THE OFFICIAL FOOTBALL ASSOCIATION

NON-LEAGUE CLUB DIRECTORY 1998

EDITOR TONY WILLIAMS

ISBN 1-869833-42-2

Published by Tony Williams Publications Ltd.
Printed by WBC Book Manufacturers Ltd. (Bridgend)
Typeset by Formatvisual, Typecast, Nina Whatmore, Keith Rye & T.W. Publications

Distributed by Tony Williams Publications Ltd.
Helland, North Curry, Taunton TA3 6DU.
Tel: 01823 490080 Fax: 01823 490281

Cover photograph: Neil Coates, Dorchester Town's captain, tackles Steve Thompson, one of Woking's FA Cup heroes, in their FA Trophy match.
Photo: Eric Marsh

Introduction

The Twentieth Directory doesn't differ too much from last year's book but we have tried to include junior leagues within the geographical districts in which they act as feeders to the powerful families above them.

We are gradually encouraging clubs to send us team photos with captions which eventualy will give us the opportunity to give you photos of every senior non-League player, while Steve Whitney's wonderful records of all senior players' clubs does give a superb record of all our top players.

Every FA Umbro Trophy and FA Carlsberg Vase club is featured within all the senior competitions while we continue our match by match records of the FA Cup, Trophy and Vase.

The County Cups and, of course, the section featuring the special worlds of AFA, Scottish, Welsh, Schools and Womens football are covered as are the competition in the off shore islands of Guernsey, Jersey and the Isle of Man. The FA Sunday and FA Youth Cups also have their place but we do appreciate the real heart of the Non-League Pyramid is built around the three major 'families' - The Southern League (Dr. Martens), The Northern Premier League (UniBond) and The Isthmian League (ICIS) while we obviously accept the Vauxhall Conference is a superbly promoted and well respected 'icing at the top' of the pyramid!

Acknowledgements

This Directory is a massive undertaking and cannot be published without the good will of a huge team of helpers.

The League Secretaries who compile their league records and write the review of their season.

The Club Secretaries who bring their club details up-to-date and try to find photos and programmes for us to use.

The Staff at The Football Association who have always been a great help, especially in the competitions department, who do such a great job for all the 'pyramid' clubs.

The Team Talk Photographers Team who have covered matches up and down the country in all weathers without financial reward with tremendous loyalty and a true love of the game - Paul Barber, Peter Barnes, Clive Butchins, Andrew Chitty, Keith Clayton, Alan Coomes, Graham Cotterill, Paul Dennis, Tim Durrant, Tim Edwards, Keith Gillard, Ken Gregory, Garry Letts, Peter Lirettoc, Eric Marsh, Rob Monger, Ian Morsman, John Newton, Dennis Nicholson, Ray Pruden, Kevin Rolfe, Francis Short, Colin Stevens, Neil Thaler, Roger Turner, Alan Watson, Gordon Whittington, Martin Wray.

Our Sponsors who have so many exciting new ideas which will benefit the game at our level. Their support will be monitored through Team Talk and I hope that clubs will also be able to benefit greatly from their plans.

All Contributors who so kindly send in ideas, records, statistics for football at all levels - Mike Ford - 'Bureau of Non-League Football' (League Tables & County Cup Results), Mandy Sabat & Steve Clark (Football Association), Nick Robinson (Icis League), Dennis Strudwick (Dr Marten's League), Duncan Bayley (Unibond League League), Wally Goss (A.F.A.), Mike Simmonds (Schools Football), Jeremy Biggs, Trevor Bailey (Sunday Football), Bob Morrison - 'First XI Sports Agency', Dudley Jackson, Stewart Davidson (Scottish Football), Bill Berry - 'Non-League Traveller' (League & Club Addresses), Robert Errington, Gareth Davies (North Wales Football), Rob Kelly, Peter Bentley, Mike Wilson, Leslie G Moore, Richard Ralph, Andy Molden, Steve Layzell, Jon Weaver, John Bullen, Dave Edmunds, Steve Davies, Colin Timbrell, Paul Gardner, Mike Amos, Alan Turvey, Keith Masters, David Halford, Cathy Gibb (Womens' Football), Rob Grillo, Mark Jones, Peter Goringe, Jonathon Rouse, William Hughes, Andy Snowley, Dave Dorey, Keith Dixon, Rod Phillips, Tim Lancaster.

We thank you all very much indeed and hope you enjoy the finished article!

TW

Contents

Only the major leagues are listed in this section. The full list will be found in the index of leagues on page 1016.

The county section starts at Page 877 and runs through the various county associations in alphabetical order.

Editorial

Another exciting season brought much to enthuse about within the world of the semi-professional pyramid of football leagues.

Macclesfield Town claimed their Nationwide League place after overhauling Kidderminster Harriers and holding off Stevenage Borough but the majority of football followers felt desperately sorry for Hereford United who lost out to Brighton & Hove Albion in their fight for Football League survival.

From our point of view United will probably make a more popular member of the Vauxhall Conference with their cosy Edger Street ground and very friendly administration.

Their membership of the Conference gives the competition a sixth club who can be expected to attract regular 2,000 plus attendances and, when you consider the state of many Third Division clubs whose supporters create very little atmosphere within fairly depressing stadia, it can be seen that there will be some very favourable comparisons made between the competitions in the months ahead.

This will make the decision of the Nationwide club chairmen even more ridiculous as they turned down the professional observations of a top firm of accountants, who advised them that part time football within a regional structure was the only sensible way ahead.

The Conference clubs, with their smart stadia, positive forward looking attitudes and pleasantly old fashioned happy sociable spirit off the field, would have injected fresh life into the Hartlepools and Torquays of the Nationwide League. But no, the heads went deeper into the sand and no progress was made.

It will happen some time but the Vauxhall Conference is getting stronger and serious thought will have to be given to the national structure when the merger happens. Will the Conference disappear or will it promote its present clubs and form new North and South Divisions below the Nationwide Divisions Three North and South?

Hopefully this tricky problem will have been thought out before the move ever has to take place and no doubt The Football Association National League Systems Committee, which looks after Pyramid matters, will have this in mind.

It would be good for football if the many fine qualities of top semi-professional football were able to influence the Third Division clubs many of whom have long lost their soul and the fun that should be there for all to appreciate.

Regular readers of this Directory and Team Talk will know how strongly I feel about our England Team, who represent the largest section of football in their country but doesn't have a tournament in which it can show its strengths on the International stage.

I cannot believe a tournament is so difficult to set up if the desire really exists. Last season a potential sponsor emerged for a series of Inter-League games aiming to provide the England coach with enough talent on show in representative matches to pick a strong squad for an end-of-season tournament, which would also help with sponsorship money.

Many of the Inter-League games were to be played below Premier Feeder League level which didn't really directly help the England squad, but the inclusion of our FA XI (usually containing Conference players) against The Dr. Martens League XI will mean all three feeder leagues will play FA XI's this season so the new England coach will have three high quality trials in which he can see his potential England players.

Hopefully club chairmen and managers will make sure they co-operate and ensure their players will be made available if selected for these trials.

Having said that, the whole operation would appear so much more important if a prestigious tournament was waiting for the England squad at the end of the season. I know that FA Representative Committee chairman Alan Turvey and the appropriate FA department under Adrian Titcombe and Mandy Clark will be trying their hardest to give this England squad the status they deserve.

Senior football in this country is welcoming foreigners from all over the world into its clubs. Those who are world class can benefit our game on and off the field, but many newcomers are really no better than the talent we possess throughout England.

We are extremely pleased to announce that The Football Association are endorsing the 'Non-League Club Directory' and our monthly Team Talk Magazine.

Regular readers know that we make great efforts to promote The FA Umbro Trophy and FA Carlsberg Vase in particular while also highlighting the first two thirds of the FA Cup competition sponsored by Littlewoods and, of course, our England Semi-Professioinal International side and the trial games played by the F.A. XIs.

Hopefully we will be able to make even more of the football public aware of the massive contributions The Football Association makes towards the administration of the national winter sport and we look forward to working closely with the Football Association staff and committees to promote football in the best possible light.

It has never been more important for our good young players to be reorganised at an early age and their progress to be monitored through until the time that they are ready to hold their own at the top level.

Good monitoring, coaching and sophisticated care and grooming will prevent so many millions of pounds leaving the country and will, of course, reward our junior clubs for the work they put in on behalf of these youngsters.

Our sponsors, Price, Patrick & Associates Ltd., will be helping football with their exciting new projects and we will be keeping clubs up-to-date with the benefits available to them through Team Talk, our monthly magazine now in its seventh year.

This season will probably see the Vauxhall Conference clubs produce near record attendances especially if their championship is well contested by three or four powerful clubs.

The Dr. Martens Premier Division also has some well supported potential challengers in Bromsgrove Rovers, Nuneaton Borough, Burton Albion and Worcester City. While Kingstonian and Dagenham & Redbridge of the ICIS League have already enjoyed gates of over 1,000 in the first couple of home games and in the UniBond League, Barrow, Boston United and Altrincham can attract big crowds. So let's sit back and hope we can enjoy four well contested battles, creating exciting atmospheres in which football can always be appreciated.

Add a lively and well contested FA Umbro Trophy and FA Carlsberg Vase Competitions and some impressive FA Cup performances by our semi-professional underdogs and you have the ingredients of a great season.

Despite this being the 21st year for the Directory I'm still as excited about the prospects as ever and we will be looking forward to presenting the campaign to you through Team Talk magazine as the season unfurls.

Please let me know if you have any special ideas for the twenty-first edition next year and thank you all for your support once again and may I wish you all a happy and successful year.

TONY WILLIAMS

Editorial Team
Tony Williams (Editor)
Keith Rye & George Brown (House Editors)
Steve Whitney & Bill Mitchell
Editorial Address
Tony Williams Publications, Helland, North Curry, Taunton, Somerset TA3 6DU
Tel: 01823 490080 Fax: 01823 490281

We appreciate that we have a long way to go in our effort to display the many leagues at the foot of the pyramid in a logical order both for standard and geography but a great effort has been put in this year to ensure the layout of the book is easier to follow. We hope you agree but perhaps you may have some ideas we could incorporate for our 21st birthday edition next season?

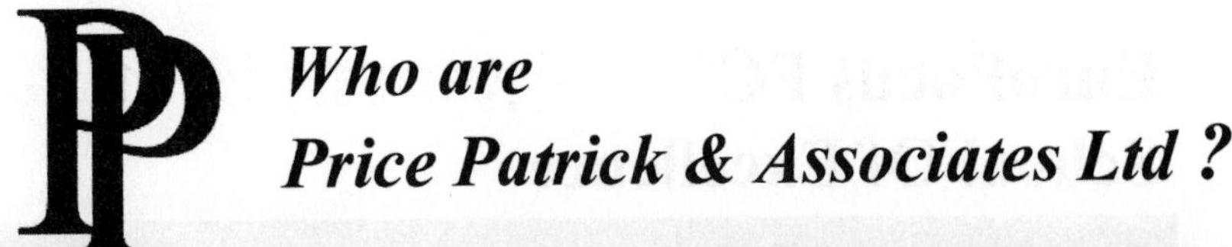
Who are
Price Patrick & Associates Ltd ?

Price Patrick & Associates Ltd

Price Patrick & Associates Ltd. is a management company dedicated to sport.

Investment In Sport

Price Patrick have been making a significant financial investment in developing management systems that are easy and friendly to use.

Computerised Systems For Football Management

The company has developed a number of systems for football clubs. including the EuroFocus FC School of Excellence, which is being used in an ever growing number of clubs, including the Premier Division.

Consultancy Focus on Technology

In addition we provide consultancy services in the area of business development, and the use of the technology in the support of long term objectives.

Equipment Supply And Installations

We can provide both hardware and software to meet your club's computing requirements.

Of particular importance to clubs is our practical experience and ability to assess equipment needs, define requirements, prepare procedures and install and commission networked computer systems.

Support Services & Training

Price Patrick & Associates provide a full support service, including a help desk from our offices in Berkshire, London, and Surrey.

Comprehensive training has to be considered as a vital stage in the implementation of any system, and full training on all of our management systems is available.

The company can supply courses on most commercially available software packages, including word processing and financial packages

Setting Future Sports Management Standards

EuroFocus FC
School Of Excellence

A "Professional System" - That Sets Future Management Standards

Introduction

Price Patrick & Associates Ltd. have a significant financial investment in Sport. As part of our "Sports Development" programme we are pleased to announce that the "School Of Excellence Management System" is now available.

The system was developed over a period of seven months, and in close co-operation between experienced football professionals and I.T. analysts and consultants.

The School Of Excellence Management System provides a comprehensive Youth Development standard which will assist Clubs in protecting their 'youth investment', and provides indepth support for youth development programmes.

Player Registrations

The registration facility uses a highly developed "User friendly" interface, making data input a simple task. The Medical and Injury management facility provide a full history of incidents critical to the continued well being of the Players.

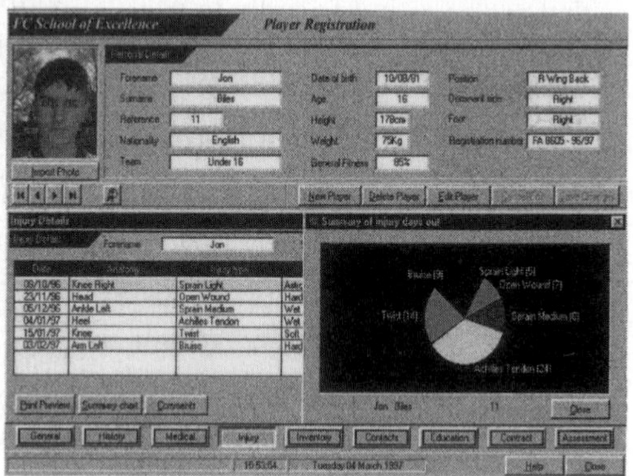

Careful attention to detail has been made to tailor the registration requirement for both the amateur and professional games, and includes registration details as currently required by the F.A.

Features Overview

Player information	**Player Playing History**
Medical Records	**Injury Management**
Player Contacts	**Player Education**
Player Contracts	**Full Player Reporting**

The system provides excellent search facilities.The user can select a wide variety of criteria, including technical, physical and psychological attributes. Searches can be also be made against age, squad, position, dominant side etc.

Player Assessments

The assessment system which forms part of the School Of Excellence is fully user definable. Categories and Attributes can be based on the foundations developed by the F.A. and other knowledgeable bodies. These categories can be further extended to include the Club's coaching requirements.

Setting Up Categories & Attributes

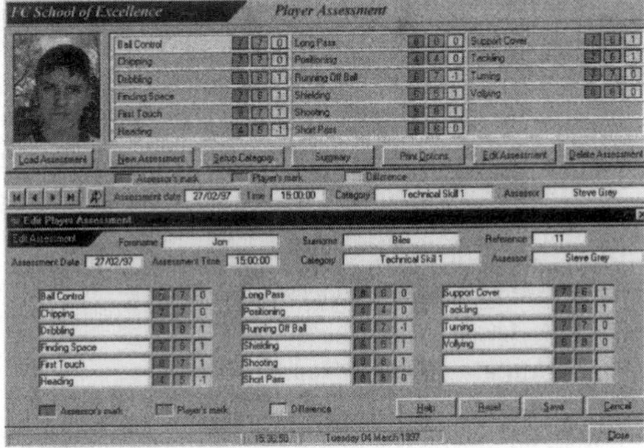

The system provides a unique communication tool between the Coach and the Player.

Assessments are made against a predefined set of attributes that are individually assessed both by Player and Coach.

The assessment system also provides a focus for the improvement of communications between the Club and Parents, utilising printed reports.

Graphic Output Of Assessment

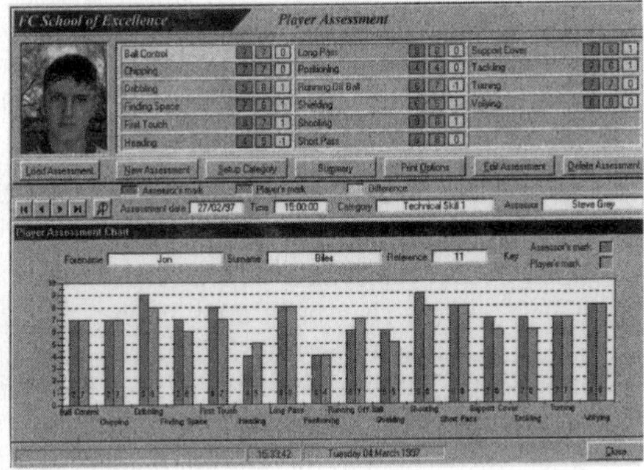

Operational Benefits

Reduced Administration	**Information on Demand**
Detailed Registration	**Detailed Reports**
Technical Assessments	**Psychological Assessments**
Injury Management	**Electronic Data Transfer**

In Support Of Youth Development

This is an often talked about subject, but what do we really mean. Is it just time spent with youngsters letting them play their matches and shouting from the sidelines or does it involve more than this?

True youth development is to provide a learning and truly supportive environment where personal aptitude, diet, fitness and health awareness, technical skills, teamwork, and knowledge of the game and its rules can be nurtured and perfected.

The objective is to ensure each player is taken carefully, caringly and, above all, safely along the path to reach his or her full potential in a competitive environment for the benefit of country, club and player.

The responsibility therefore placed upon coaches and their assistants is considerable. They must draw upon experience and a deep knowledge of the game together with reviewing and assimilating new understanding and ways of coaching on an ongoing basis. Even this is not enough, they must be able to communicate their skills effectively with their players and report on progress to directors, managers and not least parents.

This reporting on all aspects of individual and team progress is essential to justify the levels of financial support that will need to be made as a joint contribution towards success.

As coaching becomes more and more professional within a structured national framework then the amount of information both generated and required will be significant. The sometimes challenging transition of changing from a long established, time consuming, manual systems to newly introduced computer based systems will have to be made to allow for detailed registration, performance monitoring, medical and injury management, effective reporting, accurate recording and to reduce administration time and cost.

Price Patrick & Associates are fully supportive of current initiatives in the development of youth in football.

Surrey Youth v Lancashire Youth

FA County Youth Cup - Semi Final

Photograph: D Nicholson

The appointment of Howard Wilkinson as Technical Director of the Football Association in January 1996 and his recent introduction of a "Quality Charter" are seen as a very positive and long awaited approach. These FA initiatives deserve to be fully endorsed.

We shall continue to develop and produce management systems that meet the stated requirements of the F.A. and other governing bodies, in this country and world-wide.

EuroFocus FC series have been designed to cover all areas of football from boys clubs and amateur clubs right up to the top professional teams. This is achieved by using carefully constructed modules that cater for an identified and specific area of football club management.
Each module is extremely functional and powerful in its own right.

Sponsorship
By Local Business & Other Organisations

Price Patrick realise that the cost of management systems and supporting computer equipment may be difficult for a club to finance.

We provide a unique opportunity for companies and organisations to sponsor the management systems.

Business has for a very long time recognised the promotional potential from success in football.

The time is now exactly right for business to be associated with the movement for a structured approach to youth development in clubs.

Price Patrick will be pleased to provide an information pack to interested clubs and or business organisations on this sponsorship option.

Girls and Women's Football

Women's World Cup in the USA 1999

Women's football is developing at a fast pace. The draw for the 1997/1999 European Qualifying Competition for the 3rd FIFA Women's World Cup took place, in Geneva on 19th February 1997.
A total of 34 countries entered the qualifying competition. Qualifying matches will be played against each group member in home and away matches. These qualifying matches are due to begin in September 1997.

Ladies Pool Game
Portsmouth
versus
FC Concordia (Switzerland)

England are in Group 3 along with Norway, Germany, Netherlands.
For the record: Group 1 Sweden, Spain, Iceland, Ukraine.
Group 2 Italy, Finland, France, Switzerland.
Group 4 Russia, Denmark, Portugal, Belgium.

Top Attendances 1996-97

( ) = 195-96 Average

	TEAM	AGG	PLD	OVER 2,000	1,000	HIGHEST			AVERAGE	
1	Stevenage Borough	60,496	21	20	1	5,760	v	Macclesfield	2,880	(1,895)
2	Yeovil Town	58,259	21	17	4	8,007	v	Enfield	2,774	(2,032)
3	Kidderminster	55,858	21	18	3	6,081	v	Bromsgrove	2,659	(2,030)
4	Woking	54,504	21	19	2	3,420	v	Kidderminster	2,595	(2,385)
5	Rushden & Diamonds	52,800	21	20	1	5,170	v	Kettering	(2,514	(2,168)
6	Kettering Town	35,896	21	3	17	4,628	v	Rushden & Diamonds	1,709	(1,426)
7	Aldershot Town	35,290	21	2	19	2,262	v	Basingstoke	1,680	(1,656)
8	Macclesfield	29,551	21	2	16	3,004	v	Bromsgrove	1,407	(1,264)
9	Hednesford Town	27.582	21	2	15	2,368	v	Woking	1,313	(1,310)
10	Barrow	24,472	22	-	15	1,452	v	Marine1,112	(1,217)	
11	Dover Athletic	22,474	21	-	14	1,671	v	Rushden	1,070	(1,002)
12	Slough Town	22,443	21	1	12	2,055	v	Woking	1,068	(1,019)
13	Nuneaton Borough	21,424	21	-	9	1,607	v	Atherstone	1,020	(1,101)
14	Morecambe	21,213	21	-	9	1,438	v	Stevenage Borough	1,010	(881)
15	Cheltenham Town	20.902	21	1	7	3,005	v	Gloucester	995	(714)
16	Gloucester City	20,504	21	1	6	2,154	v	Cheltenham	976	(821)
17	Southport	20,362	21	-	8	1,546	v	Macclesfield	970	(944)
18	Kings Lynn	20,360	21	-	8	1,476	v	Gresley	969	(1,032)
19	Northwich Victoria	20,316	21	-	7	1,527	v	Macclesfield	967	(827)
20	Boston United	20,676	22	-	9	1,487	v	Barrow	939	(881)
21	Telford United	18,591	21	-	5	1,860	v	Kidderminster	885	(816)
22	Bromsgrove Rovers	17,778	21	1	1	2,548	v	Kidderminster	846	(1,071)
23	Halifax Town	17,668	21	1	2	2,191	v	Macclesfield	841	(838)
24	Burton Albion	17,651	21	1	2	2,537	v	Gresley	840	(724)
25	Gresley Rovers	17,548	21	-	4	1,760	v	Burton	835	(646)
26	Enfield	17,273	21	-	4	1,349	v	Yeovil Town	822	(866)
27	Altrincham	17,271	21	-	3	1,334	v	Northwich	822	(887)
28	Halesowen Town	17,117	21	-	3	1,406	v	Cheltenham	815	(793)
29	Tamworth	16,183	20	-	2	1,339	v	VS Rugby	809	(562)
30	Farnborough Town	16,921	21	-	4	1,479	v	Woking	805	(810)
31	Worcester City	15,992	21	-	1	1,270	v	Cheltenham	761	(817)
32	Chelmsford City	15,971	21	-	2	1,114	v	Gravesend	760	(810)
33	Welling United	14,997	21	-	3	1,101	v	Woking	714	(615)
34	Bath City	14,483	21	-	3	1,258	v	Northwich	690	(516)
35	Sittingbourne	14,276	21	-	2	1,028	v	Gravesend	679	(687)
36	Newport AFC	14,054	21	-	-	944	v	Merthyr Tydfil	669	(882)
37	Hayes	13,984	21	-	4	1,327	v	Woking	665	(461)
38	Stalybridge Celtic	13,598	21	-	1	1,067	v	Kidderminster	647	(615)
39	Sutton United	13,538	21	-	2	1,281	v	Yeovil Town	644	(543)
40	Crawley Town	13,523	21	-	-	943	v	Hastings Town	643	(710)
41	Weymouth	13,495	21	-	1	1,132	v	Newport	642	(686)
42	Gravesend & Northfleet	13,334	21	-	1	1,303	v	Sittingbourne	634	(534)
43	Dagenham & Redbridge	13,167	21	-	2	1,181	v	Yeovil Town	627	(790)
44	Merthyr Tydfil	13,079	21	-	1	1,109	v	Newport	622	(419)
45	Dorchester Town	12,756	21	-	-	868	v	Salisbury City	607	(641)
46	Gateshead	12,353	21	-	1	1,276	v	Kidderminster	588	(623)

THE NON-LEAGUE CLUB DIRECTORY

AWARDS 1996-97

FOOTBALLER OF THE YEAR
Howard Forinton

MANAGER OF THE YEAR
Paul Futcher

INDIVIDUAL MERIT AWARDS
Ted Hardy
Bernard Manning Junior
Alan O'Dell
Lee Hughes

* * * * *

REGIONAL CLUB AWARDS

NORTH EAST	Whitby Town
NORTH WEST	Trafford
MIDLANDS	Tamworth
EAST of ENGLAND	Stamford
HOME COUNTIES NORTH	Enfield
HOME COUNTIES SOUTH	AFC Lymington
WEST of ENGLAND	Yeovil Town
WALES	Llansantffraid
F.A. CUP	Hednesford Town

Non-League Footballer of the Year

Howard Forinton
(Oxford City - Yeovil Town)

To be considered to be The Non-League Footballer of the Year a player's individual consistency and brilliance must really be seen to have helped his club actually achieve something. In the case of Howard Forinton a bright start to the season with Oxford City brought him seventeen goals, selection for the ICIS League and an FA XI and a £17,500 move to Yeovil Town.

He arrived as his new club became locked in a dour battle with Enfield for promotion to the Conference. Three points were desperately needed from every match and every goal was vital as pressure was built up by the game. In this atmosphere Howard was inspirational to all around him, his goals seemed to get more spectacular by the match and he scored 26 goals in 24 games including six doubles in the vital last seven league games!

This brought Howard Forinton 43 goals in the season, a £75,000 transfer to Birmingham City, and for his club a thrilling ICIS championship and a place in the Vauxhall Conference. A magnificent effort!

Manager of the Year

Paul Futcher

(Gresley Rovers)

Paul Futcher enjoyed a long and successful professional career as a player, making over 650 League appearances for the likes of Luton Town, Manchester City and Derby County, while he represented England at Under-23 level and also played for the Football League XI. Then, towards the end of the 1995/96 season, along with another former League and international star, Garry Birtles, Paul took over as player-manager of Dr. Martens Premier Division club Gresley Rovers and, without spending a penny in transfer fees, led the little Derbyshire club to the championship in his first full season in charge. He led from the front too as, at the age of 40, Paul hardly missed a match, organising his defence and still looking a very accomplished player, whilst Birtles did his bit from the bench. This managerial team also achieved a quite remarkable record as their Gresley squad didn't lose a single player through suspension and no player was sent off during the season. Sadly for the club, Gresley were unable to take their place in the Vauxhall Conference due to their new ground not being ready in time. Paul has now accepted an offer to take over in the Conference at Southport.

Individual Merit Awards

Ted Hardy (Dagenham & Redbridge Manager)

After a long and very successful career as a non-League manager, most people, including perhaps Ted himself, thought that at the age of 68 his days of managing a top club had long gone. However, following a succession of disappointing managerial appointments, Dagenham & Redbridge turned to Ted in the hope that he could weave some magic to keep them in the Vauxhall Conference. He couldn't, and again many thought that Ted had been out of management too long. But, during 1996/97, his first full season in charge, Ted led his team to Wembley in the FA Umbro Trophy final and, although they eventually lost out to Woking in a close fought contest, Ted proved that the old magic is still there, and, who knows, will perhaps mount a serious challenge to regain a place in the Conference next season.

Bernard Manning Jr (Radcliffe Borough Chairman)

A lot of people outside of Radcliffe Borough Football Club thought that Bernard Manning Junior's elevation to the chair was nothing more than a publicity stunt. However, the son of the controversial comedian has, along with his fellow directors, worked miracles not only to provide manager Kevin Glendon with the finances to build a UniBond League First Division championship winning team, but also to make their Strainton Park ground a true community stadium with all weather floodlit facilities for the locals to utilise. This has all been achieved by money raising activities, hard work and grants, and not by relying on a 'sugar daddy'.

Alan Odell (Retired FA Councellor - Middlesex)

Alan Odell, having previously served Uxbridge FC as secretary, joined the Football Association as assistant accountant in 1963 and was appointed secretary of their International Committee in 1966. His retirement in 1989 coincided with the sad death of his friend Alec Smith, the Middlesed County FA Councillor, and Alan was voted in to represent the County at Lancaster Gate until last year. Alan has been a constant supporter of the England Semi-Professional side since its conception and he has worked for the good of football, his county and his beloved Uxbridge Football Club without every being drawn away from his beliefs for political reasons. Our thanks go to Alan Odell a real 'football' man.

Lee Hughes (Kidderminster Harriers & England)

Having been carefully looked after in the club's excellent youth scheme Lee Hughes soon made his mark in the Kidderminster Harriers first team and his consistent goalscoring led to his selection for the England Semi-Professional squad as the youngest 'cap'. Last season he led the Conference goalscoring chart all season and although reaching the elusive 30 mark he unluckily picked up an injury that prevented him helping Harriers in their desperate end of season championship chase. It was bad luck for 'Kiddy' but Lee has achieved one of his ambitions by being signed by his home town professional club West Bromwich Albion for £200,000.

Club Awards

North East

Whitby Town

Although both Newcastle Blue Star and Whickham had won the FA Vase in the past, both were members of the Wearside League when achieving their respective 1978 and 1981 successes. Therefore, in 1997 Whitby Town earned the Northern League its first senior non-League trophy since Bishop Auckland were FA Amateur Cup winners in 1958. That in itself was noteworthy enough, but the men from Upgang Lane also gained promotion to the UniBond League as Northern League champions, winning the title by nine points and scoring 130 goals into the bargain. A truly great season.

North West

Trafford

When the non-League Pyramid was developed, it provided opportunities for clubs to move swiftly through divisions, as long as their on-the-field achievements were matched by suitable ground developments off it. Trafford are a classic example of this. Formed only in 1990, they have climbed through from the Mid-Cheshire League via the North West Counties League and into the UniBond League and, during that climb, have developed their Shawe View ground into one of the most picturesque in the North-West. To top off a truly great 1996/97 season, Trafford's reserve side also won their league, league cup and Manchester Amateur Cup. They are a club going places.

Midlands

Tamworth

Tamworth have tremendous support, both home and away. Unfortunately, since gaining promotion to the Southern League in 1988/89, a season when they also lifted the FA Vase, many managers have tried and failed to bring promotion to the Premier Division for their vast army of fans. That was until 1996/97, when Paul Hendrie's second season in charge saw Tamworth win the Midland Division title by a massive 26 points margin. The Lamb outfit are undoubtedly a 'sleeping giant' that has been dormant for far too long. Their enthusiastic followers will be hoping that this is the start of something big for their club.

East of England

Stamford

During the 1970s and 80s, Stamford fans were used to success. They went to Wembley three times as FA Vase finalists and celebrated five United Counties League championships. However, since 1982 their cupboard has been bare. That was until 1996/97 when the UCL Championship flag once again flew at Wothorpe Road. Stamford's boss Steve Evans isn't everyone's 'cup of tea'. However, much of his own money went into bringing star names such as Olympic Champion Daley Thompson, former Scottish international David Speedie and ex-FA Cup winner Dave Bennett to the club. It put Stamford back on the map and into the headlines, and alongside an excellent youth policy produced a title-winning side again for the Lincolnshire town.

Home Counties North

Enfield

A club with such an excellent pedigree should really be competing in the top semi-professional sphere and every season Enfield appear to be equipped to move up. They have been desperately close for so long that their loyal supporters have to show terrific morale to keep the club's spirits up. Last season Enfield had the best defensive record, avoided defeat away from home, had the best goal difference and 95 points but still couldn't quite clinch that vital top spot. It was a terrific season with an excellent FA Cup run which would have been considered a great year for any other club. Good luck to the 'Es' in the future.

Home Counties South

AFC Lymington

Frequently, when clubs are knocked out of cup competitions early, many say: "Well, at least we can concentrate on the league". This is often just an excuse. In AFC Lymington's case, it was proved to be perfectly correct as they proceeded to go the entire league season unbeaten in the Jewson Wessex League, creating a whole host of new records along the way, including the highest points total (110), most victories (35), least goals against (22), most away wins (19), biggest winning points margin (25) and best goal difference (90). In any 'normal' season, runners-up Wimborne Town's 85 points would surely have been enough to secure the title.

South West

Yeovil Town

A quite incredibly intense two club race developed in the ICIS Premier League and both Enfield and the eventual champions Yeovil Town deserve immense credit for not cracking under the pressure. Graham Roberts had built a new squad and their spirit as will as undoubted quality enabled them to embark on an eighteen match unbeaten league run-in, inspired by massive emotional support and a single mindedness not often seen at senior semi-professional level. Other highlights of the season included a league attendance of 8,007 v Enfield, Jerry Gill's cap for England, Howard Forinton's goals and a Cup Final success against Bristol City.

Wales

Llansantffraid

The formation of the League of Wales didn't completely endear itself to all followers of non-League football. But what it did do was to enable little clubs like Llansantffraid to compete in European football. It must only have ever been a pipe dream for fans of this village club that, one day, they would see their team in the European Cup Winners' Cup, but they did, and they enjoyed every moment of their involvement in which the club was a credit to their league.

FA Cup

Hednesford Town

Hednesford Town have come a long way in a very short space of time. Since joining the Vauxhall Conference in 1995, the 'Pitmen' have develped into one of the top clubs in non-League football's leading competition and have become feared cup opponents. Beating Nationwide Second Division promotion hopefuls Blackpool in The Second Round was noteworthy enough, but they then overcame York City in the third round and gave the all star Middlesbrough side the fright of their lives before bowing out to a late winner in a 3-2 defeat. But, not only did Hednesford just lose out to the eventual finalists, they also earned great tributes for their style of play and for the conduct of their terrific support.

The Football Association Challenge Cup

Sponsored by LITTLEWOODS Pools

Non League Roll of Honour

FIRST ROUND (32)

Dr Martens (5)
Ashford Town
Shepshed Dynamo
Merthyr Tydfil
Cheltenham Town
Sudbury Town

Vauxhall Conference (14)
Southport
Woking
Hayes
Rushden & Diamonds
Morecambe
Welling United
Stalybridge Celtic
Kidderminster Harriers
Farnborough Town
Hednesford Town
Macclesfield Town
Northwich Victoria
Altrincham
Stevenage Borough

ICIS (6)
Dagenham & Redbridge
Boreham Wood
Bromley
Enfield
Hendon
St Albans City

Unibond (3)
Boston United
Colwyn Bay
Runcorn

Northern
Consett
Whitby Town

Jewson Eastern (1)
Wisbech Town

N.W.Co. (1)
Newcastle Town

SECOND ROUND (9)

Hednesford Town
St Albans City
Woking
Boston United
Enfield
Stevenage Borough
Boreham Wood
Sudbury Town
Ashford Town

THIRD ROUND (3)

Hednesford Town
Stevenage Borough
Woking

FOURTH ROUND (1)

Hednesford Town

1996-97 (non-league) Review

***Oldham Town 2 Halifax Town 3** (F.A. Cup 1st Qualifying Round). Former Leeds United player, Bobby Davison of Halifax Town takes on the Oldham Town defence during his sides 3-2 victory.* Photo: Colin Stevens

***Stalybridge Celtic 2 Ashton United 1** (F.A. Cup 3rd Qualifying Round) Ashton United 'keeper David Pierce keeps hold of the ball despite the attentions of Stalybridge opponent Steve Charles, and his own team mate Steve Caswell.* Photo: Colin Stevens

SECTION 1

Preliminary Round Results – Sat. 31 Aug. 1996

	Workington	1 v 0	Worksop Town
	Ossett Town	3 v 1	Armthorpe Welfare
	Eastwood Hanley	0 v 1	Crook Town
	St Helens T	2 v 2	Peterlee Newtown
r	*Peterlee Newtown*	*1 v 2*	*St Helens T*
	Hebburn	0 v 5	Dunston Federation Brewery

1st Qualifying Round – Saturday 14 September

	St Helens	0 v 0	Gateshead
r	*Gateshead*	*5 v 1*	*St Helens*
	Billingham Town	0 v 0	Dunston Fed. Brewery
r	*Dunston Fed. Brew.*	*0 v 2*	*Billingham Town*
	Workington	3 v 1	Crook Town
	Buxton	1 v 2	Ossett Town

2nd Qualifying Round – Saturday 28th September

Gateshead	5 v 1	Osset Town
Billingham Town	0 v 1	Workington

3rd Qualifying Round – Saturday 12th October

Gateshead	4 **v** 0	Workington

SECTION 2

Preliminary Round Results – Sat. 31 Aug. 1996, 3.00pm

	Harrogate Town	6 v 0	Whitley Bay
	Pontefract Collieries	1 v 2	Pickering Town
	Alnwick Town	0 v 0	Consett
r	*Consett*	*2 v 0*	*Alnwick*
	Esh Winning	1 v 3	Oldham Town
	Northallerton	0 v 1	Morpeth Town

1st Qualifying Round – Saturday 14 September

Oldham Town	2 v 3	Hali f.a.x Town
Durham City	5 v 1	Morpeth Town
Harrogate Town	0 v 1	Consett
Bishop Auckland	3 v 1	Pickering Town

2nd Qualifying Round – Saturday 28th September

Halifax Town	1 v 4	Bishop Auckland
Durham City	1 v 1*	Consett

3rd Qualifying Round – Saturday 12th October

Bishop Auckland	0 **v** 1	Consett

*(Durham City Eliminated for playing ineligable player)

SECTION 3

Preliminary Round Results – Sat. 31 Aug. 1996, 3.00pm

Flixton	4 v 1	RTM Newcastle
Blackpool (Wren) Rov	1 v 2	Hucknall Town
Bootle	2 v 0	Seaham Red Star
Brandon United	3 v 1	Tadcaster Albion
Ryhope CA	1 v 2	Arnold Town

1st Qualifying Round – Saturday 14 September

	Brandon United	0 v 6	Morecambe
	Gretna	1 v 1	Arnold Town
r	*Arnold Town*	*3 v 0*	*Gretna*
	Flixton	2 v 0	Bootle
	Guiseley	4 v 0	Hucknall Town

2nd Qualifying Round – Saturday 28th September

	Morecambe	4 v 1	Guiseley
	Arnold Town	0 v 0	Flixton
r	*Flixton*	*2 v 0*	*Arnold Town*

3rd Qualifying Round – Saturday 12th October

Morecambe	6 v 2	Flixton

SECTION 4

Preliminary Round Results – Sat. 31 Aug. 1996, 3.00pm

Netherfield	3 v 0	Shildon
Ossett Albion	2 v 1	Brigg Town
Nantwich Town	5 v 0	South Shields
Ferryhill Athletic	1 v 2	Yorkshire Amateur
Harrogate Railway	5 v 2	Stockton

1st Qualifying Round – Saturday 14 September

	Yorkshire Amateur	0 v 1	Stalybridge Celtic
	Ashton United	3 v 0	Harrogate Railway
	Netherfield	3 v 1	Nantwich Town
	Accrington Stanley	1 v 1	Ossett Albion
r	*Ossett Albion*	*2 v 1*	*Accrington Stanley*

2nd Qualifying Round – Saturday 28th September

Stalybridge Celtic	4 v 1	Ossett Albion
Ashton United	2 v 0	Netherfield

3rd Qualifying Round – Saturday 12th October

Stalybridge Celtic	2 v 1	Ashton United

SECTION 5

Preliminary Round Results – Sat. 31 Aug. 1996, 3.00pm

Willington	2 v 1	Borrowash Victoria
Ashington	4 v 5	Ashfield United
Newcastle Town	1 v 0	Denaby United
Murton	1 v 0	Congleton Town

1st Qualifying Round – Saturday 14 September

Murton	1 v 3	Frickley Athletic
Easington Colliery	2 v 7	Winsford United
Willington	1 v 3	Newcastle Town
Bradford (Park Ave.)	1 v 0	Ashfield United

2nd Qualifying Round – Saturday 28th September

Frickley Athletic	1 v 0	Bradford (Park Ave.)
Winsford United	0 v 1	Newcastle Town

3rd Qualifying Round – Saturday 12th October

	Frickley Athletic	1 v 1	Newcastle Town
r	*Newcastle Town*	*2 v 1*	*Finckley Athletic*

SECTION 6

Preliminary Round – Sat. 31 Aug. 1996, 3.00pm

	Washington	0 v 0	Bridgnorth Town
r	*Bridgnorth*	*2 v 1*	*Washington*
	Eccleshill United	2 v 1	Hallam
	Trafford	2 v 1	Clitheroe
	Glasshoughton Welfare	1 v 2	Matlock Town

1st Qualifying Round – Saturday 14 September

	Matlock Town	0 v 1	Leek Town
	Tow Law Town	1 v 1	Gainsborough Trinity
r	*Gainsborough Trinity*	*2 v 0*	*Tow Law Town*
	Bridgnorth	2 v 1	Trafford
	Eastwood Town	1 v 0	Eccleshill United

2nd Qualifying Round – Saturday 28th September

Leek Town	1 v 0	Eastwood Town
Gainsborough Trinity	2 v 1	Bridgnorth

3rd Qualifying Round – Saturday 12th October

Leek Town	2 v 0	Gainsborough Trinity

r = Replay

Stapenhill 3 Salford City 0 *(F.A. Cup Preliminary Round)   Salford no. 9 John Main closely marshalled by Stapenhills Cheetan.*

Lancaster City 6 Blakenall 0 *(F.A. Cup 2nd Qualifying Round)   Steve Hartley, centre, steers home the first of Lancaster's six goals watched by team mate Antony Key.* Photo: Dennis Nicholson

Heanor Town 3 Sheffield 4 *(F.A. Cup Preliminary Round)   Mark Flanagan's shot evades the Sheffield defence to register Heanor's second goal.*

SECTION 7

Preliminary Round – Sat. 31 Aug. 1996, 3.00pm

	Shotton Comrades	0	v	4	Garforth Town
	Cheadle Town	0	v	0	Burscough
r	*Burscough*	*2*	*v*	*0*	*Cheadle T.*
	Whitby Town	6	v	2	Whickham
	Hatfield Main	0	v	0	Farsley Celtic
r	*Farsley Celtic*	*2*	*v*	*1*	*Hatfield Main*

1st Qualifying Round – Saturday 14 September

	Farsley Celtic	1	v	0	Knowsley United
	Warrington Town	0	v	1	Hyde United
	Garforth Town	1	v	3	Whitby Town
	Mossley	3	v	1	Burscough

2nd Qualifying Round – Saturday 28th September

	Farsley Celtic	3	v	1	Mossley
	Hyde United	0	v	1	Whitby Town

3rd Qualifying Round – Saturday 12th October

	Farsley Celtic	0	v	1	Whitby Town

SECTION 8

Preliminary Round Results – Sat. 31 Aug. 1996, 3.00pm

	Droylsden	1	v	5	Stocksbridge Park Steels
	Thackley	0	v	4	Selby Town
	Kidsgrove Athletic	0	v	3	Chester-Le-Street Town
	Rossendale United	1	v	1	Castleton Gabriels
r	*Castleton Gabriels*	*2*	*v*	*4*	*Rossendale United*
	Louth United	2	v	2	Guisborough Town
r	*Guisborough Town*	*4*	*v*	*1*	*Louth United*

1st Qualifying Round – Saturday 14 September

	Rossendale United	0	v	5	Southport
	Burton Albion	1	v	0	Guisborough Town
	Stocksbridge P. Steels	4	v	2	Chester-Le-Street Town
	Emley	3	v	0	Selby Town

2nd Qualifying Round – Saturday 28th September

	Southport	1	v	1	Emley
	Emley	2	v	3	Southport
	Burton Albion	2	v	1	Stocksbridge Park Steels

3rd Qualifying Round – Saturday 12th October

	Southport	4	v	1	Burton Albion

SECTION 9

Preliminary Round Results – Sat. 31 Aug. 1996, 3.00pm

	Heanor Town	3	v	4	Sheffield
	Horden CW	0	v	4	Atherton Collieries
	Shifnal Town	1	v	2	Chadderton
	Belper Town	1	v	1	Leigh RMI
r	*Leigh RMI*	*3*	*v*	*1*	*Belper Town*

1st Qualifying Round – Saturday 14 September

	Leigh RMI	2	v	0	Alfreton Town
	Radcliffe Borough	0	v	2	Marine
	Sheffield	2	v	1	Chadderton
	Billingham Synthonia	1	v	0	Atherton Collieries

2nd Qualifying Round – Saturday 28th September

	Leigh RMI	1	v	1	Billingham Synthonia
r	*Billingham Synthonia*	*2*	*v*	*3*	*Leigh RMI*
	Marine	1	v	0	Sheffield

3rd Qualifying Round – Saturday 12th October

	Leigh RMI	2	v	0	Marine

r = Replay ***2r*** = 2nd replay

SECTION 10

Preliminary Round Results – Sat. 31 Aug. 1996, 3.00pm

	Harworth CI	0	v	0	Blidworth MW
r	*Blidworth*	*2*	*v*	*2*	*Harworth CI*
2r	*Blidworth*	*2*	*v*	*1*	*Harworth CI*
	Evenwood Town	3	v	1	Darwen
	Stapenhill	3	v	0	Salford City
	Liversedge	0	v	0	Atherton LR 0
r	*Atherton LR*	*2*	*v*	*2*	*Liversedge*

1st Qualifying Round – Saturday 14 September

	Atherton	1	v	0	Ikeston Town
	West Auckland Town	1	v	3	Bamber Bridge
	Blidworth	0	v	1	Stapenhill
	Curzon Ashton	1	v	0	Evenwood Town

2nd Qualifying Round – Saturday 28th September

	Atherton LR	3	v	2	Curzon Ashton
	Bamber Bridge	5	v	3	Stapenhill

3rd Qualifying Round – Saturday 12th October

	Atherton LR	1	v	1	Bamber Bridge
r	*Bamber Bridge*	*2*	*v*	*0*	*Atherton LR*

SECTION 11

Preliminary Round Results – Sat. 31 Aug. 1996, 3.00pm

	Kimberley Town	3	v	0	Rossington Main
	Prudhoe Town	1	v	1	Maine Road
r	*Maine Road*	*1*	*v*	*2*	*Prudhoe Town*
	Blakenall	3	v	0	Glossop North End
	North Ferriby United	4	v	0	Great Harwood Town 0

1st Qualifying Round – Saturday 14 September

	North Ferriby United	4	v	1	Chorley
	Lincoln United	2	v	2	Lancaster City
r	*Lancaster City*	*3*	*v*	*2*	*Lincoln United*
	Rossington Main	1	v	2	Blakenall
	Bedlington Terriers	4	v	0	Prudhoe Town

2nd Qualifying Round – Saturday 28th September

	North Ferriby United	1	v	0	Bedlington Terriers
	Lancaster City	6	v	0	Blakenall

3rd Qualifying Round – Saturday 12th October

	North Ferriby United	0	v	2	Lancaster City

SECTION 12

Preliminary Round Results – Sat. 31 Aug. 1996, 3.00pm

	Bedworth United	2	v	2	Paget Rangers
r	*Paget Ranger*	*1*	*v*	*2*	*Bedworth United*
	Wellingborough Town	0	v	3	Cogenhoe United
	Banbury United	0	v	1	VS Rugby
	Rocester	5	v	1	Bolehall Swifts
	Halesowen Harriers	2	v	2	Long Buckby
r	*Long Buckby*	*1*	*v*	*1*	*Halesowen Hariers*
2r	*Halesowen Harriers*	*2*	*v*	*1*	*Long Buckby*

1st Qualifying Round – Saturday 14 September

	Rocester	0	v	3	Kettering Town
	Hinckley Athletic	5	v	1	Halesowen Harriers
	Bedworth United	3	v	3	VS Rugby
r	*VS Rugby*	*0*	*v*	*3*	*Bedworth United*
	Atherstone United	3	v	1	Cogenhoe United

2nd Qualifying Round – Saturday 28th September

	Kettering Town	0	v	0	Atherstone United
r	*Atherstone United*	*1*	*v*	*6*	*Kettering Town*
	Hinckley Athletic	1	v	1	Bedworth United
r	*Bedworth United*	*3*	*v*	*1*	*Hinckley Athletic*

3rd Qualifying Round – Saturday 12th October

	Kettering Town	0	v	1	Bedworth United

***Desborough 2 Bilston 2** (F.A. Cup 2nd Qualifying Round) Desborough's Roy Stewart is flanked by Bilston defenders Dave Braithwaite and Tim Preece during this epic F.A. Cup Tie.* Photo: Ray Pruden

***Witham Town 2 Grantham Town 5** (F.A. Cup Preliminary Round) Grantham's Adrian Speed gets in a fierce tackle on Witham Towns Gary Coe and Wendle Nightingale.* Photo: John Robinson

***Hednesford 4 Tamworth 2** (F.A. Cup 3rd Qualifying Round) It's going in! Tamworth open their account at Hednesford via Ian Bennett.* Photo: Paul Barber

SECTION 13

Preliminary Round Results – Sat. 31 Aug. 1996, 3.00pm

	Stafford Rangers	1 v 1	Redditch United
r	*Redditch United*	*0 v 1*	*Stafford Rangers*
	Chasetown	2 v 0	Boldmere St Michaels
	Barwell	0 v 2	Bilston Town
	West Midlands Police	1 v 2	Westfields
	Lye Town	0 v 4	Desborough Town

1st Qualifying Round – Saturday 14 September

	Westfield	0 v 4	Rushden & Diamonds
	Leicester Utd (Withdrawn)		Desborough Town (Withdrawn)
	Stafford Ragners	0 v 1	Bilston Town
	Gresley Rovers	2 v 1	Chasetown

2nd Qualifying Round – Saturday 28th September

	Rushden & Diamonds	4 v 0	Gresley Rovers
	Desborough Town	2 v 2	Bilston Town
r	*Bilston Town*	*5 v 2*	*Desborough Town*

3rd Qualifying Round – Saturday 12th October

	Rushden & Diamonds	1 v 0	Bilston Town

SECTION 14

Preliminary Round Results – Sat. 31 Aug. 1996, 3.00pm

	Dudley Town	1 v 3	Tamworth
	Rushall Olympic	1 v 3	Pelsall Villa
	Willenhall Town	1 v 0	Hinckley Town
	Newport Pagnell Town	0 v 1	Wednesfield
	Northampton Spencer	1 v 0	Oldbury United

1st Qualifying Round – Saturday 14 September

	Wednesfield	0 v 0	Hednesford Town
r	*Hednesford Town*	*6 v 0*	*Wednesfield*
	Racing Club	1 v 1	Northampton Spencer
r	*Northampton Spencer*	*2 v 2*	*Racing Club*
2r	*Racing Club*	*5 v 1*	*Northampton Spencer*
	Tamworth	4 v 1	Willenhall Town
	Evesham United	4 v 0	Pelsall Villa

2nd Qualifying Round – Saturday 28th September

	Hednesford Town	6 v 1	Evesham United
	Racing Club	0 v 5	Tamworth

3rd Qualifying Round – Saturday 12th October

	Hednesford Town	4 v 2	Tamworth

SECTION 15

Preliminary Round Results – Sat. 31 Aug. 1996, 3.00pm

	Stourport Swifts	0 v 4	Pershore Town
	Stratford Town	0 v 2	Shepshed Dynamo
	Knypersley Victoria	4 v 0	Stewarts & Lloyds
	Sutton Coldfield Town	0 v 0	Moor Green
	Replay: Moor Green	*3 v 2*	*Sutton Coldfield Town*

1st Qualifying Round – Saturday 14 September

	Moor Green	1 v 2	Solihull Borough
	Stourbridge	1 v 0	Halesowen Town
	Pershore Town	1 v 2	Knypersley Victoria
	Sandwell Borough	0 v 0	Shepshed Dynamo
r	*Shepshed Dynamo*	*5 v 2*	*Sandwell Borough*

2nd Qualifying Round – Saturday 28th September

	Solihull Borough	1 v 1	Shepshed Dynamo
r	*Shepshed Dynamo*	*1 v 0*	*Solihull Borough*
	Stourbridge	0 v 0	Knypersley Victoria
r	*Knypersley Victoria*	*1 v 0*	*Stourbridge*

3rd Qualifying Round – Saturday 12th October

	Shepshed Dynamo	1 v 0	Knypersley Victoria

r = Replay

SECTION 16

Preliminary Round Results – Sat. 31 Aug. 1996, 3.00pm

	Rothwell Town	5 v 1	Bourne Town
	Watton United	1 v 4	Bedford Town
	Wingate & Finchley	0 v 1	Spalding United
	Fakenham Town	2 v 2	Maldon Town
r	*Maldon Town*	*2 v 0*	*Fakenham Town*
	Burnham Ramblers	1 v 1	Great Yarmouth Town
r	*Great Yarmouth Town*	*3 v 1*	*Burnham Ramblers*

1st Qualifying Round – Saturday 14 September

	Maldon Town	2 v 7	Boston United
	Sudbury Wanderers	1 v 1	Great Yarmouth Town
r	*Great Yarmouth Town*	*0 v 1*	*Sudbury Wanderers*
	Rothwell Town	2 v 3	Spalding United
	Bishop's Stortford	2 v 0	Bedford Town

2nd Qualifying Round – Saturday 28th September

	Boston United	3 v 0	Bishop's Stortford
	Sudbury Wanderers	3 v 2	Spalding United

3rd Qualifying Round – Saturday 12th October

	Boston United	10 v 1	Sudbury Wanderers

SECTION 17

Preliminary Round Results – Sat. 31 Aug. 1996, 3.00pm

	Witham Town	2 v 5	Grantham Town
	Tilbury	1 v 1	Diss Town
r	*Diss Town*	*1 v 0*	*Tilbury*
	Lowestoft Town	1 v 2	Boston Town
	Wroxham	2 v 2	Great Wakering Rovers
r	*Great Wakering Rovers*	*0 v 1*	*Wroxham*
	Haverhill Rovers	5 v 1	Holbeach United

1st Qualifying Round – Saturday 14 September

	Wroxham	3 v 2	Kings Lynn
	Canvey Island	3 v 1	Haverhill Rovers
	Grantham Town	2 v 0	Boston Town
	Cambridge City	6 v 1	Diss Town

2nd Qualifying Round – Saturday 28th September

	Wroxham	1 v 1	Cambridge City
r	*Cambridge City*	*2 v 0*	*Wroxham*
	Canvey Island	1 v 1	Grantham Town
r	*Grantham Town*	*0 v 1*	*Canvey Island*

3rd Qualifying Round – Saturday 12th October

	Cambridge City	0 v 3	Canvey Island

SECTION 18

Preliminary Round Results – Sat. 31 Aug. 1996, 3.00pm

	Wivenhoe Town	2 v 2	Raunds Town
r	*Raunds Town*	*3 v 0*	*Wivenhoe Town*
	March Town United	2 v 1	Barkingside
	East Thurrock United	4 v 2	Mirrlees Blackstone
	Bury Town	4 v 1	Milton Keynes
	Saffron Walden Town	2 v 2	Newmarket Town
r	*Newmarket Town*	*0 v 0*	*Walden Town (Abandoned)*
ar	*Newmarket Town*	*3 v 0*	*Walden Town*

1st Qualifying Round – Saturday 14 September

	Bury Town	0 v 0	Heybridge Swifts
r	*Heybridge Swifts*	*3 v 0*	*Bury Town*
	Wisbech Town	2 v 1	Newmarket Town
	Raunds Town	2 v 4	East Thurrock United
	Chelmsford City	5 v 0	March Town United

2nd Qualifying Round – Saturday 28th September

	Heybridge Swifts	1 v 1	Chelmsford City
	Chelmsford City	2 v 1	Heybridge Swifts
	Wisbech Town	2 v 1	East Thurrock United

3rd Qualifying Round – Saturday 12th October

	Chelmsford City	2 v 3	Wisbech Town

***Ruislip Manor 1 Clacton Town 1** (F.A. Cup Preliminary Round) First-half action from Grosvenor Vale, as Town's centre forward Sid Edwards brings out a superb reflex save from Manor's 'keeper Stuart Amey to deny a gaol.*

Photo: Martin Wray

***Baldock Town 2 Tiptree United 0** (F.A. Cup 1st Qualifying Round) Brian Stean nets the Reds first goal.*

***Arlesey Town 0 Stevenage Borough 3** (F.A. Cup 1st Qualifying Round) Arlesey on the attack.* Photo: Stephen Ayres

SECTION 19

Preliminary Round Results – Sat. 31 Aug. 1996, 3.00pm

	Home				Away
	Corby Town	5	v	1	Eynesbury Rovers
	Haringey Borough	0	v	3	Hornchurch
	Soham Town Rangers	0	v	2	Stamford
	Cornard United	0	v	2	Gorleston
	Basildon United	0	v	2	Woodbridge Town

1st Qualifying Round Results – Sat. 14 September

	Home				Away
	Gorleston	1	v	2	Sudbury Town
	Billericay Town	4	v	0	Woodbridge Town
	Corby Town	4	v	1	Stamford
	Purfleet	5	v	1	Hornchurch

2nd Qualifying Round – Saturday 28th September

	Home				Away
	Sudbury Town	2	v	1	Purfleet
	Billericay Town	0	v	0	Corby Town
r	*Corby Town*	*1*	*v*	*1*	*Billericay Town*
2r	*Corby Town*	*3*	*v*	*1*	*Billericay Town*

3rd Qualifying Round – Saturday 12th October

	Home				Away
	Sudbury Town	1	v	0	Corby Town

SECTION 20

Preliminary Round – Sat. 31 Aug. 1996, 3.00pm

	Home				Away
	Leyton Pennant	0	v	0	Collier Row & Romford
r	*Collier Row & Romford*	*1*	*v*	*0*	*Leyton Pennant*
	Tiptree United	1	v	0	Hadleigh United
	Harefield United	2	v	4	Halstead Town
	Arlesey Town	3	v	1	Potton United
	Southend Manor	0	v	5	Braintree Town

1st Qualifying Round – Saturday 14 September

	Home				Away
	Arlesey Town	0	v	3	Stevenage Borough
	Marlow	0	v	2	Braintree Town
	Collier R. & Romford	1	v	1	Halstead Town
r	*Halstead Town*	*4*	*v*	*0*	*Collier R. & Romford*
	Baldock Town	2	v	0	Tiptree United

2nd Qualifying Round – Saturday 28th September

	Home				Away
	Stevenage Borough	1	v	1	Baldock Town
r	*Baldock Town*	*1*	*v*	*2*	*Stevenage Borough*
	Braintree Town	3	v	1	Halstead Town

3rd Qualifying Round – Saturday 12th October

	Home				Away
	Stevenage Borough	3	v	1	Braintree Town

SECTION 21

Preliminary Round – Sat. 31 Aug. 1996, 3.00pm

	Home				Away
	Berkhamsted Town	2	v	3	Chesham United
	Ruislip Manor	1	v	1	Clacton Town
r	*Clacton Town*	*3*	*v*	*2*	*Ruislip Manor*
	Concord Rangers	2	v	2	Barking
r	*Barking*	*1*	*v*	*0*	*Concord Rangers*
	Hoddesdon Town	0	v	1	Stotfold
	Potters Bar Town	5	v	1	Cheshunt

1st Qualifying Round – Saturday 14 September

	Home				Away
	Stotford	0	v	2	Hayes
	Hertford Town	1	v	2	Potters Bar Town
	Chesham United	3	v	1	Barking
	Grays Athletic	6	v	0	Clacton Town

2nd Qualifying Round – Saturday 28th September

	Home				Away
	Hayes	1	v	1	Grays Athletic
r	*Grays Athletic*	*0*	*v*	*0*	*Hayes*
2r	*Hayes*	*2*	*v*	*0*	*Grays Athletic*
	Potters Bar Town	0	v	4	Chesham United

3rd Qualifying Round – Saturday 12th October

	Home				Away
	Hayes	1	v	0	Chesham United

SECTION 22

Preliminary Round results – Sat. 31 Aug. 1996, 3.00pm

	Home				Away
	Uxbridge	2	v	1	Leighton Town
	Hillingdon Borough	1	v	4	Stowmarket Town
	Felixstowe Port & Town	0	v	1	Clapton
	Langford	0	v	4	Brackley Town
	Royston Town	1	v	0	Southall

1st Qualifying Round – Saturday 14 September

	Home				Away
	Brackley Town	1	v	1	Dagenham & Redbridge
r	*Dagenham & Redbridge*	*1*	*v*	*0*	*Braddey Town*
	Wembley	0	v	2	Royston Town
	Uxbridge	5	v	1	Clapton
	Harrow Borough	4	v	1	Stowmarket Town

2nd Qualifying Round – Saturday 28th September

	Home				Away
	Dagenham & Redbridge	0	v	0	Harrow Borough
r	*Harrow Borough*	*0*	*v*	*2*	*Dagenham & Redbridge*
	Royston Town	0	v	5	Uxbridge

3rd Qualifying Round – Saturday 12th October

	Home				Away
	Dagenham & Redbridge	3	v	0	Uxbridge

SECTION 23

Preliminary Round results – Sat. 31 Aug. 1996, 3.00pm

	Home				Away
	Edgware Town	1	v	1	Flackwell Heath
r	*Flackwell Heath*	*1*	*v*	*1*	*Edgware Town*
2r	*Flackwell Heath*	*0*	*v*	*3*	*Edgware Town*
	Brimsdown Rovers	1	v	3	Tring Town
	Ford United	1	v	0	Harwich & Parkeston
	Welwyn Garden City	2	v	0	Wootton Blue Cross
	Erith & Belvedere	2	v	2	Kingsbury Town
r	*Kingsbury Town*	*0*	*v*	*1*	*Erith & Belvedere*

1st Qualifying Round – Saturday 14 September

	Home				Away
	Welwyn Garden City	1	r	4	Aylesbury United
	Barton Rovers	2	v	2	Erith & Belvedere
r	*Erith & Belvedere*	*1*	*v*	*2*	*Barton Rovers*
	Edgware Town	3	v	3	Ford United
r	*Ford United*	*2*	*v*	*8*	*Edgware Town*
	Boreham Wood	8	v	1	Tring Town

2nd Qualifying Round – Saturday 28th September

	Home				Away
	Aylesbury United	0	v	3	Boreham Wood
	Barton Rovers	1	v	2	Edgware Town

3rd Qualifying Round – Saturday 12th October

	Home				Away
	Boreham Wood	3	v	2	Edgware Town

SECTION 24

Preliminary Round results – Sat. 31 Aug. 1996, 3.00pm

	Home				Away
	Hemel Hempstead	1	v	0	Ware
	Bowers United	2	v	1	Hanwell Town
	Stansted	2	v	1	Aveley
	Biggleswade Town	0	v	1	London Colney
	Sheppey United	1	v	2	Harlow Town

1st Qualifying Round – Saturday 14 September

	Home				Away
	London Colney	0	v	0	St Albans City
r	*St Albans City*	*4*	*v*	*1*	*London Colney*
	Hampton	2	v	1	Harlow Town
	Hemel Hempstead	0	v	1	Stansted
	Yeading	6	v	0	Bowers United

2nd Qualifying Round – Saturday 28th September

	Home				Away
	St Albans City	1	v	1	Yeading
r	*Yeading*	*0*	*v*	*1*	*St Albans City*
	Hampton	2	v	2	Stansted
r	*Stansted*	*2*	*v*	*1*	*Hampton*

3rd Qualifying Round – Saturday 12th October

	Home				Away
	St Albans City	5	v	1	Stansted

r = Replay
2r = 2nd Replay

***Tonbridge 1 Leatherhead 0** (F.A. Cup Preliminary Round) 'Angels' goalkeeper Joe Radford collects the ball at the Longmead Stadium.*
Photo: Tim Edwards

***Sittingbourne 4 Tooting & Mitcham 5** (F.A. Cup 2nd Qualifying Round) Goal no. 4!! As Tooting's David Kempton fires the ball past the outstretched Bourne defender Ricky Pearson and past the 'keeper.*
Photo: Martin Wray

***Tooting & Mitcham 0 Staines Town 1** (F.A. Cup 3rd Qualifying Round) Tooting & Mitchams Andy Symes dives to his left to save a penalty.*
Photo: Garry Letts

SECTION 25

Preliminary Round results – Sat. 31 Aug. 1996, 3.00pm

	Margate	0 v 1	Banstead Athletic
	Bedfont	1 v 2	Tunbridge Wells
	Peacehaven&Telscombe	5 v 0	Dorking
	Portfield	1 v 3	Three Bridges
	Selsey	3 v 1	Thamesmead Town

1st Qualifying Round – Saturday 14 September

	Three Bridges	1 v 6	Farnborough Town
	Bracknell Town	4 v 2	Selsey
	Banstead Athletic	1 v 3	Peacehaven & Telscombe
	Carshalton Athletic	6 v 0	Tunbridge Wells

2nd Qualifying Round – Saturday 28th September

	Farnborough Town	3 v 2	Carshalton Athletic
	Bracknell Town	5 v 2	Peacehaven & Telscombe

3rd Qualifying Round – Saturday 12th October

	Farnborough Town	3 v 2	Bracknell Town

SECTION 26

Preliminary Round results – Sat. 31 Aug. 1996, 3.00pm

	Dartford	1 v 1	Horsham
r	*Horsham*	*1 v 0*	*Dartford*
	Ashford Town (Middx)	2 v 0	Slade Green
	Shoreham	0 v 1	Wealdstone
	Southwick	0 v 0	Oakwood
r	*Oakwood*	*1 v 2*	*Southwick*
	Wick	0 v 2	Herne Bay

1st Qualifying Round – Saturday 14 September

	Southwick	1 v 2	Welling United
	Walton & Hersham	1 v 1	Herne Bay
r	*Herne Bay*	*1 v 0*	*Walton & Hersham*
	Horsham	1 v 0	Wealdstone
	Dulwich Hamlet	2 v 0	Ashford Town (Middx)

2nd Qualifying Round – Saturday 28th September

	Welling United	2 v 1	Dulwich Hamlet
	Herne Bay	1 v 0	Horsham

3rd Qualifying Round – Saturday 12th October

	Welling United	2 v 0	Herne Bay

SECTION 27

Preliminary Round results – Sat. 31 Aug. 1996, 3.00pm

	Worthing	0 v 1	Fisher
	Merstham	3 v 2	Deal Town
	Langney Sports	1 v 3	Chalfont St Peter
	Mile Oak	5 v 1	Lancing
	Croydon Athletic	2 v 0	Lewes

1st Qualifying Round – Saturday 14 September

	Mile Oak	0 v 3	Dover Athletic
	Hendon	2 v 0	Croydon Athletic
	Fisher	3 v 2	Chalfont St Peter
	Aldershot Town	8 v 1	Merstham

2nd Qualifying Round – Saturday 28th September

	Dover Athletic	2 v 0	Aldershot Town
	Hendon	0 v 0	Fisher
r	*Fisher*	*0 v 1*	*Hendon*

3rd Qualifying Round – Saturday 12th October

	Dover Athletic	0 v 1	Hendon

r = Replay **2r** = 2nd replay

SECTION 28

Preliminary Round results – Sat. 31 Aug. 1996, 3.00pm

	Tonbridge	1 v 0	Leatherhead
	Raynes Park Vale	1 v 4	Burnham
	Pagham	1 v 4	Northwood
	Ringmer	7 v 0	Steyning Town
	Whitehawk	1 v 6	Whitstable Town

1st Qualifying Round – Saturday 14 September

	Ringmer	1 v 2	Chertsey Town
	Molesey	3 v 1	Whitstable Town
	Tonbridge	2 v 0	Northwood
	Hastings Town	2 v 0	Burnham

2nd Qualifying Round – Saturday 28th September

	Chertsey Town	2 v 3	Hastings Town
	Molesey	0 v 0	Tonbridge
r	*Tonbridge*	*1 v 2*	*Molesey*

3rd Qualifying Round – Saturday 12th October

	Hastings Town	2 v 1	Molesey

SECTION 29

Preliminary Round results – Sat. 31 Aug. 1996, 3.00pm

	St Leonards Stamcroft	2 v 0	Metropolitan Police
	Viking Sports	2 v 0	Corinthian
	Arundel	3 v 0	Canterbury City
	Hailsham Town	2 v 2	Redhill
r	*Redhill*	*2 v 1*	*Hailsham Town*
	Hassocks	1 v 3	Egham Town

1st Qualifying Round – Saturday 14 September

	Redhill	0 v 1	Crawley Town
	Croydon	3 v 1	Egham Town
	St Leondards Stamcroft	4 v 1	Arundel
	Bromley	4 v 0	Viking Sports

2nd Qualifying Round – Saturday 28th September

	Crawley Town	0 v 4	Bromley
	Croydon	0 v 7	St Leondards Stamcroft

3rd Qualifying Round – Saturday 12th October

	Bromley	1 v 1	St Leonards Stamcroft
r	*St Leonards Stamcroft*	*2 v 5*	*Bromley*

SECTION 30

Preliminary Round results – Sat. 31 Aug. 1996, 3.00pm

	Whyteleafe	3 v 3	Chatham Town
r	*Chatham Town*	*2 v 0*	*Whyteleafe*
	Corinthian-Casuals	1 v 1	Chipstead
r	*Chipstead*	*2 v 4*	*Corinthian-Casuals*
	Burgess Hill Town	4 v 1	Epsom & Ewell
	Horsham YMCA	6 v 1	Littlehampton Town
	East Grinstead	2 v 3	Folkestone Invicta

1st Qualifying Round – Saturday 14 September

	Horsham YMCA	2 v 3	Sittingbourne
	Staines Town	2 v 0	Folkestone Invicta
	Chatham Town	1 v 2	Burgess Hill Town
	Tooting & Mitcham Utd	5 v 0	Corinthian-Casuals

2nd Qualifying Round – Saturday 28th September

	Sittingbourne	4 v 5	Tooting & Mitcham Utd
	Staines Town	2 v 1	Burgess Hill Town

3rd Qualifying Round – Saturday 12th October

	Tooting & Mitcham Utd	0 v 1	Staines Town

Buckingham Town 3 Hungerford Town 6 *(F.A. Cup 1st Qualifying Round) Action from Ford Street. As Hungerford striker Chris Brown races past his Robins marker.* Photo: Martin Wray

Weston-super-Mare 2 Brislington 0 *(F.A. Cup Preliminary Round Jon Bowering climbs above Tony Ricketts and Jeff Hazel to head an attempt on the visitors goal during his sides 2-0 F.A. Cup victory. Bowering scored the second of Weston's goals.* Photo: K. Gregory

Clevedon Town 4 Dorchester Town 1 *(F.A. Cup 1st Qualifying Round) Paul Thorpe, a 70th minute substitute, hits a powerful drive in the quest to pull back Dorchester's deficit at the hands of Dr. Martens League Southern Division Clevedon Town. Clevedon ran out 4-1 victors.* Photo K. Gregory

SECTION 31

Preliminary Round results – Sat. 31 Aug. 1996, 3.00pm

	Wimborne Town	1	v	1	Andover
r	*Andover*	*0*	v	*1*	*Wimborne Town*
	Eastleigh	0	v	3	Hungerford Town
	Cove	1	v	0	Ash United
	Wokingham Town	0	v	0	Fareham Town
r	*Fareham Town*	*4*	v	*1*	*Wokingham Town*

1st Qualifying Round – Saturday 14 September

	Fareham Town	2	v	1	Worcester City
	Witney Town	1	v	1	Oxford City
r	*Oxford City*	*2*	v	*3*	*Witney Town*
	Wimborne Town	5	v	0	Cove
	Buckingham Town	3	v	6	Hungerford Town

2nd Qualifying Round – Saturday 28th September

Fareham Town	4	v	2	Hungerford Town
Witney Town	2	v	1	Wimborne Town

3rd Qualifying Round – Saturday 12th October

Fareham Town	0	v	1	Witney Town

SECTION 32

Preliminary Round results – Sat. 31 Aug. 1996, 3.00pm

Thatcham Town	2	v	0	Brockenhurst
Lymington	6	v	1	Windsor & Eton
Bemerton Heath Harl.	2	v	0	Bicester Town
Maidenhead United	0	v	1	Havant Town

1st Qualifying Round – Saturday 14 September

	Havant Town	0	v	3	Bashley
	Basingstoke Town	0	v	3	Gloucester City
	Thatcham Town	1	v	1	Bemerton Heath
r	*Bemerton Heath*	*2*	v	*3*	*Thatcham Town*
	Thame United	1	v	1	Lymington
r	*Lymington*	*11*	v	*13*	*Thame United*

2nd Qualifying Round – Saturday 28th September

Bashley	4	v	3	Thame United
Gloucester City	1	v	3	Thatcham Town

3rd Qualifying Round – Saturday 12th October

Bashley	0	v	1	Thatcham Towv

SECTION 33

Preliminary Round results – Sat. 31 Aug. 1996, 3.00pm

Fleet Town	2	v	0	Waterlooville
Godalming & Guildford	5	v	2	Carterton Town
Bournemouth	1	v	3	Abingdon Town
Gosport Borough	2	v	1	Ryde
Portsmouth Royal Navy	1	v	6	Camberley Town

1st Qualifying Round – Saturday 14 September

	Gosport Borough	0	v	1	Cheltenham Town
	Weymouth	2	v	0	Camberley Town
	Fleet Town	0	v	3	Abingdon Town
	Salisbury City	0	v	0	Godalming & Guildford
r	*Godalming & Guildford*	*0*	v	*2*	*Salisbury City*

2nd Qualifying Round – Saturday 28th September

Cheltenham Town	4	v	3	Salisbury City
Weymouth	1	v	0	Abingdon Town

3rd Qualifying Round – Saturday 12th October

Cheltenham Town	1	v	0	Weymouth

SECTION 34

Preliminary Round results – Sat. 31 Aug. 1996, 3.00pm

Cirencester Town	1	v	0	Yate Town
Mangotsfield United	6	v	1	Chippenham Town
Falmouth Town	3	v	0	Barnstaple Town
Devizes Town	2	v	0	Westbury United
Melksham Town	2	v	1	Bridgwater Town

1st Qualifying Round – Saturday 14 September

	Devizes Town	2	v	2	Bath City
r	*Bath City*	*3*	v	*1*	*Devizes Town*
	Bideford	2	v	6	Melksham Town
	Cirencester Town	2	v	0	Falmouth Town
	Newport AFC	5	v	2	Mangotsfield United

2nd Qualifying Round – Saturday 28th September

Bath City	5	v	2	Newport AFC
Melksham Town	0	v	1	Cirencester Town

3rd Qualifying Round – Saturday 12th October

Bath City	2	v	0	Cirencester Town

SECTION 35

Preliminary Round results – Sat. 31 Aug. 1996, 3.00pm

Weston-Super-Mare	2	v	0	Brislington
Torrington	3	v	0	Paulton Rovers
Endsleigh	0	v	3	Bristol Manor Farm
St Blazey	2	v	0	Minehead
Glastonbury	2	v	4	Calne Town

1st Qualifying Round – Saturday 14 September

St Blazey	0	v	7	Merthyr Tydfil
Trowbridge Town	3	v	0	Calne Town
Weston-Super-Mare	4	v	0	Bristol Manor Farm
Forest Green Rovers	4	v	5	Torrington

2nd Qualifying Round – Saturday 28th September

Merthyr Tydfil	3	v	1	Torrington
Trowbridge Town	2	v	1	Weston-Super-Mare

3rd Qualifying Round – Saturday 12th October

Merthyr Tydfil	1	v	0	Trowbridge Town

SECTION 36

Preliminary Round results – Sat. 31 Aug. 1996, 3.00pm

Welton Rovers	3	v	2	Saltash United
Frome Town	3	v	0	Elmore
Tuffley Rovers	2	v	5	Taunton Town
Bridport	0	v	1	Clevedon Town

1st Qualifying Round – Saturday 14 September

Clevedon Town	4	v	1	Dorchester Town
Backwell United	0	v	6	Yeovil Town
Welton Rovers	0	v	6	Taunton Town
Tiverton Town	3	v	0	Frome Town

2nd Qualifying Round – Saturday 28th September

	Clevedon Town	0	v	2	Tiverton Town
	Yeovil Town	0	v	0	Taunton Town
r	*Taunton Town*	*3*	v	*5*	*Yeovil Town*

3rd Qualifying Round – Saturday 12th October

Tiverton Town	0	v	2	Yeovil Town

r = Replay **2*r*** = 2nd replay

4th ROUND QUALIFYING

Date 26th October

Ashford T 3 — **Kingstonian** 1
White 20; Curruthers 41, 50 — Darlington 90
Attn: 1,089

Barrow 1 — **Altrincham** 1
McDonald 29 — Hardy 55
1,861

Altrincham *4* — ***Barrow*** *0*
France 28, Hardy 53, 80; Harris 80
Attn: 1,141

Bath City 0 — **Cheltenham T** 0
1,088

Cheltenham T *4* — ***Bath City*** *1*
Boyle 90, Eaton 91; Smith 95, Howells 110 — Davis 35
Attn: 1,018
After Extra Time

Bedworth U 0 — **Boston United** 2
Williams 37; Chambers 89
Attn: 1,174

Boreham Wood 5 — **Thatcham T** 0
Robbins 27, 78, 83; Nisbet 37; Liburd 69
Attn: 522

Bromley 1 — **Sutton United** 0
Sharman 72
Attn: 1,063

Canvey Island 0 — **Sudbury T** 1
Brown 35

Cinderford T 0 — **Farnborough T** 4
Boothe 60, 71; Gavin 73; Day 75
Attn: 784

Colwyn Bay 1 — **Nuneaton B** 0
Donnelly 38

Gateshead 0 — **Consett** 1
McCloud 49
Attn: 856

Gravesend & N 1 — **Stevenage B** 5
Lovell 20 — Webster 27 pen; Crawshaw 45; Beevor 58; Venables 62; Browne 78
Attn: 1,330

Hastings Town 1 — **Hendon** 1
Simmons 50 pen — Darlington 12
753

Hendon *2* — ***Hastings Town*** *0*
Richardson 32; Darlington 34
Attn: 512

Hayes 1 — **Slough** 0
Brady 72
Attn: 1,803

Staines Town 0 Welling 1 *Wellings Robin Trott "Scores" but the goal was ruled out.* Photo: K. Gillard

Hednesford T ....2 **Telford U** 0
Lawrence 16
Street 90
Attn: 1,343

Hitchin T ....1 **Wisbech T**....................2
Coley 30 — Williams 45
Attn: 942 — Munns 63

Lancaster City........1 **Morecambe**.................1
Diggle 44 — Hartley 75 og
Attn: 2,500

Morecambe.................2 ***Lancaster City***..............2
Burns 35 — Flannery 31
McKnearney 105 — Borrowdale 112
Attn: 2,725

Morecambe.................4 ***Lancaster City***...............2
Leaver 4 — Shirley 13
Jackson 36 — Coleman 80
Norman 43, 60
Attn: 2,454

Leigh RMI ....2 **Runcorn** 4
Evans 74 pen — Wallace 1 og
Ridings 77 — Lee 30
Carragher 53
Heavey 75
Attn: 920

Merthyr.......................2 **Yeovil T** 1
Abraham 28 — Gill 67
Summers 82
Attn: 1,514

Newcastle T ....4 **Bamber Bridge**..........0
Ritchie 1, Dunn 55
Burndred 60, 69
Attn: 455

Newport IoW ....1 **Dag & Red**....................4
Barsdell 86 — Pratt 7
Pickering 52
Davidson 63
Naylor 78
Attn: 924

Thatchanm Town 0 Boreham Wood 5 *Glen Damen (Thatcham Town) tangles with Wood's Junior Samuels.*
Photo: Clive S. Butchins

Rushden & D ....2 **Bognor Regis T** 0
Collins 72, 83
Attn: 1,844

Shepshed D..............2 **Bromsgrove R** 0
King 55
Chamberlain 86
Attn: 969

Spennymoor U.......2 **Southport** 2
Innes 52, 55 — McDonald 21
Attn: 558 — Whittaker 63

Southport....................2 ***Spennymoor U***.............1
Clark 9 — Alderson 85
McDonald 60
Attn: 990

Staines T.....................0 **Welling U** 1
Attn: 250 — Dennis 29

Stalybridge C ....1 **Leek T** 0
Jones 40
Attn: 974

Whitby T ....2 **Blyth Spartans**...........1
Logan 44 — Henderson 23
Hodgson 63
Attn: 830

Witney T ....0 **St Albans C**..................4
Martin 48
Phillips 60 og
Bashir 62
Daly 73
Attn: 606

Witton Alb ....1 **Kidderminster H** 4
Wilde 54 — Henry 31 og
Doherty 37p, Olney 40
Hughes 62
Attn: 926

Hayes 1 Slough 0 *Slough are awarded a penalty, but do not score.*
Photo: Eric Marsh

FIRST ROUND PROPER

Date 16th November

Ashford Town 2 Dagenham & R 2
Warrilow 26 / Stimson 15
Dent 72 / Creaser 67 Attn: 1,813
Ashford Town: *Munden, Morris (sub 75 mins Chambers), O'Brien, Donn, Warrilow, Wynter, Wheeler, White, Allon, Dent, Ross. Subs not used: Parks, O'Leary.*
Dagenham: *Gothard, Culverhouse, Davidson, Double, Conner, Creaser, Parrat, Pratt, Rogers, Stimson, Naylor. Subs not used: Johnson, Oakley, John.*
Referee: *M. R. Halsey (Welwyn Garden City)*

Replay

Dagenham & R 1 Ashford Town 1
Rogers 5 / White 76 Attn: 2,424
aet: Ashford Town won 4-3 on penalties.
Dagenham: *Gothard, Culverhouse (sub 46 mins Jacques 6), Davidson, Double, Connor, Creaser, Parrat (sub 101 mins John), Pratt, Rogers, Stimson (sub 88 mins Johnson), Naylor.*
Ashford: *Munden, Morris (sub 46 mins Donn 6), O'Brien, Allon, Warrilow, Wynter, Wheeler, White, Caruthers (sub 111 mins Chambers), Dent, Ross. Sub not used: Parks.*
Referee: *M. Halsey (Welwyn Garden City).*

Blackpool 1 Wigan 0

Boreham Wood 1 Rushden & D 1
Robbins 9 / Hackett 27 Attn: 1,567
Boreham Wood: *Shepphard, Daly (sub 39 mins Fox), Joyce (sub 64 mins Holligdale), Hatchett, Nisbet, Harrigan, Prutton, Heffer, Robbins, Samuels (sub 83 mins Samuels), Shaw.*
Rushden & D: *Davies, Wooding, Tucker, Holden, Rodwell, Wilson, King 9, Butterworth (sub 75 mins Bailey), Alford (sub 75 mins Wilkin), Collins, Hackett. Sub no used: Capone.*
Referee: *A. P. Durso (Billericay, Essex).*

Replay

Rushden & D 2 Boreham Wood 3
Wilkin 15 / Heffer 45, M. Samuels 72,
Collins 90 / D.Samuels 90 Attn: 2,619
Rushden & D: *Davies, Wooding (sub 81 mins Capone), Tucker, Holden, Rodwell, Smith, King (sub 46 mins Bailey), Butterworth, Wilkin, Collins, Hackett (sub 88 mins Furnell.*
Boreham W: *Shepphard, Daly, Joyce, Howard, Nisbet, Harrigan, Prutton, Heffer, Robbins (sub 81 mins Samuels D), Samuels T, Shaw. Subs not used Holligdale, Fox.*
Referee: *A. P. D'Urso (Billericay, Essex).*

Boston United 3 Morecambe 0
Chambers 21, 57, 85 Attn: 2,935
Boston: *Bastock, Armstrong (sub 82 mins Melson 7), Withe, Fee, Hardy, Chambers S, Chambers L, Appleby, Brown, Williams, Mason. Subs not used: Munton, Cooke.*
Morecambe: *Banks, Knowles, Lavelle, Miller, Hughes, Burns, Cain (sub 66 mins Monk 7), Grimshaw, McCluskie (sub 70 mins Ceroala), Norman (sub 74 mins McKearney), Leaver 6.*
Referee: *U. D. Rennie (Sheffield).*

Brentford 2 Bournemouth 0

Bristol Rovers 1 Exeter 2

Bromley 1 Enfield 3
Kane 9 / West 18, 26, 67 Attn: 2,709
Bromley: *Wietecha, Rawlings, Campbell (sub 60 mins Dennington), Coles, Campfield (sub 60 mins Hope), Odedgi, Sharman, Loveday (sub 68 mins Francis), Warden, Tompkins, Cane.*
Enfield: *Pape, Harrigan, Underwood, Carstairs, Terry, St Hilaire, Moran, Edwards, West, Annon, Gentle. Subs not used: Gentle, Marchal, Marchal.*
Referee: *R. Styles (Waterlooville).*

Burnley 2 Lincoln 1

Cambridge Utd 3 Welling 0
Beall 2, Kyd 20
Barnwell 34 Attn: 3,187
Welling: *Knight, Watts, Cooper, Trott, Copley (sub 84 mins Farley), Horton, Brown D, (sub 84 mins Lewington), Rutherford, Morah, Dennis, Lakin. Sub not used: Smith.*
Referee: *G. Singh (Wolverhampton).*

Cardiff 2 Hendon 0
White 31
Middleton 88 Attn: 2,592
Hendon: *Wagenaar, White, Clarke, Murphy, Warmington, Kelly, Adams (sub 48 mins Kelly), Price, Darlington (sub 57 mins Bolton), Richardson, Lewis. Sub not used: Smart.*
Referee: *C.R. Wilkes (Gloucester)*

Carlisle 6 Shepshed Dynamo 0
Peacock 36, Davidson 16 og
Conway 61, Corbett 34 og
Archdeacon 74 pen
McAlindon 87 Attn: 4,394
Shepshed Dynamo: *Selby, Doughty (sub 77 mins Igoe), Bancroft, Knight, Rowe (sub 77 mins Chamberlain), Davidson, O'Kane, Corbett, Akeredolu, Riddel (sub 68 mins Parkins), Hare.*
Referee: *T. Leake (Darwin)*

Chester 3 Stalybridge 0
Rimmer 52, 87
Milner 89 3,151
Stalybridge: *Williams, Bates, Coathup, Hine, Bordman, Hall, Burke, Jones, Trott, Arnold, Charles. Subs not used: Powell M, Powell C, Challender.*
Referee: *D.B. Allison (Lancaster).*

Chesterfield 1 Bury 0

Colchester 1 Wycombe 2

Colwyn Bay 1 Wrexham 1
Roberts 68 / Hughes 76 Attn: 4,679
Colwyn Bay: *Roberts R, McCosh, Fuller, Harley, Graham, Price, Dulson, Roberts G (sub 89 mins Drury), Williams, Donnelly, Rigby. Subs not used: Mann, Caton.*
Referee: *T. Lunt (Ashton-in-Makerfield).*

***Andy Holmes** wins this heading dual for Newcastle Town against Notts County.*

***Sudbury Town 0 Brighton** 0 (F.A. Cup 1st Round Proper) Brighton's George Parris and Jason Peake (8) are split by Sudbury Town's Ian Brown shot on goal. This effort going just wide of the post.*

Photo: Andrew Chitty

***Bromley 1 Enfield 3** (F.A. Cup 1st Round Proper) Enfields Steve West (quarters shirt front) heads in his second goal of the game after 26 minutes.*

Photo: Garry Letts

Replay

***Wrexham* 2 *Colwyn Bay* 0**
Hughes 45, 81 Attn: 4,106
Colwyn Bay: *Roberts R, McCosh, Fuller, Harley (sub 79 mins Caton), Graham, Price, Dulson, Roberts G (sub 39 mins Drury), Williams, Donnelly, Rigby. Sub not used: Mann.*
Referee: *T. Lunt (Ashton-in-Makerfield).*

Crewe 4 Kidderminster 1
Macauley 16 — Yates 64
Murphy 28, 56
Lightfoot 73 Attn: 4,651
Kidderminster: *Steadman, Bignot, Prindiville, Weir, Brindley, Yates, Webb (sub 80 mins Casey), Willetts 6 (sub 66 mins Deakin), Hughes, McCue (sub 66 mins Olney 6), Doherty 7.*
Referee: *P. Robinson (Hull).*

Farnborough 2 Barnet 2
Wingfield 31 — Devine 72, 89
Boothe 39 Attn: 2,566
Farnborough: *MacKenzie, Stemp, Underwood, Day, Williams, Harford (sub 82 mins McAvoy), Boothe, Harlow, Gavin, Baker, Wingfield (sub 81 mins Mintram). Sub not used: Denny.*
Referee: *P. Alcock (Redhill).*

Replay

***Barnet* 1 *Farnborough* 0**
Devine 72 Attn: 2,215
Farnborough: *MacKenzie, Stemp (sub 89 mins McAvoy), Underwood, Williams, Mintram, Harford, Boothe, Harlow, Gavin, Robson, Wingfield. Subs not used: Rowe, Denny.*
Referee: *K.A. Leach (Wolverhampton).*

Gillingham 1 Hereford 0

Hartlepool 0 York 0

Replay

***York* 3 *Hartlepool* 0**

Hednesford 2 Southport 1
Russell 11
O'Connor 68
Collins 84 og Attn: 2,060
Hednesford: *Cooksey, Carty, Russell, Simpson, Comyn, Collins, McNally (sub 65 mins Devine), Lambert, Hemmings, Street, O'Connor. Subs not used: Brant, Essex.*
Referee: *Mr R. Poulain (Huddersfield).*

Leyton Orient 2 Merthyr 1
Winston 73 — Evans 47
West 87 Attn: 4,421
Merthyr: *Wager, Barnhouse, Downs, Abraham, O'Brien, Wimbledon, Mardenborough (sub 55 mins Ramsey), Wigley, Rees (sub 83 mins Pascoe), Evans (sub 78 mins Summers), Jones.*
Referee: *C.T. Finch (Bury St Edmunds).*

Macclesfield 0 Rochdale 2
Deary 10
Johnson 32 Attn: 3,134
Macclesfield: *Oakes, Tinson, Edey, Payne, Howarth, Sorvel, Circuit (sub 75 mins Bradshaw), Wood, Coates (sub 66 mins Williams), Power, Mitchell 6. Sub not used: Mottram..*
Referee: *R. D. Fernandez (Doncaster).*

Mansfield 4 Consett 0
Ford 30, Eustace 42
Doolan 45, Wood 74 Attn: 3,183
Consett: *Lee, Woodward, Gray (sub 46 mins Hagen), Quinn, Sugden, Smith, Rowell, Suddes, McCleod, Outterside, Brown (sub 86 mins Clarke). Sub not used: Kelly.*
Referee: *B. Burns (Scarborough).*

Newcastle Town 0 Notts County 2
(At Stoke City) Attn: 3,918

Northampton T. 0 Watford 1

Northwich 2 Walsall 2
Cooke 37, 77 — Wilson 48,
Lightbourne 52 Attn: 3,142
Northwich: *Greygoose, Ward, Fairclough, Crookes, Simpson, Bishop, Humphreys, Walters, Steele (sub 74 mins Tate), Crooke, Vicary (sub 70 mins Duffy). Sub not used: Reddish.*
Referee: *B. Coddington.*

Replay

***Walsall* 3 *Northwich* 1**
Lightborne 33, 50 — *Tait 69*
Wilson 41 pen Attn: 3,491

Peterborough U 0 Cheltenham T 0
Attn: 5,271
Cheltenham: *Molloy, Wotton (sub 90 mins Bloomer), Wring, Banks, Freeman, Victory, Howells, Wright, Boyle (sub 57 mins Eaton), Smith (sub 90 mins Chenowealth), Clarke.*
Referee: *Mike Pearce.*

Replay

***Cheltenham T* 1 *Peterborough U* 3**
Smith 116 — *Charlery 91, Grazioli 108*
Charlery 120 Attn: 4,160
Cheltenham: *Molloy, Wotton, Banks, Freeman, Wring, Victory (sub 90 mins Bloomer), Howells, Wright (sub 105 mins Chenowealth), Clarke, Smith, Eaton (sub 73 mins Boyle).*
Referee: *M. E. Pierce (Portsmouth).*

Plymouth 5 Fulham 0

Preston 4 Altrincham 1
Reeves 17, 30, 36 — Shepherd 78 pen
Ashcroft 79 Attn: 8,286
Altrincham: *Dickins, Shepherd, Heesom, France, Maddox, Doherty, Hardy (sub 85 mins Cain), Harris, Pritchard, Carmody, Rimmer. Sub not used: Carrol.*
Referee: *A. Wilkie (County Durham).*

Runcorn 1 Darlington 4
Heavy 28 — Naylor 8
Shaw 33, Crosby 67
Brumwell 75 Attn: 1,268
Runcorn: *Morris, O'Shaunessy, Ashton, Callaghan, Finlay, Chadwick (sub 68 mins Carragher), Whalley, Heavey, Dunn, Randles, Lee. Subs not used: McClelland, Warder.*
Referee: *E. Wolstenholme (Blackburn).*

Scunthorpe 4 Rotherham 1

Shrewsbury 1 Scarborough 1

Replay

***Scarborough* 1 *Shrewsbury* 0**

Stevenage 2 **Hayes** 2
Catlin 37 Williams 2
Hayles 74 Haynes 40 Attn: 3,288

Stevenage: *Gallagher, Webster, Mutchell, Grime (sub 64 mins Venables), Smith, Barrowcliff, Beevor, Browne (sub 90 mins Crawshaw), Cretton, Catlin, Hayles. Sub not used: Wilmot.*
Hayes: *Meara, Brady, Goodliffe, Kelly, Cox, Bunce, Hyatt, Hooper, Williams (sub 88 mins Roberts, J), Haynes (sub 77 mins Bartley), Wilkinson. Sub no used: Randall.*
Referee: *S. G. Bennett.*

Replay

Hayes *0* ***Stevenage*** *2*
Hayles 22, 79 Attn: 2,965

Hayes: *Meara, Brady (sub 46 mins Randall), Goodliffe, Kelly, Cox, Brunce, Hyatt, Hooper, Williams, Haynes, Wilkinson. Subs not used: Bartley, Roberts J.*
Stevenage: *Gallagher, Kirby, Mutchell, Sodje, Smith, Cretton, Beevor, Trebble, Venables (sub 77 mins Crawshaw), Catlin 7, Hayles (sub 84 mins Browne). Sub not used: Wilmot.*
Referee: *F. Bennett (Redhill).*

Stockport 2 **Doncaster** 1

Sudbury Town 0 **Brighton** 0
Attn: 3,112

Replay

Brighton *1* ***Sudbury*** *1*
Maskell 43 *Brown 23* Attn: 3,902
Aet; 90 mins 1-1: Sudbury win 4-3 on pens.

Sudbury: *Mokler, Girling (sub 74 mins Ball), Stafford 6 (sub 60 mins Reilly), Adams (sub 105mins Rolph), Tracey, Carter, Cheatham, Brown, McClean, Smith, English..*
Referee: *D. R. Elleray (Harrow-on-the-Hill).*

Swansea 1 **Bristol City** 1

Replay

Bristol City *1* ***Swansea*** *0*
Agostino 1 Attn: 8,017

Torquay 0 **Luton** 1

Wisbech 1 **St Albans** 2
Munns 50 Howell 55, 89 Attn: 2,509

Wisbech: *Edmunds, Shelton, Lindsay, Sharman, Moore, Massinghams (sub 89 mins Topliss), Parrot, Ward, Munns, Williams (sub 64 mins Gallagher), Setchell. Sub not used: Minet.*
St Albans: *Howells, Polston, Omogbehin (sub 33 mins Risley), Bashir, Mudd, Coleman, Cobb, Howell, Clark, Evans, Haworth. Subs not used: Martin, Thomas.*
Referee: *D. Orr (Iver, Bucks).*

Whitby Town 0 **Hull City** 0
Attn: 3,337

Replay

Hull City *8* ***Whitby Town*** *4*
Darby 9, 30, 45 *Pitman 10, 47 pen*
89, 98, 107 *50 pen*
Peacock 97 *Robinson 21*
Mann 118 Attn: 2,900

Whitby Town: *Campbell, Martin (sub 91 mins Hall), Logan, Goodrick, Pearson, Cooke, Borthewick (sub 91 mins Goodchild), Hodgson, Robinson (sub 105 mins Robertson), Toman, Pitman.*
Referee: *R. Pearson (Peterlee).*

Woking 2 **Millwall** 2
Foster 3 Savage
Walker 56 Crawford Attn: 5,448

Woking: *Batty, Howard, Taylor, Foster, Brown, Jones, Thompson, Wye, Steele, Hunter, (sub 85 mins Hay), Walker, Subs not used: Ellis, Wye, L..*
Referee: *G. Willard (Worthing).*

Replay

Millwall *0* ***Woking*** *1*
Walker 9 Attn: 6,084

Woking: *Batty, Howard, Taylor, Foster, Brown, Jones, Thompson, Wye S, Steele, Hunter (sub 84 mins Hay), Walker 9. Subs not used: Ellis, Wye L.*
Referee: *G. S. Willard (Worthing).*

Brendan Hackett *(Diamonds) scores to equalize against Boreham Wood.* Photo: Peter Barnes

SECOND ROUND RESULTS

Date 7th December

(Reports first published in *Team Talk*)

Barnet 3 **Wycombe** 3

Replay:Tuesday Dec 17, 7.45

Blackpool 0 **Hednesford** 1

O'Connor 87 Attn: 4,583

Hednesford *Cooksey, Russell, Collins, Simpson, Essex, Comyn, Hemmings, Lambert, Lake, Devine (sub 46mins Harnett), O'Connor. Subs not used: Lawrence, Dandy.

A simple tap in by ace goalscorer Joe O'Connor with three minutes to go set up a complete contrast in emotions. The Blackpool supporters were distraught and many started shouting for the departure of the manager and board, while Hednesford fans were delirious with joy as they celebrated reaching the Third Round for the first time in their 116 year history.

Keith Russell had finished a great run with a shot tipped onto the post before the alert predator gave manager/joint owner John Baldwin 'the greatest day of his life'. During the game the midlanders managed to frustrate the famous League side and a post plus great work by goalkeeper Scott Cooksey kept them in the game. Many of the more gracious Blackpool supporters gave 'The Pitmen' a great reception to cap a day they will always remember.

Bristol City 9 **St. Albans** 2

Goodridge 13, Agostino 22, 42, 48, 76, Kuhl 25, Hewlett 43, 55, Nugent 81

Clark 54, Daly 66

Attn: 7,136

St. Albans Howells, Mudd, Poiston, Coleman (sub 64mins Risely), Daly, Evans, Bashir, Cobb, ***Howell** (sub 46mins Blackman), Haworth (sub 87mins Martin), Clark.

ICIS League side St Albans had a taste of this year's FA Cup glory, having won their way through the punishing Qualifying matches. They were rewarded with an away draw at Football League Division 2 highflyers Bristol City, and the club decided to see the trip out in style.

Team Talk met up with the lads Saturday mid-day, at the Hilton International in Bristol City Centre, where they had spent the overnight pre-match preparations in Premier League style. The players, managers, directors and entire club back-room set up had made the trip, and were getting a taste for the big time. Chairman Bernard Tominey was enjoying his third recent trip to the city having watched Bristol City twice prior to the game as part of the club's preparations. He was at home in the resplendent surroundings of the Hilton and confidently gave us his only prediction "The match will definitely be played at Ashton Gate". Pretty safe bet there. Bernard had received a good luck fax from none other than press favourite Graham Taylor who had sent best wishes from Watford FC, a side with whom St Albans share a decent local relationship. The St Albans side is not short of professional links with training facilities often enjoyed by Arsenal and Spurs using Clarence Park for reserve games.

The Chairman was joined in the lounge by Managing Director Graham McDougall, a man used to this quality of life. Graham was enthusing about the support they had received from the ICIS League, who had supplied sweatshirts, and Adidas, who had sent them tracksuits from Germany.

At the sharp end, the managers and players were relaxing low key in a crucial period of the mental preparation for the game. Manager Alan Randall was sprawled on his bed, in a room shared with his assistant Erskine Smart. While the TV played SKY's lunchtime football build-up programme, Alan was working on some finer points of team selection on Hilton note-paper. The first impression of these two men was that they were not here for the day-out. The manager's opening gambit was clear: "We're 90 minutes away from Old Trafford". In recognising that this was a big game, the confidence of teams from the higher echelons of pyramid football today understand that results are not impossible, and the promise of an even bigger day out is a potent drug. "This is not the end of the rainbow for us" commented Alan.

However, the reality exists of the other side of the coin and a big defeat, and the management team were keen to ensure that "we must get total concentration for the first twenty", the strategy being to get doubt into the big side's psyche and turn the fans around.

Having had Bristol City watched, Alan Randall was aware of the pace of winger Gregory Goodridge. Whilst noting that he often "flattered to deceive", his pace would be a factor. "Our plan is to kick him – in the tunnel".

Player-coach Erskine Smart, unavailable from being Cup-tied after a loan spell at Dulwich Hamlet, summed up the mood of the camp: "We want more of this" he said.

Randall was adamant that his players were up for it, and said that none of them would freeze. We went to look for them to find out. The players were mostly together in the lounge, avidly watching Sky on the big screen. A great spirit with more than the usual amount of banter and self-mocking humour. "Golden boy" Greg Howell and captain Kevin Mudd were at the centre of the majority, with the large self-confidence of Rob Haworth demanding that he "would score within 30 minutes". Naseem Bashir was then collecting money for the club bet, which saw the lads place 50 quid on themselves at 11/1.

Ashton Gate's 10,000 crowd was swelled by the St Albans travelling army. The town had caught the travelling dose of cup fever and over 1000 townsfolk made their way down the M4 and into the Wedlock Stand at Ashton Gate. Amongst their numbers were three prospective parliamentary candidates, a few sensible politicians who had realised their election prospects would be seriously harmed by not being at St Albans big day. We met the army off the coaches and a large number met us with the first priority question of the day for travelling football supporters: "Where's the pub, mate?". And against our better judgement we directed them to The Robins.

In the crowd were several families, one of which was prominent with their vocal support was the Howarth's, kinsfolk of the afore-mentioned Rob. Mr Howarth senior was clear: "We're a decent side, you know."

Unfortunately on the day, the Saints recent patchy form told against an in-form City side and a 9-2 defeat ended the dream. Alan Randall remained upbeat and held on to his sense of humour with his final assessment: "Everything went to plan for the first 12 and a half minutes".

Cambridge **0** **Woking** **2**
Walker 74,
Taylor 83 Attn: 5,857

Woking Batty, Howard, Taylor, Foster, Brown, Jones, Thompson, Wye, S, Steele, (Sub 83 mins Ellis), Hay, (Sub 89 mins Hunter), Walker. Sub not used: Wye, L.

It's that man again! Clive Walker having impressed all those who saw him in the two excellent team performances against Millwall, produced another goal. This time it was a 30 yard cracker and if that wasn't enough, he started the move which Robin Taylor finished off to eliminate Cambridge and put Woking into the Third Round once again. Geoff Chappell and Colin Lippiatt have kept Woking around the top of the Conference with a steady flow of players moving in and out of the club. The club's facilities are improving all the time and surely they must join the Nationwide League within the next couple of years.

Cardiff **0** **Gillingham** **2**

Carlisle **1** **Darlington** **0**

Chester **1** **Boston** **0**
Milner 5 Attn: 3,344

Boston Bastock, Armstrong (sub 83mins Melson), Withe, Fee, Hardy, Chambers, S, Chambers, L, Appleby, Brown, Cooke (sub 74mins Smaller), Mason (sub 71mins Munton).

The least that Boston deserved from this encounter was a replay at York Street. Even the home team's sponsors recognised that, by giving the man of the match award to their keeper, Ronnie Sinclair. His greatest contribution was to save Boston's best chance, a penalty awarded in the 18th minute after Phil Brown had been brought down by Julian Alsford. Unfortunately player manager Greg Fee hesitated nervously in his run up, then helped Sinclair by side footing the ball only slightly to his right, so the City man was able to fall and grab gratefully.

This miss came when Chester were one up, having gained the lead in the fifth minute when Andy Milner was sent clear on the right to fire his shot across Paul Bastock and into the Boston net. Shortly afterwards Chester skipper, Peter Jackson, was booked for an unnecessary fracas in the centre circle. This was of greater signifance just before half time, when he pulled back Leroy Chambers and was walking even before referee Winter could extricate the red card.

As the first half progressed Chester became more and more anxious. Boston created many chances with Leroy Chambers, Brown and raiding wingback, Simon Armstrong, said to be a Manchester United target, prominent. Richard Mason on the other flank also had his moments and forced Sinclair to another fine save from a 25 yard free kick. Stuart Rimmer had a couple of Chester chances although his fellow attackers were frequently caught in the Pilgrims' offside trap. City must have been close to a penalty themselves two minutes after Fee's failure but Boston looked in most trouble when goalkeeper Bastock delayed clearing back passes.

The Deesiders looked better organised defensively in the second half but Leroy Chambers, Chris Cook, Mason twice, and even defender Martin Hardy, all had equaliser chances. Chester's Kevin Racliffe showed his managerial nerves with increasingly frequent charges from the dugout to tunnel as his side's luck held out, but Sinclair kept his net empty and was far and away his side's best player.

Boston's large and vociferous support will have been pleased by their team's efforts but disappointed that they were not able to turn their pressure and skill into a score. On this form they should be able to look forward to a Conference return at the season's end, which, long term, beats any Cup run.

Chester City: Ronnie Sinclair, Ross Davidson, Iain Jenkins, Matthew Woods, Peter Jackson, Julian Alsford, David Flitcroft, Chris Priest, Andy Milner (sub Spencer Whelan 90th min.), Stuart Rimmer, Neil Fisher (sub Kevin Noteman 71st min.).

Boston United: Paul Bastock, Simon Armstrong (sub Mark Melson 83rd min.), Chris Withe, Greg Fee. Martin Hardy, Steve Chambers, Leroy Chambers, Steve Appleby, Phil Brown Chris Cook (sub Carl Smaller 74th min.), Richard Mason (sub Darren Munton 89th min.).

Referee: Mr J.T. Winter (Stockton on Tees).

Chesterfield **2** **Scarborough** **0**

Enfield **1** **Peterborough U.** **1**
Marshall 19 Charlery 52 Attn: 2,847
Replay: Tuesday Dec 17, 7.45

Enfield Pape, Harrigan, Underwood, Carstairs, Terry, Fitzgerald, Moran, Edwards 6 (sub 75mins Gentle, J), West, Marchal, S (sub 63mins St. Hilaire), Annon. Sub not used: Gentle, D.

A delightful lob from Shaun Marshall after 19 minutes seemed to be enough to see Enfield through to the Third Round with another League scalp. But a wild tackle from centre half Hannigan led to a red card and a rearguard action that still only gave 'The Posh' two chances. Unfortunately Charlery, another ex-non League striker, from Fisher Athletic headed home a centre just after half time and then a replay suited everyone.

Peterborough U **4** **Enfield** **1**

I've seen little of the ICIS League, the London area being outside of my stomping ground, but I like Enfield. The club must surely rank as one of the football's unluckier sides. Last season, they were runners-up to Hayes, only goal difference separating the two. Hayes had a goal difference of 44; Enfield's was 43. Such ill-fortune seems to be the story of Enfield's life in recent seasons.

The 94/95 season saw Enfield win the league only to be refused promotion to the Vauxhall Conference as, after much debate, it was decided that the club's accounts did not satisfy Conference requirements.

Going back a bit further, 1986 saw the club romp to the Conference championship. Unfortunately, this was one year before promotion to the Football League was made automatic.

My sympathies lie with the club and its long-suffering fans, therefore, and this explains why I made the long drive over the bleak Fenlands to the London Road ground. That and the fact that the match looked promising.

Enfield, of course, have an FA Cup record to be proud of, and I was pretty confident that they would join their old League sparring partners, Woking and Stevenage in the Third Round (Enfield have been runners-up to both clubs in recent seasons). Peterborough, on the other hand, looked no more like a Goliath than Enfield looked like a David. Prior to this match they had won only four of twenty-three league games this season, leaving them in twenty-first position in Division Two.

In the first fifteen minutes neither side gained the upperhand or looked dangerous near the opposition's goal-mouth. The exception was Enfield's Martin St. Hilaire who was causing problems for Peterborough with his speed and determination.

In the nineteenth minute, though, the game changed completely. A David Morrison free-kick from 30 yards out wasn't cleared by the Enfield defence and Scott Houghton's strike gave the home team the lead.

Within a minute Peterborough had their second when Ken Charlery headed into the back of the net from inside the six-yard box. The scoreline wasn't a fair reaction of the game so far, but it was obvious that Enfield's defence was going to pay a heavy price if they didn't sort themselves out. Forwards were being left unmarked, defenders were stumbling over each other, the ball wasn't being cleared and there was a lack of control and decisiveness about the visitor's defence.

Ten minutes after Charlery had put the Posh two-up, Martin St. Hilaire scored from a corner, picking up on a flick by Jimmy Carstairs. This was the goal he had always looked like getting and Enfield were back in this game.

The goal brought Enfield to life and they started to play some fluent, passing football. But, in the thirty-fifth minute of the game Martin Carruthers killed off the match with a beautiful swerving shot from the edge of the box that beat the keeper to end in the right-hand corner of the net. Six minutes into the second-half and Martin Carruthers made it four, meeting a cross a few yards in front of goal and slotting the ball home.

This was effectively the end of the contest. Peterborough seemed content with the score and Enfield felt it beyond them to salvage the game. The remainder of the second-half was an aimless affair, despite three substitutions by each side. The only Enfield player who seemed to play with any sense of urgency was Matt Edwards who never stopped battling away in midfield.

The final whistle blew and the Enfield players went to take the salute from their fans. That the fans never stopped singing to the home crowd throughout the match is a credit to them; but this time it was not bad luck that led to Enfield's downfall. They were outplayed by a team which didn't play particularly well and I'm sure the manager and the players were disappointed. Newspapers tend to use expressions such as "brave minnows" on occasion such as this, but Enfield are no minnows and could have had more out of their cup run than a Second Round exit in front of a crowd of less than 4,000.

Hull	**1**	**Crewe**	**5**
Leyton Orient	**1**	**Stevenage**	**2**
Channing 9		Browne1, Catlin 22	
			Attn: 6,980

Stevenage Gallagher, Kirby, Mutchell, Sodje, Smith, Barrowcliff, Beevor, Browne, Catlin, Cretton, Hayles (sub 77mins Crawshaw), Subs not used: Wilmot, Adams.

Stevenage produced one of the upsets of the round by knocking out Third Division strugglers Leyton Orient in a thrilling battle at Brisbane Road. The fact that the kick off was delayed for 15 minutes, due to crowd congestion, only added to the excitement and anticipation of the travelling Stevenage fans. This was the first time Stevenage Borough had reached the second round and they must have fancied their chances after Leyton Orient needed a late winner against Merthyr Tydfil in the last round.

Stevenage had a dream start when a long Gallagher goal kick was flicked on by the Orient defender, Joseph, whose mistake let Boro' striker Corey Browne in to slide the ball past the ageing goalkeeping legend Peter Shilton, after only 54 seconds.

This early setback stunned Leyton Orient who out played Stevenage for the next 10 minutes before finally getting their reward when some poor Stevenage defending allowed Justin Channing to head in a well flighted cross at the far post.

A scrappy period followed, in which neither team took control of the match. This spell was broken after 22 minutes when the ball found Stevenage midfielder Neil Catlin on the edge of the penalty area. He flicked the ball over the last Orient defender and smashed the ball low and wide of the advancing Shilton.

Stevenage took charge of the match for the rest of the half, and their pressure should have been rewarded. A mix up between an Orient defender and Shilton put Boro's star man, Barry Hayles through clear on goal. As he took the ball round Shilton, who had advanced out of his area, Hayles was blatantly brought crashing down to the ground. The furious Stevenage fans demanded Shilton be sent off but perhaps his reputation made the referee only book him. The resultant free kick was wasted by Stevenage and Leyton Orient were let off the hook.

Half time could not come too soon for Orient but Stevenage knew there was a lot of defending to be done in the second half as the half-time match facts showed Stevenage with two shots on target and two goals.

The second half was dominated by Orient who should have made more of their many chances but were denied again and again by the superb goalkeeping of Des Gallagher. The first chance for Orient came from a corner which Stevenage failed to clear and a shot from point blank range was saved and held by the quick reactions of Gallagher.

It wasn't all Orient, however, and Stevenage had the chance to go three up when Crawshaw came on for Hayles and was not picked up which gave him the chance to break down the right. His cross was half cleared and the ball was read left to Browne who cut inside and pulled it back for ırrowcliff, who squandered the chance from 10 yards.

Orient looked very dangerous from set pieces and a succssion of corners threatened an equaliser. The towering Orit players somehow failed to make contact with Gallagher ger tipping the ball away each time and eventually the danr was over.

Stevenage defended stoutly and were just holding on after e referee had allowed five minutes of stoppage time. As Oriıt took a throw in the final whistle blew and the Stevenage ns went ecstatic. The match was the most historic victory of evenage's short but eventful history. Players and crowd celbrated together long after the final whistle. A money spinning e beckons in the next round for Stevenage.

uton	**2**	**Boreham Wd**	**1**
larshall 67, 84		Robbins 60	Attn: 5,332

ioreham W Sheppard, Daly, Joyce (sub 88mins Holligdale), loward, Nisbet, Harrigan, Prutton, Holligdale, Robbins, Samuels, (sub 78mins Samuels, D), Shaw. Sub not used: Hatchett.

ollowing a cross from Tony Samuels, Terry Robins scored his ninth goal to jointly lead the FA Cup goalscorers list this season. For the last twenty minutes this looked enough to give the CIS club a home replay but Dwight Marshall an ICIS old boy rom Grays Athletic via Plymouth, equalised after 67 minutes nd much to 'The Hatters' relief scored the winner with just ix minutes to go.

lansfield	**0**	**Stockport**	**3**
Notts Co.	**3**	**Rochdale**	**1**
reston	**2**	**York**	**3**
udbury	**1**	**Brentford**	**3**
		McGhee 51, Taylor 58, 74	Attn: 3,973

udbury Molker, Girling, Stafford (sub 80mins Ball), Adams (sub)mins Reilly), Tracey, Carter, Cheatham, Brown, McClean, Smith, nglish. Sub not used: French.

aying the game at Colchester, Sudbury enjoyed an attennce of nearly 4,000 but despite taking the lead through nristian McLean following a corner after 24 minutes, the ivision Two leaders showed their class and came back with ree second half goals despite another excellent display by alkeeper Steve Mokler.

/alsall	**1**	**Burnley**	**1**

eplay: Tuesday Dec 17 7.45

/atford	**5**	**Ashford**	**0**
zeley 50, 72			
onnolly 76, 81, 89			Attn: 7,590

shford Munden, Morris, O'Brien, Allon, Warrilow, Wynter, heeler, White (sub 69mins Chambers), Caruthers, Dent, Ross. bs not used: Donn, Parks.

Ashford's first day out for thirty years was sweet enough until around 4.30pm. Battling valiantly against a sharp and inventive Watford side, they were only 1-0 down, and striker Nicky Dent had just thundered in a 35 yard drive which Kevin Miller was lucky to tip over. A shock was still on the cards.

Then the dream faded as Watford scored four times in the last 18 minutes. The gulf between the Nationwide second division and the semi-pro game was cruelly exposed, as defensive blunders were gratefully accepted.

Before the match, Ashford manager Neil Cugley reckoned that the first 20 minutes would be vital. He must have been pleased, because at the end of that period Ashford had soaked up an early storm of pressure with few problems. Six corners had rained in on Maurice Munden's goal but he and a stout defence, marshalled by Tommy Warrilow, had coped comfortably.

Then, in the best move of the first half, Jeff Ross broke on the left, exchanged passes with Dent, and fed the ball to an unmarked Jason Wheeler on 18 yards. Wheeler's powerful shot beat Miller, but was just touched away by Watford's Keith Millen on the line.

Watford continued to apply pressure, and looked dangerous on the flanks, through Gary Penrice and Tommy Mooney, but Munden was able to deal comfortably with high balls. Ashford, however, broke well from midfield, and were by no means flattered to go in for half time level at 0-0.

Watford broke the deadlock soon after the interval when the confident Darren Bazeley picked up a fine crossfield ball from Steve Palmer and shot powerfully under Munden's dive.

On 72 minutes it was 2-0 when Paul O'Brien, under no pressure, lost possession and Bazeley was allowed to run on and fire in another good shot.

Then Watford substitute David Connelly carved a hat trick in 13 minutes as Ashford legs began to fail. A horrible blunder from Warrilow on 76 minutes let Connelly in for the easiest of chances, and he popped up twice more in the last five minutes to complete the rout.

After the game, Ashford's two best players Dent and Wheeler vented their disappointment at the scoreline, but had to admit that Watford had taken their chances well. "They are a class act who will be pushing for promotion at the end of the season" said Wheeler.

Finally, a tribute and a prediction. Although he did not get on the scoresheet, Watford striker Gifton Noel-Williams had a great game. Strong and inventive, he harried the Ashford defence with probing runs all afternoon, despite close and sometimes unfriendly attention from Ashford defenders. Noel-Williams is only 16 and has just become Watford's youngest ever goal scorer. Given his age and his potential, he looks a future international striker. So when Alan Shearer moves over, remember that you heard it first in Team Talk.

THIRD AND FOURTH ROUND RESULTS

4th & 25th January 1997

THIRD ROUND

Stevenage Bor. (0) 0 Birmingham C. (1) 2

No doubt both clubs thoroughly appreciated the increased gate revenue from playing this tie in Birmingham, but Stevenage would have been particularly difficult to beat at home, whereas the First Division club, once Borough's initial burst of enthusiasm had been weathered, rarely felt threatened by the Conference champions in the security of St Andrews.

This is not to say Stevenage didn't acquit themselves admirably. Barry Hayles was involved with three chances and one of these needed to be taken early in the game to boost the confidence of the semi professionals and create doubts in the Brummie hearts.

However it was the artistic Sodje who, attempting an over elaborate back heel, was robbed on the edge of the penalty area and allowed Devlin to set up Francis with an open goal after 27 minutes.

The Conference side continued to play well but without really worrying 'The Blues' but the penalty given against the luckless Sodje midway through the second half was harsh to say the least. Top scorer Devlin who had tumbled in the area took the opportunity to increase his goal tally and Borough's brave cup run was over.

After all last season's fuss about the grading of their ground, you cannot help wishing they had presented their stadium to the senior football world for this tie and who knows it might well have made all the difference to the result. It clearly would have improved Stevenage Borough's Football League credibility.

Stevenage: Gallagher, Mutchell, Kirby, Sodje, Smith, Webster (Adams 53), Catlin (Trebble 72), Barrowcliff, Beevor, Browne (Crawshaw 80), Hayles. **Booked:** Catlin.
Birmingham City: Bennett, Grainger (Johnson 76), Bruce, Ablett, Bass, Bowen, Tait, Horne, Holland (Legg 71), Francis, Devlin. **Sub:** Kristenson. **Booked:** Bruce, Albett. **Goals:** Francis (26), Delvin (63).
Referee: M Pierce (Portsmouth)

Hednesford Town (1) 1 York City (0) 0

Having enjoyed the club's most memorable victory at Blackpool in the previous round perhaps it was asking too much for the Staffordshire townsfolk to be presented with another league scalp but a capacity crowd packed in and were rewarded with an excellent cup tie played in a good spirit.

Scoot Cooksey again proved his worth when most needed but when the home side won a much contested corner just before half time, the visitors were still unsettled as Paul Carty's shot from the edge of the penalty area beat the packed defence and 'keeper Clarke before Gary Himsworth handled on the line.

A red card had to be shown and Keith Russell duly scored to send the 'The Pitman' off for half time with Keys Park buzzing.

With their ten men battling valiantly and the memories of cup victories over Everton and Manchester United to draw upon, York battled gamely but vital chances were missed and Hednesford settled down to deservedly qualify for the glory game with Middlesbrough.

The last minutes were desperate but they just made the final whistle more emotional!

Hednesford Town: Kooksey, Fitzpatrick, Simpson, Comyn, Collins, Carty, McNally, Lambert, Lake, Russell, O'Connor. **Subs:** Devlin, Essex, Street. **Booked:** McNally, Collins, Carty, Comyn.
York City: Clarke, McMillian, Sharples, Barras, Atkinson (Tutill 60), Himsworth, Pepper, Pouton (Murty 65), Stephenson, Tolson, Bull. **Subs:** Warrington (9). **Booked:** Pouton, Sharples, Stephenson, Tolson. Sent off: Himsworth.
Referee: T Heilbron (Newton Aycliffe)

Coventry City (0) 1 Woking (0) 1

This much delayed Third Round match eventually went ahead three weeks late, on Fourth Round day, but it was well worth the wait!

The Cards gave notice of their intentions as early as the third minute, diminutive midfielder Scott Steele controlling the ball well with his back to goal before turning, finding space and unleashing a shot from 25 yards which went straight past the upright with home keeper Steve Ogrizovic at full stretch. At the other end, Woking defender Terry Howard was forced to head behind following a dangerous cross from the left by John Salako. On 18 minutes another Salako cross was met by Noel Whelan, whose first time shot from 15 yards clipped the framework behind the goal. Eight minutes latter, Woking keeper Laurance Batty spread himself brilliantly to deny the impressive Darren Huckerby a certain goal after a spell of 'head tennis' and an eventual flick on by Whelan had put him clear. Woking however, easily matched the Premiership side stride for stride and some delightful triangular passing moves involving Steele, Shane Wye, and the ageless Clive Walker had the Coventry defence chasing shadows, but they seemed to lack a killer touch up front, new signing Justin Jackson from Morecambe being ineligible.

On 42 minutes, City almost took the lead. A long throw on the right reached Eion Jess, who played a neat ball inside to Huckerby. His shot from 20 yards took a wicked deflection off Howard, but Batty was just able to scramble across goal and finger tip the ball onto the post. On the stroke of half time, a scene reminiscent of the Seventies saw Walker shake off his marker and sprint down the left before delivering another of his trademark deep, hanging crosses to the far post which Ogrizovic met just before the head of Junior Hunter.

At the start of the second half, City stepped up a gear and initially threatened to overwhelm the Cards, but gradually Woking got to grips with the increased pace and began to look comfortable once again. On 62 minutes, Tom Jones showed he was enjoying the green, green grass by playing a magnificent defence-splitting pass to Walker on the left. Scott Steele made a superb run inside him, taking the defender away, allowing Walker the space to cut in and try a shot from 18 yards, unfortunately with his weaker foot, which still had Ogrizovic scrambling across goal to make the save.

Once again City stepped up the pressure, and only Batty's legs denied skipper Gary McAllister, when Whelan looking suspiciously offside. Two superb sliding tackles, Kevan Brown on Whelan and Steve Foster on Huckerby, continued to frustrate the Sky Blues, Robin Taylor made a crucial interception to deny McAllister a clear sight of goal and Foster kicked Huckerby's header off the line.

On 74 minutes, City finally got a breakthrough. Salako shook off the attentions of Shane Wye on the left, took the ball down to the goal line and crossed. McAllistar took a wild swing and missed completely, allowing the ball to run on to the unmarked Jess, who drilled it past Batty from ten yards.

To their credit, Woking refused to lie down and mounted a series of assaults on the Coventry goal, but an equaliser just seemed beyond them. In the very last minute though, yet another patient build up resulted in Jones picking out Taylor on the edge of the area. His header across goal was met by former Wycombe midfielder Steve Thompson. His initial header back, rebounded to him off a defender, and he was first to react, poking the ball beyond Ogrizovic into the far corner, sending the 4000-plus Woking fans into raptures. It was certainly no more than they deserved. At the end, the Woking players and supporters applauded and cheered each other for fully 20 minutes.

At this stage I have traditionally nominated a man of the match. On this occasion the award goes to the whole Woking team, for a quality, truly memorable team performance.

Coventry City: Ogrizovic, Shaw, Borrows, Williams, Richardson, Telfer, McAllistar, Jess, Salako, Huckerby, Whelan. **Subs:** Hall, Ducros, Filan (g). **Goal:** Jess (75). **Booked:** Telfer.
Woking: Batty, S Wye, Howard, Brown, Foster, Taylor, Jones, Thompson, Steele, Hunter (Hay 80), Walker. **Subs:** Ellis, L Wye. Goal: Thompson (90). **Booked:** Howard.
Referee: M Riley (Leeds).

Woking (1) 1 Coventry City (1) 2

Full marks to Woking who were the first non-League club to hold a Premier League club in the FA Cup – their away draw must have made everyone wonder!

Their beautiful new stand looked splendid and their Kingfield ground acted as a typical example of a famous old amateur and now semi professional club being transformed for the modern professional game it would clearly love to join.

Coventry City were truly frightened by the prospect of failure and the poor quality of their play and the frayed nerves shown by Huckerby and his supporting colleagues after a foul by Kevan Brown, really set up the prospect of a little more FA Cup history making for 'The Cards'.

However, the resulted free kick brought a deflection, a flick on and a tap in for Whelan.

This should have calmed the Premier team but no, Woking again came back to play cultured sensible football and Clive Walker centered from the right for Scott Steele to turn in an equaliser at the near post.

Coventry's football was at best, ragged but despite some quality touches from Walker, and superb pressure which lifted the crowd, it was Steve Ogrizovic who kept his team in the game and as so often happens, the part timers were pressured into defensive mistakes in front of brave Laurence Batty. Two deflections finished with the luckless Steve Foster heading into the corner of his net instead of past the post.

A couple more efforts by Walker couldn't bring a goal and another wonderful cup run was over.

Manager Geoff Chapples and his backroom team were understandably proud of their players and the fans were thrilled.

Coventry were very happy indeed – they can now go to Blackburn Rovers as comfortable underdogs and start enjoying the FA Cup.

Woking: Batty, S Wye, Howard, Brown, Foster, Taylor, Thompson, Jones, Steele, Walker, Hay (Hunter 85). **Subs:** Ellis, L Wye. **Booked:** Taylor, Brown.
Coventry City: Ogrizovic, Telfer, Shaw, Borrows, Williams, Hall, McAllistar, Richardson, Whelan, Jess (Strachan 89), Huckerby (Ndlovu 68). **Sub:** Filan (g). **Booked:** Huckerby, Borrows, Williams.
Referee: M. Riley (Leeds).

FOURTH ROUND

Hednesford Town (1) 2 Middlesbrough (1) 3

Hednesford have scored – O'Connor of course!

The word spread round non-League grounds all over the country at one minute past three on Saturday 25th January.

Then we all expected the worst when Middlesbrough's equaliser was reported, through a muddled own goal, but half time at 1-1 sounded encouraging.

We then lost interest as our own games took over but late news from all the airwaves brought despair as Coventry took the lead against Woking and Manchester United appeared to have eliminated Wimbledon. Rumour had it that Hednesford were out but when the results came flashing through the FA Cup had struck again.

Equalisers for Woking and Wimbledon brought replays and plucky Hednesford not only scored a second but at 1-2 down with two minutes to go, O'Connor hit a post a goal and two more goals were still to follow, what a fantastic finish to a memorable Cup run!

"It was what we are all in the game for – a wonderful dream come true that makes all the day-today hard work really worthwhile."

Hednesford Town manager John Baldwin still hadn't come down to earth four days after his teams wonderful Fourth Round performance in the FA Cup at Middlesbrough. The joys and excitement of the competition can surely never have been so clearly appreciated.

"The winning goal at Blackpool was a great moment which meant so much to the club and its supporters and then our performance against York City was excellent.

Most of the reporters sent in their reports early and didn't really emphasise the fact we played them off the park in the second half, but to succeed when we knew the winners would play Middlesbrough was a thrill in itself and the thought of taking on all those star names was certainly intimidating.

I found the real satisfaction was pitting our wits against famous managers and players. We did our homework for all the games and the players were never allowed to just think about going along to enjoy the experience and the day out. We went out to do our job and the lads all knew their particular responsibilities.

However much a manager tells his full time professionals to give respect to part time opposition, you know that players deep down might think it's going to be easy.

Once that feeling has set in, it's practically impossible to move them up a gear and if the opposition are from the lower leagues like Blackpool and York City you do have a chance if your players have the desire and can concentrate on the game plan without being too overawed. (We lost to Canvey Island last season!)

This season it came right for us twice and we very nearly caused a major upset at The Riverside Stadium.

The locals had really been uplifted by the cup run and it was great to see a smile back on the face of the community who had recently had a pit closed down in the area. Everyone was up for the trip and although we took some stick for taking the game to Middlesbrough I'm sure the sixty coach loads who helped make up the biggest ever away support (7,000) to have visited the new stadium, will treasure that day all their lives

The demand for replica shirts, scarfs, hats and wigs was just too great for us to satisfy and everything was sold out immediately it went on sale. The atmosphere before the game was just magnificent and I must admit that during the day I cried countless times – the emotion of seeing our club – it's players and supporters alike, enjoying a dream world that they had all deserved, was sometimes just too much!

I saw one of my oldest players Steve Essex marking Ravanelli and one of the youngest Stuart Lake, who had been out on loan with Nuneaton Borough, marking Emerson and at training there were a few relieved faces when I gave the man for man marking job of looking after Juninho to Wayne Simpson!

He did a great job however, and what an experience for him to treasure for the rest of his life.

All the players were heroes and perhaps their efforts will bring them individual rewards. There cannot be many better goalkeepers than Scott Cooksey in non-League football while Joe O'Connor has scored over 300 goals for me in the last seven seasons and Andy turned down a two year contract at West Bromwich Albion to become an accountant and play football for us.

Obviously we knew that man for man Middlesbrough were obviously better than us, but as a team – that was a different matter!

The desire, spirit and pride matched the concentration the whole team shared in doing their individual jobs. The national press were mystified that a non-League club should actually pass the ball around, create and take chances and not rely on the old fashioned kick and rush blustering of years gone by.

We will always wonder what would have happened if instead of striking the post at 1-2 down, we had equalised – but we'll never know!

We do know we played well, enjoyed every second of the experience and have only happy memories of the day.

Middlesbrough Football Club treated the players, management, administrators and supporters as equals, we appreciated that and on the day I think we proved them right!"

Hednesford: Cooksey, Fitzpatrick, Essex, Comyn, Collins, Simpson, Carty, Lambert, Lake (Devine 85), Russell (McNally 85), O'Connor. Sub: Hemmings. **Goals:** O'Connor (14,90). Booked: Simpson, McNally.
Middlesbrough: Roberts, Kinder, Festa, Vickers, Whyte, Juninho, Mustoe, Emerson, Moore, Beck (Fjortoft 75), Ravanelli. Subs: Liddle, Ormerod. **Goals:** Lambert (og 26), Fjortoft (86), Ravanelli (88).
Referee: M Bodenham (Looe, Cornwall).

1996-97 REVIEW

Woking celebrate! *A victorious quartet line up for the camera, (left to right) Clive Walker, Darren Hay, Laurence Batty and Manager Geoff Chappel*

Photo: Martin Wray

FIRST QUALIFYING ROUND

Saturday 19th October

	Home	Score	Away	Attn
	Atherstone United	0 v 2	Whitley Bay	Attn: 218
	Atherton LR	1 v 1	Moor Green	Attn: 150
r	*Moor Green*	*6 v 1*	*Atherton LR (22/10)*	Attn: 130
	Stafford Rangers	1 v 2	Curzon Ashton	Attn: 408
	Droylsden	1 v 1	Leigh RMI	Attn: 140
r	*Leigh RMI*	*1 v 3*	*Droylsden (22/10)*	Attn: 112
*	Nuneaton B.	0 v 3	Congleton Town	Attn: 902
	Alfreton Town	4 v 4	Bilston Town	Attn: 156
r	*Bilston Town*	*4 v 1*	*Alfreton Town*	Attn: 151
	Warrington Town	0 v 2	Lancaster City	Attn: 106
	Bedworth United	0 v 0	Gretna	Attn: 262
†	Gretna	1 v 4	Bedworth United	Attn: 118
	Hinckley Town	0 v 2	Worksop Town	Attn: 124
	Harrogate Town	2 v 3	Knowsley United	Attn: 172
	Grantham Town	1 v 0	Leek Town	Attn: 295

	Home	Score	Away	Attn	
	Racing Club Warick	1 v 2	Frickley Athletic	Attn: 103	
	Tamworth	2 v 2	Great Harwood T.	Attn: 506	
r	*Great Harwood T.*	*1 v 0*	*Tamworth*	Attn: 189	
	Paget Rangers	0 v 1	Eastwood Town	Attn: 110	
	Buxton	2 v 1	VS Rugby	Attn: 204	
	Matlock Town	1 v 4	Winsford United	Attn: 253	†
	Stocksbridge P. S.	1 v 0	Sutton Coldfield T.	Attn: 130	
	Solihull Borough		Leicester United	*(walkover for Solihull Borough - Leicester United withdrawn)*	
	Witton Albion	3 v 3	Workington	Attn: 286	
r	*Workington*	*1 v 0*	*Witton Albion*	Attn: 285	
	Netherfield	2 v 3	Farsley Celtic	Attn: 75	
	Cirencester Town	2 v 2	Cambridge City	Attn: 127	
r	*Cambridge City*	*6 v 5*	*Cirencester Town*	Attn: 195	‡
	Workington Town	1 v 0	Erith & Belvedere	Attn: 196	
	Ashford Town	4 v 1	Hitchin Town	Attn: 544	

* BEST ATTENDANCE † LARGEST AWAY VICTORY ‡ LARGEST AGGREGATE § LARGEST HOME VICTORY

Gary Smith *of Tamworth bursting through the Great Harwood defence* Photo: Tim Durant

Hitchin keeper **Lee Pearce** *takes this corner under no pressure at Ashford.* Photo: Alan Coomes

	Home	Score	Away	Attn
	Tonbridge	0 v 2	Aylesbury United	Attn: 438
	Fareham Town	2 v 2	Weymouth	Attn: 244
§ r	*Weymouth*	*7 v 0*	*Fareham Town*	*Attn: 547*
	Whyteleafe	0 v 1	Yeading	Attn: 84
	Baldock Town	3 v 2	Stourbridge	Attn: 251
	Margate	1 v 2	Aldershot Town	Attn: 487
	Buckingham Town	0 v 1	Forest Green Rovers	Attn: 88
	Hendon aet	1 v 1	Thame United	Attn: 162
r	*Thame United*	*1 v 1**	*Hendon*	Attn: 126
2r	*Thame United*	*0 v 3*	*Hendon*	Attn: 132
	Chesham United	1 v 1	Walton & Hersham	Attn: 416
r	*Walton & Hersham*	*1 v 3*	*Chesham United*	Attn: 237
	Bishop's Stortford	3 v 0	Croydon	Attn: 337
	Hampton	4 v 1	Trowbridge Town	Attn: 173
	Raunds Town	4 v 1	Barton Rovers	Attn: 101
	Canvey Island	0 v 1	Heybridge Swifts	Attn: 361
	Gravesend & Northfleet	2 v 2	St. Leonards Stamcroft	Attn: 424
r	*St. Leonards Stamcroft*	*4 v 3*	*Gravesend & Northfleet*	Attn: 440
	Yate Town	1 v 3	Kings Lynn	Attn: 168
	Sitingbourne	3 v 2	Fleet Town	Attn: 519
	Weston-s-Mare	2 v 0	Worthing	Attn: 251
	Newport (IW)	3 v 3	Leyton Pennant	Attn: 335
r	*Leyton Pennant* aet	*2 v 1**	*Newport (IW)*	Attn: 204
	Abingdon Town	0 v 2	Evesham United	Attn: 194
	Maidenhead Utd	4 v 2	Corby Town	Attn: 131
	Bromley	1 v 0	Uxbridge	Attn: 250
	Cinderford Town	2 v 3	Havant Town	Attn: 215
	Grays Athletic	2 v 1	Bashley	Attn: 103
	Billericay Town	3 v 0	Berkhamsted Town	Attn: 258
	Fisher	2 v 2	Molesey	Attn: 129
r	*Molesey*	*1 v 2*	*Fisher*	Attn: 125
	Marlow	1 v 1	Witney Town	Attn: 160
r	*Witney Town*	*2 v 1*	*Marlow (22/10)*	Attn: 167
	Dorchester Town	1 v 0	Waterlooville	Attn: 408

* *After Extra Time*

SECOND QUALIFYING ROUND

Saturday 9th November

	Home	Score	Away	Attendance
	Moor Green	2 v 1	Ilkeston Town	Attn: 255
	Workington	1 v 0	Redditch United	Attn: 251
	Farsley Celtic	1 v 1	Worksop Town	Attn: 164
r	*Worksop Town* aet	*2 v 1*	*Worksop Town*	Attn: 217
	Stocksbridge P. S.	2 v 2	Shepshed Dynamo	Attn: 250
r	*Shepshed Dynamo*	*0 v 1*	*Stocksbridge P.S.*	Attn: 185
	Buxton	1 v 0	Eastwood Town	Attn: 222
	Congleton Town	1 v 3	Solihull Town	Attn: 223
	Whitley Bay	0 v 1	Bradford (Park Ave)	Attn: 214
	Bliston Town	4 v 0	Great Harwood T.	Attn: 122
	Lancaster City	2 v 0	Droylsden	Attn: 236
	Lincoln United	3 v 4	Frickley Athletic	Attn: 161
	Grantham Town	2 v 1	Winsford United	Attn: 285
	Curzon Ashton	0 v 2	Bedworth United	Attn: 110
	Knowsley United	3 v 2	Flixton	Attn: 80
	Heybridge Swifts	2 v 1	Grays Athletic	Attn: 270
†‡	Oxford City	1 v 6	Basingstoke Town	Attn: 325
	Weymouth	4 v 1	Clevedon Town	Attn: 630
	Aylesbury United	1 v 1	Sittingbourne	Attn: 506
r	*Sittingbourne*	*v*	*Aylesbury United*	Attn: 482
	Salisbury City	1 v 0	Witney Town	Attn: 391
	Weston-s-Mare	1 v 3	Raunds Town	Attn: 241
	Forest Green Rov.	1 v 2	Cambridge City	Attn: 236
	Maidenhead Utd	1 v 3	Bromley	Attn: 217
*	Aldershot Town	3 v 0	Chesham United	Attn: 1943
	Hendon	1 v 3	Sutton United	Attn: 402
	Hampton	0 v 1	St. Leonards Stramcroft	Attn: 225

	Home	Score	Away	Attendance
	Chertsey Town	1 v 1	Yeading	Attn: 222
r	*Yeading*	*v*	*Chertsey Town*	Attn: 154
	Fisher Athletic	1 v 1	Havant Town	Attn:
r	*Havant Town*	*2 v 3*	*Fisher Athletic*	Attn: 146
	Dartford	1 v 1	Tooting & Mitcham Utd	Attn: 461
r	*Tooting & Mitcham Utd*	*2 v 3*	*Dartford*	Attn: 194
	Wokington Town	2 v 0	Leyton Pennant	Attn: 260
	Billricay Town	0 v 4	Dorchester Town	Attn: 345
	Staines Town	0 v 1	Kings Lynn	Attn: 292
‡§	Ashford Town	6 v 1	Bishop's Stortford	Attn: 572
	Baldock Town	0 v 1	Evesham United	Attn: 198

***Lee Pearce** (left) wins possession from **David Mehew** of Weston during the Trophy tie between two teams from different regions of the Dr. Martens League.*

Photo: Ken Gregory

* BEST ATTENDANCE † LARGEST AWAY VICTORY ‡ LARGEST AGGREGATE § LARGEST HOME VICTORY

THIRD QUALIFYING ROUND

Saturday 30th November

	Bradford (Park Ave)	1 v 1	Barrow	Attn: 425
r	*Barrow*	*0 v 1*	*Bradford (Park Ave)*	*Attn: 620*
	Marine	0 v 1	Gainsborough Trinity	Attn: 233
	Buxton	1 v 1	Grantham Town	Attn: 190
r	*Grantham Town*	*0 v 1*	*Buxton*	*Attn: 227*
	Runcorn	2 v 1	Solihull Borough	Attn: 369
	Moor Green	6 v 1	Dudley Town	Attn: 175
	Ashton United	1 v 0	Burton Albion	Attn: 354
	Colwyn Bay	1 v 0	Frickley Athletic	Attn: 264
‡	Blyth Spartans	7 v 3	Bilston Town	Attn: 436
	Worksop Town	0 v 0	Lancaster City	Attn: 346
r	*Lancaster City*	*4 v 2*	*Worksop Town*	*Attn: 144*
	Bishop Auckland	2 v 1	Stocksbridge Park S.	Attn: 191
	Spennymoor Utd	1 v 0	Radcliffe Borough	Attn: 196
	Bedworth United	2 v 0	Accrington Stanley	Attn: 381
†	Rothwell Town	1 v 7	Workington	Attn: 213
	Knowsley United	2 v 2	Emley	Attn: 132
r	*Emley*	*5 v 2*	*Knowsley United*	*Attn: 205*
	Dartford	0 v 0	Dulwich Hamlet	Attn: 286
	Dulwich Hamlet	v	Dartford	Attn: 110
	Bromley	1 v 1	Worcester City	Attn: 345
r	*Worcester City*	*2 v 0*	*Bromley*	*Attn: 502*
	Sutton United	0 v 2	Dorchester Town	Attn: 512
*	Aldershot Town	1 v 3	Dagenham & Redbridge	Attn: 1686
	Crawley Town	0 v 2	Chelmsford City	Attn: 619
	Yeovil Town	2 v 0	Evesham United	Attn: 1366
	Carshalton Ath.	0 v 3	Heybridge Swifts	Attn: 217
§	St Leonards Stamcroft	6 v 0	Purfleet	Attn: 344

	Weymouth	2 v 0	Ashford Town	Attn: 849
	Raunds Town	4 v 2	Bognor Regis Town	Attn: 190
	Harrow Borough	2 v 2	Salisbury City	Attn: 175
r	*Salisbury City*	*2 v 1*	*Harrow Borough*	*Attn: 175*
	Sudbury Town	2 v 3	Cheltenham Town	Attn: 369
	Cambridge City	1 v 1	Newport AFC	Attn: 346
r	*Newport AF C*	*4 v 0*	*Cambridge City*	*Attn: 414*
	Sittingbourne	0 v 0	Yeading	Attn: 474
r	*Yeading*	*3 v 1*	*Sittingbourne*	*Attn: 142*
	Basingstoke	0 v 1	Hastings Town	Attn: 372
	St Albans City	3 v 1	Kings Lynn	Attn: 525
	Gloucester City	3 v 1	Kingstonian	Attn: 752
	Fisher Athletic	1 v 2	Workingham Town	Attn: 168

***John Magee** St. Leonards Stamcroft (left) scored a hat-trick in this F.A. Trophy 3rd Round Qualifying match but was stopped this time by a Purfleet defender.*
Photo: Alan Coomes

FIRST ROUND PROPER

Saturday 18th January 1997

	Home	Score	Away
‡	**Ashton United** Williams 7, Twigg 34 Brown 37, Wilson 50, 61	**5 v 3**	**Moor Green** Moore 11 Pearce 67, 89 *Att: 180*
	Bath City Penny 85	**1 v 1**	**Stevenage Bor.** Browne 48 *Att: 682*
r	***Stevenage Bor.*** Browne 13, 73, 81 Trebble 37, Hayes 51 Catlin 90	***6 v 1***	***Bath City*** Brooks 89 *Att: 1,344*
	Blyth Spartans Moat 25	**1 v 1**	**Grantham Town** Grocock 90 *Att: 667*
r	***Grantham*** Dakin 85pen *aet*	***1 v 1***	***Blyth Spartans*** Pyle 53 *Att: 687*
2r	***Grantham*** Munton 21, Glasser 105, Brandy 118	***3 v 1***	***Blyth Spartans*** Bond 10 *Att: 874* *aet*
	Bromsgrove R. Hunt 67, Crisp 83	**2 v 1**	**Merthyr Tydfil** Rees 26 *Att: 691*
	Cheltenham T Victory 13	**1 v 2**	**Dulwich Hamlet** Lillington 46 Whitmarsh 47 *Att: 703*
§	**Colwyn Bay** Limbert 1 Drury 13 Williams 29, 43, 89 Lawton 57	**6 v 0**	**Lancaster City** *Att: 335*
	Dover Athletic	**0 v 2**	**Dagenham & R** Stimson 1 Naylor 18 *Att: 783*
	Emley Francis 43 Reynolds 51	**2 v 1**	**Boston Utd** Williams 49 *Att: 504*
	Enfield Annon 53	**1 v 3**	**Boreham Wood** Nisbet 7 Samuels 37, 57 *Att: 693*
	Gainsborough T. Matthew 83	**1 v 3**	**Bradford (P A)** Blair 27, Gabbiadini 60, Megson 87 *Att: 631*
	Gateshead Thompson 86	**1 v 2**	**Runcorn** Ellis 73 Carragher 75 *Att: 380*
	Gresley Rovers Garner 6pen, 18 Wardle 34	**3 v 3**	**Altrincham** Terry 30pen McGoona 39 Harris 75 *Att: 927*

r = Replay ***2r*** *= 2nd replay aet = after extra time*

★ *BEST ATTENDANCE* † *LARGEST AWAY VICTORY* ‡ *LARGEST AGGREGATE* § *LARGEST HOME VICTORY*

Boreham Woods ***Andy Prutton*** *(right) tries a shot while Enfield defender* ***Steve McGrath*** *takes avoiding action.*

Photo: Clive Butchins

r *Altrincham* **1 v 0** *Gresley Rovers*
Harris 57 — *Att: 567*

Guiseley 2 v 1 Telford United
Parsley 39, Abbott 61 — Langford 38
Att: 778

Hastings Utd 1 v 3 Salisbury C
Ullathorne 30 — Chalk 55, Emms 58, Webb 74
Att: 389

Hyde United 4 v 2 Bedworth United
Kimmins 30, 53, Owen 46, Carroll 71 — Graham 16, Penney 79
Att: 512

Kettering 0 v 1 Chelmsford
Docking 80
Att: 1,528

★ **Kidderminster H. 3 v 0 Macclesfield T.**
Weir 34, Hughes 85, Doherty 88
Att: 2,815

Morecambe 3 v 1 Chorley
Norman 13, Ceroalo 38, Monk 89 — Ross 66
Att: 937

Northwich V. 3 v 1 Hednesford Town
Tait 39, Bishop 68, 85pen — Carty 58
Att: 1,109

Raunds Town 0 v 1 Welling United
Lakin 41
Att: 437

Rushden & D 1 v 2 Farnborough T.
Wilkins 86 — Underwood 31, Wingfield 66
Att: 1,759

Slough Town 2 v 2 Dorchester Town
Hercules 16, Blackford 33 — Lisk 58, Pickard 63
Att: 744

r *Dorchester Town* **1 v 1** *Slough Town*
Taylor 39 pen — Blackford 13
Att: 635

2r *Slough Town* **1 v 2** *Dorchester Town*
Hercules 34 — Pickard 35, Taylor 54
Att: 641

Southport 0 v 0 Halesowen Town
Att: 1,005

r *Halesowen Town* **0 v 2** *Southport*
Whittaker 15, 84
Att: 866

Spennymoor U. 0 v 2 Bishop Auckland
Bayles 29, 69
Att: 482

St. Albans Citu 2 v 0 Weymouth
Kelly 2, Clark 18pen
Att: 592

St. Leonards S. 1 v 0 Newport AFC
Miles 89pen
Att: 501

Stalybridge Cel. 0 v 1 Halifax Towm
Brook 13
Att: 1014

Wokingham T. 0 v 1 Woking
Thompson 28
Att: 1,575

Worcester City 1 v 2 Heybridge Swifts
Molloy 57 — Keen 5, Cranfield 35
Att: 724

Workington 2 v 5 Bamber Bridge †
Collins 4, Dobie 41 — Spencer 23, Phoenix 27, Eaves 38, Hill 84, Okone 89
Att: 313

Yeading 0 v 3 Gloucester City
Kemp 41, Nevin 85og, Burns 89
Att: 245

Yeovil Town 2 v 2 Hayes
Birkby 25, 90 — Randall 55, 65
Att: 2,310

r *Hayes* **2 v 2** *Yeovil Town*
Roberts 78, Cox 90, aet — Batmore 7, Engwell 69
Att: 657

2r *Yeovil Town* **1 v 2** *Hayes*
Harvey pen 37 — Randall 10, 64
Att: 2,310

Tony Jenkins *(Merthyr Tydfil) takes on* ***Nick Amos*** *(Bromsgrove).* Photo: Alan Coomes

SECOND ROUND PROPER

Saturday 8th February 1997

Ashton United 3 v 1 Bamber Bridge
Twigg 55, Robinson 86, Wilson 88 — Leitch 21
Att: 323

Bishop Auck. 3 v 2 Northwich Vic.
Ellison 18, 83, Waller 65 pen — Bishop 60 og, Cooke 87
Att: 705

Boreham Wood 0 v 1 Stevenage B.
— Browne 12
Att: 1,242

Bradford (PA) 0 v 1 Morecambe
— Grimshaw 18
Att: 915

Bromsgrove R. 1 v 1 Hyde United
Taylor 81 — Owen 72
Att: 971

r ***Hyde United 2 v 2 Bromsgrove R.***
aet
Att:

2r **Bromsgrove R. 0 v 2 Hyde United**
Att: 642

Colwyn Bay 2 v 0 Southport
Donnelly 49 pen, Drury 84
Att: 928

Dagenham & R 2 v 1 Chelmsford City
Garvey 28 og, Broom 38 — Davidson 33
Att: 1,351

Farnborough 0 v 2 Altrincham
— Doherty 15, Hardy 35
Att: 691

Gloucester City 3 v 0 Halifax Town §
Holmes 62 Watkins 66, 80
Att: 1,118

Grantham T. 0 v 1 Heybridge Swifts
— Adcock 82
Att: 1,223

Hayes 1 v 2 Runcorn
Francis 58 — Warder 52, 77
Att: 668

Kidderminster 0 v 0 Emley *
Att: 2,301

r ***Emley 1 v 5 Kidderminster*** ‡†
Att: 1,021

Salisbury City 1 v 1 Dorchester Town
Browne 53 — Taylor 67
Att: 727

r ***Dorchester Town 3 v 2 Salisbury City***
Att: 713

St. Albans City 1 v 1 Woking
Howell 68 pen — Jackson 10
Att: 2,015

r ***Woking 3 v 1 St. Albans City***

St. Leonards 2 v 1 Dulwich Hamlet
McGee 23, White 46 — Jones 45 og
Att: 776

Welling United 1 v 1 Guiseley
Dennis 5 — Matthews 45
Att: 778

r ***Guiseley 1 v 0 Welling United***
aet
Att: 523

* *BEST ATTENDANCE* † *LARGEST AWAY VICTORY* ‡ *LARGEST AGGREGATE* § *LARGEST HOME VICTORY*

Emley's ***Chris Maples*** *shows a safe pair of hands as Kidderminster apply the pressure.* Photo: Peter Barnes

THIRD ROUND PROPER

Saturday 1st March 1997

	Home	Score	Away
	Altrincham *Att: 653*	**0 v 1**	**Bishop Auckland** Peverill 59 pen
	Ashton Utd Robinson 30, Bell 44	**2 v 0**	**Hyde Utd** *Att: 1,190*
	Colwyn Bay Dulson 44, Lawton 84	**2 v 2**	**St. Leonards S.** McGee 69, Miles 71 *Att: 555*
r	**St. Leonards S.** *aet*	**0 v 0**	**Colwyn Bay** *Att: 817*
2r	**St. Leonards S.** Ruddy 80 *aet*	**1 v 2**	**Colwyn Bay** Roberts 4, Drury 53 *Att: 1151*
*	**Dorchester** Killick 7, Pickard 67	**2 v 3**	**Woking** Steele 21, 90, Ellis 82 *Att: 2,942*
	Gloucester City Burns 5, Kemp 35 Ellis 44 og	**3 v 1**	**Runcorn** Finley 50 *Att: 1,129*
	Heybridge S. Caldon 22, 50, Harding 63	**3 v 0**	**Kidderminster H.** *Att: 1,187*
	Morecambe	**0 v 0**	**Dagenham & R.** *Att: 971*
r	**Dagenham & R** Naylor 85, 107 *aet*	**2 v 1**	**Morecambe** Norman 31 *Att: 788*
	Stevenage Bor. Catlin 90	**1 v 0**	**Guiseley** *Att: 2,152*

*Hyde United's England Semi-Pro player **Ged Kimmins** in action against Ashton United. Unfortunately he could not inspire his team as local rivals Ashton United progressed to the next round by virtue of a 2-0 victory.*

Photo: Colin Stevens

* *BEST ATTENDANCE*

***Gary Caldon** beats **Dareen Steadman** to score Heybridge Swifts second goal against Kidderminster Harriers.*

Photo: Roger Turner

Dagenham's ***Tony Rogers*** *celebrates after scoring in the last minute against Ashton United.* Photo: Alan Coomes

Darren Hay *(Woking) wins the ball from Ashley Vickers (Heybridge Swifts).* Photo: Roger Turner

FOURTH ROUND PROPER

Saturday 22nd March 1997

Bishop Auckland 0 v 0 Gloucester City
Att: 832

r **Gloucester City 4 v 3 Bishop Auckland**
Watkin 10,56 — Ellison 33
Holmes 61, 74 — Peverill 75
Att: 1,829

Dagenham & R 1 v 0 Ashton United
Rogers 89 — Att: 1,281

Heybridge S. 0 v 1 Woking
Att: 2,477 — Ellis 67

Stevenage Bor. 2 v 0 Colwyn Bay *
R. Roberts 15
Sodje 44 — Att: 3,082

BEST ATTENDANCE

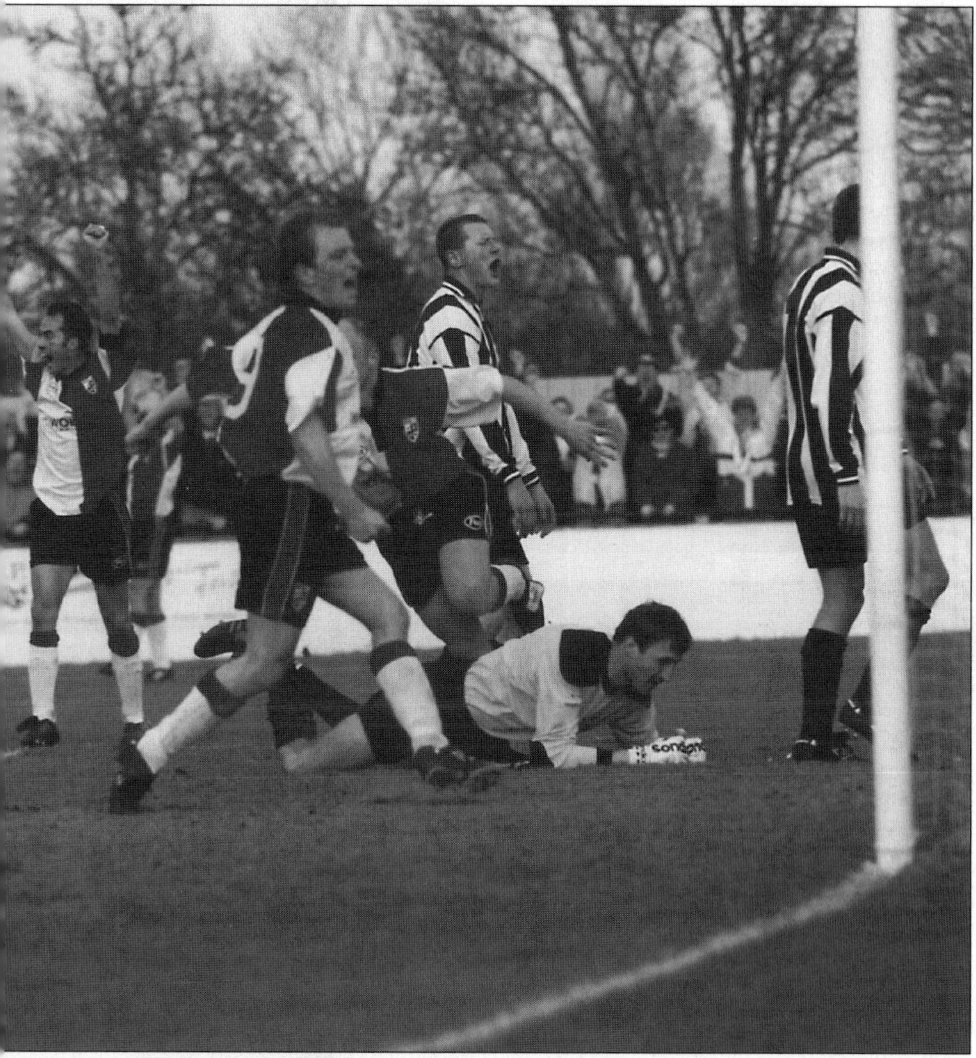

*Woking's **Andrew Ellis** (far right behind keeper) runs to the fans after scoring the only goal after 67 minutes in their Fourth Round clash against Heybridge Swifts.*
Photo: Garry Letts

SEMI FINAL TIES

1st Leg – Saturday 5 April 1997

DAGENHAM & REDBRIDGE 0 v 0 GLOUCESTER CITY

Att: 2,077

Team: Gothard, Culverhouse, Davidson (John 88) Double, Conner, Creaser, Parratt, Pratt, Rogers, Broom, Naylor (Simson 81)

Team: Coles, Holloway, McGrath, Thorne, Kemp, Burns, Fergusson, Webb, Holmes (Mings 14), Watkins, Cooper

WOKING 1 v 0 STEVENAGE BOROUGH

Taylor 32

Att: 3,769

Team: Batty, Howard, Taylor, Foster, Brown, S Wye, Ellis Thompson (L Wye 41), Steele, Hay, Jackson (Hunter 58)

Team: Wilmot, Kirby, Mutchell, Sodje, Smith (Hayles 58), Barrowcliff, Hooper, Browne, Crawshaw, Beevor, Catlin

2nd Leg – Saturday 12 April 1997

GLOUCESTER CITY 2 v 2 DAGENHAM & REDBRIDGE

Watkins 38, Mings 116

aet

Conner 87, Pratt 99

Att: 4,000

Team: Coles, Holloway (Kirkup 34), Johnson (McGrath 106), Thorne, Kemp, Burns, Fergusson, Webb, Holmes (Mings 95), Watkins

Team: Gothard, Culverhouse, Davidson, Double (Jacques 74), Connor, Creaser, Parratt, Pratt, Rogers, Broom (John 101), Naylor (Simson 69)

STEVENAGE BOROUGH 2 v 1 WOKING

Hayles 1, Crawshaw 119

aet

Hay 92

Att: 5,163

Team: Gallagher, Kirby, Mutchell, Sodje, Smith (Browne 58), Barrowcliff, Hooper, Adams, Crawshaw, Catlin, Hayles (Trebble 83)

Team: Batty, Howard, Taylor, L Wye (Timothy 105), Brown, S Wye, Thompson (Jones 112), Ellis, Steele, Jackson (Hay 65), Walker

Dagenham & Redbridge drew with Gloucester City 2-2 on aggregate.

Woking drew with Stevenage Borough 2-2 on aggregate.

Replays – Wednesday 16 April 1997

DAGENHAM & REDBRIDGE 2 v 1 GLOUCESTER CITY

Stimson 29, 51

at Slough Town FC

Holmes 11

Att: 2,053

Team: Gothard, Culverhouse, Davidson, Jacques, Conner Creaser, Parratt, Pratt, Rogers, Broom, Stimson (Naylor 66)

Team: Coles, Mings (Milsom 79), Johnson, Thorne, Kemp, Burns, Fergusson, Webb (Tucker 85), Holmes, Watkins, Cooper

*** WOKING 2 v 1 STEVENAGE BOROUGH**

Walker 20, Ellis 65

at Watford FC

Soloman 84

Att: 5,810

Team: Batty, Howard, Taylor, Foster, Brown, S Wye, Thompson, Ellis, Steele (L Wye 68), Hay, Walker

Team: Gallagher, Kirby, Mutchell, Sodje, Smith, Barrowcliff, Hooper, Browne, Catlin (Trebble 65) Soloman, Hayles

* *BEST ATTENDANCE*

When the draw for the FA Umbro Trophy Semi-Finals was made the fact that the two Conference favourites Stevenage Borough and Woking were drawn together brought mixed reactions.

Many had hoped that their meeting in the Final would have attracted a big attendance and a glamourous fixture, while others were pleased that a club from outside the Conference would actually be reaching Wembley for the first time since Leek Town played Barrow in 1990.

Woking had beaten their Hertfordshire rivals twice in the Conference and had scored three times on both occasions. They were unbeaten away in cup ties this season despite visiting Millwall and Coventry City and were out of the Conference championship race so perhaps they were favourites.

Stevenage however were certainly determined to achieve something after a year of disappointments and political wrangling. They also had a fresh Barry Hayles keen to make his mark on a season in which he had to endure the frustration of acting as a mere spectator for three months because of injury.

A first minute goal seemed to vindicate all that the omens had promised but Borough dug in and

Stevenage Borough's *'wall' against* ***Woking*** *in their Semi Final tie.* Photo: Garry Letts

at the end of a tough uncompromising ninety minutes Steve Thompson's goal was all there was between the teams.

Anything you can do we can do just as well, must have been the feeling in the Stevenage camp as they tore into the Cardinals and scored in the first minute of the second leg through Hayles.

Again no quarter was asked or given, and in front of an impressive 5,163 the tie went into extra time and this time it was Woking's turn to score quickly through Hay.

Borough's equaliser, scored by Crawshaw, prolonged the agony and it was on to Watford where just under 6,000 saw the Surrey club produce a performance which could have earned them a clearer victory than the 2-1 scoreline. Their goals were scored by Walker and Ellis before Soloman raised some flickering hopes for Stevenage in the last few minutes.

Woking deserved to reach their third final in four years but their potential opponents were also well matched in semi-finals that saw the more varied attacking skills of Gloucester City from Dr. Martens League, facing the dour but impressive team work of Dagenham & Redbridge of the ICIS League that produced machine like pressure.

Gloucester had earned a replay from a goalless draw at Bishop Auckland in the quarter final and they did it again at Dagenham. Their ace goal scorer Dale Watkins gave them an exciting lead in the second leg and it wasn't until late in the game that the Daggers machine finally ground down the opposition and produced a goal, in fact it brought two - from Conner three minutes

Gary Crawshaw *(Stevenage) holds off* ***Kevan Brown*** *(Woking).* Photo: Mark V. Sandom

***Robin Taylor** – centre – (Woking) scorer of the only goal at Kingfield against Stevenage Borough.* Photo: Eric Marsh

before the final whistle and for Pratt just nine minutes into extra time.

What an emotional time for the fabulous Gloucester supporters who had given their side such impressive support all season. They were three minutes from Wembley and suddenly they were losing sight of the twin towers altogether.

*Gloucester City's **Cooper** and **Webb** win the midfield battle.* Photo: Roger Turner

Cometh the hour, cometh the goal scorer and this time it was substitute Adie Mings who crashed in a glorious equaliser and a third meeting was set up at Slough.

Once again Gloucester's flair saw them take the lead when Holmes knocked in a rebound after just eleven minutes. If the Daggers goalkeeper Paul Gothard was at fault he soon redeemed himself and kept his side in touch with a brilliant save at the foot of the post. But gradually the ICIS club's power wore City down and Stimson replied on the half hour, Conner and Creaser gradually took a grip on the west country attack and Watkins became noticeably edgy. His frustration eventually gave the referee no option other than to dismiss him for a second cautionable offence but even more upsetting was Stimson's quite brilliant 25 yard drive which gave the excellent David Coles no chance at all and Gloucester just too much to do.

So a rock hard defence and flashes of individual brilliance had taken Dagenham to their third FA Trophy Final and Ted Hardy their manager to his fourth Wembley Final.

The final should give Woking's ball players the chance to pass the ball around beautifully on Wembley's open spaces but watch out for the Daggers' work rate and their determination to battle their way into the game. The longer it goes without Woking taking a commanding lead the stronger the ICIS club will become.

FA UMBRO TROPHY AT A GLANCE

First Round

Gainsborough Trinity 1
Bradford Park Avenue 3

Morecambe 3
Chorley 1

Dover Athletic 0
Dagenham & Red. 2

Kettering Town 0
Chelmsford City 1

Ashton United 5
Moor Green 3

Workington 2
Bamber Bridge 5

Bromsgrove Rovers 2
Merthyr Tydfil 1

Hyde United 4
Bedworth United 2

Rushden & Diamonds 1
Farnborough Town 2

Gresley Rovers 3/0
Altrincham 3/1

Spennymoor United 0
Bishop Auckland 2

Northwich Victoria 3
Hednesford Town 1

Yeading 0
Gloucester City 3

Stalybridge Celtic 0
Halifax Town 1

Yeovil Town 2/2*/1
Hayes 2/2*/2

Gateshead 1
Runcorn 2

Blyth Spartans 1/1*/1*
Grantham Town 1/1*/3*

Worcester City 1
Heybridge Swifts 2

Kidderminster Harriers 3
Macclesfield Town 0

Emley 2
Boston United 1

Hastings Town 1
Salisbury City 3

Slough Town 2/2*/1
Dorchester Town 2/2*/2

St Albans City 2
Weymouth 0

Wokingham Town 0
Woking 1

Enfield 1
Boreham Wood 3

Bath City 1/1
Stevenage Borough 1/6

Raunds Town 0
Welling United 1

Guiseley 2
Telford United 1

Colwyn Bay 6
Lancaster City 0

Southport 0/2
Halesowen Town 0/0

St Leonards Stamcroft 1
Newport AFC 0

Cheltenham Town 1
Dulwich Hamlet 2

Second Round

Bradford Park Avenue 0
Morecambe 1

Dagenham & Red. 2
Chelmsford City 1

Ashton United 3
Bamber Bridge 2

Bromsgrove Rov. 1/2*/0
Hyde United 1/2*/2

Farnborough Town 0
Altrincham 2

Bishop Auckland 3
Northwich Victoria 2

Gloucester City 3
Halifax Town 0

Hayes 1
Runcorn 2

Grantham Town 0
Heybridge Swifts 1

Kidderminster Harr. 0/5
Emley 0/1

Salisbury City 1/2
Dorchester Town 1/3

St Albans City 1/1
Woking 1/3

Boreham Wood 0
Stevenage Borough 1

Welling United 1/0
Guiseley 1/1

Colwyn Bay 2
Southport 0

St Leonards Stamcroft 2
Dulwich Hamlet 1

Third Round

Morecambe 0/1
Dagenham & Red. 0/2

Ashton United 2
Hyde United 0

Altrincham 0
Bishop Auckland 1

Gloucester City 3
Runcorn 1

Heybridge Swifts 3
Kidderminster Harr. 0

Dorchester Town 2
Woking 3

Stevenage Borough 1
Guiseley 0

Colwyn Bay 2/0*/2
St Leonards Stam. 2/0*/1

Fourth Round

Dagenham & Red. 1
Ashton United 0

Bishop Auckland 0/3
Gloucester City 0/4

Heybridge Swifts 0
Woking 1

Stevenage Borough 2
Colwyn Bay 0

Semi-Final

Dag. & Red. 0/2*/2
Gloucester C 0/2*/1

Woking 1/1*/2
Stevenage Boro 0/2/1

Final

DAGENHAM & REDBRIDGE
WOKING

FINAL

Sunday 18 May 1997

DAGENHAM & REDBRIDGE 0 v 1 WOKING

at Wembley Stadium

Hay 112
Att: 24,376

Dagenham & Redbridge		Woking	
1	Gothard	1	Batty
2	Culverhouse	2	Brown
3	Connor	3	Howard
4	Creaser	4	Foster
5	Jacques	5	Taylor
6	Davidson	6	S Wye
7	Pratt	7	Thompson
8	Parratt	8	Ellis
9	Broom	9	Steele
10	Rogers	10	Walker
11	Stimson	11	Jackson

Substitutes
John *for Stimson 65th minute*
Double *for Jacques 75th minute*
Naylor *for Pratt 81st minute*

Referee:
J Winter
(North Riding FA)

Substitutes
Hay *for Jackson 77th minute*
L Wye *for Steele 108th minute*
Jones *for Thompson 115th minute*

It was a nice change to see an 'outsider' challenging the quite natural dominance of the Vauxhall Conference at Wembley in this year's FA Umbro Trophy Final.

The neutrals were definitely behind Dagenham & Redbridge from the ICIS League and the east end of London, while the aristocrats of Woking, who by their exciting cup performances over the years, had been transformed into a 'big' club in the public's eyes were the 'giants' and red hot favourites.

It was Woking however who were definitely the footballing side with Clive Walker again an inspiration and a danger every time he touched the ball. Having outplayed Millwall and Cambridge United and held Premier League Coventry City to two very close games through their passing games, Wembley would really be Woking's perfect stage.

But those who knew the 'Daggers' and their wily old manager Ted Hardy had a feeling that a war of attrition might finish with a very frustrated Woking losing their poise and possibly the match.

Ted had stated through Team Talk that he was a firm believer in strength down the spine of his side and in England International Paul Gothard he had an outstanding goalkeeper, Steve Conners and Glyn Creaser, two very experienced centre backs who were 'giants' of the non-League game, and up front an olf fashioned centre forward in Tony Rogers thundered around without too much pace but a lot of determination.

There was no doubt from the early exchanges that if Woking were to win the Trophy they would have to match the 'Daggers' spirit and effort. From the hustle and bustle epitomised by the non stop Dean Parratt to the thundering headed clearances of the centre backs the message was there for Woking - the gauntlet had been thrown down and would the Cardinals match the physical challenge and make their more sophisticated football win the day?

The first half was not a spectacle of beauty but it was fascinating to see how Woking reacted to the constant challenge and excellent closing down. The artistry of Scot Steele flickered in and out of the game, Walker added class when in possession but the massive and very noisy Red and Blue Army were driving their men on and half time came with the game in deadlock.

This situation could have remained through 120 minutes as far as Dagenham were concerned as their game plan appeared to be developing as expected. The Woking players were wondering whether the extra physical effort on a hot day at the end of a long season was within their capabilities and could it be that Dagenham might just convert a set piece?

The class of Woking was still more likely to create chances but Gothard was enjoying a great day behind his two 'power houses' but then the turning part of the game occurred.

The robust Rogers had caught Steve Foster with an elbow earlier in the game but a second 'collision' angered the defender and caused much 'handbag' waving. Sadly for Dagenham & Redbridge when the dust settled there was Mr. Winters with a red card held high and the ICIS club were down to ten men and an even less penetrative attack.

Even more effort came from the depleted side but now Woking sensed it was their day. Substitutes added some life to Dagenham's counter

Wokings ***Steve Foster*** *(4) and* ***Scott Steele*** *(9) are perfectly placed to see* ***Darren May's*** *header enter the net for the decisive goal of the game.* Photo: Gordon Whittington

attacks and the height of Vincent John, plus the speed and skill of Courtney Naylor and David Pratt, did seem to give them more variety up front, but could they hold on for a replay?

Extra time came and Woking still looked more likely to score. Set pieces were well used by both sides and if anything Laurance Batty just had the edge over his England colleague in the opposite goal when it came to long crosses. Darren Hay had come on for Justin Jackson and this gave the Surrey club a more threatening aerial attacking option.

Indeed they did convert a cross from the hard work of Steve Thompson but the ball was adjudged to have crossed the byline so the 'goal' was ruled out.

This was a warning however and from their next corner Darren Hay rose to thunder a deep cross just under the bar and put an end to a brave battle by the eastenders.

Class had won the day but a spirited battle, typical of the ICIS club and their popular manager, had given us a fascinating match.

A good crowd of 24,376 had enjoyed their Wembley day out and created an excellent atmosphere. Woking made it three Trophy wins in three visits and, if it was a niggle for the Daggers supporters to wonder if they could have won with eleven men, they made up for it with plenty of post match celebrations and plans for regaining their Conference place next season.

FA UMBRO TROPHY ATTENDANCES 1996/1997

	Total Attenance	*Average Attendance*	*Largest Attendance*	
1st Qualifying Round	16,312	337	902	Nuneaton Borough
2nd Qualifying Round	11,687	365	1,943	Aldershot Town
3rd Qualifying Round	16,039	501	1,686	Aldershot Town
1st Round Proper	35,674	1,115	2,815	Kidderminster Harriers
2nd Round Proper	22,295	1,393	2,301	Kidderminster Harriers
3rd Round Proper	13,535	1,692	1,692	Dorchester Town
4th Round Proper	8,501	2,125	3,082	Stevenage Borough
Semi Finals	22,871	3,812	5,163	Replay at Watford
Final	24,376	24,376	24,376	Wembley
Total	**171,290**	**3,968**		

PAST F.A. TROPHY FINALS

1970 **MACCLESFIELD TOWN 2** (Lyond, B Fidler) — **TELFORD UNITED 0** — Ref: K Walker, Att: 28,000.

Macclesfield: Cooke, Sievwright, Bennett, Beaumont, Collins, Roberts, Lyons, B Fidler, Young, Corfield, D Fidler.
Telford: Irvine, Harris, Croft, Flowers, Coton, Ray, Fudge, Hart, Bentley, Murray, Jagger.

1971 **TELFORD UTD 3** (Owen, Bentley, Fudge) — **HILLINGDON BORO. 2** (Reeve, Bishop) — Ref: D Smith, Att: 29,500

Telford: Irvine, Harris, Croft, Ray, Coton, Carr, Fudge, Owen, Bentley, Jagger, Murray.
Hendon: Lowe, Batt, Langley, Higginson, Newcombe, Moore, Fairchild, Bishop, Reeve, Carter, Knox.

1972 **STAFFORD RANGERS 3** (Williams 2, Cullerton) — **BARNET 0** — Ref: P Partridge, Att: 24,000

Stafford R.: Aleksic, Chadwick, Clayton, Sargeant, Aston, Machin, Cullerton, Chapman, Williams, Bayley, Jones.
Barnet: McClelland, Lye, Jenkins, Ward, Embrey, King, Powell, Rerry, Flatt, Easton, Plume.

1973 **SCARBOROUGH 2** (Leask, Thompson) — **WIGAN ATHLETIC 1 aet** (Rogers) — Ref: H Hackney, Att: 23,000

Scarboro: Garrow, Appleton, Shoulder, Dunn, Siddle, Fagan, Donoghue, Franks, Leask (Barmby), Thompson, Hewitt.
Wigan: Reeves, Morris, Sutherland, Taylor, Jackson, Gillibrand, Clements, Oats (McCunnell), Rogers, King, Worswick.

1974 **MORECAMBE 2** (Richmond, Sutton) — **DARTFORD 1** (Cunningham) — Ref: B Homewood, Att: 19,000

Morecambe: Coates, Pearson, Bennett, Sutton, Street, Baldwin, Done, Webber, Roberts (Galley), Kershaw, Richmond.
Dartford: Morton, Read, Payne, Carr, Burns, Binks, Light, Glozier, Robinson (Hearne), Cunningham, Halleday.

1975 **MATLOCK TOWN 4** (Oxley, Dawson, T Fenoughty, N Fenoughy) — **SCARBOROUGH 0** — Ref: K Styles, Att: 21,000

Matlock: Fell, McKay, Smith, Stuart, Dawson, Swan, Oxley, N Fenoughy, Scott, T Fenoughty, M Fenoughty.
Scarborough: Williams, Hewitt, Rettitt, Dunn, Marshall, Todd, Houghton, Woodall, Davidson, Barnby, Aveyard.

1976 **SCARBOROUGH 3** (Woodall, Abbey, Marshall(p)) — **STAFFORD R. 2 aet** (Jones 2) — Ref: R Challis, Att: 21,000

Scarboro: Barnard, Jackson, Marshall, H Dunn, Ayre (Donoghue), HA Dunn, Dale, Barmby, Woodall, Abbey, Hilley.
Stafford: Arnold, Ritchie, Richards, Sargeant, Seddon, Morris, Chapman, Lowe, Jones, Hutchinson, Chadwick.

1977 **SCARBOROUGH 2** (Dunn(p), Abbey) — **DAGENHAM 1** (Harris) — Ref: G Courtney, Att: 21,500

Scarboro: Chapman, Smith, Marshall (Barmby), Dunn, Ayre, Deere, Aveyard, Donoghue, Woodall, Abbey, Dunn.
Dagenham: Hutley, Wellman, P Currie, Dunwell, Moore, W Currie, Harkins, Saul, Fox, Harris, Holder.

1978 **ALTRINCHAM 3** (King, Johnson, Rogers) — **LEATHERHEAD 1** (Cook) — Ref: A Grey, Att: 20,000

Altrincham: Eales, Allan, Crossley, Bailey, Owens, King, Morris, Heathcote, Johnson, Rogers, Davidson (Flaherty).
Leatherhead: Swannell, Cooper, Eaton, Davies, Reid, Malley, Cook, Salkeld, Baker, Boyle (Bailey).

1979 **STAFFORD RANGERS 2** (A Wood 2) — **KETTERING TOWN 0** — Ref: D Richardson, Att: 32,000

Stafford: Arnold, F Wood, Willis, Sargeant, Seddon, Ritchie, Secker, Chapman, A Wood, Cullerton, Chadwick (Jones).
Kettering: Lane, Ashby, Lee, Eastell, Dixey, Suddards, Flannagan, Kellock, Phipps, Clayton, Evans (Hughes).

1980 **DAGENHAM 2** (Duck, Maycock) — **MOSSLEY 1** (Smith) — Ref: K Baker, Att: 26,000

Dagenham: Huttley, Wellman, Scales, Dunwell, Mooore, Durrell, Maycock, Horan, Duck, Kidd, Jones (Holder).
Mossley: Fitton, Brown, Vaughan, Gorman, Salter, Polliot, Smith, Moore, Skeete, O'Connor, Keelan (Wilson).

1981 **BISHOP'S STORTFORD 1** (Sullivan) — **SUTTON UNITED 0** — Ref: J Worrall, Att: 22,578

Stafford: Moore, Blackman, Brame, Smith (Worrell), Bradford, Abery, Sullivan, Knapman, Radford, Simmonds, Mitchell.
Sutton: Collyer, Rogers, Green, J Rains, T Rains, Stephens (Sunnucks), Waldon, Pritchard, Cornwell, Parsons.

1982 **ENFIELD 1** (Taylor) — **ALTRINCHAM 0** — Ref: B Stevens, Att: 18,678

Enfield: Jacobs, Barrett, Tone, Jennings, Waite, Ironton, Ashford, Taylor, Holmes, Oliver (Flint), King. Altrincham: Connaughton, Crossley, Davison, Bailey, Cuddy, King (Whitbread), Allan, Heathcote, Johnson, Rogers, Howard.

1983 **TELFORD UTD 2** (Mather 2) — **NORTHWICH VICTORIA 1** (Bennett) — Ref: B Hill, Att: 22,071

Telford: Charlton, Lewis, Turner, Mayman (Joseph), Walker, Easton, Barnett, Williams, Mather, Hogan, Alcock.
Northwich: Ryan, Fretwell, Murphy, Jones, Forshaw, Ward, Anderson, Abel (Bennett), Reid, Chesters, Wilson.

1984 **NORTHWICH VICTORIA 1** (Chesters) — **BANGOR CITY 1** (Whelan) — Ref: J Martin, Att: 14,200

Replay **NORTHWICH 2** (Chesters(p), Anderson) — **BANGOR 1** (Lunn) — Att: 5,805 (at Stoke)

Northwich: Ryan, Fretwell, Dean, Jones, Forshaw (Power 65), Bennett, Anderson, Abel, Reid, Chesters, Wilson.
Bangor: Letheren, Cavanagh, Gray, Whelan, Banks, Lunn, Urqhart, Morris, Carter, Howat, Sutcliffe (Westwood 105).
Same teams in replay.

1985 **WEALDSTONE 2** (Graham, Holmes) — **BOSTON UNITED 1** (Cook) — Ref: J Bray, Att: 20,775

Wealdstone: Iles, Perkins, Bowgett, Byatt, Davies, Greenaway, Holmes, Wainwright, Donnellan, Graham (N Cordice 89), A Cordice.
Boston: Blackwell, Casey, Ladd, Creane, O'Brien, Thommson, Laverick (Mallender 78), Simpsom, Gilbert, Lee, Cook.

1986 **ALTRINCHAM 1** (Farrelly) — **RUNCORN 0** — Ref: A Ward, Att: 15,700

A'cham: Wealands, Gardner, Densmore, Johnson, Farrelly, Conning, Cuddy, Davison, Reid, Ellis, Anderson. Sub: Newton.
Runcorn: McBride, Lee, Roberts, Jones, Fraser, Smith, S Crompton (A Crompton), Imrie, Carter, Mather, Carrodus.

1987 **KIDDERMINSTER H. 0** — **BURTON ALBION 0** — Ref: D Shaw, Att: 23,617

Replay **KIDDERMINSTER H. 2** (Davies 2) — **BURTON ALBION 1** (Groves) — Att: 15,685 (at West Brom)

K'minster: Arnold, Barton, Boxall, Brazier (sub Hazlewood in rep), Collins (sub Pearson 90 at Wembley), Woodall, McKenzie, O'Dowd, Tuohy, Casey, Davies. sub: Jones.
Burton: New, Essex, Kamara, Vaughan, Simms, Groves, Bancroft, Land, Dorsett, Redfern, (sub Wood in replay), Gauden. Sub: Patterson.

1988 **ENFIELD 0** — **TELFORD UNITED 0** — Ref: L Dilkes, Att: 20,161

Replay **ENFIELD 3** (Furlong 2, Howell) — **TELFORD 2** (Biggins, Norris(p)) — Att: 6,912 (at West Brom)

Enfield: Pape, Cottington, Howell, Keen (sub Edmonds in rep), Sparrow (sub Hayzleden at Wembley), Lewis (sub Edmonds at Wembley), Harding, Cooper, King, Furlong, Francis.
Telford: Charlton, McGinty, Storton, Nelson, Wiggins, Mayman (sub Cunningham in rep (sub Hancock)), Sankey, Joseph, Stringer (sub Griffiths at Wembley, Griffiths in rep), Biggins, Norris.

1989 **TELFORD UNITED 1** (Crawley) — **MACCLESFIELD TOWN 0** — Ref: T Holbrook, Att: 18,102

Telford: Charlton, Lee, Brindley, Hancock, Wiggins, Mayman, Grainger, Joseph, Nelson, Lloyd, Stringer. Subs: Crawley, Griffiths.
Macclesfield: Zelem, Roberts, Tobin, Edwards, Hardman, Askey, Lake, Hanton, Imrie, Burr, Timmons. Subs: Devomshire, Kendall.

1990 **BARROW 3** (Gordon 2, Cowperthwaite) — **LEEK TOWN 0** — Ref: T Simpson. Att: 19,011

Barrow: McDonnell, Higgins, Chilton, Skivington, Gordon, Proctor, Doherty (Burgess), Farrell (Gilmore), Cowperthwaite, Lowe, Ferris.
Leek: Simpson, Elsby (Smith), Pearce, McMullen, Clowes, Coleman (Russell), Mellor, Somerville, Sutton, Millington.

1991 **WYCOMBE W. 2** (Scott, West) — **KIDDERMINSTER H. 1** (Hadley) — Ref: J Watson, Att: 34,842

Wycombe: Granville, Crossley, Cash, Kerr, Creaser, Carroll, Ryan, Stapleton, West, Scott, Guppy (Hutchinson).
Kidderminster: Jones, Kurila, McGrath, Weir, Barnett, Forsyth, Joseph (Wilcox), Howell (Whitehouse), Hadley, Lilwall, Humphries.

1992 **COLCHESTER UTD 3** (Masters, Smith, McGavin) — **WITTON ALBION 1** (Lutkevitch) — Ref: K P Barratt, Att: 27,806

Colchester: Barrett, Donald, Roberts, Knsella, English, Martin, Cook, Masters, McDonough (Bennett 65), McGavin, Smith.
Witton: Mason, Halliday, Coathup, McNeilis, Jim Connor, Anderson, Thomas, Rose, Alford, Grimshaw (Joe Connor), Lutkevitch (McCluskie).

1993 **WYCOMBE W. 4** (Cousins, Kerr, Thompson, Carroll) — **RUNCORN 1** (Shaughnessy) — Ref: I J Borritt, Att: 32,968

Wycombe: Hyde, Cousins, Cooper, Kerr, Crossley, Thompson (Hayrettin 65), Carroll, Ryan, Hutchinson, Scott, Guppy. Sub: Casey.
Runcorn: Williams, Bates, Robertson, Hill, Harold (Connor 62), Anderson, Brady (Parker 72), Brown, Shaughnessy, McKenna, Brabin.

1994 **WOKING 2** (D Brown, Hay) — **RUNCORN 1** (Shaw (pen)) — Ref: Paul Durkin, Att: 15,818

Woking: L Batty, M Tucker, L Wye, G Berry, K Brown, A Clement, D Brown (K Rattray 32), C Fielder, S Steele, D Hay (D Puckett 46), C Walker.
Runcorn: A Williams, J Bates, P Robertson, N Shaw, A Lee, G Anderson, K Thomas, J Connor, I McInerney (G Hill 71), K McKenna, G Brabin. Sub: N Parker.

1995 **WOKING 2** (Steele, Fielder) — **KIDDERMINSTER H. 1 aet** (Davies) — Ref: D J Gallagher, Att: 17,815

Woking: L Batty, M Tucker, L Wye, C Fielder, K Brown, J Crumplin (K Rattray 42), S Wye, A Ellis, S Steele, D Hay (R Newberry 112), C Walker. Sub: T Read (gk).
Kidderminster: K Rose, S Hodson, P Bancroft, P Webb, C Brindley (N Cartwright 94), R Forsyth, J Deakin, M Yates, D Humphreys (L Hughes 105), P Davies, J Purdie. Sub: M Dearlove (gk).

1996 **MACCLESFIELD TOWN 3** (Payne, OG, Hemmings) — **NORTHWICH VICTORIA 1** (Williams) — Ref: Mike D Reed, Att: 8,672

Macclesfield: Ryan Price, Cec Edey, Mark Gardiner, Steve Payne, Neil Howarth (C), Neil Sorvel, Darren Lyons, Steve Wood (Kevin Hulme 83), Marc Coates, Phil Power, Tony Hemmings (Paul Cavell 88).
Northwich Victoria: Dean Greygoose, Derek ward, Chris Duffy, Dave Burgess (Wes Simpson 87), Graham Abel (Lee Steele), Steve Walters, Carwyn Williams, Brian Butler (C), Ian Cooke, Delwyn Humphries, Darren Vicary.

Wokings Football Club at the Peacock Centre. Photo: Eric Marsh

'The Friendly Final' the managers, ***Ted Hardy*** *(left) with* ***Geoff Chapple*** *at Wembley.* Photo: Roger Turner

Woking 'keeper ***Laurence Batty*** *and defender* ***Terry Howard*** *foil Dagenham's* ***Courtnay Naylor.***

Photo: Ian Morsman

FIRST QUALIFYING ROUND

Saturday 7th September 1996

Pentrith	2 v 0	Darwen
Ashington	2 v 3	Tadcaster Albion
aet		
Billingham Town	1 v 2	Blackpool (Wren) R.
aet		
Evenwood Town	0 v 2	Morpeth Town
Stockton	6 v 4	Newcastle Benfield P.
Horden CW	0 v 3	Harrogate Railway
W. Allotment Cel.	0 v 2	Holker Old Boys
(at Newcastle Benfield Park FC)		
Rossendale United	0 v 2	Nelson
Cheadle Town	1 v 2	Merseyside Police
Heanor Town	1 v 2	Hall Road Rangers
Vauxhall GM	3 v 0	Castleton Gabriels
Abbey Hey	1 v 2	Shirebrook Town
Staveley MW	0 v 2	Hallam
Ramsbottom Utd	0 v 1	Tetley Walker
Harworth CI	1 v 0	Pontefract Collieries
Liversedge	1 v 4	Formby
Salford City	0 v 2	Bacup Borough
St Helens Town	3 v 4	Haslingden
aet		
S. Normanton A.	0 v 1	Kimberley Town
Burscough	3 v 2	Heswall
Brodsworth	0 v 2	Borrowash Victoria
Denaby United	2 v 0	Atherton Collieries
Glapwell	2 v 1	Glasshoughton Wel.
Long Eaton United	0 v 4	Skelmersdale United
Parkgate	3 v 2	Rainworth MW
Holwell Sports	2 v 2	Birstall United
aet		
r Birstall United	*1 v 1*	*Holwell Sports*
aet		
2r Holwell Sports	*1 v 2*	*Birstall United*
Kings Heath	1 v 0	Halesowen Harriers
aet		
Wellingborough T.	2 v 4	Gedling Town
Northampton Spen.	0 v 3	Chasetown
Dunkirk	6 v 4	Cradley Town
Stratford Town	3 v 2	Oldbury United
aet		
Meir KA	2 v 0	Newport Pagnell T.
Northfield Town	v	Wednesfield
(walkover for Wednesfield – Northfield Town removed)		
Friar Lane OB	5 v 2	Coleshill Town
March Town Utd	1 v 2	Brightlingsea United
Downham Town	1 v 2	Saffron Walden T.
Thetford Town	0 v 4	Haverhill Rovers
Watton United	0 v 3	Whitton United
Great Wakering R.	6 v 0	Mildenhall Town
Great Yarmouth T.	0 v 2	Southend Manor
Basildon United	1 v 3	Soham Town Rang.
Somersham Town	1 v 2	Braintree Town
Clacton Town	1 v 4	Sudbury Wanderers
New Bradwell St P.	0 v 3	Stansted
Hanwell Town	5 v 0	East Ham United

★ *BEST ATTENDANCE* † *LARGEST AWAY VICTORY* ‡ *LARGEST AGGREGATE* § *LARGEST HOME VICTORY*

Abbey Hey 1 Shirebrook Town 2 *(F.A. Carlsberg Vase – First Qualifying Round). Abbey Hey were unlucky to lose. 2-1 to Shirebrook Town.* Photo: Colin Stevens

Broadbridge Heath 3 Leatherhead 9 *(F.A. Carlsberg Vase – First Qualifying Round). Nigel Webb scored four goals for Leatherhead and his brother Tony saved a penalty. Here Nigel Webb is tackled by Tony Beckingham.* Photo: Tim Edwards

	Milton Keynes	2 v 2	Viking Sports
	aet		
r	*Viking Sports*	*6 v 1*	*Milton Keynes*
	Totternhoe	3 v 5	Flackwell Heath
	aet		
	Brimsdown Rovers	1 v 2	Bedford United
	Hertford Town	1 v 4	Ford United
	Southall	1 v 2	Potters Bar Town
	(at Potters Bar Town FC)		
	Feltham	5 v 1	Biggleswade Town
	(at Biggleswade Town FC)		
	Tring Town	2 v 1	Wingate & Finchley
	St Margaretsbury	1 v 7	East Thurrock United
	(at East Thurrock United FC)		
	London Colney	5 v 0	Tottenham Omada
	Clapton	2 v 0	Kingsbury Town
*	Wealdstone	4 v 0	Kempston Rovers *Att: 241*
	Haringey Borough	0 v 3	Amersham Town
	Deal Town	6 v 3	Horsham YMCA
	aet		
†‡	Broadbridge Heath	3 v 9	Leatherhead
	Sheppey United	2 v 0	Folkestone Invicta
	Epsom & Ewell	3 v 1	Tunbridge Wells
	Walton Casuals	1 v 3	Pagham
	East Preston	2 v 1	Sidley United
	Netherne	0 v 2	Eastbourne Town
	Lewes	4 v 0	Woolwich Town
	Newhaven	1 v 2	Cray Wanderers
	Langney Sports	3 v 2	Canterbury City
	Selsey	3 v 0	Faversham Town

Ashford T. (Middx)	4 v 0	Saltdean United	
Cobham	0 v 4	Egham Town	
Chipstead	2 v 1	Ash United	
aet			
Redhill	2 v 1	Croydon Athletic	
Hailsham Town	7 v 0	East Grinstead	§
Three Bridges	2 v 5	Beckenham Town	
aet			
Steyning Town	0 v 4	Bedfont	
Corinthian-Casuals	3 v 2	Crowborough Ath.	
aet			
Lambourn Sports	0 v 1	Bournemouth	
Portsmouth R. Navy	0 v 3	Kintbury Rangers	
Cove	0 v 3	Swindon Superm.	
Abingdon United	5 v 0	Sherborne Town	
North Leigh	1 v 0	Ryde	
Andover	2 v 4	Downton	
Petersfield Town	2 v 4	Reading Town	
aet			
Westbury United	1 v 4	Sandhurst Town	
(at Warminster Town FC)			
Barnstaple Town	0 v 1	Melksham Town	
Liskeard Athletic	2 v 0	Larkhall Athletic	
St Blazey	1 v 2	Dawlish Town	
Odd Down	3 v 2	Hallen	
Old Georgians	4 v 0	Tuffley Rovers	
Shortwood United	4 v 0	Exmouth Town	
Brislington	1 v 3	Porthleven	
Endsleigh	2 v 1	Bristol Manor Farm	
St Austell	1 v 2	Bridgwater Town	
aet			

SECOND QUALIFYING ROUND

Saturday 5th October 1996

	Home	Score	Away
	Nelson	2 v 4	Easington Colliery
	Washington *aet*	2 v 2	Shotten Comrades
r	*Shotten Comrades*	*3 v 1*	*Washington*
	Blackpool (W.) Rov. *aet*	4 v 2	Ryhope CA
	Tadcaster Albion	2 v 6	Brandon United
	Bedlington Terriers	5 v 0	Stockton
	Seaton Delaval A.	0 v 1	Thackley
	Alnwick Town	2 v 1	Willington
	Annfield Plain *aet*	6 v 3	Pickering Town
	Whickham	2 v 1	Marske United
	Norton & S. Anc. *aet*	3 v 4	Ferryhill Athletic
	Armthorpe Wel.	1 v 2	Ossett Albion
	Esh Winning	1 v 2	Ponteland Utd
	Crook Town	4 v 1	Jarrow Roofing B.
	Holker Old Boys	2 v 1	Yorkshire Amateur
	Penrith *aet*	2 v 2	South Shields
r	*South Shields*	*4 v 3*	*Penrith*
	Harrogate Railway	1 v 3	Morpeth Town
	Selby Town	0 v 1	Denaby United
	Eccleshill United *aet*	1 v 1	Bootle
r	*Bootle*	*0 v 2*	*Eccleshill*
	Merseyside Police	1 v 4	Newcastle Town
	Garforth Town	0 v 4	Hucknall Town
	Ashfield United *aet*	1 v 1	Sandiacre Town
r	*Sandiacre Town*	*0 v 1*	*Ashfield Utd*
	Maltby Main	0 v 2	Arnold Town
	Bacup Borough	1 v 5	Vauxhall GM
	Worsbro B. MW	4 v 0	Radford
	Parkgate	1 v 0	Hall Road Rangers
	Borrowash Vic.	2 v 0	Blidworth MW
	Glapwell	3 v 2	Maghull
	Sheffield	4 v 2	Rossington Main
	Douglas H. S. OB	0 v 3	Nantwich Town
§	**Formby**	**8 v 1**	**Shirebrook Town**
	Burscough *aet*	0 v 0	Glossop North End
r	*Glossop North End*	*0 v 3*	*Burscough*
	Haslingden	4 v 0	Daisy Hill
	Chadderton	0 v 1	Poulton Victoria
	Kidsgrove Athletic	0 v 1	Grove United
	Hallam	5 v 1	Nettleham
	Maine Road	0 v 1	Tetley Walker
	Harworth CI	1 v 7	Ossett Town
	Nuthall	4 v 5	Skelmersdale United

	Home	Score	Away
	Oldham Town	7 v 0	Kimberly Town
	Louth United	3 v 1	Wythenshawe Am.
	Blakenall *aet*	1 v 2	Boldmere St. Mich.
	Stourport Swifts	3 v 2	Wednesfield
	Brierley Hill Town *aet*	1 v 4	Stewarts & Lloyds
	West Midlands Pol. *aet*	3 v 6	Sandwell Borough
	Knowle *aet*	0 v 1	Shifnal Town
	Gedling Town	7 v 1	Westfields
	Pershore Town	2 v 1	Highgate United
	Malvern Town	0 v 3	St Andrews
	Banbury United	0 v 1	Cogenhoe United
	Knypersley Vict.	2 v 3	Desborough Town
	Walsall Wood	1 v 2	Chasetown
	Worcester Athl. *aet*	1 v 3	Long Buckby
	Rushall Olympic	0 v 2	Stratford Town
	Friar Lane OB	2 v 1	Meir KA
	Gornal Athletic	1 v 5	Bloxwich Town
	Stapenhill	3 v 1	Pegasus Juniors
	Kings Heath	0 v 3	Oadby Town
	Darlaston	1 v 2	Brackley Town
	Dunkirk	0 v 0	Rocester
r	*Rocester* *aet*	*2 v 2*	*Dunkirk*
2r	*Dunkirk*	*2 v 0*	*Rocester*
	Tividale	1 v 2	Barrow Town
	Birstall United	0 v 1	Bolehall Swifts
	Witham Town *aet*	1 v 1	Mirrlees Blackstone
r	*Mirrlees Blackstone*	*3 v 3*	*Witham Town*
2r	*Witham Town*	*5 v 1*	*Mirrlees Blackstone*
	Bourne Town *aet*	0 v 3	Saffron Walden T.
	Great Wakering R.	3 v 0	Newmarket Town
	Stamford AFC *aet*	0 v 0	St Neots Town
r	*St Neots Town*	*3 v 4*	*Stamford AFC*
	Haverhill Rovers	1 v 3	Fakenham Town
	Felixstowe Port & T	2 v 1	Stowmarket Town
	Ipswich Wanderers	1 v 0	Wroxham
	Histon	7 v 0	Norwich Town
	Whitton United	2 v 1	Warboys Town
	Eynesbury Rovers	3 v 2	Burnham Ramblers
	Sawbridgeworth T.	1 v 2	Southend Manor.
	Brightlingsea Utd	1 v 2	Swaffham Town
	Soham T. Rangers	0 v 4	Harwich & Park.
	Cornard United	**2 v 9**	**Braintree Town ‡†**

	Spalding United	4 v 1	Sudbury Wanderers
	Lowestoft Town	6 v 1	Chatteris Town
	Maldon Town	4 v 1	Hullbridge Sports
	Stanway Rovers	1 v 1	Tiptree United
	aet		
r	*Tiptree United*	*2 v 0*	*Stanway Rovers*
	Holbeach United	0 v 3	Boston Town
	aet		
	Woodbridge Town	2 v 1	Ely City
	Chalfont St Peter	4 v 1	Amersham Town
	Harefield United	1 v 5	Leverstock Green
	Stansted	1 v 0	Cheshunt
	Letchworth	0 v 5	Edgware Town
	Waltham Abbey	1 v 2	Cockfosters
	Brache Sparta	3 v 2	Hillingdon Borough
	Tring Town	1 v 3	Viking Sports
	Royston Town	4 v 0	Bowers United
	Brentwood	2 v 1	Hanwell Town
	Wealdstone	1 v 0	Hoddesdon Town
	Aveley	2 v 0	Harpenden Town
	Barkingside	3 v 0	Ruislip Manor
	Wootton Blue C.	*v*	Shillington
	(walkover for Wootton Blue Cross – Shillington withdrawn)		
	Feltham	5 v 2	Flackwell Heath
	Clapton	1 v 1	Brook House
	aet		
r	*Brook House*	*2 v 3*	*Clapton*
	aet		
	East Thurrock Utd	1 v 0	Hemel Hempstead
	Stotfold	3 v 2	Hornchurch
	Concord Rangers	5 v 3	Welwyn Gard. City
	Bedford United	2 v 0	Leighton Town
	Tilbury	0 v 2	Ford United
	Potters Bar Town	0 v 2	Ware
	Harlow Town	1 v 0	Bedford Town
	Langford	1 v 1	London Colney
	aet		
r	*London Colney*	*2 v 0*	*Langford*
	Potton United	3 v 1	Beaconsfield SYCOB
	Hythe United	1 v 2	Windsor & Eton
	Bracknell Town	2 v 1	Camberley Town
	Epsom & Ewell	4 v 1	Eastbourne Town
	Eastbourne Utd	2 v 4	Ringmer
	Lewes	1 v 3	Chatham Town
	Godalming & Guild.	3 v 1	Deal Town
	Mile Oak	0 v 0	Southwick
	aet		
r	*Southwick*	*2 v 0*	*Mile Oak*
	Chichester City	0 v 2	Selsey
	Langney Sports	2 v 1	Egham Town
	Oakwood	0 v 3	Wick
	Cray Wanderers	4 v 0	Merstham
	Bedfont	0 v 1	Slade Green
	Chipstead	1 v 2	Redhill
	Beckenham Town	2 v 1	Corinthian
	aet		
	East Preston	2 v 5	Hassocks
	Sheppey United	3 v 2	Cranleigh
	Shoreham	0 v 0	Herne Bay
	aet		
r	*Herne Bay*	*4 v 0*	*Shoreham*
	Arundel	2 v 1	Corinthian-Casuals
	Greenwich Bor.	3 v 1	Portfield
	Worthing United	1 v 6	Leatherhead
	Littlehampton T	0 v 1	Hailsham Town
	Farnham Town	1 v 3	Horsham
	aet		
	Pagham	3 v 1	Raynes Park Vale
	Lancing	0 v 4	Whitstable Town
	Ashford T. (Middx)	4 v 0	Crockenhill
	North Leigh	2 v 0	Bournemouth
	Amesbury Town	2 v 1	Sandhurst Town
	Downtown	3 v 2	Bicester Town
	Bemerton Heath H.	1 v 0	Swindon Supermarine
	aet		
	Totton AFC	1 v 4	Reading Town
	Kintbury Rangers	3 v 5	Brockenhurst
	Christchurch	3 v 1	Cowes Sports
	First Tower United	3 v 0	Hungerford Town
	Milton United	1 v 4	Wantage Town
	Carterton Town	2 v 0	Holmer Green
	BAT Sports	3 v 1	Didcot Town
	Gosport Borough	2 v 0	Eastleigh
	Calne Town	1 v 3	Abingdon United
	Backwell United	5 v 1	Warminster Town
	Crediton United	0 v 4	Minehead
	Fairford Town	0 v 2	Porthleven
	Old Georgians	2 v 3	Ilfracombe Town
	Cadbury Heath	1 v 1	Frome Town
	aet		
r	*Frome Town*	*0 v 0*	*Cadbury Hth*
	aet		
2r	*Cadbury Hth*	*2 v 1*	*Frome Town*
	Glastonbury	1 v 2	Almondsbury Town
	aet		
	Chard Town	2 v 3	Bridport
	Chippenham Town	3 v 1	Bishop Suton
	Endsleigh	2 v 1	Welton Rovers
	Bridgwater Town	**6 v 0**	**Liskeard Athletic** *Att: 328* *
	Bideford	3 v 2	Harrow Hill
	Dawlish Town	1 v 0	Elmore
	Shortwood Utd	3 v 2	Wellington Town
	aet		
	Torrington	3 v 1	DRG AFC
	Keynsham Town	2 v 3	Devizes Town
	Melksham Town	1 v 3	Saltash United
	Odd Down	2 v 0	Newquay

* BEST ATTENDANCE † LARGEST AWAY VICTORY ‡ LARGEST AGGREGATE § LARGEST HOME VICTORY

FIRST ROUND PROPER

Saturday 2nd November 1996

	Burscough		1 v 2	Trafford	Att: 139
	Skelmersdale Utd	aet	0 v 2	Formby	Att: 96
§	**Poulton Victoria**		**7 v 0**	**Ferryhill Ath.**	Att: 139
	Whitby Town		2 v 1	Crook Town	Att: 302
	Blackpool (W) Rov.		1 v 0	Consett	Att: 122
†	**Shildon**		**0 v 7**	**Bedlington Ter.**	Att: 126
	Annfield Plain		0 v 2	Vauxhall	Att: 129
§	**Haslingden**		**7 v 0**	**Alnwick Town**	Att: 105
	Peterlee Newtown		0 v 2	Tetley Walker	Att: 42
	Brandon Utd		5 v 1	Oldham Town	Att: 62
	Easington Colliery		3 v 0	Whickham	Att: 54
	Ossett Town		1 v 3	Holker Old Boys	Att: 87
	Sheffield	aet	3 v 4	RTM Newcastle	Att: 50
	North Ferriby Utd		3 v 1	Parkgate	Att: 132
	Shotton Comrades		1 v 2	Tow Law Town	Att: 85
	South Shields		1 v 0	Northallerton	Att: 180
	Grove United		0 v 2	Thackley	Att: 51
	Ossett Albion		4 v 1	Ponteland Utd	Att: 125
	Eccleshill United		0 v 3	Morpeth Town	Att: 97
	Denaby United		2 v 0	Worsbro Bdg MW	Att: 90
	Hallam		3 v 1	Hartfield Main	Att: 120
	Long Buckby	aet	1 v 1	Oadby Town	Att: 53
r	*Oadby Town*		*4 v 0*	*Long Buckby*	Att: 190
	Barrow Town		1 v 6	Sandwell Borough	Att: 135
	Borrowash Vic.		1 v 3	Arnold Town	Att: 119
‡	**Stewarts & Lloyds**		**5 v 3**	**Anstey Nomads**	Att: 29
	Stratford Town		0 v 1	Brackley Town	Att: 176
	Glapwell		3 v 1	Pelsall Villa	Att: 90
	Boldmere St Mich.	aet	3 v 2	Ashfield United	Att: 69
	Newcastle Town		4 v 0	Lye Town	Att: 150
	Stapenhill		4 v 2	Friar Lane OB	Att: 89
	Bloxwich Town	aet	1 v 1	Hucknall Town	Att: 93
r	*Hucknall Town*		*v*	*Bloxwich Tn.*	Att: 143
	Stourport Swifts		1 v 2	Hinckley Athletic	Att: 86
	Cogenhoe United		1 v 0	Chasetown	Att: 65
	St Andrews	aet	4 v 2	Desborough Town	Att: 72
	Gedling Town		2 v 0	Shifnal Town	Att: 80
	Dunkirk		2 v 1	Bolehall Swifts	Att: 79
	Nantwich Town		3 v 1	Willenhall Town	Att: 145
	Pershore Town		2 v 3	Louth United	Att: 111
	London Colney	aet	0 v 1	Harlow Town	Att: 90
	Brantree Town		3 v 1	Great Wakering R.	Att: 239
	Concord Rangers		3 v 1	Witham Town	Att: 45
	Clapton	aet	1 v 2	Southend Manor	Att: 68
	Hadleigh United		0 v 2	Swaffham Town	Att: 54
	Chalfont St Peter	aet	2 v 1	Leverstock Green	Att: 101
	Cockfosters		1 v 2	Boston Town	Att: 140
	Spalding United	aet	1 v 1	Wealdstone	Att: 271
r	*Wealdstone*		*v*	*Spalding*	Att: 239
	Fakenham Town		1 v 2	Woodbridge Town	Att: 176
	Viking Sports		1 v 3	Brache Sparta	Att: 55
	Gorleston		3 v 2	Ipswich Wand.	Att: 158
	Stotfold	aet	2 v 2	Feltham	Att: 123
	Feltham		*v*	*Stotfold*	Att: 51
	Ford United		0 v 1	Avelay	Att: 107
	Saffron Walden T.		1 v 0	Harwich & Park.	Att: 109
	Wootton Blue C.		1 v 4	Northwood	Att: 150
	Royston Town		0 v 1	Wisbech Town	Att: 312

	Ware	4 v 0	Felixstowe P&T	Att: 158
	Histon	5 v 0	Stansted	Att: 63
	East Thurrock Utd	1 v 2	Lowestoft Town	Att: 175
	Tiptree United	4 v 1	Barkingside	Att: 51
	Brentwood	2 v 0	Maldon Town	Att: 82
	Stamford	3 v 1	Edgware Town	Att: 168
	Potton United	3 v 0	Whitton United	Att: 123
	Bedford United	0 v 4	Eynesbury Rovers	Att: 110
	Whitehawk	2 v 1	Bat Sports	Att: 85
	Wantage Town	2 v 4	Bracknell Town	Att: 56
	Langney Sports *aet*	2 v 3	Chatham Town	Att: 151
	Ringmer	1 v 3	Burnham	Att: 111
	Arundel	0 v 6	Greenwich Bor.	Att: 71
	Dorking	0 v 2	Reading Town	Att: 75
	Ashford T.(Middx)	1 v 0	Horsham	Att: 101
	Carterton Town	1 v 3	North Leigh	Att: 89
	Abingdon United aet	1 v 0	Epsom & Ewell	Att: 71
	Southwick	1 v 3	Whitstable Town	Att: 103
	Slade Green	2 v 0	Thamesmead Town	Att: 102
	Burgess Hill Town	1 v 0	Leatherhead	Att: 315
	Windsor & Eton	0 v 3	Thatcham Town	Att: 194
	Beckenham Town	2 v 1	Redhill	Att: 75
	Wick	1 v 0	Cray Wanderers	Att: 169
	Hassocks	1 v 3	Herne Bay	Att: 120
	Sheppey United	3 v 1	Pagham	Att: 70
	Hallisham Town *aet*	3 v 1	Furness	Att: 140
‡	First Tower Utd	6 v 2	Godalming&Guild.	Att: 87
	Selsey	0 v 3	Gosport Borough	Att: 130
	Torpoint Athletic	2 v 3	Chippenham Town	Att: 76
	Torrington	1 v 2	Odd Down	Att: 61
*	Shortwood Utd	0 v 2	Tiverton Town	Att: 327
	Bideford	3 v 1	Endsleigh	Att: 60
	Porthleven aet	2 v 3	Bemerton Heath H.	Att: 140
	Bridgwater Town	2 v 0	Downton	Att: 310
	Minehead	3 v 4	Amesbury Town	Att: 58
	Devizes Town	0 v 1	Christchurch	Att: 66
	Backwell United	2 v 0	Ilfracombe Town	Att: 65
	Almondsbury Town	1 v 3	Paulton Rovers	Att: 67
	Saltash United	4 v 2	Cadbury Heath	Att: 69
	Brockenhurst	5 v 2	Dawlish Town	Att: 41
	Truro City	4 v 0	Bridport	Att: 124
	Lymington AFC	0 v 2	Wimborne Town	Att: 227

* *BEST ATTENDANCE* † *LARGEST AWAY VICTORY*

‡ *LARGEST AGGREGATE* § *LARGEST HOME VICTORY*

***Bridgwater Town 2 Downton 0** (F.A. Carlsberg Vase – First Round Proper). Dave Kitchener of Bridgwater fires in a shot as the late afternoon gloom descends on an entertaining Vase tie between the Western League and Wessex League rivals.* Photo: Ken Gregory

SECOND ROUND PROPER

Saturday 23rd November 1996

	Home	Score	Away
	Haslingden	1 v 2	Trafford *Att: 72*
	North Ferriby Utd	4 v 0	Hebburn *Att: 173*
	Blackpool (W.) Rov. *aet*	1 v 1	South Shields *Att: 136*
r	*South Shields*	*3 v 1*	*Blackpool (W.) Rov.* *Att: 225*
	Brandon United	0 v 3	Brigg Town *Att: 62*
	Chester-Le-St. T.	1 v 3	Dunston FB *Att: 114*
‡	Tow Law Town	5 v 2	Murton *Att: 65*
	Guisborough Town	2 v 0	Prudhoe Town *Att: 143*
	Whitby Town	1 v 0	Billingham Synthonia *Att: 361*
	Poulton Victoria	3 v 1	RTM Newcastle *Att: 97*
	Seaham Red Star	0 v 4	Ossett Albion *Att: 52*
	Mossly	2 v 1	Morpeth Town *Att: 146*
†	Formby	0 v 5	Tetley Walker *Att: 77*
	Durham City	2 v 1	Easlington Colliery *Att: 175*
	Cammell Laird	0 v 2	Bedlington Terriers *Att: 132*
	West Auckland T	2 v 3	Holker Old Boys *Att: 40*
	Vauxhall GM	3 v 1	Clitheroe *Att: 102*
	Stewarts & Lloyds	3 v 2	Glapwell *Att: 51*
	Boldmere St. Mich,	3 v 1	Belper Town *Att: 203*
†	Dunkirk	0 v 5	Cogenhoe Unite *Att: 105*
	Hallam	1 v 1	Sandwell Borough *Att: 98*
r	*Sandwell Borough*	*0 v 1*	*Hallam* *Att: 72*
	Oadby Town	3 v 1	Arnold Town *Att: 210*
	Hinckley Athletic	2 v 0	Eastwood Hanley *Att: 212*

* *BEST ATTENDANCE* † *LARGEST AWAY VICTORY* ‡ *LARGEST AGGREGATE* § *LARGEST HOME VICTORY*

Brache Sparta 1 Wisbech Town 3 *(F.A. Carlsberg Vase – Second Round Proper). Andy Sharman nets for Wisbech at Brache Sparta.*

	Home	Score	Away	Attendance	
	Denaby United	2 v 4	Newcastle Town	Att: 188	
	Bridgnorth Town *aet*	2 v 2	Stapenhill	Att: 97	
r	*Stapenhill*	*1 v 2*	*Bridgnorth Town*	Att: 116	
	Brackley Town	2 v 4	Hucknall Town	Att: 215	
	Gelding Town	2 v 1	Barwell	Att: 74	
	Thackley *aet*	0 v 0	Louth United	Att: 102	
r	*Louth United*	*2 v 1*	*Thackley*	Att: 71	
	Nantwich Town	2 v 1	St. Andrews	Att: 100	
	Bury Town *aet*	1 v 2	Collier Row & Rom	Att: 333	
	Histon	3 v 2	Ware	Att: 101	
‡	Wivenhoe Town	3 v 4	Harlow Town	Att: 219	
	Woodbridge Town	2 v 0	Brentwood	Att: 148	
	Northwood	3 v 1	Calfront St. Peter	Att: 171	
	Wembley	0 v 1	Spalding United	Att: 142	
	Swaffham Town *aet*	1 v 1	Saffron Walden T.	Att: 130	
r	*Saffron Walden Town*	*3 v 0*	*Swaffham Town*	Att: 136	
	Feltham *aet*	2 v 4	Braintree Town	Att: 78	
	Boston Town	1 v 3	Barking	Att: 139	
	Eynesbury Rovers	1 v 2	Concord Rangers	Att: 130	
	Stamford AFC	2 v 0	Lowerstoft Town	Att: 379	
	Diss Town	2 v 1	Potton United	Att: 328	
	Halstead Town	2 v 1	Gorleston	Att: 192	
	Tiptree United	0 v 3	Southend Manor	Att: 41	
	Aveley *aet*	2 v 2	Arlesey Town	Att: 112	
r	*Arlesey Town*	*3 v 2*	*Aveley*	Att: 169	
	Brache Sparta *aet*	1 v 3	Wisbech Town	Att: 250	
	Ashford T. (Middx)	0 v 1	Burnham	Att: 83	
	Burgess Hill Town	3 v 0	North Leigh	Att: 254	
	Sheppey United	0 v 1	Metropolitan Police	Att: 56	
	Wick	2 v 4	Thatcham Town	Att: 171	
	Banstead Athletic	2 v 0	Bracknell Town	Att: 55	
	Abingdon United	0 v 3	Herne Bay	Att: 96	
	Reading Town	2 v 1	Chatham Town	Att: 120	
	Whitstable Town	1 v 0	Slade Green	Att: 135	
	Beckenham Town	2 v 5	Peacehaven & Tel.	Att: 150	‡
	First Tower United *aet*	4 v 2	Halisham Town	Att: 73	
	Whitehawk	2 v 3	Greenwich Bor.	Att: 82	
	Gosport Borough	0 v 2	Saltash United	Att: 124	
	Chippenham Town	6 v 0	Amesbury Town	Att: 79	§
	Tiverton Town	3 v 0	Bideford	Att: 355	
	Paulton Rovers *aet*	0 v 0	Taunton Town	Att: 193	
r	*Taunton Town*	*2 v 1*	*Paulton Rovers*	Att: 302	
	Odd Down	0 v 1	Bemerton Health H.	Att: 56	
	Falmouth Town	1 v 2	Truro City	Att: 530	*
	Christchurch	0 v 2	Mangotsfield Ut	Att: 175	
	Bridgwater Town	2 v 1	Brockenhurst	Att: 271	
	Wimborne Town	5 v 1	Backwell United	Att: 209	

(abandoned after 71 mins due to floodlight failure 1-2 att 269)

North Ferriby United 4 Hebburn 0 *(F.A. Carlsberg Vase – Second Round Proper). The Hebburn defence comes under pressure from North Ferriby's John Dearth.*
Photo: Ray Pruden

THIRD ROUND PROPER

Saturday 14th December 1996

	Home	Score	Away	Attendance
	Brigg Town	1 v 3	Tow Law Town	Att: 289
	South Shields	1 v 3	Bedlington Terriers	Att: 182
	Louth United *aet*	2 v 4	Whitby Town	Att: 147
	Dunston FB	5 v 0	Holker Old Boys	Att: 129
	Tetley Walker *aet*	1 v 0	Trafford	Att: 120
	Hallam	1 v 3	North Ferriby Utd	Att: 122
	Guisborough Town *(at Whitby Town FC)*	4 v 3	Poulton Victoria	Att: 111
	Ossett Albion	0 v 1	Nantwich Town	Att: 117
	Vauxhall GM	1 v 3	Mossley	Att: 130
	Gedling Town	0 v 1	Durham City	Att: 116
	Hucknall Town	2 v 1	Newcastle Town	Att: 367
	(abandoned 1-0 after 33 mins due to an injury to a match official Att: 493)			
	Woodbridge Town	3 v 1	Halstead Town	Att: 224
	Hinckley Athletic	0 v 1	Stamford AFC	Att: 255
	Oadby Town	1 v 3	Cogenhoe United	Att: 170
	Spalding United *aet*	1 v 1	Bridgnorth Town	Att: 259
r	*Bridgnorth Town*	*1 v 2*	*Spalding United*	Att: 150
	Barking *aet*	1 v 1	Saffron Walden T.	Att: 127
r	*Saffron Walden Town*	*1 v 3*	*Barking*	Att: 146
	Northwood *aet*	2 v 1	Harlow Town	Att: 177
	Histon	2 v 1	Metropolitan Police	Att: 51
	Stewarts & Lloyds	0 v 1	Southend Manor	Att: 58
	Collier Row & Rom.	2 v 2	Braintree Town	Att: 321
	(abandoned after 112 mins due to a floodlight failure)			
r	*Braintree Town* *aet*	*1 v 1*	*Collier Row & Rom.*	Att: 312
2r	*Collier Row & Rom.*	*3 v 1*	*Braintree Town*	Att: 239
★	Wisbech Town	3 v 0	Diss Town	Att: 834
	Concord Rangers *aet*	1 v 1	Greenwich Borough	Att: 98
r	*Greenwich Borough*	*1 v 3*	*Concord Rangers*	Att: 86
	Arlesey Town	3 v 0	Boldmere St Michaels	Att: 195
	Burgess Hill Town *aet*	0 v 1	Bemerton Heath H.	Att: 310
	Bridgwater Town	1 v 3	Taunton Town	Att: 731
	Mangotsfield Utd	2 v 1	Chippenham Town	Att: 160
‡§	Tiverton Town	8 v 0	Peacehaven & Tel.	Att: 550
†	First Tower United	1 v 5	Reading Town	Att: 169
	Burnham	1 v 2	Whitstable Town	Att: 158
	Herne Bay	3 v 0	Saltash United	Att: 242
	Banstead Athletic	3 v 1	Truro City	Att: 100
	Thatcham Town	4 v 1	Wimborne Town	Att: 200

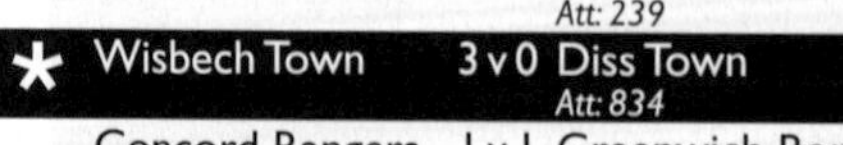

Thatcham Town 4 Wimborne Town 1 *(F.A. Carlsberg Vase – Third Round Proper).* Photo: Eric Marsh

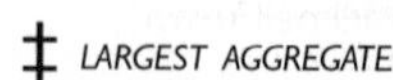

★ BEST ATTENDANCE † LARGEST AWAY VICTORY ‡ LARGEST AGGREGATE § LARGEST HOME VICTORY

***Banstead* 3 *Truro City* 1** *(F.A. Carlsberg Vase Third Round Proper). That's nice! Banstead's Ian Kilpatrick (left) admires Nigel Pugh's fancy footwork for Truro.*
Photo: Dennis Nicholson

***Arlesey Town* 3 *Boldmere St Michaels* 0** *(F.A. Carlsberg Vase Third Round Proper). Arlesey on the attack.*

FOURTH ROUND PROPER

Saturday 11th January 1997

	Stamford AFC *aet*	1 v 1	North Ferriby Utd	Att: 338
r	*North Ferriby Utd*	*1 v 0*	*Stamford AFC*	Att: 318
	Guisborough Town *aet*	4 v 2	Tow Law Town	Att: 153
	Mossley	3 v 2	Cogenhoe United	Att: 214
	Bedlington Terriers	4 v 1	Dunston Fed. Brew.	Att: 140
	Tetley Walker	0 v 1	Durham City	Att: 200
*	Hucknall Town	2 v 5	Spalding United	Att: 645
	Whitby Town	3 v 1	Nantwich Town	Att: 513
	Barking	1 v 0	Woodbridge Town	Att: 164
	Arlesey Town	2 v 3	Herne Bay	Att: 327
	Southend Manor	0 v 1	Wisbech Town	Att: 420
	Mangotsfield Utd	2 v 3	Taunton Town	Att: 396
	Thatcham Town	0 v 1	Tiverton Town	Att: 568
	Concord Rangers	0 v 0	Whitstable Town	Att: 133
r	*Whitstable Town*	*2 v 1*	*Concord Rangers*	Att: 305
	Bemerton H. H.	0 v 1	Collier Row & Rom.	Att: 465
	Histon	0 v 2	Northwood	Att: 138
	Reading Town	0 v 2	Banstead Athletic	Att: 253

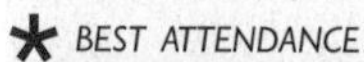

* *BEST ATTENDANCE*

Reading Town 0 Banstead Athletic 2 *(F.A. Carlsberg Vase Fourth Round Proper).* Photo: Ian Morsman

Stamford AFC 1 North Ferriby United 1 *(F.A. Carlsberg Vase Fourth Round Proper). Header by Dean Elston (Stamford) scrambled away by North Ferriby defence for corner kick.* Photo: Tony Emery

Tiverton's Grimshaw challenges the Thatcham defence. Photo: Neil Thaler

FIFTH ROUND PROPER

Saturday 1st February 1997

	Guisborough Town	2 v 0	Wisbech Town	*Att: 585*
	Taunton Town	3 v 0	Spalding United	*Att: 665*
	North Ferriby Utd	1 v 0	Whitstable Town	*Att: 338*
	Durham City	0 v 2	Northwood	*Att: 448*
	Mossley	1 v 0	Barking	*Att: 413*
	Whitby Town	1 v 0	Tiverton Town *	*Att: 1179*
	Banstead Athletic	2 v 0	Herne Bay	*Att: 224*
	Collier Row & Rom *aet*	2 v 2	Bedlington Terriers	*Att: 506*
r	*Bedlington Terriers*	*2 v 1*	*Collier Row & Rom.*	*Att: 715*

* *BEST ATTENDANCE*

Mossley 1 Barking 0 *(F.A. Carlsberg Vase Fifth Round Proper). Barking keeper Marc Baker catches safely watched by fellow team mates and Bernie Hughes of Mossley.*
Photo: Colin Stevens

SIXTH ROUND PROPER

Saturday 22nd February 1997

Northwood *aet*	0 v 1	Banstead Athletic *Att: 912*	Whitby Town	5 v 1	Mossley *Att: 1543*
Guisborough Town	3 v 0	Taunton Town *Att: 845*	North Ferriby Utd	2 v 0	Bedlington Terriers *Att: 707*

***Mossley** fans wish their team luck before the kick off against **Whitby Town**. Unfortunately the team came up against a very powerful Whitby Town side who won 5-1.* Photo: Colin Stevens

***Whitby Town 5 Mossley 1** (F.A. Carlsberg Vase Sixth Round Proper). Mossley keeper Rod Bates is unable to stop Whitby Town's first goal, scored by Lawrie Pearson who is partly hidden in this shot.* Photo: Colin Stevens

SEMI FINALS

1st Leg – Saturday 15 March 1997

GUISBOROUGH TOWN **0 v 2** **NORTH FERRIBY UNITED**
France 25, 46
Att: 923

BANSTEAD ATHLETIC **0 v 1** **WHITBY TOWN**
Pearson 4
Att: 1,228

2nd Leg – Saturday 22 March 1997

NORTH FERRIBY UNITED **1 v 1** **GUISBOROUGH TOWN**
Flounders 80
Breckon 20
Att: 1,359

North Ferriby United won 3-1 on aggregate

WHITBY TOWN **1 v 1** **BANSTEAD ATHLETIC**
Pitman 89
Sweeney 21
Att: 2,006

Whitby Town won 2-1 on aggregate

There was no doubt that Whitby Town had emerged as red hot favourites before the Semi Final Draw. So at the excellently presented evening at Lancaster Gate the relief of Guisborough Town and North Ferriby United was obvious to see when the Northern League favourites were paired with ICIS club Banstead Athletic.

The Northern League were also relieved to see their two clubs separated but would a real north east 'derby' be a good crowd puller for Wembley?

Banstead Athletic were drawn at home in their first leg and a respectable crowd of 1,228 was boosted by a host of ground hoppers and southern photographers. Full marks to the home club for organisation and a well contested tie with only a fourth minute goal from Pearson keeping the teams apart, but the 'experts' thought Whitby would cruise through the home 'leg'!

North Ferriby United having suffered the memories of 1989 when they won their semi final at Tamworth 2-1, only to lose 1-3 at home, were determined to do better. Their first leg at Guisborough produced two heroes: goalkeeper Paul Sharp and goalscorer Darren France, who had been given the 'nod' over Andy Flounders and thanked manager Tim Holte with two vital goals – after 25 minutes, a far post header, and then heading in a long through ball just after half time. Paul Sharpe was outstanding, his manager reckoned it was the best display by any goalkeeper that he had had the privilege of working with and he thoroughly deserved the Man of the Match award for 'Probably the Best Moment'.

Sadly, the Guisborough attendance didn't reach the four figure mark and reporters were given the impression that the Cleveland club didn't appear to have any real conviction that they could reach Wembley.

However both ties were nicely balanced although the home clubs were hotly favoured despite history pointing out the fact that not many clubs in two legged semi finals find playing at home a definite advantage.

The pressure of being expected to win, the club officials often being under stress as they cope with all the big match administration and the fact the opposition seem more relaxed all add up to a tense occasion and many a player 'freezing' when it matters most.

Indeed the home team jitters struck again and within twenty minutes both the favourites were knocked back by goals and the doubters were beginning to wonder if that glorious week they had enjoyed planning a Wembley trip had pushed their luck too far.

North Ferriby supporters remembered the nightmares of 1989 and Whitby rued the chances missed at Banstead the previous week.

Guisborough and Banstead supporters on the other hand, having travelled with little real conviction, were suddenly noisy and excited.

Banstead Athletic 0 Whitby Town 1 *(F.A. Carlsberg Vase Semi-final – first leg). Whitby's Mitch Cook (front player) challenges Banstead's Simon Liddle for the ball.* Photo: Garry Letts

The tension built and, true to the FA Vase tradition, what seemed foregone conclusions were suddenly anybody's game at both venues.

Guisborough really took the game to North Ferriby and certainly frightened the home side but couldn't quite get the equaliser. The atmosphere was tremendous with a tuneful and noisy supporters 'band' and, although Andy Flounders, the experienced goalscorer who had been to Wembley with Brigg Town last season, had not enjoyed one of his best games, experience told and he was in the right place to calm United's nerves with a goal ten minutes from the end.

Once again away performances had far surpassed both clubs' home efforts and North Ferriby had eventually deserved to reach Wembley and become the first 'United' to play in a Vase final!

Back at Whitby a crowd of over 2,000 had been shocked by Banstead's equalising goal from Sweeney.

After 21 minutes a long cross from wide on the left wing, sent accurately over by Steve Latusk, was met at the far post by Liddle whose neat header rocketed past the helpless David Campbell.

It took the Seasiders until half-time to come to terms with this shock and indeed it was the excellent Campbell who prevented the visitors from taking a lead when he dived at the feet of Simon Liddle.

Toman did have a chance for Whitby and Scott Tarr saved brilliantly from David Goodrich so honours were even as the teams went in for half time.

Borthwick's facial injury kept him out of the second period but Whitby came out rejuvenated and now had the pace and size of Robinson up front. For Banstead Errol Vassell replaced Steve Latusk and both sides had all to play for as the game swept swiftly from end to end.

Whitby looked the more likely to score but

on 63 minutes John Sweeney appeared to control the ball with his hand on the blind side of the referee but the ensuing scramble was cleared and the Seasiders still offered most threat as Goodrich and Andy Toman went close.

With just two minutes to go before extra time was needed, a long free kick into the Banstead penalty area wasn't cleared and, after a desperate scramble, ace goalscorer Paul Pitman blasted it into the roof of the net to send the town into ecstasy.

Banstead Athletic had really frightened the high flying Northerners and everyone present had been given a thrilling afternoon's football.

The Whitby chairman, Graham Manser, was extremely eloquent on BBC Radio 5's 6.06 programme when he described the town's pride in reaching Wembley in such a great competition.

It should be a terrific final and with the super Carlsberg support it will be a memorable Wembley weekend ahead for all involved.

Goal! *Whitby's 4th minute winner against Banstead (F.A. Carlsberg Vase Semi-final 1st leg).* Photo: Peter Lirettoc

FA CARLSBERG VASE ATTENDANCES '96/'97

	Total Attenance	Average Attendance	Largest Attendance	
First Qualifying Round	6,813	73	241	Wealdstone
Second Qualifying Round	15,777	98	328	Bridgwater Town
First Round	11,741	112	327	Shortwood United
Second Round	10,853	169	530	Falmouth Town
Third Round	7,851	245	834	Wisbech Town
Fourth Round	5,690	316	648	Huchnall Town
Fifth Round	5,073	563	1,179	Whitby Town
Sixth Round	4,007	1,001	1,543	Whitby Town
Semi-Final	5,516	1,379	2,006	Whitby Town
Final	11,098	11,098		Wembley
Total	**78,729**	**1,504**		

FINAL

Saturday 10th May 1997

NORTH FERRIBY UNITED 0 v 3 WHITBY TOWN

Graeme Williams, David Logan
Andy Toman
Att: 11,098

at Wembley Stadium

North Ferriby United		Whitby Town	
1	Paul Sharp	1	David Campbell
2	John Deacey	2	Graeme Williams
3	Andy Smith	3	David Logan
4	Steve Brentano (c)	4	David Goodchild
5	Jimmy Walmsley	5	Lawrie Pearson
6	Mike Smith	6	Mitch Cook
7	Kenny Harrison	7	Kenny Goodrick
8	Darren Phillips	8	Neil Hodgson (C)
9	Darren France	9	Graham Robinson
10	Andy Flounders	10	Andy Toman
11	Mark Tennison	11	Paul Pitman

Substitutes
Jay Horne *for Kenny Harrison*
Shane Milner *for Darren Phillips*
Paul Newman *for Darren France*

Referee:
Graham Poll
(Hertfordshire)

Substitutes
Stephen Pyle *for Andy Toman*
Mike Hall *for Paul Pitman*
John Borthwick *for Kenny Goodrick*

There has always been a passion for football in the North East but despite spectacular new stadia and playing revivals at Newcastle, Middlesbrough and Sunderland in recent seasons the Northern League clubs have struggled to cope as attendances dwindled.

The great Amateur Cup days when thousands travelled to Wembley to support famous clubs such as Bishop Auckland and Crook Town are just memories but, when the Northern League clubs were 'relegated' to the FA Vase instead of competing in the FA Trophy, there was definitely a 'silver lining' to be considered.

The late Arthur Clark, the Northern League's most loyal supporter, was disappointed with the demotion but he was sure that there was now a very real possibility of more Wembley visits for 'his' clubs.

Sadly Arthur died during the season and ironically it was Whitby Town, a club who had been devastated by dubious red tape which prevented their promotion to the Unibond League in 1995, who were the first Northern League club to reach Wembley.

Meeting them on the 10th May were North Ferriby United from the North East Counties League and many pundits forecast another small attendance which could well have had serious repercussions within the competition if the previous year's all time low of 7,340 had been repeated.

Again the final was between two northern clubs but this time a lively 11,098 watched the game – more than all the Scottish league games played that day except the Celtic and Rangers fixtures!

Both finalists had played through a crowded fixture congestion that would have had Manchester United and Middlesbrough officials sulking but, whereas North Ferriby just failed to keep their promotion challenge going to the end, Whitby steamed through to sail into the Unibond League as the unassailable and all conquering Federation Brewery Northern League champions.

This aura of invincibility was obviously of vital importance at Wembley where they were brimming with confidence from the very start.

However it took 27 minutes for a goal to be scored and, although Whitby looked the sharper side, North Ferriby kept in the game with Flounders and France, both experienced goalscorers, always capable of taking a half chance.

United's captain Steve Brentano had experienced a winning Vase Final with Bridlington and he certainly steadied his side as they battled to hold the lively seasiders. The first goal was going to be all important and it came from an excellent move started by David Logan, Whitby's wing-back with a really 'cultured' left foot. His pass to skipper Neil Hodgson resulted in a shot, a fine save by Paul Sharp and a rebound which Logan smashed into the roof of the net to set the Whitby fans alight. Blue and white wigs and banners took over and the confidence gained and lost after the goal was plain to see.

North Ferriby did battle to gain more possession either side of half time but you sensed they were hanging on desperately, hoping some lucky bounce or incident might just get them back into the game.

It wasn't to be however and Whitby's other full-back, Graeme Williams, picked his spot and drove home an excellent goal after good work from Andy Toman and Mitch Cook after 61 minutes.

With the comfort of a two goal lead any tension still in Whitby's game evaporated and a third goal tucked in from an angle by Toman completed a comprehensive victory with fifteen minutes to go.

An enjoyable match with the usual honest endeavour associated with FA Vase finals eased to a quiet finish. North Ferriby United although well beaten on the day had made history for the club, they had battled courageously and had been to Wembley. For most clubs this just remains an ambition.

Whitby Town although a Yorkshire club like their rivals had brought honour back to the famous Northern League, albeit just before leaving for life in the Unibond. I'm sure there will be more to follow them down to Wembley finals in years to come – look out for the Terriers from Bedlington!

They were right! Photo: Peter Lirettoc

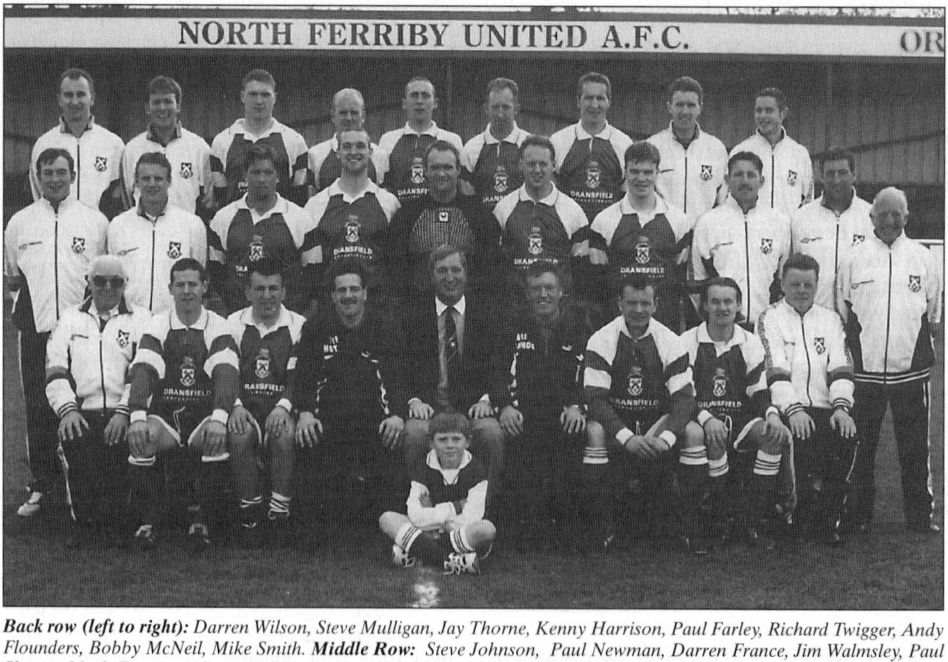

Back row (left to right): *Darren Wilson, Steve Mulligan, Jay Thorne, Kenny Harrison, Paul Farley, Richard Twigger, Andy Flounders, Bobby McNeil, Mike Smith.* ***Middle Row:*** *Steve Johnson, Paul Newman, Darren France, Jim Walmsley, Paul Sharpe, Mark Tennison, Steve Fisher, Darren Phillips, Dave England,* ***Front Row:*** *Ken Foxon, Steve Brentano, John Deacey, Tim Hotte, Les Hare, Brian France, Andy Smith, Shane Miller, Alan Stephenson, Colin Naylor, Graeme Blackhall.*

***Paul Sharp's** gallent attempt cannot stop **David Logans** shot from crashing into the next – and Whitby Town go into the lead.*
Photo: Graham Cotterill

Whitby Town goal scoring machine Paul Pitman (player with ball) holds off a North Ferriby defender before whiping in a dangerous cross during the Vase Final.
Photo Andrew Chitty

*Ferriby's **Darren France** shoots for goal in the F.A. Carlsberg Vase Final.*
Photo Garry Letts

PAST F.A. VASE FINALS

1975 Att: 9,500 **HODDESDON TOWN 2** v **1 EPSOM & EWELL** Ref: Mr R Toseland

Hoddesdon (Scorers: Sedgwick 2.)
Galvin, Green, Hickey, Maybury, Stevenson, Wilson, Bishop, Picking, Sedgwick, Nathan, Schofield.

Epsom & Ewell (Scorer: Wales)
Page, Bennett, Webb, Wales, Worby, Jones, O'Connell, Walker, Tuite, Eales, Lee.

1976 Att: 11,848 **BILLERICAY TOWN 1** v **0 STAMFORD** (aet) Ref: Mr A Robinson

Billericay (Scorer: Aslett)
Griffiths, Payne, Foreman, Pullin, Bone, Coughlan, Geddes, Aslett, Clayden, Scott, Smith.

Stamford
Johnson, Kwiatowski, Marchant, Crawford, Downs, Hird, Barnes, Walpole, Smith, Russell, Broadbent.

1977 Att: 14,000 **BILLERICAY TOWN 1** v **1 SHEFFIELD** aet Ref: Mr J Worrall

Billericay (Scorer: Clayden)
Griffiths, Payne, Bone, Coughlan, Pullin, Scott, Wakefield, Aslett, Clayden, Woodhouse, McQueen. Sub: Whettell.

Sheffield (Scorer: Coughlan og)
Wing, Gilbody, Lodge, Hardisty, Watts, Skelton, Kay, Travis, Pugh, Thornhill, Haynes. Sub: Strutt.

Replay Att: 3,482 **BILLERICAY TOWN 2** v **1 SHEFFIELD** at Nottingham Forest

Billericay (Scorers: Aslett, Woodhouse)
Griffiths, Payne, Pullin, Whettell, Bone, McQueen, Woodhouse, Aslett, Clayden, Scott, Wakefield.

Sheffield (Scorer: Thornhill)
Wing, Gilbody, Lodge, Strutt, Watts, Skelton, Kay, Travis, Pugh, Thornhill, Haynes.

1978 Att: 16,858 **NEWCASTLE BLUE STAR 2** v **1 BARTON ROVERS** Ref: Mr T Morris

Newcastle (Scorers: Dunn, Crumplin)
Halbert, Feenan, Thompson, Davidson, S Dixon, Beynon, Storey, P Dixon, Crumplin, Callaghan, Dunn. Sub: Diamond.

Barton Rovers (Scorer: Smith)
Blackwell, Stephens, Crossley, Evans, Harris, Dollimore, Dunn, Harnaman, Fossey, Turner, Smith. Sub: Cox.

1979 Att: 17,500 **BILLERICAY TOWN 4** v **1 ALMONDSBURY GREENWAY** Ref: Mr C Steel

Billericay (Scorers: Young 3, Clayden.)
Norris, Blacka;;er, Bingham, Whettell, Bone, Reeves, Pullin, Scott, Clayden, Young, Groom. Sub: Carrigan.

Almondsbury (Scorer: Price)
Hamilton, Bowers, Scarrett, Sulllivan, Tudor, Wookey, Bowers, Shehean, Kerr, Butt, Price. Sub: Kilbaine.

1980 Att: 11,500 **STAMFORD 2** v **0 GUISBOROUGH TOWN** Ref: Neil Midgeley

Stamford (Scorers: Alexander, McGowan.)
Johnson, Kwiatkowski, Ladd, McGowan, Bliszczak I, Mackin, Broadhurst, Hall, Czarnecki, Potter, Alexander. Sub: Bliszczak S.

Guisborough
Cutter, Scott, Thornton, Angus, Maltby, Percy, Skelton, Coleman, McElvaney, Sills, Dilworth. Sub: Harrison.

1981 Att: 12,000 **WHICKHAM 3** v **2 WILLENHALL** aet Ref: Mr R Lewis

Whickham (Scorers: Scott, Williamson, Peck og)
Thompson, Scott, Knox, Williamson, Cook, Ward, Carroll, Diamond, Cawthra, Robertson, Turnbull. Sub: Alton.

Willenhall (Scorers: Smith, Stringer)
Newton, White, Darris, Woodall, Heath, Fox, Peck, Price, Matthews, Smith, Stringer. Sub: Trevor.

1982 Att: 12,500 **FOREST GREEN ROVERS 3** v **0 RAINWORTH M.W.** Ref: Mr K Walmsey

Forest Green (Scorers: Leitch 2, Norman.)
Moss, Norman, Day, Turner, Higgins, Jenkins, Guest, Burns, Millard, Leitch, Doughty. Sub: Dangerfield.

Rainworth M.W.
Watson, Hallam, Hodgson, Slater, Sterland, Oliver, Knowles, Raine, Radzi, Reah, Cornerfield. Sub: Robinson.

1983 Att: 13,700 **V.S. RUGBY 1** v **0 HALESOWEN TOWN** Ref: Mr B Daniels

VS Rugby (Scorer: Crawley)
Burton, McGinty, Harrison, Preston, Knox, Evans, ingram, Setchell, Owen, Beecham, Crawley. Sub: Haskins.

Halesowen Town
Coldicott, Penn, Edmonds, Lacey, Randall, Shilvock, Hazelwood, Moss, Woodhouse, P Joinson, L Joinson. Sub: Smith

1984 (Att: 8,125) **STANSTED 3** v **2 STAMFORD** Ref: Mr T Bune

Stanstead (Scorers: Holt, Gillard, Reading.)
Coe, Williams, Hilton, Simpson, Cooper, Reading, Callanan, Holt, Reevs, Doyle, Gillard. Sub: Williams.

Stamford (Scorers: Waddicore, Allen.)
Parslow, Smitheringate, Blades, McIlwain, Lyon, Mackin, Genovese, Waddicore, Allen, Robson, Beech. Sub: Chapman.

1985 (Att: 16,715 **HALESOWEN TOWN 3** v **1 FLEETWOOD TOWN** Ref: Mr C Downey

Halesowen (Scorers: Moss 2, L Joinson)
Pemberton, Moore, Lacey, Randle (Rhodes), Sherwood, Heath, Penn, Woodhouse, P Joinson, L Joinson, Moss.

Southall
MacKenzie, James, McGovern, Croad, Holland, Powell (Richmond), Pierre, Richardson, Sweales, Ferdinand, Rowe.

1986 (Att: 18,340) **HALESOWEN TOWN 3** v **0 SOUTHALL** Ref: Mr D Scott

Halesowen (Scorers: Moss 2, L Joinson.)
Pemberton, Moore, Lacey, Randle (Rhodes), Sherwood, Heath, Penn, Woodhouse, P Joinson, L Joinson, Moss.

Southall
Mackenzie, James, McGovern, Croad, Holland, Powell (Richmond), Pierre, Richardson, Sweales, Ferdinand, Rowe.

1987 (Att: 4,254) **ST. HELENS 3** v **2 WARRINGTON TOWN** Ref: Mr T Mills

St Helens (Scorers: Layhe 2, Rigby.)
Johnson, Benson, Lowe, Bendon, Wilson, McComb, Collins (Gledhill), O'Neill, Cummins, Lay, Rigby. Sub: Deakin.

Warrington (Scorers: Reid, Cook.)
O'Brien. Copeland, Hunter, Gratton, Whalley, Reid, Brownville (Woodyer), Cook, Kinsey, Looker (Hill), Hughes.

1988 (Att: 15,000) **COLNE DYNAMOES 1** v **0 EMLEY** Ref: Mr A Seville

Colne Dynamoes (Scorer: Anderson)
Mason, McFafyen, Westwell, Bentley, Dunn, Roscoe, Rodaway, Whitehead (Burke), Diamond, Anderson, Wood (Coates).

Emley
Dennis, Fielding, Mellor, Codd, Hirst (Burrows), Gartland (Cook), Carmody, Green, Bramald, Devine, Francis.

1989 (Att: 26,487) **TAMWORTH 1** v **1 SUDBURY TOWN** aet Ref: Mr C Downey

Tamworth (Scorer: Devaney)
Bedford, Lockett, Atkins, Cartwright, McCormack, Myers, Finn, Devaney, Moores, Gordon, Stanton. Subs: Rathbone, Heaton.

Sudbury Town (Scorer: Hubbick)
Garnham, Henry, G Barker, Boyland, Thorpe, Klug, D Barker, Barton, Oldfield, Smith, Hubbick. Subs: Money, Hunt.

Replay (Att: 11,201) **TAMWORTH 3** v **0 SUDBURY TOWN** at Peterborough

Tamworth (Scorers: Stanton 2, Moores.)
Bedford, Lockett, Atkins, Cartwright, Finn, Myers, George, Devaney, Moores, Gordon, Stanton. Sub: Heaton.

Sudbury Town
Garnham, Henry, G Barker, Boyland, Thorpe, Klug, D Barker, Barton, Oldfield, Smith, Hubbick. Subs: Money, Hunt.

1990 (Att: 7,932) **YEADING 0** v **0 BRIDLINGTON TOWN** aet Ref: Mr R Groves

Yeading
Mackenzie, Wickens, Turner, Whiskey (McCarthy), Croad, Denton, Matthews, James (Charles), Sweates, Impey, Cordery.

Bridlington
Taylor, Pugh, Freeman, McNeill, Warburton, Brentano, Wilkes (Hall), Noteman, Gauden, Whiteman, Brattan (Brown).

Replay (Att: 5,000) **YEADING 1** v **0 BRIDLINGTON TOWN** at Leeds Utd FC

Yeading (Scorer: Sweales)
Mackenzie, Wickens, Turner, Whiskey, Croad (McCarthy), Schwartz, Matthews, James, Sweates, Impey (Welsh), Cordery.

Bridlington
Taylor, Pugh, Freeman, McNeill, Warburton, Brentano, Wilkes (Brown), Noteman, Gauden (Downing), Whiteman, Brattan.

1991 (Att: 11,314) **GRESLEY ROVERS 4** v **4 GUISELEY** aet Ref: Mr C Trussell

Gresley (Scorers: Rathbone, Smith 2, Stokes.)
Aston, Barry, Elliott (Adcock), Denby, Land, Astley, Stokes, K Smith, Acklam, Rathbone, Lovell (Weston).

Guiseley (Scorers: Tennison 2, Walling, A Roberts.)
Maxted, Bottomley, Hogarth, Tetley, Morgan, McKenzie, Atkinson (Annan), Tennison, Walling, A Roberts, B Roberts.

Replay (Att: 7,585) **GUISELEY 3** v **1 GRESLEY ROVERS** at Bramall Lane

Guiseley (Scorers: Tennison, Walling, Atkinson.)
Maxted, Annan, Hogarth, Tetley, Morgan, McKenzie (Bottomley), Atkinson, Tennison (Noteman), Walling, A Roberts, B Roberts.

Gresley (Scorer: Astley.)
Aston, Barry, Elliott, Denby, Land, Astley, Stokes (Weston), K Smith, Acklam, Rathbone, Lovell (Adcock).

1992 (Att: 10,772) **WIMBORNE TOWN 5** v **3 GUISELEY** Ref: Mr M J Bodenham

Wimborne (Scorers: Richardson, Sturgess 2, Killick 2.)
Leonard, Langdown, Wilkins, Beacham, Allan, Taplin, Ames, Richardson, Bridle, Killick, Sturgess (Lovell), Lynn.

Guiseley (Scorers: Noteman 2, Colville.)
Maxted, Atkinson, Hogarth, Tetley (Wilson), Morgan, Brockie, A Roberts, Tennison, Noteman (Colville), Annan, W Roberts.

1993 (Att: 9,061) **BRIDLINGTON TOWN 1** v **0 TIVERTON TOWN** Ref: Mr R A Hart

Bridlington Town (Scorer: Radford.)
Taylor, Brentano, McKenzie, Harvey, Bottomley, Woodcock, Grocock, A Roberts, Jones, Radford (Tyrell), Parkinson. Sub: Swailes.

Tiverton Town
Nott, J Smith, N Saunders, M Saunders, Short (Scott), Steele, Annunziata, K Smith, Everett, Daly, Hynds (Rogers).

1994 (Att: 13,450) **DISS TOWN 2** v **1 TAUNTON TOWN** Ref: Mr K. Morton

Diss Town (Scorers: Gibbs (p), Mendham.)
Woodcock, Carter, Wolsey (Musgrave), Casey (Bugg), Hartle, Smith, Barth, Mendham, Miles, Warne, Gibbs.

Taunton Town (Scorer: Fowler)
Maloy, Morris, Walsh, Ewens, Graddon, Palfrey, West (Hendry), Fowler, Durham, Perrett (Ward), Jarvis.

1995 (Att: 13,670) **ARLESEY TOWN 2** v **1 OXFORD CITY** Ref: Mr G S Willard

Arlesey (Scorers: Palma, Gyalog.)
Young, Cardines, Bambrick, Palma (Ward), Hull, Gonsalves, Gyalog, Cox, Kane, O'Keefe, Marshall (Nicholls). Sub: Dodwell.

Oxford (Scorer: S Fontaine)
Fleet, Brown (Fisher), Hume, Shepherd, Muttock, Hamilton (Kemp), Thomas, Spittle, Sherwood, S Fontaine, C Fontaine. Sub: Torres.

1996 (Att: 7,340) **BRIGG TOWN 3** v **0 CLITHEROE** Ref: Mr S J Lodge

Brigg (Scorers: Stead 2, Roach)
Gawthorpe, Thompson, Rogers, Greaves (Clay), Buckley (Mail), Elston, C Stead, McLean, N Stead (McNally), Flounders, Roach.

Clitheroe
Nash, Lampkin, Rowbotham (Otley), Baron, Westwell, Rovine, Butcher, Taylor (Smith), Grimshaw, Darbyshire, Hill (Dunn).

FA CARLSBERG VASE AT A GLANCE

3rd Round

Hallam 1
North Ferriby Utd 3

Hinckley Athletic 0
Stamford AFC 1

Concord Rngrs 1*/3
Greenwich Boro 1*/1

Burnham 1
Whitstable Town 2

Collier Row & R 2**/1*/3
Braintree Town 2**/1*/1

Burgess Hill Town 0*
Bemerton Hth Hqns 1*

South Shields 1
Bedlington Terriers 3

Dunston FB 5
Holker Old Boys 0

Guisborough Town 4+
Poulton Victoria 3+

Brigg Town 1
Tow Law Town 3

Wisbech Town 3
Diss Town 0

Stewarts & Lloyds 0
Southend Manor 1

Bridgwater Town 1
Taunton Town 3

Mangotsfield United 2
Chippenham Town 1

Spalding United 1*/2
Bridgnorth Town 1*/1

Hucknall Town 2++
Newcastle Town 1++

Louth United 2*
Whitby Town 4*

Ossett Albion 0
Nantwich Town 1

Tiverton Town 8
Peacehaven & Tels 0

Thatcham Town 4
Wimborne Town 1

Vauxhall GM 1
Mossley 3

Oadby Town 1
Cogenhoe United 3

Barking 1*/3
Saffron Walden Tn 1*/1

Woodbridge Town 3
Halstead Town 1

Banstead Athletic 3
Truro City 1

First Tower United 1
Reading Town 5

Herne Bay 3
Saltash United 0

Arlesey Town 3
Boldmere St Michaels 0

Gedling Town 0
Durham City 1

Tetley Walker 1*
Trafford 0*

Northwood 2*
Harlow Town 1*

Histon 2
Metropolitan Police 1

North Ferriby Utd 1*/1
Stamford AFC 1*/0

Concord Rangers 0*/1
Whitstable Town 0*/2

Collier Row & R 1
Bemerton Hth Hqns 0

Bedlington Terriers 4
Dunston F Brewery 1

Guisborough Town 4
Tow Law Town 2

Wisbech Town 1
Southend Manor 0

Taunton Town 9
Mangotsfield United 2

Spalding United 5
Hucknall Town 2

Whitby Town 3
Nantwich Town 1

Tiverton Town 1
Thatcham Town 0

Mossley 3
Cogenhoe United 2

Barking 1
Woodbridge Town 0

Banstead Athletic 2
Reading Town 0

Herne Bay 3
Arlesey Town 2

Durham City 1
Tetley Walker 0

Northwood 2
Histon 0

5th Round

North Ferriby Utd 1
Whitstable Town 0

Collier Row & R 2*/1
Bedlington Terriers 2*/2

Guisborough Town 2
Wisbech Town 0

Taunton Town 3
Spalding United 0

Whitby Town 1
Tiverton Town 0

Mossley 1
Barking 0

Banstead Athletic 2
Herne Bay 0

Durham City 0
Northwood 2

6th Round

North Ferriby Utd 2
Bedlington Terriers 0

Guisborough Town 3
Taunton Town 0

Whitby Town 5
Mossley 1

Banstead Athletic 1
Northwood 0

Semi-Finals

North Ferriby Utd 2/1
Guisborough Town 0/1

Whitby Town 1/1
Banstead Athletic 0/1

Final

NORTH FERRIBY UTD
WHITBY TOWN

* After extra time
\+ At Whitby Town FC
** Abandoned after 112 minutes due to a floodlight failure
++ Abandoned 1-0 after 33 minutes due to an injury to a match official

***Whitby Town** celebrate – what a feeling!* Photo: Garry Letts

*The proud skipper **Neil Hodgson** (Whitby Town FC)*
Photo: Neil Thaler

*North Ferriby's Goalie **Paul Sharp** punches clear against Whitby.*
Photo: Alan Coomes

F.A. SUNDAY CUP 1996-97

EXEMPTIONS to SECOND ROUND.

Allerton	Nicosia
Capel Plough	Park Royals
Croxteth & Gilmoss RBL	Queens Park
Hammer	Salerno
Hartlepool Lion Hotel	Saltbox
Lebeq tavern	St Joseph's (Luton)
Lodge Cottrell	*(Holders)*

FIRST ROUND

Byes: Greenacres Tavern, Hundred acre, Morden Nomads, Holderness United, Old Oak & Nelson Victoria

	Bolton Woods	4 v 2	Britannia
	Dudley & Weetslade	5 v 5*	A3
(R)	A3	4 v 2	Dudley & Weetslade
	Caldway	2 v 1	East Bowling Unity
	Shankhouse United	0 v 3	Andy J Leisure (Walford)
	Crown	1 v 2	Dock
	Fiddlers	3 v 0	BRNESC
	Hartlepool Staincliffe Hotel	3 v 4	Lobster
	Oakenshaw	0 v 1	Boulevard Mode Force
	Newfield	4 v 0	Seaton Sluice SC
	Stanley Road	2 v 1	Clubmoor Nalgo
	Littlewoods Athletic	2 v 3	Northwood
	Sandon	2 v 5*	Humbledon Plains Farm
	Seymour	4 v 3	Stockton Rosewood Social
	The Tiger	1 v 3	Manfast
	Almithak	1 v 1*	Albion Sports
(R)	Albion Sports	3 v 0	Almithak
	Boundary	1 v 3	Eden Vale
	Park Inn	2 v 0	Baildon Junction Athletic
	Caversham Park	1 v 5	Marston Sports
	Romulus	0 v 1	BRSC Aidan
	Reading Borough	0 v 1	Rover Sports
	Sandwell	2 v 1	Golden Bottle
	Courage	1 v 3	Luton Old Boys
	Slade Celtic	4 v 3*	Broad Plain House
	Clifton Albion	5 v 1	Gamlingay Eagles
	Heathfield	4 v 2	Brookvale Athletic
	Dulwich	2 v 1	Fownhope
	Melton Youth Old Boys	0 v 6	Ashwell Globe
	Hobbies United	4 v 3	Leicester City Bus
	Watford Labour	0 v 2	Grosvenor Park
	Sawston Keys	4 v 2	New Inn Keynsham
	Duke of York	2 v 1	Bedmond Only
	Olympic Star	1 v 0	Theale
	Warriors	3 v 1	Hanham
	Continental	1 v 2	Kendall Albion
	St Joseph's (Bristol)	2 v 3	Bournemouth Electric
	Cavaliers	3 v 3*	Pitsea
(R)	Pitsea	3 v 2	Cavaliers
	St Joseph's (S. Oxhey)	3 v 4	Bournemouth
	Ouzavich	3 v 0	Roofwork
	Leavesden Sports & Soc.	2 v 2*	Belstone
(R)	Belstone	2 v 3	Leavesden Sports & Soc.
	Oakwood Sports	3 v 2	Italia Wasteels
	Cherry Tree (Warley)	1 v 2	Chequers
	Winter Royals	5 v 0	Peckham
	Ford Basildon	5 v 1	Berner United
	Celtic SC (Luton)	2 v 0	Oxford Road Social
	Forest Athletic	1 v 0	Coach & Horses

SECOND ROUND

	Saltbox	3 v 3*	Dock
(R)	Dock	3 v 2	Saltbox
	Seymour	0 v 2	A3
	Andy J Leiasure (Walford)	2 v 0	Caldway
	Nelson Victoria	2 v 1	Bolton Woods
	Boulevard Mode Force	0 v 3	Stanley Road
	Eden Vale	5 v 1	Lobster
	Croxteth & Gilmoss RBL	2 v 0	Humbledon Plains Farm
	Northwood	4 v 2	Newfield
	Hartlepool Lion Hotel	4 v 0	Fiddlers
	Nicosia	4 v 3	Queens Park AFC
	Albion Sports	3 v 4	Allerton
	Park Inn	2 v 1	Manfast
	Salerno	2 v 4	Marston Sports
	BRSC Aidan	1 v 2	Sandwell
	Rovers Sports	2 v 3	Luton Old Boys
	Heathfield	1 v 3	Slade Green
	Dulwich	1 v 1*	Clifton Albion
(R)	Clifton Albion	4 v 2	Dulwich
	Hobbies United	0 v 3	Ashwell Green
	Grosvenor Park	2 v 1	Duke of York
	Sawston Keys	3 v 0	Lebeq Tavern
	Kendall Albion	0 v 3	Olympic Star
	Greenacres Tavern	0 v 3	Warriors
	Morden Nomads	0 v 1	Capel Plough
	Bournemouth Electric	5 v 2	St Joseph's (Luton)
	Pitsea	0 v 1	Hammer
	Leavesden Sports & Soc.	5 v 4	Bournemouth
	Oakwood Sports	2 v 1	Ouzavich
	Holderness United	2 v 0	Hundred Acres
	Park Royals	1 v 2	Forest Athletic
	Old Oak	1 v 3	Winter Royals
	Celtic SC (Luton)	3 v 1	Ford Basildon
	Lodge Cottrell	5 v 4	Chequers

THIRD ROUND

	Allerton	0 v 2	A3
	Park Inn	2 v 1*	Slade Celtic
	Dock	0 v 1	Clifton Albion
	Northwood	2 v 0	Olympic Star
	Hartlepool Lion Hotel	3 v 0	Nelson Victoria
	Croxteth & Gilmoss RBL	0 v 3	Marston Sports
	Nicosia	2 v 5	Stanley Road
	Eden Vale	2 v 1*	Andy J Leisure (Walford)
	Winter Royals	3 v 5	Warriors
	Sandwell	0 v 4	Oakwood Sports
	Ashwell Globe	2 v 1*	Lodge Cottrell
	Bournemouth Electric	4 v 1	Holderness United
	Leavesden Sports & Soc.	1 v 3	Capel Plough
	Forest Athletic	1 v 1*	Luton Old Boys
(R)	Luton Old Boys	0 v 1	Forest Athletic
	Celtic SC (Luton)	3 v 1	Grosvenor Park
	Sawston Keys	2 v 5*	Hammer

FOURTH ROUND

Hartleppol Lion Hotel	1 v 2	Marston Sports
Northwood	6 v 0	Clifton Albion
Stanley Road	0 v 3	A3
Eden Vale	3 v 1*	Park Inn
Capel Plough	1 v 3	Forest Athletic
Bournemouth Electric	0 v 2*	Ashwell Globe
Celtic SC (Luton)	7 v 0	Oakwood Sports
Hammer	2 v 3*	Warriors

FIFTH ROUND

Eden Vale	3 v 0	Ashwell Globe
Northwood	2 v 1*	Celtic SC (Luton)
Marston Sports	4 v 1	Forest Athletic
A3	3 v 0	Warriors

SEMI-FINALS

EDEN VALE	0 v 2	NORTHWOOD
(Crosby S.L.)		*(Hull S.L.)*

Att: 391 at Altrincham F.C.

MARSTON SPORTS	1 v 0	A3
(Wolverhampton S.L.)		*(Liverpool Business S.L.)*

Att: 300 at Macclesfield Town F.C.

FINAL

MARSTON SPORTS	1 v 0	NORTHWOOD

Att: 1000 at Mansfield Town F.C.

F.A. YOUTH CUP 1996-97

(* - After extra Time)

EXTRA PRELIMINARY ROUND

	Home	Score	Away
	Darlington	1 v 5	Hartlepool United
	Harrogate Town	5 v 2	Shotton Comrades
	Hull City	0 v 1	Mansfield Town
	Southport	1 v 1	Lincoln City
(R)	Lincoln City	2 v 0	Southport
	Bury	0 v 0	Stockport County
(R)	Stockport County	0 v 1	Bury
	Wigan Athletic	2 v 0	Rochdale
	Leigh RMI	2 v 3	Cheadle Town
	Bootle	0 v 1	Port Vale
	Stalybridge Celtic	3 v 3	Willenhall Town
(R)	Willenhall Town	0 v 1	Stalybridge Celtic
	Nuneaton Borough	3 v 0	Banbury United
	Stratford Town	1 v 5	Hinckley Athletic
	Bedworth United	1 v 4	Kidderminster Harriers
	Bromsgrove Rovers	2 v 1	Pelsall Villa
	Newport Pagnell T.	2 v 2	Gornal Athletic
	tie awarded to Gornal Ath.	*-*	*Newport Pagnell T. withdrawn*
	Lye Town	1 v 0	Stourbridge
	Basildon United	2 v 2	Wivenhoe Town
(R)	Wivenhoe Town	3 v 0	Basildon United
	Cambridge United	5 v 0	Bishop's Stortford
	Cambridge City	8 v 2	Gorleston
	Ipswich Wanderers	3 v 2	Gt Wakering Rovers
	Sudbury Town	4 v 0	Hitchin Town
	Barnet	4 v 0	Potters Bar Town
	Harefield United	2 v 1	Northwood
	Uxbridge	4 v 6	Hillingdon Borough
	Royston Town	9 v 2	Kingsbury Town
	Wingate & Finchley	2 v 2	Clapton
(R)	Clapton	1 v 3	Wingate & Finchley
	Marlow	2 v 2	Hampton
(R)	Hampton	7 v 0	Marlow
	Viking Sports	v	Slough Town
	w/o Viking Sports	*-*	*Slough Town withdrawn*
	Staines Town	3 v 0	Tooting & Mitcham Utd
	Carshalton Athletic	2 v 0	Redhill
	Hastings Town	1 v 0	Dartford
	Sittingbourne	2 v 1	Dover Athletic
	Thamesmead Town	2 v 2	Herne Bay
	Herne Bay	1 v 0	Thamesmead Town
	Ashford Town	0 v 1	Faversham Town
	Shoreham	7 v 3	Leatherhead
	Crawley Town	0 v 3	Oakwood
	Windsor & Eton	3 v 1	Bedfont
	Bracknell Town	8 v 0	Horsham YMCA
	Bognor Regis Town	4 v 2	Eastbourne Town
	Egham Town	1 v 4	Ashford T. (Middx)
	Langney Sports	1 v 0	Basingstoke Town
	Maidenhead United	1 v 2	Eastleigh
	Oxford City	2 v 0	Waterlooville
	Forest Green Rovers	0 v 1	Worcester City
	Gloucester City	2 v 1	Cheltenham Town
	Bristol Rovers	5 v 0	Paulton Rovers

PRELIMINARY ROUND

	Home	Score	Away
	Guisborough Town	1 v 2	Hartlepool United
	Scarborough	5 v 0	Harrogate Town
	Lancaster City	0 v 4	Barnsley
	Carlisle United	4 v 0	Barrow
	Bolton Wanderers	3 v 0	Mansfield Town
	Frickley athletic	1 v 3	lincoln City
	Chorley	1 v 2	Hallam
	Scunthorpe United	1 v 1	Farsley Celtic
(R)	Farsley Celtic	0 v 0*	Scunthorpe United
	Farsley Celtic won 7-6	*on*	*kicks from the penalty mark*
	Worksop Town	0 v 2	Bury
	Chadderton	1 v 5	Wigan Athletic
	Chesterfield	0 v 5	Chester City
	Marine	3 v 1	Warrington Town
	Northwich Victoria	3 v 1	Cheadle Town
	Nantwich Town	1 v 2	Port Vale
	Louth United	4 v 2	Shifnal Town
	Stalybridge Celtic	1 v 2	Walsall Wood
	Bilston Town	0 v 2	Nuneaton Borough
	Redditch United	6 v 1	Hinckley athletic
	Birstall United	0 v 5	Burton Albion
	Kidderminster Harriers	5 v 2	Chasetown
	Lutterworth Town	1 v 1	Bromsgrove Rovers
(R)	Bromsgrove Rovers	7 v 0	Lutterworth Town
	Cradley Town	1 v 3	Gornal Athletic
	Bolehall Swifts	0 v 6	Northampton Spencer
	Lye Town	2 v 0	Rothwell Town
	Braintree Town	0 v 5	Wivenhoe Town
	Billericay Town	0 v 2	Cambridge United
	Wisbech Town	0 v 0	Southend Manor
(R)	Southend Manor	3 v 4	Wisbech Town
	Cambridge City	1 v 0	Eynesbury Rovers
	Thetford Town	1 v 4	Ipswich Wanderers
	Stevenage Borough	1 v 0	Sudbury Town
	ST Albans City	3 v 1	Waltham Abbey
	Maldon Town	2 v 3	Hornchurch
	Cheshunt	1 v 4	Barnet
	Beaconsfield SYCOB	2 v 1	Harefield United
	Wembley	1 v 0	Collier Row & Romford
	Hillingdon Borough	8 v 1	Hemel Hempstead
	Bedford Town	3 v 5	Royston Town
	Chesham United	5 v 0	Wingate & Finchley
	Aveley	4 v 1	Welwyn Garden C.
	Ruislip Manor	1 v 0	Flackwell Heath
	Sutton United	8 v 2	Hampton
	Banstead Athletic	1 v 3	Viking Sports
	Hayes	1 v 3	Farnborough Town
	Staines Town	2 v 2	Kingstonian
(R)	Kingstonian	2 v 2	Staines Town
	Staines won 4-2 on	*kicks*	*from the penalty mark*
	Bromley	2 v 3	Carshalton Athletic
	Whitstable Town	1 v 1	Hastings Town
(R)	Hastings Town	2 v 0	Whitstable Town
	Tonbridge	2 v 1	Chatham Town
	Sittingbourne	3 v 0	Croydon
	Chipstead	1 v 6	Herne Bay
	Gravesend & Northfleet	1 v 1	Faversham Town
(R)	Faversham Town	0 v 2	Gravesend & Northfleet
	Folkestone Invicta	0 v 1	Margate
	Three Bridges	2 v 4	Erith & Belvedere
	Merstham	1 v 2	Shoreham
	Walton & Hersham	3 v 0	Oakwood
	Ringmer	2 v 8	Corinthian
	Southwick	3 v 2	Raynes Park Vale
	St Leonards Stamcroft	5 v 2	Windsor & Eton
	Lewes	0 v 3	Bracknell Town
	Camberley Town	6 v 1	Whitehawk
	Bognor Regis Town	3 v 0	Burgess Hill Town
	Portfield	0 v 5	Ashford T. (Middx)
	Aldershot Town	3 v 2	Langney Sports
	Thatcham Town	1 v 7	Wokingham Town
	Horsham	3 v 2	Thame United
	Romsey Town	1 v 3	Eastleigh
	Witney Town	3 v 1	Oxford City
	Fareham Town	3 v 5	Yeovil Town
	Weymouth	0 v 3	Havant Town
	Mangotsfield United	2 v 2	Worcester City
(R)	Worcester City	1 v 0	Mangotsfield United
	Yate Town	2 v 4	Gloucester City
	Chippenham Town	0 v 3	Cirencester Town
	Bristol Rovers	8 v 0	Odd Down

FIRST ROUND QUALIFYING

	Home	Score	Away
	Barnsley	2 v 0	Scarborough
	Carlisle United	0 v 0	Hartlepool United
(R)	Hartlepool United	2 v 1	Carlisle United
	Hallam	3 v 3	Lincoln City
(R)	Lincoln City	5 v 1	Hallam
	Farsley Celtic	1 v 4	Bolton Wanderers
	Chester City	3 v 0	Wigan Athletic
	Marine	0 v 1	Bury
	Louth United	0 v 5	Port Vale
	Walsall Wood	1 v 1	Northwich Victoria
(R)	Northwich Victoria	0 v 1	Walsall Wood
	Burton Albion	3 v 1	Redditch United
	Kidderminster Harriers	0 v 4	Nuneaton Borough
	Northampton Spencer	0 v 1	Gornal Athletic
	Lye Town	1 v 1	Bromsgrove Rovers
(R)	Bromsgrove Rovers	4 v 0	Lye Town
	Wisbech Town	1 v 5	Cambridge United
	Cambridge City	1 v 3	Wivenhoe Town
	St Albans City	0 v 2	Stevenage Borough
	Hornchurch	1 v 1	Ipswich Wanderers
(R)	Ipswich Wanderers	0 v 1	Hornchurch
	Wembley	3 v 0	Beaconsfield SYCOB
	Hillingdon Borough	3 v 1	Barnet
	Aveley	2 v 2	Chesham United
(R)	Chesham United	2 v 3	Aveley
	Ruislip Manor	2 v 3	Royston Town
	Farnborough Town	1 v 1	Viking Sports
(R)	Viking Sports	4 v 0	Farnborough Town
	Staines Town	1 v 1	Sutton United
(R)	Sutton United	9 v 2	Staines Town
	Tonbridge	2 v 0	Hastings Town
	Sittingbourne	3 v 1	Carshalton Athletic
	Margate	1 v 6	Gravesend & Northfleet
	Erith & Belvedere	1 v 3	Herne Bay
	Corinthian	3 v 1	Walton & Hersham

	Southwich	2 v 0	Shoreham
	Camberley Town	4 v 3	Bracknell Town
	Bognor Regis T.	6 v 1	St Leonards Stamcroft
	Wokingham Town	2 v 1	Aldershot Town
	Horsham	2 v 4	Ashford T. (Middx)
	Yeovil Town	5 v 0	Witney Town
	Havant Town	2 v 3	Eastleigh
	Cirencester Town	1 v 1	Gloucester City
(R)	Gloucester City	2 v 2*	Cirencester Town

Cirencester won 5-3 on kicks from the penalty mark.

	Bristol Rovers	6 v 0	Worcester City

SECOND ROUND QUALIFYING

	Barnsley	3 v 0	Hartlepool United
	Lincoln City	0 v 0	Bolton Wanderers
(R)	Bolton Wanderers	2 v 0	Lincoln City
	Chester City	0 v 2	Bury
	Port Vale	7 v 0	Walsall Wood
	Burton Albion	0 v 1	Nuneaton Borough
	Gornal Athletic	1 v 2	Bromsgrove Rovers
	Cambridge United	3 v 1	Wivenhoe Town
	Stevenage Borough	7 v 1	Hornchurch
	Wembley	2 v 3	Hillingdon Borough
	Aveley	3 v 0	Royston Town
	Viking Sports	1 v 1	Sutton United
(R)	Sutton United	1 v 2	Viking Sports
	Tonbridge	1 v 1	Sittingbourne
(R)	Sittingbourne	1 v 0	Tonbridge
	Gravesend & Northfleet	6 v 3	Herne Bay
	Corinthian	3 v 2	Southwick
	Camberley Town	0 v 2	Bognor Regis T.
	Wokingham Town	8 v 1	Ashford T. (Middx)
	Yeovil Town	4 v 1	Eastleigh
	Cirencester Town	1 v 1	Bristol Rovers
(R)	Bristol Rovers	2 v 1	Cirencester Town

FIRST ROUND PROPER

	Rotherham United	3 v 1	Barnsley
	Notts County	0 v 0	Bury
(R)	Bury	2 v 0	Notts County
	Huddersfield Town	0 v 0	Leicester City
(R)	Leicester City	0 v 1	Huddersfield Town
	Preston North End	0 v 1	Port Vale
	Shrewsbury Town	0 v 5	Wrexham
	Grimsby Town	5 v 0	Bradford City
	Leeds United	2 v 2	Sheffield Wednesday
(R)	Sheffield Wednesday	0 v 4	Leeds United
	Blackburn Rovers	3 v 1	Blackpool
	Newcastle United	1 v 2	Burnley
	Everton	3 v 0	Nuneaton Borough
	Bolton Wanderers	5 v 0	Derby County
	Walsall	3 v 0	Bromsgrove Rovers
	Peterborough United	2 v 1	Stevenage Borough
	Hereford United	1 v 3	Luton Town
	Rushden & Diamonds	6 v 1	Hillingdon Borough
	Welling United	0 v 1	Wolverhampton Wands.
	Enfield	0 v 0	Boreham Wood
(R)	Boreham Wood	1 v 2	Enfield
	Leighton Town	0 v 3	Watford
	Birmingham City	3 v 0	Boldmere St Michaels
	Northampton Town	0 v 5	Chelsea
	Charlton Athletic	6 v 1	Aveley
	Cambridge United	2 v 4	Colchester United
	Bognor Regis T.	1 v 4	Viking Sports
	Reading	2 v 1	Dulwich Hamlet
	Plymouth Argyle	3 v 0	Brighton & Hove A.
	Exeter City	0 v 7	Torquay United
	Bristol Rovers	4 v 1	Woking
	Oxford United	2 v 1	Cardiff City
	Croydon Athletic	1 v 5	Gravesend & Northfleet
	Wycombe Wanderers	5 v 0	Corinthian
	Fulham	0 v 3	Gillingham
	Yeovil Town	3 v 3	Bournemouth AFC
(R)	Bournemouth AFC	4 v 0	Yeovil Town
	Southampton	1 v 0	Sittingbourne
	Wokingham Town	1 v 4	Swansea City

SECOND ROUND

	Tranmere Rovers	2 v 0	Grimsby Town
	Oldham Athletic	3 v 0	York City
	Blackburn Rovers	2 v 0	Port Vale
	Bury	1 v 0	Huddersfield Town
	Bolton Wanderers	1 v 1	Sheffield United
(R)	Sheffield United	4 v 5*	Bolton Wanderers
	Coventry City	2 v 1	Aston Villa
	Liverpool	5 v 3	Burnley
	Manchester City	2 v 2	Walsall
(R)	Walsall	2 v 4	Manchester City
	Manchester United	7 v 0	Wrexham
	Rotherham United	2 v 1	Stoke City
	Nottingham Forest	3 v 1	Middlesbrough
	Leeds United	2 v 0	Crewe Alexandra
	Sunderland	1 v 0	Birmingham City
	West Bromwich A.	1 v 2	Everton
	Oxford United	1 v 1	Luton Town
(R)	Luton Town	3 v 2	Oxford United
	Enfield	1 v 1	Gravesend & Northfleet
(R)	Gravesend & Northfleet	2 v 0	Enfield
	Ipswich Town	1 v 0	Arsenal
	Chelsea	2 v 3	Crystal Palace
	Bournemouth AFC	2 v 1	Portsmouth
	Swansea City	0 v 6	Norwich City
	Charlton Athletic	2 v 1	Brentford
	Millwall	1 v 0	Gillingham
	Viking Sports	0 v 2	Wimbledon
	Wolverhampton Wands.	2 v 3	Wycombe Wanderers
	Leyton Orient	1 v 2	Bristol City
	Colchester United	1 v 3	West Ham United
	Rushden & Diamonds	2 v 2	Southend United
(R)	Southend United	4 v 0	Rushden & Diamonds
	Bristol Rovers	0 v 0	Queens Park Rangers
	Queens Park Rangers	1 v 0	Bristol Rovers
	Southampton	1 v 3*	Tottenham Hotspur
	Torquay United	1 v 1	Swindon Town
(R)	Swindon Town	0 v 2	Torquay United
	Plymouth Argyle	1 v 2	Peterborough United
	Watford	8 v 0	Reading

THIRD ROUND

	Nottingham Forest	1 v 0	Rotherham United
	Manchester City	1 v 2	Leeds United
	Oldham Athletic	1 v 2	Sunderland
	Bury	0 v 0	Blackburn Rovers
(R)	Blackburn Rovers	3 v 2	Bury
	Bolton Wanderers	1 v 2	Everton
	Liverpool	1 v 2	Manchester United
	Coventry City	0 v 1	Tranmere Rovers
	Southend United	2 v 3	Watford
	Norwich City	5 v 1	Wycombe Wanderers
	Torquay United	0 v 2	Luton Town
	Crystal Palace	2 v 1	West Ham United
	Bristol City	2 v 3	Bournemouth AFC
	Queens Park Rangers	3 v 2	Wimbledon
	Tottenham Hotspur	5 v 2	Gravesend & Northfleet

at Gravesend & Northfleet FC

	Charlton Athletic	5 v 4	Ipswich Town

FOURTH ROUND

	Leeds United	2 v 0	Queens Park Rangers
	Norwich City	1 v 1	Everton
(R)	Everton	0 v 2	Norwich City
	Nottingham Forest	0 v 3	Blackburn Rovers
	Charlton Athletic	0 v 2	Tottenham Hotspur
	Sunderland	2 v 5	Luton Town
	Manchester United	1 v 1	Watford
(R)	Watford	3 v 2	Manchester United
	Bournemouth AFC	0 v 3	Tranmere Rovers
	Peterborough United	1 v 3	Crystal Palace

FIFTH ROUND

	Luton Town	0 v 0	Watford
(R)	Watford	1 v 1*	Luton Town

Luton Town won 5-3 on kicks from the penalty mark.

	Leeds United	0 v 0	Tranmere Rovers
(R)	Tranmere Rovers	0 v 1	Leeds United
	Blackburn Rovers	2 v 1	Norwich City
	Crystal Palace	1 v 0	Tottenham Hotspur

SEMI-FINALS

Luton Town	1 v 2	Leeds United
Leeds United	1 v 0	Luton Town

Crystal Palace	2 v 1	Blackburn Rovers
Blackburn Rovers	2 v 2	Crystal Palace

FINAL

Leeds United 2 v 1 Crystal Palace
Att: 6649

Crystal Palace 0 v 1 Leeds United
Att: 4759

A mixed Season for our England International Squad

The International season was a difficult one for new coach Ron Reid and his assistant Graham Allner as preparation for the Irish game was ruined by the weather but an away draw with Holland and a fine FA XI win against Highland League left everyone in good spirits and looking forward to the next campaign.

Ron has now joined Oldham Athletic as assistant manager/coach and Graham is concentrating on Kidderminster Harriers matters, so there will be a new regime in charge and I sincerely hope there will be an International Tournament on which they can concentrate their efforts

The first England trial played on a very wet Guy Fawkes night at Hyde resulted in an emphatic 3-0 victory for the FA XI, made up of Conference players plus the late selection of Boston United's very promising young left back, Richard Mason, over a very competitive Unibond League XI. This was the FA's first success in this fixture since the 1990-91 season and was particularly pleasing for Ron Reid in his first representative match as England's semi-professional international team manager, it was also good to see his assistant manager Graham Allner and England physio Jimmy Conway with the team as well.

The playing surface at Ewen Fields was magnificent and despite driving rain, the game produced some excellent football without the pitch cutting up or the pace slacking off. It was certainly a credit to the senior non-League clubs in the north of England.

The first half saw the FA XI with the wind at their backs, looking dangerous through the power of Mike Norbury and Ian Cooke and the impressive pace and control of Stuart Terry and Darren Vicary.

Some tough tackling resulted in Norbury retiring with a twisted knee and Stuart Terry with an ankle injury, but an unfortunate misunderstanding as Gus Wilson passed back to his 'keeper (who had come out to collect the through ball) resulted in a soft 'own goal' to give the FA a half time lead. 'Keeper Kevin O'Brien had also made some very good saves but the Unibond side must have fancied their chances of taking the game with the elements in the second half. FA manager Ron Reid made a vital change for the second half:

"I thought we were playing too deep so I asked Wayne Simpson to sit in just in front of the back four and allow Steve Walters more freedom."

This worked a treat, especially as the left flank combined well, with Phil Power, Neil Sorvel and the outstanding Richard Mason setting up two goals both scored by Walters. The powerful Cooke also took a bad knock but bravely battled on and helped with an excellent knock down for the third goal.

It was a good team performance built on Macclesfield's impressive central defensive duo of Neil Howarth and Steve Payne and second half 'keeper Billy Stewart looked good facing the gale.

For the Unibond League the mobile strike power of Ged Kimmins and Neil Morton promised much but were eventually controlled. The wind made it extremely difficult to build attacks although Jon Gautrey and Vince Brockie both worked hard. It was a shame that Brian Ross, Greg Fee and Deniol Graham were unavailable and the impressive Des Hazel did not last the ninety minutes.

FA XI Team: Price (Macclesfield), Simpson (Hednesford), Prindiville (Kidderminster H), Walters (Northwich V), Howarth (Macclesfield), Payne (Macclesfield), Terry (Altrincham), Sorvel (Macclesfield), Norbury (Halifax T), Cooke (Northwich V), Vicary (Northwich V), Subs: Bates (Stalybridge C), Stewart (Southport), Mason (Boston United), Power (Macclesfield).

Unibond XI Team; O'Brien (Marine), Gallagher (Hyde United), Wilson (Hyde United), Mayers (Chorley), Baldwin (Accrington Stanley), Gautrey (Marine), Hazell (Guiseley), Brockie (Hyde United), Kimmins (Hyde United), Morton (Barrow), Marginson (Chorley). Subs: Maxwell (Gainsborough Town), Johnson (Knowsley), Proctor (Marine), Bullock (Leek Town).

Englands past results and a list of International cap winners can be found on page 1012

Final England Trials Completed

If it was the weather that spoiled the day in the north, it was a freak traffic jam that did it's best to disrupt the ICIS League's big evening at Dagenham as over 200,000 vehicles clogged up the east of London and the jam remained for nine hours!

Amazingly the players all managed to get to the ground and a very competitive match was won 1-0 by the League XI.

ICIS Football League 1 FA XI 0

Al James Hannigan had been in the headlines following his dismissal in the FA Cup when Enfield entertained Peterborough United, it was a happier story at Dagenham as he headed in an inch perfect free kick from Graham Kemp mid-way through the first half and this proved to be the winner.

Clive Walker and Kevan Brown (Woking) and David Harlow and Phil Wingfield (Farnborough Town) worked hard for the FA but a spirited display by the ICIS League under the guidance of Graham Roberts saw them hold on to their slender lead and Paul Gothard (Dagenham & Redbridge) plus Rob Cousins and Jerry Gill (Yeovil Town) impressed enough to be picked for the FA XI to play Combined Services at Oxford City.

*England Captain **Paul Webb.*** Photo: Sportsfile

ICIS Football League: Paul Gothard (Dagenham & Redbridge), Jerry Gill (Yeovil Town), Micky Engwell (Yeovil Town), AL James Hannigan (Enfield), Steve Conner (Dagenham & Redbridge), Rob Cousins (Yeovil Town), John Richardson (Hendon), Jon Daly (St.Albans City), Steve West (Enfield), Howard Forinton (Oxford City), **Subs:** Andy Riley (Sutton United), Paul Turner (Yeovil Town), Clive Gartell (Sutton United), Daniel Honey (Yeading) (GK), Paul Whitmarsh (Dulwich Hamlet)

FA XI: Laurence Batty (Woking), Gary Smart (Forest Green Rov.), Phil Wingfield (Farnborough Town), Mark Smith (Stevenage Borough), Steve Munday (Dover Athletic), Stephen Foster (Woking), David Harlow (Farnborough Town), Paul Barrowcliff (Stevenage Borough), Chris Boothe (Farnborough Town), Corey Browne (Stevenage Borough) Clive Walker (Woking), **Subs:** Wayne Stemp (Farnborough), Kevan Brown (Woking), Robin Taylor (Woking), Fred Hyatt (Hayes), Des Gallagher (Stevenage Borough)

FA XI v British Students

Sadly the weather prevented the FA XI'S match being played against the British Students XI at the West Riding County FA. The original squad selected was:

Matt Dickins (Altrincham), Steve Dickinson (Guiseley), Steve Chambers (Boston United) Paul Stoneman (Halifax Town), Paul Stoneman (Halifax Town), Paul Ellender (Gainsborough Trinity), Sam Kitchen (Gateshead), Richard Annan (Stalybridge Celtic), Kevin Hulme (Halifax Town), Vince Brockie (Hyde United), Mark Todd (Blythe Spartans), David Nolan (Hyde United), Michael Norbury (Halifax Town), Ged Kimmins (Hyde United), Paul Thompson (Gateshead), Tony Carroll (Hyde United). **Team Manager:** Ron Reid, **Assistant Manager:** Alan Smith, **Trainer/Pyhsiotherapist:** Paul Smith

FA XI 5 Combined Service 0
(at Oxford City)

With a sharp frost taking a grip of the pitch during the evening both sides did well to produce an entertaining and fast moving match. And when you consider the quality of the FAXI's attack, which included the country's equal top scorer Lee Hughes of Kidderminster, last years overall top scorer Darren Collins, one of the ICIS leagues leading scorers Howard Forington and Kidderminster's second top scorer Neil Doherty, it wasn't surprising that the Services defence just could not cope!

It did take twenty minutes to open the scoring however, and it was a gem when it arrived! Following a corner from Doherty, Cousins headed back across goal and the man in form, Lee Hughes leapt to smash in an overhead scissor kick of which Jurgen Klinsmen would have been proud.

Within a couple of minutes local hero Howard Forington drove in a low shot which skidded off the hardening turf and deceived 'keeper Elliott.

***Alan Turvey** chairman of the F.A.'s Representative Committee awards **Ken Cramman** with his first international cap which he won last season.*
Photo: Peter Barnes

Riley, the Royal Navy's versatile defender was working hard stemming the flow of FA attacks and Thompson never stopped in his efforts to lift his side, but spurred on by internationals Paul Webb and Ken Cramman the FA kept pushing forward and it was no surprise when Lee Hughes cracked in a third from a pass by Jerry Gill.

With the playing surface becoming very tricky in the second half, the quality of the FAXI was even more noticeable and playing sensible possession football further goals were scored by Hughes to complete his hat-trick following a pass from Darren Collins and a powerful header from centre half Cliff Hercules who has certainly settled down well at the back following many years as a striker where he accumulated nearly 300 goals.

Defensively the FA were not really tested but the squad kept its 'shape' played neat and disciplined football throughout and Richard Mason produced his second sound performance at left back. It was also good to see Basingstoke Towns' excellent season acknowledged with the selection of lively Paul Coomes.

The pitch played well considering the weather but local support for the fixture was disappointing. About half the attendance came from Yeovil Town players, officials, supporters and the parents of Rob Cousins and Jerry Gill, who both showed they were comfortable amongst the experienced internationals.

Ron Reid has watched three games a week, but his FA games have suffered a little from the weather. So he will be sitting down to select his squad for Ireland without the ideal preparation but with plenty of options.

FA XI: Paul Gothard (Dagenham & Redbridge), Jerry Gill (Yeovil Town), Rob Cousins (Yeovil Town), Cliff Hercules (Slough Town), Richard Mason (Boston United), Paul Webb (Kidderminster Harriers), Gary Butterworth (Rushden & Diamonds), Ken Cramman (Rushden & Diamonds), Neil Doherty (Kidderminster Harriers), Howard Farington (Oxford City), Lee Hughes (Kidderminster Harriers). **Sub:** Darren Steadman (Kidderminster Harriers), Mark Tucker & Darren Collins (Rushden & Diamonds), Steve Appleby (Boston United).

Combined Services: I. Elliott (Army), P. Willetts, D. Wilson (RN), A. Higgins (Army), T. Price, G. Wotton (RAF), S. RIley (RN), N. Thompson (RN), C. McGuire (RAF), N. Thwaites (RN), W. Haig (RN), **Subs:** P. Barton (RN), L. Innes, S. Johnston, A. Bird, P. Tagg (Army).

***Neil Doherty** of Kidderminster Harriers.*
Photo: Sportsfile

Ireland 2 England 0

Ron Reid's first Semi-Professional International since taking over at the beginning of the season coincided with quite incredible gales and storms spreading right across Ireland for practically the whole duration of the visit to Dublin.

Having had to replace goalkeeper Laurance Batty, one of Woking's FA Cup heroes, with the equally heroic Scott Cooksey from Hednesford, and Paul Power of Macclesfield with David Leworthy who had scored three goals since joining Rushden & Diamonds from Dover Athletic, the squad reported on Sunday morning after travelling from all over the country.

The Forte Post House at Dublin Airport proved an excellent headquarters and the tour planners had given the squad forty-eight hours in which to train, organise set pieces and generally get a feel for Ron's tactics.

The training grounds were excellent with the choice of twelve pitches all in good condition, as you would expect as they were also to be used by the full Republic of Ireland squad for their international preparations.

But however suitable the venue, any real coaching and serious match preparation was proved impossible by a mixture of gale force, icy winds and heavy rain. The managerial team of Ron, Graham Allner, his assistant and physio Jimmy Conway could hardly make themselves heard let alone achieve any serious planning as their lads froze every time they paused to listen to instructions.

It was tragic that the pre match planning which Ron had so successfully presented with Tony Jennings last season, (when three goals were scored from practiced moves) was just not possible for this match.

In fact it was the Irish who benefited from their own practice after just four minutes when a free kick twenty-five yards out was taken by Gormly after a dummy by Mooney and a short pass to his right saw the Shelbourne goalscoring ace Stephen Geoghegan hit a fierce swerving right footed drive high into the top of the net.

In the first fifteen minutes the home side's understanding was very apparent and some

The England Team *Back row (left to right): Jim Conway (Physio), David Harlow (Farnborough Town), Lee Hughes (Kidderminster Harriers), Neil Howarth (Macclesfield Town), Scott Cooksey (Hednesford Town), Ron Reid (Manager), Paul Gothard (Dagenham & Redbridge), Kevan Brown (Woking), Joe O'Connor (Hednesford Town), Wayne Simpson (Hednesford Town), Graham Allner (Assistant Manager).* ***Front Row (left to right):*** *David Leworthy and Ken Cramman (Rushden & Diamonds), Neil Doherty (Kidderminster Harriers), Paul Webb (Captain: Kidderminster Harriers), Jerry Gill (Yeovil Town), Ged Kimmins (Hyde United), Gary Butterworth (Rushden & Diamonds), Mark Gardiner (Macclesfield Town).*

Photograph © Sportsfile, Dublin.

slick passing saw Geoghegan through again but he pulled his shot just wide of the far post as Scott Cooksey narrowed the angle.

It wasn't long however before some lively pressure pulled the visitor's defence out of position and it was Geoghegan again who added the killer touch that gave the Irish a deserved two goal lead.

At this stage it looked as if England could be in for a drubbing but the midfield trio of skipper Paul Webb, Kenny Cramman and the outstanding Gary Butterworth dug in and steadied the side.

Jerry Gill had his hands full trying to cope with the flying winger Rutherford but at half time when honours were about even the ex-Hudderfield Town and Birmingham City player moved inside in the second half.

Under half of the England team hadn't featured in last years two internationals so it wasn't surprising that team understanding was sometimes lacking, but it was disappointing that a number of senior players didn't really manage to produce their best form.

The second half saw all four substitutes used and it was good to see Ged Kimmin's fly past his full back in one of our most positive moves late in the game.

David Leworthy recalled to the side after two years, battled away, often as a lone central striker and he lead his line with skill and much hard work right to the final whistle.

Joe O'Connor *of Hednesford.* Photo: Sportsfile

Paul Gothard *of Dagenham & Redbridge.*
Photo: Sportsfile

Paul Gothard came on as a substitute goalkeeper for the last fifteen minutes and can be pleased with his faultless 'cameo' performance which included the best save of the match, low down to his left in the last five minutes.

Yes, the opposition was good and the lack of preparation was frustrating and limiting, but everyone felt a little 'flat' after the game as we all knew we could have done better.

Hopefully the squad will be able to prepare properly in Holland before the next International and perhaps the memories of this game should be wiped away as we look positively ahead.

Ireland: Henderson (Bohemians), Tresson (Drogheda United), Scully (Shelbourne), McDonnell (St Patrick's Athletic), D. Geoghegan (Shelbourne), Mooney (Bohemians), Hutton (Derry City), Gormley (St Patrick's), Rutherford (Shelbourne), Morley (Shelbourne), S. Geoghegan (Shelbourne). Subs: O'Dowd (Derry City) and Cahill (Cork City) for Henderson and Mooney (both at half-time), Lynch (St Patrick's), Cousins (Shamrock Rovers) and Colwell (UCD) for Scully, Gormley and Rutherford (all 88 mins).

England: Cooksey (Hednesford), Gill (Yeovil), Brown (Woking), Howarth (Macclesfield), Gardiner (Macclesfield), Doherty (Kidderminster), Butterworth (Rushden & Diamonds), Webb (Kidderminster), Cramman (Rushden & Diamonds), Leworthy (Rushden & Diamonds), Hughes (Kidderminster Harriers). Subs: O'Connor (Hednesford) for Doherty (55 mins), Kimmins (Hyde United) for Hughes (69 mins) Harlow (Farnborough) for Webb (73 mins), Gothard (Dagenham & Redbridge) for Cooksey (78 mins).

England draw 0-0 in Holland

An encouraging display in Appingedam where a goalless draw was fought out with the Amateurs of Holland, gave manager Ron Reid much more satisfaction.

Despite the bad luck of losing four of his original squad through injury, training went well and by the time the team took the field they had the confidence of knowing they were well prepared and comfortable with the tactics.

Indeed England started well and dominated the first half and with Lee Hughes outstanding they had two 'goals' disallowed, but sadly hadn't managed to convert their pressure into goals by half time.

In the second half the Dutch came back to take the initiative and with Hughes now injured England were pinned back, so in the end a draw was probably a fair result.

Skipper Paul Webb and the experienced David Leworthy were the pick of the visitors but now the third important representative match sadly cannot be classed an International as The Highland League (not Scotland) are the opposition. So Ron's strongest squad will be selected under the title of an FAXI for the game on Saturday 10th May. (Incidentally what a very sad dilemma many fans will face as it's the same day as the FA Carlsberg Vase Final – we don't have many big fixtures, so two on the same date is aggravating).

ENGLAND TEAM v HOLLAND

1. Ryan Price	–	Macclesfield T
2. Marcus Bignot	–	Kiddermimster H
3. Ken Cramman	–	Rushden & D
4. David Harlow	–	Farnborough T
5. Steve Payne	–	Macclesfield T
6. Garry Butterworth	–	Rushden & D
7. Paul Webb (C)	–	Kidderminster H
8. Steve Walters	–	Northwich V
9. David Leworthy	–	Rushden & D
10. Chris Byrne	–	Macclesfield T
11. Lee Hughes	–	Kidderminster H

Substitutes used:

Joe O'Connor for Lee Hughes (38 mins)
Steve Prindiville for David Harlow (72 mins)

Substitutes not used:

13. Scott Cooksey – Hednesford Town
14. Ian Cooke – Northwich Victoria
16. Wes Simpson – Northwich Victoria

*England Captain **Paul Webb** seen here shaking hands with the Irish captain.* Photo: Sportsfile

FA XI beats the Highland Select for the first time

HIGHLAND LEAGUE SELECT (0) 1
FA XI (1) 5

The FA Representive side were too strong and technically superior for the Highland League squad as Ron Reid's side rattled in five goals at Allan Park, Cove. The preparation for the fixture had been combed to the last detail, and the squad had enjoyed the comfort of a short flight from Heathrow, setting down in Aberdeen on the Thursday evening.

The Cove Rangers Club excelled in their handling of the fixture, with the hospitality afforded to the travelling English squad, and to the supporters that trekked north, warm and genuine. With ambitious plans to improve the 2,000 capacity at Allan Park, coupled with the existing facilities for social functions and hospitality/press requirements, the supporters of the Aberdeen based club should have faith in their board's drive to move forward.

The last fixture between these respective sides had resulted in a 4-3 victory for the Scots at St Albans City in 1994/95. Their was never to be any repeat of this though. The Highland League has lost the Inverness contingent since those days, and with it the Ross County players, thus diminishing the talent available for selection from the far north – certainly a vast area, although only with a population similar to Sheffield!

The English had a torrid start with the home side tearing into their midfield and back four in terrrier like fashion. This twenty minute battering was controlled though, and it was the Kidderminster Harriers connection that stabbed the homesters so cruelly in the back with a breakaway goal against the run of play after 23 minutes.

Steve Prindiville and Lee Hughes worked the ball down the left wing, before Hughes deposited the ball onto the foot of Hednesford Town's Joe O'Connor, the striker converting the chance with Ivor Pirie stranded, the Peterhead

New England "cap" ***David Harlow*** *of Farnborough Town scored twice against the Highland League.*
Photo: Ian Morsman

Englands FA XI line up at Cove Rangers on May 10th 1997. Back Row (left to right): G. Allner (assistant manager), L. Hughes (Kidderminster), M. Bignall (Morecambe), M. Smith (Stevenage Borough), S. MacKenzie (Farnborough Town), R. Reid (manager), B. Stewart (Southport), P. Ellender (Gainsborough Town), P. Moran (Enfield), J. O'Connor (Hednesford), J. Conway (physio). Front Row: S. Prindiville, M. Bignot (Kidderminster Harriers), S. Terry (Altrincham), G. Butterworth (Rushden & Diamonds), R. Cousins (Yeovil Town), D. Harlow (Farnborough Town), B. Hayles (Stevenage Borough), K. Cramman (Rushden & Diamonds). Photo: F. T. Lancaster

custodion left to search in vain for answers to his back four's generous misgivings. Pirie rescued his side twice before the interval, Hughes' header testing him after 25 minutes, and then a minute before the break the Kidderminster man drove in a shot that the keeper held well following Rob Cousins' slide rule pass.

The twelve minutes after half time were a personal disaster for Pirie though. Lee Hughes was as surprised as anyone to see his 55th minute shot escape the keeper's grasp to make the score 2-0, and then a handling offence outside the box saw the Peterhead man dismissed.

This was the end for the Highlanders, as substitute Barry Hayles (Stevenage Borough), found himself clear to score the FA XI's third, and when confronted by Huntly's John Gardiner, a 40 year old replacement, the striker made no mistake past the veteran goalkeeper. Farnborough Town's David Harlow tucked home the fourth goal, and although a swift reply from Steve King (Peterhead) reduced the arrears, King's header crashing past Billy Stewart, the Southport goalkeeper, a man who had performed admirably all afternoon.

The rout was duly competed two minutes from time – again it was the English substitutes that did the damage, Barry Hayles got in a right wing cross that fell to Harlow, the Farnborough man steadied himself, brought the ball under control and drove it past Gardiner.

Tim Lancaster

HIGHLAND LEAGUE XI: Pirie, Morrision (Cheyne), King, Morland, Paterson, D. Milne (Brown), Park (Presslie), Clark, Macpherson (Gardiner), Whyte (C. Milne), Stephen.

FA XI: Stewart (Mackenzie), Bignot, Prindiville, Cousins (Crammen), Smith, Ellender, Terry, Butterworth, Hughes, Bignall (Hayles), O'Connor (Harlow).

REFERE: M. Pocock, Aberdeen.

Attendance: 450

Highland League – Final Table

		Home			Away			Goals		
	P	W	D	L	W	D	L	F	A	Pts
Huntly	30	11	3	1	12	1	2	86	26	73
Keith	30	12	0	3	9	3	3	76	36	66
Peterhead	30	9	3	3	8	4	3	77	30	58
Lossiemouth	30	10	2	3	8	2	5	66	31	58
Clach	30	10	4	1	6	1	8	59	46	53
Fraserbrugh	30	8	3	4	7	4	4	56	38	52
Cove R	30	8	1	6	7	4	4	84	47	50
Deveronvale	30	10	2	3	6	0	9	55	54	50
Elgin City	30	6	3	6	7	1	7	64	66	43
Wick Acad	30	4	5	6	5	3	7	41	46	35
Rothes	30	5	3	7	4	5	6	44	52	35
Forres Mechs	30	6	2	7	2	3	10	40	60	29
Buckie Th	30	4	1	10	4	3	8	41	55	28
Brora R	30	3	6	6	2	4	9	43	88	25
Nairn Co	30	2	2	11	2	1	12	21	93	15
Fort William	30	1	1	13	1	2	12	31	116	9

GM Vauxhall Conference

Founded: 1979 **President:** J C Thompson MBIM, MInst.M,FID

Chairman: W J King **Vice-Chairman:** G F Smith **Chief Executive:** P D Hunter

Secretary: J A Moules, 24 Barnehurst Road, Bexleyheath, Kent DA7 6EZ
Tel: 01322 521116 Fax: 01322 526793

After three seasons failing to provide a champion club possessing the Nationwide Division Three criteria, it was of the utmost importance that this season's top club would be able to make the historic step up to the full time professional world.

Kidderminster Harriers, Macclesfield Town and Stevenage Borough had all been manoeuvred out of contention as the last three Conference champions and they, along with Woking and Rushden & Diamonds, were the pre-season favourites. All five had acceptable grounds and all five were ambitious.

The Harriers' soon moved well ahead while Woking and Stevenage Borough enjoyed exciting FA Cup runs. The Cardinals beat Millwall after a replay and Cambridge United away, before taking Premier League Coventry City to a second tie and a very close game indeed. The quality of their football was an eye opener for the millions of television viewers and, when Hednesford Town also beat Blackpool and York City before giving the Middlesbrough All Stars a very real shock, only just losing 2-3, the football public had to think seriously about the quality of Conference football.

Kidderminster Harriers with young Lee Hughes racing away at the top of the Conference goalscoring chart were well out in front, but Macclesfield had games in hand and Stevenage were still in touch.

At the other end Bath City looked in real trouble and while Hayes and Welling United seemed to be struggling it was also noticeable that the once all-conquering Altrincham might just have lost their way.

Perhaps the key result for the championship was Kidderminster's 3-0 home Trophy success against Macclesfield. This left the Cheshire club able to mount a single minded challenge, as all their rivals fancied a bid for a Wembley Final as well.

With mid field ace Steve Wood regularly scoring vital goals 'The Silkmen' started playing off their games in hand and won them!

They actually took the lead and although 'Kiddy' fought back you sensed that Sammy McIlroy's squad were on a 'roll' and their consistency gave their challengers very little hope.

Bromsgrove Rovers and Altrincham were sinking fast as Hayes made a brilliant recovery and Welling just avoided sinking too dramatically into the bottom three. One had to feel sorry for Bath City, however, who finished more like champions accordng to the form chart but still couldn't avoid the drop.

The relegation battles were thrilling to the end, while the championship was very professionally won with great confidence by an excellent squad well managed by Sammy McIlroy. What a shame Macclesfield's previous chairman was not alive to see his club move into the Football League.

For Kidderminster, their challenge was really checked when Lee Hughes was injured playing for England and they then found goals hard to come by in the crucial run in. They did win the Spalding League Cup and fellow challengers Stevenage and Woking met in the FA Umbro Trophy Semi-Final before Geoff Chapple's side went on to beat Dagenham & Redbridge in the Final at Wembley.

With attendances well up, good FA Cup results and their champions off to compete in the Nationwide Division Three, prospects look good for a really competitive season ahead and watch those attendance figures!

TW

GM VAUXHALL CONFERENCE 1996-97 - LEAGUE TABLE & RESULTS GRID

		Home					*Away*							Clean Sheets - FA Cup & Trophy & League games only	
	P	**W**	**D**	**L**	**F**	**A**	**W**	**D**	**L**	**F**	**A**	**Pts.**	**G.D.**	/	**Top Scorers** (Competitions as listed in league bulletin)
Macclesfield Town	**42**	15	4	2	41	11	11	5	4	39	19	**90**	50	23	Wood - 16; Power -12; Byrne 11; Sorvel - 8; Askey - 7
Kidderminster Harriers	**42**	14	4	3	48	18	12	3	6	36	24	**85**	42	22	Hughes - 34; Doherty - 16; Olney - 10; Webb - 8; Yates - 7
Stevenage Borough	**42**	15	4	2	53	23	9	6	6	34	30	**82**	34	16	Hayles - 21; Browne - 19; Crawshaw - 18; Catlin - 11
Morecambe	**42**	10	5	6	34	23	9	4	8	35	33	**66**	13	12	Jackson - 19; Norman - 18; Burns, Grimshaw & McCluskie 8
Woking	**42**	10	5	6	41	29	8	5	8	30	34	**64**	8	11	Walker - 18; Steele - 16; Hay - 11; Thompson - 7
Northwich Victoria	**42**	11	5	5	31	20	6	7	8	30	34	**63**	7	11	Steele - 15; Tait - 11; Cooke - 10; Bishop & Walters - 6
Farnborough Town	**42**	9	6	6	35	29	7	7	7	23	24	**61**	5	11	Boothe - 24; Wingfield - 16; Gavin - 13; Harlow - 8; Robson - 6
Hednesford Town	**42**	10	7	4	28	17	6	5	10	24	33	**60**	2	19	O'Connor - 24; Russell - 9; Street - 8; Lambert - 7
Telford United	**42**	6	7	8	21	30	10	3	8	25	26	**58**	-10	16	Gray - 12; Fowler & Langford - 5; Turner - 4
Gateshead	**42**	8	6	7	32	27	7	5	9	27	36	**56**	-4	13	Thompson - 22; Bos & Proudlock - 8; Harkus - 6
Southport	**42**	8	5	8	27	28	7	5	9	24	33	**55**	-10	13	Whittaker - 27; Gamble - 9; Butler, Davenport & McDonald - 5
Rushden & Diamonds	**42**	8	8	5	30	25	6	3	12	31	38	**53**	-2	10	Alford - 15; Collins - 14; Wilkin - 10; Leworthy - 8; Cramman - 7
Stalybridge Celtic	**42**	9	5	7	35	29	5	5	11	18	29	**52**	-5	12	Burke - 15; Arnold & Charles - 13; Trott - 9; Hall & Jones - 7
Kettering Town	**42**	9	4	8	30	28	5	5	11	23	34	**51**	-9	13	Norman - 11; Lynch - 8; Mustafa - 7; May - 5; Lyne - 4
Hayes	**42**	7	7	7	27	21	5	7	9	27	34	**50**	-1	13	Randall - 16; Haynes - 11; Williams - 8; Goodliffe & Roberts - 7
Slough Town	**42**	7	7	7	42	32	5	7	9	20	33	**50**	-3	14	Abbott - 18; West - 9; Hercules - 6; Blackford & Owusu - 5
Dover Athletic	**42**	7	9	5	32	30	5	5	11	25	38	**50**	-11	11	Leworthy - 13; Strouts - 11; Reina - 7; Dobbs & Theodosiou - 5
Welling United	**42**	9	2	10	24	26	4	7	10	26	34	**48**	-10	10	Dennis - 22; Morah - 11; Lakin & Rutherford - 6; Trott - 4
Halifax Town	**42**	9	5	7	39	37	3	7	11	16	37	**48**	-19	10	Norbury - 15; Brook - 10; Horsfield - 9; Lyons - 4; Horner - 3
Bath City	**42**	9	5	7	27	28	3	6	12	26	52	**47**	-27	8	Davis - 21; Penny - 8; Colbourne - 7; Harrington, Withey & Wyatt - 4
Bromsgrove Rovers	**42**	8	4	9	29	30	4	1	16	12	37	**41**	-26	5	Mainwaring - 9; Crisp - 8; Taylor - 7; Burgher, Gardner & Grocutt - 3
Altrincham	**42**	6	3	12	25	34	3	9	9	24	39	**39**	-24	7	Hardy - 18; Terry - 14; Doherty - 6; Harris - 5; McGoona - 4

Home Team \ Away Team	Altrin. 1	Bath 2	Brom. 3	Dover 4	Farnb. 5	Gates. 6	Halif. 7	Hayes 8	Hedn. 9	Kett. 10	Kidd. 11	Macc. 12	More. 13	N.Vic. 14	Rush. 15	Slou. 16	S'port 17	Stalyb. 18	Steve. 19	Telford 20	Welling 21	Woking 22
1. Altrincham		1-3 (648)	3-1 (727)	1-2 (646)	0-3 (643)	0-1 (764)	2-1 (673)	0-2 (746)	1-1 (670)	4-3 (791)	0-1 (848)	0-1 (1285)	0-1 (894)	2-3 **(1334)**	4-3 (1037)	0-1 (967)	1-0 (793)	1-0 (692)	1-2 (700)	2-3 (714)	1-1 (731)	1-1 (888)
2. Bath City	1-2 (619)		1-0 (646)	2-1 (544)	1-1 (1166)	3-0 (465)	0-0 (567)	3-1 (377)	2-1 (385)	0-2 (660)	0-3 (571)	0-3 (955)	2-1 (509)	3-2 **(1258**	3-2 (960)	0-0 (822)	0-2 (531)	0-2 (530)	0-0 (587)	2-3 (499)	3-1 (831)	1-1 (1001)
3. Bromsgrove Rovers	4-0 (562)	2-1 (716)		3-1 (803)	1-1 (729)	2-2 (752)	3-0 (686)	2-2 (557)	1-0 (814)	1-2 (898)	0-1 **(2548)**	0-3 (833)	2-3 (652)	0-5 (638)	0-1 (1109)	4-1 (686)	0-1 (762)	0-1 (734)	1-1 (922)	2-1 (788)	1-0 (708)	0-3 (881)
4. Dover Athletic	2-2 (1114)	2-2 (1164)	2-0 (1023)		0-0 (715)	0-1 (1058)	2-2 (1037)	1-0 (1005)	2-2 (1158)	0-1 (966)	0-5 (1186)	2-1 (948)	3-0 (953)	2-2 (722)	1-1 **(1671)**	0-0 (1129)	0-1 (1259)	2-1 (700)	3-3 (1619)	1-4 (890)	2-1 (1127)	5-1 (1030)
5. Farnborough Town	1-1 (823)	4-1 (807)	2-1 (529)	2-3 (1015)		1-2 (677)	3-0 (675)	1-1 (689)	1-0 (794)	0-2 (1106)	2-1 (613)	0-1 (647)	2-2 (770)	2-2 (728)	2-2 (961)	2-1 (892)	3-3 (707)	1-0 (696)	3-1 (1148)	0-2 (705)	2-1 (460)	1-2 **(1479)**
6. Gateshead	1-1 (635)	5-0 (423)	1-0 (694)	1-3 (622)	1-0 (578)		0-1 (466)	1-1 (476)	0-1 (694)	1-1 (767)	3-1 **(1276)**	0-0 (487)	0-3 (402)	5-1 (489)	1-0 (632)	2-1 (472)	2-2 (511)	0-2 (448)	2-2 (652)	2-3 (361)	1-2 (532)	3-2 (816)
7. Halifax Town	1-1 (842)	4-5 (655)	1-0 (608)	1-3 (709)	3-0 (694)	2-0 (679)		2-1 (684)	1-0 (623)	2-1 (790)	2-3 (786)	3-3 **(2191)**	1-1 (883)	0-3 (1078)	1-3 (948)	4-1 (793)	2-0 (792)	4-1 (664)	4-2 (1171)	0-3 (663)	1-1 (608)	0-4 (807)
8. Hayes	3-1 (470)	0-1 (1183)	1-0 (521)	2-0 (535)	0-0 (537)	0-0 (404)	0-0 (521)		4-0 (674)	2-1 (468)	0-1 (434)	0-2 (684)	2-3 (490)	1-1 (591)	1-1 (1043)	5-0 (768)	1-1 (753)	0-2 (595)	1-3 (1097)	0-1 (485)	1-1 (363)	3-2 **(1327)**
9. Hednesford Town	2-2 (1138)	2-0 (1054)	3-0 (1276)	1-1 (1010)	0-1 (1156)	0-0 (1060)	1-1 (1017)	2-0 (1040)		0-0 (1121)	1-4 **(2587)**	4-1 (2177)	2-1 (1463)	3-0 (1096)	1-0 (1252)	2-1 (852)	0-1 (1149)	2-1 (1035)	0-0 (1440)	0-0 (1440)	0-3 (851)	2-0 **(2368)**
10. Kettering Town	3-1 (1039)	1-1 (1444)	2-0 (1578)	1-1 (1290)	3-1 (1092)	4-1 (1329)	4-1 (1541)	2-2 (1608)	0-2 (766)		3-1 (2305)	1-4 (3461)	0-2 (1362)	1-0 (1378)	1-5 **(4628)**	0-0 (1379)	0-1 (1575)	1-0 (1509)	1-2 (1874)	0-1 (1406)	2-3 (1420)	0-0 (1912)
11. Kidderminster Harriers	1-1 (2679)	6-0 (3305)	1-2 **(6081)**	4-1 (2349)	2-3 (2492)	3-2 (1658)	3-0 (2523)	5-1 (2121)	2-1 (2661)	4-0 (2754)		0-0 (2331)	2-2 (3009)	1-0 (2794)	1-0 (2603)	1-2 (2087)	3-0 (3139)	1-1 (1718)	3-0 (2356)	1-0 (2723)	3-2 (1559)	1-0 (2916)
12. Macclesfield Town	1-1 (2382)	2-2 (1091)	4-0 **(3004)**	1-0 (1209)	3-0 (1431)	3-0 (1763)	1-0 (951)	1-0 (909)	4-0 (1003)	2-0 (1250)	0-1 (1606)		0-0 (1161)	0-1 (1375)	2-1 (1304)	2-0 (1013)	3-2 (1601)	2-0 (792)	2-1 (1723)	2-1 (1054)	1-1 (1102)	5-0 (1826)
13. Morecambe	2-0 (1085)	1-1 (917)	1-0 (940)	3-1 (802)	1-1 (897)	4-0 (788)	1-0 (711)	2-4 (1012)	2-2 (1088)	5-2 (1205)	2-3 (1175)	1-0 (1306)		2-0 (1160)	2-0 (1040)	0-0 (704)	2-1 (733)	0-0 (862)	1-2 **(1438)**	0-1 (1100)	1-2 (877)	1-2 (1360)
14. Northwich Victoria	2-2 (1292)	1-0 (769)	1-0 (722)	0-2 (964)	1-1 (702)	4-2 (823)	2-2 (911)	2-1 (972)	2-1 (924)	2-1 (1055)	1-1 (1234)	2-1 **(1527)**	1-0 (1436)		1-2 (769)	0-1 (849)	5-1 (701)	0-1 (814)	0-1 (1021)	1-0 (742)	0-0 (877)	1-2 (1208)
15. Rushden & Diamonds	3-2 (2521)	4-1 (1853)	1-2 (2144)	1-1 (2110)	0-2 (2298)	0-4 (2214)	1-0 (2629)	2-2 (3134)	0-2 (2618)	1-0 **(5170)**	1-1 (2529)	1-1 (2242)	2-1 (2145)	1-1 (2112)		2-2 (1980)	3-0 (2218)	1-1 (2156)	0-1 (3288)	2-0 (2554)	3-0 (2096)	1-1 (2589)
16. Slough Town	0-1 (1240)	5-2 (1032)	2-0 (1158)	2-2 (843)	1-1 (975)	0-1 (638)	1-0 (760)	1-3 (1106)	2-2 (1120)	1-1 (1032)	0-2 (1610)	0-0 (1096)	2-0 (1104)	3-4 (703)	5-0 (1325)		1-1 (661)	4-1 (822)	1-6 (1298)	6-0 (1002)	3-3 (869)	3-0 **(2055)**
17. Southport	1-3 (803)	3-1 (786)	0-0 (741)	0-1 (935)	0-3 (905)	1-1 (673)	2-1 (1543)	0-2 (702)	1-2 (1023)	2-2 (676)	3-0 (1423)	1-5 **(1546)**	3-1 (802)	0-0 (1077)	2-1 (1225)	0-1 (1117)		3-0 (1051)	0-0 (965)	0-1 (925)	3-2 (884)	4-1 (560)
18. Stalybridge Celtic	1-0 (725)	2-2 (545)	3-0 (585)	4-2 (579)	2-0 (617)	2-5 (274)	2-3 (614)	3-1 (634)	1-2 (643)	3-1 (684)	4-1 **(1067)**	0-1 (887)	2-1 (474)	0-1 (701)	2-0 (788)	2-2 (511)	2-2 (493)		0-3 (735)	0-0 (430)	0-0 (710)	0-2 (702)
19. Stevenage Borough	2-1 (2287)	2-1 (2574)	3-0 (2552)	4-1 (2009)	3-1 (2041)	4-1 (2015)	6-0 (2117)	2-0 (1807)	3-2 (2744)	0-0 (2864)	2-2 **(6489)**	2-3 (5760)	4-2 (2655)	2-0 (2501)	4-1 (2836)	2-2 (2834)	2-1 (2903)	1-1 (2685)		3-0 (2089)	2-1 (2382)	0-3 (4352)
20. Telford United	0-0 (878)	1-1 (549)	3-1 (814)	1-0 (709)	2-0 (816)	0-3 (697)	1-1 (759)	0-0 (812)	1-1 (1236)	1-0 (771)	0-2 **(1860)**	0-3 (1015)	2-3 (721)	2-2 (969)	0-5 (900)	0-2 (872)	1-0 (839)	1-1 (554)	2-3 (1060)		2-0 (746)	1-2 (1014)
21. Welling United	1-0 (601)	2-0 (485)	1-2 (501)	1-0 (1082)	0-2 (757)	2-0 (697)	0-1 (688)	1-0 (433)	1-2 (702)	1-2 (854)	0-1 (781)	0-3 (874)	1-4 (602)	1-1 (527)	0-1 (747)	3-2 (534)	2-3 (700)	2-0 (697)	2-0 (1078)	2-1 (566)		1-1 **(1171)**
22. Woking	7-1 (2701)	2-2 (2317)	1-3 (2044)	1-1 (1926)	0-2 (2379)	1-1 (2300)	2-2 (2331)	1-2 (3352)	2-0 (2313)	2-1 (2968)	2-1 **(3420)**	2-3 (2346)	1-2 (2373)	3-1 (3091)	4-2 (2768)	2-0 (3208)	0-1 (2858)	3-2 (2382)	3-1 (2466)	0-0 (2744)	2-1 (1664)	

SPALDING CHALLENGE CUP

First Round

STALYBRIDGE CELTIC	3	v	1	TELFORD UNITED
HALIFAX TOWN	0	v	1	ALTRINCHAM
FARNBOROUGH TOWN	3	v	2	HAYES
BATH CITY	0	v	2	WELLING UNITED
DOVER ATHLETIC	2	v	3	RUSHDEN & DIAMONDS
KETTERING TOWN	1	v	0	SLOUGH TOWN

Second Round

NORTH

STALYBRIDGE CELTIC	2	v	1	SOUTHPORT
BROMSGROVE ROVERS	3	v	1	NORTHWICH VICTORIA
GATESHEAD	1	v	3	MORECAMBE
HEDNESFORD TOWN	1	v	6	KIDDERMINSTER HARRIERS
ALTRINCHAM	0	v	1	MACCLESFIELD TOWN

SOUTH

KETTERING TOWN	0	v	2	FARNBOROUGH TOWN
RUSHDEN & DIAMONDS	1	v	0	STEVENAGE BOROUGH
WOKING	0	v	2	WELLING UNITED

Third Round

KIDDERMINSTER HARRIERS	1	v	0	RUSHDEN & DIAMONDS
MACCLESFIELD TOWN	1	v	0	BROMSGROVE ROVERS
WELLING UNITED	1	v	2	FARNBOROUGH TOWN
MORECAMBE	3	v	3	STALYBRIDGE CELTIC
(R) STALYBRIDGE CELTIC	0	v	1	MORECAMBE

SEMI-FINAL

1st Leg FARNBOROUGH TOWN 2 v 2 KIDDERMINSTER HARRIERS
Att: 370

2nd Leg KIDDERMINSTER HARRIERS 1 v 1 FARNBOROUGH TOWN
Att: 927

Kidderminster win on away goals rule

1st Leg MORECAMBE 0 v 2 MACCLESFIELD TOWN
Att: 513

2nd Leg MACCLESFIELD TOWN 4 v 1 MORECAMBE
Att: 826

FINAL

1st Leg MACCLESFIELD TOWN 1 v 1 KIDDERMINSTER HARRIERS
Davenport 65 Att: 1320 Prindiville 40

2nd Leg KIDDERMINSTER HARRIERS 0 v 0 MACCLESFIELD TOWN
Att: 2212

A.E.T. Kidderminster win on away goals rule.

TEN YEAR CLUB RECORD - G.M. Vauxhall Conference

	87-88	88-89	89-90	90-91	91-92	92-93	93-94	94-95	95-96	96-97
ALTRINCHAM	14	14	16	3	18	10	10	4	12	22r
AYLESBURY UNITED	-	20	-	-	-	-	-	-	-	-
BARNET	2	8	2	1	-	-	-	-	-	-
BARROW	-	-	14	10	22	-	-	-	-	-
BATH CITY	20	-	-	20	9	7	12	12	18	20p
BOSTON UNITED	16	3	18	18	8	22	-	-	-	-
BROMSGROVE ROVERS	-	-	-	-	-	2	18	13	11	21r
CHELTENHAM TOWN	13	15	11	16	21	-	-	-	-	-
CHORLEY	-	17	20	-	-	-	-	-	-	-
COLCHESTER UNITED	-	-	-	2	1	-	-	-	-	-
DAGENHAM	22	-	-	-	-	-	-	-	-	-
DAGENHAM & REDBRIDGE	-	-	-	-	-	3	6	15	22	-
DARLINGTON	-	-	1	-	-	-	-	-	-	-
DOVER ATHLETIC	-	-	-	-	-	-	8	16	20	17
ENFIELD	12	13	22	-	-	-	-	-	-	-
FARNBOROUGH TOWN	-	-	21	-	5	21	-	14	10	7
FISHER ATHLETIC	15	18	19	22	-	-	-	-	-	-
GATESHEAD	-	-	-	17	14	14	11	7	5	10
HALIFAX TOWN	-	-	-	-	-	-	13	8	15	19
HAYES	-	-	-	-	-	-	-	-	-	15
HEDNESFORD TOWN	-	-	-	-	-	-	-	-	3	8
KETTERING TOWN	3	2	5	4	3	13	2	6	16	14
KIDDERMINSTER HARRIERS	7	5	13	13	19	9	1	11	7	2
LINCOLN CITY	1	-	-	-	-	-	-	-	-	-
MACCLESFIELD TOWN	11	7	4	7	13	18	7	1	4	1p
MAIDSTONE UNITED	9	1	-	-	-	-	-	-	-	-
MERTHYR TYDFIL	-	-	9	9	4	16	20	20	-	-
MORECAMBE	-	-	-	-	-	-	-	-	9	4
NORTHWICH VICTORIA	17	10	15	12	11	11	15	10	8	6
REDBRIDGE FOREST	-	-	-	-	7	-	-	-	-	-
RUNCORN	4	6	3	8	16	19	5	9	21	-
RUSHDEN & DIAMONDS	-	-	-	-	-	-	-	-	-	12
SLOUGH TOWN	-	-	-	19	20	5	21	-	17	16
SOUTHPORT	-	-	-	-	-	-	4	3	6	11
STAFFORD RANGERS	6	19	17	15	17	6	9	21	-	-
STALYBRIDGE CELTIC	-	-	-	-	-	12	14	18	14	13
STEVENAGE BOROUGH	-	-	-	-	-	-	-	5	1	3
SUTTON UNITED	8	12	8	21	-	-	-	-	-	-
TELFORD UNITED	5	16	12	6	6	15	17	19	13	9
WEALDSTONE	21	-	-	-	-	-	-	-	-	-
WELLING UNITED	19	11	6	11	12	20	16	17	19	18
WEYMOUTH	10	21	-	-	-	-	-	-	-	-
WITTON ALBION	-	-	-	-	10	17	22	-	-	-
WOKING	-	-	-	-	-	8	3	2	2	5
WYCOMBE WANDERERS	18	4	10	5	2	1	-	-	-	-
YEOVIL TOWN	-	9	7	14	15	4	19	22	-	-

PAST SEASONS - GM Vauxhall Conference

THE TOP THREE

Max. Pts.	Season	Pts	CHAMPIONS		Pts	Runners-up	Pts	3rd Place
(76)	1979/80	56	Altrincham		54	Weymouth	49	Worcester C.
(76)	1980/81	54	Altrincham		51	Kettering T.	47	Scarborough
(126)	1981/82	93	Runcorn		86	Enfield	77	Telford Utd.
(126)	1982/83	84	Enfield		83	Maidstone U.	79	Wealdstone
(105)	1983/84	70	Maidstone U.		69	Nuneaton Bor.	65	Altrincham
(105)	1984/85	62	Wealdstone		58	Nuneaton Bor.	57*	Dartford
(105)	1985/86	76	Enfield		69	Frickley Ath.	67	Kidderminster
(126)	1986/87	91	Scarborough	*(Promoted - D4)*	85	Barnet	73	Maidstone Utd.
(126)	1987/88	82	Lincoln City	*(Promoted - D4)*	80	Barnet	75	Kettering Town
(126)	1988/89	84	Maidstone Utd.	*(Promoted - D4)*	76	Kettering Town	74	Boston Utd.
(126)	1989/90	87	Darlington	*(Promoted - D4)*	85	Barnet	70	Runcorn
(126)	1990/91	87	Barnet	*(Promoted - D4)*	85	Colchester U.	82	Altrincham
(126)	1991/92	94	Colchester Utd.	*(Promoted - D4)*	94	Wycombe Wdrs	73	Kettering Town
(126)	1992/93	83	Wycombe Wdrs.	*(Promoted - D3)*	68	Bromsgrove R.	67	Dagenham & R.
(126)	1993/94	75	Kidderminster H.		72	Kettering T.	67	Woking
(126)	1994/95	80	Macclesfield T.		75	Woking	72	Southport
(126)	1995/96	91	Stevenage B.		83	Woking	76	Hednesford T.
(126)	1996/97	90	Macclesfield T.	*(Promoted - D3)*	85	Kidderminster H.	82	Stevenage Bor.

* Indicates position achieved through goal difference.

LEAGUE CUP

SPALDING CHALLENGE CUP
BOB LORD TROPHY
DRINKWISE CUP

	Winner	*Runner-up*
1979/80	Northwich Victoria	*Altrincham*
1980/81	Altrincham	*Kettering Town*
1981/82	Weymouth	*Enfield*
1982/83	Runcorn	*Scarborough*
1983/84	Scarborough	*Barnet*
1984/85	Runcorn	*Maidstone United*
1985/86	Stafford Rangers	*Barnet*
1986/87	Kettering Town	*Hendon (Isthmian)*
1987/88	Horwich RMI (NPL)	*Weymouth*
1988/89	Barnet	*Hyde United (HFS)*
1989/90	Yeovil Town	*Kidderminster H.*
1990/91	Sutton United	*Barrow*
1991/92	Wycombe Wdrs	*Runcorn*
1992/93	Northwich V.	*Wycombe Wdrs*
1993/94	Macclesfield T.	*Yeovil Town*
1994/95	Bromsgrove R.	*Kettering T.*
1995/96	Bromsgrove R.	*Macclesfield T.*
1996/97	Kidderminster H.	*Macclesfield T.*

CHAMPIONSHIP SHIELD

(Conference Champions v Trophy Winners)

	Winner	*Runner-up*
1980	Northwich V	*Altrincham*
1981	Altrincham	*Kettering T.*
1982	Runcorn	*Weymouth*
1983	Enfield	*Runcorn*
1984	Maidstone U.	*Scarborough*
1985	Runcorn	*Wealdstone*
1986	Stafford R.	*Enfield*
1987	Kidderminster H.	*Scarborough*
1988	Lincoln City	*Enfield*
1989	Maidstone Utd.	*Telford Utd.*
1990	Darlington	*Barrow*
1991	Wycombe W.	*Barnet*
1992	Wycombe W.	*Colchester Utd*
1993	Wycombe W.	*Northwich Vics*
1994	Woking	*Kidderminster H.*
1995	Macclesfield	*Woking*
1996	Macclesfield	*Stevenage B.*

CONFERENCE DIARY

August 1996 May 1997

1st - 26th August

Stevenage Borough will defend their title after the dismissal of the club's appeal against a High Court decision not to promote the Hertfordshire outfit to the Third Division. **Woking** open their impressive new £1.3 Million, 2,000-seater stand at Kingfield. The latter two clubs are installed as joint favourites to win the championship with **Macclesfield Town** and newcomers **Rushden & Diamonds** joint second favourites at 6-1. **Telford United** confirm the sale of their Buck's Head ground to the local Wrekin District Council. Steve Joel is confirmed as the new manager of **Southport**, taking over from Billy Ayre who has joined Swansea City as assistant-manager, whilst **Dover Athletic** appoint former Chelmsford City boss Joe O'Sullivan as their new manager. **Kettering Town** break their transfer record by paying Bromsgrove Rovers £26,000 for Recky Carter and Craig Gaunt. Another new managerial appointment is at **Northwich Victoria**, where their ex-stalwart centre-half Mark Hancock takes over from Brian Kettle, who was dismissed shortly after the FA Umbro Trophy final defeat in May. **Kidderminster Harriers** show their commitment to go for a second title in three years by signing Telford United's Marcus Bignot for £10,000, experienced goalkeeper Fred Barber and winger Neil Doherty from Birmingham, full-back Steve Prindiville from relegated Dagenham & Redbridge and one-time England under-21 international striker Ian Olney from Oldham. **Rushden & Diamonds**, newly-promoted from the Southern League, continue to splash out on players, paying £35,000 to bring in England defender Mark Tucker from Woking, £40,000 on England midfielder Kenny Cramman from Gateshead and £6,000 on Cambridge United goalkeeper Martin Davies. One of the busiest managers prior to the start of the season is new **Bath City** boss Steve Millard. However, most of his business is outgoing as the Twerton Park club lose many of their most experienced players. **Stevenage Borough** make a record-breaking start to the 96/97 campaign by beating **Halifax Town** 6-0 at Broadhall Way. **Souhtport** sell midfielder Martin McDonald to Third Division Doncaster for £20,000 whilst **Rushden & Diamonds** buy again, shelling out £40,000 on Halesowen Town's giant defender Jim Rodwell.

27th August - 8th September 1996

Southport are the early leaders with **Woking** and **Altrincham** close by. The early season Bank Holiday clash between **Stevenage Borough** and **Macclesfield Town** sees the Cheshire side inflict a first defeat of the campaign on the defending champions. Meanwhile, joint-second favourites **Rushden & Diamonds** suffer their heaviest defeat since being formed in 1992, going down 5-0 at **Slough Town** to leave the Northamptonshire club rooted to the bottom of the table. A season's best crowd of 2,744 see **Woking** being held to a draw at Kingfield against **Telford United. Hayes** open their account as a Conference club, beating **Bromsgrove Rovers** 1-0 at Church Road. Rovers' 22-year-old defender, Adie Smith, goes to Premiership clun Coventry City on trial. Speculation linking the 1995/96 *Mail on Sunday* player of the year, Barry Hayles, with a move away from **Stevenage Borough** is ended for the time being at least when the England striker signs a new two-year contract.

9th - 22nd September 1996

Peter Wragg steps down as manager of **Stalybridge Celtic**, ending a three-year spell at Bower Fold. Experienced midfielder David Frain is put in temporary charge of team affairs. England striker Leroy May switches from **Kidderminster Harriers** to **Kettering Town** for a £15,000 fee. County neighbours **Rushden & Diamonds** finally open their Conference account with a 3-1 win at **Halifax Town. Bromsgrove Rovers** suffer their fifth straight defeat, going down 3-0 at home to **Macclesfield Town. Woking** suffer their first home defeat since December 26th 1994 when **Farnborough Town** win 2-0 at Kingfield. **Hayes** also lose a long-standing home record by losing 1-0 to **Kidderminster Harriers.** It was Hayes' first loss at Church Road since December 1995. The 1st qualifying round of the FA Cup produces no defeats for Conference clubs, although **Bath City**, held at Devizes Town, **Gateshead**, who draw 0-0 at St.Helens Town and **Hednesford Town**, also goalless at Wednesfield, face replays. Both **Morecambe** and **Farnborough Town** bag six goals apiece, away at Brandon United and Three Bridges respectively.

Michael Knowles of Morecambe (hooped socks) just manages to keep control despite the tackle from Philip Wingfield of Farnbrough Town.

Photo: Andrew Chitty.

23rd September - 6th October 1996

All three Conference clubs comfortably negotiate their FA Cup replays, scoring 14 goals between them. **Macclesfield Town** are dealt a massive blow when they learn of the death of their esteemed chairman Arthur Jones, who had been a guiding light at the Moss Rose since 1991. **Bromsgrove Rovers** end their seven-match run of defeats by beating **Altrincham** 4-0 at the Victoria Ground. **Woking** set another attendance-high when 2,768 see Clive Walker score a hat-trick in the 4-2 victory over **Rushden & Diamonds. Dover Athletic** lose summer recruit Udo Onwere, who moves back into the League by joining Blackpool. **Stevenage Borough** continue to lead the table with **Slough Town** separating two other title favourites, **Kidderminster Harriers** and **Macclesfield Town.** Former Northwich Victoria and Southport boss Brian Kettle is the new manager of **Stalybridge Celtic.** Paul Thompson provides the best individual return so far by scoring four of **Gateshead's** five goals in their victory over Ossett Town in the second qualifying round of the FA Cup. Only **Halifax Town** are beaten, losing 4-1 at home to UniBond Leaguers Bishop Auckland, although **Southport, Kettering Town, Stevenage Borough** and **Hayes** are all held at home by lower league sides.

7th - 20th October 1996

Ronnie Reid is announced as the new manager of the England semi-professional team with **Kidderminster Harriers'** boss Graham Allner as his number two. **Welling United** sign Jamaican international striker Lennie Dennis from Sutton United on a permanent basis following a successful loan spell at Park View Road. The Wings were on the wrong end of a 3-0 defeat which earned **Rushden & Diamonds** their first home win of the season. **Southport, Kettering Town** and **Stevenage Borough** all safely negotiate FA Cup replays but **Hayes** are held 0-0 in their replay at Grays Athletic. The scorer of **Stevenage Borough's** last minute cup winner against Baldock Town, defender Efitobor Sodje, is the subject of a bid by Second Division Bristol Rovers, who had unsuccessfully bid for his team-mate Barry Hayes earlier this season. **Macclesfield Town** became only the second team ever to retain the JC Thompson Championship Shield by beating **Stevenage Borough** 2-1 after extra-time.

21st October - 3rd November 1996

Telford United defender Steve Foster joins **Woking** for a £10,000 fee whilst leading Conference scorer Lee Hughes declines an offer to trial with an un-named Premiership club. His club **Kidderminster Harriers** set a new season's best run of 11 matches without defeat by drawing 1-1 at **Northwich Victoria.** Lloyd Owusu becomes the first player to score four goals in a league game in **Slough Town's** 6-0 home win over **Telford United.** Gary Johnson is sacked as manager of **Kettering Town** after a run of nine games without a win. Striker Recky Carter also departs Rockingham Road, joining Dr Martens League side Solihull Borough for £17,500. **Hednesford Town** end a 76-year wait to reach the 1st round proper of the FA Cup after beating Conference rivals **Telford United** at Keys Park. However, **Gateshead** (defeated at home by Consett), **Bromsgrove Rovers** (2-0 losers at Shepshed Dynamo) and **Slough Town** (beaten by Hayes), will not be in the hat for the next round. **Altrincham, Southport, Morecambe** and **Bath City** all face tricky replays.

4th - 17th November 1996

Defending champions **Stevenage Borough** set a new seasons best attendance record when 4,352 watch the 3-0 home defeat by **Woking. Kidderminster Harriers** suffer their first defeat since August 31st when losing 3-2 at home to **Farnborough Town,** whilst **Kettering Town** end their nine-game winless run by beating **Gateshead** 4-1 under the guidance of caretaker boss Steve Berry. **Bath City** bow out of the FA Cup, losing their fourth qualifying round replay 4-1 at Cheltenham Town. However, there are wins for **Southport,** at home to Spennymoor United, and for **Altrincham,** 4-0 at home to Barrow. **Morecambe's** replay against neighbours Lancaster City attracts a massive crowd of 2,726, who see the UniBond League outfit hold the Conference side to a 2-2 draw after extra-time. Yeovil Town's player-manager Graham Roberts is offered the vacant managerial position at **Kettering Town. Hednesford Town** make their first money signing for over a year by paying out an undisclosed four-figure fee for **Macclesfield Town** winger Tony Hemmings. **Morecambe** equal a campaign best of 11 matches without defeat by recording a 3-2 win at **Telford United.** The Shrimps also progressed in the FA Cup by finally beating Lancaster 4-2 in front of another 2500-plus crowd at Christie Park.

18th November - 1st December 1996

Former England defender Graham Roberts decides to remain with Yeovil Town instead of becoming the new boss of **Kettering Town**, whilst Wayne Clarke resigns as manager of **Telford United** and is quickly replaced by ex-Shrewsbury defender Jake King. It isn't a particularly distinguished time for Conference clubs in the 1st round of the FA Cup. **Woking** do well to hold Second Division Millwall to a 2-2 draw at Kingfield in the live Sky Sports match but only **Hednesford Town** are definitely through after beating league rivals **Southport** at Keys Park. There are replays for **Northwich Victoria** (against Walsall), **Rushden & Diamonds** (Boreham Wood), **Stevenage Borough** (Hayes) and **Farnborough Town** (Barnet). **Hayes** pay out one of their highest ever fees to sign Enfield midfielder Joe Francis. **Kettering Town** decide to appoint Steve Berry, who has been in caretaker charge since the departure of Gary Johnson, as their new player-manager. **Morecambe** set a new seasonal best by beating **Rushden & Diamonds** 2-0 to extend their unbeaten run to twelve games. Diamonds' record signing, England striker Carl Alford, asks for a transfer. Another England player, Steve Taylor, re-joins **Bromsgrove Rovers** from Hednesford Town. Struggling **Bath City** extend their run of games without a win to ten after drawing 1-1 with **Woking**.

2nd - 15th December 1996

Mark Hancock resigns as manager of **Northwich Victoria**, due to business commitments, after only five months in charge. Veteran striker Clive Walker is wanted as player-coach by **Rushden & Diamonds**. Meanwhile, his goal earns **Woking** a tremendous 1-0 victory over Millwall in their FA Cup 1st round replay at the New Den. The Cards are one of only two Conference clubs to progress after replays as **Farnborough Town, Rushden & Diamonds** and **Northwich Victoria** all perish. **Stevenage Borough** win the all-Conference replay against **Hayes**. **Woking** celebrate by hammering **Altrincham** 7-1 at Kingfield in the league. Former player Phil Wilson returns to the Drill Field to take over as manager of **Northwich Victoria**. Wilson had been in charge of UniBond League leaders Leek Town. **Gateshead** manager Colin Richardson becomes full-time at the International Stadium. After five straight away defeats, **Rushden & Diamonds** end that sequence in style by beating **Telford United** 5-0 at the Buck's Head. The Vauxhall Conference may only have had three clubs in the 2nd round of the FA Cup, but they do the league proud by all achieving memorable victories. **Hednesford Town** win 1-0 at Blackpool, courtesy of Joe O'Connor's 87th minute strike, **Woking** beat Cambridge United at the Abbey Stadium and **Stevenage Borough** win 2-1 at Leyton Orient.

16th December 1996 - 5th January 1997

Gateshead sign Senegal international striker Ally Dia, who caused something of a stir when turning out for Premiership side Southampton under 'false' pretences. **Woking** keep Clive Walker to his contract, thus scuppering his hopes of becoming player-coach at **Rushden & Diamonds**. League leaders **Kidderminster Harriers** complete their seventh straight win in beating **Kettering Town** 4-0. It is the best sequence of results since 1994/95. Kettering wing back Kofi Nyamah moves to Stoke City for £25,000. Steve Joel resigns as manager of **Southport**, who put former England striker Peter Davenport in temporary charge. A Boxind Day crowd of 6,081 see **Kidderminster Harriers** lose for the first time in eight games in their derby match with neighbours **Bromsgrove Rovers**. **Kettering Town** use £9,000 of the money received for Nyamah's transfer by signing England forward Dave Venables from Stevenage Borough. **Bath City** endure a disasterous Christmas, losing 4-1 at **Farnborough Town** and then 6-0 at **Kidderminster Harriers** to leave them four points adrift at the bottom of the table. Harriers are now twelve points ahead of nearest rivals **Macclesfield Town** at the top.

6th - 19th January 1997

Bad weather hits the fixture programme for the first time. Only **Stevenage Borough** are able to play their 3rd round FA Cup tie at 'home' to Birmingham City. A crowd of 15,365 at St.Andrews see the Conference side put up a valiant effort before bowing out 2-0. **Farnborough Town** are £15,000 richer following the transfer of their former goalkeeper Maik Taylor from Barnet to Southampton for £500,000. Yet another England semi-pro international joins **Rushden & Diamonds**. Full back Simeon Hodson moves to Nene Park from **Kidderminster Harriers**, taking the number of internationals to eleven at Diamonds. **Hednesford Town** sign the former Derby and Leicester striker Phil Gee, who was forced to retire from the full-time game through injury. England striker David Leworthy asks **Dover Athletic** for a transfer, citing the extensive travelling from his Portsmouth home as the reason for wanting to move from The Crabble. **Bath City's** first win in eight games, a 2-1 success at home to **Morecambe**, lifts them to within one point of second from bottom **Rushden & Diamonds**.

Kenny Cramman (Rushden & Diamonds) takes on the Stalybridge defence with a yellow ball (it is!) on a snow covered pitch just before the New Year.
Photo: Colin Stevens

20th January - 2nd February 1997

Colin Richardson leaves **Gateshead** by mutual consent after three years in charge. The Tynesiders have slipped to 15th in the table. **Dover Athletic** are also on the look out for a new boss after the resignation of Joe O'Sullivan. **Woking** smash their transfer record by paying out £30,000 to sign **Morecambe's** top scorer Justin Jackson. Yet another England international, midfielder Simon Stapleton, finds his way to **Rushden & Diamonds** via **Slough Town**. **Hednesford Town's** marvellous FA Cup campaign continues with an excellent 1-0 win in the delayed tie against York City. **Woking** must still wait, however, as their game at Coventry again falls foul of the weather. **Hednesford Town** come down to earth in the FA Umbro Trophy however, losing 3-1 at **Northwich Victoria** in the 1st round. There are also defeats for **Telford United** (at Guiseley), **Gateshead** (at Runcorn), **Kettering Town** (at home to Chelmsford City) and managerless **Dover Athletic** (at home to Dagenham & Redbridge). **Woking's** FA Cup tie against Coventry finally goes ahead on 4th round day, and the Cards put up yet another superb performance to hold the Premiership club to a 1-1 draw at Highfield Road in front of a crowd of 16,040. Meanwhile, in the 4th round, **Hednesford Town** put up a tremendous show against the stars of another Premiership side, Middlesbrough, before finally bowing out 3-2 to a Ravenelli winner. The Pitmen will have some consolation from a 27,511 attendance at the Riverside.

3rd - 16th February 1997

Former Northern Ireland international goalkeeper Jim Platt is the new manager of **Gateshead**. Erstwhile **Southport** caretaker boss Peter Davenport joins **Macclesfield Town** as a player after losing out to Ronnie Moore in the contest to become 'Port's new manager. There was something of a party atmosphere at Keys Park as 2,368 - **Hednesford Town's** second highest Conference attendance, welcomed the Pitmen back from their FA Cup exploits. Amongst the crowd was over 20 scouts from Premiership and Nationwide clubs. **Telford United's** midfielder Mark Turner attends a trial with Premiership club Leeds United. **Stevenage Borough's** hopes of retaining their Conference title is dealt a severe blow when top scorer Barry Hayles breaks his leg against **Welling United**. The only piece of good news for the England striker is that the break isn't a bad one. A crowd of 6,064 saw a Steve Foster own goal eleven minutes from time bring an end to **Woking's** marvellous FA Cup run. The Cards' cup farewell against Coventry City was broadcast live on Radio Five Live with highlights shown later on BBC's *Match of the Day*. The 2nd round of the FA Umbro Trophy isn't particularly productive for Conference clubs with four bowing out to lower league opposition and four more facing tricky replys. The only sides definitely through are **Stevenage Borough**, **Morecambe** and **Altrincham**, who belied their league position to earn a fine 2-1 win at **Farnborough Town**.

17th February - 1st March 1997

John Carroll's ten-month spell as manager of **Halifax Town** comes to an end after a 5-4 home defeat by **Bath City**, a result which lifted the Twerton Park club off the bottom of the table. Veteran coach George Mulhall and ex-Eire international midfielder Keiran O'Regan are put in temporary charge of team affairs. **Gateshead's** new boss Jim Platt signs his fifth new player in three weeks with north-easterner Steve Cuggy joining on loan from Dr Martens Leaguers Hastings Town and midfielder Tony Skedd arriving from UniBond League Spennymoor United. FA Umbro Trophy replays see mainly good news for Conference clubs, although **Welling United** are beaten at Guiseley and **Bromsgrove Rovers** face a second replay after drawing 2-2 at Hyde United. **Kidderminster Harriers** keep up their hopes of a 'double' by winning their replay at Emley 5-1. **Bath City**, fresh from their first away win of the season at **Halifax Town**, sign former Manchester United and Northern Ireland full back Jimmy Nichol, recently sacked as manager of Millwall. However, his debut for the Romans was ended 17 minutes early when he was sent-off for his second bookable offence. **Bromsgrove Rovers** lose their second replay against UniBond League side Hyde United 2-0 at the Victoria Ground. Despite spending heavily on players, **Rushden & Diamonds'** 1-0 defeat at **Gateshead** leaves them rock bottom of the table.

2nd March - 16th March 1997

Former Wimbledon goalkeeper Hans Segers joins **Woking** after Laurence Batty broke a finger which could keep the England international out of the game for two months. Ex-Ipswich, Arsenal and England midfielder Brian Talbot is brought in by **Rushden & Diamonds** as head coach. Diamonds' home game against **Slough Town**, which finished 2-2, ended the Rebels run of four consecutive defeats but the Berkshire club still have failed to win in 13 games. The 3rd round of the FA Umbro Trophy sees victories for **Stevenage Borough** over Guiseley and **Woking** at Dorchester Town, although it needed a 90th minute Scott Steele goal to see off their Dr Martens League opponents. **Altrincham** are beaten at home by Bishop Auckland in a game which saw the UniBond Leaguers' visiting fans cause problems at Moss Lane, and, most surprisingly, **Kidderminster Harriers**, the favourites, are beaten 3-0 at ICIS League Heybridge Swifts. In the other tie, **Morecambe** are held to a goalless draw at home by former Conference club Dagenham & Redbridge. Following Brian Talbot's arrival at **Rushden & Diamonds**, manager Roger Ashby moves 'upstairs' to become director of football. Their local derby against **Kettering Town** sees a crowd of 4,628 at Rockingham Road witness an amazing 5-1 win by the Conference newcomers. **Gateshead's** on loan Dutchman, Gijsbert Bos, nets an eleven-minute hat-trick in the Tynesiders' 5-2 win at **Stalybridge Celtic**. Dagenham & Redbridge end **Morecambe's** interest in this year's FA Umbro Trophy by winning the replay 2-1 at Victoria Road. **Kidderminster Harriers'** star striker Lee Hughes nets his 24th and 25th goals of the season to earn his team a 3-0 win over **Halifax Town**, but Harriers are now four points behind leaders **Macclesfield Town**.

17th - 31st March 1997

The Sports Ground Initiative awards **Halifax Town** a grant of £400,000 to develop their Shay ground. The grant goes towards the planned merger between Town and Halifax Blue Sox, the Rugby Super League team. **Hayes** lose striker Mark Hall, albeit only temporarily. He has been called up into the Barbados Caribbean Cup squad. In an attempt to squash rumours of an impending departure, **Woking** offer veteran Clive Walker an extension to his contract. Former Glasgo Rangers winger Ted McMinn joins **Slough Town** upon his return from a spell playing in Australia. **Bath City** announce that Dr Martens League side Trowbridge Town will groundshare at Twerton Park next season. **Rushden & Diamonds'** improvement under Brian Talbot continues and their vital 1-0 win at fellow relegation candidates **Bromsgrove Rovers** pushes the Northants side to four points ahead of their rivals with four games in hand. **Woking** reach their third FA Umbro Trophy semi-final in four years with a 1-0 win at ICIS League Heybridge Swifts. **Stevenage Borough** join them after defeating UniBond Leaguers Colwyn Bay 2-0 at Broadhall Way. **Macclesfield Town**b extend their sequence of victories to seven wity a 3-0 win against **Gateshead**. A crowd of 5,170 see **Rushden & Diamonds** complete a league 'double' over neighbours **Kettering Town**. They then snatch experienced goalkeeper Steve Cherry from their county rivals after the ex-Notts County stalwart had made only a handful of appearances for the Poppies. **Morecambe** sign Mike Bignall from **Stevenage Borough** for £6,000. **Altrincham** move to within one defeat of the Conference record of seven, after defeats at **Stevenage Borough** and **Welling United**.

Action from Woking v Gateshead.

Photo: Eric Marsh

1st April - 13th April 1997

Macclesfield Town's run of eight straight victories comes to an end with a 4-1 defeat at **Hednesford Town.** The Pitmen's winger, Keith Russell, moves to Second Division Blackpool for £50,000. The loan signing of Gijbert Bos from Lincoln proves successful for **Gateshead** as he wins the *Mail on Sunday* goalscorers award for March. The Dutchmen netted seven times during the month. It's a touch of nepotism as **Telford United** midfielder Mark Turner moves to Hereford United after an unsuccessful trial at Leeds. Hereford's manager is Graham Turner, Mark's father. England semi-pro international midfielder Kenny Lowe moves from **Gateshead** to Darlington. The leading Conference clubs, **Macclesfield Town, Kidderminster Harriers** and **Stevenage Borough**, all achieve the Football League's criteria for entry. **Bromsgrove Rovers** maintain their late rally to avoid the drop with a 1-0 win over **Hednesford Town**. Meanwhile, **Slough Town's** 1-0 victory over **Halifax Town**, their first win since October 19th, virtually secures their Conference place for next season. **Woking** take a 1-0 lead into the second leg of the FA Umbro Trophy semi-final after a first minute Robin Taylor goal separates the two Conference sides.

14th - 27th April 1997

Stevenage Borough and **Woking** meet at Watford's Vicarage Road in the FA Umbro Trophy semi-final replay after the two sides fought out a 2-2 aggregate scoreline over the two legged affair. The replay goes the way of the twice former winners, when goals from Andy Ellis and Clive Walker secure a 2-1 win for the Cards. Founder members **Altrincham** continue their slide by hitting the bottom of the table for the first time in 18 years. Meanwhile, fellow relegation candidates **Bath City** maintain their improvement with a 3-2 win over **Rushden & Diamonds**. **Gateshead's** upturn in fortunes since the arrival of Jim Platt as manager continues with their fourth successive victory - a 1-0 win at **Dover Athletic**. Former England midfielder Brian Talbot is confirmed as head coach at **Rushden & Diamonds**, signing an incredible five-year contract at Nene Park. **Kidderminster Harriers** return to the top of the table following a 3-2 win at **Morecambe. Halifax Town** announce that they are to share their Shay home with local Rugby league club Halifax Blue Sox. The share agreement will bring over £720,000-worth of improvements to the stadium.

28th April - End of Season

Macclesfield Town are now just one win away from securing the title and promotion to the Nationwide League. **Bromsgrove Rovers** become the first side to have relegation confirmed after a 4-0 defeat at the Moss Rose. Fellow relegation candidates **Altrincham** ended their 15-match run without a win by beating **Kettering Town** 4-3 at Moss Lane. Erstwhile **Rushden & Diamonds** manager Roger Ashby is appointed as Sports Development Director at Nene Park. Former England under-21 international Dean Coney is released by **Farnborough Town** after six years with the Cherrywood Road club. Another Conference 'veteran', **Hednesford Town** defender Steve Essex, announces his retirement from the game at the age of 36. **Altrincham** and **Bath City** join Bromsgrove Rovers in being confirmed as relegation candidates. Altrincham lose 2-1 at home to Stevenage Borough in midweek whilst Bath are condemned to a bottom three place despite a last-day win over Northwich Victoria. **Halifax Town's** final day victory over Stevenage ends Bath's Conference tenure. **Kidderminster Harriers** gain some silverware by winning the Spalding Cup. A crowd of 2,212 - the best for a Spalding Cup final for four years, see Harriers clinch the trophy on the away goals rule, following a 1-1 draw at Aggborough. It is the first time Graham Allner's men have won the Spalding Cup. Meanwhile, Harriers' highly-rated striker Lee Hughes lifts the *Mail on Sunday* Goalscorer of the Year award, becoming only the third player since the merit awards began in 1987 to score over 30 goals. It is his final effort for the Worcestershire club though, as it is confirmed that he is to join West Bromwich Albion for an initial £200,000 fee. Hughes is a life-long Albion fan. **Macclesfield Town** more than make up for that disapponitment by clinching the Conference title with a resounding 4-1 win at **Kettering Town** on the final day. **Woking** win the FA Umbro Trophy for the third time in four years when Darren Hay's extra-time winner secures a 1-0 win over ICIS Leaguers Dagenham & Redbrige at Wembley. The teams who finsihed in the bottom three have relegation confirmed as the champions of the ICIS League, Yeovil Town, the UniBond League, Leek Town, and the Dr Martens League runners-up, Cheltenham Town, are all accepted for promotion. Both Bath and Bromsgrove will play in the Dr Martens League next season whilst Altrincham will return to the UniBond after an eighteen-year gap. The Robins' relegation leaves only **Kettering Town**, **Northwich Victoria** and **Telford United** as original founder members of the Alliance Premier League.

Macclesfield Town celebrate after clinching the Conference Championship and gaining promotion.
Photo: Andrew Chitty

Formed:
1892

CHELTENHAM TOWN

Chairman: Paul Baker **Vice Chairman:** Arthur Hayward

Secretary: Reg Woodward
3 Harveys Lane, Winchcombe, Glos. GL54 5QS. (01242 602261)

Commercial Manager: P G Cook

Press Officer: Arthur Hayward

The Robins return to the Vauxhall Conference after a five year gap, coming up as runners-up to Gresley Rovers in the Dr. Martens Premier Division. Cheltenham always looked in contention for promotion but were never going to catch runaway leaders Gresley.

Cheltenham shocked many when they dispensed with the services of manager Chris Robinson midway through the campaign. The former Atherstone United boss had led the club to the top three and it did seem a rather strange decision at the time. To take his place, the Robins turned to Steve Cotterill, ironically signed by Robinson in December 1996. A former Wimbledon and Bournemouth striker, Cotterill was well versed with the non-League game, having actually begun his career at Whaddon Road and then turning out for Alvechurch and Burton Albion before becoming a professional. His full time career was ended by injury and promotion to the Conference means that, due to a clause in his insurance pay-out, he will be unable to play himself.

Cheltenham have a more than useful squad of players, and in Jimmy Smith and Jason Eaton a prolific striking duo who have now been joined by £10,000 signing Dale Watkins, who netted over 30 goals for neighbours Gloucester City last season. However, survival in their first season back at the top will be a triumph.

L-R, Back Row: Mike Davis (Res. Team Man.), Stephen Murphy, Chris Banks, Ross Casey, Mark Freeman, Steve Book, Steve Cotterill (Manager), Ryan Gannaway, Mike Duff, Mark Crisp, Darren Wright, Jamie Victory, Bob Bloomer (Asst. Man.). Front Row: Wally Attwood (Kit Man.), Michael Jackson, Christy Fenwick, Jimmy Smith, Jason Eaton, Keith Knight, Lee Howells, Russell Milton, Dale Watkins, Steve Benton, John Atkinson (Physio).

Cheltenham Town

Match No.	Date	Venue H/A	Competition	Opponents	Result	League Pos.	Attendance	Goalscorers (Times if known)
1	Aug 17	H	DML	Sittingbourne	Won 2-0		703	Chenoweth 72, Boyle 90
2	Aug 20	A	DML	Dorchester Town	Won 3-1		754	Eaton 42, Howells 72, 88
3	Aug 24	A	DML	King's Lynn	Won 2-0		1253	Victory 50, Hughes 77
4	Aug 26	H	DML	Salisbury City	Lost 0-2	3	1017	
5	Aug 31	A	DML	Gravesend & Northfleet	Won 3-1	2	566	Bellingham 17, Banks 49, Boyle 90
6	Sep 3	H	DML	Atherstone United	Won 2-0		610	Banks 57, 61
7	Sep 8	A	DML	Chelmsford City	Won 4-2	2	870	Boyle 10, 40, Wright 52, Howells 79
8	**Sep 14**	**A**	**FAC 1 Q**	**Gosport Borough**	**Won 1-0**		**212**	**Banks 83**
9	Sep 21	A	DML	Baldock Town	Lost 0-1	3	321	
10	Sep 24	H	DML	Dorchester Town	Drew 1-1	3	536	Victory 88
11	**Sep 28**	**H**	**FAC 2 Q**	**Salisbury City**	**Won 4-3**		**714**	**Wright 13, Eaton (3) 38, 56, 63**
12	Oct 5	H	DML	Crawley Town	Lost 1-2	6	810	Howells 39
13	**Oct 9**	**A**	**DMLC**	**Newport A.F.C.**	**Lost 1-2**		**346**	**Smith 18**
14	**Oct 12**	**H**	**FAC 3 Q**	**Weymouth**	**Won 1-0**		**805**	**Smith 70**
15	Oct 16	A	DML	Salisbury City	Won 2-1		310	Boyle 6, Smith 30 (pen)
16	Oct 19	H	DML	Sudbury Town	Lost 0-2	6	867	
17	**Oct 26**	**A**	**FAC 4 Q**	**Bath City**	**Drew 0-0**		**1088**	
18	**Oct 29**	**H**	**FAC 4QR**	**Bath City**	**Won 4-1***		**1018**	**Boyle 90, Eaton 91, Smith 95, Howells 110**
19	Nov 2	H	DML	Ashford Town	Won 6-0	5	854	Victory 4, 18, Smith 8, Boyle 42, Howells 45, 61
20	**Nov 6**	**A**	**GSC SF**	**Cirencester Town**	**Won 2-1**		**197**	**Eaton (2)**
21	Nov 9	A	DML	Worcester City	Drew 2-2	6	1270	Howells 37, Smith 46
22	**Nov 12**	**H**	**DMLC**	**Newport A.F.C.**	**Won 5-0**		**696**	**Smith (3) 23, 51, 58, John 73 (og), Eaton 82**
23	**Nov 16**	**A**	**FAC 1**	**Peterborough**	**Drew 0-0**		**5271**	
24	Nov 23	H	DML	Cambridge City	Won 1-0	5	906	Wring 12
25	**Nov 27**	**H**	**FAC 1 R**	**Peterborough**	**Lost 1-2**		**4160**	**Smith 112 (pen)**
26	**Nov 30**	**A**	**FAT 3 Q**	**Sudbury Town**	**Won 3-2**		**480**	**Freeman 68, Eaton 81, Smith 90**
27	Dec 7	H	DML	Gravesend & Northfleet	Lost 0-1	6	705	
28	**Dec 10**	**H**	**DMC**	**Gloucester City**	**Won 1-0**		**590**	**Eaton 54**
29	Dec 14	A	DML	Crawley Town	Drew 3-3	7	448	Chenoweth 45, 55, Boyle 64
30	Dec 18	A	DML	Newport A.F.C.	Won 5-1		511	Chenoweth 16, 77, Bloomer 18, Boyle 54, 89
31	Dec 21	H	DML	Merthyr Tydfil	Won 2-0	4	801	Bloomer 79, Howells 85
32	Dec 26	A	DML	Gloucester City	Lost 1-2	4	2154	Victory 68
33	Dec 28	H	DML	Nuneaton Borough	Won 2-0	4	1068	Wright 9, Victory 34
34	Jan 11	H	DML	Baldock Town	Won 3-2	3	761	Freeman 2, Symonds 30, Smith 81
35	**Jan 14**	**H**	**DMC**	**Forest Green Rovers**	**Lost 0-1**		**443**	
36	**Jan 18**	**H**	**FAT 1**	**Dulwich Hamlet**	**Lost 1-2**		**703**	**Victory 13**
37	Jan 25	A	DML	Sittingbourne	Lost 0-1	4	598	
38	Feb 1	H	DML	King's Lynn	Lost 1-2	4	704	Chenoweth 41
39	Feb 11	H	DML	Halesowen Town	Won 2-1		747	Knight 69, Howells 73
40	Feb 15	H	DML	Chelmsford Town	Won 1-0	4	763	Wright 63
41	Feb 18	A	DML	Cambridge City	Won 4-1		227	Smith 20, 83, Freeman 43, Boyle 47
42	Feb 22	A	DML	Gresley Rovers	Lost 0-2	5	1010	
43	Mar 1	A	DML	Merthyr Tydfil	Drew 2-2	3	543	Boyle 21, Symonds 85
44	Mar 8	H	DML	Worcester City	Won 2-0	2	1009	Howells 56, Wright 58
45	Mar 11	A	DML	Atherstone United	Drew 0-0		375	
46	Mar 15	H	DML	Hasting Town	Won 2-1	2	412	Howells 52, Victory 60
47	Mar 22	H	DML	Burton Albion	Drew 3-3	2	1066	Banks 22, Smith 67, Victory 73
48	Mar 25	H	DML	Gresley Rovers	Drew 2-2		1396	Chenoweth 9, Dunwell 45
49	Mar 29	A	DML	Halesowen Town	Won 5-1		1406	Knight 60, Dunwell 73, 75 (pen), Wright 81, Boyle 87
50	Mar 31	H	DML	Gloucester City	Drew 1-1	2	3005	Wright 48
51	Apr 5	A	DML	Nuneaton Borough	Lost 0-1	2	1241	
52	Apr 12	H	DML	Hastings Town	Won 1-0	2	1009	Wright 52
53	Apr 19	A	DML	Ashford Town	Drew 1-1	2	574	Wright 82
54	Apr 22	A	DML	Sudbury Town	Won 4-1	2	240	Eaton 18, 37, Dunwell 31, Freeman 42
55	Apr 26	H	DML	Newport A.F.C.	Drew 0-0	2	1565	
56	May 3	A	DML	Burton Albion	Drew 0-0	2	1142	
57	**May 6**	**A**	**GSC F**	**Gloucester City**	**Won 2-1**		**520**	**Howells, Boyle**

* After Extra Time

Cheltenham Town

1	2	3	4	5	6	7	8	9	10	11	12	14	15	Mth No.
Maloy	Clarke	Wring	Banks	Freeman	Victory	Wright	Bloomer	Eaton	Bellingham	Chenoweth	Boyle	Howells	Hughes	1
Maloy	Clarke	Wring	Banks	Freeman	Victory	Wright	Bloomer	Eaton	Bellingham	Chenoweth	Boyle	Howells	Hughes	2
Maloy	Clarke	Wring	Banks	Freeman	Victory	Wright	Howells	Boyle	Bellingham	Chenoweth	Wotton	Bloomer	Hughes	3
Maloy	Clarke	Wring	Banks	Freeman	Victory	Wright	Howells	Boyle	Bellingham	Chenoweth	Wotton	Bloomer	Hughes	4
Maloy	Clarke	Wring	Wotton	Freeman	Victory	Wright	Banks	Hughes	Bellingham	Howells	Bloomer	Boyle	Chenoweth	5
Maloy	Clarke	Wring	Wotton	Freeman	Victory	Wright	Banks	Hughes	Bellingham	Howells	Bloomer	Boyle	Chenoweth	6
Maloy	Clarke	Wring	Wotton	Freeman	Victory	Wright	Banks	Boyle	Bellingham	Howells	Chenoweth	Bloomer	Hughes	7
Maloy	**Clarke**	**Wring**	**Wotton**	**Freeman**	**Victory**	**Wright**	**Banks**	**Boyle**	**Bellingham**	**Howells**	**Chenoweth**	**Burden**	**Bloomer**	**8**
Maloy	Clarke	Wring	Wotton	Freeman	Victory	Wright	Banks	Boyle	Bellingham	Howells	Chenoweth	Bloomer	Eaton	9
Maloy	Duff	Wring	Wotton	Freeman	Victory	Wright	Banks	Eaton	Chenoweth	Bloomer	Clarke	Howells	Bellingham	10
Maloy	**Duff**	**Wring**	**Wotton**	**Freeman**	**Victory**	**Wright**	**Banks**	**Eaton**	**Chenoweth**	**Bloomer**	**Clarke**	**Howells**	**Bellingham**	**11**
Maloy	Wotton	Bloomer	Banks	Freeman	Victory	Howells	Wright	Eaton	Smith	Chenoweth	Clarke	Duff	Bellingham	12
Gannaway	**Clarke**	**Duff**	**Wotton**	**Freeman**	**Victory**	**Wright**	**Banks**	**Boyle**	**Smith**	**Chenoweth**	**Bloomer**	**Wring**	**Bellingham**	**13**
Gannaway	**Bloomer**	**Wotton**	**Banks**	**Freeman**	**Victory**	**Chenoweth**	**Wright**	**Eaton**	**Smith**	**Clarke**	**Howells**	**Boyle**	**Maloy**	**14**
Gannaway	Bloomer	Wring	Banks	Wotton	Victory	Howells	Wright	Boyle	Smith	Clarke	Pick	Chenoweth	Eaton	15
Gannaway	Bloomer	Wring	Banks	Wotton	Victory	Howells	Wright	Boyle	Smith	Clarke	Duff	Chenoweth	Eaton	16
Maloy	**Wotton**	**Wring**	**Banks**	**Freeman**	**Victory**	**Howells**	**Wright**	**Eaton**	**Smith**	**Clarke**	**Bloomer**	**Chenoweth**		**17**
Maloy	**Wotton**	**Wring**	**Banks**	**Freeman**	**Victory**	**Howells**	**Wright**	**Eaton**	**Smith**	**Clarke**	**Bloomer**	**Boyle**	**Gannaway**	**18**
Maloy	Wotton	Wring	Banks	Freeman	Victory	Howells	Wright	Boyle	Smith	Clarke	Bloomer	Pick	Eaton	19
Maloy	**Bloomer**	**Wring**	**Pick**	**Freeman**	**Victory**	**Chenoweth**	**Wright**	**Eaton**	**Smith**	**Clarke**	**Parker**	**Bellingham**	**Gannaway**	**20**
Maloy	Wotton	Wring	Banks	Freeman	Victory	Howells	Wright	Boyle	Smith	Clarke	Eaton	Bloomer	Chenoweth	21
Gannaway	**Wotton**	**Wring**	**Pick**	**Freeman**	**Victory**	**Howells**	**Wright**	**Boyle**	**Smith**	**Clarke**	**Eaton**	**Chenoweth**	**Bloomer**	**22**
Maloy	**Wotton**	**Wring**	**Banks**	**Freeman**	**Victory**	**Howells**	**Wright**	**Boyle**	**Smith**	**Clarke**	**Eaton**	**Chenoweth**	**Bloomer**	**23**
Maloy	Wotton	Wring	Banks	Freeman	Victory	Chenoweth	Wright	Eaton	Smith	Clarke	Boyle	Bloomer	Pick	24
Maloy	**Wotton**	**Wring**	**Banks**	**Freeman**	**Victory**	**Howells**	**Wright**	**Eaton**	**Smith**	**Clarke**	**Boyle**	**Bloomer**	**Chenoweth**	**25**
Maloy	**Wotton**	**Wring**	**Banks**	**Freeman**	**Victory**	**Chenoweth**	**Wright**	**Eaton**	**Smith**	**Clarke**	**Parker**	**Bloomer**	**Gannaway**	**26**
Maloy	Wotton	Wring	Banks	Chenoweth	Victory	Howells	Wright	Eaton	Smith	Bloomer	Boyle	Parker	Duff	27
Maloy	**Wotton**	**Wring**	**Banks**	**Freeman**	**Chenoweth**	**Boyle**	**Wright**	**Eaton**	**Smith**	**Bloomer**	**Duff**	**Parker**	**Gannaway**	**28**
Maloy	Wotton	Wring	Banks	Duff	Chenoweth	Boyle	Wright	Eaton	Smith	Bloomer	Burden	Parker	Gannaway	29
Gannaway	Wotton	Wring	Banks	Duff	Victory	Chenoweth	Wright	Boyle	Smith	Bloomer	Clarke	Burden	Howells	30
Gannaway	Wotton	Wring	Banks	Duff	Victory	Chenoweth	Wright	Boyle	Smith	Bloomer	Clarke	Howells	Cotterill	31
Gannaway	Wotton	Wring	Banks	Freeman	Victory	Chenoweth	Wright	Boyle	Cotterill	Bloomer	Clarke	Howells	Duff	32
Gannaway	Wotton	Wring	Banks	Freeman	Victory	Chenoweth	Wright	Howells	Cotterill	Bloomer	Duff	Parker	Clarke	33
Gannaway	Wotton	Wring	Banks	Freeman	Victory	Chenoweth	Wright	Boyle	Symonds	Bloomer	Smith	Howells	Clarke	34
Gannaway	**Clarke**	**Wring**	**Banks**	**Duff**	**Victory**	**Chenoweth**	**Wright**	**Cotterill**	**Symonds**	**Bloomer**	**Smith**	**Howells**	**Boyle**	**35**
Gannaway	**Wotton**	**Wring**	**Banks**	**Freeman**	**Victory**	**Chenoweth**	**Wright**	**Howells**	**Smith**	**Bloomer**	**Cotterill**	**Duff**	**Clarke**	**36**
Gannaway	Duff	Wring	Banks	Freeman	Victory	Chenoweth	Clarke	Boyle	Smith	Bloomer	Wright	Symonds	Parker	37
Gannaway	Duff	Knight	Banks	Freeman	Victory	Chenoweth	Clarke	Boyle	Smith	Bloomer	Wright	Symonds	Wring	38
Gannaway	Duff	Knight	Banks	Clarke	Victory	Chenoweth	Wright	Symonds	Smith	Bloomer	Wring	Boyle	Howells	39
Gannaway	Duff	Knight	Banks	Clarke	Victory	Howells	Wright	Boyle	Smith	Bloomer	Chenoweth	Wring	Wotton	40
Skeen	Wotton	Symonds	Banks	Freeman	Victory	Howells	Wright	Boyle	Smith	Bloomer	Chenoweth	Clarke	Wring	41
Gannaway	Wotton	Symonds	Banks	Freeman	Victory	Howells	Wright	Boyle	Smith	Bloomer	Chenoweth	Knight	Clarke	42
Gannaway	Clarke	Knight	Banks	Freeman	Victory	Howells	Wright	Boyle	Smith	Chenoweth	Symonds	Duff	Cotterill	43
Gannaway	Clarke	Knight	Banks	Freeman	Victory	Howells	Wright	Boyle	Smith	Bloomer	Chenoweth	Symonds	Cotterill	44
Gannaway	Clarke	Knight	Banks	Freeman	Victory	Howells	Wright	Boyle	Symonds	Bloomer	Chenoweth	Smith	Duff	45
Gannaway	Clarke	Knight	Banks	Freeman	Victory	Howells	Wright	Boyle	Symonds	Bloomer	Chenoweth	Smith	Cotterill	46
Gannaway	Clarke	Knight	Banks	Chenoweth	Victory	Howells	Wright	Dunwell	Smith	Bloomer	Symonds	Duff	Cotterill	47
Maloy	Chenoweth	Knight	Banks	Freeman	Victory	Howells	Wright	Dunwell	Smith	Bloomer	Symonds	Duff	Cotterill	48
Maloy	Chenoweth	Knight	Banks	Freeman	Victory	Howells	Wright	Dunwell	Boyle	Bloomer	Eaton	Duff	Cotterill	49
Maloy	Chenoweth	Knight	Banks	Freeman	Victory	Howells	Wright	Dunwell	Boyle	Bloomer	Eaton	Duff	Cotterill	50
Maloy	Duff	Knight	Clarke	Freeman	Victory	Howells	Wright	Dunwell	Boyle	Bloomer	Chenoweth		Symonds	51
Maloy	Duff	Knight	Cotterill	Freeman	Victory	Howells	Wright	Dunwell	Boyle	Bloomer	Clarke	Smith		52
Maloy	Duff	Knight	Cotterill	Freeman	Victory	Howells	Wright	Dunwell	Boyle	Bloomer	Eaton	Chenoweth	Clarke	53
Maloy	Duff	Knight	Banks	Freeman	Victory	Howells	Wright	Dunwell	Eaton	Bloomer	Boyle	Chenoweth	Cotterill	54
Maloy	Duff	Knight	Banks	Freeman	Victory	Howells	Wright	Dunwell	Eaton	Bloomer	Chenoweth	Boyle	Cotterill	55
Maloy	Duff	Knight	Banks	Freeman	Victory	Howells	Wright	Dunwell	Eaton	Bloomer	Chenoweth	Boyle	Cotterill	56
Maloy	**Duff**	**Benton**	**Banks**	**Clarke**	**Victory**	**Howells**	**Wright**	**Boyle**	**Eaton**	**Bloomer**	**Chenoweth**	**Casey**	**Symonds**	**57**

STEVE COTTERILL (MANAGER)

Date of Appointment	21.01.97
Date of Birth:	20.07.64
Place of Birth:	Cheltenham

PREVIOUS CLUBS

As manager	Sligo Rovers (L.o.Ireland)
As player	Cheltenham T., Alvechurch, Burton Albion, Wimbledon, Brighton & H.A., AFC Bournemouth.

HONOURS

As manager	European Qualification with Sligo Rovers. Promotion to Vauxhall Conference 96-97.
As player	3 x professional "Player of the Year" awards.

Physio:
John Atkinson

Opposite:

Jimmy Smith
Cheltenham Town
Top Goalscorer
1996-97

MATCHDAY PROGRAMME

Number of pages	24
Price	£1.00
Programme Editor	Paul Godfrey 01242 517554
Other club publications:	None
Local Newspapers:	Western Daily Press Gloucestershire Echo
Local Radio Stations:	BBC Radio Gloucester 603 Cheltenham Radio

1997-98 PLAYING SQUAD

PLAYER	Birthplace Honours	Birthdate	CLUBS
GOALKEEPERS			
Kevin Maloy	Taunton		Weston-s-Mare, Taunton T., Blackpool, Exeter C., Taunton T., Cheltenham T.
Ryan Gannaway	Gloucester		Shortwood Utd., Forest Green Rovers, Cheltenham T.
DEFENDERS			
Dean Clarke	Hereford	28.7.77	Hereford Utd., Cheltenham T.
Lee Howells	Bristol		Brisbane C. (Aust), Bristol Rovers, Cheltenham T.
Steve Benton	Bristol		Clevedon T., Bristol City, Cheltenham T.
Bob Bloomer	Sheffield	21.6.66	Bristol Rovers, Chesterfield, Cheltenham T.
Mark Freeman	Birmingham SLP	27.1.70	Gloucester C., Hednesford T., Willenhall, Bilston, Wolves, Bilston, £7.5k to Cheltenham T.
Chris Banks	Stone, Staffs.	12.11.65	Bath C., Exeter C., Port Vale, £10k to Cheltenham T.
MIDFIELDERS			
Paul Chenoweth	Bristol	5.2.73	Bath C., Bristol Rovers, £15k to Cheltenham T.
Andy Hughes	W: Youth		Fairford, Swindon T., Wolves, Chelsea, Cheltenham T.
Jamie Victory	London	14.11.75	AFC Bournemouth, West Ham Utd., Cheltenham T.
Keith Knight	Cheltenham E: Schoolboy	16.2.69	Halesowen T., Gloucester C., Trowbridge T., Yeovil T., Trowbridge T., Gloucester C., Reading, P/E to Cheltenham T.
FORWARDS			
Jimmy Smith	Johnstone	22.11.69	Salisbury C., Torquay Utd., £5k to Cheltenham T.
Jason Eaton	Bristol	29.1.69	Gloucester C., Bristol C., Clevedon T., Bristol Rovers, £15k to Cheltenham T.
Martin Boyle	Bristol		Bath C., Mangotsfield T., Trowbridge T., Bristol Rovers, £10k to Cheltenham T.
John Symonds	Coventry	3.9.70	Bedworth U., Nuneaton B., Hinckley T., Derby Co., £6k to Cheltenham T.

DEPARTURES - (During the season):
Jimmy Wring (Newport AFC), Phil Serjeant (Clevedon T.), Gary Wotton (Hayes), gary Pick (Newport AFC), Mark Bellingham (Halesowen T.), Dave Elsey (Cirencester T.).

(During the close season):
None

PLAYERS ON LOAN: None.

Whaddon Road, Cheltenham

ADDRESS: Whaddon Road, Cheltenham, Gloucestershire GL52 5NA
TELEPHONE NUMBER: 01242 573558

SIMPLE DIRECTIONS: M5 jct 10, A4019 through Cheltenham centre and join B4632 Prestbury Road. Whaddon Rd turning on right. Grd 1 mile town centre & 2 miles Cheltenham (BR).

CAPACITY: 5,000 **COVERED TERRACING:** 3,000 **SEATED** 1,000

SOCIAL FACILITIES: Clubhouse open every evening. Three bars - clubroom, lounge, Robin's Nest. Open before and after Saturday matches. Nest & clubroom available for private hire.

CLUB SHOP: Sells souvenirs of all descriptions incl. metal badges.

Cheltenham Fact File

Nickname: Robins **Sponsors:** Endsleigh Insurance
Club Colours: Red & white stripes/white/white.
Change Colours: Yellow & blue halves/blue/blue.
Midweek matchday: Tuesday
Reserves' League: Central Conference

PREVIOUS - **Leagues:** Local leagues to 1932, Birmingham Combination 32-35, Southern 35-85, GMV Conf 85-92, Southern League 92-97.
Names: None.
Grounds: Whaddon Lane, Carter's Field (pre-war).

CLUB RECORDS - **Win:** 12 - 0 v Chippenham Rovers, FA Cup 3rd Qual., 2.11.35.
Defeat: 1 - 10 v Merthyr Tydfil, Southern League, 8.3.52.
Attendance: 8,326 v Reading, FA Cup 1st Rd 56-57.
Career Goalscorer: Dave Lewis 290 (1970-83).
Career Appearances: Roger Thorndale 701 (58-76).
Transfer fee paid: £20,000 to Kidderminster Harriers (Kim Casey).
Transfer fee received: £60,000 (initial) from Southampton for Christer Warren.

BEST SEASON - **FA Cup:** 3rd Rd Proper 33-34 (lost 1-2 at Blackpool).
League clubs defeated: Carlisle United 33-34.
FA Trophy: Quarter Final, 85-86 & 88-89.
FA Amateur Cup: N/A.

Players progressing to Football League: Paul Tester (Shrewsbury), Brett Angell (Derby), Keith Knight (Reading), Peter Shearer (Bournemouth), Simon Brain (Hereford), Chris Burns (Portsmouth), Christer Warren (Southampton), Steve Jones (Swansea), Peter Rushworth (Leicester), Roy Shiner (Huddersfield), Peter Goring (Arsenal).

96-97 Captain: Mark Freeman.
96-97 Player of the Year: Jamie Victory (Supporters). Darren Wright (Players).
96-97 Top Goalscorer: Jimmy Smith (14)

HONOURS: Southern Lg 84-85 R-up 92-93 94-95 96-97, Midland Div 82-83, Lg Cup 57-58 (R-up 68-69 84-85), Championship Shield 58-59, Merit Cup 84-85), Nth Glos. Snr Professional Cup (30 times), Midland Floodlit Cup 85-86 86-87 87-88.

Formed:
1983

DOVER ATHLETIC

Chairman: Mr J T Husk

Secretary: Mr J F Durrant

Directors: J T Husk, A G Husk, J F Durrant, K F Stamp, G A Goodacre, D Hammond, C J Harman, T J Parmenter.

Commercial Manager: Jean Haves

Press Officer: Commercial Office

During the close season of 1996, Dover fans were looking forward to Peter Taylor's first full season in charge at The Crabble. Then, just before the campaign got underway, Taylor left to become manager of the England Under-21 set up and former Chelmsford City boss Joe O'Sullivan took over.

It was a difficult task for O'Sullivan taking on a squad he knew little about and results suffered. Dover found goals hard to come by despite the presence of the prolific David Leworthy, and eventually O'Sullivan departed with the Lilywhites near the foot of the table. The club then surprised everyone by appointing Bill Williams as O'Sullivan's replacement.

Williams had a good track record during the 1980s but he had been out of football management since leaving Maidstone United some ten years ago. He brought in the experienced coach Clive Walker as his number two and between them they proceeded to steer Dover to the relative safety of 17th place.

Optimism is much higher at The Crabble now, with an excellent crop of youngsters coming through. Their need for a striker is still there and they will miss England midfielder Russell Milton but at least they are still members of the Vauxhall Conference, something that looked very unlikely for most of the 1996/97 season.

Left-Right - Back: Gary Stebbing, Stuart Munday, Lee Palmer, Scott Daniels, Ricky Peina, Phil Barber.
Middle: Frank Brooks (Physio), John Budden, Charlie Mitten, Liburd Henry, Jimmy Strouts, Ron Fearon, Neil Le Bihan, Clive Walker (Asst. Man.).
Front: Steve Jones, Ryan McCabe, Jake Leberl, Bill Williams (Manager), Darren Adams, Paul Wilson, Gerald Dobbs.

Dover Athletic

Match No.	Date	Venue H/A	Competition	Opponents	Result	League Pos.	Attendance	Goalscorers (Times if known)
1	Aug 17	A	VC	Hednesford Town	Drew 1-1	10	1010	Strouts 85
2	Aug 20	H	VC	Hayes	Won 1-0		1005	Reina 25
3	Aug 24	H	VC	Kidderminster Harriers	Lost 0-5		1186	
4	Aug 26	A	VC	Bath City	Lost 1-2	18	544	Leworthy 63
5	Aug 31	A	VC	Macclesfield Town	Lost 0-1	20	1209	
6	Sep 3	H	VC	Woking	Won 5-0		1030	Leworthy 31,47, 51, Milton 56, Dobbs 89
7	Sep 7	H	VC	Altrincham	Drew 2-2	13	1114	Reina 31, Lyndsay 88 (pen)
8	Sep 10	A	VC	Kettering Town	Drew 1-1		1290	Strouts 28
9	**Sep 14**	**A**	**FAC 1 Q**	**Mile Oak**	**Won 3-0**		**395**	**Leworthy (2, 1p), Theodosiou**
10	Sep 17	H	VC	Slough Town	Drew 0-0		1129	
11	Sep 21	A	VC	Gateshead	Won 3-1	12	622	Dobbs 18, Strouts 32, Theodosiou 51
12	Sep 24	A	VC	Woking	Drew 1-1		1926	Leworthy
13	**Sep 28**	**H**	**FAC 2 Q**	**Aldershot Town**	**Won 2-0**		**1793**	**Leworthy (2) 9,44**
14	Oct 1	H	VC	Bath City	Drew 2-2		1164	Dobbs 35, Reina 70
15	Oct 5	A	VC	Northwich Victoria	Lost 0-2	13	964	
16	**Oct 8**	**H**	**SCC**	**Rushden & Diamonds**	**Lost 2-3**		**723**	**Lindsay 21, Reina 46**
17	**Oct 12**	**H**	**FAC 3 Q**	**Hendon**	**Lost 0-1**		**1117**	
18	Oct 15	H	VC	Farnborough Town	Drew 0-0		715	
19	Oct 19	A	VC	Bromsgrove Rovers	Lost 1-3	14	803	Theodosiou 71
20	Nov 2	H	VC	Halifax Town	Drew 2-2	13	1037	Dobbs 4, Strouts 90
21	Nov 9	A	VC	Rushden & Diamonds	Drew 1-1	14	2110	Leworthy 55
22	Nov 23	H	VC	Telford United	Lost 1-4	17	890	Strouts 42
23	Nov 30	A	VC	Stevenage Borough	Lost 1-4	17	2009	Strouts 45
24	Dec 7	A	VC	Kidderminster Harriers	Lost 1-4	19	2349	Leworthy 56
25	Dec 14	H	VC	Northwich Victoria	Drew 2-2	20	722	O'Connell 52, Milton 90
26	Dec 21	H	VC	Stalybridge Celtic	Won 2-1		700	Hanlon 42, Leworthy 89
27	Dec 26	A	VC	Welling United	Lost 0-1		1082	
28	Dec 28	A	VC	Farnborough Town	Won 3-2	16	1015	Milton 15, Hanlon 68, Theodosiou 76
29	Jan 4	A	VC	Hayes	Lost 0-2	18	535	
30	**Jan 18**	**H**	**FAT 1**	**Dagenham & Redbridge**	**Lost 0-2**		**783**	
31	Jan 25	A	VC	Stalybridge Celtic	Lost 2-4	16	579	Theodosiou 1, Reina 9
32	Feb 1	H	VC	Kettering Town	Lost 0-1	21	966	
33	Feb 8	H	VC	Macclesfield Town	Won 2-1	19	948	Brown 71, Stebbing 80
34	Feb 15	H	VC	Bromsgrove Rovers	Won 2-0	16	1023	Strouts 17, Brown 73
35	Feb 18	H	VC	Welling United	Won 2-1	14	1127	Munday 21 (pen), Milton 66
36	Feb 22	A	VC	Southport	Won 1-0	14	935	Strouts 81
37	Mar 1	H	VC	Southport	Lost 0-1	14	1259	
38	Mar 15	A	VC	Halifax Town	Won 3-1	14	709	Adams 36, 47, Strouts 41
39	Mar 22	A	VC	Morecambe	Lost 1-3	14	802	Reina 82
40	Mar 29	H	VC	Rushden & Diamonds	Drew 1-1		1671	Stebbing 25
41	Mar 31	A	VC	Slough Town	Drew 2-2	17	843	Haag 24, Adams 84
42	Apr 5	H	VC	Morecambe	Won 3-0	16	953	Munday 73 (pen), Strouts 78, Reina 86
43	Apr 8	H	VC	Stevenage Borough	Drew 3-3	17	1619	Reina 8, Strouts 73, Adams 90
44	Apr 12	H	VC	Gateshead	Lost 0-1		1058	
45	Apr 19	A	VC	Altrincham	Won 2-1	14	646	Budden 83, Adams 88
46	Apr 26	A	VC	Telford United	Lost 0-1	16	709	
47	May 3	H	VC	Hednesford Town	Drew 2-2	17	1158	Dobbs 76, Wilson 79

Dover Athletic

1	2	3	4	5	6	7	8	9	10	11	12	14	15	Mth No.
Horne	Lindsey	Pilkington	Budden	Daniels	O'Connell	Stebbing	Milton	Reina	Leworthy	Strouts	Sowerby	Jones	Mitten	1
Horne	Lindsey	Pilkington	Budden	Daniels	O'Connell	Stebbing	Milton	Reina	Leworthy	Strouts	Sowerby	Onwere	Munday	2
Horne	Munday	Pilkington	Budden	Daniels	O'Connell	Stebbing	Milton	Reina	Leworthy	Lindsey	Sowerby	Onwere	Strouts	3
Horne	Lindsey	Munday	Theodosiou	Daniels	O'Connell	Stebbing	Milton	Sowerby	Leworthy	Strouts	Onuere	Jones	Pilkington	4
Horne	Munday	Barber	Theodosiou	Daniels	O'Connell	Stebbing	Milton	Reina	Leworthy	Strouts	Lindsey	Sowerby	Pilkington	5
Horne	Munday	Barber	Theodosiou	Daniels	O'Connell	Stebbing	Milton	Reina	Leworthy	Strouts	Dobbs	Lindsey	Budden	6
Horne	Munday	Barber	Theodosiou	Daniels	O'Connell	Stebbing	Milton	Reina	Leworthy	Strouts	Dobbs	Lindsey	Budden	7
Horne	Munday	Barber	Theodosiou	Daniels	O'Connell	Stebbing	Dobbs	Reina	Leworthy	Strouts	Pilkington	Lindsey	Budden	8
Horne	**Munday**	**Barber**	**Theodosiou**	**Budden**	**O'Connell**	**Stebbing**	**Dobbs**	**Reina**	**Leworthy**	**Strouts**	**Pilkington**	**Lindsey**	**Jones**	**9**
Horne	Munday	Barber	Theodosiou	Daniels	O'Connell	Stebbing	Dobbs	Reina	Leworthy	Strouts	Budden	Lindsey	Pilkington	10
Horne	Lindsey	Barber	Theodosiou	Budden	O'Connell	Stebbing	Dobbs	Reina	Leworthy	Strouts	Pilkington	Jones	McCabe	11
Horne	Lindsey	Barber	Theodosiou	Daniels	O'Connell	Stebbing	Dobbs	Budden	Leworthy	Strouts	Pilkington	Jones	McCabe	12
Horne	**Lindsey**	**Barber**	**Theodosiou**	**Daniels**	**O'Connell**	**Stebbing**	**Dobbs**	**Reina**	**Leworthy**	**Strouts**	**Budden**	**Sowerby**	**Jones**	**13**
Horne	Munday	Barber	Theodosiou	Daniels	O'Connell	Stebbing	Dobbs	Reina	Leworthy	Strouts	Lindsey	Budden	Sowerby	14
Horne	Munday	Barber	Theodosiou	Daniels	O'Connell	Stebbing	Dobbs	Reina	Leworthy	Lindsey	Budden	Strouts	Sowerby	15
Horne	**Munday**	**Barber**	**Budden**	**Daniels**	**O'Connell**	**Stebbing**	**Dobbs**	**Reina**	**Lindsey**	**Strouts**	**Jones**	**Morrish**	**Theodosiou**	**16**
Horne	**Munday**	**Barber**	**Theodosiou**	**Daniels**	**O'Connell**	**Stebbing**	**Dobbs**	**Reina**	**Leworthy**	**Lindsey**	**Budden**	**Strouts**	**Jones**	**17**
Horne	Munday	Barber	Budden	Daniels	O'Connell	Stebbing	Dobbs	Reina	Lindsey	Strouts	Theodosiou	Jones	Morrish	18
Horne	Munday	Barber	Theodosiou	Budden	O'Connell	Stebbing	Dobbs	Reina	Lindsey	Strouts	Morrish	Jones	McCabe	19
Horne	Munday	Barber	Budden	Daniels	O'Connell	Stebbing	Dobbs	Strouts	Leworthy	Lindsey	Theodosiou	McCabe	Jones	20
Horne	Munday	Barber	Lindsey	Morrish	O'Connell	Stebbing	Dobbs	Strouts	Leworthy	Milton	Budden	Theodosiou	Jones	21
Horne	Budden	Barber	McCabe	Daniels	Morrish	Stebbing	Dobbs	Strouts	Leworthy	Milton	Theodosiou	Jones	Sykes	22
Horne	Munday	Barber	Budden	Daniels	Morrish	Stebbing	Dobbs	Strouts	Leworthy	Milton	Theodosiou	McCabe	Jones	23
Horne	Munday	Barber	Budden	Daniels	O'Connell	Stebbing	Dobbs	Hanlon	Leworthy	Strouts	Milton	Theodosiou	Mitten	24
Horne	Munday	Barber	Budden	Daniels	O'Connell	Stebbing	Lindsey	Hanlon	Leworthy	Milton	Dobbs	Theodosiou	Morrish	25
Horne	Munday	Barber	Theodosiou	Morrish	O'Connell	Stebbing	Dobbs	Hanlon	Leworthy	Milton	Budden	Lindsey	Shepherd	26
Horne	Munday	Barber	Theodosiou	Morrish	O'Connell	Stebbing	Dobbs	Hanlon	Leworthy	Milton	Strouts	Lindsey	Shepherd	27
Horne	Budden	Barber	Theodosiou	Morrish	Lindsey	Stebbing	Sowerby	Hanlon	Strouts	Milton	McCabe	Sykes	Guiver	28
Horne	Budden	Barber	Theodosiou	Morrish	O'Connell	Lindsey	Dobbs	Hanlon	Strouts	Sowerby	Milton	McCabe	Shepherd	29
Horne	**Munday**	**Barber**	**Budden**	**Morrish**	**Theodosiou**	**Stebbing**	**Dobbs**	**Lindsey**	**Strouts**	**Milton**	**Reina**	**McCabe**	**Shepherd**	**30**
Horne	Munday	McCabe	Theodosiou	Daniels	Lindsey	Stebbing	Strouts	Reina	Sowerby	Milton	Budden	Dobbs	Shepherd	31
Fearon	Munday	McCabe	Theodosiou	Budden	Lindsey	Stebbing	Strouts	Reina	Dobbs	Milton	Sowerby	Morrish	Shepherd	32
Horne	Munday	Palmer	Daniels	Budden	Stebbing	G Dobbs	Strouts	Reina	Brown	Milton	Lindsey	Theodosiou	Barber	33
Fearon	Munday	Palmer	Daniels	Budden	Stebbing	G Dobbs	Strouts	Reina	Brown	Milton	Lindsey	O'Connell	Barber	34
Fearon	Munday	Palmer	Daniels	Budden	Stebbing	G Dobbs	Strouts	Reina	Brown	Milton	Lindsey	O'Connell	Barber	35
Fearon	Munday	Palmer	Daniels	Budden	Stebbing	G Dobbs	Strouts	Lindsey	Adams	Milton	McCabe	O'Connell	Barber	36
Fearon	Lindsey	Palmer	Daniels	Budden	Stebbing	G Dobbs	Strouts	Reina	Brown	Milton	Adams	O'Connell	Barber	37
Fearon	Lindsey	Palmer	Daniels	Budden	Barber	G Dobbs	Strouts	Reina	Adams	Milton	McCabe	O'Connell	Wilson	38
Fearon	Lindsey	Palmer	Daniels	Budden	Barber	Stebbing	Strouts	Reina	Adams	Milton	O'Connell	Morrish	Wilson	39
Fearon	Munday	Palmer	Daniels	O'Connell	Stebbing	Haag	Lindsey	Reina	Adams	Milton	Barber	Morrish	Wilson	40
Fearon	Munday	Palmer	Daniels	O'Connell	Stebbing	Lindsey	Haag	Reina	Adams	Milton	Wilson	Morrish	Barber	41
Fearon	Munday	Palmer	Daniels	Budden	Stebbing	Dobbs	Strouts	Reina	Adams	Milton	Barber	Lindsey	O'Connell	42
Fearon	Munday	Palmer	Daniels	Budden	Stebbing	Dobbs	Strouts	Reina	Adams	Milton	Lindsey	Mitten	Barber	43
Fearon	O'Connell	Palmer	Daniels	Budden	Stebbing	Dobbs	Strouts	Barber	Adams	Milton	Morrish	Wilson	McCabe	44
Fearon	Barber	Palmer	Daniels	Budden	Stebbing	Dobbs	Strouts	Reina	Adams	Milton	O'Connell	Wilson	Morrish	45
Fearon	Lindsey	Palmer	Daniels	Budden	Stebbing	Dobbs	Strouts	Reina	Adams	Milton	O'Connell	Barber	Wilson	46

BILL WILLIAMS (MANAGER)

Date of Appointment	24.01.97
Date of Birth:	23rd August 1942
Place of Birth:	Esher, Surrey.

PREVIOUS CLUBS

As manager	Durban City (SA), Sacramento Gold (ASL), Atlanta Chiefs (NASL), Maidstone Utd.
As coach	None
As player	Portsmouth, West Brom. A., Q.P.R., Gillingham, Maidstone Utd.

HONOURS

As manager	Championships with Durban City (x2), Sacramento (x2), Atlanta. GMVC & F.Lge 4 with Maidstone U.
As player	England: Youth (8).

Assistant Manager / Coach: Clive Walker

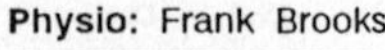

Physio: Frank Brooks

Rick Reina takes on the Mile Oak defence in last season's FA Cup match.

Photo: Roger Turner

MATCHDAY PROGRAMME

Number of pages	40
Price	£1.50
Programme Editor	Chris Collings 01304 822074

Other club publications:

"Tales from the River End" (fanzine)

Local Newspapers:	Dover Express East Kent Mercury
Local Radio Stations:	Radio Kent Invicta FM

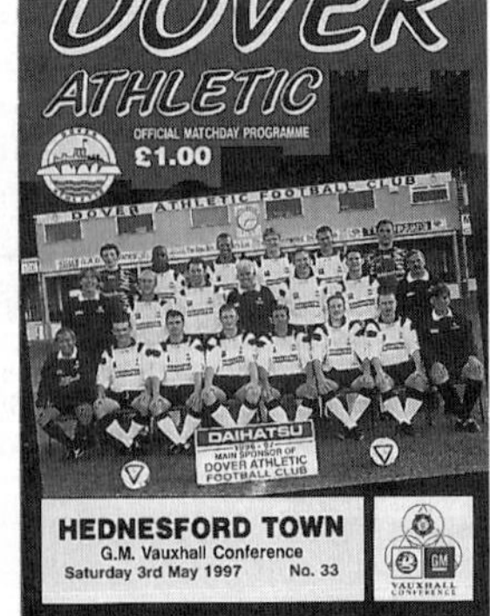

1997-98 PLAYING SQUAD

PLAYER	Birthplace Honours	Birthdate	CLUBS
GOALKEEPERS			
Ron Fearon	Romford	19.11.60	Leyton O., Southend U., Ipswich T., Leyton O., Ipswich T., Sutton U., Reading, Q.P.R., Dover A.
Charlie Mitten	Kent		Thamesmead T., Dover A.
DEFENDERS			
Gerard Dobbs	Lambeth	24.1.71	Wimbledon, Dover A.
Gary Stebbing	Croydon E: Youth	11.8.65	Dagenham & Redb., Kettering, Maidstone U., Ostend (Bleg), Crystal Pal., Dover A.
Stuart Munday	Newham	28.9.72	Brighton & H.A., Dover A.
Scott Daniels	Benfleet	22.11.69	Exeter C., Colchester U., Dover A.
David Scott	Carlisle SLP, SLS, E.Univ.	15.4.67	Hastings T., Canterbury C., Hastings T., Penrith, Dover A.
Luke Morrish	Greenwich	14.11.77	Carshalton A., Southend U., Dover A.
MIDFIELDERS			
Scott Lindsey	Walsall	4.5.72	Gillingham, Bridlington T., Sutton Coldfield T., Tamworth, Burton Alb., Stafford R., Goole T., Scunthorpe U., Dover A.
Phil Barber	Tring	10.6.65	Bristol C., Millwall, Crystal Pal., Aylesbury U., Dover A.
Iain O'Connell	Southend SLP	9.10.70	Southend U., Dover A.
Russell Milton	London E: Semi-Pro		Instant Dict (H.K.), Double Flower (H.K.), Arsenal, Dover A.
James Strouts	York Army		Sittingbourne, Harrogate T., Frickley A., Harrogate R.A., Dover A.
FORWARDS			
Ricky Reina	Kent		Sing Tao (H.K.), Folkestone Invicta, Gillingham, Dover A.
Liam Fox	Dover		from Youth team Dover A.
Steve Lawrence	Gilbert & Elice Is.		from Youth team Dover A.

DEPARTURES - (During the season):
Udo Onware (Blackpool T.), Jermaine Darlington (Hendon), david Leworthy (Rushdn & D.), Colin Sowerby (Billericay T.), Brian Horne (Millwall).

(During the close season): None

PLAYERS ON LOAN: None

Crabble Athletic Ground, Dover

GROUND ADDRESS: Crabble Athletic Ground, Lewisham Road, River, Dover, Kent. CT17 0JB.
Telephone: 01304 822373

SIMPLE DIRECTIONS: Follow the A2 from Canterbury until you pass the Forte Posthouse Hotel on your left and approach a roundabout with MacDonald's drive-in restuarant and a petrol station at the roundabout on your left. Turn right signposted to Town Centre and go down the hill. At the mini-roundabout at the bottom turn left. At the next traffic lights turn right and follow the road under the railway bridge. The ground is up the hill on your left.

CAPACITY: 6,500 **SEATED:** 1,000 **COVERED TERRACING:** 4,900

CLUB SHOP: At the ground, open matchdays for general souvenirs, programmes, replica shirts (home & away) etc. Also at Worthington Street in the town, open daily. Contact Jean Haves 01304 240041.

SOCIAL FACILITIES: Social Club open 7 days a week. Meals available. Steward - Gavin Hughes 01304 822306.

Dover Fact File

Nickname: Lilywhites **Club Sponsors:** Daihatsu (UK) Ltd.

Club colours: White shirts, black shorts and black & white socks.

Change colours: Red shirts, red shorts and black & red socks.

Reserve team league: Winstonlead Kent League Div.2.

Midweek home matchday: Tuesday

PREVIOUS - **Leagues:** Kent League, Southern League.
Grounds None

CLUB RECORDS: **Attendance:** 4,035 v Bromsgrove Rovers, Beazer Homes League April 1992

Win: 7-0 v Weymouth 3rd April 1990.

Defeat: 1-7 v Poole Town.

Career Goalscorer: Lennie Lee - 160.

Career Appearances: Jason Bartlett - 539.

Transfer Fee paid: £50,000 for David Leworthy from Farnborough Town - Aug. 1993.

Transfer Fee received: £11,500 for Tony Rogers from Chelmsford City 1992.

Past players who progressed to the Football League: None

1996-97 Captain: Scott Daniels

1996-97 Top Goalscorer: David Leworthy (13) - now with Rushden & Diamonds

1996-97 Player of the Year: Jimmy Strouts

HONOURS: Beazer Homes League Premier Division Champions 1989/90, 1992/93; Beazer Homes League Southern Division Champions 1987/88; Beazer Homes League Championship Match Winners 1990 & 1993; Premier Inter League Cup Winners 1990/91; Southern League Cup Winners 1991/92; Kent Senior Cup Winners 1990/91, Runners-up 1993/94, 1996/97.

Formed:
1967

FARNBOROUGH TOWN

Chairman: Tony Alper **President:** Charles Mortimer

Football Secretary: Terry Parr

Commercial Manager: Alan Humphries

Directors: B Blewett, C Mortimore, M McCarthy, G Darcey, A Gillespie, T Parr, A Spaven, J Jeremiah, H Carter, J Robinson.

The Hampshire club continue to defy the many pundits who continually name them amongst the favourites to be relegated each season.

Manager Alan Taylor has developed a squad which has a good mix of youth and experience with Football League scouts making regular journeys to Cherrywood Road.

Striker Chris Boothe again did very well last season with 25 goals, whilst midfielder Phil Wingfield chipped in with a very valuable 16. Veteran defender Dean Coney has decided to hang up his boots but Taylor has made some useful summer signings which should ensure another solid campaign for the 'Boro.

What must please the management team is that Farnborough have gained a reputation for being a hard side to beat. No doubt the fact that this will be 'Boro's fourth consecutive season in the top non-League competition after several yo-yo years helps, but the development of their younger players is perhaps the key to their stability.

L-R, Back Row: Phil Wingfield, Chris Boothe, Darren Robson, Stuart MacKenzie, Paul Hartford, Stuart Collar, Jon Underwood, Neil Baker, David Mehew, Keith Rowlands.
Middle Row: Simon Read (Res. Team Man.), Dave Beard (Coach), Ron Manville (Kit/Ground), Cliff Cobb (Physio), Mike Savage (Coach).
Front Row: Spencer Mintram, Steve Baker, Jamie Laidlaw, Wayne Stemp, Ken Ballard (Asst. Man.), Alan Taylor (Manager), David Harlow, Martin Rowlands, Barry Miller.

Farnborough Town

Match No.	Date	Venue H/A	Competition	Opponents	Result	League Pos.	Attendance	Goalscorers (Times if known)
1	Aug 17	A	VC	Telford United	Lost 0-2	19	816	
2	Aug 20	H	VC	Kidderminster Harriers	Won 2-1		613	Boothe 31, Harlow 83
3	Aug 24	H	VC	Macclesfield Town	Lost 0-1		647	
4	Aug 26	A	VC	Welling United	Won 2-0	11	757	Harlow 56, Gavin 86
5	Aug 31	H	VC	Gateshead	Lost 1-2	14	677	Mintram 49
6	Sep 3	H	VC	Hayes	Drew 1-1		689	Wingfield 23
7	Sep 10	A	VC	Woking	Won 2-0		2379	Wingfield 19, Harlow 22
8	**Sep 14**	**A**	**FAC 1 Q**	**Three Bridges**	**Won 6-1**		**557**	**Boothe 8, 35, Harlow 30, Baker 57, Robson 83, Gavin 87**
9	Sep 17	A	VC	Rushden & Diamonds	Won 2-0		2298	Boothe 42, Wingfield 63
10	Sep 21	H	VC	Morecambe	Drew 2-2	8	729	Boothe (2) 40,67
11	Sep 24	H	VC	Bromsgrove Rovers	Won 2-1		529	Gavin 24, Robson 42
12	**Sep 28**	**H**	**FAC 2 Q**	**Carshalton Athletic**	**Won 3-2**		**655**	**Boothe (2) 4, 45, Wingfield 31**
13	Oct 5	A	VC	Hednesford Town	Won 1-0	7	1156	Boothe 77
14	**Oct 12**	**H**	**FAC 3 Q**	**Bracknell Town**	**Won 3-2**		**695**	**Boothe (2) 67 (pen), 70, Coney 87**
15	Oct 15	A	VC	Dover Athletic	Drew 0-0		715	
16	Oct 19	H	VC	Stevenage Borough	Won 3-1	7	1148	Wingfield 49, Boothe 50, Baker 77
17	**Oct 22**	**H**	**HSC 2**	**Fleet Town**	**Won 4-3**		**262**	**Gavin (2), Wingfield, Boothe**
18	**Oct 26**	**A**	**FAC 4 Q**	**Cinderford Town**	**Won 4-0**		**784**	**Boothe 61, 70, Gavin 73, Day 75**
19	**Oct 29**	**H**	**SCC**	**Hayes**	**Won 3-2**		**317**	**Gavin (3) 21, 39, 89**
20	Nov 2	A	VC	Kidderminster Harriers	Won 3-2	7	2492	Gavin 38, 81, Boothe 51
21	Nov 9	H	VC	Kettering Town	Lost 0-2	8	1106	
22	**Nov 16**	**H**	**FAC 1**	**Barnet**	**Drew 2-2**		**2566**	**Wingfield 31, Boothe 39**
23	**Nov 19**	**A**	**SCC**	**Kettering Town**	**Won 2-0**		**503**	**Harford 32, Boothe 54**
24	Nov 23	A	VC	Altrincham	Won 3-0	7	643	Day 45, Underwood 68, Gavin 80
25	**Nov 26**	**A**	**FAC 1 R**	**Barnet**	**Lost 0-1**		**2215**	
26	Nov 30	H	VC	Southport	Drew 3-3	7	707	Wingfield 22, Gavin 45, Boothe 60
27	**Dec 3**	**H**	**HSC 3**	**BAT Sports**	**Won 8-0**		**128**	**Boothe (2), Harlow, Denny, Wingfield, Gavin**
28	Dec 7	A	VC	Northwich Victoria	Drew 1-1	7	702	Boothe 22
29	Dec 14	H	VC	Slough Town	Won 2-1	7	892	Robson 77, Underwood 80
30	Dec 21	A	VC	Bromsgrove Rovers	Drew 1-1		729	Harlow 40 (pen)
31	Dec 26	H	VC	Bath City	Won 4-1		807	Wingfield 7, 62, Gavin 71, Janson 80
32	Dec 28	H	VC	Dover Athletic	Lost 2-3	7	1015	Gavin 5, Stubbing 53 (og)
33	Jan 11	A	VC	Slough Town	Drew 1-1	7	975	Williams 66
34	**Jan 18**	**A**	**FAT 1**	**Rushden & Diamonds**	**Won 2-1**		**1759**	**Underwood 31, Wingfield 66**
35	**Jan 21**	**H**	**HSC 4**	**Newport IoW**	**Won 2-0**		**188**	**Harlow, Gavin**
36	Jan 25	H	VC	Rushden & Diamonds	Drew 2-2	7	961	Underwood 17, Coney 25
37	**Jan 28**	**A**	**SCC**	**Welling United**	**Won 2-1**		**312**	**Harlow 85, 112**
38	Feb 1	A	VC	Stalybridge Celtic	Lost 0-2	7	617	
39	**Feb 4**	**H**	**SCC**	**Kidderminster Harriers**	**Drew 2-2**		**370**	**Boothe 33, 60**
40	**Feb 8**	**H**	**FAT 2**	**Altrincham**	**Lost 0-2**		**691**	
41	Feb 15	H	VC	Stalybridge Celtic	Won 1-0	7	696	Wingfield 8
42	Feb 18	A	VC	Kettering Town	Lost 1-3	7	1092	Boothe 36
43	Feb 22	A	VC	Halifax Town	Lost 0-3	8	694	
44	Mar 1	A	VC	Macclesfield Town	Lost 0-3	9	1431	
45	**Mar 4**	**N**	**HSC SF**	**Basingstoke Town**	**Lost 1-2**		**417**	**Robson**
46	Mar 8	A	VC	Southport	Won 3-0	7	905	Robson 36, 66, Wingfield 68
47	Mar 11	A	VC	Hayes	Drew 0-0		537	
48	Mar 15	A	VC	Morecambe	Drew 1-1	7	897	Baker 7
49	Mar 18	H	VC	Welling United	Won 2-1	5	460	Wingfield 59, 62
50	Mar 22	H	VC	Northwich Victoria	Drew 2-2	5	728	Gavin 16, Underwood 79
51	**Mar 24**	**A**	**SC SF 2**	**Kidderminster Harriers**	**Drew 1-1**		**927**	**Underwood**
52	Mar 29	H	VC	Altrincham	Drew 1-1		823	Mintram 8
53	Mar 31	H	VC	Halifax Town	Won 3-0	5	675	Boothe 17, Harlow 24, Wingfield 31
54	Apr 5	A	VC	Gateshead	Lost 0-1	5	578	
55	Apr 14	A	VC	Stevenage Borough	Lost 1-3	5	2041	Robson 73
56	Apr 24	H	VC	Woking	Lost 1-2		1479	Boothe 54
57	Apr 26	H	VC	Hednesford Town	Won 1-0	7	794	Wingfield 27
58	Apr 29	A	VC	Bath City	Drew 1-1		1166	Boothe 85
59	May 3	H	VC	Telford United	Lost 0-2	7	702	

Farnborough Town

1	2	3	4	5	6	7	8	9	10	11	12	14	15	Mth No.
MacKenzie	Stemp	Williams	Coney	Underwood	Robson	Boothe	Harlow	Gavin	Baker	Wingfield	McAvoy	Denny	Rowe	1
MacKenzie	Stemp	Underwood	Coney	Day	Robson	Boothe	Harlow	Gavin	Baker	Wingfield	McAvoy	Denny	Rowe	2
MacKenzie	Stemp	Underwood	Coney	Day	Robson	Boothe	Harlow	Gavin	Baker	Wingfield	Williams	Denny	Rowe	3
MacKenzie	Stemp	Underwood	Coney	Day	Robson	Boothe	Harlow	Gavin	Harford	Denny	Williams	Mintram	Stedman	4
MacKenzie	Stemp	Underwood	Coney	Mintram	Robson	Boothe	Harlow	Gavin	Harford	Denny	Williams	Baker	Rowe	5
MacKenzie	Stemp	Underwood	Coney	Mintram	Harford	Boothe	Harlow	Denny	Baker	Wingfield	McAvoy	Robson	Gavin	6
MacKenzie	Stemp	Underwood	Coney	Mintram	Robson	Boothe	Harlow	Harford	Baker	Wingfield	Williams	Denny	Gavin	7
MacKenzie	**Stemp**	**Underwood**	**Coney**	**Mintram**	**Robson**	**Boothe**	**Harlow**	**Harford**	**Baker**	**Wingfield**	**Williams**	**Denny**	**Gavin**	**8**
MacKenzie	Stemp	Underwood	Coney	Mintram	Robson	Boothe	Harlow	Harford	Baker	Wingfield	Gavin	Williams	Rowe	9
MacKenzie	Stemp	Underwood	Coney	Mintram	Robson	Boothe	Harlow	Harford	Baker	Wingfield	Williams	Gavin	Denny	10
MacKenzie	Stemp	Underwood	Coney	Mintram	Robson	Boothe	Harlow	Harford	Baker	Wingfield	Williams	Gavin	Denny	11
MacKenzie	**Stemp**	**Underwood**	**Coney**	**Mintram**	**Robson**	**Boothe**	**Harlow**	**Gavin**	**Baker**	**Wingfield**	**Williams**	**Denny**	**Rowe**	**12**
MacKenzie	Stemp	Underwood	Coney	Mintram	Robson	Boothe	Harlow	Harford	Baker	Wingfield	Williams	Gavin	Denny	13
MacKenzie	**Stemp**	**Underwood**	**Coney**	**Mintram**	**Robson**	**Boothe**	**Harlow**	**Harford**	**Baker**	**Wingfield**	**Williams**	**Gavin**	**Denny**	**14**
MacKenzie	Stemp	Underwood	Coney	Mintram	Robson	Boothe	Harlow	Harford	Baker	Wingfield	Day	Gavin	Denny	15
MacKenzie	Stemp	Underwood	Coney	Mintram	Robson	Boothe	Harlow	Harford	Baker	Wingfield	Day	Gavin	Denny	16
Rowe	**Williams**	**Underwood**	**Day**	**Mintram**	**Harford**	**Denny**	**Harlow**	**Gavin**	**Baker**	**Wingfield**	**Boothe**	**Robson**	**McAvoy**	**17**
MacKenzie	**Stemp**	**Underwood**	**Day**	**Mintram**	**Robson**	**Boothe**	**Harlow**	**Gavin**	**Baker**	**Wingfield**	**Williams**	**Denny**	**Rowe**	**18**
Rowe	**Stemp**	**Underwood**	**Day**	**Williams**	**Robson**	**Denny**	**Harlow**	**Gavin**	**Baker**	**Wingfield**	**McAvoy**	**Stedman**	**Ross**	**19**
MacKenzie	Stemp	Underwood	Day	Williams	Robson	Boothe	Harlow	Gavin	Baker	Wingfield	McAvoy	Denny	Rowe	20
MacKenzie	Stemp	Underwood	Day	Williams	Denny	Boothe	Harlow	Gavin	Baker	Wingfield	McAvoy	Stedman	Rowe	21
MacKenzie	**Stemp**	**Underwood**	**Day**	**Williams**	**Harford**	**Boothe**	**Harlow**	**Gavin**	**Baker**	**Wingfield**	**McAvoy**	**Denny**	**Mintram**	**22**
MacKenzie	**Stemp**	**Underwood**	**Day**	**Mintram**	**Harford**	**Boothe**	**Harlow**	**Gavin**	**Baker**	**Wingfield**	**Williams**	**Denny**	**Jansen**	**23**
MacKenzie	Stemp	Underwood	Day	Mintram	Harford	Boothe	Harlow	Gavin	Robson	Wingfield	Williams	Jansen	Rowe	24
MacKenzie	**Stemp**	**Underwood**	**Williams**	**Mintram**	**Harford**	**Boothe**	**Harlow**	**Gavin**	**Robson**	**Wingfield**	**McAvoy**	**Denny**	**Rowe**	**25**
MacKenzie	Williams	Underwood	Day	Mintram	Harford	Boothe	Harlow	Gavin	Robson	Wingfield	McAvoy	Denny	Rowe	26
Rowe	**Baker**	**Williams**	**Day**	**Mintram**	**Harford**	**Boothe**	**Harlow**	**Denny**	**Robson**	**Wingfield**	**Gavin**	**Jansen**	**Hayward**	**27**
MacKenzie	Stemp	Underwood	Williams	Mintram	Harford	Boothe	Harlow	Gavin	Baker	Robson	Hayward	Denny	Rowe	28
MacKenzie	Stemp	Underwood	Coney	Williams	Harford	Boothe	Harlow	Gavin	Baker	Wingfield	Stedman	Denny	Robson	29
MacKenzie	Stemp	Underwood	Robson	Williams	Harford	Boothe	Harlow	Gavin	Baker	Wingfield	Mintram	Denny	Rowe	30
MacKenzie	Stemp	Underwood	Denny	Williams	Robson	Jansen	Harlow	Gavin	Baker	Wingfield	Dobson	Boothe	Rowe	31
MacKenzie	Stemp	Underwood	Coney	Williams	Robson	Denny	Harlow	Gavin	Baker	Wingfield	Day	Jansen	Rowe	32
MacKenzie	Williams	Underwood	Coney	Day	Robson	Mintram	Harlow	Gavin	Baker	Wingfield	Stedman	Denny	Jansen	33
MacKenzie	**Stemp**	**Underwood**	**Coney**	**Day**	**Williams**	**Harford**	**Harlow**	**Gavin**	**Baker**	**Wingfield**	**Robson**	**Denny**	**Rowe**	**34**
MacKenzie	**Stemp**	**Underwood**	**Williams**	**Mintram**	**Robson**	**Boothe**	**Harlow**	**Gavin**	**Harford**	**Wingfield**	**Day**	**Denny**	**Jansen**	**35**
MacKenzie	Stemp	Underwood	Coney	Day	Williams	Harford	Harlow	Gavin	Baker	Wingfield	Robson	Boothe	Mintram	36
MacKenzie	**Stemp**	**Underwood**	**Williams**	**Robson**	**Harford**	**Boothe**	**Harlow**	**Gavin**	**Baker**	**Wingfield**	**Coney**	**Mintram**	**Denny**	**37**
MacKenzie	Stemp	Underwood	Coney	Williams	Harford	Boothe	Harlow	Gavin	Baker	Wingfield	Day	Robson	Mintram	38
MacKenzie	**Stemp**	**Underwood**	**Coney**	**Williams**	**Harford**	**Boothe**	**Harlow**	**Gavin**	**Baker**	**Wingfield**	**Day**	**Robson**	**Mintram**	**39**
MacKenzie	**Stemp**	**Williams**	**Coney**	**Robson**	**Harford**	**Boothe**	**Harlow**	**Gavin**	**Baker**	**Wingfield**	**Day**	**Mintram**	**Denny**	**40**
MacKenzie	Stemp	Underwood	Coney	Day	Robson	Denny	Harlow	Gavin	Baker	Wingfield	Mintram	Harford	Boothe	41
MacKenzie	Stemp	Underwood	Coney	Day	Robson	Boothe	Harlow	Gavin	Baker	Denny	Harford	Mintram	Rowe	42
MacKenzie	Stemp	Underwood	Coney	Harford	Robson	Boothe	Harlow	Gavin	Baker	Wingfield	Day	Jansen	Mintram	43
MacKenzie	Stemp	Underwood	Mintram	Day	Robson	Boothe	Harlow	Gavin	Jansen	Wingfield	Stedman	Dobson	Hayward	44
MacKenzie	**Stemp**	**Mintram**	**Stedman**	**Day**	**Robson**	**Boothe**	**Harlow**	**Gavin**	**Jansen**	**Wingfield**	**Rowe**	**Hayward**	**Dobson**	**45**
MacKenzie	Stemp	Mintram	N Baker	Day	Robson	Boothe	Harlow	Gavin	Harford	Wingfield	Stedman	Hayward	Rowe	46
MacKenzie	Stemp	Mintram	N Baker	Day	Robson	Boothe	Harlow	Gavin	Harford	Wingfield	Underwood	Hayward	Rowe	47
MacKenzie	Stemp	Mintram	N Baker	Day	Robson	Boothe	Harlow	Gavin	S Baker	Wingfield	Underwood	Hayward	Rowe	48
MacKenzie	Stemp	Mintram	N Baker	Day	Robson	Boothe	Harlow	Gavin	S Baker	Wingfield	Underwood	Stedman	Rowe	49
MacKenzie	Stemp	Mintram	N Baker	Day	Robson	Boothe	Harlow	Gavin	S Baker	Wingfield	Underwood	Hayward	Dobson	50
MacKenzie	**Stemp**	**Mintram**	**N Baker**	**Day**	**Robson**	**Boothe**	**Harlow**	**Gavin**	**Underwood**	**Wingfield**	**Stedman**	**Dobson**	**Rowe**	**51**
MacKenzie	Stemp	Mintram	N Baker	Day	Robson	Boothe	Harlow	Gavin	Underwood	Wingfield	Coney	S Baker	Hayward	52
MacKenzie	Stemp	Mintram	N Baker	Day	Robson	Boothe	Harlow	Gavin	Underwood	Wingfield	Coney	Dobson	Hayward	53
MacKenzie	Stemp	Stedman	N Baker	Day	Robson	Boothe	Harlow	Gavin	Underwood	Wingfield	Dobson	Rowe	Hayward	54
MacKenzie	Stemp	Mintram	N Baker	S Baker	Robson	Boothe	Harlow	Gavin	Underwood	Wingfield	Coney	Rowlands	Hayward	55
MacKenzie	Stemp	Mintram	N Baker	S Baker	Robson	Boothe	Harlow	Gavin	Underwood	Wingfield	Coney	Rowlands	Hayward	56
MacKenzie	Stemp	Mintram	N Baker	Day	Robson	Boothe	Harlow	S Baker	Underwood	Wingfield	Coney	Gavin	Rowlands	57
MacKenzie	Stemp	Mintram	N Baker	Underwood	Robson	Boothe	Harlow	S Baker	Rowlands	Wingfield	Day	Hayward	Gavin	58
MacKenzie	Stemp	Mintram	N Baker	Underwood	Robson	Boothe	Harlow	S Baker	Rowlands	Wingfield	Day	Hayward	Gavin	59

ALAN TAYLOR (MANAGER)

Date of Appointment	August 1993
Date of Birth:	05.12.53
Place of Birth:	Barking

PREVIOUS CLUBS

As manager	Chesham United
As coach	Fulham (Youth team)
As player	West Ham United, AFC Bournemouth

HONOURS

As manager	Southern League 93-94
As player	-

Assistant Mananager:
Ken Ballard

Coaches:
M Savage,
M Critchell,
D Beard

Physios:
A Morris,
C Cobb.

Scout:
R Brandon

Farnborough Town's defender, Wayne Stemp, clears his line.
Photo: Andy Donnison.

MATCHDAY PROGRAMME

Number of pages	40
Price	£1.20
Programme Editor	Michael O'Connor
Other club publications:	"Simon Read's Haircut" (fanzine)
Local Newspapers:	Farnborough News
Local Radio Stations:	BBC Southern Counties

1997-98 PLAYING SQUAD

PLAYER	Birthplace Honours	Birthdate	CLUBS
GOALKEEPERS			
Stuart Mackenzie	Tooting FAV	21.3.65	Hounslow, Southall, Hounslow, Harrow Borough, Yeading, £3,250 to Farnborough
DEFENDERS			
Wayne Stemp	Epsom BHL	9.9.70	Brighton, Woking, Staines T, Bognor Regis T
Neil Baker	Southampton	(18 yrs)	Southampton, Wycombe Wanderers
Spencer Mintram	Brighton		Brighton, Lewes, Worthing, £5k to Farnborough
Richard Williams	Surrey		Tottenham Hotspur
Barry Miller	Surrey	(22 yrs)	Brentford (A), Wokingham T, Epsom & Ewell, Wokingham T
MIDFIELDERS			
Phil Wingfield	London		Walton & Hersham, Kingstonian, Walton & Hersham, Hayes, Kingstonian, £7,500 to Farnborough
Steve Baker	Newcastle BHL	2.12.61	Southampton, Leyton Orient, Aldershot
David Harlow	Epsom ESP	2.11.67	Fulham, Farnborough T, Kingstonian, £10k to Farnborough
Darren Robson	Woolwich	18.11.69	Petersfield U, Andover, Waterlooville, Basingstoke T, Gosport B, Southwick, Worthing
Jon Underwood	Surrey		Wokingham T
Paul Harford	Chelmsford	21.10.74	Arsenal, Blackburn R
FORWARDS			
Chris Boothe	London BHL		Hanwell T
David Mehew	Camberley Div 3	29.10.67	Leeds U (A), Bristol Rovers, Walsall, Yate T, Weston-Super-Mare, Bath C.(Free).
Keith Rowlands	London	(22 yrs)	Hanwell T (Free)
Jamie Laidlaw	Doncaster	27.7.77	Swindon T (A), Yeovil T, Bashley (Free).

DEPARTURES - (During the season): Andy Liney (Released), Gordon McAvoy (Fleet T), Ricky Denny (Aldershot T), Micky Ross (Bognor Regis T)
(During the close season): Dean Coney (Retired), Keith Day & Pat Gavin (Released)

PLAYERS ON LOAN: None

Cherrywood Road, Farnborough

ADDRESS:
John Roberts Ground, Cherrywood Road, Farnborough, Hampshire GU14 8UD.
TELEPHONE NUMBER: 01252 541469. **Club Newsline:** 0898 88 44 07.

SIMPLE DIRECTIONS:
M3 exit 4, A325 towards Farnborough, right into Prospect Avenue (club signposted), 2nd right into Cherrywood Rd, ground on right. 20-30 min walk from Farnborough Main, Farnborough North and Frimley BR stations. Whippet mini-bus route 12 passes ground.

CAPACITY: 4,900 **SEATED:** 561 **COVERED TERRACING:** 1,350

SOCIAL FACILITIES:
Clubhouse open pub hours and matchdays. Hot pies, bar meals, crisps etc. Darts, pool, fruit machines & jukebox.

CLUB SHOP:
Boro' Leisurewear shop sells all types of club leisurewear and matchballs (contact Commercial Manager (01252 549328)). Supporters Club shop sells old progs, scarves, badges etc (contact Sandy Turnball).

Farnborough Fact File

Nickname: The "Boro" **Club Sponsor:** Jewson
Club Colours: Yellow & blue
Change colours: Red & black
Midweek matchday: Tuesday
Reserves' League: Suburban League (Premier Division)

PREVIOUS - **Leagues:** Surrey Senior 68-72/ Spartan 72-76/ Athenian 76-77/ Isthmian 77-89/ Alliance Premier (GMV Conference) 89-90 91-93/ Southern 90-91 93-94.
Grounds: Queens Road, Farnborough (1969-1976)

CLUB RECORDS - **Attendance:** 3,581 v Brentford 22/11/95 (FA Cup).
Win: 11-0 v Chertsey Town (H), Spartan League 72-73.
Defeat: 2-10 v Worplesdon (H), Surrey Senior League Division One 68-69.
Career Goalscorer: Simon Read 209, 1986-1994.
Season Goalscorer: Simon Read 53, 1988-89.
Career Appearances: Brian Broome 529, 1980-1994.
Transfer Fee Paid: £10,000 to Kingstonian for David Harlow December 1994.
Transfer Fee Received: £50,000 from Dover Athletic for David Leworthy, August 1993.

BEST SEASON - **FA Cup:** 3rd Rd Proper replay 91-92 (lost 0-1 at West Ham United after 1-1 draw).
League clubs defeated: Torquay United 91-92.
FA Trophy: Quarter Final 92-93.

Past Players progressing to Football League: Dennis Bailey (Crystal Palace & Birmingham City), Paul Mortimer (Charlton Athletic), Tommy Jones (Aberdeen & Swindon Town), Allan Cockram (Brentford), Paul Holsgrove (Millwall & Reading), Maik Taylor (Barnet, Southampton).

1996-97 Captain: Dean Coney (now left the club).

1996-97 Top Goalscorer: Chris Boothe (28)

1996-97 Player of the Year: David Harlow

HONOURS: Southern Lg 90-91 93-94, Isthmian Lg R-up 88-89 (Div 1 84-85, Div 2 78-79), Athenian Lg Div 2 78-79, Spartan Lg 72-73 73-74 74-75 (Lg Cup 74-75), London Spartan Lg 75-76 (Lg Cup 75-76), Hants Snr Cup 74-75 81-82 83-84 85-86 90-91 (R-up 93-94), FA Trophy QF 92-93, FA Vase SF 75-76 76-77.

GATESHEAD

Formed: 1977

Chairman: John Gibson

President: J C Thomas

Vice Chairman: Peter Robinson

Director: Norman Lakey

General Manager: Mark Donnelly

Fixture Secretary: Arthur Waggott

Press Officer: Andy Wilson

Commercial Manager: Cheryl Smith

After a couple of excellent seasons under manager Colin Richardson, which resulted in finishing positions of seventh and fifth respectively, Gateshead surprisingly struggled during the first half of last season. So much so that the ambitious Tynesiders dispensed with Richardson's sevices and brought in ex-Northern Ireland goalkeeper Jim Platt, who had been so successful at Darlington the previous season.

A number of changes were made by the new boss and Gateshead embarked on a terrific 21-game run which eventually lifted them to tenth place - a great achievement considering they were hovering around the relegation places when Platt arrived.

Striker Paul Thompson enjoyed a good campaign, netting 23 goals and earning a big money move to Stevenage Borough, whilst one of Platt's shrewdest moves was to sign Gijsbert Bos on loan from Lincoln. His goals went a long way to helping Gateshead's improved form and earned the striker March's Goalscorer Of The Month Award. Despite valiant attempts to make the Dutchman's move to the International Stadium, his form with them persuaded Rotherham to sign him during the summer.

The 1997/98 season will be a very interesting one for the Tynesiders as they have decided to go 'full time'. To justify that, Gateshead will need to be challenging for the title.

Gateshead

Match No.	Date	Venue H/A	Competition	Opponents	Result	League Pos.	Attendance	Goalscorers (Times if known)
1	Aug 17	A	VC	Kidderminster Harriers	Lost 2-3	15	1658	Harkus 45, Foreman 82
2	Aug 21	H	VC	Northwich Victoria	Won 5-1		489	Ord 42, Proudlock 47, 84, Thompson 52, Foreman 58
3	Aug 24	A	VC	Telford United	Won 3-0		697	Hughes og, 57, Lowe 79, Harkus 83
4	Aug 26	H	VC	Altrincham	Drew 1-1	6	635	Proudlock 24
5	Aug 31	A	VC	Farnborough Town	Won 2-1	4	677	Pearson 45, Thompson 65
6	Sep 3	A	VC	Halifax Town	Lost 0-2		679	
7	Sep 7	A	VC	Bath City	Lost 0-3	9	465	
8	Sep 11	H	VC	Southport	Drew 2-2		511	Proudlock 35, Harkus 89
9	**Sep 14**	**A**	**FAC 1**	**St Helens**	**Drew 0-0**		**113**	
10	**Sep 18**	**H**	**FAC 1 R**	**St Helens**	**Won 5-1**		**220**	**Foreman 3, Dowson 46, Harkus 57, Lowe 59, Ord 73**
11	Sep 21	H	VC	Dover Athletic	Lost 1-3	15	622	Harkus 20
12	Sep 25	H	VC	Macclesfield Town	Drew 0-0		487	
13	**Sep 28**	**H**	**FAC 2 Q**	**Ossett Town**	**Won 5-1**		**400**	**Thompson (4) 41, 65, 69, 79, Lowe 35**
14	Oct 5	A	VC	Bromsgrove Rovers	Drew 2-2	14	757	Thompson 32 (pen), J Robson 46
15	**Oct 12**	**H**	**FAC 3 Q**	**Workington**	**Won 4-0**		**460**	**Proudlock 27, Kitchen 46, Thompson 7, 82**
16	Oct 16	H	VC	Morecambe	Lost 0-3		402	
17	Oct 19	A	VC	Rushden & Diamonds	Won 4-0	13	2214	Proudlock 19, Thompson 31, Pearson 56, Watson 86
18	**Oct 26**	**H**	**FAC 4 Q**	**Consett**	**Lost 0-1**		**856**	
19	Nov 2	A	VC	Kettering Town	Lost 1-4	14	1329	Conlon 32
20	Nov 9	H	VC	Welling United	Lost 1-2		532	Conlon 60
21	Nov 16	H	VC	Slough Town	Won 2-1	13	472	Thompson 46, Harkus 65
22	**Nov 20**	**H**	**SCC**	**Morecambe**	**Lost 1-3**		**166**	**Thompson 20**
23	Nov 23	A	VC	Stevenage Borough	Lost 1-4	14	2015	Ord 32
24	Nov 26	A	VC	Southport	Drew 1-1		673	Watson 75
25	Nov 30	A	VC	Hayes	Drew 0-0	14	404	
26	Dec 11	A	VC	Morecambe	Lost 0-4		788	
27	Dec 14	H	VC	Bath City	Won 5-0	13	423	Watson 8, Thompson 56, Dia 83, J Robson 85
28	Dec 21	A	VC	Hednesford Town	Drew 0-0		1060	
29	Dec 26	H	VC	Stalybridge Celtic	Lost 0-2		448	
30	Dec 28	H	VC	Halifax Town	Lost 0-1	15	466	
31	Jan 11	H	VC	Telford United	Lost 2-3	15	361	Thompson 77 (pen), Dia 83
32	**Jan 18**	**H**	**FAT 1**	**Runcorn**	**Lost 1-2**		**380**	**Thompson 86**
33	Feb 1	A	VC	Slough Town	Won 1-0	16	638	Thompson 82
34	Feb 8	H	VC	Kettering Town	Drew 1-1	16	767	Thompson 24 (pen)
35	Feb 15	H	VC	Hednesford Town	Lost 0-1	17	694	
36	Feb 22	H	VC	Rushden & Diamonds	Won 1-0	17	632	Proudlock 39
37	Mar 1	H	VC	Hayes	Drew 1-1	17	476	Thompson 41 (pen)
38	Mar 4	A	VC	Stalybridge Celtic	Won 5-2		274	Wrightson 4, Bos 39, 49, 50, Proudlock 63
39	Mar 8	H	VC	Woking	Won 3-2	14	816	Thompson 12 (pen), Bos 28, Cuggy 38
40	Mar 15	A	VC	Northwich Victoria	Lost 2-4	15	823	Bos 55, 89 (pen)
41	Mar 22	A	VC	Macclesfield Town	Lost 0-3	15	1763	
42	Mar 29	H	VC	Bromsgrove Rovers	Won 1-0		694	Grocutt 85 (pen)
43	Mar 31	A	VC	Altrincham	Won 1-0	14	764	Bos 70
44	Apr 5	H	VC	Farnborough Town	Won 1-0	13	578	Bos 34
45	Apr 12	A	VC	Dover Athletic	Won 1-0		1058	Innes 63
46	Apr 19	A	VC	Woking	Won 1-1	9	2300	Thompson 55
47	Apr 23	H	VC	Stevenage Borough	Drew 2-2		652	Robson 7, Thompson 76 (pen)
48	Apr 26	A	VC	Welling United	Lost 0-2	10	697	
49	May 3	H	VC	Kidderminster Harriers	Won 3-1	10	1276	Thompson 45, Edgcumbe 79, Skedd 90

Gateshead

1	2	3	4	5	6	7	8	9	10	11	12	14	15	Mth No.
Sherwood	Pearson	Ord	Howarth	Hague	Kitchen	Proudlock	Harkus	Thompson	Lowe	Rowe	Foreman	Watson	J Robson	1
Sherwood	Watson	Ord	Pearson	Hague	Kitchen	Proudlock	Foreman	Thompson	Lowe	Rowe	Harkus	Howarth	Henderson	2
Sherwood	Watson	Ord	Pearson	Hague	Kitchen	Proudlock	Foreman	Thompson	Lowe	Rowe	Harkus	J Robson	G Robson	3
Sherwood	Watson	Ord	G Robson	Hague	Kitchen	Proudlock	Foreman	Thompson	G Robson	Rowe	Harkus	J Robson	Howarth	4
Sherwood	Watson	Ord	Pearson	Hague	Kitchen	Proudlock	Foreman	Thompson	Lowe	Pearson	Harkus	J Robson	Howarth	5
Sherwood	Watson	Ord	G Robson	Hague	Kitchen	Proudlock	Foreman	Thompson	Lowe	Pearson	Haukus	J Robson	Howarth	6
Sherwood	Watson	Ord	J Robson	Hague	Kitchen	Proudlock	Foreman	Thompson	Lowe	Rowe	Harkus	Dowson	Pearson	7
Sherwood	Watson	Ord	Kitchen	Wrightson	Hague	Proudlock	Harkus	Thompson	Lowe	Rowe	Foreman	Dowson	Pearson	8
Sherwood	**Watson**	**Ord**	**Kitchen**	**Wrightson**	**Dowson**	**Proudlock**	**Pearson**	**Foreman**	**Lowe**	**Rowe**	**Hague**	**J Robson**	**Howarth**	**9**
Sherwood	**Robson**	**Ord**	**Kitchen**	**Wrightson**	**Dowson**	**Pearson**	**Harkus**	**Foreman**	**Lowe**	**Rowe**	**Watson**	**Henderson**	**Howarth**	**10**
Sherwood	Watson	Dowson	Howarth	Wrightson	Kitchen	J Robson	Harkus	Foreman	Lowe	Rowe	Proudlock	Ord	Hague	11
Sherwood	Watson	Ord	G Robson	Wrightson	Kitchen	Proudlock	Harkus	Thompson	Lowe	Rowe	Houston	Dowson	Hague	12
Sherwood	**Robson**	**Ord**	**Hague**	**Wrightson**	**Kitchen**	**Proudlock**	**G Robson**	**Thompson**	**Lowe**	**Rowe**	**Brady**	**Dowson**	**Foreman**	**13**
Sherwood	Watson	Ord	G Robson	Wrightson	Kitchen	J Robson	Connolly	Thompson	Lowe	Hague	Houston	Dowson	Brady	14
Sherwood	**Watson**	**Ord**	**G Robson**	**Wrightson**	**Kitchen**	**J Robson**	**Proudlock**	**Thompson**	**Lowe**	**Hague**	**Connolly**	**Brady**	**Rowe**	**15**
Sherwood	Watson	Ord	G Robson	Wrightson	Kitchen	J Robson	Proudlock	Thompson	Brady	Rowe	Hague	Connolly	Houston	16
Sherwood	Watson	Dowson	Hague	Wrightson	Kitchen	Pearson	Proudlock	Thompson	Lowe	Rowe	Houston	Connolly	Brady	17
Sherwood	**Watson**	**Dowson**	**Hague**	**Wrightson**	**Kitchen**	**Pearson**	**Proudlock**	**Thompson**	**Lowe**	**Rowe**	**G Robson**	**J Robson**	**Ord**	**18**
Sherwood	J Robson	Dowson	Pearson	Wrightson	Kitchen	Ord	Conlon	G Robson	Lowe	Rowe	Hague	Watson	Proudlock	19
Harper	Pearson	Ord	Brady	Hague	Kitchen	G Robson	Conlon	Thompson	Lowe	Rowe	Watson	Connolly	Dowson	20
Harper	Wrightson	Dowson	G Robson	Hague	Kitchen	Conlon	Harkus	Thompson	Lowe	Rowe	Watson	Connolly	Pearson	21
Sherwood	**Wrightson**	**Dowson**	**Ord**	**Hague**	**Kitchen**	**Pearson**	**Conlon**	**Thompson**	**Lowe**	**Rowe**	**Watson**	**Connolly**	**Houston**	**22**
Harper	Watson	Ord	Brady	Wrightson	Kitchen	Pearson	Conlon	Thompson	Lowe	Rowe	Hague	Connolly	Sherwood	23
Harper	Watson	Dowson	Ord	Wrightson	Kitchen	Smith	Bracy	Thompson	Lowe	Rowe	Houston	Howarth	Sherwood	24
Harper	Watson	Dowson	Ord	Wrightson	Kitchen	G Robson	Harkus	Thompson	Brady	Rowe	Hague	Howarth	Houston	25
Harper	Watson	Dowson	J Robson	Ord	Kitchen	Pearson	Dixon	Thompson	Lowe	Rowe	Thornton	Brady	Howarth	26
Harper	Watson	Ord	Brady	Wrightson	Kitchen	Dixon	Dia	Thompson	Lowe	Rowe	J Robson	Pearson	Thornton	27
Harper	Watson	Ord	J Robson	Wrightson	Kitchen	Dixon	Dia	Thompson	Lowe	Rowe	Pearson	Thornton	Lagaville	28
Harper	Watson	Ord	Pearson	Wrightson	Kitchen	Dixon	Dia	Thompson	Lowe	Rowe	Hague	J Robson	Proudlock	29
Harper	Watson	Ord	Pearson	Wrightson	Kitchen	Dixon	Dia	Thompson	Lowe	Rowe	Hague	J Robson	Proudlock	30
Harper	Watson	Ord	Bracy	Wrightson	Hague	Proudlock	Dia	Thompson	Lowe	Thornton	Pearson	G Robson	Dixon	31
Sherwood	**Watson**	**Ord**	**Bracy**	**Wrightson**	**Kitchen**	**G Robson**	**Proudlock**	**Thompson**	**Lowe**	**Thornton**	**Pearson**	**Hague**	**J Robson**	**32**
Harper	Watson	Byrne	G Robson	Kitchen	Ord	Pearson	J Robson	Thompson	Proudlock	Rowe	Dia	Brady	Howarth	33
Sherwood	Watson	Byrne	G Robson	Kitchen	Ord	Pearson	Edgcumbe	Thompson	Proudlock	Rowe	J Robson	Lowe	Dia	34
Sherwood	J Robson	Rowe	G Robson	Wrightson	Kitchen	Pearson	Edgcumbe	Thompson	Proudlock	Skedd	Lowe	Key	Cuggy	35
Sherwood	J Robson	Rowe	G Robson	Wrightson	Kitchen	Cuggy	Bos	Thompson	Proudlock	Skedd	Lowe	Pearson	Edgcumbe	36
Sherwood	J Robson	Rowe	G Robson	Wrightson	Kitchen	Cuggy	Bos	Thompson	Proudlock	Skedd	Lowe	Ord	Edgcumbe	37
Sherwood	Watson	Ord	G Robson	Wrightson	Kitchen	J Robson	Bos	Thompson	Proudlock	Rowe	Lowe	Dixon	Key	38
Sherwood	Watson	Ord	G Robson	Wrightson	Kitchen	J Robson	Bos	Thompson	Proudlock	Rowe	Lowe	Skedd	Cuggy	39
Sherwood	Watson	Ord	G Robson	Wrightson	Kitchen	J Robson	Bos	Thompson	Proudlock	Rowe	Lowe	Skedd	Cuggy	40
Sherwood	J Robson	Ord	G Robson	Wrightson	Kitchen	Pearson	Bos	Proudlock	Lowe	Skedd	Thompson	Watson	Key	41
Johnson	Watson	Ord	G Robson	Wrightson	Kitchen	Innes	Bos	Thompson	Bowey	Proudlock	Skedd	Pearson	Dia	42
Johnson	Watson	Ord	G Robson	J Robson	Kitchen	Innes	Bos	Thompson	Bowey	Skedd	Pearson	Dia	Key	43
Johnson	Watson	Ord	G Robson	J Robson	Rowe	Innes	Bos	Thompson	Bowey	Pearson	Proudlock	Skedd	Byrne	44
Johnson	Watson	Ord	G Robson	J Robson	Kitchen	Innes	Bos	Key	Bowey	Rowe	Pearson	Thompson	Wrightson	45
Johnson	Watson	Rowe	G Robson	Wrightson	Kitchen	Key	Innes	Thompson	Bowey	J Robson	Skedd	Byrne	Pearson	46
Johnson	Watson	Byrne	G Robson	Wrightson	Kitchen	Key	Innes	Thompson	Bowey	Rowe	Ord	Skedd	Pearson	47
Johnson	Watson	Byrne	G Robson	Ord	Kitchen	Key	Innes	Thompson	Bowey	Rowe	Skedd	Pearson	Sherwood	48

JIM PLATT

Date of Appointment	January 1997
Date of Birth:	26th January 1952
Place of Birth:	Ballymena, Northern Ireland

PREVIOUS CLUBS

As manager	Darlington, Ballymena, Coleraine
As coach	Darlington (Director of Coaching)
As player	Ballymena Utd., Middlesbrough, Hartlepool Utd., Cardiff C., Coleraine.

HONOURS

As manager	R-up 3rd Div Play-offs 1996 (Darlington)
As player/manager	Irish Cup (Ballymena & Coleraine)
	R-up Irish Lge (Coleraine)
As player	Northern Ireland - 23 caps incl. 1982 World Cup Finals

Manager's Assistant: Jack Watson **Player Coach:** Gary Robson **Physio:** Bev Dougherty

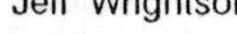
Jeff Wrightson

Kenny Lowe

MATCHDAY PROGRAMME

Number of pages	36
Price	£1.20
Programme Editor	Andy Wilson (0191 478 3883)
Other club publications:	"A Different Corner" (fanzine)
Local Newspapers:	Gateshead Post Newcastle Chronicle & Journal Sunderland Echo Sunday Sun
Local Radio Stations:	BBC Radio Newcastle Metro FM Century Radio

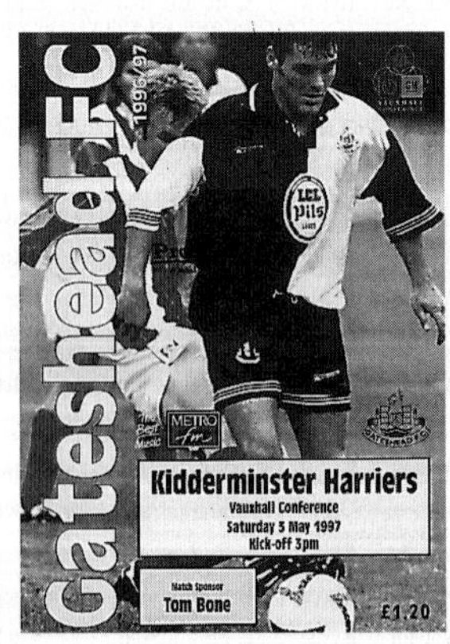

1997-98 PLAYING SQUAD

PLAYER	Birthplace Honours	Birthdate	CLUBS
GOALKEEPERS			
Steve Sherwood	Selby Div 4	10.12.53	Chelsea, Watford, Grimsby T, Stalybridge C
Frank Johnson	South Shields	24.2.77	Darlington
DEFENDERS			
Justin Robson	Durham NPL, NCEL	29.4.63	Newcastle U, Gateshead, Newcastle Blue Star, North Shields, Bridlington T, Durham C, Gretna
Sam Kitchen	Rintein	11.6.67	Yorkshire Main, Goole T, Stafford R, Goole T, Frickley A, Leyton Orient, Doncaster R
Wes Byrne	Dublin	9.2.77	Middlesbrough, Darlington
Derek Ord	Gateshead	18.1.63	North Shields, Blyth Spartans, Gateshead, Chester-le-Street, Spennymoor U, Bishop Auckland, Durham C, Gretna
MIDFIELDERS			
Steve Bowey	Durham	10.7.74	Bristol R, Forest Green R
Brian Rowe	Sunderland	24.10.71	Doncaster R
Gary Robson	Chester-le-Street FL XI	6.7.65	W.B.A., Bradford C
Tony Skedd	North Cleveland	19.5.75	Hartlepool U, Spennymoor U
Lee Innes	Durham	28.2.76	Sheffield U, Darlington
FORWARDS			
Steve Harkus	Newcastle	18.2.68	Hebburn, South Shields, Blyth Spartans
Paul Proudlock	Hartlepool	25.10.65	Hartlepool U, Middlesbrough, Carlisle U
Paul Thompson	Newcastle	17.4.73	Hartlepool U
Graham Robinson	South Africa SA u-21, FAV		Whitby T

DEPARTURES -
(During the season): Alan Dowson (Walton & Hersham), Stuart Connolly (Lancaster C), Darren Foreman (Barrow), Tony Lagaville (Released), Paul Hague (Tow Law T), Ian Brady (Halifax T), Kenny Lowe (Darlington)
(During the close season): Mark Thornton, John Watson, Jeff Wrightson, Andy Howarth (Released)

PLAYERS ON LOAN: Paul Conlon (Sunderland), Steve Cuggy (Hastings T), Gijsbert Bos (Lincoln C)

International Stadium, Gateshead

ADDRESS:
International Stadium, Neilson Road, Gateshead, NE10 0EF
TELEPHOE NUMBER: 0191 4783883 **Fax:** 0191 4771315.
SIMPLE DIRECTIONS:
From the South follow A1(M) to Granada services (Birtley), take right hand fork marked A194(M) (Tyne Tunnel, South Shields) follow A194 to first roundabout, turn left onto A184 - then 3 miles to stadium. Turn right at traffic lights into Neilson Road.
BY RAIL to Newcastle Central Station, transfer to the Metro System and then to Gateshead Stadium.

CAPACITY: 11,795 **SEATED:** 11,795 **COVERED TERRACING:** 3,300

SOCIAL FACILITIES: Bar inside Tyne & Wear stand open before, during and after matches. The Stadium Public House adjacent to ground.

CLUB SHOP: Sells replica shirts, baseball caps, sweatshirts, badges, scarves, programmes, coffee mugs, pennants, fanzines, ski hats. Contact: Mark Donnelly (0191 4783883).

Gateshead Fact File

Nickname: The Tynesiders **Sponsors:** Cameron Hall Developments Ltd
Club colours: Black & white shirts, black shorts, white socks.
Change colours: All yellow.
Midweek home matchday: Wednesday
Reserves League: Vaux Wearside League

PREVIOUS - **Leagues:** Football League Division 3 North 1930-1958, Football Lge Div.4 1958-1960, Northern Counties League 1960-1962, North Regional League 1962-1968, Northern Premier League 1968-1970, Wearside League 1970-1971, Midland League 1971-1972, Northern Premier League 1973-1983, Alliance Premier League 1983-1985, Northern Premier League 1985-1986, Vauxhall Conference 1986-1987, Northern Premier League 1987-1990.
Grounds: Redheugh Park - 1930-1971

CLUB RECORDS - **Attendance:** 11,750 v Newcastle United (Pre-Season Friendly. 7th August 1995)
Win: 8-0 v Netherfield, Northern Premier League.
Defeat: 0-9 v Sutton United - 22/09/90 - GMVC.
Career goalscorer: Bob Topping
Career appearances: Simon Smith - 450 - 1985-1994
Transfer fee paid: £9,000 for Paul Cavell (Dagenham & Redbridge).
Transfer fee received: For Kenny Cramman from Rushden & Diamonds

BEST SEASON - **FA Cup:** Quarter Final, 1952-53.
FA Trophy: Quarter Final, 0-1 v Wycombe W. (A) 13.3.93

Past players who progressed to the Football League: Osher Williams (Southampton, Stockport, Port Vale, Preston), John McGinley (Sunderland, Lincoln), Billy Askew (Hull City, Newcastle United), Lawrie Pearson (Hull City, Port Vale), Ian Johnson (Northampton Town), Ken Davies (Stockport), Kenny Lowe (Birmingham C., Barnet, Darlington, Stoke C.)

1996-97 Top scorer: Paul Thompson (22)
1996-97 Player of the Year: Paul Thompson

HONOURS:
Football League Division 3 North R-up 1931-32, 1949-50; Northern Premier League Champions 1982-83, 1985-86; Northern Premier League R-up 1989-90; Northern Premier League Cup Finalists 1989-90; Multipart Shield 1985-86.

Formed:
1911

HALIFAX TOWN

Chairman: J C Stockwell **President:** S J Brown

Vice Chairman: C O Holland

Football Secretary: Derek A Newiss

Commercial Manager: David Worthington Tel: 01422 353423

It took a final day victory over Stevenage Borough for Halifax to secure their Vauxhall Conference status but they still became the lowest placed former Football League club since promotion and relegation began. Manager John Carroll eventually paid the price with his job and the improvement in form following the appointment of George Mulhall and Kieran O'Regan as caretaker bosses earned the duo the posts on a permanent basis during the summer.

Despite their disappointments on the field optimism is high at Halifax with The Shay undergoing a face life and, thanks to the amalgamation with Rugby League club Halifax Blue Sox, the building of a new £720,000 stand. The squad had undergone quite a bit of re-shaping under the new management team and a number of useful signings have been made, ensuring that the club shouldn't need to suffer the traumas of last season.

L-R, Back Row: Paul Hand, Darren Lyons, Peter Jackson, Lee Williams, Paul Stoneman, Noel Horner, Geoff Horsfield, Ady Thackeray, Mark Bradshaw. Middle: Alan Russell-Cox (Physio), Martin Ayscough, Chris Newton, Gareth Hamlet, Paul Trudgill, Michael Rosser, Karl Cochrane, Phil McDonald, Ryan Gonsalves, Billy Callaghan, David Worthington (Res. Team Man.). Front: Damian Place, Willie Griffiths, Kieran O'Regan (PLayer/Coach), George Mulhall (Manager), Jamie Paterson, Jon Brown, Gary BRook, Kevin Hulme. Photo: Courtesy Halifax Evening Courier.

Halifax Town

Match No.	Date	Venue H/A	Competition	Opponents	Result	League Pos.	Attendance	Goalscorers (Times if known)
1	Aug 17	A	VC	Stevenage Borough	Lost 0-6	22	2117	
2	Aug 20	H	VC	Altrincham	Drew 1-1		842	Brook 44
3	Aug 24	H	VC	Slough Town	Won 4-1		793	Worthington 46, Horner 54, J Brown 84, Midwood 85
4	Aug 26	A	VC	Southport	Lost 1-2	17	1543	Horner 90
5	Aug 31	A	VC	Kettering Town	Lost 1-4	21	1541	Norbury 29
6	Sep 3	H	VC	Gateshead	Won 2-0		679	Norbury 62, Brook 66
7	Sep 7	H	VC	Rushden & Diamonds	Lost 1-3	19	948	Norbury 21
8	Sep 10	A	VC	Altrincham	Lost 1-2		673	Brook 22
9	**Sep 14**	**A**	**FAC**	**Oldham Town**	**Won 3-2**		**452**	**Hendrick 10, Brook (2) 48, 50**
10	Sep 17	H	VC	Stalybridge Celtic	Won 4-1		664	Ellison 8, Norbury 39, 60, Trotter 69
11	Sep 21	A	VC	Hayes	Drew 0-0	16	523	
12	Sep 24	H	VC	Telford United	Lost 0-3		663	
13	**Sep 28**	**H**	**FAC**	**Bishop Auckland**	**Lost 1-4**		**628**	**Norbury 32**
14	Oct 1	A	VC	Macclesfield Town	Lost 0-1		951	
15	Oct 5	H	VC	Kidderminster Harriers	Lost 2-3	19	786	Norbury 49, Horner 59
16	**Oct 8**	**H**	**SCC**	**Altrincham**	**Lost 0-1**		**379**	
17	Oct 19	H	VC	Woking	Lost 0-4	21	807	
18	Nov 2	A	VC	Dover Athletic	Drew 2-2	21	1037	McInerney 39, Hulme 58
19	Nov 9	A	VC	Bath City	Drew 0-0	20	567	
20	Nov 23	H	VC	Welling United	Drew 1-1	19	608	Brook 5
21	Nov 30	H	VC	Kettering Town	Won 2-1	20	790	Horsfield 61, Davison 74
22	Dec 7	A	VC	Stalybridge Celtic	Won 3-2	18	814	Stoneman (p) 12, Davidson 35, Horsfield 79
23		**H**	**WRFA**	**Bradford City**	**Won 2-1**		**482**	**Worthington, Norbury**
24	Dec 14	H	VC	Morecambe	Drew 1-1	17	883	Brook 90
25	Dec 21	A	VC	Woking	Drew 2-2		2331	Horsfield 59, Lyons 80
26	Dec 26	H	VC	Northwich Victoria	Lost 0-3		1078	
27	Dec 28	A	VC	Gateshead	Won 1-0	18	466	Norbury 90
28	**Jan 18**	**A**	**FAT 1**	**Stalybridge Celtic**	**Won 1-0**		**973**	**Brook 13**
29	Jan 28	H	VC	Bromsgrove Rovers	Won 1-0	16	608	Norbury 89 (pen)
30	Feb 1	A	VC	Bromsgrove Rovers	Lost 0-3	19	686	
31	**Feb 8**	**A**	**FAT 2**	**Gloucester City**	**Lost 0-3**		**1118**	
32	Feb 15	H	VC	Bath City	Lost 4-5	20	655	Horsfield 15, 81, Lyons 32, Martin 71
33	Feb 22	H	VC	Farnborough Town	Won 3-0	19	694	Brook 13, Horsfield 61, Day 72 (og)
34	Mar 1	A	VC	Welling United	Won 1-0	16	688	
35	Mar 4	H	VC	Hednesford Town	Won 1-0		623	Brook 64
36	Mar 8	A	VC	Kidderminster Harriers	Lost 0-3	16	2523	
37	Mar 15	H	VC	Dover Athletic	Lost 1-3	17	709	Stoneman 19
38	Mar 17	A	VC	Northwich Victoria	Drew 2-2	16	911	Norbury 32 (pen), Horsfield 65
39	Mar 28	H	VC	Southport	Won 2-0		792	Murphy 36, Martin 38
40	Mar 31	A	VC	Farnborough Town	Lost 0-3	18	675	
41	Apr 5	A	VC	Slough Town	Lost 0-1	18	760	
42	Apr 8	A	VC	Hednesford Town	Drew 1-1	17	1017	Lyons 67
43	Apr 12	A	VC	Telford United	Drew 1-1	18	759	Norbury 39
44	Apr 16	A	VC	Morecambe	Lost 0-1		711	
45	Apr 19	H	VC	Hayes	Won 2-1	18	684	Norbury 40, Lyons 74
46	Apr 26	A	VC	Rushden & Diamonds	Lost 0-1	19	2629	
47	Apr 30	H	VC	Macclesfield Town	Drew 3-3		2191	Murphy 45, Horsfield 81, Hulme 85
48	May 3	H	VC	Stevenage Borough	Won 4-2	19	1171	Norbury (3) 27, 41, 56, Horsfield 90

Halifax Town

1	2	3	4	5	6	7	8	9	10	11	12	14	15	Mth No.
Woods	Brown	Mudd	O'Regan	Trotter	Lee	Cochrane	Stoneman	Worthington	Brook	Midwood	Horner	Hendrick	Davison	1
Woods	Brown	Mudd	O'Regan	Trotter	Lee	Hendrick	Stoneman	Worthington	Brook	Davison	Horner			2
Woods	Horner	Mudd	O'Regan	Trotter	Brown	Hendrick	Stoneman	Worthington	Brook	Davison	Midwood	Cochrane	Brown	3
Woods	Horner	Mudd	O'Regan	Cochrane	Brown	Hendrick	Stoneman	Worthington	Brook	Davison	Midwood	Cameron	Brown	4
Woods	Horner	Jon Brown	O'Regan	Harold	Lee	Midwood	Jim Brown	Norbury	Brook	Worthington	Hendrick	Cochrane	Davison	5
Woods	Horner	Mudd	O'Regan	Harold	Lee	Hendrick	Jon Brown	Norbury	Brook	Jim Brown	Davison	Midwood	Worthington	6
Woods	Horner	Mudd	O'Regan	Harold	Lee	Hendrick	Jon Brown	Norbury	Brook	Jim Brown	Davison	Trotter	Worthington	7
Woods	Horner	Trotter	O'Regan	Harold	Lee	Stoneman	Jon Brown	Norbury	Brook	Jim Brown	Davison	Hendrick	Midwood	8
Heyes	**Lee**	**Brown**	**O'Regan**	**Trotter**	**Stoneman**	**Hendrick**	**Davison**	**Norbury**	**Brook**	**Brown**	**Worthington**	**Midwood**	**McInerney**	**9**
Woods	Horner	Brown	O'Regan	Trotter	Stoneman	Hendrick	Ellison	Norbury	Brook	Brown	Worthington	McInerney	Davison	10
Woods	Horner	Jon Brown	O'Regan	Lee	Stoneman	Hendrick	Worthington	Norbury	Brook	Jim Brown	Davison	McInerney	Midwood	11
Woods	Horner	Jon Brown	O'Regan	Lee	Stoneman	Hendrick	Worthington	Norbury	Brook	Jim Brown	Cameron	McInerney	Ellison	12
Woods	**Horner**	**Mudd**	**O'Regan**	**Lee**	**Stoneman**	**Hendrick**	**Jon Brown**	**Norbury**	**Brook**	**Jim Brown**	**Davison**	**McInerney**	**Worthington**	**13**
Woods	Jon Brown	Mudd	O'Regan	Trotter	Stoneman	Horner	Beckford	Davison	Brook	McInerney	Jim Brown	Hendrick	Worthington	14
Heyes	Jon Brown	Mudd	O'Regan	Trotter	Stoneman	Horner	Beckford	Davison	Brook	McInerney	Norbury	Jim Brown	Midwood	15
Heyes	**Horner**	**Mudd**	**O'Regan**	**Trotter**	**Stoneman**	**Midwood**	**Beckford**	**Norbury**	**Brook**	**McInerney**	**Jim Brown**	**Worthington**	**Cameron**	**16**
Gibson	Horner	Mudd	O'Regan	Stoneman	Beckford	Francis	Hulme	Norbury	Davison	McInerney	Horsfield	Midwood	Worthington	17
Gibson	Cox	Mudd	O'Regan	Goulding	Trotte	Horsfield	Hulme	Norbury	Brook	McInerney	Worthington	Woods	Place	18
Gibson	Cox	Mudd	O'Regan	Goulding	Stoneman	Horsfield	Hulme	Norbury	Brook	McInerney	Worthington	Trotter	Woods	19
Woods	Cox	Mudd	O'Regan	Goulding	Stoneman	Horner	Hulme	Horsfield	Brook	McInerney	Worthington	Trotter	Brown	20
Woods	Cox	Mudd	O'Regan	Goulding	Stoneman	Horner	Hulme	Horsfield	Brook	McInerney	Worthington	Davison	Brown	21
Woods	Brown	Mudd	O'Regan	Cox	Stoneman	Horner	Hulme	Horsfield	Davison	McInerney	Worthington	Brook	Kelly	22
Woods	**Brown**	**Mudd**	**O'Regan**	**Cox**	**Stoneman**	**Horner**	**Worthington**	**Horsfield**	**Davison**	**McInerney**	**Brook**	**Midwood**	**Norbury**	**23**
Woods	Brown	Mudd	O'Regan	Cox	Stoneman	Horner	Hulme	Norbury	Davison	McInerney	Brook	Midwood	Worthington	24
Woods	Cox	Mudd	O'Regan	Goulding	Stoneman	Lyons	Worthington	Norbury	Horsfield	McInerney	Davison	Horner	Brook	25
Woods	Cox	Mudd	Horner	Goulding	Stoneman	Lyons	Hulme	Norbury	Horsfield	Worthington	Davison	Brook	Place	26
Woods	Horner	Mudd	Martin	Goulding	Stoneman	Lyons	Brook	Norbury	Horsfield	Worthington	Davison	Place		27
Woods	**Brown**	**Mudd**	**McInerney**	**Goulding**	**Stoneman**	**Horner**	**Hulme**	**Horsfield**	**Brook**	**Worthington**	**Davison**	**Cox**	**Place**	**28**
Woods	Brown	Mudd	McInerney	Cox	Stoneman	Lyons	Hulme	Norbury	Brook	Worthington	Davison	Horsfield	Horner	29
Woods	Brown	Mudd	O'Regan	Cox	Stoneman	Horsfield	Hulme	Norbury	Brook	Worthington	Davison	Lyons	Horner	30
Woods	**Cox**	**Mudd**	**O'Regan**	**Goulding**	**Stoneman**	**Horner**	**Hulme**	**Norbury**	**Horsfield**	**McInerney**	**Davison**	**Brook**	**Brown**	**31**
Woods	Brown	Mudd	O'Regan	Goulding	Cox	Francis	Martin	Horsfield	Brook	Lyons	Davison	Norbury	Horner	32
Woods	Brown	Mudd	O'Regan	Cox	Horner	Horsfield	Davison	Norbury	Brook	Martin	Goulding	Worthington	Lyons	33
Woods	Brown	Mudd	O'Regan	Cox	Horner	Hulme	Horsfield	Norbury	Brook	Martin	Davison	Goulding	Lyons	34
Woods	Brown	Mudd	O'Regan	Cox	Horner	Hulme	Davison	Norbury	Brook	Martin	Goulding	Worthington	Lyons	35
Woods	Brown	Mudd	O'Regan	Cox	Horner	Hulme	Davison	Norbury	Brook	Martin	Lyons			36
Woods	Horner	Mudd	O'Regan	Norbury	Cox	Hulme	Stoneman	Horsfield	Brook	Worthington	Lyons	Goulding	Hand	37
Woods	Horner	Mudd	O'Regan	Norbury	Martin	Hulme	Stoneman	Horsfield	Brook	Worthington	Cox	Lyons	Place	38
Woods	Brown	Mudd	O'Regan	Murphy	Cox	Lyons	Martin	Horsfield	Horner	Worthington	Davison	Hand	Griffiths	39
Woods	Horner	Mudd	O'Regan	Murphy	Brown	Lyons	Martin	Horsfield	Brook	Worthington	Davison	Griffiths	Hand	40
Woods	Brown	Murphy	O'Regan	Norbury	Cox	Martin	Hulme	Horsfield	Brook	Worthington	Mudd	Lyons	Davison	41
Woods	Brown	Mudd	O'Regan	Cox	Murphy	Lyons	Hulme	Norbury	Horsfield	Martin	Horner	Brook	Worthington	42
Woods	Brown	Mudd	O'Regan	Cox	Murphy	Lyons	Hulme	Norbury	Horsfield	Martin	Horner	Worthington	Brock	43
Woods	Brown	Mudd	O'Regan	Cox	Murphy	Lyons	Worthington	Norbury	Brook	Martin	Horner	Stoneman	Horsfield	44
Woods	Brown	Mudd	O'Regan	Cox	Murphy	Lyons	Worthington	Norbury	Brook	Martin	Stoneman	Horner	Horsfield	45
Woods	O'Regan	Mudd	Martin	Stoneman	Murphy	Lyons	Hulme	Norbury	Brook	Horner	Worthington	Davison	Cox	46
Woods	Brown	Mudd	Martin	Stoneman	Murphy	Lyons	Hulme	Norbury	Brook	O'Regan	Horner	Worthington	Horsfield	47
Woods	Brown	Mudd	Martin	Stoneman	Murphy	Lyons	Hulme	Norbury	Brook	O'Regan	Horner	Worthington	Horsfield	48

	GEORGE MULHALL MANAGER	KIERAN O'REGAN PLAYER/COACH
Date of Appointment	22.02.97	22.02.97
Date of Birth:	08.05.36	22.02.97
Place of Birth:	Standburn (Scotland)	Cork City
PREVIOUS CLUBS		
As manager	Halifax T., Bradford C., Bolton Wanderers.	-
As coach	Bolton Wanderers	-
As player	Aberdeen, Sunderland.	Brighton & H.A., Swindon T., Huddersfield T., W.B.A.
HONOURS		
As manager	-	-
As player	Scotland: 3 full caps.	Rep. of Ireland: 4 full caps.

Physio:
Alan Russell Cox

Opposite:

Player/Assistant Manager, Kieran O'Regan, showing the new Halifax Town home strip.

MATCHDAY PROGRAMME

Number of pages	28
Price	£1.50
Programme Editor	David Worthington 01422 353423
Other club publications:	None
Local Newspapers:	Halifax Courier Yorkshire Post Telegraph Argus
Local Radio Stations:	Pulse Radio Radio Leeds

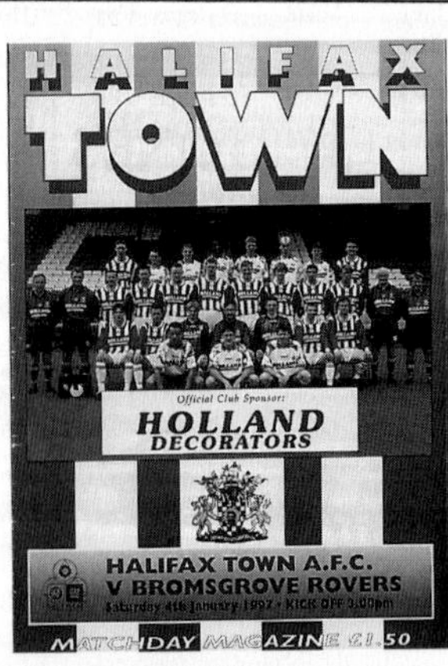

1997-98 PLAYING SQUAD

PLAYER	Birthplace Honours	Birthdate	CLUBS
GOALKEEPERS			
Andy Woods	Colchester	15.1.76	Oldham A
DEFENDERS			
Paul Stoneman	Whitley Bay	26.2.73	Blackpool
Paul Mudd	Hull ES	13.11.70	Hull C, Scarborough, Scunthorpe U, Lincoln C
Nathan Murray	South Shields ES, EY	10.9.75	Newcastle U, Carlisle U
Paul Cox	Nottingham	1.1.72	Notts Co, Kettering T, Gresley R, Ilkeston T
Paul Hand	Halifax		From YTS
MIDFIELDERS			
Kevin Hulme	Franworth FAT	2.12.67	Radcliffe B, Bury, Doncaster R, Lincoln C, Macclesfield T
Damian Place	Halifax		From YTS
Keiran O'Regan	Cork Ei: 4.	9.11.63	Tramore A, Brighton, Swindon T, Huddersfield T, W.B.A.
Jon Brown	Barnsley	8.9.66	Denaby U, Exeter C
Darren Lyons	Blakeley GMVC, FAT, BLT	9.11.66	Oldham A, Rhyl, Droylsden, Macclesfield T, Leek T, Mossley, Ashton U, Bury, Southport, Macclesfield T, Winsford U
FORWARDS			
Gary Brook	Dewsbury NCEL	9.5.64	Ossett A, Frickley A, Newport Co, Scarborough, Blackpool, Frickley A, Boston U
Michael Midwood	Burnley	19.4.76	Huddersfield T
Geoff Horsefield	Barnsley	1.11.73	Worsborough Bridge MW, Scarborough, Halifax T, Guiseley, Witton A

DEPARTURES - (During the season): Mik Trotter & Darren Heyes (VS Rugby), Karl Thomas (Stalybridge C), John Francis (Emley), Andy Lee (Knowsley U), Lee Ellison (Bishop Auckland), Karl Cochrane (Ossett A), Jason Beckford (Altrincham), Tony Kelly (Released), Ian Brady (Stalybridge C), Derek Goulding (Released), John Francis (Farsley Celtic)
(During the close season): Mike Norbury (Hednesford T)

PLAYERS ON LOAN - Dean Martin (Rochdale), Paul Gibson (Manchester U), Jamie Murphy (Doncaster R)

The Shay, Halifax

GROUND ADDRESS: The Shay, Halifax, West Yorkshire HX1 2YS.
Telephone: 01422 345543. **Fax:** 01422 349487.

SIMPLE DIRECTIONS:
From North: Take A629 to Halifax Town Centre. Take 2nd exit at roundabout into Broad Street and follow signs for Huddersfield (A629) into Skircoat Road. From South, East & West: Exit M62 junction 24 and follow Halifax (A629) signs to Town centre into Skircoat Road for ground.

CAPACITY: 5,149 **SEATED:** 1,878 **COVERED TERRACING:** 2,600

SOCIAL FACILITIES:
No facilities on the ground.
(N.B. The ground details and social facilities could change next season depending on ground work proposals)

CLUB SHOP:
19A Westgate, Halifax. Phone/Fax: 01422 353423. Contact Dave Worthington.

Halifax Town Fact File

Nickname: The Shaymen **Club Sponsors:** J C Holland Decorators
Club colours: Blue shirts with white trim, blue shorts white trim, white stockings
Change colours: Old gold shirts with black trim, black shorts, black stockings
Reserves' League: Bolton & District Combination, North West Alliance Div.
Midweek home matchday: Tuesday 7.45pm KO

PREVIOUS - **Grounds:** Sandhall Lane 1911-15, Exley 1919-21.
Leagues: Yorkshire Combination 1911-12, Midland League 1912-21, Division 3 North 1921-58, Division 3 1958-63, 1969-76, 1992, Division 4 1963-69.

CLUB RECORDS - **Attendance:** 36,885 v Tottenham - 5th Round FA Cup - 14.02.53
Win: 12-0 v West Vale Ramblers - 1st Qualifying Round FA Cup - 1913-14
Defeat: 0-13 v Stockport County - Division 3 North - 1933-34
Career goalscorer: Albert Valentine
Career appearances: John Pickering
Transfer fee paid: £50,000 for Ian Juryeff (Hereford United).
Transfer fee received: £250,000 for Wayne Allison (Watford).

BEST SEASON - **FA Cup:** 5th Round, 1913-14, 52-53.
FA Trophy: 3rd Round, 93-94.

Past players who progressed to the Football League: N/A
1996-97 Captain: K O'Regan, J Brown, K Hulme.
1996-97 Top scorer: Mike Norbury (15)
1996-97 Player of the Year: Andy Woods.

HONOURS: Promoted to Division 3 1968-69

Formed:
1909

HAYES

President: Les Lovering **Chairman:** Derek Goodall

Vice-Chairman: Trevor Griffith

Football Secretary: John Bond Jnr.

General Manager: Terry Brown **Press Officer:** Trevor Griffith (01895 638013)

Despite the fact that Hayes finished only three points ahead of the relegation places, the Missioners still did extremely well in their debut season as a Vauxhall Conference club.

Attendances increased by 38 per cent and the team played an exciting and refreshing brand of football.

Manager Terry Brown continually dabbled in the transfer market but found a real gem right on his door step - young striker Jason Roberts. Roberts attracted the scouts to Church Road throughout the campaign. His fellow striker, Martin Randall, also enjoyed a good season, netting seventeen goals and earning the player of the year award.

Hayes have invested wisely on their Church Road Stadium, which has taken on a new look since the club won promotion from the ICIS League. Although the Missioners have ambitions, they are realistic enough to know that finishing mid-table this season would represent success and further progress for this happy and friendly club.

L-R, Back Row: Gary Williams, Darron Wilkinson, Paul Watkins, Jason Roberts, Russell Meara, Carl Bartley, Ross Pickett, Nathan Bunce, Eddie Mee. Middle Row: Dave Killick (Yth Dev. Off.), Jimmy Sugrue, Jason Goodliffe, Steve Baker, Nick Roddis, Junior Haynes, Martin Randall, Karl Ballard (Sports Therapist), Ray Girvan (Yth Team Man.). Front Row: Terry Brown (Manager), Freddie Hyatt, Lee Flynn, Derek Goodall (Chairman), Warren Kelly, Jon Brady, Willy Wordsworth (Asst. Man). Photo: Ray Peploe

Hayes

Match No.	Date	Venue H/A	Competition	Opponents	Result	League Pos.	Attendance	Goalscorers (Times if known)
1	Aug 17	H	VC	Southport	Drew 1-1	11	753	Goodliffe 13
2	Aug 20	A	VC	Dover Athletic	Lost 0-1		1005	
3	Aug 24	A	VC	Stalybridge Celtic	Lost 1-3		634	Williams 39
4	Aug 26	H	VC	Rushden & Diamonds	Drew 1-1	21	1043	Haynes 11
5	Aug 31	H	VC	Bromsgrove Rovers	Won 1-0	16	521	Clarke (og) 52
6	Sep 3	A	VC	Farnborough Town	Drew 1-1		689	Williams 12
7	Sep 7	A	VC	Kettering Town	Drew 2-2	15	1608	Haynes (2) 78,89
8	Sep 10	H	VC	Kidderminster Harriers	Lost 0-1		434	
9	**Sep 14**	**A**	**FAC 1 Q**	**Stotfold**	**Won 2-0**		**238**	**Brady 32, Pickett 61**
10	Sep 21	H	VC	Halifax Town	Drew 0-0	20	521	
11	Sep 24	H	VC	Welling United	Drew 1-1		363	Haynes 90
12	**Sep 28**	**H**	**FAC 2 Q**	**Grays Athletic**	**Drew 1-1**		**377**	**Wilkinson 53**
13	**Oct 1**	**A**	**FAC 2QR**	**Grays Athletic**	**Drew 0-0**		**264**	
14	Oct 5	H	VC	Telford United	Lost 0-1	20	485	
15	**Oct 7**	**H**	**FAC 2QR2**	**Grays Athletic**	**Won 2-0**		**328**	**Williams 73, Bartley 90**
16	**Oct 12**	**H**	**FAC3Q**	**Chesham United**	**Won 1-0**		**633**	**Haynes 69**
17	Oct 15	A	VC	Welling United	Lost 0-1		433	
18	Oct 19	H	VC	Altrincham	Won 3-1	19	470	Williams 9, 11, Haynes 47
19	**Oct 22**	**H**	**ICS**	**Kingstonian**	**Won 4-2**		**264**	**Goodliffe, Hyatt, Adams (2)**
20	**Oct 26**	**H**	**FAC 4 Q**	**Slough Town**	**Won 1-0**		**1803**	**Brady 72**
21	**Oct 29**	**A**	**SCC**	**Farnborough Town**	**Lost 2-3**	20	**317**	**Hyatt 33, Bunce 64**
22	Nov 2	A	VC	Northwich Victoria	Lost 1-2	20	972	Haynes 28
23	Nov 4	A	VC	Kidderminster Harriers	Lost 1-5		2121	Haynes 55
24	Nov 9	H	VC	Stalybridge Celtic	Lost 0-2	15	595	
25	**Nov 16**	**A**	**FAC 1**	**Stevenage Borough**	**Drew 2-2**		**3288**	**Williams 2, Haynes 40**
26	Nov 23	A	VC	Macclesfield Town	Lost 0-1	22	909	
27	**Nov 26**	**H**	**FAC 1 R**	**Stevenage Borough**	**Lost 0-2**		**2965**	
28	Nov 30	H	VC	Gateshead	Drew 0-0	22	404	
29	Dec 7	A	VC	Morecambe	Won 4-2	21	1012	Randall 6, 54, Roberts 20, Williams 35
30	Dec 14	A	VC	Hednesford Town	Lost 0-2	21	1040	
31	Dec 21	H	VC	Kettering Town	Won 2-1		468	Randall 2, Cox 53
32	Dec 28	H	VC	Woking	Won 3-2	20	1327	Haynes 16, 83, Cox 86
33	Jan 4	H	VC	Dover Athletic	Won 2-0	16	535	Francis 37, Roberts 55
34	**Jan 7**	**H**	**MSC**	**Wingate & Finchley**	**Won 4-3**		**85**	**Randall, Mee, J Roberts (2)**
35	Jan 11	H	VC	Stevenage Borough	Lost 1-3	16	1097	Hall 2
36	**Jan 18**	**A**	**FAT 1**	**Yeovil Town**	**Drew 2-2**		**2458**	**Randall 56, 65**
37	**Jan 21**	**H**	**FAT 1 R**	**Yeovil Town**	**Drew 2-2***		**607**	**Roberts 78, Cox 90**
38	Jan 25	A	VC	Altrincham	Won 2-0	15	746	Randall 36, 47
39	**Jan 27**	**A**	**FAT 1 R2**	**Yeovil Town**	**Won 2-1**		**2310**	**Randall 56, 65**
40	Feb 1	H	VC	Macclesfield Town	Lost 0-2	17	684	
41	**Feb 4**	**A**	**MSC**	**Northwood**	**Lost 2-3***			**Hayes, J Roberts**
42	**Feb 8**	**H**	**FAT 2**	**Runcorn**	**Lost 1-2**		**635**	**Francis 58**
43	Feb 11	A	VC	Bath City	Lost 1-3		377	Flynn 50
44	Feb 15	A	VC	Telford United	Drew 0-0	18	812	
45	Feb 17	A	VC	Stevenage Borough	Lost 0-2	18		
46	Feb 22	H	VC	Slough Town	Won 5-0	18	768	Randall 10, 37, 64 (p), Hall 56, Goodliffe 77 (p)
47	Mar 1	A	VC	Gateshead	Drew 1-1	18	476	Hall 79
48	Mar 8	H	VC	Morecambe	Lost 2-3	18	558	Randall 36, Goodliffe 79 (pen)
49	Mar 11	H	VC	Farnborough Town	Drew 0-0		537	
50	Mar 15	A	VC	Slough Town	Won 3-1	17	1100	Williams 63, Roberts 66, 79
51	Mar 22	A	VC	Bromsgrove Rovers	Drew 2-2	17	557	Randall 46, Roberts 74
52	Mar 25	A	VC	Woking	Won 2-1	16	3352	Hall 33, Lillington 46
53	Mar 29	H	VC	Hednesford Town	Won 4-0		674	Goodliffe 48, 52 (pen), Randall 57, Roberts 83
54	Mar 31	A	VC	Rushden & Diamonds	Drew 2-2	12	3134	Francis 7, Cox 48
55	Apr 5	H	VC	Northwich Victoria	Drew 1-1	15	591	Randall 26 (pen)
56	Apr 19	A	VC	Halifax Town	Lost 1-2	18	684	Goodliffe 56 (pen)
57	Apr 26	H	VC	Bath City	Lost 0-1		1183	
58	May 3	A	VC	Southport	Won 2-0	11	702	Goodliffe 5, Flynn 12

* After Extra Time

Hayes

1	2	3	4	5	6	7	8	9	10	11	12	14	15	Mth No.
Meara	Brady	Flynn	Kelly	Bunce	Goodliffe	Scott	Roddis	Williams	Randall	Wilkinson	Bartley	Haynes	Sugrue	1
Meara	Brady	Flynn	Kelly	Bunce	Goodliffe	Scott	Roddis	Williams	Randall	Wilkinson	Bartley	Haynes	Sugrue	2
Meara	Brady	Flynn	Kelly	Bunce	Goodliffe	Sugrue	Roddis	Williams	Haynes	Wilkinson	Randall	J Roberts	Lewis	3
Meara	Brady	Flynn	Kelly	Bunce	Goodliffe	Sugrue	Roddis	Williams	Haynes	Lewis	Hyatt	Wilkinson	Randall	4
Meara	Brady	Flynn	Kelly	Bunce	Goodliffe	Sugrue	Rodddis	Williams	Haynes	Lewis	Scott	Wilkinson	Randall	5
Meara	Brady	Clasp	Kelly	Bunce	Wilkinson	Sugrue	Roddis	Williams	Haynes	Lewis	Fickett	Sugrue	Randall	6
Meara	Brady	Clasp	Kelly	Bunce	Goodliffe	Wilkinson	Roddis	Williams	Pickett	Lewis	Sugrue	Bartley	Haynes	7
Meara	Brady	Clasp	Pickett	Bunce	Goodliffe	Sugrue	Wilkinson	Williams	Haynes	Lewis	Cox	Bartley	Randall	8
Meara	**Brady**	**Clasp**	**Kelly**	**Cox**	**Goodliffe**	**Bunce**	**Pickett**	**Williams**	**Haynes**	**Wilkinson**	**Sugrue**	**Randall**	**O'Brien**	**9**
Meara	Brady	Clasp	Kelly	Cox	Goodliffe	Sugrue	Adams	Williams	Haynes	Wilkinson	Bartley	Mee	O'Brien	10
Meara	Brady	Clasp	Kelly	Cox	Goodliffe	Bartley	Adams	Williams	Haynes	Wilkinson	Sugrue	Mee	Bunce	11
Meara	**Brady**	**Bunce**	**Kelly**	**Cox**	**Goodliffe**	**Sugrue**	**Bartley**	**Williams**	**Haynes**	**Wilkinson**	**Clasp**	**Mee**	**O'Brien**	**12**
Meara	**Brady**	**Bunce**	**Kelly**	**Cox**	**Goodliffe**	**Sugrue**	**Wise**	**Bartley**	**Haynes**	**Wilkinson**	**Bartley**	**Mee**	**Bunce**	**13**
Meara	Brady	Wise	Kelly	Cox	Goodliffe	Roddis	Adams	Williams	Haynes	Wilkinson	Bunce	Bartley	D Roberts	14
Meara	**Brady**	**Wise**	**Kelly**	**Cox**	**Goodliffe**	**Roddis**	**Bunce**	**Williams**	**Haynes**	**Wilkinson**	**Bartley**	**Sugrue**	**Randall**	**15**
Meara	**Brady**	**Wise**	**Kelly**	**Cox**	**Goodliffe**	**Roddis**	**Bunce**	**Williams**	**Haynes**	**Wilkinson**	**Bartley**	**Sugrue**	**Randall**	**16**
Oderoynbo	Brady	Wise	Kelly	Cox	Bunce	Adams	Hall	Williams	Haynes	Wilkinson	Goodliffe	Hyatt	Randall	17
Meara	Brady	Goodliffe	Kelly	Cox	Bunce	Hyatt	Hall	Williams	Haynes	Wilkinson	Adams	Randall	J Roberts	18
Meara	**Brady**	**Goodliffe**	**Sugrue**	**Cox**	**Bunce**	**Hyatt**	**Adams**	**Bartley**	**Randall**	**Wise**	**Hall**	**Stevens**	**J Roberts**	**19**
Meara	**Brady**	**Goodliffe**	**Kelly**	**Cox**	**Bunce**	**Hyatt**	**Sugrue**	**Williams**	**Randall**	**Wilkinson**	**Bartley**	**Wise**	**J Roberts**	**20**
Meara	**Brady**	**Goodliffe**	**Adams**	**Cox**	**Bunce**	**Hyatt**	**Hall**	**Bartley**	**J Roberts**	**Wilkinson**	**Baker**	**Randall**	**Haynes**	**21**
Meara	Brady	Goodliffe	Adams	Bartley	Bunce	Hyatt	Baker	Williams	Haynes	Wilkinson		J Roberts	Hall	22
Meara	Brady	Goodliffe	Adams	J Roberts	Bunce	Hyatt	Hall	Williams	Haynes	Wilkinson	Bartley	Cox	Randall	23
Meara	Brady	Goodliffe	Hooper	Cox	Bunce	Hyatt	Hall	Williams	Donoghue	Wilkinson	J Roberts	Adams		24
Meara	**Brady**	**Goodliffe**	**Kelly**	**Cox**	**Bunce**	**Hyatt**	**Hooper**	**Williams**	**Haynes**	**Wilkinson**	**Randall**	**Bartley**	**J Roberts**	**25**
Meara	Brady	Goodliffe	Kelly	Cox	Bunce	Hyatt	Hooper	Williams	Francis	Wilkinson	Haynes	Hedge	Hall	26
Meara	**Brady**	**Goodliffe**	**Kelly**	**Cox**	**Bunce**	**Hyatt**	**Hooper**	**Williams**	**Haynes**	**Wilkinson**	**Randall**	**Bartley**	**J Roberts**	**27**
Meara	Randall	Goodliffe	Kelly	Cox	Bunce	Adams	Hooper	Hall	Haynes	Wilkinson	Williams	Roddis	J Roberts	28
Meara	Brady	Duncan	Kelly	Goodliffe	Williams	Hayrettin	Hall	Randall	J Roberts	Wilkinson	Roddis	Haynes	Adams	29
Meara	Brady	Duncan	Hooper	Roddis	Williams	Hayrettin	Hall	Randall	Haynes	Wilkinson	Hyatt	Wise		30
Meara	Brady	Duncan	Kelly	Cox	Williams	Hayrettin	Hall	Randall	J Roberts	Wilkinson	Francis	Haynes	Goodliffe	31
Meara	Goodliffe	Duncan	Kelly	Cox	Haynes	Hayrettin	Hall	Randall	J Roberts	Wilkinson	Francis	Williams	Brady	32
Meara	Brady	Goodliffe	Bunce	Cox	Randall	Francis	Hall	Haynes	J Roberts	Wilkinson	Mee	Hyatt	Roddis	33
Ferme	**Duncan**	**Flynn**	**Goodliffe**	**Bunce**	**Williams**	**Adams**	**Hyatt**	**Francis**	**Randall**	**Haynes**	**Mee**	**Brady**	**J Roberts**	**34**
Meara	Duncan	Goodliffe	Bunce	Cox	Randall	Francis	Hall	Haynes	J Roberts	Wilkinson	Brady	G Williams	Hayrettin	35
Meara	**Brady**	**Flynn**	**Bunce**	**Cox**	**Randall**	**Francis**	**Hall**	**Williams**	**J Roberts**	**Hayrettin**	**Haynes**	**O'Brien**	**Roddis**	**36**
Meara	**Wilkinson**	**Haynes**	**Goodliffe**	**Cox**	**Randall**	**Francis**	**Hall**	**Williams**	**J Roberts**	**Hayrettin**	**Flynn**	**Brady**	**Roddis**	**37**
Meara	Brady	Duncan	Williams	Cox	Goodliffe	Francis	Hall	Randall	J Roberts	Wilkinson	Haynes	Flynn	Hayrettin	38
Meara	**Brady**	**Flynn**	**Goodliffe**	**Cox**	**Randall**	**Francis**	**Hall**	**Williams**	**J Roberts**	**Wilkinson**	**Hayrettin**	Haynes	Roddis	39
Meara	Brady	Duncan	Goodliffe	Hayrettin	Randall	Francis	Hall	Williams	J Roberts	Wilkinson	Flynn	Haynes	Roddis	40
Meara	**Brady**	**Flynn**	**Bird**	**Hayrettin**	**Duncan**	**Haynes**	**Roddis**	**Williams**	**J Roberts**	**Wilkinson**	**Bunce**	**Francis**	**O'Brien**	**41**
Meara	**Brady**	**Flynn**	**Goodliffe**	**Bunce**	**Hayrettin**	**Francis**	**Hall**	**Haynes**	**J Roberts**	**Wilkinson**	**Evans**	**Stevens**	**O'Brien**	**42**
Meara	Brady	Flynn	Bunce	Duncan	Goodliffe	Francis	Hall	Ansah	J Roberts	Wilkinson	Haynes	Hayrettin	Hyatt	43
Meara	Brady	Duncan	Goodliffe	Williams	Bunce	Roddis	Francis	Ansah	Randall	Wilkinson	Hall	Haynes	J Roberts	44
Meara	Brady	Goodliffe	Duncan	Bunce	Williams	Roddis	Ansah	Randall	J Roberts	Wilkinson	Francis	Haynes	Hall	45
Meara	Brady	Duncan	Goodliffe	Cox	Bunce	Roddis	Hall	Randall	J Roberts	Wilkinson	O'Brien	Haynes	Hyatt	46
Meara	Brady	Duncan	Goodliffe	Cox	Williams	Roddis	Hall	Randall	J Roberts	Wilkinson	Wotton	Bunce	Hyatt	47
Meara	Wotton	Duncan	Goodliffe	Cox	Williams	Roddis	Hall	Randall	J Roberts	Wilkinson	O'Brien	Haynes	Hyatt	48
Meara	Wotton	Duncan	Goodliffe	Cox	Williams	Roddis	Hall	Randall	Haynes	Wilkinson	O'Brien	J Roberts	Hyatt	49
Meara	Brady	Duncan	Goodliffe	Cox	Williams	Roddis	Hall	Randall	Haynes	Hyatt	Wotton	J Roberts	Bunce	50
Meara	Brady	Wotton	Goodliffe	Cox	Bunce	Roddis	Hyatt	Randall	Lillington	Wilkinson	Duncan	J Roberts	Francis	51
Meara	Wotton	Brady	Francis	Cox	Goodliffe	Lillington	Hall	Randall	J Roberts	Wilkinson	Duncan	Bunce	Hyatt	52
Meara	Wotton	Brady	Francis	Cox	Goodliffe	Lillington	Hall	Randall	J Roberts	Wilkinson	Duncan	Bunce	Hyatt	53
Meara	Brady	Wotton	Duncan	Cox	Bunce	Francis	Lillington	Randall	Hall	Wilkinson	Hyatt	Roddis	J Roberts	54
Meara	Brady	Wotton	Francis	Cox	Bunce	Lillington	Hall	Randall	J Roberts	Wilkinson	Hyatt	Roddis	Duncan	55
Meara	Brady	Duncan	Goodliffe	Cox	Williams	Roddis	Francis	Randall	J Roberts	Hyatt	Lillington	Wotton	Bunce	56
Meara	Brady	Duncan	Kelly	Cox	Goodliffe	Francis	Hall	Randall	J Roberts	Wilkinson	Williams	Bartley	Roddis	57
Meara	Brady	Flynn	Kelly	Cox	Goodliffe	Roddis	Hall	Randall	J Roberts	Wilkinson	Williams	Bunce	Duncan	58

TERRY BROWN (MANAGER)

Date of Appointment	November 1993
Date of Birth:	5th August 1952
Place of Birth:	Hillingdon

PREVIOUS CLUBS

As manager	
As coach	Wokingham Town
As player	Hayes, Slough Town, Hayes, Wokingham Town

HONOURS

As manager	ICIS League Championship 95-96
As player	None

Assistant Manager: Willy Wordsworth **Coach:** Dave Killick **Physio:** Karl Ballard

Gary Williams gets up well to get in his header, in the match against Rushden & Diamonds.

Photo: Peter Barnes.

MATCHDAY PROGRAMME

Number of pages	24
Price	£1.20
Programme Editor	Robert Frape
	0181 848 8848
Other club publications:	None
Local Newspapers:	Hayes Gazette
Local Radio Stations:	Capital Radio

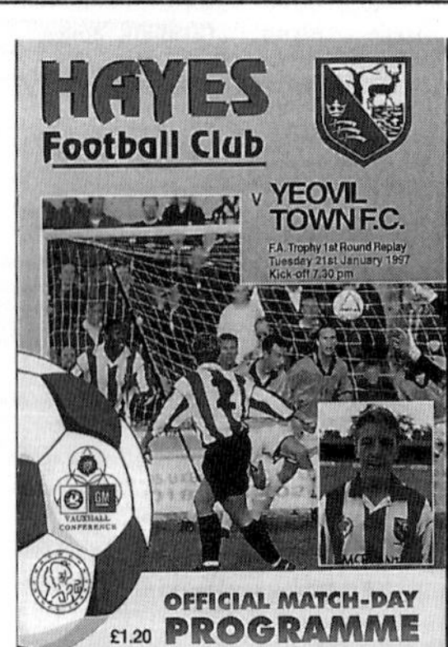

1997-98 PLAYING SQUAD

PLAYER	Birthplace Honours	Birthdate	CLUBS
GOALKEEPERS			
Russell Meara	Hammersmith ILP	12.7.74	Southampton, Brighton, Barnet, Aylesbury U, Wokingham T
DEFENDERS			
Jon Brady	Newcastle(Aust) ILP	14.1.75	Adamstown Rosebuds (Aust), Swansea C, Brentford, Hayes, Mjolner (Nor)
Warren Kelly	Watford ILP	18.4.68	Hemel Hempstead, St.Albans C
Andy Cox	Hemel H ILP, FA XI	1.5.69	Chipperfield, Tring T, Berkhamsted T, St.Albans C, £6k to Hayes
Jason Goodliffe	Hillingdon ILP	7.3.74	Brentford
Nathan Bunce	Hillingdon	2.5.75	Brentford, Yeading, £2k to Hayes
Iain Duncan	Oxford	31.7.72	Leicester C, Thatcham T, Basingstoke T, Wealdstone, Windsor & Eton, Wokingham T
MIDFIELDERS			
Steve Baker	Hillingdon ILP	31.5.74	Brentford, Brook House, Hayes, Southall, Yeading
Nick Roddis	Rotherham	18.2.73	Nottingham F, Boston FC, Boston U, Yeading
Darron Wilkinson	Reading ILP	24.11.69	Wokingham T, Brighton, Kuitan (HK)
Freddie Hyatt	West London ILP	18.1.68	Ruislip, Burnham, Wokingham T
Gary Wotton	Devon Combined Services	8.7.74	Plymouth A, Reading, Yeovil T, Dorchester T, Liskeard A, Weston-Super-Mare, Cheltenham T
FORWARDS			
Martin Randall	Pinner ILP	3.3.73	Northwood, £1,500 to Hayes
Carl Bartley	Peckham	6.10.76	Fulham, Dulwich Hamlet
Gary Williams	Adelaide (Aust) ILP	19.6.69	Luton T, Vauxhall Motors, Stevenage B, Baldock T, Hitchin T
Willie Lillington	London		Wimbledon, Molesey, Dulwich Hamlet
Mark Hall	Islington Barbados Int.	13.1.73	Tottenham H, Southend U, Torquay U, Grays A
Junior Haynes	Croydon	16.4.76	Tottenham H, Luton T, Barnet, Hendon
Jason Roberts	London		From Youth Team

DEPARTURES -
(During the season): Dean Hooper (Stevenage B), Corey Donoghue (Hitchin T), Junior Lewis (Hendon), Ross Pickett (Yeading), Jimmy Sugrue (Aldershot T), Neal Stevens (Hendon), Andy Ansah (Heybridge S) (Conwy U), Nick Harland (Rhyl), Tony Bullock (Barnsley)

PLAYERS ON LOAN - Keiran Adams (Barnet)

Church Road, Hayes

GROUND ADDRESS: Townfield House, Church Road, Hayes, Middx UB3 2LE.

TELEPHONE NUMBER: 0181 573 2075. Fax: 0181 573 2075. **Club News:** 0891 884484. **Buzzline:** 0891 101922.

SIMPLE DIRECTIONS: M25, M4, A312 (Hayes By-Pass), A4020 (Uxbridge Road), Church Road on left.

CAPACITY: 6,500 **SEATED:** 450 **COVERED TERRACING:** 2,000

CLUB SHOP:
Wide range of programmes, replica kits, souvenirs and books. Contact Lee Hermitage c/o Hayes FC.

SOCIAL FACILITIES:
Clubhouse open Sat. 12.00 - 3.00pm, 4.45 - 11.00pm. Sun. 12.00 - 3.00pm, 7.00 - 11.00pm. Midweek 7.00 - 11.00pm. Match nights 6.30 - 11.00pm. Some cold snacks available.

Hayes Fact File

Nickname: The Missioners **Club Sponsors:**

Club colours: Red and white shirts, black shorts, and black socks.

Change colours: Blue shirts, blue shorts, blue socks.

Reserve team league: Suburban Premier.

Midweek home matchday: Tuesday.

PREVIOUS - **Leagues:** Local leagues 09-14; Gt Western Suburban 19-22; London 22-24; Spartan 24-30; Athenian 30-71; Isthmian 71-96. **Ground:** Botwell Common.

CLUB RECORDS - **Attendance:** 15,370 v Bromley - FA Amateur Cup - 10.2.51.

Win: Unknown **Defeat:** Unknown

Transfer fee paid: £6,000 to Hendon for Gary Keen, 1990
to Enfield for Joe FRancis, 1996

Transfer fee received: £30,000 from QPR for Les Ferdinand - 1987.

Career goalscorer: Unknown.

Career appearances: Reg Leather - 701.

BEST SEASON - **FA Amateur Cup:** Runners-up 30-31

FA Cup: 2nd Round (replay) 72-73, 0-1 v Reading (H) after 0-0.
Also 2nd Rd. 90-91, 92-93.

League clubs defeated: Fulham, Bristol Rovers, Cardiff City.

FA Trophy: Quarter Final 78-79, 1-2 v Runcorn (A).

1996-97 Captain: Warren Kelly

1996-97 Top scorer: Martin Randall (18)

1996-97 Player of the Year: Jason Roberts

Past players who progressed to the Football League: Cyril Bacon (Orient 1946), Phil Nolan (Watford 1947), Dave Grommbridge (Orient 1951), Jimmy Bloomfield (Brentford 1952), Derek Neale & Les Champleover (Brighton 1956 & 57), Gordon Phillips (Brentford 1963), Robin Friday (Reading 1974), Les Smith (A Villa), Cyrille Regis (WBA 1977), Les Ferdinand (QPR 1987), Derek Payne (Barnet 1988), Paul Hyde (Wycombe 1991), Dean Hooper (Swindon 1995).

HONOURS: ICIS League Premier Div. 95-96, FA Amateur Cup R-up 30-31, Isthmian Lg R-up 78-79, 87-88, Athenian Lg 56-57, Spartan Lg 27-28, Gt Western Suburban Lg 20-24, London Snr Cup 31-32, 80-81, Middx Snr Cup 19-21, 25-26, 30-31, 35-36, 39-40, 49-50, 81-82, 95-96, London Charity Cup 60-61, Middx Charity Cup (15 times), Middx Premier Cup 87-88, 88-89, Suburban Lg (North) 88-89, 91-92, 96-97.

Formed:
1880

HEDNESFORD TOWN

President: Nigel Tinsley

Chairman: Mick Smith

Vice-Chairman: John Baldwin

Secretary: Ritchie Murning

Commercial Manager / Press Officer: Terry Brumpton

The Pitmen completed their second season in the Vauxhall Conference in a top eight position, with crowds at their highest ever levels and having taken part in a superb FA Cup run. Players such as Joe O'Connor and Scott Cooksey gained international recognition and, in just two years, the club's profile was lifted enormously.

Manager John Baldwin, now entering his ninth season in charge, has seen his team progress from the lower reaches of the Southern League Midland Division to being tipped now as potential champions of non-League football's premier competition. Despite last season's successes, Baldwin has made a number of changes to his squad, including signing a number of highly experienced former professionals. The manager would like to see his team embark on another fairy tale run to the Fourth Round of the FA Cup but his number one priority is mounting a challenge for promotion to the Football League, something the bookies certainly believe is possible.

L-R, Back Row: John Cotterill, Dave Harnett, Leighton Derry, Keith Russell, Paul Carty, Tyron Street, Luke Yates. Middle: Pete Windsor (Kit Man.), Stuart Lake, Steve Essex, Scott Cooksey, Gavin Brant, Andy Comyn, Colin Lambert, Don Drakeley (Physio). Front: Bernard McNally, Gary Fitzpatrick, Kevin Collins, John Baldwin (Manager), John Allen (Asst. Man.), Wayne Simpson, Steve Devine, Steve Taylor. Photo: Mr & Mrs C Rogers

Hednesford Town

Match No.	Date	Venue H/A	Competition	Opponents	Result	League Pos.	Attendance	Goalscorers (Times if known)
1	Aug 17	H	VC	Dover Athletic	Drew 1-1	12	1010	Lambert 66
2	Aug 19	H	VC	Stevenage Borough	Drew 0-0		1440	
3	Aug 24	A	VC	Woking	Lost 0-2		2363	
4	Aug 26	A	VC	Stalybridge Celtic	Won 2-1	13	643	Street 70, O'Connor 73
5	Aug 31	H	VC	Bath City	Won 2-0	8	1054	Devine 55, O'Connor 84
6	Sep 2	H	VC	Northwich Victoria	Won 3-0		1096	Cotterill 44, O'Connor 72, Comyn 75
7	Sep 7	A	VC	Morecambe	Drew 2-2	5	1088	O'Connor 37, McNally 70 (pen)
8	Sep 9	H	VC	Bromsgrove Rovers	Won 3-0		1276	Comyn 17, Lambert 49, O'Connor 68
9	**Sep 14**	**A**	**FAC 1 Q**	**Wednesfield**	**Drew 0-0**		**486**	**\Lambert 26, Street 31, O'Connor 40,**
10	**Sep 16**	**H**	**FAC R**	**Wednesfield**	**Won 6-0**		**743**	**Devine 48, Comyn 68, Fitzpatrick 75**
11	Sep 21	A	VC	Slough Town	Drew 2-2	6	1120	O'Connor, Street
12	**Sep 28**	**H**	**FAC 2 Q**	**Evesham United**	**Won 6-1**		**635**	**O'Connor 44, 50, 55, Lawrence 77, Essex 81, Street 85**
13	Sep 30	H	VC	Rushden & Diamonds	Won 1-0		1252	McNally 30
14	Oct 5	H	VC	Farnborough Town	Lost 0-1	9	1156	
15	**Oct 12**	**H**	**FAC 3 Q**	**Tamworth**	**Won 4-2**		**1290**	**Street 8, Russell 10, 55, O'Connor 50**
16	Oct 15	A	VC	Kettering Town	Won 2-0		766	Russell 45 (pen), Lambert 69
17	Oct 19	H	VC	Southport	Lost 0-1	10	1149	
18	**Oct 26**	**H**	**FAC 4 Q**	**Telford United**	**Won 2-0**		**1343**	**Lawrence 16, Street 89**
19	Nov 2	A	VC	Welling United	Won 2-1	9	702	O'Connor 5, 36
20	**Nov 4**	**H**	**SSC**	**Port Vale**	**Won 3-0**		**390**	**Fitzpatrick, Harnett (2)**
21	Nov 9	H	VC	Altrincham	Drew 2-2	10	1138	Russell 22, O'Connor 81
22	**Nov 16**	**H**	**FAC**	**Southport**	**Won 2-1**		**2060**	**Russell 10, O'Connor 65**
23	**Nov 18**	**H**	**BSC**	**Coventry City**	**Lost 0-1**		**245**	
24	Nov 23	A	VC	Kidderminster Harriers	Lost 1-2	10	2661	Lambert 89
25	Nov 26	A	VC	Bath City	Lost 1-2		385	Hartnett 52
26	Nov 30	H	VC	Stalybridge Celtic	Won 2-1	9	1035	O'Connor 5, Lawrence 45
27	**Dec 2**	**H**	**SSC**	**Kidderminster Harriers**	**Lost 1-6**		**333**	**Dandy 68 (pen)**
28	**Dec 7**	**A**	**FAC 2**	**Blackpool**	**Won 1-0**		**4583**	**O'Connor 87**
29	Dec 14	H	VC	Hayes	Won 2-0	9	1040	Fitzpatrick 6, Lake 58
30	Dec 21	H	VC	Gateshead	Drew 0-0		1060	
31	Dec 26	A	VC	Telford United	Drew 1-1		1236	Russell 90 (pen)
32	Dec 28	A	VC	Southport	Won 2-1	9	1023	Lake 53, Lambert 64
33	**Jan 13**	**H**	**FAC 3**	**York City**	**Won 1-0**		**3169**	**Russell 43 (pen)**
34	**Jan 18**	**A**	**FAT 1**	**Northwich Victoria**	**Lost 1-3**		**1109**	**Carty 60**
35	**Jan 25**	**N (A)**	**FAC 4**	**Middlesbrough**	**Lost 2-3**		**27,511**	**O'Connor 14, 90**
36	Feb 1	H	VC	Woking	Won 2-0	8	2368	Russell 38, Lake 44
37	**Feb 3**	**H**	**SSC 2 Rnd**	**Tamworth**	**Won 2-0**		**2541**	**Harnett, Street**
38	Feb 8	A	VC	Rushden & Diamonds	Won 2-0		2618	Carty 50, Street 73
39	Feb 11	A	VC	Macclesfield Town	Lost 0-4		1003	
40	Feb 15	A	VC	Gateshead	Won 1-0	5	694	O'Connor 70
41	Feb 22	H	VC	Morecambe	Won 2-1	5	1463	O'Connor 58, Street 79
42	Mar 1	H	VC	Telford United	Drew 0-0	5	1440	
43	Mar 4	A	VC	Halifax Town	Lost 0-1	5	623	
44	**Mar 6**	**H**	**SSC 3 Rnd**	**Stoke City**	**Won 5-3***		**1311**	**Street, O'Connor (3), McKenzie**
45	Mar 15	A	VC	Stevenage Borough	Lost 2-3	6	2744	Fitzpatrick 17, O'Connor 32
46	Mar 17	H	VC	Kidderminster Harriers	Lost 1-4	6	2587	Russell 34
47	Mar 22	H	VC	Kettering Town	Drew 0-0	7	1121	
48	Mar 25	A	VC	Altrincham	Drew 1-1	6	670	Carty 90 (pen)
49	Mar 29	A	VC	Hayes	Lost 0-4		674	
50	Mar 31	H	VC	Macclesfield Town	Won 4-1	7	2177	Lambert 13, Mason 49 (pen), O'Connor 76, 84
51	Apr 5	A	VC	Bromsgrove Rovers	Lost 0-1	7	814	
52	Apr 7	H	VC	Halifax Town	Drew 1-1	7	1007	Fitzpatrick 62
53	Apr 12	A	VC	Northwich Victoria	Lost 1-2	7	928	Mason 22 (pen)
54	**Apr 15**	**A**	**SSC**	**Macclesfield**	**Drew 1-1***		**505**	**O'Connor**
55	Apr 19	H	VC	Slough Town	Won 2-1	5	852	Carty 65, Francis 81
56	Apr 21	H	VC	Welling United	Lost 0-3		851	
57	Apr 26	A	VC	Farnborough Town	Lost 0-1	8	794	
58	May 3	A	VC	Dover Athletic	Drew 2-2	8	1158	Francis 53, 65

* After Extra Time

Hednesford Town

1	2	3	4	5	6	7	8	9	10	11	12	14	15	Mth No.
Cooksey	Carty	Collins	Comyn	Essex	Russell	Devine	Lambert	Taylor	McNally	Fitzpatrick	Derry	Simpson	Cotterill	1
Cooksey	Carty	Collins	Simpson	Essex	Comyn	Devine	Lambert	Taylor	McNally	Fitzpatrick	Yates	Lake	Street	2
Cooksey	Carty	Collins	Simpson	Essex	Comyn	Devine	Lambert	Taylor	McNally	Fitzpatrick	Street	Yates	Harnett	3
Cooksey	Comyn	Collins	Simpson	Essex	Carty	McNally	Fitzpatrick	Taylor	Lambert	O'Connor	Devine	Street	Yates	4
Cooksey	Carty	Collins	Simpson	Comyn	Fitzpatrick	McNally	Lambert	Street	Devine	O'Connor	Essex	Taylor	Yates	5
Cooksey	Cotterill	Collins	Simpson	Comyn	McNally	Fitzpatrick	Lambert	Street	Edwards	O'Connor	Essex	Taylor	Yates	6
Cooksey	Cotterill	Collins	Simpson	Comyn	McNally	Fitzpatrick	Lambert	Street	Edwards	O'Connor	Essex	Taylor	Lake	7
Cooksey	Carty	Collins	Simpson	Comyn	Lake	McNally	Lambert	Street	Edwards	O'Connor	Yates	Essex	Taylor	8
Cooksey	**Carty**	**Collins**	**Simpson**	**Comyn**	**Fitzpatrick**	**McNally**	**Lambert**	**Street**	**Devine**	**O'Connor**	**Essex**	**Taylor**	**Cotterill**	**9**
Cooksey	**Carty**	**Devine**	**Simpson**	**Comyn**	**Essex**	**McNally**	**Lambert**	**Street**	**Fitzpatrick**	**O'Connor**	**Taylor**	**Cotterill**	**Derry**	**10**
Cooksey	Carty	Devine	Simpson	Essex	Comyn	Fitzpatrick	Lambert	Street	McNally	O'Connor	Cotterill	Taylor	Collins	11
Cooksey	**Carty**	**Devine**	**Simpson**	**Essex**	**Comyn**	**Fitzpatrick**	**Lambert**	**Street**	**McNally**	**O'Connor**	**Cotterill**	**Collins**	**Lawrence**	**12**
Cooksey	Carty	Devine	Simpson	Essex	Comyn	McNally	Lambert	Street	Fitzpatrick	O'Connor	Cotterill	Collins	Lawrence	13
Cooksey	Cotterill	Devine	Simpson	Essex	Comyn	Fitzpatrick	Lambert	Street	McNally	O'Connor	Collins	Lawrence	Lake	14
Cooksey	**Russell**	**Devine**	**Simpson**	**Comyn**	**Collins**	**Fitzpatrick**	**Lambert**	**Street**	**McNally**	**O'Connor**	**Lawrence**	**Essex**	**Carty**	**15**
Cooksey	Russell	Devine	Simpson	Essex	Comyn	Fitzpatrick	Lambert	Street	McNally	O'Connor	Lawrence	Cotterill	Collins	16
Cooksey	Russell	Edwards	Simpson	Essex	Comyn	Fitzpatrick	Lambert	Street	McNally	O'Connor	Lawrence	Collins	Cotterill	17
Cooksey	**Carty**	**Russell**	**Simpson**	**Comyn**	**Collins**	**McNally**	**Lambert**	**Lawrence**	**Street**	**O'Connor**	**Fitzpatrick**	**Devine**	**Brant**	**18**
Cooksey	Carty	Devine	Simpson	Comyn	Collins	McNally	Lambert	Lawrence	Street	O'Connor	Fitzpatrick	Cotterill	Essex	19
Brant	**Cotterill**	**Yates**	**Broadhurst**	**Essex**	**Collins**	**Dandy**	**Fitzpatrick**	**Harnett**	**Street**	**Derry**	**Palmer**	**McNally**	**Devine**	**20**
Cooksey	Carty	Russell	Simpson	Comyn	Collins	McNally	Devine	Lawrence	Street	O'Connor	Essex	Fitzpatrick	Hemmings	21
Cooksey	**Carty**	**Russell**	**Simpson**	**Comyn**	**Collins**	**McNally**	**Lambert**	**Hemmings**	**Street**	**O'Connor**	**Devine**	**Brant**	**Essex**	**22**
Brant	**Yates**	**Russell**	**Broadhurst**	**Essex**	**Collins**	**Dandy**	**Devine**	**Lawrence**	**Harnett**	**Derry**	**Corbett**	**Street**	**Comyn**	**23**
Cooksey	Carty	Russell	Simpson	Comyn	Collins	Devine	Lambert	Hemmings	Street	O'Connor	Essex	Brant	Lake	24
Cooksey	Russell	Hemmings	Simpson	Comyn	Collins	Lake	Lambert	Harnett	Street	O'Connor	Essex	Devine	Dandy	25
Cooksey	Russell	Hemmings	Comyn	Essex	Collins	Lake	Lambert	Lawrence	Devine	O'Connor	Dandy	Harnett	Broadhurst	26
Brant	**Carty**	**Hemmings**	**Broadhurst**	**Essex**	**Collins**	**Dandy**	**Lake**	**Harnett**	**Devine**	**O'Connor**	**Yates**	**Unitt**	**Palmer**	**27**
Cooksey	**Russell**	**Collins**	**Simpson**	**Essex**	**Comyn**	**Hemmings**	**Lambert**	**Lake**	**Devine**	**O'Connor**	**Lawrence**	**Dandy**	**Harnett**	**28**
Cooksey	Carty	Collins	Simpson	Comyn	Fitzpatrick	Divine	Lake	Russell	Hemmings	O'Connor	Lawrence	Holmes	Dandy	29
Cooksey	Russell	Collins	Simpson	Comyn	Fitzpatrick	Hemmings	Devine	Holmes	Lake	O'Connor	Lawrence	Street	Dandy	30
Cooksey	Russell	Collins	Simpson	Comyn	Lake	Hemmings	Lambert	Holmes	Street	O'Connor	Devine	Fitzpatrick	McNally	31
Cooksey	Fitzpatrick	Collins	Simpson	Essex	McNally	Lake	Lambert	Russell	Carty	O'Connor	Lawrence	Holmes	Devine	32
Cooksey	**Carty**	**Russell**	**Simpson**	**Comyn**	**Collins**	**McNally**	**Lambert**	**Lake**	**Fitzpatrick**	**O'Connor**	**Devine**	**Essex**	**Street**	**33**
Cooksey	**Carty**	**Russell**	**Simpson**	**Comyn**	**Collins**	**Dandy**	**Lambert**	**Lake**	**Fitzpatrick**	**O'Connor**	**Devine**	**Hemmings**	**Essex**	**34**
Cooksey	**Carty**	**Russell**	**Simpson**	**Essex**	**Comyn**	**Collins**	**Lambert**	**Lake**	**Fitzpatrick**	**O'Connor**	**McNally**	**Hemmings**	**Devine**	**35**
Cooksey	Hemmings	Russell	Simpson	Essex	Collins	McNally	Devine	Lake	Fitzpatrick	O'Connor	Street	Lawrence	Dandy	36
Cooksey	**Russell**	**Harnett**	**Simpson**	**Essex**	**Collins**	**Devine**	**Dandy**	**Lawrence**	**Fitzpatrick**	**Street**	**Broadhurst**	**Derry**	**Brant**	**37**
Cooksey	Carty	Russell	Simpson	Essex	Comyn	Collins	Lambert	Devine	Fitzpatrick	Hemmings	Street	Dandy	Harnett	38
Cooksey	Carty	Hemmings	Comyn	Essex	Collins	Lake	Lambert	Street	Fitzpatrick	O'Connor	Harnett	Dandy	Broadhurst	39
Cooksey	Carty	Hemmings	Comyn	Essex	Collins	Street	Lambert	Lake	Fitzpatrick	O'Connor	Devine	Harnett	Broadhurst	40
Cooksey	Carty	Hemmings	Comyn	Essex	Collins	Street	Lambert	Lake	Fitzpatrick	O'Connor	Devine	Simpson	Russell	41
Cooksey	Russell	Hemmings	Comyn	Essex	Collins	Street	Lambert	Devine	Fitzpatrick	O'Connor	Carty	Harnett	Dandy	42
Cooksey	Carty	Mason	Comyn	Essex	Collins	Devine	Lambert	Russell	Fitzpatrick	O'Connor	Street	Hemmings	Harnett	43
Cooksey	**Fitzpatrick**	**Mason**	**Comyn**	**Essex**	**Street**	**Devine**	**Lambert**	**Russell**	**Carty**	**O'Connor**	**Harnett**	**McKenzie**	**Dandy**	**44**
Cooksey	Carty	Russell	Simpson	Essex	Comyn	Collins	Lambert	Lake	Fitzpatrick	O'Connor	Street	Mason	Devine	45
Cooksey	Carty	Russell	Simpson	Essex	Comyn	Collins	Lambert	Lake	Fitzpatrick	O'Connor	Street	Mason	Devine	46
Cooksey	Russell	Mason	Simpson	Comyn	Fitzpatrick	Carty	Lambert	Lake	Street	O'Connor	Francis	McKenzie	Collins	47
Cooksey	Fitzpatrick	Mason	Comyn	Essex	Carty	Simpson	Lake	Ecclestone	Russell	O'Connor	Francis	Street	Collins	48
Cooksey	Broadhurst	Mason	Comyn	Essex	Simpson	Street	Hemmings	Ecclestone	Collins	O'Connor	Francis	McKenzie	Rowlands	49
Cooksey	Broadhurst	Collins	Comyn	Essex	Street	Francis	Lambert	Ecclestone	Mason	O'Connor	Hemmings	McKenzie	Rowlands	50
Cooksey	Comyn	Collins	Simpson	Essex	Street	Francis	Fitzpatrick	McKenzie	Mason	O'Connor	Hemmings	Rowlands	Cotterill	51
Brant	Cotterill	Collins	Simpson	Comyn	McNally	Carty	Fitzpatrick	McKenzie	Hemmings	Francis	Rowlands	Derry	Harnett	52
Cooksey	Carty	Collins	Simpson	Comyn	Street	Fitzpatrick	Lake	Francis	Hemmings	O'Connor	Essex	Mason	McKenzie	53
Cooksey	**Carty**	**Mason**	**Simpson**	**Essex**	**Street**	**Fitzpatrick**	**Lambert**	**Lake**	**Francis**	**O'Connor**	**McKenzie**	**Lutz**	**Rowlands**	**54**
Cooksey	Fitzpatrick	Mason	Simpson	Comyn	Collins	Carty	Lake	Francis	McNally	O'Connor	Essex	Cotterill	McKenzie	55
Cooksey	Cotterill	Collins	Simpson	Essex	Comyn	Carty	Lake	Francis	Fitzpatrick	O'Connor	Hemmings	Mason	McKenzie	56
Cooksey	Fitzpatrick	Collins	Simpson	Comyn	Carty	Francis	Lake	McKenzie	Hemmings	O'Connor	Mason	Harnett	Rowlands	57
Cooksey	Carty	Collins	Simpson	Essex	Comyn	Fitzpatrick	Lake	Francis	Mason	O'Connor	McKenzie	Harnett	Rowlands	58

JOHN BALDWIN (MANAGER)

Date of Appointment	January 1990
Date of Birth:	05.05.54
Place of Birth:	London
PREVIOUS CLUBS	
As manager	Electricity, Harrisons.
As coach	
As player	Hednesford Town
HONOURS	
As manager	Southern League Prem Div. 94-95
As player	England: Youth. British Universities

Assistant Manager: John Allen **Physio:** Don Drakeley

Keith Russell, seen here in action against Telford United, gained a dream move to Blackpool last season.

MATCHDAY PROGRAMME

Number of pages	48
Price	£1.20
Programme Editor	Terry Brumpton
Other club publications:	None
Local Newspapers:	Express & Star Chase Post; Cannock Mercury Lichfield Trader; The Chronicle
Local Radio Stations:	Radio WM; BRMB: WABC; Beacon: Signal; BBC Radio Stoke.

1997-98 PLAYING SQUAD

PLAYER	Birthplace Honours	Birthdate	CLUBS
GOALKEEPERS			
Scott Cooksey	Birmingham ESP, SLP	24.6.72	Derby Co, Shrewsbury T, Bromsgrove R, Peterborough U
DEFENDERS			
Wayne Simpson	Newcastle ESP, SLP, FA XI	19.9.68	Port Vale, Stafford Rangers
Andy Comyn	Wakefield	2.8.68	Manchester Utd., Alvechurch, Aston Villa, Derby County, Plymouth A, W.B.A.
Paul Blades	Peterborough EY, Div 2	5.1.65	Derby Co, £700k to Norwich C, £325k to Wolverhampton W, £110k to Rotherham U
Nigel Niblett	Stratford SLC, FA XI	12.8.67	Snitterfield Sports, Stratford T, VS Rugby, £5k to Telford U, £10k to Hednesford T
Kevin Collins	Birmingham FAT, SLP	21.7.64	Boldmere St.Michaels, Shrewsbury T, Stourbridge, Pelsall Villa, Burton A, Kidderminster H, Rushall Olympic
Paul Edwards	Birkenhead	25.12.63	Altrincham, Crewe A, Coventry C, Wolverhampton W, W.B.A.
MIDFIELDERS			
Gary Fitzpatrick	Birmingham Ei u-20, SLP	5.8.71	Leicester C, VS Rugby, Moor Green, Rannberg (Swe)
Richard Mason	Sheffield	5.6.77	Sheffield Wed, Boston U
Bernard McNally	Shrewsbury NI, WC	17.10.63	Shrewsbury T, W.B.A.
Paul Ware	Congleton Div 2	7.11.70	Stoke C, Stockport Co
Paul Carty	Birmingham SLP	22.10.66	Everton, Nuneaton B, Bromsgrove R, Tamworth
Stuart Lake	Stone SLP	15.10.75	Walsall
Robbie Dennison	Banbridge NI, Div 3, Div 4	30.4.63	Glenavon, £40k to W.B.A., £20k to Wolverhampton W
FORWARDS			
Mike Norbury	Hemsworth	22.1.69	Ossett T, Scarborough, Bridlington T, Cambridge U, Preston, Doncaster R, Guiseley, Stafford Rangers, Halifax T, £10k to Hednesford T
Charlie Ntamark	Paddington Cameroon Int.	22.7.64	Boreham Wood, Walsall
Joe O'Connor	Wolverhampton ESP, SLP	20.10.67	Lye T, Stafford Rangers
Tony Hemmings	Burton FAT	21.9.67	Rocester, Northwich Victoria, Wycombe W, Macclesfield T
Tony Ecclestone	Birmingham		Wolverhampton U, Tamworth, Bloxwich T

DEPARTURES - (During the season): Luke Yates (Nuneaton B), Steve Taylor (Bromsgrove R), Keith Russell (Blackpool), George Lawrence (Rushden & D), Phil Gee (Shepshed D), Steve Devine (Gresley R)
(During the close season): Steve Essex (Retired), Leighton Derry (Released), Gavin Brant (Bloxwich T)

PLAYERS ON LOAN - Steve Rowlands (Walsall)

Keys Park, Hednesford

GROUND ADDRESS: Keys Park, Hednesford, Cannock, Staffordshire.
TEL. NO. 01543 422870

SIMPLE DIRECTIONS: M6 J11 to Cannock, through traffic lights to island , 3rd exit, next island, 2nd exit onto Lichfield Rd. Next island 1st exit, next island straight on, next island 3rd exit, continue to mini-island. Keys Park is straight on (signposted from 2nd island.)

CAPACITY: 3,500 **SEATED:** 770 **COVERED TERRACING:** 1,000

CLUB SHOP: Yes. Open throughout the week.

SOCIAL FACILITIES: Strikers Bar open matchdays and every evening except Sunday 7-11. No food available. Chase Suite hold functions.

Hednesford Fact File

Nickname: The Pitmen **Club Sponsors:** Miras Contracts
Club colours: White shirts & black & red trim, black shorts, white trim.
Change colours: Gold shirts, navy sleeves, navy shorts, gold trim.
Reserve team league: Central Conference League, and Endsleigh Midland Combination (Reserve Div.).
Midweek home matchday: Monday.

PREVIOUS - **Grounds:** The Tins (behind Anglesey Hotel) until 1904, Cross Keys until 1995.
Leagues: Walsall & District/ Birmingham Combination 08-15 45-53/ West Mids 19-39 53-72 74-84/ Midland Counties 72-74.

CLUB RECORDS - **Attendance:** 10,000 v Walsall, FA Cup 1919-20
Win: 12-1 v Birmingham City- Birmingham Wartime League Cup 40-41
v Redditch United, Birmingham Combination 52-53.
Defeat: 0-15 v Burton , Birmingham Combination 24-25.
Career goalscorer: Tosh Griffiths
Career appearances: Kevin Foster
Transfer fee paid: £12,000 for Steve Burr (Macclesfield Town 1991)
Transfer fee received: £50,000 for Dave Hanson (Leyton Orient)

BEST SEASON - **FA Cup:** 1996-97, 4th Round v Middlesbrough (2-3 at Middlesbrough).
League clubs defeated: Blackpool, York City.
FA Trophy: 1977-78, 2nd Round.

Past players who progressed to the Football League:
Brian Horton (Port Vale 1970), Vernon Allatt (Halifax Town 1979), Chris Brindley (Wolverhampton W. 1986), Dave Hanson (Leyton Orient), Keith Russell (Blackpool 1997).

1996-97 Captain: Kevin Collins
1996-97 Top scorer: Joe O'Connor (24)
1996-97 Player of the Year: Scott Cooksey (Supporters'). Andy Comyn (Players').

HONOURS:
Welsh Cup R-up 91-92: Southern League Prem. Div. 94-95; Midland Div. R-up 91-92; Lge. Cup R-up 86-87: West Midlands. Lge 77-78; R-up 83-84; Lge. Cup 83-84: Birmingham Combination 09-10, 50-51; R-up 12-13, 52-53: Staffs Senior Cup 69-70, 73-74; R-up 92-93: Birmingham Senior Cup 35-36; R-up 93-94.

HEREFORD UNITED

Formed: 1924

Chairman: P S Hill FRICS

President: A Bush

Directors: D H Vaughan, J Simmons, R Fry (Managing).

Secretary: Joan Fennessy (01432 276666)

Hereford United have featured amongst most football lovers' favourite clubs for their original giant-killing (especially the defeat of Newcastle United), their mascot, which is a huge good looking bull and the happy-go-lucky attitude of their chairman and directors, plus the friendly atmosphere of their Edgar Street ground.

So when they finally sank into a desperate position at the foot of Division Three last season no-one really wanted to see them lose their Nationwide place.

Manager Graham Turner has always been a popular figure in the game and when Brighton scored that desperate equaliser to send Hereford down, there was much sympathy but of course nothing positive to help the club.

The players will remain as full-time professionals, the manager's offer of resignation has been refused and hopefully the club will re-group and quickly adapt to Conference football. It won't be easy but it will certainly be character building!

L-R, Back Row: Gavin Mahon, Andy de Bont, Trevor Matthewson, Chris Mackenzie, Gary Cook. Middle: Simon Shakeshaft, Jamie Pitman, Brian McGorry, Neil Grayson, John Brough, Richard Walker, Chris Hargreaves, Rob Warner, Keith Downing. Front: Tony Agana, Ian Foster, David Norton, Graham Turner, Murray Fishlock, Roy Jordan, Ian Rodgerson.

Hereford United

Match No.	Date	Venue H/A	Competition	Opponents	Result	League Pos.	Attendance	Goalscorers (Times if known)
1	Aug 17	A		Fulham	Lost 0-1		5277	
2	**Aug 21**	**H**	**CC**	**Cambridge United**	**Won 3-0**		**1952**	**Norton, Smith, A Foster**
3	Aug 24	H		Doncaster Rovers	Won 1-0		2877	Stoker
4	Aug 27	H		Hull City	Lost 0-1		2820	
5	Aug 31	A		Colchester United	Drew 1-1		2723	Smith
6	**Sep 3**	**A**	**CC**	**Cambridge United**	**Drew 1-1**		**1164**	**Smith**
7	Sep 7	H		Hartlepool United	Lost 0-1		2729	
8	Sep 10	A		Swansea City	Lost 0-4		2479	
9	Sep 14	A		Darlington	Lost 0-1		3271	
10	**Sep 18**	**A**	**CC**	**Middlesbrough**	**Lost 0-7**		**17136**	
11	Sep 21	H		Rochdale	Won 3-0		2140	A Foster, Hargreaves, Mahon
12	**Sep 24**	**H**	**CC**	**Middlesbrough**	**Lost 0-3**		**4522**	
13	Sep 28	A		Mansfield Town	Lost 1-3		1889	Preedy
14	Oct 1	H		Scunthorpe United	Won 3-2		1776	Hibbard, Smith, A Foster
15	Oct 5	H		Scarborough	Drew 2-2		2524	Smith, A Foster
16	Oct 12	A		Torquay United	Lost 1-2		2073	Hargreaves
17	Oct 15	A		Brighton & Hove A	Won 1-0		3444	A Foster
18	Oct 19	H		Leyton Orient	Won 2-0		2831	Smith, Stoker
19	Oct 26	A		Chester City	Won 3-1		2301	A Foster (2), Brough
20	Oct 29	H		Cambridge United	Lost 0-1		2372	
21	Nov 2	H		Barnet	Drew 1-1		2066	A Foster
22	Nov 9	A		Wigan Athletic	Lost 1-4		3414	Preedy
23	**Nov 16**	**A**	**FAC 1**	**Gillingham**	**Lost 0-1**		**5280**	
24	Nov 19	H		Lincoln City	Drew 1-1		1382	Stoker
25	Nov 23	A		Cardiff City	Lost 0-2		3900	
26	Nov 30	H		Chester City	Lost 1-2		2212	Smith
27	Dec 3	A		Exeter City	Drew 1-1		2189	Cross
28	**Dec 7**	**H**	**AWS**	**Milwall**	**Lost 0-4**		**1710**	
29	Dec 14	H		Carlisle United	Lost 2-3		1890	Matthewson, Smith
30	Dec 21	A		Northampton Town	Lost 0-1		4238	
31	Dec 26	H		Swansea City	Lost 0-1		4204	
32	Dec 28	A		Hartlepool United	Lost 1-2		1923	Smith
33	Jan 11	H		Mansfield Town	Lost 0-1		1873	
34	Jan 18	A		Scunthorpe United	Lost 1-5		1986	A Foster
35	Jan 25	A		Cambridge United	Won 1-0		3010	Hargreaves
36	Feb 1	H		Wigan Athletic	Won 3-1		2532	Fishlock, Beeston, A Foster
37	Feb 4	H		Darlington	Drew 1-1		2003	Beeston
38	Feb 8	A		Barnet	Won 3-2		2439	Hargreaves, A Foster (2)
39	Feb 16	H		Cardiff City	Drew 1-1		4967	A Foster
40	Feb 18	A		Rochdale	Drew 0-0		1074	
41	Feb 22	A		Lincoln City	Drew 3-3		2957	Smith, Matthewson, Williams
42	Mar 1	H		Exeter City	Lost 1-2		2735	Williams
43	Mar 8	H		Northampton Town	Lost 1-2		2995	A Foster
44	Mar 15	A		Carlisle United	Won 3-2		5063	A Foster (3)
45	Mar 21	A		Doncaster Rovers	Lost 0-1		2483	
46	Mar 28	H		Fulham	Drew 0-0		4473	
47	Mar 31	A		Hull City	Drew 1-1		2818	A Foster
48	Apr 5	H		Colchester United	Won 1-0		2535	McGorry
49	Apr 12	A		Scarborough	Drew 1-1		2332	Williams
50	Apr 19	H		Torquay United	Drew 1-1		2862	Agana
51	Apr 26	A		Leyton Orient	Lost 1-2		5599	Agana
52	May 3	H		Brighton & Hove A				

Hereford United

1	2	3	4	5	6	7	8	9	10	11	12	14	15	Mth No.
de Bont	Norton	Fishlock	Smith	Brough	Townsend	Pitman	Downing	A Foster	I Foster	Mahon	Stoker	Hargreaves	McBlay	1
de Bont	**Norton**	**Fishlock**	**Smith**	**Brough**	**Townsend**	**Pitman**	**Downing**	**A Foster**	**I Foster**	**Mahon**	**Stoker**	**MacKenzie**	**Hargreaves**	**2**
de Bont	Norton	Fishlock	Smith	Brough	Townsend	Stoker	Downing	A Foster	Hargreaves	Mahon	Pitman	I Foster	Cook	3
de Bont	Norton	Fishlock	Smith	Brough	Townsend	Stoker	Downing	A Foster	Hargreaves	Mahon	Pitman	I Foster	Cook	4
de Bont	Norton	Fishlock	Smith	Brough	Townsend	Stoker	Downing	A Foster	Hargreaves	Mahon	Pitman	I Foster	Cook	5
de Bont	**Norton**	**Fishlock**	**Smith**	**Brough**	**Townsend**	**Stoker**	**Downing**	**A Foster**	**Hargreaves**	**Mahon**	**Sutton**	**I Foster**	**MacKenzie**	**6**
de Bont	Norton	Fishlock	Smith	Brough	Townsend	Stoker	Downing	A Foster	Hargreaves	Mahon	Sutton	Pitman	I Foster	7
de Bont	Norton	Fishlock	Smith	Brough	Townsend	Pitman	Downing	A Foster	I Foster	Button	Mahon	Stoker	Hargreaves	8
de Bont	Norton	Fishlock	Smith	Brough	Sutton	Stoker	Hargreaves	A Foster	I Foster	Mahon	Townsend	Downing	Cook	9
de Bont	**Pilman**	**Sutton**	**Smith**	**Brough**	**Townsend**	**Mahon**	**Stoker**	**A Foster**	**I Foster**	**Hargreaves**	**Cook**	**MacKenzie**	**Preedy**	**10**
de Bont	Downing	Hibbard	Smith	Brough	Sutton	Pitman	Stoker	A Foster	Hargreaves	Mahon	Townsend	Bartlett	Preedy	11
de Bont	Warner	Hibbard	Smith	Brough	Sutton	Downing	Stoker	A Foster	Hargreaves	Mahon	Townsend	Cook	Preedy	12
de Bont	Norton	Hibbard	Forsyth	Brough	Sutton	Warner	Stoker	Cook	Hargreaves	Mahon	Townsend	Bartlett	Preedy	13
de Bont	Norton	Hibbard	Smith	Brough	Forsyth	Cook	Stoker	A Foster	Hargreaves	Preedy	Sutton	Mahon	I Foster	14
de Bont	Norton	Hibbard	Smith	Brough	Forsyth	Cook	Stoker	A Foster	Hargreaves	Preedy	Townsend	Warner	Bartlett	15
de Bont	Norton	Matthewson	Smith	Law	Forsyth	Cook	Stoker	A Foster	Hargreaves	Mahon	Brough	Hibbard	Ellison	16
de Bont	Norton	Matthewson	Smith	Law	Forsyth	Cook	Stoker	A Foster	Hargreaves	Brough	Hibbard	Warner	Preedy	17
de Bont	Norton	Matthewson	Smith	Law	Forsyth	Cook	Stoker	A Foster	Hargreaves	Brough	Hibbard	Warner	Preedy	18
de Bont	Norton	Matthewson	Smith	Law	Forsyth	Cook	Stoker	A Foster	Hargreaves	Brough	Hibbard	Warner	Preedy	19
de Bont	Norton	Matthewson	Smith	Law	Forsyth	Cook	Stoker	A Foster	Hargreaves	Brough	Hibbard	Warner	Preedy	20
de Bont	Norton	Matthewson	Smith	Law	Forsyth	Cook	Stoker	A Foster	Hargreaves	Brough	Hibbard	Warner	Preedy	21
de Bont	Norton	Matthewson	Smith	Law	Forsyth	Cook	Stoker	A Foster	Hargreaves	Brough	Hibbard	Kottlia	Preedy	22
de Bont	**Norton**	**Matthewson**	**Smith**	**Law**	**Hibbard**	**Cook**	**Stoker**	**A Foster**	**Hargreaves**	**Brough**	**Preedy**	**Townsend**	**Warner**	**23**
de Bont	Norton	Matthewson	Smith	Law	Forsyth	Cook	Stoker	A Foster	Hargreaves	Brough	Warner	Townsend	Preedy	24
de Bont	Norton	Matthewson	Smith	Law	Forsyth	O'Toole	Stoker	A Foster	Hargreaves	Brough	Cook	Warner	Preedy	25
de Bont	Norton	Matthewson	Smith	Hibbard	Law	Mahon	Stoker	A Foster	Hargreaves	Brough	Cook	Preedy	I Foster	26
de Bont	Norton	Matthewson	Smith	Warner	Cross	Cook	Stoker	A Foster	Hargreaves	Brough	Law	I Foster	Preedy	27
de Bont	**Norton**	**Matthewson**	**Smith**	**Warner**	**Cross**	**Cook**	**Stoker**	**A Foster**	**Hargreaves**	**Brough**	**Law**	**I Foster**	**Preedy**	**28**
de Bont	Norton	Matthewson	Smith	Warner	Law	Cook	Hargreaves	A Foster	Cross	Brough	Fishlock	I Foster	Kottlia	29
de Bont	Norton	Fishlock	Smith	Matthewson	Law	Cook	Hargreaves	A Foster	Cross	Brough	Mahon	Warner	I Foster	30
de Bont	Norton	Fishlock	Smith	Law	Matthewson	Hargreaves	Stoker	Kottlia	Cross	Brough	Warner	I Foster	A Foster	31
de Bont	Norton	Fishlock	Smith	Brough	Matthewson	Hargreaves	Stoker	Kottlia	Cross	Warner	Mahon	I Foster	A Foster	32
Wood	Norton	Fishlock	Smith	Brough	Matthewson	Hargreaves	Stoker	A Foster	Kottlia	Law	I Foster	Preedy	Warner	33
Wood	Norton	Fishlock	Smith	Brough	Matthewson	Hargreaves	Stoker	A Foster	Kottlia	Downing	I Foster	Preedy	Mahon	34
Wood	Norton	Fishlock	Smith	Beeston	Matthewson	Hargreaves	Stoker	A Foster	Kottlia	Downing	Brough	Warner	Mahon	35
Wood	Norton	Fishlock	Smith	Beeston	Matthewson	Hargreaves	Warner	A Foster	Kottlia	Downing	Brough	I Foster	Pitman	36
Wood	Norton	Fishlock	Smith	Beeston	Matthewson	Hargreaves	Warner	A Foster	Kottlia	Downing	Brough	I Foster	Pitman	37
Wood	Norton	Fishlock	Smith	Beeston	Matthewson	Hargreaves	Warner	A Foster	Kottlia	Downing	Brough	I Foster	Pitman	38
Wood	Norton	Fishlock	Smith	Beeston	Matthewson	Hargreaves	Warner	A Foster	Kottlia	Downing	Brough	Williams	Pitman	39
Wood	Norton	Fishlock	Smith	Beeston	Matthewson	Hargreaves	Warner	A Foster	Kottlia	Cook	Brough	Williams	Pitman	40
Wood	Norton	Fishlock	Smith	Beeston	Matthewson	Brough	Warner	A Foster	Kottlia	Downing	Cook	Williams	Pitman	41
Wood	Norton	Fishlock	Smith	Beeston	Matthewson	Jordan	Warner	I Foster	Williams	Downing	Brough	Cook	Pitman	42
Wood	Norton	Fishlock	Smith	Beeston	Matthewson	Hargreaves	Warner	A Foster	Williams	Downing	Brough	Cook	Jordan	43
Wood	Norton	Fishlock	Smith	Brough	Matthewson	Hargreaves	Warner	A Foster	Williams	Cook	Jordan	I Foster	Pitman	44
Wood	Norton	Fishlock	Smith	Pitman	Matthewson	Hargreaves	Warner	A Foster	Williams	Cook	Townsend	I Foster	Hibbard	45
Wood	Norton	Fishlock	Smith	**Sandeman**	Matthewson	Hargreaves	McGorry	A Foster	Agana	Turner	Townsend	Warner	Hibbard	46
Wood	Norton	Fishlock	Smith	**Sandeman**	Matthewson	Hargreaves	McGorry	A Foster	Agana	Turner	Townsend	Warner	Hibbard	47
Wood	Norton	Fishlock	Smith	**Sandeman**	Matthewson	Hargreaves	McGorry	A Foster	Waner	Turner	Brough	I Foster	Hibbard	48
Wood	Norton	Fishlock	Brough	**Sandeman**	Matthewson	Hargreaves	McGorry	A Foster	Williams	Turner	Warner	I Foster	Hibbard	49
Wood	Norton	Fishlock	Smith	**Sandeman**	Matthewson	Hargreaves	McGorry	A Foster	Williams	Turner	Brough	Warner	Agana	50
Wood	Norton	Fishlock	Brough	**Sandeman**	Matthewson	Hargreaves	McGorry	A Foster	Williams	Turner	Warner	deBont	Agana	51

GRAHAM TURNER (MANAGER)

Date of Appointment	August 1995
Date of Birth:	5th October 1947
Place of Birth:	Ellesmere Port

PREVIOUS CLUBS

As manager	Shrewsbury T., Aston Villa, Wolverhampton W.
As coach	None
As player	Wrexham, Chester City, Shrewsbury T.

HONOURS

As manager	League: Div.3 78-79 (Shrewsbury), Div.4 87-88, Div.3 88-89; S.V.T. 87-88 (Wolves)
As player	England - Youth cap.

Physio: Simon Shakeshaft B.Sc, BA Hons.

Neil Grayson in action against Farnborough Town

Photo: Andrew Chitty

MATCHDAY PROGRAMME

Number of pages	32
Price	£1.50
Programme Editor	Gary Watts
Other club publications:	None
Local Newspapers:	Hereford Times Evening News
Local Radio Stations:	BBC Hereford & Worcester

1997-98 PLAYING SQUAD

PLAYER	Birthplace Honours	Birthdate	CLUBS
GOALKEEPERS			
Chris Mackenzie	Northampton	14.5.72	Corby T
Andy Debont	Wolverhampton	7.2.74	Wolverhampton W
DEFENDERS			
Murray Fishlock	Marlborough	23.9.73	Swindon T, Gloucester C, Trowbridge T
Robert Warner	Stratford	20.4.77	From YTS
Trevor Matthewson	Sheffield GMVC, ANMC	12.2.63	Sheffield Wed, Newport Co, Stockport Co, £13k to Lincoln C, £45k to Birmingham C, Preston, Bury, Witton A
David Norton	Cannock EY	3.3.65	Aston Villa, Notts Co, Hull C, Northampton T
Ian Rodgerson	Hereford	9.4.66	Cardiff C., Hereford Utd., £35k to Cardiff C., £50k to Birmingham C., £140k Sunderland, Cardiff C.
Richard Walker	Derby	9.11.71	Notts County, (Loan - Mansfield T.)
MIDFIELDERS			
John Brough	Ilkeston	8.1.73	Notts County, Shrewsbury T., Telford Utd.
Jamie Pitman	Trowbridge	6.1.76	Swindon T
Gavin Mahon	Birmingham	2.1.77	Wolverhampton W
Brian McGorry	Liverpool	16.4.70	Weymouth, AFC Bournemouth, Peterborough U, Wycombe W
FORWARDS			
Tony Agana	London ESP	2.10.63	Welling U, Weymouth, £35k to Watford, £45k to Sheffield U, £750k to Notts Co
Chris Hargreaves	Cleethorpes	12.5.72	Grimsby T, Hull C, W.B.A.
Neil Grayson	York	1.1.64	Rowntree Mac., Doncaster R., York C., Chesterfield, Gateshead, Boston Utd., Northampton T.

DEPARTURES -
(During the close season): Adrian Foster (Rushden & Diamonds), Dean Smith (Leyton O.), Mark Turner (Telford), John Williams (Walsall), Trevor Wood, Bradley Sandeman, Quentin Townsend, Phil Preedy, Mark Hibbard.

Edgar Street, Hereford

GROUND ADDRESS: Edgar Street, Hereford. HR4 9JU.

TELEPHONE NUMBERS: 01432 276666. Fax 01432 .

SIMPLE DIRECTIONS: From Hereford city centre follow signs to Leominster (A49) into Edgar Street. Car parking for 1000 (approx.) available near the ground. Nearest railway station Hereford.

CAPACITY: 8,843 **SEATED:** 2,761 **COVERED TERRACING:** 6,082

SOCIAL FACILITIES: Clubhouse open on matchdays.

CLUB SHOP: Yes.

Hereford Fact File

Nickname: The Bulls **Sponsors:**

Club Colours: White shirts, black trim; black shorts, white trim; black socks, white tops

Change Colours: Red & black quarters; black shorts; black socks.

Midweek matchday: Wednesday

Reserve League: Central Conference

Local Press: Herefordshire Times, Evening News.

Local Radio: BBC Hereford & Worcester

PREVIOUS -
Leagues: Southern League, Birmingham League, Birmingham Combination, Football League (74-97).
Names: None
Ground: None

CLUB RECORDS -
Attendance: 18,114 v Sheffield Wed., FA Cup 3rd Rd, 4.1.58
Career Goalscorer: Unknown
Career Appearances: unknown
Win: 6-0 v Burnley (A), Div. 4 24.1.87.
Defeat: 0-6 v Rotherham Utd (A), Div. 4 29.4.89
Transfer Fee Paid: £75,000 to Walsall for Dean Smith, 7.94.
Transfer Fee Received: £250,000 for Darren Peacock from Q.P.R., 3.91
+ a further £240,000 when he moved to Newcastle Utd. 3.91.

BEST SEASON -
FA Trophy: N/A
FA Cup: 4th Rd 71-72, 76-77, 81-82, 89-90, 91-92.

Players Progressing to Football Lge: Not applicable yet.

96-97 Captain: David Norton
96-97 Player of the Year: Dean Smith
96-97 Top scorer: Adrian Foster

HONOURS: Welsh Cup 89-90, r-up 3 times, League Div. 3 75-76

KETTERING TOWN

Formed:
1872

President: S Chapman

Chairman: P Mallinger

Vice-Chairman: P Oliver

Secretary/Press Officer: G P Knowles

Commercial Manager: B Baker

Although they showed an improvement of two places in the league over the previous campaign, this was still a highly disappointing campaign for a club that should be challenging at the top, not hovering around the relegation zone.

Manager Gary Johnson paid the price for some poor results with his job midway through the season and, after Yeovil's Graham Roberts turned down the post, experienced midfielder Steve Berry was handed his first managerial position.

There is no doubting Berry's abilities as a player but many Poppies supporters felt that a manager with a higher profile was required to take the club back to where they feel it belongs.

During 1996/97, Kettering made some mistakes in the transfer market. They made some big money signings such as Leroy May and Recky Carter who were both swiftly sold on at a loss, but they did have the boost of a £25,000 fee from Kofi Nyamah's transfer to Stoke.

Unfortunately, many Kettering fans will now settle for finishing above county rivals Rushden & Diamonds in the league instead of expecting a tilt at the title, and that is perhaps all they will realistically have to look forward to.

L-R, Back: Eddie King, Paul Miles, Danny Kelly, Kevin Shoemake, Alan Judge, Russell Stock, Neil Lyne. Middle: Peter Barnett, Craig Norman, Craig Gaunt, Luke Dowling, Leroy May, Rob Marshall, Kofi Nyamah, Lawrie Dudfield, Dean Holliday. Front: Darren Harmon, Jamie March, John Gaunt, Richard Nugent, Steve Berry, Tony Lynch, Tarkan Mustafa.

Kettering Town

Match No.	Date	Venue H/A	Competition	Opponents	Result	League Pos.	Attendance	Goalscorers (Times if known)
1	Aug 17	A	VC	Macclesfield Town	Lost 0-2	20	1250	
2	Aug 20	H	VC	Welling United	Lost 2-3		1420	Stock 74, Harmon 76 (pen)
3	Aug 24	A	VC	Bath City	Won 2-0		660	Pope 3, Mustafa 86
4	Aug 26	H	VC	Woking	Drew 0-0	14	1912	
5	Aug 31	H	VC	Halifax Town	Won 4-1	9	1541	Mustafa 24, Nugent 70, Pope 85, Lynch 88
6	Sep 3	A	VC	Bromsgrove Rovers	Won 2-1		898	Nugent 15, Mustafa 82
7	Sep 7	H	VC	Hayes	Drew 2-2	7	1608	Stock 31, Nyamah 33
8	Sep 10	H	VC	Dover Athletic	Drew 1-1		1290	Nyamah 40
9	**Sep 14**	**A**	**FAC**	**Rocester**	**Won 3-0**		**237**	**Pope 15 (pen), Mustafa 34, Lynch 55**
10	Sep 17	A	VC	Telford United	Lost 0-1		771	
11	Sep 21	H	VC	Southport	Lost 0-1	13	1575	
12	Sep 24	A	VC	Slough Town	Drew 1-1		1032	Woodsford 25
13	**Sep 28**	**H**	**FAC**	**Atherstone United**	**Drew 0-0**		**1278**	
14	**Oct 1**	**A**	**FAC R**	**Atherstone United**	**Won 6-1**		**682**	**Nyamah 45, Carter 55, 76, Norman 65 (p), May 83, 89**
15	Oct 5	A	VC	Stalybridge Celtic	Lost 1-3	15	684	Berry 21
16	**Oct 8**	**H**	**SCC**	**Slough Town**	**Won 1-0**		**762**	**May 18**
17	**Oct 12**	**H**	**FAC 3 Q**	**Bedworth United**	**Lost 0-1**		**1461**	
18	Oct 15	H	VC	Hednesford Town	Lost 0-2		766	
19	Oct 19	A	VC	Morecambe	Lost 2-5	17	1205	Gaunt 1, Stock 44
20	Oct 26	A	VC	Woking	Lost 1-2	17	2968	Nugent 62
21	Nov 2	H	VC	Gateshead	Won 4-1	15	1329	Lynch (3) 2, 23, 47, Norman 81 (pen)
22	Nov 9	A	VC	Farnborough Town	Won 2-0	13	1106	May 51, 65
23	**Nov 19**	**H**	**SCC**	**Farnborough Town**	**Lost 0-2**		**503**	
24	Nov 23	H	VC	Bromsgrove Rovers	Won 2-0	13	1578	Lynch 31, Mustafa 85
25	Nov 30	A	VC	Halifax Town	Lost 1-2		790	Norman 37 (pen)
26	Dec 7	H	VC	Slough Town	Drew 0-0	13	1379	
27	Dec 14	A	VC	Kidderminster Harriers	Lost 0-4	15	2754	
28	Dec 21	A	VC	Hayes	Lost 1-2		468	Harmon 90
29	Jan 1	A	VC	Northwich Victoria	Lost 1-2	20	1055	Lyne 22
30	**Jan 18**	**H**	**FAT 1**	**Chelmsford City**	**Lost 0-1**		**1528**	
31	Jan 25	H	VC	Bath City	Won 1-0	16	1444	Norman 38
32	Feb 1	A	VC	Dover Athletic	Won 1-0	15	966	Slawson 76
33	Feb 8	A	VC	Gateshead	Drew 1-1	16	767	Norman 74
34	Feb 15	A	VC	Stevenage Borough	Drew 0-0	15	2864	
35	Feb 18	H	VC	Farnborough Town	Won 3-1	13	1092	Berry 12, Venables 33, Lynch 87
36	Feb 22	H	VC	Kidderminster Harriers	Won 3-1	13	2305	Lyne 2, Norman 13 (pen), Lynch 50
37	Mar 1	H	VC	Stalybridge Celtic	Won 1-0	11	1509	Norman 24
38	Mar 8	H	VC	Rushden & Diamonds	Lost 1-5	13	4628	Pearson 45, Butterworth 83
39	Mar 11	H	VC	Altrincham	Won 3-1	10	1039	Lyne 1, Norman 70, 78
40	Mar 15	H	VC	Telford United	Lost 0-1	10	1406	
41	Mar 18	A	VC	Rushden & Diamonds	Lost 0-1	10	5170	
42	Mar 22	A	VC	Hednesford Town	Drew 0-0	11	1120	
43	Mar 25	H	VC	Stevenage Borough	Lost 1-2	11	1874	Norman 75 (pen)
44	Mar 29	H	VC	Northwich Victoria	Won 1-0		1378	Wilkes 12
45	Mar 31	A	VC	Welling United	Won 2-1	10	854	Norman 53, Mustafa 56
46	Apr 2	A	VC	Southport	Drew 2-2	9	676	Wilkes 62, Mustafa 84
47	Apr 12	H	VC	Morecambe	Lost 0-2	11	1362	
48	Apr 26	A	VC	Altrincham	Lost 3-4	13	791	Gaunt 53, Pearson 63, 89
49	May 3	H	VC	Macclesfield Town	Lost 1-4	14	3451	Lyne 8

Kettering Town

1	2	3	4	5	6	7	8	9	10	11	12	14	15	Mth No.
Judge	Marshall	Norman	Gaunt	Nugent	Berry	Mustafa	Harding	Stock	Carter	Lynch	Harmon	March	Shoemake	1
Judge	Marshall	Norman	Gaunt	Nugent	Berry	Mustafa	Harding	Harmon	Carter	Lynch	Stock	March	Shoemake	2
Judge	Marshall	Norman	Gaunt	Nugent	Berry	Nyamah	Harding	Pope	Carter	Lynch	Mustafa	Stock	Harmont	3
Judge	Marshall	Norman	Gaunt	Nugent	Berry	Nyamah	Harding	Pope	Carter	Lynch	Harmon	Mustafa	March	4
Judge	Marshall	Norman	Gaunt	Nugent	Berry	Mustafa	Nyamah	Pope	Carter	Lynch	March	Harding	Stock	5
Judge	Marshall	Norman	Gaunt	Nugent	Berry	Mustafa	Nyamah	Pope	Carter	Lynch	Harmon	Harding	Stock	6
Judge	Harmon	Norman	Gaunt	Nugent	Berry	Mustafa	Nyamah	Pope	Carter	Lynch	Harding	March	Stock	7
Judge	Marshall	Norman	Gaunt	Nugent	Berry	Mustafa	Nyamah	Pope	Harmon	Lynch	Harding	March	Stock	8
Judge	**Marshall**	**Norman**	**Gaunt**	**Nugent**	**Berry**	**Mustafa**	**Nyamah**	**Pope**	**Harmon**	**Lynch**	**March**	**Shoemake**	**Stock**	**9**
Judge	Marshall	Norman	Gaunt	Nugent	Berry	Mustafa	Nyamah	Pope	Harmon	Lynch	March	Shoemake	Stock	10
Judge	Marshall	Norman	Harmon	Nugent	Berry	Mustafa	Nyamah	May	Pope	Lynch	March	Shoemake	Stock	11
Shoemake	Marshall	Norman	Stock	Nugent	Berry	Mustafa	Nyamah	Woodsford	Pope	Lynch	Harmon	Judge	March	12
Shoemake	**Marshall**	**Norman**	**Gaunt**	**Nugent**	**Berry**	**Mustafa**	**Nyamah**	**May**	**Carter**	**Pope**	**Stock**	**Judge**	**Harmon**	**13**
Shoemake	**Marshall**	**Norman**	**Gaunt**	**Nugent**	**Berry**	**Mustafa**	**Nyamah**	**May**	**Carter**	**Stock**	**March**	**Harmon**	**Judge**	**14**
Shoemake	Marshall	Norman	Gaunt	Nugent	Berry	Mustafa	Nyamah	May	Carter	Woodsford	March	Stock	Harmon	15
Shoemake	**Marshall**	**Norman**	**Gaunt**	**Nugent**	**Berry**	**Harmon**	**Nyamah**	**May**	**Woodsford**	**Stock**	**March**	**Carter**	**Judge**	**16**
Shoemake	**Marshall**	**March**	**Gaunt**	**Nugent**	**Berry**	**Mustafa**	**Nyamah**	**May**	**Pope**	**Harmon**	**Lynch**	**Stock**	**Judge**	**17**
Shoemake	Marshall	Norman	Gaunt	Nugent	Berry	Stock	Nyamah	May	Pope	Lynch	Harmon	March	Judge	18
Shoemake	Marshall	Norman	Gaunt	Nugent	Berry	Stock	Nyamah	May	Pope	Lynch	March	Judge	Pope	19
Shoemake	Marshall	Norman	Gaunt	Nugent	Berry	Nyamah	Stock	May	March	Lynch	Pope	Dudfield	Judge	20
Shoemake	Marshall	Norman	Gaunt	Nugent	Berry	Pope	Nyamah	May	Lynch	March	Harmon	Stock	Dudfield	21
Shoemake	Marshall	Norman	Gaunt	Nugent	Berry	Harmon	Nyamah	May	Lynch	Pope	Dudfield	Judge	Stock	22
Kelly	**Marshall**	**Norman**	**Gaunt**	**Nugent**	**Stock**	**Harmon**	**Dudfield**	**May**	**Lynch**	**Pope**	**Mustafa**	**Shoemake**	**King**	**23**
Shoemake	Marshall	March	Gaunt	Nugent	Berry	Harmon	Stock	Dudfield	Lynch	Pope	Mustafa	Judge	King	24
Shoemake	Marshall	March	Gaunt	Norman	Berry	Harmon	Stock	May	Lynch	Pope	Mustafa	Judge	Dudfield	25
Shoemake	Marshall	March	Gaunt	Norman	Berry	Harmon	Nyamah	May	Lynch	Lyne	Mustafa	Stock	Judge	26
Shoemake	Marshall	March	Gaunt	Norman	Berry	Mustafa	Nyamah	Stock	Lyne	Flatts	May	Harmon	Dudfield	27
Judge	Marshall	March	Gaunt	Nugent	Berry	Harmon	Venables	Lyne	May	Flatts	Mustafa	Lynch	Stock	28
Shoemake	Harmon	March	Gaunt	Nugent	Berry	Venables	Pearson	Lyne	Lynch	McMahon	Slawson	Judge	Dudfield	29
Shoemake	**Harmon**	**Norman**	**Gaunt**	**Nugent**	**Berry**	**Venables**	**Stock**	**Lyne**	**Lynch**	**Slawson**	**Judge**	**Dudfield**	**Miles**	**30**
Turley	Harmon	Norman	Gaunt	Nugent	Berry	Venables	McMahon	Lyne	Pearson	Slawson	Lynch	Marshall	March	31
Turley	Harmon	Norman	Gaunt	Nugent	Berry	Venables	McMahon	Lyne	Pearson	Slawson	Marshall	March	Dudfield	32
Turley	Harmon	Norman	Gaunt	Nugent	Berry	Venables	McMahon	Lynch	Pearson	Slawson	Marshall	Dudfield	March	33
Turley	Harmon	March	Gaunt	Nugent	Berry	Venables	Norman	Marshal	Pearson	Slawson	Lynch	Dudfield	Miles	34
Turley	Harmon	March	Gaunt	Nugent	Berry	Venables	Norman	Marshal	Pearson	Slawson	Lynch	Dudfield	Miles	35
Turley	Harmon	March	Gaunt	Marshall	Berry	Venables	Norman	Lyne	Lynch	Slawson	Dudfield	Mustafa	Miles	36
Turley	Marshall	March	Gaunt	Norman	Berry	Venables	Dudfield	Lyne	Lynch	Slawson	Mustafa	Holliday	Miles	37
Shoemake	Marshall	March	Gaunt	Nugent	Berry	Mustafa	Norman	Lyne	Lynch	Pearson	Dudfield	Dowling	Miles	38
Cherry	Marshall	March	Gaunt	Nugent	Berry	Harmon	Norman	Lyne	Pearson	Slawson	Lynch	Mustafa	Dudfield	39
Cherry	Harmon	March	Gaunt	Marshall	Berry	Mustafa	Norman	Lyne	Pearson	Slawson	Lynch	Wilkes	Dudfield	40
Cherry	Harmon	March	Gaunt	Marshall	Berry	Mustafa	Norman	Lyne	Wilkes	Slawson	Pearson	Stock	Dudfield	41
Judge	Harmon	March	Gaunt	Marshall	Stock	Mustafa	Norman	Lyne	Wilkes	DeVito	Pearson	Shoemake	Dudfield	42
Judge	Harmon	March	Lyne	Marshall	Berry	Venables	Norman	Pearsort	Wilkes	Slawson	Mustafa	DeVito	Dudfield	43
Judge	Marshall	March	Gaunt	Norman	Berry	Mustafa	Stock	Lyne	Wilkes	Slawson	Dudfield	Smith	DeVito	44
Judge	Smith	March	Marshall	Norman	Berry	Mustafa	Stock	Lyne	Wilkes	Slawson	Dudfield	Miles	DeVito	45
Turley	Smith	March	Marshall	Norman	Berry	Mustafa	Stock	Dudfield	Wilkes	Slawson	Miles	Judge	DeVito	46
Turley	Smith	March	Marshall	Lyne	Berry	Mustafa	Norman	Wilkes	Pearson	Slawson	Dudfield	Miles	DeVito	47
Judge	Harmon	Smith	Gaunt	Tallentire	Berry	Mles	Stock	Pearson	Wilkes	Lyne	Mustafa	Dudfield	DeVito	48
Judge	Marshall	March	Gaunt	Tallentire	Berry	Wilkes	Norman	Lyne	Pearson	Harmon	Smith	Dudfield	Miles	49

STEVE BERRY (MANAGER)

Date of Appointment	November 1996
Date of Birth:	4th April 1963
Place of Birth:	Gosport, Hants.

PREVIOUS CLUBS

As manager	None
As coach	
As player	Portsmouth, Sunderland, Newport Co., Swindon T.,, Aldershot, Northampton T., Instant Dict (Hong Kong), Stevenage Bor.

HONOURS

As manager	None
As player	GM Vauxhall Conference 95-96.

Assistant Manager: John Gaunt **Coach:** John Gaunt **Physio:** Peter Barnett

Craig Norman - Top Goalscorer, Player of the Year, Players P.o.Y.

Craig Gaunt - Captain

MATCHDAY PROGRAMME

Number of pages	32
Price	£1.30
Programme Editor	Avalon Print
	01604 670050

Other club publications:

"Poppies at the Gates of Dawn" (Fanzine)

Local Newspapers:	Evening Telegraph Chronicle & Echo Herald & Post; Citizen
Local Radio Stations:	Radio Northampton Northants 96; KCBC

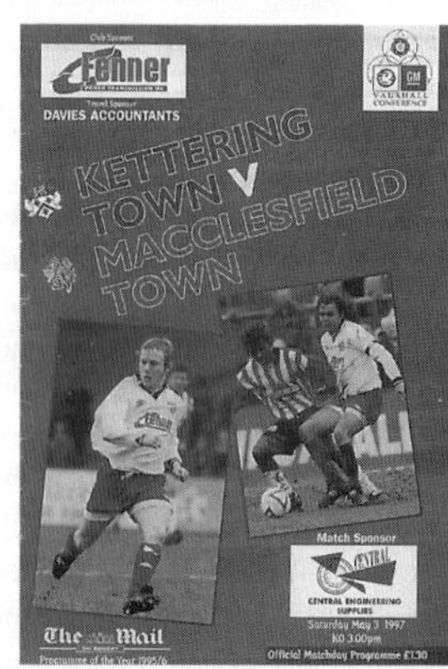

1997-98 PLAYING SQUAD

PLAYER	Birthplace Honours	Birthdate	CLUBS
GOALKEEPERS			
Simon Sheppard	Clevedon EY	7.8.73	Watford, Reading, Bishop's Stortford, Boreham Wood
DEFENDERS			
Craig Gaunt	Sutton-in-Ashfield BLT	31.3.73	Arsenal, Scarborough, Bromsgrove R, £6k to Kettering T
Craig Norman	Perivale	21.3.75	Chelsea
Eddie King	Haverhill	2.12.78	From Youth Team
Mark Tucker	Woking ESP, FAT	27.4.72	Fulham, Woking, £45k to Rushden & Diamonds
Kenny Webster	Hammersmith GMVC	2.3.73	Arsenal, Peterborough U, Stevenage B, Harrow Borough
Paul Miles	Haverhill	18.9.78	From Youth Team
Rob Mutchell	Solihull GMVC	3.1.74	Oxford U, Barnet, Telford U, Stevenage B
MIDFIELDERS			
Steve Berry	Gosport GMVC	4.4.63	Portsmouth, Sunderland, Swindon T, Northampton T, Instant Dict (HK), Stevenage B
Dave Venables	Horsham ESP, GMVC	6.11.67	Eastbourne U, Crawley T, Wealdstone, Stevenage B, £9k to Kettering T
Neil Lyne	Leicester	4.4.70	Leicester U, Nottingham F, Shrewsbury T, Cambridge U, Hereford U
Gary Pick	Leicester	9.7.71	Leicester U, Stoke C, Hereford U, Cambridge U, Worcester C, Cheltenham T, Newport AFC
FORWARDS			
Chris Pearson	Leicester	5.1.76	Hinckley T, Notts Co, Hinckley T, £5k to Kettering T
Tim Wilkes	Nottingham		Notts Co
Tony Kelly	Meridan	14.2.66	Bristol C, Dulwich H, Cheshunt, Enfield, St.Albans C, £20k to Stoke C, £10k to Bury, £30k to Leyton Orient, St.Albans C
Lawrie Dudfield	Kettering	7.5.80	From Youth Team

DEPARTURES - (During the season): Kofi Nyamah (Stoke C), Neil Pope (Sudbury T), Mark Flatts (Released), Recky Carter (Solihull B), Leroy May (Enfield), Steve Cherry (Rushden & D), Tony Lynch (Peterborough U), Richard Nugent (Hendon)
(During the close season): Luke Dowling (Leicester C), Rob Marshall (Stevenage B), Russell Stock (King's Lynn), Kevin Shoemake, Alan Judge, Darren Harmon, Jamie March, Scott Smith, Steve Slawson, Tarkan Mustapha (Released)

PLAYERS ON LOAN - Sam McMahon (Leicester C), Billy Turley (Northampton T), Jamie Woodsford (Luton T), Claudio DeVito (Northampton T)

Rockingham Road, Kettering

GROUND ADDRESS: Rockingham Road, Kettering, Northants, NN16 9AW.

TELEPHONE NUMBERS: 01536 83028/410815 (Office). 01536 410962 (Social Club). **Fax:** 01536 412273.

SIMPLE DIRECTIONS: M1 junction 15, A43 to Kettering use A14 and Kettering Northern by pass, turn right A6003, ground half a mile. From North M1 or M6 use junction 19 then A14 to Kettering. Exit junction 7 A1 use A14 at Huntingdon then as above. British Rail - Inter-City Midland - 50mins from London (St.Pancras), 20mins from Leicester.

CAPACITY: 6,100 **SEATED:** 1,800 **COVERED TERRACING:** 2,200

CLUB SHOP: Open before and after matches, and office staff will open on request on non-match days. Situated in front of main stand. Also Ken Burton's Sports in town centre.

SOCIAL FACILITIES: Social Club (Poppies), Vice-Presidents Bar & Sponsor's Lounge.

Kettering Fact File

Nickname: Poppies **Club Sponsors:** Fenner Power Transmission UK.

Club colours: Red & white shirts, red socks, red socks.

Change colours: White shirts, navy shorts, white socks.

Midweek home matchday: Tuesday

PREVIOUS - **Leagues:** Southern League, Northants League, Midland League, Birmingham League, Central Alliance, United Counties League.
Grounds: North Park / Green Lane.

CLUB RECORDS - **Attendance:** 11,536 Kettering v Peterborough (pre-Taylor report).
Win: 16-0 v Higham YMCI (FA Cup 1909)
Defeat: 0-13 v Mardy (Southern League Div. 2, 1911/12)
Transfer fee paid: £25,000 to Macclesfield for Carl Alford, 1994.
Transfer fee received: £150,000 from Newcastle United for Andy Hunt.
Career goalscorer: Roy Clayton 171 (1972 - 1981)
Career appearances: Roger Ashby.

BEST SEASON - **FA Cup:** 4th Round - 1988-89, 1-2 v Charlton Ath.; 91-92, 1-4 v Blackburn R.
League clubs defeated: Swindon T., Millwall, Swansea C., Halifax T. & Maidstone.
FA Trophy: Runners-up 78-79.

1996-97 Captain: Craig Gaunt

1996-97 Top scorer: Craig Norman

1996-97 Player of the Year: Craig Norman (Supporters' & Players')

Past players who progressed to the Football League: Billy Kellock (Peterborough), Gary Wood (Notts Co.), Dave Longhurst (Nott'm Forest), Scott Endersby (Ipswich), Steve Fallon (Cambridge U.), Andy Rogers (Plymouth), Martyn Foster (Northampton), Cohen Griffith (Cardiff C.), Andy Hunt (Newcastle), Richard Brown (Blackburn R.).

HONOURS: Premier Inter League Cup winners; FA Trophy Runners-up 78-79; Alliance Premier League r-up (x3); Southern League Winners, County Cup Winners, Daventry Charity Cup Winners (x2); Northants Senior Cup (x25); Maunsell Cup Winners (x12).

KIDDERMINSTER HARRIERS

Formed:
1886

Chairman: David L Reynolds **Vice-Chairman:** Lionel Newton

Directors: G R Lane, J R Painter, C C Youngjohns.

Secretary: Roger Barlow

Commercial Manager: Mark Searl

For most clubs, finishing second and winning the Spalding Cup would represent a wonderful season, but for Harriers' boss Graham Allner, success would only have been finishing above Macclesfield Town and winning the promotion that was so cruelly denied them in 1994.

There is no doubting who Kidderminster's star of the 1996/97 campaign was - striker Lee Hughes. His 34 goals earned him a dream move to his favourite club, West Bromwich Albion, and both Harriers and the England semi-professional side will greatly miss this talented 21-year-old.

Many Harriers' fans have expressed worries that Allner hasn't replaced Hughes with another proven goalscorer, but they are very hard to come by, and besides, Harriers already posses the likes of veterans Paul Davies and Kim Casey plus ex-Villa star Ian Olney.

With Bromsgrove Rovers' Adie Smith signed to add strength to an already solid defence, Kidderminster will again be challenging for promotion in what promises to be one of the most open competitions for a number of years.

L-R, Back: Craig Riley, Kevin Willetts, James McCue, Kim Casey, Mark Shepherd, Neil Doherty, Marcus Bignot, John Deakin, Robert Dew. Middle: M Etherington (Team Attendant), Mark Dearlove, Ian Olney, Darren Steadman, Kevin Rose, Danny Watson, Martin Weir, Steve Prindiville, Archie Richards (Team Attendant). Front: Graham Allner (Manager), Neil Cartwright, Lee Hughes, Paul Davies (Coach), Mark Yates (Captain), Chris Brindley, Paul Webb, Simeon Hodson, Jim Conway (Physio/Asst. Man.)

Kidderminster Harriers

Match No.	Date	Venue H/A	Competition	Opponents	Result	League Pos.	Attendance	Goalscorers (Times if known)
1	Aug 17	H	VC	Gateshead	Won 3-2	6	1658	Doherty 9, Webb 68, Hughes 90
2	Aug 20	A	VC	Farnborough Town	Lost 1-2		613	Davies 66
3	Aug 24	A	VC	Dover Athletic	Won 5-0		1186	Webb 22, 87, Hughes 65, 66, 85
4	Aug 26	H	VC	Slough Town	Lost 1-2	8	2087	Bignot 51
5	Aug 31	A	VC	Southport	Lost 0-1	12	1423	
6	Sep 2	H	VC	Stalybridge Celtic	Drew 1-1		1718	Hughes 34
7	Sep 7	H	VC	Welling United	Won 3-2	8	1559	Hughes (3) 1, 11, 61
8	Sep 10	A	VC	Hayes	Won 1-0		434	Weir 73
9	Sep 14	H	VC	Macclesfield Town	Drew 0-0	5	2331	
10	Sep 16	H	VC	Stevenage Borough	Won 3-0		2356	Prindiville 20, Brindley 52, Hughes 89
11	Sep 21	A	VC	Altrincham	Won 1-0	3	848	Doherty 28
12	Sep 24	A	VC	Bath City	Won 3-0	2	571	Willetts (2) 47, 73, Hughes 90
13	Oct 5	A	VC	Halifax Town	Won 3-2	2	786	Willetts 30, Yates 33, Hughes 60
14	Oct 12	H	VC	Telford United	Won 1-0	1	2723	Webb 87
15	Oct 14	H	VC	Rushden & Diamonds	Won 1-0	1	2603	Casey 48
16	Oct 19	A	VC	Northwich Victoria	Drew 1-1	1	1234	Doherty 51
17	**Oct 26**	**A**	**FAC 4 Q**	**Witton Albion**	**Won 4-1**		**926**	**Henry 31 (og), Doherty 38 (p), Olney 41, Hughes 62**
18	Nov 2	H	VC	Farnborough Town	Lost 2-3	1	2492	Doherty 35 (pen), Webb 63
19	Nov 4	H	VC	Hayes	Won 5-1	1	2121	Doherty 34, 65, Webb 56, Yates 64, McCue 67
20	Nov 9	A	VC	Slough Town	Won 2-0	1	1610	Hughes 69, Doherty 75
21	**Nov 16**	**A**	**FAC**	**Crewe Alexandra**	**Lost 1-4**		**4651**	**Yates 63**
22	Nov 23	H	VC	Hednesford Town	Won 2-1	1	2661	Yates 69, Hughes 86
23	Nov 30	A	VC	Telford United	Won 2-0	1	1860	Doherty 45, Hughes 62
24	**Dec 2**	**A**	**SSC**	**Hednesford Town**	**Won 6-1**		**333**	**Davies 18, 64, Cartwright 22, 36, Casey 26, Olney 60**
25	Dec 7	H	VC	Dover Athletic	Won 4-1	1	2349	Hughes 25, 73, Yates 26, Doherty 33
26	Dec 10	A	VC	Macclesfield Town	Won 1-0	1	1606	Hughes 85
27	Dec 14	H	VC	Kettering Town	Won 4-0	1	2754	Yates 45, Hughes 56, 90, Willetts 84
28	**Dec 16**	**H**	**SSC**	**Rushden & Diamonds**	**Won 1-0**		**811**	**Hughes 32 (pen)**
29	Dec 21	A	VC	Rushden & Diamonds	Drew 1-1	1	2529	Doherty 90 (pen)
30	Dec 26	H	VC	Bromsgrove Rovers	Lost 1-2	1	6081	Hughes 42
31	Dec 28	H	VC	Bath City	Won 6-0	1	3305	Hughes 14, 60, Doherty 33, 37 (2 p), Yates 82, Casey 87
32	Jan 4	H	VC	Northwich Victoria	Won 1-0	1	2794	Olney 14
33	**Jan 18**	**H**	**FAT 1**	**Macclesfield Town**	**Won 3-0**		**2815**	**Weir 33, Hughes 84, Doherty 87**
34	Jan 25	A	VC	Stevenage Borough	Drew 2-2	1	6489	Olney 13, 25
35	**Jan 27**	**H**	**WSC**	**Halesowen Town**	**Lost 0-3**		**898**	
36	**Feb 4**	**A**	**SSC**	**Farnborough Town**	**Drew 2-2**		**370**	**Cartwright 37, Casey 55**
37	**Feb 8**	**H**	**FAT 2**	**Emley**	**Drew 0-0**		**2301**	
38	**Feb 11**	**A**	**FAT 2 R**	**Emley**	**Won 5-2**		**1021**	**Hughes 32, Webb 45, 63, Olney 50, Willetts 60**
39	Feb 15	H	VC	Altrincham	Drew 1-1	1	2679	Hughes 41
40	Feb 22	A	VC	Kettering Town	Lost 1-3	2	2305	Weir 45
41	**Mar 1**	**A**	**FAT 3**	**Heybridge Swifts**	**Lost 0-3**		**1187**	
42	Mar 8	H	VC	Halifax Town	Won 3-0	2	2523	Doherty 7, Hughes 66, 81
43	Mar 11	A	VC	Bromsgrove Rovers	Won 1-0	2	2548	Hughes 27
44	Mar 15	A	VC	Welling United	Won 1-0	2	781	Olney 4
45	Mar 17	A	VC	Hednesford Town	Won 4-1	1	2587	Hughes 10, Dawes 14, Weir 26, Casey 33
46	Mar 22	A	VC	Stalybridge Celtic	Lost 1-4	2	1067	Davies 80
47	**Mar 24**	**H**	**SCC**	**Farnborough Town**	**Drew 1-1**		927	Davies 120
48	Mar 29	H	VC	Morecambe	Drew 2-2	2	3009	Hughes 31, 86 (pen)
49	Mar 31	A	VC	Woking	Lost 1-2	2	3420	Olney 2
50	**Apr 12**	**A**	**SCC F**	**Macclesfield Town**	**Drew 1-1**		1320	Prindiville 40
51	Apr 14	H	VC	Woking	Won 1-0	2	2916	Olney 81
52	Apr 19	A	VC	Morecambe	Won 3-2	1	1175	Doherty 45, Norman 76 (og), Yates 84
53	Apr 26	H	VC	Southport	Won 3-0		3139	Davies 10, Brindley 14, Olney 44
54	**Apr 28**	**H**	**SCC F**	**Macclesfield Town**	**Drew 0-0**		**2212**	
55	May 3	A	VC	Gateshead	Lost 1-3	2	1276	Hughes 69

Kidderminster Harriers

1	2	3	4	5	6	7	8	9	10	11	12	14	15	Mth No.
Barber	Bignot	Prindiville	Weir	Brindley	Yates	Webb	Willetts	McCue	Davies	Doherty	Hughes	Casey	Deakin	1
Barber	Bignot	Prindiville	Weir	Brindley	Yates	Webb	Willetts	McCue	Davies	Doherty	Hughes	Casey	Deakin	2
Barber	Bignot	Prindiville	Weir	Brindley	Yates	Webb	Willetts	Hughes	Davies	Doherty	Olney	Casey	Deakin	3
Barber	Bignot	Prindiville	Weir	Brindley	Yates	Webb	Willetts	Hughes	Davies	Doherty	Olney	Casey	Deakin	4
Barber	Bignot	Prindiville	Weir	Brindley	Yates	Webb	Willetts	Hughes	Olney	Doherty	McCue	Casey	Deakin	5
Barber	Bignot	Prindiville	Weir	Brindley	Yates	Webb	Willetts	Hughes	Olney	Doherty	McCue	Casey	Deakin	6
Barber	Bignot	Prindiville	Weir	Brindley	Yates	Webb	Willetts	Hughes	Olney	Doherty	McCue	Casey	Deakin	7
Barber	Bignot	Prindiville	Weir	Brindley	Yates	Webb	Willetts	Hughes	McCue	Doherty	Davies	Casey	Deakin	8
Barber	Bignot	Prindiville	Weir	Brindley	Yates	Deakin	Willetts	Hughes	McCue	Doherty	Olney	Casey	Cartwright	9
Barber	Bignot	Prindiville	Weir	Brindley	Yates	Deakin	Willetts	Hughes	Olney	Doherty	McCue	Casey	Cartwright	10
Steadman	Bignot	Prindiville	Hodson	Brindley	Yates	Deakin	Willetts	Hughes	Olney	Doherty	McCue	Casey	Cartwright	11
Steadman	Bignot	Prindiville	Weir	Brindley	Yates	Cartwright	Willetts	Hughes	Olney	Doherty	McCue	Casey	Hodson	12
Steadman	Bignot	Prindiville	Weir	Brindley	Yates	Cartwright	Willetts	Hughes	Olney	Doherty	McCue	Casey	Webb	13
Steadman	Bignot	Prindiville	Weir	Brindley	Yates	Webb	Willetts	Hughes	Olney	Doherty	McCue	Casey	Cartwright	14
Steadman	Bignot	Prindiville	Weir	Brindley	Yates	Webb	Willetts	Hughes	Casey	Doherty	McCue	Davies	Cartwright	15
Steadman	Bignot	Prindiville	Weir	Brindley	Yates	Webb	Willetts	Hughes	Olney	Doherty	McCue	Casey	Cartwright	16
Steadman	**Bignot**	**Prindiville**	**Weir**	**Brindley**	**Yates**	**Webb**	**Willetts**	**Hughes**	**Olney**	**Doherty**	**McCue**	**Casey**	**Cartwright**	**17**
Steadman	Bignot	Prindiville	Weir	Brindley	Yates	Webb	Willetts	Hughes	Olney	Doherty	McCue	Casey	Cartwright	18
Steadman	Bignot	Prindiville	Weir	Brindley	Yates	Webb	Willetts	Hughes	McCue	Doherty	Deakin	Casey	Cartwright	19
Steadman	Bignot	Prindiville	Weir	Brindley	Yates	Deakin	Willetts	Hughes	McCue	Doherty	Olney	Casey	Cartwright	20
Steadman	**Bignot**	**Prindiville**	**Weir**	**Brindley**	**Yates**	**Webb**	**Willetts**	**Hughes**	**McCue**	**Doherty**	**Olney**	**Casey**	**Deakin**	**21**
Steadman	Bignot	Prindiville	Weir	Brindley	Yates	Webb	Willetts	Hughes	McCue	Doherty	Olney	Casey	Deakin	22
Steadman	Bignot	Prindiville	Weir	Brindley	Yates	Webb	Willetts	Hughes	McCue	Doherty	Olney	Casey	Deakin	23
Rose	**Bignot**	**Willetts**	**Webb**	**Dearlove**	**Yates**	**Deakin**	**Casey**	**Olney**	**Davies**	**Cartwright**	**Shepherd**	**Riley**	**Wills**	**24**
Steadman	Bignot	Prindiville	Weir	Brindley	Yates	Webb	Willetts	Hughes	McCue	Doherty	Olney	Casey	Deakin	25
Steadman	Bignot	Prindiville	Weir	Brindley	Yates	Webb	Willetts	Hughes	McCue	Doherty	Olney	Casey	Deakin	26
Steadman	Bignot	Prindiville	Weir	Brindley	Yates	Webb	Willetts	Hughes	Olney	Doherty	McCue	Casey	Deakin	27
Steadman	**Bignot**	**Prindiville**	**Webb**	**Dearlove**	**Yates**	**Deakin**	**Willetts**	**Hughes**	**Davies**	**McCue**	**Shepherd**	**Casey**	**Wills**	**28**
Steadman	Bignot	Prindiville	Weir	Brindley	Yates	Webb	Willetts	Hughes	Olney	Doherty	McCue	Casey	Deakin	29
Steadman	Bignot	Prindiville	Weir	Brindley	Yates	Webb	Willetts	Hughes	Olney	Doherty	McCue	Casey	Deakin	30
Steadman	Bignot	Prindiville	Weir	Brindley	Yates	Webb	Willetts	Hughes	Olney	Doherty	McCue	Casey	Deakin	31
Steadman	Bignot	Prindiville	Weir	Deakin	Yates	Webb	Willetts	Hughes	Olney	Doherty	McCue	Casey	Cartwright	32
Steadman	**Bignot**	**Prindiville**	**Weir**	**Cartwright**	**Deakin**	**Webb**	**Willetts**	**Hughes**	**Olney**	**Doherty**	**McCue**	**Casey**	**Dearlove**	**33**
Steadman	Bignot	Prindiville	Weir	Brindley	Deakin	Webb	Willetts	Hughes	Olney	Doherty	McCue	Casey	Cartwright	34
Rose	**Bignot**	**Prindiville**	**Dearlove**	**Brindley**	**Yates**	**Deakin**	**Casey**	**McCue**	**Davies**	**Cartwright**	**Shepherd**	**Watson**	**Riley**	**35**
Steadman	**Bignot**	**Prindiville**	**Weir**	**Webb**	**Yates**	**Deakin**	**Casey**	**McCue**	**Davies**	**Cartwright**	**Shepherd**	**Doherty**	**Dearlove**	**36**
Steadman	**Bignot**	**Prindiville**	**Weir**	**Brindley**	**Yates**	**Webb**	**Willetts**	**Hughes**	**Olney**	**Doherty**	**McCue**	**Cartwright**	**Deakin**	**37**
Steadman	**Bignot**	**Prindiville**	**Weir**	**Brindley**	**Yates**	**Webb**	**Willetts**	**Hughes**	**Olney**	**Doherty**	**McCue**	**Cartwright**	**Deakin**	**38**
Steadman	Bignot	Prindiville	Weir	Deakin	Yates	Webb	Willetts	Hughes	Olney	Doherty	McCue	Cartwright	Casey	39
Steadman	Bignot	Prindiville	Weir	Deakin	Yates	Webb	Willetts	Hughes	Olney	Doherty	McCue	Casey	Cartwright	40
Steadman	**Bignot**	**Willetts**	**Weir**	**Brindley**	**Yates**	**Webb**	**Deakin**	**Hughes**	**McCue**	**Doherty**	**Davies**	**Casey**	**Rose**	**41**
Barber	Bignot	Willetts	Weir	Brindley	Webb	Yates	Deakin	Hughes	Davies	Doherty	McCue	Casey	Dearlove	42
Barber	Bignot	Prindiville	Weir	Brindley	Yates	Webb	Willetts	Hughes	Olney	Doherty	Davies	Casey	Deakin	43
Barber	Willetts	Prindiville	Weir	Deakin	Yates	Webb	Casey	Hughes	Olney	Doherty	Davies	Dearlove	Steadman	44
Barber	Willetts	Prindiville	Weir	Deakin	Yates	Webb	Casey	Hughes	Olney	Davies	Cartwright	McCue	Dearlove	45
Barber	Willetts	Prindiville	Weir	Deakin	Yates	Dearlove	Casey	Hughes	Olney	Davies	Cartwright	McCue	Steadman	46
Steadman	Bignot	Prindiville	Weir	Deakin	Yates	Dearlove	Willetts	Hughes	Olney	Davies	McCue	Casey	Cartwright	47
Barber	Bignot	Prindiville	Weir	Brindley	Yates	Webb	Deakin	Hughes	Olney	Doherty	Davies	Casey	Dearlove	48
Barber	Bignot	Prindiville	Weir	Brindley	Yates	Webb	Casey	Hughes	Olney	Doherty	Davies	McCue	Dearlove	49
Barber	Bignot	Prindiville	Willetts	Brindley	Yates	Webb	Casey	Shepherd	Olney	Doherty	McCue	Davies	Steadman	50
Barber	Bignot	Prindiville	Weir	Brindley	Yates	Webb	Casey	Shepherd	Olney	Willetts	Davies	Doherty	McCue	51
Steadman	Bignot	Prindiville	Weir	Brindley	Yates	Webb	Willetts	Davies	Olney	Doherty	Casey	McCue	Shepherd	52
Steadman	Bignot	Prindiville	Weir	Brindley	Yates	Webb	Willetts	Davies	Olney	Doherty	Shepherd	Casey	Deakin	53
Steadman	**Bignot**	**Prindiville**	**Weir**	**Brindley**	**Yates**	**Webb**	**Willetts**	**Hughes**	**Olney**	**Davies**	**Shepherd**	**Casey**	**Deakin**	**54**
Steadman	Bignot	Prindiville	Weir	Brindley	Yates	Webb	Willetts	Hughes	Olney	Doherty	Davies	Casey	Deakin	55

GRAHAM ALLNER (MANAGER)

Date of Appointment	October 1983
Date of Birth:	7th September 1949
Place of Birth:	Birmingham

PREVIOUS CLUBS

As manager	AP Leamington
As Asst. Man.	Cheltenham Town
As player	Walsall, Worcester City, Stafford Rangers, Alvechurch.

HONOURS

As manager	GMV Conference 93-94; FA Trophy 86-87 Southern League (with Leamington)
As player	England: Youth, Middlesex Wanderers.

Assistant Manager: Jimmy Conway **Coach:** Paul Davies **Physio:** Jimmy Conway

Mark Yates (No. 6) pressurising the Emley goalkeeper during their FA trophy match last season.
Photo: Peter Barnes.

MATCHDAY PROGRAMME

Number of pages	36
Price	£1.50
Programme Editor	Steve Thomas
Other club publications:	None
Local Newspapers:	Kidderminster Shuttle / Times Kidderminster Chronicle Evening Mail; Express & Star Worcester Evening News
Local Radio Stations:	BBC Hereford & Worcester Radio Wyvern Beacon Radio; BRMB.

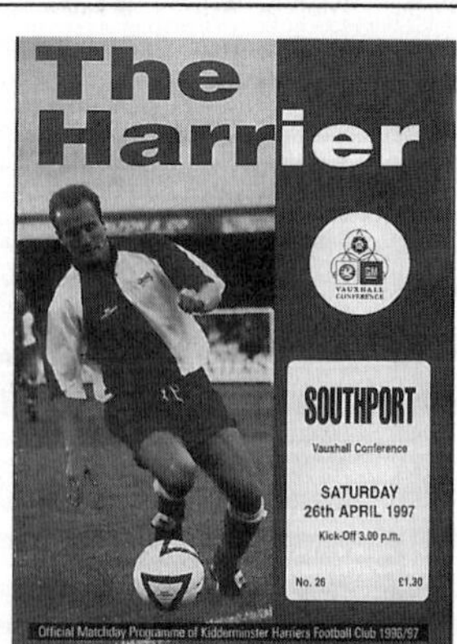

1997-98 PLAYING SQUAD

PLAYER	Birthplace Honours	Birthdate	CLUBS
GOALKEEPERS			
Fred Barber	Ferryhill FL XI	26.8.63	Darlington, £50k to Everton, £100k to Walsall, £25k to Peterborough U, £25k to Luton T, Birmingham C
Darren Steadman	Kidderminster ES	26.1.70	From YTS
DEFENDERS			
Steve Prindiville	Harlow ESP	26.12.68	Leicester C, Chesterfield, Mansfield T, Doncaster R, Wycombe W, Halifax T, Dagenham & Redbridge
Martin Weir	Birmingham GMVC, FA XI, Middx Wanderers	4.7.68	Birmingham C
Chris Brindley	Stoke GMVC, FAT, FA XI	5.7.69	Hednesford T, Wolverhampton W, Telford U, £20k to Kidderminster H
Marcus Bignot	Birmingham ESP	28.8.74	Birmingham C, Telford U, £10k to Kidderminster H
Kevin Willetts	Gloucester FA XI, Middx Wanderers	15.8.62	Sharpness, Cheltenham T, Forest Green R, Gloucester C, Weston-Super-Mare
Adie Smith	Birmingham BLT		Willenhall T, Birmingham C, Bromsgrove R, £10k to Kidderminster H
Steve Lilwall	Birmingham SLP	15.2.70	Moor Green, Kidderminster H, £60k to W.B.A., Rushden & Diamonds
MIDFIELDERS			
Mark Yates	Birmingham	24.1.70	Birmingham C, Burnley, Doncaster R
Neil Cartwright	Stourbridge GMVC	20.2.71	W.B.A.
John Deakin	Sheffield GMVC	29.9.66	Barnsley, Doncaster R, Grimsby T, Frickley A, Shepshed Alb, Birmingham C, Carlisle U, Wycombe W
Neil Doherty	Barrow ESP, FAT, NPL, FA XI	21.2.69	Watford, Barrow, £40k to Birmingham C
Paul Webb	Wolverhampton ESP, GMVC, SLP, FA XI	30.11.67	Bilston T, Shrewsbury T, Bromsgrove R, £17,500 to Kidderminster H
FORWARDS			
Paul Davies	Kidderminster ESP, GMVC, FAT, FA XI	9.10.60	Cardiff C, Trowbridge T, SC Hercules (Holl)
Kim Casey	Birmingham ESP, GMVC, FAT	3.3.61	Sutton Coldfield T, AP Leamington, Gloucester C, Kidderminster H, Cheltenham T, Wycombe W, Solihull B
James McCue	Glasgow	29.6.75	W.B.A., Partick Thistle, £5k to Kidderminster H
Ian Olney	Luton E u-21	17.12.69	Aston Villa, £700k to Oldham A

DEPARTURES - (During the season): Simeon Hodson (Rushden & D), Leroy May (Kettering T)
(During the close season): Mark Dearlove (Bridgnorth T), Kevin Rose (Released)

PLAYERS ON LOAN: None.

Aggborough, Kidderminster

GROUND ADDRESS: Aggborough Staduim, Hoo Road, Kidderminster, DY10 1NB.

TELEPHONE NUMBERS: 01562 823931 **Fax:** 01562 827329.

SIMPLE DIRECTIONS: From North - exit M5 at junction 3, follow A456 to Kidderminster and on reaching the town at first traffic lights turn left into Chester Road. At next traffic lights turn right into Comberton Road, continue past station and Hoo Road is on the left halfway down the hill. From the South & West - exit M5 at junction 6. Follow A449 to Kidderminster. At first roundabout (Adjacent to railway viaduct) turn right into Chester Road and first left into Hoo Road. From London direction via M42 then follow M5 north to junction 4 (Lydiate Ash). Exit motorway turn left and follow A491 towards Stourbridge. At Hagley roundabout turn left and follow A456 to Kidderminster as above.

CAPACITY: 6,237 **SEATED:** 1,100 **COVERED TERRACING:** 4,690

CLUB SHOP:
Open Monday to Friday 9am-5pm, plus 1st XI match days.

SOCIAL FACILITIES:
Lounge bar for members, officials & players. Social & supporters club (3 bars) open to visiting supporters before & after the match, temporary admission fee 50p. Hot & cold food available.

Kidderminster Fact File

Nickname: Harriers **Sponsors:** Not yet known for 97-98
Club colours: Red & white
Change colours: Yellow & black
Reserve team league: Central Conference
Midweek home matchday: Mondays 7.45pm.

PREVIOUS - **Leagues:** Birmingham League 1889-1890, 1891-1939, 1947-1948, 1960-1962, Midland League 1890-1891, Southern League 1939-1945 (Abandoned - World War II), 1948-1960, 1972-1983, Birmingham Combination 1945-1947, West Midlands League 1962-1972.
Grounds: None **Names:** None

CLUB RECORDS - **Attendance:** 9,155 - Hereford United - FA Cup 1st Round Proper 27.11.48.
Win: 25-0 v Hereford (H) - 12.10.1889 - Birmingham Senior Cup 1st Rnd.
Defeat: 0-13 v Darwen (A) - 24.01.1891 - FA Cup 1st Rnd Proper.
Transfer fee paid: £20,000 for Chris Brindley from Telford - 1992
Transfer fee received: £60,000 each for Paul Jones from Wolves - 1991 & Steve Lilwall from W.B.A - 1992.
Career goalscorer: Peter Wassall 432 - 1963-1974
Career appearances: Brendan Wassall 686 - 1962-1974

BEST SEASON - **FA Cup:** 5th Round 1993-94. 0-1 v West Ham United.
League clubs defeated: Birmingham City, Preston North End.
FA Trophy: Winners 86-87, R-up 90-91, 94-95.

1996-97 Captain: Mark Yates

1996-97 Top scorer: Lee Hughes (34)

1996-97 Player of the Year: Lee Hughes

Recent past players who progressed to the Football League: Lee Hughes (West Brom. A.), Richard Forsyth (Birmingham C., now Stoke C.), Paul Jones (Wolverhampton W., now Stockport Co.), Dave Barnett (Barnet, now Birmingham C.), Steve Lilwall (West Brom. A.).

HONOURS: GMV Conference Champions 1994, R-up 1997; FA Trophy Winners 1987, Runners-up 1991, 1995; Spalding Cup 1997, Welsh FA Cup Runners-up 1986, 1989; Southern League Cup 1980; Worcester Senior Cup (19); Birmingham Senior Cup (7); Staffordshire Senior Cup (4); West Midland League Champions (6), Runners-up (3); Southern Premier Runners-up (1); West Midland League Cup winners (7); Keys Cup winners (7); Border Counties Floodlit League Champions (3), Camkin Floodlit Cup Winners (3); Bass County Vase Winners (1); Conference Fair Play Trophy (4).

Formed
1946

LEEK TOWN

President: G Heath **Chairman:** L Davis

Secretary: Michael Rowley
62 London Rd., Chesterton, Newcastle, Staffs. ST5 7DY. Tel: 01782 562890

Press Officer: Rob Bailey **Commercial Manager:** Rob Bailey

In 1995/96, Leek Town finished seventeenth in the UniBond League Premier Division. Two seasons earlier they were denied promotion to the Vauxhall Conference as runners-up due to their Harrison Park ground being deemed as unsuitable. Leek were then forced to have a season in the Dr. Martens League, which proved to be a financial disaster for the club and they very nearly went under. What a tribute then to find, two years later, that Leek are a Vauxhall Conference club with a ground most would be proud of.

On the field, much of the praise for Leek's success must go to Phil Wilson, the former boss of Stalybridge Celtic and a number of other north-west clubs. He tranformed Leek's fortunes and even when he departed for Northwich Victoria, the seeds were well and truly set. The club also acted shrewdly by appointing Wilson's number two, Peter Ward, as his successor, thereby ensuring stability for the vital run-in.

A number of useful signings have been made for the new season, including mid fielder Ray Walker as player-coach, but Leek may still find life tough in the Conference.

Players L-R, Back: J Evans, J Diskin, D Trott, T Bullock, M Filson, N Cutler, M Beeby, M Ogley, N Ellis, S Soley. Front: D Bancroft, S Leicester, S Locke, M Bates, P Ward (Manager), G Bauress (Asst. Man), S Tobin, J Porter, J Carter, M Hawkes.

Leek Town

Match No.	Date	Venue H/A	Competition	Opponents	Result	League Pos.	Attendance	Goalscorers (Times if known)
1	Aug 24	A	UL	Frickley Athletic	Won 3-2		190	Harland 73, Filson 74, Batho 88
2	Aug 26	H	UL	Winsford United	Won 3-1		371	Harland 5, Soley 12, Bancroft 63
3	Aug 31	H	UL	Spennymoor United	Drew 1-1	3	358	Soley 25
4	Sep 3	A	UL	Runcorn	Won 2-0		430	Bancroft 33, Bauress 68
5	Sep 7	A	UL	Bamber Bridge	Won 4-0	1	254	Batho (3) 4, 33, 71, Bancroft 51
6	Sep 10	H	UL	Alfreton Town	Won 4-1	1	320	Batho 45, Bancroft 57, Bauress 85 (p), Carter 86
7	**Sep 14**	**A**	**FAC 1 Q**	**Matlock Town**	**Won 1-0**		**375**	**Filson 74**
8	Sep 18	A	UL	Winsford United	Won 2-0	1	261	Soley 23, Filson 28
9	Sep 21	H	UL	Chorley	Won 1-0	1	405	Batho 72
10	Sep 24	A	UL	Buxton	Won 2-0	1	437	Soley 25, Beeby 76
11	**Sep 28**	**H**	**FAC 2 Q**	**Eastwood Town**	**Won 1-0**		**432**	**Soley 34**
12	Oct 1	H	UL	Boston United	Won 1-0	1	486	Filson 60
13	Oct 5	A	UL	Marine	Drew 0-0	1	501	
14	Oct 8	H	UL	Buxton	Drew 1-1	1	702	Soley 66
15	**Oct 12**	**H**	**FAC 3 Q**	**Gainsborough Trinity**	**Won 2-0**		**577**	**Ellis 15, Batho 78**
16	Oct 16	A	UL	Accrington Stanley	Won 2-1	1	415	Soley 77, Bancroft 85
17	**Oct 19**	**A**	**FAT 1 Q**	**Grantham Town**	**Lost 0-1**		**295**	
18	Oct 22	H	UL	Runcorn	Drew 1-1	1	429	Carter 5
19	**Oct 26**	**A**	**FAC 4 Q**	**Stalybridge Celtic**	**Lost 0-1**		**974**	
20	**Oct 29**	**H**	**ULC**	**Gainsborough Trinity**	**Drew 0-0**		**227**	
21	Nov 2	H	UL	Guiseley	Lost 1-3	1	391	Leicester 79
22	Nov 9	A	UL	Hyde United	Lost 1-3	2	609	Filson 54
23	**Nov 12**	**A**	**SSC**	**Pelsall Villa**	**Won 3-1**		**105**	**Carter 35, Eastwood 55, Bauress 81 (p)**
24	Nov 16	A	UL	Bishop Auckland	Drew 1-1	2	226	Soley 72
25	Nov 27	A	UL	Knowlsey United	Lost 2-3	2	53	Eastwood 56, 73
26	Nov 30	H	UL	Bamber Bridge	Won 4-1	2	302	Soley 30, Bauress 45, Carter 74, Batho 85
27	**Dec 3**	**A**	**ULCC**	**Gainsborough Trinity**	**Lost 0-1**		**232**	
28	Dec 7	H	UL	Lancaster City	Won 2-1	2	346	Soley 58, 63
29	Dec 10	H	UL	Gainsborough Trinity	Won 1-0	1	226	Eastwood 30
30	Dec 14	A	UL	Blyth Spartans	Won 1-0	1	732	Ellis 42
31	Dec 21	H	UL	Accrington Stanley	Won 2-1	1	363	Soley 10, Bancroft 86
32	Jan 4	A	UL	Barrow	Lost 0-3	1	1107	
33	Jan 18	H	UL	Knowsley United	Won 2-0	1	372	Soley 14, 23 (pen)
34	Feb 1	A	UL	Lancaster City	Won 3-0	1	238	Soley 43, 45, Filson 90
35	Feb 8	A	UL	Witton Albion	Won 2-1	1	584	Diskin 21, Filson 45
36	**Feb 4**	**H**	**SSC**	**Knypersley Athletic**	**Won 1-0**		**243**	**Filson 46**
37	Feb 15	H	UL	Frickley Athletic	Won 3-0	1	417	Filson 18, Tobin 22, Higginbottom 31
38	Feb 22	H	UL	Blyth Spartans	Won 4-0	1	582	Soley 26, Higginbottom 31, Beeny 49, Carter 68
39	Mar 1	A	UL	Gainsborough Trinity	Won 1-0	1	517	Ellis 43
40	Mar 4	A	UL	Chorley	Drew 0-0	1	139	
41	Mar 8	H	UL	Emley	Drew 0-0	1	660	
42	**Mar 12**	**H**	**SSC**	**Bilston Town**	**Lost 1-2***		**220**	Soley 83
43	Mar 15	H	UL	Hyde United	Drew 0-0		1065	
44	Mar 22	A	UL	Guiseley	Lost 0-2	1	480	
45	Mar 29	H	UL	Marine	Lost 0-1	1	696	
46	Mar 31	A	UL	Colwyn Bay	Lost 1-3	1	498	Trott 35
47	Apr 5	H	UL	Bishop Auckland	Won 1-0	1	425	Soley 63
48	Apr 9	A	UL	Boston United	Won 2-0	1	1108	Soley 36, Trott 75
49	Apr 12	A	UL	Alfreton Town	Drew 1-1	1	401	Tobin 87
50	Apr 14	A	UL	Emley	Won 3-2	1	452	Jones 48 (og), Soley 69 (pen), 78
51	Apr 19	H	UL	Witton Albion	Won 2-1	1	679	Evans 24, Beeby 26
52	Apr 22	H	UL	Colwyn Bay	Won 1-0	1	866	Tobin 60
53	Apr 26	A	UL	Spennymoor United	Won 1-0	1	151	Carter 77
54	May 3	H	UL	Barrow	Won 2-1	1	733	Soley 86, Ellis 90

Leek Town

1	2	3	4	5	6	7	8	9	10	11	12	14	15	Mth No.
Bullock	Locke	Bates	Ogley	Diskin	Soley	Bancroft	Carter	Harland	Filson	Bauress	Batho	Beeby	Gilford	1
Bullock	Locke	Bates	Ogley	Diskin	Soley	Bancroft	Carter	Harland	Filson	Bauress	Hawkes	Beeby	Batho	2
Bullock	Locke	Bates	Ogley	Diskin	Soley	Bancroft	Hawkes	Harland	Filson	Bauress	Beeby	Batho	Carter	3
Bullock	Locke	Bates	Ogley	Diskin	Soley	Bancroft	Carter	Harland	Filson	Bauress	Beeby	Batho	Hawkes	4
Bullock	Locke	Bates	Ogley	Diskin	Batho	Bancroft	Carter	Harland	Filson	Bauress	Hawkes	Beeby	Kiely	5
Bullock	Locke	Bates	Ogley	Diskin	Batho	Bancroft	Carter	Harland	Filson	Bauress	Hawkes	Beeby	Leicester	6
Bullock	**Locke**	**Bates**	**Ogley**	**Diskin**	**Batho**	**Hawkes**	**Carter**	**Harland**	**Filson**	**Bauress**	**Beeby**	**Leicester**	**Shaw**	**7**
Bullock	Locke	Bates	Beeby	Diskin	Soley	Bancroft	Carter	Batho	Filson	Bauress	Leicester	Harland	K Wilson	8
Bullock	Locke	Bates	Ogley	Diskin	Soley	Bancroft	Beeby	Batho	Harland	Bauress	Leicester	Shaw	K Wilson	9
Bullock	Locke	Bates	Ogley	Diskin	Soley	Bancroft	Beeby	Batho	Filson	Bauress	Leicester	Harland	K Wilson	10
Bullock	**Locke**	**Bates**	**Ogley**	**Diskin**	**Soley**	**Bancroft**	**Carter**	**Batho**	**Filson**	**Bauress**	**Leicester**	**Harland**	**Beeby**	**11**
Bullock	Locke	Bates	Ogley	Beeby	Soley	Bancroft	Carter	Batho	Filson	Bauress	Leicester	Harland	K Wilson	12
Bullock	Locke	Bates	Ogley	Beeby	Bancroft	Ellis	Carter	Batho	Harland	Bauress	K Wilson	Kiely	Diskin	13
Bullock	Locke	Bates	Ogley	Beeby	Soley	Ellis	Carter	Batho	Harland	Bauress	Bancroft	Kiely	Diskin	14
Bullock	**Locke**	**Bates**	**Ogley**	**Diskin**	**Soley**	**Bancroft**	**Ellis**	**Kiely**	**Filson**	**Bauress**	**Leicester**	**Batho**	**Carter**	**15**
Bullock	Locke	Bates	Ogley	Diskin	Soley	Bancroft	Leicester	Batho	Filson	Bauress	Kiely	Carter	Harland	16
Bullock	**Locke**	**Bates**	**Ogley**	**Diskin**	**Soley**	**Bancroft**	**Leicester**	**Batho**	**Filson**	**Bauress**	**Kiely**	**Carter**	**Beeby**	**17**
Bullock	Locke	Bates	Ogley	Diskin	Soley	Bancroft	Carter	Ellis	Filson	Bauress	Batho	Kiely	Leicester	18
Bullock	**Locke**	**Bates**	**Ogley**	**Diskin**	**Soley**	**Bancroft**	**Carter**	**Ellis**	**Filson**	**Bauress**	**Leicester**	**Batho**	**Beeby**	**19**
Bullock	**Locke**	**Bates**	**Ogley**	**Diskin**	**Soley**	**Ellis**	**Carter**	**Batho**	**Filson**	**Bauress**	**Leicester**	**Bancroft**	**Beeby**	**20**
Bullock	Beeby	Bates	Ogley	Diskin	Soley	Filson	Eastwood	Ellis	Leicester	Bauress	Carter	Locke	Batho	21
Bullock	Locke	Bates	Ogley	Diskin	Evans	Leicester	Ellis	Higginbotham	Filson	Bauress	Carter	Batho	Beeby	22
Bullock	**Locke**	**Bates**	**Beeby**	**Diskin**	**Leicester**	**Bancroft**	**Carter**	**Batho**	**Eastwood**	**Bauress**	**McKie**	**Wilson K**	**Ogley**	**23**
Bullock	Locke	Bates	Beeby	Diskin	Soley	Leicester	Carter	Eastwood	Higginbotham	Bauress	Batho	Bancroft	Wilson K	24
Bullock	Locke	Bates	Beeby	Diskin	Soley	Leicester	Tobin	Batho	Bancroft	Bauress	Eastwood	Wilson K	Carter	25
Bullock	Locke	Bates	Beeby	Diskin	Soley	Leicester	Tobin	Eastwood	Bancroft	Bauress	Carter	Batho	Evans J	26
Bullock	**Locke**	**Bates**	**Beeby**	**Diskin**	**Soley**	**Leicester**	**Carter**	**Batho**	**Bancroft**	**Bauress**	**Ellis**	**Ogley**	**Wilson K**	**27**
Bullock	Locke	Bates	Beeby	Diskin	Soley	Leicester	Tobin	Eastwood	Higginbotham	Bauress	Ogley	Evans J	Bancroft	28
Bullock	Locke	Bates	Ogley	Diskin	Soley	Leicester	Tobin	Eastwood	Higginbotham	Bauress	Beeby	Evans J	Bancroft	29
Bullock	Locke	Bates	Ogley	Diskin	Soley	Ellis	Tobin	Eastwood	Filson	Bauress	Beeby	Leicester	Bancroft	30
Bullock	Locke	Bates	Ogley	Diskin	Soley	Ellis	Tobin	Eastwood	Filson	Bauress	Beeby	Leicester	Bancroft	31
Bullock	Locke	Bates	Ogley	Diskin	Soley	Ellis	Tobin	Eastwood	Filson	Evans J	Beeby	Leicester	Bancroft	32
Holmes	Locke	Beeby	Ogley	Diskin	Soley	Ellis	Tobin	Filson	Higginbotham	Evans J	Eastwood	Leicester	Bancroft	33
Bullock	Locke	Beeby	Ogley	Diskin	Soley	Ellis	Tobin	Filson	Higginbotham	Evans J	Leicester	Batho	Bauress	34
Bullock	Locke	Beeby	Ogley	Diskin	Soley	Ellis	Tobin	Filson	Higginbotham	Evans J	Leicester	Batho	Bauress	35
Bullock	**Locke**	**Beeby**	**Ogley**	**Diskin**	**Soley**	**Ellis**	**Tobin**	**Filson**	**Higginbotham**	**Bauress**	**Evans J**	**Leicester**	**Bancroft**	**36**
Bullock	Locke	Beeby	Ogley	Diskin	Soley	Ellis	Tobin	Filson	Higginbotham	Bauress	Evans J	Evans G	Bancroft	37
Bullock	Leicester	Beeby	Ogley	Diskin	Soley	Ellis	Tobin	Filson	Higginbotham	Evans J	Carter	Batho	Bancroft	38
Bullock	Locke	Beeby	Ogley	Diskin	Soley	Ellis	Tobin	Filson	Higginbotham	Bauress	Evans J	Leicester	Evans G	39
Bullock	Locke	Beeby	Ogley	Diskin	Soley	Leicester	Tobin	Filson	Higginbotham	Bauress	Evans J	Bancroft	Evans G	40
Bullock	Locke	Beeby	Ogley	Diskin	Soley	Leicester	Tobin	Evans	Higginbotham	Bauress	Evans J	Bancroft	Carter	41
Bullock	**Locke**	**Beeby**	**Ogley**	**Carter**	**Evans J**	**Leicester**	**Tobin**	**Evans G**	**Bancroft**	**Bauress**	**Soley**	**Parker**	**Ellis**	**42**
Bullock	Locke	Beeby	Ogley	Diskin	Soley	Ellis	Tobin	Filson	Carr-Lawton	Bauress	Leicester	Evans J	Hawkes	43
Bullock	Leicester	Beeby	Ogley	Diskin	Soley	Ellis	Tobin	Filson	Hawkes	Bauress	Locke	Evans J	Carr-Lawton	44
Cutler	Locke	Beeby	Ogley	Diskin	Soley	Ellis	Tobin	Evans J	Hawkes	Bauress	Leicester	Carr-Lawton	Bancroft	45
Cutler	Locke	Beeby	Ogley	Diskin	Soley	Ellis	Tobin	Trott	Carr-Lawton	Bauress	Evans J	Bancroft	Parker	46
Cutler	Locke	Beeby	Ogley	Bates	Soley	Ellis	Tobin	Trott	Evans J	Bauress	Carr-Lawton	Bancroft	Parker	47
Cutler	Bates	Beeby	Ogley	Diskin	Soley	Ellis	Tobin	Trott	Evans J	Bauress	Locke	Carr-Lawton	Bancroft	48
Cutler	Bates	Beeby	Ogley	Diskin	Soley	Ellis	Tobin	Trott	Evans J	Bauress	Locke	Bancroft	Hawkes	49
Cutler	Bates	Beeby	Ogley	Diskin	Soley	Ellis	Tobin	Trott	Filson	Bauress	Bancroft	Locke	Evans J	50
Cutler	Bates	Beeby	Ogley	Diskin	Soley	Ellis	Tobin	Evans J	Filson	Bauress	Bancroft	Locke	Hawkes	51
Cutler	Evans J	Beeby	Ogley	Diskin	Soley	Ellis	Tobin	Trott	Filson	Bauress	Bancroft	Locke	Bates	52
Cutler	Locke	Beeby	Bates	Diskin	Soley	Ellis	Bancroft	Trott	Filson	Bauress	Parker	Carter	Tobin	53
Cutler	Locke	Beeby	Bates	Diskin	Soley	Ellis	Tobin	Carter	Filson	Bauress	Bancroft	Leicester	Parker	54

PETER WARD (MANAGER)

Date of Appointment	30th November 1996
Date of Birth:	10th May 1948
Place of Birth:	Kidsgrove (Stoke-on-Trent)

PREVIOUS CLUBS

As manager	Kidsgrove Ath. (x2), Newcastle T., Hanley T., Nantwich T.
As coach	Nantwich T., Kidsgrove A., Newcastle T.
As player	Kidsgrove A., English Electric, Blythe Matthey.

HONOURS

As manager	Northern Prem. Lge 96-97 (Leek), Mid-Cheshire Lge & Cup (Newcastle T.)
As player	Mid-Cheshire Lge & Cup, Leek Cup, Hanley Cup.

Assistant Manager: Gary Bauress **Player Coach:** R Walker **Physio:** K Birch-Martin

Leek Town salute their fans with the Unibond Premier Trophy which they won so convincingly.

Photo: John Taylor

MATCHDAY PROGRAMME

Number of pages	36
Price	£1.20
Programme Editor	Mike Cope
Other club publications:	None
Local Newspapers:	Leek Post & Times Evening Sentinel
Local Radio Stations:	Radio Stoke Signal Radio

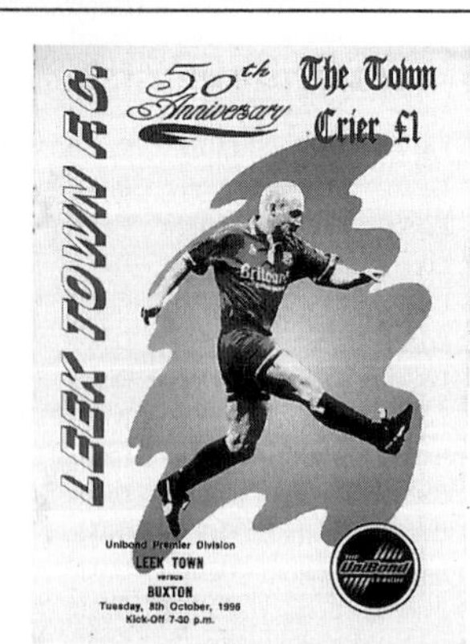

1997-98 PLAYING SQUAD

PLAYER	Birthplace Honours	Birthdate	CLUBS
GOALKEEPERS			
Chris Holmes	Stoke		Alsager T, Nantwich T, Ashton U, Nantwich T, Kidsgrove A
DEFENDERS			
Gary Bauress	Liverpool ULP	19.1.71	Everton, Tranmere R, Stalybridge C, Ashton U, Stalybridge C
Mark Ogley	Barnsley ULP	10.3.67	Burnley, Carlisle U, Aldershot, York C, Altrincham, Stalybridge C
Martin Filson	Manchester ULP	25.6.68	Tranmere R, Wrexham, Rhyl, Stalybridge C, Halifax T, Dagenham & Redbridge, Caernarfon T
John Diskin	Manchester ULP		Nantwich T
Iain Brunskill	Ormskirk ES, EY	5.11.76	Liverpool, Bury
Dale Hawtin	Crewe	28.12.75	Crewe A
MIDFIELDERS			
Ray Walker	North Shields EY, FAYC	28.9.63	Aston Villa, Port Vale
Steve Tobin	Manchester GMVC, BLT, ULP	24.3.75	Leeds U, Macclesfield T, Flixton
Mick Bates	Stoke ULP		Arsenal, Port Vale, Eastwood Hanley
Steve Soley	Liverpool ULP		Avon A, Warrington T
Jamie Evans	Sheffield ULP		Sheffield U, Grantham T, Matlock T
FORWARDS			
Stuart Leicester	Altrincham ULP	11.8.66	Irlam T, Stalybridge C, Macclesfield T, Stalybridge C, Witton A, Ashton U
Richard Batho	Stoke ULP		Kidsgrove A, Redgate Clayton
Wayne Biggins	Sheffield Div 3	20.11.61	Lincoln C, Matlock T, King's Lynn, £7,500 to Burnley, £40k to Norwich C, £150k to Manchester C, £250k to Stoke C, £200k to Barnsley, Celtic, Stoke C, Oxford U, Wigan A
Dean Cunningham	Stoke	28.5.77	Port Vale
Dean Trott	Barnsley	13.5.67	Ossett A, Frickley A, Boston U, Northampton T, Gateshead, Stalybridge C, £5k to Leek
Marc Hawkes	Stoke ULP	22.9.76	Stoke C, Leek T, Shrewsbury T

DEPARTURES - (During the season): Nigel Shaw (Knypersley V), Paul Higginbotham (Conwy U), Nick Harland (Rhyl), Tony Bullock (Barnsley)
(During the close season): Stuart Locke (Leigh RMI)

Harrison Park, Leek

GROUND ADDRESS: Harrison Park, Macclesfield Road, Leek ST13 8LD
TEL. NO. 01538 399278 Fax: 01538 399826

SIMPLE DIRECTIONS: Opposite Courtaults chemical works on A523 Macclesfield to Buxton road half a mile out of Leek heading towards Macclesfield.

CAPACITY: 3,600 **SEATED:** 625 **COVERED TERRACING:** 2,675

RECORD ATTENDANCE: 5,312 v Macclesfield Town, F.A. Cup Second Qualifying Round 73-74.

CLUB SHOP: Contact club on 01538 399278.

SOCIAL FACILITIES: Clubhouse open nightly & weekend lunchtimes. 01538 383734

Leek Town - Fact File

Nickname: The Blues **Club Sponsors:** Britannia/F Ball & Co Ltd
Club colours: All blue
Change colours: All yellow
Reserve team league:
Midweek home matchday: tuesday
Newsline: 0891 122727.

PREVIOUS - **Leagues:** Staffs County, Manchester 51-54 57-73, West Mids (B'ham) 54-56, Cheshire County 73-82, North West Counties 82-87, Northern Premier 87-94, Southern League 94-95, Northern Premier 95-97.

Names: Abbey Green Rovers/ Leek Lowe Hamil. **Grounds:** None

CLUB RECORDS - **Win:** Unknown
Defeat: Unknown
Transfer fee paid: £2,000 for Simon Snow (Sutton Town)
Transfer fee received: £30,000 for Tony Bullock (Barnsley)
Career goalscorer: Dave Suttons 144.
Career appearances: Gary Pearce 447.

BEST SEASON - **FA Cup:** 2nd Rd 90-91 (0-4 v Chester (A) after 1-1).
League clubs defeated: Scarborough 90-91.
FA Trophy: Runners-up 89-90, Q-F 85-86.

1996-97 Captain: Gary Bauress
1996-97 Top scorer: Steve Soley (23)
1996-97 Player of the Year: Steve Soley

Past players who progressed to the Football League: Geoff Crosby (Stockport 1952), Bill Summerscales (1970), Mark Bright (1981) & Martyn Smith (1984) all to Port Vale, Paul Edwards (Crewe 1989), Tony Bullock (Barnsley 1997).

HONOURS: FA Trophy R-up 89-90; Northern Premier Lg 96-97, R-up 93-94 (Div 1 89-90, Div 1 Cup R-up 88-89, Presidents Cup R-up 93-94, Lg Shield 90-91); North West Co's Lg Cup 84-85 (Charity Shield 84-85); Cheshire County Lg 74-75 (Challenge Shield 74-75); Manchester Lg 51-52 71-72 72-73 (Lg Cup 72-73); Staffs Snr Cup 95-96, R-up 54-55 81-82 95-96, Jnr Cup 51-52 70-71 (R-up 47-48 48-49 49-50)); Staffs Co. Lg 50-51 69-70 70-71 73-74 (R-up 47-48 49-50, Lg Cup 70-71 73-74); Leek Post Charity Shield 46-47; Leek Cup 47-48 52-53 70-71 71-72 (R-up 46-47); May Bank Cup 47-48 50-51 71-72; Hanley Cup 48-49 70-71 (R-up 49-5); Mid Cheshire Lg Div 2 87-88 (Div 2 Cup 87-88); Evans Halshaw Floodlit Cup Winners 93-94 94-95; Doc Martens(Southern Lg) Cup Finalists 94-95; Unibond Lge Chall Cup R-up 95-96

Formed:
1920

MORECAMBE

President: Jim Bowen

Chairman: Rod Taylor

Directors: P McGuigan,
R Danson, D Derham.

Vice-Chairman: Graham Hodgson

Company & Football Secretary: Neil Marsdin

Commercial Manager: Peter Howard

The Shrimps enjoyed an excellent 1996/97 season, finishing in fourth spot in the league, reaching the semi-final of the Spalding Cup and the First Round of the FA Cup. Manager Jimmy Harvey led his troops to their best finishing position, following on from ninth place secured the previous campaign, and he did so with a squad which cost very little and without top scorer Justin Jackson, who was sold to Woking for a club record £30,000 fee.

Off the field, too, things are really bubbling, with Christie Park continually being upgraded, leaving it almost ready now for Football League grading, and with the club being handed the north-west's 'Programme for Sporting Excellence' scheme.

One or two very useful new signings have been made for the new season and the Shrimps will be regarded as one of the favourites for the title - and rightly so.

Back Row: Robert Howarth, David Miller, Stuart Drummond, Brian Healy, Kenny Mayers, Steve McIlhargey, Andy Banks, Steve Hodgson, Tony Hughes, Mark Ceroalo, Mike Bignall, Ian Monk.
Front Row: Paul Rushton, John Norman, Dave McKearney, Tony Hesketh (Asst. Man.), Jim Harvey (Manager), Andrew Grimshaw, Paul Burns, Gary Williams. Photo: Michael Williamson

Morecambe

Match No.	Date	Venue H/A	Competition	Opponents	Result	League Pos.	Attendance	Goalscorers (Times if known)
1	Aug 17	H	VC	Woking	Lost 1-2	16	1360	Miller 18
2	Aug 21	H	VC	Macclesfield Town	Won 1-0		1306	Monk 51
3	Aug 24	A	VC	Stevenage Borough	Lost 2-4		2655	Sodje 21 (og), Jackson 36
4	Aug 26	H	VC	Telford United	Lost 0-1	19	1100	
5	Aug 31	A	VC	Welling United	Won 4-1	13	602	Jackson (2) 16, 54, Burns (2) 74, 77
6	Sep 3	A	VC	Altrincham	Won 1-0		2242	Norman 35
7	Sep 7	H	VC	Hednesford Town	Won 2-0	10	1088	McKearney (2) 67, 79
8	Sep 10	A	VC	Macclesfield Town	Drew 0-0		1161	
9	**Sep 14**	**A**	**FAC 1 Q**	**Brandon United**	**Won 6-0**		**237**	**Leaver 23, 30, Grimshaw 37, Ceroalo 67, 84, Norman 80**
10	Sep 21	A	VC	Farnborough Town	Drew 2-2	14	770	Norman 16, Jackson 52
11	**Sep 28**	**H**	**FAC 2 Q**	**Guiseley**	**Won 4-1**		**729**	**Knowles 33, Jackson (2) 54, 90, Norman 64**
12	Oct 2	H	VC	Northwich Victoria	Won 2-0		1160	McKearney 65 (pen), McCluskie 87
13	Oct 5	A	VC	Slough Town	Won 2-1	10	1104	McCluskie 75, Monk 80
14	**Oct 12**	**H**	**FAC 3 Q**	**Flixton**	**Won 6-2**		**727**	**Norman 8, 9, 89, Jackson 38, McCluskie 65, 88**
15	Oct 16	A	VC	Gateshead	Won 3-0		402	Jackson 61, 84, McCluskie 78
16	Oct 19	H	VC	Kettering Town	Won 5-2	6	1205	Jackson 8, 45, Norman 14 (og), McCluskie 76, Burns 88
17	**Oct 26**	**A**	**FAC 4 Q**	**Lancaster City**	**Drew 1-1**		**2500**	**McKearney 73**
18	**Oct 30**	**H**	**FAC 4QR**	**Lancaster City**	**Drew 2-2**		**2726**	**Burns 36, McKearney 99 (pen)**
19	Nov 2	H	VC	Bath City	Drew 1-1	8	917	Jackson 58
20	**Nov 6**	**H**	**FAC4QR2**	**Lancaster City**	**Won 4-2**		**2454**	**Leaver 4, Norman 43, 60, Jackson 36**
21	Nov 9	A	VC	Telford United	Won 3-2	7	721	Burns 29, 55 (2 pens), Grimshaw 66
22	**Nov 16**	**A**	**FAC 1**	**Boston United**	**Lost 0-3**		**2955**	
23	**Nov 20**	**A**	**SCC**	**Gateshead**	**Won 3-1**		**166**	**Ceroalo 6, Knowles 58, Leaver 63**
24	Nov 23	H	VC	Rushden & Diamonds	Won 2-0	6	1040	Monk 31, Burns 63
25	Nov 26	A	VC	Stalybridge Celtic	Lost 1-2		474	Ceroalo 75
26	Nov 30	A	VC	Bromsgrove Rovers	Won 3-2	6	652	Norman 12, Jackson 44, Monk 46
27	Dec 7	H	VC	Hayes	Lost 2-4	6	1012	Shirley 28, Burns 68 (pen)
28	Dec 11	H	VC	Gateshead	Won 4-0		788	Monk 9, Jackson 55, 78, Norman 80
29	Dec 14	A	VC	Halifax Town	Drew 1-1	3	883	Jackson 1
30	**Dec 18**	**H**	**SCC**	**Stalybridge Celtic**	**Drew 3-3**		**407**	**Grimshaw 50, 59, Norman 66**
31	Dec 21	H	VC	Altrincham	Won 2-1		1088	Jackson 63, 65
32	Dec 28	A	VC	Northwich Victoria	Lost 0-1	5	1436	
33	Jan 11	A	VC	Bath City	Lost 1-2	6	509	Norman 22
34	**Jan 18**	**H**	**FAT 1**	**Chorley**	**Won 3-1**		**937**	**Norman 13, Ceroalo 38, Monk 89**
35	Jan 25	H	VC	Bromsgrove Rovers	Won 1-0	5	940	Ceroalo 39
36	Feb 1	A	VC	Rushden & Diamonds	Lost 1-2	5	2145	Udall 51
37	**Feb 8**	**A**	**FAT 2**	**Bradford (PA)**	**Won 1-0**		**915**	**Grimshaw 18**
38	Feb 15	H	VC	Welling United	Lost 1-2	6	877	Norman 17 (og)
39	Feb 22	A	VC	Hednesford Town	Lost 1-2	7	1463	Ceroalo
40	**Feb 25**	**A**	**SCC**	**Stalybridge Celtic**	**Won 1-0**		**335**	**Shirley 117**
41	**Mar 1**	**H**	**FAT 3**	**Dagenham & Redbridge**	**Drew 0-0**		**972**	
42	**Mar 3**	**A**	**FAT 3 R**	**Dagenham & Redbridge**	**Lost 1-2**		**788**	**Norman 31**
43	Mar 8	A	VC	Hayes	Won 3-2		558	McCluskie 23, Knowles 25, Norman 89
44	Mar 15	H	VC	Farnborough Town	Drew 1-1	8	897	Grimshaw 64
45	Mar 22	H	VC	Dover Athletic	Won 3-1	6	802	Bignall 27, Cain 38, 63
46	**Mar 25**	**A**	**SC**	**Macclesfield Town**	**Lost 1-4**		**826**	**Healy 13 (lost 1-6 agg)**
47	Mar 29	A	VC	Kidderminster Harriers	Drew 2-2		3009	Bignall 25, 69
48	Mar 31	H	VC	Stevenage Borough	Lost 1-2	8	1438	Healy 24
49	Apr 5	A	VC	Dover Athletic	Lost 0-3	8	953	
50	Apr 8	A	VC	Southport	Lost 1-3	8	802	Bignall 49
51	Apr 12	A	VC	Kettering Town	Won 2-0		1362	Bignall 72, Norman 79
52	Apr 16	H	VC	Halifax Town	Won 1-0		711	Monk 89
53	Apr 19	H	VC	Kidderminster Harriers	Lost 2-3	6	1175	Bignall 43, Healy 75
54	Apr 22	H	VC	Stalybridge Celtic	Drew 0-0		862	
55	Apr 26	H	VC	Slough Town	Drew 0-0	6	704	
56	Apr 29	H	VC	Southport	Won 2-1		733	McCluskie 78, Healy 85
57	May 3	A	VC	Woking	Won 2-1	4	2373	Hodgson 53, Grimshaw 58

Morecambe

1	2	3	4	5	6	7	8	9	10	11	12	14	15	Mth No.
McIlhargey	McKearney	Annan	Miller	Hughes	West	Monk	Burns	Jackson	Norman	Sang	Ceraolo	McCluskie	Rushton	1
McIlhargey	McKearney	Annan	Miller	Hughes	Grimshaw	Monk	Sang	Jackson	Norman	Leaver	Knowles	McCluskie	Rushton	2
McIlhargey	McKearney	Annan	Miller	Hughes	Grimshaw	Monk	Sang	Jackson	Norman	Leaver	Knowles	McCluskie	Rushton	3
McIlhargey	McKearney	Annan	Miller	Hughes	Knownes	Monk	Sang	Jackson	Norman	Leaver	West	McCluskie	Rushton	4
McIlhargey	West	Annan	Miller	Hughes	Grimshaw	Monk	McKearney	Jackson	Norman	Leaver	Burns	McCluskie	Knowles	5
McIlhargey	West	Annan	Miller	Rushton	Grimshaw	Monk	McKearney	Jackson	Norman	Leaver	Lavelle	McCluskie	Knowles	6
McIlhargey	Knowles	Annan	West	Rushton	Grimshaw	Monk	McKearney	Jackson	Norman	Leaver	Lavelle	McCluskie	Sang	7
McIlhargey	Knowles	Annan	West	Rushton	Grimshaw	Monk	McKearney	Jackson	Norman	Leaver	Lavelle	McCluskie	Sang	8
McIlhargey	**Knowles**	**Annan**	**West**	**Rushton**	**Grimshaw**	**Monk**	**McKearney**	**Jackson**	**Norman**	**Leaver**	**Lavelle**	**Ceraolo**	**Sang**	**9**
McIlhargey	Knowles	Annan	West	Rushton	Grimshaw	Monk	McKearney	Jackson	Norman	Leaver	Burns	Ceraolo	Hughes	10
McIlhargey	**Knowles**	**Annan**	**West**	**Rushton**	**Grimshaw**	**Monk**	**McKearney**	**Jackson**	**Norman**	**Leaver**	**Burns**	**McCluskie**	**Hughes**	**11**
McIlhargey	Knowles	Lavelle	Hughes	Rushton	Grimshaw	Monk	McKearney	Jackson	Norman	Leaver	Cain	McCluskie	West	12
McIlhargey	Knowles	Cain	Hughes	Rushton	Grimshaw	Monk	McKearney	Jackson	Norman	Leaver	Burns	McCluskie	West	13
McIlhargey	**Knowles**	**Lavelle**	**Rushton**	**Hughes**	**Grimshaw**	**Monk**	**McKearney**	**Jackson**	**Norman**	**Leaver**	**Burns**	**McCluskie**	**West**	**14**
McIlhargey	Knowles	Lavelle	Hughes	Rushton	Burns	Cain	McKearney	Jackson	Norman	Leaver	Sang	McCluskie	West	15
McIlhargey	Knowles	Lavelle	Hughes	Rushton	Burns	Cain	McKearney	Jackson	Norman	Leaver	Grimshaw	McCluskie	West	16
McIlhargey	**Knowles**	**Annan**	**Hughes**	**Rushton**	**Burns**	**Grimshaw**	**McKearney**	**Jackson**	**Norman**	**Leaver**	**Cain**	**McCluskie**	**Miller**	**17**
McIlhargey	**Knowles**	**Annan**	**Hughes**	**Rushton**	**Burns**	**Monk**	**McKearney**	**Jackson**	**Norman**	**Leaver**	**Lavelle**	**McCluskie**	**Miller**	**18**
McIlhargey	Knowles	Annan	Miller	Rushton	Burns	Cain	Grimshaw	Jackson	Norman	Leaver	Lavelle	McCluskie	Sang	19
McIlhargey	**Knowles**	**Annan**	**Miller**	**Rushton**	**Burns**	**Monk**	**McKearney**	**Jackson**	**Norman**	**Leaver**	**Lavelle**	**McCluskie**	**Grimshaw**	**20**
Banks	Knowles	Lavelle	Miller	Rushton	Burns	Monk	Grimshaw	Jackson	Norman	Leaver	Cain	McCluskie	West	21
Banks	**Knowles**	**Lavelle**	**Miller**	**Hughes**	**Burns**	**Cain**	**Grimshaw**	**McCluskie**	**Norman**	**Leaver**	**McKearney**	**Monk**	**Ceraolo**	**22**
Banks	**Knowles**	**Lavelle**	**Miller**	**Hughes**	**Burns**	**Monk**	**McKearney**	**Ceraolo**	**Norman**	**Leaver**	**West**	**McCluskie**	**Grimshaw**	**23**
Banks	Knowles	Lavelle	West	Hughes	Burns	Monk	McKearney	Ceraolo	Norman	Leaver	Rushton	McCluskie	Grimshaw	24
Banks	Knowles	Lavelle	West	Hughes	Burns	Monk	McKearney	Ceraolo	Norman	Leaver	Jackson	Rushton	Grimshaw	25
McIlhargey	Knowles	Lavelle	Rushton	Hughes	Burns	Monk	McKearney	Jackson	Norman	Shirley	Ceraolo	McCluskie	Miller	26
McIlhargey	Knowles	Lavelle	Rushton	Hughes	Burns	Monk	McKearney	Jackson	Norman	Shirley	Ceraolo	McCluskie	Miller	27
Banks	Knowles	Annan	Miller	Hughes	Burns	Monk	McKearney	Jackson	Norman	Shirley	Ceraolo	McCluskie	Hodgson	28
Banks	Knowles	Annan	Miller	Hughes	Burns	Monk	McKearney	Jackson	Norman	Shirley	Ceraolo	Grimshaw	Rushton	29
Banks	**Knowles**	**Annan**	**Miller**	**Hughes**	**Burns**	**Monk**	**McKearney**	**Jackson**	**Norman**	**Shirley**	**Ceraolo**	**Grimshaw**	**Leaver**	**30**
McIlhargey	Knowles	Annan	Miller	Hughes	Burns	Monk	McKearney	Jackson	Norman	Shirley	Ceraolo	Rushton	Leaver	31
McIlhargey	Burns	Annan	Miller	Hughes	Grimshaw	Monk	Grimshaw	Jackson	Norman	Shirley	Ceraolo	Rusthon	Leaver	32
McIlhargey	Knowles	Lavelle	Miller	Rushton	Burns	Monk	McKearney	Jackson	Norman	Leaver	Ceraolo	Cain	Sang	33
McIlhargey	**Knowles**	**Annan**	**Miller**	**Rushton**	**Burns**	**Monk**	**McKearney**	**Ceraolo**	**Norman**	**Leaver**	**Lavelle**	**Cain**	**McCluskie**	**34**
McIlhargey	Knowles	Annan	Udall	Hughes	Burns	Monk	McKearney	Ceraolo	Norman	Shirley	Healey	Cain	McCluskie	35
McIlhargey	Knowles	Annan	Udall	Hughes	Burns	Monk	McKearney	Ceraolo	Norman	Healy	Lavelle	Shirley	McCluskie	36
McIlhargey	**Burns**	**Leaver**	**Rushton**	**Hughes**	**Grimshaw**	**Monk**	**Healy**	**Ceraolo**	**McCluskie**	**McKearney**	**Williams**	**Lavelle**	**Udall**	**37**
McIlhargey	Burns	Leaver	Rushton	Hughes	Healy	Monk	McKearney	Ceraolo	McCluskie	Shirley	Williams	Norman	Grimshaw	38
McIlhargey	Burns	Annan	Rushton	Hughes	Healy	Monk	Grimshaw	Ceraolo	Norman	Leaver	Williams	Shirley	McKearney	39
McIlhargey	**Burns**	**Annan**	**Rushton**	**Hughes**	**Healy**	**Monk**	**Grimshaw**	**Ceraolo**	**Norman**	**Leaver**	**McCluskie**	**McKearney**	**Shirley**	**40**
McIlhargey	**Burns**	**Leaver**	**Rushton**	**Hughes**	**Healy**	**Monk**	**Grimshaw**	**Ceraolo**	**Norman**	**McKearney**	**Williams**	**Lavelle**	**McCluskie**	**41**
McIlhargey	**Burns**	**Knowles**	**Rushton**	**Hughes**	**Healy**	**Monk**	**Grimshaw**	**Ceraolo**	**Norman**	**McKearney**	**Williams**	**Lavelle**	**McCluskie**	**42**
McIlhargey	Knowles	Mckearney	West	Hughes	Healy	Burns	Grimshaw	McCluskie	Norman	Shirley	Williams	Lavelle	Hodgson	43
Banks	Knowles	Mckearney	West	Hodgson	Healy	Burns	Grimshaw	McCluskie	Norman	Shirley	Cain	Lavelle	Monk	44
Banks	McKearney	Lavelle	West	Hughes	Healy	Cain	Knowles	Bignall	Norman	Shirley	Williams	Burns	Monk	45
Banks	**Knowles**	**Lavelle**	**West**	**Hughes**	**Healy**	**Cain**	**McKearney**	**Bignall**	**Norman**	**Shirley**	**Williams**	**Burns**	**Monk**	**46**
McIlhargey	Knowles	Lavelle	West	Rushton	Healy	Cain	McKearney	Bignall	Norman	Shirley	Williams	Burns	Monk	47
McIlhargey	Knowles	Lavelle	West	Hodgson	Healy	Cain	McKearney	Bignall	Norman	Shirley	Williams	Burns	Monk	48
McIlhargey	Knowles	Lavelle	West	Hodgson	Healy	Monk	McKearney	Bignall	Cain	Shirley	Williams	Burns	Drummond	49
McIlhargey	Knowles	Lavelle	West	Hodgson	Grimshaw	Monk	Burns	Bignall	Norman	Williams	McCluskie	Annan	Drummond	50
McIlhargey	Knowles	Lavelle	Mckearney	Hodgson	Grimshaw	Monk	Burns	Bignall	Norman	Shirley	McCluskie	Williams	Drummond	51
McIlhargey	Knowles	Burns	Mckearney	Hodgson	Grimshaw	Monk	Healy	Bignall	Norman	Williams	McCluskie	Cain	Drummond	52
McIlhargey	Knowles	Burns	Mckearney	Hodgson	Grimshaw	Monk	Healy	Bignall	Norman	Williams	McCluskie	Cain	Drummond	53
McIlhargey	Knowles	Lavelle	Mckearney	Hodgson	Grimshaw	Monk	Healy	Bignall	Norman	Cain	Burns	Drummond	McCluskie	54
McIlhargey	Burns	Lavelle	Mckearney	Hodgson	Drummond	Monk	Healy	Bignall	Norman	Knowles	Williams	Cain	McCluskie	55
McIlhargey	Knowles	Burns	Mckearney	Hodgson	Grimshaw	Monk	Healy	Bignall	Norman	Shirley	Drummond	McCluskie	Lavelle	56
McIlhargey	Knowles	Burns	Mckearney	Hodgson	Grimshaw	Monk	Healy	Bignall	Norman	Shirley	Drummond	McCluskie	Lavelle	57

JIM HARVEY (MANAGER)

Date of Appointment	June 1994
Date of Birth:	2nd May 1958
Place of Birth:	Lurgan, Northern Ireland

PREVIOUS CLUBS

As manager	
As assistant manager	Morecambe (Jan - June 1994)
As player	Glenavon, Arsenal, Hereford Utd., Bristol City, Tranmere Rovers, Crewe Alexandra.

HONOURS

As manager	None
As player	N. Ireland - u23., Leyland Daf winner, Mercantile Trophy Winner, promotion from Division 4 & Division 3.

Assistant Manager: Tony Hesketh **Physio:** David Edge

Dave McKearney, players Player of the Year pictured before the kick off of the match against Rushden & Diamonds.

MATCHDAY PROGRAMME

Number of pages	48
Price	£1.20
Programme Editor	Martin Shaw
Other club publications:	"Corpus Christie" (fanzine) "Going Up?" (part fanzine)
Local Newspapers:	Morecambe Visitor Morecambe Guardian Lancashire Evening Post The Citizen
Local Radio Stations:	Radio Lancashire Red Rose Radio Bay Radio

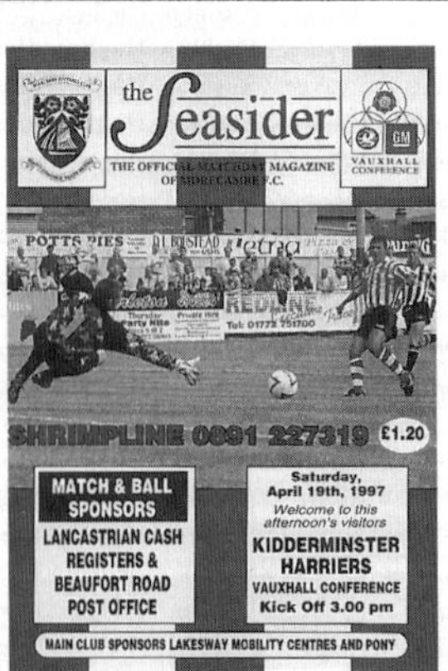

1997-98 PLAYING SQUAD

PLAYER	Birthplace Honours	Birthdate	CLUBS
GOALKEEPERS			
Steve McIlhargey	Glasgow	10.12.62	Blantyre Celtic, Walsall, Blackpool
Andy Banks	Preston	21.4.76	Preston, Bury
DEFENDERS			
David Miller	Burnley	8.1.64	Burnley, Tranmere R, Colne Dynamoes, Preston, £30k to Carlisle U, £25k to Stockport Co, Wigan A
Paul Burns	Liverpool	1.10.67	Grimsby T, Burscough, Prescot, Caernarfon T, Altrincham, Accrington Stanley
Paul Rushton	Chester	25.1.74	Crewe A
Dave McKearney	Crosby	20.6.68	Prescot, Bolton W, Northwich Victoria, Crewe A, Wigan A, Chorley
Paul West	Birmingham	22.6.72	Alcester T, Port Vale, Bradford C, Wigan A
Tony Hughes	Liverpool EY	3.10.73	Crewe A
Steve Hodgson	Kendal	28.8.76	From Youth Team
MIDFIELDERS			
Michael Knowles	Morecambe	3.3.74	From Youth Team
Andy Grimshaw	Bacup NPL	30.3.64	Rossendale U, Manchester U, Bury, Colne Dynamoes, Witton A
David Leaver	Preston NPL		Leyland Daf, Bamber Bridge
Kenny Mayers	Manchester NPL, FA XI		Bamber Bridge, £12k to Chorley
John Norman	Birkenhead	26.6.71	Tranmere R, Bury, Heswall, Mold A
Stuart Drummond	Preston	11.12.75	From Youth Team
Brian Healy	Durham FA XI		West Auckland T, Billingham T, Bishop Auckland, Gateshead, Spennymoor U
FORWARDS			
Jim McCluskie	Rawtenstall NPL XI	29.9.66	Rochdale, Mossley, Hyde U< Witton A, Accrington Stanley
Marek Ceraolo	Birkenhead	10.11.75	Crewe A
Mike Bignall	Liverpool		Wrexham, Runcorn, Stevenage B, £6k to Morecambe
Mark Shirley	Liverpool		Nottingham F, Netherley RBL, Caernarfon T, Ashton U, Lancaster C

DEPARTURES - (During the season): Glen Johnstone (Gretna), Neil Sang (Chorley), Justin Jackson (Woking)
(During the close season): Ian Cain (Chorley), Ben Lavelle (Bamber Bridge)

PLAYERS ON LOAN: None.

Christie Park, Morecambe

GROUND ADDRESS: Christie Park, Lancaster Road, Morecambe, Lancashire LA4 5TJ

TELEPHONE NUMBERS: 01524 411797 Fax: 01524 411797

SIMPLE DIRECTIONS: From south leave M6 motorway at junction 34. Follow signs for Morecambe through Lancaster, on A589, go straight across the first 2 roundabouts, and at the third (with the Shrimp pub on your left), follow the signs for Town Centre - Christie Park is approx. 600 metres on your left.

CAPACITY: 6,000 **SEATED:** 2,000 **COVERED TERRACING:** 1,000

RECORD ATTENDANCE: 9,324 v Weymouth FA Cup 4.1.62

CLUB SHOP: On ground and open on matchdays, also commercial office open Monday to Friday 9.00 - 5.00 selling the same goods.

SOCIAL FACILITIES: J B's open normal licensing hours.

Morecambe Fact File

Nickname: The Shrimps **Club sponsor:** Oasis Leisure

Club colours: Red shirts, black shorts, red & white socks.

Change colours: White shirts, black shorts, black & white socks.

Midweek home matchday: Tuesdays, 7.45pm kick-off.

PREVIOUS - **Leagues:** Lancs Combination 1920-68, Northern Premier 1968-1995.
Grounds: Woodhill Lane 1920-25, shared with cricket club who still play there.

CLUB RECORDS - **Win:** 16-0 v Rossendale Utd, Lancs Combination Sept 1967 (Arnold Timmins scored 8)
Defeat: 0-7 v Darwen, November 7th 1953
Transfer fee paid: £7,500 to Fleetwood for Ian Cain, 1988
Transfer fee received: £30,000 from Woking for Justin Jackson, January 1997
Career Goalscorer:
Keith Borrowdale 289 goals 1956-68, 78-79 Lancashire Combination.
John Coleman 130 goals 1990-1995 (Northern Premier League)
Career Appearances: Steve Done 523 + 7 sub. (1968-78)

BEST SEASON - **FA Cup:** 3rd Round 1961-62, 0-1 v Weymouth.
League clubs defeated: Chester City.
FA Trophy: Winners 73-74, Q-final 72-73, 77-78, 93-94.

96-97 Captain: Dave McKearney

96-97 Player of the Year: Michael Knowles

96-97 Top Goalscorer: Justin Jackson (19)

Past players who progressed to the Football League: Fred Blondel & Malcolm Darling (Bury 1946 & 78), Herbert Harrison (Accrington 1947), Gordon Milne (Preston 1956), Ray Charnley (Blackpool 1957), Geoff Slack (Stockport 1958), Ron Mitchell (Leeds 1958), Derek Armstrong (Carlisle 1961), Alan Taylor (Rochdale 1973), John Coates (Southport via Burscough & Skelmersdale 1975), Keith Galley (Southport 1975), Brian Thompson (West Ham 1977), David Eyres (Blackpool), Kenny Lowe (Barnet via Barrow), Steve Gardner (Bradford City), Dave Lancaster (Chesterfield).

HONOURS: FA Trophy 73-74, Northern Premier Lg Presidents Cup 91-92, NPL Runners-up 94-95, Lancs Combination(5) 24-25 61-63 66-68 (R-up 25-26, Lg Cup 26-27 45-46 64-65 66-68), Lancs Jnr Cup (now ATS Tphy)(8) 25-27 61-63 68-69 85-87 92-93, 95-96; Lancs Snr Cup 67-68, Lancs Lg Div 2 83-84.

NORTHWICH VICTORIA

Formed:
1874

Chairman: Rod J Stich **Vice Chairman:** Dave Stone

President & Football Secretary: Derek Nuttall

Company Secretary: Graham Fenton

Other Directors: A Stich (Chief Exec.), Rod Stich, Roger Stubbs, Graham Cookson, Dave Edgeley

It was Northwich's best season in the Vauxhall Conference since 1982.

That simply says it all, and much of the success goes down to the managerial appointments - firstly of Mark Hancock and then ex-Leek boss Phil Wilson.

It was Mark Hancock, given the job when Brian Kettle departed shortly after the FA Umbro Trophy final in May 1996, who brought stability to the club and ensured that a talented squad of players maintained the progress shown under Kettle's guidance.

Lee Steele enjoyed a good campaign scoring the goals, but his summer transfer to Shrewsbury leaves the Vics a little short of fire power in attack.

However, Phil Wilson, who left Leek's promotion charge to take over at one of his former clubs as a player, is a very shrewd boss and he will no doubt find a suitable replacement for Steele.

With the Drill Field undergoing extensive redevelopment, exciting times are ahead, and Northwich could well be dark horses for the championship in 1997/98.

L-R, Back Row: Don Page, Steve Walters, Wayne Fairclough, Wes Simpson, Chris Duffy, Dean Greygoose, Paul Tait, Delwyn Humphreys, Ian Cooke, Eddie Bishop, Phil Lea (Physio). Front: John Stannard, Darren Vicary, Dominic Crookes, Phil Wilson (Manager), John Williams (Dir. of Football), Lee Steele, Derek Ward, Shane Reddish.
Photo: Courtesy Northwich Chronicle.

Northwich Victoria

Match No.	Date	Venue H/A	Competition	Opponents	Result	League Pos.	Attendance	Goalscorers (Times if known)
1	Aug 17	H	VC	Bath City	Won 1-0	9	769	Bishop 33
2	Aug 21	A	VC	Gateshead	Lost 1-5		489	Steele 75
3	Aug 24	A	VC	Rushden & Diamonds	Drew 1-1		2112	Vicary 12
4	Aug 26	H	VC	Bromsgrove Rovers	Won 1-0	7	722	Richardson 29 (og)
5	Aug 31	H	VC	Stevenage Borough	Lost 0-1	11	1021	
6	Sep 2	A	VC	Hednesford Town	Lost 0-3		1096	
7	Sep 9	H	VC	Rushden & Diamonds	Lost 1-2		769	Steele 20
8	Sep 14	H	VC	Telford United	Won 1-0	15	742	Walters 56
9	Sep 17	A	VC	Southport	Drew 0-0		1077	
10	Sep 21	A	VC	Stalybridge Celtic	Won 1-0	11	701	Duffy 25
11	Sep 28	H	VC	Macclesfield Town	Won 2-1	9	1527	Howarth 36 (og), Cooke 95
12	Oct 2	A	VC	Morecambe	Lost 0-2		1160	
13	Oct 5	H	VC	Dover Athletic	Won 2-0	13	964	Humphreys 49 (pen), Stebbing 19 (og)
14	Oct 12	A	VC	Altrincham	Won 3-2	6	1334	Steele 14, 29, Crookes 21
15	Oct 19	H	VC	Kidderminster Harriers	Drew 1-1	8	1234	Humphreys 41 (pen)
16	Oct 26	A	VC	Macclesfield Town	Won 1-0		1375	Cooke 34
17	Nov 2	H	VC	Hayes	Won 2-1	4	972	Steele 11, 37
18	Nov 9	A	VC	Woking	Lost 1-3	5	3091	Bishop 69 (pen)
19	**Nov 16**	**H**	**FAC 1**	**Walsall**	**Drew 2-2**		**3142**	**Cooke 38, 79**
20	**Nov 19**	**A**	**SCC**	**Bromsgrove Rovers**	**Lost 1-3**		**271**	**Tait 20**
21	Nov 23	A	VC	Slough Town	Lost 0-1	8	849	
22	**Nov 26**	**A**	**FAC 1 R**	**Walsall**	**Lost 1-3**		**3491**	**Tait 69**
23	Nov 30	A	VC	Welling United	Drew 1-1	8	527	Walters 88
24	Dec 7	H	VC	Farnborough Town	Drew 1-1	8	702	Crookes 1
25	Dec 14	A	VC	Dover Athletic	Drew 2-2		722	Tait 8, Steele 40
26	Dec 20	H	VC	Southport	Won 5-1		701	Vicary 6, 75, Tait 23, 44, Steele 51
27	Dec 26	A	VC	Halifax Town	Won 3-0		1078	Simpson 18, Steele 87, 89
28	Dec 28	H	VC	Morecambe	Won 1-0	3	1436	Steele 20
29	Jan 4	A	VC	Kidderminster Harriers	Lost 0-1	4	2794	
30	Jan 11	H	VC	Kettering Town	Won 2-1	4	1056	Humphreys 58, Walters 70
31	**Jan 18**	**H**	**FAT 1**	**Hednesford Town**	**Won 3-1**		**1109**	**Tait 39, Bishop 70, 87 (pen)**
32	Jan 25	A	VC	Telford United	Drew 2-2	4	969	Steele 22, Cooke 29
33	Feb 1	H	VC	Altrincham	Drew 2-2	4	1292	Walters 42, Steele 79
34	**Feb 8**	**A**	**FAT 2**	**Bishop Auckland**	**Lost 2-3**		**705**	**Bishop 60, Cooke 87**
35	Feb 15	A	VC	Slough Town	Won 4-3	3	703	Vicary 24, Cooke (3) 37, 64, 89
36	Feb 22	H	VC	Welling United	Drew 0-0	4	877	
37	Mar 1	A	VC	Bromsgrove Rovers	Won 5-0	4	638	Tait (3) 9, 41, 54, Duffy 51, Stannard 65
38	Mar 8	A	VC	Stevenage Borough	Lost 0-2	4	2501	
39	Mar 15	H	VC	Gateshead	Won 4-2	4	823	Walters 28 (pen), Tait 32, Bishop 38, Stannard 57
40	Mar 17	H	VC	Halifax Town	Drew 2-2	4	911	Tait 3, Walters 5
41	Mar 22	A	VC	Farnborough Town	Drew 2-2	4	728	Crookes 25, Steele 90
42	Mar 29	A	VC	Kettering Town	Lost 0-1		1378	
43	Mar 31	H	VC	Stalybridge Celtic	Lost 0-1	4	814	
44	Apr 5	A	VC	Hayes	Drew 1-1	4	591	Vicary 45
45	Apr 12	H	VC	Hednesford Town	Won 2-1	4	928	Tait 83 (pen), Steele 89
46	Apr 26	H	VC	Woking	Lost 1-2	5	1208	Stannard 32
47	May 3	A	VC	Bath City	Lost 2-3	6	1258	Steele 28, Tait 32

Northwich Victoria

1	2	3	4	5	6	7	8	9	10	11	12	14	15	Mth No.
Greygoose	Reddish	Duffy	Burgess	Simpson	Bishop	Lewis	Walters	Cooke	Steele	Vicary	Tait	Woods	Davies	1
Greygoose	Ward	Duffy	Burgess	Simpson	Bishop	Lewis	Reddish	Cooke	Steele	Vicary	Tait	Davies	Crookes	2
Greygoose	Crookes	Duffy	Burgess	Simpson	Bishop	Ward	Reddish	Cooke	Steele	Vicary	Tait	Abbey	Lewis	3
Greygoose	Reddish	Duffy	Burgess	Simpson	Bishop	Ward	Walters	Cooke	Steele	Vicary	Tait	Humphreys	Crookes	4
Greygoose	Reddish	Duffy	Burgess	Simpson	Bishop	Ward	Walters	Cooke	Steele	Vicary	Tait	Crookes	Humphreys	5
Woods	Ward	Duffy	Burgess	Crookes	Bishop	Fairclough	Reddish	Cooke	Steele	Tait	Vicary	Walters	Humphreys	6
Greygoose	Crookes	Fairclough	Reddish	Simpson	Bishop	Tait	Walters	Cooke	Steele	Duffy	Vicary	Ward	Clarke	7
Greygoose	Reddish	Fairclough	Crookes	Simpson	Bishop	Duffy	Walters	Cooke	Steele	Vicary	Ward	Burgess	Davies	8
Greygoose	Reddish	Fairclough	Crookes	Simpson	Bishop	Duffy	Walters	Cooke	Steele	Vicary	Ward	Burgess	Davies	9
Greygoose	Reddish	Fairclough	Crookes	Simpson	Bishop	Duffy	Walters	Cooke	Steele	Vicary	Ward	Burgess	Humphreys	10
Greygoose	Reddish	Duffy	Crookes	Simpson	Bishop	Humphreys	Walters	Humphreys	Cooke	Vicary	Steele	Burgess	Ward	11
Greygoose	Ward	Duffy	Crookes	Simpson	Bishop	Humphreys	Walters	Humphreys	Cooke	Vicary	Steele	Burgess	Carthy	12
Greygoose	Ward	Duffy	Crookes	Simpson	Bishop	Humphreys	Walters	Steele	Cooke	Vicary	Burgess	Hutchinson	Reddish	13
Greygoose	Ward	Duffy	Crookes	Simpson	Bishop	Humphreys	Reddish	Steele	Cooke	Vicary	Burgess	Hutchinson	Fairclough	14
Greygoose	Ward	Duffy	Crookes	Simpson	Bishop	Humphreys	Reddish	Steele	Cooke	Vicary	Burgess	Walters	Fairclough	15
Greygoose	Ward	Duffy	Crookes	Simpson	Bishop	Humphreys	Walters	Steele	Cooke	Vicary	Fairclough	Burgess	Reddish	16
Greygoose	Fairclough	Duffy	Crookes	Simpson	Bishop	Ward	Walters	Steele	Cooke	Vicary	Tait	Reddish	Burgess	17
Greygoose	Fairclough	Duffy	Crookes	Simpson	Bishop	Ward	Walters	Steele	Cooke	Vicary	Tait	Burgess	Reddish	18
Greygoose	**Ward**	**Fairclough**	**Crookes**	**Simpson**	**Bishop**	**Humphreys**	**Walters**	**Steele**	**Cooke**	**Vicary**	**Tait**	**Reddish**	**Duffy**	**19**
Greygoose	**Ward**	**Duffy**	**Cooke**	**Simpson**	**Bishop**	**Humphreys**	**Walters**	**Steele**	**Tait**	**Vicary**	**Reddish**	**Fairclough**	**Carthy**	**20**
Greygoose	Ward	Fairclough	Crookes	Simpson	Bishop	Humphreys	Reddish	Steele	Cooke	Vicary	Duffy	Tait	Page	21
Greygoose	**Reddish**	**Fairclough**	**Crookes**	**Simpson**	**Bishop**	**Humphreys**	**Duffy**	**Steele**	**Cooke**	**Vicary**	**Tait**	**Burgess**	**Ward**	**22**
Greygoose	Ward	Fairclough	Crookes	Simpson	Bishop	Reddish	Walters	Steele	Tait	Duffy	Page	Vicary	Abbey	23
Greygoose	Reddish	Fairclough	Crookes	Simpson	Bishop	Duffy	Walters	Humphreys	Tait	Vicary	Steele	Ward	Page	24
Greygoose	Ward	Duffy	Crookes	Fairclough	Reddish	Humphreys	Walters	Steele	Tait	Vicary	Page	Abbey	Briggs	25
Greygoose	Ward	Duffy	Crookes	Fairclough	Bishop	Reddish	Walters	Steele	Tait	Vicary	Page	Humphreys	Simpson	26
Greygoose	Ward	Duffy	Crookes	Simpson	Bishop	Reddish	Walters	Steele	Tait	Vicary	Stannard	Humphreys	Page	27
Greygoose	Ward	Duffy	Crookes	Simpson	Stannard	Reddish	Walters	Steele	Tait	Vicary	Cooke	Humphreys	Page	28
Greygoose	Ward	Duffy	Crookes	Simpson	Cook	Reddish	Walters	Steele	Tait	Vicary	Stannard	Humphreys	Page	29
Greygoose	Ward	Duffy	Crookes	Simpson	Fairclough	Tait	Walters	Steele	Cooke	Vicary	Humphreys	Stannard	Page	30
Greygoose	**Ward**	**Duffy**	**Fairclough**	**Simpson**	**Bishop**	**Reddish**	**Tait**	**Steele**	**Cooke**	**Vicary**	**Humphreys**	**Hughes**	**Briggs**	**31**
Greygoose	Ward	Fairclough	Crookes	Simpson	Bishop	Reddish	Tait	Steele	Cooke	Humphreys	Vicary	Duffy	Briggs	32
Greygoose	Ward	Duffy	Crookes	Simpson	Bishop	Reddish	Walters	Steele	Cooke	Tait	Vicary	Humphreys	Fairclough	33
Greygoose	**Ward**	**Duffy**	**Crookes**	**Simpson**	**Bishop**	**Reddish**	**Walters**	**Steele**	**Cooke**	**Tait**	**Vicary**	**Humphreys**	**Fairclough**	**34**
Greygoose	Ward	Fairclough	Crookes	Simpson	Bishop	Reddish	Walters	Steele	Cooke	Vicary	Tait	Humphreys	Stannard	35
Greygoose	Ward	Fairclough	Crookes	Simpson	Tait	Reddish	Walters	Steele	Humphreys	Vicary	Stannard	Duffy	Carthy	36
Greygoose	Ward	Fairclough	Crookes	Simpson	Duffy	Reddish	Walters	Steele	Tait	Vicary	Stannard	Hughes	Carthy	37
Greygoose	Duffy	Fairclough	Crookes	Simpson	Bishop	Reddish	Walters	Humphreys	Tait	Vicary	Stannard	Ward	Steele	38
Greygoose	Stannard	Fairclough	Crookes	Simpson	Bishop	Reddish	Walters	Humphreys	Tait	Vicary	Cooke	Ward	Duffy	39
Greygoose	Stannard	Fairclough	Crookes	Simpson	Bishop	Reddish	Walters	Humphreys	Tait	Vicary	Cooke	Ward	Steele	40
Greygoose	Stannard	Fairclough	Crookes	Simpson	Bishop	Reddish	Walters	Humphreys	Tait	Vicary	Cooke	Steele	Ward	41
Greygoose	Ward	Fairclough	Crookes	Simpson	Tait	Reddish	Walters	Humphreys	Cooke	Vicary	Steele	Stannard	Duffy	42
Hughes	Ward	Stannard	Crookes	Simpson	Steele	Reddish	Walters	Tait	Cooke	Vicary	Humphreys	Duffy	Carthy	43
Hughes	Ward	Fairclough	Crookes	Simpson	Duffy	Humphreys	Walters	Cooke	Tait	Vicary	Steele	Stannard	Carthy	44
Hughes	Ward	Duffy	Crookes	Fairclough	Cooke	Reddish	Walters	Humphreys	Tait	Vicary	Steele	Stannard	Carthy	45
Hughes	Ward	Duffy	Crookes	Fairclough	Stannard	Reddish	Humphreys	Steele	Tait	Vicary	Carthy	Hughes	Greygoose	46
Greygoose	Ward	Fairclough	Crookes	Simpson	Duffy	Reddish	Walters	Steele	Tait	Stannard	Humphreys	J Hughes	RHughes	47

PHIL WILSON (MANAGER)

Date of Appointment	December 1996
Date of Birth:	6th December 1950
Place of Birth:	Wallasey

PREVIOUS CLUBS

As manager	Caernarfon T., Stalybridge C., Leek T.
As coach	
As player	New Brighton, Runcorn, Mossley, Altrincham, Northwich Vics.

HONOURS

As manager	NPL 91-92
As player	FA Trophy 84, R-up 80, 83. NPL (x2), APL

Director of Football: John Williams **Physio:** Phil Lea

Lee Steele, Vics' top scorer last season, getting the better of Richard Nugent of Kettering.

MATCHDAY PROGRAMME

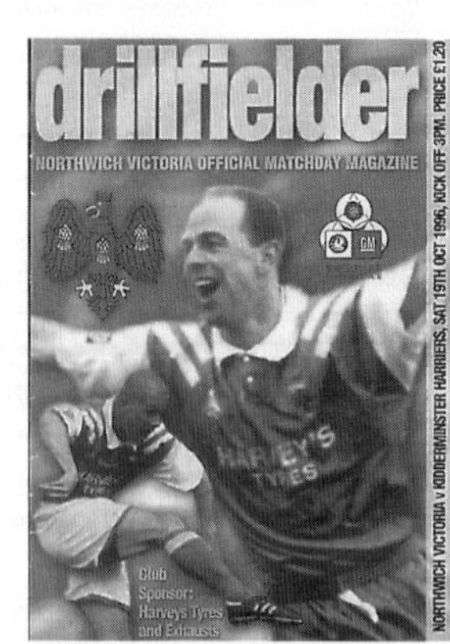

Number of pages	32
Price	£1.20
Programme Editor	William Hughes
Other club publications:	1997 Yearbook by William Hughes £3
Local Newspapers:	Northwich Guardian (Wed.) Northwich Chronicle (Wed.) Daily Post Manchester Evening News Pink (Sat.)
Local Radio Stations:	GMR (BBC Manchester) Piccadilly Radio; Signal Radio

1997-98 PLAYING SQUAD

PLAYER	Birthplace Honours	Birthdate	CLUBS
GOALKEEPERS			
Dean Greygoose	Thetford E: Y	8.12.64	Camb. Utd, Leyton Orient, Crystal Palace, Crewe Alexandra, Holywell T, Northwch V.
DEFENDERS			
Dave Burgess	Liverpool	20.1.60	Tranmere R, Grimsby T, Blackppol, Carlisle U., Northwich V.
Derek Ward	Birkenhead	17.5.72	Bury, Southport, Northwich V.
Wayne Fairclough	Nottingham	27.4.68	Notts Co, Mansfield, Chesterfield, Northwich V.
Wes Simpson	Winsford	29.3.77	Crewe Alexandra
MIDFIELDERS			
Chris Duffy	Manchester	31.10.73	Crewe Alexandra, Wigan Ath.
Jason Gallagher	Liverpool	25.3.72	Marine, Ternia (Belg), Witton A.
Shane Reddish	Bolsover	20.9.69	Mansfield T, Doncaster R, Carlisle U, Hartlepool U
Steve Walters	Plymouth E: Y	9.1.72	Crewe Alexandra
Eddie Bishop	Liverpool	28.11.62	Winsford U, Northwich V, Altrincham, Runcorn, Tranmere R., Chester C., Northwich V.
FORWARDS			
Delwyn Humphries	Shrewsbury E: SP, GMVC, FAT, SSC	13.2.65	Newtown, Bridgnorth T, Kidderminster H., £10k to Northwich V.
Paul Tait	Newcastle	24.10.74	Everton, Wigan Athletic, Runcorn, Northwich V.
Lee Steele	Liverpool		Bootle
Darren Vicary	Liverpool		Cammell Lairds
Ian Cooke	Bebington	1.11.73	Cammell Lairds

DEPARTURES - (During the season): Jeff Parker (Barrow), Lee Cooper (Knowsley U), Neil Hardy (Altrincham), Rob Radcliffe (Macclesfield T), Rob Hilton (Tetley Walker), George Oghani (Guiseley - Loan), Charlie Boyd (Congleton T - Loan), Steve Holden (Released), Hugh McAuley (Skelmersdale U), Darren Tinson (Macclesfield T), Charlie Boyd (Winsford U), Paul Clayton (Released), Graeme Hughes (Released), Neil Ogden (Released).
(During close season): George Oghani (Released), Brian Butler (Southport), Mark Jones (Hyde U), Graham Abel (Chorley), Carwyn Williams (Macclesfield T).

LOAN PLAYERS: Jon Sunderland (Blackpool), Mike Edwards (Tranmere R).

Drill Field, Northwich

GROUND ADDRESS: The Drill Field, Drill Field Road, Northwich, Cheshire. CW9 5HN.

TELEPHONE NUMBERS: 01606 41450. Fax: 01606 330577. Internet address: http://www.u-net.com/~sandiway/home.htm. **Club Newsline:** 0891 12 27 13

SIMPLE DIRECTIONS: Leave M6 at Junc.19 and follow A556 towards Chester. At second roundabout (approx. 6 miles), turn right onto A533. Ground on right behind Volunteer Public House.

CAPACITY: 6,000 **SEATED:** 660 **COVERED TERRACING:** 3,500

CLUB SHOP: Located inside ground. Open match days. Manager: Andy Dakin.

SOCIAL FACILITIES: Large social club with members lounge and seperate function room - both available for hire Tel: 0606 43120. Food available on matchdays with prior notice. Bass beers, Pool, Darts, TV.

Northwich Fact File

Nickname: The Vics, Greens

Club Sponsors: Harvey's Tyres.

Club colours: Green & white shirts, green shorts and white socks.

Change colours: Yellow

Midweek home matchday: Monday.

Reserve Team's league: None.

PREVIOUS - **Leagues:** The Combination 1890-1892, Football League Div.2 1892-94, The Combination 1894-1898, The Cheshire League 1898-1900, Manchester League 1900-12, Lancashire 1912-19, Cheshire County League 1919-68, Northern Premier League 1968-79.
Grounds: None

CLUB RECORDS - **Attendance:** 11,290 v Witton Albion, Cheshire League, Good Friday 1949.
Win: 17-0 v Marple Ass. 15.12.1883 **Defeat:** 3-10 v Port Vale 7.2.1931
Career Goalscorer: Peter Burns 160 - 1955-65.
Career Appearances: 970 by Ken Jones 1969-85.
Transfer Fee paid: £10,000 to Hyde United for Malcolm O'Connor - August 1988 and to Kidderminster Harriers for Delwyn Humphreys - September 1995.
Transfer Fee received: £50,000 from Chester City for Neil Morton - October 1990.

BEST SEASON - **FA Cup:** Quarter Finals 1883-84
League clubs defeated: Rochdale, Peterborough, Watford, Chester C., Crewe Alex.
FA Trophy: Winners 83-84, R-up 82-83 95-96.

Past players who progressed to the Football League in the last five years:
Tony Hemmings (Wycombe W.), Tony Bullock (Barnsley), Darren Tinson (Macclesfield).

1996-97 **Captain:** Shane Reddish

1996-97 **Top Goalscorer:** Lee Steele (15)

1996-97 **Player of the Year:** Wes Simpson

HONOURS: Welsh Cup Runners-up 1881/82,1888-89; FA Trophy 1983/84, Runners-up 1982/83 & 1995/96; Bob Lord Trophy 1979/80, 92/93; Northern Premier League Runners-up 1976/77; Northern Premier League Cup 1972/73, Runners-up 1978/79; Cheshire County League Champions 1956/57, Runners-up 1924/25, 47/48; Cheshire County League Cup 1925/35; Manchester League Champions 1902/03, Runners-up 1900/01, 03/04, 07/08, 08/09, 11/12; The Combination Runners-up 1890/91; Cheshire Senior Cup 1880-81, 81/82, 82/83, 83/84, 84/85, 85/86, 1928/29, 36/37, 49/50, 54/55, 71/72, 76/77, 78/79, 83/84, 93/94. Runners-up 1891/92, 96/97, 1905/06, 08/09, 47/48, 50/51, 63/64, 1965/66, 69/70, 70/71, 77/78, 85/86; Staffordshire Senior Cup 1978/79, 79/80, 89/90, Runners-up 1986/87, 90/91; Cheshire Amateur Cup 1901/02, Runners-up 1898/99, 02/93, Northwich Senior Cup 1948/49, 58/59, 59/60, 63/64, 64/65, 65/66, 67/68, 68/69, 69/70, 71/72, 74/75, Runners-up 1953/54, 54/55, 55/56, 57/58, 60/61, 61/62, 72/73; Mid Cheshire Senior Cup 1984/85, 85/86, 87/88, 89/90, 91/92, 93/94, 94/95, 96/97, Runners-up 1982/83, 83/84, 90/91, 92/93; North-West Floodlit League 1966/67, 75/76; Cheshire League Lancashire Combination Inter-League Cup 1961/62; Guardian Charity Shield 1985/86, 86/87, 87/88.

RUSHDEN & DIAMONDS

Formed
1992

President: D Attley **Chairman:** W M Griggs CBE

Managing Director: M G Darnell

Football Secretary: David Joyce Tel: 01933 279466 (H) 01933 652000 (B)

Press Officer: David Joyce **Commercial Manager:** Bernard Lake

The ambitious Northamptonshire club's summer signings have taken their spending to over half a million pounds on their squad of players. Some of those players have been moved on since former England star Brian Talbot replaced the long serving Roger Ashley as head coach but it is now imperative that Diamonds make a challenge at the top end of the table rather than flirt with relegation.

There is no doubting that Diamonds posses the facilities to progress. Nene Park is without doubt the best stadium in non-League football and, in chairman Max Griggs, they have a man who is determined to see his club in the Football League.

In the end, a finishing position of twelfth flattered Diamonds a little, but it certainly brought in the crowds, with an average of 2,514 watching - a figure beaten only by promotion chasers Kidderminster and Stevenage and well ahead of neighbouring Kettering.

The close season has seen their expensive squad trimmed and it still has, on paper, as much talent, if not more, than most. Perhaps expectations are too high, especially for a club that is still only five years old. However, with the backing of Mr. Griggs, a big following and a superb stadium, nothing less than a championship challenge will do.

L-R, Back Row: Michael Mison, Andrew Chapman, Julian Capone, Adam Cann, Kenny Cramman, Simeon Hodson, Glen Fuff, Brendan Hackett. Middle: Billy Jeffrey (Asst. Head Coach), Steve Stott, Carl Alford, Darren Watts, Steve Cherry, Martin Davies, Tim Wooding, Darren Collins, Simon Parsell (Physio). Front: Adrian Foster, Andy Peaks, Gary Butterworth, Brian Talbot Head Coach), Danny O'Shea, Jim Rodwell, Paul Underwood. Missing: Simon Stapleton, David Gilmore, Malcolm Ndekwe, John Hamsher.

Rushden & Diamonds

Match No.	Date	Venue H/A	Competition	Opponents	Result	League Pos.	Attendance	Goalscorers (Times if known)
1	Aug 17	A	VC	Altrincham	Lost 3-4	14	1037	Cramman (2) 17, 54, Collins 47
2	Aug 20	A	VC	Slough Town	Lost 0-5		1325	
3	Aug 24	H	VC	Northwich Victoria	Drew 1-1		2112	Collins 47
4	Aug 26	A	VC	Hayes	Drew 1-1	22	1043	Alford 30
5	Aug 31	H	VC	Stalybridge Celtic	Drew 1-1	22	2156	Cramman 87
6	Sep 3	H	VC	Macclesfield Town	Drew 1-1		2242	Wilkin 88
7	Sep 7	A	VC	Halifax Town	Won 3-1	16	948	Rodwell 29, Collins 58, Cramman 74
8	Sep 9	A	VC	Northwich Victoria	Won 2-1		769	Wilson 45, Rodwell 83
9	**Sep 14**	**A**	**FAC 1 Q**	**Westfields**	**Won 4-0**		**518**	**Wilkin 23, Furnell (3) 29, 52, 87**
10	Sep 17	H	VC	Farnborough Town	Lost 0-2		2298	
11	Sep 21	A	VC	Woking	Lost 2-4	18	2768	Wilkin 15, Bailey 70
12	Sep 24	H	VC	Stevenage Borough	Lost 0-1		3288	
13	**Sep 28**	**H**	**FAC 2 Q**	**Gresley Rovers**	**Won 4-0**		**1875**	**King 23, Alford (2) 33, 75, Collins 69**
14	Sep 30	A	VC	Hednesford Town	Lost 0-1		1252	
15	Oct 5	H	VC	Welling United	Won 3-0	16	2296	Watts 5 (og), Stott 69, Cramman 86
16	**Oct 8**	**A**	**SCC**	**Dover Athletic**	**Won 3-2**		**723**	**Cramman 53, Wilkin 57, 89**
17	**Oct 12**	**H**	**FAC 3 Q**	**Bilston Town**	**Won 1-0**		**1605**	**Collins 60**
18	Oct 14	A	VC	Kidderminster Harriers	Lost 0-1		2603	
19	Oct 19	H	VC	Gateshead	Lost 0-4	18	2214	
20	**Oct 26**	**H**	**FAC 4 Q**	**Bognor Regis Town**	**Won 2-0**		**1844**	**Collins 72, 83**
21	Nov 2	A	VC	Southport	Lost 1-2	19	1225	King 22
22	Nov 9	H	VC	Dover Athletic	Drew 1-1	19	2110	Alford 56
23	**Nov 16**	**A**	**FAC 1**	**Boreham Wood**	**Drew 1-1**		**1567**	**Hackett 27**
24	**Nov 19**	**H**	**SCC**	**Stevenage Borough**	**Won 1-0**		**1073**	**Collins 66**
25	Nov 23	H	VC	Morecambe	Lost 0-2	20	1040	
26	**Nov 26**	**H**	**FAC 1 R**	**Boreham Wood**	**Lost 2-3**		**2619**	**Wilkin 15, Collins 90**
27	Nov 30	H	VC	Bath City	Won 4-1	18	1853	Collins 5, Wilkin 47, 81, Capone 84
28	Dec 7	A	VC	Telford United	Won 5-0		900	Collins 41, 90, Alford 67, 86, Rodwell 60
29	Dec 14	H	VC	Bromsgrove Rovers	Lost 1-2	19	2144	Alford 4
30	**Dec 16**	**A**	**SCC**	**Kidderminster Harriers**	**Lost 0-1**		**811**	
31	Dec 21	H	VC	Kidderminster Harriers	Drew 1-1		2529	Alford 39 (pen)
32	Dec 28	A	VC	Stalybridge Celtic	Lost 0-2	21	788	
33	**Jan 18**	**H**	**FAT 1**	**Farnborough Town**	**Lost 1-2**		**1759**	**Wilkin 86**
34	Jan 25	A	VC	Farnborough Town	Drew 2-2	21	961	Leworthy 37, Stapleton 74
35	Feb 1	H	VC	Morecambe	Won 2-1	20	2145	Leworthy 71, Cramman 77
36	Feb 8	H	VC	Hednesford Town	Lost 0-2	21	2618	
37	Feb 15	A	VC	Macclesfield Town	Lost 1-2	22	1304	Leworthy 36
38	Feb 22	A	VC	Gateshead	Lost 0-1	22	632	
39	Mar 1	H	VC	Slough Town	Drew 2-2	21	1980	Capone 14, 72
40	Mar 8	A	VC	Kettering Town	Won 5-1	20	4628	Alford 7, Hackett 36, Leworthy 62, 81, Butterworth
41	Mar 15	A	VC	Bromsgrove Rovers	Won 1-0	20	1109	83
42	Mar 18	H	VC	Kettering Town	Won 1-0	18	5170	Alford 76
43	Mar 22	H	VC	Telford United	Won 2-0	16	2554	Stott 45
44	Mar 25	A	VC	Welling United	Won 1-0	14	747	Rodwell 22, Leworthy 75
45	Mar 29	A	VC	Dover Athletic	Drew 1-1		1671	Leworthy 82
46	Mar 31	H	VC	Hayes	Drew 2-2	16	3134	Hackett 19
47	Apr 5	H	VC	Southport	Won 3-0	14	2218	Collins 36, Alford 83
48	Apr 12	A	VC	Bath City	Lost 2-3	17	960	Alford 19, 82, Leworthy 84
49	Apr 21	A	VC	Stevenage Borough	Lost 1-4		2836	Alford 50, Stapleton 70
50	Apr 26	H	VC	Halifax Town	Won 1-0	15	2629	Alford 37
51	Apr 29	H	VC	Woking	Drew 1-1		2589	Hackett 79
52	May 3	H	VC	Altrincham	Won 3-1	12	2521	Collins 83
								Butterworth 23, Shepherd 34 (og), King 73

Rushden & Diamonds

1	2	3	4	5	6	7	8	9	10	11	12	14	15	Mth No.
Benstead	Peaks	Ashby	Stott	Rodwell	Hannigan	Wilkin	Butterworth	Alford	Collins	Cramman	Hackett	Wooding	King	1
Benstead	Peaks	Ashby	Stott	Rodwell	Hannigan	Hackett	Butterworth	Wilkin	Collins	Cramman	Kirkup	Wooding	King	2
Benstead	Wooding	Ashby	Stott	Rodwell	Cramman	King	Butterworth	Alford	Collins	Hackett	Wilkin	Kirkup	Wilson	3
Benstead	Wooding	Ashby	Stott	Rodwell	Cramman	King	Butterworth	Alford	Collins	Hackett	Bailey	Kirkup	Wilson	4
Davies	Wooding	Ashby	Stott	Rodwell	Wilson	Hackett	Butterworth	Alford	Collins	Cramman	Kirkup	Wilkin	King	5
Davies	Wooding	Ashby	Stott	Rodwell	Wilson	Wilkin	Butterworth	Alford	Collins	Cramman	Kirkup	Hackett	King	6
Davies	Wooding	Ashby	Stott	Rodwell	Wilson	Wilkin	Butterworth	Alford	Collins	Cramman	Furnell	Hackett	Peaks	7
Davies	Wooding	Ashby	Stott	Rodwell	Wilson	Wilkin	Butterworth	Furnell	Collins	Cramman	Kirkup	Hackett	Peaks	8
Davies	**Wooding**	**Ashby**	**Stott**	**Rodwell**	**Wilson**	**Wilkin**	**Butterworth**	**Furnell**	**Collins**	**Cramman**	**Kirkup**	**Hackett**	**Peaks**	**9**
Davies	Wooding	Ashby	Stott	Rodwell	Wilson	Wilkin	Butterworth	Furnell	Collins	Cramman	Kirkup	Hackett	Alford	10
Davies	Wooding	Ashby	Stott	Rodwell	Wilson	Wilkin	Butterworth	Bailey	Hackett	Cramman	Kirkup	Furnell	Peaks	11
Davies	Wooding	Ashby	Stott	Rodwell	King	Wilkin	Butterworth	Alford	Collins	Cramman	Kirkup	Hackett	Wilson	12
Davies	**Wooding**	**Ashby**	**Stott**	**Rodwell**	**King**	**Wilkin**	**Butterworth**	**Alford**	**Collins**	**Cramman**	**Kirkup**	**Peaks**	**Wilson**	**13**
Davies	Wooding	Lilwall	Stott	Rodwell	King	Wilkin	Butterworth	Alford	Collins	Cramman	Kirkup	Peaks	Wilson	14
Davies	Wooding	Lilwall	Stott	Rodwell	King	Morrison	Butterworth	Alford	Collins	Cramman	Wilkin	Smith	Furnell	15
Davies	**Wooding**	**Lilwall**	**Stott**	**Rodwell**	**King**	**Morrison**	**Butterworth**	**Wilkin**	**Collins**	**Cramman**	**Peaks**	**Smith**	**Furnell**	**16**
Davies	**Wooding**	**Lilwall**	**Stott**	**Rodwell**	**Smith**	**King**	**Butterworth**	**Wilkin**	**Collins**	**Cramman**	**Furnell**	**Bailey**	**Hackett**	**17**
Davies	Wooding	Lilwall	Smith	Rodwell	King	Bailey	Butterworth	Wilkin	Collins	Cramman	Furnell	Peaks	Hackett	18
Davies	Wooding	Ashby	Smith	Rodwell	Bailey	Morrison	Butterworth	Alford	Collins	Cramman	King	Wilkin	Hackett	19
Davies	**Wooding**	**Lilwall**	**Holden**	**Rodwell**	**Peaks**	**King**	**Butterworth**	**Alford**	**Collins**	**Wilson**	**Wilkin**	**Bailey**	**Hackett**	**20**
Davies	Wooding	Lilwall	Holden	Rodwell	Wilson	King	Butterworth	Alford	Collins	Peaks	Morrison	Wilkin	Hackett	21
Davies	Wooding	Hackett	Holden	Rodwell	Wilson	King	Butterworth	Alford	Collins	Peaks	Morrison	Wilkin	Bailey	22
Davies	**Wooding**	**Tucker**	**Holden**	**Rodwell**	**Wilson**	**King**	**Butterworth**	**Alford**	**Collins**	**Hackett**	**Capone**	**Wilkin**	**Bailey**	**23**
Davies	**Wooding**	**Tucker**	**Holden**	**Rodwell**	**Wilson**	**King**	**Morrison**	**Bailey**	**Collins**	**Hackett**	**Capone**	**Wilkin**	**Alford**	**24**
Davies	Wooding	Tucker	Holden	Rodwell	Wilson	King	Butterworth	Bailey	Collins	Hackett	Morrison	Wilkin	Furnell	25
Davies	**Wooding**	**Tucker**	**Holden**	**Rodwell**	**Smith**	**King**	**Butterworth**	**Wilkin**	**Collins**	**Hackett**	**Capone**	**Bailey**	**Furnell**	**26**
Davies	Wooding	Tucker	Holden	Rodwell	Smith	Capone	Butterworth	Wilkin	Collins	Hackett	Cramman	Bailey	Furnell	27
Davies	Hodson	Tucker	Holden	Rodwell	Smith	Cramman	Butterworth	Wilkin	Collins	Hackett	Alford	King	Peaks	28
Davies	Hodson	Tucker	Peaks	Ashby	Smith	Cramman	Butterworth	Wilkin	Collins	Alford	Furnell	King	Bailey	29
Davies	**Wooding**	**Tucker**	**Holden**	**Ashby**	**Smith**	**Cramman**	**Butterworth**	**Wilkin**	**Collins**	**Alford**	**Furnell**	**King**	**Bailey**	**30**
Davies	Hodson	Ashby	Holden	Rodwell	Smith	Cramman	Butterworth	Ayorinde	Collins	Alford	Hackett	King	Bailey	31
Davies	Hodson	Ashby	Holden	Rodwell	Smith	Cramman	Butterworth	Ayorinde	Tucker	Alford	Hackett	King	Wilkin	32
Davies	**Hodson**	**Tucker**	**Holden**	**Rodwell**	**Stott**	**Cramman**	**Butterworth**	**Alford**	**Collins**	**Capone**	**Furnell**	**King**	**Wilkin**	**33**
Davies	Hodson	Ashby	Stott	Rodwell	Stapleton	Cramman	Butterworth	Collins	Leworthy	Alford	King	Tucker	Capone	34
Benstead	Hodson	Ashby	Stott	Rodwell	Stapleton	Cramman	Butterworth	Collins	Leworthy	Alford	King	Furnell	Capone	35
Benstead	Hodson	Ashby	Stott	Rodwell	Capone	Cramman	Butterworth	Collins	Leworthy	Alford	King	Tucker	Furnell	36
Davies	Hodson	Ashby	Stott	Rodwell	Tucker	Cramman	Capone	Collins	Leworthy	Alford	Wilkin	Peaks	Hackett	37
Davies	Hodson	Ashby	Crossley	Rodwell	Stapleton	Cramman	Butterworth	Collins	Leworthy	Capone	Alford	Hackett	Peaks	38
Davies	Hodson	Hackett	Crossley	Rodwell	Stott	Capone	Butterworth	Alford	Leworthy	Peaks	Collins	Bailey	Cramman	39
Davies	Hodson	Cramman	Peaks	Rodwell	Stott	Capone	Butterworth	Alford	Leworthy	Hackett	Collins	Bailey	Stapleton	40
Davies	Hodson	Cramman	Peaks	Rodwell	Stott	Capone	Butterworth	Alford	Leworthy	Hackett	King	Bailey	Stapleton	41
Davies	Hodson	Cramman	Peaks	Rodwell	Stott	Capone	Butterworth	Alford	Leworthy	Hackett	King	Bailey	Stapleton	42
Cherry	Stapleton	Cramman	Peaks	Rodwell	Stott	Capone	Butterworth	Alford	Leworthy	Hackett	King	Bailey	Fuff	43
Cherry	Stapleton	Cramman	Peaks	Rodwell	Stott	Capone	Butterworth	Alford	Leworthy	Hackett	Collins	Bailey	King	44
Cherry	Hodson	Cramman	Peaks	Rodwell	Stott	Capone	Butterworth	Alford	Leworthy	Hackett	Collins	Stapleton	King	45
Cherry	Hodson	Cramman	Peaks	Rodwell	Stott	King	Butterworth	Collins	Leworthy	Hackett	Alford	Wilkin	Stapleton	46
Cherry	Hodson	Cramman	Peaks	Rodwell	Stott	Collins	Butterworth	Alford	Leworthy	Hackett	Bailey	Wilkin	Stapleton	47
Cherry	Hodson	Cramman	Peaks	Rodwell	Stott	King	Butterworth	Alford	Collins	Hackett	Wilkin	Furnell	Stapleton	48
Cherry	Hodson	Cramman	Peaks	Rodwell	Stott	Collins	Butterworth	Alford	Leworthy	Hackett	Bailey	Chapman	Stapleton	49
Cherry	Hodson	Cramman	Peaks	Rodwell	Stott	Collins	Butterworth	Alford	Leworthy	Hackett	King	Ashby	Stapleton	50
Cherry	Hodson	Cramman	Peaks	Rodwell	Stott	Collins	Butterworth	Alford	Leworthy	Hackett	King	Furnell	Fuff	51
Cherry	Hodson	Cramman	Peaks	Rodwell	Stott	Collins	Butterworth	Alford	Leworthy	Hackett	King	Furnell	Allardyce	52

BRIAN TALBOT (HEAD COACH)

Date of Appointment: April 1997

Date of Birth: 21st July 1953
Place of Birth: Ipswich

PREVIOUS CLUBS
As manager: West Bromwich Albion, Kettering T., Hibernians (Malta)
As coach
As player: Ipswich T., Arsenal, Watford, Stoke C., Fulham, Aldershot.

HONOURS
As manager: Maltese Championship.
As player: England - 6 full, 1 'B' & u23 caps
FA Cup winner x 2, Texaco Cup winner.

Assistant Coach: Billy Jeffrey **Physios:** Peter Brown / Simon Parsell

Steve Stott (left) and Darren Collins chasing back to cover this break from Halifax Town. Photo: Peter Barnes.

MATCHDAY PROGRAMME

Number of pages	48
Price	£1.30
Programme Editor	Ted Carrol
Other club publications:	
Local Newspapers:	Northants Evening Telegraph Chronicle & Echo Citizen Herald & Post
Local Radio Stations:	Radio Northampton KCBC Northants 96 Radio Diamonds

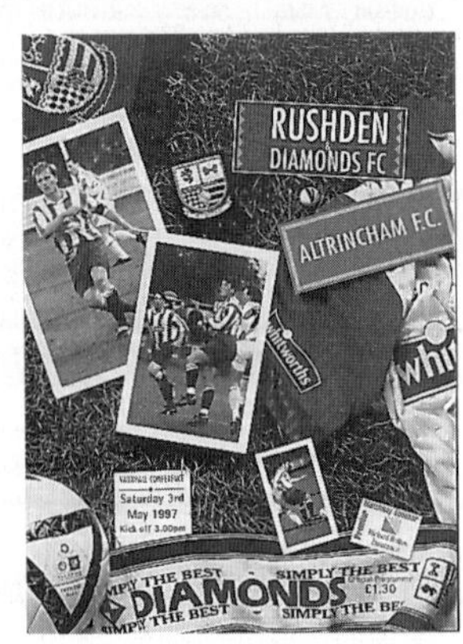

1997-98 PLAYING SQUAD

PLAYER	Birthplace Honours	Birthdate	CLUBS
GOALKEEPERS			
Steve Cherry	Nottingham EY	5.8.60	Derby County, Walsall, Plymouth Argyle, Notts County, Watford, Rotherham U, Kettering T
Martin Davies	Swansea Welsh u-21	28.6.74	Coventry C, Cambridge U, £6k to Rushden & Diamonds
DEFENDERS			
Jim Rodwell	Lincoln SLP	20.11.70	Darlington, Sabam (Malaysia), Bury, Boston FC, Boston U, Bedworth U, Hednesford T, Nuneaton B, Halesowen T, £40K to Rushden & Diamonds
Tim Wooding	Wellingborough SLP	5.7.73	Norwich C, AFC Bournemouth
Simeon Hodson	Lincoln ESP, GMVC	5.3.66	Notts Co, Charlton A, Lincoln C, Newport Co, W.B.A., Doncaster R, Kidderminster H, £10k to Rushden & Diamonds
Glen Fuff	Northampton		Northampton T
Danny O'Shea	Kennington Div 3	26.3.63	Arsenal, Exeter C, £5k to Southend U, Cambridge U, Northampton T
Andy Peaks	Northampton SLP, SLM	25.11.70	Northampton T
Gary Butterworth	Peterborough ESP, SLP	8.9.69	Peterborough U, Dagenham & Redbridge, £20k to Rushden & Diamonds
Paul Underwood	London		Sutton U, Kingstonian, Carshalton A, Enfield, £50k to Rushden & Diamonds
MIDFIELDERS			
Steve Stott	Leeds ESP, SLP	3.2.65	Alvechurch, Bromsgrove R, £18k to Kettering T, £30k to Rushden & Diamonds
Kenny Cramman	Gateshead ESP	17.8.65	Hartlepool U, Bishop Auckland, Gateshead, £40k to Rushden & Diamonds
Mike Mison	London	8.11.75	Fulham
Brendan Hackett	Wolverhampton SLP	2.3.66	Bilston T, Redditch U, Stourbridge, Dudley T, Worcester C, Gloucester C, Telford U, Hednesford T
Simon Stapleton	Oxford ESP, GMVC, FAT, ILP	10.12.68	Portsmouth, Bristol Rovers, Wycombe Wanderers, Slough T, £6k to Rushden & Diamonds
FORWARDS			
Carl Alford	Denton ESP, SLP	11.2.72	Rochdale, Stockport Co, Burnley, Witton A, £1,700 to Macclesfield T, £25k to Kettering T, £85k to Rushden & Diamonds
Darren Collins	Winchester ESP, SLP	24.5.67	Petersfield U, Northampton T, Aylesbury U, Enfield, £20k to Rushden & Diamonds
Andy Furnell	Peterborough	13.2.77	Peterborough U
Adrian Foster	Kidderminster	19.3.71	W.B.A., Torquay U, £60k to Gillingham, Hereford U

DEPARTURES -
(During the season): Terry Wilson (Ilkeston T), Andy Kirkup (Gloucester C), Al-James Hannigan (Enfield)
(During the close season): Graham Benstead & David Leworthy (Kingstonian), Steve Lilwall (Kidderminster H), Mark Tucker (Kettering T), Neil Smith, Kevin Wilkin, Ian King, Nick Ashby, Steve Holden & Richard Bailey (Released)

PLAYERS ON LOAN: Sam Ayorinde (Leyton O), Dave Morrison (Peterborough U), Matt Crossley (Wycombe W)

Nene Park, Irthlingborough

GROUND ADDRESS: Nene Park, Station Road, Irthlingborough, Northants (01933 652000).

TELEPHONE NUMBER: 01933 652000. Fax: 01933 650418. **Newsline:** 0891 44 00 33.

SIMPLE DIRECTIONS:
South from M1 exit 15, A45 bypassing Northampton until A6 - 1st exit North - ground approx 400 yards right. North & West from A14 exit A6 South (Bedford), follow A6 for approx 6 miles, ground on left. East from A14 exit A45 (Northampton) follow A45 for approx 4 miles to A6 - 3rd exit North - ground approx 400 yards on right.

CAPACITY: 6,635. **SEATED:** 4,654. **COVERED:** 4,182

SOCIAL FACILITIES:
Lounge facilities. Open all day, every day. Full restaurant facilities.

CLUB SHOP / DOC SHOP:
Sells programmes, replica shirts, scarves, hats, footwear etc. Contact Bernard Lake (01933 652000, extn.2263).

Rushden & Diamonds Fact File

Nickname: Diamonds **Team Sponsors:** Whitworths Ltd
Club colours: White, red & blue trim, shirts, blue shorts, white socks.
Change colours: Blue shirts, white shorts, red socks.
Reserve team league: Capital League (midweek), Endsleigh Insurance Midland Football Comb.
Midweek home matchday: Tuesday.

PREVIOUS -
Grounds: Rushden Town: Hayden Road, Rushden (pre-1992). Irthlingborough Diamonds: Manton Road, Irthlingborough.
Leagues: Rushden Town: Midland 1894-1901/ Utd Co's 01-04, 19-56, 61-83, Central Alliance 61-83. Irthlingborough Diamonds: Rushden Yth/Rushden & Dist/Kettering Am. Rushden & Diamonds: Southern League 92-96.
Grounds:

CLUB RECORDS -
Attendance: 5,170 v Kettering Town - GM Vauxhall Conference March 1997
Win: 7-0 v Redditch Utd (H), Southern League Midland Div. 7/5/94.
Defeat: 0-5 v Slough Town (A), GM Vauxhall Conference 96/97.
Career goalscorer: Darren Collins 81.
Career appearances: Andy Peaks - 154.
Transfer fee paid: £85,000 to Kettering Town for Carl Alford - 1996.
Transfer fee received: £18,000 from Kingstonian for David Leworthy - June 1997.

1996-97 Captain: Gary Butterworth

1996-97 Top scorer: Carl Alford (15)

1996-97 Player of the Year: Gary Butterworth

Past players who progressed to the Football League: From Rushden Town: Gordon Inwood (WBA 1949), Robert Peacock (Northampton 1957). From Irthlingborough Diamonds: Scott Endersby (Ipswich), Steve Brown & Dave Johnson (Northampton),

HONOURS:
Rushden Town: Southern Lg Midland Div R-up 88-89, Utd Co's Lg 02-03, 26-27, 29-30, 31-32, 34-38, 63-64, 72-73, R-up 12 times, Lg Cup 33-35, 36-38, 46-47, Northants Snr Cup 25-28, 29-31, 34-35, 36-37, 57-58, 77-78, FA Vase QF 89-90. Irthlingborough Diamonds: Utd Co's Lg 70-71, 76-77, 78-79, 82-83, KO Cup 78-79, 80-81, Northants Snr Cup 80-81. **Rushden & Diamonds:** Southern Lg Premier Div 95-96, Southern Lg Midland Div 94-95, Northants Snr Cup 94-95, Daventry Charity Cup 92-93, Campri Leisurewear Cup 92-93, FA Trophy S/F 94-95.

SLOUGH TOWN

Formed:
1890

Chairman: A A Thorne

Vice-Chairman: B A Thorne **Chief Executive:** Bob Breen

Secretary / Press Officer: Trevor Gorman
Tel: 01753 523358 (B) Address - c/o the club.

Commercial Manager: Bob Breen (Chief Exec.)

The Rebels had a very inconsistent 1996/97 season.

The first half of the campaign saw Brian McDermott's men show genuine championship form as they climbed into a top five spot.

However, rather than building upon this good start, Slough then slumped to such an extent that they did not record a single win during the period from November 16th to March 8th. This eventually saw the Rebels finish in 16th position.

There is no doubt that injuries were a major contributing factor in Slough's loss of form but their poor defensive record (65 goals conceded) was perhaps more significant.

Slough's poor end of season run has left them as one of the bookmakers' favourites for the drop - however, Brian McDermott, now entering his third season in charge, has made a number of summer signings which should, at the least, ensure survival for another year.

L-R - Back: Stuart Bannister, Mark Pye, Terry Angus, Ted McMinn, Tony Nolan, Lloyd Owusu, Terry Mitchell, Gary Abbott, Kevin McGoldrick. Middle: Dave Brown, Kevin Hill, Dean White, Wayne Watts, Danny Wicks, Ben Miles, Cliff Hercules, Paul Wilkerson, Derek Simpson, Mark Fiore, Robert Smith, Brian Burke, Brian McDermott. Front: Grant Eaton, Paul Hardyman, Mark West, Gary McGinnis, Alan Thorne, Gary Brazil, Lee Randall, Danny Bolt, Byron Walton.

Slough Town

Match No.	Date	Venue H/A	Competition	Opponents	Result	League Pos.	Attendance	Goalscorers (Times if known)
1	Aug 17	H	VC	Stalybridge Celtic	Won 4-1	2	822	Bolt 8 (p), Abbott 44, West 51, Blackford 83
2	Aug 20	H	VC	Rushden & Diamonds	Won 5-0		1325	Hercules 29, Abbott 48, 52, 59, West 66
3	Aug 24	A	VC	Halifax Town	Lost 1-4		793	Hercules 78
4	Aug 26	A	VC	Kidderminster Harriers	Won 2-1	2	2087	West 70, Blackford 75
5	Aug 31	H	VC	Altrincham	Lost 0-1	5	1240	
6	Sep 3	H	VC	Bath City	Won 5-2		1032	West 3, Abbott 25, 60, 88, Bolt 62
7	Sep 7	A	VC	Southport	Won 1-0	3	1117	West 34
8	Sep 10	A	VC	Welling United	Lost 2-3		534	West (2) 51, 80
9	Sep 14	H	VC	Bromsgrove Rovers	Won 2-0	2	1158	Abbott 9, Blackford 19
10	Sep 17	A	VC	Dover Athletic	Drew 0-0		1129	
11	Sep 21	H	VC	Hednesford Town	Drew 2-2	2	1120	Stapleton 43, West 61
12	Sep 24	H	VC	Kettering Town	Drew 1-1		1032	Abbott 4
13	Sep 28	A	VC	Bromsgrove Rovers	Lost 1-4	3	686	Walton 27
14	Oct 1	H	VC	Woking	Won 3-0		2055	Smith 51, Stapleton 62, Bolt 87 (pen)
15	Oct 5	H	VC	Morecambe	Lost 1-2	4	1104	Stapleton 58
16	**Oct 8**	**A**	**SCC**	**Kettering Town**	**Lost 0-1**		**702**	
17	Oct 19	H	VC	Telford United	Won 6-0	4	1002	Owusu (4) 20, 39, 51, 61, Abbott 36, West 81
18	**Oct 26**	**A**	**FAC 4 Q**	**Hayes**	**Lost 0-1**		**1803**	
19	Nov 2	A	VC	Altrincham	Won 1-0	3	967	Owusu 76
20	Nov 9	H	VC	Kidderminster Harriers	Lost 0-2	4	1610	
21	Nov 16	A	VC	Gateshead	Lost 1-2		472	Hague 83 (og)
22	Nov 23	A	VC	Northwich Victoria	Won 1-0	3	849	Bateman 33
23	Nov 30	H	VC	Macclesfield Town	Drew 0-0	5	1096	
24	Dec 7	A	VC	Kettering Town	Drew 0-0	4	1379	
25	Dec 14	A	VC	Farnborough Town	Lost 1-2	6	892	Murphy 52
26	Dec 20	H	VC	Welling United	Drew 3-3		869	Hercules 2, Bateman 51, Abbott 61
27	Dec 26	A	VC	Stevenage Borough	Drew 2-2		2834	Abbott (2) 10, 39
28	Dec 28	A	VC	Woking	Lost 0-2	8	3208	
29	Jan 1	H	VC	Stevenage Borough	Lost 1-6	9	1298	Fiore 63
30	Jan 11	H	VC	Farnborough Town	Drew 1-1	8	975	Mernagh 71
31	**Jan 14**	**H**	**BBSC**	**Buckingham Town**	**Won 6-0**		**254**	**Fiore, Pye, Mernagh (2), Abbott, Blackford**
32	**Jan 18**	**H**	**FAT 1**	**Dorchester Town**	**Drew 2-2**		**744**	**Hercules 16, Blackford 35**
33	**Jan 21**	**A**	**FAT 1 R**	**Dorchester Town**	**Drew 1-1**		**685**	**Blackford 13**
34	Jan 25	A	VC	Macclesfield Town	Lost 0-2	8	1013	
35	**Jan 27**	**H**	**FAT**	**Dorchester Town**	**Lost 1-2**		**641**	**Hercules**
36	Feb 1	H	VC	Gateshead	Lost 0-1	9	638	
37	Feb 15	H	VC	Northwich Victoria	Lost 3-4	11	703	Brazil 27, Clement 32, Barclay 74
38	Feb 22	A	VC	Hayes	Lost 0-5	11	768	
39	Mar 1	A	VC	Rushden & Diamonds	Drew 2-2	11	1980	Hercules 48, Fiore 90
40	Mar 8	H	VC	Telford United	Won 2-0	11	872	Hardyman 13, Abbott 39
41	**Mar 11**	**H**	**BBSC**	**Wycombe**	**Lost 2-3**		**562**	**Nolan, Brazil**
42	Mar 15	H	VC	**Wanderers**	Lost 1-3	13	1100	Smart 48
43	Mar 22	H	VC	Hayes	Drew 1-1	13	661	Abbott 43
44	Mar 29	A	VC	Southport	Drew 0-0		822	
45	Mar 31	H	VC	Bath City	Drew 2-2	13	843	Brazil 53, Abbott 68
46	Apr 5	H	VC	Dover Athletic	Won 1-0	12	760	Hercules 15
47	Apr 19	A	VC	Halifax Town	Lost 1-2	15	852	Brazil 52
48	Apr 26	A	VC	Hednesford Town	Drew 0-0	14	704	
49	May 3	A	VC	Morecambe	Drew 2-2	17	511	Abbott 28, 72

Slough Town

1	2	3	4	5	6	7	8	9	10	11	12	14	15	Mth No.
Wilkerson	Smart	McGinnis	Micklewhite	Hercules	Bateman	Blackford	Stapleton	West	Abbott	Bolt	Wallon	Fiore	Mernagh	1
Wilkerson	Smart	McGinnis	Micklewhite	Hercules	Bateman	Blackford	Stapleton	West	Abbott	Bolt	Wallon	Paris	Mernagh	2
Wilkerson	Smart	McGinnis	Micklewhite	Hercules	Bateman	Blackford	Stapleton	West	Abbott	Bolt	Wallon	Paris	Mernagh	3
Wilkerson	Smart	McGinnis	Micklewhite	Hercules	Bateman	Blackford	Stapleton	West	Abbott	Bolt	Wallon	Fiore	Clement	4
Miles	Smart	McGinnis	Micklewhite	Hercules	Bateman	Blackford	Stapleton	West	Abbott	Bolt	Wallon	Fiore	Clement	5
Miles	Smart	McGinnis	Micklewhite	Hercules	Bateman	Blackford	Stapleton	West	Abbott	Bolt	Wallon	Fiore	Clement	6
Miles	Smart	McGinnis	Micklewhite	Hercules	Bateman	Blackford	Stapleton	West	Abbott	Bolt	Wallon	Fiore	Clement	7
Miles	Smart	Clement	Micklewhite	Smith	Bateman	Blackford	Stapleton	West	Abbott	Bolt	Wallon	Fiore	Owusu	8
Miles	Smart	Clement	Micklewhite	Smith	Bateman	Blackford	Stapleton	West	Abbott	Fiore	Wallon	Bolt	Owusu	9
Miles	Smart	Clement	Micklewhite	Smith	Bateman	Blackford	Stapleton	West	Abbott	Wallon	Bolt	Fiore	Owusu	10
Miles	Smart	Clement	Micklewhite	Smith	Bateman	Blackford	Stapleton	West	Abbott	Bolt	Wallon	Fiore	Owusu	11
Miles	Smart	Walton	Micklewhite	Smith	Bateman	Blackford	Stapleton	West	Abbott	Bolt	Clement	Fiore	Owusu	12
Miles	Smart	Walton	Micklewhite	Hercules	Smith	Blackford	Stapleton	West	Abbott	Fiore	Bateman	Bolt	Owusu	13
Miles	Smart	Smith	Micklewhite	Hercules	Bateman	Blackford	Stapleton	West	Abbott	Bolt	Wallon	Fiore	Owusu	14
Miles	Smart	Smith	Micklewhite	Hercules	Bateman	Blackford	Stapleton	West	Abbott	Bolt	McGinnis	Fiore	Owusu	15
Miles	**Smart**	**Smith**	**McGinnis**	**Hercules**	**Bateman**	**Clement**	**Stapleton**	**West**	**Owusu**	**Wallon**	**Mernagh**	**Ealon**	**Micklewhite**	**16**
Miles	Smart	McGinnis	Fiore	Bateman	Smith	Blackford	Stapleton	Owusu	Abbott	Simpson	West	Micklewhite	Paris	17
Wilkerson	**Smart**	**McGinnis**	**Owusu**	**Hercules**	**Smith**	**Blackford**	**Stapleton**	**West**	**Abbott**	**Simpson**	**Fiore**	**Wallon**	**Paris**	**18**
Wilkerson	Smart	McGinnis	Owusu	Clement	Smith	Blackford	Stapleton	Walton	Abbott	Simpson	Fiore	Mernagh	Ealon	19
Wilkerson	Smart	McGinnis	Owusu	Clement	Smith	Blackford	Stapleton	Walton	Abbott	Simpson	Bateman	Pye	Fiore	20
Wilkerson	Smart	McGinnis	Wallon	Clement	Smith	Blackford	Pye	Hercules	Owusu	Simpson	Bateman	Ealon	Bolt	21
Wilkerson	Smart	McGinnis	Bateman	Clement	Smith	Blackford	Pye	Hercules	Bolt	Simpson	Fiore	Paris	Ealon	22
Wilkerson	Smart	McGinnis	Bateman	Clement	Smith	Fiore	Pye	Hercules	Murphy	Simpson	Stapleton	Bolt	Mernagh	23
Wilkerson	Smart	McGinnis	Bateman	Clement	Smith	Fiore	Pye	Hercules	Abbott	Simpson	Stapleton	Bolt	Murphy	24
Wilkerson	Smart	Bolt	Bateman	Clement	Smith	Fiore	Stapleton	Hercules	Abbott	West	Pye	Eaton	Murphy	25
Wilkerson	Smart	McGinnis	Bateman	Clement	Smith	Fiore	Pye	Hercules	Abbott	Bolt	Simpson	Blackford	Murhpy	26
Wilkerson	Smart	Murphy	Bateman	Clement	Smith	Fiore	Blackford	Hercules	Abbott	Simpson	McGinnis	Stapleton	Mernagh	27
Wilkerson	Blackford	McGinnis	Bateman	Clement	Smith	Fiore	Stapleton	Murphy	Abbott	Simpson	Ealon	Mernagh	Paris	28
Wilkerson	Blackford	McGinnis	Bateman	Clement	Smith	Fiore	Stapleton	Murphy	Abbott	Ealon	Simpson	Mernagh	Paris	29
Wilkerson	McGinnis	Cash	Stapleton	Hercules	Smith	Fiore	Pye	Murphy	Abbott	Blackford	Bolt	Mernagh	Paris	30
Wilkerson	**Smart**	**Simpson**	**Bateman**	**McGinnis**	**Smith**	**Fiore**	**Pye**	**Mernagh**	**Abbott**	**Blackford**	**Bolt**	**Paris**	**Murphy**	**31**
Wilkerson	**Smart**	**Simpson**	**McGinnis**	**Hercules**	**Smith**	**Fiore**	**Pye**	**Bateman**	**Abbott**	**Blackford**	**Bolt**	**Murphy**	**Clement**	**32**
Wilkerson	**Smart**	**Simpson**	**Clement**	**Bateman**	**Smith**	**Fiore**	**Pye**	**Hercules**	**Murphy**	**Blackford**	**Bolt**	**Abbott**	**McGinnis**	**33**
Wilkerson	Smart	Cash	McGinnis	Hercules	Bateman	Fiore	Clement	Murphy	Bolt	Blackford	Abbott	Pye	Smith	34
Wilkerson	**Smart**	**Simpson**	**Clement**	**Bateman**	**Smith**	**McGinnis**	**Pye**	**Hercules**	**Abbott**	**Blackford**	**Bolt**	**Murphy**	**Ealon**	**35**
Wilkerson	Smart	Cash	Mernaugh	Bateman	Smith	McGinnis	Pye	Hercules	Abbott	Blackford	Bolt	Murphy	Simpson	36
Wilkerson	Smart	Cash	Bateman	Hercules	Clement	Fiore	Eaton	Brazil	Barclay	Bolt	Simpson	Mernagh	Blackford	37
Imber	Smart	Simpson	Bateman	Hercules	Clement	Fiore	Blackford	Brazil	Abbott	Bolt	Barclay	Mernagh	Ealon	38
Imber	Smart	Hardyman	Bateman	Hercules	Clement	Fiore	Blackford	Brazil	Abbott	McGinnis	Barclay	Nolan	Owusu	39
Imber	Smart	Hardyman	Bateman	Nolan	McMinn	Fiore	Blackford	Brazil	Abbott	McGinnis	Barclay	Clement	Ealon	40
Imber	**Smart**	**Murphy**	**Bateman**	**Nolan**	**McGinnis**	**Fiore**	**Clement**	**Brazil**	**Barclay**	**Blackford**	**Mernagh**	**Simpson**	**Ealon**	**41**
Imber	Smart	Hardyman	Bateman	Nolan	McMinn	Fiore	Clement	Brazil	Abbott	McGinnis	Owusu	Murphy	Ealon	42
Imber	Smart	Hardyman	Bateman	Hercules	McMinn	Fiore	Blackford	Brazil	Abbott	McGinnis	Nolan	Clement	Owusu	43
Miles	Smart	Hardyman	Bateman	Hercules	McMinn	Fiore	Blackford	Brazil	Abbott	McGinnis	Nolan	Bolt	Owusu	44
Miles	Smart	Hardyman	Bateman	Hercules	McMinn	Fiore	Owusu	Brazil	Abbott	McGinnis	Nolan	Bolt	Ealon	45
Miles	Smart	Hardyman	Bateman	Hercules	McMinn	Fiore	Owusu	Brazil	Abbott	McGinnis	Nolan	Bolt	Blackford	46
Miles	Smart	Hardyman	Bateman	Hercules	McMinn	Fiore	Blackford	Brazil	Abbott	McGinnis	Mernagh	Bolt	Paris	47
Wilkerson	Smart	Hardyman	Bateman	Hercules	McMinn	Fiore	Blackford	Brazil	Abbott	McGinnis	Owusu	Simpson	Ealon	48

BRIAN McDERMOTT MANAGER)

Date of Appointment	February 1996
Date of Birth:	8th April 1961
Place of Birth:	Slough

PREVIOUS CLUBS

As manager	None
As coach	None
As player	Arsenal, Oxford Utd., Cardiff C., Exeter C., Yeovil T., South China (Hong Kong), Marlow, Stamco.

HONOURS

As manager	None
As player	England - Youth Int.

Assistant Manager: David Brown **Physio:** Kevin McGoldrick

Left:
Gary Abbott, Slough Town's top goalscorer last season.
Photo: Andrew Chitty

Right:
Player of the Year,
Cliff Hercules, when he was a bit younger and still a striker.
Photo: Eric Marsh

MATCHDAY PROGRAMME

Number of pages	36
Price	£1.50
Programme Editor	Committee
Other club publications:	"Rebels without a Clue" (fanzine)
Local Newspapers:	Slough Observer Slough Express
Local Radio Stations:	Thames Valley FM Star FM

1997-98 PLAYING SQUAD

PLAYER	Birthplace Honours	Birthdate	CLUBS
GOALKEEPERS			
Paul Wilkerson	Hertford	11.12.74	Watford
DEFENDERS			
Gary McGinnis	Dundee Sc u-21	21.10.63	Celtic, Dundee U, St.Johnstone, Happy Valley (HK)
Gary Smart	Totnes	29.4.64	Wokingham T, Oxford U, Stevenage B, Hayes
Danny Bolt	Wandsworth	5.2.76	Fulham
Gary Blackford	Redhill ILP	25.9.68	Whyteleafe, Croydon, Fisher A, Barnet, Dagenham & Redbridge, Enfield
Cliff Hercules	Aylesbury ILP, FA XI	16.8.63	Oving, Aylesbury U, £10k to Slough T
Derek Simpson	Lanark	23.12.78	Reading
Steve Bateman	Berkhamsted ILP, FAYC	23.4.65	Everton, Chesham U, Harrow Borough
MIDFIELDERS			
Mark Pye	Hammersmith ILP, FA XI	29.2.68	West Ham U, North Greenford U, Harrow Borough, Enfield, £5,500 to Slough T
Mark Fiore	Southwark	21.3.61	Wimbledon, Plymouth A
Ted McMinn	Castle Douglas SLC	28.9.62	Glenafton A, Queen of the South, £50k to Glasgow Rangers, £225k to Seville (Sp), £300k to Derby Co, £115k to Birmingham C, Burnley, Australia
Gary Brazil	Tunbridge Wells	19.9.62	Crystal Palace, Sheffield U, £12,500 to Preston, £50k to Newcastle U, £110k to Fulham, Barnet
FORWARDS			
Mark West	Wycombe ESP, FAT	16.2.66	West Ham U, Reading, Wycombe W
Gary Abbott	Catford ESP, ILP	7.11.64	Welling U, £15k to Barnet, £40k to Enfield, £30k to Welling U, £12k to Enfield
Gavin Mernagh	Slough	11.6.78	Q.P.R.

DEPARTURES -
(During the season): Gary Micklewhite (QPR), Simon Stapleton (Rushden & D), Andy Clement (Yeovil T)

PLAYERS ON LOAN - Ben Miles (Swansea), Dominic Barclay (Bristol C), Paul Hardyman (Barnet)

Wexham Park Stadium, Slough

ADDRESS: Wexham Park Stadium, Wexham Road, Slough, Berkshire. SL2 5QR.
TELEPHONE NUMBER: 01753 523358 Fax: 01753 516956.

GROUND DIRECTIONS:
From North: M25 J16 East London M40 J1 - South A412 through Iver Heath to George Green. 2nd set lights turn right by George PH, George Green. Church Lane 1 mile to end, then small roundabout, turn left, ground 1/4 mile on right.
From East: M25 J15/M4 J5 to A4 West to Co-Op Superstore on right, A412 North (Uxbridge), dual carriageway to 4th set lights. Church Lane, then as from North.
From South: If M25 then as from East. From Windsor A355 under M4 J6 to A4, turn right, pass Brunel Bus station on left, Tesco Superstore, also on left, then first left, Wexham Road, signposted Wexham Park Hospital, ground just over 1 mile on left. From West: If M4 J6 then as from South.

CAPACITY: 5,000 **SEATED:** 450 **COVERED TERRACING:** 1,890

SOCIAL FACILITIES: Rebels bar & Lounge bar open weekdays 7pm-11pm, weekends lunchtime/evenings. Banqueting hall for all types of functions. 25 bay golf driving range.
CLUB SHOP: Contact John Linlow (0753 571710).

Slough Town Fact File

Nickname: The Rebels **Club Sponsor:** The Cable Corporation
Club colours: Amber shirts, navy blue shorts, amber socks
Change colours: All white
Midweek home matchday: Tuesdays

PREVIOUS - **Leagues:** Southern Alliance 1892-93/ Berks & Bucks 1901-05/ Gt Western Suburban 1906-19/ Spartan 1920-39/ Herts & Middx 1940-45/ Corinthian 1946-63/ Athenian 1963-73/ Isthmian 1973-90, 94-95/ Alliance Prem. (GMVC) 90-94.
Grounds: Dolphin Playing Fields & Stadium, Chalvey Road Sports Ground, York Road Maidenhead 1920, Centre Sports Ground 1936-42.

CLUB RECORDS - **Attendance:** 8,000 - Schoolboys u15 Final Slough v Liverpool - 1976
Win: 17-0 v Railway Clearing House - 1921-22.
Defeat: 1-11 v Chesham Town 1909/10.
Transfer fee paid: £18,000 for Colin Fielder from Farnborough - 1991
Transfer fee received: £22,000 from Wycombe Wanderers for Steve Thompson
Career goalscorer: Terry Norris 84 - 1925/26
Career appearances: Terry Reardon 458 - 1964/81

BEST SEASON - **FA Cup:** 2nd Round Proper, 79-80 (Yeovil T), 82-83 (Bishop's Stortford), 85-86 (Leyton O.), 86-87 (Swansea C.). **League clubs defeated:** Millwall, 1-0 (H) Jan. 1983
FA Trophy: Semi-Final, 1976-77, 2-6 (agg) v Dagenham.

1996-97 Captain: Gary McGinnis
1996-97 Top scorer: Gary Abbott (18)
1996-97 Player of the Year: Cliff Hercules

Past players who progressed to the Football League: Bill McConnell, Peter Angell, Dennis Edwards, Ralph Miller, John Delaney, Paul Barron, Dave Kemp, Roy Davies, Mickey Droy, Eric Young, Alan Paris, Tony Dennis.

HONOURS: FA Amateur Cup R-up 72-73; Great Western Suburban League R-up 19-20: Spartan League R-up 20-21 21-22 31-32 32-33 38-39; Herts & Middx League R-up 43-44; Corinthian League 50-51 (R-up 45-46 46-47 57-58); Athenian League 67-68 71-72 72-73 (R-up 68-69, Div 1 64-65, Memorial Shield 64-65 71-72 72-73); Isthmian League 80-81 89-90 R-up 94-95, (Div 2 R-up 73-74), League Shield 80-81 89-90 (R-up 94-95); Berks & Bucks Senior Cup(9) 02-03 19-20 23-24 35-36 54-55 70-72 76-77 80-81.

Formed:
1881

SOUTHPORT

Chairman: Charles Clapham **President:** Jack Carr

Football Secretary: Ken Hilton Tel: 01704 894504 (H) 01704 840775 (B)
34 Mill Lane, Burscough, Ormskirk, Lancs. L40 5TS

Press Officer: Ken Hilton (see above)

Southport began the 1996/97 season as many pundits' dark horse for the championship. That they ended the campaign in eleventh place was more to do with the managerial upheavals at Haig Avenue than anything else.

Billy Ayre, who had done such a good job during his tenure in charge, opted for a return to the full time game as assistant-manager at Swansea and, after his former number two Steve Joel had been given a go in sole charge, Ronnie Moore took over, only then to be swiftly linked with virtually every managerial vacancy going in the Second and Third Divisions.

He eventually moved back to one of his former clubs, Rotherham, and during the last close season, Southport managed to persuade Paul Futcher to leave Gresley Rovers, whom he had led to the Dr. Martens Premier Division championship, and take over at Haig Avenue.

The appointment of Futcher should prove to be a shrewd move, and Southport will again, justifiably, be amongst the favourites for the Conference title.

L-R, Back Row: Andy Whittaker, Kevin Formby, Dave Thompson, John Deary.
Middle: Mel Singleton (Physio), Brian Ross, David Gamble, Billy Stewart, Leroy Dove, John Bagnall, Phil Horner, Phil Bolland, Max Thompson (Asst. Man.).
Front: Tim Ryan, Ged Kielty, Paul Mitten, Paul Futcher (player/manager), Brian Butler, Andy Farley, Paul Jones.

Southport

Match No.	Date	Venue H/A	Competition	Opponents	Result	League Pos.	Attendance	Goalscorers (Times if known)
1	Aug 17	A	VC	Hayes	Drew 1-1	13	753	Whittaker 75
2	Aug 20	H	VC	Stalybridge Celtic	Won 3-0		1051	Jones 2, Clark 32, Whittaker 43
3	Aug 24	A	VC	Bromsgrove Rovers	Won 1-0		762	Davenport 80
4	Aug 26	H	VC	Halifax Town	Won 2-1	1	1543	Gamble 44, 72 (2 pens)
5	Aug 31	H	VC	Kidderminster Harriers	Won 1-0	1	1423	Whittaker 68
6	Sep 3	A	VC	Telford United	Lost 0-1		839	
7	Sep 7	H	VC	Slough Town	Lost 0-1	4	1117	
8	Sep 11	A	VC	Gateshead	Drew 2-2		511	Davenport 24, 81
9	**Sep 14**	**A**	**FAC 1 Q**	**Rossendale**	**Won 5-0**		**445**	**McDonald 30, Whittaker (3) 55, 57, 71, Vickers 8**
10	Sep 17	H	VC	Northwich Victoria	Drew 0-0		1077	
11	Sep 21	A	VC	Kettering Town	Won 1-0	5	1575	Davenport 21
12	**Sep 28**	**H**	**FAC 2 Q**	**Emley**	**Drew 1-1**		**848**	**Farley 45**
13	**Sep 30**	**A**	**FAC R**	**Emley**	**Won 3-2***		**434**	**Butler 34, Whittaker 104, McDonald 11**
14	Oct 5	A	VC	Stevenage Borough	Lost 1-2	11	2903	Jones 34
15	**Oct 12**	**H**	**FAC 3 Q**	**Burton Albion**	**Won 4-1**		**1078**	**Whittaker 27, Dove 60, McDonald 66, Clark 9**
16	Oct 19	A	VC	Hednesford Town	Won 1-0	11	1149	Whittaker 51
17	**Oct 22**	**A**	**SCC**	**Stalybridge Celtic**	**Lost 1-2**		**224**	**Clark 59**
18	**Oct 26**	**A**	**FAC 4 Q**	**Spennymoor United**	**Drew 2-2**		**558**	**McDonald 22, Whittaker 65**
19	**Oct 29**	**H**	**FAC 4QR**	**Spennymoor United**	**Won 2-1**		**990**	**Clark 9, McDonald 70**
20	Nov 2	H	VC	Rushden & Diamonds	Won 2-1	11	1225	Butler 36, Whittaker 77
21	Nov 6	A	VC	Altrincham	Lost 0-1	11	793	
22	Nov 9	H	VC	Macclesfield Town	Lost 1-5	12	1546	Anderson 45
23	**Nov 16**	**A**	**FAC 1**	**Hednesford Town**	**Lost 1-2**		**2060**	**Simpson 82 (og)**
24	Nov 26	H	VC	Gateshead	Drew 1-1		673	Butler 70
25	Nov 30	A	VC	Farnborough Town	Drew 3-3	11	707	Whittaker 67, Gamble 70, Butler 79
26	Dec 7	H	VC	Bromsgrove Rovers	Drew 0-0	11	741	
27	Dec 14	H	VC	Altrincham	Lost 1-3	12	803	Gamble 67
28	Dec 20	A	VC	Northwich Victoria	Lost 1-5		701	Whittaker 46
29	Dec 28	H	VC	Hednesford Town	Lost 1-2	14	1023	Whittaker 7
30	Jan 4	H	VC	Bath City	Won 3-1	12	786	Davenport 20, Jones 45, Whittaker 62
31	**Jan 18**	**H**	**FAT 1**	**Halesowen Town**	**Drew 0-0**		**1005**	
32	**Jan 21**	**A**	**FAT 1 R**	**Halesowen Town**	**Won 2-0**		**866**	**Whittaker 14, 83**
33	Jan 25	H	VC	Welling United	Won 3-2	12	884	Horner 56, Whittaker 64, 83
34	Feb 1	A	VC	Bath City	Won 2-0	12	531	Whittaker 30, Gamble 49
35	**Feb 8**	**A**	**FAT 2**	**Colwyn Bay**	**Lost 0-2**		**928**	
36	Feb 11	A	VC	Stalybridge Celtic	Drew 2-2	10	493	Gamble 34, Farley 71
37	Feb 15	A	VC	Woking	Won 1-0	10	2858	Whittaker 33
38	Feb 22	H	VC	Dover Athletic	Lost 0-1	10	935	
39	Mar 1	A	VC	Dover Athletic	Won 1-0	10	1259	Butler 84
40	Mar 8	H	VC	Farnborough Town	Lost 0-3	10	905	
41	Mar 15	A	VC	Macclesfield Town	Lost 2-3	11	1601	Price 59 (og), Horner 76
42	Mar 22	A	VC	Slough Town	Drew 1-1	12	661	Whittaker 76
43	Mar 28	A	VC	Halifax Town	Lost 0-2		792	
44	Mar 31	H	VC	Telford United	Lost 0-1	15	925	
45	Apr 2	H	VC	Kettering Town	Drew 2-2		676	Whittaker 78, Rogers 90
46	Apr 5	A	VC	Rushden & Diamonds	Lost 0-3	17	2218	
47	Apr 8	H	VC	Morecambe	Won 3-1	14	802	Haw 16, Sharratt 27, Whittaker 34
48	Apr 12	A	VC	Welling United	Won 3-2		700	Gamble (3) 47, 62, 89 (2 pens)
49	Apr 19	H	VC	Stevenage Borough	Drew 0-0	10	965	
50	Apr 26	A	VC	Kidderminster Harriers	Lost 0-3	11	3139	
51	Apr 29	A	VC	Morecambe	Lost 1-2		733	Dove 90
52	May 1	H	VC	Woking	Won 4-1		560	Whittaker (3) 1, 5, 52, Dove 71
53	May 3	H	VC	Hayes	Lost 0-2	11	702	

* After Extra Time

Southport

1	2	3	4	5	6	7	8	9	10	11	12	14	15	Mth No.
Stewart	Anderson	Farley	Horner	Jones	Butler	Clark	Whittaker	Carroll	Gamble	McDonald	Griffiths	Powell	Vickers	1
Stewart	Anderson	Farley	Horner	Jones	Butler	Clark	Whittaker	Davenport	Carroll	McDonald	Gamble	Griffiths	Vickers	2
Stewart	Anderson	Farley	Horner	Jones	Butler	Clark	Whittaker	Davenport	Carroll	McDonald	Gamble	Griffiths	Vickers	3
Stewart	Clark	Farley	Horner	Jones	Butler	Carroll	Whittaker	Davenport	Gamble	McDonald	Griffiths	Vickers	Eyre	4
Stewart	Clark	Farley	Horner	Jones	Butler	Carroll	Whittaker	Davenport	Gamble	McDonald	Griffiths	Vickers	Eyre	5
Stewart	Clark	Farley	Horner	Jones	Butler	Eyre	Whittaker	Vickers	Gamble	Griffiths	Davenport	Carroll	Dove	6
Stewart	Clark	Farley	Horner	Jones	Butler	Eyre	Whittaker	Davenport	Gamble	McDonald	Carroll	Vickers	Dove	7
Stewart	Anderson	Farley	Horner	Jones	Butler	Carroll	Whittaker	Davenport	Gamble	McDonald	Borwick	Vickers	Blakeman	8
Stewart	**Anderson**	**Farley**	**Horner**	**Jones**	**Butler**	**Carroll**	**Whittaker**	**Davenport**	**Gamble**	**McDonald**	**Vickers**	**Borwick**	**Blakeman**	**9**
Stewart	Anderson	Farley	Horner	Jones	Butler	Carroll	Whittaker	Davenport	Gamble	McDonald	Blakeman	Vickers	Borwick	10
Stewart	Anderson	Farley	Horner	Dove	Butler	Carroll	Whittaker	Davenport	Gamble	Clark	Vickers	Borwick	Blakeman	11
Stewart	**Clark**	**Farley**	**Horner**	**Jones**	**Butler**	**Dove**	**Whittaker**	**Davenport**	**Gamble**	**McDonald**	**Carroll**	**Anderson**	**Borwick**	**12**
Stewart	**Clark**	**Farley**	**Horner**	**Jones**	**Butler**	**Dove**	**Whittaker**	**Davenport**	**Gamble**	**McDonald**	**Anderson**	**Carroll**	**Vickers**	**13**
Stewart	Clark	Farley	Horner	Jones	Butler	Dove	Whittaker	Davenport	Gamble	McDonald	Carroll	Vickers	Anderson	14
Stewart	**Dove**	**Farley**	**Horner**	**Jones**	**Butler**	**Clark**	**Whittaker**	**Davenport**	**Gamble**	**McDonald**	**Anderson**	**Carroll**	**Vickers**	**15**
Stewart	Anderson	Farley	Horner	Jones	Butler	Clark	Whittaker	Davenport	Gamble	McDonald	Dove	Vickers	Preece	16
Stewart	**Anderson**	**Farley**	**Dove**	**Jones**	**Butler**	**Clark**	**McDonald**	**Daley**	**Gamble**	**Preece**	**Davenport**	**Horner**	**Blakeman**	**17**
Stewart	**Anderson**	**Farley**	**Horner**	**Jones**	**Butler**	**Clark**	**Whittaker**	**Preece**	**Gamble**	**McDonald**	**Blakeman**	**Davenport**	**Dove**	**18**
Stewart	**Anderson**	**Blakeman**	**Horner**	**Jones**	**Butler**	**Clark**	**Whittaker**	**Preece**	**Gamble**	**McDonald**	**Davenport**	**Dove**	**McAuley**	**19**
Stewart	Anderson	Blakeman	Horner	Jones	Butler	Clark	Whittaker	Preece	Gamble	McDonald	Dove	Davenport	Morgan	20
Stewart	Anderson	Blakeman	Horner	Jones	Butler	Clark	Whittaker	Preece	Gamble	McDonald	Davenport	Morgan	Dove	21
Stewart	Anderson	Dove	Horner	Jones	Butler	Clark	Whittaker	Davenport	Gamble	Preece	Morgan	Blakeman	McAuley	22
Stewart	**Anderson**	**Eyre**	**Horner**	**Jones**	**Butler**	**Clark**	**Whittaker**	**Preece**	**Gamble**	**McDonald**	**Davenport**	**Morgan**	**Dove**	**23**
Stewart	Anderson	Rogers	Horner	Dove	Butler	Clark	Whittaker	Davenport	Preece	Sharratt	Gamble	Morgan	Jones	24
Stewart	Anderson	Rogers	Horner	Dove	Butler	Turner	Whittaker	Davenport	Preece	Sharratt	Gamble	Morgan	Jones	25
Stewart	Anderson	Rogers	Horner	Dove	Butler	Kenworthy	Whittaker	Preece	Farley	Sharratt	Gamble	Davenport	Jones	26
Stewart	Anderson	Farley	Horner	Jones	Butler	Kenworthy	Whittaker	Mayers	Preece	Sharratt	Gamble	Davenport	Turner	27
Stewart	Clark	Rogers	Horner	Dove	Butler	Preece	Whittaker	Davenport	Mayers	Sharratt	Turner	Gamble	Farley	28
Stewart	Farley	Rogers	Horner	Jones	Butler	Clark	Whittaker	Mayers	Blakeman	Sharratt	Anderson	Turner	Davenport	29
Stewart	Farley	Rogers	Horner	Jones	Preece	Mayers	Whittaker	Davenport	Blakeman	Sharratt	Gamble	Dove	Morgan	30
Stewart	**Farley**	**Rogers**	**Horner**	**Jones**	**Dove**	**Clark**	**Whittaker**	**Davenport**	**Anderson**	**Sharratt**	**Blakeman**	**Morgan**	**R Horner**	**31**
Stewart	**Farley**	**Rogers**	**Horner**	**Dove**	**Anderson**	**Clark**	**Whittaker**	**Morgan**	**Gamble**	**Sharratt**	**Turner**	**P Clarke**	**Blakeman**	**32**
Stewart	Farley	Rogers	Horner	Dove	Butler	Clark	Whittaker	Morgan	Gamble	Sharratt	Turner	Anderson	Blakeman	33
Stewart	Farley	Rogers	Horner	Dove	Butler	Clark	Whittaker	Turner	Gamble	Sharratt	Anderson	Jones	Morgan	34
Stewart	**Farley**	**Rogers**	**Horner**	**Dove**	**Butler**	**Clark**	**Whittaker**	**Turner**	**Gamble**	**Sharratt**	**Anderson**	**Jones**	**Morgan**	**35**
Stewart	Farley	Rogers	Horner	R Horner	Butler	Clark	Whittaker	Turner	Gamble	Sharratt	Dove	Morgan	Blakeman	36
Stewart	Farley	Rogers	Horner	R Horner	Butler	Clark	Whittaker	Turner	Gamble	Sharratt	Morgan	Dove	Blakeman	37
Stewart	Farley	Moran	Horner	R Horner	Butler	Clark	Whittaker	Turner	Gamble	Sharratt	Morgan	Dove	Blakeman	38
Stewart	Farley	Moran	Horner	R Horner	Butler	Clark	Whittaker	Mitten	Gamble	Sharratt	Dove	Rogers	Turner	39
Stewart	Farley	Rogers	Horner	R Horner	Butler	Clark	Moran	Mitten	Gamble	Sharratt	Haw	Dove	Morgan	40
Stewart	Moran	Rogers	Horner	R Horner	Butler	Clark	Whittaker	Haw	Gamble	Sharratt	Farley	Dove	Blakeman	41
Stewart	Farley	Rogers	Horner	R Horner	Moran	Clark	Whittaker	Haw	Gamble	Sharratt	Dove	Blakeman	Morgan	42
Stewart	Farley	Rogers	Horner	R Horner	Moran	Clark	Whittaker	Duerden	Gamble	Sharratt	Dove	Blakeman	Haw	43
Stewart	Farley	Rogers	Dove	R Horner	Moran	Clark	Whittaker	Duerden	Gamble	Sharratt	Haw	Blakeman	Ellison	44
Stewart	Farley	Rogers	Blakeman	R Horner	Moran	P Horner	Whittaker	Duerden	Gamble	Sharratt	Haw	Ellison	Morgan	45
Stewart	Farley	Rogers	Blakeman	R Horner	Moran	P Horner	Whittaker	Duerden	Gamble	Sharratt	Haw	Ellison	Morgan	46
Stewart	Clark	Rogers	Horner	R Horner	Moran	Haw	Whittaker	Duerden	Gamble	Sharratt	Farley	Blakeman	Ellison	47
Stewart	Farley	Rogers	Blakeman	R Horner	Clark	Haw	Whittaker	Duerden	Gamble	Ellison	Sharratt	Marsden	Whitehead	48
Stewart	Farley	Rogers	Horner	R Horner	Clark	Haw	Whittaker	Duerden	Gamble	Sharratt	Butler	Blakeman	Morgan	49
Stewart	Farley	Clark	Horner	R Horner	Butler	Haw	Whittaker	Duerden	Gamble	Sharratt	Blakeman	Moran	Rogers	50
Stewart	Clark	Rogers	Horner	Dove	Butler	Haw	Whittaker	Duerden	Gamble	Moran	Farley	Sharratt	R Horner	51
Stewart	Farley	Rogers	Dove	R Horner	Moran	Clark	Whittaker	Duerden	Gamble	Sharratt	Horner	Haw	Blakeman	52
Stewart	Farley	Rogers	Dove	R Horner	Moran	Clark	Whittaker	Duerden	Gamble	Sharratt	Horner	Haw	Blakeman	53

PAUL FUTCHER (MANAGER)

Date of Appointment	June 1997
Date of Birth:	25th September 1956
Place of Birth:	Chester

PREVIOUS CLUBS

As manager	Darlington, Gresley Rovers.
As coach	None
As player	Chester C., Luton T., Manchester C., Oldham A., Derby Co., Barnsley, Halifax T., Grimsby.

HONOURS

As manager	Southern Lge Prem. 1996-97, Derbys. Sen. Cup (x2) (Gresley R.)
As player	England: u21 (11).

Assistant Manager: Peter Davenport **Physio:** Mark Thompson

John Deary from Rochdale - with over 550 League appearances

Brian Ross from Chorley - an experienced semi-pro International

TWO NEW SUMMER SIGNINGS

MATCHDAY PROGRAMME

Number of pages	36
Price	£1.20
Programme Editor	Derek Hitchcock (01704 579458)
Assistant Editor	Martin Hagan
Other club publications:	
Local Newspapers:	Southport Visitor Southport Advertiser The Champion
Local Radio Stations:	Radio Merseyside Red Rose Radio City Radio Lancashire

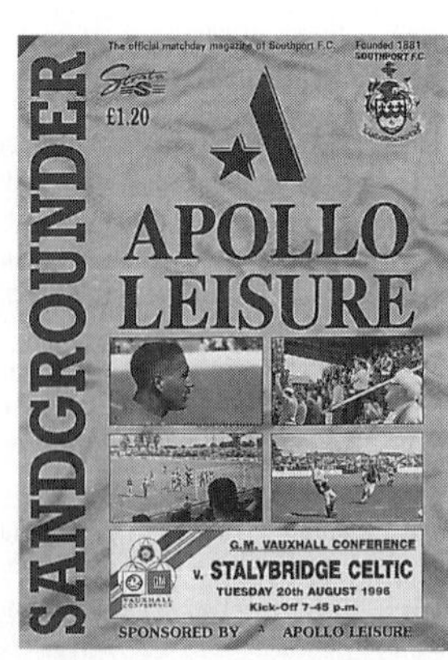

1997-98 PLAYING SQUAD

PLAYER	Birthplace Honours	Birthdate	CLUBS
GOALKEEPERS			
Billy Stewart	Liverpool	1.1.68	Liverpool, Wigan A, Chester C, Northampton T, Chester C
Peter Croasdale	Blackpool	1.1.77	Blackpool
DEFENDERS			
Leroy Dove	Manchester NPL, FA XI	27.4.63	Prestwich Heys, Droylsden, Buxton
Chris Blakeman	Southport	3.6.78	From Youth Team
Phil Horner	Leeds EY	10.11.68	Leicester C, Halifax T, Blackpool
Lee Anderson	Bury	4.10.73	Bury, Altrincham
Martin Clark	Accrington	12.9.70	Accrignton Stanley, Crewe A
Dave Rogers	Liverpool	25.8.75	Tranmere R, Chester C
Paul Futcher	Chester E u-21, FL XI	25.9.56	Chester C, £100k to Luton T, £350k to Manchester C, £150k to Oldham A, £44k to Derby Co, £30k to Barnsley, Halifax T, £10k to Grimsby T, Droylsden, Gresley R
MIDFIELDERS			
Brian Butler	Salford ESP, BLT	4.7.66	Blackpool, Stockport Co, Halifax T, Northwich Victoria
Dave Gamble	Liverpool NPL	23.3.71	Grimsby T, Altrincham
Chris Borwick	Preston	30.10.76	Preston
Andy Farley	Preston	18.12.74	From Youth Team
FORWARDS			
Chris Sharratt	West Kirby	13.8.70	Bangor C, Caernarfon T, Stalybridge C, Wigan A, Macclesfield T, Altrincham
Steve Haw	Liverpool NPL	9.11.62	Wigan A, Runcorn, Kirkby T, Marine, Altrincham, Marine, Southport, Chorley
Franis Powell	Burnley	17.6.77	Burnley, Rochdale
Andy Whittaker	Preston	29.1.68	Bamber Bridge, Netherfield, Barrow

DEPARTURES -
(During the season): Rod McDonald (Chester C), Phil Daley (Bangor C), Peter Davenport (Macclesfield T), Roger Preece (Telford U), Alex Jones (Lancaster C), Bryan Griffiths (Bangor C)

PLAYERS ON LOAN: Kenny Mayers (Chorley), Jon Kenworthy (Tranmere), Ian Duerden (Burnley)

Haig Avenue, Southport

GROUND ADDRESS:
Haig Avenue, Southport, Merseyside. PR9 7DR.
TELEPHONE NUMBER:
Ground: 01704 533422 Ticket Office: 01704 530182 Fax: 01704 533422.
Club Newsline: 0891 44 68 36
SIMPLE DIRECTIONS:
Signposted from all entrances to town.
CAPACITY: 6,012 **SEATED:** 1,880 **COVERED TERRACING:** 1,100
SOCIAL FACILITIES:
Open 7.30-11.00 every night and match days. (Tel: 01704 530182).
CLUB SHOP:
Scarves, replica kits, programmes and various other souvenirs for sale. Contact D Hitchcock, c/o Southport F.C.

Southport Fact File

Nickname: The Sandgrounders
Club Sponsors: Apollo Leisure
Club colours: Old Gold & black
Change colours: White & black
Midweek home matchday: Tuesday
Reserves' League: North West Combination

PREVIOUS -
Grounds: Ash Lane
Leagues: Northern Premier League, Football League, Lancashire Combination
Names: None

CLUB RECORDS -
Attendance: 20,000 v Newcastle United - FA Cup - 1932
Record win: 8-1 v Nelson - 01.01.31.
Record defeat: 0-11 v Oldham - 26.12.62
Career goalscorer: Alan Spence 98
Career appearances: Arthur Peat 401 - 1962-72
Transfer fee paid: £20,000 for Martin McDonald from Macclesfield Town - 1995.
Transfer fee received: £25,000 from Rochdale for Steve Whitehall - 1991

BEST SEASON -
FA Cup: Quarter Final, 1931-32. Lost to Newcastle Utd.
(The first Division 3 North team to reach the Quarter Finals)
FA Trophy: 3rd Round replay, 85-86, 1-6 (A) v Kidderminster Harriers, after 1-1 (H)

1996-97 Captain: Brian Butler
1996-97 Top scorer: Andy Whittaker (27)
1996-97 Player of the Year: Billy Stewart

Past players who have progressed to the Football League:
Shaun Teale, Andy Mutch, Steve Whitehall, Tony Rodwell.

HONOURS: Football League Division Four Champions 1972/73 (Runners-up 1966/67); Northern Premier League Champions 1992/93 (League Cup Winners 1990/91, League Shield 1993/94); Third Division North Section Cup Winners 1937/38; Liverpool Senior Cup Winners 1930/31, 1931/32, 1943/44, 1957/58 (shared), 1963/64 (shared), 1974/75, 1990/91, 1992/93 (Runners-up 1993/94); Lancashire Senior Cup Winners 1904/05; Lancashire Junior Cup (now ATS Challenge Trophy) Winners 1919/20, 1992/93 (Runners-up 1993/94).

Formed:
1909

STALYBRIDGE CELTIC

President: Joe Jackson **Chairman:** Peter Barnes
Vice Chairman: Derek Wolstenholme
Football Secretary: Martyn Torr Address - c/o the club
Tel: 0161 628 3387 (H) 0161 338 2828 (B) 0161 338 8256 (Fax)
Commercial Manager: Keith Mogford Tel: 0161 338 2828 (B)
Press Officer: Keith Trudgeon Tel: 0161 331 4426 (B) 0161 304 8934 (H)

A so-so season for the Bower Fold club.

Had it not been for a poor last month or so, Celtic could have easily beaten their best ever finishing position of twelfth. But, as it was, they had to settle for one place lower, following a run-in of four draws and a defeat.

Brian Kettle, appointed during the early part of the 96/97 campaign, certainly added a lot more steel to the side and Celtic became a hard outfit to beat.

However, despite the presence of record signing Ian Arnold and Brendan Burke in attack, their goal return didn't match the strength of their defence. Arnold has now moved on to Kidderminster Harriers, leaving Stalybridge even lighter up front, and that could be the difference between a top ten finish and a flirtation with relegation for the ambitious Bower Fold club.

Back Row: Tommy Martin (Asst. Man.), Craig Powell, David Hall, Harvey Willetts, David Williams, Dean Trott, Greg Challender, Craig Boardman, Steve Jones, Brian Kettle (Manager). Front: Darren Vine, Mark Powell, Ian Arnold, Lee Coathup, Brendan Burke, Jamie Bates, Steve Charles, Mark Hine.

Stalybridge Celtic

Match No.	Date	Venue H/A	Competition	Opponents	Result	League Pos.	Attendance	Goalscorers (Times if known)
1	Aug 17	A	VC	Slough Town	Lost 1-4	21	822	Vine 39
2	Aug 20	A	VC	Southport	Lost 0-3		1051	
3	Aug 24	H	VC	Hayes	Won 3-1		634	Trott 48, Burke (2) 54, 82
4	Aug 26	H	VC	Hednesford Town	Lost 1-2	20	643	Hall 59
5	Aug 31	A	VC	Rushden & Diamonds	Drew 1-1	18	2156	Charles 35
6	Sep 2	A	VC	Kidderminster Harriers	Drew 1-1		1718	Arnold 65 (pen)
7	Sep 7	H	VC	Woking	Lost 0-2	21	702	
8	Sep 10	H	VC	Telford United	Drew 0-0		430	
9	**Sep 14**	**A**	**FAC 1 Q**	**Yorkshire Amateurs**	**Won 1-0**		**146**	**Charles 38**
10	Sep 17	A	VC	Halifax Town	Lost 1-4		664	Charles 14
11	Sep 21	H	VC	Northwich Victoria	Lost 0-1	22	701	
12	**Sep 24**	**H**	**CSC**	**Winsford United**	**Won 3-2**		**207**	**Challender, Vine, Arnold**
13	**Sep 28**	**H**	**FAC 2 Q**	**Ossett Albion**	**Won 4-1**		**516**	**Trott 2, 59, Hall 18, Charles 83**
14	Oct 1	A	VC	Altrincham	Lost 0-1		692	
15	Oct 5	H	VC	Kettering Town	Won 3-1	22	684	Jones 17, Charles 44, Burke 84
16	**Oct 8**	**H**	**SCC**	**Telford United**	**Won 3-1***		**278**	**Burke 70, 115, Hall 118**
17	**Oct 12**	**H**	**FAC 3 Q**	**Ashton United**	**Won 2-1**		**1027**	**Burke 23 (pen), Jones 52**
18	Oct 15	A	VC	Macclesfield Town	Lost 0-2		792	
19	Oct 19	A	VC	Bath City	Won 2-0	22	530	Arnold 45, Burke 85
20	**Oct 22**	**H**	**SCC**	**Southport**	**Won 2-1**		**224**	**Jones 65, Burke 86**
21	**Oct 26**	**H**	**FAC 4 Q**	**Leek Town**	**Won 1-0**		**974**	**Jones**
22	Nov 2	H	VC	Bromsgrove Rovers	Won 3-0	17	585	Charles 17, Arnold 37, Burke 90
23	**Nov 5**	**A**	**CSC 2 Rnd**	**Nantwich Town**	**Lost 1-3**		**176**	**Burke**
24	Nov 9	A	VC	Hayes	Won 2-0	15	595	Charles 28, Jones 51
25	**Nov 16**	**A**	**FAC 1**	**Chester City**	**Lost 0-3**		**3151**	
26	Nov 26	H	VC	Morecambe	Won 2-1		474	Arnold 54, Charles 90
27	Nov 30	A	VC	Hednesford Town	Lost 1-2	15	1035	Arnold 56
28	Dec 7	H	VC	Halifax Town	Lost 2-3	16	814	Burke 66, 69
29	Dec 14	H	VC	Macclesfield Town	Lost 0-1		887	
30	**Dec 18**	**A**	**SCC**	**Morecambe**	**Drew 3-3***		**407**	**Trott 24, Hall 42, 89**
31	Dec 21	A	VC	Dover Athletic	Lost 1-2		700	Charles 27
32	Dec 26	A	VC	Gateshead	Won 2-0		448	Hall 14, Arnold 46
33	Dec 28	H	VC	Rushden & Diamonds	Won 2-0	13	788	Charles 35, Trott 51
34	Jan 11	A	VC	Bromsgrove Rovers	Won 1-0	12	734	Trott 35
35	Jan 14	A	VC	Telford United	Drew 1-1		554	Trott 84
36	**Jan 18**	**H**	**FAT 1**	**Halifax Town**	**Lost 0-1**		**973**	
37	Jan 25	H	VC	Dover Athletic	Won 4-2	11	579	Trott 3, Hall 36, Arnold 68, Daniels 76 (og)
38	Feb 1	H	VC	Farnborough Town	Won 2-0	10	617	Burke 50, Trott 81
39	Feb 11	H	VC	Southport	Drew 2-2		493	Arnold 68, 90
40	Feb 15	A	VC	Farnborough Town	Lost 0-1	12	696	
41	Feb 22	H	VC	Stevenage Borough	Lost 0-3	12	735	
42	**Feb 25**	**H**	**SCC**	**Morecambe**	**Lost 0-1**		**335**	
43	Mar 1	A	VC	Kettering Town	Lost 0-1	13	1509	
44	Mar 4	H	VC	Gateshead	Lost 2-5		274	Charles 22, Jones 73
45	Mar 8	H	VC	Altrincham	Won 1-0	12	725	Burke 64
46	Mar 15	A	VC	Woking	Lost 2-3	13	2382	Arnold 68, 87
47	Mar 22	H	VC	Kidderminster Harriers	Won 4-1	10	1067	Charles 27, Burke 36, Jones 47, 51
48	Mar 29	H	VC	Welling United	Drew 0-0		710	
49	Mar 31	A	VC	Northwich Victoria	Won 1-0	11	814	Hine 90
50	Apr 5	H	VC	Bath City	Drew 2-2	11	545	Arnold 10, 41
51	Apr 22	A	VC	Morecambe	Drew 0-0		862	
52	Apr 26	H	VC	Stevenage Borough	Drew 1-1	12	2685	Goldbourne 82
53	Apr 29	A	VC	Welling United	Lost 0-2		617	
54	May 3	H	VC	Slough Town	Drew 2-2	13	511	Charles 51, Burke 82 (pen)

* After Extra Time

Stalybridge Celtic

1	2	3	4	5	6	7	8	9	10	11	12	14	15	Mth No.
Willetts	Bates	Coathup	O'Shaughnessy	Boardman	Hine	Burke	Vine	Jones	Trott	Challender	Frain	Powell M	Heaton	1
Willetts	Bates	Coathup	O'Shaughnessy	Jones	Challender	Burke	Vine	Trott	Hine	Charles	Boardman	Frain	Powell M	2
Willetts	Bates	Coathup	O'Shaughnessy	Boardman	Frain	Burke	Vine	Jones	Trott	Charles	Arnold	Hall	Powell M	3
Willetts	Bates	Coathup	O'Shaughnessy	Boardman	Hall	Burke	Hine	Trott	Arnold	Charles	Vine	Challender	Powell M	4
Willetts	Bates	Coathup	Frain	Boardman	Hall	Goodacre	Todd	Powell C	Arnold	Charles	Challender	Powell M	Heaton	5
Willetts	Bates	Coathup	Frain	Boardman	Hall	Todd	Hine	Trott	Arnold	Charles	Challender	Vine	Powell M	6
Willetts	Bates	Coathup	Charles	Boardman	Hall	Todd	Jones	Trott	Arnold	Challender	Vine	Powell C	Powell M	7
Willetts	Bates	Coathup	Hine	Boardman	Hall	Todd	Jones	Trott	Arnold	Charles	Powell C	Heaton	Powell M	8
Willetts	**Bates**	**Coathup**	**Hine**	**Boardman**	**Hall**	**Todd**	**Powell M**	**Trott**	**Arnold**	**Charles**	**Powell C**	**Challender**	**Vine**	**9**
Willetts	Bates	Coathup	Hine	Boardman	Hall	Burke	Todd	Trott	Arnold	Charles	Vine	Challender	Powell M	10
Willetts	Bates	Coathup	Hine	Boardman	Hall	Burke	Challender	Trott	Arnold	Charles	Vine	Powell M	Powell C	11
Willetts	**Bates**	**Charles**	**Hine**	**Boardman**	**Hall**	**Burke**	**Challender**	**Vine**	**Arnold**	**Powell C**	**Powell M**	**Trott**	**Frain**	**12**
Willetts	**Bates**	**Coathup**	**Hine**	**Boardman**	**Hall**	**Burke**	**Challender**	**Trott**	**Arnold**	**Charles**	**Todd**	**Powell M**	**Jones**	**13**
Willetts	Bates	Coathup	Hine	Boardman	Hall	Burke	Jones	Vine	Arnold	Charles	Frain	Todd	Heaton	14
Williams	Bates	Coathup	Hine	Boardman	Hall	Burke	Jones	Powell M	Arnold	Charles	Todd	Frain	Vine	15
Williams	**Powell M**	**Coathup**	**Todd**	**Boardman**	**Hall**	**Burke**	**Jones**	**Frain**	**Arnold**	**Charles**	**Hine**	**Vine**	**Heaton**	**16**
Williams	**Bates**	**Coathup**	**Hine**	**Boardman**	**Hall**	**Burke**	**Powell M**	**Jones**	**Arnold**	**Charles**	**Vine**	**Todd**	**Challender**	**17**
Williams	Bates	Coathup	Powell M	Boardman	Hall	Burke	Jones	Trott	Arnold	Charles	Hine	Powell C	Challender	18
Williams	Bates	Coathup	Hine	Boardman	Hall	Burke	Jones	Powell M	Arnold	Charles	Trott	Powell C	Challender	19
Williams	**Bates**	**Coathup**	**Hine**	**Boardman**	**Hall**	**Burke**	**Jones**	**Powell M**	**Arnold**	**Charles**	**Trott**	**Powell C**	**Challender**	**20**
Williams	**Bates**	**Coathup**	**Hine**	**Boardman**	**Hall**	**Burke**	**Jones**	**Trott**	**Arnold**	**Charles**	**Powell M**	**Powell C**	**Challender**	**21**
Williams	Bates	Coathup	Hine	Boardman	Hall	Burke	Jones	Trott	Arnold	Charles	Challender	Powell M	Vine	22
Willetts	**Challender**	**Coathup**	**Hine**	**Jones**	**Hall**	**Burke**	**Powell M**	**Trott**	**Arnold**	**Charles**	**Boardman**	**Powell C**	**Vine**	**23**
Williams	Bates	Coathup	Hine	Boardman	Hall	Burke	Jones	Trott	Arnold	Charles	Powell M	Challender	Powell C	24
Williams	**Bates**	**Coathup**	**Hine**	**Boardman**	**Hall**	**Burke**	**Jones**	**Trott**	**Arnold**	**Charles**	**Challender**	**Powell M**	**Powell C**	**25**
Williams	Bates	Powell M	Hine	Boardman	Hall	Burke	Jones	Trott	Arnold	Charles	Challender	Vine	Powell C	26
Williams	Powell M	Coathup	Hine	Boardman	Hall	Burke	Jones	Trott	Arnold	Charles	Challender	Howard	Vine	27
Williams	Powell M	Coathup	Hine	Boardman	Hall	Burke	Jones	Trott	Arnold	Charles	Vine	Powell C	Challender	28
Willetts	Bates	Coathup	Hine	Boardman	Hall	Burke	Jones	Trott	Arnold	Charles	Vine	Powell C	Challender	29
Willetts	**Bates**	**Powell M**	**Hine**	**Boardman**	**Hall**	**Burke**	**Jones**	**Trott**	**Arnold**	**Thomas G**	**Charles**	**Challender**	**Powell C**	**30**
Williams	Bates	Thomas G	Hine	Boardman	Hall	Powell M	Challender	Trott	Arnold	Charles	Burke	Jones	Vine	31
Williams	Powell M	Thomas G	Hine	Boardman	Hall	Thomas K	Challender	Trott	Arnold	Charles	Coathup	Bates	Jones	32
Williams	Powell M	Thomas G	Hine	Boardman	Hall	Thomas K	Challender	Trott	Arnold	Charles	Vine	Jones	Coathup	33
Williams	Powell M	Thomas G	Hine	Boardman	Hall	Thomas K	Challender	Trott	Arnold	Charles	Burke	Jones	Coathup	34
Williams	Powell M	Coathup	Hine	Boardman	Hall	Jones	Challender	Trott	Burke	Thomas G	Vine	Ellis	Thomas K	35
Williams	**Powell M**	**Coathup**	**Hine**	**Boardman**	**Hall**	**Burke**	**Jones**	**Trott**	**Arnold**	**Thomas G**	**Challender**	**Thomas K**	**Vine**	**36**
Williams	Powell M	Coathup	Hine	Jones	Hall	Burke	Challender	Trott	Arnold	Thomas G	Boardman	Thomas K	Ellis	37
Williams	Powell M	Coathup	Hine	Boardman	Hall	Burke	Jones	Trott	Arnold	Thomas G	Challender	Thomas K	Jackson	38
Williams	Powell M	Coathup	Hine	Boardman	Hall	Burke	Jones	Trott	Arnold	Thomas G	Charles	Thomas K	Jackson	39
Williams	Powell M	Coathup	Hine	Boardman	Hall	Burke	Jones	Trott	Thomas K	Thomas G	Charles	Jackson	Arnold	40
Williams	Powell M	Coathup	Hine	Boardman	Hall	Burke	Jones	Trott	Arnold	Thomas G	Charles	Challender	Thomas K	41
Williams	**Powell M**	**Coathup**	**Hine**	**Boardman**	**Hall**	**Jones**	**Challender**	**Trott**	**Arnold**	**Charles**	**Thomas K**	**Vine**	**Thomas G**	**42**
Williams	Powell M	Coathup	Challender	Boardman	Hall	Burke	Jones	Trott	Arnold	Charles	Thomas G	Crane	Hine	43
Williams	Powell M	Coathup	Hine	Hall	Charles	Burke	Crane	Trott	Arnold	Thomas G	Boardman	Challender	Jones	44
Westhead	Powell M	Coathup	Hine	Boardman	Hall	Burke	Jones	Trott	Charles	Thomas G	Arnold	Crane	Bates	45
Westhead	Powell M	Coathup	Hine	Boardman	Trott	Burke	Jones	Charles	Arnold	Thomas G	Crane	Vine	Bates	46
Westhead	Powell M	Thomas G	Hine	Boardman	Hall	Burke	Jones	Trott	Goldbourne	Charles	Bates	Crane	Vine	47
Westhead	Powell M	Thomas G	Hine	Boardman	Hall	Burke	Jones	Goldbourne	Arnold	Charles	Coathup	Bates	Crane	48
Westhead	Powell M	Thomas G	Coathup	Boardman	Hall	Burke	Jones	Goldbourne	Arnold	Charles	Bates	Crane	Hine	49
Westhead	Powell M	Thomas G	Hine	Boardman	Hall	Burke	Jones	Bates	Arnold	Charles	Coathup	Crane	Goldbourne	50
Westhead	Bates	Coathup	Hine	Boardman	Hall	Burke	Jones	Vine	Charles	Thomas G	Powell M	Crane	Goldbourne	51
Coathup	Bates	Powell M	Hine	Boardman	Hall	Burke	Jones	Vine	Thomas G	Charles	Goldbourne	Crane	Heaton	52
Westhead	Bates	Powell M	Hine	Boardman	Hall	Burke	Jones	Vine	Charles	Thomas G	Goldbourne	Crane		53

BRIAN KETTLE (MANAGER)

Date of Appointment	November 1996
Date of Birth:	22nd April 1956
Place of Birth:	Prescot

PREVIOUS CLUBS

As manager	South Liverpool, Southport, Northwich Vic.
As coach	None
As player	Liverpool, Wigan Athletic, Houston Hurricanes (USA), Runcorn, South Liverpool.

HONOURS

As manager	Northern Premier League
As player	England - Youth cap

Asst. Manager: Tommy Martin **Physio:** Dave Pover

BRENDON BURKE - Team Captain

DAVID HALL - 96-97 Player of the Year

MATCHDAY PROGRAMME

Number of pages	40
Price	£1.30
Programme Editor	Nick Shaw (0161 633 1117)
Other club publications:	None
Local Newspapers:	Manchester Evening News Manchester Evening News Pink (Sat. eve.) Aston Reporter, Ashton Advertiser
Local Radio Stations:	G.M.R. (BBC Manchester) Piccadilly Radio

1997-98 PLAYING SQUAD

PLAYER	Birthplace Honours	Birthdate	CLUBS
GOALKEEPERS			
Mark Statham	Davyhulme	7.3.76	Nottingham Forest, Wigan Athletic, Witton Albion
DEFENDERS			
Ian Patterson	Chatham	4.4.73	Sunderland, Burnley, Wigan A
Jamie Bates	Manchester		Maine Road, Runcorn
Lee Coathup	Singapore	2.5.67	Everton, Newtown, Vauxhall GM, Stalybridge C, Witton A
David Hall	Manchester	19.10.73	Oldham A, Halifax T
Steve O'Shaughnessy	Wrexham EY	13.10.67	Leeds U, Bradford C, Rochdale, Exeter C, Darlington, Stalybridge C, Barry T
Ian Brady	Liverpool		Heswall, Bootle, Runcorn, Gateshead, Halifax T
MIDFIELDERS			
Steve Charles	Sheffield ES	10.5.60	Sheffield U, Wrexham, Mansfield T, Scarborough
Steve Jones	Stoke		Stoke C, Stafford Rangers, Eastwood Hanley, Leek T, £3,500 to Stalybridge C
Gary Thomas	Manchester	16.12.67	Winsford U, Witton A, Southport, Chorley
Ronnie Gouldbourne	Liverpool		Liverpool, Knowsley U
FORWARDS			
Ian Arnold	Durham ESP	4.7.72	Middlesbrough, Carlisle U, £10k to Kettering T, £15k to Stalybridge C
Darren Vine	Sheffield	22.12.76	Sheffield U
Sam Goodacre	Sheffield	1.12.70	Sheffield U, Scunthorpe U
Carwyn Williams	Pwllheli	21.10.74	Crewe A, Northwich V, Macclesfield T
Brendan Burke	Manchester FA XI	13.10.70	Manchester U, Mosssley, Witton A, £12k to Stalybridge C

DEPARTURES -
(During the season): Peter Byrne (Knowsley U), Mark Todd (Blyth S), David Frain (Alfreton T), Craig Powell (Curzon Ashton), Robbie Jackson, Greg Challender & David Williams (Released)

PLAYERS ON LOAN - Matt Westhead (Bolton W)

Bower Fold, Stalybridge

GROUND ADDRESS:
Bower Fold, Mottram Road, Stalybridge, Cheshire SK15 2RT.

TELEPHONE NUMBER:
0161 338 2828 Fax: 0161 338 8256 Mobile: 0860 841765.

SIMPLE DIRECTIONS:
M6 to A556 to M63 to M67; end of Motorway through roundabout to traffic lights, left; left at end into Molltram Road, up hill, down hill into Stalybridge, ground on left next to Hare & Hounds pub.

CAPACITY: 6,000 **SEATED:** 1,300 **COVERED TERRACING:** 1,300

RECORD ATTENDANCE:
9,753 v WBA - FA Cup replay - 1922-23

CLUB SHOP:
Contact Keith Mogford for details (0161 338 2828)

SOCIAL FACILITIES:
Clubhouse open matchdays and evenings during the week. Food available on matchdays.

Stalybridge Celtic Fact File

Nickname: Celtic
Club Sponsors: Manro Perfordmance Chemicals Ltd.
Club colours: Blue shirts with white sleeves, blue shorts, blue socks.
Change colours: Green and white hooped shirts, green shorts, green socks.
Midweek home matchday: Tuesday
Reserves' League: None

PREVIOUS - **Leagues:** Lancashire Combination 1911-12, Central Lge 1912-21, Football Lge 1921-23, Cheshire Co. Lge 1923-1982, North West Co's 1982-87, Northern Prem. Lge 1987-92.
Grounds: None **Names:** None

CLUB RECORDS - **Win:** 16-2 twice; v Manchester NE 1/5/26; v Nantwich 22/10/32
Defeat: 0-6 v Northwich Victoria
Career appearances: Kevin Booth 354
Career goalscorer: Not known
Goalscorer (in a season): Chris Camden 45, 1991-92
Transfer fee paid: £15,000 to Kettering Town for Ian Arnold 1995
Transfer fee received: £3,000 for Martin Filson from Halifax Town

BEST SEASON - **FA Cup:** Second Round 1993-94, 1-3 v Carlisle United (A)
League clubs defeated: None
FA Trophy: Third Round 1991-92, 0-1 v Witton Albion (A).

1996-97 Captain: Brendon Burke
1996-97 Top scorer: Brendon Burke (15)
1996-97 Player of the Year: David Hall
Past players who progressed to the Football League: Too numerous to list.

HONOURS: Northern Premier Lg Prem Div 91-92, NPL R-up 90-91 (Div.1 R-up 87-88); Cheshire Cnty Lg 79-80 (R-up 77-78), Lg Cup 21-22 (R-up 46-47,81-82); Challenge Shield 77-78 (runners-up 79-80), Reserves Div R-up 81-82), NW Co's Lg 83-84, 86-87 (Lge Cup R-up 83-84), Champions v Cup Winners Trophy 83-84, Lancs Comb Div 2 11-12; Cheshire Snr Cup 52-53 (R-up 54-55, 80-81; Manchester Snr Cup 22-23 (Intermediate Cup 57-58, 68-69 (R-up 56-57, 67-68, 69-70)); Challenge Shield 54-55, (Junior Cup 62-63), Lancs Floodlit Cup 88-89 (R-up 89-90); Reporter Cup R-up 74-75; Edward Case Cup 77-78.

STEVENAGE BOROUGH

Formed
1976

President: Rod Resker

Chairman: Victor Green

Club Secretary: Janice Hutchings
Address - c/o the club.
Tel: 01438 743322 (B) Fax: 01438 743666

Commercial Manager: Clive Abrey
Press Officer: Paul Fry (01438 748684)

One cannot argue with Stevenage Borough's record since joining non-League football's top competition. Fifth, first and third represents a terrific achievement.

All defending champions find it extremely difficult the following season and Borough couldn't quite match their achievements of 1995/96 as visiting sides tried that much harder to dent the title winners' pride.

What must have pleased Borough's officials though was the attendance figures - an incredible 52 per cent up on the previous season, ending with an average of 2,881.

Manager Paul Fairclough made changes to his championship winning squad and has done so again during the last close season, even more dramatically. They will certainly miss Barry Hayles' goals and Efetobor Sodje's presence at the back, but Fairclough always seems able to come up with replacements and no doubt he will do so again.

L-R, Back Row: Brian Hierons (Res Physio), Miguel Luque (Res Mgr), Bill Bannister (Res Asst Mgr), Efetobor Sodje, Des Gallagher, Nicholas Grime, Neil Trebble, Dave Venables, Richard Wilmot, Corey Browne, Eric Richards (Kit), Robbie Scott (Scout). Middle: Shaun Stevens, Matthew Vier, Mike Bignall, Paul Peterson (Asst Mgr), Paul Fairclough (Manager), Noel Blackwell (Coach), Kenny Webster, Dominic Grime, Barry Hayles. Front: Alan Paris, Mark Smith, Neil Catlin, Scott Cretton, Stuart Beevor, Gary Crawshaw, Paul Barrowcliff, Rob Mutchell, John Ugbah.

Stevenage Borough

Match No.	Date	Venue H/A	Competition	Opponents	Result	League Pos.	Attendance	Goalscorers (Times if known)
1	**Aug 10**	**A**	**HCCF**	**St Albans City**	**Won 4-2***			**Sodje, Hayles (2), Ugbah**
2	Aug 17	H	VC	Halifax Town	Won 6-0	1	2117	Bignall 9,18, Barrowcliff 46, Sodje 67, Browne 71, 82
3	Aug 19	A	VC	Hednesford Town	Drew 0-0		1440	
4	Aug 24	H	VC	Morecambe	Won 4-2		2655	Webster 69 (p), Hayles 72, 77, Venables 79
5	Aug 26	A	VC	Macclesfield Town	Lost 1-2	5	1723	Hayles 80
6	Aug 31	A	VC	Northwich Victoria	Won 1-0	3	1021	Hayles 20
7	Sep 2	H	VC	Welling United	Won 2-1		2382	Bignall (2) 21, 26
8	Sep 5	A	VC	Telford United	Won 3-2	1	1060	Crawshaw (2) 20, 32, Trebble 48
9	Sep 9	H	VC	Bath City	Won 2-1		2574	Bates 4, Browne 63
10	**Sep 14**	**A**	**FAC 1 Q**	**Arlesey Town**	**Won 3-0**		**1564**	**Browne (2) 73, 85, Ugbah 84**
11	Sep 16	A	VC	Kidderminster Harriers	Lost 0-3		2356	
12	Sep 21	H	VC	Bromsgrove Rovers	Won 3-0	1	2552	Browne (2) 5, 80, Hayles 78
13	Sep 24	A	VC	Rushden & Diamonds	Won 1-0		3288	Ugbah 19
14	**Sep 28**	**H**	**FAC 2 Q**	**Baldock Town**	**Drew 1-1**		**1865**	**Crawshaw 26**
15	**Oct 2**	**A**	**FAC R**	**Baldock Town**	**Won 2-1**		**1588**	**Crawshaw 26, Sodje 89**
16	Oct 5	H	VC	Southport	Won 2-1	1	2903	Crawshaw 7, Barrowcliff 41
17	**Oct 7**	**H**	**JTCM**	**Macclesfield Town**	**Lost 1-2***		**1828**	**Hayles**
18	**Oct 12**	**H**	**FAC 3 Q**	**Braintree Town**	**Won 3-1**		**1970**	**Webster 2 (p), Trebble 31, Crawshaw 81**
19	Oct 15	A	VC	Woking	Lost 1-3		2466	Trebble 83
20	Oct 19	A	VC	Farnborough Town	Lost 1-3	3	1148	Webster 52 (pen)
21	**Oct 26**	**A**	**FAC 4 Q**	**Gravesend & Northfleet**	**Won 5-1**		**784**	**W'ster 27(p), C'shaw 45, B'vor 58, V'bles 62, Br'ne 78**
22	**Oct 28**	**H**	**HCC 2**	**Hitchin Town**	**Won 4-2**		**522**	**Catlin, Trebble (3)**
23	Nov 2	H	VC	Woking	Lost 0-3	6	4352	
24	Nov 9	A	VC	Bromsgrove Rovers	Drew 1-1	6	922	Trebble 51
25	**Nov16**	**H**	**FAC 1**	**Hayes**	**Drew 2-2**		**3288**	**Catlin 37, Hayles 74**
26	**Nov 19**	**A**	**SCC**	**Rushden & Diamonds**	**Lost 0-1**		**1073**	
27	Nov 23	H	VC	Gateshead	Won 4-1	5	2015	Adams (3) 51, 67, 76, Trebble
28	**Nov 26**	**A**	**FAC 1 R**	**Hayes**	**Won 2-0**		**2965**	**Hayles 22, 79**
29	Nov 30	H	VC	Dover Athletic	Won 4-1	4	2009	Catlin 46, Trebble 63, Adams 77, Hayles 86
30	**Dec 7**	**A**	**FAC 2**	**Leyton Orient**	**Won 2-1**		**6980**	**Browne 1, Catlin 22**
31	Dec 14	H	VC	Telford United	Won 3-0		2089	Crawshaw 36 (p), Catlin 58, Browne 60
32	Dec 21	A	VC	Bath City	Drew 0-0		587	
33	Dec 26	H	VC	Slough Town	Drew 2-2	6	2834	Hayles 4, Browne 31
34	Jan 1	A	VC	Slough Town	Won 6-1	3	1298	Kirby 3, Hayles 23, Catlin 40, Beevor 52,71, Browne 70
35	**Jan 4**	**H+**	**FAC 3**	**Birmingham City**	**Lost 0-2**		**15365**	
36	Jan 11	A	VC	Hayes	Won 3-1	2	1097	Hayles 47, Beevor 62, Catlin 69
37	**Jan 18**	**A**	**FAT 1**	**Bath City**	**Drew 1-1**		**682**	**Browne 48**
38	**Jan 20**	**H**	**FAT 1 R**	**Bath City**	**Won 6-1**		**1344**	**Browne 15, 72, 81, Trebble 37, Hayles 51, Catlin 90**
39	Jan 25	H	VC	Kidderminster Harriers	Drew 2-2	3	6489	Catlin 21, Browne 76
40	Feb 1	A	VC	Welling United	Lost 0-2	3	1078	
41	**Feb 8**	**A**	**FAT 2**	**Boreham Wood**	**Won 1-0**		**1242**	**Browne 12**
42	Feb 15	H	VC	Kettering Town	Drew 0-0	3	2864	
43	Feb 17	H	VC	Hayes	Won 2-0		1807	Sodje 13, Hooper 38
44	Feb 22	A	VC	Stalybridge Celtic	Won 3-0	3	735	Crawshaw 40, Soloman 55, Browne 80
45	**Mar 1**	**H**	**FAT 3**	**Guiseley**	**Won 1-0**		**2152**	**Catlin 90**
46	Mar 8	H	VC	Northwich Victoria	Won 2-0		2501	Sodje 73, Barrowcliff 85
47	Mar 15	H	VC	Hednesford Town	Won 3-2	3	2744	Crawshaw 13, Soloman 19, Barrowcliff 32
48	Mar 17	H	VC	Altrincham	Won 2-1	3	2287	(pen)
49	**Mar 22**	**H**	**FAT Q F**	**Colwyn Bay**	**Won 2-0**		**3082**	Crawshaw 11, Catlin 48
50	Mar 25	A	VC	Kettering Town	Won 2-1	3	1874	**Roberts 15 (og), Sodje 44**
51	Mar 29	H	VC	Macclesfield Town	Lost 2-3	3	5760	Crawshaw 51, 58 (pen)
52	Mar 31	A	VC	Morecambe	Won 2-1		1438	Crawshaw 29, Catlin 52
53	**Apr 5**	**A**	**FAT S F**	**Woking**	**Lost 0-1**		**3769**	Mison 8, Barrowcliff 75 (pen)
54	Apr 8	A	VC	Dover Athletic	Drew 3-3	3	1619	
55	**Apr 12**	**H**	**FAT S F**	**Woking**	**Won 2-1**		**5163**	Crawshaw 27, 87, Mison 66
56	Apr 14	H	VC	Farnborough Town	Won 3-1	3	2041	**Hayles 1, Crawshaw 119**
57	**Apr 16**	**N**	**FAT S F**	**Woking**	**Lost 1-2**		**5870**	Hayles 12, 49, 87
58	Apr 19	A	VC	Southport	Drew 0-0	3	965	**Soloman 84**
59	Apr 21	H	VC	Rushden & Diamonds	Won 4-1		2836	
60	Apr 23	A	VC	Gateshead	Drew 2-2	3	652	Hayles 19, Sodje 50, Mison 66, Kimby 90
61	Apr 26	H	VC	Stalybridge Celtic	Drew 1-1	3	2685	Mison 53, Soloman 60
62	Apr 30	A	VC	Altrincham	Won 2-1	3	780	Mison 35
63	May 3	A	VC	Halifax Town	Lost 2-4	3	1171	Hayles 25, 90
								Stoneman 20 (og), Hayles 39

+ Played at St Andrews

Stevenage Borough

1	2	3	4	5	6	7	8	9	10	11	12	14	15	Mth No.
Gallagher	**Webster**	**Paris**	**Sodje**	**Smith**	**Barrowcliff**	**Beevor**	**Browne**	**Venables**	**Catlin**	**Hayles**	**Ugbah**	**Bignall**	**Stevens**	**1**
Gallagher	Webster	Paris	Sodje	Smith	Barrowcliff	Beevor	Browne	Venables	Catlin	Bignall	Ugbah	Trebble	Wilmot	2
Gallagher	Webster	Paris	Sodje	Smith	Barrowcliff	Beevor	Browne	Venables	Catlin	Bignall	Ugbah	Trebble	Wilmot	3
Gallagher	Webster	Paris	Sodje	Smith	Barrowcliff	Beevor	Browne	Venables	Catlin	Bignall	Hayles	Ugbah	Wilmot	4
Gallagher	Webster	Paris	Sodje	Smith	Barrowcliff	Ugbah	Browne	Venables	Bignall	Hayles	Trebble	Beevor	Wilmot	5
Gallagher	Webster	Paris	Sodje	Smith	Barrowcliff	Beevor	Trebble	Crawshaw	Bignall	Hayles	Ugbah	Mutchell	Wilmot	6
Gallagher	Webster	Paris	Sodje	Smith	Barrowcliff	Beevor	Ugbah	Crawshaw	Bignall	Hayles	Trebble	Mutchell	Wilmot	7
Gallagher	Webster	Paris	Sodje	Smith	Barrowcliff	Beevor	Ugbah	Crawshaw	Bignall	Trebble	Hayles	Mutchell	Wilmot	8
Gallagher	Webster	Paris	Sodje	Smith	Barrowcliff	Beevor	Ugbah	Bates	Browne	Trebble	Stevens	Mutchell	Wilmot	9
Wilmot	**Webster**	**Mutchell**	**Sodje**	**Smith**	**Barrowcliff**	**Beevor**	**Ugbah**	**Bignall**	**Browne**	**Venables**	**Paris**	**Stevens**	**Gallagher**	**10**
Gallagher	Webster	Paris	Sodje	Smith	Barrowcliff	Beevor	Ugbah	Venables	Browne	Hayles	Bignall	Crawshaw	Wilmot	11
Gallagher	Webster	Paris	Sodje	Smith	Barrowcliff	Beevor	Ugbah	Mutchell	Browne	Hayles	Crawshaw	Catlin	Wilmot	12
Gallagher	Webster	Paris	Sodje	Smith	Barrowcliff	Beevor	Ugbah	Catlin	Browne	Hayles	Venables	Crawshaw	Wilmot	13
Gallagher	**Mutchell**	**Paris**	**Sodje**	**Smith**	**Barrowcliff**	**Beevor**	**Ugbah**	**Crawshaw**	**Browne**	**Bignall**	**Catlin**	**Venables**	**Wilmot**	**14**
Wilmot	**Mutchell**	**Paris**	**Sodje**	**Smith**	**Barrowcliff**	**Beevor**	**Catlin**	**Crawshaw**	**Browne**	**Hayles**	**Trebble**	**Ugbah**	**Stevens**	**15**
Wilmot	Webster	Mutchell	Sodje	Smith	Barrowcliff	Beevor	Venables	Crawshaw	Trebble	Hayles	Ugbah	Browne	Imber	16
Wilmot	**Webster**	**Mutchell**	**Sodje**	**Smith**	**Barrowcliff**	**Beevor**	**Venables**	**Crawshaw**	**Trebble**	**Hayles**	**Ugbah**	**Browne**	**Imber**	**17**
Wilmot	**Webster**	**Mutchell**	**Sodje**	**Smith**	**Barrowcliff**	**Beevor**	**Venables**	**Crawshaw**	**Browne**	**Trebble**	**Paris**	**Ugbah**	**Imber**	**18**
Wilmot	Webster	Mutchell	Sodje	Smith	Barrowcliff	Beevor	Ugbah	Crawshaw	Venables	Trebble	Paris	Ugbah	Imber	19
Wilmot	Webster	Mutchell	Sodje	Smith	Barrowcliff	Venables	Beevor	Crawshaw	Browne	Endersby	Trebble	Catlin	Imber	20
Wilmot	**Webster**	**Mutchell**	**Sodje**	**Smith**	**Barrowcliff**	Beevor	Catlin	Crawshaw	Browne	Venables	Trebble	Ugbah	Gallagher	21
Gallagher	**Webster**	**Vier**	**Cretton**	**Paris**	**Ugbah**	**Venables**	**Catlin**	**Endersby**	**Browne**	**Trebble**	**Beevor**	**Bignall**	**Wilmot**	**22**
Wilmot	Webster	Mutchell	Sodje	Smith	Barrowcliff	Catlin	Venables	Endersby	Crawshaw	Hayles	Paris	Browne	Trebble	23
Gallagher	Kirby	Mutchell	Sodje	Smith	Barrowcliff	Cretton	Beevor	Crawshaw	Catlin	Trebble	Hayles	Browne	Vier	24
Gallagher	**Webster**	**Mutchell**	**O'Grime**	**Smith**	**Barrowcliff**	**Beevor**	**Browne**	**Cretton**	**Catlin**	**Hayles**	**Crawshaw**	**Venables**	**Wilmot**	**25**
Gallagher	**Grime**	**Butler**	**Cretton**	**Smith**	**Adams**	**Beevor**	**Browne**	**Catlin**	**Vier**	**Hayles**	**Venables**	**Crawshaw**	**Mutchell**	**26**
Gallagher	Kirby	Mutchell	Cretton	Smith	Adams	Beevor	Browne	Catlin	Grime	Hayles	Venables	Trebble	Crawshaw	27
Gallagher	**Kirby**	**Mutchell**	**Sodje**	**Smith**	**Cretton**	**Beevor**	**Trebble**	**Venables**	**Catlin**	**Hayles**	**Crawshaw**	**Browne**	**Wilmot**	**28**
Gallagher	Kirby	Mutchell	Sodje	Smith	Cretton	Beevor	Adams	Catlin	Trebble	Hayles	Barrowcliff	Venables	Crawshaw	29
Gallagher	**Kirby**	**Mutchell**	**Sodje**	**Smith**	**Barrowcliff**	**Beevor**	**Browne**	**Catlin**	**Cretton**	**Hayles**	**Crawshaw**	**Adams**	**Wilmot**	**30**
Gallagher	Kirby	Mutchell	Sodje	Smith	Barrowcliff	Adams	Browne	Catlin	Cretton	Crawshaw	Venables	Beevor	Webster	31
Gallagher	Kirby	Mutchell	Sodje	Smith	Barrowcliff	Adams	Browne	Catlin	Webster	Crawshaw	Trebble	Beevor	Cretton	32
Gallagher	Kirby	Mutchell	Sodje	Smith	Barrowcliff	Adams	Browne	Catlin	Webster	Hayles	Crawshaw	Beevor	Cretton	33
Gallagher	Kirby	Mutchell	Sodje	Smith	Barrowcliff	Hooper	Browne	Catlin	Beevor	Hayles	Crawshaw	Adams	Trebble	34
Gallagher	**Kirby**	**Mutchell**	**Sodje**	**Smith**	**Barrowcliff**	**Beevor**	**Browne**	**Catlin**	**Webster**	**Hayles**	**Crawshaw**	**Adams**	**Trebble**	**35**
Wilmot	Kirby	Mutchell	Sodje	Smith	Barrowcliff	Hooper	Browne	Catlin	Beevor	Hayles	Crawshaw	Adams	Trebble	36
Gallagher	**Kirby**	**Mutchell**	**Hooper**	**Smith**	**Barrowcliff**	**Adams**	**Browne**	**Catlin**	**Beevor**	**Hayles**	**Crawshaw**	**Trebble**	**Wilmot**	**37**
Gallagher	**Kirby**	**Mutchell**	**Hooper**	**Smith**	**Barrowcliff**	**Trebble**	**Browne**	**Catlin**	**Beevor**	**Hayles**	**Adams**	**Catlin**	**Wilmot**	**38**
Gallagher	Kirby	Mutchell	Hooper	Smith	Barrowcliff	Trebble	Browne	Catlin	Beevor	Hayles	Crawshaw	Adams	Sodje	39
Gallagher	Kirby	Mutchell	Sodje	Smith	Barrowcliff	Hooper	Browne	Catlin	Beevor	Hayles	Adams	Crawshaw	Trebble	40
Gallagher	**Kirby**	**Mutchell**	**Sodje**	**Smith**	**Barrowcliff**	**Hooper**	**Browne**	**Adams**	**Beevor**	**Crawshaw**	**Catlin**	**Catlin**	**Wilmot**	**41**
Gallagher	Kirby	Mutchell	Sodje	Smith	Barrowcliff	Hooper	Browne	Catlin	Crawshaw	D Grime	Adams	Bignall	Cretton	42
Gallagher	Kirby	Mutchell	Sodje	Smith	Barrowcliff	Hooper	Browne	Adams	Beevor	Crawshaw	Cretton	Alen	Wilmot	43
Gallagher	Kirby	Mutchell	Sodje	Smith	Barrowcliff	Hooper	Browne	Adams	Soloman	Crawshaw	Cretton	Alen	Catlin	44
Gallagher	**Kirby**	**Mutchell**	**Sodje**	**Smith**	**Barrowcliff**	**Hooper**	**Browne**	**Crawshaw**	**Soloman**	**Adams**	**Bignall**	**Catlin**	**Wilmot**	**45**
Gallagher	Kirby	Mutchell	Sodje	Smith	Barrowcliff	Hooper	Beevor	Crawshaw	Soloman	Bignall	Catlin	Adams	Gentle	46
Gallagher	Kirby	Mutchell	Sodje	Smith	Barrowcliff	Hooper	Catlin	Crawshaw	Soloman	Gentle	Adams	Beevor	Hayles	47
Gallagher	Kirby	Mutchell	Sodje	Smith	Beevor	Hooper	Catlin	Crawshaw	Soloman	Gentle	Adams	Hayles	Browne	48
Gallagher	**Kirby**	**Mutchell**	**Sodje**	**Smith**	**Beevor**	**Hooper**	**Browne**	**Crawshaw**	**Soloman**	**Catlin**	**Trebble**	**Adams**	**Cretton**	**49**
Gallagher	Kirby	Mutchell	Sodje	Smith	Beevor	Hooper	Gentle	Crawshaw	Soloman	Catlin	Adams	Browne	Trebble	50
Gallagher	Kirby	Mutchell	Sodje	Smith	Beevor	Hooper	Catlin	Crawshaw	Soloman	Gentle	Barrowcliff	Browne	Hayles	51
Wilmot	Kirby	Mutchell	Sodje	Smith	Barrowcliff	Hooper	Browne	Catlin	Mison	Hayles	Trebble	Adams	Gentle	52
Wilmot	**Kirby**	**Mutchell**	**Sodje**	**Smith**	**Barrowcliff**	**Hooper**	**Beevor**	**Crawshaw**	**Catlin**	**Browne**	**Hayles**	**Adams**	**Imber**	**53**
Gallagher	Kirby	Mutchell	Mison	Cretton	Barrowcliff	Hooper	Browne	Crawshaw	Beevor	Hayles	Trebble	Adams	Imber	54
Gallagher	**Kirby**	**Mutchell**	**Sodje**	**Smith**	**Browne**	**Barrowcliff**	**Hooper**	**Adams**	**Crawshaw**	**Catlin**	**Hayles**	**Trebble**	**Trebble**	**55**
Gallagher	Kirby	Mutchell	Sodje	Mison	Barrowcliff	Hooper	Beevor	Crawshaw	Gentle	Hayles	Adams	Browne	Wilmot	56
Gallagher	**Kirby**	**Mutchell**	**Sodje**	**Smith**	**Barrowcliff**	**Hooper**	**Browne**	**Catlin**	**Crawshaw**					**57**
Gallagher	Kirby	Mutchell	Sodje	Smith	Barrowcliff	Hooper	Mison	Gentle	Soloman	Hayles	Browne	Trebble	Wilmot	58
Wilmot	Kirby	Mutchell	Sodje	Smith	Barrowcliff	Hooper	Mison	Gentle	Soloman	Hayles	Trebble	Catlin	Browne	59
Wilmot	Kirby	Mutchell	Sodje	Smith	Barrowcliff	Hooper	Mison	Gentle	Trebble	Soloman	Beevor	Hayes	Browne	60
Wilmot	Kirby	Mutchell	Sodje	Smith	Barrowcliff	Hooper	Mison	Browne	Soloman	Hayles	Trebble	Beevor	Cretton	61
Wilmot	Kirby	Mutchell	Sodje	Smith	Beevor	Hooper	Mison	Crawshaw	Trebble	Hayles	Browne	Gentle	Cretton	62
Wilmot	Kirby	Mutchell	Sodje	Smith	Barrowcliff	Hooper	Mison	Crawshaw	Trebble	Hayles	Cretton	Browne	Gentle	63

PAUL FAIRCLOUGH (MANAGER)

Date of Appointment	August 1990
Date of Birth:	31st January 1950
Place of Birth:	Liverpool

PREVIOUS CLUBS

As manager	Hertford Town
As coach	Hemel Hempstead, Finchley.
As player	Harlow Town, St Albans City, Hertford Town

HONOURS

As manager	GMVC 95-96, Isthmian Lge. Prem. 93-94, Div.1 91-92
As player	None

Assistant Manager: Noel Blackwell **Coach:** John Harding **Physio:** Keith Allinson

Rob Mutcher chasing the ball while keeping an eye on Birmingham's Barry Horne during their FA Cup mtach last season.

Photo: Tim Durant

MATCHDAY PROGRAMME

Number of pages	36
Price	£1.20
Programme Editor	Paul Fry (01438 748684)
Other club publications:	The Borough Yearbook "Gitts is Up" (fanzine)
Local Newspapers:	Stevenage Gazette; Comet Stevenage Mercury; Herald
Local Radio Stations:	Chiltern Radio BBC Three Counties Radio

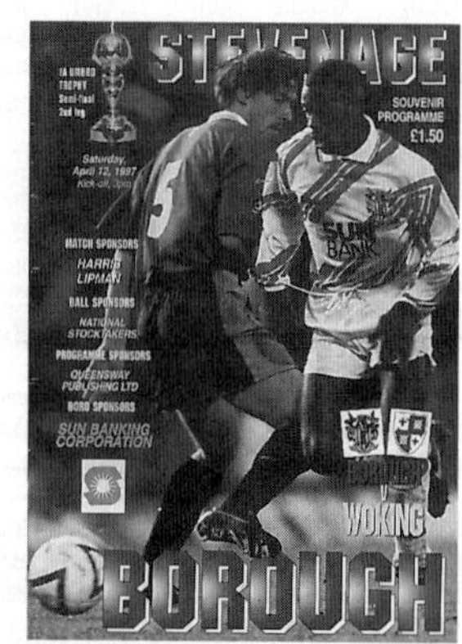

1997-98 PLAYING SQUAD

PLAYER	Birthplace Honours	Birthdate	CLUBS
GOALKEEPERS			
Des Gallagher	Luton GMVC, ILP	23.1.62	Watford, Eaton Bray U, Stevenage B, Dunstable
Richard Wilmot	Matlock GMVC	29.8.69	Pirton, Hitchin T, Stevenage B, Scunthorpe U, Halifax T, Hitchin T
DEFENDERS			
Mark Smith	Luton ESP, GMVC, ILP		Hitchin T, Letchworth GC, Hitchin T, Woking, Hitchin T
Ryan Kirby	Chingford	6.9.74	Arsenal, Doncaster R, Northampton T
Shaun Stevens	Chertsey	8.3.76	Wycombe Wanderers
Scott Cretton	Luton		From Youth Team
MIDFIELDERS			
Corey Browne	Edmonton ESP, GMVC	2.7.70	Kingsbury T, Fulham, Haringey B, Exeter C, Wealdstone, Dover A, £1k to Stevenage B
Stuart Beevor	Welwyn G. C. GMVC	23.4.75	Stevenage B, Hatfield T
Neil Catlin	Amersham	15.9.72	Marlow, Thame U, Flackwell Heath, Marlow, Maidenhead U, Marlow, Slough T
Jason Solomon	Welwyn G. C. EY	6.10.70	Watford, Wycombe Wanderers, Fulham
Tom Meredith	Enfield	27.10.77	Peterborough U
Dean Hooper	Harefield	13.4.71	Hayes, Swindon T, Hayes
Paul Barrowcliff	London GMVC		Hendon, Ruislip Manor, Hayes, Harrow Borough, Kingstonian, Wycombe Wanderers, Sutton U, Aylesbury U
FORWARDS			
Gary Crawshaw	Reading GMVC, ILP	4.2.71	Luton T, Wycombe Wanderers, Staines T, Hendon
Neil Trebble	Hitchin	16.2.69	Stevenage B, Scunthorpe U, Preston, Scarborough

DEPARTURES -
(During the season): Alan Paris & Kenny Webster (Harrow Borough), Dave Venables (Kettering T), Mike Bignall (Morecambe), John Ugbah (Carshalton A)
(During the close season): Barry Hayles (Bristol R), Rob Mutchell (Kettering T), Efetobor Sodje (Macclesfield T)

PLAYERS ON LOAN: Noel Imber (Chelsea), Dominic Gentle (Enfield), Mike Mison (Fulham), Tom Meredith (Peterborough)

Broadhall Way, Stevenage

GROUND ADDRESS:
Stevenage Stadium, Broadhall Way, Stevenage, Herts SG2 8RH (01438 743322).

TELEPHONE NUMBER: 01438 743322 Fax: 01438 743666.

SIMPLE DIRECTIONS:
Stevenage South exit off A1(M) - ground on right at second roundabout. Spectators are however advised to go straight on at this roundabout and park in the Showground opposite the stadium. The stadium is one mile from Stevenage BR station. Buses SB4 and SB5.

CAPACITY: 6,546 **SEATED:** 2,002 **COVERED TERRACING:** 2,000

CLUB SHOP:
Sells programmes, scarves and other club merchandise. Contact Bob Ellis c/o the Club.

SOCIAL FACILITIES:
Tel.: 01438 367059. Clubhouse at ground open Monday to Friday 7 - 11pm, Saturday noon - 2.00 & 4.30 - 11pm, Sunday: All day from noon.

Stevenage Borough Fact File

Nickname: Boro' **Club Sponsors:** Sun Banking Corporation
Reserve Team's League: Essex & Herts Border Combination & Capital League.
Club colours: White & red striped shirts, white with red trim shorts & white with red trim socks.
Change colours: Blue and yellow shirts, yellow shorts, yellow socks.
Midweek home matchday: Monday

PREVIOUS - **Leagues:** Chiltern Youth 76-79/ Wallspan South Combination 79-80/ United Counties 80-84/ Isthmian 84-94.
Grounds: King George V Playing Field 1976-80.

CLUB RECORDS - **Attendance:** 6,489 v Kidderminster H., GM Vauxhall Conference 25.1.97
Win: 11-1 v British Timken Athletic (H), United Counties League Div.1, 1980-81.
Defeat: 0-7 v Southwick (H), Isthmian League Div. 1, 1987-88.
Career goalscorer: Barry Hayles
Career appearances: Martin Gittings
Transfer fee paid: Undisclosed.
Transfer fee received: Undisclosed.

BEST SEASON - **FA Cup:** 3rd Round 1996-97. 0-2 v Birmingham City (A).
League clubs defeated: Leyton Orient (7.12.96, 2nd Rd., 2-1)
FA Trophy: Semi Final 1996-97. 1-2 v Woking in Replay at Watford.

1996-97 Captain: Paul Barrowcliff
1996-97 Top scorer: Barry Hayles (21)
1996-97 Player of the Year: Robert Mitchell

Past players who progressed to the Football League: Richard Wilmot & Neil Trebble (Scunthorpe Utd) 1993, Simon Clark (Peterborough United) 1994, Leo Fortune West (Gillingham) 1995, Phil Simpson (Barnet) 1995.

HONOURS: GM Vauxhall Conference 95-96, Isthmian Lge Prem 93-94, Div 1 91-92, Div 2 (North) 85-86 90-91; Utd Counties Lg Div 1 80-81 (Div 1 Cup 80-81), Herts Snr Cup R-up 85-86, 93/94; Herts Charity Cup R-up 93-94, Herts Charity Shield R-up 83-84, Herts Charity Cup R-up 93/94; Televised Sports Snr Floodlit Cup 89-90, Eastern Professional F'lit Cup Group winners 81-82 85-86 86-87 88-89 90-91 91-92, South Co's Comb. Cup 91-92; Essex & Herts Border Comb.(Reserves) 94/95, Essex & Herts (Western Div) 95-96.

TELFORD UNITED

Formed:
1876

President: G E Smith **Chairman:** A H Esp

Secretary: Mike Ferriday 199 Trench Road, Telford, Shropshire. TF2 7DX.
Tel: 01952 605193 (H) 01952 292929 (B)

Commercial Manager: Clair Finnegan. Tel: 01952 270767
Press Officer: Robert Cave Tel: 01952 270767

Season 1996/97 was one of some changes and disruption for the club. After an impressive start to the season, esults began to fall away, and the club made first round exits in both the F.A. Cup and F.A. Trophy, manager ayne Clarke felt unable to strengthen the squad as he would have wished, and everyone at the club were sorry hen the affair culminated in his resignation in November. He was replaced by former Shrewsbury Town and rexham favourite Jake King, who made an immediate impact, the team winning his first game in charge 4-1 at over's Crabble ground. He also set about starting reserve and youth teams for 1997/98, and appointed Mark earney as assistant manager and long time club favourite Antone Joseph as reserve team manager.

Despite a difficult spell after the Dover game, results improved immeasurably, and the team were able to finish e season in ninth place, chalking up an impressive ten away wins in the process.

Supporters were looking forward to this season in a spirit of some optimism, but then came the second anagerial hammer blow as Shrewsbury Town parted company with manager Fred Davies. The lure of league otball as manager of the club who brought him into the professional game proved just too strong for Jake to stay t Telford. In his short time as manager he had proved himself to be of the highest quality, and he will be a hard act follow. However, after some deliberation the club has appointed former Wolves and Manchester City favourite teve Daley to take charge of team affairs. Although this will be his first managerial appointment, Steve brings a ealth of football knowledge and experience with him, and it is very much hoped that he will be able to build on ake King's excellent work.

A further blow was the resignation of Brian Taylor from the board of directors. Brian has been a great benefactor th club, and his enthusiasm and hard work on the board will be sorely missed.

The season also saw an unprecedented five ex-players signed for league clubs, and all at the club wish Steve oster at Bristol Rovers and Peter Wilding, Roger Preece, Martyn Naylor and Mark Wiliams every success at hrewsbury.

Rollo Sheridan

-R, Back Row: Mark Turner, Brian Caswell, Steve Eccleston, Brett Wilcox, Brian Gray, Derek Dudley, Darren imkin, Nigel Niblett, Steve Foster, Chris Harrison, Mark Keorney. Front: Lee Fowler, Kevin Ashley, Justin Ellitts, rian Taylor, Wayne Clarke, Tony Esp, Lee Robinson, Tim Langford, Jan Purdie.

Telford United

Match No.	Date	Venue H/A	Competition	Opponents	Result	League Pos.	Attendance	Goalscorers (Times if known)
1	Aug 17	H	VC	Farnborough Town	Won 2-0	4	816	Purdie 24, Gray 60
2	Aug 20	A	VC	Bromsgrove Rovers	Lost 1-2		788	Russell 40
3	Aug 24	H	VC	Gateshead	Drew 0-0		697	
4	Aug 26	A	VC	Morecambe	Won 1-0	12	1100	Gray 37
5	Aug 31	A	VC	Woking	Drew 0-0	10	2744	
6	Sep 3	H	VC	Southport	Won 1-0		839	Gray 84
7	Sep 7	H	VC	Stevenage Borough	Lost 2-3	12	1060	Woods 46, Turner 79
8	Sep 10	A	VC	Stalybridge Celtic	Drew 0-0		430	
9	Sep 14	A	VC	Northwich Victoria	Lost 0-1	12	742	
10	Sep 17	H	VC	Kettering Town	Won 1-0		771	Gray 88
11	Sep 21	A	VC	Welling United	Lost 1-2	9	566	Page 22
12	Sep 24	A	VC	Halifax Town	Won 3-0		663	Russell (2) 1, 44, Niblett 52
13	Sep 28	H	VC	Altrincham	Drew 0-0	6	878	
14	Oct 1	H	VC	Bromsgrove Rovers	Won 3-1		814	Gray 38, Foster 75, Gardiner 80 (og)
15	Oct 5	A	VC	Hayes	Won 1-0	5	485	Ashley 90
16	**Oct 8**	**A**	**SCC**	**Stalybridge Celtic**	**Lost 1-3***		**272**	**Turner 57**
17	Oct 12	A	VC	Kidderminster Harriers	Lost 0-1	5	2723	
18	Oct 15	H	VC	Bath City	Drew 1-1		549	Gray 36
19	Oct 19	A	VC	Slough Town	Lost 0-6	5	1002	
20	**Oct 26**	**A**	**FAC 4 Q**	**Hednesford Town**	**Lost 0-2**		**1343**	
21	Nov 2	H	VC	Macclesfield Town	Lost 0-3	10	1015	
22	Nov 9	H	VC	Morecambe	Lost 2-3	11	721	Fowler 44 (pen), Niblett 56
23	Nov 23	A	VC	Dover Athletic	Won 4-1	9	890	Langford 11, Turner 26, Gray 69, 84
24	Nov 30	H	VC	Kidderminster Harriers	Lost 0-2	10	1860	
25	Dec 7	H	VC	Rushden & Diamonds	Lost 0-5	10	900	
26	Dec 14	A	VC	Stevenage Borough	Lost 0-3	11	2089	
27	Dec 21	A	VC	Macclesfield Town	Lost 1-2		1054	Gray 58
28	Dec 26	H	VC	Hednesford Town	Drew 1-1		1236	Rodosthenous 31
29	Dec 28	H	VC	Welling United	Won 2-0	10	746	Gray 13, 46
30	Jan 11	A	VC	Gateshead	Won 3-2	10	361	Fowler 2 (pen), Turner 69, Gray 90
31	Jan 14	H	VC	Stalybridge Celtic	Drew 1-1	10	554	Robinson 59
32	**Jan 18**	**A**	**FAT 1**	**Guiseley**	**Lost 1-2**		**778**	**Langford 37**
33	Jan 25	H	VC	Northwich Victoria	Drew 2-2	10	969	Langford 24, Fowler 66 (pen)
34	Feb 8	A	VC	Bath City	Won 3-2	9	499	Fowler 52, Wilding 65, Purdie 89
35	Feb 15	H	VC	Hayes	Drew 0-0	9	812	
36	Feb 22	A	VC	Altrincham	Won 3-2	9	714	Gray 45, Fowler 48 (pen), Langford 54
37	Mar 1	A	VC	Hednesford Town	Drew 0-0	6	1440	
38	Mar 8	H	VC	Slough Town	Lost 0-2	8	872	
39	Mar 15	A	VC	Kettering Town	Won 1-0	9	1406	Preece 39
40	Mar 22	A	VC	Rushden & Diamonds	Lost 0-2	9	2554	
41	Mar 29	H	VC	Woking	Lost 1-2		1014	Langford 22
42	Mar 31	A	VC	Southport	Won 1-0	9	925	Purdie 77
43	Apr 12	H	VC	Halifax Town	Drew 1-1	9	759	Wilding 6
44	Apr 26	H	VC	Dover Athletic	Won 1-0	9	709	Purdie 35
45	May 3	A	VC	Farnborough Town	Won 2-0	9	705	Niblett 24, Ashley 83

* After Extra Time

Telford United

1	2	3	4	5	6	7	8	9	10	11	12	14	15	Mth No.
Hughes	Ashley	Fowler	Wilcox	Foster	Simkin	Robinson	Russell	Gray	Turner	Purdie	Kearney	Ecclestone	Niblett	1
Hughes	Ashley	Fowler	Wilcox	Foster	Simkin	Robinson	Russell	Gray	Turner	Purdie	Kearney	Ecclestone	Niblett	2
Hughes	Ashley	Fowler	Ecclestone	Foster	Simkin	Robinson	Russell	Gray	Turner	Purdie	Woods	Niblett	Kearney	3
Hughes	Ecclestone	Fowler	Robinson	Foster	Niblett	Woods	Kearney	Gray	Turner	Purdie	Naylor	Simkin	Russell	4
Hughes	Ecclestone	Fowler	Robinson	Foster	Niblett	Woods	Kearney	Gray	Turner	Purdie	Ashley	Simkin	Russell	5
Hughes	Ecclestone	Fowler	Robinson	Foster	Niblett	Woods	Kearney	Gray	Turner	Purdie	Ashley	Simkin	Russell	6
Hughes	Ecclestone	Fowler	Robinson	Foster	Niblett	Woods	Kearney	Gray	Turner	Purdie	Ashley	Simkin	Russell	7
Jones	Ashley	Kearney	Russell	Foster	Niblett	Woods	Simkin	Gray	Turner	Purdie	Ecclestone	Naylor	Dudley	8
Jones	Ashley	Fowler	Robinson	Foster	Niblett	Woods	Kearney	Gray	Turner	Purdie	Simkin	Russell	Ecclestone	9
Jones	Ashley	Fowler	Robinson	Foster	Niblett	Woods	Kearney	Gray	Turner	Page	Naylor	Russell	Ecclestone	10
Jones	Ashley	Fowler	Robinson	Kearney	Niblett	Woods	Naylor	Gray	Turner	Page	Ecclestone	Russell	Hughes	11
Jones	Ecclestone	Kearney	Robinson	Foster	Niblett	Ashley	Russell	Gray	Turner	Page	Martin	Fowler	Hughes	12
Jones	Ashley	Fowler	Robinson	Foster	Niblett	Russell	Kearney	Gray	Turner	Page	Hughes	Woods	Ecclestone	13
Jones	Ashley	Fowler	Robinson	Foster	Niblett	Woods	Kearney	Gray	Turner	Page	Russell	Purdie	Ecclestone	14
Jones	Ashley	Fowler	Robinson	Foster	Niblett	Woods	Kearney	Gray	Turner	Page	Ecclestone	Purdie	Russell	15
Jones	**Ecclestone**	**Kearney**	**Wilcox**	**Foster**	**Challinor**	**Woods**	**Russell**	**Gray**	**Turner**	**Purdie**	**Page**	**Naylor**	**Ashley**	**16**
Jones	Ashley	Kearney	Robinson	Challinor	Niblett	Fowler	Purdie	Gray	Turner	Page	Wilcox	Russell	Ecclestone	17
Jones	Ashley	Fowler	Wilcox	Kearney	Niblett	Robinson	Page	Gray	Turner	Purdie	Naylor	Russell	Ecclestone	18
Jones	Ecclestone	Fowler	Wilcox	Kearney	Niblett	Ashley	Robinson	Russell	Page	Purdie	Naylor	Turner	Ecclestone	19
Jones	**Ashley**	**Kearney**	**Robinson**	**Ecclestone**	**Niblett**	**Naylor**	**Page**	**Russell**	**Turner**	**Fowler**	**Wilcox**	**Purdie**	**Martin**	**20**
Jones	Ecclestone	Fowler	Kearney	Niblett	Wilcox	Turner	Todd	Purdie	Page	Martin	Woods	Russell	Robinson	21
Jones	Naylor	Fowler	Robinson	Kearney	Niblett	Woods	Wilcox	Gray	Turner	Purdie	Page	Russell	Martin	22
Jones	Ecclestone	Fowler	Kearney	Niblett	Robinson	Naylor	Langford	Gray	Turner	Purdie	Wilcox	Russell	Joseph	23
Jones	Ecclestone	Fowler	Kearney	Niblett	Robinson	Wilcox	Turner	Purdie	Gray	Langford	Ashley	Russelll	Naylor	24
Jones	Ashley	Kearney	Ecclestone	Niblett	Robinson	Naylor	Turner	Gray	Langford	Purdie	Wilcox	Joseph	Russell	25
Jones	Kearney	Ecclestone	Niblett	Challinor	Ashley	Robinson	Turner	Langford	Gray	Purdie	Martin	Joseph	Naylor	26
Jones	Ashley	Niblett	Ecclestone	Wilcox	Kearney	Purdie	Turner	Robinson	Gray	Langford	Martin	Joseph	Naylor	27
Jones	Ashley	Fowler	Wilcox	Kearney	Niblett	Challinor	Robinson	Gray	Rodosthenous	Purdie	Langford	Turner	Ecclestone	28
Jones	Ashley	Fowler	Wilcox	Ecclestone	Niblett	Challinor	Robinson	Gray	Rodosthenous	Purdie	Langford	Turner	Naylor	29
Jones	Ashley	Fowler	Wilcox	Wilding	Niblett	Challinor	Robinson	Gray	Rodosthenous	Purdie	Langford	Turner	Ecclestone	30
Jones	Ashley	Kearney	Wilcox	Wilding	Niblett	Challinor	Robinson	Gray	Rodosthenous	Purdie	Ecclestone	Turner	Langford	31
Jones	**Ashley**	**Fowler**	**Wilcox**	**Wilding**	**Niblett**	**Challinor**	**Robinson**	**Gray**	**Langford**	**Purdie**	**Kearney**	**Ecclestone**	**Turner**	**32**
Jones	Ashley	Fowler	Wilcox	Wilding	Niblett	Challinor	Kearney	Turner	Langford	Purdie	Naylor	Ecclestone	Joseph	33
Jones	Naylor	Fowler	Ecclestone	Wilding	Challinor	Joseph	Kearney	Turner	Langford	Purdie	Ashley	Croft	Martin	34
Jones	Naylor	Fowler	Ecclestone	Wilding	Challinor	Joseph	Kearney	Gray	Langford	Purdie	Turner	Croft	Rose	35
Jones	Naylor	Fowler	Wilcox	Wilding	Niblett	Challinor	Preece	Gray	Langford	Kearney	Purdie	Ecclestone	Ashley	36
Jones	Naylor	Fowler	Wilcox	Wilding	Niblett	Challinor	Preece	Gray	Langford	Kearney	Purdie	Ecclestone	Ashley	37
Jones	Naylor	Fowler	Wilcox	Wilding	Niblett	Challinor	Preece	Gray	Langford	Kearney	Williams	Ecclestone	Purdie	38
Jones	Naylor	Fowler	Wilcox	Ecclestone	Niblett	Challinor	Preece	Gray	Langford	Kearney	Turner	Williams	Purdie	39
Jones	Naylor	Fowler	Wilcox	Ecclestone	Niblett	Turner	Preece	Gray	Langford	Kearney	Purdie	Williams	Ashley	40
Jones	Naylor	Fowler	Wilcox	Ecclestone	Niblett	Challinor	Kearney	Gray	Langford	Purdie	Dudley	Williams	Ashley	41
Dudley	Naylor	Fowler	Wilcox	Wilding	Niblett	Challinor	Preece	Gray	Williams	Purdie	Ecclestone	Kearney	Ashley	42
Dudley	Naylor	Fowler	Joseph	Wilding	Niblett	Challinor	Ashley	Gray	Williams	Purdie	Jones	Langford	Rose	43
Dudley	Naylor	Ashley	Joseph	Wilding	Niblett	Challinor	Preece	Gray	Langford	Purdie	Jones	Williams	Rose	44
Dudley	Naylor	Fowler	Wilcox	Wilding	Niblett	Challinor	Preece	Gray	Langford	Purdie	Jones	Ashley	Williams	45

STEVE DALEY MANAGER)

Date of Appointment	June 1997
Date of Birth:	1st April 1953
Place of Birth:	Barnsley

PREVIOUS CLUBS

As manager	None
As assistant manager	None
As player	Wolverhampton W., Manchester City, Burnley, Seattle (USA), Walsall, San Diego (USA).

HONOURS

As manager	N/A
As player	England: B, Youth.

Assistant Manager: Jon Purdie **Reserve Team Man.:** Antone Joseph **Physio:** Paul Heath

Lee Fowler 96-97 P.o.Y.

Nigel Niblett 96-97 Captain (now with Hednesford T.)

MATCHDAY PROGRAMME

Number of pages	32
Price	£1.30
Programme Editor	Rollo Sheridan
	01952 406570
Other club publications:	None
Local Newspapers:	Shropshire Star Telford Journal
Local Radio Stations:	BBC Radio Shropshire Beacon Radio

1997-98 PLAYING SQUAD

PLAYER	Birthplace Honours	Birthdate	CLUBS
GOALKEEPERS			
Derek Dudley	Birmingham	2.2.70	Aston Villa, Sutton Coldfield T, Stourbridge, Worcester C, VS Rugby, W.B.A., Halesowen T, £1,000 to Telford U
DEFENDERS			
Kevin Ashley	Birmingham	31.12.68	Birmingham C, £500k to Wolverhampton W, Peterborough U
Paul Challinor	Newcastle (Staffs)	6.4.76	Birmingham C, Baldock T
Lee Fowler	Nottingham	26.1.69	Stoke C, Preston, Doncaster R, Halifax T
MIDFIELDERS			
Brett Wilcox	Sutton Coldfield	27.12.68	Kidderminster H, Bridgnorth T, Shifnal T
Mark Turner	Bebbington	4.10.72	Wolverhampton W, Northampton T, Telford U, Hereford U
Lee Robinson	Wythenshawe	23.11.73	Burnley
Scott Colcombe	West Bromwich	15.12.71	W.B.A., Torquay U, Doncaster R
Nick Colley	Birmingham		Chasetown, Halesowen T
Lee Martin	Birmingham	3.10.76	Shrewsbury T
Steve Eccleston	Birmingham	17.1.67	Welshpool, Bridgnorth T, Tamworth, Atherstone U, Hednesford T, Bridgnorth T
Steve Palmer	Birmingham		Wednesfield
FORWARDS			
Jon Purdie	Corby ES, GMVC, FAT, FA XI	22.2.67	Arsenal, Wolverhampton W, Oxford U, Brentford, Shrewsbury T, Worcester C, Cheltenham T, Kidderminster H
Brian Gray	Birmingham	25.11.72	Birmingham C, Bromsgrove R
Tim Langford	Kingswinford GMVC	12.9.65	Halesowen T, Telford U, Wycombe W
Damon Russell	Wales	10.4.67	Congleton T, Welshpool
Ryan Daley	Birmingham		Wednesfield
Evran Wright	Wolverhampton	17.1.64	Springvale-Tranco, Stourbridge, Oldbury U, Stourbridge, Halesowen T, Walsall, Barry T, Stafford Rangers, Bilston T, Halesowen T, £3k to Telford U

DEPARTURES -
(During the season): Don Page (Northwich V), Ken Hughes (Released), Mark Todd (Blyth S), Steve Foster (Woking), Darren Simkin (Blakenall), Mark Turner (Hereford U)
(During the close season): Peter Wilding, Mark Kearney, Mark Williams, Roger Preece & Martin Naylor (Shrewsbury T), Justin Ellits (Released)

Bucks Head, Telford

ADDRESS: Bucks Head Ground, Watling Street, Wellington, Telford, Shropshire TF1 2NJ.

TELEPHONE NUMBER: 01952 223838. Fax: 01952 246431.

SIMPLE DIRECTIONS:
M54 Junction 6, A518 to B5061 (Watling Street). Ground is on several bus routes.

CAPACITY: 4,600 **SEATED:** 1,200 **COVERED TERRACING:** 1,500

SOCIAL FACILITIES:
Social club adjacent to ground - open matchdays and selected other hours.

CLUB SHOP:
Contact Shirley Finnigan on 01952 223838 for details.

Telford United Fact File

Nickname: Lilywhites **Club Sponsors:** Eastern Generation.

Club colours: White shirts, black shorts, white socks.

Change colours: Orange shirts, orange shorts and orange socks.

Midweek home matchday: Tuesday

Reserves' League: None

PREVIOUS - **Leagues:** Southern League, Cheshire League, Birmingham League.
Name: Wellington Town (prior to 1969). **Grounds:** None

CLUB RECORDS - **Attendance:** 13,000 v Shrewsbury Town - Birmingham League - 1936.
Win: Unknown. **Defeat:** Unknown. **Career appearances:** Unknown
Career goalscorer: Jack Bentley
Transfer fee paid: £10,000 to Northwich Victoria for Paul Mayman.
Transfer fee received: £50,000 from Scarborough for Stephen Norris.

BEST SEASON - **FA Cup:** 5th Round 84-85, 0-3 v Everton (A), 47,402. Also 4th Rd. 83-84, 3rd Rd. 86-87, 2nd Rd. 82-83, 85-86, 91-92.
League clubs defeated: Wigan, Rochdale, Stockport C., Darlington, Stoke C., Lincoln U., Bradford C.
FA Trophy: Winners 71-72, 82-83, 88-89. R-up 69-70, 87-88.

1996-97 Captain: Nigel Niblett

1996-97 Top scorer: Brian Gray (12)

1996-97 Player of the Year: Lee Fowler

Past Players who progressed to the Football League: A.Walker (Lincoln City), G.French (Luton Town), K.McKenna (Tranmere Rovers), S.Norris (Scarborough), David Pritchard (Bristol Rovers) 1994, Sean Parrish (Doncaster Rovers) 1994, Steve Foster (Bristol R.); Peter Wilding, Roger Preece, Mark Williams & Martyn Naylor - all to Shrewsbury 1997.

HONOURS: FA Trophy Winners 71-72, 82-83, 88-89. R-up 69-70, 87-88; Birmingham League 1920-21, 1934-35, 1935-36; Cheshire League 1945-46, 1946-47, 1951-52; Edward Case Cup 1952-53, 1954-55; Welsh Cup 1901-02, 1905-06, 1939-40; Birmingham Senior Cup 1946-47; Walsall Senior Cup 1946-47; Birmingham League Challenge Cup 1946-47; Shropshire Senior Cup (30); Southern League Cup 1970-71; Midland Floodlit Cup 1970-71; Midland Floodlit Cup 1970-71, 1982-83, 1988-89, Runners-up 1969-70, 1987-88.

WELLING UNITED

Formed:
1963

President: E Brackstone

Chairman: P Websdale
Vice Chairman: S Pain

Secretary: Barrie Hobbins Tel: 0181 301 1196 (B) Fax: 0181 301 5676
Address - c/o the club

Commercial Manager: S Wells

Press Officer: Paul Carter

Three successive victories at the end of the season ensured Welling's continued presence in the Conference after looking relegation certainties for most of the campaign.

Manager Kevin Hales moved away from Welling's usual policy of playing youngsters and fielded a much more experienced team last season. Lennie Dennis enjoyed a marvellous time, netting 25 goals and finishing second to Lee Hughes in the top scorers' chart but he has now gone, along with defender Wayne Brown (both to Kingstonian) and Hales will now have to revert again to his younger players. Player of the year, Robin Troff, has also departed, leaving Welling with real defensive problems.

Almost every one of the Wings' twelve campaigns in the Vauxhall Conference have begun with them as one of the favourites for relegation. They have survived thus far - but for how long?

L-R, Back Row: Wayne Brown, Lew Watts, Lennie Dennis, Colin Lewinston, Paul Copley, Andy Harris, Robin Trott, John Farley, Ollie Morah. Front: Danny Smith, Barry Lakin, Mike Rutherford, Peter Green (Physio), Kevin Hayles (Manager), Ray Burgess (Asst. Man.), Gary Cooper, Duncan Horton, Dereck Brown. Photo: Keith Gillard

Welling United

Match No.	Date	Venue H/A	Competition	Opponents	Result	League Pos.	Attendance	Goalscorers (Times if known)
1	Aug 17	H	VC	Bromsgrove Rovers	Lost 1-2	17	501	Trott 73
2	Aug 20	A	VC	Kettering Town	Won 3-2		1420	Cooper 2, Dennis 21, Morah 34
3	Aug 24	A	VC	Altrincham	Drew 1-1		731	Morah 10
4	Aug 26	H	VC	Farnborough Town	Lost 0-2	15	757	
5	Aug 31	H	VC	Morecambe	Lost 1-4	19	602	Rutherford 79
6	Sep 2	A	VC	Stevenage Borough	Lost 1-2		2382	Dennis 2
7	Sep 7	A	VC	Kidderminster Harriers	Lost 2-3	22	1559	Dennis 26 (pen), 85
8	Sep 10	H	VC	Slough Town	Won 3-2		534	Dennis (3) 10, 23, 30
9	**Sep 14**	**A**	**FAC 1 Q**	**Southwick**	**Won 2-1**		**150**	**Appiah (2) 65, 70**
10	Sep 21	H	VC	Telford United	Won 2-1	17	566	Lakin 12, Dennis 47 (pen)
11	Sep 24	A	VC	Hayes	Drew 1-1		363	Dennis 41
12	**Sep 28**	**H**	**FAC 2 Q**	**Dulwich Hamlet**	**Won 2-1**		**721**	**Rutherford 53, Morah 61**
13	Oct 5	A	VC	Rushden & Diamonds	Lost 0-3	18	2296	
14	**Oct 8**	**A**	**SCC**	Bath City	Won 2-0		237	Dennis 25, Rutherford 49
15	**Oct 12**	**H**	**FAC 3 Q**	**Herne Bay**	**Won 2-0**		**742**	**Trott 54, Morah 64**
16	Oct 15	H	VC	Hayes	Won 1-0		433	Dennis 78
17	Oct 19	A	VC	Macclesfield Town	Drew 1-1	16	1102	Rutherford 20
18	**Oct 26**	**A**	**FAC 4 Q**	**Staines Town**	**Won 1-0**		**273**	**Dennis 25**
19	Nov 2	H	VC	Hednesford Town	Lost 1-2	18	702	Dennis 26 (pen)
20	Nov 9	H	VC	Gateshead	Won 2-1	16	532	Dennis 80, Morah 88
21	**Nov 16**	**A**	**FAC 1**	**Cambridge United**	**Lost 0-3**		**3187**	
22	Nov 23	A	VC	Halifax Town	Drew 1-1	15	608	Smith 89
23	**Nov 26**	A	**KSC**	**Fisher Athletic**	**Lost 1-2***			**Watts**
24	Nov 30	H	VC	Northwich Victoria	Drew 1-1	16	527	Dennis 42 (pen)
25	**Dec 3**	**A**	**SSC**	**Woking**	**Won 2-0**		**597**	**Lakin, Dennis**
26	Dec 7	H	VC	Bath City	Won 2-0	14	485	Morah 39, Lakin 90
27	Dec 14	H	VC	Woking	Drew 1-1	14	1171	Dennis 5
28	Dec 20	A	VC	Slough Town	Drew 3-3		869	Lakin 4, Rutherford 87, Watts 88
29	Dec 26	H	VC	Dover Athletic	Won 1-0		1082	Rutherford 2
30	Dec 28	A	VC	Telford United	Lost 0-2	12	746	
31	**Jan 19**	**A**	**FAT 1**	**Raunds Town**	**Won 1-0**		**437**	**Lakin 40**
32	Jan 25	A	VC	Southport	Lost 2-3	14	884	Lakin 7, Morah 86
33	**Jan 28**	**H**	**SSC**	**Farnborough Town**	**Lost 1-2***		**312**	**Morah 46**
34	Feb 1	H	VC	Stevenage Borough	Won 2-0	14	1078	Morah 44, Downs 90
35	**Feb 8**	**H**	**FAT 2**	**Guiseley**	**Drew 1-1**		**778**	**Dennis 5**
36	**Feb 11**	**A**	**FAT 2 R**	**Guiseley**	**Lost 0-1**		**537**	
37	Feb 15	A	VC	Morecambe	Won 2-1	13	877	Copley 10, Dennis 82
38	Feb 18	A	VC	Dover Athletic	Lost 1-2	13	1127	Morah 35
39	Feb 22	A	VC	Northwich Victoria	Drew 0-0	15	877	
40	Mar 1	H	VC	Halifax Town	Lost 0-1	15	688	
41	Mar 8	H	VC	Macclesfield Town	Lost 0-3	17	874	
42	Mar 11	A	VC	Woking	Lost 1-2		1664	Foster 4 (og)
43	Mar 15	H	VC	Kidderminster Harriers	Lost 0-1	18	781	
44	Mar 18	A	VC	Farnborough Town	Lost 1-2	19	460	Baker 45 (og)
45	Mar 22	H	VC	Altrincham	Won 1-0	18	601	Trott 53
46	Mar 25	H	VC	Rushden & Diamonds	Lost 0-1	18	747	
47	Mar 29	A	VC	Stalybridge Celtic	Drew 0-0		710	
48	Mar 31	H	VC	Kettering Town	Lost 1-2	19	854	Dennis 65 (pen)
49	Apr 12	H	VC	Southport	Lost 2-3	19	700	W Brown 16, Dennis 66 (pen)
50	Apr 19	A	VC	Bath City	Lost 1-3	20	831	Lakin 54
51	Apr 21	A	VC	Hednesford Town	Won 3-0		851	Dennis 54, Trott 62, Morah 83
52	Apr 26	H	VC	Gateshead	Lost 0-2	18	697	
53	Apr 29	H	VC	Stalybridge Celtic	Won 2-0		617	Farley 37, Morah 80
54	May 3	A	VC	Bromsgrove Rovers	Lost 0-1	18	708	

* After Extra Time

Welling United

1	2	3	4	5	6	7	8	9	10	11	12	14	15	Mth No.
Knight	Watts L	Cooper	Trott	Brown W	Horton	Brown D	Rutherford	Morah	Dennis	Lakin	Farley	Copley	Smith	1
Knight	Watts L	Cooper	Trott	Brown W	Horton	Brown D	Rutherford	Morah	Dennis	Copley	Farley	Smith	Dimmock	2
Knight	Watts	Cooper	Trott	Copley	Horton	Brown D	Rutherford	Morah	Dennis	Farley	Smith	Dimmock	Wastell	3
Knight	Watts	Cooper	Trott	Copley	Horton	Brown D	Rutherford	Morah	Dennis	Farley	Smith	Dimmock	Wastell	4
Knight	Watts	Cooper	Trott	Copley	Hales	Brown D	Rutherford	Morah	Dennis	Farley	Smith	Dimmock	Appiah	5
Knight	Watts	Cooper	Trott	Copley	Horton	Brown D	Rutherford	Morah	Dennis	Farley	Smith	Appiah	Wastell	6
Wastell	Watts	Cooper	Trott	Copley	Horton	Brown D	Rutherford	Smith	Dennis	Farley	Dimmock	Appiah	Watts S	7
Knight	Watts	Cooper	Trott	Copley	Horton	Brown D	Rutherford	Smith	Dennis	Zorioich	Farley	Appiah	Watts S	8
Knight	**Watts**	**Cooper**	**Trott**	**Copley**	**Horton**	**Brown D**	**Rutherford**	**Appiah**	**Smith**	**Lakin**	**Farley**	**Dimmock**	**Watts S**	**9**
Knight	Watts	Cooper	Trott	Copley	Horton	Brown D	Rutherford	Morah	Dennis	Lakin	Smith	Farley	Watts S	10
Knight	Watts	Cooper	Trott	Copley	Horton	Brown D	Rutherford	Morah	Dennis	Lakin	Smith	Farley	Watts S	11
Knight	**Watts**	**Cooper**	**Trott**	**Copley**	**Horton**	**Brown D**	**Rutherford**	**Morah**	**Smith**	**Lakin**	**Farley**	**Watts S**	**Dimmock**	**12**
Knight	Watts	Cooper	Trott	Copley	Horton	Brown D	Rutherford	Morah	Dennis	Lakin	Smith	Dimmock	Farley	13
Knight	Lakin	Farley	Trott	Copley	Horton	Brown D	Rutherford	Morah	Dennis	Smith	Dimmock	Watts S	Cooper	14
Knight	**Watts**	**Cooper**	**Trott**	**Copley**	**Horton**	**Brown D**	**Rutherford**	**Morah**	**Dennis**	**Lakin**	**Farley**	**Dimmock**	**Smith**	**15**
Knight	Watts	Cooper	Trott	Copley	Horton	Brown D	Rutherford	Morah	Dennis	Lakin	Farley	Dimmock	Smith	16
Knight	Watts	Cooper	Trott	Copley	Horton	Brown D	Rutherford	Morah	Dennis	Lakin	Smith	Farley	Lewington	17
Knight	**Watts**	**Cooper**	**Trott**	**Copley**	**Horton**	**Brown D**	**Rutherford**	**Morah**	**Dennis**	**Lakin**	**Farley**	**Smith**	**Lewington**	**18**
Knight	Watts	Cooper	Trott	Copley	Horton	Brown D	Rutherford	Morah	Dennis	Lakin	Farley	Smith	Dimmock	19
Knight	Watts	Cooper	Trott	Copley	Horton	Brown D	Rutherford	Morah	Dennis	Lakin	Farley	Smith	Lewington	20
Knight	**Watts**	**Cooper**	**Trott**	**Copley**	**Horton**	**Brown D**	**Rutherford**	**Morah**	**Dennis**	**Lakin**	**Farley**	**Smith**	**Lewington**	**21**
Knight	Watts	Farley	Trott	Copley	Horton	Brown D	Rutherford	Morah	Dennis	Lakin	Watts S	Smith	Lewington	22
Knight	**Watts**	**Farley**	**Trott**	**Copley**	**Horton**	**Smith**	**Rutherford**	**Morah**	**Appiah**	**Lakin**	**Watts S**	**Dimmock**	**Lewington**	**23**
Knight	Smith	Farley	Trott	Copley	Horton	Tierling	Rutherford	Morah	Dennis	Lakin	Watts S	Dimmock	Lewington	24
Lewington	**Tierling**	**Cooper**	**Trott**	**Copley**	**Horton**	**Farley**	**Rutherford**	**Smith**	**Dennis**	**Lakin**	**Watts S**	**Dimmock**	**Knight**	**25**
Knight	Tierling	Cooper	Trott	Copley	Horton	Brown D	Rutherford	Morah	Dennis	Lakin	Farley	Smith	Lewington	26
Knight	Watts	Cooper	Trott	Copley	Horton	Brown	Rutherford	Morah	Dennis	Lakin	Smith	Watts S	Lewington	27
Knight	Watts	Cooper	Trott	Copley	Horton	Brown	Rutherford	Smith	Dennis	Lakin	Farley	Watts S	Lewington	28
Knight	Watts	Cooper	Trott	Copley	Horton	Brown D	Rutherford	Morah	Dennis	Lakin	Smith	Farley	Lewington	29
Knight	Watts	Cooper	Trott	Copley	Corbyn	Brown D	Rutherford	Morah	Dennis	Lakin	Smith	Farley	Watts S	30
Knight	**Tierling**	**Farley**	**Trott**	**Copley**	**Hales**	**Brown D**	**Smith**	**Morah**	**Dennis**	**Lakin**	**Watts S**	**Dimmock**	**Lewington**	**31**
Knight	Tierling	Farley	Trott	Copley	Horton	Brown D	Smith	Morah	Dennis	Lakin	Watts S	Dimmock	Hales	32
Knight	**Tierling**	**Cooper**	**Trott**	**Copley**	**Horton**	**Brown D**	**Rutherford**	**Morah**	**Dennis**	**Lakin**	**Smith**	**Farley**	**Watts S**	**33**
Knight	Tierling	Cooper	Trott	Watts	Horton	Brown D	Rutherford	Morah	Dennis	Lakin	Smith	Farley	Watts S	34
Knight	**Tierling**	**Cooper**	**Trott**	**Watts**	**Horton**	**Brown D**	**Rutherford**	**Morah**	**Dennis**	**Lakin**	**Smith**	**Farley**	**Lewington**	**35**
Knight	**Tierling**	**Cooper**	**Trott**	**Watts**	**Horton**	**Brown D**	**Rutherford**	**Morah**	**Dennis**	**Lakin**	**Smith**	**Farley**	**Lewington**	**36**
Knight	Watts	Farley	Trott	Copley	Horton	Brown D	Rutherford	Morah	Dennis	Smith	Lakin	Dimmock	Lewington	37
Knight	Watts	Farley	Trott	Copley	Horton	Brown D	Rutherford	Morah	Dennis	Lakin	Smith	Dimmock	Lewington	38
Knight	Watts	Cooper	Trott	Copley	Horton	Brown D	Rutherford	Morah	Smith	Lakin	Farley	Dimmock	Watts S	39
Knight	Watts	Cooper	Trott	Copley	Horton	Brown D	Farley	Morah	Smith	Lakin	Brown W	Dimmock	Watts S	40
Knight	Watts	Cooper	Trott	Copley	Horton	Brown D	Farley	Morah	Dennis	Lakin	Smith	Brown W	Watts S	41
Lewington	Watts	Cooper	Trott	Copley	Horton	Brown D	Rutherford	Morah	Dennis	Lakin	Brown W	King	Smith	42
Knight	Watts	Cooper	Brown W	Copley	Horton	Brown D	Rutherford	Morah	Dimmock	Lakin	Smith	Farley	King	43
Lewington	Watts	Cooper	Trott	Copley	Horton	Brown D	Rutherford	Morah	Dimmock	Smith	Lakin	Brown W	King	44
Knight	Watts	Cooper	Trott	Copley	W Brown	Brown D	Rutherford	Morah	Jones	Lakin	King	Farley	Dimmock	45
Knight	Watts	Cooper	Trott	Copley	W Brown	Brown D	Rutherford	Morah	Jones	Rattray	Lakin	Farley	Dimmock	46
Knight	Watts	Farley	Trott	Copley	Horton	Brown D	Rutherford	Morah	Jones	Brown W	Lakin	Dimmock	King	47
Knight	Watts	Cooper	Trott	Copley	Horton	Brown D	Rutherford	Morah	Jones	Rattray	Dennis	Farley	Lakin	48
Knight	Brown W	Farley	Trott	Copley	Horton	Brown D	Rutherford	Morah	Dennis	Rattray	Smith	King	Dimmock	49
Knight	Tierling	Farley	Trott	Copley	Horton	Brown D	Rutherford	Morah	Dennis	Rattray	Lakin	Dimmock	Smith	50
Knight	Lakin	Farley	Trott	Copley	Horton	Brown D	Rutherford	Morah	Dennis	Smith	Lewington	Dimmock	King	51
Knight	Lakin	Farley	Trott	Copley	Horton	Brown D	Rutherford	Morah	Dennis	Rattray	Brown W	Smith	Dimmock	52
Knight	Lakin	Farley	Trott	Copley	Horton	Brown D	Rutherford	Morah	Dennis	Rattray	Brown W	Smith	Watts L	53
Knight	Lakin	Farley	Trott	Copley	Horton	Brown D	Rutherford	Morah	Dennis	Rattray	Smith	King	Watts L	54

KEVIN HALES (MANAGER)

Date of Appointment	August 1995
Date of Birth:	13th January 1961
Place of Birth:	Dartford

PREVIOUS CLUBS

As manager	None
As coach	None
As player	Chelsea, Leyton Orient

HONOURS

As manager	None
As player	None

Assistant Manager: Ray Burgess **Coach:** Kevin Hales **Physio:** Peter Green

PARK VIEW ROAD - Welling United's home.

MATCHDAY PROGRAMME

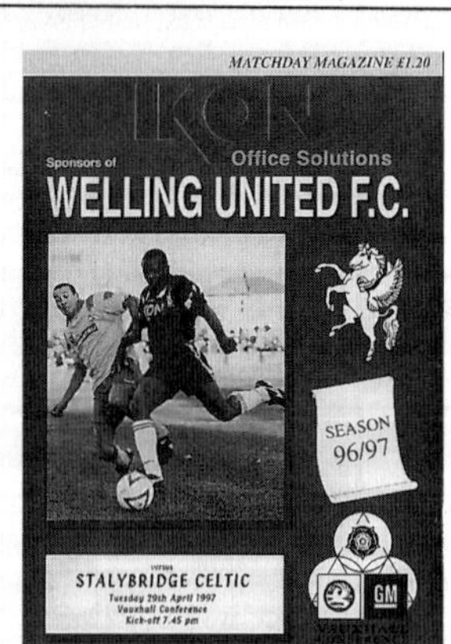

Number of pages	32
Price	£1.20
Programme Editor	Barrie Hobbins
Other club publications:	"Winning isn't Everything" (Fanzine)
Local Newspapers:	Kentish Times Bexleyheath & Welling Mercury
Local Radio Stations:	Radio Kent Radio Invicta R.T.M.

1997-98 PLAYING SQUAD

PLAYER	Birthplace Honours	Birthdate	CLUBS
GOALKEEPERS			
Glen Knight	London		Millwall
DEFENDERS			
Duncan Horton	Maidstone GMVC	18.2.67	Charlton A, Maidstone U, Barnet, Wycombe Wanderers
Richard Corbyn	Kent		Gillingham, Margate
Wayne Brown	Waterloo FA XI	19.1.70	From Youth Team
Paul Copley	Dartford	13.8.70	Slade Green, Crockenhill
Robin Trott	Orpington	17.8.74	Gillingham
MIDFIELDERS			
Lewis Watts	Maidstone	14.9.74	Gravesend & Northfleet, Fisher A
Mike Rutherford	Woolwich	6.6.72	Q.P.R.
Dereck Brown	London ESP, FAT, FA XI	8.8.63	Wembley, Hendon, Wembley, Hendon, Woking, Walton & Hersham
Danny Smith	London	7.9.75	From YTS
John Farley	Greenwich	18.2.73	Lewisham Elms
Barry Lakin	Dartford	19.9.73	Leyton Orient
FORWARDS			
Ollie Morah	Islington ES, EY, FAYC	3.9.72	Tottenham H, Swindon T, Sutton U, Cambridge U
Mark Cooper	Watford	5.4.67	Cambridge U, Tottenham H, £105k to Gillingham, Leyton Orient, Barnet, Northampton T
Murray Jones	Bexley	7.10.64	Southend U, Welling U, Epsom & Ewell, Greenwich B, Croydon, Carshalton A, Crystal Palace, Bristol C, Exeter C, Grimsby T, Brentford, Sittingbourne, Welling U, Guang Dong (China), Kingstonian, Sutton U
Tyrone King	Kent		Sittingbourne
Richard Dimmock	Woolwich	27.3.79	Charlton A

DEPARTURES -

(During the season): James Wastell (Redhill), Sam Appiah (Erith)
(During the close season): Lennie Dennis (Kingstonian)

PLAYERS ON LOAN - Danny Evans (Dartford), Kevin Rattray (Barnet)

Park View Road, Welling

GROUND ADDRESS:
Park View Road Ground, Welling, Kent DA16 1SY.

TELEPHONE NUMBER: 0181 301 1196. Fax: 0811 301 5676. **Welling Wingsline:** 0891 80 06 54.

SIMPLE DIRECTIONS: M25, then A2 towards London. Take Welling turn-off, ground 1 mile. By rail to Welling station (BR) - ground 3/4 mile.

CAPACITY: 5,500 **SEATED:** 500 **COVERED TERRACING:** 1,500

SOCIAL FACILITIES:
Clubhouse open on match days

CLUB SHOP:
On sale programmes (League & non-League), scarves, mugs, caps, hats, badges, replica kits and Conference merchandise - matchday manager Peter Mason.

Welling United Fact File

Nickname: The Wings **Club Sponsors:**

Club colours: Red shirts, red shorts, white socks.

Change colours: White shirts, blue shorts, blue socks.

Midweek home matchday: Tuesday

Reserves' League: Capital League

PREVIOUS - **Leagues:** Eltham & District League 1963/71, London Spartan League 1971/77, Athenian League 1977/79, Southern League 1979/86.
Grounds: Butterfly Lane, Eltham - 1963/78

CLUB RECORDS - **Attendance:** 4,100 v Gillingham, FA Cup
Record win: 7-1
Record defeat: 0-7
Goalscorer (career): John Bartley - 533
Appearances (career): Nigel Ransom - 1,066 & Ray Burgess - 1,044.
Record transfer fee paid: £30,000 for Gary Abbott from Enfield
Record transfer fee received: £95,000 from Birmingham City for Steve Finnan. 1995.

BEST SEASON -
FA Cup: 3rd Round 1988-89, 0-1 v Blackburn R.
League clubs defeated: Gillingham
FA Trophy: Quarter Final 1988-89, 0-1 v Macclesfield.

1996-97 Captain: Mike Rutherford

1996-97 Top scorer: Lennie Dennis (22)

1996-97 Player of the Year: Robin Trott

Past players who progressed to the Football League: Paul Barron (Plymouth, Arsenal, Stoke, WBA, C. Palace, QPR), Andy Townsend (Southampton, Norwich, Chelsea), Ian Thompson (AFC Bournemouth), John Bartley (Millwall), Dave Smith (Gillingham, Bristol City), Murray Jones (C. Palace, Bristol City, Exeter City), Kevin Shoemaker (Peterborough), Tony Agana (Watford, Sheffield Utd), Duncan Horton (Barnet), Mark Hone (Southend), Steve Finnan & Steve Barnes (Birmingham City).

HONOURS: London Spartan League 1978; Southern League Premier Division 1985/86; Kent Senior Cup 1985/86; London Senior Cup 1989/90; London Challange Cup 1991/92, Runners-up 1993/94.

WOKING

Formed
1889

President: Leslie A Gosden MBE

Chairman: Jon Davies

Secretary: Phil J Ledger
Tel: 01483 725295 (H) 0831 271369 (M)
19 Ainsdale Way, Woking, Surrey. GU21 3PP.

Vice Chairman: Terry Molloy

Commercial Projects Manager: Philip Shorter

Press Officer: Terry Molloy

Commercial Assistant: Rosemary Hurl

Club Administrator: Sue Day

Another tremendous campaign for Woking, winning the FA Umbro Trophy again and enjoying another superb FA Cup run, plus finishing fifth in the league despite a torrid fixture backlog.

But things weren't quite right at Kingfield, and when very little celebration took place after the final whistle at Wembley last May, one could sense that something was amiss.

Sure enough, chairman Phil Ledger departed and this move was swiftly followed by the departures of both long serving manager Geoff Chapple and goalscoring hero Clive Walker.

From a long list of candidates, the Cards chose former Nottingham Forest star John McGovern to take over the reins from Chapple. Whoever got the job was going to find it extremely difficult following on from the almost legendary Chapple and undoubtedly John McGovern, despite his playing pedigree, will find that this is the case.

Nonetheless expectations, as usual, are high at Kingfield but they may have to be tempered a little - at least for the time being.

Back Row: Robin Taylor, Dave Timothy, Junior Hunter, Clive Walker.
Middle: Malcolm Hague (Kit), Steve Foster, Terry Howard, Steve Wood, John Gregory, Lawrence Batty, Aiden Kilner, Justin Jackson, Tom Jones, Colin Lippiatt, Barry Kimber (Physio).
Front: Shane Wye, Steve Thompson, Darren Hay, Kevan Brown, Geoff Chapple, Scot Steele, Andy Ellis, Lloyd Wye, Mascot.

Woking

Match No.	Date	Venue H/A	Competition	Opponents	Result	League Pos.	Attendance	Goalscorers (Times if known)
1	Aug 17	A	VC	Morecambe	Won 2-1	8	1360	Hay 13, Hunter 59
2	Aug 20	H	VC	Bath City	Drew 2-2		2317	Thompson 74, Taylor 89
3	Aug 24	H	VC	Hednesford Town	Won 2-0		2363	Hay (2) 27, 87
4	Aug 26	A	VC	Kettering Town	Drew 0-0	4	1912	
5	Aug 31	H	VC	Telford United	Drew 0-0	6	2744	
6	Sep 3	A	VC	Dover Athletic	Lost 1-5		1030	Thompson 25
7	Sep 7	A	VC	Stalybridge Celtic	Won 2-0	6	702	Walker 45, Hay 67
8	Sep 10	H	VC	Farnborough Town	Lost 0-2		2379	
9	Sep 14	A	VC	Altrincham	Drew 1-1	8	888	Maddox 61 (og)
10	Sep 21	H	VC	Rushden & Diamonds	Won 4-2	7	2768	Walker (3) 28(p), 54, 60(p), Jones 54
11	Sep 24	H	VC	Dover Athletic	Drew 1-1	8	1926	Walker 23
12	Oct 1	A	VC	Slough Town	Lost 0-3		2055	
13	Oct 5	H	VC	Macclesfield Town	Lost 2-3	12	2849	Walker 33, Steele 83
14	Oct 15	H	VC	Stevenage Borough	Won 3-1		2466	Thompson 26, Walker 27, Payne 68
15	Oct 19	A	VC	Halifax Town	Won 4-0	9	807	Grazioli (3) 62, 76, 85, Walker 69 (p)
16	Oct 26	H	VC	Kettering Town	Won 2-1	6	2968	Grazioli 44, Walker 74
17	**Oct 29**	**H**	**SSC**	**Ashford Town**	**Won 3-0**		**590**	**Steele, Ellis, Walker**
18	Nov 2	A	VC	Stevenage Borough	Won 3-0	5	4352	Grazioli 1, 25, Howard 54
19	Nov 9	H	VC	Northwich Victoria	Won 3-1	3	3091	Steele 33, 84, Walker 51 (p)
20	**Nov 15**	**H**	**FAC 1**	**Millwall**	**Drew 2-2**		**5448**	**Foster 3, Walker 55 (pen)**
21	Nov 23	A	VC	Bath City	Drew 1-1	4	1001	Steele 55
22	**Nov 26**	**A**	**FAC 1 R**	**Millwall**	**Won 1-0**		**6084**	**Walker 9**
23	Nov 30	H	VC	Altrincham	Won 7-1	3	2701	Foster 5, Walker 14, Taylor 25, 51 (og), Thompson 30, Hay 56, 83
24	**Dec 3**	**H**	**SSC**	**Welling United**	**Lost 0-2**		**597**	
25	**Dec 7**	**A**	**FAC 2**	**Cambridge United**	**Won 2-0**		**5857**	**Walker 74, Taylor 83**
26	Dec 14	A	VC	Welling United	Drew 1-1	5	1171	Steele 4
27	**Dec 17**	**A**	**SSC 2**	**Walton & Hersham**	**Lost 1-3**			**Wye, Ellison**
28	Dec 21	H	VC	Halifax Town	Drew 2-2		2332	Steele 3, 26
29	Dec 26	A	VC	Hayes	Lost 2-3		1327	Hunter 50, 69
30	Dec 28	H	VC	Slough Town	Won 2-0	4	3208	Walker 29, Taylor 57
31	**Jan 19**	**A**	**FAT 1**	**Wokingham Town**	**Won 1-0**		**1575**	**Thompson 28**
32	**Jan 25**	**A**	**FAC 4**	**Coventry City**	**Drew 1-1**		**16,040**	**Thompson 90**
33	Feb 1	A	VC	Hednesford Town	Lost 0-2	6	2368	
34	**Feb 4**	**H**	**FAC 4 R**	**Coventry City**	**Lost 1-2**		**6064**	**Steele 36**
35	**Feb 8**	**A**	**FAT 2**	**St Albans City**	**Drew 1-1**		**2015**	**Jackson 10**
36	**Feb 11**	**H**	**FAT 2 R**	**St Albans City**	**Won 3-1**		**1907**	**Jackson 6, Hay 59, Steele 60**
37	Feb 15	H	VC	Southport	Lost 0-1	8	2858	
38	Feb 22	A	VC	Bromsgrove Rovers	Lost 0-3	6	881	Walker 5, 54, Jackson 40
39	**Mar 1**	**A**	**FAT 3**	**Dorchester Town**	**Won 3-2**		**2942**	**Steele 21, 90, Ellis 82**
40	Mar 8	A	VC	Gateshead	Lost 2-3	9	816	Walker 81 (pen), Hay 90
41	Mar 11	H	VC	Welling United	Won 2-1		1664	Steele 61, Hay 84
42	Mar 15	H	VC	Stalybridge Celtic	Won 3-2	5	2382	Hay 42, Steele 45, Thompson 90
43	**Mar 22**	**A**	**FAT Q F**	**Heybridge Swifts**	**Won 1-0**		**2477**	**Ellis 69**
44	Mar 25	H	VC	Hayes	Lost 1-2	8	3352	Steele 79
45	Mar 29	A	VC	Telford United	Won 2-1		1014	Ellis 52, Steele 62
46	Mar 31	H	VC	Kidderminster Harriers	Won 2-1	6	3420	Batty 53 (pen), Hay 72
47	**Apr 5**	**H**	**FAT S F**	**Stevenage Borough**	**Won 1-0**		**3769**	**Taylor 1**
48	Apr 8	H	VC	Bromsgrove Rovers	Lost 1-3	6	2044	Taylor 51
49	**Apr 12**	**A**	**FAT S F**	**Stevenage Borough**	**Lost 1-2**		**5163**	**Hay 92**
50	Apr 14	A	VC	Kidderminster Harriers	Lost 0-1	6	2916	
51	**Apr 16**	**N**	**FAT S F R**	**Stevenage Borough**	**Won 2-1**		**5810**	**Walker 32, Ellis 63**
52	Apr 19	H	VC	Gateshead	Drew 1-1	7	2300	Foster 86
53	Apr 22	A	VC	Macclesfield Town	Lost 0-5		1826	
54	Apr 24	A	VC	Farnborough Town	Won 2-1		1479	Day 33 (og), Foster 85
55	Apr 26	A	VC	Northwich Victoria	Won 2-1	4	1208	Timothy 14, Kilner 83
56	Apr 29	A	VC	Rushden & Diamonds	Drew 1-1		2589	Jackson 60
57	May 1	A	VC	Southport	Lost 1-4		560	Wye 60
58	May 3	H	VC	Morecambe	Lost 1-2	5	2373	Steele 89

Woking

1	2	3	4	5	6	7	8	9	10	11	12	14	15	Mth No.
Batty	Wood	Wye	Fielder	Brown	Jones	Thompson	Ellis	Steele	Hay	Walker	Hunter	Garner	Taylor	1
Batty	Wood	Wye	Fielder	Brown	Jones	Thompson	Ellis	Steele	Hay	Walker	Hunter	Garner	Taylor	2
Batty	Wood	Wye	Fielder	Brown	Jones	Thompson	Ellis	Steele	Hay	Walker	Hunter	Garner	Taylor	3
Batty	Wood	Wye	Fielder	Brown	Jones	Thompson	Ellis	Steele	Hay	Walker	Hunter	Garner	Taylor	4
Batty	Wood	Wye	Fielder	Brown	Jones	Thompson	Ellis	Steele	Hay	Walker	Hunter	Garner	Taylor	5
Batty	Wood	Wye	Timothy	Brown	Jones	Thompson	Ellis	Steele	Hunter	Walker	Hay	Garner	Taylor	6
Batty	Palmer	Wye	Fielder	Brown	Jones	Thompson	Ellis	Steele	Hay	Walker	Hunter	Garner	Taylor	7
Batty	Palmer	Wye	Fielder	Brown	Jones	Thompson	Ellis	Steele	Hay	Walker	Hunter	Garner	Taylor	8
Batty	Palmer	Wye	Taylor	Brown	Jones	Thompson	Ellis	Hunter	Hay	Timothy	Walker	Steele	Fielder	9
Batty	Palmer	Wye	Taylor	Brown	Jones	Thompson	Ellis	Timothy	Hunter	Walker	Hay	Steele	Fielder	10
Batty	Palmer	Wye	Taylor	Brown	Jones	Thompson	Ellis	Timothy	Hunter	Walker	Hay	Steele	Fielder	11
Batty	Palmer	Taylor	Fielder	Brown	Jones	Thompson	Ellis	Timothy	Hay	Walker	Howard	Steele	Garner	12
Gregory	Palmer	Taylor	Fielder	Brown	Jones	Thompson	Ellis	Timothy	Hay	Walker	Howard	Steele	Garner	13
Batty	Howard	Timothy	Foster	Brown	Jones	Thompson	Wye	Grazioli	Payne	Walker	Taylor	Steele	Hanley	14
Batty	Howard	Taylor	Foster	Brown	Jones	Thompson	Wye	Grazioli	Payne	Walker	Ellis	Steele	Hanley	15
Batty	Howard	Taylor	Foster	Brown	Jones	Wye	Ellis	Grazioli	Payne	Walker	Fielder	Steele	Gregory	16
Batty	**Howard**	**Steele**	**Foster**	**Brown**	**Jones**	**Wye**	**Ellis**	**Grazioli**	**Payne**	**Walker**	**Fielder**	**Wimcoll**	**Gregory**	**17**
Batty	Howard	Taylor	Foster	Brown	Jones	Thompson	Wye	Steele	Grazioli	Walker	Ellis	Payne	Hunter	18
Batty	Howard	Taylor	Foster	Brown	Jones	Thompson	Wye	Steele	Grazioli	Walker	Ellis	Hunter	Payne	19
Batty	**Howard**	**Taylor**	**Foster**	**Brown**	**Jones**	**Thompson**	**Wye**	**Steele**	**Hunter**	**Walker**	**Ellis**	**Hay**	**Wye**	**20**
Batty	Howard	Taylor	Foster	Brown	Jones	Thompson	Wye	Steele	Hunter	Walker	Ellis	Hay	Wye	21
Batty	**Howard**	**Taylor**	**Foster**	**Brown**	**Jones**	**Thompson**	**Wye**	**Steele**	**Hunter**	**Walker**	**Ellis**	**Hay**	**Wye**	**22**
Batty	Howard	Taylor	Foster	Brown	Jones	Thompson	Wye	Steele	Hay	Walker	Ellis	Timothy	Wye	23
Batty	Howard	Taylor	Wye	Brown	Jones	Ellis	Wye	Kay	Hay	Walker	Timothy	Ellison	Gregory	24
Batty	**Howard**	**Taylor**	**Foster**	**Brown**	**Jones**	**Thompson**	**Wye**	**Steele**	**Hay**	**Walker**	**Ellis**	**Hunter**	**Wye**	**25**
Batty	Howard	Taylor	Foster	Brown	Jones	Thompson	Wye	Steele	Hay	Walker	Ellis	Hunter	Wye	26
Gregory	**Wye**	**Taylor**	**Foster**	**Brown**	**Ellis**	**Thompson**	**Wye**	**Steele**	**Ellison**	**Walker**	**Jones**	**Timothy**	**Brooks**	**27**
Batty	Howard	Wye	Foster	Brown	Jones	Thompson	Wye	Steele	Hay	Walker	Ellis	Hunter	Timothy	28
Batty	Howard	Taylor	Foster	Brown	Jones	Thompson	Wye	Steele	Hunter	Walker	Ellis	Hay	Wye	29
Batty	Howard	Taylor	Foster	Brown	Jones	Thompson	Wye	Steele	Hunter	Walker	Ellis	Hay	Wye	30
Batty	**Howard**	**Taylor**	**Foster**	**Brown**	**Jones**	**Thompson**	**Wye**	**Steele**	**Hay**	**Walker**	**Ellis**	**Hunter**	**Wye**	**31**
Batty	**Howard**	**Taylor**	**Foster**	**Brown**	**Jones**	**Thompson**	**Wye**	**Steele**	**Hunter**	**Walker**	**Hay**	**Ellis**	**Wye**	**32**
Batty	Howard	Taylor	Foster	Brown	Jones	Thompson	Wye	Steele	Jackson	Walker	Timothy	Hay	Wye	33
Batty	**Howard**	**Taylor**	**Foster**	**Brown**	**Jones**	**Thompson**	**Wye**	**Steele**	**Hay**	**Walker**	**Ellis**	**Hunter**	**Wye**	**34**
Batty	**Howard**	**Wye**	**Foster**	**Brown**	**Jones**	**Thompson**	**Wye**	**Steele**	**Jackson**	**Walker**	**Ellis**	**Hay**	**Timothy**	**35**
Batty	**Howard**	**Taylor**	**Foster**	**Brown**	**Jones**	**Thompson**	**Wye**	**Steele**	**Jackson**	**Walker**	**Ellis**	**Hay**	**Wye**	**36**
Batty	Howard	Taylor	Foster	Brown	Jones	Thompson	Wye	Steele	Jackson	Walker	Ellis	Hay	Wye	37
Batty	Howard	Wye	Foster	Brown	Wye	Thompson	Ellis	Steele	Jackson	Walker	Hay	Jones	Taylor	38
Segers	**Howard**	**Wye**	**Foster**	**Brown**	**Wye**	**Thompson**	**Ellis**	**Steele**	**Jackson**	**Walker**	**Jones**	**Hay**	**Taylor**	**39**
Gregory	Howard	Wye	Foster	Brown	Wye	Thompson	Ellis	Steele	Jackson	Walker	Hay	Jones	Taylor	40
Hyde	Howard	Taylor	Foster	Brown	Wye	Jones	Ellis	Steele	Hay	Walker	Jackson	Wye	Hunter	41
Gregory	Howard	Taylor	Foster	Brown	Wye	Thompson	Ellis	Steele	Hay	Walker	Jackson	Jones	Wye	42
Gregory	**Howard**	**Taylor**	**Foster**	**Brown**	**Wye**	**Thompson**	**Ellis**	**Steele**	**Hay**	**Walker**	**Wye**	**Jackson**	**Timothy**	**43**
Gregory	Howard	Taylor	Foster	Brown	Wye	Thompson	Ellis	Steele	Hay	Walker	Jackson	Wye	Timothy	44
Batty	Howard	Taylor	Foster	Brown	Wye	Thompson	Ellis	Steele	Jackson	Timothy	Hay	Wye	Gregory	45
Batty	Howard	Taylor	Foster	Brown	Wye	Thompson	Ellis	Steele	Jackson	Timothy	Wood	Wye	Hay	46
Batty	**Howard**	**Taylor**	**Foster**	**Brown**	**Wye**	**Thompson**	**Ellis**	**Steele**	**Hay**	**Jackson**	**Hunter**	**Wye**	**Jones**	**47**
Gregory	Howard	Taylor	Wood	Brown	Timothy	Wye	Ellis	Steele	Hay	Huntr	Jackson	Wye	Jones	48
Batty	**Howard**	**Taylor**	**Wye**	**Brown**	**Wye**	**Thompson**	**Ellis**	**Steele**	**Jackson**	**Walker**	**Hay**	**Timothy**	**Jones**	**49**
Batty	Howard	Taylor	Foster	Brown	Wye	Wye	Ellis	Jones	Jackson	Hunter	Timothy	Wood	Gregory	50
Batty	**Howard**	**Taylor**	**Foster**	**Brown**	**Wye**	**Thompson**	**Ellis**	**Steele**	**Hay**	**Walker**	**Wye**	**Jackson**	**Jones**	**51**
Gregory	Howard	Wye	Foster	Brown	Jones	Thompson	Taylor	Hunter	Jackson	Walker	Ellis	Kilner	Wood	52
Gregory	Howard	Wye	Foster	Brown	Jones	Thompson	Hunter	Jackson	Hay	Walker	Ellis	Kilner	Betsy	53
Gregory	Howard	Wye	Foster	Brown	Salsman	Kamara	Kilner	Hunter	Jackson	Walker	Timothy	Ellis	Brooks	54
Gregory	Hunter	Wye	Foster	Brocks	Timothy	Kamara	Betsy	Kilner	Jackson	Walker	Wye	Ellis	Batty	55
Batty	Howard	Wye	Foster	Taylor	Wye	Thompson	Ellis	Timothy	Jackson	Walker	Hunter	Kamara	Kilner	56

JOHN McGOVERN (MANAGER)

Date of Appointment	July 1997
Date of Birth:	28th October 1949
Place of Birth:	Montrose

PREVIOUS CLUBS

As manager	
As player/manager	Bolton Wanderers
As player	Hartlepool U., Derby C., Leeds U., Nottingham Forest

HONOURS

As manager	
As player	S: u23 (2); European Cup 78-79,79-80, Div. 1 71-72, 78-79; Div. 2 68-69; League Cup 77-78, 78-79, R-up 79-80.

Assistant Manager / Coach: Brian Finn **Physio:** Barry Kimber

Kevan Brown holds the FA Umbro Trophy aloft at Wembley. Photo: P C W Barnes

MATCHDAY PROGRAMME

Number of pages	40
Price	£1.30
Programme Editor	Paul Beard
Other club publications:	"Winning isn't Everything" (fanzine)
Local Newspapers:	Woking News & Mail Woking Herald Surrey Advertiser
Local Radio Stations:	BBC Surrey Sussex County Sound BBC Southern Counties

1997-98 PLAYING SQUAD

PLAYER	Birthplace Honours	Birthdate	CLUBS
GOALKEEPERS			
Laurence Batty	Westminster ESP, FAT, ILP	15.2.64	Maidenhead U, Fulham, Brentford, Farense (Belg)
DEFENDERS			
Terry Howard	Stepney E u-19, FAT	26.2.66	Chelsea, Leyton Orient, Wycombe W
Steve Wood	Bracknell Div 2, Div 3	2.2.63	Reading, Millwall, Southampton, Oxford U
Kevan Brown	Andover ESP, FAT, Div 3	25.6.68	Southampton, Brighton, Aldershot
Lloyd Wye	Wokingham FAT, ILP, NZL, FA XI	14.5.67	Southampton, Woking, Wanganui (NZ)
Robin Taylor	Leicester FAT, British Students		Cambridge C, Hinckley T, Kettering T, Peterborough U, Kettering T, Port Vale, Dagenham & Redbridge
MIDFIELDERS			
Andy Ellis	Cardiff FAT, WSP		Barry T, Inter Cardiff, Barry T
Scott Steele	Motherwell FAT, SS	19.9.71	Airdrie
Tom Jones	Aldershot ESP, FAT, Div 2	7.10.64	Chelsea, Franborough T, Weymouth, Aberdeen, Swindon T, Reading
Steve Thompson	Plymouth ESP, GMVC, FAT, ILP	12.1.63	Bristol C, Torquay U, Saltash U, Slough T, Wycombe W
FORWARDS			
Clive Walker	Oxford FAT, ES	26.5.57	Chelsea, Sunderland, Q.P.R., Fulham, Brighton
Darron Hay	Hitchin FAT	17.12.69	Biggleswade T, Cambridge U
Junior Hunter	Lambeth	1.2.75	Cambridge U, Kettering T, Hendon
Justin Jackson	Nottingham FAT	26.6.65	Bolton W, Ayr U, Penrith, Ilkeston T, Morecambe, £30k to Woking

DEPARTURES - (During the season): Simon Garner (Wealdstone), Colin Fielder (Yeovil T), Russ Watkinson (Southampton), Noel Imber (Slough T)
(During the close season): Steve Foster (Bristol R)

PLAYERS ON LOAN - Lee Palmer (Cambridge U), Guiliano Grazioli (Peterborough), Hans Segers (Wimbledon), Paul Hyde (Leicester C)

Kingfield Stadium, Woking

GROUND ADDRESS:
Kingfield Stadium, Kingfield, Woking, Surrey. GU22 9AA.
TELEPHONE NUMBER: 01483 772470

SIMPLE DIRECTIONS:
M25 J10 or 11, signposted from outskirts of Town. Ground 1 mile. Woking B.R.Station & buses from Woking.

CAPACITY: 6,000 **SEATED:** 2,500 **TERRACING - Covered:** 1,400 **Uncovered:** 2,100

SOCIAL FACILITIES:
Clubhouse open on matchdays. Food available.

CLUB SHOP:
Phone 01483 772470 for details.

Woking Fact File

Nickname: The Cards **Club Sponsors:** Woking Borough Council
Club colours: Red/white halves & black shorts
Change colours: Yellow and Navy
Reserve team's league: Capital League
Midweek home matchday: Tuesday 7.45pm.

PREVIOUS - **Grounds:** Wheatsheaf, Ivy Lane (pre 1923) **Leagues:** Isthmian 1991/92

CLUB RECORDS - **Attendance:** 6,000 v Swansea, FA Cup - 1978/79
v Coventry C., FA Cup - 1996-97
Win: 17-4 v Farnham, 1912-13.
Defeat: 0-16 v New Crusaders, 1905-06.
Career goalscorer: C Mortimore 331, 1953-65
Career appearances: B Finn 564, 1962-74
Transfer fee paid: £30,000 for Justin Jackson (Morecambe) - 1996
Transfer fee received: £150,000 from Bristol Rovers for Steve Foster, May 1997.

BEST SEASON - **FA Cup:** 3rd Round replay 96-97, 1-2 (H) v Coventry after 1-1 (A)
League clubs defeated: Cambridge U., Millwall (96-97)
FA Trophy: Winners 93-94, 94-95, 96-97.
FA Amateur Cup: Winners 75-58.

1996-97 Captain: Kevan Brown
1996-97 Top scorer: Clive Walker (18)
1996-97 Player of the Year: Steve Thompson

Past players who progressed to the Football League: Ray Elliott (M'wall 1946), Charlie Mortimore (A'shot 1949), Robert Edwards (Chelsea 1951), Ron Newman (Portsmouth 1955), Mervyn Gill (Southampton 1956), John Mortimore (Chelsea 1951), Reg Stratton (Fulham 1959), George Harris (Newport 1961), Norman Cashmore (A'shot 1963), Alan Morton (C.Palce 1967), William Holmes (Millwall 1970), Richard Forbes (Exeter 1979), Kevin Rattray (Gillingham 1995), Steve Foster (Bristol Rovers 1997).

HONOURS: FA Trophy 93-94, 94-95, 96-97; FA Amateur Cup 57-58; GM Vauxhall Conference R-up 94-95, 95-96; Isthmian League R-up 56-57, Lge AC Delco Cup 90-91, Div.1 R-up 89-90, Div.2 South 86-87, Reserve Section (2); West Surrey Lge (4), London Senior Cup R-up 82-83; Surrey Senior Cup 12-13, 26-27, 55-56, 56-57, 71-72, 90-91, 93-94, 95-96; Surrey Senior Shield (9); Surrey Premier Cup (2); Surrey Invitation Cup 66-67; Surrey Intermediate Cup (2); Channel Islands Victory Cup (2); Suburban Lge (2), Lge Cup (2); Diadora Premier Division 91-92; Isthmian League Charity Shield 91-92, 92-93; Vauxhall Championship Shield 94-95, R-up 95-96.

Formed:
1895

YEOVIL TOWN

Chairman: John Fry **President:** S N Burfield

Secretary: Jean Cotton Address - c/o the club
Tel: 01935 423662 Fax: 01935 473956

Commercial Manager: Alan Skirton

Press Officer: Jean Cotton (see above)

A two club promotion race over six months with hardly a week, when neither club has a lead of more than two points, really sorts out the men from the boys. Yeovil Town and Enfield both took up the challenge magnificently but the Somerset club were probably given an extra lift by usually having a small lead and they definitely had the advantage of the quite outstanding Howard Forinton.

'The Non-League Footballer of the Year' eventually took it upon himself to see his club into the Conference with 24 goals in 22 games including six doubles in the last seven games. Jerry Gill was selected for England at right back but he and Paul Turner scored double figures from mid-field while Warren Patmore (top scorer with 29) and Ian Birkby were also consistent.

Great attendances certainly helped and the club's financial situation is now greatly improved in all ways. An FA Cup run ended in the Fourth Qualifying Round at Merthyr Tydfil and three Trophy games with Hayes were entertaining but not productive. The County Cup was won but the club did concentrate on promotion and this single mindedness paid off to give Graham Roberts and his squad a wonderful reward, having attracted 8,007 to the Enfield ICIS match, and 6,000 turned up to see relegated Chertsey on the last day of the season and found it a memorable day of celebration.

It may take a little time to acclimatize in the Conference, but the club is now developing a firmer financial foundation so expectations are high for the season ahead.

Left to right - Back Row: Chris White, Dean Birkby, Kevin Brabrook, Lee Harvey, Rob Cousins, Owen Pickard. Middle: Colin Fielder (Player Coach), Tony Pennock, Nick Stone, Terry Cotton (Asst. Manager). Front: Steve Browne, Chris Seymour, Andy Clement, Graham Roberts (Manager), Micky Engwell (Captain), Al James Hannigan, Warren Patmore. Missing: Graham Kemp, Steve Winter.

Yeovil Town

Match No.	Date	Venue H/A	Competition	Opponents	Result	League Pos.	Attendance	Goalscorers (Times if known)
1	Aug 17	A	IL	Grays Athletic	Won 3-2		385	Harvey, Patmore (2)
2	Aug 20	H	IL	Dagenham & Redbridge	Drew 0-0		2255	
3	Aug 24	H	IL	Bromley	Won 1-0		1810	Turner
4	Aug 26	A	IL	Hitchin Town	Won 1-0	1	537	Patmore
5	Aug 31	A	IL	Dulwich Hamlet	Lost 1-4	6	711	Turner
6	**Sep 3**	**H**	**GIC**	**Molesey**	**Won 6-1**		**911**	**Harvey (2), Moores (2), Laidlaw, Gill**
7	Sep 7	H	IL	Hendon	Won 2-0	3	1904	Gill, Harvey
8	**Sep 14**	**H**	**FAC 1 Q**	**Backwell United**	**Won 6-0**		**1614**	**Patmore (3), Gill, Harvey, Turner**
9	Sep 17	H	IL	Carshalton Athletic	Won 3-0		1846	Gill, Engwell, Moores
10	Sep 21	A	IL	Kingstonian	Won 3-0	1	676	Gill, Patmore, Laidlaw
11	**Sep 28**	**H**	**FAC 2 Q**	**Taunton Town**	**Drew 0-0**		**3303**	
12	**Sep 30**	**A**	**FAC 2QR**	**Taunton Town**	**Won 5-3**		**2500**	**Birkby, Turner, Patmore (2), Gill**
13	Oct 5	H	IL	Harrow Borough	Won 2-1	1	2116	Patmore, Turner
14	**Oct 12**	**A**	**FAC 3 Q**	**Tiverton Town**	**Won 2-0**		**2380**	**Patmore, Seymour**
15	Oct 19	A	IL	St Albans City	Won 3-2	1	851	Patmore, Gill, Birkby
16	Oct 22	H	IL	Yeading	Won 2-0	1	2285	Whale, Harvey (pen)
17	**Oct 26**	**A**	**FAC 4 Q**	**Merthyr Tydfil**	**Lost 1-2**		**1514**	**Gill**
18	Nov 2	A	IL	Aylesbury United	Drew 0-0	1	864	
19	**Nov 5**	**A**	**GIC**	**Yeading**	**Drew 1-1**		**150**	**Patmore**
20	Nov 9	A	IL	Enfield	Lost 0-3	1	1349	
21	Nov 12	A	IL	Boreham Wood	Won 3-0	1	333	Gill (2), Kemp
22	Nov 16	H	IL	Sutton United	Won 3-2	1	2803	Birkby (2), Patmore
23	Nov 23	A	IL	Purfleet	Drew 1-1	1	347	Moores
24	**Nov 26**	**H**	**GIC**	**Yeading**	**Lost 0-1**		**908**	
25	**Nov 30**	**H**	**FAT 3 Q**	**Evesham United**	**Won 2-0**		**1366**	**Birkby, Turner**
26	**Dec 3**	**H**	**SSC**	**Frome Town**	**Won 7-0**		**251**	**Birkby 2, Patmore 2, Moores, Pounder, Braybrook**
27	Dec 7	A	IL	Chertsey Town	Won 2-0	1	452	Birkby (pen), Patmore
28	Dec 14	H	IL	Heybridge Swifts	Won 1-0	1	2101	Birkby
29	Dec 21	A	IL	Bishop's Stortford	Won 1-0	1	466	Birkby
30	Dec 28	H	IL	Grays Athletic	Won 2-0	1	2184	Patmore (2)
31	**Jan 11**	**H**	**IL FMC**	**Carshalton Athletic**	**Won 2-0**		**764**	**Birkby, Gill**
32	**Jan 18**	**H**	**FAT1**	**Hayes**	**Drew 2-2**		**2458**	**Birkby (2)**
33	**Jan 21**	**A**	**FAT 1 R**	**Hayes**	**Drew 2-2**		**607**	**Patmore, Engwell**
34	Jan 25	A	IL	Dagenham & Redbridge	Won 1-0	1	1181	Birkby
35	**Jan 27**	**H**	**FAT 1R2**	**Hayes**	**Lost 1-2**		**2310**	**Harvey (pen)**
36	Feb 1	H	IL	Hitchin Town	Won 1-0	1	2004	Forinton
37	Feb 8	A	IL	Carshalton Athletic	Won 1-0	1	603	Fielder
38	**Feb 11**	**H**	**IL FMC**	**Bognor Regis Town**	**Won 3-2**			**Moores, Laidlaw, Pounder**
39	Feb 15	H	IL	Kingstonian	Lost 2-3	2	2242	Forinton (2)
40	Feb 22	H	IL	St Albans City	Won 3-1	2	2168	Gill, Patmore, Forinton (pen)
41	**Feb 26**	**A**	**SSC**	**Paulton Rovers**	**Won 1-0**		**222**	**White**
42	Mar 1	A	IL	Yeading	Drew 0-0	2	409	
43	Mar 4	H	IL	Dulwich Hamlet	Won 6-1	2	1707	Forinton (3), Turner, Fielder, Birkby
44	Mar 8	A	IL	Harrow Borough	Won 3-2	1	447	Gill, Turner, Birkby
45	Mar 11	A	IL	Hendon	Won 3-1	1	372	Forinton, Birkby, Gill
46	**Mar 13**	**H**	**SSC**	**Brislington**	**Won 4-2**		**406**	**Forinton (2), Pounder, Turner**
47	Mar 15	H	IL	Boreham Wood	Drew 0-0	1	3195	
48	**Mar 18**	**H**	**IL FMC**	**Maidenhead United**	**Lost 0-1**		**434**	
49	Mar 22	H	IL	Aylesbury United	Won 3-2	1	2011	Forinton (2), Gill
50	Mar 25	H	IL	Enfield	Drew 2-2	1	8007	Engwell, Turner
51	Mar 29	A	IL	Staines Town	Drew 1-1	1	510	Patmore
52	Mar 31	A	IL	Oxford City	Won 2-0	1	869	Patmore (2)
53	Apr 5	H	IL	Bishop's Stortford	Won 1-0	1	2628	Forinton
54	Apr 8	H	IL	Staines Town	Won 3-1	1	2808	Forinton (2), Patmore
55	Apr 12	A	IL	Sutton United	Won 3-0	1	1281	Forinton (2), Patmore
56	Apr 19	H	IL	Purfleet	Won 4-3	1	3004	Forinton (2), Patmore, Turner
57	Apr 22	H	IL	Oxford City	Won 4-1	1	3275	Forinton (2), Patmore (2)
58	Apr 26	A	IL	Heybridge Swifts	Drew 0-0	1	875	
59	Apr 29	A	IL	Bromley	Won 2-1	1	979	Forinton (2)
60	May 3	H	IL	Chertsey Town	Won 4-0	1	6013	Forinton (2), Pennock (pen), Turner
61	**May 5**	**H**	**SSC F**	**Bristol City**	**Won 2-1**		**1111**	**Forinton, Gill**

Yeovil Town

1	2	3	4	5	6	7	8	9	10	11	12	14	15	Mth No.
Pennock	Gill	Cousins	Braybrook	Harvey	Seymour	Pounder	Whale	Patmore	Birkby	Kemp	Moors	Laidlaw	White	1
Pennock	Gill	Engwell	Pounder	Harvey	Seymour	Cousins	Whale	Patmore	Birkby	Kemp	Laidlaw	Braybrook	Brown	2
Pennock	Gill	Engwell	Roberts	Turner	Seymour	Pounder	Whale	Patmore	Cousins	Kemp	Birkby	Harvey	Braybrook	3
Pennock	Gill	Engwell	Roberts	Harvey	Cousins	Seymour	Turner	Patmore	Birkby	Kemp	Whale	Pounder	Braybrook	4
Pennock	Gill	Engwell	Roberts	Harvey	Cousins	Pounder	Whale	Patmore	White	Turner	Laidlaw	Braybrook	Kemp	5
Pennock	**Gill**	**Engwell**	**White**	**Harvey**	**Cousins**	**Braybrook**	**Turner**	**Laidlaw**	**Moors**	**Pounder**	**Harris**	**Whale**	**Patmore**	**6**
Pennock	Gill	Engwell	White	Turner	Harvey	Pounder	Laidlaw	Moors	Cousins	Braybrook	Patmore	Whale	Kemp	7
Pennock	**Gill**	**Engwell**	**White**	**Harvey**	**Cousins**	**Pounder**	**Turner**	**Moore**	**Patmore**	**Braybrook**	**Laidlaw**	**Roberts**	**Whale**	**8**
Pennock	Gill	Engwell	White	Harvey	Cousins	Pounder	Turner	Patmore	Moors	Braybrook	Laidlaw	Roberts	Whale	9
Pennock	Gill	Engwell	White	Harvey	Cousins	Pounder	Turner	Patmore	Moors	Braybrook	Whale	Roberts	Laidlaw	10
Pennock	**Gill**	**Engwell**	**White**	**Harvey**	**Cousins**	**Pounder**	**Turner**	**Patmore**	**Moors**	**Braybrook**	Whale	Roberts	Kemp	**11**
Pennock	**Gill**	**Engwell**	**Roberts**	**Harvey**	**Cousins**	**White**	**Turner**	**Patmore**	**Birkby**	**Kemp**	**Laidlaw**	**Brown**	**Pounder**	**12**
Pennock	Gill	White	Roberts	Harvey	Cousins	Pounder	Turner	Patmore	Birkby	Kemp	Whale	Braybrook	Laidlaw	13
Pennock	**Gill**	**White**	**Seymour**	**Harvey**	**Cousins**	**Pounder**	**Turner**	**Patmore**	**Birkby**	**Kemp**	**Whale**	**Braybrook**	**Moors**	**14**
Pennock	Gill	Seymour	Harvey	Braybrook	Cousins	Pounder	Turner	Patmore	Birkby	Kemp	Whale	Laidlaw	Moors	15
Pennock	Gill	Whale	Seymour	Harvey	Cousins	Pounder	Turner	Patmore	Birkby	Kemp	Roberts	Moors	Braybrook	16
Pennock	**Gill**	**Engwell**	**Seymour**	**Harvey**	**Cousins**	**Braybrook**	**Turner**	**Moors**	**Birkby**	**Pounder**	**Roberts**	**Whale**	**Laidlaw**	**17**
Pennock	Gill	Engwell	Roberts	Seymour	Cousins	White	Turner	Patmore	Moors	Kemp	Birkby	Harvey	Pounder	18
Pennock	**Gill**	**Engwell**	**Roberts**	**Harvey**	**Cousins**	**Pounder**	**Turner**	**Laidlaw**	**Birkby**	**Braybrook**	**Patmore**	**Moors**	**White**	**19**
Pennock	Gill	Engwell	Roberts	Harvey	Cousins	White	Turner	Patmore	Pounder	Kemp	Moors	Birkby	Whale	20
Seymour	Gill	Engwell	Roberts	Harvey	Cousins	Pounder	Turner	Patmore	Birkby	Kemp	Whale	Braybrook	Moors	21
Tyler	Gill	Engwell	Roberts	Harvey	Cousins	Whale	Turner	Patmore	Birkby	Kemp	Moors	Pounder	White	22
Tyler	Gill	Engwell	White	Harvey	Cousins	Whale	Turner	Patmore	Birkby	Kemp	Moors	Pounder	Braybrook	23
Seymour	**Gill**	**Engwell**	**White**	**Harvey**	**Cousins**	**Whale**	**Turner**	**Patmore**	**Birkby**	**Kemp**	**Moors**	**Pounder**	**Braybrook**	**24**
K Harvey	Gill	Engwell	Seymour	Harvey	Cousins	White	Turner	Patmore	Moors	Braybrook	Birkby	Pounder	Whale	25
J Smith	**Gill**	**Pounder**	**Seymour**	**Harvey**	**Cousins**	**White**	**Moors**	**Patmore**	**Birkby**	**Braybrook**	**Whale**	**Miller**	**D Smith**	**26**
Tyler	Gill	Engwell	Seymour	Cousins	White	Fielder	Turner	Patmore	Birkby	Braybrook	Moors	Pounder	Kemp	27
Tyler	Gill	Engwell	Seymour	Harvey	Cousins	Pounder	Whale	Moors	Birkby	Kemp	Patmore	Braybrook	White	28
Pennock	Gill	Engwell	White	Harvey	Cousins	Fielder	Turner	Moors	Birkby	Kemp	Pounder	Whale	Braybrook	29
Pennock	Gill	Engwell	Roberts	Harvey	Cousins	Fielder	Turner	Patmore	Birkby	Pounder	Kemp	Braybrook	White	30
Pennock	**Gill**	**Engwell**	**Roberts**	**Harvey**	**Cousins**	**Fielder**	**Pounder**	**Patmore**	**Birkby**	**Kemp**	**Braybrook**	**Collier**	**White**	**31**
Pennock	**Gill**	**Engwell**	**Seymour**	**Harvey**	**Cousins**	**Fielder**	**Turner**	**Patmore**	**Birkby**	**Kemp**	**Braybrook**	**Pounder**	**White**	**32**
Pennock	**Gill**	**Engwell**	**Roberts**	**Harvey**	**Cousins**	**Fielder**	**Turner**	**Patmore**	**Birkby**	**Seymour**	**Kemp**	**Whale**	**Moors**	**33**
Pennock	Gill	Engwell	Roberts	Harvey	Cousins	Fielder	Turner	Forinton	Birkby	Seymour	Kemp	Pounder	White	34
Pennock	**Gill**	**Engwell**	**Roberts**	**Harvey**	**Cousins**	**Fielder**	**Turner**	**Patmore**	**Birkby**	**Kemp**	**Pounder**	**Browne**	**White**	**35**
Pennock	Gill	Engwell	Seymour	Harvey	Cousins	Fielder	Turner	Forinton	Birkby	Peters	Patmore	Pounder	Braybrook	36
Pennock	Harvey	Engwell	Braybrook	Patmore	Cousins	Fielder	Turner	Forinton	Birkby	Peters	White	Moors	Browne	37
Pennock	**Pounder**	**Whale**	**Braybrook**	**Harvey**	**Cousins**	**White**	**Browne**	**Moors**	**Laidlaw**	**Kemp**	**Patmore**	**Turner**	**Miller**	**38**
Pennock	Gill	Kemp	Roberts	Harvey	Cousins	Fielder	Turner	White	Forinton	Pounder	Braybrook	Browne	Patmore	39
Pennock	Gill	Engwell	White	Patmore	Cousins	Fielder	Turner	Forinton	Birkby	Kemp	Harvey	Roberts	Brown	40
Pennock	**White**	**Pounder**	**Brown**	**Harvey**	**Cousins**	**Fielder**	**Turner**	**Forinton**	**Birkby**	**Patmore**	**Braybrook**	**Moors**	**Gill**	**41**
Pennock	Gill	Engwell	White	Browne	Cousins	Fielder	Turner	Patmore	Birkby	Forinton	Pounder	Harvey	Braybrook	42
Pennock	Gill	Engwell	Roberts	White	Cousins	Fielder	Turner	Seymour	Birkby	Forinton	Harvey	Browne	Pounder	43
Pennock	Gill	Engwell	Roberts	Browne	Cousins	Fielder	Turner	Forinton	Birkby	Kemp	Pounder	Harvey	Adams	44
Pennock	Gill	Engwell	Roberts	White	Cousins	White	Turner	Forinton	Birkby	Kemp	Patmore	Harvey	Adams	45
Pennock	**White**	**Pounder**	**Braybrook**	**Harvey**	**Cousins**	**Fielder**	**Turner**	**Patmore**	**Forinton**	**Kemp**	**Engwell**	**Moors**	**Collier**	**46**
Pennock	Gill	Engwell	Roberts	White	Cousins	Adams	Browne	Patmore	Birkby	Kemp	Harvey	Pounder	Adams	47
Pennock	**Pounder**	**Engwell**	**Adams**	**Harvey**	**Cousins**	**Fielder**	**Browne**	**Patmore**	**Birkby**	**Moors**	**Kemp**	**Collier**	**Miller**	**48**
Pennock	Gill	Engwell	Roberts	Harvey	Cousins	Braybrook	Turner	Forinton	Birkby	Browne	Patmore	Adams	Pounder	49
Pennock	Gill	Engwell	Roberts	Clement	Cousins	Fielder	Turner	Forinton	Birkby	Patmore	Harvey	Kemp	Browne	50
Pennock	Gill	Kemp	Roberts	Harvey	Cousins	Fielder	Browne	Patmore	Pounder	Forinton	Birkby	Braybrook	Adams	51
Pennock	Gill	Clement	Harvey	White	Cousins	Fielder	Kemp	Forinton	Patmore	Browne	Birkby	Moors	Braybrook	52
Pennock	Gill	Clement	White	Harvey	Cousins	Fielder	Turner	Patmore	Forinton	Kemp	Pounder	Roberts	Moors	53
Pennock	Gill	White	Roberts	Harvey	Cousins	Puttnem	Turner	Kemp	Forinton	Puttnem	Patmore	Moors	Browne	54
Pennock	Gill	Puttnam	White	Harvey	Cousins	Fielder	Turner	Patmore	Forinton	Browne	Pounder	Roberts	Moors	55
Pennock	Gill	White	Browne	Harvey	Cousins	Fielder	Turner	Patmore	Forinton	Puttnem	Clement	Roberts	Birkby	56
Pennock	Gill	Puttnam	Roberts	Harvey	Cousins	Fielder	Turner	Patmore	Forinton	Browne	Birkby	Clement	White	57
Pennock	Gill	White	Browne	Harvey	Cousins	Fielder	Turner	Patmore	Forinton	Puttnem	Birkby	Clement	Adams	58
Pennock	Gill	White	Browne	Harvey	Cousins	Fielder	Turner	Patmore	Forinton	Puttnem	Birkby	Clement	Adams	59
Pennock	Gill	Puttnam	Roberts	Harvey	Cousins	Fielder	Turner	Patmore	Forinton	Browns	Birkby	White	Clement	60
Roberts	**Gill**	**Pounder**	**Clement**	**Harvey**	**Cousins**	**Adams**	**Fielder**	**Forinton**	**Birkby**	**Braybrook**	**Browne**	**Turner**	**Kemp**	**61**

GRAHAM ROBERTS (MANAGER)

Date of Appointment	1995
Date of Birth:	3rd July 1959
Place of Birth:	Southampton
PREVIOUS CLUBS	
As manager	Enfield
As coach	Slough, Stevenage Borough
As player	Dorchester, Weymouth, Portsmouth (NC), Tottenham Hotspur, Glasgow Rangers, Chelsea, W.B.A.
HONOURS	
As manager	ICIS Prem. 96-97.
As player	England - 6 full & 1 'B' cap. UEFA Cup 84; FA Cup 81,82; Div. 2 89, Scot. Prem. 87, Scot. Lg. Cup 88.

Assistant Manager: Terry Cotton **Player/Coach:** Colin Fielder **Physio:** Terry Hardwell

Jerry Gill (left) and Howard Forinton both moved to Birmingham City during the close season.
Photo: Garry Letts

MATCHDAY PROGRAMME

Number of pages	48
Price	£1.50
Programme Editor	Bryan Moore
Other club publications:	None
Local Newspapers:	Western Gazette Western Daily Press Bristol Evening Post Sunday Independent.
Local Radio Stations:	Radio Bristol Somerset Sound Orchard FM.

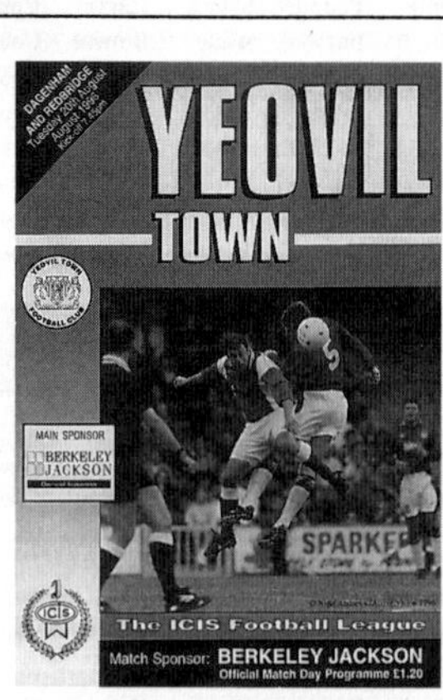

1997-98 PLAYING SQUAD

PLAYER	Birthplace Honours	Birthdate	CLUBS
GOALKEEPERS			
Tony Pennock	Swansea ILP	10.4.71	Stockport Co, Wigan A, Hereford U
DEFENDERS			
Chris White	Chatham ILP	11.12.70	Portsmouth, Peterborough U, Exeter
Lee Harvey	London ILP	2.10.69	Hemel Hempstead, Aylesbury U, Slough T
Micky Engwell	Chadwell St.Mary ILP	27.9.66	Southend U, Chelmsford C, Barking, Crewe A, Chesham U, Harrow Borough, Enfield, Grays A
Graham Roberts	Southampton E: 6, EUFAC 84, FAC 81,82, Div 2 89, Scot.Prem. 87, S.L.C 88, ILP	3.7.59	Sholing Sports, AFC Bournemouth, Portsmouth, Dorchester T, £6k to Weymouth, £85k to Tottenham H, Glasgow Rangers, £475k to Chelsea, £250k to W.B.A., Enfield, Slough T, Stevenage B
Andy Clement	Cardiff FAT, ILP	12.11.67	Wimbledon, Plymouth A, Woking, Slough T
Al-James Hannigan	London ILP, SLP	26.1.71	Arsenal, Barnet, Harwich & Parkeston, Harlow T, Marlow, Enfield, £5k to Rushden & Diamonds, £6k to Enfield
MIDFIELDERS			
Chris Seymour	Reading ILP	14.9.71	Reading, Newbury T
Colin Fielder	Winchester FAT, SLP, ILP, FA XI	5.1.64	Aldershot, Farnborough T, £18k to Slough T, Woking
Rob Cousins	Bristol ILP	9.1.71	Bristol C, Bath C
Graham Kemp	Birmingham ILP	21.6.68	Shrewsbury T, Reading, Newbury T
Paul Turner	London ILP	13.11.68	Arsenal, Cambridge U, Farnborough T, Enfield
Steve Browne	London ILP	21.6.64	Charlton A, Fulham, Maidstone U, Dartford, Grays A, Newmont Travel, Wealdstone, Sutton U, Kingstonian, Sutton U, Yeading, Wealdstone, Walton & Hersham, Yeovil T, Hendon
FORWARDS			
Dean Birkby	Castleford ILP	3.3.71	Mangotsfield U, Clevedon T, Mangotsfield U, Gloucester C, Yate T, Bath C, £10k to Yeovil T
Owen Pickard	Barnstaple	18.11.69	Plymouth A, Hereford U, Dorchester T
Warren Patmore	Kingsbury ILP	14.8.71	Northwood, Cambridge U, Millwall, Northampton T, Ards
Kevin Braybrook	Basingstoke	11.2.77	Portsmouth

DEPARTURES -
(During the season): Leroy Whale (Fareham T), Jamie Laidlaw (Bashley), Rob Peters (Released)
(During the close season): Howard Forinton & Jerry Gill (Birmingham C), Chris Moors, Danny Adams (Released)

PLAYERS ON LOAN - Mark Tyler (Peterborough U), Dave Puttnam (Gillingham)

Huish Park, Yeovil

GROUND ADDRESS: Huish Park, Lufton Way, Yeovil Somerset, BA22 8YF.

TELEPHONE NUMBERS: 01935 423662. Fax 01935 73956.

SIMPLE DIRECTIONS: Leave A303 at Cartgate r'about, take A3088 signposted Yeovil. 1st exit at next r'about, 1st exit at next r'about into Lufton Way. Railway station - Yeovil Pen Mill (Bristol/Westbury to Weymouth) 2.5 miles from ground. Bus service from stations on Saturday.

CAPACITY: 8,720 **SEATED:** 5,212 **COVERED TERRACING:** 3,508

SOCIAL FACILITIES: Matchdays hot + cold food available. Meals can be ordered provided advance notice is given. All weather astro turf pitch available for bookings 9am-10pm.

CLUB SHOP: Open on matchdays selling full range of souvenirs, match programmes, scarves, hats, replica kits and badges.

Yeovil Fact File

Nickname: Glovers **Sponsors:** ADG Electrical, Gillingham, Dorset.

Club Colours: Green & white/white/green & white

Change Colours: Yellow with black flashings.

Midweek matchday: Tuesday

Reserve League: Screwfix Direct, Western Lge Div 1

Local Press: Western Gazette, Western Daily Press, Bristol Evening Post, Sunday Independent.

Local Radio: Radio Bristol, Somerset Sound, Orchard FM.

PREVIOUS -
Leagues: Western League, London Combination, Southern League, Alliance Premier, Isthmian, GMV Conference, Isthmian.
Names: Yeovil & Petters Utd
Ground: The Huish until 1993

CLUB RECORDS -
Attendance: 8,612 v Arsenal 3rd Rd FA Cup 02/1/93.
Scorer: Dave Taylor 285 1960-69
Career Appearances: Len Harris, 691, 1958-72
Career Goalscorer: Unknown
Win: 10-0 v Kidderminster Harriers (H), Southern Lge. 27.12.1955
v Bedford Town (H), Southern Lge. 4.3.61
Defeat: 0-8 v Manchester Utd., FA Cup 5th Rd. 12.2.49 at Maine Rd. (81,565).
Transfer Fee Paid: £17,500 to Oxford City for Howard Forinton 1.97.
Transfer Fee Received: £75,000 for Mark Shail from Bristol City.
for Howard Forinton from Birmingham City 1997

BEST SEASON -
FA Trophy: Semi-Final 70-71 71-72.
FA Cup: 5th Rd 1948-49 3rd Rd 92-93.
League clubs beaten: (14)

Players Progressing to Football Lge: Over 40 players & 18 managers including, since 1985, Nigel Jarvis (Torquay), Ian Davies (Bristol Rovers), Alan Pardew (Crystal Palace), Paul Miller (Wimbledon) John McGinlay (Bolton), Guy Whittingham (Portsmouth), Mark Shail (Bristol City), Malcom McPherson (West Ham), Howard Forinton & Jerry Gill (Birmingham City).

96-97 Captain: Mickey Engwell
96-97 Player of the Year: Rob Cousins
96-97 Top scorer: Warren Patmore (30)

HONOURS: Southern Lge 54-55, 63-64, 70-71, R-up 23-24, 31-32, 34-35, 69-70, 72-73. Southern Lge Cup 48-49, 54-55, 60-61, 65-66. Vauxhall-Opel Lge (Isthmian) 87-88, R-up 85-86, 86-87. ICIS Prem. (Isthmian) 96-97; AC Delco Cup 87-88. Bob Lord Trophy 89-90, R-up 93-94.

NORTHERN PREMIER LEAGUE

PYRAMID SECTION

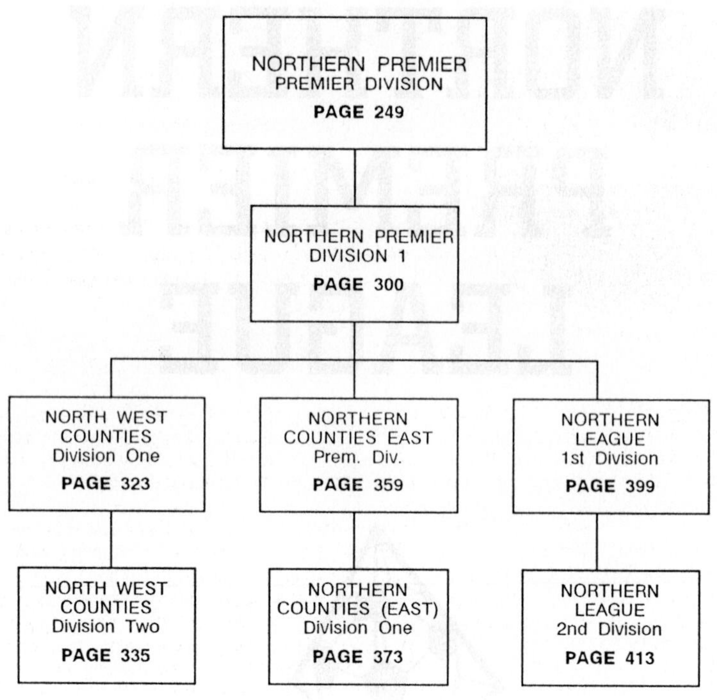

FEEDER & OTHER FEATURED LEAGUES

CENTRAL MIDLANDS
Page 379

WEARSIDE LEAGUE
Page 421

NOTTS ALLIANCE
Page 391

NORTHERN ALLIANCE
Page 427

Manchester League - Page 341; Mid Cheshire Lge. - Page 345; West Cheshire Lge - Page 349; West Lancs. League - Page 353; East Lancs. League - Page 355; Teeside League - Page 431

UniBond League

President N White F.S.C.A.

Chairman Ken Marsden

Vice-Chairman K F Brown

Secretary & Treasurer R Duncan Bayley
22 Woburn Drive, Hale, Altrincham, Cheshire WA15 8LZ
Tel: 0161 980 7007 (H & B) Fax: 0161 904 8850 Mob: 0378 669772

Perhaps the biggest success for the UniBond League was the securing of a further three year deal with the League's Sponsors, Henkel, which will take the Northern Premier League into the Millenium under the UniBond banner. The deal is worth £300,000 over the period and, at a time when semi-professional clubs are being hard hit financially by the double whammy of the National Lottery and televised football, is a most welcome addition to clubs' finances.

Away from the playing action the big talking point of the UniBond season was the number of managerial changes with over two thirds of the 45 member Leagues having changed managers by the end of the campaign! On the field, however, both Divisions saw some tough battles before the respective Championships were decided. In the top flight, up to half a dozen clubs were in contention with six weeks left but the sheer consistency of Leek Town wore down all their challengers leaving the Staffordshire club to celebrate their 50th Anniversary in style, gaining, at the same time, the promotion to the Vauxhall Conference that they had been denied in the corridors of power three years earlier. After their exploits of 1995/96, Hyde United had been most people's favourites for the title but sixteen draws cost them dear whilst both Barrow and Boston United promised much but failed to deliver when it mattered.

The surprise package of the season were Emley but, perhaps, they shouldn't have been for their manager Ronnie Glavin also took unfashionable Frickley Athletic to the foothills of the title race in 1993-94. But pipping everybody for runners-up spot were Bishop Auckland who finished like an express train in the final furlong to win eight and draw one of their final ten games. The North East side also had the Division's leading goalscorer Nick Peverill - who hit forty goals in the season including 28 in the league. At the bottom Buxton struggled all season and were never going to repeat the 'Houdini' impression they had performed the previous season. The 'Bucks' were joined in the relegation spots by Witton Albion, whose form collapsed once their major backer withdrew in October.

The race to replace Buxton and Witton in the Premier Division went to a photo finish with four clubs contesting the issue until the final fortnight when Farsley Celtic, enjoying their best season since joining the League, faltered to leave both the Championship and runners-up spot undecided going into the final day. Radcliffe Borough eventually took the main honour but Leigh, celebrating their Centenary, had an anxious wait to hear whether they had cause for a double celebration. Lincoln United's game with Whitley Bay was delayed due to an injured player and there were still ten minutes to play when Leigh's game finished. So close was Leigh and Lincoln that at 4.45pm the Lancashire side were up providing United didn't add to their 1-0 lead over Bay. They didn't and the Hilton Park outfit created history by becoming the first club to return to the top flight after being relegated to the First Division.

At the bottom of this Division it looked at Christmas as though Gretna and Warrington Town were doomed. But both put together useful runs, which saw the Scottish side escape although Warrington's brave bid just failed. The Cheshire club were joined in the relegation places by Curzon Ashton and Atherton LR, the latter dropping like a stone after enjoying mid-season security in mid-table. But the unsung hero of this Division was surely Alan McGreevy, Flixton's reserve team boss. The Manchester based club, in their first season of UniBond action, lost their major backer, their manager and virtually their entire team in October, but cometh the hour, cometh the man and McGreevy stepped into the breach and did a magnificent job to keep Flixton in mid-table under such arduous circumstances.

The UniBond League Challenge Cup served up an all Lincolnshire final for the first time in the history of the League and a crowd of almost 3,000 witnessed a titanic struggle between Gainsborough Trinity and Boston United before Grant Morrow scored the only goal of the game duing extra time for Trinity against the 'Pilgrims', who were left to reflect what might have been. Five of the winning side were former 'Pilgrims' whilst the winning manager, Ernie Moss, had also spent time at York Street as assistant manager!

In the other domestic cups, nobody could surely deny Ashton United's right to win the Unifilla First Division Cup for the second time. In a 22 club competition they played 990 minutes of soccer, experiencing two 4-4 draws and a 3-3 draw plus two penalty shoot outs before winning the trophy with a 5-4 Second Leg success over newcomers Stocksbridge PS to add to a three goal lead from the First Leg. In the Second Leg, the Division's top scorer Paddy Wilson added another brace to his tally but was outdone in what became known as the 'Wilson' show when namesake Darren Wilson notched a treble! The UniBond League President's Cup went to Blyth Spartans to give the much travelled goalkeeper John Burridge his first success as a manager. But their success was only achieved after Runcorn had twice wiped out a First Leg deficit.

In the FA Cup, the UniBond League didn't quite capture any full time scalps but they came close to providing shocks. Boston United disposed of Conference outfit Morecambe and then took Chester City all the way in the Second Round Proper before losing to the only goal of the game after the 'Pilgrims' had missed a penalty. Another Football League outfit to struggle to overcome UniBond League opposition were Wrexham who went on to contest a place in the semi-finals with Chesterfield. Colwyn Bay had the better of the first game and took the lead before giving another excellent account of themselves in a replay which sufficiently impressed Wrexham boss Brian Flynn to comment after his side's defeat by Chesterfield at the Quarter Final stage: "Of course I'm disappointed we didn't reach the last four but, then again, I think how lucky we were to overcome Colwyn Bay of the UniBond League in the First Round. Everything else after that was a bonus." The other UniBond League club to appear in the First Round were Runcorn and they also gave Darlington a shock when they levelled an early goal before succumbing in the second period.

Pictured left to right - Dick Norris (Executive Director Henkel Ltd), Ken Marsden (Chairman UniBond League), Duncan Bailey (Secretary UniBond League) and Rob Jenkins (UniBond Sponsorship Executive).

CHALLENGE CUP 96-97

FIRST ROUND

Ashton United 4v2 Bradford P.A.
(After 0-0)
Congelton Town 0v2 Flixton
Curzon Ashton 3v2 Atherton L.R.
Droylsden 1v2 Warrington Town
Frickley Athletic 1v0 Farsley Celtic
Gt. Harwood Town 2v1 Workington
Harrogate Town 3v2 Stocksbridge P.S.
Lincoln United 3v1 Alfreton Town
Matlock Town 4v1 Buxton
Netherfield 2v3 Lancaster City
(After 2-2)
Radcliffe Borough 3v1 Leigh
(After 0-0)
Whitley Bay 0v2 Gretna
Worksop Town 5v2 Eastwood Town
(After 1-1 & Extra Time)

SECOND ROUND

Ashton United 0v2 Guiseley
Bamber Bridge 1v5 Radcliffe Borough
Barrow 1v0 Gretna
Blyth Spartans 1v2 Emley
Boston United 3v0 Lincoln United
(After 1-1)
Flixton 2v0 Warrington Town
Frickley Athletic 1v0 Bishop Auckland
Gainsborough Trinity 1v0 Leek Town
(After 0-0)
Gt. Harwood Town 2v1 Chorley
Lancaster City 0v2 Accrington Stanley
Marine 1v3 Knowsley United
Matlock Town 3v1 Worksop Town
Spennymoor United 4v3 Harrogate Town
Winsford United 3v1 Runcorn
Witton Albion 0v5 Colwyn Bay

THIRD ROUND

Accrington Stanley 4v1 Flixton
Boston United 3v2 Hyde United
(After 1-1)
Colwyn Bay 3v2 Winsford United
Emley 1v0 Spennymoor United
Gainsborough Trinity 3v0 Frickley Athletic
Gt. Harwood Town 0v1 Knowsley United
(After 2-2)
Matlock Town 1v4 Guiseley
Radcliffe Borough 2v1 Barrow

FOURTH ROUND

Boston United 2v1 Emley
Gainsborough Trinity 2v1 Knowsley United
Guiseley 0v2 Colwyn Bay
(After 2-2)
Radcliffe Borough 0v3 Accrington Stanley
(After 0-0)

SEMI-FINALS

Accrington Stanley 1v0 Gainsborough Trinity
Gainsborough Trinity 3v1 Accrington Stanley

Boston United 1v0 Colwyn Bay
Colwyn Bay 1v3 Boston United

FINAL

Boston United 0v1 Gainsborough Trinity
AET - at Lincoln City FC

PRESIDENT'S CUP

FIRST ROUND

Bamber Bridge 2v3 Runcorn
Barrow 5v4 Accrington Stanley
Blyth Spartans 2v1 Spennymoor United
(After 2-2)
Boston United 5v2 Gainsborough Trinity
Curzon Ashton 0v3 Alfreton Town
(After 0-0)
Emley 0v1 Radcliffe Borough
Farsley Celtic 2v0 Guiseley
(After 1-1)
Worksop Town 3v0 Lincoln United

SECOND ROUND

Farsley Celtic 2v1 Boston United
(AET and 1-1)
Radcliffe Borough 3v1 Alfreton Town
Runcorn 3v1 Barrow
Worksop Town 1v2 Blyth Spartans
(After 2-2)

SEMI-FINAL (2 legs)

Blyth Spartans (0) 1v0 (0) Radcliffe Borough
Farsley Celtic (0) 1v2 (0) Runcorn

FINAL (2 legs)

Blyth Spartans (1) 3v2 (0) Runcorn

FIRST DIVISION CUP

FIRST ROUND

Droylsden 4v0 Flixton
(After 0-0)
Eastwood Town 0v1 Harrogate Town
Leigh 1v1 Ashton United
(After 3-3, AET, Ashton won on pens. 6-5)
Netherfield 2v1 Gretna
Stocksbridge P.S. 2v1 Matlock Town
Workington 1v0 Whitley Bay

SECOND ROUND

Atherton LR 1v0 Workington
Bradford P.A. 0v2 Harrogate Town
Droylsden 4v4 Ashton United
(After 1-1, AET, Ashton won on pens 4-1)
Farsley Celtic 1v2 Stocksbridge PS
Gt Harwood Town 2v3 Netherfield
(After 1-1)
Lincoln United 2v1 Worksop Town
(After 2-2)
Radcliffe Borough 1v0 Curzon Ashton
Warrington Town 0v8 Congleton Town

THIRD ROUND

Harrogate Town 2v1 Atherton LR
Netherfield 0v3 Ashton United
(After 4-4)
Radcliffe Borough 5v1 Lincoln United
Stocksbridge PS 1v0 Congleton Town

SEMI-FINALS (2 legs)

Harrogate Town (1) 2v2 (2) Ashton United (AET)
Stocksbridge PS (1) 0v0 (1) Radcliffe Borough
(AET - Stocksbridge won on away goals)

FINAL (2 legs)

Ashton United (3) 5v4 (0) Stocksbridge PS

UNIBOND LEAGUE - PREMIER DIVISION 1996-97

		Home					Away							Clean Sheets - FA Cup & Trophy & League games only	
	P	W	D	L	F	A	W	D	L	F	A	Pts.	G.D.	/	Top Scorers (Competitions as listed in league bulletin)
Leek Town	**44**	15	5	2	37	13	13	4	5	34	22	**93**	36	24	Soley - 23; Filson - 9; Batho - 8; Bancroft & Carter - 6
Bishop Auckland	**44**	12	6	4	49	24	11	8	3	39	19	**83**	45	13	Peverell - 40; Ellison - 18; Bayles - 10; McKinlay & Milroy - 5
Hyde United	**44**	12	8	2	49	20	10	8	4	44	26	**82**	47	18	Carroll & Kimmins - 21; Nolan - 20; James - 14; Owen - 12
Emley	**44**	12	5	5	54	30	11	7	4	35	24	**81**	35	16	Graham - 29; Hurst - 11; Lacey, Williams & Wilson - 10
Barrow	**44**	11	8	3	37	17	12	3	7	34	28	**80**	26	14	Morton - 26; Green - 14; Marginson - 5; 6 players - 3
Boston United	**44**	12	7	3	43	25	10	6	6	31	22	**79**	27	15	L Chambers - 25; Brown - 23; Williams - 14; Mason - 8
Blyth Spartans	**44**	10	8	4	40	22	12	3	7	34	27	**77**	25	12	Young - 24; Henderson - 13; Moat - 10; Bond & McGargle - 8
Marine	**44**	11	8	3	32	16	9	7	6	21	21	**75**	16	25	McNally - 14; Gautrey - 8; Blackhurst - 7; Draper - 5
Guiseley	**44**	13	4	5	32	16	7	7	8	31	38	**71**	9	15	Matthews - 24; Davison - 7; Blackstone - 6; 3 players - 5
Gainsborough Trinity	**44**	11	4	7	31	16	7	8	7	34	30	**66**	19	16	Maxwell - 18; Morrow - 17; Ellender - 8; Tilly - 5
Accrington Stanley	**44**	11	4	7	45	36	7	8	7	32	34	**66**	7	6	Ormorod - 28; Smith - 16; Welch - 15; Greenwood - 9
Runcorn	**44**	10	6	6	32	25	5	9	8	31	37	**60**	1	13	Dunn - 17; Heavey - 16; Lee - 9; Carmichael & Watson - 8
Chorley	**44**	7	6	9	39	35	9	3	10	30	31	**57**	3	11	Ross - 18; Trundle - 12; Blackstone & Marginson - 8
Winsford United	**44**	6	8	8	24	24	7	6	9	26	32	**53**	-6	8	Russell - 23; Burr - 10; Lyons - 7; Bishop - 4
Knowsley United	**44**	8	8	6	37	31	4	6	12	21	48	***49**	-21	6	Johnston & Stannard - 13; Kinney -12; Weathers - 9
Colwyn Bay	**44**	6	8	8	40	35	5	5	12	20	41	**46**	-16	14	Roberts - 16; Williams - 14; Donnelly - 12; Drury - 11
Lancaster City	**44**	8	3	11	23	34	4	6	12	25	41	**45**	-27	15	Coleman - 17; Diggle - 16; Borrowdale - 12; Trainor - 7
Frickley Athletic	**44**	7	4	11	38	41	5	4	13	24	50	**44**	-29	5	Armstrong - 15; Dring & Duffy - 9; Hatto & Thorpe - 8
Spennymoor United	**44**	7	6	9	35	29	3	4	15	17	39	**40**	16	8	Shaw - 19; Innes - 12; Alderson - 10; Cowell - 7
Bamber Bridge	**44**	4	4	14	30	51	7	3	12	29	48	**40**	-40	3	O'Neill - 11; Edwards & Spencer - 8; Leitch - 7
Alfreton Town	**44**	7	5	10	26	33	1	8	13	19	50	**37**	-38	5	Stafford - 9; Eshelby - 6; Pickering - 4; 3 players - 3
Witton Albion	**44**	4	8	10	25	40	1	6	15	16	51	**29**	-50	6	Watson - 9; Wilde - 6; Brenchley & Gayle - 5
Buxton	**44**	2	4	16	11	36	3	8	11	22	50	**27**	-53	5	Botchett & Hall - 8; Lee 7; March - 5

* 1 point deducted for breach of rules

Home Team / Away Team	Acc.S 1	Alfret. 2	Bamb. 3	Barr. 4	B.Auc. 5	Blyth 6	Bost. 7	Buxt. 8	Chor. 9	Colw. 10	Emley 11	Frick. 12	Gains. 13	Guis. 14	Hyde 15	Knows 16	Lanc. 17	Leek 18	Mari. 19	Runc. 20	Spen. 21	Winsf. 22	Witt. 23
1.Accrington Stanley		4-2 (501)	4-1 (768)	1-2 **(882)**	1-4 (371)	2-3 (513)	3-1 (417)	5-3 (374)	0-3 (747)	3-1 (432)	1-1 (521)	4-0 (412)	0-4 (480)	1-2 (455)	3-2 (574)	1-1 (333)	2-1 (377)	1-2 (415)	1-0 (444)	2-2 (702)	2-0 (321)	0-0 (367)	4-1 (423)
2.Alfreton Town	1-3 (277)		2-1 (201)	2-3 (289)	1-1 (253)	1-2 (256)	1-2 (397)	1-2 (313)	0-3 (205)	2-1 (218)	0-0 (249)	1-0 (124)	0-1 (225)	4-5 (283)	0-3 (238)	2-0 (197)	1-0 (232)	1-1 **(401)**	0-1 (281)	1-1 (175)	2-1 (230)	1-1 (229)	2-1 (192)
3.Bamber Bridge	1-1 **(787)**	2-2 (365)		1-3 (661)	1-2 (281)	0-1 (226)	0-2 (293)	2-2 (331)	0-2 (768)	2-3 (318)	0-3 (254)	5-1 (291)	1-1 (253)	6-4 (325)	1-4 (417)	1-2 (205)	0-2 (323)	0-4 (254)	1-0 (389)	0-5 (375)	1-3 (166)	1-2 (344)	4-2 (301)
4.Barrow	4-3 (1122)	3-0 (867)	1-1 (1414)		0-1 (1229)	2-2 (977)	0-1 (972)	0-0 (786)	3-0 (1015)	1-0 (871)	3-0 (1230)	2-0 (1152)	2-2 (1096)	1-1 (968)	1-1 (1165)	1-1 (1332)	3-0 (1142)	3-0 (1107)	0-1 **(1452)**	1-1 (1288)	1-0 (896)	2-1 (1259)	3-1 (1132)
5.Bishop Auckland	1-1 (173)	2-2 (127)	2-0 (183)	0-1 (282)		1-3 (375)	1-0 (144)	5-0 (205)	1-3 (211)	3-1 (193)	0-1 (172)	2-2 (142)	3-3 (185)	1-0 (245)	3-0 (122)	4-1 (151)	4-2 (142)	1-1 (226)	2-2 (204)	2-0 (225)	4-1 **(389)**	2-0 (174)	5-0 (164)
6.Blyth Spartans	1-1 (602)	2-1 (535)	2-1 (513)	1-0 (587)	0-0 (580)		1-2 (569)	5-0 (374)	1-3 (641)	0-0 (505)	1-1 (382)	6-3 (428)	1-1 (551)	1-1 (583)	2-1 (687)	6-0 (515)	3-1 (487)	0-1 **(732)**	1-1 (429)	3-2 (520)	2-0 (509)	1-2 (648)	0-0 (587)
7.Boston United	3-1 (1011)	1-1 (1023)	1-1 (811)	3-5 **(1487)**	1-1 (706)	2-1 (1283)		3-0 (865)	3-0 (1003)	3-2 (976)	4-1 (679)	2-3 (966)	1-1 (801)	1-1 (709)	0-0 (1391)	1-0 (819)	4-2 (937)	0-2 (1108)	2-0 (942)	2-2 (1035)	2-0 (422)	2-0 (634)	2-1 (1068)
8.Buxton	1-3 (271)	0-1 (316)	0-1 (189)	0-1 (223)	1-1 (173)	1-2 (194)	0-2 (176)		0-1 (201)	2-2 (155)	0-3 (215)	1-3 (220)	2-1 (227)	0-1 (148)	0-3 (105)	0-0 (188)	1-0 (180)	0-2 (437)	0-2 (289)	0-2 (257)	0-2 (152)	1-2 (241)	1-1 **(487)**
9.Chorley	1-1 (594)	2-1 (312)	1-3 (537)	1-3 **(867)**	1-1 (411)	1-3 (344)	3-4 (349)	2-2 (195)		4-0 (296)	1-2 (323)	0-1 (306)	3-4 (398)	1-0 (569)	3-3 (519)	2-2 (297)	0-2 (337)	0-0 (139)	2-1 (340)	4-0 (526)	1-0 (300)	0-1 (407)	6-1 (373)
10.Colwyn Bay	0-2 (381)	1-1 (287)	5-2 (304)	1-2 (394)	1-2 (314)	3-0 (339)	1-5 (297)	3-4 (312)	1-1 (235)		3-2 (268)	5-0 (275)	0-2 (241)	1-1 (390)	1-3 (313)	5-0 (317)	1-1 (363)	3-1 **(498)**	0-0 (193)	3-3 (269)	1-1 (310)	1-2 (283)	0-0 (427)
11.Emley	3-1 (210)	4-0 (222)	1-2 (212)	3-0 (415)	2-0 (258)	3-2 (268)	1-1 (303)	3-0 (163)	1-0 (307)	0-1 (211)		3-3 (427)	3-3 (282)	4-0 (312)	2-4 (419)	2-4 (250)	2-2 (271)	2-3 (452)	5-1 **(645)**	2-1 (253)	3-0 (249)	1-1 (170)	4-1 (205)
12.Frickley Athletic	0-1 (209)	7-2 (190)	1-0 (112)	0-2 (195)	0-4 (129)	2-2 (153)	2-2 (239)	3-1 (132)	2-1 (224)	3-4 (127)	1-2 (277)		2-2 (157)	0-1 **(254)**	0-3 (178)	0-2 (200)	3-1 (165)	2-3 (190)	0-1 (144)	1-1 (206)	5-2 (228)	3-2 (138)	1-2 (108)
13.Gainsborough Trinity	2-2 (511)	3-0 (453)	0-2 (423)	3-0 (457)	0-1 (401)	0-1 (474)	1-1 **(748)**	1-1 (442)	3-0 (440)	2-0 (430)	0-3 (573)	2-0 (527)		1-0 (545)	0-1 (610)	2-0 (318)	1-1 (408)	0-1 (517)	0-1 (433)	4-1 (406)	1-0 (532)	2-0 (293)	3-0 (383)
14.Guiseley	1-0 (512)	1-1 (334)	5-0 (513)	3-1 (410)	0-0 (254)	2-1 (331)	1-0 (328)	2-0 (382)	1-4 (462)	0-1 (417)	2-0 **(610)**	1-0 (207)	1-0 (432)		2-3 (423)	1-0 (387)	1-1 (312)	2-0 (480)	0-1 (297)	0-1 (299)	2-1 (362)	1-1 (345)	3-0 (355)
15.Hyde United	7-2 (578)	5-0 (440)	2-2 (478)	1-0 (653)	1-1 (615)	0-2 (523)	2-2 (509)	2-0 (604)	3-2 (622)	1-1 (427)	1-2 (576)	5-1 (449)	2-1 (443)	2-2 (543)		4-0 (421)	0-0 (400)	3-1 (609)	1-1 (487)	2-0 **(670)**	4-0 (415)	0-0 (548)	1-0 (565)
16.Knowsley United	1-1 (87)	1-1 (56)	5-0 (52)	0-3 **(228)**	0-5 (50)	0-1 (92)	0-0 (90)	4-1 (51)	4-1 (133)	3-0 (96)	0-1 (85)	0-0 (86)	0-1 (72)	2-2 (50)	3-3 (120)		3-1 (70)	3-2 (53)	3-1 (116)	1-1 (96)	2-2 (60)	0-3 (72)	2-1 (85)
17.Lancaster City	1-2 (301)	1-0 (146)	2-3 (217)	1-0 **(605)**	2-1 (245)	1-0 (228)	0-1 (243)	1-0 (142)	4-1 (302)	1-1 (154)	1-3 (286)	1-3 (262)	0-2 (214)	1-2 (197)	0-4 (410)	2-2 (222)		0-3 (238)	0-2 (141)	0-2 (197)	1-0 (275)	1-1 (161)	2-1 (182)
18.Leek Town	2-1 (363)	4-0 (320)	4-1 (302)	2-1 (733)	1-0 (425)	4-0 (582)	1-0 (486)	1-1 (702)	1-0 (405)	1-0 (866)	0-0 (660)	3-0 (417)	1-0 (226)	1-3 (391)	0-0 **(1065)**	2-0 (372)	2-1 (346)		0-1 (696)	1-1 (429)	1-1 (358)	3-1 (371)	2-1 (679)
19.Marine	2-1 (417)	1-1 (316)	2-0 (311)	1-1 (514)	2-3 (342)	0-3 (402)	1-0 (427)	3-0 (303)	1-0 **(533)**	0-0 (342)	0-0 (474)	3-1 (229)	2-0 (373)	1-2 (490)	1-1 (387)	2-2 (267)	5-1 (381)	0-0 (501)		1-0 (528)	1-0 (311)	3-0 (264)	0-0 (347)
20.Runcorn	1-3 (342)	1-0 (261)	1-2 (273)	0-0 (395)	1-3 (191)	1-0 (454)	1-1 (501)	1-1 (356)	0-2 (401)	5-0 (349)	1-1 (428)	0-0 (338)	2-1 (353)	2-0 (433)	1-3 (377)	1-0 (311)	3-2 **(559)**	0-2 (430)	1-1 (363)		1-0 (344)	4-3 (302)	4-0 (386)
21.Spennymoor United	0-0 (192)	3-2 (202)	2-1 (237)	1-2 **(329)**	1-5 (307)	0-2 (319)	1-3 (254)	0-1 (152)	0-0 (278)	1-2 (197)	2-3 (162)	3-1 (167)	1-2 (164)	4-1 (242)	1-1 (172)	5-0 (262)	1-1 (192)	0-1 (151)	0-0 (215)	6-0 (293)		2-0 (156)	1-1 (256)
22.Winsford United	1-1 (188)	1-0 (198)	4-2 (102)	1-2 (183)	1-2 (180)	0-2 (188)	0-1 (148)	1-1 (254)	0-1 (182)	3-0 (145)	2-2 (186)	1-0 (93)	1-1 (124)	1-1 (128)	2-1 (222)	3-1 (201)	0-1 (146)	0-2 (261)	0-1 (195)	0-0 (182)	1-1 (220)		1-1 **(278)**
23.Witton Albion	0-1 (530)	1-1 (406)	1-3 (404)	2-2 (480)	1-1 (232)	1-1 (317)	1-0 (349)	2-2 (269)	2-2 (373)	1-0 (258)	1-4 (351)	0-2 (239)	2-1 (535)	2-1 (443)	0-0 (527)	1-3 (312)	1-2 (463)	1-2 (584)	2-2 (443)	1-5 **(615)**	1-2 (360)	1-3 (338)	

FIRST DIVISION LEAGUE TABLE 1996-97

			Home					Away					
		P	W	D	L	F	A	W	D	L	F	A	Pts
1	Radcliffe Borough	42	15	2	4	47	17	11	5	5	30	16	85
2	Leigh	42	12	5	4	33	19	12	6	3	32	14	83
3	Lincoln United	42	13	3	5	43	26	12	5	4	35	21	83
4	Farsley Celtic	42	10	6	5	32	18	13	2	6	43	30	77
5	Worksop Town	42	12	5	4	38	15	8	7	6	30	23	*69
6	Stocksbridge Park Steels	42	11	5	5	39	26	8	6	7	27	28	68
7	Bradford Park Avenue	42	11	2	8	28	25	9	6	6	30	25	68
8	Ashton United	42	10	7	4	38	24	7	7	7	35	28	65
9	Great Harwood Town	42	10	5	6	30	17	6	7	8	26	29	60
10	Droylsden	42	7	7	7	38	35	8	7	6	31	32	59
11	Matlock Town	42	9	4	8	35	35	7	6	8	26	34	58
12	Whitley Bay	42	8	7	6	26	21	6	5	10	21	33	54
13	Flixton	42	7	5	9	26	27	8	2	11	31	45	52
14	Netherfield	42	7	6	8	24	24	5	8	8	30	32	50
15	Eastwood Town	42	8	8	5	25	19	4	6	11	17	31	50
16	Gretna	42	5	10	6	31	33	5	8	8	24	35	48
17	Harrogate Town	42	6	5	10	30	39	7	3	11	25	37	47
18	Congleton Town	42	8	4	9	31	31	4	5	12	16	33	45
19	Workington	42	7	8	6	33	29	3	4	14	12	34	42
20	Curzon Ashton	42	4	4	13	25	37	4	6	11	23	42	34
21	Warrington Town	42	2	11	8	20	32	3	7	11	22	47	33
22	Atherton Laburnam Rovers	42	3	4	14	22	40	4	5	12	23	45	30

* 3 points deducted for breach of rule

RESULTS GRID 1996-97

	HOME TEAM	1	2	3	4	5	6	7	8	9	10	11	12	13	14	15	16	17	18	19	20	21	22
1	Ashton U	*	4-1	0-0	0-1	4-0	1-1	2-0	1-2	1-0	2-1	4-2	2-2	2-1	2-1	2-0	2-2	1-3	1-2	2-2	1-1	2-0	2-2
2	Atherton LR	0-2	*	1-3	1-2	3-3	3-3	0-2	0-2	1-3	0-1	2-0	1-2	0-2	2-2	1-3	1-4	0-1	0-1	3-1	1-1	1-0	1-2
3	Bradford PA	0-1	4-2	*	3-0	1-2	0-5	1-1	2-1	0-1	2-1	3-1	1-0	0-3	0-1	1-0	3-2	0-1	2-0	2-0	1-2	1-0	1-1
4	Congleton T	2-7	4-1	0-1	*	1-1	0-1	2-0	0-2	3-2	0-3	2-0	5-1	0-1	0-3	1-1	2-0	0-0	2-0	2-3	1-3	1-1	3-0
5	Curzon A.	0-0	0-1	0-1	1-1	*	3-3	2-1	2-4	1-2	1-2	1-2	1-3	0-1	2-2	0-1	1-3	0-3	3-1	3-0	1-3	3-1	0-2
6	Droylsden	3-3	3-1	2-2	2-1	0-0	*	2-2	1-2	2-3	0-0	2-2	3-1	3-2	1-2	1-2	1-0	3-1	1-3	2-3	1-1	3-1	2-3
7	Eastwood T	2-1	0-0	1-1	0-0	3-2	0-0	*	3-1	3-0	2-0	0-2	2-0	0-0	0-1	1-2	2-2	1-0	2-2	1-0	1-2	0-1	1-1
8	Farsley C	2-3	0-2	1-0	3-0	1-2	3-0	3-1	*	1-1	3-0	1-1	3-0	0-0	2-0	1-1	2-1	0-1	2-1	1-1	1-1	1-2	1-0
9	Flixton	0-0	1-0	2-1	0-1	2-1	1-3	1-2	2-2	*	0-2	2-3	5-0	0-1	1-1	0-0	1-0	1-3	1-2	1-2	2-2	1-0	1-2
10	G Harwood T	0-2	4-1	1-2	2-1	0-0	0-1	1-0	2-3	4-1	*	0-0	1-0	1-1	2-3	2-0	0-0	0-2	1-0	6-0	2-0	1-0	0-0
11	Gretna	1-1	2-2	2-2	1-1	1-1	0-1	1-3	3-0	0-3	2-2	*	1-2	1-2	1-1	3-3	1-3	1-0	1-1	3-3	3-1	2-1	1-0
12	Harrogate T	2-2	4-1	3-1	1-2	4-2	4-4	3-0	0-5	3-2	0-2	0-0	*	0-2	0-3	1-2	1-1	2-2	1-2	0-3	1-0	0-1	0-2
13	Leigh	2-0	1-0	1-2	3-2	2-0	1-3	2-0	1-2	4-1	1-1	0-0	2-0	*	2-1	1-1	3-1	2-2	1-1	1-0	1-0	2-1	0-1
14	Lincoln U	1-2	3-1	2-1	1-0	0-1	0-1	2-1	0-4	8-2	2-1	4-1	4-1	1-2	*	4-1	2-2	2-1	2-2	2-2	1-0	1-0	1-0
15	Matlock T	2-2	4-1	0-2	2-0	1-4	0-2	3-0	1-2	4-0	2-2	2-1	0-2	2-1	1-4	*	3-3	0-2	2-1	2-2	3-0	1-0	0-4
16	Netherfield	1-0	2-2	0-3	1-0	2-0	1-0	0-1	1-0	0-1	1-1	0-1	0-1	0-3	1-1	5-1	*	0-1	2-2	0-0	5-0	1-1	1-5
17	Radcliffe B	2-0	2-0	2-0	3-2	3-1	4-0	2-0	3-0	3-2	2-1	5-2	2-0	0-1	0-1	3-1	1-1	*	0-1	3-0	1-2	5-1	1-1
18	Stocksbridge	2-2	0-1	3-2	2-0	2-2	3-0	1-0	3-4	3-2	2-4	2-2	1-1	0-0	2-1	0-2	1-0	0-2	*	5-0	2-0	3-0	2-1
19	Warrington T	0-4	2-3	0-0	2-2	3-1	2-2	0-0	1-1	1-2	1-1	3-1	0-4	1-1	0-1	1-1	0-0	0-3	1-2	*	0-1	1-1	1-1
20	Whitley B	3-2	2-0	3-4	0-0	1-0	1-0	1-1	2-1	0-2	0-0	0-1	1-1	1-2	0-1	1-0	1-2	1-1	1-0	5-1	*	0-0	2-2
21	Workington	2-1	1-1	0-0	4-0	3-0	4-0	1-1	0-2	1-1	4-1	1-1	0-2	0-4	2-4	3-4	0-3	1-1	2-2	0-0	2-1	*	2-0
22	Worksop T	1-0	2-2	1-2	1-0	5-0	1-1	1-1	2-3	2-0	2-0	1-1	2-1	2-2	0-1	2-0	4-0	1-0	0-1	2-0	2-0	4-0	*

Altrincham return after 18 years in the Conference

A very happy Altrincham team after defeating Farnborough Town in last season's FA Trophy. Photo: Eric Marsh.

Moss Lane, Altrincham.

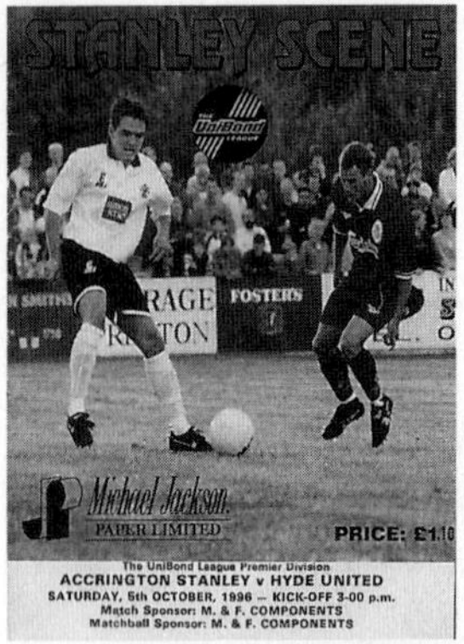

ACCRINGTON STANLEY

Formed: 1968 **Nickname:** Reds
Colours: Red/white/red
Change colours: All white with purple trim
Midweek home matchday: Tuesday **Newsline:** 0891 227 343.
Reserve Team's League: North West Alliance.

Chairman: Eric Whalley **President:** J C Prescott/J Hudson
Secretary: Philip Terry, 8 Princess Street, Colne, Lancs BB8 9AN (01286 866768).
Manager: Tony Greenwood **Asst Manager:** Phil Entwistle
Osteopath: Martin Dixon D.O.
Press Officer: John de Maine **Commercial Director:** John de Maine

PROGRAMME DETAILS
Pages: 32 **Price:** £1
Editor: P Terry/D Ellis.
(01282 866768)

GROUND - Address: Crown Ground, off Livingstone Road, Accrington (01254 383235). **Directions:** Arriving on A680 from Clayton-le-Moors Livingstone Road is on left 50 yds past Crown Hotel. From M62/M66, through town centre on A680 - Livingstone Road 500 yds on right after Victoria Hospital. One and a half miles from Accrington (BR).
Capacity: 4,000 **Cover:** 1,650 **Seats:** 700 **Floodlights:** Yes
Clubhouse: Open two nights and matchdays. Private functions. Well stocked tea sar in ground.
Club Shop: Yes, selling replica kits, sweaters, t-shirts, videos, photos etc. Contact John De Maine. **Metal Badges:** Yes
Youth League: Lancs Youth Floodlit League. **Sponsors:** Asda.

PREVIOUS - Leagues: Lancs Combination 70-78/ Cheshire County 78-82/ North West Counties 82-87.

CLUB RECORDS - Attendance: 2,270 v Gateshead 14/11/92 FA Cup 1st Rd *(10,081 v Crewe Alexandra, F.A. Cup Second Round Proper 5/12/92 - played at Ewood Park, Blackburn).* **Scorer:** David Hargreaves 318. **Appearances:** Chris Grimshaw 352. **Win:** 9-0 v Ashton Town, Lancashire Combination 75-76. **Defeat:** 1-9 v Runcorn (A), FA Cup 2nd Qual Rd replay 85-86. **Fees - Paid:** £2,250 for Bernie Hughes (Droylsen 90-91). **Received:** £50,000 for Brett Ormerod (Blackpool March 97)
Best FA Cup season: Second Rd Proper 92-93 (lost 1-6 at home to Crewe Alexandra).
League clubs defeated in FA Cup: None.
Players progressing to Football League: David Hargreaves (Blackburn R. 77), Ian Blackstone (York C.), Gus Wilson (Crewe), Glen Johnstone (Preston), Darren Lyons (Bury), Martin Clark (Crewe 92-93), Mark Wright (Wigan 93-94), Paul Collings (Bury 93-94), Brett Ormerod (Blackpool 96-97)
96-97 Captain: Jez Baldwin **96-97 P.o.Y.:** Pete Smith
96-97 Top scorer: Brett Ormerod **96-97 Players P.o.Y.:**
Local Press: Accrington Observer, Lancashire Evening Telegraph.
Local Radio Stations: Radio Lancashire, Red Rose Radio.

HONOURS: N West Counties Lg R-up 86-87, Cheshire County Lg Div 2 80-81 (R-up 79-80), Lancs Comb 73-74 77-78 (R-up 71-72 75-76, Lg Cup 71-72 72-73 73-74 76-77), George Watson Trophy 71-72 73-74 74-75, John Duckworth Trophy 85-86, Lancs Junior Cup (now ATS Trophy) R-up 85-86 96-97, FA Trophy 1st Rd 72-73 78-79 92-93, Lancs under-18 Yth Cup 89-90. N.W.All Div Cup 94-95, Anglo-Barbados Cup 1995.

Accrington Stanley: *Photo - Neil Thaler*

Accrington Stanley

Match No.	Date	Venue H/A	Competition	Opponents	Result	League Pos.	Attendance	Goalscorers (Times if known)
1	Aug 24	A	UL	Colwyn Bay	Won 2-0		381	Thornton 60, Welch 69
2	Aug 26	H	UL	Barrow	Lost 1-2		882	Welch 70
3	Aug 31	H	UL	Runcorn	Drew 2-2	11	702	Taylor 55, Welch 82
4	Sep 3	A	UL	Marine	Lost 1-2		417	Edmonds 14
5	Sep 7	A	UL	Witton Albion	Won 1-0	8	530	Rawstron 28
6	Sep 11	H	UL	Bishop Auckland	Lost 1-4	13	371	Rawstron 74
7	**Sep 14**	**H**	**FAC 1 Q**	**Ossett Albion**	**Drew 1-1**		**394**	**Moulden 42**
8	**Sep 17**	**A**	**FAC 1QR**	**Ossett Albion**	**Lost 1-2**		**344**	**Rogerson 84**
9	Sep 21	A	UL	Boston United	Lost 1-3	17	1011	Welch 61
10	Sep 25	H	UL	Lancaster City	Won 2-1		377	Welch 53, 68
11	Sep 28	A	UL	Alfreton Town	Won 3-1	11	277	Smith 51, Hirst 61, Rogerson 88
12	Oct 2	H	UL	Chorley	Lost 0-3		747	
13	Oct 5	H	UL	Hyde United	Won 3-2	10	574	Welch 8, Edmonds 56, Smith 90
14	Oct 11	A	UL	Knowsley United	Drew 1-1		87	Taylor 80
15	Oct 12	A	UL	Chorley	Drew 1-1	9	594	Ormerod 27
16	Oct 16	H	UL	Leek Town	Lost 1-2	12	415	Ormerod 86
17	Oct 22	A	UL	Blyth Spartans	Drew 1-1		602	Edmonds 83
18	Oct 26	H	UL	Alfreton Town	Won 4-2	9	501	Midwood 76, 87, Welch 79, 85
19	Nov 2	A	UL	Gainsborough Trinity	Drew 2-2	10	511	Miles 57, Midwood 75
20	Nov 9	H	UL	Emley	Drew 1-1	11	521	Ormerod 90
21	**Nov 12**	**A**	**ULC**	**Lancaster City**	**Won 2-0**		**247**	**Rawstron 16, Midwood 70**
22	Nov 16	A	UL	Winsford United	Drew 1-1	14	188	Molloy 58
23	**Nov 20**	**H**	**LFA ATS**	**Blackpool (Wrn) Rovers**	**Won 6-1**		**165**	**Smith 2, Mills 24, Ormerod 45,81,83, Welch 79**
24	Nov 23	H	UL	Witton Albion	Won 4-1	11	423	Ormerod 3, Smith 7, 50, Rawstron 31
25	**Nov 26**	**A**	**ULFC**	**Barrow**	**Lost 4-5**		**492**	**Ormerod (3) 5, 25, 70, Welch 37**
26	**Nov 30**	**A**	**FAT 3 Q**	**Bedworth United**	**Lost 0-2**		**391**	
27	**Dec 4**	**H**	**ULCC**	**Flixton**	**Won 4-1**		**155**	**Edmonds 8, Ormerod 21, 85, Greenwood 72**
28	Dec 7	H	UL	Blyth Spartans	Lost 2-3	13	513	Smith 32, Quick 52
29	Dec 11	A	UL	Bishop Auckland	Drew 1-1		173	Ormerod 45
30	Dec 14	H	UL	Guiseley	Lost 1-2	15	455	Ormerod 87
31	Dec 21	A	UL	Leek Town	Lost 1-2		363	Smith 36
32	Dec 26	H	UL	Bamber Bridge	Won 4-1	13	768	Rogerson 19, 30, Ormerod 41, 62
33	Jan 11	H	UL	Gainsborough Trinity	Lost 0-4	12	480	
34	**Jan 15**	**H**	**LFA ATS**	**Skelmerdale United**	**Won 3-1**		**152**	**Greenwood 40, Rogerson 44, Ormerod 85**
35	Jan 18	A	UL	Barrow	Lost 3-4	15	1122	Ormerod (3) 40, 42, 75 (pen)
36	Jan 25	A	UL	Lancaster City	Won 2-1	15	301	Ormerod 8, Smith 24
37	Feb 1	H	UL	Marine	Won 1-0	11	444	Ormerod 56
38	**Feb 5**	**H**	**LFA ATS**	**Barrow**	**Won 4-1**		**301**	**Greenwood 26, Ormerod 48, 90, Edmonds 59**
39	Feb 8	A	UL	Buxton	Won 3-1	11	271	Edmonds 64, Quick 86, Smith 90
40	**Feb 11**	**H**	**ULCC**	**Radcliffe Borough**	**Drew 0-0**		**244**	
41	Feb 15	A	UL	Hyde United	Lost 2-7	10	578	Ormerod 80, 82
42	Feb 22	A	UL	Emley	Lost 1-3	11	210	Smith 10
43	**Feb 26**	**H**	**L ATS FAC**	**Great Harwood Town**	**Won 2-1**		**644**	**Greenwood 22, 59**
44	Mar 1	H	UL	Winsford United	Drew 0-0	12	367	
45	**Mar 4**	**A**	**ULCC**	**Radcliffe Borough**	**Won 3-0**		**237**	**Ormorod 9, 85, Thompson 45**
46	Mar 8	A	UL	Frickley Athletic	Won 1-0	12	209	Welch 90
47	**Mar 12**	**H**	**ULCC**	**Gainsborough Trinity**	**Won 1-0**		**263**	**Smith 67**
48	Mar 15	H	UL	Boston United	Won 3-1	11	417	Welch 34, Edmonds 62, Greenwood 87
49	**Mar 18**	**A**	**ULCC**	**Gainsborough Trinity**	**Lost 1-3**		**446**	**Greenwood 15**
50	Mar 22	A	UL	Spennymoor United	Drew 0-0	12	192	
51	Mar 29	H	UL	Colwyn Bay	Won 3-1	11	432	Gelling 7, 53, Smith 39
52	Mar 31	A	UL	Bamber Bridge	Drew 1-1	11	787	Welch 62
53	Apr 5	H	UL	Buxton	Won 5-3	11	374	Robertson 24, 57 (p), Rawstron 40, Mills 55 Greenwood 67
54	Apr 12	A	UL	Guiseley	Lost 0-1		512	
55	Apr 16	H	UL	Spennymoor United	Won 2-0		321	Smith 4, 82
56	Apr 19	A	UL	Runcorn	Won 3-1	10	342	Welch 34, Smith 57, Mills 69
57	**Apr 22**	**H**	**L FAT F**	**Southport**	**Lost 0-3**		**1345**	
58	Apr 26	H	UL	Frickley Athletic	Won 4-0	11	412	Smith 10, Mills 15, og 17, Greenwood 41
59	Apr 30	H	UL	Knowsley United	Drew 1-1	11	335	Bolland 42 (og)

ACCRINGTON STANLEY PLAYING SQUAD 1997-98

Goalkeepers : Steve Berryman (Bamber B, Leyland Daf, Altrincham, Preston, Barnet, Camb.U, Exeter, Hartlepool), **Rob Mulloy** (Nelson, Crosshills, Colne Dynamoes)

Defenders: Ollie Parillon (Barrow, Morecambe, Horwich RMI, Leyland Motors), Les Thompson (Burnley, Maidstone U, Hull), Peter Mellor (Witton A, Droylsden, Barrow, Radcliffe B, Hyde U), **Chris Molloy** (Leigh RMI, Hyde U, Mossley, Altrincham, St.Helens T, Witton A, York), **Mark Rawstron** (Great Harwood T, Rossendale U, Great Harwood T, Bacup B, Rossendale U, Whitworth Valley, Bacup B, Burnley (A)), **Neil Edmonds** (Stalybridge C, East Bengal (Ind), Stalybridge C, Chorley, Rochdale, Oldham), **Jez Baldwin** (Bamber B, Fleetwood, Bamber B, Leyland Celtic), **Paul Robertson** (Witton A, Doncaster, Runcorn, Bury, Stockport, York), **Matt Moxham** (Youth team)

Midfielders: Brian Welch (Barrow, Burnley, Hebburn), **Darren Quick** (Salford C, Blackpool (T)), **Ged Walsh** (Great Harwood T, Bacup B, Rossendale U, Bacup B), **Rodger Wilkins** (Great Harwood T), **John Kennedy** (Barrow, Netherfield, Hartlepool), **Danny Mills** (Atherton Coll, Daisy Hill), **Stuart Gelling** (Lancaster, Fleetwood, Knowsley, Liverpool), **Lee George** (Bury), **Daniel Parr** (Youth team)

Forwards: Peter Smith (Barrow, Gt. Harwood, BAC Preston, Barrow), **Nigel Greenwood** (Bamber B, Halifax, Preston, Bury, Preston), **Darren Davies** (Leyland M, Preston, Leyland M), **Micky Seddon** (Clitheroe, Leyland M, Warrington, Acc. Stanley, Clitheroe, St. Helens, Horwich, Bolton), **Alan Hughes** (Blackpool Mechs, Fleetwood, Blackpool, Watford), **Paul Machiter** (Youth team)

TOWN TALK
85p
SPAR
Official Programme of
Alfreton Town F.C.
UniBond League
Premier Division
Season 1996/97
Supported by
Alfreton
Town Council
Chad
THE UniBond LEAGUE

PROGRAMME DETAILS:
Pages: 32 **Price:** £1
Editor: Chris Tacey
(01773 511012)

ALFRETON TOWN

Formed: 1959 **Nickname:** The Reds
Colours: Red & white/red/red
Change colours: Yellow/blue/yellow.
Midweek home matchday: Tuesday
Reserve League: None, Under 12s & 11s

Chairman: Sean Egan **Vice Chairman:** Dave Gregory
Secretary:
Roger Taylor, 9 Priory Rd, Alfreton, Derbyshire DE55 7JT (01773 835121).
Manager: Steve Dolby **Comm. Man.:** Elite Sporting Promotions
Press Officer: Chris Tacey (01773 511012) **Physio:** Kevin Grundy

GROUND - Address: Town Ground, North Street, Alfreton, Derbyshire (01773 830277). **Directions:** M1 junction 28 and follow A38 towards Derby for 1 mile, left onto B600, right at main road to town centre and after half a mile turn left down North Street - ground on right. Half mile from Alfreton & Mansfield Parkway (BR) station. Buses 242 & 243 from both Derby and Mansfield.
Capacity: 5,000 **Cover:** 1,000 **Seats:** 350 **Floodlights:** Yes
Clubhouse: Clubhouse on ground for members. Hot & cold food & drinks available on ground. Supporters Clubs just outside ground open 11am-4pm matchdays and 7-11pm at night.
Club Shop: Sells programmes (English & Scottish Lge + non-Lge), club badges, pens, key rings, ties, sewn-on badges. Contact Mr Brian Thorpe, 13 Oakland St., Alfreton. (01773 836251)
Sponsors: Alfreton Town council.

PREVIOUS - Leagues: Central Alliance *(before reformation 21-25)* 59-61/ Midland (Counties) *25-27* 61-82/ Northern Counties (East) 82-87.

CLUB RECORDS: - Attendance: 5,023 v Matlock Tn, Central All 60. **Scorer:** J Harrison 303. **Appearances:** J Harrison 560. **Win:** 15-0 v Loughborough, Midland Lge. 69-70. **Defeat:** 2-9 v Worksop 61, 0-8 v Bridlington 92. **Fees - Paid:** £1,000 for R Mountain (Matlock). **Received:** £7,000 for Paul Eshelby (Ilkeston Tn 96-97)
Best Season - FA Cup: 1st Rd 3rd replay 69-70. Also 1st Rd 73-74. **FA Trophy:** 1st Rd Proper 94-95
League clubs defeated in FA Cup: Lincoln 24-25, but none since club's reformation in 1959.
Players progressing to Football League: M Wright (68), A Kowalski (73), A Henson (81), Philip Greaves (86) (All Chesterfield), A Woodward (Grimsby T. 70), A Taylor (Chelsea 72), R Greenhough Chester C. 85), K Smith (Exeter C. 89).
96-97 - Captain: Phil Stafford **Top Scorer:** Phil Stafford **P.o.Y.:** Neil Pickering
Local Newspapers: Derbyshire Times, Derby Evening Telegraph, Chad, Ripley & Heanor News.
Local Radio: Radio Derby.

HONOURS: Northern Counties (E) Lg 84-85 (Lg Cup 84-85); Midland Cou Lg 69-70 73-74 76-77 (R-up 71-72 80-81 81-82), Lg Cup 71-72 72-73 73-74; Derbyshire Sen Cup 60-61 69-70 72-73 73-74 81-82 94-95, R-up 62-63 64-65 77-78 79-80 84-85 87-88 92-93, Div Cup (N) 64-65; Evans Halshaw Floodlit Cup 87-88 95-96; Cent All Lg. R-Up 63-64; NPL Div 1 R-Up 95-96.

Alfreton Town FC.

Alfreton Town

Match No.	Date	Venue H/A	Competition	Opponents	Result	League Pos.	Attendance	Goalscorers (Times if known)
1	Aug 24	H	UL	Bishop Auckland	Drew 1-1		253	Cheetham 13
2	Aug 28	A	UL	Boston United	Drew 1-1		1023	Eshelby 77
3	Aug 31	A	UL	Bamber Bridge	Drew 2-2	13	365	Cheetham 14, Pickering 86 (pen)
4	Sep 4	H	UL	Buxton	Lost 1-2		313	Haigh 43
5	Sep 7	H	UL	Lancaster City	Won 1-0	11	232	Eshelby 81
6	Sep 10	A	UL	Leek Town	Lost 0-4		320	
7	**Sep 14**	**A**	**FAC 1 Q**	**Leigh RMI**	**Lost 0-2**		**165**	
8	Sep 18	H	UL	Emley	Drew 0-0	18	249	
9	Sep 21	A	UL	Blyth Spartans	Lost 1-2		535	Eshelby 35
10	Sep 25	H	UL	Hyde United	Lost 0-3		258	
11	Sep 28	H	UL	Accrington Stanley	Lost 1-3	20	277	Stafford 78
12	**Oct 1**	**A**	**ULC**	**Lincoln United**	**Lost 1-3**		**127**	**Stafford 45**
13	Oct 5	A	UL	Winsford United	Lost 0-1	21	198	
14	Oct 9	H	UL	Witton Albion	Won 2-1		192	Eshelby 37, Weston 64
15	Oct 12	A	UL	Guiseley	Drew 1-1	20	334	McFadzean 45
16	Oct 15	A	UL	Runcorn	Lost 0-1	20	261	
17	**Oct 19**	**H**	**FAT 1 Q**	**Bilston Town**	**Drew 4-4**		**156**	**Weston 14, Stafford 56, 81, Maybury 77 (p)**
18	**Oct 22**	**A**	**FAT 1QR**	**Bilston Town**	**Lost 1-4**		**151**	**Eves 2**
19	Oct 26	A	UL	Accrington Stanley	Lost 2-4	21	501	Maybury 78, Ashley 86
20	Nov 2	A	UL	Knowsley United	Drew 1-1	20	56	Eshelby 49
21	Nov 9	A	UL	Witton Albion	Drew 1-1	20	406	Stafford 56
22	Nov12	A	UL	Gainsborough Trinity	Lost 0-3	21	453	
23	Nov 16	H	UL	Guiseley	Lost 4-5	21	283	Dawes 14, Maybury 23 (p), Pickering 81, Eshelby 89
24	Nov 23	A	UL	Marine	Drew 1-1	20	316	Dawes 25
25	**Nov 27**	**H**	**ULPC**	**Curzon Ashton**	**Drew 0-0**		**94**	
26	Dec 7	A	UL	Chorley	Lost 1-2	20	312	Frain 23
27	Dec 14	H	UL	Colwyn Bay	Won 2-1	20	218	Schofield 34, Pickering 73
28	Dec 28	A	UL	Frickley Athletic	Lost 2-7	20	490	Straw 72, Phelan 76 (pen)
29	Jan 18	H	UL	Winsford United	Drew 1-1	20	229	Stafford 5
30	Jan 25	H	UL	Marine	Lost 0-1	20	281	
31	Feb 1	A	UL	Colwyn Bay	Drew 1-1	21	287	Weston 60
32	Feb 8	H	UL	Knowsley United	Won 2-0	18	197	Frain 25, Hirst 75
33	Feb 15	A	UL	Spennymoor United	Lost 2-3	20	202	Pickering 41, Walsh 88
34	**Feb 19**	**A**	**ULPC**	**Radcliffe Borough**	**Lost 1-3**		**117**	**Stafford 32**
35	Feb 22	H	UL	Barrow	Lost 2-3	20	289	Atkinson 38, Warren 44
36	Mar 1	H	UL	Chorley	Lost 0-3	20	205	
37	Mar 5	A	UL	Bishop Auckland	Drew 2-2		127	Parkins 57, Stafford 65
38	Mar 8	A	UL	Barrow	Lost 0-3	20	807	
39	Mar 15	H	UL	Runcorn	Drew 1-1	21	175	Warren 75
40	Mar 17	A	UL	Hyde United	Lost 0-5		440	
41	Mar 22	H	UL	Bamber Bridge	Won 2-1	21	201	Stafford 50, Dawes 79
42	Mar 26	H	UL	Gainsborough Trinity	Lost 0-1		255	
43	Mar 29	H	UL	Spennymoor United	Won 2-1	21	230	Powell 1, 13
44	Mar 31	H	UL	Boston United	Lost 1-2	21	397	Clyde 84 (og)
45	Apr 8	A	UL	Buxton	Won 1-0		316	Warren 83
46	Apr 12	H	UL	Leek Town	Lost 1-1	20	401	Pickering 68 (pen)
47	Apr 15	A	UL	Lancaster City	Lost 0-1		146	
48	Apr 22	H	UL	Frickley Athletic	Won 1-0		124	Warren 1
49	Apr 26	A	UL	Emley	Lost 0-4	21	222	
50	May 3	H	UL	Blyth Spartans	Lost 1-2	21	256	Brady 53

ALFRETON TOWN PLAYING SQUAD 1997-98

Goalkeepers: Phil Yeomans (Kiveton Park, Denaby), **Paul Norton** (Eastwood T, Ilkeston, Alfreton, Gainsborough T, Worksop, Bridlington, Hartlepool, Sheffield U)

Defenders: Neil Pickering (Worksop, Sutton T, Crookes), **Lee Hirst** (Coventry, Scarborough), **Andy Glenister** (Matlock, Rossington Main, Scarborough), **Darren Schofield** (Denaby, Alfreton), **Martin Dick** (Long Eaton, Gresley R, Borrowash V, Hucknall, Long Eaton, Derby), **Nicky Phelan** (Hucknall, Hallam, Worksop), **Ian Straw** (Gresley R, Buxton, Burton A, Grimsby, Southampton), **Matthew Warren** (Gresley R, Derby)

Midfielders: Craig Weston (Belper, Gresley R, Grantham, Belper, Burton A), **Scott Elliot** (Gresley R, Long Eaton), **Darren England** (South Normanton, Blackwell MW), **Graeme Rigg** (Belper, Gresley R, Mickleover RBL, Burton A, Nottingham F), **Lee Ellis** (Buxton, Gresley R), **David Frain** (Stalybridge, Stockport, Rochdale, Sheffield U, Dronfield U), **Chris Parkins** (Shepshed D, Eastwood T, Mansfield)

Forwards: Phil Stafford (Ashfield U, Sheffield Aurora, Sutton T, Frickley, Denaby, Sheffield, Goole, Gainsborough T), **John McFadzean** (Sheffield Aurora, Sheffield, Denaby, Rotherham), **Craig Powell** (Curzon Ashton, Stalybridge, Sheffield U), **Bob Dawes** (Sheffield Aurora, Mosborough T)

PROGRAMME DETAILS
Pages: 36, **Price:** £1.20
Editors: Robert Muir

ALTRINCHAM

Formed: 1903 **Nickname:** The Robins
Colours: Red & white striped shirts, black shorts and white socks.
Change colours: Yellow/green/green
Midweek matchday: Tuesday **Reserve's League:** Bolton & Dist

Chairman: Gerry Berman **President:** Noel White
Vice-Chairman: Len Rosenfield **Vice President:** Bill King
Secretary: Graham Heathcote
Manager: John King **Asst Manager:** Graham Heathcote
Physio: Mandy Johnson **Trainer:** Les Attwood
Press Officer: Mark Harris **Commercial Manager:** Bert Green

GROUND - Address: Moss Lane, Altrincham, Cheshire WA15 8AP. Tel: 0161 928 1045. Fax: 0161 926 9934. **Directions:** M6 junction 19; A556/M56 (Manchester Airport) to junction 7; signs Hale and Altrincham; through 1st traffic lights and 3rd right into Westminster Road and continue into Moss Lane. Ground on right.
Capacity: 6,085 **Cover:** Yes **Seats:** 1,054 **Floodlights:** Yes
Clubhouse: Two snack bars on ground for pies, crisps, soft drinks and chocolate etc; bar under the stand open on match days only.
Club Shop: Yes **Youth League:** Altrincham Youth
Sponsor: Carole Nash Insurance Brokers

PREVIOUS - Leagues: Manchester League 03-11, Lancashire Combination 11-19, Cheshire County Lge 19-68, Northern Premier Lge 68-79, GMVC 79-97; **Grounds:** Pollitts Field - 1903-1910

CLUB RECORDS - Attendance: 10,275 - Altrincham Boys v Sunderland Boys - English Schools Shield 3rd Round 28.02.25: **Scorer:** Jack Swindells 252 - 1965-71: **Appearances:** John Davison 677 - 1971-86: **Win:** 9-2 v Merthyr Tydfil,Vauxhall Conference, Feb 1991: **Defeat:** Unknown: **Fees - Paid:** £10,000 to Telford United for Ken McKenna - 1990: **Received:** From Crewe Alexandra for Paul Edwards - 1988.
Players progressing to Football League: G Barrow (Wigan Athletic 81), E Bishop (Tranmere Rovers 88), F Carrodus (Manchester City 69), T Carke (Shrewsbury Town 93), P Conning (Rochdale, 86), R Dale/ N Daws/ S Johnson/ A Reid (Bury, 51 77 92 92), P Edwards (Crewe, 88), B Green (Exeter City, 62), J Hughes/ A Kilner (Stockport County, 76 90), J Kennedy/ E Robinson (West Brom, 48 57), S March (Port Vale, 59), Charlie Mitten (Halifax Town, 65), B Phillips (Middlesbrough, 54), J Rogers (Wigan Athletic, 82), P Showler (Barnet, 91), Nelson Stiffle (Chesterfield, 54), J Street (Barrow, 69), C Freeman (Doncaster Rovers 93).
Local Press: Sale & Altrincham Messenger, Sale & Altrincham Express, Manchester Evening News
Local Radio Stations: GMR (BBC), Signal Radio, Piccadilly Radio.
HONOURS: Alliance Premier League Champions 1980,1981; FA Trophy Winners 1978,1986; Bob Lord Trophy Winners 1981; N.P.L. Cup Winners 1970; N.P.L. Shield Winners 1980; Cheshire County League Winners 1966,1967; Cheshire County League Cup Winners 1951,1953,1964; Cheshire Senior Cup Winners 1905,1934,1967,1982; Manchester League Champions 1905; Cheshire Amateur Cup Winners 1904.

Altrincham

Match No.	Date	Venue H/A	Competition	Opponents	Result	League Pos.	Attendance	Goalscorers (Times if known)
1	Aug 17	H	VC	Rushden & Diamonds	Won 4-3		1037	Sharratt 38, Terry 43, og 82, Hardy 89
2	Aug 20	A	VC	Halifax Town	Drew 1-1		842	Terry 10
3	Aug 24	H	VC	Welling United	Drew 1-1		731	Hardy 56
4	Aug 26	A	VC	Gateshead	Drew 1-1	9	635	Hardy 11
5	Aug 31	A	VC	Slough Town	Won 1-0	7	1240	Pybus 90
6	Sep 3	H	VC	Morecambe	Lost 0-1		894	
7	Sep 7	A	VC	Dover Athletic	Drew 2-2	11	1114	Hardy 7, Terry 90 (pen)
8	Sep 10	H	VC	Halifax Town	Won 2-1		673	Hardy 13, Terry 60
9	Sep 14	H	VC	Woking	Drew 1-1	7	888	Terry 5
10	Sep 17	A	VC	Bromsgrove Rovers	Lost 0-4		562	
11	Sep 21	H	VC	Kidderminster Harriers	Lost 0-1	10	848	
12	Sep 28	A	VC	Telford United	Drew 0-0	11	878	
13	Oct 1	H	VC	Stalybridge Celtic	Won 1-0		692	Johnson 68
14	Oct 5	A	VC	Bath City	Won 2-1	6	619	Johnson 60, France 63
15	**Oct 8**	**A**	**SCC**	**Halifax Town**	**Won 1-0**		**879**	**Terry 107 (pen)**
16	Oct 12	H	VC	Northwich Victoria	Lost 2-3	7	1334	France 2, Hardy 46
17	Oct 19	A	VC	Hayes	Lost 1-3	12	470	Terry 57
18	**Oct 26**	**A**	**FAC 4 Q**	**Barrow**	**Drew 1-1**		**1861**	**Hardy 55**
19	**Oct 29**	**H**	**FAC 4QR**	**Barrow**	**Won 4-0**		**1141**	**France 28, Heesom 55, Hardy 53,80**
20	Nov 2	H	VC	Slough Town	Lost 0-1	12	967	
21	Nov 6	H	VC	Southport	Won 1-0	11	793	Pritchard 6
22	Nov 9	A	VC	Hednesford Town	Drew 2-2	10	1138	Hardy 40, 61
23	**Nov 16**	**A**	**FAC 1**	**P.N.E.**	**Lost 1-4**		**8286**	**Shepherd 80 (pen)**
24	Nov 23	H	VC	Farnborough Town	Lost 0-3	11	643	
25	Nov 30	A	VC	Woking	Lost 1-7	12	2701	Hardy 21
26	**Dec 7**	**H**	**SCC**	**Macclesfield Town**	**Lost 0-1**		**903**	
27	Dec 14	A	VC	Southport	Won 3-1	10	803	Doherty 60, Hardy 69, Cain 90
28	Dec 21	A	VC	Morecambe	Lost 1-2		1088	Hardy 83
29	Dec 28	H	VC	Bromsgrove Rovers	Won 3-1	11	727	Terry 3, 90, Doherty 10
30	**Jan 18**	**A**	**FAT 1**	**Gresley Rovers**	**Drew 3-3**		**927**	**Terry 32 (pen), McGoona 39, Hardy 75**
31	**Jan 21**	**H**	**FAT 1**	**Gresley Rovers**	**Won 1-0**		**1344**	**Harris 67**
32	Jan 25	H	VC	Hayes	Lost 0-2	13	746	
33	Jan 28	H	VC	Macclesfield Town	Lost 0-1	13	1285	
34	Feb 2	A	VC	Northwich Victoria	Drew 2-2	13	1292	Harris 73, Doherty 84
35	**Feb 8**	**A**	**FAT 2**	**Farnborough Town**	**Won 2-0**		**691**	**Doherty 15, Hardy 35**
36	Feb 15	A	VC	Kidderminster Harriers	Drew 1-1	14	694	McGoona 84
37	Feb 22	H	VC	Telford United	Lost 2-3	16	714	Terry 68, Doherty 89
38	**Mar 1**	**H**	**FAT 3**	**Bishop Auckland**	**Lost 0-1**		**653**	
39	Mar 8	A	VC	Stalybridge Celtic	Lost 0-1	19	725	
40	Mar 11	A	VC	Kettering Town	Lost 1-3		1039	Terry 34
41	Mar 15	H	VC	Bath City	Lost 1-3	19	648	Hardy 90
42	Mar 17	A	VC	Stevenage Borough	Lost 1-2	19	2287	Hardy 25
43	Mar 22	A	VC	Welling United	Lost 0-1	20	601	
44	Mar 25	H	VC	Hednesford Town	Drew 1-1	20	670	Hardy 40
45	Mar 29	A	VC	Farnborough Town	Drew 1-1		823	Limbert 33
46	Mar 31	H	VC	Gateshead	Lost 0-1	20	764	
47	Apr 5	A	VC	Macclesfield Town	Drew 1-1	20	2383	Terry 65
48	Apr 19	H	VC	Dover Athletic	Lost 1-2	22	646	Harris 71
49	Apr 26	H	VC	Kettering Town	Won 4-3	21	791	Terry 30(pen), Doherty 31, Harris 86, Ayorinde 88
50	Apr 29	H	VC	Stevenage Borough	Lost 1-2	22	780	Ayorinde 77
51	May 3	A	VC	Rushden & Diamonds	Lost 2-3	22	2521	McGoona 83, 89

ALTRINCHAM PLAYING SQUAD 1997-98

Goalkeepers: Matt Dickins (Stockport, Blackburn, Lincoln C, Sheffield U)

Defenders: Paul France (Burnley, Bristol C, Huddersfield), **George Shepherd** (Macclesfield, Hyde U, Bolton, Manchester C), **Barry Butler** (Barrow, Chester, Atherton T), **Ian Horrigan** (Morecambe, Barrow, Conwy U, Knowsley, Prescot, Liverpool), **Richard Brown** (USA, Stalybridge, Kettering, USA, Blackburn, Kettering, Boston U, Ilkeston, Sheffield Wed.), **Mark Maddox** (Local football)

Midfielders: Mick Carmody (Emley, Tranmere, Emley, Huddersfield), **Stuart Terry** (Bangor C), **Neil Hardy** (Northwich V, Crewe), **Marc Limbert** (Connah's Quay N, Everton)

Forwards: Ian Doyle (Local football), **Ricky Harris** (Hyde U, Runcorn, Hyde U, Altrincham, Ashton U), **Danny McGoona** (Coonah's Quay N), **Lee Kissock** (Youth team), **Paul Cain** (Local football)

BAMBER BRIDGE

Founded: 1952 **Nickname:** Brig
Colours: White/black/white.
Change Colours: All yellow
Midweek Matches: Tuesday
Reserve Teams League: North West Alliance.

President: Harold Hargreaves **Chairman:** D Allan
Vice Chairman: Brian Ginty **Secretary & Press Officer:** D G Spencer, 11 Tennyson Place, Walton-le-Dale, Preston, Lancs PR5 4TT (011772 34355).
Manager: Martin Eatough **Commercial Manager:** Nigel Webster.
Asst Manager: Dave Sargent **Physio:** A Jones
GROUND Address: Irongate, Brownedge Road, Bamber Bridge, Preston, Lancs. Tel Nos: Club Office 01772-909690; Social Club 01772-909695; Fax No. 01772-909691. 627387).
Directions: M6 Junct 29, A6 (Bamber Bridge Bypass) towards Walton-le-Dale, to r'bout, A6 London Road to next r'bout, 3rd exit signed Bamber Bridge (Brownedge Road) and first right. Ground 100 yds at end of road on left. Just over a mile from Bamber Bridge (BR).
Seats: 250 **Cover:** 800 **Capacity:** 2,500 **Floodlights:** Yes
Clubhouse: On ground, open all day Saturday matchdays, every evening and Sunday lunchtimes. Refreshment cabin on ground serves hot & cold drinks, pies, sandwiches crisps etc during matches.
Club Shop: Sells hats, cups, scarves, key rings, badges etc plus large selection of programmes. Contact Russ Rigby (01772 909690)
Sponsors: Baxi Partnership

PROGRAMME DETAILS:
Pages: 36 **Price:** £1.
Editor: Dave Rowland.
(01772 465659)

PREVIOUS - **Leagues:** Preston & District 52-90/ North West Counties 90-93.
Ground: King George V Ground, Higher Walton 1952-86.

CLUB RECORDS - **Attendance:** 2,300 v Czech Republic, Pre-Euro 96 Friendly.
Win: 8-0 v Curzon Ashton N.W.Co. 94-95.
Transfer Fee Paid: £10,000 to Horwich R.M.I.for Mark Edwards.
Transfer Fee Received: £15,000 from Wigan Athletic for Tony Back, 1995.

Best Season - **FA Vase:** Semi Final 91-92 (lost 0-2 on agg to Wimborne Tn).
FA Cup: Second Qualifying Round 92-93 (0-4 v Spennymoor United {H}).

96-97 Captain: Darren Brown **96-97 P.o.Y.:** Wayne Maddock **96-97 Top scorer:** Neil Spencer

HONOURS: Nth West Co's Lge R-up 92-93 (Div 2 91-92, F'lit Cup R-up 91-92), Preston & Dist Lge(4) 80-81 85-87 89-90 (R-up 78-79 82-83 84-85), Guildhall Cup 78-79 80-81 84-85 89-90 (R-up 77-78 79-80 87-88), Lancs Amtr Shield 81-82 (R-up 80-81 89-90), Lancastrian Brigade Cup 76-77 89-90 90-91. A.T.S.Lancs Trophy Winners 94-95, R-Up 95-96, Unibond Challenge Cup Winners 94-95, Unibond 1st Div R-Up.94-95. Unibond Northern Prem Div Champions 95-96.

Bamber Bridge's Neil Spencer with a flying header, saved by Workington's keeper Lee Copeland.
Photo - Alan Watson

Bamber Bridge

Match No.	Date	Venue H/A	Competition	Opponents	Result	League Pos.	Attendance	Goalscorers (Times if known)
1	Aug 17	H	Ch Shield	Hyde United	Lost 2-4		353	Royle 44, Doherty 65 (pen)
2	Aug 24	A	UL	Spennymoor United	Lost 1-2		237	O'Neill 84
3	Aug 26	H	UL	Chorley	Lost 0-2		768	
4	Aug 31	H	UL	Alfreton Town	Drew 2-2	20	365	Hill 42, Milligan 44
5	Sep 3	A	UL	Colwyn Bay	Lost 2-5		304	O'Neill 33, 75
6	Sep 7	H	UL	Leek Town	Lost 0-4	23	254	
7	Sep 10	A	UL	Barrow	Drew 1-1		1414	Edwards 60
8	Sep 14	A	FAC 1 Q	West Auckland	Won 3-1		87	O'Neill 56, Spencer 60, 85
9	Sep 21	A	UL	Buxton	Won 1-0	22	189	Edwards 64
10	Sep 24	H	UL	Knowsley United	Lost 1-2	22	205	O'Neill 14
11	Sep 28	H	FAC 2 Q	Stapenhill	Won 5-3		237	Edwards (3) 14, 41, 81(p), Taylor 17, Eaves 89
12	Oct 5	H	UL	Boston United	Lost 0-2	22	293	
13	Oct 8	H	UL	Barrow	Lost 1-3	22	661	Spencer 42
14	Oct 12	A	FAC 3 Q	Atherton L R	Drew 1-1		239	Edwards 60
15	Oct 15	H	FAC 3QR	Atherton L R	Won 2-0		277	Spencer 18, Edwards 75
16	Oct 19	A	UL	Hyde United	Drew 2-2	22	478	Takashashi 86, Leitch 90
17	Oct 22	A	UL	Marine	Lost 0-2	22	311	
18	Oct 26	A	FAC 4 Q	Newcastle Town	Lost 0-4		455	
19	Nov 6	A	UL	Knowsley United	Lost 0-5	22	52	
20	Nov 9	A	UL	Guiseley	Lost 0-5	22	513	
21	Nov 16	H	UL	Gainsborough Trinity	Drew 1-1	22	253	Edwards 81
22	Nov 19	H	ULC	Radcliffe Borough	Lost 1-5		116	Spencer 85
23	Nov 23	A	UL	Blyth Spartans	Lost 1-2	22	513	O'Neill 80
24	Nov 26	H	ULPC	Runcorn	Lost 2-3		168	O'Neill 51, Leitch 74
25	Nov 30	A	UL	Leek Town	Lost 1-4		302	O'Neill 44
26	Dec 7	H	UL	Emley	Lost 0-3	22	254	
27	Dec 10	H	UL	Lancaster City	Lost 0-2		323	
28	Dec 14	A	UL	Winsford United	Lost 2-4	23	102	O'Neill 21, Eaves 35
29	Dec 21	H	UL	Witton Albion	Won 4-1	22	301	Eaves 19, Helme 28, Okorie 75, Todhunter 89
30	Dec 28	A	UL	Accrington Stanley	Lost 1-4		768	Lancaster 74
31	Jan 11	H	UL	Frickley Athletic	Won 5-1	21	291	M'gan 13, Eaves 20, L'caster 55, V'kers 79, Ok'ie 89
32	Jan 18	A	FAT 1	Workington	Won 5-2		313	Spencer 23, Eaves 38, Ph'nix 27, Hill 84, Ok'ie 89
33	Jan 25	A	UL	Witton Albion	Won 3-1	22	404	Hill 23, Vickers 44, Eaves 65
34	Feb 1	H	UL	Hyde United	Lost 1-4	22	417	Lancaster 89
35	Feb 8	A	FAT 1	Ashton United	Lost 1-3		323	Leitch 21
36	Feb 15	A	UL	Emley	Won 2-1	22	212	Woodward 17, Maddock 58
37	Feb 22	H	UL	Winsford United	Lost 1-2	22	344	Brown 18
38	Mar 4	A	UL	Lancaster City	Won 3-2	21	217	Leitch 26, Milligan 38, Maddock 48
39	Mar 8	H	UL	Buxton	Drew 2-2	21	331	Lancaster 62, Maddock 64
40	Mar 11	A	UL	Chorley	Won 3-1		537	Leitch 57, Lancaster 60, Vickers 84
41	Mar 15	H	UL	Marine	Won 1-0	20	389	Brennan 20
42	Mar 18	H	UL	Spennymoor United	Lost 1-3		166	Vickers 49
43	Mar 20	H	L FA ATS T	Southport	Lost 1-3		553	Spencer 59
44	Mar 22	A	UL	Alfreton Town	Lost 1-2	20	201	Vickers 6
45	Mar 29	A	UL	Gainsborough Trinity	Won 2-0		423	O'Neill 70, Spencer 85
46	Mar 31	H	UL	Accrington Stanley	Drew 1-1	20	787	Hoskin 14
47	Apr 2	A	UL	Bishop Auckland	Lost 0-2		183	
48	Apr 5	A	UL	Frickley Athletic	Lost 0-1	21	112	
49	Apr 8	H	UL	Colwyn Bay	Lost 2-3		318	Maddock 49, Leitch 56
50	Apr 12	H	UL	Runcorn	Lost 0-5	21	375	
51	Apr 14	A	UL	Runcorn	Won 2-1		273	Brennan 36, Vickers 40
52	Apr 19	A	UL	Boston United	Drew 1-1	20	811	Maddock 25
53	Apr 22	H	UL	Blyth Spartans	Lost 0-1		226	
54	Apr 26	H	UL	Guiseley	Won 6-4	20	325	B'nan 24, Sp'cer 49, M'dock 58, H'kin 65, L'tch 84, O'N'll 86
55	May 1	H	UL	Bishop Auckland	Lost 1-2	20	281	Hoskin 30

BAMBER BRIDGE PLAYING SQUAD 1997-98

Goalkeepers: Stuart Barton (Atherton LR, Bamber B, Lancaster, Darwen, Bamber B, Fisher A)

Defenders: Stuart Phoenix (Leigh RMI, St.Helens T, Wigan), **Mark Milligan** (Youth team), **Darren Brown** (Great Harwood T, Preston), **Denis Hill** (Clitheroe, Great Harwood T), **Gordon Dugdale** (Burnley (T)), **Paul Taylor** (Bury), **Dave Burgess** (Northwich V, Carlisle, Blackpool, Grimsby, Tranmere), **Simon Woodward** (Darwen, Bamber B), **Paul Byron** (Netherfield, Lancaster, Acc. Stanley, Morecambe, Bamber B, Morecambe, Bamber B, Fleetwood, Southport, Hartlepool, Blackburn,Sunderland), **Jay Fairhurst** (Hednesford)

Midfielders: David Eaves (Morecambe, Preston), **Neil Spencer** (Atherton LR, Bamber B), **Damian Corcoran** (Preston), **Grant Leitch** (Chorley, Altrincham, Halifax, Blackpool), **Mark Brennan** (Bangor C, Marine, Ashton U, Chorley, Southport, Morecambe, Sth. Liverpool, Bootle, Sth.Liverpool), **Stuart Todhunter** (Barrow, Workington, Barrow, Preston, Workington), **Kelechi Okerie** (Sarpsborg (Nor), Ashton U, Kalmar IF (Swe), St.Mirren, Grimsby, Doncaster)

Forwards: Mark Edwards (Horwich RMI, Ashton U, Stalybridge C, Horwich RMI, Witton A, Chorley, Horwich RMI, St.Helens T), **Steve O'Neill** (Altrincham,Bootle, Marine), **Wayne Maddock** (Morecambe, Barrow, Netherfield, Marine, BAC Preston, Leyland Motors), **David Ward** (Blackpool), **Ashley Hoskin** (Barrow, Acc. Stanley, Burnley Bank Hall, Wrexham, Burnley), Matt Helme (Witton A,Skelmersdale, Burscough, Warrington, Fleetwood, Burscough), Dave Lancaster (Rochdale, Bury, Rochdale, Chesterfield, Blackpool, Colne D), Ian Vickers (Southport, Blackpool)

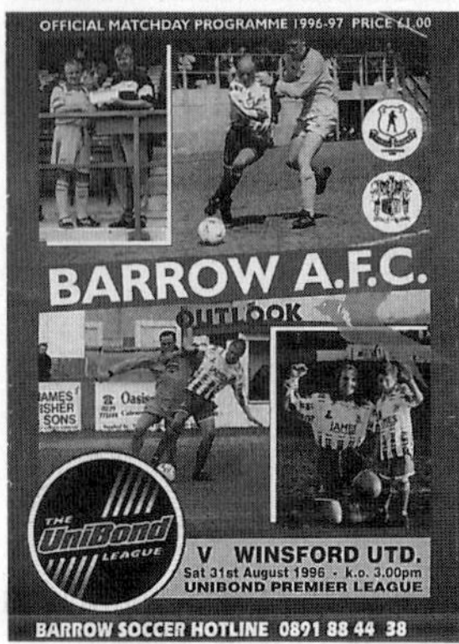

PROGRAMME DETAILS:
Pages: 24 **Price:** £1
Editor: D Gardner

BARROW

Founded: 1901 **Nickname:** Bluebirds
Colours: Blue & White Hoops/Blue/Blue & white hoops.
Change colours: Green white trim/Green/Green.
Midweek home matchday: Tuesday
Reserve League: Bolton Combination

Barrow A.F.C. Hotline:
0891 88 44 38

Chairman: Stephen Vaughan **President:**
Secretary: Pat Brewer, c/o the club 01229 820346 or 01229 828913 (H)
Press Off.: Phil Yelland, 83 Camus Ave., Edinburgh EH10 6QY 0131 445 1010
Manager: Owen Brown

GROUND Address: Holker Street Ground, Wilkie Rd, Barrow-in-Furness, Cumbria LA14 5UH (01229 820346/823839). Commercial Office: (at ground) 01229 823061 - Manager Mrs Linda Barker.
Directions: M6 to junction 36, A590 to Barrow, enter Barrow on Park Road and after about 2 miles turn left into Wilkie Rd - ground on right.B.R.1/4 mile .
Capacity: 3,500 **Cover:** 1,200 **Seats:** 1000+. **Floodlights:** Yes
Clubhouse: Barrow Sports & Leisure centre next to ground. Open matchdays and Functions only. Snack bars on grd.
Club Shop: Yes Contact: Linda Barker. **Metal Badges:** Yes
Sponsors:
PREVIOUS - Leagues: Lancs Comb 01-21/Football Lge 21-72/N Prem 72-79 83-84 86-89/GMVC 79-83 84-86 89-92. **Grounds:** The Strawberry & Little Park, Roose.

CLUB RECORDS - Record Attendance: 6,002 v Enfield, FA Trophy Semi-Final, Apr 88. **Goalscorer:** Colin Cowperthwaite 282 (Dec '77-Dec '92). **Appearances:** Colin Cowperthwaite 704. **Defeat:** 1-10 v Hartlepools Utd, Football Lge Div 4, 1959. **Win:** 12-0 v Cleator, FA Cup 1920. **Transfer Fees - Paid:** £9,000 for Andy Whittaker (Ashton Utd, July 94). **Received:** £40,000 for Kenny Lowe (Barnet, Jan 91). **Best Season - FA Cup:** Third Round Proper on nine occasions including once as a non-League club (90-91, lost 0-1 at Bolton Wanderers).
Players progressing to Football League: I McDonald, N McDonald, J Laisby, B Diamond, F Gamble, B Knowles, G Skivington, P Byron, L Edwards, K Lowe, M Dobie, T Rigby, N Doherty.
96-97 Captain: **96-97 P.o.Y.:** **96-97 Top scorer:**
Local Press: North West Evening Mail, Barrow & West Cumberland Advertiser
Local Radio Stations: BBC Radio Furness, BBC Radio Cumbria, Red Rose, Bay Radio.
HONOURS: FA Trophy 89-90 (SF 87-88), Nth Prem Lge 83-84 88-89 (Lge Cup R-up 87-88, Lge Shield 84-85), Bord Lord Trophy R-up 90-91, Cumbrian Cup 82-83 83-84 (R-up 84-85), Lancs Floodlit Cup R-up 86-87, Lancs Sen Cup 54-55 (R-up 51-52 65-66 66-67 69-70), Lancs Challenge Trophy 80-81 (R-up 81-82 84-85), Lancs Comb 20-21 (R-up 13-14, Div 2 R-up 04-05 10-11).

Barrow AFC

Barrow

Match No.	Date	Venue H/A	Competition	Opponents	Result	League Pos.	Attendance	Goalscorers (Times if known)
1	Aug 24	H	UL	Knowsley United	Drew 1-1		1332	Morton 75 (pen)
2	Aug 26	A	UL	Accrington Stanley	Won 2-1		882	Morton 11, Green 67
3	Aug 31	H	UL	Winsford United	Won 2-1	4	1259	Edwards 30 (og), Morton 67
4	Sep 3	A	UL	Chorley	Won 3-1		867	Morton 4 (pen), 74, Green 88
5	Sep 7	A	UL	Guiseley	Lost 1-3	4	410	Humphreys 73
6	Sep 10	H	UL	Bamber Bridge	Drew 1-1	2	1414	Morton 90
7	Sep 14	A	UL	Colwyn Bay	Won 2-1	2	394	Green 1, Morton 4
8	Sep 21	A	UL	Hyde United	Lost 0-1	5	653	
9	Sep 24	A	UL	Marine	Drew 1-1	4	504	O'Keefe 74
10	Sep 28	H	UL	Witton Albion	Won 3-1	4	1132	Ford 16, O'Keefe 23, Green 37
11	Oct 5	H	UL	Bishop Auckland	Lost 0-1	7	1229	
12	Oct 8	A	UL	Bamber Bridge	Won 3-1	4	661	McGuire 64, 78, Morton 72 (pen)
13	Oct 12	A	UL	Blyth Spartans	Lost 0-1	4	587	
14	Oct 15	H	UL	Chorley	Won 3-0	4	1015	Ford 5, Brown 65, Morton 75
15	Oct 19	H	UL	Emley	Won 3-0	2	1230	Green 18, Morton 33, 46
16	Oct 23	A	UL	Knowsley United	Won 3-0	2	228	Morton 12, Hennigan 30, Parker 36
17	**Oct 26**	**H**	**FAC 4 Q**	**Altrincham**	**Drew 1-1**		**1861**	**McDonald 29**
18	**Oct 29**	**A**	**FAC 4QR**	**Altrincham**	**Lost 0-4**		**1141**	
19	Nov 2	H	UL	Frickley Athletic	Won 2-0	2	1152	Doolan 18, Green 36
20	Nov 9	A	UL	Spennymoor United	Won 2-1	1	329	Doolan 61 (pen), Brown 84
21	Nov 12	H	UL	Marine	Lost 0-1	1	1452	
22	Nov 16	A	UL	Emley	Lost 0-3	1	415	
23	**Nov 19**	**H**	**ULC**	**Gretna**	**Won 1-0**		**472**	**McDonald 35**
24	Nov 23	H	UL	Boston United	Lost 0-1	3	972	
25	**Nov 26**	**H**	**ULPC**	**Accrington Stanley**	**Won 5-4**		**492**	**M'ton (3) 47(p), 60, 78, H'phreys 37, H'gan 90**
26	**Nov 30**	**A**	**FAT 3 Q**	**Bradford (PA)**	**Drew 1-1**		**425**	**Foreman 79**
27	**Dec 3**	**H**	**FAT 3QR**	**Bradford (PA)**	**Lost 0-1**		**620**	
28	Dec 7	A	UL	Runcorn	Drew 0-0	5	395	
29	Dec 14	H	UL	Buxton	Drew 0-0	5	786	
30	Dec 21	A	UL	Gainsborough Trinity	Lost 0-3	6	457	
31	Dec 28	A	UL	Bishop Auckland	Won 1-0	5	282	Green 3
32	Jan 4	H	UL	Leek Town	Won 3-0	4	1101	Fahy 38, Marginson 57, O'Keefe 89
33	Jan 11	A	UL	Winsford United	Won 2-1	4	183	Green 34, McAuley 55
34	Jan 18	H	UL	Accrington Stanley	Won 4-3	2	1122	Green 10, 45, Morton 54, Dollan 69 (p)
35	Jan 21	H	UL	Lancaster City	Won 3-0	1	1142	Parker 33, Morton 51, Fahy 69
36	Jan 25	H	UL	Runcorn	Drew 1-1	1	1288	Humphreys 67
37	Feb 1	A	UL	Boston United	Won 5-3	1	1487	Morton (4) 17, 78, 85, 90, Grugel 55
38	**Feb 5**	**A**	**LFA ATS**	**Accrington Stanley**	**Lost 1-3**		**301**	**Marginson 8**
39	Feb 8	H	UL	Gainsborough Trinity	Drew 2-2	2	1096	Morton 12, Cooper 45
40	Feb 11	A	UL	Lancaster City	Lost 0-1	2	605	
41	Feb 15	H	UL	Guiseley	Drew 1-1	2	968	Green 76
42	Feb 22	A	UL	Alfreton Town	Won 3-2	2	289	Green 55, McCauley 67, Marginson 88
43	Mar 1	A	UL	Buxton	Won 1-0	2	223	Green 6
44	**Mar 4**	**A**	**ULPC**	**Runcorn**	**Lost 1-3**		**236**	**Fahy 26**
45	Mar 8	H	UL	Alfreton Town	Won 3-0	2	867	Cooper 5, 77, Glenston 19 (og)
46	Mar 22	H	UL	Blyth Spartans	Drew 2-2	2	977	Hennigan 45, Green 63
47	Mar 29	A	UL	Witton Albion	Drew 2-2		480	Marginson 15, Green 31
48	Mar 31	H	UL	Hyde United	Drew 1-1	2	1165	Morton 81
49	Apr 5	H	UL	Colwyn Bay	Won 1-0	2	871	Morton 29
50	Apr 12	A	UL	Frickley Athletic	Won 2-0	2	195	Marginson 60, Doherty 90
51	Apr 19	H	UL	Spennymoor United	Won 1-0	2	896	Morton 47
52	May 3	A	UL	Leek Town	Lost 1-2	5	733	Parker 65

BARROW PLAYING SQUAD 1997-98

Goalkeepers: Steve Farrelly (Rotherham, Macclesfield, Knowsley, Chester)

Defenders: Jeff Parker (Northwich V, Brunei Darussalam, Northwich V, Crewe, Everton), **Danny Vaughan** (Nantwich, Wigan, Crewe, Liverpool), **Carl MacAuley** (Lancaster, Witton Alb, Vauxhall GM, Prescot Cables, Bromborough Pool), **JohnDoolan** (Wigan, Knowsley), **Andy Lee** (Knowsley, Halifax, Runcorn, Telford, Altrincham, Witton Alb, Colne D, Telford, Altrincham, Runcorn, Camb. U, Tranmere, Stafford R, Bangor C, Wrexham, Liverpool)

Midfielders: Stuart Humphries (Atherton LR, Ellesmere Port, St. Helens T), **Jimmy Brown** (Witton A, Runcorn, Morecambe, Vauxhall GM, Bootle), **Gerard Hennigan** (Everton), **Ian Leeming** (Youth team), **Steve Eyre** (Southport, Runcorn, Chorley, Stockport, Wigan, Burnley)

Forwards: Neil Morton (Altrincham, Wigan, Chester, Northwich V, Crewe), **Andy Green** (Altrincham, Knowsley U, Morecambe, Macclesfield T, Binche (Belg), South Liverpool, Bootle), **Chris Speak** (Blackpool), **Lee O'Keefe** (Holker OB, Workington, Morecambe, Workington), **Karl Marginson** (Chorley, Macclesfield, Rotherham, Ashton U, Droylsden, Curzon Ashton, Blackpool, Stockport), **Lee Cooper** (Burscough, Stockbridge, Ashton U, Knowsley, Northwich V, St. Helens, Southport, Worcester, St. Helens, Maghull)

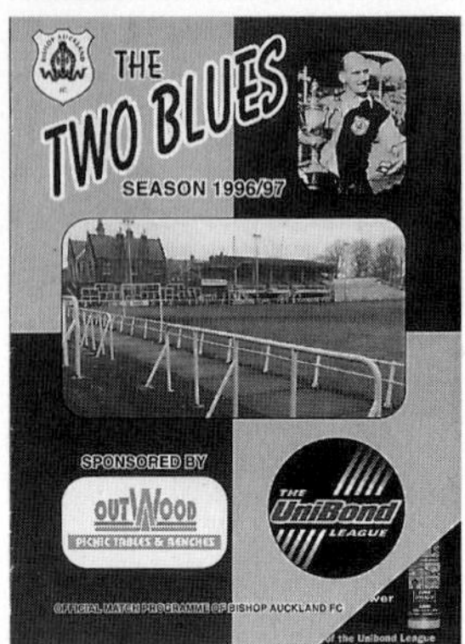

PROGRAMME DETAILS:
Pages: 28 **Price:** £1.
Editor: Bobby Wake
(01388 609428)

BISHOP AUCKLAND

Formed: 1886 **Nickname:** Bishops
Colours: Sky & Navy blue
Change colours: Red & white.
Midweek home matchday: Wednesday.
Reserve Team: None.

Chairman: **President:** B T Newton
Vice-Chairman: C Backhouse **Secretary:** Tony Duffy, 8 Ennerdale Grove, West Auckland, Co.Durham. DL14 9LN. (01388 833410)
Manager: Tony Lee **Asst Mgr:** Tony Boylan
Press Officer: Secretary **Physio:** Dave Nesbitt
Commercial Manager: Brian Collinson
GROUND Address: Kingsway, Bishop Auckland, County Durham (01388 603686). **Directions:** A1 to Scotch Corner (Turn off A68 from A1) or M6 Junc A38 (A685 to Brough), then follow signs to Bishop Auckland. Ground in town centre (rear of Newgate Str). Half mile from station.
Capacity: 3,500 **Cover:** 2,000 **Seats:** 600 **Floodlights:** Yes
Clubhouse: Open every lunchtime and evening noon-4 & 7-11pm, and Saturday matchdays noon-4 & 5-6 & 7-11pm. Large bar, pool, juke box. Also snack bar within grounds sells hot & cold pies & drinks.
Club Shop: Yes **Metal Badges:** £3.00. **Sponsors:**

PREVIOUS - Leagues: N East Counties 1889-90/ Northern Alliance 1890-91/ Northern 1893-1988.
CLUB RECORDS - Attendance: 17,000 v Coventry, FA Cup 2nd Rd 6/12/52. **Appearances:** Bob Hardisty. **Win:** 13-0. **Defeat:** 1-7. **Fees - Paid:** £2,000. **Received:** £9,000 for David Laws. **Best Season - FA Cup:** 4th Rd 54-55 (lost 1-3 at home to York City). **League clubs beaten in FA Cup:** Crystal Palace, Ipswich 54-55, Tranmere 56-57.
Players progressing to Football League: B Paisley (Liverpool), F Richardson & S O'Connell (Chelsea 46 & 54), R Hardisty & K Williamson (Darlimgton 46 & 52), W Shergold (Newport 47), N Smith (Fulham 48), R Steel & K Murray (Darlington 50), A Adey (Doncaster 50), F Palmer & A Stalker (Gateshead 51 & 58), A Sewell (Bradford City 54), G Barker (Southend 54), J Major (Hull 55), H Sharratt (Oldham 56), F McKenna (Leeds 56), J Barnwell (Arsenal 56), D Lewis (Accrington Stanley 57), C Cresswell (Carlisle 58), W Bradley (Man Utd), L Brown (Northampton), P Baker (Southampton), M Gooding (Rotherham), K Nobbs & A Toman (Hartlepool), P Hinds (Dundee Utd).
96-97 Capain: Dave Lobb **96-97 P.o.Y.:** D Lobb/ N Peverell **96-97 Top scorer:** Nick Peverell 40
Local Newspapers: Northern Echo, Evening Gazette, N'castle Journal.
Local Radio Stations: Radio Cleveland, Radio Tees, Radio Metro, Radio Newcastle.
HONOURS: FA Amateur Cup 1895-96, 1899-1900 13-14 20-22 34-35 38-39 54-56 57-58 (R-up(8) 01-02 05-06 10-11 14-15 45-46 49-51 53-54); FA Trophy QF 78-79 88-89 96-97; Northern Lg(19) 1898-99 1900-02 08-10 11-12 20-21 30-31 38-39 46-47 49-52 53-56 66-67 84-86, R-up (17) 78-79 86-87 96-97, Lg Cup(7) 49-51 53-55 59-60 66-67 75-76), D'ham Chall Cup 1891-92 98-99 1930-31 38-39 51-52 55-56 61-62 66-67 84-85 85-86 87-88 96-97, HFS Loans Lg Div 1 R-up 88-89. Plus tournaments in Isle of Man, Spain, Portugal etc.

Bishop Auckland: Back Row (L-R); Ian Lowe, Dave McKinlay, Nick Scaife, Chris Lynch, Nick Peverell, Simon Bishop, Michael Ward, Mark Taylor, Lee Ellison, Tony Lee (Mgr), Tony Boylan (Asst Mgr). Front Row; Alan Gray, George Adams, David Lobb, Michael Parkinson, David Bayles, David Gallagher, Dave Nesbitt (Physio).

Bishop Auckland

Match No.	Date	Venue H/A	Competition	Opponents	Result	League Pos.	Attendance	Goalscorers (Times if known)
1	Aug 24	A	UL	Alfreton Town	Drew 1-1		253	Peverell 39
2	Aug 31	A	UL	Hyde United	Drew 1-1	16	615	Peverell 15
3	Sep 4	H	UL	Blyth Spartans	Lost 1-3		375	Dixon 55
4	Sep 7	H	UL	Buxton	Won 5-0	14	205	Peverell (3) 20, 79, 81, Webb 45, Dixon 70
5	Sep 11	A	UL	Accrington Stanley	Won 4-1		371	Peverell (3) 59, 62, 82, Banks 43
6	Sep 14	H	FAC 1 Q	Pickering Town	Won 3-1		187	Carter 36, Bolam 57, 61
7	Sep 17	A	UL	Blyth Spartans	Drew 0-0		580	
8	Sep 21	H	UL	Winsford United	Won 2-0	7	174	West 43, Lobb 77
9	Sep 25	H	UL	Frickley Athletic	Drew 2-2	9	142	West 75, Banks 77
10	Sep 28	A	FAC 2 Q	Halifax Town	Won 4-1		628	Bolam 3, Scaife 15, Dixon 45, Milroy 69
11	Oct 2	H	UL	Guiseley	Won 1-0		245	Milroy 74
12	Oct 5	A	UL	Barrow	Won 1-0	4	1229	Peverell 87
13	Oct 12	H	FAC 3 Q	Consett	Lost 0-1		362	
14	Oct 14	A	UL	Emley	Lost 0-2		258	
15	Oct 19	H	UL	Marine	Drew 2-2	12	204	Bayles 44, Waller 45
16	Oct 23	H	UL	Emley	Lost 0-1		172	
17	Oct 26	A	UL	Winsford United	Won 2-1	6	180	Milroy 22, Bayles 51
18	Oct 30	H	DSC	Seaham Red Star	Won 5-1		83	Peverell 21, Scaife 37, Bayles 44, Sinclair 77, 80
19	Nov 2	H	UL	Colwyn Bay	Won 3-1	6	193	Peverell 48, 70, Dixon 71
20	Nov 5	A	USC	Frickley Athletic	Lost 0-1		86	
21	Nov 9	A	UL	Chorley	Drew 1-1	7	411	Scaife 69
22	Nov 10	H	UL	Leek Town	Drew 1-1	10	226	Peverell 24
23	Nov 20	H	DSC	Bolden C.A.	Won 8-1		56	Lynch, Bayles, Jenson, P'rell (3), McK'ley (2)
24	Nov 23	A	UL	Gainsborough Trinity	Won 1-0	8	401	Adams 85
25	Nov 30	H	FAT 3 Q	Stocksbridge P.S.	Won 2-1		191	Waller 45, Milroy 90
26	Dec 11	H	UL	Accrington Stanley	Drew 1-1	9	173	Gallagher 71
27	Dec 14	A	UL	Knowsley United	Won 5-0	9	50	Ellison (3) 39, 43, 56, Peverell 65, 68
28	Dec 21	H	UL	Runcorn	Won 2-0	5	225	Gallagher 82, Milroy 86
29	Dec 28	H	UL	Barrow	Lost 0-1	8	282	
30	Jan 13	A	DSC	Durham City	Won 2-1		310	Peverell 76, 82
31	Jan 18	A	FAT 1	Spennymoor United	Won 2-0		482	Bayles 30, 69
32	Jan 25	A	UL	Buxton	Drew 1-1	10	173	Peverell 15
33	Feb 1	H	UL	Gainsborough Trinity	Drew 3-3	10	185	Ellison 47, 55, McKinley 84
34	Feb 8	H	FAT 2	Northwich Victoria	Won 3-2		705	Ellison 19, 83, Waller 66
35	Feb 10	H	DSC	West Auckland	Won 6-1		180	Peverell (4) 15, 20, 34, 45, Ellison 10, McKinley 65
36	Feb 15	H	UL	Chorley	Lost 1-3	11	211	Waller 59 (pen)
37	Feb 22	A	UL	Marine	Won 3-2	10	342	Peverell 26, 77, Lobb 32
38	Feb 25	A	UL	Frickley Athletic	Won 4-0	9	129	Adams 17, Ellison 73, 87, Peverell 83
39	Mar 1	A	FAT 3	Altrincham	Won 1-0		653	Peverell 59 (pen)
40	Mar 5	H	UL	Alfreton Town	Drew 2-2	9	127	Ellison 15, Parkinson 40
41	Mar 11	A	UL	Guiseley	Drew 0-0		254	
42	Mar 13	H	UL	Lancaster City	Won 4-2		142	Adams 35, Ellison (3) 59, 70, 85
43	Mar 15	H	UL	Witton Albion	Won 5-0	9	164	Lobb 4, Woodhouse 7, McKinlay 16, Bayles 22, Peverill 69
44	Mar 16	H	UL	Boston United	Won 1-0	9	144	Milner 39
45	Mar 18	A	UL	Witton Albion	Drew 1-1	7	232	Rowntree 45
46	Mar 22	H	FAT Q F	Gloucester City	Drew 0-0		832	
47	Mar 25	A	FAT QFR	Gloucester City	Lost 3-4		1829	Ellison 35, Peverill 74, Lynch 76
48	Mar 29	A	UL	Lancaster City	Lost 1-2	9	245	Peverill 21
49	Mar 31	H	DSC Final	Spennymoor United	Won 2-0		450	Bayles 19, Ellison 40
50	Apr 2	H	UL	Bamber Bridge	Won 2-0		183	Parkinson 39, Peverill 83
51	Apr 5	A	UL	Leek Town	Lost 0-1	9	197	
52	Apr 9	H	UL	Hyde United	Won 3-0	6	122	Bayles 39, Peverill 44, Parkinson 55
53	Apr 19	H	UL	Knowsley United	Won 4-1	7	151	Gray 45, Peverill 38, 90, Ellison 69
54	Apr 21	H	UL	Spennymoor United	Won 4-1		389	Peverill 4, 55, Ellison 45, 87
55	Apr 26	A	UL	Runcorn	Won 3-1	6	191	Adams 8, Ward 27, Bayles 83
56	Apr 29	A	UL	Spennymoor United	Won 5-1		307	Woodhouse (3) 6, 12, 87, Todd 22 (og), Peverill 34
57	May 1	A	UL	Bamber Bridge	Won 2-1		281	Lynch 20, Peverill 69
58	May 3	A	UL	Boston United	Drew 1-1	2	706	Lee 58

BISHOP AUCKLAND PLAYING SQUAD 1997-98

Goalkeepers: Simon Bishop (Northallerton, Whitby, Guisborough, Newcastle U)

Defenders: Steve West (Youth team), **Mark Foster** (Willington, B Auckland, Ferryhill, Shildon), **David McKinlay** (Bradford C, Middlesbrough), **David Lobb** (Hartlepool T, Peterlee Newtown), **Michael Waller** (Northallerton, B Auckland, Northallerton, South Bank, Middlesbrough), **Nick Scaife** (Gateshead, Halifax, York, Whitby), **Chris Lynch** (Hartlepool), **Alan Gray** (Doncaster), **Michael Driscoll** (Norton, Easington CW, Guisborough, Doncaster, Middlesbrough (J)), **Mark Taylor** (Netherfield, Northampton, Fulham, Middlesbrough)

Midfielders: George Adams (Shildon), **Andrew Banks** (Billingham Syn., Ipswich), **Steve Carter** (Jarrow Roofing, B Auckland, Durham, Scarborough, Durham,Northallerton, N Shields, Scarborough, Manchester U), David Gallagher (Guisborough, Marske U), Mike Parkinson (Seaham RS, Newcastle U), **David Bayles** (Shildon, Consett, West Auckland, B.Auckland), **Tony Lee** (Guisborough, Whitby, B.Auckland, Ferryhill, Northallerton, Newcastle U), **Keith Oliver** (Hartlepool)

Forwards: Paul Dobson (Gateshead, Darlington, Lincoln, Scarborough, Doncaster, Torquay, Horden CW, Hartlepool, Newcastle U), **Stuart Jewson** (Tow Law, Inglewood Falcons (Aust), Middlesbrough), **Nick Peverell** (York, Hartlepool, Middlesbrough), **Jon Bolam** (Chester-le-Street, Walkers), **Jon Milroy** (West Auckland, Blyth S, Cockfield, Dunston Fed., Ferryhill), **Lee Ellison** (Halifax, Crewe, Leicester C, Darlington), **Michael Ward** (Billingham Syn., Nth Ormesby, Northallerton)

PROGRAMME DETAILS:
Pages: 64 **Price:** 80p
Editor: Brian Grey.
(011912 745305)

BLYTH SPARTANS

Formed: 1899 **Nickname:** Spartans
Colours: Green & white stripes
Change colours: Claret
Midweek Matches: Tuesday
Reserve Team's League:

Chairman: Mike Mitchell
Secretary: Scott Sawyer, 53 Ninth Avenue, Blyth, Northumberland NE24 2TE (01670 355669).
Press Officer: Ken Teasdale
Manager: John Burridge **Assistant Manager:** Dereck Bell

GROUND Address: Croft Park, Blyth, Northumberland. (01670) 354818
Directions: Through Tyne tunnel heading north on A19, take Cramlington turn, follow signs for Newsham/Blyth. Right fork at railway gates in Newsham, down Plessey Rd, ground can be seen on left behind chip shop and before Masons Arms. Buses X24, X25, X26, X1 from Newcastle.
Seats: 300 **Cover:** 1,000 **Capacity:** 6,000 **Floodlights:** Yes
Clubhouse: Open every night plus Saturday & Sunday lunch & matchdays. Available for wedding functions. Pies & sandwiches available.
Souvenir Shop: Sells hats, pennants, programmes etc. Contact: Kevin Little (01670 362168) or Stan Watson (01912-739138)
Sponsors: Federation Brewery.

PREVIOUS - Leagues: Northumberland 01-07/ Northern Alliance 07-13/ 46-47/ North Eastern 13-14 19-39 47-58 62-64/ Northern Combination 45-46/ Midland 58-60/ Northern Counties 60-62/ Northern 62-94.
CLUB RECORDS - Attendance: **Win:** **Defeat:** **Appearances:** **Goal Scorer:** **Transfer Fee - Received:** £30,000 for Les Mutrie (Hull City) 1979. **Paid:** **Best Season - FA Trophy:** Quarter-Final replay 79-80 82-83. **FA Amateur Cup:** Semi-Final 71-72. **FA Cup:** 5th Rd replay 77-78 (lost to Wrexham). 1st Round on 46 occasions.
League Clubs defeated in FA Cup: Ashington, Gillingham 22-23, Crewe Alexandra, Stockport County 71-72, Chesterfield, Stoke City 77-78, Bury 95-96.
Players progressing to Football League: William McGlen (Manchester Utd 46), Joe Roddom (Chesterfield 48), Henry Mills (Huddersfield 48), John Allison (Reading 49), James Kelly (Watford 49), Robert Millard (Reading 49), Jim Kerr (Lincoln 52), James Milner (Burnley 52), John Hogg (Portsmouth 54), John Allison (Chesterfield 55), John Inglis (Gateshead 57), John Longland (Hartlepool 58), Alan Shoulder (Newcastle 79), Les Mutrie (Hull City 79), Steve Carney (Newcastle 80), Craig Liddle (Middlesbrough 94), Paul O'Connor (Hartlepool 95).
Local Newspapers: Newcastle Journal & Evening Chronicle.
96-97 Captain: John Gamble **Top Scorer:** Stuart Young **P.o.Y.:** Michael Farrey

HONOURS: Nth Lg(10) 72-73 74-76 79-84 86-88 94-95, (R-up 71-72 73-74 77-78 84-85 94-95), Lg Cup(5) 72-73 77-79 81-82 91-92 94-95, Presidents Cup 96-97; Nth Eastern Lg 35-36 (R-up 22-23, Lg Cup 49-50 54-55); Northumberland Lg 03-04; Northern All. 08-09 12-13 (R-up 46-47); Northumberland Snr Cup (19); Shields Gazette Cup 95-96.

Blyth Spartan FC:

Blyth Spartans

Match No.	Date	Venue H/A	Competition	Opponents	Result	League Pos.	Attendance	Goalscorers (Times if known)
1	Aug 24	A	UL	Marine	Won 3-0		402	Raffell 31, Young 61, 83
2	Aug 26	H	UL	Spennymoor United	Won 2-0		509	Henderson 34, 35
3	Aug 31	H	UL	Witton Albion	Drew 0-0	2	587	
4	Sep 4	A	UL	Bishop Auckland	Won 3-1		375	Young (3) 35, 80, 86
5	Sep 7	H	UL	Hyde United	Won 2-1	2	687	Young 18, Switzer 90 (og)
6	Sep 14	A	UL	Runcorn	Lost 0-1	3	454	
7	Sep 17	H	UL	Bishop Auckland	Drew 0-0		580	
8	Sep 21	H	UL	Alfreton Town	Won 2-1	2	535	Young 37, Bond 71
9	Sep 24	A	UL	Spennymoor United	Won 2-0	2	319	Pyle 37, Young 40
10	Sep 28	A	UL	Colwyn Bay	Lost 0-3	2	339	
11	Oct 5	H	UL	Chorley	Lost 1-3	2	641	Gamble 38
12	Oct 8	A	UL	Lancaster City	Lost 0-1	2	228	
13	Oct 12	H	UL	Barrow	Won 1-0	2	587	Young 63
14	Oct 19	A	UL	Gainsborough Trinity	Won 1-0	3	474	Henderson 49
15	Oct 22	H	UL	Accrington Stanley	Drew 1-1	4	602	Locker 11
16	**Oct 26**	**A**	**FAC 4 Q**	**Whitby Town**	**Lost 1-2**		**832**	**Henderson 23**
17	**Oct 30**	**H**	**ULC**	**Emley**	**Lost 1-2**		**336**	**Young 67**
18	Nov 2	A	UL	Buxton	Won 2-1	4	194	Walker 21, Raffell 67
19	Nov 9	H	UL	Boston United	Lost 1-2	5	569	Walker 84
20	Nov 12	A	UL	Frickley Athletic	Drew 2-2	3	153	Walker 19, Cole 72
21	Nov 16	H	UL	Buxton	Won 5-0	3	374	Moat (3) 17, 61, 73, Farrey 26, Bernabia 28
22	Nov 23	H	UL	Bamber Bridge	Won 2-1	1	513	Moat 34, Henderson 90
23	**Nov 26**	**A**	**ULPC**	**Spennymoor United**	**Drew 2-2**		**214**	**Todd 24 (pen), Young 44**
24	**Nov 30**	**H**	**FAT 3 Q**	**Bilston Town**	**Won 7-3**		**436**	**Farrey, Pyle (3) 9, 36, 69, Young (3) 39, 54, 81**
25	Dec 7	A	UL	Accrington Stanley	Won 3-2	1	513	Young 27, Moat 41, Henderson 85
26	**Dec 11**	**H**	**ULPC**	**Spennymoor United**	**Won 2-1**		**389**	**Young 44, Moat 49**
27	Dec 14	H	UL	Leek Town	Lost 0-1	4	732	
28	Dec 21	A	UL	Winsford United	Won 2-0	3	188	Todd 59 (pen), Young 66
29	Dec 26	H	UL	Guiseley	Drew 1-1	3	583	Pyle 19
30	Jan 4	H	UL	Knowsley United	Won 6-0	3	515	Bond 6, 26, Young (3) 31, 77, 78, Farrey
31	Jan 11	A	UL	Boston United	Lost 1-2	3	1283	34
32	**Jan 18**	**H**	**FAT 1**	**Grantham Town**	**Drew 1-1**		**667**	Moat 85
33	**Jan 21**	**A**	**FAT 1 R**	**Grantham Town**	**Drew 1-1***		**687**	**Moat 25**
34	Jan 25	H	UL	Winsford United	Lost 1-2	4	648	**Pyle 53**
35	**Jan 27**	**A**	**FAT 1R2**	**Grantham Town**	**Lost 1-3***		**874**	Young 18
36	Feb 1	A	UL	Guiseley	Lost 1-2	5	331	**Bond 17**
37	**Feb 11**	**A**	**NSC**	**Morpeth Town**	**Lost 2-6**		**410**	Page 67
38	Feb 15	H	UL	Runcorn	Won 3-2	5	520	**Todd 48, Pyle 72**
39	**Feb 18**	**H**	**ULPC**	**Worksop Town**	**Drew 2-2**		**336**	McGarole (3) 20, 36, 64
40	Feb 22	A	UL	Leek Town	Lost 0-4	6	582	**Walker 67, McGargle 69**
41	Mar 1	A	UL	Witton Albion	Drew 1-1	6	317	
42	Mar 8	H	UL	Colwyn Bay	Drew 0-0	8	505	Fletcher 10
43	Mar 15	A	UL	Knowsley United	Won 1-0	8	92	
44	Mar 22	A	UL	Barrow	Drew 2-2	9	977	Farrey 30
45	Mar 25	H	UL	Emley	Drew 1-1		382	McGargle 1, Page 60
46	Mar 29	A	UL	Hyde United	Won 2-0		523	Walker 36
47	Mar 30	A	UL	Chorley	Won 3-1	7	344	Henderson 16, 36
48	**Apr 2**	**H**	**ULPC**	**Radcliffe Borough**	**Won 1-0**		**543**	Henderson 43, Moat 51, Page 89
49	Apr 5	A	UL	Emley	Lost 2-3	7	268	**Moat**
50	Apr 12	H	UL	Gainsborough Trinity	Drew 1-1	9	551	Fletcher 45, Bond 42
51	Apr 19	H	UL	Marine	Drew 1-1	9	429	Henderson 75
52	Apr 22	A	UL	Bamber Bridge	Won 1-0		226	Henderson 85
53	**Apr 24**	**A**	**ULPC F1**	**Runcorn**	**Won 1-0**		**223**	Henderson 2
54	Apr 26	H	UL	Lancaster City	Won 3-1	8	487	**McGargle 77**
55	Apr 29	H	UL	Frickley Athletic	Lost 0-1		428	Graham 9 (og), Henderson 54 (pen), Fletcher 88
56	**May 1**	**H**	**ULPC F2**	**Runcorn**	**Won 3-2**		**770**	Henderson 39, 81, Page 47, McGargle 82, Bond 79, 90
57	May 3	A	UL	Alfreton Town	Won 2-1	7	256	**Wilson 16, 40, Henderson 72**
								McGargle 86, Henderson 89

* After Extra Time

BLYTH SPARTANS PLAYING SQUAD 1997-98

Goalkeepers: John Burridge (Queen of the South, Northampton, Witton Alb, Grimsby, Darlington, Notts Co, Manchester C, Falkirk, Dumbarton, Newcastle U, Aberdeen, Lincoln, Scarborough, Newcastle U, Southampton, Sheffield U, Wolves, QPR, Crystal Palace, Aston Villa, Blackpool, Workington)

Defenders: Anthony Cole (Berwick R, Gateshead, St.Johnstone, Middlesbrough), **Steve Raffell** (Bedlington Terriers, Blyth S, Boston U, Doncaster), **Steve Locker** (Bedlinton Terriers, Whitley Bay, Blyth S, Hartlepool, Nottingham F), **Jamie Burt** (Carlisle)

Midfielders: Tony Cosgrove (Middlesbrough), **John Gamble** (Fleetwood T, Bishop Auckland, Seaham RS, Newcastle Blue Star, Queen of the South), **Darren Nicholls** (Hebburn, Gateshead, Blyth Spartans), **Peter Kirkham** (Darlington, Newcastle U), **Michael Farrey** (Gateshead, Chester-le-Street, Whickham), **Steve Walker** (Doncaster, Blyth S, Morpeth, Whitley Bay, Morpeth), **Mark Todd** (Telford, Stalybridge, Rotherham, Sheffield U, Manchester U), **Willie Wilson** (BedlingtonTerriers, Gretna, Dunston Fed.), **Joe McGiven** (Sunderland, Watford)

Forwards: Richie Bond (Bishop Auckland, Carlisle, Blackpool, Blyth Spartans), **Damian Henderson** (Hartlepool, Scunthorpe, Scarborough, Leeds), **Don Page** (Northwich V, Telford, Matlock, Scarborough, Chester, Doncaster, Rotherham,Wigan, Runcorn), **Steve Adams** (Ashington)

BOSTON UNITED

PROGRAMME DETAILS:
Pages: 44 **Price:** £1
Editor: Secretary

Founded: 1934 **Nickname:** The Pilgrims
Colours: Amber/black/amber
Change colours: All blue or white/green/blue
Midweek matchday: Wednesday **Newsline:** 0898 121 539.
Reserve League: Lincolnshire League.
Chairman: S.Burgess **President:** Mr A E Bell
Vice-Chairman:
General Manager / Secretary / Commercial Manager: John Blackwell, 14-16 Spain Place, Boston, Lincs PE26 6HN 01205 364406 (office).
Manager: Gregg Fee **Asst Manager:** Chris Cook
GROUND Address: York Street, Boston, Lincs (0205 364406-office, 365524/5-matchday no., 354063-fax).
Directions: A1 to A17 Sleaford-Boston, over rail crossing, bear right at Eagle pub to lights over haven Bridge, thru lights opposite New Store, right into York Street. Ground just off town centre.
Capacity: 8,771 **Cover:** 8,771 **Seats:** 1,826 **Floodlights:** Yes
Clubhouse: (0205 362967) Open every day except Tuesday. Live entertainment Saturday, pool, darts, dominoes, Sunday football teams.
Club Shop: At club office (as secretary's address, above) not ground.
Metal Badges: Yes (2 types) **Sponsors:** Batemans Brewery.
PREVIOUS - Leagues: Midland 21-58 62-64/ Southern 58-61/ Central Alliance 61-62/ United Counties 65-66/ West Midlands (Regional) 66-68/ Northern Premier 68-79/ Alliance Premier (Conference) 79-93. **Names:** Boston Town/ Boston Swifts. **Grounds:** None.
CLUB RECORDS - Attendance: 10,086 v Corby Town, floodlight inauguration 1955. **Scorer:** Jimmy Rayner 55, 66-67. **Appearances:** Billy Howells, 500+. **Win:** 14-0 v Spilsby Town, Grace Swan Cup, 1992-93. **Transfer Fees - Paid:** £14,000 for Micky Nuttell (Wycombe Wanderers). **Received:** £25,000 for Gary Jones (Southend United, 1993).
Best FA Cup season: Third Rd Proper replay 73-74 (lost 1-6 at home to Derby County after 0-0 draw).
League clubs defeated in FA Cup: Derby 55-56, Southport 70-71, Hartlepool 71-72, Crewe 82-83.
Players progressing to Football League: Jim Smith (Colchester), Steve Thompson (Lincoln), Brendon Phillips (Mansfield), Gordon Simmonite (Blackpool), Simon Garner (Blackburm), John Froggatt & Bobby Svarc (Colchester), David Gilbert, Neil Grayson, Jamie Pascoe, Robbie Curtis, Dean Trott (Northampton), Tim Dalton (Bradford C.), Gary Jones (Southend).
96-97 Captain: Martin Hardy **96-97 P.o.Y.:** Chris White **96-97 Top scorer:** Phil Brown
HONOURS: FA Trophy R-up 84-85, Northern Prem Lg 72-73 73-74 76-77 77-78 (R-up 71-72), Lg Cup 73-74 75-76 (R-up 77-78), Challenge Shield 73-74 74-75 76-77 77-78), Lincs Snr Cup 34-35 36-37 37-38 45-46 49-50 54-55 55-56 76-77 78-79 85-86 87-88 88-89, E Anglian Cup 60-61, Central All 61-62 (Lg Cup 61-62), Utd Counties Lg 65-66 (Lg Cup 65-66), W Mids (Reg) Lg 66-67 67-68, Eastern Professional Floodlit Cup 71-72 (R-up 76-77), Non-League Champion of Champions Cup 72-73 73-74 76-77 77-78, Midland Lg R-up 55-56, Unibond Prem Lge R-Up 95-96.

Boston United F.C. 1996-97. Back Row: Simon Armstrong, John Rawdon, Royston Kent, Nick Maddison, Paul Bastock, Martin Bunce, Mark Melson, Martin Hardy, Martin King. Middle Row: Dick Creasey (Res Mgr), Gerald Starling (Physio), Sean Maloney, Darren Gibbons, Matthew Price, Steve Burdas, Tom Ryan, Joe Vauchan, Glen Maddison, Jamie Cox, Chris Cook (Asst Mgr), David Young (Kit). Front Row: Paul Banks, Leroy Chambers, Paul Casey, Steve Appleby, Phil Brown, Richard Mason (now Hednesford Tn), Carl Smaller, Darren Munton (now Lincoln Utd), Neil Timby, Gregg Fee (Player/Mgr). *Photo courtesy of A & K Markham (Boston).*

Boston United

Match No.	Date	Venue H/A	Competition	Opponents	Result	League Pos.	Attendance	Goalscorers (Times if known)
1	Aug 24	A	UL	Runcorn	Drew 1-1		501	Cook 67
2	Aug 28	H	UL	Alfreton United	Drew 1-1		1023	Gray 88
3	Aug 31	H	UL	Chorley	Won 3-0	8	1003	Armstrong 2, Brown 87, Mason 87
4	Sep 3	A	UL	Frickley Athletic	Drew 2-2		239	Cook 31, Williams 49
5	Sep 7	A	UL	Marine	Lost 0-1	10	427	
6	Sep 11	H	UL	Emley	Won 4-1	7	679	Brown 28, Chambers 33, Williams 60, 68
7	**Sep 14**	**A**	**FAC 1 Q**	**Maldon Town**	**Won 7-2**		**235**	**Fee, L Chambers , Mason (4), Munton**
8	Sep 18	H	UL	Buxton	Won 3-0		865	Brown 2, 49, Williams 22
9	Sep 21	H	UL	Accrington Stanley	Won 3-1	3	1011	Williams 44, Armstrong 63, Brown 86
10	Sep 24	A	UL	Guiseley	Lost 0-1	5	328	
11	**Sep 28**	**H**	**FAC 2 Q**	**Bishop's Stortford**	**Won 3-0**		**977**	**Williams 42, Appleby 67, L Chambers**
12	Oct 1	A	UL	Leek Town	Lost 0-1		486	**89**
13	Oct 5	A	UL	Bamber Bridge	Won 2-0	6	293	
14	Oct 9	H	UL	Guiseley	Drew 1-1	7	709	Hardy 37, Munton 76
15	**Oct 12**	**H**	**FAC 3 Q**	**Sudbury Wanderers**	**Won 10-1**		**422**	Fee 30 (pen)
16	Oct 15	A	UL	Buxton	Won 2-0	6	176	W'ams (3), H'dy, Ch'bers, M'son, Ap'by (2), Sm'ler, A'strng
17	Oct 19	H	UL	Colwyn Bay	Won 3-2	4	976	Fee 11 (pen), Chambers 20
18	**Oct 26**	**A**	**FAC 4 Q**	**Bedworth United**	**Won 2-0**		**1174**	Munton 50, Smaller 87, Brown 90
19	**Oct 29**	**A**	**ULC**	**Lincoln United**	**Drew 1-1**		**242**	**Williams 37, S Chambers 89**
20	Nov 2	H	UL	Witton Albion	Won 2-1	5	1068	**Hardy 52**
21	Nov 9	A	UL	Blyth Spartans	Won 2-1	4	569	Armstrong 12, Chambers 70
22	Nov 11	A	UL	Emley	Drew 1-1	6	303	Brown 21, Chambers 72
23	**Nov 16**	**H**	**FAC 1**	**Morecambe**	**Won 3-0**		**2935**	L Chambers 2
24	**Nov 20**	**H**	**ULC**	**Lincoln United**	**Won 3-0**		**278**	**L Chambers 21, 56, S Chambers 83**
25	Nov 23	A	UL	Barrow	Won 1-0	4	972	**Brown 24, 80, Nelson 38**
26	**Nov 27**	**H**	**ULPC**	**Gainsborough Trinity**	**Won 5-2**		**250**	Armstrong 80
27	Nov 30	A	UL	Witton Albion	Lost 0-1	5	349	**Brown 3, 52, L Chambers 12, 26, Smaller 48**
28	**Dec 2**	**A**	**ULCC**	**Hyde United**	**Drew 1-1**		**296**	
29	**Dec 7**	**A**	**FAC 2**	**Chester City**	**Lost 0-1**		**3344**	**L Chambers 25**
30	**Dec 11**	**H**	**ULCC**	**Hyde United**	**Won 3-2**		**496**	
31	Dec 14	H	UL	Runcorn	Drew 2-2	7	1035	**L Chambers 56, 88, Smaller 89**
32	Dec 21	A	UL	Hyde United	Drew 2-2	7	509	L Chambers 17, 28
33	Jan 4	A	UL	Colwyn Bay	Won 5-1	7	297	S Chambers 59, Cox 90 (og)
34	Jan 11	H	UL	Blyth Spartans	Won 2-1	5	1283	Hardy 17, Chambers 46, Brown (3) 81, 87, 88
35	**Jan 18**	**A**	**FAT 1**	**Emley**	**Lost 1-2**		**504**	Williams 59, Brown 90
36	Jan 25	A	UL	Spennymoor United	Won 3-1	5	254	**Williams 49**
37	**Jan 29**	**H**	**ULPC**	**Farsley Celtic**	**Drew 1-1**		**423**	Brown 33, Williams 70, Chambers 84
38	Feb 1	H	UL	Barrow	Lost 3-5	6	1487	**Withe 44**
39	Feb 8	A	UL	Winsford United	Won 1-0	4	148	Williams 28, Cook 77, Stanhope 89
40	Feb 15	A	UL	Knowsley United	Drew 0-0	4	90	Brown 53
41	**Feb 19**	**H**	**ULCC**	**Emley**	**Won 2-1**		**225**	
42	Feb 19	H	UL	Hyde United	Drew 0-0	5	1391	**L Chambers 43, Mason 50**
43	Feb 26	H	UL	Gainsborough Trinity	Drew 1-1	4	801	
44	Mar 1	H	UL	Lancaster City	Won 4-2	4	937	S Chambers 62
45	Mar 4	A	UL	Gainsborough Trinity	Drew 1-1		748	Cook 23, Brown 57, 75, Smaller 62
46	Mar 8	A	UL	Lancaster City	Won 1-0	4	243	Hardy 27
47	Mar 15	A	UL	Accrington Stanley	Lost 1-3	4	417	Nelson 70
48	Mar 16	A	UL	Bishop Auckland	Lost 0-1		144	Fee 38 (pen)
49	.Mar 22	H	UL	Knowsley United	Won 1-0	4	819	
50	Mar 29	H	UL	Frickley Athletic	Lost 2-3		966	Stanhope 86
51	Mar 31	A	UL	Alfreton Town	Won 2-1	5	397	Chambers 24, Brown 83
52	**Apr 2**	**A**	**ULCC**	**Colwyn Bay**	**Won 3-1**		**445**	Warren 9 (og), L Chambers 38
53	Apr 5	H	UL	Marine	Won 2-0	4	942	**Brown 82, Cook 85, L Chambers 90**
54	Apr 9	H	UL	Leek Town	Lost 0-2		1108	Cook 11, Hardy 51
55	Apr 12	A	UL	Chorley	Won 4-3	5	349	
56	Apr 19	H	UL	Bamber Bridge	Drew 1-1	5	811	Fee 48 (pen), S Chambers 53, L Chambers 67, Withe 70
57	Apr 24	H	UL	Spennymoor United	Won 2-0		422	Brown 64
58	Apr 26	H	UL	Winsford United	Won 2-0	5	634	Armstrong 8, Fee 85 (pen)
59	**Apr 29**	**H**	**ULCC F**	**Gainsborough Trinity**	**Lost 0-1**		**2890**	Appleby 34, Stanhope 81
60	May 3	H	UL	Bishop Auckland	Drew 1-1	6	706	

BOSTON UNITED PLAYING SQUAD 1997-98

Goalkeepers: Paul Bastock (Kettering, Camb. U, Coventry)

Defenders: Greg Fee (Mansfield, Sheffield Wed., Boston U, Kettering, Bradford C), **Martin Hardy** (Matlock, Boston U, Worksop, Notts Co), **Chris Withe** (Shrewsbury, Mansfield, Bury, Notts Co, Bradford C, Newcastle)

Midfielders: Steve Appleby (Bourne, Boston U, Bourne, Kettering, Bourne), **Steve Chambers** (Mansfield, Sheffield Wed.(A)), **Neil Timby** (Boston T, Bourne), **Andy Stanhope** (K. Lynn, Peterborough), **Mark Melson** (Youth team)

Forwards: Phil Brown (Kettering, Lincoln C, Stockport, Chesterfield), **Chris Cook** (Boston, Boston U, K. Lynn, Altrincham, Boston U), **Terry Maddigan** (Local football), **Simon Armstrong** (Skegness T), **Carl Smaller** (Boston T, Grimsby), **Leroy Chambers** (Chester, Sheffield Wed)

CHORLEY

PROGRAMME DETAILS:
Pages: 32 **Price:**£1.
Editor: Alan Robinson

Formed: 1883 **Founded:** The Magpies
Colours: White & black stripes/black/black & white
Change colours: All yellow
Midweek matchday: Tuesday
Reserve League: Alliance League.

Chairman: Jack Kirkland **President:** Dr P J Wren.
Vice Chairman: **Commercial Manager:** Ernie Howe.
Secretary / Press Officer: Mick Wearmouth, 6 Avondale Road, Chorley, Lancs. PR7 2ED (01257 271395).
Manager: Brian Griffiths **Asst Manager:** Ken Wright

GROUND Address: Victory Park, Duke Street, Chorley, Lancs (01257 263406). **Directions:** M61 jct 6, A6 to Chorley, going past Yarrow Bridge Hotel on Bolton Rd turn left at 1st lights into Pilling Lane, 1st right into Ashley Str., ground 2nd left. From M6; jct 27, follow signs to Chorley, left at lights, continue for two and a half miles on A49, right onto B5251, on entering Chorley turn right into Duke Street 200yds after Plough Hotel. Quarter mile from Chorley (BR).
Capacity: 9,000 **Cover:** 4,000 **Seats:** 900 **Floodlights:** Yes
Clubhouse: (01257 275662). Open every evening. Entertainment at weekends. Snacks available. **Club Shop:** Yes. **Sponsors:** Coloroll.

PREVIOUS - Leagues: Lancs Alliance 1890-94/ Lancs 94-1903/ Lancs Comb. 03-68 69-70/ Northern Premier 68-69 70-72 82-88/ Cheshire County 72-82/ GMV Conference 88-90. **Grounds:** Dole Lane 1883-1901/ Rangletts Park 01-05/ St George's Park 05-20.

CLUB RECORDS - Attendance: 9,679 v Darwen, 1931-32. **Goalscorer:** Peter Watson. **Fees - Paid:** Undisclosed fee tp Marine for Brian Ross 1995. **Received:** £22,500 for Paul Mariner (Plymouth, 1973). **Best Season - FA Cup:** 2nd Rd 86-87 (lost in replay at Preston), 90-91 (lost at Shrewsbury). **FA Trophy:** Semi-Final 1995-96.
Players progressing to Football League: Charles Ashcroft (Liverpool 1946), William Healey (Arsenal 1949), Stan Howard (Huddersfield 1952), Derek Hogg (Leicester 1952), William Norcross (Southport 1959), Micky Walsh (Blackpool 1971), Paul Mariner (Plymouth 1973), Graham Barrow (Wigan 1976), Steve Galliers (Wimbledon 1977), Kevin Tully (Bury 1980), Geoff Twentyman (Preston 1983), Gary Buckley (Bury 1984), Chris Hunter (Preston 1984).
96-97 Captain: **96-97 P.o.Y.:** **96-97 Top scorer:**
Local Newspapers: Lancs Evening Post, Chorley Guardian. **Local Radio:** Radio Lancs, Red Rose.

HONOURS: Northern Premier Lg 87-88, Cheshire Co. Lg 75-76 76-77 81-82, Lancs Comb. 19-20 22-23 27-28 28-29 32-33 33-34 45-46 59-60 60-61 63-64 (R-up 21-22 26-27 48-49 62-63 64-65 65-66, Lg Cup 24-25 58-59 62-63), Lancs Lg 1896-97 98-99, Lancs Alliance 1892-93 (R-up 94-95), Lancs Jnr Cup 1894-95 1908-09 23-24 39-40 45-46 57-58 58-59 60-61 63-64 64-65 75-76 79-80 81-82 82-83, FA Tphy QF (replay) 76-77.

Chorley FC:

Chorley

Match No.	Date	Venue H/A	Competition	Opponents	Result	League Pos.	Attendance	Goalscorers (Times if known)
1	Aug 24	H	UL	Guiseley	Won 1-0		569	Trundle 47
2	Aug 26	A	UL	Bamber Bridge	Won 2-0		768	Blackstone 34, Ross 48
3	Aug 31	A	UL	Boston United	Lost 0-3	7	1003	
4	Sep 3	H	UL	Barrow	Lost 1-3		867	Haw 29
5	Sep 7	H	UL	Gainsborough Trinity	Lost 3-4	12	398	Haw 37, Mayers 74, Trundle 82
6	Sep 10	A	UL	Lancaster City	Lost 1-4	19	302	Ward 45
7	**Sep 14**	**A**	**FAC 1 Q**	**North Ferriby United**	**Lost 1-4**		**283**	**Ross 86**
8	Sep 17	H	UL	Knowsley United	Drew 2-2		297	Procter 36, Ross 74
9	Sep 21	A	UL	Leek Town	Lost 0-1	19	405	
10	Sep 24	H	UL	Witton Albion	Won 6-1	14	373	Thorpe 13, Mayers 14, 22, Trundle 52, 63, Ross 55
11	Oct 2	A	UL	Accrington Stanley	Won 3-0		747	Marginson 61, Abel 74, Ross 84
12	Oct 5	A	UL	Blyth Spartans	Won 3-1	7	641	Marginson (3) 26, 28, 76
13	Oct 8	H	UL	Runcorn	Won 4-0		526	Abel 18, Marginson 25, 26, Finlay 50 (og)
14	Oct 12	H	UL	Accrington Stanley	Drew 1-1	5	594	Blackstone 52
15	Oct 15	A	UL	Barrow	Lost 0-3		1015	
16	Oct 19	A	UL	Spennymoor United	Drew 0-0	8	278	
17	Oct 22	H	UL	Winsford United	Lost 0-1		407	
18	Oct 26	A	UL	Frickley Athletic	Lost 1-2	12	224	Worthington 67
19	Nov 2	H	UL	Hyde United	Drew 3-3	11	519	Blackstone 25, 56, Haw 40
20	Nov 9	H	UL	Bishop Auckland	Drew 1-1	12	411	Blackstone 20
21	Nov 12	A	UL	Colwyn Bay	Drew 1-1	11	235	Blackstone 71
22	Nov 16	H	UL	Spennymoor United	Won 1-0	11	300	Marginson 26
23	Nov 26	H	UL	Marine	Won 2-1	10	340	Marginson 27, Thomas 54
24	Nov 30	A	UL	Hyde United	Lost 2-3	10	622	Ross 21, 50
25	Dec 7	H	UL	Alfreton Town	Won 2-1	9	312	Ross 73, 74
26	Dec 14	A	UL	Emley	Lost 0-1	10	307	
27	Dec 21	A	UL	Guiseley	Won 4-1	9	462	Trundle (3) 23, 26, 42, Blackstone 71
28	Dec 26	A	UL	Marine	Lost 0-1	10	533	
29	**Jan 14**	**H**	**LFA ATS**	**Atherton L R**	**Lost 1-2**		**171**	**Blackstone 48**
30	**Jan 18**	**A**	**FAT 1**	**Morecambe**	**Lost 1-3**		**937**	**Ross 56**
31	Jan 25	H	UL	Gainsborough Trinity	Lost 0-3	11	440	
32	Feb 1	H	UL	Emley	Lost 1-2	14	323	Ross 40
33	Feb 15	A	UL	Bishop Auckland	Won 3-1	12	211	Sang 6, Potts 31, Trundle 85
34	Feb 22	H	UL	Frickley Athletic	Lost 0-1	13	306	
35	Mar 1	A	UL	Alfreton Town	Won 3-0	11	205	Ross 27, Wright 43, Proctor 44
36	Mar 4	H	UL	Leek Town	Drew 0-0		139	
37	Mar 8	A	UL	Runcorn	Won 2-0	11	401	Sang 21, Ross 23
38	Mar 11	H	UL	Bamber Bridge	Lost 1-3		637	McGhee 80
39	Mar 15	H	UL	Lancaster City	Lost 0-2	12	337	
40	Mar 18	H	UL	Buxton	Drew 2-2		195	Fleming 60, Ward 71
41	Mar 22	A	UL	Winsford United	Won 1-0	11	182	Ross 89
42	Mar 29	A	UL	Knowsley United	Lost 1-4		133	Trundle 45
43	Mar 30	H	UL	Blyth Spartans	Lost 1-3	12	344	Mayers 62
44	Apr 5	A	UL	Witton Albion	Drew 2-2	13	373	Sang 45, Ross 67
45	Apr 12	H	UL	Boston United	Lost 3-4	13	349	Mayers 13, Trundle 27, Ross 54
46	Apr 19	H	UL	Colwyn Bay	Won 4-0	13	296	Ross 13, 61, Sang 51, Trundle 85
47	May 3	A	UL	Buxton	Won 1-0	13	201	Trundle 35

CHORLEY PLAYING SQUAD 1997-98

Goalkeepers: Simon Marsh (Hyde U, Blackpool (T)), **Chris Clarke** (Rochdale, Bolton)

Defenders: Paul Fleming (Halifax T, Mansfield, Halifax T), **Mark Wright** (Wigan, Huddersfield, Everton), **Andy Thorpe** (Buxton, Witton Alb, Melbourne (Aust),Stockport, Tranmere, Stockport), **Tony Ward** (Marine, Chorley, Wigan, Everton), **Shaun McHugh** (Bamber B, Fleetwood T, Clitheroe, Chorley, Barrow, Feniscowles, Ipswich (T)), **Graham Abel** (Northwich V, Crewe, Chester, Runcorn, Northwich V), **Neil Sang** (Morecambe, Runcorn, Ilkeston, Macclesfield, Caernarfon, Stalybridge, Torquay, Everton), **Gil Brookes** (Bamber B, Preston)

Midfielders: Kenny Mayers (Bamber Bridge, Horwich RMI), **Jimmy Proctor** (Rochdale), **Mark Calvert** (Scarborough, Hull), **Paul Loughlin** (Warrington, Cheadle, Bamber B, Chorley), **Steve Grunshaw** (Gt.Harwood, Clitheroe, Blackburn)

Forwards: Brian Ross (Marine, Chorley, Winsford U, Northwich V, Rochdale, Manchester U (A)), **Lee Trundle** (Burscough, St.Dominics), **Ian Blackstone** (Southport, Scarborough, York, Harrogate RA), **Colin Potts** (Rochdale), **Kyle Hayton** (Bamber B, Preston), **Danny Worthington** (Youth team)

PROGRAMME DETAILS:
Pages: 28 **Price:** 80p
Editor: M Richardson
(011492 878953)

COLWYN BAY

Formed: 1885
Nickname: 'Bay' or 'Seagulls'
Colours: Maroon with wide blue stripes/maroon/maroon.
Change colours: White/navy/navy
Midweek home matchday: Tuesday
Reserve Team: None.

Chairman: Glynne Owens
Vice Chairman: J A Humphreys
Secretary / Press Officer: Alan J Banks, 15 Smith Avenue, Old Colwyn, N Wales LL29 8BE. 01492 516941 (H), 01492 515133 (B).
Manager: Bryn Jones 01244 531974 (H), 01244 812154 (B)
Assistant Manager: Dave Brett **Physio:** John Carmichael
GROUND Address: Llanelian Road, Old Colwyn, N.Wales. (01492 516554)
Directions: M55 North Wales Coast - approaching Colwyn Bay take 1st exit signposted Old Colwyn, left at bottom slip road, straight over r'bout into Llanelian Rd - ground half mile on right. 2 miles from Colwyn Bar BR station.
Capacity: 2,500 **Seats:** 250 **Cover:** 700 **Floodlights:** Yes
Clubhouse: Open matchdays only.
Club Shop: Yes - contact: A Holden 01492 534287
Metal Badges: Yes **Sponsors:** Colwyn Shopping Centre

PREVIOUS - Grounds: Eiras Park 1930-82/ Llanelian Road 82-92/ Northwich Victoria FC 92-93/ Ellesmere Port Stadium 94-95 *(two years in exile due to dispute with FAW over the League of Wales).* **Leagues:** Nth Wales Coast 01-21 33-35/ Welsh National 21-30/ Nth Wales Comb. 30-31/ Welsh Lg (Nth) 45-84/ North West Counties 84-91.

CLUB RECORDS - Attendance: 5,000 (at Eiras Park) v Borough United, 1964. **Win:** **Defeat:** **Scorer:** Peter Donnelly **Appearances:** Bryn A Jones
Best FA Cup season: Second Round Proper 95-96. **League clubs defeated in FA Cup:** None.
96-97 Captain: Peter Donnelly **96-97 P.o.Y.:** Craig Lawton **96-97 Top scorer:** Graham Roberts (16)
Local Newspapers: North Wales Weekly News, North Wales Pioneer.

HONOURS: Northern Premier Lg Div 1 91-92 (Div 1 Cup 91-92), North West Counties Lg R-up 90-91 (Div 3 R-up 83-84, Lg Cup 88-89, Floodlit Cup 90-91), Welsh Cup SF 91-92, Welsh National Lg R-up 27-28 29-30, Nth Wales Comb. 30-31, Welsh Lg Nth 64-65 82-83 83-84 (R-up 35-36 45-46 63-64, Lg Cup 27-28), Alves Cup 63-64, Cookson Cup 73-74 79-80 80-81 81-82 83-84, Barritt Cup 79-80 81-82 83-84, Nth Wales Coast Chal. Cup 30-31 31-32 81-82 82-83 83-84 95-96, Nth Wales Coast Jnr Cup 1898-99.

Colwyn Bay FC. Back Row (L-R): Lee Harley, Dave Fuller, Richie Roberts, Steve Mann, Colin Caton, Glen Graham, Gary McCosh, Mark Price, Gareth Drury. Front Row: Matthew McQuillan, Craig Lawton, Craig Dulson, Graham Roberts, Peter Donnelly, Neil Rigby.

Colwyn Bay

Match No.	Date	Venue H/A	Competition	Opponents	Result	League Pos.	Attendance	Goalscorers (Times if known)
1	Aug 24	H	UL	Accrington Stanley	Lost 0-2		381	
2	Aug 26	A	UL	Knowsley United	Lost 0-3		96	
3	Aug 31	A	UL	Gainsborough Trinity	Lost 0-2	23	430	
4	Sep 3	H	UL	Bamber Bridge	Won 5-2		304	Roberts 8, 20, Donnelly 29, Fuller 53, Drury 84
5	Sep 7	A	UL	Emley	Won 1-0	13	211	Roberts 20
6	Sep 9	H	UL	Witton Albion	Drew 0-0	15	427	
7	Sep 14	H	UL	Barrow	Lost 1-2	15	394	Donnelly 28
8	Sep 17	A	UL	Marine	Drew 0-0	15	342	
9	Sep 28	H	UL	Blyth Spartans	Won 3-0	12	339	Jones 25, Fuller 76, 80
10	Sep 30	A	UL	Hyde United	Drew 1-1		427	Donnelly 84
11	Oct 5	A	UL	Guiseley	Won 1-0	11	417	Roberts 86
12	Oct 9	H	UL	Winsford United	Lost 1-2		283	Roberts 20
13	Oct 12	H	UL	Spennymoor United	Drew 1-1	14	310	Jones 46
14	Oct 19	A	UL	Boston United	Lost 2-3	16	976	Jones 32, Donnelly 84
15	Oct 22	H	UL	Lancaster City	Drew 1-1	16	363	Gelling 6
16	**Oct 26**	**H**	**FAC 4 Q**	**Nuneaton Borough**	**Won 1-0**		**1026**	**Donnelly 38**
17	**Oct 29**	**A**	**ULC**	**Witton Albion**	**Won 5-0**		**209**	**Roberts 25, 29, Williams 63, 73, Dulson 84**
18	Nov 2	A	UL	Bishop Auckland	Lost 1-3	17	193	Williams 89
19	Nov 3	A	UL	Spennymoor United	Won 2-1	17	197	Donnelly 26, Williams 42
20	Nov 6	A	UL	Winsford United	Lost 0-3	17	145	
21	Nov 9	H	UL	Gainsborough Trinity	Lost 0-2	17	241	
22	Nov 12	H	UL	Chorley	Drew 1-1	17	235	Donnelly 60
23	**Nov 16**	**H**	**FAC 1**	**Wrexham**	**Drew 1-1**		**4679**	**Roberts 63**
24	Nov 23	H	UL	Frickley Athletic	Won 5-0		275	Williams 24, 45, Drury (3) 27, 65, 82
25	**Nov 26**	**A**	**FAC 1 R**	**Wrexham**	**Lost 0-2**		**4106**	
26	**Nov 30**	**H**	**FAT 3 Q**	**Frickley Athletic**	**Won 1-0**		**264**	**Lawton 41**
27	**Dec 3**	**H**	**ULCL**	**Winsford United**	**Won 3-2**		**160**	**Bishop 86 (og), Williams 88, Lawton 90**
28	Dec 10	H	UL	Runcorn	Drew 3-3	17	269	Drury 7, Williams 26, 43
29	Dec 14	A	UL	Alfreton Town	Lost 1-2	17	218	Graham 88
30	Dec 21	H	UL	Emley	Won 3-2	16	268	Limbert 31, Donnelly 55, 65
31	Dec 26	H	UL	Knowsley United	Won 5-0		427	Rob'ts 9, D'nelly 16, Drury 31, Li'bert 55, L'ton 75
32	Jan 4	H	UL	Boston United	Lost 1-5	16	297	Dancy 6
33	Jan 11	A	UL	Runcorn	Lost 0-5	16	349	
34	**Jan 18**	**H**	**FAT 1**	**Lancaster City**	**Won 6-0**		**335**	**Drury 13, W'ams 29, 43, 89, L'ton 87, L'bert 1**
35	Jan 25	H	UL	Guiseley	Drew 1-1	16	390	Williams 41
36	Feb 1	H	UL	Alfreton Town	Drew 1-1	16	287	Williams 10
37	**Feb 8**	**H**	**FAT 2**	**Southport**	**Won 2-0**		**928**	**Donnelly 49 (pen), Drury 85**
38	Feb 24	H	UL	Buxton	Lost 3-4	18	312	Dulson 28, Roberts 51, McCosh 88
39	**Feb 25**	**H**	**ULCC**	**Guiseley**	Drew 2-2	17	240	Lawton 33, 85
40	**Mar 1**	**H**	**FAT 3**	**St Leonards Stamcroft**	**Drew 2-2**		**555**	**Dulson 44, Lawton 84**
41	**Mar 6**	**A**	**FAT 3 R**	**St Leonards Stamcroft**	**Drew 0-0***		**827**	
42	Mar 8	A	UL	Blyth Spartans	Drew 0-0	18	505	
43	**Mar 10**	**A**	**FAT 3R2**	**St Leonards Stamcroft**	**Won 2-1**		**1151**	**Roberts 5, Drury 53**
44	**Mar 12**	**A**	**ULCC**	**Guiseley**	**Won 2-0**	18	**188**	**Drury 67, Donnelly 89**
45	Mar 15	A	UL	Buxton	Drew 2-2		155	Lawton 57, Drury 68
46	**Mar 18**	**A**	**NWC FAC**	**Porthmadoc**	**Drew 1-1**		**155**	**Roberts 75 (Lost 1-4 on Penalties)**
47	**Mar 22**	**A**	**FAT Q F**	**Stevenage Borough**	**Lost 0-2**		**3082**	
48	**Mar 25**	**A**	**ULCC**	**Boston United**	**Lost 0-1**		**521**	
49	Mar 29	A	UL	Accrington Stanley	Lost 1-3		432	Roberts 75
50	Mar 31	H	UL	Leek Town	Won 3-1	18	498	Lawton 7, Fuller 74, Roberts 88
51	**Apr 2**	**H**	**ULCC**	**Boston United**	**Lost 1-3**		**445**	**Donnelly 83 (pen)**
52	Apr 5	A	UL	Barrow	Lost 0-1	18	871	
53	Apr 8	A	UL	Bamber Bridge	Won 3-2		318	Roberts 13, Donnelly 57, Lawton 87
54	Apr 12	H	UL	Bishop Auckland	Lost 1-2	17	314	Roberts 70
55	Apr 19	A	UL	Chorley	Lost 0-4	17	296	
56	Apr 22	A	UL	Leek Town	Lost 0-1		866	
57	Apr 24	H	UL	Marine	Drew 0-0		193	
58	Apr 26	H	UL	Hyde United	Lost 1-3	17	313	Dulson 29
59	Apr 29	A	UL	Witton Albion	Lost 0-1	16	258	
60	May 1	A	UL	Frickley Athletic	Won 4-3		127	Lawton 2, Jones 34, Brett 37, Hughes 62
61	May 3	A	UL	Lancaster City	Drew 1-1	16	154	T Jones 59

* After Extra Time

COLWYN BAY PLAYING SQUAD 1997-98

Goalkeepers: Richie Roberts (Christleton), **Neil Griffiths** (Flint, Conwy U,Warrington, Rhyl)

Defenders: Dave Fuller (Southport, Witton Alb, Bangor C, Gainsborough T, Bangor C), **Glen Graham** (Flint, Mostyn, Holywell), **Gary McGosh** (Local football), **Steve Mann** (Caernarfon, Mold A, Newtown, Upton T, Connah's Quay N), **Mark Price** (Connah's Quay N, Holywell, Upton T), **Mark Woods** (Pieksamaki (Fin), C.Bay, Flint, United Services), **Colin Caton** (Witton Alb, C.Bay, Rhyl)

Midfielders: Lee Harley (Flint, Chester), **Dave Brett** (Chester, C.Bay), **Craig Dulson** (Stalybridge), **Les Armor** (Caernarfon, Stalybridge, Bangor C, Rhyl, C.Bay), **Gareth Drury** (Vauxhall GM, Knowsley, Marine), **Craig Lawton** (Port Vale, Manchester U)

Forwards: Peter Donnelly (Northwich V, C.Bay, Rhyl, Oswestry, Chester), **Graham Roberts** (Macclesfield, C.Bay, Caernarfon, Flint, Mold A, British Steel), **Matthew Wild** (Christleton), **Jason McKinlay** (Droylsden, Congleton, Macclesfield), **Tommy Jones** (Holywell, Conwy U, Llandudno, C.Bay), **Marc Williams** (Altrincham, Stockport, Bangor C, Porthmadog, Llanberis), **Lewis Coady** (Wrexham)

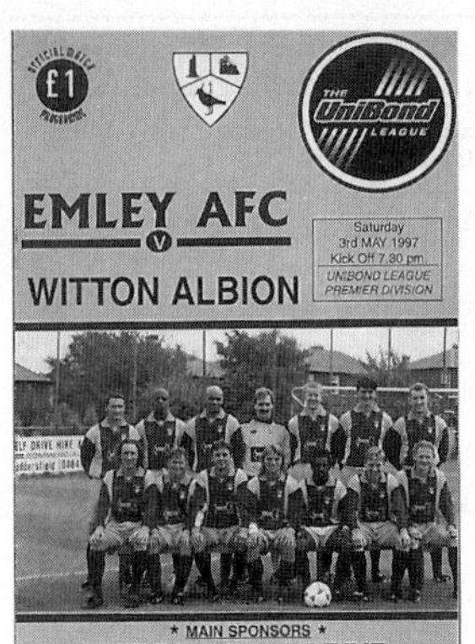

PROGRAMME DETAILS:
Pages: 34 **Price:** £ 1
Editor: Alan Blackman
(01924 403959)

EMLEY

Formed: 1903 **Nickname:**
Colours: Maroon and blue/blue/maroon.
Change Colours: All yellow.
Midweek matchday: Monday.
Reserve League: Nth Co's (E) Res Div.

Chairman: Peter Matthews. **President:** Peter Maude
Secretary: Richard Poulain, 17, Smithy Lane, Skelmanthorpe, Huddersfield HD8 9DF. (01484 860323 H & Fax, 0374 252131 Mob, 01484 438800 ext 238 B).
Manager: Ronnie Glavin. **Asst Manager:** Peter Price
Physio: Daryl Brook. **Press Officer:** Secretary

GROUND Address: Emley Welfare Sports Ground, Emley, Huddersfield (01924 848398. Office: 840087). **Directions:** Follow Huddersfield signs from M1 junct 38, left onto A636 at r'bout, then right after about 3/4 mile for Emley. 7 miles from Huddersfield (BR) station - buses to Emley Cross.
Capacity: 3,000 **Cover:** 1,000 **Seats:** 250 **Floodlights:** Yes
Clubhouse: (01924 848398). Members' social club open five nights a week and Saturday & Sunday. Bingo, discos, occasional caberet.
Club Shop: Yes Contact Mrs Linda Sykes (01484 656406)
Sponsors: Arrow Self Drive

Previous Leagues: Huddersfield/ Yorkshire 69-82/ Northern Counties East 82-89.
CLUB RECORDS - Attendance: 5,134 v Barking, Amateur Cup Third Round Proper 1/2/69. *9,035 v Bolton Wanderers, FA Cup 1st Rd Proper 17/11/92.* **Goalscorer:** Mick Pamment 305. **Appearances:** Ray Dennis 751. **Transfer Fee Received:** £20,000 for Colin Alcide (Lincoln City 95).
Best FA Cup season: First Round Proper 91-92 (0-3 v Bolton Wanderers at Huddersfield).
Players progressing to Football League: A Sweeney (Hartlepool Utd 79), G Cooper (Huddersfield Tn 84), J Francis (Sheffield Utd 88), S Smith (Crewe Alexandra 1992), C Alcide (Lincoln City 95)
96-97 Captain: Ian Banks **96-97 P.o.Y.:** Neil Lacey **96-97 Top scorer:** Deiniol Graham
Local Newspapers: Huddersfield Examiner, Huddersfield & District Chronicle.
Local Radio Stations: Radio Leeds, Radio Sheffield, Pulse FM.
HONOURS: FA Vase R-up 87-88 (SF 86-87), FA Trophy 4th Rd 90-91, FA Amateur Cup 3rd Rd replay 69-70, Northern Prem Lg Div 1 R-up 90-91, Northern Counties E Lg(2) 87-89 (R-up 85-86), Yorkshire Lg 75-76 77-78 79-80 81-82 (R-up(5) 72-74 76-77 78-79 80-81, Lg Cup 69-70 78-79 81-82, Div 2 R-up 69-70, Sheffield & Hallamshire Senior Cup 75-76 79-80 80-81 83-84 88-89 90-91 91-92, Huddersfield Challenge Cup 82-83 83-84 85-86, Huddersfield Lg(4) 65-69.

Emley FC: *Photo: Peter Barnes.*

Emley

Match No.	Date	Venue H/A	Competition	Opponents	Result	League Pos.	Attendance	Goalscorers (Times if known)
1	Aug 26	H	UL	Marine	Won 5-1		645	Graham (3) 11, 42, 61, Proctor 48 (og), Willams 70 (p)
2	Aug 31	A	UL	Knowsley United	Won 1-0	5	85	Lacey 18
3	Sep 2	H	UL	Hyde United	Lost 2-4		419	Graham 44, 74 (pen)
4	Sep 7	H	UL	Colwyn Bay	Lost 0-1	9	211	
5	Sep 11	A	UL	Boston United	Lost 1-4	16	679	Graham 79
6	**Sep 14**	**H**	**FAC 1 Q**	**Selby Town**	**Won 3-0**		**163**	**Graham 54, 60, Banks 63**
7	Sep 18	A	UL	Alfreton Town	Drew 0-0		249	
8	Sep 21	A	UL	Runcorn	Drew 1-1	14	428	Reynolds 21
9	Sep 23	H	UL	Gainsborough Trinity	Drew 3-3	18	282	O'Donnell 13, Graham 33, Lacey 58
10	**Sep 28**	**A**	**FAC 2 Q**	**Southport**	**Drew 1-1**		**848**	**David 16**
11	**Sep 30**	**H**	**FAC 2QR**	**Southport**	**Lost 2-3***		**462**	**Reynolds 79, O'Donnell 92**
12	Oct 5	H	UL	Lancaster City	Drew 2-2	18	271	Williams 43, Graham 53
13	Oct 8	A	UL	Gainsborough Trinity	Won 3-0		573	Thompson 8, Wilson 28, Graham 39
14	Oct 12	A	UL	Winsford United	Drew 2-2	16	186	David 66, Nicholson 67 (pen)
15	Oct 14	H	UL	Bishop Auckland	Won 2-0		258	Waller 34 (og), Graham 77
16	Oct 19	A	UL	Barrow	Lost 0-3	13	1230	
17	Oct 23	A	UL	Bishop Auckland	Won 1-0		172	Thompson 73
18	Oct 26	H	UL	Buxton	Won 3-0	7	163	Graham 38, Wilson 40, Lacey 59
19	**Oct 30**	**A**	**ULC**	**Blyth Spartans**	**Won 2-1**		**336**	**Banks 21, Williams 73**
20	Nov 2	H	UL	Spennymoor United	Won 3-0	7	249	Hurst 74, Graham 76, Wilson 79
21	**Nov 6**	**A**	**S & H SC**	**Worsborough B**	**Drew 1-1**		**195**	**Lacey 45**
22	Nov 9	A	UL	Accrington Stanley	Drew 1-1	8	521	Wilson 89
23	Nov 11	H	UL	Boston United	Drew 1-1		303	David 3
24	Nov 16	H	UL	Barrow	Won 3-0	7	415	Francis 42, Hurst 59, 73
25	Nov 23	A	UL	Lancaster City	Won 3-1	7	286	Graham 17, 19, Reynolds 85
26	**Nov 27**	**H**	**S & H SC**	**Worsborough B**	**Won 5-2**		**125**	**Williams 23, Lacey 41, Francis 46, 67, Reynolds 49**
27	**Nov 30**	**A**	**FAT 3 Q**	**Knowsley United**	**Drew 2-2**		**132**	**Graham 53, Wilson 89**
28	**Dec 2**	**H**	**FAT 3 Q**	**Knowsley United**	**Won 5-2**		**205**	**Graham (3) 21, 28, 62, Lacey 73, Nicholson 90**
29	Dec 7	A	UL	Bamber Bridge	Won 3-0	4	254	Graham 40, 67, Williams 84
30	**Dec 10**	**H**	**S & H SC**	**Ecclesfield RR**	**Won 12-0**		**132**	**⁺ See Foot of List**
31	Dec 14	H	UL	Chorley	Won 1-0	3	307	Williams 88
32	Dec 21	A	UL	Colwyn Bay	Lost 2-3	4	268	Francis 14, Limbert 51 (og)
33	Dec 26	H	UL	Frickley Athletic	Drew 3-3	4	427	David 28, Graham 36, Hirst 66
34	Dec 28	A	UL	Guiseley	Lost 0-2	4	610	
35	**Jan 13**	**H**	**S & H SC**	**Stocksbridge PS**	**Won 3-0**		**242**	**Graham (3) 60, 84, 87**
36	**Jan 18**	**H**	**FAT 1**	**Boston United**	**Won 2-1**		**504**	**Francis 43, Reynolds 51**
37	**Jan 20**	**H**	**ULSC**	**Spennymoor United**	**Won 1-0**		**180**	**Williams 90**
38	Jan 25	H	UL	Knowsley United	Lost 2-4	8	250	Francis 7, Thompson 9
39	**Jan 27**	**H**	**ULPC**	**Radcliffe Borough**	**Lost 0-1**		**160**	
40	Feb 1	A	UL	Chorley	Won 2-1	7	323	Banks 5, Fearon 89
41	**Feb 8**	**A**	**FAT 2**	**Kidderminster Harriers**	**Drew 0-0**		**2312**	
42	**Feb 11**	**H**	**FAT 2 R**	**Kidderminster Harriers**	**Lost 1-5**		**1021**	**Banks 84**
43	Feb 15	H	UL	Bamber Bridge	Lost 1-2	9	212	Lacey 67
44	**Feb 19**	**A**	**ULCC**	**Boston United**	**Lost 1-2**		**225**	**Graham 64**
45	Feb 22	H	UL	Accrington Stanley	Won 3-1	9	210	Lacey 18, Reynolds 36, Banks 90
46	Mar 1	A	UL	Spennymoor United	Won 3-2	8	162	Thompson 10, Fearon 43, Tonks 79
47	Mar 3	H	UL	Guiseley	Won 4-0	5	312	Hurst 17, Thompson 62, Banks 75, Wilson 80
48	**Mar 6**	**H**	**S & H SC**	**Worksop Town**	**Won 1-0**		**191**	**Fearon 84**
49	Mar 8	A	UL	Leek Town	Drew 0-0	5	660	
50	Mar 15	H	UL	Winsford United	Drew 1-1	7	170	Lacey 16
51	Mar 22	A	UL	Hyde United	Won 2-1	8	576	Williams 3, Lacey 57
52	Mar 25	A	UL	Blyth Spartans	Drew 1-1		382	Thompson 59
53	Mar 29	H	UL	Runcorn	Won 2-1		253	Thompson 31, 61
54	Mar 31	A	UL	Frickley Athletic	Won 2-1	4	277	Hurst 39, Thompson 55
55	Apr 5	H	UL	Blyth Spartans	Won 3-2	5	268	Wilson 13, Graham 83, Thompson 78
56	Apr 8	A	UL	Witton Albion	Won 4-1		351	Banks 21, 51 (2 pens), Thompson 24, Hurst 67
57	Apr 12	A	UL	Marine	Drew 0-0	4	474	
58	Apr 14	H	UL	Leek Town	Lost 2-3		452	Ogley 24 (og), Hurst 44 (pen)
59	Apr 19	A	UL	Buxton	Won 3-0	3	215	Wilson 8, 85, Hurst 53
60	Apr 26	H	UL	Alfreton Town	Won 4-0	4	222	Tonks 5, Wilson 34, Fearon 61, Hurst 84
61	May 3	H	UL	Witton Albion	Won 4-1	4	205	Tonks 33, Thompson 56, 58, Hurst 59

⁺ Scorers v Ecclesfield RR: Williams 8, 15, Reynolds 35, 56, Wood 49, Tonks 62, Graham 64, Jones 65, Francis (3) 71, 75, 87, Marples 88 (pen)

* After Extra Time

EMLEY PLAYING SQUAD 1997-98

Goalkeepers: Chris Marples (Chesterfield, York, Stockport, Chesterfield, Goole, Sutton T), **Ray Dennis** (Ossett Alb, Barrow, Emley, Altrincham, Emley)

Defenders: Nicky Wood (Huddersfield), **Nicky Bramald** (Ossett Alb, Emley), **Steve Nicholson** (Farsley C, Leeds U), **Neil Lacey** (Frickley, Gateshead, Frickley, Goole, Denaby), **Glynn Hurst** (Barnsley, Tottenham H), **Richard Coyles** (Glasshoughton W, Emley), **Sean Fearon** (Rotherham)

Midfielders: Ian Banks (Darlington, Rotherham, Barnsley, WBA, Bradford C, Huddersfield, Leicester C, Barnsley), **Mike Thompson** (Frickley, Ashfield U, Frickley, Goole, Scunthorpe), **Paul David** (Bradley R), **Chris Hirst** (South Africa), **Mark Wilson** (Bradford PA, Farsley C, Shepshed Alb, Frickley, Huddersfield, Rotherham), **Simon Jones** (Local football)

Forwards: Deniol Graham (Dag & Red, Halifax, Barnsley, Manchester U), **Paul Viner** (Bradford PA, Eccleshill U, Guiseley, Torquay), **Carey Williams** (Denaby, Rotherham, Denaby, Brunsmere Ath), **Michael Reynolds** (Local football), **Chris Shaw** (Ossett T, Pontefract Coll, South Shields, Langley Park)

PROGRAMME DETAILS:
Pages: 40 **Price:** £1
Editor: D Fisher

FRICKLEY ATHLETIC

Formed: 1866
Nickname: The Blues
Colours: All blue
Change colours: Yellow & black.
Midweek home matchday: Tuesday
Reserves' League: None

Chairman: Mike Twiby
Financial Secretary: D Fisher
Secretary / Treasurer: D Fisher, 31 Vickers Ave., South Elmsall WF9 3LW. (01977 643316)
Manager: Ian Thompson

GROUND Address: Westfield Lane, South Elmsall, Pontefract (01977 642460).
Directions: Follow signs for South Elmsall from A1 and A638. Left at Superdrug warehouse, right at T junction and immediately left up Westfield Lane. Left into Oxford Road (opposite Westfield Hotel) - ground at bottom on right. Two miles from South Elmsall (BR).
Capacity: 6,000 **Cover:** 2,500
Seats: 800 **Floodlights:** Yes
Clubhouse: On ground
Club Shop: Yes **Sponsors:** Berwin & Berwin

PREVIOUS - **Leagues:** Sheffield; Yorkshire 22-24; Midland Counties 24-33 34-60 70-76; Cheshire County 60-70; Northern Premier 76-80; GMV Conference (Alliance Premier) 80-87.
Name: Frickley Colliery Athletic.

CLUB RECORDS - **Attendance:** 6,500 v Rotherham United, FA Cup First Round 1971. **Scorer:** K Whiteley.
Fee Paid: £1,800. **Fee Received:** £12,500 for Paul Shirtliff (Boston Utd).

BEST SEASON - **FA Trophy:** Quarter-Finals 84-85.
FA Cup: 3rd Rd 1985-86 (1-3 v Rotherham H). 2nd Rd 84-85 (0-1 at Darlington). 1st Rd 36-37 57-58 63-64 71-72 73-74 83-84 86-87 88-89.
League clubs defeated: Hartlepool United 85-86.

HONOURS: Alliance Premier Lg R-up 85-86, Midland Counties Lg R-up 72-73 (Lg Cup 75-76), Yorkshire Lg R-up 23-24, Sheffield & Hallamshire Senior Cup 27-28 56-57 60-61 62-63 66-67 78-79 85-86 87-88 89-90, Sheffield Association Lg 20-21 (R-up 11-12).

Players progressing to Football League: Dennis Smith & Jack Brownsword (Hull 1946), Stan Scrimshaw (Halifax 1947), William Callaghan (Aldershot 1949), Leo Dickens 1950), John Ashley & Graham Caulfield (York 1950 & 67), Ron Barritt (Leeds 1951), John Pickup (Bradford PA 1955), Tom Hymers & Arthur Ashmore & Stewart Gray (Doncaster 1958 & 66 & 78), Colin Roberts (Bradford City 1959), Derek Downing (Middlesbrough 1965), Graham Reed & Russell Wilcox (Northampton 1985 & 86), Will Foley (Swansea 1986), Gary Brook (Newport 1987), Wayne Scargill (Bradford City 94-95),Andy Hayward (Rotherham Utd.).

96-97 Captain: Mark Hancock **96-97 Top Scorer:** Scott Armstrong (17) **96-97 P.o.Y.:** Scott Armstrong

Local Newspapers: South Yorks Times, Hemsworth & South Elmsall Express.
Local Radio Stations: Radio Sheffield, Radio Hallam, Radio Leeds.

Frickley Athletic

Match No.	Date	Venue H/A	Competition	Opponents	Result	League Pos.	Attendance	Goalscorers (Times if known)
1	Aug 24	H	UL	Leek Town	Lost 2-3		190	Duffty 58, Dickenson 89 (pen)
2	Aug 26	A	UL	Gainsborough Trinity	Lost 0-2		527	
3	Aug 31	A	UL	Lancaster City	Won 3-1	14	262	Coleman og 1, Dring 18, Armstrong 43
4	Sep 3	H	UL	Boston United	Drew 2-2		239	Hardy og 3, Yates 53
5	Sep 7	H	UL	Runcorn	Drew 1-1	15	206	Armstrong 41
6	Sep 10	A	UL	Spennymoor United	Lost 1-3	20	167	Dring 86
7	**Sep 14**	**A**	**FAC 1 Q**	**Murton**	**Won 3-1**		**85**	**Thorpe 36, Field 42, Dring 61**
8	Sep 21	A	UL	Knowsley United	Drew 0-0	20	86	
9	Sep 25	A	UL	Bishop Auckland	Drew 2-2	19	142	Fields 10, Dring 64
10	**Sep 28**	**H**	**FAC 2 Q**	**Bradford (PA)**	**Won 1-0**		**269**	**Armstrong 77**
11	**Oct 1**	**H**	**ULC**	**Farsley Celtic**	**Won 1-0**		**99**	**Duffty 70**
12	Oct 5	A	UL	Buxton	Won 3-1	19	220	Stubbs 44, Kelly 60, N Dempsey 87
13	**Oct 12**	**H**	**FAC 3 Q**	**Newcastle Town**	**Drew 1-1**		**246**	**Thorpe 77**
14	**Oct 15**	**A**	**FAC 3QR**	**Newcastle Town**	**Lost 1-2**		**102**	**Thorpe 24**
15	**Oct 19**	**A**	**FAT 1 Q**	**R C Warwick**	**Won 2-1**		**103**	**Thorpe 18, Hatto 51 (pen)**
16	Oct 22	H	UL	Spennymoor United	Won 5-2		228	Hatto 37 (p), 70, Armstrong 53, 58, Duffey 75
17	Oct 26	H	UL	Chorley	Won 2-1	17	224	Hatto 4 (pen), Armstrong 38
18	Nov 2	A	UL	Barrow	Lost 0-2		1152	
19	**Nov 5**	**H**	**ULC**	**Bishop Auckand**	**Won 1-0**		**85**	**Dring 80**
20	**Nov 9**	**A**	**FAT 2 Q**	**Lincoln United**	**Won 4-3**		**161**	**Fields 60, Armstrong 72, Duffty 83, Thorpe 87**
21	Nov 12	H	UL	Blyth Spartans	Drew 2-2	18	153	Armstrong 7, Hatto 44
22	Nov 23	A	UL	Colwyn Bay	Lost 0-5	18	275	
23	Nov 26	H	UL	Hyde United	Lost 0-3		178	
24	**Nov 30**	**A**	**FAT 3 Q**	**Colwyn Bay**	**Lost 0-1**		**264**	
25	Dec 7	H	UL	Winsford United	Won 3-2	18	138	Armstrong 30, Field 60, 76
26	**Dec 10**	**H**	**S & H SC**	**Norton Woodside**	**Won 6-1**		**69**	**Dr'ng, St'bbs, Th'pe, A'strng, T'son, N D'sey**
27	Dec 14	A	UL	Witton Albion	Won 2-0	18	239	Dring 27, Armstrong 37
28	**Dec 17**	**A**	**ULCC**	**Gainsborough Trinity**	**Lost 0-3**		**275**	
29	Dec 21	H	UL	Knowsley United	Lost 0-2	18	200	
30	Dec 26	A	UL	Emley	Drew 3-3	18	427	Field 14, Thorpe 45, 83
31	Dec 28	H	UL	Alfreton Town	Won 7-2	18	190	Duffty (4), Hatto, Dring, Armstrong
32	Jan 11	A	UL	Bamber Bridge	Lost 1-5	18	291	Lancaster 45
33	**Jan 13**	**H**	**S & H SC**	**Worksop Town**	**Lost 1-2**		**139**	**Hancock 63**
34	Jan 18	H	UL	Buxton	Won 3-1	17	132	Dempsey 22, 68, Armstrong 29
35	Jan 25	A	UL	Hyde United	Lost 1-5	17	449	Hatto 3 (pen)
36	Jan 28	A	UL	Guiseley	Lost 0-1		207	
37	Feb 1	H	UL	Witton Albion	Lost 1-2	17	108	Lancaster 81
38	Feb 8	H	UL	Lancaster City	Won 3-1	16	165	Duffty 10, Lancaster 23, 77
39	Feb 15	A	UL	Leek Town	Lost 0-3	18	417	
40	Feb 22	A	UL	Chorley	Won 1-0	16	306	Dring 68
41	Feb 25	H	UL	Bishop Auckland	Lost 0-4		129	
42	Mar 1	H	UL	Marine	Lost 0-1	16	144	
43	Mar 8	H	UL	Accrington Stanley	Lost 0-1	17	209	
44	Mar 15	H	UL	Guiseley	Lost 0-1	17	254	
45	Mar 22	A	UL	Runcorn	Drew 0-0	17	338	
46	Mar 29	A	UL	Boston United	Won 3-2	17	966	Fuller 5, Clyde 37 (og), Armstrong 85
47	Mar 31	H	UL	Emley	Lost 1-2	17	277	Armstrong 12
48	Apr 5	H	UL	Bamber Bridge	Won 1-0	15	112	Armstrong 45
49	Apr 8	A	UL	Marine	Lost 1-3	16	229	Yates 7
50	Apr 12	H	UL	Barrow	Lost 0-2	16	195	
51	Apr 15	H	UL	Gainsborough Trinity	Drew 2-2		157	Dickinson 8, Kelly 14
52	Apr 19	A	UL	Winsford United	Lost 0-1	16	93	
53	Apr 22	A	UL	Alfreton Town	Lost 0-1		124	
54	Apr 26	A	UL	Accrington Stanley	Lost 0-4	16	412	
55	Apr 29	A	UL	Blyth Spartans	Lost 3-6		428	Kelly 67, Hatto 68, 80
56	May 1	H	UL	Colwyn Bay	Lost 3-4	18	127	Field 58, Hancock 84, 89 (2 penalties)

FRICKLEY ATHLETIC PLAYING SQUAD 1997-98

Goalkeepers: Tommy Allen (BCCI)

Defenders: Glyn Yates (Maltby MW, Gainsborough T, Boston U, Maltby MW), **Paul Taylor** (BCCI), **Ian Thompson** (Altrincham, Frickley, Goole, Worksop, Goole,Worksop, Gainsborough T), **David O'Sullivan** (Worksop, Frickley, East Stirling), **Mark Hancock** (Wharncliffe Arms, Grimethorpe MW), **Gary Hatto** (Ossett T, Frickley, Doncaster, Huddersfield)

Midfielders: Chris Hilton (Rotherham), **Glen Dempsey** (ICI Blackley, Horwich, ICI Blackley), **Darren Fields** (Pontefract Coll, Grimethorpe CW, Barnsley), **Kevin Kelly** (Huddersfield), **Justin Dickinson** (Tickhill)

Forwards: Gary Duffy (Rotherham), **Ian Dring** (Yeovil), **Darren Lancaster** (Maltby Main, Blackpool R, Blackpool), **Terry Stubbs** (BCCI), **Scott Armstrong** (Huddersfield), **Simon Fuller** (Ossett T, Bradford C)

GAINSBOROUGH TRINITY

PROGRAMME DETAILS:
Pages: 32 **Price:** £1
Editor: Basil Godley
(01427 611612)

Formed: 1873 **Nickname:** The Blues
Colours: Blue Shirts, White Shorts, Blue Socks.
Change colours: Green & white/green/green
Midweek home matchday: Wednesday
Reserve Team's League:

Chairman: John Davis. **President:** Ken Marsden.
Secretary: Frank Nicholson, 9 North Street, Morton, Gainsborough, Lincs DN21 3AS. Tel. 01427 615239, Fax 01427 615239.
Manager: Ernie Moss. **Asst Manager:** Phil Tingay.
Physio: Ernie Beaumont.
Commercial Director: Tim Hanson. **Press Officer:** Frank Nicholson
GROUND Address: The Northolme, Gainsborough, Lincs DN21 2QW (01427 613295 - office or 01427 615625 - club) (Fax 01427 613295)
Directions: The Northolme is situated near the town centre 250 yards from the Magistrates Court and the Post Office. Two miles from Lea Road (BR).
Capacity: 3,500 **Cover:** 2,500 **Seats:** 238 **Floodlights:** Yes
Clubhouse: Executive 'Club on the Park' (01427 615625) open Saturday matchday lunchtimes. Restaurant facilities.
Club Shop: Yes, contact Nigel Tasker on 01522 542014.
Metal Badges: Yes **Sponsors:** Eastern Generation.

PREVIOUS - Leagues: Mid.Counties 1889-96, 12-60, 61-68, Football Lge 1896-1912, Cent Alliance 60-61.

CLUB RECORDS - Attendance: 9,760 v Scunthorpe Utd. Midland Lge. 1948. **Fee Paid:** £3,000 for Stuart Lowe (Buxton 89-90). **Received:** £30,000 for Tony James (Lincoln 1988). **Win:** 7-0 v Fleetwood Town and Great Harwood Town. **Defeat:** 2-7 v Hyde Utd.
Best Season - FA Cup: 3rd Rd 1886-87, 1st Rd on 33 occasions. **FA Trophy:** 2nd Rd, 2nd replay 86-87.
Players progressing to Football League: Since 1980 - Stewart Evans (Sheffield Utd 1980), Tony James, Ian Bowling & John Schofield (Lincoln 1988), Dave Redfern (Stockport 1991), Richard Logan (Huddersfield 1993), Glenn Humphries (Hull City).
96-97 Captain: Mick Matthews **96-97 P.o.Y.:** Chris Timons **96-97 Top scorer:** Jason Maxwell
Local Newspapers: Gainsborough News, Lincolnshire Echo. **Local Radio Stations:** BBC Radio Lincs, Lincs FM

HONOURS: Northern Premier Lge Cup 81-82 96-97 (R-up 71-72), Midland Co's Lge 1890-91, 1927-28, 48-49, 66-67 (R-up 1891-92, 95-96, 1913-14, 28-29), Lincs Senior Cup (15) 1889-90, 92-93, 94-95, 97-98, 1903-05, 06-07, 10-11, 46-49, 50-51, 57-59, 63-64

Gainsborough Trinity 96-97

Gainsborough Trinity

Match No.	Date	Venue H/A	Competition	Opponents	Result	League Pos.	Attendance	Goalscorers (Times if known)
1	Aug 24	A	UL	Witton Albion	Lost 1-2		535	Morrow 51
2	Aug 26	H	UL	Frickley Athletic	Won 2-0		527	Maxwell 3, Nicholson 69
3	Aug 31	H	UL	Colwyn Bay	Won 2-0	6	430	Williams 48, Maxwell 83
4	Sep 7	A	UL	Chorley	Won 4-3	5	398	Maxwell (3) 41, 57, 59, Tilly 55
5	Sep 10	H	UL	Guiseley	Won 1-0	4	545	Maxwell 67
6	**Sep 14**	**A**	**FAC 1 Q**	**Tow Law Town**	**Drew 1-1**			**Ellender 90**
7	**Sep 17**	**H**	**FAC 1QR**	**Tow Law Town**	**Won 2-0**		**519**	**Williams 37, Stiles 59**
8	Sep 21	H	UL	Marine	Lost 0-1	8	433	
9	Sep 23	A	UL	Emley	Drew 3-3	10	282	Morrow 7, Ellender 89, Cooper 90
10	**Sep 28**	**H**	**FAC 2 Q**	**Bridgnorth**	**Won 2-1**		**624**	**Morrow 30, Maxwell 38**
11	Oct 1	H	UL	Spennymoor United	Won 1-0		522	Smith 23
12	Oct 5	A	UL	Runcorn	Lost 1-2	8	353	Nicholson 62
13	Oct 8	H	UL	Emley	Lost 0-3		573	
14	**Oct 12**	**A**	**FAC 3 Q**	**Leek Town**	**Lost 0-2**		**577**	
15	Oct 16	A	UL	Winsford United	Drew 1-1		124	Ellender 27
16	Oct 19	H	UL	Blyth Spartans	Lost 0-1	14	474	
17	Oct 26	A	UL	Hyde United	Lost 1-2	15	443	Morrow 65 (pen)
18	**Oct 29**	**A**	**UKC**	**Leek Town**	**Drew 0-0**		**222**	
19	Nov 2	H	UL	Accrington Stanley	Drew 2-2	16	511	Smith 18, Tilly 61
20	Nov 9	A	UL	Colwyn Bay	Won 2-0	16	241	Maxwell 5, Riley 26
21	Nov 12	H	UL	Alfreton Town	Won 3-0		453	Riley 37, 45, Tilly 74
22	Nov 16	A	UL	Bamber Bridge	Drew 1-1	13	253	Ward 12 (og)
23	Nov 23	H	UL	Bishop Auckland	Lost 0-1	14	401	
24	**Nov 27**	**A**	**ULPC**	**Boston United**	**Lost 2-5**		**250**	**Morrow 60, Nicholson 88**
25	**Nov 30**	**A**	**FAT 3 Q**	**Marine**	**Won 1-0**		**233**	**Maxwell 62**
26	**Dec 3**	**H**	**ULCC**	**Leek Town**	**Won 1-0**		**232**	**Timmons 3**
27	Dec 7	H	UL	Knowsley United	Won 2-0	13	318	Maxwell 26, Ellender 42
28	Dec 10	A	UL	Leek Town	Lost 0-1		226	Eastwood 30
29	Dec 14	A	UL	Lancaster City	Won 2-0	12	214	Morrow 71, Nicholson 80
30	**Dec 17**	**H**	**ULCC**	**Frickley Athletic**	**Won 3-0**		**275**	**Morrow (3) 19, 86, 90**
31	Dec 21	H	UL	Barrow	Won 3-0	11	457	Ellender 11, Tilly 83, Morrow 85
32	Jan 11	A	UL	Accrington Stanley	Won 4-0	12	480	Circuit 7, 50, Morrow 20, Maxwell 66
33	**Jan 18**	**H**	**FAT**	**Bradford (PA)**	**Lost 1-3**		**631**	**Matthews 83**
34	Jan 25	H	UL	Chorley	Won 3-0	9	440	Taylor 70, Morrow 81, Maxwell 90
35	Feb 1	A	UL	Bishop Auckland	Drew 3-3	9	165	Morrow 45, Maxwell 52, Timmons 60
36	Feb 8	A	UL	Barrow	Drew 2-2	9	1096	Parker 58 (og), Tilly 70
37	Feb 15	H	UL	Witton Albion	Won 3-0	8	383	Matthews 2, Maxwell 10, Morrow 79
38	**Feb 18**	**H**	**ULCC**	**Knowsley United**	**Won 2-1**		**323**	**Ellender 25, Maxwell 42**
39	Feb 22	A	UL	Boston United	Drew 1-1		801	Morrow 37
40	Feb 26	H	UL	Leek Town	Lost 0-1	10	517	
41	Mar 1	A	UL	Guiseley	Lost 0-1	9	432	
42	Mar 4	H	UL	Boston United	Drew 1-1		748	Dempsey 4
43	Mar 8	A	UL	Marine	Lost 0-2	10	373	
44	**Mar 12**	**A**	**ULCC**	**Accrington Stanley**	**Lost 0-1**		**263**	
45	Mar 15	A	UL	Spennymoor United	Won 2-1	10	164	Maxwell 19, Price 26
46	**Mar 18**	**H**	**ULCC**	**Accrington Stanley**	**Won 3-1**		**446**	**Maxwell 1, Matthews 52, Morrow 89**
47	Mar 22	H	UL	Lancaster City	Drew 1-1	10	408	Riley 87
48	Mar 26	A	UL	Alfreton Town	Won 1-0		255	Ellender 26
49	Mar 29	H	UL	Bamber Bridge	Lost 0-2	10	423	
50	Mar 31	A	UL	Buxton	Lost 1-2		228	Price 68 (pen)
51	Apr 2	H	UL	Buxton	Drew 1-1		442	Morrow 7
52	Apr 5	H	UL	Winsford United	Won 2-0	10	293	Maxwell 53, Morrow 60
53	Apr 12	A	UL	Blyth Spartans	Drew 1-1	10	551	Circuit 71
54	Apr 15	A	UL	Frickley Athletic	Drew 2-2	11	157	Ellender 31, Price 89 (pen)
55	Apr 22	H	UL	Runcorn	Won 4-1		406	Circuit 17, Matthews 26, Maxwell 48, Timmons 52
56	Apr 26	A	UL	Knowsley United	Won 1-0	10	72	Taylor 82
57	**Apr 29**	**A**	**ULCC F**	**Boston United**	**Won 1-0**		**2890**	**Morrow 97**
58	May 3	H	UL	Hyde United	Lost 0-1	10	610	

GAINSBOROUGH TRINITY PLAYING SQUAD 1997-98

Goalkeepers: Gary Ingham (Maltby MW, Bridlington, Goole, Shepshed Chart., Gainsborough T, Rotherham)

Defenders: Nigel Downing (Armthorpe W, Hatfield M, Armthorpe W, Rossington M, Sheffield Wed (J)), **Chris James** (Boston U, Worksop, Bridlington, Scarborough, Worksop, Sheffield), **Steve Price** (Oldham), **Paul Ellender** (Scunthorpe), **Neil Beech** (Sheffield U), **Will Davies** (K.Lynn, Derby), **Chris Timons** (Leyton O, Gainsborough T, Mansfield, Clipstone MW)

Midfielders: Kevin Riley (Armthorpe W, Harworth CI), **Jason Maxwell** (Buxton, Grantham, Appleby Frodingham, Scunthorpe (J)), **Richard Taylor** (Matlock, Frecheville Comm., Scarborough), **Mark Dempsey** (Frickley, Buxton, Altrincham, Macclesfield, Rotherham, Sheffield U, Manchester U), **Steve Circuit** (Macclesfield, Boston U, Halifax, Stafford R, Sheffield U)

Forwards: Mark Smith (Boston U, Scunthorpe, Grimsby, Huddersfield, Rochdale, Kettering, Scunthorpe, Gainsborough T, Worksop, Sheffield U), **Mick Matthews** (Kuitan (HK), Kitchee (HK), Boston U, Hull, Scarborough, Stockport, Scarborough, Halifax, Scunthorpe, Wolves), **Nick Tilly** (Matlock, Belper, Matlock, Sheffield, Matlock, Crookes), **Max Nicholson** (Torquay, Scunthorpe,Hereford, Doncaster)

GUISELEY

Formed: 1909 **Nickname:**
Colours: White/blue/white.
Change colours: Yellow/Navy
Midweek home matchday: Tuesday.
Reserves' League: Bolton & Dist Comb, Alliance Div

Chairman: Philip Rogerson **President:**
Secretary: Alan Walker, Riva Bungalow, Goose Lane, Hawksworth LS20 8PL (01943 875955)
Match Secretary: Bruce Speller, (01943 874534)
Manager: Steve Richards. **Asst Manager:** Greg Abbott.
Physio: John Rhodes
Commercial Manager: Les Wood (01132 509181)
Press Officer: John Martin (01943 879473)
GROUND Address: Nethermoor, Otley Road, Guiseley, Leeds LS20 8BT (0943 873223).
Directions: Via M1 to M62 junction 28, follow Leeds road to Leeds ring-road to junction of A65 at Horsforth. At r-about turn left onto A65 through Rawdon to Guiseley centre. Ground quarter of a mile past traffic lights, on the right, entrance on A65 opposite Silver Cross factory. Additional car parking available off Ings Crescent. Five mins walk from Guiseley (BR/Metro) station.
Capacity: 3,000 **Cover:** 1,040 **Seats:** 427 **Floodlights:** Yes

PROGRAMME DETAILS:
Pages: 40 **Price:** £1
Editor: Les Wood
(01532 509181)

Clubhouse: (01943 872872) Open before and after all games (closes 11pm). Snack bar within ground open before and during matches.
Club Shop: Sells programmes, various items of clothing, key rings, badges, mugs etc. Phone Jennifer Roseron 01943 879236 **Metal Badges:** Yes **Sponsors:** OHS Ltd.

PREVIOUS - Leagues: West Riding Co. Amtr/ West Yorks/ Yorkshire 68-82/ Northern Co's (East) 82-91.

CLUB RECORDS - Attendance: 2,486 v Bridlington Town, FA Vase Semi Final 1st Leg 89-90. **Best Season - FA Cup:** First Round Proper 1994-95 (lost 1-4 at Valley Parade). **FA Vase:** Winners 1990-91. **FA Trophy:** Semi-Final 1994-95.
Players progressing to Football League: Keith Walwyn (York City), Frank Harrison (Halifax Town), Dean Walling (Carlisle United), Richard Annan (Crewe Alexandra).
96-97 Captain: Chris Lee **96-97 P.o.Y.:** Steve Dickinson
96-97 Top scorer: Neil Matthews (25) **96-97 Supporters P.o.Y.:** Peter Atkinson
Local Newspapers: Yorkshire Evening Post, Bradford Telegraph & Argus, Airedale & Wharfedale Observer, Wharfe Valley Times.

HONOURS: FA Vase 90-91 (R-up 91-92, SF 89-90), FA Trophy SF 94-95, Northern Premier Lg Div 1 94-95 (Presidents Cup 94-95, Div 1 Cup 92-93), Northern Counties (East) Lg 90-91 (Lg Cup 90-91), West Riding County Cup(5 inc 94-95), Yorkshire Lg R-up 79-80 81-82 (Lg Cup 79-80).

Guiseley AFC: Back Row (L-R); John Rhodes (Physio), Marc Ledingham, Gavin Haigh, Simon Portrey, Paul Bottomley, Lee Adamson, Steve Dickinson, Paul Stevenson, Gavin Warbouys, Colin Hogarth, Steve Richards (Mgr). Front Row; Elliot Beddard, Neil Grayson, Ben Davey, Matt Edeson, Matt Flanagan, Peter Atkinson, Greg Abbott, Des Hazel.

Guiseley

Match No.	Date	Venue H/A	Competition	Opponents	Result	League Pos.	Attendance	Goalscorers (Times if known)
1	Aug 24	A	UL	Chorley	Lost 0-1		569	
2	Aug 26	H	UL	Lancaster City	Drew 1-1	19	312	Matthews 44
3	Sep 2	A	UL	Spennymoor United	Lost 1-4		242	Stevenson 63
4	Sep 7	H	UL	Barrow	Won 3-1	20	410	Graham 31, Matthews 55, 89
5	Sep 10	A	UL	Gainsborough Trinity	Lost 0-1	22	545	
6	**Sep 14**	**H**	**FAC 1 Q**	**Hucknall Town**	**Won 4-0**		**313**	**Flanagan, Matthews (3) 47, 60, 84**
7	Sep 17	H	UL	Spennymoor United	Won 2-1	14	362	Matthews 35 (pen), Graham 86
8	Sep 21	A	UL	Witton Albion	Lost 1-2	16	443	Matthews 83 (pen)
9	Sep 24	H	UL	Boston United	Won 1-0	15	328	Hook 34
10	**Sep 28**	**A**	**FAC 2 Q**	**Morecambe**	**Lost 1-4**		**729**	**Matthews 48 (pen)**
11	Oct 2	A	UL	Bishop Auckland	Lost 0-1		245	
12	Oct 5	H	UL	Colwyn Bay	Lost 0-1	20	417	
13	Oct 9	A	UL	Boston United	Drew 1-1		709	Parsley 81
14	Oct 12	H	UL	Alfreton Town	Drew 1-1	18	334	Matthews 71
15	Oct 19	A	UL	Runcorn	Lost 0-2		433	
16	Oct 22	H	UL	Hyde United	Lost 2-3	19	423	Parsley 37, Hook 79
17	Oct 26	H	UL	Knowsley United	Won 1-0	19	387	Hazel 61
18	Oct 28	A	UL	Buxton	Won 1-0		148	Foreman 55
19	Nov 2	A	UL	Leek Town	Won 3-1	13	391	Davison 19, 46, Hook 69
20	Nov 9	H	UL	Bamber Bridge	Won 5-0	10	513	Davison 43, 72, Abbott 45, Hazel 58, Matthews 88
21	Nov 12	H	UL	Buxton	Won 2-0		382	Davison 57, Abbott 73
22	Nov 16	A	UL	Alfreton Town	Won 5-4	8	283	Davison 69, 79, Lee 7, Hook 59, Matthews 66
23	**Nov 26**	**H**	**ULPC**	**Farsley Celtic**	**Drew 1-1**		**253**	**Ledingham 46**
24	Nov 30	A	UL	Winsford United	Drew 1-1	9	128	Elvidge 55
25	Dec 7	H	UL	Witton Albion	Won 3-0	8	358	Ledingham 33, Varadi 66, Matthews 82
26	**Dec 9**	**A**	**WRSC**	**Harrogate Railway**	**Won 2-1***		**98**	**Bottomley 26, Atkinson 120**
27	Dec 14	A	UL	Accrington Stanley	Won 2-1	6	544	Varadi 2, Bottomley 30
28	Dec 21	H	UL	Chorley	Lost 1-4	8	562	Varadi 52
29	Dec 26	A	UL	Blyth Spartans	Drew 1-1	6	583	Hazel 38
30	Dec 28	H	UL	Emley	Won 2-0	6	610	Abbott 20, Matthews 78
31	**Jan 18**	**H**	**FAT 1**	**Telford United**	**Won 2-1**		**778**	**Parsley 39, Abbott 61**
32	Jan 25	A	UL	Colwyn Bay	Drew 1-1	7	390	Matthews 49
33	Jan 28	H	UL	Frickley Athletic	Won 1-0	4	207	Matthews 31
34	Feb 1	H	UL	Blyth Spartans	Won 2-1	4	334	Matthews 10 (pen), 75
35	**Feb 8**	**A**	**FAT 2**	**Welling United**	**Drew 1-1**		778	**Matthews 44**
36	**Feb 11**	**H**	**FAT 2 R**	**Welling United**	**Won 1-0***		**523**	**Matthews 102**
37	Feb 15	A	UL	Barrow	Drew 1-1	6	968	Matthews 12
38	Feb 22	H	UL	Gainsborough Trinity	Won 1-0	4	432	Blackstone 43
39	**Feb 25**	**A**	**ULCC**	**Colwyn Bay**	**Drew 2-2**		**240**	**Green 25, Hunter 52**
40	**Mar 1**	**A**	**FAT 3**	**Stevenage Borough**	**Lost 0-1**		**2152**	
41	Mar 3	A	UL	Emley	Lost 0-4		312	
42	Mar 8	H	UL	Winsford United	Drew 1-1	7	345	Atkinson 35 (pen)
43	Mar 11	H	UL	Bishop Auckland	Drew 0-0		254	
44	**Mar 13**	**H**	**ULCC**	**Colwyn Bay**	**Lost 0-2**		**188**	
45	Mar 15	A	UL	Frickley Athletic	Won 1-0	6	254	Blackstone 46
46	Mar 22	H	UL	Leek Town	Won 2-0	6	480	Hazel 24, Hunter 39
47	Mar 24	A	UL	Hyde United	Drew 2-2		543	Hook 51, Hogarth 87
48	Mar 31	A	UL	Marine	Won 2-1	6	490	Matthews 67, Hazel 88
49	Apr 12	H	UL	Ackrington Stanley	Won 1-0	8	512	Blackstone 68
50	Apr 15	H	UL	Marine	Lost 0-1		297	
51	Apr 19	A	UL	Lancaster City	Won 2-1	8	197	Matthews 17 (pen), 71
52	Apr 22	A	UL	Knowsley United	Drew 2-2		50	Blackstone 55, Hunter 85
53	Apr 26	A	UL	Bamber Bridge	Lost 4-6	9	325	Hunter 6, 20, Blackstone 46, 89
54	May 3	H	UL	Runcorn	Lost 0-1	9	299	

* After Extra Time

GUISELEY PLAYING SQUAD 1997-98

Goalkeepers: Steve Dickinson (Bradford C)

Defenders: Steve Richards (Doncaster, Halifax, Scarborough, Camb.U, Lincoln C, Gainsborough T, York, Hull), **Peter Atkinson** (Otley T), **Paul Bottomley** (Bridlington, Guiseley, Garforth), **Neil Parsley** (Witton Alb, Exeter, WBA, Huddersfield, Leeds U, Witton Alb), **Colin Hogarth** (Lancaster, Guiseley, Harrogate T, Guiseley, Otley T, Thackley), **Steve Hook** (Chorley, Bury, Goole, Halifax), **Marc Ledingham** (Hull), **Paul Ryan** (Youth team)

Midfielders: Colin Hunter (Harrogate RA), **Gavin Haigh** (Hull), **Richard Hepworth** (Armthorpe W), **Greg Abbott** (Hull, Guiseley, Halifax, Bradford C, Coventry), **Chris Lee** (Hull, Scarborough, Rochdale, Bradford C), **Matthew Flanagan** (Youth team), **Ben Davey** (Hull), **Paul Olsson** (Darlington, Hartlepool, Scarborough, Exeter, Hull), **Richard Cooper** (Gainsborough T, Yeovil, Weymouth, Exeter, Lincoln C, Sheffield U)

Forwards: Neil Matthews (Gainsborough T, Dag & Red, Lincoln C, Stockport, Halifax, Grimsby), **Des Hazel** (Chesterfield, Rotherham, Sheffield Wed), **Simon Parke** (Bradford PA), **John Rickers** (Mansfield)

HYDE UNITED

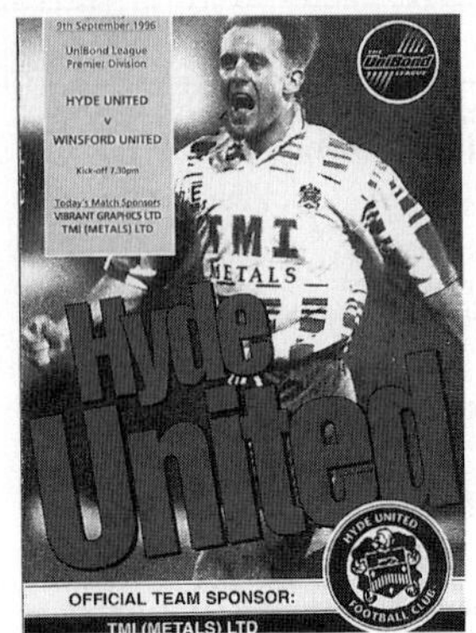

PROGRAMME DETAILS
Pages: 32 **Price:** £1.
Editor: M Dring

Formed: 1919 **Nickname:** The Tigers
Colours: Red & black/black/black
Change colours: Yellow/black/yellow & black
Midweek home matchday: Monday

Chairman: S C Hartley **Vice Chairman:**
Secretary / Press Officer: Ray Stanley, 15 Balmain Avenue, Gorton, Manchester M18 7PF (0161 223 2445)
Manager: Mike McKenzie **Coach:** Billy Garton
Commercial Manager: Roy Ollerenshaw **Physio:** G Clowes
GROUND Address: Tameside Stadium, Ewen Fields, Walker Lane, Hyde SK14 5PL (0161 368 1031).
Directions: On entering Hyde follow signs for Tameside Leisure Park - in Walker Lane take 2nd car park entrance nr Leisure Pool, follow road around to the stadium. Quarter of a mile from Newton (BR).
Capacity: 4,000 **Cover:** 2,000 **Seats:** 400 **Floodlights:** Yes
Clubhouse: (0161 368 1621). Open most nights, full facilities, 150 seats. Stewards: Lil & Doug.
Club Shop: Replica shirts, scarves, sports shirts, baseball caps, bronx hats, badges. Contact either Roy Ollerenshaw (0161 612 1781) or Secretary
Club Sponsors: TMI Metals.

PREVIOUS Leagues: Lancs & Cheshire 19-21 / Manchester 21-30 / Cheshire County 30-68 70-82/Northern Prem. 68-70

CLUB RECORDS - Attendance: 9,500 v Nelson, FA Cup 1952. **Scorer:** P O'Brien 247. **Appearances:** S Johnson 623. **Defeat:** (as Hyde F.C.) 0-26 v Preston North End, F.A. Cup. **Fee Paid:** £8,000 for Jim McCluskie (Mossley, 1989). **Fee Received:** £50.000 for Colin Little (Crewe Alexandra) 1995.
Best F.A. Cup season: 1st Rd 54-55 (v Workington), 83-84 (v Burnley),94-95 v Darlington.
Players progressing to Football League: C McClelland & J Webber & P Barry (B'burn 1946 & 47 & 48), L Battrick (Manc. City 1968), J Hilton (Wrexham 1950), D Teece (Hull 1952), R Calderbank & William Bell & Neil Colbourne (R'dale 1953 & 74 & 80), Jeff Johnson (Stockport 1976), David Constantine & Donald Graham (Bury 1979), George Oghani (Bolton 1983), Kevin Glendon (Burnley 1983), Peter Coyne (Swindon 1984), Colin Little (Crewe Alex. 1995)
96-97 Captain: Billy Garton **96-97 Supp P.o.Y.:** Val Owen **96-97 Players P.o.Y.:** Val Owen
Local Newspapers: North Cheshire Herald & Hyde Reporter. **Local Radio Stations:** GMR, Picadilly.

HONOURS: FA Trophy SF 88-89 94-95 95-96; Premier Inter-Lge Cup R-up(2) 88-90; NPL R-up(2) 87-89 (Lg Cup 85-86 88-89 95-96 (R-up 83-84 94-95), Chal. Shield 96-97, (R-up 86-87 90-91); Cheshire Co. Lg(3) 54-56 81-82 (Lg Cup 33-34 52-53 54-55 72-73 81-82, Lg Chal. Shield(2) 80-82; Manchester Lg(5) 20-23 28-29 29-30 (Lg (Gilgryst) Cup(4) 27-29 49-50 70-71); Cheshire Snr Cup 45-46 62-63 69-70 80-81 89-90 96-97; Manchester Prem. Cup 93-94, 94-95, 95-96, Senior Cup 74-75, Int Cup 55-56 56-57(jt), Junior Cup 21-22 68-69; Lancs & Cheshire F'lit Cup(2) 54-56; Ashton Chal. Cup(6) 30-34 39-40 47-48; Hyde Chal Cup(2) 27-29; Reporter Cup(3) 72-74 75-76; Gavin Nicholson Mem Trophy 79-80; Lancs F'lit Trophy(2) 86-88; Edward Case Cup(4) 56-8 59-60 80-81.

Hyde United 1996-97: Back Row (L/R): Terry Mojram, Andy Reid, David Nulan, Tony Camilleri, Martin Jones, Billy Garton, Paul Cox, Vinnie Brockie, Prince Moncrieffe, Darren Esdaille, Paul Varden, Arthur Williams, George Switzer. Front Row; Gary Henshaw, Lutel James, Gus Wilson, Tony Carroll, Jason Gallagher, Jason Donnelly, Ged Kimmins, Val Owen. *Photo - John Newton.*

Hyde United

Match No.	Date	Venue H/A	Competition	Opponents	Result	League Pos.	Attendance	Goalscorers (Times if known)
	Aug 17	A	U Shield	Bamber Bridge	Won 4-2		353	Kimmins 16, Owen 36, Valden 70, 88
1	Aug 24	A	UL	Lancaster City	Won 4-0		410	Carroll 9, Gallagher 32, Owen 71, Nelson 80
2	Aug 26	H	UL	Runcorn	Won 2-0		670	Varden 55, Nolan 90 (pen)
3	Aug 31	H	UL	Bishop Auckland	Drew 1-1	1	615	Nolan 19
4	Sep 2	A	UL	Emley	Won 4-2		419	Carroll 9, 80, Nolan 58 (pen), 84
5	Sep 7	A	UL	Blyth Spartans	Lost 1-2	3	687	Nolan 17
6	Sep 9	H	UL	Winsford United	Drew 0-0		548	
7	**Sep 14**	**A**	**FAC 1 Q**	**Warrington Town**	**Won 1-0**		**334**	**Kimmins 79**
8	Sep 17	A	UL	Witton Albion	Lost 0-6	4	527	
9	Sep 21	H	UL	Barrow	Won 1-0	4	653	Carroll 76
10	Sep 25	A	UL	Alfreton Town	Won 3-0	3	238	Carroll 64, Owen 70, Kimmins 83
11	**Sep 28**	**H**	**FAC 2 Q**	**Whitby Town**	**Lost 0-1**		**507**	
12	Sep 30	H	UL	Colwyn Bay	Drew 1-1		427	Kimmins 88
13	Oct 5	A	UL	Accrington Stanley	Lost 2-3	3	576	Nolan 45 (pen), Donnelly 82
14	Oct 7	H	UL	Marine	Drew 1-1		587	Moncrieffe 30
15	Oct 12	A	UL	Knowsley	Drew 3-3	3	120	Nolan 7, James 27, Moncrieffe 32
16	Oct 15	A	UL	Spennymoor United	Drew 1-1	5	172	Donnelly 70
17	Oct 19	H	UL	Bamber Bridge	Drew 2-2	5	478	James 30, Owen 31
18	Oct 22	A	UL	Guiseley	Won 3-2		423	Carroll 10, Kimmins 52, 83
19	Oct 26	H	UL	Gainsborough Trinity	Won 2-1	3	443	Carroll 53, James 79
20	**Oct 29**	**H**	**ULC**	**Curzon Ashton**	**Won 3-0**		**263**	**Carroll 24, 70, Nolan 58 (pen)**
21	Nov 2	A	UL	Chorley	Drew 3-3	3	579	James 39, Nolan 76 (p), Gallagher 85
22	Nov 9	H	UL	Leek Town	Won 3-1	3	609	Brockie 20, Donnelly 24, Cox 45
23	**Nov 18**	**H**	**UCSC**	**Witton Albion**	**Won 2-1**		**311**	**Donnelly 7, Carroll 74**
24	Nov 23	A	UL	Runcorn	Won 3-1	2	377	Brockie 32, Carroll 44, 46
25	Nov 26	A	UL	Frickley Athletic	Won 3-0		178	Kimmins 34, 84, Brockie 75
26	Nov 30	H	UL	Chorley	Won 3-2	1	622	Carroll 15, 62, Owen 83
27	**Dec 2**	**H**	**ULCC**	**Boston United**	**Drew 1-1**		**296**	**Nolan 88**
28	Dec 7	A	UL	Marine	Drew 1-1	1	387	Brockie 35
29	**Dec 11**	**A**	**ULCC**	**Boston United**	**Lost 2-3**		**496**	**Carroll 60, Cox 90**
30	Dec 21	H	UL	Boston United	Drew 2-2	2	509	Kimmins 15, 77
31	Dec 26	H	UL	Buxton	Won 2-0	2	604	Cox 59, Kimmins 61
32	Dec 28	A	UL	Winsford United	Lost 1-2	2	222	Owen 84
33	**Jan 18**	**H**	**FAT 1**	**Bedworth Town**	**Won 4-2**		**512**	**Kimmins 30, 54, Owen 46, Parnell 73**
34	Jan 25	H	UL	Frickley Athletic	Won 5-1	3	449	K'mins 12, 75, Brockie 25, C'roll 79, M'crieffe 87
35	Feb 1	A	UL	Bamber Bridge	Won 4-1	3	417	Carroll 44, Kimmins (3) 45, 46, 58
36	**Feb 8**	**A**	**FAT 2**	**Bromsgrove Rovers**	**Drew 1-1**		**971**	**Owen 73**
37	**Feb 10**	**H**	**FAT 2 R**	**Bromsgrove Rovers**	**Drew 2-2***		**707**	**Owen 59, Nolan 73**
38	Feb 15	H	UL	Accrington Stanley	Won 7-2	3	578	Carroll, Nolan (p), Owen (2), Kimmins, James (2)
39	**Feb 17**	**A**	**FAT 2 R**	**Bromsgrove Rovers**	**Won 2-0**		**642**	**Nolan 51, James 66**
40	Feb 19	A	UL	Boston United	Drew 0-0	3	1391	
41	**Mar 1**	**A**	**FAT 3**	**Ashton United**	**Lost 0-2**		**1118**	
42	**Mar 3**	**H**	**UCSC**	**Vauxhall Sports**	**Won 3-1**		**288**	**Nolan 1, Owen 41, Williams 25 (og)**
43	Mar 8	H	UL	Knowsley United	Won 4-0	3	421	Kimmins 36, Nolan 45, James 62, Carroll 87
44	**Mar 11**	**A**	**UCSC**	**Vauxhall GM**	**Lost 1-2**		**120**	**Moncrieffe 80**
45	Mar 15	A	UL	Leek Town	Drew 0-0	3	1065	
46	Mar 17	H	UL	Alfreton Town	Won 5-0		440	Nolan 19 (pen), 70, Leberl 73, Kimmins 77, James 84
47	Mar 22	H	UL	Emley	Lost 1-2	3	576	Henshaw 49
48	Mar 24	H	UL	Guiseley	Drew 2-2		543	James 26, Leberl 75
49	Mar 29	H	UL	Blyth Spartans	Lost 0-2		523	
50	Mar 31	A	UL	Barrow	Drew 1-1	3	1165	Lee 55 (og)
51	Apr 5	H	UL	Spennymoor United	Won 4-0	3	415	James 7, Owen 54, Carroll 38, 50
52	Apr 9	A	UL	Bishop Auckland	Lost 0-3		122	
53	Apr 12	H	UL	Witton Albion	Won 1-0	3	565	Moncrieffe 50
54	**Apr 19**	**N**	**UCSC F**	**Macclesfield Town**	**Won 3-0***		**1005**	**Kimmins 99, James 103, 115**
55	Apr 21	H	UL	Lancaster City	Drew 0-0		100	
56	Apr 23	A	UL	Buxton	Won 3-0		105	Murray 37, James 41, Brockie 84
57	Apr 26	A	UL	Colwyn Bay	Won 3-1	3	313	Moncrieffe 19, Leberl 61, Nolan 86
58	May 3	A	UL	Gainsborough Trinity	Won 1-0	3	610	Nolan 81 (pen)

* After Extra Time

HYDE UNITED PLAYING SQUAD 1997-98

Goalkeepers: Martin Jones (Tranmere)

Defenders: George Switzer (Darlington, Manchester U), **Billy Garton** (Witton Alb, Salford, Manchester U), **Andy Reid** (Altrincham, Bury, Altrincham, Runcorn, Southport, Witton Alb), **Jason Gallagher** (Caernarfon, Witton Alb, Marine, Ternia (Belg), Newton), **Paul Cox** (Altrincham, Bramhall, Sale U), **Gus Wilson** (Crewe, Runcorn, Acc.Stanley, Droylsden, Flixton, Northwich V)

Midfielders: Gary Henshaw (Runcorn, Chorley, Swansea, Bolton, Grimsby), **David Nolan** (Barrow, Chester, Bromborough Pool, Prescot), **Jason Donnelly** (Winsford, Maine Road, Trafford), **Val Owen** (Local football), **Vince Brockie** (Guiseley, Goole, Doncaster, Leeds U), **Phil Taylor** (Ayr U), **Tony Camilleri** (Radcliffe B, Hyde U, Winsford, Mossley, Winsford, Southport, Hyde U, Lancaster, Buxton,Clitheroe, Radcliffe B, Irlam, Salford), **Darren Pybus** (Trafford, Droylsden, Altrincham, Maine Road, Hyde U, Crewe, Wythenshawe Am, Maine Road, York)

Forwards: Ged Kimmins (Salford), **Tony Carroll** (Bamber B, Radcliffe B), **Lutel James** (Guiseley, Selby, Guiseley, Yorkshire Am), **Prince Moncrieffe** (West Indies), **Nigel Evans** (Droyslden), **Jimmy Cameron** (Flixton, Halifax, Winsford, Runcorn, Winsford, Acc.Stanley, Buxton, Maine Road)

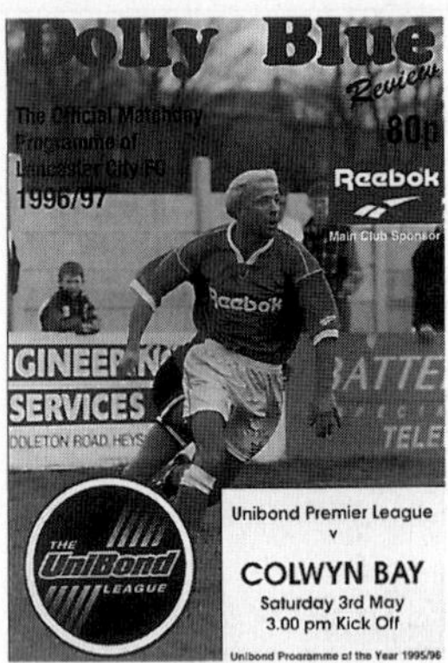

PROGRAMME DETAILS:
Pages: 32 **Price:** 80p
Editor: Paul Wilkinson
(c/o the club)

LANCASTER CITY

Formed: 1902 **Nickname:** Dolly Blues
Colours: Blue/white/blue
Change colours: All yellow
Midweek matchday: Tuesday.
Reserve League: North Western Alliance.
Club Fanzines: The Mad Axeman, Bambula Azzurri.

Chairman: Terry McWilliams **President:** M Woodhouse.
Vice-Chairman: K Lancaster. **Secretary:** Mike Sparks, 30 Salisbury Road, Lancaster LA1 5PJ (01524 33483).
Manager: Gordon Rayner **Coach:** Wayne Harrison
Physio: D McKevitt/F Charlton/D Hughes
Commercial Manager / Press Officer: Mike Hoyle (c/o the club).

GROUND Address: Giant Axe, West Road, Lancaster LA1 5PE (01524 382238 Office). **Directions:** M6 junc 33, follow into city, left at lights immediately after Waterstones bookshop, 2nd right, pass railway station on right, follow road down hill, ground 1st right. 5 mins walk from both bus & rail stations.
Capacity: 2,500 **Cover:** 800. **Seats:** 300 **Floodlights:** Yes
Clubhouse: "The Dolly Blue Tavern" just outside the ground. Two bars,hot and cold food available. Also a new tea bar inside ground serving food and drinks.
Club Shop: Inside ground, selling metal badges, pennants, programmes and other souvenirs etc. Contact Dave Crawford at club.
Sponsors: Reebok

PREVIOUS - Leagues: Lancs Combination 05-70/ Northern Premier 70-82/ North West Counties 82-87. **Name:** Lancaster Town. **Ground:** Quay Meadow 05-06 (club's 1st 2 games only!)

CLUB RECORDS - Attendance: 7,500 v Carlisle, FA Cup 1936. **Appearances:** Edgar J Parkinson. **Win:** 8-0 v Leyland Motors (A), 83-84. **Defeat:** 0-10 v Matlock T, NPL Division One, 73-74.
Best FA Cup season: 2nd Rd 46-47 (01-4 v Gateshead) 72-73 (1-2 v Notts County).
League Clubs defeated in FA Cup: Barrow, Stockport County 21-22.
Players progressing to Football League: J McNamee (Workington 75), B O'Callaghan (Stoke C.), I Stevens (Stockport Co. 86), G Johnstone (P.N.E. 93), M Clark & W Collins (Crewe Alex.), G Wilson (Crewe Alex.).
96-97 Captain: B Stimpson **96-97 Top Scorer:** J Coleman **96-97 P.o.Y:** S Trainer
Local Newspapers: Lancaster Guardian, Morcambe Visitor, Lancashire Evening Post and Lancaster Citizen.
Local Radio Stations: Red Rose, Radio Lancashire and Bay Radio.

HONOURS: Northern Prem. Lg Cup R-up 79-80 (Div 1 Cup R-up 90-91), Lancs Combination 21-22 29-30 34-35 35-36 (R-up 19-20 22-23 27-28 51-52, Lg Cup 21-22, Div 2 R-up 14-15), Lancs Jun. Cup (ATS Challenge Trophy) 27-28 28-29 30-31 33-34 51-52 74-75 (R-up 06-07 08-09 19-20 26-27), FA Vase 2nd Rd 86-87 90-91, FA Trophy 3rd Rd 74-75 75-76, Lancs Yth (u18) Cup 87-88 88-89 (R-up 86-87 89-90), President's Cup 1994-95. Unibond Div 1 95-96, Lge Cup 95-96.

Lancaster City: Back row (L-R): Coach, Trainer, S Trainor, B Stimpson, S Diggle, M Thornley, P Borrowdale, P Craven, S Phillips, Gordon Rayner (Mgr). Front Row: P Lodge, S Hartley, S Gelling, A McDonald, J Flannery, M Flanagan, R Evans
Photo - Neil Thaler.

Lancaster City

Match No.	Date	Venue H/A	Competition	Opponents	Result	League Pos.	Attendance	Goalscorers (Times if known)
1	Aug 24	H	UL	Hyde United	Lost 0-4		410	
2	Aug 26	A	UL	Guiseley	Drew 1-1	22	312	Coleman 90
3	Aug 31	H	UL	Frickley Athletic	Lost 1-3		262	Key 39
4	Sep 3	A	UL	Witton Albion	Won 2-1	21	463	McNeilis 46, Diggle 85
5	Sep 7	A	UL	Alfreton Town	Lost 0-1		232	
6	Sep 10	H	UL	Chorley	Won 4-1	14	302	Coleman (4) 18, 34, 52, 60
7	**Sep 14**	**A**	**FAC 1 Q**	**Lincoln United**	**Drew 2-2**		**139**	**Diggle 36, Coleman 68**
8	**Sep 17**	**H**	**FAC 1QR**	**Lincoln United**	**Won 3-2**		**229**	**Diggle 23, 31, Trainor 80**
9	Sep 21	H	UL	Spennymoor United	Won 1-0	12	275	Shirley 13
10	Sep 25	A	UL	Accrington Stanley	Lost 1-2	16	377	Coleman 12
11	**Sep 28**	**H**	**FAC 2 Q**	**Blakenall**	**Won 6-0**		**250**	**Hartley, Coleman (2), Borrowdale (2), Diggle**
12	**Oct 1**	**H**	**ULC**	**Netherfield**	**Drew 2-2**		**183**	**Diggle 60, Short 82 (og)**
13	Oct 5	A	UL	Emley	Drew 2-2	18	271	O'Donnell 58 (og), Diggle 74
14	Oct 8	H	UL	Blyth Spartans	Won 1-0	17	228	Diggle 16
15	**Oct 12**	**A**	**FAC 3 Q**	**North Ferriby United**	**Won 2-0**		**383**	**Coleman 11, Borrowdale 27**
16	**Oct 19**	**A**	**FAT 1 Q**	**Warrington Town**	**Won 2-0**		**104**	**Coleman 56, Borrowdale 90**
17	Oct 22	A	UL	Colwyn Bay	Drew 1-1	18	363	Gelling 6
18	**Oct 26**	**H**	**FAC 4 Q**	**Morecambe**	**Drew 1-1**		**2500**	**Diggle 44**
19	**Oct 30**	**A**	**FAC 4QR**	**Morecambe**	**Drew 2-2**		**2725**	**Flannery 31, Borrowdale 112**
20	Nov 2	A	UL	Runcorn	Drew 2-2	19	559	Shirley 56, Borrowdale 76
21	**Nov 4**	**A**	**FAC 4QR**	**Morecambe**	**Lost 2-4**		**2454**	**Shirley 13, Coleman 80**
22	**Nov 9**	**H**	**FAT 2 Q**	**Droylsden**	**Won 2-0**		**236**	**Shirley 19, Key 44**
23	Nov 16	A	UL	Marine	Lost 1-5	19	381	Borrowdale 22
24	**Nov 19**	**H**	**LFA ATS T**	**Blackpool Mechs**	**Won 9-1**		**135**	**C'man (4), McNeilis (2), F'nery, G'ling, B'dale**
25	Nov 23	H	UL	Emley	Lost 1-3	19	286	Borrowdale 6
26	Nov 26	H	UL	Winsford United	Drew 1-1		161	Armstrong 20
27	**Nov 30**	**A**	**FAT 3 Q**	**Worksop Town**	**Drew 0-0**		**346**	
28	**Dec 3**	**H**	**FAT 3QR**	**Worksop Town**	**Won 4-2**		**144**	**Armstrong 16, Coleman 28, Trainor 37, 83**
29	Dec 7	A	UL	Leek Town	Lost 1-2	19	346	Stimpson 79 (pen)
30	Dec 10	A	UL	Bamber Bridge	Won 2-0	19	323	Armstrong 5, Stimpson 89
31	Dec 14	H	UL	Gainsborough Trinity	Lost 0-2	19	214	
32	Jan 4	H	UL	Spennymoor United	Drew 1-1	18	192	Cain 14
33	**Jan 18**	**A**	**FAT 1**	**Colwyn Bay**	**Lost 0-6**		**335**	
34	Jan 21	A	UL	Barrow	Lost 0-3	19	1142	
35	Jan 25	H	UL	Accrington Stanley	Lost 1-2	19	301	Diggle 34
36	Feb 1	H	UL	Leek Town	Lost 0-3	19	238	
37	Feb 8	A	UL	Frickley Athletic	Lost 1-3	16	165	Diggle 11
38	Feb 11	H	UL	Barrow	Won 1-0		605	Diggle 14
39	Feb 15	A	UL	Winsford United	Won 1-0	19	146	Diggle 13
40	Feb 22	H	UL	Knowsley United	Drew 2-2	19	222	Key 80, Trainor 82
41	Mar 1	A	UL	Boston United	Lost 2-4	19	937	Borrowdale 28, Trainor 28
42	Mar 4	H	UL	Bamber Bridge	Lost 2-3	19	217	Borrowdale 2, Lodge 64
43	Mar 8	H	UL	Boston United	Lost 0-1	19	243	
44	Mar 11	H	UL	Witton Albion	Won 2-1		182	Diggle 69, Graham 71
45	Mar 13	A	UL	Bishop Auckland	Lost 2-4		142	Flannery 87, 90
46	Mar 15	A	UL	Chorley	Won 2-0	19	337	McNeilis 12, Diggle 59
47	Mar 18	H	UL	Marine	Lost 0-2		141	
48	Mar 22	A	UL	Gainsborough Trinity	Drew 1-1	19	408	Diggle 71
49	Mar 25	A	UL	Buxton	Lost 0-1			
50	Mar 29	H	UL	Bishop Auckland	Won 2-1	19	245	Graham 55, McKinlay 90 (og)
51	Apr 5	H	UL	Runcorn	Lost 0-2	19	197	
52	Apr 12	A	UL	Knowsley United	Lost 1-3	19	70	Dobie 26
53	Apr 15	H	UL	Alfreton Town	Won 1-0		146	Craven 52
54	Apr 19	H	UL	Guiseley	Lost 1-2	19	197	Borrowdale 26
55	Apr 21	A	UL	Hyde United	Drew 0-0		400	
56	Apr 26	A	UL	Blyth Spartans	Lost 1-3	18	487	Dobie 67 (pen)
57	Apr 29	H	UL	Buxton	Won 1-0		142	Trainor 3
58	May 3	H	UL	Colwyn Bay	Drew 1-1	17	154	A Jones 45

LANCASTER CITY PLAYING SQUAD 1997-98

Goalkeepers: Mark Thornley (Morecambe, Fleetwood, Matlock, Stafford R, Alfreton, Sutton T, Belper, Alfreton), **Lee Williams** (Bradford PA, Ovenden West Riding)

Defenders: Steve McNeilis (Witton Alb, Colne D, Northwich V, Burscough, Formby), **Steve Hartley** (Blackpool R) , **Paul Tomlinson** (Morecambe, Mossley, Burscough), **Jay Flannery** (Southport, Bamber B), **Alex Jones** (Southport, Stalybridge, Halifax, Rochdale, Motherwell, Rochdale, Carlisle, Preston, Oldham), **Peter Craven** (Farsley C, Bradford PA, Halifax, Preston, Halifax, Guiseley, Eccleshill U, Farsley C, Eccleshill U), **Barrie Stimpson** (Morecambe, Barrow, Lancaster, Barrow, Colne D, Morecambe, Gateshead, Hartlepool, Chesterfield, Hartlepool), **Robbie Armstrong** (Morecambe, Rhyl, Southport, Kirkby), **Alan McDonald** (Barrow, Chorley, Southport, Altrincham, Acc.Stanley, Witton Alb, Southport, Gen.Chemicals, St.Helens, Formby), **Jimmy Graham** (Guiseley, Hull, Rochdale, Bradford C)

Midfielders: Tony Key (Leek, Eastwood Hanley, Stoke), **Paul Lodge** (Bangor C, Southport, Morecambe, Witton Alb, Macclesfield, Southport, Barrow, Stockport, Bolton, Preston, Everton), **Lee Margerison** (Bradford PA, Gainsborough T, Slough, Bradford C), **Steve Horrocks** (Morecambe)

Forwards: Stuart Diggle (Fleetwood, Blackpool R, Southport, Blackpool Mech, Halifax, Blackpool), **Peter Borrowdale** (Morecambe, Blackpool Mech, Netherfield), **Stuart Connolly** (Gateshead, Ayr U), **Mark Dobie** (Workington, Queen of the South, Barrow, Gretna, Darlington, Torquay, Camb.U, Gretna, Workington), **Steve Trainor** (Fleetwood, Blackpool R, Fleetwood, Runcorn, Fleetwood, Blackpool)

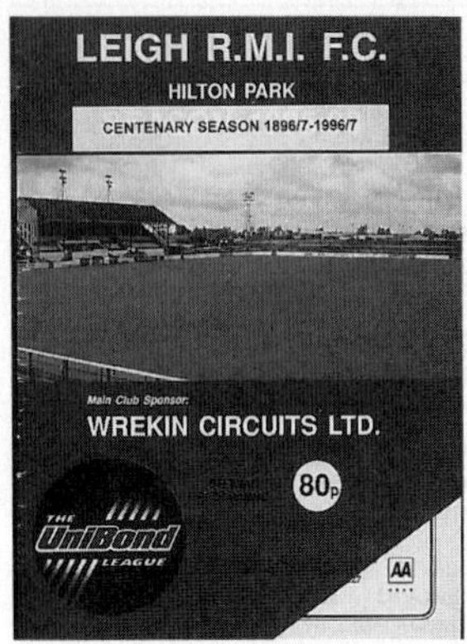

LEIGH R.M.I. F.C.
HILTON PARK
CENTENARY SEASON 1896/7-1996/7
Main Club Sponsor:
WREKIN CIRCUITS LTD.
80p
THE UniBond LEAGUE
AA

LEIGH R.M.I.

Formed: 1896 **Nickname:** Railwaymen
Colours: Red & white stripes/black/black
Change colours: All Yellow
Midweek home matchday: Tuesday
Reserve Team's League: Preston & District League

Chairman: Chris Healey **President:** G H Fisher
Secretary: Alan Robinson, 55 Janice Drive, Fulwood, Preston, Lancs. PR2 9TY. 01772 719266 (H) 01942 743743 (Club)
Manager: Steve Waywell **Asst Manager/Coach:** Kevin Booth

GROUND Address: Hilton Park, Kirkhall Lane, Leigh. WN7 1RN. 01942 743743 (Office). **Directions:** From M61 at junction 5, follow the Westhoughton sign to r'about, then follow signs to Leigh. Keep on main road to the traffic lights, turn left into Leigh Road, carry on about 3 miles to the traffic lights. Turn left and first right to the next set of lights. Turn right onto Atheleigh Way, A579 at the first set of traffic lights, turn left (B & Q on right), at the next set of lights turn right (Leigh town centre), at the 2nd opening on right turn into Prescott St., carry on to top, turn right, ground on left.
Capacity: 8000 **Cover:** 4,000 **Seats:** 2,000 **Floodlights:** Yes
Clubhouse: Yes. **Club Shop:** Not yet **Sponsors:** Wrekin Circuits Ltd
PREVIOUS - Name: Horwich R.M.I. to 1995. **Ground:** Grundy Hill, Horwich to 1994. **Leagues:** Lancs Alliance 1891-97/ Lancs 1897-1900/ Lancs Comb 17-18 19-39 46-68/ Cheshire County 68-82/ North West Counties 82-83.

PROGRAMME DETAILS:
Pages: 32 **Price:** 80p
Editor:

CLUB RECORDS - Attendance: 4,500. **Appearances:**
Goalscorer: **Fee Paid:** **Fee Received:** £5,000 for Tony McDonald (Chorley).
Best season - FA Trophy: Quarter Final 90-91 **FA Cup:** 1st Rd 28-29, 82-83. - **League clubs defeated:** None.
Players progressing to Football League: Harold Lea (Stockport 58), David Holland (Stockport 59), Jim Cunliffe (Stockport 60), Frank Wignall (Everton 58), Gary Cooper (Rochdale 73), Tony Caldwell (Bolton 83), Raymond Redshaw (Wigan 84), Tony Ellis (Oldham 86).
Local Newspapers: Bolton Evening News. **Local Radio:** Radio Lancs, Red Rose Radio, G.M.R.
96-97 Captain: Mark Schofield **96-97 P.o.Y.:** Graham Hill **96-97 Top Scorer:** Chris Shaw

HONOURS: Premier Inter League (GMAC) Cup 87-88, Cheshire County Lg 78-79 (Challenge Shield 78-79), Lancs Combination 57-58 (R-up 29-30 55-56 66-67, Lg Cup 28-29 53-54 56-57 65-66, Div 2 R-up 48-49 50-51), West Lancs Lg 10-11 11-12, Lancs Junior Cup 24-25 29-30 (R-up 53-54 57-58 62-63 82-83), Lancs Floodlit Trophy 84-85 (R-up 83-84), Lancs FA Cup 84-85, NPL Div 1 R-up 96-97.

Leigh RMI: Back Row (L-R); Paul Wheeler, Mark Schofield, Garaham Hill, Dave Felgate, Mick Charlton, Dave Ryding. Front Row; Matt Weston, Mick Wallace, Mascot, Keith Evans, Chris Shaw, Chris Bermingham.

Leigh RMI

Match No.	Date	Venue H/A	Competition	Opponents	Result	League Pos.	Attendance	Goalscorers (Times if known)
1	Aug 24	H	UL	Droylsden	Lost 1-3		205	Evans
2	Aug 26	A	UL	Atherton L R	Won 2-0		198	Evans (2)
3	**Aug 31**	**A**	**FAC Pre**	**Belper Town**	**Drew 1-1**		**256**	**Wallace**
4	**Sep 3**	**H**	**FAC R**	**Belper Town**	**Won 3-1**		**205**	**Ridings, Evans, McKenna**
5	Sep 7	A	UL	Whitley Bay	Won 2-1		138	Ridings, Bermingham
6	Sep 10	H	UL	Warrington Town	Won 1-0		146	Ridings
7	**Sep 14**	**H**	**FAC 1 Q**	**Alfreton Town**	**Won 2-0**		**165**	**Shaw (2)**
8	Sep 21	H	UL	Stocksbridge P S	Drew 1-1		164	Shaw
9	Sep 24	A	UL	Netherfield	Won 3-0		120	Wallace, Bermingham, Evans
10	**Sep 28**	**H**	**FAC 2 Q**	**Billingham Synthonia**	**Drew 1-1**		**195**	**Shaw**
11	**Oct 2**	**A**	**FAC 2 Q R**	**Billingham Synthonia**	**Won 3-2**		**238**	**Shaw, Evans, Leishman**
12	Oct 5	A	UL	Worksop Town	Drew 2-2		309	Wheeler, Evans
13	Oct 8	A	UL	Flixton	Won 1-0		171	Evans
14	**Oct 12**	**H**	**FAC 3 Q**	**Marine**	**Won 2-0**		**334**	**Bermingham, Shaw**
15	**Oct 15**	**H**	**Lg CC 1**	**Radcliffe Borough**	**Drew 0-0**		**110**	
16	**Oct 19**	**A**	**FAT 1 Q**	**Droylsden**	**Drew 1-1**		**140**	**Wallace**
17	**Oct 22**	**H**	**FAT R**	**Droylsden**	**Lost 1-3**		**112**	**Hill**
18	**Oct 25**	**H**	**FAC 4 Q**	**Runcorn**	**Lost 2-4**		**820**	**Ridings, Evans**
19	**Oct 29**	**A**	**Lg CC 1 R**	**Radcliffe Borough**	**Lost 1-3**		**144**	**Shaw**
20	Nov 2	A	UL	Bradford Park Ave	Won 3-0		304	Shaw (3)
21	Nov 4	H	UL	Ashton United	Won 2-0		141	Ridings, Evans
22	Nov 9	A	UL	Gretna	Won 2-1		65	Shaw, Bermingham
23	**Nov 11**	**A**	**UC 1**	**Ashton United**	**Drew 3-3**		**130**	**Fahey, Evans, Bermingham**
24	Nov 16	H	UL	Lincoln United	Won 2-1		216	Shaw, McKenna
25	**Nov 25**	**H**	**ATS T**	**Bacup Borough**	**Won 4-0**		**83**	**Wallace, Shaw (2), Evans**
26	Nov 30	H	UL	Atherton L R	Won 1-0		230	Ridings
27	Dec 3	H	UL	Curzon Ashton	Won 2-0		101	Shaw, Evans
28	Dec 7	A	UL	Stocksbridge P S	Drew 0-0		165	
29	**Dec 10**	**H**	**UC R**	**Ashton United**	**Drew 1-1**		**106**	**Evans**
30	Dec 14	H	UL	Matlock Town	Drew 1-1		140	Shaw
31	**Jan 14**	**A**	**ATS T 2**	**Burscough**	**Lost 0-1**		**115**	
32	Jan 18	H	UL	Congleton Town	Won 3-2		135	Shaw (2), Evans
33	Jan 25	A	UL	Eastwood Town	Drew 0-0		127	
34	Feb 1	A	UL	Matlock Town	Drew 1-1		196	Shaw
35	Feb 3	A	UL	Ashton United	Lost 1-2		166	Shaughnessy
36	Feb 8	H	UL	Whitley Bay	Won 1-0		133	Wheeler
37	Feb 11	A	UL	Warrington Town	Drew 1-1		101	Shaw
38	Feb 15	A	UL	Droylsden	Lost 2-3		128	Schofield, Shaughnessy
39	Feb 18	H	UL	Farsley Celtic	Lost 1-2		110	Evans
40	Feb 22	H	UL	Worksop Town	Lost 0-1		143	
41	Mar 1	A	UL	Congleton Town	Won 1-0		153	Shaw
42	Mar 4	H	UL	Harrogate Town	Won 2-0		104	Booth, Ridings
43	Mar 8	H	UL	Bradford Park Ave	Lost 1-2		162	Schofield
44	Mar 11	H	UL	Eastwood Town	Won 2-0		104	Shaw, Evans
45	Mar 15	A	UL	Lincoln United	Won 2-1		210	Evans (2)
46	Mar 22	A	UL	Harrogate Town	Won 2-0		154	Shaw, Sellars (og)
47	Mar 25	H	UL	Workington	Won 2-1		132	James, Shaughnessy
48	Mar 29	H	UL	Netherfield	Won 3-1		128	Ridings, Shaw, Bermingham
49	Mar 31	A	UL	Radcliffe Borough	Won 1-0		529	Hill
50	Apr 5	H	UL	Flixton	Won 4-1		130	James, Ridings, Shaw (2)
51	Apr 10	A	UL	Farsley Celtic	Drew 0-0		147	
52	Apr 12	A	UL	Curzon Ashton	Won 1-0		142	Shaw
53	Apr 19	H	UL	Great Harwood Town	Drew 1-1		191	Evans
54	Apr 22	A	UL	Great Harwood Town	Drew 1-1		130	Schofield
55	Apr 26	A	UL	Workington	Won 4-0		189	James, Ridings, Shaw, Bermingham
56	Apr 29	H	UL	Radcliffe Borough	Drew 2-2		830	James, Evans
57	May 3	H	UL	Gretna	Drew 0-0		151	

LEIGH RMI PLAYING SQUAD 1997-98

Goalkeepers: David Felgate (Wigan, Chester, Wolves, Bury, Bolton, Grimsby, Lincoln, Bolton, Blaenau Ffestiniog)

Defenders: Mike Wallace (Netherfield, Chorley, Witton Alb, Stockport, Manchester C), **Mike Charlton** (Ramsbottom U), **Steve Walmsley** (Stantondale), **Steve Byrne** (Ashton U, Runcorn, Vauxhall GM), **Graham Hill** (Runcorn, Curzon Ashton, Atherton Coll), **Damian Berry** (Bury), **Lee Anderson** (Southport, Altrincham, Bury), **Tony Edwards** (Chorley, Barrow, Altrincham, Runcorn, Marine,Witton Alb, Skelmersdale, Liverpool (J)), **Andy Burns** (Acc.Stanley, Wythenshawe Am), **Kevin Booth** (Flixton, Stalybridge, Curzon Ashton, Stalybridge, Bacup B, Stalybridge)

Midfielders: Jamie Fahey (St.Helens, Everton (J)), **Chris Bermingham** (Flixton, Tetley Walker), **Dave Ridings** (Crewe, Rochdale, Curzon Ashton, Lincoln C, Halifax, Curzon Ashton), **Mark Schofield** (Chorley, Southport, Horwich, Wigan), **Peter Smythe** (Curzon Ashton, Altrincham, Horwich, Manchester U), **Tony Briffa** (Runcorn, Acc.Stanley, Leigh, Curzon Ashton, Salford), **Martin James** (Acc.Stanley, Rotherham, Stockport, Preston)

Forwards: Chris Shaw (Ashton U, Witton Alb, Ashton U, Oldham T, Radcliffe B), **Keith Evans** (Hyde U, Ashton U, Curzon Ashton, Irlam, Preston), **Matthew Weston** (Droylsden, Altrincham, Ipswich (T)), **Steve Shaughnessy** (Droylsden, Flixton, Acc.Stanley, Stalybridge, Runcorn, Maine Road, Tranmere), **Paul Wheeler** (Stalybridge, Chester, Stockport, Hereford, Hull, Cardiff, Aberaman, Bristol R), **Tom McKenna** (Acc.Stanley, East Stirling, Gt.Harwood, Amazulu (SA), Rossendale, Bamber B, Castleton Gab., Stenhousemuir, Airdrie, Rochdale)

PROGRAMME DETAILS:
Pages: 24 **Price:** 80p
Editor: David Wotherspoon

MARINE

Formed: 1894 **Nickname:** The Mariners
Colours: White/black/black
Change colours: All Yellow
Midweek matchday: Tuesday
Reserve Team's League: Lancashire League Division One.

Chairman: Tom Culshaw **President:** David Bryant.
Secretary: John Wildman, 4 Ashbourne Avenue, Blundellsands, Liverpool L23 8TX (0151 924 5248).
Manager: Roly Howard **Asst Mgr/Coach:** Roger Patience
Press Officer: David Wotherspoon **Physio:** John Bradshaw
GROUND Address: Rossett Park, College Road, Crosby, Liverpool (0151 924 1743). **Directions:** College Road is off main Liverpool-Southport road (A565) in Crosby. Ground ten minutes walk from Crosby & Blundellsands (Mersey Rail). Bus No. 92.
Capacity: 2,500 **Cover:** 1,900 **Seats:** 400 **Floodlights:** 210 lux
Clubhouse: Open daily. Concert Hall (250 seats), Members Lounge (100 seats). **Club Shop:** Sells replica kit, baseball caps, polo shirts, scarves, badges, mugs, pens/pencils, bookmarks, car stickers, combs, tax disc holders. (Dave Rannard 0151 924 0076
Sponsors: Johnsons the Cleaners

PREVIOUS - Leagues: I Zingari/ Liverpool Co. Comb./ Lancs Combination 35-39 46-69/ Cheshire County 69-79. **Name:** Waterloo Melville. **Ground:** Waterloo Park 1894-1903.

CLUB RECORDS - Attendance: 4,000 v Nigeria, Friendly 49. **Goalscorer:** Paul Meachin 200. **Appearances:** Peter Smith 952. **Win:** 14-2 v Rossendale United (A), Cheshire County League 25/2/78. **Defeat:** 1-7 v Dulwich Hamlet, FA Amateur Cup final at West Ham, 1932. **Fee Paid:** £6,000 for Jon Penman (Southport October 1995). **Fee Received:** £20,000 for Richard Norris (Crewe 96). **Best FA Cup year:** 3rd Rd 92-93 (lost 1-3 at Crewe Alexandra).
League clubs defeated in FA Cup: Barnsley 75-76, Halifax Town 92-93.
Players progressing to Football League: A Sharrock, S Brooks (Southport 73 & 77), A Jones (Leeds 60), G Williams (Preston 72), J Lacy (Fulham & Spurs), P Beesly (Sheffield Utd), M Kearney (Everton 81), A Finlay (Shrewsbury 81), P Cook (Norwich), P Edwards (Crewe & Coventry), I Nolan (Tranmere), J McAteer (Liverpool), R Norris (Crewe 96).
96-97 Captain: Jon Gautrey **96-97 Top Scorer:** Paul McNally **96-97 P.o.Y:** Paul McNally
Local Press: Crosby Herald, Liverpool Echo, Daily Post **Local Radio:** BBC, Radio Merseyside, Radio City.

HONOURS: FA Amtr Cup R-up 31-32 (SF 46-47), FA Trophy SF 83-84 91-92, Northern Prem Lg 94-95 (R-up 85-86 91-92, Lg Cup 84-85 91-92 (R-up 80-81 85-86), Presidents Cup R-up 83-84 86-87), Cheshire Co. Lg 73-74 75-76 77-78 (R-up 72-73), Lancs Comb. R-up 46-47 (Lg Cup 46-47 63-64 68-69), Liverpool Comb. 27-28 30-31 33-34 34-35 (Lg Cup 30-31), Lancs Tphy 87-88 90-91, Lancs Jnr Cup 78-79, Lancs Amtr Cup 21-22 25-26 30-31 31-32 32-33, Liverpool Snr Cup 78-79 84-85 87-88 89-90 94-95, Liverpool Non-Lge Cup 68-69 75-76 76-77, Liverpool Chal. Cup 42-43 44-45 71-72.

Back Row (L-R): Roger Patience (Asst Mgr), John King, Graham Rowlands, Phil Greenhalgh, Keith Proctor, Kevin O'Brien, Andy Draper, Andy Rooney, Paul McNally, Roly Howard (Manager(, Eddie Murray. Front Row; John Dempsey (Asst Physio), John Bradshaw (Physio), Ian Renshaw, Jim Blackhurst, Andy Cavanagh, Robbie Cowley, Jon Gautrey, Ian Baines, Mick McDonough

Photo - Suzy James

Marine

Match No.	Date	Venue H/A	Competition	Opponents	Result	League Pos.	Attendance	Goalscorers (Times if known)
1	Aug 24	H	UL	Blyth Spartans	Lost 0-3		403	
2	Aug 26	A	UL	Emley	Lost 1-5		645	Rowlands 82
3	Aug 31	A	UL	Buxton	Won 2-0	15	298	McNally 42, Cowley 87
4	Sep 3	H	UL	Accrington Stanley	Won 2-1		417	Gautrey 28, Renshaw 87
5	Sep 7	H	UL	Boston United	Won 1-0	6	427	Renshaw 61
6	Sep 11	A	UL	Knowsley United	Lost 1-3	9	116	McNally 83
7	**Sep 14**	**A**	**FAC 1 Q**	**Radcliffe Borough**	**Won 2-0**		**250**	**Gautrey 20, McDonough 79**
8	Sep 17	H	UL	Colwyn Bay	Drew 0-0		342	
9	Sep 21	A	UL	Gainsborough Trinity	Won 1-0	6	433	McDonough 86
10	Sep 24	H	UL	Barrow	Drew 1-1	8	504	Renshaw 18
11	**Sep 28**	**H**	**FAC 2 Q**	**Sheffield**	**Won 1-0**		**247**	**Renshaw 83**
12	Oct 1	A	UL	Witton Albion	Drew 2-2		443	Gautrey 46, Blackhurst 89
13	Oct 5	H	UL	Leek Town	Drew 0-0	11	501	
14	Oct 7	A	UL	Hyde United	Drew 1-1	11	487	McNally 77
15	**Oct 12**	**A**	**FAC 3 Q**	**Leigh RMI**	**Lost 0-2**		**334**	
16	Oct 15	H	UL	Knowsley United	Drew 2-2		267	Gautrey 28, Rowlands 88
17	Oct 19	A	UL	Bishop Auckland	Drew 2-2	10	204	McNally 14, Rooney 54
18	Oct 22	H	UL	Bamber Bridge	Won 2-0	10	311	Draper 31, McNally 55
19	**Oct 28**	**H**	**ULC**	**Knowsley United**	**Lost 1-3**		**161**	**Cowley 13**
20	Nov 2	A	UL	Winsford United	Won 1-0	9	195	McDonough 49
21	Nov 9	H	UL	Runcorn	Won 1-0	6	528	McNally 49
22	Nov 12	A	UL	Barrow	Won 1-0		1452	Gautrey 37
23	Nov 16	H	UL	Lancaster City	Won 5-1	4	381	Draper (2), McNally, Barnicle, McDonough
24	**Nov 19**	**H**	**LFA ATS T**	**Great Harwood Town**	**Lost 0-1**		**97**	
25	Nov 23	H	UL	Alfreton Town	Drew 1-1	6	316	Barnicle 12
26	Nov 26	A	UL	Chorley	Lost 1-2		340	Draper 26
27	**Nov 30**	**H**	**FAT 3 Q**	**Gainsborough Trinity**	**Lost 0-1**		**233**	
28	Dec 7	H	UL	Hyde United	Drew 1-1	6	387	McNally 39
29	**Dec 10**	**A**	**LSC**	**Bootle**	**Lost 1-3**		**110**	**Cavanagh 40**
30	Dec 26	H	UL	Chorley	Won 1-0		533	Cowley 42
31	Jan 18	H	UL	Witton Albion	Drew 0-0	8	347	
32	Jan 25	A	UL	Alfreton Town	Won 1-0	6	281	McNally 48
33	Feb 1	A	UL	Accrington Stanley	Lost 0-1	8	444	
34	Feb 8	A	UL	Spennymoor United	Drew 0-0	8	215	
35	Feb 15	H	UL	Buxton	Won 3-0	7	303	McNally 10, Blackhurst 17, Daley 62
36	Feb 22	H	UL	Bishop Auckland	Lost 2-3	8	342	McNally 45, Gautrey 64 (pen)
37	Feb 25	A	UL	Runcorn	Drew 1-1		363	McNally 24
38	Mar 1	A	UL	Frickley Athletic	Won 1-0	7	144	Gautrey 38 (pen)
39	Mar 8	H	UL	Gainsborough Trinity	Won 2-0	6	373	Blackhurst 22, Draper 27
40	Mar 11	H	UL	Winsford United	Won 3-0		264	Blackhurst 37, 54, 57
41	Mar 15	A	UL	Bamber Bridge	Lost 0-1	5	389	
42	Mar 18	A	UL	Lancaster City	Won 2-0		141	Daley 10, Blackhurst 75
43	Mar 29	A	UL	Leek Town	Won 1-0		696	Ogley 31 (og)
44	Mar 31	H	UL	Guiseley	Lost 1-2	8	490	McNally 1
45	Apr 5	A	UL	Boston United	Lost 0-2	4	942	
46	Apr 8	H	UL	Frickley Athletic	Won 3-1		229	Cavanagh 42, Rowlands 49, Daley 60
47	Apr 12	H	UL	Emley	Drew 0-0	7	474	
48	Apr 15	A	UL	Guiseley	Won 1-0		297	Gautrey 70 (pen)
49	Apr 19	A	UL	Blyth Spartans	Drew 1-1	6	429	Nulty 81
50	Apr 24	A	UL	Colwyn Bay	Drew 0-0	7	193	
51	May 3	H	UL	Spennymoor United	Won 1-0	8	311	McNally 48

MARINE PLAYING SQUAD 1997-98

Goalkeepers: Kevin O'Brien (Sth Liverpool, Chorley, Runcorn, Burscough, Rhyl, Maghull, Everton)

Defenders: Ian Baines (Southport, Knowsley, Rhyl, Knowsley, Southport, Kirkby), **Keith Proctor** (Youth team), **Andy Rooney** (Barrow, Marine, Altrincham, Runcorn, Crewe, Everton), **Phil Greenhalgh** (Youth team), **Ray Moss** (Youth team), **AndyDraper** (Local football), **Mark Nulty** (Youth team)

Midfielders: Paul McNally (Warrington, Southport, Stalybridge, Runcorn, Oswestry), **Jon Gautrey** (Southport, Bolton), **Graham Rowlands** (Coastal (USA), Southport, Formby, Southport, Preston), **Ian Renshaw** (Youth team), **Andy Cavanagh** (Burscough, Southport), **Eddie Murray** (Altrincham, Tranmere, Stork, Maghull), **Tom Barnicle** (Youth team)

Forwards: Jimmy Blackhurst (Southport, Sth Liverpool, Marine), **Karl O'Neill** (Everton (T)), **Mick McDonough** (Burscough, Witton Alb, Burscough, Everton (T)), **Phil Daley** (Bangor C, Southport, Lincoln C, Wigan, Newton, Kirkby)

RADCLIFFE BOROUGH

PROGRAMME DETAILS:
Pages: 28 **Price:** 80p
Editor: David Johnson
(01772 495306)

Formed: 1949 **Nickname:** Boro'
Colours: Blue/blue/white.
Change colours: All white.
Midweek home matchday: Tuesday
Reserve Team: None.

Chairman: Bernard Manning Jnr **President:** A A Swarbrick
Vice Chairman: R Doyle **Company Secretary:** Graham E Fielding
Club Secretary: David Murgatroyd, 62 Croston Rd., Lostock Hall, Preston, PR5 5LA. 01772 314768 (H), 0161 724 8363 (B)
Manager: Kevin Glendon **Coach:** Frankie Bunn
Press Officer: **Physio:** Roy Davies
Comm. Co-ordinator: Mike Lester (0161 724 8346, Fax 0161 723 3178)

GROUND Address: Stainton Park, Pilkington Road, Radcliffe, Lancs M26 0PE (0161 724 5937-club), (0161-724-8346 Office) and FAX 0161 723 3178. 9197).
Directions: M62 junction 17 - follow signs for Whitefield and Bury. Take A665 to Radcliffe. Thro' town centre, turn right into Unsworth St. (opposite Turf Hotel). Ground on left half mile Colshaw Close East. 1/2 mile from Radcliffe (BR).
Capacity: 3,000 **Cover:** 1,000 **Seats:** 350 **Floodlights:** Yes
Clubhouse: (0161 724 5937) 'The Borough'- public house on ground. No food available.
Club Shop: Yes - contact Ryan Davies at ground.(0161-724-5937). **Sponsors:** Martin Darlington Transport

PREVIOUS - Ground: Bright Street 1949-70. **Leagues:** South East Lancs/ Manchester 53-63/ Lancs Combination 63-71/ Cheshire County 71-82/ North West Counties 82-87.

CLUB RECORDS - Attendance: 1,468 v Caernarvon Town, N.W.C. Lge 83. **Goalscorer:** Gary Haworth. **Appearances:** Chris Lilley. **Fee Paid:** £5,000 for Gary Walker (Buxton, 1991). **Fee Received:** £5,000 for Kevin Hulme (Bury, 1989). **Best season - FA Trophy:** 3rd Rd v Gateshead 1995-96. **FA Cup:** 2nd Qual. Rd replay 75-76 (1-4 at Rossendale Utd after 2-2 draw).
Players progressing to Football League: Jim Hayman (Bury 1950), Ian Wood (Oldham Athletic 1965), Robert Hutchinson (Rochdale 1974), Gary Hawarth (Rochdale 1984), Kevin Hulme (Bury 1989).
96-97 - Captain: Simon Whittle **P.o.Y.:** Loz Greenhalgh **Top scorer:** Ian Lunt
Local Press: Radcliffe Times, Bolton Evening News, Manchester Evening News.
Local Radio: Greater Manchester Radio (GMR), Piccadilly.

HONOURS: Unibond Lge Div One Champ 96-97; North West Counties Lg 84-85 (Div 2 82-83); Lancs Combination Lg Cup 69-70; Manchester Lg R-up 55-56 (Lg Cup 58-59 joint).

Radcliffe Borough FC: Back Row; Ian Philips, Peter McClae, Ian Lunt, Hraham Haddon, Andy Johnson, Colin McCrory, John Ryan, Joe Connor, Simon Whittle (Capt), Andy Kilner, Bernard Manning Jnr (Chr). Front Row; Mike Farrelly, Levi Edwards, Andy Brown, Jason Astley, Jon Senior, David Bean, Loz Greenhalgh, Neil Moss.

Radcliffe Borough

Match No.	Date	Venue H/A	Competition	Opponents	Result	Attendance	Goalscorers
1	Aug 24	A	UL	Worksop	Lost 0-1	814	
2	Aug 26	H	UL	Stocksbridge	Lost 0-1	180	
3	Aug 31	H	UL	Gretna	Won 5-2	141	Senior (2), Whittle, Bean, Lunt
4	Sep 7	A	UL	Bradford PA	Won 1-0	313	Lunt
5	Sep 10	H	UL	Farsley Celtic	Won 3-0	112	Bunn, Lunt, Connor
6	**Sep 14**	**H**	**FAC 1 Q**	**Marine**	**Lost 0-2**	**290**	
7	Sep 17	A	UL	Warrington	Won 3-0	88	Lunt, Astley, Edwards
8	Sep 21	A	UL	Netherfield	Won 1-0	117	Bean
9	Sep 24	H	UL	Curzon Ashton	Won 3-1	150	Edwards, Lunt (2)
10	Sep 28	H	UL	Worksop	Drew 1-1	165	Connor
11	Oct 5	H	UL	Lincoln	Lost 0-1	275	
12	Oct 8	A	UL	Workington	Drew 1-1	229	Bean
13	Oct 12	H	UL	Netherfield	Drew 1-1	170	Edwards
14	**Oct 15**	**A**	**ULC 1**	**Leigh**	**Drew 0-0**	**110**	
15	Oct 19	A	UL	Flixton	Won 3-1	184	McCrae, Lunt (2)
16	Oct 22	H	UL	Harrogate	Won 2-0	176	Ryan, Farrelly
17	Oct 26	A	UL	Matlock	Won 2-0	271	Edwards (2)
18	**Oct 29**	**H**	**ULC 1 R**	**Leigh**	**Won 3-1**	**244**	**Moss, Farrelly, McCrae**
19	Nov 2	H	UL	Whitley Bay	Lost 1-2	205	Lunt
20	Nov 5	A	UL	Atherton L R	Won 1-0	119	McCrae
21	Nov 9	A	UL	Ashton United	Won 3-1	194	Lunt (2), Connor
22	**Nov 12**	**H**	**MC 1**	**Chadderton**	**Won 1-0**	**167**	**Moss**
23	Nov 16	H	UL	Congleton	Won 3-2	175	McCrory, Ryan, Lunt
24	**Nov 19**	**A**	**ULC 2**	**Bamber Bridge**	**Won 5-1**	**116**	**Royle, Ryan (2), Astley, Brown**
25	Nov 23	H	UL	Droylsden	Won 4-0	244	McCrory (2), Lunt (2)
26	**Nov 27**	**A**	**FAT 3 Q**	**Spennymoor United**	**Lost 0-1**	**196**	
27	Dec 7	H	UL	Eastwood Town	Won 2-0	210	McCrory, Lunt
28	**Dec 10**	**H**	**U Div 1 C**	**Curzon Ashton**	**Won 1-0**	**102**	**Kamard (og)**
29	Dec 13	A	UL	Great Harwood	Won 2-0	233	Phillips, McCrory
30	**Dec 17**	**H**	**ULC 3**	**Barrow**	**Won 2-1**	**228**	**Lunt (2)**
31	Dec 21	H	UL	Atherton	Won 2-0	261	Lunt, McCrory
32	Dec 26	H	UL	Warrington	Won 3-0	220	Greenhaigh, Connor, McCrory
33	**Jan 14**	**H**	**ATS T**	**Barrow**	**Lost 0-1**	**188**	
34	Jan 18	H	UL	Flixton	Won 3-2	245	Ryan, Whittle, McCrae
35	Jan 25	A	UL	Harrogate	Drew 2-2	204	Lunt (2)
36	**Jan 29**	**H**	**MC 2**	**Glossop NE**	**Lost 1-3**	**140**	**Moss**
37	Feb 1	H	UL	Bradford PA	Won 2-0	288	Connor, McCrae
38	**Feb 4**	**H**	**U Div 1 C**	**Lincoln United**	**Won 5-1**	**160**	**Lunt (2), Edwards, Graham, Senior**
39	Feb 8	A	UL	Eastwood Town	Lost 0-1	170	
40	**Feb 11**	**A**	**ULC 4**	**Accrington Stanley**	**Drew 0-0**	**244**	
41	Feb 15	H	UL	Workington	Won 5-1	270	Connor (2), Brown, Edwards, Lunt
42	**Feb 18**	**H**	**PRES C**	**Alfreton Town**	**Won 3-1**	**117**	**Lunt, McCrory, Moss**
43	Feb 22	A	UL	Stocksbridge	Won 2-0	242	Lunt, McDonald
44	Mar 1	A	UL	Curzon Ashton	Won 3-0	150	Lunt, Whittle, McDonald
45	**Mar 4**	**H**	**PRES C**	**Accrington Stanley**	**Lost 0-3**	**237**	
46	Mar 8	A	UL	Droylsden	Lost 1-3	160	McDonald
47	Mar 14	H	UL	Great Harwood	Won 2-1	366	Edwards, Connor
48	**Mar 17**	**H**	**PRES C SF**	**Blyth Spartans**	**Drew 0-0**	**268**	
49	**Mar 20**	**H**	**U Dv1 C SF**	**Stourbridge PS**	**Won 2-1**	**180**	**Mcdonald, Whittle**
50	**Mar 25**	**A**	**U Dv1 C SF2**	**Stourbridge PS**	**Lost 0-1**	**295**	
51	Mar 29	A	UL	Gretna	Lost 0-1	112	
52	Mar 31	H	UL	Leigh RMI	Lost 0-1	529	
53	**Apr 2**	**A**	**PRES C SF2**	**Blyth Spartans**	**Lost 0-1**	**543**	
54	Apr 5	A	UL	Whitley Bay	Drew 1-1	141	McCrory
55	Apr 15	H	UL	Ashton United	Won 2-0	276	Lunt, Connor
56	Apr 19	A	UL	Congleton	Drew 0-0	165	
57	Apr 21	A	UL	Farsley Celtic	Won 1-0	132	McDonald
58	Apr 26	A	UL	Lincoln United	Lost 1-2	196	McDonald
59	Apr 29	A	UL	Leigh RMI	Drew 2-2	830	Lunt, Bean

RADCLIFFE BOROUGH PLAYING SQUAD 1997-98

Goalkeepers: Andy Johnston (Barrow, Knowsley, St.Helens, Barrow)

Defenders: Simon Whittle (Netherfield, Cheadle, Acc.Stanley, Chorley, Irlam, Horwich, Bolton), **David Bean** (Cheadle, Radcliffe B), **Ian Phillips** (Wythenshawe Am), **Mike Farrelly** (Winsford, Macclesfield, Altrincham, Preston), **Lawrence Greenhalgh** (Warrington, Rossendale, Bury), **Danny Donachie** (Leigh, Carlisle)

Midfielders: John Ryan (Stalybridge, Bury, Rochdale, Chesterfield, Mansfield, Oldham, Sheffield Wed, Newcastle, Oldham), **Jon Senior** (Ashton U, Leigh, Acc.Stanley, Southport, Horwich, Northwich V, Horwich, Bolton), **Levi Edwards** (Buxton, Radcliffe B, Winsford, Hyde U, Stockport, Altrincham, Crewe, Oldham, Manchester U, Ashton U, Barrow), **Paul Lyons** (Rochdale, Manchester U (T)), **Luke Hardman** (Youth team), **Joe Connor** (Runcorn, Witton Alb, Hyde U, Mossley, Hyde U, Stockport), **Graham Haddon** (Witton Alb, Horwich, Bamber B, Horwich, Radcliffe B, Leyland M, Horwich)

Forwards: Frankie Bunn (Stalybridge, Oldham, Luton), **Ian Lunt** (Curzon Ashton, Droylsden, Curzon Ashton, Winsford, Witton Alb, Altrincham), **Colin McCrory** (Curzon Ashton, Droylsden, Rossendale, Droylsden, Curzon Ashton, Irlam, Horwich, Curzon Ashton), **Andy Graham** (West Kirby, Radcliffe B, Hyde U, Northwich V, Staines, Wycombe, Wealdstone, Hyde U, Lancaster, Oldham, Bramhall), **Andy Kilner** (Fredrickstad (Belg), Radcliffe B, Chorley, Witton Alb, Stockport, Jonsereds IF (Swe), Vanessborgs IF (Swe), IF Halmin (Swe), Burnley), **Jason Astley** (Mossley, Radcliffe B, Mossley, Witton Alb)

RUNCORN A.F.C
MATCHDAY MAGAZINE

PREMIER DIVISION
RUNCORN v BAMBER BRIDGE
Tuesday, 15th April, 1997 Kick Off: 7.30pm
MAIN CLUB SPONSOR ICI
PROGRAMME SPONSOR ROBERT GLEAVE & SONS LTD.
PROGRAMME PRICE: £1.00

RUNCORN

Formed: 1918 **Nickname:** The Linnets
Colours: Yellow/green/yellow.
Change colours:
Midweek home matchday: Tuesday
Reserve Team's league: Northwest Alliance
Youth Team's league: Altrincham & Dist

Chairman: Dr David Robertson **Vice Chairman:** Tony Bamber
Secretary: Chris Henshall, 58 Minerva Close, Warrington, Cheshire WA4 2XN. Tel. 01925 650311 (Home), Tel/Fax 01928 560076 (Business).
Asst Secretary: Rob Ellison, 24 Cross Lane, Grappenhall, Warrington, Cheshire WA4 2LR. Tel. 01925 266999 (Home), 0802 480313 (Mobile).
Manager: Derek Brownbill **Assistant Manager:** Alan Blair
GROUND Address: Canal Street, Wivern Place, Runcorn, Cheshire WA7 1RZ. Tel. 01928 560076. Fax 01928 560076.
Directions: From South: Leave M56 (junct 11). Follow A56 to Warrington for 1.5 miles. Turn left at roundabout onto A558 signposted Liverpool for 3 miles. Take left hand slipway sign posted Football Ground. From North: Leave M62 (junct 7). Travel via Widnes and over Runcorn bridge. Follow signs for Northwich for 1 mile. Take left hand slipway sign posted Football Ground.
Capacity: 4,600 **Cover:** 1,200 **Seats:** 441 **Floodlights:** Yes
Clubhouse: Open on matchdays. Light snacks available.

PROGRAMME DETAILS:
Pages: 32 **Price:** £ 1.20
Editor:

Club Shop: Selling usual club memorabilia. Contact Phil Wainwright. Tel. 01928 560075. **Metal Badges:** Yes
PREVIOUS - Leagues: Lancs Combination/ Cheshire Co. Lg/ Northern Prem. Lg/ Alliance Prem./ GMV Conference.
CLUB RECORDS - Attendance: 10,111 v Preston - FA Cup 1938-39. **Goalscorer:** Alan Ryan. **Win:** 11-0 v Congelton. **Defeat:** 0-8 v South Shields. **Fee Paid:** £17,000 for Simon Rudge from Hyde United. **Fee Received:** £80,000 for Ian Woan from Nottingham Forest.
Players progressing to Football League: Mark McCarrick, Eddie Bishop, Jim Cumbes, Graham Abel, Barry Knowles, Mark Jones, Don Page, David Pugh, Ian Woan, Gary Brabin, Paul Robertson, Mike Smith.
96-97 Captain: Carl Ruffer **96-97 P.o.Y.:** Carl Ruffer **96-97 Top scorer:** Joey Dunn
Local Newspapers: Runcorn Weekley News, Liverpool Echo, Runcorn World, Manchester Evening News.
Local Radio Stations: Radio Merseyside, GMR.
HONOURS: Lancs Jnr Cup 1918-19; Cheshire Lg 1919-20, 36-37, 38-39, 39-40, 62-63; Cheshire Snr Cup 24-25, 35-36, 61-62, 64-65, 67-68, 73-74, 74-75, 84-89 (5 times), R-up 93-94; Cheshire Co. Bowl 37-38; Northern Premier Lg 75-76, 80-81; NPL Chall Cup 74-75, 79-80, 80-81; NPL Challenge Shield 80-81, 81-82; Alliance Premier Lg 81-82, Gola Lg Championship Shield 82-83, 85-86; Bob Lord Trophy 82-83, 84-85, R-up 91-92. FA Trophy R-up 85-86, 92-93, 93-94.

Runcorn AFC: Back Row (L-R): Ian Baker (Asst Comm Mgr), Tommy Ellis (Kit Mgr), Mal Liptrot (Trainer), Aidan Warder, Ian Callaghan, Paul Heavey, Mark Morris, Mark Ashton, Chris Lee, Joey Dunn, Phil Chadwick. Middle Row: Neil Cook, Steve Carragher, Neil Whalley, Peter Ellis, Carl Ruffer (Cpt), Gary Randles, Liam Watson, Gary Carey (Dir). Front Row: Kevin Warburton (Comm Mgr), Miss Janine Owen (Dir), John Brown (Life Vice President), Tony Loftus (Dir), Glen Jones (Dir), Tony Bamber (Vice Chr), Dr David Robertson (Chr), George Worrall (President), Alan Blair (Asst Mgr), Chris Henshall (Sec), Rob Ellison (Astt Sec), Alan Jones (Youth Mgr). *Photo - Weston Point Studios*

Runcorn

Match No.	Date	Venue H/A	Competition	Opponents	Result	League Pos.	Attendance	Goalscorers (Times if known)
1	Aug 24	H	UL	Boston United	Drew 1-1		501	Randles 75
2	Aug 26	A	UL	Hyde United	Lost 0-2		670	
3	Aug 31	A	UL	Accrington Stanley	Drew 2-2	17	702	Randles 7, Dunn 45
4	Sep 3	H	UL	Leek Town	Lost 0-2		430	
5	Sep 7	A	UL	Frickley Athletic	Drew 1-1	22	206	Dunn 10
6	Sep 9	A	UL	Buxton	Won 2-0		257	Langley 39, Dunn 67
7	Sep 14	H	UL	Blyth Spartans	Won 1-0	8	454	Dunn 26
8	Sep 21	H	UL	Emley	Drew 1-1	11	428	Dunn 6
9	**Sep 24**	**H**	**CSC**	**Congleton Town**	**Drew 1-1***		**230**	**Thomas 71**
10	Sep 28	A	UL	Spennymoor United	Lost 0-6		293	
11	**Oct 1**	**A**	**CSC**	**Congleton Town**	**Lost 1-3**		**254**	**Ellis 31**
12	Oct 5	H	UL	Gainsborough Trinity	Won 2-1	14	353	Chadwick 75, Heavey 86
13	Oct 8	A	UL	Chorley	Lost 0-4		526	
14	Oct 12	A	UL	Witton Albion	Won 5-1	15	615	Heavey 5, Dunn (3) 3, 48, 81 (p), Carraghor 78
15	Oct 15	H	UL	Alfreton Town	Won 1-0		261	Heavey 79
16	Oct 19	H	UL	Guiseley	Won 2-0	6	433	Carraghor 35, Heavey 61
17	Oct 22	A	UL	Leek Town	Drew 1-1	8	429	Dunn 77
18	**Oct 26**	**A**	**FAC 4 Q**	**Leigh RMI**	**Won 4-2**		**920**	**Wallace 1 (og), Lee 30, Carraghor 53, Heavey**
19	**Oct 30**	**A**	**ULC**	**Winsford United**	**Lost 1-3**		**154**	**75**
20	Nov 2	H	UL	Lancaster City	Won 3-2	8	559	**Dunn 47**
21	Nov 9	A	UL	Marine	Lost 0-1	9	528	Ruffer 81, Carraghor 84, Dunn 89
22	Nov 12	H	UL	Winsford United	Won 4-3	9	302	
23	**Nov 16**	**H**	**FAC 1**	**Darlington**	**Lost 1-4**		**1268**	Chadwick 40, Lee 52, N Ashton 71, Ruffer 78
24	Nov 23	H	UL	Hyde United	Lost 1-3	10	377	**Heavey 29**
25	**Nov 26**	**A**	**ULPC**	**Bamber Bridge**	**Won 3-2**		**168**	Dunn 9
26	**Nov 30**	**H**	**FAT 3 Q**	**Solihull Borough**	**Won 2-1**		**350**	**Dunn 9, Watson 56, Heavey 89**
27	Dec 7	H	UL	Barrow	Drew 0-0	12	392	**Dunn 37, 50**
28	Dec 10	A	UL	Colwyn Bay	Drew 3-3		269	
29	Dec 14	A	UL	Boston United	Drew 2-2	11	1035	Lee 14, 75, Carragher 78
30	Dec 21	A	UL	Bishop Auckland	Lost 0-2	13	225	Whalley 8, Watson 83
31	Jan 11	H	UL	Colwyn Bay	Won 5-0	11	349	
32	**Jan 18**	**A**	**FAT 1**	**Gateshead**	**Won 2-1**		**380**	Watson 20, 40, 66, Carraghor 60, Heavey 87
33	Jan 25	A	UL	Barrow	Drew 1-1	13	1288	**Ellis 72, Carragher 74**
34	Feb 1	H	UL	Buxton	Drew 1-1	12	356	Dunn 72 (pen)
35	**Feb 8**	**A**	**FAT 2**	**Hayes**	**Won 2-1**		**635**	Watson 12
36	Feb 15	A	UL	Blyth Spartans	Lost 2-3	14	520	**Warder 54, 77**
37	Feb 22	H	UL	Spennymoor United	Won 1-0	12	344	Dunn 60, Ruffer 90
38	Feb 25	H	UL	Marine	Drew 1-1		363	Heavey 8
39	**Mar 1**	**A**	**FAT 3**	**Gloucester City**	**Lost 1-3**		**1029**	Carragher 13
40	**Mar 4**	**H**	**ULPC**	**Barrow**	**Won 3-1**		**236**	**Finlay 50**
41	Mar 8	H	UL	Chorley	Lost 0-2	14	401	**Lee 5, Heavey 21, 55**
42	**Mar 11**	**H**	**ULPC**	**Farsley Celtic**	**Drew 0-0**		**234**	
43	Mar 15	A	UL	Alfreton Town	Drew 1-1	13	175	
44	**Mar 19**	**A**	**ULPC**	**Farsley Celtic**	**Won 2-1**		**197**	Ellis 65
45	Mar 22	H	UL	Frickley Athletic	Drew 0-0	13	338	**Carragher 49, Chadwick 65**
46	Mar 25	H	UL	Witton Albion	Won 4-0	13	386	
47	Mar 29	A	UL	Emley	Lost 1-2	13	253	Lee 31, 41, Dunn 64, Chadwick 84
48	Mar 31	H	UL	Knowsley United	Won 1-0	13	311	Randles 88
49	Apr 2	A	UL	Winsford United	Drew 0-0	12	182	Ruffer 10
50	Apr 5	A	UL	Lancaster City	Won 2-0	12	197	
51	Apr 9	A	UL	Knowsley United	Drew 1-1		56	Lee 53, 73
52	Apr 12	A	UL	Bamber Bridge	Won 5-0	11	375	Randles 56
53	Apr 15	H	UL	Bamber Bridge	Lost 1-2		273	Dunn 39, Brooks 48, Heavey (3) 56, 87, 89
54	Apr 19	H	UL	Accrington Stanley	Lost 1-3	12	342	Whalley 73
55	Apr 22	A	UL	Gainsborough Trinity	Lost 1-4		406	Heavey 24
56	**Apr 24**	**H**	**ULPC F**	**Blyth Spartans**	**Lost 0-1**		**223**	Heavey 37
57	Apr 26	H	UL	Bishop Auckland	Lost 1-3	12	191	
58	**May 1**	**A**	**ULPC FL**	**Blyth Spartans**	**Lost 2-3**		**770**	Watson 74
59	May 3	A	UL	Guiseley	Won 1-0	12	299	**Whalley 10, Watson 27**
								Randles 53

* After Extra Time

RUNCORN PLAYING SQUAD 1997-98

Goalkeepers: Mark Morris (Wrexham)

Defenders: Steve Carragher (Wrexham, Preston), **Carl Ruffer** (Everton (T)), **Mark Ashton** (Curzon Ashton, Warrington, Mossley, Castleton Gab, Mossley), **Alan Finley** (Stockport, Shrewsbury, Marine), **Peter Ellis** (Knowsley), **Neil Boardman** (Curzon Ashton, Warrington)

Midfielders: Neil Whalley (Witton Alb, Altrincham, Preston, Warrington), **IanCallaghan** (Curzon Ashton, Warrington, Droylsden, Hyde U, Northwich V, Bolton), **Gary Randles** (Curzon Ashton, Warrington, Interox, Greenalls, Warrington, Tetley Walker, Bolton (J)), **Aiden Warder** (Curzon Ashton, Warrington, Altrincham, Warrington, Monks Sports, Bolton (J)), **Matty Brooks** (Atherton LR, Wigan), **Steve Ashton** (Southport)

Forwards: Liam Watson (Witton Alb, Marine, Preston, Warrington, Burscough, Maghull), **Joey Dunn** (Atherton LR, Curzon Ashton, Warrington, Caernarfon,Warrington, Marine, Burscough, Altrincham, Formby, Sth Liverpool, Earle), **Paul Heavey** (Curzon Ashton, Warrington, Preston, Netherfield), **Chris Lee** (Curzon Ashton, Warrington, Chorley, Knowsley, Ford M), **Phil Chadwick** (Bamber B, Atherton Coll, Glossop, Hyde U, Droylsden), **Gavin McDonald** (Atherton LR,Warrington, Irlam, Chesterfield), **Bryan Griffiths** (Bangor C, Southport, Telford, Blackpool, Wigan, St.Helens)

SPENNYMOOR UNITED

PROGRAMME DETAILS:
Pages: 32 **Price:** 80p
Editor: Gary Nunn

Founded: 1904 **Nickname:** The Moors
Club colours: Black & white stripes/black/white.
Change colours: All red
Midweek home matches: Tuesday
Reserve Team: None
Local Press: Northern Echo; The Journal.

Chairman: Barry Hindmarch **Vice Chairman:** J Norman
President: T Beaumont MA
Secretary: Jim Nutt, 41 Warwick Close, Grange Estate, Spennymoor, County Durham DL16 6UU (01388 812179).
Manager: Matt Pearson **Asst Manager:** Dave Barton
Physio: Alan Jackson **Coach:** Managerial team
Commercial Mgr: Des Beamson
Press Off.: Gary Nunn 01388 810831

GROUND Address: Brewery Field, Durham Road, Spennymoor, County Durham DL16 6JN (01388 811934).
Directions: From South; A1(M), A167, A688, straight on at mini-r'bout, 3rd exit at next large r'bout (St Andrews church opposite), pass Asda on left, straight on at junction, pass Salvin Arms (Durham Rd), ground 200 yds on left. From A167 North - leave at Croxdale (N.E.S.S. factory), right at cemetary on left - this is Durham Rd - ground half mile on right. Nearest rail station is Durham - buses from there.
Capacity: 7,500 **Seats:** 300
Cover: 2,000 **Floodlights:** Yes
Clubhouse: (01388 814100) Open eves. 7-11, Sat 12-11, Sun 12-2 & 7-10.30. Bar snacks. Tea bar in ground.
Club Shop: Sells replica kit, memorabilia, programmes etc. Contact Peter Fletcher (01388 814100).
Sponsors: Home: Rothmans (Spennymoor). Away: Welland Medical (Leicester)

PREVIOUS -
Ground: Wood Vue 1901-1904.
Leagues: Northern 05-08 60-90; North Eastern 08-37 38-58; Wearside 37-38; Midland Counties 58-60; Northern Counties (East) 90-93.

CLUB RECORDS -
Attendance: 7,202 v Bishop Auckland, Durham County Challenge Cup 30/3/57.
Win: 19-0 v Eden Colliery, North Eastern Lge 6/2/37
Defeat: 0-16 v Sunderland 'A', Durham Snr Cup 4/1/02 (Half-time: 0-10)
Scorer: Dougie Humble 200+ **Appearances:** Ken Banks 600+
Fee Paid: £2,500 for Dean Gibb (Seaham Red Star, 1991)
Fee Received: £20,000 for Michael Heathcote (Sunderland, 1988)

BEST SEASON -
FA Trophy: Semi Final 77-78.
FA Cup: 3rd Rd 36-37 (lost 1-7 at West Bromwich Albion).
League clubs defeated: Hartlepool 27-28, Southport 75-76.

HONOURS:
Northern Premier Lg Cup 93-94 (Div 1 R-up 93-94), Northern Lg(6) 67-68 71-72 73-74 76-79 (R-up(3) 74-75 79-81, Lg Cup(5) 65-66 67-68 79-81 86-87, Turney Wylde Cup 80-81, J R Cleator Cup 80-81 86-87), Northern Counties (East) Lg 92-93 (Lg Cup 92-93), Durham Challenge Cup 29-30 44-45 45-46 53-54 62-63 67-68 72-73 73-74 74-75 75-76 78-79 82-83 93-94; Durham Benevolent Bowl 26-27 29-30 31-32 47-48 58-59 60-61, North Eastern Lg(4) 09-10 44-46 56-57 (Lg Cup 28-29).

Players progressing to Football League: Over fifty, including: H. Hubbick (Burnley, 3.25), T. Dawson (Charlton, 3.39), T. Flockett (Charlton, 4.49), J. Smallwood (Chesterfield, 12.49), J. Oakes (Aldershot, 5.54), J. Adams (Luton Town, 53), Alan Moore (Chesterfield), Michael Heathcote (Sunderland, 5.87), Jason Ainsley (Hartlepool, 94).

Spennymoor United

Match No.	Date	Venue H/A	Competition	Opponents	Result	League Pos.	Attendance	Goalscorers (Times if known)
1	Aug 24	H	UL	Bamber Bridge	Won 2-1		237	Innes 40, 76
2	Aug 26	A	UL	Blyth Spartans	Lost 0-2		509	
3	Aug 31	A	UL	Leek Town	Drew 1-1	12	358	Innes 75
4	Sep 3	H	UL	Guiseley	Won 4-1		242	Alderson 5, Shaw 21, 61, Cowell 53
5	Sep 7	A	UL	Winsford United	Drew 1-1	7	220	Cowell 72
6	Sep 10	H	UL	Frickley Athletic	Won 3-1		107	Shaw 33, 64, Innes 41
7	Sep 14	H	UL	Witton Albion	Drew 1-1	5	256	Shaw 80
8	Sep 17	A	UL	Guiseley	Lost 1-2		362	Innes 31
9	Sep 21	A	UL	Lancaster City	Lost 0-1	9	275	
10	Sep 24	H	UL	Blyth Spartans	Lost 0-2		319	
11	Sep 28	H	UL	Runcorn	Won 6-0	6	293	Innes (2), Shaw, Hunter, Healy, Purvis
12	Oct 1	A	UL	Gainsborough Trinity	Lost 0-1		522	
13	Oct 5	H	UL	Knowsley United	Won 5-0	5	262	Innes 43, A'rson 46, Shaw 51, P'ron 59, Todd
14	Oct 12	A	UL	Colwyn Bay	Drew 1-1	6	310	76
15	Oct 15	H	UL	Hyde United	Drew 1-1		172	Hunter 27
16	Oct 19	H	UL	Chorley	Drew 0-0	7	278	Ainsley 84
17	Oct 22	A	UL	Frickley Athletic	Lost 2-5	11	228	
18	**Oct 26**	**H**	**FAC 4 Q**	**Southport**	**Drew 2-2**		**558**	Innes 8, Alderson 23
19	**Oct 29**	**A**	**FAC 4QR**	**Southport**	**Lost 1-2**		**990**	**Innes 52, 55**
20	Nov 2	A	UL	Emley	Lost 0-3	12	249	**Alderson 85**
21	Nov 3	H	UL	Colwyn Bay	Lost 1-2		197	
22	Nov 9	H	UL	Barrow	Lost 1-2	15	329	Cowell 89
23	**Nov 13**	**A**	**DSC**	**Whickham**	**Won 5-0**		**100**	Shaw 10
24	Nov 16	A	UL	Chorley	Lost 0-1	16	300	**Healy 12, Shaw 48, 83, Alderson 72, Ainsley 86**
25	**Nov 20**	**A**	**DSC**	**Jarrow Roofing**	**Won 3-1**		**60**	
26	Nov 23	H	UL	Winsford United	Won 2-0	15	156	**Shaw 14, 23, Cowell 57**
27	**Nov 26**	**H**	**ULPC**	**Blyth Spartans**	**Drew 2-2**		**214**	Hunter 2, Ferguson 27
28	**Nov 30**	**H**	**FAT 3 Q**	**Radcliffe Borough**	**Won 1-0**		**196**	**Ainsley 58, Thompson 86 (og)**
29	Dec 7	A	UL	Buxton	Won 2-0	15	152	**Todd 23**
30	**Dec 11**	**A**	**ULPC**	**Blyth Spartans**	**Lost 1-2**		**389**	Shaw 38, Dobson 47
31	**Dec 17**	**H**	**ULPC**	**Harrogate Town**	**Won 4-1**		**86**	**Ainsley 29**
32	Jan 4	H	UL	Lancaster City	Drew 1-1	17	192	**Shaw 22, Dobson 48, Ainsley 86, Todd 89**
33	**Jan 18**	**H**	**FAT 1**	**Bishop Auckland**	**Lost 0-2**		**482**	Innes 16
34	**Jan 20**	**A**	**ULCC**	**Emley**	**Lost 0-1**		**180**	
35	Jan 25	H	UL	Boston United	Lost 1-3	17	254	
36	Feb 1	A	UL	Knowsley United	Drew 2-2	18	60	Ferguson 11
37	Feb 8	H	UL	Marine	Drew 0-0	18	215	Shaw 15, Alderson 23
38	**Feb 11**	**H**	**DSC Cup**	**Murton**	**Won 3-1**		**136**	
39	Feb 15	H	UL	Alfreton Town	Won 3-2	16	202	**Shaw 25, 89, Cowell 87**
40	Feb 22	A	UL	Runcorn	Lost 0-1	17	344	Shaw 26, Cowell 60, Innes 85
41	Mar 1	H	UL	Emley	Lost 2-3	17	162	
42	Mar 8	A	UL	Witton Albion	Won 2-1	16	360	Shaw 24 (pen), O'Hara 31
43	Mar 15	H	UL	Gainsborough Trinity	Lost 1-2	16	164	Alderson 40, 59
44	Mar 18	A	UL	Bamber Bridge	Won 3-1		166	Hunter 5
45	Mar 22	H	UL	Accrington Stanley	Drew 0-0	15	192	Alderson 8, 11, Bates 81
46	Mar 29	A	UL	Alfreton Town	Lost 1-2	16	230	
47	**Mar 31**	**A**	**DSC**	**Bishop Auckland**	**Lost 0-2**		**450**	Todd 23
48	Apr 5	A	UL	Hyde United	Lost 0-5	17	415	
49	Apr 12	H	UL	Buxton	Lost 0-1	18	152	
50	Apr 16	A	UL	Accrington Stanley	Lost 0-2		321	
51	Apr 19	A	UL	Barrow	Lost 0-1		896	
52	Apr 21	A	UL	Bishop Auckland	Lost 1-4		389	
53	Apr 24	A	UL	Boston United	Lost 0-2		422	Adamson 18
54	Apr 26	H	UL	Leek Town	Lost 0-1	19	151	
55	Apr 29	H	UL	Bishop Auckland	Lost 1-5		307	
56	May 3	A	UL	Marine	Lost 0-1	19	311	Cowell 47

SPENNYMOOR UNITED PLAYING SQUAD 1997-98

Goalkeepers: Adrian Swan (Billingham T, Darlington)

Defenders: Richie Watson (Billingham T, B Auckland, Billingham T, Whitley Bay, Billingham T), **Wes Saunders** (Torquay, Dundee, Carlisle, Newcastle U), **Graham Pepper** (Darlington, Newcastle U (T)), **Andy Elliott** (Dunston Fed), **Ralph Petitjean** (B Auckland, Spennymoor, Ferryhill), **Andy Purvis** (Blackpool), **GaryO'Hara** (Port Vale, Leeds U (T)), **Lee Adamson** (Murton, Harrogate T, Whitby, Murton), **Mark Elliott** (Darlington, Washington, Chester-L-S), **Graham Paxton** (Berwick R, Brandon U, B Stortford, Sawbridgeworth, Norwich (J))

Midfielders: David Robson (Dundton Fed, Spennymoor, Murton), **Paul Wratten** (B.Auckland, Hartlepool, Manchester U), **David Hunter** (Dunston Fed, Blyth S, Dunston Fed, Whitley Bay, Blyth S, Ipswich), **Gary Cowell** (Ferryhill), **Ralph Richards** (Billingham T), **Andy Howarth** (Gateshead), **Kevin Todd** (B Auckland, Berwick R, Whitley Bay, Newcastle Blue Star, Darlington, Newcastle U, Ryhope CA)

Forwards: Paul Dobson (Chester-L-S, B Auckland, Gateshead, Darlington, Lincoln C, Scarborough, Doncaster, Torquay, Horden CW, Hartlepool, Newcastle U), **Mark Ferguson** (Durham, Ipswich, Middlesbrough, Durham), **Andrew Shaw** (Whitley Bay, B Auckland, Crook), **Ritchie Alderson** (Whickham, Whitley Bay, Newcastle U (T))

PROGRAMME DETAILS:
Pages: 24 **Price:** 80p
Editor: A Maylor
Tel: 01606 552763

WINSFORD UNITED

Founded: 1883 **Nickname:** Blues
Colours: Royal/white/royal
Change colours: Maroon/white/white.
Midweek home matchday: Monday.
Reserve Team's league:

Chairman: M Morgan **President:** A Bayliss
Vice Chairman: D.Cotterill. **Secretary:** Peter Warburton, 3 Massey Avenue, Winsford, Cheshire CW7 3DU (01606 554295).
Manager: Dalton Steele **Asst Manager:** John Imrie
GROUND Address: Barton Stadium, Wharton, Winsford, Cheshire CW7 3EU (01606 593021).
Directions: From north; M6 junction 19, A556 towards Northwich to Davenham, then A5018 to Winsford. From south; M6 junction 18, A54 through Middlewich to Winsford. Ground quarter mile off main road in Wharton area of town. 1 mile from Winsford (BR).
Capacity: 6,000 **Cover:** 5,000 **Seats:** 250 **Floodlights:** Yes
Clubhouse: Mon-Sat 8-11pm, Sun 8-10.30pm
Club Shop: Yes - contact E Welch
Sponsors: Dickson Motors Ltd, Winsford (Ford).

PREVIOUS - Leagues: The Combination 02-04/ Cheshire County 19-40 47-82/ North West Counties 82-87. **Name:** Over Wanderers (prior to 1914).

CLUB RECORDS - Attendance: 7,000 v Witton Albion 1947. **Goalscorer:** Graham Smith 66. **Appearances:** Edward Harrop 400. **Fee Paid:** Nil. **Fee Received:** £6,000 for Neville Southall from Bury.
Best Season - F.A. Cup: 2nd Rd 1887-88. 1st Rd 1975-76 1991-92. **F.A. Trophy:** Qtr Finals 77-78.
League clubs defeated: None.
Players progressing to Football League: W Foulkes (Chester 48), C Marsh (Leeds U. 48), B Nicol (Rochdale 49), E Johnson (Coventry 52), W Hughes (Liverpool 54), R Lewis (Luton 54), W Heggie (Accrington 55), J Richardson (Birmingham C. 59), J Abbott (Crewe Alex. 61), R Walters (Shrewsbury 62), P Mullington (Rochdale 78), Neville Southall (Bury 80), Mark Came (Bolton Wanderers 84), Dave Bamber (Blackpool), Bob Sutton (West Ham U.), J Richardson (Sheffield U.), Stanley Wood (W.B.A.), R Pearce (Luton T.).
Local Newspapers: Winsford Chronicle, Winsford Guardian. **Local Radio:** Signal, Piccadilly.

HONOURS: Northern Premier Lg R-up 92-93, Div 1 R-up 91-92, Lg Cup 92-93, Presidents Cup 92-93, Div 1 Cup SF 89-90; Cheshire County Lg 20-21 76-77 (R-up 74-75 79-80), Lg Cup 49-50 55-56 59-60 76-77 78-79 79-80 80-81 (R-up 36-37 68-69 77-78); Cheshire Snr Cup 58-59 79-80 92-93; Mid-Cheshire Snr Cup 90-91 92-93 (R-up 88-89); Cheshire Amateur Cup 00-01 02-03; Lancs Comb/Cheshire County Inter-Lg Cup 62-63.

Winsford United FC. *Photo - Keith Clayton*

Winsford United

Match No.	Date	Venue H/A	Competition	Opponents	Result	League Pos.	Attendance	Goalscorers (Times if known)
1	Aug 24	H	UL	Buxton	Drew 1-1		254	Burr 55
2	Aug 26	A	UL	Leek Town	Lost 1-3		371	Russell 28
3	Aug 31	A	UL	Barrow	Lost 1-2	21	1279	Lyons 76 (pen)
4	Sep 4	H	UL	Knowsley United	Won 3-1		201	Russell 35, Edwards 36, Burr 57
5	Sep 7	H	UL	Spennymoor United	Drew 1-1	16	220	Russell 90
6	Sep 9	A	UL	Hyde United	Drew 0-0	17	548	
7	**Sep 14**	**A**	**FAC 1 Q**	**Easington Colliery**	**Won 7-2**		**43**	**Allen, Burr (2), Stokes, Newton, Dawson (2)**
8	Sep 18	H	UL	Leek Town	Lost 0-2		261	
9	Sep 21	A	UL	Bishop Auckland	Lost 0-2	21	174	
10	**Sep 24**	**A**	**CSC**	**Stalybridge Celtic**	**Lost 2-3**		**188**	**Russell 3, Burr 39**
11	**Sep 28**	**H**	**FAC 2 Q**	**Newcastle Town**	**Lost 0-1**		**162**	
12	Oct 2	A	UL	Knowsley United	Won 3-0		72	J Bishop 62, Lyons 88, Russell 90
13	Oct 5	H	UL	Alfreton Town	Won 1-0	15	198	Newton 53
14	Oct 9	A	UL	Colwyn Bay	Won 2-1		283	Case 40, Russell 70
15	Oct 12	H	UL	Emley	Drew 2-2	13	186	Russell 14, Gorman 83
16	Oct 16	H	UL	Gainsborough Trinity	Drew 1-1	15	124	Russell 15
17	**Oct 19**	**A**	**FAT 1 Q**	**Matlock Town**	**Won 4-1**		**253**	**Burr 17, 87, Russell 69, Dicken 84**
18	Oct 22	A	UL	Chorley	Won 1-0		407	Wenton 12
19	Oct 26	H	UL	Bishop Auckland	Lost 1-2	13	180	Lyons 36
20	**Oct 30**	**H**	**ULC**	**Runcorn**	**Won 3-1**		**154**	**Russell 5, 54, Lyons 10**
21	Nov 2	H	UL	Marine	Lost 0-1	9	195	
22	Nov 6	H	UL	Colwyn Bay	Won 3-0		145	Russell 10, 37, Bishop 20
23	**Nov 9**	**A**	**FAT 2 Q**	**Grantham**	**Lost 1-2**		**288**	**Russell 32**
24	Nov 12	A	UL	Runcorn	Lost 3-4		302	Russell 22, Bishop 44, Burr 67
25	Nov 16	H	UL	Accrington Stanley	Drew 1-1	15	188	Baldwin 35 (og)
26	Nov 23	A	UL	Spennymoor United	Lost 0-2	16	156	
27	Nov 26	A	UL	Lancaster City	Drew 1-1		161	Lyons 24
28	Nov 30	H	UL	Guiseley	Drew 1-1	14	128	Lyons 4
29	**Dec 3**	**A**	**ULCC**	**Colwyn Bay**	**Lost 2-3**		**160**	**Came 42, Allen 27**
30	Dec 7	A	UL	Frickley Athletic	Lost 2-3	16	138	German 31, Lyons 41
31	Dec 14	H	UL	Bamber Bridge	Won 4-2	14	102	Lyons 22, Russell 40, 74, Talbot 77
32	Dec 21	H	UL	Blyth Spartans	Lost 0-2	15	188	
33	Dec 28	H	UL	Hyde United	Won 2-1	14	222	Allen 66, Russell 88 (pen)
34	Jan 11	H	UL	Barrow	Lost 1-2	15	183	Bishop 56
35	Jan 18	A	UL	Alfreton Town	Drew 1-1	13	229	Russell 33
36	Jan 25	A	UL	Blyth Spartans	Won 2-1	12	648	Russell 27, Vine 39
37	Feb 8	A	UL	Boston United	Lost 0-1		148	
38	Feb 15	H	UL	Lancaster City	Lost 0-1	15	146	
39	Feb 22	A	UL	Bamber Bridge	Won 2-1	14	344	Russell 8, 59
40	Mar 1	A	UL	Accrington Stanley	Drew 0-0	14	367	
41	Mar 8	A	UL	Guiseley	Drew 1-1	13	345	Vine 5
42	Mar 11	A	UL	Marine	Lost 0-3		264	
43	Mar 15	A	UL	Emley	Drew 1-1	14	170	Russell 3
44	Mar 22	H	UL	Chorley	Lost 0-1	14	182	
45	Mar 29	A	UL	Buxton	Won 2-1		201	Hockenhull 3, Burr 52
46	Mar 31	H	UL	Witton Albion	Drew 1-1	14	278	Stokes 19
47	Apr 2	A	UL	Gainsborough Trinity	Lost 0-2	14	293	
48	Apr 5	H	UL	Runcorn	Drew 0-0	14	182	
49	Apr 15	A	UL	Witton Albion	Won 3-1		338	Stokes 39, Dicken 55, Hockenhull 79
50	Apr 19	H	UL	Frickley Athletic	Won 1-0	14	93	Hockenhull 40
51	Apr 26	A	UL	Boston United	Lost 0-2	14	634	

WINSFORD UNITED PLAYING SQUAD 1997-98

Goalkeepers: John Bagnall (Chester, Bury, Wigan, Chester, Preston)
Defenders: Dan Leeming (Northwich V, Stafford R, Everton), **Danny Goodall** (Blackburn), **Mark Came** (Exeter, Chester, Bolton, Winsford), **Elfyn Edwards** (Southport, Halifax, Macclesfield, Altrincham, Runcorn, Tranmere, Wrexham), **Gary Talbot** (Barnton, Wilmslow Alb, Rhyl), **Chris Blundell** (Northwich V, Rochdale, Oldham)
Midfielders: David German (Macclesfield, Halifax, Sheffield U), **Jason Danskin** (Northwich V, Winsford, Witton Alb, Mansfield, Everton), **Paul Newton** (Flixton, Witton Alb, Winsford, Radcliffe B, Cheadle, Stockport, Flixton, Manchester C), **Steve Pope** (Local football), **Paul Allen** (Bamber B, Buxton, Leek, Stalybridge, Fleetwood, Buxton, Fleetwood, Southport, Preston, Bolton)
Forwards: Andy Hockenhull (St.Helens, Tetley Walker, St.Helens), **Darryl Dickin** (Congleton, Grove U), **Lee Raby** (Local football)

SEASON 1996/97
DIVISION 1
MATCHDAY PROGRAMME
ASHTON
UNITED F.C.
Division 1 Cup
Second leg
ASHTON UNITED
v
STOCKSBRIDGE
Wednesday 30th April 1997
70p

PROGRAMME DETAILS:
Pages: 22 **Price:** 70p
Editor: Debbie Quaile

ASHTON UNITED

Formed: 1878 **Nickname:** Robins
Colours: Red & white halves/black/red
Change colours: Yellow/white/yellow
Midweek matchday: Monday
Club Sponsors:

Chairman: T N Styring **President:** D C N Jones
Vice Chairman: J Milne
Secretary: Debbie Quaile, 19 Quickwood, off Carrhill Road, Mossley, Lancs OL5 0SF (H 01457 834208, B 0161 200 4925)
Manager: John Coleman **Asst Manager:** Jimmy Bell
Press Officer: T Liversidge **Physio:** Geoff Johnson
GROUND Address: Surrey Street, Hurst Cross, Ashton-u-Lyne OL6 8DY. Tel; 0161 339 4158. (office) 01613 301511 (Social Club). Fax 0161 339 4158.
Directions: M62 jct 20, A627(M) to Oldham, keep in righthand 2 lanes, leave at Ashton sign after 2 miles passing Belgrade Hotel, take A627 at next island, keep in left lane and take slip road signed Ashton-under-Lyme, at island follow Stalybridge/Park Road sign, go straight ahead for 3 miles to ground at Hurst Cross. BR to Charles Street (Ashton), or Stalybridge. Buses 331, 332, 337, 408 (Ashton-Stalybridge) all pass ground.
Seats: 250 **Cover:** 750 **Capacity:** 4,500 **Floodlights:** Yes
Clubhouse: Open 11am-11pm. Refreshment bar open matchdays.
Club Shop: Yes - contact Mr K Lee (0161 330 9800).
PREVIOUS - Name: Hurst 1878-1947. **Ground:** Rose Hill 1878-1912. **Leagues:** Manchester/ Lancs Combination 12-23 48-64 66-68/ Midland 64-66, Cheshire Co. 23-48 68-82/ North West Counties 82-92.
CLUB RECORDS - Attendance: 11,000 v Halifax Town, FA Cup First Round 1952. **Scorer:** Mark Edwards, 37. **Appearances:** Micky Boyle, 462. **Fees Paid:** £9,000 for Andy Whittaker (Netherfield, 1994). **Fees Received:** £15,000 for Karl Marginson (Rotherham, March 1993).
Best FA Cup season: 1st Rd replay 52-53 (lost 1-2 at Halifax after 1-1 draw). Also 1st Rd 55-56 (lost 1-6 at Southport).
Players progressing to Football League: A Ball (Blackpool), J Mahoney (Stoke C.), B Daniels (Manchester C.), R Jones (Rotherham U.), A Arrowsmith (Liverpool), N Stiffle (Crystal Palace), K Marginson (Rotherham U.).
96-97 Captain: Paul Clowes **96-97 Top Scorer:** Paddy Wilson **96-97 P.o.Y.:** Steve Caswell
HONOURS: Northern Premier League Division 1 Cup 94-95, Manchester Senior Cup 1884-85 13-14 75-76 77-78, Manchester League 11-12, Lancs Comb. Div 2 60-61 (League Cup 62-63), Manchester Prem. Cup 79-80 82-83 92-93, North West Counties League 91-92 (Challenge Cup 91-92, Div 2 87-88, Floodlit League 90-91, Challenge Shield 92-93), Manchester Challenge Shield 35-36 38-39 49-50 53-54 (R-up 34-35 39-40), Manchester Intermediate Cup 58-59 62-63 65-66 (R-up 60-61 64-65), Manchester Jnr Cup(4) 1894-95 10-12 32-33, Unifilla Div 1 Cup 96-97.

Ashton United FC: Back Row (L-R); Stewart Anderson, Geoff Johnston (Physio), Ronnie Lee (Kit), Paul Clowes, Darren Wilson, Jimmy Bell (Player/Asst Mgr), John McKenna, Chris Wood, David Robinson, Karl Bell, Darren Twigg, David Pearce. Front Row; Alan Shirley, Paddy Wilson, John Coleman (Player/Mgr), John Brown, Terry Williams, Steve Caswell.
Photo - John Newton

BELPER TOWN

Formed: 1883 **Nickname:** Nailers
Colours: Gol/black/black
Change colours: All white
Midweek home matchday: Tuesday

Chairman: Phil Varney **President:** Alan Benfield
Secretary: David Laughlin, Lorne Cottage, 1 Hagg Lane, Fritchley, Derbys DE56 2HJ (01773 856556).
Manager: Martin Rowe **Asst Manager:** Eddie Green
Press Officer: Nigel Oldrini

GROUND Address: Christchurch Meadow, Bridge Street, Belper (01773 856556).
Directions: From M1 North, Jnct 28 onto A38 towards Derby, turn off at A610 (Ripley/Nottingham), then 4 exit at roundabout towards Ambergate. At junction with A6 (Hurt Arms Hotel) left to Belper. Ground on right past traffic lights. 400 yards from Belper (BR).
Capacity: 2,640 **Cover:** 1,000 **Seats:** 200 **Floodlights:** Yes
Clubhouse: Open matchdays, bar, hot & cold food available
Club Shop: Yes manager Andy Smithurst 01773 570967

PROGRAMME DETAILS:
Pages: 28 **Price:** 70p
Editor: Neil Laughlin

PREVIOUS - Leagues: Central Alliance 57-61/ Midland Co's 61-82. **Grounds:** Acorn Ground prior to 1951. **Names:** None

CLUB RECORDS - Attendance: 3,200 v Ilkeston Town, 1955. **Goalscorer:** Mick Lakin 231. **Appearances:** Gil Rhodes. **Transfer Fees - Paid:** Nil. **Received:** £700 for Brian Hall (Mansfield Town 59). **Biggest Victory:** 15-2 v Nottingham Forest 'A' 1956. **Biggest Defeat:** 0-12 v Goole Town 1965.

BEST SEASON - FA Cup: 1st Rd Prop 1887-88 (4th Qual. Rnd 1964-65). **FA Vase:** Semi-final 94-95

Players progressing to Football League:
96-97 - Captain: Mark Townsend **P.o.Y.:** Corin Holness **Top scorer:** Brendan Morgan
Local Newspapers: Belper News, Derby Evening Telegraph, Belper Express
Local Radio Stations: BBC Radio Derby.

HONOURS: Northern Counties East Lge 84-85, Midland Counties Lg 79-80; Central Alliance Lge 58-59; Derbys Snr Cup 58-59 60-61 62-63 79-80

Belper Town's Mark Townsend powers a header in at Christchurch Meadow in their match against Hatfield Main

PROGRAMME DETAILS:
Pages: 36 **Price:** £1.00
Editor: Tim Clapham

BRADFORD PARK AVENUE

Formed: 1907 **Nickname:** Avenue
Reformed: 1988
Colours: Green & white/white/green & white
Change colours: Red, amber & black/black/black
Midweek Matches: Wednesday
Reserve Team's league: Bolton Comb All

Chairman: Mike Firth **President:** Charlie Atkinson
Secretary: Alan Hirst, 24 Quarryfields, Mirfield, West Yorks WF14 0NT. Tel. 01924 480349 (H) 01924 474477 (B).
Manager: Trevor Storton **Asst Manager:** Bobby Barr
Res Team Manager: Dave Heeley **Physio:** Ray Killick.
Press Officer: Tim Clapham. **Commercial Manager:** Garry Sawyer

GROUND Address: Horsfall Stadium, Cemetery Road, Bradford, West Yorks BD6 2NG. **Directions:** M62 Jct 26. Go along M606 to the end. At the roundabout go along the A6036 (signposted Halifax) and pass Odsal Stadium on left hand side. At next roundabout take the 3rd exit A6036 (Halifax), in approx. 1 mile turn left into Cemetery Road (by Kings Head Pub). Ground 150 yards on left.
Capacity: 5,000 **Cover:** 2,000. **Seats:** 1,247 **Floodlights:** Yes
Clubhouse: No
Club Shop: Yes - contact Trevor Hutchinson (01274 785657)

PREVIOUS - Leagues: Southern 07-08; Football 08-70; Northern Prem 70-74; West Riding County Amtr 88-89; Central Mids 89-90; N. W. Counties 90-95. **Grounds:** Park Ave 07-73; Valley Parade 73-74; Manningham Mills 88-89; Bramley R.L.F.C., McLaren Field 89-93; Batley 93-96.

CLUB RECORDS - Attendance: 32,810 v Blackpool, War Cup 1944
Win: 11-0 v Denby Dale FAC 1908 **Defeat:** 0-7 v Barnsley 1911
Scorer: Len Shackleton 171 1940-46 **Appearances:** Tommy Farr 542 1934-50
Fee Received: £ 34,000 for K Hector (derby County 1966)
Fee Paid: £ 24,500 for L Leuty (Derby County 1950)
Best FA Cup year: Qtr finals 1912-13, 19-20, 45-46

96-97 Captain: Phil Sharpe **96-97 Top Scorer:** Ricardo Gabbiadini 17 **96-97 P.o.Y.:** Tony Brown

HONOURS: Football Lge Div 2 R-up 1914; 3rd Div N 28; Yorkshire Lge 21, 23; Midland Lge 32; West Riding Snr Cup 11,13,25,27,32,36,51,53,63, County Cup 29, 90-91, N.W.C. Lg Champions 94-95, N.W.C. Carling Challenge Trophy 94-95.

Bradford Park Avenue: Back Row (L-R); Joe Richardson, Nick Hey, David Blair, Clive Freeman, Karl Lenaghan, Tony Brown, Milton Brown, Ricardo Gabbiadini. Front Row; Gary Chapman, Mark Price, Phil Sharpe, Kevin Megson, Richard Harrison, Wayne Benn, Neil Grayston. *Photo - Bradford Telegraph & Argus*

PROGRAMME DETAILS:
Pages: 36 **Price:** 60p
Editor: A Tomlinson
(01484 718907)

BUXTON

Formed: 1877 **Nickname:** The Bucks
Colours: Royal & white/royal/royal
Change colours: All yellow with blue trim
Midweek home matchday: Tuesday

Chairman: K Perrins **Vice Chairman:** S Dakin
Secretary / Press Officer: J B Goodwin, 97 Tongue Lane, Fairfield, Buxton, Derbys. SK17 7LL. 01298 25068 (H).
Manager: Wayne Goodison **Asst Manager: Physio:** K Perrins

GROUND Address: The Silverlands, Buxton, Derbyshire (01298 24733).
Directions: 200 yards of Buxton Market Place, opposite County Police HQ. Half mile from Buxton (BR).
Capacity: 4,000 **Cover:** 2,500 **Seats:** 490 **Floodlights:** Yes
Clubhouse: (01298 23197). Open nightly + Sunday lunchtimes. Tetleys beers, no hot food.
Club Shop: Contact P Scott (01298 72159).
Sponsors: Josiah Tetley.

PREVIOUS - Leagues: The Combination 1891-99/ North Derbyshire/ E Cheshire/ Manchester 1907-32/ Cheshire County 32-73.

CLUB RECORDS - Attendance: 6,000 v Barrow, FA Cup 1st rd 51-52. **Goalscorer:** Dave Herbert. **Appearances:** Mick Davis. **Transfer Fees - Paid:** £5,000 for Gary Walker (Hyde United, 1989). **Received:** £16,500 for Ally Pickering (Rotherham, 1989). **Best Season - FA Trophy:** Quarter Finals 70-71 71-72. **FA Cup:** 3rd Rd 51-52. Also 2nd Rd 58-59, 1st Rd 62-63.
League clubs defeated in FA Cup: Aldershot 51-52.
Players progressing to Football League: Peter Robinson (Notts Co 1950), John Higgins (Bolton 1950), Maurice Brooks (Stockport 1951), Ray Parker (Bradford City 1951), Fred Marlow (Grimsby 1951), Ian Greaves (Man Utd 1953), John Brindley (Chesterfield 1953), Les Ferriday (Walsall 1954), John Good (Tranmere 1955), Jimmy Anders (Bradford PA 1956), William Haydock (Man City 1959), Anthony Parkes (Blackburn 1970), Andy Proudlove (Sheffield Wednesday 1975), Graham Collier (York City 1978), Harry Charlton (Darlington 1979), Ally Pickering (Rotherham 1990).
96-97 Captain: **96-97 P.o.Y.:** **96-97 Top scorer:**
Local Newspapers: Buxton Advertiser, Matlock Mercury. **Local Radio Stations:** Radio Derby.

HONOURS: Northern Premier Lg Cup 90-91 (Presidents Cup R-up 81-82), Cheshire County 72-73 (R-up 46-47 62-63, Lg Cup 56-57 57-58 68-69), Manchester Lg 31-32 (R-up 04-05 28-29 29-30 30-31, Lg Cup 25-26 26-27), Derbyshire Senior Cup 38-39 44-45 45-46 56-57 59-60 71-72.

Buxton FC's home end at the Silverlands. *Photo - Keith Clayton*

OFFICIAL
MATCHDAY
PROGRAMME
CONGLETON TOWN F.C.
vs RADCLIFFE BOROUGH
15th APRIL 1997
MAIN SPONSORS
CONGLETON
TOWN COUNCIL
60p
PROGRAMME
SPONSORED BY
BROMLEY
GARAGE

PROGRAMME DETAILS:
Pages: 48 **Price:** 60p.
Editor: Paul Marshall.

CONGLETON TOWN

Formed: 1901 **Nickname:** Humbugs/Bears
Colours: White & black flashes/black/black & white
Change colours: All red.
Midweek home matchday: Tuesday.
Reserve Team: N/A.

Chairman: Barry Machin
Secretary and Press Officer: David Wilcock, 4,Maxwell Rd., Congleton, Cheshire. CW12 3HY.(H) 01260 276347 or (W) 01260 270275.
Manager: Tommy Lawson **Physio:**
GROUND Address: Booth Street Ground, Crescent Road, Congleton, Cheshire (0260 274460).
Directions: On approach to Congleton via Clayton bypass take second right after fire station, into Booth Street. Two miles from Congleton (BR).
Capacity: 5,000 **Cover:** 1,200 **Seats:** 250 **Floodlights:** Yes
Clubhouse: Open match days only.
Club Shop: Yes. Contact: Robert Fletcher.
PREVIOUS - Leagues: Crewe & Dist/ North Staffs/ Macclesfield/ Cheshire 20-39 46-65 78-82/ Mid Cheshire 68-78/ North West Counties 82-87.
Name: Congleton Hornets *(prior to current club's formation in 1901).*

CLUB RECORDS - Attendance: 7,000 v Macclesfield, League 53-54. **Goalscorer:** Mick Biddle (150+). **Appearances:** Ray Clack (600+). **Fee Paid:** None. **Fee Received:** £5,000 for D Frost (Leeds).
Best season - FA Trophy: 3rd Qualifying Rd 89-90 90-91. **FA Vase:** 4th Rd 76-77 80-81. **FA Cup:** 1st Rd 89-90 (lost 0-2 at Crewe). **(League clubs defeated):** None.
Players progressing to Football League: Ron Broad (Crewe 1955), Jack Mycock (Shrewsbury 1958), Steve Davies (Port Vale 1987), L Hamlet (Leeds), Jimmy Quinn (West Ham, N Ireland), Ian Brightwell (Man City).
96-97 Captain: Graham Harrison **96-97 P.o.Y.:** Graham Harrison **96-97 Top Scorer:** Darren Washington
Local Press: Congleton Chronicle, Staffs Evening Sentinel. **Local Radio:** Radio Stoke, Signal.
HONOURS: North West Counties League R-up 85-86, Cheshire County League R-up 20-21 21-22 (Div 2 81-82), Mid Cheshire League 73-74 75-76 77-78 (R-up 69-70 71-72 76-77, League Cup 71-72), Cheshire Senior Cup 20-21 37-38.

Congleton Town FC: Back Row (L-R): Tommy Lawson (Mgr), Albert Altenor, Marc Borland, Paul Abbey, Richard Witten, Steven Rothwell, Stuart Heeps, Darren Washington, David Waller, Ian Parr, Paul Cuddy. Front Row: Billy O'Neil, Mark Aitken, Brian Holmes, Craig Murphy, Peter Weston, Graham Harrison (Cpt), Mark Ansell, Ian Marshall.

PROGRAMME DETAILS:
Pages: 20 **Price:** 80p
Editor: Martin Crookall

DROYLSDEN

Formed: 1892 **Nickname:** The Bloods
Colours: Red & white/black/black
Change colours: Green/white/green.
Midweek home matchday: Wednesday.
Reserve Team: None.

Chairman: David Pace
Secretary: Bernard King, 22 Hart Street, Droylsden, Manchester M43 7AW. Tel. 0161 2855232 (Home), Fax 0161 3701426.
Manager: David Pace
Asst Manager: Alan Blair.

GROUND Address: The Butchers Arms Ground, Market Street, Droylsden, Manchester (0161 370 1426).
Directions: 4 miles east of Manchester via A662 Ashton New Road, behind Butchers Arms Hotel.
Capacity: 3,500 **Cover:** 2,000 **Seats:** 500 **Floodlights:** Yes
Clubhouse: Pub hours except atchdays. Pool and darts.
Shop: Yes **Metal Badges:** Yes.
Sponsors: Alpha Court Windows/ Hastings Taxis.

PREVIOUS - Leagues: Manchester/ Lancs Com 36-39 50-68/ Cheshire County 39-50 68-82/ NW Counties 82-87.

CLUB RECORDS - Attendance: 4,250 v Grimsby, FA Cup 1st rd 1976. **Scorer:** E Gillibrand 78 (1931-32). **Win:** 13-2 v Lucas Sports Club. **Fee Received:** £11,000 for Tony Naylor (Crewe).
FA Cup - Best Season: 2nd Rd 78-79. **League clubs defeated:** Rochdale 78-79.
Players progressing to Football League: Albert Butterworth & F Letchford (Blackpool 1931), William Davies & Maurice Randall (Crewe 1947), William Mellor (Accrington 1950), Geoff Tonge (Bury 1960), David Campbell (WBA 1962), Kevin Randall (Bury 1965), Peter Litchfield (Preston 1979), Tony Naylor (Crewe 1990).
Local Press: Droylsden Reporter (0161 303 1910), Advertiser. **Local Radio:** BBC Manchester.

HONOURS: Northern Prem League Division 1 Runners-up 89-90 (Division 1 Cup 87-88), NW Counties League Division 2 86-87, Cheshire County League Runners-up 39-40 45-46 (League Cup 77-78 (Runners-up 76-77)), Lancs Comb Division 2 Runners-up 55-56 58-59 62-63, Manchester League 30-31 32-33 (League Cup 23-24 33-34), Manchester Premier Cup 80-81 (Runners-up 83-84 90-91 93-94), Manchester Senior Cup 72-73 75-76 78-79 (Runners-up 72-73 75-76 78-79), Manchester Intermediate Cup 59-60 64-65 69-70, Manchester Challenge Shield 46-47.

Droylsden's top marksman Billy O'Callaghan in action against Ashton United

PROGRAMME DETAILS:
Pages: 24 **Price:** 50p
Editor: Jim McVea

EASTWOOD TOWN

Formed: 1953 **Nickname:** The Badgers
Colours: Black & white stripes/black/black
Change Colours: Yellow/blue/yellow.
Midweek home matchday: Tuesday

Chairman: George Belshaw **Vice Chairman:** Roy Cheatle
Secretary / Press Officer: Paddy Farrell, 7 Primrose Rise, Newthorpe, Notts NG16 2BB (Tel/Fax: 01773 715500).
Manager: Bryan Chambers **Physio:** Derek Myatt.

GROUND Address: Coronation Park, Eastwood, Notts (01773 715823).
Directions: From North - M1 jct 27, follow Heanor signs via Brinsley to lights in Eastwood. Turn left then first right after Fire Station - ground entrance on Chewton Street. From South - M1 jct 26, A610 to Ripley, leave at 1st exit (B6010), follow to Eastwood, left at lights, first left at 'Man in Space' - ground entrance on Chewton Street. Nearest station - Langley Mill. Buses every 10 mins (R11, R12 or R13) from Victoria Centre, Nottingham - approx 40 mins.
Capacity: 5,500 **Cover:** 1,150 **Seats:** 200 **Floodlights:** Yes
Clubhouse: Social club open normal licensing hours (Sat 11am-11pm, midweek matches 6.30-11pm). Hot & cold food available. Steward; Richard James (01773 715823)
Club Shop: Sells programmes, mugs, scarves, badges etc. Contact R K Storer (0115 938 5239). **Sponsors:**

PREVIOUS - Leagues: Notts Alliance 53-61/ Central Alliance 61-67/ East Midlands 67-71/ Midland Counties 71-82/ Northern Counties (East) 82-87. **Names:** None - predecessors Eastwood Collieries disbanded in 1953. **Previous Ground:** Coronation Park 1953-65 - previous pitch now town bowling green.

CLUB RECORDS - Attendance: 2,723 v Enfield, FA Amateur Cup, February 1965. **Goalscorer:** Martin Wright. **Appearances:** Arthur Rowley, over 800 1st team games, but not a single booking, 1955-76. **Win:** 26-0. **Defeat:** 1-7. **Fee Paid:** £500 for Jamie Kay, Gainsborough Trinity 90-91. **Fee Received:** £72,500 for Richard Liburd (Middlesbrough 92-93). **Best F.A. Cup season:** Final Qual. Rd replay 75-76 (0-1 at Wycombe W.).
Players progressing to Football League: J Butler (Notts County 57), A Woodcock A Buckley Andrew Todd (Nottm Forest), P Richardson (Derby), S Buckley (Luton), R Liburd (Middlesbrough 92-93), Martin Bullock (Barnsley 94-95), Neil Illman (Plymouth 95-96), Lee Marshall (Scunthorpe 97).
96-97 Captain: Mark Place **96-97 P.o.Y.:** Martin Chadbourne **96-97 Top scorer:** Kris Hoy
Local Press: Eastwood Advertiser, Nottingham Evening Post, Derby Telegraph.
Local Radio: Radio Nottingham, Radio Trent.

HONOURS: Northern Counties (East) Lg R-up 82-83 84-85, Midland Counties Lg 75-76 (R-up 74-75 77-78, Lg Cup 77-78 79-80), Central Alliance 63-64 (R-up 64-65), Notts Alliance 56-57 (R-up 53-54 54-55 55-56 57-58 58-59 59-60, Lg Cup 55-56), East Midlands Lg R-up 68-69, Notts Senior Cup 75-76 77-78 78-79 79-80 82-83 83-84 88-89 89-90 91-92 (R-up 57-58 63-64 65-66), Evans Halshaw Floodlit Cup 94-95 R-up 89-90, Notts Intermediate Cup 86-87, Ripley Hospital Charity Cup(6) 76-81, FA Trophy 1st Rd 78-79, FA Amateur Cup 3rd Rd replay 67-68.

Back Row (L-R): Martyn Chadbourne, Neil Cluxton, Glenn Kirkwood, Richard Parkin, Mark Haran, Paul Gould, Carl Flint, Richard Mellon. Front Row: Asa Ingall, Jamie Marshall, Mark Place (Cpt), Kris Hoy, Lee Marshall

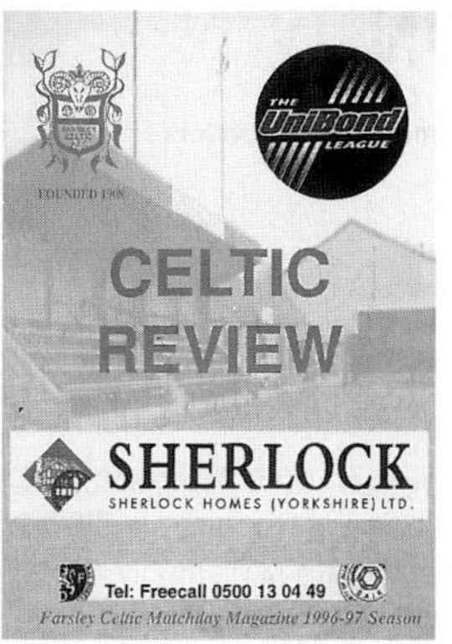

PROGRAMME DETAILS:
Pages: 26 **Price:**
Editor: Keith Huggins.

FARSLEY CELTIC

Formed: 1908 **Nickname:** Villagers
Colours: Sky & navy/navy/navy
Change colours: Yellow/yellow/navy & red
Midweek home matchday: Wednesday
Reserve Team's League: Northern Counties (E) Reserve Div.

Chairman: John E Palmer **Vice Chairman:**
Secretary: Mrs Margaret Lobley, 29 Spring Bank Road, Farsley, Leeds, West Yorks LS28 5LS (01132 575675)
Manager: Martin Haresign **Coach:** J Macay
Press Officer: **Physio:** Ian McGready
GROUND Address: Throstle Nest, Newlands, Farsley, Pudsey, Leeds LS28 5BE (01532 561517). **Directions:** From North East: A1 south to Wetherby, A58 to Leeds, at 1st island (approx 8 miles) take 3rd exit (A6120 ring-rd), follow Bradford signs to 12th r'bout (approx 12 miles) - 1st exit (B6157 Stanningley). From M62 jct 26, M606 (Bradford) to r'bout, 4th exit (A6177) passing McDonalds on left, continue on Rooley Lane - Sticker Lane passing Morrisons store on left to lights (approx 3 miles) - right onto A647 (Leeds) to 2nd r'bout, 2nd exit (B6157 Stanningley). Continue 800yds passing Police & Fire Stations on left. Turn left down New Street at Tradex warehouse before turning right into Newlands. Ground at bottom of road. 1 mile from New Pudsey (BR).
Capacity: 4,000 **Cover:** 1,000 **Seats:** 430 **Floodlights:** Yes
Clubhouse: Lounge, games room and committee room open every evening and Friday and weekend lunchtimes. New multi-purpose Leisure Centre available evenings and afternoons.
Club Shop: League & non-League programmes & magazines. Club badges, scarves, ties, sweaters, training suits, polo & T-shirts. Various souvenirs & photos. Contact Brian Falkingham, 27 Rycroft Ct., Leeds LS13 4PE. 0113 255 0749
PREVIOUS - Grounds: Red Lane, Farsley/ Calverley Lane, Farsley (prior to 1948).
Leagues: West Riding County Amateur/ Leeds Red Triangle/ Yorkshire 49-82/ Northern Counties (East) 82-87.

CLUB RECORDS - Attendance: 11,000 (at Elland Road) v Tranmere Rovers, FA Cup 1st Rd 1974.
Win: **Defeat:** **Scorer:** **Appearances:** **Fee Paid:** **Fee Received:**
Best Season - FA Amateur Cup: Third Round, 34-35. **FA Cup:** 1st Rd 74-75 (see above). Lost 0-2. **FA Vase:** Quarter Final 87-88.
Players progressing to Football League: Barry Smith (Leeds 1951), Paul Madeley (Leeds 1962), William Roberts (Rochdale 1988), Stuart McCall (Bradford City, Everton, Scotland).
96-97 Captain: Wayne Noteman **96-97 P.o.Y.:** Craig Taylor **96-97 Top scorer:** Robbie Whelans
Local Press: Yorkshire Evening Post, Telegraph & Argus, Pudsey Times.
Local Radio: Radio Leeds, Radio Aire, Radio Pennine.

HONOURS: West Riding County Cup 57-58 59-60 66-67 70-71 83-84 87-88 95-96; Yorkshire League 59-60 68-69 (R-up 57-58 58-59 70-71 71-72); Div 2 51-52; League Cup 62-63 63-64 66-67 96-97.

Farsley Celtic: Back Row (L-R); Nigel Smith, Paul Stevenson, Ben Carrington, Calvin Allan, Wayne Noteman, Paul Allan, Andy Waterfield, Rob Whellans, Martin Haresign (Manager). Front Row; Scott Jackson, Steve Learoyd, Phil Tumer, Billy Roberts, Shane Muzurue, Craig Taylor, Chris Stabb, Simon Woodhead. *Photo - John Newton*

The North West Counties Football League
50p
INTO THE VALLEY
FLIXTON
Official Programme
Monday 6th May 1996
3-00pm
CLUB SPONSOR
A.J. EDGE
SHIPPING & DISTRIBUTION
Versus
TRAFFORD

FLIXTON

Formed: 1960 **Nickname:** Valley Roaders
Colours: Blue & white stripes/blue/blue
Change Colours: Gold/black/black
Midweek home matchday: Tuesday
Reserve Team's league: North West Alliance

Chairman: John Mitchell **President:** F H Eadie
Secretary: Peter Rogers, 55 Benbecula Way, Davyhulme, Urmston, Manchester M41 7FW, (0161 445 2722)
Manager: David Morris **Asst Manager:** Chris Nicholson
Physio:

GROUND Address: Valley Road, Flixton, Manchester M31 2RQ (0161 748 2903). **Directions:** M63 Jct 3, B5214 (signed Urmston), follow Trafford General Hosp. signs, at 4th r'bout take 3rd exit (Woodbridge Rd), ground at top. One and a quarter miles from Flixton BR station (trains from Manchester Oxford Rd) - turn right out of station onto Flixton Rd, left after quarter mile into Woodsend Rd, at r'bout after quarter mile take 2nd exit into Woodbridge Rd - ground at top. Take any bus from Manchester Picadilly bus station to Flixton and alight at Flixton Red Lion.
Capacity: 2,000 **Cover:** 650 **Seats:** 250 **Floodlights:** Yes
Clubhouse: Open daily 1.00pm-11pm. Sandwiches available most evenings.
Club Shop: No

PROGRAMME DETAILS:
Pages: 36 **Price:** 50p
Editor: John Fradley

PREVIOUS - Leagues: South Manchester & Wythenshawe 60-63/ Lanc & Cheshire 63-73/ Manchester 73-86/ North West Counties 86-96

CLUB RECORDS - Attendance: 1,543 v Brigg Town FA Vase Semi-Final 95-96.
Goalscorer: John Mitchell. **Appearances:** John Mitchell & Stan Matthews.
Win: 10-2 Irlam 94-95. **Defeat:** 1-10 v Knowsley Utd 90-91.
Fee Paid: **Fee Received:**

BEST SEASON - FA Cup: 1st Qual. Rd replay 91-92 (lost 1-2 at Mossley after 1-1 draw.
FA Vase: Semi-final 1995-96 (see above)

96-97 Captain: **96-97 P.o.Y.:** **96-97 Top scorer:**

HONOURS: N.W.Co Div I Champions and Cup Winners 95-96 NW Co's Lg Div 2 Winners 94-95 Lg.Cup Winners 94-95, R-up 87-88 (Div 3 R-up 86-87, Div 3 Cup SF 86-87, Res. Chal. Cup 87-88 90-91 (R-up 88-89 89-90 91-92 92-93), Res. Div East 89-90, Res. Div Sth 92-93), Manc. Lg R-up 78-79 81-82 85-86 (Div 1 77-78, Div 2(res) 82-83 85-86, Open Tphy 80-81), Lancs Amtr Cup 79-80 (R-up 80-81), Manc. Chal. Tphy 83-84 (R-up x2 84-86), Manc. Prem. Cup R-up 86-87 91-92, Manc. Amtr Cup R-up 88-89.

Flixton FC, Clubhouse

GREAT HARWOOD TOWN

PROGRAMME DETAILS:
Pages: 20 **Price:** 20p
Editor: D Bennet

Formed: 1978
Nickname: Robins
Colours: All red
Change colours: All blue.
Midweek Matches: Monday.
Reserve Team's league: West Lancs Lge

Chairman: William Holden
Secretary: Peter Birtwhistle, 23 Dryden Grove, Great Harwood, Blackburn BB6 7LW.(01254 886754)
Press Officer: K Lambert
Commercial Manager: Mark Smith
Manager: M Crabbe **Asst Manager:** Dave Sargent

GROUND Address: The Showground, Wood Street, Great Harwood, Lancs (01254 883913).
Directions: M66 from Manchester to Haslingden exit, A680 through Baxenden, Accrington to Clayton-le-Moors, left at the Hyndburn Bridge Hotel into Hyndburn Road and right into Wood Street to ground. Or M6 jct 31, Clitheroe/Skipton road to Trafalgar Hotel, A677 to Blackburn, left at Moat House Hotel and follow ring-road to M65 junction, A678 to Rishton, left at lights (B6536) to Gt Harwood, right at Town Gate into Queen Str., follow signs for Lomax Square, left into Park Rd, right into Balfour Street to ground. 3 miles from Rishton (BR), 6 miles from Blackburn (BR). Various buses from Heyes Lane & Park Road to Blackburn & Accrington.

Capacity: 2,500 **Cover:** 700
Seats: 200 **Floodlights:** Yes

Clubhouse: The Sportsman just outside ground. Normal licensing hours. Full bar facilities. Squash courts and gym. Hot & cold snacks & drinks on matchdays from tea bar in ground.
Club Shop: Sells programmes, badges, key rings, shirts. Contact: J McKay (c/o club). **Club Sponsors:** None

PREVIOUS -
Name: Great Harwood Wellington.
Leagues: West Lancashire, Lancs Combination 79-82, North West Counties 82-92.
Ground: Park adjacent to the Showground until demise of Great Harwood FC in 1978.

CLUB RECORDS -
Attendance: 5,397 v Manchester Utd, 1980
Win: 7-0 v Farsley Celtic (H), NPL Div. 1 92-93
Defeat: 0-6 v Spennymoor Utd (H), NPL Div. 1 94-95

BEST SEASON -
FA Cup: 1st Qual. Round replay 92-93, 1-2 v Atherton LR (H) after 1-1 draw.
FA Vase: Quarter Finals 90-91, 1-2 v Littlehampton Town (A)

HONOURS:
North West Counties League R-up 91-92 (Div 2 90-91, Lamot Pils Tphy 89-90 (R-up 90-91), Tennents Floodlit Trophy 91-92), Lancs ATS Challenge Trophy 91-92 (R-up 90-91).

PROGRAMME DETAILS:
Pages: 28 **Price:** 80p
Editor: R MacGregor
(01387 811820)

GRETNA

Formed: 1946 **Nickname:** Black & whites
Club colours: Black & white hoops/black/black & white
Change colours: All yellow
Midweek matchday: Tuesday
Reserve Team's league:

Chairman: Brian Fulton **President:** Thomas Kerr.
Secretary: Ron MacGregor, Brackenhurst, Lochmaben, Lockerbie, Scotland DG11 1QA (01387 811820).
Manager: Michael McCartney **Physio:** William Bentley

GROUND Address: Raydale Park, Dominion Rd., Gretna, Dumfriesshire (01461 337602). **Directions:** 8 miles north of Carlisle on A74. Take slip road to Gretna over border bridge, left at Crossways Inn for Township along Annan Rd for quarter of a mile, left into Dominion Rd, ground on right. Buses leave Carlisle on the half hour. Also trains from Carlisle.
Capacity: 2,200 **Cover:** 800 **Seats:** 385 **Floodlights:** Yes
Clubhouse: Bar, lounge, TV room, concert room. Cooked meals available. Open every day. Late bar at weekends.
Club Shop: Yes, contact Alan Watson 01387 251550, matchdays & postal sales

Club Sponsors: Home Kit; Ewart Engineering, Away Kit; North British Tours

PREVIOUS Leagues: Dumfriesshire Amateur 46-47/ Carlisle & District 47-51/ Cumberland 51-52/ Northern 83-92.

CLUB RECORDS - Attendance: 2,307 v Rochdale, F.A. Cup First Round Proper, 16/11/91.
Scorer: Denis Smith **Appearances:** William Cross.
Win: 13-0 **Defeat:** 1-5.

Best season - FA Trophy: Third Round 90-91. **FA Cup:** 1st Round Proper 1991-92 (lost 1-3 in replay at Rochdale).
Players progressing to Football League: John Hamilton (Hartlepool United) 1982, Russell Black & Don Peattie (Sheffield United) 1984, Mark Dobie (Cambridge United).
96-97 Captain: Les Armstrong **96-97 Top Scorer:** Carl Harwood
96-97 Suppoerters P.o.Y.: Tony Monaghan **96-97 Players P.o.Y.:** Paul O'Hagan
Local Newspapers: Cumberland News **Local Radio:**

HONOURS: Northern Lg 90-91 91-92 (Lg Cup 90-91), Cumberland Senior Cup (9), JR Cleator Cup 89-90 90-91 91-92, Craven Cup 91-92, Carlisle & Dist. Lg (28)(Charity Shield(25), Lg Cup(20), Benevolent Cup(15)).

Gretna FC, team 96-97: Back Row (L-R); Mike McCartney (Player/Manager), Richard Close, Paul Taylor, Duncan Armstrong, G Johnstone, Paul O'Hagan, Tony Monaghan, Les Armstrong, George Norrie (Coach). Front Row; Billy Bentley (Trainer), Stuart Parkinson, Marvin Baldwin, Stuart Darley, Andy Walker, Jamie Close, Craig Pottss, Shane Bird, Colette Anstin (Physio). *Photo - John Newton*

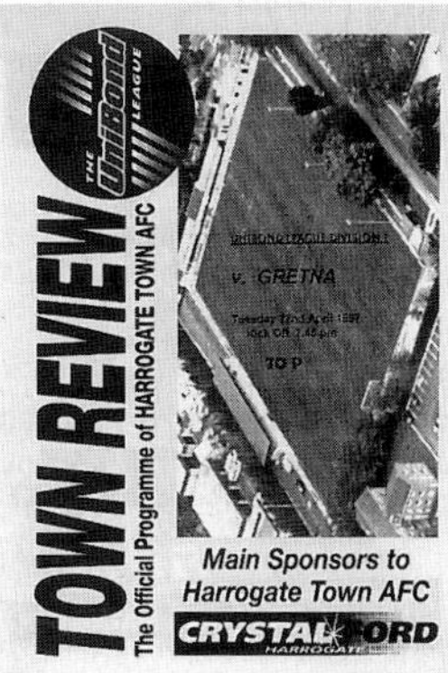

TOWN REVIEW
The Official Programme of HARROGATE TOWN AFC
v. GRETNA
Main Sponsors to
Harrogate Town AFC
CRYSTAL FORD

PROGRAMME DETAILS:
Pages: 32 **Price:** 60p
Editor: R Chambers/ T Moseley

HARROGATE TOWN

Formed: 1919 **Nickname:** Town
Colours: Yellow/black/yellow
Change colours: All blue.
Midweek home matchday: Tuesday
Reserve Team's Lge: Northern Co's (East) Reserve Div.

Chairman: George Dunnington **President:**
Managing Director: Alan Smith **General Secretary:** Roy Dalby, 123a Dene Park, Harrogate, North Yorkshire HG1 4JX (01423 567973).
Youth Development Coach: Malcolm Richardson **Coach:**

GROUND Address: Wetherby Road, Harrogate. 01423 883671 (880675-press). **Directions:** From Leeds turn right at traffic lights (Appleyard's) into Hookstone Road, continue to Woodlands Hotel (traffic lights) turn left into Wetherby Road, ground on the right. From Harrogate (BR), turn left and left again, cross road (Odeon Cinema), proceed for about 400yds to main road, cross over to The Stray (open land) using footpath which leads to Wetherby Rd, ground 200yds on left.
Capacity: 3,800 **Cover:** 600 **Seats:** 450 **Floodlights:** Yes
Clubhouse: On ground, open Tuesday, Thursday and every other Wednesday in addition to every matchday. Sandwiches available.
Club Shop: Sells scarves, ties, pens shirts and other common souvenirs.
Metal Badges: Yes **Club Sponsors:** Crystal Motors.

PREVIOUS - Names: Harrogate FC 26-34/ Harrogate Hotspurs 36-50. **Ground:** Starbeck Lane 1919-20. **Leagues:** Yorkshire 20-21 22-31 51-82/ Midland 21-22/ Northern 31-32/ Harrogate & District 36-46/ West Yorkshire 46-51/ Northern Counties (East) 82-87.

CLUB RECORDS -
Attendance: 3,208 v Starbeck LNER (now Harrogate R.A.), Whitworth Cup final 1948.
Win: 9-1 v Winsford. **Defeat:** 0-7 v Hyde Utd & v Lancaster City.
Best season - FA Vase: 4th Round 89-90. **FA Cup:** 3rd Qual. Rd 94-95 (0-3 at Bishop Auckland)

Players progressing to Football League: Tony Ingham (Leeds) 1947, Stewart Ferebee (York City 1979), Tim Hotte (Halifax Town 1985), Andy Watson (Halifax Town 1988),Ian Blackstone York City 1995)

96-97 Captain: Gary Lormer **96-97 P.o.Y.:** Jimmy Lagan **96-97 Top scorer:** Ian Hart
Local Newspapers: Yorkshire Post, Harrogate Herald Advertiser.
Local Radio: Radio Leeds, Radio York, local hospital radio.

HONOURS: Northern Premier League Division 1 Cup 89-90, Northern Counties (East) Division 1 (Nth) R-up 84-85 (Reserve Division 85-86, Reserve Division Cup 86-87), Yorkshire League Division 1 26-27 (Division 2 81-82, Division 3 R-up 71-72 80-81), West Riding County Cup 62-63 72-73 85-86, West Riding Challenge Cup 24-25 26-27.

Harrogate Town: Back Row (L-R); Micky Doig (Manager), Paul Marshall, Andy Thompson, Mike Sellers, Kevin Wolfe, Ian Hart, Elliott Beddard, Ricky Greenough, Dave Whitehead (Physio). Front Row; Mark Smitheringale, Peter Binks, Paul Cygan, Gary Lormor (Capt), Eamon Elliott, Sean Constable, Alan Matthewson, Andrew Sumpton (Mascot).
Photo - Paul Sumpton

LINCOLN UNITED

Formed: 1938 **Nickname:** United
Colours: All white
Change Colours: Red/Black.
Midweek home matchday: Wednesday
Reserve team's League: Lincolnshire.

Chairman: K Roe **President:** A Simpson
Vice Chairman: P Day **Commercial Manager:** S Eastmead.
Secretary / Press Officer: Steve Eastmead, 23 Woodvale Avenue, Doddington Park, Lincoln LN6 3RD (01522 885112 H, 01522 696400 B)
Manager: Ged Creane/John Wilkinson
Physio: Anthony Adams

PROGRAMME DETAILS:
Pages: 40 **Price:** 50p
Editor: John Wilkinson
(01522 788880)

GROUND Address: Ashby Avenue, Hartsholme, Lincoln (01522 690674).
Directions: From Newark A46 onto Lincoln relief road (A446), right at 2nd r'bout for Birchwood (Skellingthorpe Rd), go for 1 mile passing lake and Country Park, 1st right 10yds after 30mph sign into Ashby Ave., ground entrance 200 yds, opposite Old Peoples home. From north follow A57 via Saxilby until reaching A46 Lincoln Relief Road - continue on this and turn left at r'bout signed Birchwood then as above. 3 miles from Loncoln Central (BR).
Capacity: 2,714. **Seats:** 400. **Covered:** 1,084. **Floodlights:** Yes
Clubhouse: Open every day normal licensing hours. Matchday snack bar - hot & cold food & drinks.
Club Shop: Yes. Contact Jane Eastmead (01522 885112)
Sponsors: Hykeham Forum Supplies/ City Tyre Experts.

PREVIOUS - Leagues: Lincs 45-48 60-67/ Lincoln 48-60/ Yorks 67-82/ Northern Co's East 82-86/ Central Mids 82-92. **Grounds:** Skew Bridge (40s)/ Co-op Sports Ground (to mid 60s)/ Hartsholme Cricket Ground (to 82). **Name:** Lincoln Amateurs (until an ex-pro signed in 1954).

CLUB RECORDS - Attendance: 2,000 v Crook Town, FA Amateur Cup 1st Rd Proper, 1968. **Scorer:** Terry Nelson 189. **Appearances:** Brian Davies 439. **Win:** 12-0 v Pontefract Colls 95. **Defeat:** 0-7 v Huddersfield Town FA Cup 1st Round Proper 16-11-91. **Fee Paid:** £250 for Dean Dye (Sutton Town, 7.90) - only player ever bought. **Fee Received:** £3,000 for Dean Dye (Charlton Ath., 7.91).
Best FA Cup season: First Round Proper 91-92 (0-7 at Huddersfield Town).
96-97 Captain: Mike Trotter **Top Scorer:** Tony Simmons **P.o.Y.:** Billy Heath
Local Press: Lincolnshire Echo, Lincoln Standard.

HONOURS: Northern Co's (E) Lg Div 1 92-93 (Div 1 Sth 82-83, Div 2 85-86, Presidents Cup 94-95); Yorks Lg 70-71 73-74 (Lg Cup 70-71); Lincs Lg 63-64; Lincs Snr 'A' Cup 72-73 85-86 95-96, R-up 91-92 94-95, 'B' Cup 63-64 70-71; Central Mids Lg 91-92 (Wakefield Cup 90-91); Evans Halshaw Floodlit Cup R-up 92-93; Lincs I'mediate Cup(7) 67-73 80-81; N.Co.East Prem Div.Champions 94-95; Blankney Hunt Inter Lge 95-96, Cup 95-96.

Lincoln United FC

PROGRAMME DETAILS:
Pages: 32 **Price:** 70p
Editor: Ian Richardson
01629 56042

MATLOCK TOWN

Formed: 1885 **Nickname:** The Gladiators
Colours: Royal & white/royal/royal
Chamge colours: All yellow
Midweek home matchday: Tuesday
Reserve Team's league:

Chairman: Donald T Carr **Vice Chairman:** G Michael Tomlinson
Secretary: Keith F Brown, 'Barncroft', 1 Malvern Gardens, Matlock, Derbyshire DE4 3JH. 01629 584231 (H) 01335 390301 (B).
Manager: Tommy Spencer **Physio:**
Press Officer: G Michael Tomlinson 01629 583763 (H)
Commercial Manager: Mrs Sue Tomlinson

GROUND Address: Causeway Lane, Matlock, Derbyshire (01629 583866).
Directions: On A615, 500 yds from town centre and Matlock (BR).
Capacity: 7,500 **Cover:** 2,000 **Seats:** 240 **Floodlights:** Yes
Clubhouse: Gladiators Social Club, on ground, open six nights per week.
Club Shop: Yes. Contact: Sue Tomlinson (01629 583866)
Sponsors: Westons of Wirksworth/ Panasonic.

PREVIOUS - Ground: Hall Leys (last century). **Leagues:** Midland Counties 1894-96 1961-69/ Matlock & District/ Derbys Senior/ Central Alliance 24-25 47-61/ Central Combination 34-35/ Chesterfield & District 46-47.

CLUB RECORDS - Attendance: 5,123 v Burton Albion, FA Trophy 1975.
Fee Paid: £300 for Mick Chambers (Grantham) **Fee Received:** £10,000 for Ian Helliwell (York).
Best FA Cup season: 3rd Rd 76-77. 1st Rd 1885-86 86-87 86-87 87-88 1959-60 74-75 75-76 89-90.
League clubs defeated in FA Cup: Mansfield Town 76-77.
Players progressing to Football League: Keith Haines (Leeds 1959), Wayne Biggins (Burnley 1984), Darren Bradshaw (Chesterfield 1987), Les McJannet (Scarborough 1987), Ian Helliwell (York 1987).
Local Press: Matlock Mercury, Derbyshire Times. **Local Radio:** Radio Derby.

HONOURS: FA Trophy 74-75, Northern Premier League Runners-up 83-84 (League Cup 77-78, Shield 78-79), Midland Counties League 61-62 68-69, Central Alliance (North) 59-60 60-61 (Runners-up 61-62 62-63, Division 1 Cup Runners-up 61-62, Division 2 59-60, Division 2 Cup 59-60 60-61), Derbyshire Senior Cup 74-75 76-77 77-78 80-81 83-84 84-85 91-92 (Runners-up 60-61 72-73 73-74 75-76 80-81 81-82 82-83 89-90 93-94), Derbshire Divisional Cup (North) 61-62 (Runners-up 62-63), Evans Halshaw Floodlit Cup 88-89, Anglo-Italian Non-League Cup 1979.

Matlock Town's Shaun Lanaghan scores against Workington *Photo - Alan Watson*

Saturday 3rd May
1 9 9 7
v
WORKSOP
TOWN
NETHER
FIELD
THE
UniBond
LEAGUE

NETHERFIELD

Formed: 1920 **Nickname:** The Field
Colours: Black & white stripes/black/black & white
Change colours: Yellow/blue/yellow
Midweek home matchday: Tuesday
Reserve Team's League: North West Alliance.

Chairman: Ian Needham **President:** M Macklin
Secretary: Andrew Roe, 4 Lowther Park, Kendal, Cumbria LA9 6RS. 01539 731680 (H) 01524 582390 (B).
Match Secretary: Craig Campbell, 34 High Sparrowmire, Kendal Cumbria LA9 5PD 01539 725557 (H).
Manager: Stan Allan **Asst Manager:** Bruce Richardson
Press Officer: Peter Savage (01539 726488).
GROUND Address: Parkside Road, Kendal, Cumbria (01539 727472).
Directions: M6 junction 36, follow signs for Kendal (South), right at lights, left at r-bout to 'K' Village - Parkside Rd on right opposite factory main offices - ground 400 yds. A mile & a half from Oxenholme (BR) station - bus service to 'K' village, No 41 or 41A.
Capacity: 2,490 **Cover:** 1,000 **Seats:** 250 **Floodlights:** Yes
Clubhouse: The Park, open all matchdays. Pies & pasties available.
Club Shop: No. **Sponsors:** T B A

PROGRAMME DETAILS:
Pages: 36 **Price:** 80p
Editor: Peter Savage
(01539 726488)

PREVIOUS - Leagues: Westmorland/ North Lancs/ Lancs Combination 45-68/ Northern Premier 68-83/ North West Counties 83-87.

CLUB RECORDS - Attendance: 5,184 v Grimsby Town, FA Cup 1st Rd 1955. **Goalscorer:** Tom Brownlee. **Win:** 11-0 v Great Harwood 22/3/47. **Defeat:** 0-10 v Stalybridge Celtic 1/9/84. **Fee Paid:** Undisclosed for Tom Brownlee (Bradford C., 66). **Fee Received:** £10,250 for Andy Milner (Man. City 95).
Best season - FA Vase: 3rd Rd 89-90. **FA Trophy:** 2nd Rd 80-81. **FA Cup:** 2nd Rd replay 63-64 (1-4 at Chesterfield after 1-1 draw). 2nd Rd 49-50, 1st Rd 45-46 48-49 52-53 54-55 55-56 64-65.
Players progressing to Football League: John Laidlaw (Carlisle 1946), Louis Cardwell (Crewe 1947), Herbert Keen (Barrow 1953), Alec Aston (Preston 1955), Horace Langstreth (Torquay 1956), John Simpson (Lincoln 1957), Dennis Rogers (Accrington 1959), Tom Brownlee (Bradford City 1965), Peter McDonnell (Bury 1973), Keith Silken (Workington 1973), Roger Wicks (Darlington 1981), Andy Milner (Man City).
Local Press: Westmorland Gazette, Lancaster Evening Post. **Local Radio:** Radio Cumbria, Red Rose.
HONOURS: Lancs Comb. 48-49 64-65 (R-up 45-46 53-54 61-62 63-64, Lg Cup 55-56 60-61), Westmorland Snr Cup(12) 24-25 31-33 35-36 46-48 63-64 65-66 71-72 86-87 89-89 90-91.

Netherfield's Paul Renwick (light) rises above Bury players. *Photo - Westmorland Gazette*

SEASON 1996/97
STEELS
REVIEW
OFFICIAL PROGRAMME
STOCKSBRIDGE PARK STEELS
FOOTBALL CLUB
Club Sponsors
ST CHRISTOPHERS
THE UniBond LEAGUE
TODAY'S VISITORS
V
ROSSINGTON MAIN
TUESDAY
10TH DECEMBER 1996
UNIBOND LEAGUE
DIVISION ONE

STOCKSBRIDGE PARK STEELS

Formed: 1986 **Nickname:** Steels
Colours: Yellow/blue/yellow
Change colours: All blue
Midweek matches: Tuesday
Reserves' League: Beefeater County Senior.

President: C D Sedgwick **Chairman:** A Bethel
Vice-Chairman / Secretary: Michael Grimmer, 48 Hole House Lane, Stocksbridge, Sheffield S36 1BT (0114 2886470).
Manager: Mick Horne **Asst Manager:** Trevor Gough
Physio: Sean Hird **Press Officer:** Edwin O'Sullivan
Commercial Manager: Andrew Horsley (0114 2883867)

PROGRAMME DETAILS:
Pages: 28 **Price:** 80p
Editor: Edwin O'Sullivan
(0114 2884218)

GROUND Address Bracken Moor Lane, Stockbridge, Sheffield (0114 2742 882045). **Directions:** M1 jct 35a (from S), 36 (from N), A616 to Stocksbridge. On arrival in Stocksbridge turn left into Nanny Hill under the Clock Tower and continue up the hill for about 500 yds - ground on left.
Capacity: 3,500 **Cover:** 700 **Seats:** 450 **Floodlights:** Yes
Clubhouse: Open seven days (lunchtime & evenings). No food, but separate food bar open for matches.
Club Shop: No, but badges, mugs and scarves on sale.

Sponsors: St Christophers Motor Company
PREVIOUS - Ground: Stonemoor 49-51 52-53. **Names:** Stocksbridge Works, Oxley Park; clubs merged in 1986. **Leagues:** Sheffield Amateur/ Sheffield Association/ Yorkshire 49-82.

CLUB RECORDS - Attendance: 2,000 v Sheffield Wed., Floodlight opening Oct '91.
Fee Received: £15,000 for Lee Mills (Wolves, 1992).
Win: / **Defeat:** / **Scorer:** / **Appearances:**

Players progressing to Football League: Peter Eustace (Sheffield Wednesday) 1960 *(from Stocksbridge Works)*, Lee Mills (Wolverhampton Wanderers) 1992.
96-97 Captain: **96-97 P.o.Y.:** **96-97 Top Scorer:**
Local Press: Sheffield Trader, Green'un, The Star **Local Radio:**

HONOURS: Northern Lge Div 1 Cup R-up 96-97, Northern Co's East Lg 94-95, R-up 95-96, (Div 1 91-92, Lg Cup SF 92-93, Presidents Cup SF 91-92), Sheffield & Hallamshire Snr Cup 51-52 92-93 (SF 94-95), Yorks Lg 51-52 54-55 55-56 56-57 57-58 61-62 62-63 (R-up 60-61, Div 2 50-51 64-65, Div 3 70-71 74-75 (R-up 78-79), Lg Cup 61-62).

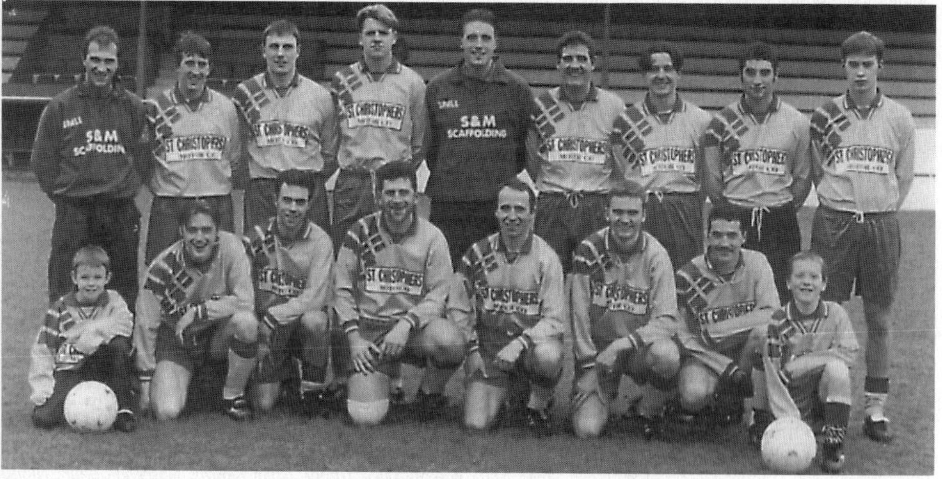

Stocksbridge Park Steels: Back Row (L-R); Sean Hird, Richard Fidler, John Fletcher, Sean Dunphy, Andy Carney, Trevor Jones, Brad Elam, Simon Marples Scott Oxley. Front Row; Mark Jones (Mascot), John Tesh, Andy Tibbenham, Craig Chadburn, Kevin Ronan, Steve Shutt, Gary Hurlestone, Liam O'Sullivan (Mascot)

Season 1996-97

Official Matchday Programme

North West Counties Football League Division One

Price 50p

PROGRAMME DETAILS:
Pages: 24 **Price:** 50p
Editor: David Murray (0161 775 7509)

TRAFFORD

Formed: 1990 **Nickname:** Th North
Colours: All White
Change colours: Red/navy/red
Midweek Matchday: Tuesday
Reserve League: NW Alliance

Chairman: David Brown **President:** K Illingworth
Secretary: Graham Foxall, 62 Grosvenor Road, Urmston M41 5AQ (0161 746 9726)

Manager: David Law **Asst Manager:** John Ferguson
Coach: Dave Higgs

GROUND Address: Shawe View, Pennybridge Lane, Flixton, Urmston, Manchester M41 5DL (0161 747 1727) **Directions:** M63 jct 4, B5158 towards Urmston, at 1st r/about take 1st exit, 1st lights turn right into Moorside Road, at next r/about 2nd exit into Bowfell Rd, at next lights turn sharp left, then immediately right into Pennybridge Lane next to Bird-in-Hand Pub, parking on left 100 yds.
Capacity: 2,500 **Cover:** 732 **Seats:** 284 **Floodlights:** Yes
Clubhouse: Yes **Club Shop:** Yes **Sponsors:** Quicks Motor Group

PREVIOUS - Leagues: Mid Cheshire 90-92, NWC 92-97. **Name:** None

CLUB RECORDS - Attendance: 433 v Flixton (NWCL 5-3-96) **Goalscorer:** Colin Small 74 **Appearances:** Jay McComb 215 **Biggest Victory:** 10-0 v Haslingden St Mary's (Lancs Amt Shield 91) **Biggest Defeat:** 0-6 v Oldham Town (NWCL Div 2 93) **Best season - FA Vase:** 5th Rd 95-96 **FA Cup:** 2nd Rd Qual 95-96
Players progressing to Football League: Anthony Vaughan (Ipswich)
96-97 Captain: John McComb **96-97 P.o.Y.:** John Eaton **96-97 Top Scorer:** Mike Turner 40
Local Press: Stretford & Urmston Messenger, Manchester Evening Echo
Local Radio: GMR Talk, Piccadilly Radio

HONOURS: Lamont Pils Trophy 93-94; NWCL Div 1 96-97, Div 2 R-up 93-94, Lge Chall Cup R-up 96-97; Res Div 93-94; Carling Chall Cup R-up 94-95; Manchester Prem Cup R-up 94-95, R-up 96-97, Res Div Champ 96-97, Cup 96-97; Manchester Amt Cup 96-97.

Trafford FC: at Old Trafford before Manchester Premier Cup Final 96-97: Back Row (L-R): John Eaton, Danny Parkin, Steve Burns, John Ferguson (Asst Mgr), Colin Small, Paul Wilson, Mike Turner, Chris Simms, Garry Vaughan, Nigel Brooks, Stuart Coburn, Andy Woodcock, Sean O'Shea, Jody Banim, Dave Law (Mgr): Front Row: Kevin Hocking (Kit), Steve Jackson, Jay McComb (Cpt), John Brady, Mike Dunphy, Dave Galloway, Dave Higgs (Coach).

Whitby Town F.C.

FEDERATION BREWERY NORTHERN LEAGUE
Main Sponsor Arnott Insurance

Official Programme

Banstead Athletic
F.A. Carlsberg Vase Semi - Final 2nd Leg
Saturday 22nd March 1997 Kick-off 3.00
Programme £1.00 Admission £5.00 Children/OAP'S £2.50

PROGRAMME DETAILS:
Pages: 38 **Price:** 80p
Editor: G Woodward
(01947 602312)

WHITBY TOWN

Formed: 1926 **Nickname:** Seasiders
Colours: All Royal Blue
Change Colours: All white.
Midweek matchday: Wednesday
Reserve League:

Chairman: Graham Miller. **President:** Brooks Mileson
Secretary: Charlie Woodward, 6 Westlands Ave, Whitby, North Yorks YO21 3DZ (01947 602312).
Manager: Harry Dunn **Asst Manager:** Steve Harland
Press Officer: Secretary **Physio:** I Jackson

GROUND Address: Turnbull Ground, Upgang Lane, Whitby, North Yorks (01947 604847). **Directions:** Take A174 road from town centre. Ground on offside travelling towards Sandsend.
Capacity: 4,000 **Cover:** 400 **Seats:** 200 **Floodlights:** Yes
Clubhouse: Mon-Fri 7-11pm, Sat 12-11pm, Sun 12-2 & 7-10.30.
Club Shop: Yes **Sponsors:** Arnott Insurance
Previous Leagues: None. **Name:** Whitby United (pre 1950). **Grounds:** None
CLUB RECORDS - Attendance: 4,000 v Scarborough, N Riding Senior Cup 18/4/65 **Goalscorer:** Paul Pitman. **Appearances:** Paul Pitman. **Win:** 11-2 v Cargo Fleet Works 1950. **Defeat:** 3-13 v Willington 24/3/28
Best FA Cup season: 2nd Round 83-84
Players progressing to Football League: Malcolm Poskett (Hartlepool, Brighton, Watford, Sammy Kemp (Huddersfield), Jimmy Mulvaney (Hartlepool, Barrow, Stockport), Bobby Veart (Hartlepool), Derek Hampton & Trevor Smith & John Linacre & Phil Linacre (Hartlepool), Mark Hine (Grimsby).
96-97 Captain: Neil Hodgson **96-97 P.o.Y.:** David Logan **96-97 Top scorer:** Paul Pitman
Local Newspapers: Whitby Gazette, Northern Echo.
Honours: FA Amateur Cup R-up 64-65, FA Trophy QF 83-84, Northern Lg 92-93 (R-up 27-28 63-64 67-68 81-82 82-83, Lg Cup 28-29 63-64 69-70 76-77 84-85 95-96), Rothmans National Cup 75-76 77-78), Nth Riding Snr Cup 64-65 67-68 82-83 89-90, N Riding Bene Cup 92-93, J R Cleator Cup 84-85 92-93, Mickey Skinner Trophy [5]

Whitby Town FC: Back Row (L-R); S Harland (Asst Mgr), H Dunn (Mgr), K Goodrick, P Cooper, A Martin, M Cook, G Robinson, D Campbell, M Williams, D Goodchild, G Williams, N Hodgson, J Borthwick, B Dewhurst (Scout), I Jackson (Physio). Front Row; A Toman, S Pyle, M Hall, L Pearson, D Logan, A Robertson, I Williams, P Pitman, D Wheeler (Goal keeping Coach).

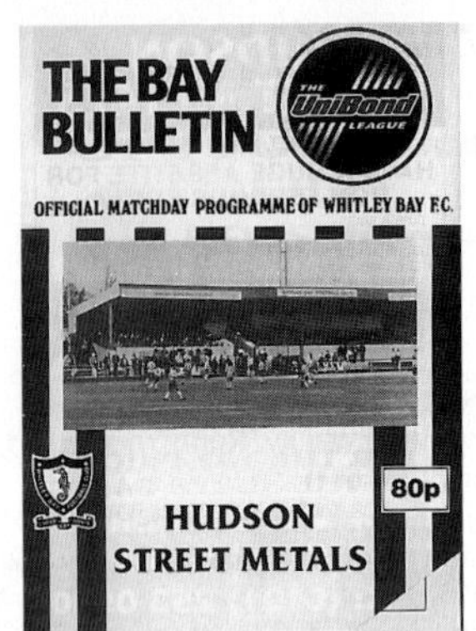

PROGRAMME DETAILS:
Pages: 24 **Price:** 80p
Editor: David Hunter
(0191 291 3637)

WHITLEY BAY

Formed: 1897 **Nickname:** The Bay
Colours: Blue & white stripes/blue/blue
Change colours: Yellow/sky blue
Midweek home matchday: Tuesday.

Chairman: Michael Robinson **Vice Chairman:** Peter Siddle
President: J Hedworth **Secretary:** Derek Breakwell, 27 kings Road, Whitley Bay, Tyne And Wear, NE26 3BD (0191 252 7940).
Manager: Patrick Lowery **Asst Manager:** Paul Walker
Coach: **Physio:** Joe Jabs
Press Officer: David Hunter **Commercial Manager:**

GROUND Address: Hillheads Park, Rink Way off Hillheads Road, Whitley Bay, Tyne & Wear NE25 8HR (0191 291 3637 Club) (Fax & matchday office 0191 291 3636).
Directions: 1 mile walk from bus station - leave St Pauls Church southward, turn right at r-about, ground 3rd left at rear of ice rink. Whitley Bay (25 mins from Newcastle) or Monkseaton metro stations, both 1 mile.
Capacity: 4,500 **Cover:** 650 **Seats:** 450 **Floodlights:** Yes
Clubhouse: Open 7-11pm, except Wed. Bar & concert room. Darts, pool.
Club Shop: Sells programmes, scarves, hats etc.
Contact Tom Moody (0191 291 1618) **Metal Badges:** Yes

PREVIOUS - Name: Whitley Bay Athletic 1950-58. **Leagues:** Tyneside 09-10, Northern Alliance 50-55, North Eastern League 55-58, Northern League 58-88.
CLUB RECORDS - Attendance: 7,301 v Hendon, FA Amateur Cup 1965. **Win:** 12-0 v Shildon 1961. **Defeat:** 1-8 v Bishop Auckland 1979. **Goalscorer:** Billy Wright 307. **Appearances:** Bill Chater 640. **Fee Paid:** £500.
Best Season - FA Amateur Cup: Semi Final 65-66 68-69. **FA Trophy:** 3rd Rd 86-87. **FA Cup:** 3rd Rd 89-90 (0-1 v Rochdale [A]). 2nd Rd 90-91 (0-1 v Barrow [H]). **League clubs defeated:** Scarborough, Preston North End 89-90.
Players progressing to Football League: W Dodd (Burnley 56), W Younger (Nottm Forest 57), R Brown (Blackpool 65), J Ritchie (Port Vale 65), John Brodie & A McCaffery (Carlisle 67 & 88), M Spelman (Wolves 69), T Harrison (Southport 77), M Miller (Gillingham 81), G Haire (Bradford City 83), S Ferebee (Darlington 87), David John Cullen (Hartlepool 97).
96-97 Captain: Chris Pearson **96-97 P.o.Y.:** Paul Greenwood **96-97 Top scorer:** Andy Blower
Local Press: The News, Guardian, Herald & Post. **Local Radio:** Radio Newcastle, Metro.
HONOURS: Northern Premier Lg Div 1 90-91 (Div 1 Cup 88-89 90-91), Northern Lg 64-65 65-66 (R-up 59-60 66-67 68-69 69-70, Lg Cup 64-65 70-71 (R-up 67-68)), Northern Alliance 52-53 53-54 (Lg Cup 52-53 53-54), Northumberland Senior Cup 52-53 60-61 63-64 64-65 67-68 68-69 69-70 70-71 72-73 86-87 (R-up 53-54 54-55 55-56 65-66 76-77 85-86 90-91).

Whitley Bay FC: Back Row (L-R); Kenny Parker (Former Mgr), Gary Anderson, Andy Blower, Philip Hildreth, Chris Pearson, Terry Burke, Steve Kendal, David Corner, Paul Brown, Tony Halliday, Darren Thompson, Patrick Lowery (Mgr). Front Row; Rob Hutchinson, Luke Hughes, Paul Greenwood, David Mosley, Stuart Ainsley, Glen Renforth, Danny Hall.

WITTON ALBION

PROGRAMME DETAILS:
Pages: 32 **Price:** £1
Editor: Phil Chadwick.
(01606 44345)

Formed: 1887 **Nickname:** The Albion
Colours: Red & white stripes
Change colours: Blue and White
Midweek matchday: Tuesday
Reserve League: None

President: T Stelfox **Chairman:** D T Lloyd
Secretary: David Leather, 34 Grosvenor Ave., Hartford, Northwich, Cheshire (01606 76488)
Manager: Kevin Tully **Coach:** Nigel Deeley
Commercial Mgr: **Physio:** Mike Carrick

GROUND Address: Wincham Park, Chapel St, Wincham, Northwich (Tel/Fax: 01606 43008) **Directions:** M6 junc 19. A556 towards Northwich, after 3 miles turn onto A559 at beginning of dual carriageway, after 3/4 mile turn left opposite Black Greyhound Inn, grd 1/2 mile on left immediately after crossing Canal Bridge.
Capacity: 4,500 **Seated:** 650 **Cover:** 2,300 **Floodlights:** Yes
Clubhouse: Concert room and Vice-Presidents room open matchdays, Tuesday, Thursday, Friday and Sunday evenings. Food available for private functions. **Club Shop:** Yes **Sponsors:** McGarage

PREVIOUS - **Leagues:** Lancs Comb./ Cheshire County/ Northern Premier/ GMV Conference 91-94.
Grounds: Central Ground, Witton Street, Northwich.

CLUB RECORDS - Attendance: 3,940 v Kidderminster Harriers - FA Trophy Semi-Final. **Win:** 6-0 v Stafford Rangers - 1992/93. **Defeat:** 0-5 v Welling United (H), GMV Conference 12/3/94. **Fee Received:** £11,500 for Peter Henderson from Chester City. **Goalscorer:** Frank Fidler 122. **Appearances:** John Goryl 652.
F.A. Cup - Best season: 1991-92 **League clubs defeated:** Halifax Town
Players progressing to the Football League: P Henderson (Chester City), Chris Nicholl (ex-Southampton manager), Phil Power (Crewe), Neil Parsley & Mike Whitlow (Leeds).
96-97 Captain: Colin Rose **96-97 Top Scorer:** Liam Watson **96-97 P.o.Y:** Mark Statham

HONOURS: Northern Prem Lge 90-91; Cheshire County Lge 48-49 49-50 53-54 (R-up 50-51), Lge Cup 53-54 75-76; Cheshire County Sen Cup (7); FA Trophy R-up 91-92 (SF 90-91 92-93).

Witton Albion FC 1997-98: Back Row (L-R): Bancroft, Washington, Boswell, Pritchard, Wright, Brenchley.
Photo: Keith Clayton Front: Gardner, Dowe, Gedman, Heeson, Carter, Roberts

WORKINGTON

Formed: 1884 (reformed 1921) **Nickname:** Reds
Colours: Red/white/red
Change colours: Jade & navy quarters/jade/jade & navy
Midweek home matchday: Tuesday
Reserve Team's League: West Cumberland.

Chairman: Jackie Donald **President:** Eric Fisher
Vice Chairman: Colin Doorbar **Secretary:** Tom Robson, 12 Derwent Bank, Seaton, Workington CA14 1EE (01900 65566).
Manager: Keith Hunton **Asst Manager:**
Press Officer: Steve Durham (01946 61380) **Physio:** Reg Cartner

GROUND Address: Borough Park, Workington, Cumbria CA14 2DT (01900 602871). **Directions:** A66 into town, right at 'T' junction, follow A596 for three quarters of a mile - ground is then visible and signposted. Ground is to north of town centre quarter of a mile from Workington (BR) station and half mile from bus station in town centre.
Capacity: 2,500 **Cover:** 800 **Seats:** 300 **Floodlights:** Yes
Clubhouse: Open matchdays and for private functions. Food on matchdays restricted menu.
Club Shop: Sells programmes, badges, magazines, pennants, photographs, replica kit, T-shirts. Contact Keith Lister (01900 812867).
Sponsors: T.B.A.

PROGRAMME DETAILS:
Pages: 28 **Price:** 60p
Editor: Steve Durham (01946 61380)

PREVIOUS - Grounds: Various 1884-1921, Lonsdale Park 21-37. **Leagues:** Cumberland Association 1890-94, Cumberland Senior League 94-1901 03-04, Lancashire League 1901-03, Lancashire Combination 04-10, North Eastern 10-11 21-51, Football League 51-77.

CLUB RECORDS - Attendance: 21,000 v Manchester Utd, FA Cup 3rd Rd 4/1/58. **Goalscorer:** Billy Charlton 193. **Appearances:** Bobby Brown 419. **Win:** 17-1 v Cockermouth Crusaders, Cumberland Senior League 19/1/01. **Defeat:** 0-9 v Chorley (A), NPL Prem. Division, 10/11/87. **Fee Paid:** £6,000 for Ken Chisholm (Sunderland, 1956). **Fee Received:** £33,000 for Ian McDonald (Liverpool, 1974).
Best Season - FA Cup: 4th Rd 33-34. 1st Rd - 53 occasions. **FA Trophy:** 1st Round replay 77-78.
Players progressing to Football League: Numerous, the best known being John Burridge.
Local Press: Evening News & Star, Times & Star. **Local Radio:** BBC Radio Cumbria, C.F.M.

HONOURS: Football League Cup QF 63-64 64-65, Football League: 5th in Div 3 65-66, 3rd Div 4 63-64, Northern Prem. Lge Presidents Cup 83-84, North Eastern Lge R-up 38-39 (Lge Cup 34-35 36-37 (R-up 37-38)), Cumberland County Cup 1886-91(x5) 95-99(x4) 1906-08(x2) 09-10 24-25 34-35 36-38(x2) 49-50 53-54 67-68 85-86 95-96 (R-up 1885-86 91-92 1899-1901(x2) 02-03 08-09 11-12 23-24 26-27 29-30 46-47 68-69 78-79).

Workington's Martin Henderson breaks clear of Stocksbridge's Richard Holmshaw. *Photo - Alan Watson*

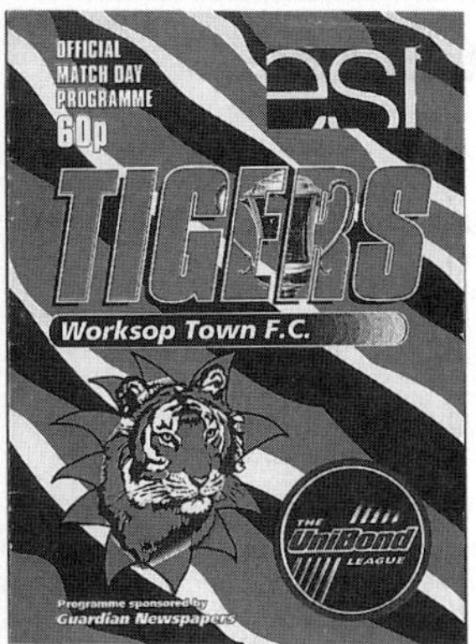

PROGRAMME DETAILS:
Pages: 28-32 **Price:** 50p
Editor: Mel Bradley
(01909 500491/500500)

WORKSOP TOWN

Formed: 1861 **Nickname:** The Tigers
Colours: Amber & black/black/black
Change colours: All white/amber/black trim
Midweek home matchday: Tuesday.
Reserve Team's League: Central Midlands Res

Chairman: Rick Knowles **Vice Chairman:** John Shuker
Club Secretary: Keith Illett, 2 Mount Avenue, Worksop, Notts (01909 487934)
General Manager: Paul Mitchell **Company Secretary:** Mel Bradley
Asst Manager: Danny Hague **Physio:** Graham Bacon
Press Officer: Mel Bradley **Commercial Manager:** Kevin Barratt

GROUND Address: Babbage Way, off Sandy Lane, Worksop, Notts S80 1UJ (01909 501911). **Directions:** M1 jct 31 (from north) jct 30 (from south), follow Worksop signs, join A57 and follow signs for Sandy Lane Industrial Estate - ground on left. 5 mins walk from station.
Capacity: 2,500 **Cover:** 1,000 **Seats:** 360 **Floodlights:** Yes.
Clubhouse: Tigers Club. Normal licensing hours. Pool, quiz nights, disco etc.
Club Shop: The Tigershop selling badges, scarves, magazines, programmes. 30 page catalogue from Steve Jarvis, 10 Wood End Drive, Ravenshead, Notts NG15 9EJ.
Sponsors: D.T.H. Engineers, Eyres of Worksop and Norwood Fisheries.

PREVIOUS - Grounds: Netherton Road, Bridge Meadow, Central Avenue (pre 1989), The Northolme (Gainsborough Trinity - shared) 89-92. **Leagues:** Midland (Counties) 1896-98 1900-30 49-60 61-68 69-74, Sheffield Assoc. 1898-99 1931-33, Central Comb. 33-35, Yorkshire 35-39, Central All. 47-49 60-61, Northern Premier 68-69.

CLUB RECORDS - Attendance: 1,503 v Sheffield Utd, friendly. *Central Avenue: 8,171 v Chesterfield, FA Cup 1925.* **Goalscorer:** Kenny Clark, 287. **Appearances:** Kenny Clark 347. **Win:** 20-0 v Staveley, 1/9/1894. **Defeat:** 1-11 v Hull City Res., 55-56. **Fees Received:** £10,000 Martin Hardy, Boston U. 87. **Best Season - FA Cup:** 3rd Rd: 1907-08 v Chelsea (A) 1-9, 21-22 v Southend (H) 1-2, 22-23 v Spurs (A) 0-0 & 0-9, 55-56 v Swindon (A) 0-1. 2nd Rd: 25-26, 1st Rd: 20-21, 26-27, 61-62, 78-79. **League Clubs defeated:** Rotherham Town 1894-95, Grimsby Town 94-95, Nelson 1921-22, Chesterfield 22-23, Coventry City 25-26, Bradford City 55-56. **FA Trophy:** 2nd Rd replay 73-74.

Players progressing to Football League: J Brown (Sheff Wed), G Dale (Chesterfield 48), A Daley (Doncaster 50), K Wood (Grimsby 51), H Jarvis (Notts Co. 51), B Taylor (Leeds 51), S Rhodes 51, D Gratton 52, A Hodgkinson 53, J Harrison 67 (Sheffield Utd), S Lloyd & P Marshall (Scunthorpe 54), A Rhodes (QPR 54), R Moore (Rotherham 55), H Mosby (Crewe 1956), L Moore (Derby 1957), H Bowery (Nottm Forest 75), T Moore (Rochdale 84), S Adams (Scarborough 87), D Moss (Doncaster 93).
96-97 Captain: Linden Whitehead **96-97 P.o.Y.:** Darren Dye **96-97 Top scorer:** Linden Whitehead
Local - Press: Worksop Guardian, Worksop Star, Nottingham Football Post.
Radio: Radio Sheffield, Radio Hallam, Radio Lincoln.

HONOURS: N.P.L. Presidents Cup 85-86 95-96, Midland Cos Lg 21-22 65-66 72-73 (R-up 62-63 66-67 73-74), Sheffield Assoc. Lg 1898-99, Sheffield & Hallamshire Snr Cup 23-24 52-53 54-55 65-66 69-70 72-73 81-82 84-85 96-97, Mansfield Charity Cup 22-23.

Worksop Town FC: Back Row (L-R): Dean Dye, Dave McNicholas, Ian Askey, Dave Cutts, Jamie Holmshaw, Gary Townsend, Steve Johnson, Darren Dye, Matt Walsh. Front Row: Lee Howard, Darren Brookes, Danny Campbell, Linden Whitehead, Terry Harris. *Photo - Paul Mitchell*

NORTH WEST COUNTIES FOOTBALL LEAGUE

HONOURS SEASON 1996/97

First Division Champions	Trafford	Runners up	Newcastle Town
Second Division Champions	Ramsbottom United	Runners up	Haslingden
League Challenge Cup Winners	Newcastle Town	Runners up	Trafford
Floodlit Trophy Winners	Penrith	Runners up	Newcastle Town
Second Division Trophy Winners	Nelson	Runners up	Garswood United
Reserve Division Champions	Trafford	Runners up	Clitheroe
Reserve Division Cup Winners	Trafford	Runners up	Clitheroe
Manchester Premier Cup Winners	Glossop North End	Runners up	Trafford

MANAGER OF THE YEAR
Division One David Law – Trafford
Division Two Ken Bridge – Ramsbottom United

PLAYER OF THE YEAR
Division One Peter Cumiskey – Prescot Cables
Division Two Matt Shiels – Nelson

PROGRAMME OF THE YEAR
Division One Newcastle Town
Division Two Skelmersdale United
Overall Winner Clitheroe

REALCO EQUIPMENT LTD FAIR PLAY AWARD
Division One Nantwich Town
Division Two Leek CSOB

LEAGUE CHALLENGE CUP 1995/96

THIRD ROUND

Vauxhall GM	1	Nantwich T.	3
Maghull	1	Glossop N.E.	2
Eastwood H.	2	Burscough	1
Trafford	2	Darwen	0
Bootle	1	Newcastle T.	3
Mossley	0	Clitheroe	3
Penrith	1	Atherton C.	0
Tetley Walker	1	Holker O.B.	2

FOURTH ROUND

Nantwich T.	1	Glossop N.E.	1*
Glossop N.E.	2	Nantwich T.	3
Eastwood H.	0	Trafford	1
Newcastle T.	2	Clitheroe	0
Penrith	1	Holker O.B.	0

SEMI-FINALS
FIRST LEG

Nantwich T.	0	Trafford	2
Newcastle T.	1	Penrith	0

SECOND LEG

Trafford	3	Nantwich T.	2
Penrith	2	Newcastle T.	4

* = Extra Time Played

FINAL

Newcastle T.	2	Trafford	1

LEADING GOAL SCORERS FOR SEASON 1996/7

DIVISION ONE		Lge	Cup	Total
Mike Turner	Trafford	31	9	40
John Scarlett	Nantwich Town	30	9	39
Tony Fyffe	Penrith	24	10	34
Graham Dodd	Atherton Collieries	24	8	32
Nicky Young	Vauxhall GM	22	9	31
Keith Johnstone	Blackpool Rovers	26	4	30
John Burndred	Newcastle Town	17	12	29
Marcus Thompson	Penrith	13	13	26
Paul Mullin	Clitheroe	21	3	24
Shaun Wade	Newcastle Town	16	8	24
Lee Cooper	Burscough	11	13	24
DIVISION TWO				
Frank Ryan	Skelmersdale United	22	9	31
Rory McDowell	Haslingden	24	6	30
Gary Laird	Garswood United	26	4	30
Mark Wilson	Formby	23	7	30
Russell Brierley	Ramsbottom United	25	3	28
Tony Plant	Tetley Walker	20	6	26

NORTH WEST COUNTIES

FEEDER TO:
NORTHERN PREMIER LEAGUE

FOUNDED: 1982
President: Canon J R Smith, MA
Chairman: J E Hinchliffe. **Treasurer:** K H Dean
Secretary: M Darby, 87 Hillary Road
Hyde, Cheshire SK14 4EB (0161 368 6243

THIRD TIME LUCKY FOR TRAFFORD

Once again the North West Counties League promotion and relegation battles went to the wire, although outside influences had a say in the relegation issues as will be explained later.

The Division One championship battle had for some weeks developed into a two horse race with TRAFFORD and NEWCASTLE TOWN leading the pack. Trafford had the points, whilst Newcastle had games in hand, but the pressure finally told when the Staffordshire side went down to Mossley whilst Trafford clinched the title with an emphatic win over Salford City in their final game.

Trafford confounded their critics as many 'experts' felt, at the start of the season, that they would be unable to maintain their challenge after the disappointment of missing out on promotion in each of the two previous seasons. Their achievement is all the more creditable as they were only formed in May 1990 and is a credit to the hard working committee as well as to the players. In season 1994/95 and 1995/96 their own success cost them dear in their league campaign. In both seasons fixture congestion as a result of success in cup competitions cost them dear. Whilst they appeared in two cup finals, and lost them both, but their end of season run in was not so congested. So at the third time of asking Trafford made no mistake and will take their place in the Unibond League for season 1997/98.

Newcastle Town took the runners up spot for the second season in succession. They will take some consolation from the fact that they defeated Trafford in the League Challenge Cup Final at Gigg Lane Bury by 2-1.

At the other end of the league table the picture is anything but clear cut. SALFORD CITY and DARWEN finished in the relegation places but neither will be playing their football in Division two next season. Darwen will retain their place in the top flight as a result of EASTWOOD HANLEY's resignation. Eastwood have led a nomadic existence over the past couple of seasons and having failed in the application to the Lottery for funds to rebuild their Trentmill Road home they feel that the club can no longer bear the cost of ground sharing. Another club leaving the league are PENRITH who are being transferred to the Northern League in order to allow two North West clubs to be relegated from the Unibond League, Atherton L.R. and Warrington Town. Salford City retain their place in the First Division as BOOTLE have failed to maintain their ground to the required standard for Division One. As a result the Liverpool outfit have been relegated to Division two by member clubs on the recommendation of the Management Committee. A timely reminder to all clubs at this level that playing criteria are not the only standards required.

In Division Two the picture was much more clear cut but again it needed a win for RAMSBOTTOM UNITED in their final game if they were to pip HASLINGDEN by goal difference. 'Rammy' duly came up with the win to take the title and leave Haslinden the runners-up spot after leading the table for weeks. Ramsbottom, in their first season in the league are to be congratulated on their achievement, both on and off the pitch. For Haslingden it is some consolation as in their first season in 1994/95 they also took the title but missed out on promotion as the Ewood Bridge facilities did not meet the requirements for Division One. Their hard working Committee have taken huge steps to ensure that there was no mistake this time.

Of the other new clubs GARSWOOD UNITED finished a creditable third and somewhat surprisingly were beaten in the final of the Second Division Trophy by NELSON having started the game as hot favourites. COLNE found their first season hard going and for most of the season occupied bottom spot. A position they held at the end of the season, and together with OLDHAM TOWN had to apply for re-election.

NELSON's success was their first piece of silverware since they joined the League and will no doubt give the club a big boost as will their success with the Lotteries Board whose grant will allow the club to provide facilities for the disabled and also floodlights.

NEWCASTLE TOWN's quest for honours saw them reach the final of the Floodlit Trophy Final for the second year in succession but they were unable to hold on to the trophy as they went down to PENRITH, winners two seasons ago.

No review of the season would be complete without reference to VAUXHALL GM. Many peoples' tip for the title, their league form was disappointing but their cup exploits were something else. Victories over Northwich Victoria, at the Drill Field, and Altrincham at Rivacres road in the Cheshire Senior Cup set up a two-legged semi-final against Hyde United and whilst they were unable to repeat the success of the earlier rounds they did themselves and the League proud.

GLOSSOP NORTH END and TRAFFORD reached the final of the Manchester County F.A. Premier Cup and in the magnificent home of Manchester United, Trafford's Final jinx struck again. They battled back from a goal down to send the game into extra time but with no further goals it was down to penalties. It was Glossop who held their nerve and in front of 2011 spectators ran out winners by 5-3.

NORTH WEST COUNTIES LEAGUE TABLES
UP TO AND INCLUDING SATURDAY 17th MAY 1997
FINAL TABLES

DIVISION ONE	*P*	*W*	*D*	*L*	*F*	*A*	*Pts*	*G/D*
Trafford	42	29	7	6	99	38	94	+61
Newcastle T.	42	27	7	8	71	31	88	+30
Clitheroe	42	23	14	5	75	36	83	+39
Penrith	42	23	10	9	75	49	79	+26
Burscough	42	22	9	11	68	48	75	+20
Eastwood H.	42	20	10	12	64	51	70	+13
Mossley	42	20	8	14	79	58	68	+21
Blackpool Rvrs.	42	17	19	9	70	47	67	+23
Prescot Cables	42	17	11	14	68	60	62	+8
Vauxhall GM	42	14	15	13	70	69	57	+1
Nantwich Town	42	14	11	17	75	74	53	+1
Glossop NE	42	14	11	17	56	67	53	–11
Bootle	42	15	8	19	61	73	53	–12
St Helens T.	42	14	6	22	65	79	48	–14
Atherton Coll.	42	12	9	21	63	85	45	–22
Kidsgrove Ath.	42	10	14	18	53	73	44	–20
Rossendale U	42	11	9	22	51	77	42	–26
Chadderton	42	10	11	21	49	80	41	–31
Holker Old Boys	42	10	9	23	60	80	39	–20
Maine Road	42	9	11	22	49	85	38	–36
Darwen	42	9	10	23	49	81	37	–32
Salford City	42	8	12	22	53	82	36	–29

DIVISION TWO	*P*	*W*	*D*	*L*	*F*	*A*	*Pts*	*G/D*
Ramsbottom U.	38	27	6	5	100	34	87	+66
Haslingden	38	27	6	5	90	32	87	+58
Garswood U.	38	26	5	7	90	38	83	+52
Tetley Walker	38	24	5	9	105	58	77	+47
Castleton Gab.	38	22	8	8	78	39	74	+39
Leek CSOB	38	22	7	9	67	49	73	+18
Formby	38	21	6	11	86	57	69	+29
Maghull	38	17	7	14	52	50	58	+2
Cheadle T.	38	15	8	15	59	63	53	–4
Skelmersdale U.	38	14	10	14	72	66	52	+6
Nelson	38	14	10	14	64	72	52	–8
Stantondale	38	11	12	15	69	69	45	–10
Middlewich Ath.	38	13	6	19	54	65	46	–11
Squires Gate	38	12	4	22	44	79	40	–35
Daisy Hill	38	10	5	23	47	76	35	–29
Bacup Borough	38	9	6	23	48	83	33	–35
Ashton Town	38	6	14	18	53	77	32	–24
Blackpool Mech.	38	7	5	26	48	88	26	–40
Oldham Town	38	6	7	25	48	113	25	–65
Colne	38	6	5	27	35	91	23	–56

NORTH WEST COUNTIES DIVISION ONE RESULTS CHART 1996–97

HOME TEAM	1	2	3	4	5	6	7	8	9	10	11	12	13	14	15	16	17	18	19	20	21	22
Atherton Coll.	*	2-4	0-4	2-2	2-2	1-2	6-1	3-0	0-0	4-3	0-0	2-1	0-2	3-0	1-3	1-1	0-0	1-1	3-1	7-4	0-2	0-1
Blackpool Rvrs.	2-0	*	1-1	5-0	1-1	0-2	3-1	2-1	2-0	5-1	2-0	1-0	0-1	2-3	1-2	0-0	2-0	0-2	5-1	3-0	1-2	1-1
Bootle	3-4	0-0	*	2-1	4-1	1-1	3-0	0-2	3-0	1-0	0-3	5-2	3-1	0-6	0-3	1-4	2-2	3-0	4-0	2-2	0-2	1-1
Burscough	5-1	1-1	3-0	*	3-1	0-1	1-0	4-3	5-2	2-0	3-0	2-0	1-0	0-1	2-3	0-2	1-0	3-0	1-0	0-3	1-1	1-1
Chadderton	1-0	1-1	0-1	0-1	*	0-3	1-1	2-0	2-1	1-1	2-3	1-0	2-4	4--0	1-2	1-2	2-1	2-0	2-1	1-0	0-4	1-1
Clitheroe	1-0	4-0	2-1	0-3	1-1	*	3-0	1-1	2-0	4-1	2-0	3-0	0-0	2-2	1-1	2-0	2-1	1-0	2-0	2-1	2-2	3-3
Darwen	2-2	2-2	0-2	0-2	2-4	1-2	*	2-3	1-2	1-0	3-5	1-5	4-3	1-1	0-2	2-3	0-1	2-3	1-1	0-2	3-1	1-1
Eastwood Han	3-0	0-0	0-0	1-1	2-1	0-4	1-0	*	1-1	1-0	2-1	4-1	4-1	1-1	1-2	2-1	1-2	1-0	3-1	4-1	2-1	2-1
Glossop NE	1-0	2-4	3-2	0-2	1-1	2-2	1-1	1-0	*	2-2	0-0	3-2	0-0	1-4	0-3	1-1	2-3	0-1	2-1	0-1	1-2	1-1
Holker OB	2-3	3-0	1-0	1-1	4-4	0-1	3-0	0-0	1-3	*	2-1	3-1	1-3	3-1	1-3	1-2	1-1	1-1	1-1	3-2	1-0	3-4
Kidsgrove Ath	1-0	2-2	0-3	1-2	1-1	0-0	4-1	1-1	4-5	1-0	*	1-1	3-1	3-4	0-0	1-2	1-1	1-1	3-0	3-3	1-3	0-4
Maine Rd	1-6	0-0	1-0	0-0	4-2	0-4	0-2	2-4	1-1	1-0	2-3	*	2-3	4-1	0-3	1-1	0-1	0-0	5-2	2-1	1-1	2-2
Mossley	2-0	1-3	3-0	4-0	2-0	0-0	1-1	1-1	1-3	2-1	4-0	1-2	*	3-2	2-1	2-2	1-2	0-2	3-1	7-2	3-0	4-0
Nantwich T.	1-1	1-0	2-2	0-1	3-0	2-2	0-1	2-2	1-2	5-1	2-0	5-0	1-2	*	0-1	1-2	1-3	0-2	1-0	4-1	1-4	1-3
Newcastle T.	3-0	1-1	1-0	0-0	4-0	0-0	0-1	1-2	1-0	2-0	3-0	2-0	2-0	1-3	*	1-1	0-4	3-1	2-0	2-0	3-1	0-1
Penrith	0-2	2-2	3-0	1-3	5-0	3-2	1-0	1-0	0-3	2-1	3-0	2-0	0-2	5-1	2-1	*	1-0	1-0	0-2	2-1	1-3	1-0
Prescot	4-1	1-2	1-2	4-3	2-2	1-0	1-3	2-0	1-0	1-0	1-1	1-1	2-2	3-1	1-1	0-3	*	6-2	1-0	2-3	0-2	2-2
Rossendale U	3-1	1-1	4-0	1-3	4-1	1-1	0-1	2-0	1-4	2-1	2-2	0-2	0-2	1-2	1-3	1-1	1-3	*	2-4	1-3	0-2	1-0
Salford City	0-1	1-4	4-2	1-1	4-0	1-3	1-1	2-1	2-0	4-4	1-2	1-1	1-1	2-2	0-2	2-2	4-3	1-1	*	0-1	0-1	2-2
St Helens T	3-0	0-1	2-3	2-0	1-0	0-2	3-2	0-2	1-2	1-3	3-0	1-1	4-3	1-1	0-1	2-2	1-1	4-3	0-2	*	0-1	4-1
Trafford	9-1	1-1	4-0	3-1	1-0	3-1	1-1	1-2	3-0	5-1	1-0	4-0	3-1	2-2	2-1	3-1	2-1	6-0	6-1	1-0	*	1-1
Vauxhall GM	5-2	2-2	3-1	0-2	2-0	3-2	1-2	1-3	1-3	1-4	0-0	5-0	2-1	2-2	0-1	1-6	4-1	3-2	0-0	2-1	1-2	*

ATHERTON COLLIERIES

Chairman: Steve Payne **Vice Chairman:** **President:** J Fielding
Secretary: Emil Anderson, 5 Almond Crescent, Standish, Wigan WN6 0AZ (01257 404055 H, 0161 288 6206 B)
Manager: Steve Walton **Asst Manager:** I Lamb **Coach:** R Hough
Physio: Trevor Ball **Commercial Manager:** D Pratano.
Ground: Atherton Collieries Football Ground, Atherton, Gt Manchester (01942 884649).
Directions: M61 Jct 5, follow sign for Westhoughton, left onto A6, right onto A579 (Newbrook Rd/Bolton Rd) into Atherton. At first set of lights turn left into High Street, 2nd left into Alder St. to ground. Quarter mile from Atherton Central (BR).
Seats: 300 **Cover:** 1,000 **Capacity:** 2,500 **Floodlights:** Yes **Founded:** 1916
Colours: Black & red stripes/black/black. **Change colours:** All red. **Nickname:** Colls
Reserves' Lge: CNWCL Res Div **Record Attendance:** 3,300 in Lancs Combination, 1920's
Midweek Matches: Tuesday **Club Sponsors:** L & I Eaton
Club Shop: Yes, selling replica shirts, programmes, enamel badges, key-rings. Contact Secretary.
Programme: 40 pages, 50p **Editor:** Secretary *(CNWCL Div 2 Programme of the Year, 93-94)*
Previous Lges: Bolton Comb. 20-50 52-71, Lancs Comb. 50-52 71-78, Cheshire Co. 78-82.
Players progressing to Football League: J Parkinson (Wigan), Russell Beardsmore (Manchester Utd).
Clubhouse: Open Mon-Fri 7-11pm, Sat 11am-11pm, Sun noon-3 & 7-10.30pm. Hot & cold food on matchdays.
Captain 96-97: **P.o.Y.:** D Owen **Top Scorer 96-97:** K Daley.
Hons: BNWCFL 3rd Div Champ 86/87; Bridge Shield 85/86; Lancs County FA Shield 19/20, 22/23, 41/42, 45/46. 56/57, 64/65; Tennents F/lit Trophy Finalist 94/95; NWCFL Div 2 R/up 95/96

ATHERTON L. R.

President: **Chairman:** Brian Horsebury. **Treasurer:** Jack Hetherington
Secretary: Steve Hartle, 32 Greensmith Way, Westhoughton, Bolton BL5 3DR (01942 840906).
Manager: Gerry Luczha **Assistant Manager:** Ian Senior **Coach:** Steve Walton
Ground: Crilly Park, Spa Road, Atherton, Greater Manchester (01942 883950).
Directions: M61 to Jct 5, follow signs for Westhoughton, left onto A6, right onto A579 (Newbrook Rd/Bolton Rd) over the railway bridge, right into Upton Rd passing Atherton Central Station, left into Springfield Rd and left again into Hillside Rd into Spa Rd and ground.
Seats: 250 **Cover:** 3 sections **Capacity:** 3,000 **Floodlights:** Yes **Club Shop:** Yes
Programme: 48 pages 70p **Editor:** Mark Salt (01942 796256)
Formed: 1954 **Nickname:** The Panthers **Sponsors:** T B A
Colours: Yellow/royal/royal **Change colours:** Red & white/black/black **Midweek Matches:** Tuesday
Reserve Team's League: North West Alliance.
Previous - Leagues: Bolton Combination/ Cheshire County 80-82/ NWCL 82-94/ NPL 94-97. **Name:** Laburnum Rovers 54-79. **Grounds:** Laburnum Road 54-56/ Hagfold 56-66.
Clubhouse: Open normal licensing hours.
Club Records - Attendance: 1,856 v Aldershot Town, FA Vase Q.-Final replay 5/3/94. **Career Scorer:** Shaun Parker. **Career Appearances:** Jimmmy Evans. **Transfer Fee Paid:** £500 for Joey Dunn from Warrington Town. **Transfer Fee Received:** £1,500 for Stuart Humphries to Barrow
Best Season: FA Cup: 3rd Qual Rd 96-97, 0-2 v Bamber Bridge. **FA Vase:** Semi-Final replay 94-95 (1-2 v Diss Town). **FA Trophy:** 1st Qual Rd 96-97
Players progressing to Football League: Barry Butler (Chester), Lee Unsworth (Crewe).
96-97 Captain: Tony Pemberton **Top Scorer:** Lee Cryer (22) **P.o.Y.:** Lee Cryer
Honours:: North West Counties Lge 92-93 93-94, Champions Trophy 92-93 93-94, F/Lit Trophy 93-94; Northern Premier Lge Div.1 Cup R-up 95-96

BLACKPOOL (Wren) ROVERS

Chairman: J Nolan **Manager:** Brian Wilson
Secretary: P Kimberley, 34 Priory Gate, South Shore, Blackpool FY4 2QE (H 01253 349853) (B 01253 737464)
Ground: Bruce Park, School Road, Marton, Blackpool, Lancs, (01253 760570)
Directions: M6 to M55, leave junc 4, left onto A583, sharp right at 1st lights (Whitehill Rd), follow signs for Airport. Ground approx 1.5 miles on right. 6 miles from Blackpool North BR station.
Seats: 500 **Cover:** 1000 **Capacity:** 1,500 **Floodlights:** Yes **Club Shop:** No.
Programme: 20 pages, 50p **Editor:** P Kimberley **Nickname:** Wrens **Clubhouse:** Open matchdays
Colours: All red **Change colours:** All blue **Founded:** 1936
Midweek matchday: Tuesday **Reserve League:** West Lancs
Record Attendance: 1,011 v Manchester City, floodlight opener Oct 1991
Previous leagues: West Lancs, Lancs Comb 72-82 **Previous Name:** Wren Rovers
96-97 Captain: John Oliver **96-97 Top Scorer:** Keith Johnstone
Honours: W Lancs Lg 69-70 70-71, (Lge Cup 70-71, 71-72); Lancs FA Shield 68-69 70-71; Lancs Comb 78-79 80-81, (R-up 77-78), Lge Cup 78-79.

BURSCOUGH

Chairman: Frank Parr **Vice Chairman:** Stuart Heaps **President:** Ken Griffin
Secretary: Stan Strickland, 109 Redgate, Ormskirk, Lancs L39 3NW (H 01695 574722) (B 01695 574722)
Manager: John Davison **Asst Manager:** Peter King. **Physio:** Rod Cottam
Ground: Victoria Park, Mart Lane, Burscough, Ormskirk, Lancs L40 0SD (01704 893237).
Directions: M6 Jct 27, follow signs thru Parbold A5209, right into Junction Lane (signed Burscough & Martin Mere) to lights, right onto A59 to Burscough Village, 2nd left over canal bridge into Mart Lane to ground. 200 yards from Burscough Bridge BR station (Wigan-Southport line). Half mile from Burscough Junction (Ormskirk Preston line).
Seats: 220 **Cover:** 1,000 **Capacity:** 3,000 **Floodlights:** Yes **Club Shop:** No
Clubhouse: 'Barons Club' (privately owned, access from outside ground). Mon-Thurs 7-11, Fri 4-11, Sat 1-11, Sun 12-3 & 7-10.30. No food. **Programme:** 36 pages, 60p **Editor/Press Officer:** Stan Strickland (01695 574722)
Colours: Green/white/green. **Change colours:** Yellow/blue/blue
Founded: 1946 **Nickname:** Linnets **Midweek Matches:** Tuesday **Sponsors:** Crown Computer Products.
Previous Leagues: Liverpool County Comb. 46-53, Lancs Comb. 53-70, Cheshire Co. 70-82.
Record Attendance: 4,798 v Wigan Athletic,F.A.Cup 3rd Qual.Rd.1950-51.
Club Record Goalscorer: Johnny Vincent 60 53-54 **Best FA Cup season:** 1st Rd 59-60 77-78 79-80 80-81.
Players progressing to Football League: S Teale (Aston Villa), L Watson (Preston), K Formby A Russell (Rochdale 94), G Martindale (Bolton 94), S Perkins (Plymouth Arg 97).
96-97 Captain: Ged Nolan **96-97 Top Scorer:** Lee Cooper **96-97 P.o.Y.:** Neil Hanson
Hons: Liverpool Challenge Cup 47-48 50-51,54-55; George Mahon Cup 47-48; Liverpool County Comb Div 1, 49-50 (Div 2 53-54, 67-68); Lancs Comb.Div 2 53-54; Lancs Comb Div 1 55-56 69-70; Lord Wavertree Cup Winners 67-68; Cheshire County League R-up 70-71, League Cup 74-75 (R-up 73-74); Lancs Jnr Cup 47-48 49-50 66-67; Liverpool Snr Cup 55/56, 71-72; Nth West Co's League 82-83 (League Cup 92-93 95-96(R-up 91-92), Challenge Shield 82-83, 95-96; Bill Tyrer Memorial Trophy 90; Liverpool Snr Non-League Cup Finalist 92-93, 95-96:

CHADDERTON

Chairman: Peter Evans **Vice Chairman:** Harry Mayall. **President:** Derek Glynn
Secretary: Ronald Manton, 42 Fife Avenue, Chadderton, Oldham, Lancs OL9 8AC, (0161 620 0368)
Manager: Dave Stewart **Asst Manager:** Paul Dixon **Physio:** Roy Houghton
Ground: Andrew Street, Chadderton, Oldham, Lancs (0161 624 9733). **Press Officer:** John Fitton
Directions: M62 Jct 20, A627(M) to Oldham. Motorway then becomes dual carriageway. Turn left at first major traffic lights A669 (Middleton Road), then first left opposite 'Harlequin' P.H. into Burnley Street - Andrew Street 2nd left. 1 mile from Oldham Werneth (BR), buses 458 & 459 (Oldham-Manchester) stop at the Harlequin.
Seats: 200 **Cover:** 700 **Capacity:** 2,500 **Floodlights:** Yes **Club Shop:** No
Clubhouse: Matchdays only. Hot & cold snack during & after games
Programme: 28-32 pages **Editor:** David Greaves **Reserves' Lge:** Carling NWCL Res. Div.
Colours: Red/White/Red. **Change colours:** White/Blue/White. **Midweek Matches:** Tuesday.
Sponsors: Royton Metals,Nationwide Building Society and Asda. **Nickname:** Chaddy **Founded:** 1947
Previous Leagues: Oldham Amateur, Manchester Amateur, Manchester 64-80, Lancs Comb. 80-82
Players progressing to Football League: David Platt (Crewe etc), John Pemberton (Crewe etc), Graham Bell (Oldham, Preston), Paul Hilton (Bury, West Ham), Don Graham (Bury).
Record Attendance: 1,500 v Guinness Exports 1969 **Record Appearances:** Billy Elwell 750+ (64-90).
96-97 Captain: Mark Bedford **96-97 P.o.Y.:** Tony Lucas **96-97 Top Scorer:** Jimmy Gemmell
Honours: Manchester Amat Lg 62-63 (North Div 55-56), Manchester Prem Cup R-up 82-83 (Challenge Tphy 71-72, R-up 72-73), Manchester Lg Div 1 66-67 (Div 2 64-65), Gilgryst Cup. 69-70, Murray Shield 65-66, Lancs Comb. Cup R-up 81-82, Alfred Pettit & Hulme Celtic Cup 61-62, Nth West Co's F/lit Tphy R-up 92-93, Manchester Yth Cup 59-60 (R-up 60-61).

CLITHEROE

Chairman: S Rush **President:** Jer Aspinall **Nickname:** The Blues **Formed:** 1877
Secretary/Press Officer: Colin Wilson, 4 Moss Street, Clitheroe, Lancs BB7 1DP (01200 424370).
Press Officer: Colin Wilson **Manager:** Denis Underwood/Gary Butcher **Physio:** Keith Lord
Ground: Shawbridge, Clitheroe, Lancs Tel: 01200 423344. **Directions:** M6 jct 31, A59 to Clitheroe (17 miles), at 5th r'bout continue for half a mile and turn left at Pendle Road. Ground one mile, behind Bridge.
Seats: 300 **Cover:** 1200 **Capacity:** 2,000 **Floodlights:** Yes **Club Shop:** Yes **Midweek matches:** Monday
Clubhouse: Open during matches. Snacks available. **Programme:** 12 pages, 60p **Editor:** Ian Rimmer
Colours: Blue & white stripes/blue/blue **Change colours:** All yellow **Reserves' Lge:** N.W.C.L.
Previous Lges: Blackburn & Dist.;Lancs Comb. 03-04 05-10 25-82. **Record Attendance:** 2,000 v Mangotsfield, FA Vase Semi-F 95-96. **Club Record - Goalscorer:** Don Francis. **Appearances:** Lindsey Wallace.
Players progressing to Football League: Ray Woods (Leeds 1950), Chris Sims (Blackburn 1960), Lee Rogerson (Wigan Ath), Carlo Nash (Crystal Palace).
96-97 Captain: Lee Sculpher **96-97 Top Scorer:** Paul Mullin **96-97 P.o.Y.:** Lee Sculpher
Hons: Lancs Comb. 79-80 (Lg Cup 34-35); Lancs Challenge Tphy 84-85; NW Co's Lg 85-86 (Div 2 84-85, Div 3 83-84; East Lancs Floodlit Trophy 94-95; FA Vase Finalists 95-96.

DARWEN

Founded: 1875 **President:** E Devlin **Chairwoman:** Mrs K Marah **Manager:** S Wilkes
Secretary: Lynn Atkinson, 58 Harwood St., Darwen, Lancs BB3 1PD (01254 761755). **Asst Man.:** M Atkinson
Ground: Anchor Ground, Anchor Road, Darwen, Lancs BB3 0BB, (01254 705627). **Physio:** Mick Sharples
Directions: A666 Blackburn/Bolton road, 1 mile north of Darwen town centre, turn right at Anchor Hotel, ground 200 yds on left. One and a half miles from Darwen (BR), bus 51 to Anchor Hotel.
Seats: 250 **Cover:** 2,000 **Capacity:** 4,000 **Floodlights:** Yes **Club Shop:** No **Clubhouse:** Matchday only.
Colours: Red & white/white/red **Change colours:** All blue **Programme:** 20 pages, 60p **Editor:** D Marah
Sponsors: Prince Moran **Midweek Matches:** Tuesday. **Reserves' League:** North West Counties
Record Gate: 9,000 v Luton, FA Cup 1909 **Previous Ground:** Barley Bank.
Prev. Lges: Football Alliance 1889-91, Football Lg 1891-99, Lancs Lg 99-03, Lancs Comb. 03-75, Ches. Co. 75-82.
96-97 Captain: S Wilkes **96-97 P.o.Y. 96-97:** N Reynolds **96-97 Top Scorer 96-97:** J Smith
Honours: Lancs Comb 31 32 73 75; Comb Cup 30 31 75; Lancs Jun Cup 73; Geo Watson Trophy 73; LFA Youth Cup 75; NWC Cup 83; Lancs F/Lit Trophy 90; NWCL Res Div Cup 94; Blackburn & Dist Youth Lge 94 95 97, Cup 94 95 97; NW All Chall Cup 96.

GLOSSOP NORTH END

Chairman: J Dillon **Secretary:** Peter Hammond, 15 Longmoor Road, Simmondley, Glossop, Derbys
President: C T Boak SK13 9NH Tel: 01457 863852 (H), 01457 854411 (B).
Manager: Ged Coyne **Asst Manager:** Tommy Martin **Physio:** TBA.
Ground: Surrey Street, Glossop, Derbys (01457 855469).
Directions: A57 (Manchester-Sheffield) to Glossop town centre, turn into Shrewsbury Street, follow to top of the hill, left at T-junction for ground. 700 yds from Glossop (BR). Buses 236 & 237 from Manchester.
Seats: 209 **Cover:** 509 **Capacity:** 2,374 **Floodlights:** Yes **Nickname:** Hillmen **Founded:** 1886
Clubhouse: Licensed bar. Hot & cold drinks and pies etc on matchdays. **Club Shop:** Yes
Programme: 32 pages, 40p **Editor:** Mr P Heginbotham, 0161 439 3932 **Press Officer:** Secretary.
Colours: Blue & white stripes/blue/blue **Change colours:** All gold. **Sponsor:** Davis Blank Furniss Solicitors.
Midweek Matches: Tuesday **Reserve's League:** North Western Alliance.
Previous - Leagues: Midland 1896-98; Football Lge 1898-1915; Manchester Lge 15-56 66-78; Lancs Combination 56-66; Cheshire County 78-82. **Names:** Glossop North End 1886-1898; Glossop FC 1898-1992.
Club Records - Attendance: 10,736 v Preston North End, FA Cup 1913/14 **Transfer fee paid:** £3,000 for Andy Gorton (Lincoln City, 1989). **Transfer fee received:** £3,000 for Andy Gorton (Oldham Athletic, 1990).
Players progressing to Football League: Jimmy Rollands (Rochdale), Ray Redshaw (Wigan Athletic).
Honours: Nth West Co's Lg Lamot Pils Trophy 90-91; Manchester Lg 27-28 (Gilgryst Cup 22-23 29-30 34-35 74-75); FA Amateur Cup QF 08-09.

HASLINGDEN

Chairman: Brian Horsbrough **Manager:** Steve Parry **Founded:** 1969
Secretary: Len Chenery, 83 Belgrave Road, Darwen, BB3 2SF (01254 704518)
Ground: Ewood Bridge, Manchester Rd, Haslingden, Lancs BB4 6JY (01706 217814).
Directions: From South: M66 Blackburn/Clitheroe exit, left at r'bout past Woolpack Hotel, sharp left at bottom of hill - ground 100yds on right. From North; M6 Jct 31, A59 to Blackburn, take ring-road at Moat House Hotel and follow signs to M65, leave M65 at jct 8 and follow signs for Bury, follow dual-c'way for about 5 miles and leave at Todmorden exit, right at lights, straight across r'bout by Woolpack Hotel, then follow as above.
Capacity: 1,500 **Floodlights:** Yes **Midweek Matches:** Tuesdays **Colours:** Tangerine/black/black
Record Gate: 551 v Blackburn, Aug. 93 **Previous Leagues:** West Lancashire (pre-1993)
Hons: N.W.Co. Lg Div 2 93-94, R-up 96-97; West Lancs Lg Div 2 80-81, R-up 92-93; Presidents Cup 71-72 80-81 92-93

MAINE ROAD F.C.

L-R Back Row: Peter Hough, Cameron Hunt, Drew Cain, Danny Glynn, John Morrey, Gareth Edwards, Mark Prescot, Mark Flowers, Andy Lowrie, Chris Nicholson. Front Row: Paul Wadsworth, Simon Savage, Steve Hall, Gordon Woods, Ian Walker, Dave Swindells, Leon Davis, Andy Sadler.

NEWCASTLE TOWN F.C.

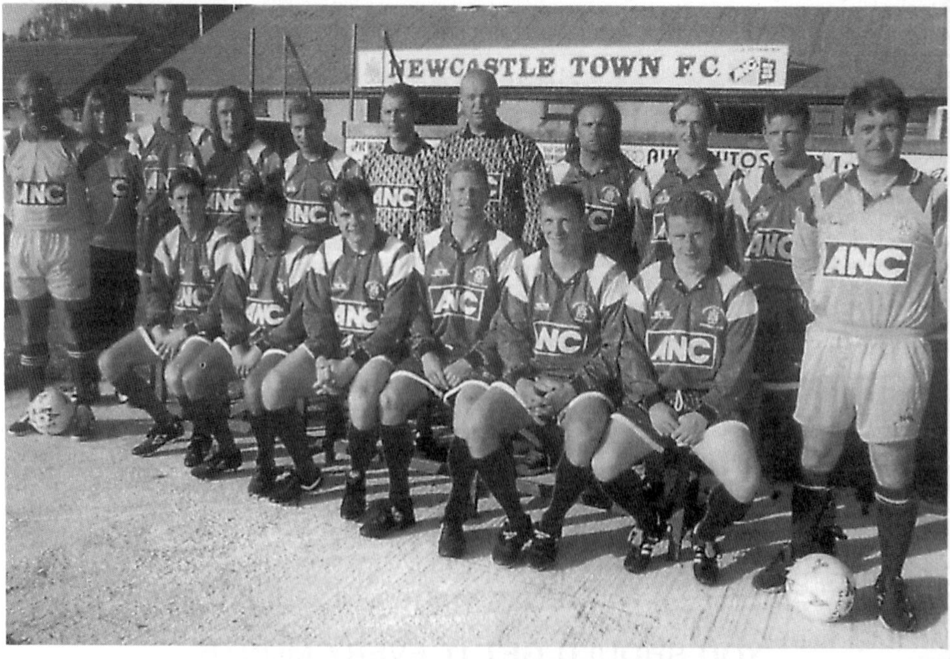

HOLKER OLD BOYS

President: R Brady **Chairman:** Ron Moffatt **Vice Chairman:** Ray Sharp
Comm. Manager: Ged Woods **Secretary:** Stewart Patton, 15 Bowfell Crescent, Barrow-in-Furness, Cumbria LA14 4PT (H 01229 832429) (B 019467 85600)
Press Officer: John Taylor
Manager: Des Johnson **Asst Manager:** Jim Capstick**Coach:** Jim Ballantyne **Physio:** Mark Hetherington
Ground: Rakesmoor Lane, Hawcoat, Barrow-in-Furness, Cumbria (01229 828176).
Directions: M6 Jct 36, A590 to Barrow-in-Furness, on entering Barrow, continue across r'bout, 2nd right (Dalton Lane) to top of road, right into Rakesmoor Lane, ground on right.
Seats: 220 **Cover:** 500 **Capacity:** 2,500 **Floodlights:** Yes **Founded:** 1936
Clubhouse: Weekdays 8-11pm, Sat noon-11pm, Sunday normal licensing hours. Pies & peas on matchdays.
Programme: 8 pages, 30p **Editor:** TBA **Club Shop:** No.
Colours: Green & yellow/green/yellow **Change colours:** Blue/red **Nickname:** Cobs.
Midweek Matches: Tuesday **Club Sponsors::** Kitchen Design Studio.
Previous Leagues: North Western/ Furness Premier/ West Lancs 70-91.
Previous Grounds: None.
Record Attendance: 1240 v Barrow ATS Tourny 95-96
Record win: 12-0 **Record defeat:** 1-8 v Newcastle T. (H) 91-92.
Club record scorer: Dave Conlin **Hons:** W Lancs Lg 86-87, R-up 85-86; Lancs Junior Shield 88-89 90-91.

KIDSGROVE ATHLETIC

Chairman: Leslie Wagg **President:** Ernie Langford
Secretary: Christine Osmond, 451 New Inn Lane, Trentham, Stoke-on-Trent, ST4 8BN (01782 644241).
Manager: Peter Ward **Coach:** Jack Heath **Physio:** Arthur Duckworth.
Ground: Clough Hall, Hollinwood Road, Kidsgrove, Stoke-on-Trent, Staffs (01782 782412).
Directions: M6 Jct 16, A500 towards Stoke, 2nd jctn onto A34 towards Manchester, turn right at 1st lights into Cedar Ave., 2nd right into Lower Ash Rd, 3rd left into Hollinwood Rd to ground. B R Kidsgrove (5mins)
Seats: 250 **Cover:** 600 **Capacity:** 4,500 **Floodlights:** Yes **Formed:** 1952
Colours: Blue/white/blue **Change Colours:**
Record Attendance: 538 **Clubhouse:** Yes
Previous Leagues: Staffordshire County, Mid Cheshire Lge.
Midweek Matches: Tuesday
Club Record Goalscorer: **Club Record Appearances:**
Honours: Mid Cheshire Lg 70-71 78-79 86-87 87-88, R-up 68-69 85-86; Lg Cup 67-68 69-70 85-86, R-up 84-85 86-87; Staffs Co. FA Vase 87-88 89-90; Staffs County Lge; Burslem & Tunstall Lge.

MAINE ROAD

Chairman: Mr R Meredith **President:** Mr F G Thompson.
Secretary: Mr K Hunter, 157 Aston Ave., Fallowfield, Manchester M14 7HN (0161 226 9937).
Manager: G Whittingham **Asst Manager:** **Physio:** E Jenkinson.
Ground: Manchester Co. FA Grnd, Brantingham Rd., Chorlton-cum-Hardy, Manchester M21 0TT (0161 862 9619).
Directions: M63 Jct 7, A56 towards City Centre, right onto A5145 Chorlton/Stockport, through lights, left at next lights into Wilbraham Rd (A6010) to Chorlton, through lights for approx 1 mile. Left into Withington Rd, first left into Brantingham Rd, ground 300 yds on left. 2 miles from Stretford (Metrolink(tram)), 3 miles from Piccadilly and Victoria (BR). Buses 85 87 103 168 188 260 261 275
Seats: 200 **Cover:** 700 **Capacity:** 2,000 **Floodlights:** Yes **Club Shop:** No
Clubhouse: Before/during/after games. Refreshment bar sells hot & cold drinks, pies, crisps, confectionary.
Programme: 48 pages, 50p **Editor:** Mr R Price (0161 442 7269) **Press Officer:** P Ramsden
Colours: All blue **Change Colours:** All yellow
Sponsors: Surface Engineers **Nickname:** Blues **Founded:** 1955
Midweek matchday: Tuesday **Reserves League:** NW Co's Lge Reserve Division.

PREVIOUS - **Leagues:** Rusholme Sunday 55-66; Manchester Amtr Sunday 66-72; Manchester 72-87.
Grounds: Hough End PF 55-73; Ward Street O.B. 73-75; Tootal Spts Ground 75-79; Leesfield 79-80. **Name:** City Supporters Rusholme

CLUB RECORDS - **Attendance:** 875 v Altrincham, FA Cup 2nd Qual. Rd 29/9/90.
Goalscorer: John Wright 140. **Appearances:** Gordon Woods 399.
Win: 15-0 v Little Hulton 2/9/86. **Defeat:** 6-10 v Old Altrinchamians 22/9/79.

Best Season -
FA Cup: 2nd Qual. 2nd replay 92-93.
FA Vase: 4th Rd 94-95.

96-97 Captain: Gordon Woods **96-97 Top scorer:** A Adamajtis/I Walker/A Lowrie (6)
Honours: Manc. Prem. Lg(4) 82-86, Cup 82-83 83-84; Manc. County Prem. Cup 87-88, Chal. Cup(4) 82-83 84-87; NW Co's Lg Div 2 89-90 (R-up 88-89).

MOSSLEY

Chairman: Vacant **President:** J Wharmby **Manager:** Benny Phillips
Secretary: Andrew Fenna, 254 Fairfied Rd., Droylsden, Manchester M43 6AN (0161 370 0508).
Ground: Seel Park, Market Street, Mossley, Lancs. (Grd 01457 832369), (Club 01457 836104).
Directions: From north; M62 Junc 20, A627M/A627 to Ashton-U-Lyne, A670 to Mossley- ground in town centre behind market place. From south; M6 Junc 19, A556, M56 to Junc 3, A5103 to manchester, then Mancunian Way (A57M) to A635. Follow Ashton signs 5 miles, the Mossley signs via A670 to town centre. Local station Mossley BR. Buses 153 from Manchester, 343 from Oldham, 350 from Ashton.
Capacity: 4,500 **Cover:** 1,500 **Seats:** 200 **Floodlights:** Yes **Club Shop:** Yes
Clubhouse: Open nights and matchdays. **Programme:** 28 Pages 50p **Editor:** John A Cawthorne
Colours: White/black/black **Change colours:** Yellow/green/green **Midweek matches:** Tuesday
Formed: 1903 **Nickname:** Lilywhites **Record Attendance:** 7,000 v Stalybridge, 1950.
Best FA Cup season: 2nd Rd replay 49-50. Also 2nd Rd 80-81, 1st Rd 69-70 77-78 78-79 79-80 81-82 83-84.
Previous Leagues: Ashton/ South East Lancs/ Lancs Combination 18-19/ Cheshire County 19-72, Northen Prem.
Players progressing to Football League: J Wright (Blackpool 46), T Bell & A Wadsworth (Oldham 46/49), A Lomas (Rochdale 50), A Tyrer (Leeds 46), E Williams (Halifax 51), J Willis (A Villa 58), M Eckershall (Torquay 59), A Roberts (Bradford PA 69), G Pierce (Huddersfield 71), E O'Keefe (Everton 79), D Young (Wigan 83).
96-97 - Captain: Bernie Hughes **Top Scorer:** Tim Crane **P.o.Y.:** Rod Bates
Honours: FA Trophy Runners-up 79-80; Northern Premier League 78-79 79-80 (R-up 80-81 81-82 82-83, Challenge Cup 78-79; NWCFL Floodlit Trophy Finalists 95-96;

NANTWICH TOWN

Chairman: R Tilley **Vice Chairman:** P Temmen **President:** J Davies
Secretary: Gary Wollaston, 68 Lunt Avenue, Crewe, CW2 7NA, (01270 668513)
Manager: Clive Jackson. **Asst Manager:** John Brydon. **Physio:** Keith Leigh.
Ground: Jackson Avenue, off London Road, Nantwich, Cheshire (01270 624098).
Directions: M6 Jct 16, A500 for Nantwich (about 8 miles), continue on A52 over railway crossing (London Rd), first right into Jackson Avenue. From Chester take A51. 3 miles from Crewe (BR).
Seats: 150 **Cover:** 555 **Capacity:** 1,500 **Floodlights:** Yes **Club Shop:** Yes
Clubhouse: Every night except Sunday 8pm-11pm. Hot pies available.
Programme: 18 pages, 65p **Editor:** Che Kerrin (01270 624098) **Club Sponsors:** Jim Barrie Plant Hire
Colours: Black & white/black/black **Change colours:** All green **Nickname:** Dabbers **Founded:** 1884
Reserves' League: Refuge Assurance **Midweek matchday:** Tuesday.
Record Attendance: 2,750 v Altrincham, Cheshire Senior Cup 66-67.
Previous - Leagues: Shropshire & Dist.; The Combination 1892-94; Lancs Comb. 12-15; Cheshire Combination 19-38; Manchester; Mid-Cheshire; Cheshire County 68-82. **Name:** Nantwich FC (pre 1973)
Club Record Goalscorer: Gerry Duffy, 42 in 61-62.
Honours: Cheshire Co. Lg 80-81; Ches. Snr Cup 75-76; Carling N.W. Co.Lg.Cup 94-95.

NEWCASTLE TOWN

Chairman: J W Walker **Vice-Chairman:** K G Walshaw **President:** K H Walshaw.
Secretary: John F Cotton, 293 Weston Road, Weston Coyney, Stoke-on-Trent, Staffs ST3 6HA (01782 333445)
Manager: Glyn Chamberlain **Asst Manager:** Trevor Brissett **Physio:** Colin Spencer
Ground: 'Lyme Valley Parkway Stadium', Lilleshall Road, Clayton, Newcastle-under-Lyne, Staffs. 01782 662351, Club 01782 662350. **Directions:** M6 jct 15, A500 for Stoke, left at r'bout A519 for Newcastle, right at 2nd r'bout into Stafford Ave., 1st left into Tittensor Road to ground. 3 miles from Stoke-on-Trent (BR).
Seats: 300 **Cover:** 1,000 **Capacity:** 4,000 **Floodlights:** Yes **Club Shop:** Yes
Clubhouse: Open Saturday matchdays noon-7.30pm and midweek 5-11pm. Hot & cold food always available.
Programme: 40 pages, 50p **Editor:** Peter Tindall (01260 28093) **Press Officer:** Ray Tatton (01782 644916)
Colours: All Royal with red & white trim **Change colours:** All yellow **Club Sponsors:** A.N.C.Ltd
Midweek Matches: Tuesday **Reserve Team:** Burslem & Newcastle Dist Lge **Nickname:** Castle **Founded:** 1964
Record Attendance: 3,948 v Notts County FA Cup Nov 96
Previous - Leagues: Hanley & Dist. Sunday; North Staffs Sunday; Potteries & Dist. Sunday; Res Refuge Ass Mid; Newcastle & Dist; Staffs Co.; Mid Cheshire. **Grounds:** Hanley Park 64-79/ Northwood Lane, Clayton 79-85.
Players progressing to Football League: C Beeston, G Shaw, P Ware, D Ritchie, D Hope, S Wade.
96-97 Captain: Kenny Lawton **96-97 Top Scorer:** John Burndred 29 **96-97 P.o.Y.:** Lyndon Beardmore
Record Scorer: Shaun Wade 97 (NWCL only) **Record appearances:** Philip Butler 270 (NWCL only).
Hons: Nth West Co's Lg Div 1 R-up 95-96 96-97, Div 2 R-up 91-92, Challenge Cup 96-97, F/Lit Trophy R-up 96-97; Lamot Pils Tphy 91-92; Mid Cheshire Lg Div 1 85-86, R-up 86-78, Div 2 82-83, 90-91, Lge Cup 84-85; Walsall Snr Cup 93-94 94-95 R-up 95-96; Sentinel Cup 94-95; Tennents Floodlit Trophy 92-93 95-96; Staffs Snr Cup R-up 95-96; Staffs M/W F/Light Lge 94-95 R-up 95-96; Umbro Over 35 Chall Cup 94-95;

RAMSBOTTOM UNITED F.C.
NORTH WEST COUNTIES DIVISION TWO CHAMPIONS 1996-97

Steve Rothwell (No. 3 stripes) scores for St. Helens Town in their FA Vase match against Haslingden at Hoghton Road.
Photo: M Thacker

PRESCOT CABLES A.F.C.

President: Mr B F Taylor **Chairman:** Ted Mercer **Vice Chairman:** D J Lace
Secretary: Dot Lace, 20 Cable Road, Prescot, Merseyside (0151 426 6440).
Manager: Arthur McCumiskey **Asst Man.:** Derek Hughes **Commercial Manager:** Arthur McCumiskey
Ground: Hoghton Road, Sutton, St Helens (01744 817225)
Directions: M62 Jct 7, take 4th exit (St Helens Linkway), exit Linkway at 3rd r/about (Sherdley) follow signs for Sutton, continue to Sutton Village, Ground just beyond St Helens Junc station 150 yards
Seats: 200 **Cover:** 550 **Capacity:** 4,400 **Floodlights:** Yes **Founded:** 1886
Clubhouse: Refreshment bar, open matchdays/evenings for hot & cold refreshments. **Club Shop:** No
Programme: 30 pages, 50p **Editor:** A McCumiskey **Midweek Matches:** Wednesday
Colours: Gold/black/black **Change colours:** Blue/blue/gold **Nickname:** Tigers.
PREVIOUS - Leagues: Liverpool Co. Comb.; Lancs Comb. 1897-98 18-20 27-33 36-67; Ches. Co. 33-36 78-82; Mid Cheshire 67-78. **Names:** Prescot Athletic; Prescot Cables 46-65 80-90; Prescot Town 65-80.
Record Gate: 8,122 v Ashton National, 1932 **Best FA Cup season:** 2nd Rd 57-58 59-60
Honours: Lancs Comb. 56-57 (Lg Cup 47-48); Ches. Lg Div 2 76-77; Mid Ches. Lg 76-77; L'pool Non-League Cup(4) 51-53 58-59 60-61; L'pool Chal. Cup(5) 28-30 48-49 61-62 77-78; George Mahon Cup 36-37.

RAMSBOTTOM UNITED

Chairman: H Williams (01706 822799)
Secretary: John Maher, 75 Ramsbottom Road, Hawkshaw, Bury BL8 4JS. (01204 852742)
Ground: Riverside Ground, Acre Bottom, Ramsbottom. (01706 822799)
Directions: M66 (North) to junction 1, take A56 towards Ramsbottom. After 1 mile turn left Bury New Road. Turn left after Trinity paper Mill along the road running parallel with the East Lancs Railway.
Colours: Blue with white trim/blue/white **Formed:** 1966 **Floodlights:** Yes
Midweek Matchday: Wednesday **Record Attendance:** 464 v Haslingden NWCFL Div 2 29/3/97
Previous Leagues: Bury Amateur League, Bolton Combination, Manchester Lge.
Honours: Bolton Comb. Div. One Champs 72-73; Bolton Comb. Prem Div. 76-77, 86-87; Manchester Lge Div. One Champs 90-91; Manchester Lge Div. 1 Cup Winners 90-91; Gilgryst Cup Winners 94-95; NWCFL Div 2 Champ 96-97, Trophy 95-96

ROSSENDALE UNITED

Chairman: J Feber **Nickname:** Rossy **Founded:** 1898
Secretary: Wendy Ennis, 4 Brow Edge, Newchurch, Rossendale, Lancs BB4 7TT (01706 212634)
Manager: Mickey Graham **Coach:** John Hughes **Physio:**
Ground: Dark Lane, Staghills Rd, Newchurch, Rossendale, Lancs BB4 7UA (Grd 01706 215119; Club 213296)
Directions: M66 Junc 18, M66 north following signs for Burnley, then A682 to Rawstenstall, take 2nd exit sign Burnley A682, at 1st lights turn right into Newchurch Rd, 1.5 miles turn right into Staghills Rd, grd 800 yards right.
Capacity: 2,500 **Cover:** Yes **Seats:** 500 **Floodlights:** Yes **Club Shop:** T.B.A.
Clubhouse: Evenings & matchdays. Hot snacks. Snooker room. Pool, darts, satellite TV, concert room.
Programme: Yes **Editor:** Bill Howarth. **Press Officer:** Kevin Proctor
Colours: Blue & white/blue/blue **Change colours:** Yellow (blue sleeves)/blue/yellow
Sponsors: T.B.A. **Midweek matchday:** Tuesday **Reserves' League:** NWCL Res. Div.
Local Radio Stations: Red Rose, Radio Lancashire.
Local Newspapers: Rossendale Free, Lancs Evening Telegraph, Rossendale Herald & Post, Rossendale Mail.
PREVIOUS - **Leagues:** North East Lancs Comb.; Lancs Comb. 1898-99 1901-70; Central Lancs 1899-1901; Cheshire County 70-82; North West Counties 82-89; Northern Premier 89-93. **Grounds:** None
CLUB RECORDS - **Attendance:** 12,000 v Bolton Wanderers FA Cup 2nd Rd 71
Win: 10-0 v Wigan Rovers, Lancs Combination 69-70.
Defeat: 0-14 v Morecambe, Lancs Comination 67-68.
Career Goalscorer: Bob Scott **Career Appearances:** Johnny Clarke 770, 1947-65.
Transfer Fee Paid: £3,000 for Jimmy Clarke (Buxton, 1992)
Transfer Fee Received: £1,500 for Dave O'Neill (Huddersfield Town, 1974).
Best Season -
FA Cup: 2nd Rd 71-72, 1-4 v Bolton at Bury FC. Also 1st Rd 75-76, 0-1 v Shrewsbury Town (H).
FA Trophy: 2nd Rd 81-82. **FA Vase:** 5th Rd 88-89
Players progressing to Football League: T Lawton, G Smith (Bradford C 52), E Hartley & W O'Loughton (Oldham 56/60), C Blunt (Burnley 64), F Eyre (Bradford PA 69), D O'Neill (Huddersfield), C Parker (Rochdale 92).
96-97 Captain: Neil Perry **96-97 P.o.Y.:** Neil Perry **96-97 Top scorer:** Darren Maloney
Honours: North West Counties Lg Div 1 88-89 (R-up 87-88 93-94), Div 2 R-up 85-86; Carling Chall Cup 93-94

St HELENS TOWN

President: Mr J Jones. **Chairman/Press Officer:** J Barrett
Secretary: W J Noctor, 95 Sutton Park Drive, Marshalls Cross, St Helens WA9 3TR (01744 816182).
Manager: James McBride **Asst Manager:** **Coach:** John Neary
Ground: Hoghton Road, Sutton, St Helens, Merseyside (Grd 01744 817225) (Club 01744 600012)
Directions: M62 Jct 7, take 4th exit (St Helens Linkway), exit Linkway at 3rd r/about (Sherdley) follow signs for Sutton, continue to Sutton Village, Ground just beyond St Helens Junc station 150 yards
Seats: 200 **Cover:** 550 **Capacity:** 4,400 **Floodlights:** Yes **Club Shop:** Yes
Clubhouse: Weekdays 8-11pm, Saturday matchdays 2-6.30pm.
Programme: 24 pages, 50p **Editor:** John McKiernan (01744 815726) **Nickname:** 'Town'
Local Newspapers: Reporter, Star, Leader,Echo.
Colours: Blue & white/white/blue **Change colours:** All yellow **Founded:** 1946
Midweek Matches: Wednesday **Reserve League:**
Previous Leagues: Lancs Comb. 03-14 49-75/ Liverpool County Combination 49-74/ Cheshire County 74-82.
Previous Grounds: Park Road 01-52; City Road 52-53.
Record Attendance: 4,000 v Manchester City, Bert Trautmann transfer match, April 1950.
Record win: 10-4 v Everton 'B' 1952
Record loss: 1-8 v Liverpool Res., L'pool Snr Cup 1950.
Players progressing to Football League: Bert Trautmann, John Connelly, John Quinn, Mike Davock, Billy Foulkes, Dave Bamber, Bryan Griffiths, Mark Leonard, Joe Paladino.
96-97 Captain: G Lowe **96-97 Top Scorer:** Steve Pennington **96-97 P.o.Y.:**
Club Record Appearances: Alan Wellens
Honours: FA Vase 86-87; Reserve Div R-up 94-95, Res Div Champions 94-95, R-Up 95-96; George Mahon Cup 49-50; Lancs Comb. 71-72, Div 2 50-51, Lg Cup R-up 70-71; Liverpool Snr Non Lge Cup R-up 76-77; Lancs Jnr Cup R-up 66-67; Bass Charrington Cup 73-74; Carling Chall Cup finalist 93-94;

SALFORD CITY

Chairman: Harold Brearley **Manager:** Alan Lord. **Asst Manager:**
Secretary: Stephen Blake, 71 Blandford Road, Salford, M6 6BD (0161 737 0922)
Press Officer: Scott White **Commercial Manager:** Stevie Plant.
Ground: Moor Lane, Kersal, Salford, Manchester (0161 792 6287).
Directions: M62 jct 17, A56 Bury New Road to Manchester, continue thro' 4 sets of lights, right into Moor Lane, ground 500 left. 4 miles from Manchester Victoria (BR). Buses 96, 139, 94, 95 to Moor Lane.
Seats: 260 **Cover:** 600 **Capacity:** 8,000 **Floodlights:** Yes **Founded:** 1940
Midweek Matches: Tuesday **Record Attendance:** 3,000 v Whickham FA Vase 1981
Colours: Tangerine/white/white **Change colours:** Blue & white stripes/blue/blue.
Prev. Names: Salford Central 40-63/ Salford Amateurs 1963 until merger with Anson Villa/ Salford FC.
Previous Ground: Crescent, Salford **Previous Leagues:** Manchester 63-80/ Cheshire Co. 80-82.
Programme: 24 pages, 50p **Editor:** Scott White **Nickname:** Ammies.
Clubhouse: Open matchdays only. Hot snacks.
Honours: Lancashire Amateur Cup 72-73 74-75 76-77; Manchester Senior Cup, Manchester Challenge Cup, Manchester Lg 74-75 75-76 76-77 78-79.

VAUXHALL MOTORS

Chairman: Tony Woodley **Secretary:** Stephen McInerney, 12 Merton Rd, Great Sutton, South Wirral L66 2SW (H 0151 356 0941) (B mobile 0385 343633)
Ground: Vauxhall Sports Ground, Rivacre Road, Hooton, Ellesmere Port, South Wirrall.
Tel: Ground 0151 327 1114, Club 0151 327 2115.
Directions: M53 junction 5, take A41 to Chester, on reaching the first set of traffic lights turn left into Hooton Green, Left at the T-junction, right at the next T-junction into Rivacre Road, ground is 250 yards on the right.
Floodlights: Yes **Colours:** All White **Club Sponsors:** James Edwards **Formed:** 1987
Midweek Matchday: Tuesday **Record Attendance:** 1,500 v English F.A. XI, 1987.
Previous Leagues: North West Counties League, West Cheshire League (to 1995)
Honours: B.N.W.C.F.L. 2nd Div Champ 88-89 95-96; Raab Karcher Chall Cup 90-91.

WARRINGTON TOWN

Chairman: TBA **Secretary:** Ian Dick, 53 Arlington Drive, Penketh, Warrington WA5 2QG. 01925 724421.
Vice Chairman: M P McShane **Press Officer:** Colin Serjent
Manager: Alan Lord **Asst Man.:** Dave Entwhistle **Coach:** Gary Bradley **Physio:** Lynda Roberts
GROUND Address: Cantilever Park, Common Lane, Latchford, Warrington WA4 2RS 01925 631932 (Club), 01925-653044 (Office). **Directions:** M6 junction 20, then A50 towards Warrington. After 2 miles turn left immediately after swing bridge into Station Road, ground 600yds on left. From town centre travel 1 mile south on A49, left at lights into Loushers Lane, ground quarter mile on right. 2 miles from Warrington Bank Quay (BR).
Capacity: 2,000 **Cover:** 650 **Seats:** 350 **Floodlights:** Yes **Formed:** 1948
Colours: Blue & yellow/blue/blue **Change colours:** All purple. **Nickname:** The Town
Midweek matchday: Tuesday **Reserve's League:** Mid-Cheshire.
Clubhouse: Weekdays 1-11pm, Sat. 12-11pm, Sun. 12-3pm, 7-10.30pm. Lounge, concert room & Sports room. Rooms for hire for all occasions. Pools, darts, dominoes & indoor bowls. Traditional bar food on matchdays.
Club Shop: Sells badges, scarves, pennants, old & new League & non-League progs, fanzines. Contact Matthew Dale
PROGRAMME: Pages: 36 **Price:** 50p **Editor:** Rick Barker 01925 604101 Tel/Fax
Local Press: Warrington Guardian, Warrington Mercury, Manchester Evening News, Liverpool Post & Echo.
Local Radio: Radio Merseyside, Radio Manchester (GMR).

PREVIOUS - Leagues: Warrington & Dist. 49-52; Mid-Cheshire 52-78; Cheshire Co. 78-82/ North West Co's 82-90; Northern Prem 90-97.
Name: Stockton Heath 1949-62. **Grounds:** London Road, Stockton Lane and Loushers Lane.

CLUB RECORDS - Attendance: 2,600 v Halesowen Town, FA Vase Semi Final 1st leg 85-86. **Goalscorer:** Steve Hughes 167. **Win:** 14-0 v Crosfields (H), Depot Cup 1951-52. **Defeat:** 0-10 v Eastwood (A), Mid-Cheshire Challenge Cup 1967-68. **Fee Paid:** £2,000 for - Paul McNally (Southport) 92 & Darren Schofield (Mossley) 93. **Fee Received:** £60,000 for Liam Watson (Preston N. E.) 92-93.

Best Season - FA Cup: 4th Qualifying Rd 94-95 (replay with Hyde Utd.). **FA Vase:** Finalists 86-87 (2-3 to St Helens Town). **FA Trophy:** Quarter-Finalists 92-93 (1-2 at Sutton United).

Players progressing to Football League: S Morris (Chester 51), J Green (Tranmere 58), R Hunt (Liverpool 59), J Richards (Wolves), J Bramhall (Tranmere 76), M Leonard (Everton), N Whalley & L Watson (Preston N.E.) 92-93.
HONOURS: N.W.C. Lge 89-90 (Lg Cup 85-86 87-88 88-89 (R-up 89-90), Div 2 R-up 86-87, Div 3 R-up 82-83, Res. Div West 89-90), Mid-Cheshire Lg 60-61 (R-up 57-58, Lg Cup 54-55 55-56) 11-12 72-73, Altrincham Amat. Cup 54-55, Warrington Yth Chall. Cup 94-95.

CLITHEROE F.C.

L-R, Back Row: Gary Butcher, Denis Underwood, Lee Sculpher, Paul Mullin, Adam Potts, Neil Baron, Lee Greenacre, Clive Bunn, Mark Heys, Steve Lampkin. Front Row: Mick Ward, Geoff Smith, Simon WEstwell (captain), Chris Grimshaw, Les Thompson, Andy Lawson, Jon Barber.
Photo: John L Newton

SECOND DIVISION CLUBS

ASHTON TOWN

President: W Pomfrett **Chairman:** G Messer **Manager:** Norman Hickson
Secretary: Chris Ashcroft, 8 Mason Close, Ashton-in-Makerfield, Wigan WN4 8SD (01942 203247).
Ground: Edge Green Street, Ashton-in-Makerfield, Wigan WN4 8SY (01942 510677).
Directions: M6 Jct 23, A49 to Ashton-in-M. Right at lights onto A58 towards Bolton. After 3/4 mile turn right at 'Rams Head' P.H. into Golbourne Rd. After 200 yds right into Edge Green Str. Ground at end.
Midweek Matches: Tuesday **Floodlights:** No **Founded:** 1965
Colours: Red with white trim/red/red **Change colours:** All sky blue **Best FA Vase season:** Prelim. Rd 84-85
Previous Leagues: Warrington, Lancs Comb. 03-11 71-78, Ches. Co. 78-82.
Record Gate: 600 v Accrington Stanley 76-77 **Hons:** Warrington Lg Guardian Cup.

BACUP BOROUGH

President: W Shufflebottom **Chairman:** W Heywood **Vice Chairman:** D Whatmough
Secretary: Frank Manning, 38 Acre Avenue, Stacksteads, Bacup OL13 0HN (H 01706 877460) (B 01706 873177)
Ground: West View, Cowtoot Lane, Blackthorn, Bacup, Lancashire (01706 878655). **Directions:** From M62, M66 onto A681 through Rawtenstall to Bacup centre, left onto A671 towards Burnley, after approx 300 yds right (immed. before the Irwell Inn) climbing Cooper Street, right into Blackthorn Lane then first left into Cowtoot Lane to ground.
Seats: 500 **Cover:** 1,000 **Capacity:** 3,000 **Floodlights:** Yes **Founded:** 1875
Clubhouse: Open matchdays. Pies and sandwiches available. **Club Shop:** No
Colours: Black & white stripes/black/black **Change colours:** All red **Midweek Matches:** Tuesday.
Programme: 12 pages, 30p **Editor:** D Whatmough (0706 875041) **Nickname:** The Boro
Previous - League: Lancs Comb. 03-82. **Name:** Bacup FC. **Ground:** None
Record Gate: 4,980 v Nelson 1947 **Honours:** Lancs Jnr Cup 10-11 (R-up 22-23 74-75); Lancs Comb. 46-47 (Lg Cup R-up 46-47 80-81; NW Co's Lg Div 2 R-up 89-90.

BLACKPOOL MECHANICS

Chairman: Henry Baldwin **Vice Chairman:** John Sanderson **President:** Gregory Gregorio
Secretary: William Singleton, c/o Club (H 01253 313444) (B 01253 761721)
Manager: Dave Rump **Asst Manager:** Gary Collings **Coach:** William Singleton
Ground: Jepson Way, Common Edge Rd, Blackpool, Lancs FY4 5DY (01253 761721).
Directions: M6 to M55, follow Airport signs. Left at r'bout along A583 (Preston New Rd) to lights, right into Whitehill Rd, becomes School Rd, to lights. Straight over main road & follow signs for Blackpool Mechanics F.C. to ground. Rail to Blackpool North - then bus 11c from Talbot Rd bus station (next to rail station) to Shovels Hotel, Common Edge Rd.
Seats: 250 **Cover:** 1,700 **Capacity:** 2,000 **Floodlights:** Yes **Founded:** 1947
Clubhouse: Match days, training nights. Dancehall. Matchday, hot food:
Club Shop: Manager Andrew Sneddon (01253 729962). Ties, sweaters, old programmes, metal badges.
Club colours: Yellow & Green/green/green **Change colours:** All blue **Nickname:** Mechs
Programme: 10 pages, 50p **Editor:** John Barlow **Commercial Manager:** John Sanderson
Midweek home matchday: Tuesday **Club Sponsors:** Yates Wine Lodge, Talbot Rd, Blackpool.
Previous - Leagues: Blackpool & Fylde Comb.; West Lancs; Lancs Comb. 62-68. **Ground:** Stanley Pk 47-49
96-97 - Captain: Alan Hughes **Top Scorer:** Alan Hughes **P.o.Y.:** Mark Williams/Stephen Littler
Record Gate: 1,200 v Morecambe, Lancs Comb, August 1968. **Honours:** Lancs Comb Bridge Shield 72-73; NW Co's. Lg Div 3 85-86; W Lancs Lg 60-61 62-63; Lancs County FA Sheild 57-58 60-61:

BOOTLE

Chairman: Frank Doran **Manager:** Steve Jackson **Founded:** 1953
Secretary: Paul Carr, 58 Orchard Hey, Old Roan, Bootle, Merseyside L30 8RY (H 0151 474 0153) (B 0151 951 4799)
Ground: Bucks Park, Northern Perimeter Road, Netherton, Bootle, Merseyside L30 7PT (0151 526 1850).
Directions: End of M57 & M58 follow signs to Bootle and Docks A5063. Turn right at next lights by Police station. Entrance 100 yds on right. Old Roan station 300yds. Bus 55 (150yds from grd), 302 341 345 350 (350yds).
Seats: 400 **Cover:** 1,400 **Capacity:** 5,000 **Floodlights:** Yes **Club Shop:**Yes.
Clubhouse: Normal pub hours. Darts & pool. **Midweek matchday:** Tuesday
Programme: 32 pages, 50p **Editor:** Secretary **Reserve League:** Liverpool Co. Comb.
Colours: All royal blue **Change colours:** Yellow/black/black **Nickname:** Bucks
Record Attendance: 750 v Carshalton Athletic, FA Trophy 2nd Rd 31/1/81.
Previous leagues: Liverpool Shipping, Liverpool County Comb., Lancs Comb. 74-78, Cheshire Lge 78-82.
Players progressing to Football League: Graeme Worsley (Shrewsbury Town 1989).
96-97 Captain: Billy Loughlin **Top Scorer:** John Lawson **P.o.Y.:** Gary McBride, Mick Gilmore
Club record appearances: Peter Cumiskey (almost 400).
Hons: North West Co. Lge Div 2 R-up 92-93 (Floodlit Tphy 93-94), Liverpool Chall. Cup 64-65 75-76 78-79, Liverpool Amtr Cup 65-66 67-68 73-74, Lancs Amtr Cup 69-70, Liverpool Co. Comb. 64-65 65-66 67-74 (x7), George Mahon Cup 66-70 (x4) 72-74 (x2), Lancs Comb. 75-76 76-77 (Lge Cup 75-76), Cheshire Co. Lge Div 2 78-79.

CASTLETON GABRIELS

Chairman: T E Butterworth **Vice Chairman:** R Butterworth
Secretary: David Lord, 34 Fairway, Castleton, Rochdale OL11 3BU (01706 522719).
Manager/Coach:: Peter Freakes **Asst. Man.:** Dave Jones **Press Officer:** Peter Wilson (01616 249602)
Ground: Butterworth Park, Chadwick Lane, off Heywood Rd., Castleton, Rochdale (01706 527103)
Directions: M62 Jct 20, A6272M to r'bout. Left towards Castleton (A664 Edinburgh Way) to next r'bout, keeping Tesco Superstore to the left, take 1st exit to next r'bout, take 2nd exit into Manchester Rd (A664), after just under mile turn right at 'Top House' P.H. into Heywood Rd., to end & ground on right.
Seats: 250 **Cover:** 500 **Capacity:** 1,500 **Floodlights:** Yes **Founded:** 1924
Clubhouse: Open seven nights a week and all day Saturday. Pie & peas and sandwiches available matchdays (pie & peas only at Reserve matches). **Reserves League:** N.W.Co. Res. Div. **Club Sponsors:** Dale Mill
Programme: 28 pages, 50p **Editor:** Peter Wilson (01616 249602) **Club Shop:** No **Nickname:** Gabs
Colours: Royal/black/black **Change colours:** Red/white/red **Midweek matches:** Tuesday
Previous Name: St Gabriels (pre-1960s) **Previous Ground:** Park pitches/ Springfield Pk 60-81.
Previous Leagues: Rochdale Alliance 24-84/ Manchester 84-89.
Record Gate: 640 v Rochdale, pre-season friendly 1991. **Record scorer (season):** Tony Diamond 17.
Record win: 8-0 v Squires Gate N.W.Co.Div 2 94 **Record defeat:** 1-10 v Blackpool Mechanics N.W.Co.Div 2 95
Players progressing to Football League: Dean Stokes (Port Vale) 92
Honours: Manc. Lg 86-87 (Murray Shield 86-87); Res Div Cup 95-96; Nth West Co's Lg Cup SF 91-92:

CHEADLE TOWN

President: Freddie Pye **Chairman:** Chris Davies **Vice-Chairman:** Clive Williams
Secretary: Susan Burton, 2 Lavington Ave., Cheadle, Stockport, Cheshire SK8 2HH (0161 491 0823).
Manager: Peter Blundell. **Physio:** John Hornbuckle **Founded:** 1961
Ground: Park Road Stadium, Park Road, Cheadle, Cheshire SK8 2AN (0161 428 2510).
Directions: M63 Jct 11, follow signs towards Cheadle (A560), first left after lights into Park Road, ground at end. 1 mile from Gatley (BR), buses from Stockport.
Seats: 300 **Cover:** 300 **Capacity:** 2,500 **Floodlights:** Yes **Club Shop:** No
Clubhouse: Open every night. Food available **Midweek Matches:** Tuesday **Reserves' Lge:** NW Counties Lge
Programme: 20 pages, 50p. **Editor:** Stuart Crawford **Press Officer:** Chris Davies (0161 428 2510).
Colours: White/black/black **Change colours:** All blue. **Previous Lges:** Manc. (pre 1987).
Club Records - Gate: 1,700 v Stockport Co., Aug 94. **Scorer:** Peter Tilley. **Appearances:** John McArdle
Players progressing to Football League: Ashley Ward (Crewe), Steve Bushell (York).
Honours: Manchester Lg Div 1 79-80 (R-up 80-81 81-82); Manchester Amtr Cup 79-80; Lamot Pils R-up 90-91; NWCFL Div 2 Trophy R-up 95-96:

COLNE

Chairman: D Blacklock (01282 696340) **Formed:** 1996
Secretary: Jean Moore, 5 Haverholt Close, Colne, BB8 9SN (01282 868857)
Ground: Colne Dynamoes Stadium, Holt House, Colne, Lancs, (01282 862545)
Directions: Enter Colne from M65 to roundabout, keep left follow signs for Keighley. At next rounabout turn left, continue on Harrison Drive over mini roundabout & follow road to ground.
Seats: 50 **Cover:** 1000 **Capacity:** 1,800 **Floodlights:** Yes **Clubhouse:** No **Club Shop:** No
Colours: All red **Change colours:** All yellow **Midweek Matchday:** Wednesday
Programme: Yes **Editor:** Ray Moore **Press Officer:** Ray Moore
Club Records - Gate: 85 v Nelson 96-97. **Scorer:** Geoff Payton. **Appearances:** Nick Roscoe
96-97 Captain: John Clark **96-97 P.o.Y.:** Nick Roscoe **96-97 Top Scorer:** Geoff Payton

DAISY HILL

Chairman: Tony Veitch **Founded:** 1894 **Reformed:** 1952
Secretary: Bob Naylor, 8 Bailey Fold, Westhoughton, Bolton, Lancs BL5 3HH (01942 813720).
Manager: Matty Wardrop **Asst Mgr:** Micky Gaynor **Physio:** Peter Rowbotham
Ground: New Sirs, St James Street, Westhoughton, Bolton, Lancs (01942 818544).
Directions: M61 Jct 5, A58 (Snydale Way/Park Road) for 1.5 miles, left into Leigh Road (B5235) for 1 mile, right into village then left between Church and School into St James Street. Ground 250 yds on left. Half mile from Daisy Hill (BR).
Seats: 200 **Cover:** 250 **Capacity:** 2,000 **Floodlights:** No **Club Shop:** No **Programme:** 38 pages 50p
Clubhouse: Open normal licensing hours during any football activity. Snacks on matchdays.
Colours: All royal blue. **Change:** Red & black stripes/black/black **Midweek Matches:** Tuesday
Reserves' Lge CNWL Res Div. **Previous Leagues:** Westhoughton; Bolton Comb.; Lancs Combination. 78-82.
Record Attendance: 2,000 v Horwich RMI, Westhoughton Charity Cup final May 1980.
Players progressing to Football League: Barry Butler (Chester City via Atherton LR).
Club Record scorer/appearances: Alan Roscoe, 300 goals. 450 games.
Honours: Bolton Combination - Prem Div 62-63 72-73 75-76 77-78, Lge Cup 59-60 61-62 71-72 72-73; Lancashire Shield 61-62 71-72 86-87.

FLEETWOOD WANDERERS FC

Chairman: J Betmead
Secretary: Alan Birkett, 22 Warren Avenue South, Fleetwood, Lancs FY7 7AZ (01253 873779
Ground: Highbury Stadium, Highbury Avenue, Fleetwood, Lancs (01253 770702)
Directions: From M55 follow signs (A583) to Fleetwood. At Nautical Campos (on left) traffic island take first left, at second island take 6th exit. Stadium is 3/4 mile on left.
Colours: Red & white/black/red & white **Floodlights:** Yes **Midweek Matches:** Tuesday **Founded:** 1997

FORMBY

Chairman: Chris Welsh **Commercial Manager:** Dave Dickinson (01704 870944)
Secretary: Paul Lawler, 13 Sefton Road, Formby, Merseyside L37 2JG (01704 878409).
Managers: Peter Hennerty, Mike Scott **Physio:** Keith Johnson **Press Officer:** Paul Lawler (01704 878409)
Ground: Brows Lane, Formby, Merseyside (01704 833505)
Directions: A565 Liverpool-Southport, turn left for Formby at lights opposite Tesco into Altcar Rd, left at T junction to r'bout (opposite Blundell Arms Hotel), take 2nd exit then sharp left into Duke Street, 1st right into Elbow Lane, ground 50yds on left. Half a mile from Formby (BR), buses from Formby & Southport stations.
Seats: 200 **Cover:** 500 **Capacity:** 2,000 **Floodlights:** No **Founded:** 1919 **Nickname:** Squirrels
Club Shop: Sells programmes, badges & souvenirs. Contact Paul Lawler (01704 878409).
Clubhouse: No. Matchday refreshment bar stocks hot food & drinks.
Colours: Yellow/blue/yellow **Change:** White/black/black **Midweek Matches:** Wednesday **Reserves:** None
Programme: 36 pages, 50p **Editor:** Paul Lawler, (01704 878409) **Club Sponsors:** DKS Packaging.
Previous Leagues: Liverpool Co. Comb. 19-68; Lancs Comb. 68-71; Ches. Co. 71-82.
96-97 Captain: Dave Walbank **96-97 P.o.Y.:** Matthew Smith **96-97 Top Scorer:** Mark Wilson (30)
Honours: Liverpool Co. Comb. 48-49, R-up 64-65; Liverpool Senior Cup 77-78, R-up 84-85; Challenge Cup 52-53 63-64 67-68, R-up 64-65; Amtr Cup 29-30 47-48 48-49; Lamot Pils Trophy 94-95; George Mahon Cup 64-65, R-up 55-56 56-57; Lancs Co FA Amt Cup 34-35:

GARSWOOD UNITED

Chairman: R Jones
Secretary: John Anelay, 128 Victoria Road, Garswood, Nr Wigan WN4 0RE (01942 519231)
Ground: Simms Lane End, Garswood Road, Garswood, Nr Wigan (01744 892258)
Directions: A580 towards Liverpool. Turn right into A58, Liverpool Road, turn left into Garswood Road, signed Garswood 3/4 mile, follow road bearing left at triangle up to crossroads, straight ahead, ground 100 yards on left
Colours: Blue & white/blue/blue **Founded:** 1967 **Floodlights:** No
Previous Leagues: Mid Cheshire, Liverpool County Comb, Warrington & Dist, St Helens Comb.
Honours: Griffiths Trophy 70-71; Worral Cup 71-72; Burtonwood Cup 72-73; Chadwick Cup 73-74; Ford Cup 74-75; Dodds Shield, Guardian Cup, Jubilee Cup 76-77; Liverpool Comb Div 2, Lord Wavertree Cup 78-79; Liverpool Jun Cup 79-80; Mid Cheshire Div 2 Cup 89-90; Whitbread Amt Cup, Mid Cheshire Div 1, Parker Cup, Wigan Cup 94-95 96-97; Mid Cheshire Div 1, Liverpool Chall Cup, Wigan Cup 95-96

L-R, Back: Roy Jones (Chairman), Frank Melia (Physio), Chris Staunton, Carl Bell, Ian Leather, Paul Dahl, Dave Williams, Paul Dickenson, Darren Kelsey, Alan Bent (Physio). Front: Joe Gibiliru, Steve Williams, Simon Corns, Jimmy Woodyer, Alan Aspinall (Manager), Gary Laird, Barry Edwardson, Lee Ogburn, Richard Murcott (Sponsor)

LEEK C.S.O.B. FC

Chairman: K J Hill **Founded:** 1945
Secretary: Stan Lockett, 5 Fitzherbert Close, Swynnerton, Stone, Staffs ST15 0PQ, (01782 796551)
Ground: Harrison Park, Macclesfield Road, Leek, Staffs, (01538 383734)
Directions: M6 south Junc 17, A534 to Congleton - follow signs for Leek (A54), carry on until junction with A523, turn right on to A523, this road is direct to Leek, ground is 8 miles, on right just into Leek.
Colours: White & red/red/white **Floodlights:** Yes **Midweek Matches:** Wednesday
Previous Leagues: Leek & Moorland Lge, Staffs County North, Refuge Midland Lge.
Honours: Refuge Midland Lge 95-96. Lge Cup 94-95 95-96; Leek Cup 94-95 95-96; Midland Ref Charity Shield 95-96; Sportsline Chall Cup 95-96.

MAGHULL

Chairman: Les Jacques **Vice Chairman:** G Fisher **President:** M Latham.
Secretary: Danny Sherlock, 14 Alexander Drive, Lydiate, Merseyside L31 2NJ (0151 526 2306).
Manager: Frank O'Brien **Coach:** Derek McLatchey **Physio:** Fred Smith.
Ground: Old Hall Field, Hall Lane, Maghull, Merseyside (0151 526 7320). **Midweek Matches:** Tuesday
Directions: M57 or M58 to end (Switch Island), A59 towards Preston (Northway) to lights at Hall Lane, turn right following signs for Maghull Station. Ground 200 yds on the left. Half mile from Maghull (Merseyrail).
Seats: None **Cover:** 75 **Capacity:** 500 **Floodlights:** No **Club Shop:** No.
Clubhouse: Fully licenced clubhouse & lounge open matchdays and midweek. Hot & cold food available.
Programme: 40 pages, 50p **Editor/Press Off.:** Andy Boyd, 0151 526 2715 **Sponsors:** John McCabe, Butchers
Colours: Blue & red stripes/blue/blue **Change:** All yellow **Reserves' League:** Liverpool County Comb.
Founded: 1921 **PREVIOUS - Leagues:** Liverpool Co. Comb.; Lancs Comb. 72-78; Cheshire Co. 78-82.
Ground: Pimbley Recreation 1921-59. **CLUB RECORDS - Attendance:** 500 v Marine, L'pool Chal. Cup 1982/83
Goalscorer: Bobby Prince **Appearances:** Bobby Prince
96-97 Captain: John McInnes **Top Scorer:** Mark Vickers **P.o.Y.:** Lee Lawson & Dave Sharples
Honours: Liverpool Co. Amtr Cup 34-35 62-63; Liverpool Co. Chal. Cup 79-80 85-86 93-94; Lancs FA Amtr Cup 48-49 57-58; Liverpool Co. Comb. 66-67; North West Co's Lg Div 2 92-93:

MIDDLEWICH ATHLETIC

Chairman: J McAteer
Secretary: Bryan Longley, 16 Northway, Holmes Chapel, Cheshire CW4 7EF (01477 537310)
Ground: Seddon Street, Middlewich (01606 835842)
Directions: M6 junc 18, A54 Middlewich to traffic lights, forward to end of dual carriageway, right into Pepper Street/Webbs Lane, second left Seddon Street, ground on right
Colours: Red & white/red/red **Founded:** 1988 **Floodlights:** No
Midweek Matches: Wednesday **Previous Leagues:** Crewe & Dist, Mid Cheshire Lge.
Honours: Crewe & Dist Prem Lge 89-90; Crewe FA Dist Cup 89-90; Mid Cheshire Dist FA Sat Cup 93-94 95-96.

TETLEY WALKER F.C.

NELSON

Chairman: Ken Broom. **Vice-Chairman:** A Barnes.
Secretary: Cyril King, 1 Grange Ave, Barrowford, Nelson, Lancashire BB9 8AN (01282 695578)
Manager: Ian Britton. **Assistant Manager:** P Rigby.
Ground: Victoria Park, Lomeshaye Way, Nelson, Lancs (01282 613820).
Directions: M65 jct 13, 1st left (A6068 Fence), 2nd left (B6249 for Nelson), 2nd right sign Lomeshaye Village to grd.
Capacity: **Seats:** 60 **Cover:** 200 **Floodlights:** Yes **Club Shop:** No **Clubhouse:** Open matchdays
Colours: Blue & white stripes/black/blue **Change colours:** White/red **Founded:** 1881
Midweek matchday: Wednesday **Reserve League:** N.W. Cos Res. Div. **Nickname:** Blues
Previous Leagues: Lancashire 1889-98 1900-01; Football League 1898-1900; Lancashire Combination 01-16 46-82; Nth West Counties 82-88; West Lancashire 88-92. **Best FA Cup season:** FA Cup 2nd Rd Proper 30-31(replay)
Honours: Lancs Lge 54-55; Lancs Comb. 1949-50 51-52; Lg Cup 49-50 50-51 59-60; Bridge Shield 75-76 81-82; Lancs Jnr Cup 54-55; NW Counties Div 2 Cup 96-97:

OLDHAM TOWN

Chairman: Ken Hughes **Manager:** T B A
Secretary: Mrs J Cooper, 1 Hannerton Road, Shaw, Oldham OL2 8HS
Ground: Whitebank Stadium, Whitebank Rd, Hollins, Oldham, Lancs OL8 3JH (0161 624 2689).
Directions: M62 jct 18, M66 to Heaton Pk, right on to A576, left at 2nd lights on to A6104, follow Victoria Ave. on to Hollinwood Ave. under bridge to roundabout take 2nd exit onto Hollins Road, follow Hollins Rd for one & a half miles to Fire Station, left on throughgate leading onto Elm Rd and follow to next left, Whitebank Rd on left.
Seats: 25 **Cover:** Yes **Capacity:** 1,000 **Floodlights:** Yes **Founded:** 1964
Clubhouse: Open evenings and matchdays.
Programme: 16 pages, 50p **Editor:** Secretary
Colours: White/blue/white **Change Colours:**
Midweek Matches: Tuesday **Previous Leagues:** Manch. Amtr/ Lancashire Comb. 81-82.
Record Attendance: 325 v Flixton, NWCL Div 2 Championship decider May 95
Honours: Div 2 R-up 94/95; Div 3 R-up 85/86; Res Div R-up 94/95, Cup 94/95:

SKELMERSDALE UNITED

Chairman: D Tomlinson **Vice Chairman:** T Garner.
Secretary: Ken Hilton, 34 Mill Lane, Burscough, Ormskirk, Lancs L40 5TJ (01704 894504).
Manager: Russ Perkins **Asst Manager:** Barry Hedley **Physio:** Billy Leigh
Ground: White Moss Park, White Moss Road, Skelmersdale, Lancs (01695 722123). **Directions:** M58 Jct 3, at 2nd r'bout take 3rd exit towards Skelmersdale, continue for approx 1 mile, ground on the right. 4 miles from Ormskirk (BR).
Seats: 250 **Cover:** 1,000 **Capacity:** 10,000 **Floodlights:** Yes **Club Shop:** No
Clubhouse: None, but matchday food bar sells hot drinks, soup, hot pies & pasties etc.
Programme: 20 pages, 50p **Editor:** Team effort **Press Officer:** Secretary
Colours: Blue & white/blue/blue **Change colours:** Yellow/black/yellow
Sponsors: Tamcos Training **Nickname:** Skemmers **Founded:** 1882
Midweek Matches: Tuesday **Record Attendance:** 7,000 v Slough FA Amat Cup 67
Best FA Cup year: 1st Rd 67-68 (0-2 at Scunthorpe), 68-69 (0-2 at Chesterfield), 71-72 (0-4 at Tranmere).
Previous Leagues: Liverpool County Combination, Lancashire Combination 1891-93 03-07 21-24 55-68 76-78, Cheshire County 68-71 78-82, Northern Premier 71-76.
Honours: FA Amateur Cup 70-71 R-up 96-97; Ches. Co. Lg 68-69 69-70, Jubilee Cup 69-70; Lancs F'lit Cup 69-70; Lancs Jnr Cup 69-70 70-71; Ashworth Cup 70-71; Barassi Anglo-Italian Cup 70-71; Lancs Non-Lge Cup 73-74 74-75; North West Co's Lg Cup R-up 82-83.

SQUIRES GATE

Chairman: P Mack **Vice President:** Brian Addison
Secretary: John Maguire, 2 Squires Court, Cairn Grove, Blackpool, Lancs FY4 2RA (01253 348512)
Manager: Paul Arnold **Assistant Manager:** John Chippendale.
Ground: School Road, Marton, Blackpool, Lancs (01253 798584).
Directions: M6 to M55 jct 4, left onto A583, turn right at the first set of lights (Whitehall Rd) and follow signs for airport. The ground is approximately one and a half miles on the right. **Record Attendance:** 600 v Everton 95
Seats: 2 rows **Cover:** One side **Capacity:** **Floodlights:** No **Clubhouse:** Yes **Formed:** 1948
Colours: Royal/black/royal **Midweek Matches:** Tuesday **Programee:** 20 pages
Previous Leagues: W. Lancs (pre-1991) **Honours:** W. Lancs Lg Div 2 80-81, Richardson Cup 86-87

STANTONDALE

President: Ken Wood **Chairman:** Roy Grundy **Vice-Chairman:** Mike Shiels
Secretary: Roy Grundy, 15 Stand Park Avenue, Netherton, Merseyside. L30 3SA. (0151 521 8277)
Mgr/Press Off.: Tommy Lawson **Asst Manager:** Garry Britton **Coach:** Eric Warren
Ground: Formby FC, Brows Lane, Formby, Merseyside L37 2LE (01704 833505)
Directions: A565 Liverpool-Southport, turn for Formby at lights opposite Tescointo Altcar Rd, left at T junction to r'bout (opposite Blundell Arms Hotel), take 2nd exit then sharp left into Duke Street, 1st right into Elbow Lane, ground 50yds on left. Half a mile from Formby (BR), buses from Formby & Southport stations.
Seats: 200 **Cover:** 500 **Capacity:** 2,000 **Floodlights:** No **Founded:** 1986 **Clubhouse:** Yes.
Programme: 28 pages, 50p **Editor:** Garry Britton (01695 23199). **Colours:** All sky blue
Midweek matches: Tuesday **Sponsors:** Charlotte Sports **Previous League:** Liverpool Co. Comb. (pre-1992)
Honours: Lamot Pils Trophy 92-93; Liverpool County Comb. Div 1 90-91, Div 2 87-88; Liverpool Jnr Cup 90-91; Liverpool Challenge Cup 91-92; McEwans Lager Cup 91-92:

TETLEY WALKER

President: John Sixsmith **Chairman:** Ray Fisher **Treasurer:** Mark Fisher
Secretary: Brian Gleave, 8 Cossack Ave., Orford, Warrington, Cheshire WA2 9PB (01925 659559).
Manager Ray Fisher **Asst.Manager:** Steve Hughes **Physio:** Peter Cowell
Ground: Tetley Walker Club, Long Lane, Orford, Warrington, Cheshire WA2 9PB (01925 634904).
Ground: M6 Junc 21A to M62 Junc 9, follow signs to Warrington town centre on A49. After about one and a half miles turn left at 2nd r'bout (next to Coachmans pub), ground about 500yds on left. Nearest station Warrington Central
Capacity: 2,000 **Seats:** 40 **Cover:** 150 **Floodlights:** No **Founded:** 1974 **Club Shop:** No
Clubhouse: Open noon-midnight. Food includes sandwiches & pies. **Midweek matches:** Tuesday
Colours: Red & blue/blue/red **Change:** Yellow & blue **Reserves' Lge:** Warrington & D.
Programme: 40 pages 50p **Editor/Press Officer:** Garry Clarke **Nickname:** Walkers **Sponsor:** Driwall
Best FA Vase Season: 4th Rd 96-97 **Previous League:** Warrington & District 1974-94.
Records - Attendance: 200 v Durham FAV 96-97 **Appearances:** Ray Arnold **Win:** 15-2 v Nelson NWCL 96-97
96-97 Captain: Steve Roberts **96-97 Top Scorer:** Tony Plant 27 **96-97 P.o.Y:** Steve Roberts
Honours: Guardian Cup 84-85 85-86 93-94 95-96 96-97; Jubilee Cup 84-85 93-94; Lge Winners 86-87 93-94:

WOODLEY SPORTS FC

Chairman: Ian Campbell **Founded:** 1970
Secretary: Ian Woodhouse, 4 Firethorn Drive, Godley, Hyde SK14 3SN (0161 351 1631 H, 0161 330 6837 B)
Ground: Lambeth Grove Stadium, Lambeth Grove, Woodley, Stockport (0161 494 6429) **Directions:** M63 Junc 15, follow signs (A560) Bredbury, take left filter at lights which brings you onto A560 Stockport Road for approx 1 mile, turn left at pub, Lowes Arms into Mill Street which goes into Mill Lane. Over bridge take 2nd right into Woodlands Avenue, then 1st leftinto Lambeth Grove. Ground 200 yards ahead. Manchester A-Z page 121 G3, Edition 8
Colours: Red & royal blue/royal/white **Floodlights:** No **Midweek Matches:** Wednesday
Record Attendance: 1,500 v Stockport County **Previous Leagues:** Lancashire & Cheshire, Manchester League.

COLNE F.C.

MANCHESTER FOOTBALL LEAGUE

President: P Morris

League Secretary: J A Warrington, 17 Broadacre, Mottram Rise, Stalybridge, Cheshire SK15 2TX

Tel: 01457 764427 (Home) Tel: 01457 855993 (Bus.) Fax: 01457 855993

FINAL LEAGUE TABLES 1996/97

DIVISION PREMIER	P	W	D	L	F	A	Pts
Highfield United	30	23	5	2	70	23	74
Abbey Hey	30	18	6	6	76	41	60
East Manchester	30	19	3	8	62	39	60
Little Hulton United	30	16	7	7	63	41	55
Dukinfield Town	30	15	8	7	48	40	53
Wythenshawe Am.	30	13	3	14	42	44	42
Woodley SC	30	10	7	13	43	45	37
Stand Athletic	30	11	4	15	46	61	37
Atherton Town	30	9	9	12	36	45	36
Mitchell Shackleton	30	10	6	14	45	56	36
Monton	30	10	4	16	43	43	34
Springhead	30	10	4	16	46	57	34
Elton Fold	30	8	10	12	43	55	34
Stockport Georgians	30	8	6	16	40	60	30
BICC	30	8	6	16	41	67	30
Wythenshawe Town	30	6	4	20	32	59	22

DIVISION ONE	P	W	D	L	F	A	Pts
Prestwich Heys	30	27	2	1	87	17	83
Tottington United	30	23	2	5	89	42	71
Gamesley	30	20	7	3	84	36	67
Willows	30	14	6	10	73	56	48
Sacred Heart	30	13	7	10	61	47	46
Old Alts	30	13	5	12	77	71	44
New Mills	30	13	3	14	70	62	42
Hollinwood	30	11	7	12	64	69	40
Milton	30	10	4	16	55	73	34
Whitworth Valley	30	9	7	14	58	84	34
Pennington	30	7	10	13	51	57	31
Breightmet United	30	8	7	15	50	69	31
GMP	30	9	4	17	35	78	31
Manchester Royal	30	8	3	19	57	85	27
Ashton Athletic	30	8	3	19	31	68	27
Whalley Range	30	7	3	20	53	81	24

MANCHESTER FOOTBALL LEAGUE CUP RESULTS 1996/97

GILGRYST CUP

Highfield United	2	Wythenshawe Town	0

MURRAY TROPHY

Pennington	0	Prestwich Heys	4

OPEN TROPHY

Manchester Royal Reserves	2	Woodley S.C. Reserves	2

Manchester Royal won on penalties

PREMIER DIVISION CLUBS 1997-98

ABBEY HEY

Secretary: Mr G Lester, 6 Newhaven Ave., Higher Openshaw, Manchester M11 1HU.
Colours: Red & navy/navy/navy **Ground:** Goredale Avenue, Gorton (0161 231 7147).
Directions: A57 towards Hyde, right into Woodland Avenue approx one & a half miles past Belle Vue junction, right again into Ryder Brow Rd, 1st left after bridge into Goredale Ave.

ATHERTON TOWN

Secretary: G Butler, 43 Hope Fold Ave., Atherton, Lancs M29 0BW (01942 870326).
Colours: Royal/white/royal **Ground:** Howe Bridge Spts Centre, Howe Bridge, Atherton (01942 870403).
Directions: A579 Atherton to Leigh road - Sports Centre on left approx one & a half miles from Atherton.

B.I.C.C.

Secretary: L. Stone, 51 Coppieridge Drive, Crumpsall,Manchester M8 4PB (01161 740 6621)
Colours: All blue **Ground:** Blackley New Road, Blackley.
Directions: Follow Rochdale Rd A664 from Manchester. Turn left at Brackley into Old Market St, then fork right into Blackley New Rd, ground 330yards on left. (01161 740 9151)

DUKINFIELD TOWN

Secretary: Paul Bishop, 21 Church Walk, Stalybridge, Cheshire (0161 303 0398).
Colours: All yellow **Ground:** Blocksages Birch Lane, Dukinfield.
Directions: To Ashton along by-pass, right at 2nd island into Dewsnap Lane, left into Birch Lane, ground 100yds on lefy behind public baths and Colliers garage.

EAST MANCHESTER

Secretary: D Wilkinson, 76 Sandy Lane, Dukinfield, Cheshire SK16 5NL (0161 330 4450).
Colours: All blue **Ground:** Gorton League Complex, Longsight
Directions: Turn into Kirkmanshulme Lane at Belle Vue (A57) junction, ground approx 880 yards on left after Pink Bank Lane.

ELTON FOLD

Secretary: Guy Mallinson 14 Lonsdale St Bury BL8 2QD (Bury 797 7090)
Colours: Blue & black/black/black **Ground:** Bolton Rd Sports Club, Bolton Rd, Bury
Directions: A58 from Bury to Bolton. 1 mile from Bury pass Wellington Pub on right 200 yards turn left into Connaught St. Halfway down turn right in between houses into car park

LITTLE HULTON UNITED

Secretary: Mrs S Macguire, 20 Holly Avenue, Walkden, Worsley (0161 799 8200).
Colours: Black & royal/black/black **Ground:** Avon Close, off Worsley Avenue, Little Hulton.
Directions: A6 from Manchester, two miles after Walkden turn left towards Tyldesley into Armitage Lane, left at Welcome pub after half mile into Madamswood Lane, 2nd right into Worsley Ave., 2nd right is Avon Close. Or, M61 jct 4, A6 towards Manchester, right into Armitage Lane and follow as above.

MITCHELL SHACKLETON

Secretary: Ian Street, 11 Senior Road, Peel Green, Eccles, M30 7PZ (0161 789 7061).
Colours: Green & white/black/black **Ground:** Salteye Park, Peel Green, Eccles (0161 788 8373).
Directions: Leave M63 at Peel Green r'bout (jct 2), take A57 Liverpool Road towards Irlam, ground entrance half mile on left behind Kara Cafew opposite Barton airport. Or, follow A57 from Manchester via Salford & Eccles, then follow Irlam signs.

MONTON AMATEURS

Secretary: T Lee, 28 Wheatley Rd, Swinton, Manchester M27 3RW (0161 793 8033).
Colours: All royal **Ground:** Granary Lane, Worsley
Directions: From Eccles Centre turn right into Worsley Rd at Patricroft Bridge. Ground approx 1 mile on left, entrance just before Bridgewater Hotel

PRESTWICH HEYS

Secretary: Stephen Howard, 28 Brandram Road, Prestwich, Manchester M25 1HJ (0161 773 4408)
Colours: Redblack/red **Ground:** Sandgate Rd, Prestwich (0161 773 8888).
Directions: Follow Old Bury Rd (A665) from Manchester to Prestwich, right into Heywood Rd, 3rd left into Mount Rd/Sandgate Rd - ground on right.

SPRINGHEAD

Secretary: K Gibson, 1 Little Oak Close, Lees, Oldham OL4 3LW (0161 627 3760).
Colours: Black & red/black/black **Ground:** St John St, Lees, Oldham (0161 627 0260).
Directions: From Oldham (Mumps r'bout) follow A669 towards Lees for approx one & a half miles, left at St John Str., grounds 500yds on right.

STAND ATHLETIC

Secretary: T H Edwards, 3 Burndale Drive, Unsworth, Bury BL9 8EN (0161 766 3432).
Colours: Yellow/black/yellow **Ground:** Elms Playing Fields, George Street, Whitefield.
Directions: From Manc. city centre proceed via Bury New Rd (A56) to Whitefield. George St. is on right just before Fire Station. Car park & changing facilities are at Whitefield Community Centre in Green Lane, off George Str.

STOCKPORT GEORGIANS

Secretary: Ged Newcombe, 7 Chiltern Close, Hazel Grove, Stockport SK7 5BQ (0161 483 0004).
Colours: Black & white/white/red **Ground:** Cromley Rd, Woodsmoor (0161 483 6581).
Directions: Follow Stockport-Hazel Grove Rd (A6), right into Woodsmoor Lane at Davenport Theatre, 1st left into Moorland Rd, left at Flowery Field for Cromley Rd.

TOTTINGTON UNITED

Secretary: Vincent Holden, 6 Ash Grove, Holcombe Brook, Ramsbottom BL0 9RS (01204 884958)
Colours: Blue & black/black/blue **Ground:** St Annes Fields, Tottington
Directions: From Bury Town centre follow B6213 to Tottington. Turn right into Laurel Street at Cenotaph. Car park in Royds Street.

WYTHENSHAWE AMATEURS

Secretary: John Sobierajsh, 5 Wensley Drive, Withington, Manchester (0161 445 3415)
Colours: Blue & white stripes/blue/blue **Ground:** Longley Lane, Northenden (0161 998 7268).
Directions: Princess Parkway from Manchester to Post House hotel, via Palatine Rd & Moor End Rd to Longley Lane - ground entrance opposite Overwood Rd.

WYTHENSHAWE TOWN

Secretary: Robert Warwick, 7 Kinsley Avenue, Wythenshawe, Manchester (0161 998 1546)
Colours: All royal **Ground:** Ericstan Park, Timpson Rd, Baguley, Manchester (0161 998 5076).
Directions: Princess Parkway from Manchester, right into Altrincham Rd (A560), left into Southmoor Rd and 1st right into Timpson Rd - ground at end.

DIVISION ONE CLUBS 1997-98

ASHTON ATHLETIC

Secretary: Jimmy Whyte, 430 Downall Green Road, Bryn, Wigan WN4 0NA (01942 205775)
Colours: Blue/black/black **Ground:** Brocstedes Park, Brocstedes Rd, North Ashton, Wigan (01942 716360).
Directions: A580 or M6 to Haydock Island, A49 to Ashton (Bryn Cross), left at lights onto Downall Green Rd, over M6, 2nd right, 2nd right is Brocstedes Rd.

BREIGHTMET UNITED

Secretary: Raymond Walsh, 94 Hatherleigh Walk, Breightmet, Bolton (01204 435197)
Colours: Black & white/black/red **Ground:** Moss Park, Back Bury Rd, Breightmet, Bolton (01204 33930).
Directions: From Manchester follow A56 Bury road, at Whitefield take A665 towards Radcliffe, at Radcliffe proceed to Bolton Rd/Countess Lane and Radcliffe Moor Rd to A58 junction, left towards Bolton - ground half mile situated behind Coopers Egg Packing station.

BRITISH AEROSPACE LOSTOCK

Secretary: Peter Hoyle, 1 Wimbourne Close, Lostock, Bolton (01204 694132)
Colours: Black & white/black/black & white **Ground:** BAE Ground, Lostock Lane, Bolton
Directions: Off A6027 (Horwich/M61 Link) into Lostock Lane. Turn left into works car park.

FAILSWORTH TOWN

Secretary: David Walton, 45 Woodend Street, Oldham, Lancs (0161 627 5480)
Colours: Black & white/white/white **Ground:** GMT White House, Heaton Park, Manchester
Directions: M66 junc 5 towards Manchester, ground approx 1mile on right behind White House GMT Club.

GAMESLEY

Secretary: Gary Weatherhead, 36 Winster Mews, Gamesley, Glossop (01457 866393)
Colours: Green & white/white/white **Ground:** Gamesley Community Centre, Melandra Castle Rd, Glossop
Directions: Follow A57 towards Glossop, at Dinting turn right at Plough Inn into Glossop Rd. Take 1st right into Cottage Lane to Melandra Castle Rd. Ground app 440 yards right.

GREATER MANCHESTER POLICE

Secretary: P Davidson, 2 Oakwood, Sale M33 5RH (0161 962 2327).
Colours: Yellow/blue/yellow **Ground:** Hough End Police Club (0161 856 1798).
Directions: Princess Parkway from central Manchester, right at Mauldeth Rd West, grd entrance half mile left.

HOLLINWOOD

Secretary: K Evans, 20 Meadow Rise, High Crompton, Shaw, Oldham OL2 7QG (01706 840987).
Colours: Blue & red/blue/blue & red **Ground:** Lime Lane, Hollinwood (0161 681 3385).
Directions: Oldham Road (A62) from Manchester to Roxy Cinema, right into Hollins Rd, 1st right into Albert Street, left at junction with Roman Road, 1st right into Lime Lane for quarter mile.

MANCHESTER ROYAL

Secretary: N Kinvic, 3 Craleigh Drive, Cheadle (01538 491 0824)
Colours: Red & black/black/red **Ground:** Barnes Hospital, Cheadle.
Directions: From Manchester, hospital entrance is on the left of Kingsway just after M63 jct 10. Keep left within hospital grounds, pitch is adjacent to motorway.

MILTON

Secretary: Mr R Curzon, 56 Abbey Crescent, Heywood OL10 4UG.
Colours: Green & yellow/black/yellow **Ground:** Athletic Stadium, Springfield Pk, Rochdale.
Directions: From Manchester via Middleton (A664) to Hollins, A6046 towards Heywood then A58 towards Rochdale - Park on left after one and a half miles. Or, M62 jct 20 then follow Heywood signs (A58) - Park on right after 1.5 miles.

NEW MILLS

Secretary: John Hackney, 46 Mellor Road, New Mills, Stockport, (01663 744546).
Colours: Amber/black/amber & black **Ground:** Church Lane, New Mills (01663 747435).
Directions: A6 to Swan Hotel, left into Albion Rd, continue to Church Rd, left into Church Lane.

OLD ALTRINCHAMIANS

Secretary: Phil Lewis, 10 Woodfield Grove, Sale, M33 6JW (0161 973 7082)
Colours: Red & black/black/black **Ground:** Crossford Bridge P.F., Meadows Rd, Sale.
Directions: From Manchester via Stretford (A56), under M63, left at lights into Dane Rd, 1st left into Meadows Rd, ground entrance at end.

PENNINGTON

Secretary: Jimmy Bowers, 137 Twist Lane, Leigh WN7 4DW (01942 208481)
Colours: White & blue/blue/blue **Ground:** Jubilee Park, Leigh Rd, Atherton (01942 894703).
Directions: From Manchester follow East Lancs Rd towards Liverpool, right at Greyhound hotel towards Leigh, in Leigh take Atherton Rd (A579), ground on left after about one & a half miles before G.M.T. offices.

SACRED HEART

Secretary: Joe Devlin, 61 Buersil Ave., Balderstone, Rochdale, Lancs OL16 4TR (01706 660989)
Colours: Red & white/red/red **Ground:** Fox Park, Belfield Mill Lane, Rochdale.
Directions: M62 jct 21, follow Rochdale signs, right at 2nd lights into Albert Royds St, grd half mile on right.

URMSTON

Secretary: Sean Brett, 3 Shuttleworth, Whalley Range, Manchester (0161 881 1962)
Colours: Sky/black/black **Ground:** Flixton Park, Flixton Road.
Directions: M63 junc 3 take Barton Rd to r/about. Then 3rd turning into Bayswater Rd. To r/about, take 2nd left Bowfell Rd, joins Flixton Rd, ground on left.

WHALLEY RANGE

Secretary: R Lapsley, 8 Withnell Rd, Burnage, Manchester M191GHN (0161 432 6158).
Colours: Red & black/black/black **Ground:** King's Rd, Chorlton (0161 881 2618).
Directions: Princess Parkway from Manchester, right at Wilbraham Rd, left at Withington Rd South, King's Rd is 1st right, ground entrance opposite Daventry Rd.

WHITWORTH VALLEY

Secretary: Mark Kirkham, 10 Hargate Avenue, Norden, Rochdale (01706 356055)
Colours: Black & white/black/red **Ground:** Rawstron Str., Whitworth (01706 853030).
Directions: Bacup road (A671) from Rochdale, after just over 2 miles turn left at Whitworth centre into Tonge Lane then 3rd right left into Crown Park Way.

WILLOWS

Secretary: Frank Miller, 11 Edmund Street, Salford, Manchester (0161 737 2411)
Colours: All red **Ground:** Salteye Park, Peel Green, Eccles
Direction: From Eccles Town centre take A57, pass under M63 at Peel Green r/about. After approx 400 yds turn left into lay-by. Ground behind Kara Cafe.

THE GREEN CONTRACT SERVICES MID-CHESHIRE LEAGUE

FOUNDED: 1948
President: R Atherton
League Secretary: E B Davies
34 Ryebank Road, Firswood, Manchester M16 0FP Tel: 0161-881 5732

BARNTON CLAIM 'THE DOUBLE'

The 1996–97 season kicked off on the 17th August with Bollington Athletic and AFC Zeneca joining the First Division taking the places of Garswood United (NWCFL) and Beeches (relegated). Hanley Town and Bollington Athletic Reserves both rejoined the league and took their places in Division Two. Last season's runners-up Barnton had a tremendous finish to the previous season and continued right through the current campaign, enabling them to win the championship in style with 81 points from a possible 90. Early in the season Grove United, Zeneca and Knutsford had all looked likely contenders for honours. Warrington Borough won four out of their first five matches before their fortunes dipped. By mid-November Linotype had moved into second place but a run of draws appeared to have dented their chances and Grove United also struck a bad patch leaving the Altrincham side to take the runners-up spot. In Division Two it looked all season like a three horse race with Lostock setting the early pace and Pilkington and Beeches all within striking distance. Chester Nomads showed some signs of upsetting the script but fell away rapidly towards the end of the season. A blip by Lostock allowed Pilkington and the Beeches to sample the top spot but they too failed to maintain their form to allow Lostock Gralam to win the championship and promotion. Beeches did enough to join them in the promotion stakes finishing in the Runners-up position taking the place of Malpas and Broadheath Cen. The former had a poor season failing to secure a single win but they are to be admired for their efforts and willpower. Styal with only one win in the second half of the season finished bottom by the narrow margin of one point.

Their fortunes changed when they were re-elected for season 97–98. Several clubs will wish to forget the League Challenge Cup competition but for the record Barnton's 1-0 win over Bramhall played on the 21st May at Winsford brought relief to the Management Committee as well as a well-deserved First Division double to Barnton the first since Congleton Town's success in 1977–78. A replay had looked likely with the floodlights showing signs of being troublesome until Paul Hennin scored the winning goal seven minutes from time, despite the panic it was a game worthy of the final tie.

The Division Two Cup had involved six replays before Beeches and Pilkington met at Barnton in the final game that was a credit to the league and both clubs. Pilkington will still be rueing the chances they missed in the second half after taking an early first half lead, but two late goals from Beeches gave them the cup in what was a very exciting finish.

In outside competitions the league were well represented in several finals and all are to be congratulated on their achievements. Grove United had a fine start in the FA Vase beating NWCFL opposition Kidsgrove Athletic away from home, but went out at home to Thackley in the next round.

Barnton, Division One League Champions and Cup Winners 1996–97

The annual inter-league match with the West Cheshire League was going well up to half-time but enforced changes during the interval helped the visitors to a deserved 3-1 win.

The league had quite a number of enquiries regarding membership throughout the season and there were six serious applications arising from which Padgate St. Oswalds were invited into the league replacing Whitchurch Alport Reserves who had resigned.

The 1997–98th season is the League's Jubilee year and the league hope to introduce a special Jubilee Cup Competition for its members. Due to a change in our sponsors name a slight change will also appear in the league's name now to be known as the:

GREEN CONTRACT SERVICES MID-CHESHIRE LEAGUE

FINAL LEAGUE TABLES 1996/1997

DIVISION ONE	P	W	D	L	F	A	Pts
Barnton	30	26	3	1	105	17	81
Linotype	30	20	6	4	76	32	66
Grove United	30	19	4	7	66	27	61
Wilmslow Albion	30	17	6	7	60	42	57
Bramhall	30	18	2	10	75	28	56
Knutsford	30	14	6	10	59	34	48
Poynton	30	13	3	14	60	61	42
AFC Zeneca	30	12	4	14	62	79	40
Chorlton Town	30	11	6	13	50	44	39
Cheadle Heath	30	11	6	13	60	64	39
Whitchurch Alport	30	11	5	14	40	45	38
Bollington Athletic	30	10	6	14	50	50	36
Rylands	30	7	9	14	41	62	30
Warrington Bro	30	8	3	19	46	93	27
Broadheath Cen	30	4	6	20	33	75	18
Malpas	30	0	3	27	16	146	3

DIVISION TWO	P	W	D	L	F	A	Pts
Lostock Gralam	30	24	4	2	113	34	76
Beeches	30	22	3	5	93	30	69
Pilkington	30	21	2	7	88	35	65
Linotype Reserves	30	15	7	8	69	46	52
Alsager	30	14	7	9	58	38	49
Grove United Res	30	15	4	11	64	56	49
Garswood United	30	11	11	8	68	50	44
Chester Nomads	30	12	7	11	61	57	43
Littlemoor	30	10	4	16	63	77	34
Chorlton Town Res	30	10	4	16	63	90	34
Poynton Res	30	7	12	11	44	50	33
Hanley Town	30	8	9	13	40	54	33
Whitchurch Alport Res	30	7	7	16	43	76	28
Bollington Ath Res	30	7	4	19	56	89	25
Rylands Res	30	5	5	20	37	121	20
Styal	30	5	4	21	48	105	19

GREEN INSULATION MID-CHESHIRE LEAGUE RESULTS CHART 1996–97

HOME TEAM	1	2	3	4	5	6	7	8	9	10	11	12	13	14	15	16
AFC Zeneca	*	0-5	3-1	0-7	4-2	1-7	3-3	0-3	3-3	4-0	6-1	1-3	3-3	6-4	3-0	4-3
Barnton	4-1	*	2-0	0-1	2-0	10-2	2-1	4-0	3-1	2-2	12-1	3-1	4-0	7-0	4-0	3-0
Bollington Athletic	2-0	0-1	*	1-4	2-0	1-2	2-1	1-0	1-1	1-1	10-0	4-0	0-2	0-2	1-3	2-3
Bramhall	2-2	0-2	0-1	*	3-0	7-2	3-0	0-2	2-1	1-2	5-0	2-0	3-0	7-0	1-0	0-2
Broadheath Cen.	4-3	0-4	3-1	1-5	*	2-4	2-3	0-3	0-1	0-3	5-1	0-4	1-1	4-0	0-2	1-4
Cheadle Heath N.	2-0	2-2	4-0	0-1	2-2	*	1-1	0-2	1-3	0-2	5-0	3-4	3-3	3-1	2-2	1-2
Chorlton Town	3-0	2-3	3-2	1-0	1-1	2-0	*	0-2	0-2	2-4	6-0	3-0	0-1	1-0	1-1	0-1
Grove United	3-2	0-4	1-1	1-0	3-0	2-1	2-2	*	2-1	1-2	17-0	2-0	3-0	5-2	0-1	0-0
Knutsford	2-1	1-3	4-1	2-1	5-0	0-1	1-0	0-2	*	2-0	7-0	1-2	1-1	4-0	0-1	4-0
Linotype	4-0	0-1	1-1	2-1	3-1	2-0	3-1	3-2	1-1	*	9-0	3-0	2-2	8-2	3-2	1-2
Malpas	2-3	0-1	1-2	0-7	1-1	1-2	0-7	1-3	0-6	1-4	*	1-1	1-1	1-2	0-1	0-4
Poynton	2-1	0-5	4-2	2-2	2-1	2-3	1-1	1-2	4-1	0-1	4-0	*	7-1	1-3	3-0	4-2
Rylands	0-1	0-4	3-3	1-2	5-0	2-1	1-2	0-2	1-1	0-3	5-1	0-3	*	1-4	1-0	2-2
Warrington Borough	0-1	1-3	0-3	1-5	2-2	5-3	4-1	0-1	1-1	1-4	3-1	4-2	0-4	*	0-4	0-4
Whitchurch Alport	2-3	0-4	1-1	0-2	1-0	0-1	0-1	0-0	1-2	1-1	3-0	4-1	2-0	5-3	*	2-4
Wilmslow Albion	2-3	1-1	0-3	2-1	0-0	2-2	2-1	1-0	1-0	0-2	4-1	5-2	3-0	1-1	3-1	*

CLUBS DIRECTORY 1997-98

A F C ZENECA

Chairman: David Lea **Manager:** Alan Duckworth
Secretary: David Stubbs, 11 Petunia Grove, Macclesfield, Cheshire SK11 7YY (01625 423160)
Ground: Mulberries Leisure Centre, Zeneca Pharmaceuticals, (01625 514040)
Colours: All green **Change Colours:** Yellow/black/black

ALSAGER

Chairman: Keith Murphy **Manager:** Mark Lawton
Secretary: Steve Whittaker, 2 Lea Close, Sandbach, Cheshire CW10 0HT (01270 761810)
Ground: The Town Ground, Woodpark, Alsager (01270 882336)
Colours: Black & white/black/black **Change Colours:**

BARNTON

Chairman: William Perrin **Manager:** Terence Murphy
Secretary: Michael Webster, 29 Townfield Lane, Barnton CW8 4LH (01606 781119)
Ground: Townfield, Townfield Lane, Barnton.
Colours: Black & white stripes/black/black **Change Colours:** Amber/blue/blue

BEECHES

Chairman: Gordon Rigby **Manager:** Gary Harper
Secretary: David Corrigan, 7 Burrows Avenue, Haydock, St Helens WA11 0DE (01744 757273).
Ground: Cowley Fields, Wynne Road, St Helens
Colours: Red & blue/navy/navy **Change Colours:** Claret & blue/maroon/maroon

BOLLINGTON ATHLETIC

Chairman: A Hall **Manager:** Glynn Ingham
Secretary: Anthony Holmes, 1 Princess Drive, Bollington, Macclesfield, Cheshire SK10 5ES (01625 574913).
Ground: Recreation Ground, Bollington.
Colours: Green & white/black/black **Change Colours:** Blue & white/blue/blue

BRAMHALL

Chairman: Mark Weaver **Manager:** Tim Wharmby
Secretary: Mrs Elaine Weaver, 25 Kimberley Street, Edgeley, Stockport SK3 8EB (0161 477 7273)
Ground: Lumb Lane, Bramhall.
Colours: Black & red/black/black **Change Colours:** Yellow/blue/blue

BROADHEATH CENTRAL

Chairman: Ian Beresford **Manager:** Steven Woods
Secretary: David Murphy, 113 Downs Drive, Timperley, Altrincham WA15 5QU (0161 718 0823).
Ground: Viaduct Rd, Broadheath, Altrincham. (0161 928 5849)
Colours: Blue & White stripes/white/white **Change Colours:** Red & black/black/black

CHEADLE HEATH NOMADS

Chairman: Roy Welsh **Manager:**
Secretary: George Gibbons, 3 Hurley Drive, Cheadle Hulme, Stockport SK8 6DH (0161 485 1343)
Ground: The Heath, Norbreck Ave, Cheadle, Stockport (0161 282 6574)
Colours: Maroon & Sky/maroon/maroon **Change Colours:** Black & white/black/black

CHESTER NOMADS

Chairman: Phil Darlington **Manager:** Bob Delgardo
Secretary: Ritz Ritzema, 22 Cross Green Upton, Chester CH2 1QR (01244 379791)
Ground: Garrison Ground, Eaton Road, Handbridge, Chester
Colours: Amber/black/amber **Change Colours:** Grey/red/white

CHORLTON TOWN

Chairman: Bert Ennis **Manager:** TBA
Secretary: Jim Calderbank, 21 South Meade, Timperley, Altrincham WA15 6QL (0161 969 1156).
Ground: Machester County FA, Brantingham Road, Chorlton
Colours: Red & black stripes/white/white **Change Colours:** Yellow or blue/blue/red

GARSWOOD UNITED RESERVES

Chairman: R Jones **Manager:** Alan Clarke
Secretary: John Anelay, 128 Victoria Road Garswood, Wigan WN4 0RE (01942 519231)
Ground: Simms Lane Ends, Garswood Road, Garswood, Nr Wigan (01744 892258).
Colours: Blue & white halves/blue/blue **Change Colours:** All red.

GROVE UNITED

Chairman: Mark Boothby **Manager:** Billey Gaffey
Secretary: Bernard Jordon, 25 Bean Leach Road, Hazel Grove, Stockport SK7 4LD (0161 456 2542).
Ground: Half Moon Lane, Alfreton Rd, Offerton/Lisburne Lane, Stockport.
Colours: Red/black/black **Change Colours:** Maroon/white/white

HANLEY TOWN

Chairman: David Bould **Manager:** Neville Chamberlain
Secretary: Mrs Joanne Shankland, 29 Ubberley Road, Bentilee, Stoke-on-Trent ST2 0EN (01782 272537)
Ground: Abbey Lane, Bucknall, Stoke-on-Trent (01782 267234)
Colours: Blue & white/white/blue **Change Colours:** Red & black/white/red

KNUTSFORD

Chairman: Simon Harris **Manager:** Ken Harrison
Secretary: Keith Jones, 20 Townfields, Cheshire WA16 8DR (01565 755711)
Ground: Manchester Road, Knutsford.
Colours: Red & black/black/black **Change Colours:** White/blue/white

LINOTYPE

Chairman: Brian Hennis **Manager:** K Gardner
Secretary: Brian McGuiness, 36 Barrington Road, Altrincham, Cheshire WA14 1HJ (0161 929 0021)
Ground: British Airways Club, Clay Lane, Timperley, Altrincham (0161 980 7354).
Colours: White/black/black **Change Colours:** Red & black/white/white

LITTLEMOOR

Chairman: Arthur McClean **Manager:** Frank Saunders
Secretary: Stanley McQuarrie, 96 Mottram Towers, Mottram St, Hillgate, Stockport SK1 3NY (0161 474 0257)
Ground: Stockport Lads Club, Hempshaw Lane, Offerton
Colours: Black & white Stripes/black/black **Change Colours:** All blue

LOSTOCK GRALAM

Chairman: Derek Washburn **Manager:** Steve Stockton
Secretary: Andrew Hough, 31 Beechwood Drive, Wincham, Northwich, Cheshire CW9 6EX (01565 733383)
Ground: Rear Slow & Easy Hotel, Manchester Road, Lostock Gralam
Colours: All blue **Change Colours:** Green & yellow halves/black/black

MALPAS

Chairman: Robert Leslie **Manager:** Martin Holden
Secretary: Bernard Lloyd, 15 Springfield Avenue, Malpas, Cheshire SY14 8QD (01948 860812).
Ground: Malpas & District Sports Club, Oxheys, Wrexham Rd, Malpas, Cheshire (01948 860662).
Colours: White/blue/red **Change Colours:** Yellow & green/green/yellow

PADGATE ST OSWALDS

Chairman: Graham Millins **Manager:** Mick Armitage
Secretary: Brian Hughes, 13 Jubilee Avenue, Padgate, Warrington WA1 3JY (01925 490924)
Ground: Bennets Rec Ground, Station Road, Padgate.
Colours: Black & white/black/red **Change Colours:** Blue & red

PILKINGTON AFC

Chairman: John Potter **Manager:** Paul Pinder
Secretary: Paul Pinder, 629 Eltonhead Road, Sutton Heath St Helens WA9 5SX (01744 816158)
Ground: Ruskin Drive, St Helens (01744 22893)
Colours: Green & black/black/black **Change Colours:** All Claret & blue

POYNTON

Chairman: John Ramsbottom **Manager:** Paul Cunningham
Secretary: Paul Burch, 24 Brooklands Avenue, Poynton, Cheshire SK12 1HZ (01625 871205).
Ground: London Rd North, Poynton (01625 875765).
Colours: Red & black/black/red & black **Change Colours:** Blue & white/blue/blue.

RYLANDS

Chairman: William Morris **Manager:** Terry Selby
Secretary: Ian Finchett, 31 Elizabeth Drive, Padgate, Warrington WA1 4JQ (01925 816911).
Ground: Gorsey Lane, Warrington (01925 35700).
Colours: Blue & black/black/black **Change Colours:** Red & royal/blue/red

STYAL

Chairman: Len Rowland **Manager:** Frank Jones
Secretary: Alan Jones, 1 Oak Brow Cottages, Atrincham Road, Styal, Wilmslow SK(4JE (01625 530270)
Ground: Altrincham Road, Styal (01625 529303)
Colours: Yellow/blue/blue **Change Colours:** Blue/black/black

WARRINGTON BOROUGH

Chairman: Harry Boon **Manager:**
Secretary: Ian Dick, 53 Arlington Drive, Penketh, Warrington, Cheshire WA5 2QG (01925 653044)
Ground: Cantilever Park, Warrington (01925 724421)
Colours: Blue & yellow/blue/blue **Change Colours:** Navy & purple/navy/navy

WHITCHURCH ALPORT

Chairman: P Wainwright **Manager:** Alan Smith
Secretary: Robert Dutton, 7 Nessina Grove, Crewe, Cheshire CW2 8EL (01270 663015)
Ground: Yockings Park, Whitchurch, Shropshire. (01948 667415)
Colours: Red/black/red **Change:** Yellow/blue/blue

WILMSLOW ALBION

Chairman: Geoff Thornton **Manager:** Malcom Winn
Secretary: David Elliott, 10 Tranmere Drive, Handforth, Wilmslow, Cheshire SK9 3BW (01625 549524)
Ground: Oakwood Farm, Styal Rd, Styal, Wilmslow (01625 535823).
Colours: Red & blue/blue/blue **Change Colours:** Black & white/black/black

CARLSBERG WEST CHESHIRE A.F.L.

President: K Halsall
Treasurer: R Prescott
Hon. Secretary: L Bullock, 8 Cambridge Road
Bromborough, Wirral L62 7JA (0151 334 3545)

SECRETARY'S REPORT: SEASON 1996/97

Each year the George Law Trophy is awarded to the club that has done the most to enhance the reputation of the Carlesberg West Cheshire League. This season there was never any doubt about the recipients. Not only did POULTON VICTORIA repeat their championship success of 12 months previously but they were also most worthy winners of the Cheshire Amateur Cup. The Wallasey outfit then went on to 'run around Wembley with the cup' having defeated Corby Caledonians 3-1 in the final of the Carlesberg Pub Cup. Congratulations go to VICS for a tremendous campaign as they again set the standards for others to follow.

Division 1 runners-up for the second consecutive season were HESWALL who eventually pipped a BROMBOROUGH POOL side who in between a poor start and finish dropped only 1 point in 18 outings. HESWALL did go one better in the Division 1 Knockout Competition, The Pyke Cup. Beaten finalists a year earlier, this time they lifted the trophy following a 1-0 replay victory over STORK. Completing a successful season the HESWALL club also retained the Wirral Senior Cup thanks to a 4-2 final win over MERSEY ROYAL, while the Reserve outfit were runaway winners of the 2nd Division. The battle for the lower Divisions' runners-up spot contested by three clubs eligible for promotion, went down to the wire with BLACON YC pipping NEW BRIGHTON on goal difference as WEST KIRBY went down to a last day defeat. BLACON will take the Division 1 place of GENERAL CHEMICALS who lost out in their relegation battle with SHELL and MORETON.

The Division 2 cup winners [West Cheshire Bowl] were SHELL RESERVES who came from behind to defeat CAMMELL LAIRD RESERVES 2-1. BLACON YC had District success in winning the Chester Senior Cup while CASTROL SOCIAL lost out on penalties in the Wirral Amateur Cup final.

POULTON VICTORIA were, unsurprisingly, our most successful club in the F.A. Carlsberg Vase reaching the third round and CAMMELL LAIRD showed signs of returning to further glories by making it 6 'all West Cheshire' finals in a row when losing to VICS in the Cheshire Amateur. LAIRDS later had some consolation as they earned themselves 36 gallons of beer for winning the Castlemaine XXXX shoot-out competition. Midway through the season the League was rocked by the news that RAY NEVIN had stepped down as the team boss at LAIRDS. This ended nearly 25 remarkable years in charge during which time the club had collected 15 Division 1 championships [including 9 in 10 years] and no fewer than 21 cup successes, a record that is likely to stand for all time.

During the season the League representative side played 2 fixtures enjoying victories in both. 3-1 v the Mid Cheshire League and 2-0 v the 1 Zingari League while the campaign had opened with MERSEY ROYAL clinching the League's charity competition, the Bill Weight Trophy. At the Annual Presentation Evening Ben McHugh of SHELL RESERVES stepped forward as the Carlsberg Player of the Year while UPTON AA received the Carlsberg Club of the Year award for having the best administration and discipline record.

DIVISION ONE	P	W	D	L	F	A	Pts	Leading Scorers		Most Man of the Match Awards
Poulton Vics	30	23	4	3	84	23	50	S Lewis	16	R Glanvill/I Doran
Heswall	30	21	4	5	79	28	46	G Steele	26	G Steele
Brom. Pool	30	22	1	7	58	26	43*	J Kearns	12	J McCreadie
M'side Police	30	16	4	10	57	39	36	A Finney	12	M Gallagher
Mond Rangers	30	15	6	9	55	54	36	A Gott	13	C Littler, K Patterson
Mersey Royal	30	13	7	10	51	42	33	A Taylor	12	J Thompson
Christleton	30	12	8	10	54	45	32	P Houghton	10	D Harding
Cammell Laird	30	12	7	10	54	45	32	W Foden	19	M Smith
Vauxhall	30	12	6	12	58	54	30	G Edwards	9	P Crane
Newton	30	8	9	13	48	56	25	S Walsh	11	A Amer
Stork	30	8	7	15	44	66	23	L Crowder	7	A Battle
Ashville	30	7	8	15	40	50	22	P Parkhill	8	A McMahon
Capenhust	30	9	3	18	44	62	21	L Oldfield	9	A Dawson
Moreton	30	8	3	19	35	70	19	D Webb	5	P Murray
Shell	30	6	4	20	37	77	16	S Wright/K Leech	11	K Leech/J Reynolds
Gen Chemicals	39	4	5	21	29	82	13	M Robinson	6	N Larkin

* 2 Points deducted for rule infringement

PYKE CUP

SEMI-FINALS

Christleton	v	Heswall	0-4	Mond Rangers	v	Stork	1-2

FINAL

Heswall v Stork 1-1, 1-0

REPRESENTATIVE GAMES

Mid Cheshire League	v	West Cheshire League	1-3 (Jimmy Kelly, Nicky Dillon, Simon Lewis)
West Cheshire League	v	1 Zingari League	2-0 (Graham Steele, John Toner)

MANAGER OF THE MONTH

August	Alvin McDonald (Poulton Vics)	September	Keith Giles (West Kirby)
October	Paul Davenport (C Laird Res)	November	Dave Jones (Blacon YC)
December	Mike Keeley (Bromboro'Pool)	January	Alvin McDonald (P. Vics)
February	Peter Ellis (Mond Rangers)	March	Gary Evason (Heswall)
April	Steve Leyland/Dave Whitcomb (Heswall Res.)		

WEST CHESHIRE BOWL

SEMI-FINAL

Cammell Laird Res	v	Castrol Social	2-1	New Brighton	v	Shell Res	2-4

FINAL

Cammell Laird Res v Shell Res 1-2

CASTLEMAINE XXXX SHOOT OUT

(Group Winners = Semi-Finalists)

SEMI-FINAL

Blacon YC	v	Mersey Royal	4-2	Cammell Laird	v	New Brighton	16-15

Final: Cammell Laird 6, Blacon YC 5

BILL WEIGHT MEMORIAL TROPHY

SEMI-FINAL

Capenhurst	v	Heswall	1-4	Poulton Victoria	v	Mersey Royal	1-1, 4-5

Final: Mersey Royal 3, Heswall 1

N.B. The 1997 Yearbook incorrectlty listed this competition as Bill Wright Trophy

CLUB DIRECTORY 1997-98

ASHVILLE FC

Secretary: Dave Walton, 15 Wellesley Road, Wallasey, Wirral, Merseyside, L44 5UR (0151 639 9196).
Ground: Villa Park, Cross Lane, Wallasey Village, Wallasey, (0151 638 2127)
Sponsor: Clinitex, Kelly Sports **Formed:** 1949 **Colours:** White/black/black

BLACON YOUTH CLUB FC

Secretary: Ron Paddock, 71 Blacon Avenue, Blacon, Chester, Cheshire CH1 5BB (01244 371240)
Ground: Cairns Crescent Playing Fields, Cairns Crescent, Blacon, Chester.
Sponsor: Acorn Glass **Formed:** 1964 **Colours:** Black & white/black/black

BROMBOROUGH POOL FC

Secretary: Trevor Patterson, 102 Princes Boulevard, Higher Bebington, Wirral L63 5LP (0151 645 1642)
Ground: Bromborough Pool Village, The Green, South View Road, Bromborough Pool.
Sponsor: **Formed:** 1884 **Colours:** All Blue

CAMMELL LAIRD FC

Secretary: Ray Steele, 46 Croft Ave, Bromborough, Wirral L62 2BR (0151 334 8998)
Ground: Kirklands, St Peters Road, Rock Ferry, Birkenhead (0151 645 5991)
Sponsor: Met Arc **Formed:** 1900 **Colours:** All blue

CAPENHURST FC

Secretary: Martin Williams, 157 Hope Farm Road, Great Sutton, South Wirral L66 2TJ (0151 339 8935)
Ground: Capenhurst Sports Ground, Capenhurst Lane, Capenhurst (0151 339 4101)
Sponsor: Atlantic Comm/Deeglass **Formed:** 1952 **Colours:** Sky & claret/claret/claret & sky

CASTROL SOCIAL FC

Secretary: Dave Bebbington, 490 Overpool Rd, Whitby, Ellesmere Port, South Wirral L66 2JJ (0151 357 1979)
Ground: Castrol Sports & Social Club, Chester Road, Whitby, Ellesmere Port (0151 355 1730)
Sponsor: Castrol/ Peninsula Restaurant **Formed:** 1954 **Colours:** Blue & white/black/black

CHRISTLETON FC

Secretary: Ken Price, 35 Canadian Ave, Hoole, Chester, Cheshire CH2 3HQ (01244 313513)
Ground: Little Heath, Christleton (01244 332153)
Sponsor: The Chester Evening Leader **Formed:** 1966 **Colours:** Red/black/red

GENERAL CHEMICALS FC

Secretary: Tony Riley, 171 Cotton Lane, Runcorn, Cheshire WA7 5JB (01928 565390)
Ground: Pavilions Club, Dandy Lane, Weston Point, Runcorn (01928 590508)
Sponsor: Maltacourt Ltd **Formed:** 1958 **Colours:** Yellow/l blue/yellow

HESWALL

Secretary: Jake Horan, 13 Reedville Road, Bebington, Wirral L63 2HS (0151 644 0459)
Ground: Gayton Park, Brimstage Road, Heswall, Wirral, (0151 342 8172)
Sponsor: Pyramids Shopping Centre **Formed:** 1891 **Colours:** Yellow/royal/yellow

MANOR ATHLETIC

Secretary: Stewart Galtress, 3 Centurion Close, Meols, Wirral L47 7BZ (0151 632 3211)
Ground: Octel Sports Club, Bridle Road, Bromborough
Sponsor: **Formed:** 1968 **Colours:** White/black/red

MERSEY ROYAL

Secretary: Dave Lawson, 7 Mount Park, Higher Bebington, Wirral L63 %rd (0151 608 2261)
Ground: Unilver Sports Ground, Bromborough
Sponsor: N S Glazier **Formed:** 1946 **Colours:** Black & green/black/black

MERSEYSIDE POLICE

Secretary: George Todd, 14 Crowther Street, St Helens, Merseyside WA10 4NH (01744 755845)
Ground: Police Club, Fairfield, Prescot Road, Liverpool L7 0JD (0151 228 2352)
Sponsor: Davies Ltd **Formed:** 1885 **Colours:** Green/black/black

MOND RANGERS

Secretary: Beverley Crilly, 26 Perrin Ave, Weston Point, Runcorn, Cheshire WA7 4BJ (01928 575938)
Ground: Pavilions Club, Sandy Lane, Weston Point, Runcorn (01928 590508)
Sponsor: Rocksavage Power Co Ltd **Formed:** 1967 **Colours:** Navy & azurte/navy/azure

MORETON FC

Secretary: Jeff Williams-Lloyd, 46 Burrell Drive, Moreton, Wirral L46 0TQ (0151 677 9840)
Ground: Elm Grove, Hoylake
Sponsor: Tilney & Co **Formed:** 1900 **Colours:** Red/black/black

NEW BRIGHTON

Secretary: Russell Holmes, 10 Rudgrave Square, Wallasey, Wirral L44 0EL (0151 638 9506)
Ground: Harrison Drive, Wallasey Village, Wallasey
Sponsor: George Major Skip Hire **Formed:** 1993 **Colours:** Red & white/white/red & white

NEWTON F C

Secretary: Alan Dabner, 41 St David Road, Claughton, Birkenhead L43 8SW (0151 653 2151)
Ground: Millcroft, Frankby Road, Greasby, Wirral (0151 677 8382)
Sponsor: Cory Bothers Shipping Ltd **Formed:** 1933 **Colours:** Gold/black/yellow

POULTON VICTORIA

Secretary: John McGraath, 1 Wernbrook Close, Noctorum, Wirral L43 9HY (0151 652 8043)
Ground: Victoria Park, Rankin Street, Wallasey (0151 638 3559)
Sponsor: Carlsberg & Bass **Formed:** 1935 **Colours:** All Royal Blue

SHELL FC

Secretary: Roy Jones, 5 Sycamore Drive, Whitby, Ellesmere Port, South Wirral L66 2PW (0151 200 1532)
Ground: Chester Road, Whitby, Ellesmere Port, South Wirral (0151 200 7080)
Sponsor: Portion Controls Ltd **Formed:** 1924 **Colours:** Yellow & blue/yellow/yellow

STORK FC

Secretary: Steve Carter, 7 Elm Road, Bebington, Wirral L63 8PF (0151 645 6697)
Ground: Unilever Sports Ground, Bromborough
Sponsor: The Village Leisure Hotel **Formed:** 1920 **Colours:** All green

UPTON ATHLETIC

Secretary: Bary Gaulton, 24 St Marks Crescent, Whitby, Ellesmere Port L66 2XD (0151 339 1504)
Ground: Cheshire County Council Sports & Social Club, Plas Newton Lane, Chester (01244 318367)
Sponsor: **Formed:** 1964 **Colours:** White/black/black

VAUXHALL MOTORS

Secretary: Carole Paisey, 26 South Road, West Kirby, Wirral L48 3HQ (0151 625 6936)
Ground: Vauxhall Sports Ground, Rivacre Road, Hooton, Ellesmere Port (0151 328 1114)
Sponsor: James Edwards/Lookers **Formed:** 1963 **Colours:** Maroon/sky/maroon

WILLASTON

Secretary: Peter Armstrong, 22 Deeside, Whitby, Ellesmere Port, South Wirral L65 6RQ (0151 200 2068)
Ground: Johnston Recreation Ground, Neston Road, Willaston, South Wirral
Sponsor: The Pollard Inn **Formed:** 1962 **Colours:** Yellow & royal/royal/royal

SGL SEAT WEST LANCASHIRE FOOTBALL LEAGUE 1996–97

President: H Johnstone
Chairman: D Procter
General Secretary: W Carr, 60 Selby Avenue, Blackpool

League President Harry Johnstone retired at the close of the season after serving the League for 50 years, he was honoured by the Football Association with the award of an inscribed medallion and the League also made a presentation for the Loyal and Dedicated service he has given to the League, he will be especially remembered for keeping the League alive between 1955 and 1959 when it was unable to function due to the forming of the Lancashire League by the County's Professional clubs and the resulting withdrawal of the 'A' Teams which at that time had so dominated the League to the extent that the Local and Village teams had been squeezed out. Non-League football in the County owe a debt to Harry for keeping the foundation intact from which today's League has grown and now stands as the county's Senior Supply League and Lancashire's only representative on the National League System.

Mr Derrick Procter Chairman for the past 14 years has been appointed as the new President.

At the Annual General Meeting the Clubs voted to accept two new clubs, Barnoldswick United and Chorley Motors; they also accepted the application for re-election of Barrow Wanderers and BAE Canberra, this will extend the Second Division to 20 teams for next season only, as the clubs also agreed to the formation of another Division for Season 1998–99 and six clubs will be relegated to provide the nucleus of the new division. It is proposed that on the formation of this division the two Senior Divisions will comprise 16 teams each.

All the Division Championships were the usual close finishes, Division 1 was won by Wyre Villa with Charnock Richard only 3 points behind. Division 2 was only decided by goal difference when Fleetwood Hesketh came with a storming finish to push Padiham, who looked early favourites to win into runners-up, this in itself was a great achievement after having had to apply for re-election the previous season, they were also runners-up in the Lancashire Challenge Shield and in the Presidents Cup, however promotion was their priority which was assured.

The fight against relegation from Division 1 was also a cliffhanger with half of the teams in the division involved in the last weeks of the season, Vickers from Barrow-in-Furness had some good results against top opponents but they had left it too late and they are in the Second Division next season for the first time since joining the League in 1962. Poulton Town, a regular also in the top division and Tempest United who only achieved senior status last season join the extended Division 2 where it will be a real scrap to avoid the bottom six places to miss the drop to the proposed new division.

Burnley United won the Richardson Cup for the first division clubs, surprisingly their opponents were relegated Tempest United.

Derrick Procter.

FINAL LEAGUE TABLES 1996/97

DIVISION ONE	P	W	D	L	F	A	Pts	G/D
Wyre Villa	34	21	6	7	96	43	69	53
Charnock Richard	34	19	9	6	67	38	66	29
Fulwood Am	34	19	8	7	74	35	65	39
Eagley	34	18	7	9	77	67	61	10
Leyland Motors Ath	34	17	7	10	76	55	58	21
Springfields	34	15	9	10	58	46	54	12
Dalton United	34	14	10	10	48	59	52	–11
Burnley United	34	13	9	12	67	61	48	6
Lancashire Constab	34	13	8	13	60	56	47	4
Blackrod Town	34	12	7	15	55	61	43	–6
Lansil	34	11	7	16	61	72	40	–11
Turton	34	11	6	17	76	88	36*	–12
Feniscowles	34	8	12	14	44	59	36	–15
Kirkham & Wesham	34	9	9	16	40	61	36	–21
Freckleton	34	9	8	17	53	67	35	–14
Vickers SC	34	9	7	18	51	67	34	–16
Poulton Town	34	8	9	17	42	64	33	–22
Tempest United	34	9	4	21	46	92	31	–46

DIVISION TWO	P	W	D	L	F	A	Pts	G/D
Fleetwood Hesketh	34	23	3	8	102	51	72	51
Padiham	34	23	3	8	90	51	72	39
Thornton Cleveleys	34	20	8	6	69	46	68	23
Hesketh Bank	34	20	7	7	73	38	67	35
Milnthorpe Corin	34	20	7	7	84	42	64*	42
Garstang	34	17	5	12	70	51	59	19
Wigan College	34	17	6	11	71	56	57	15
BAC Preston	34	16	3	15	79	83	51	–4
Preston West End	34	15	2	17	78	80	47	–2
Lythan St Annes	34	12	8	14	38	42	44	–4
Norcross & Warbreck	34	12	6	16	56	65	42	–9
Carnforth Rngs	34	12	8	14	50	51	41*	–1
Whinney Hill	34	9	10	15	62	71	37	–9
Blackpool Wren Rvr	34	9	6	19	61	88	33	–27
Glaxo	34	9	6	19	51	83	33	–32
Haslingden St.Mary's	34	9	6	19	51	77	30*	–26
BAE Canberra	34	6	8	20	45	81	26	–36
Barrow Wanderers	34	4	4	26	56	128	16	–72

* Indicates clubs with points adjustment.

DIVISION ONE CLUBS 1997-98

BLACKROD TOWN
Ground: Blackrod Comm Centre, Vicarage Rd, Blackrod (01204 692614)
Secretary: Mr D Almond (01942 793122).

BURNLEY UNITED
Ground: Barden Lane Spts Grnd, Burnley.
Secretary: Mr S Elliott (01282 414828)

CHARNOCK RICHARD
Grd: Charter Lane, Charnock Richard (01257 794288)
Secretary: Mr G S Randle (01772 496782).

DALTON UNITED
Grd: Railway Meadow, Beckside Rd, Dalton-in-Furness (01229 462799)
Secretary: Mr D Lacey (01229 464202).

EAGLEY
Grd: Eagley Sports Complex, Dunscar Bridge, Bolton (01204 306830)
Secretary: M Hackin (01204 595863).

FENISCOWLES
Ground: Livsey Branch Road, Feniscowles, Blackburn (01254 208210)
Secretary: A Akeroyd (01254 706931).

FLEETWOOD HESKETH
Ground: Fylde Road, Southport
Secretary: Mrs S Blundell, (01704 27938)

FRECKLETON
Grd: Hodgson Mem. Grnd, Bush Lane, Freckleton, Preston (01772 679139)
Secretary: Mrs L O'Reilly (01772 634773).

FULWOOD AMATEURS
Ground: Ingol, Fulwood, Preston
Secretary: Mr L Waller (01772 864019).

KIRKHAM & WESHAM
Ground: Recreation Ground, Coronation Rd, Kirkham
Secretary: Mr Pinnell

LANCASHIRE CONSTABULARY
Grd: Police HQ, Saunders Lane, Hutton, nr Preston
Secretary: E.Thistlethwait (01253 700153).

LANSIL
Ground: Opp Nelson Works, Caton Rd, Lancaster
Secretary: Mrs K Price (01524 849834)

LEYLAND MOTORS ATHLETIC
Ground: Thurston Road, Leyland, Lancs (01772 422400)
Secretary: Mr K Pownall (01772 495217)

PADIHAM
Ground: Well Street, Padiham (01282 773742)
Secretary: Mr C Baker, (01282 452395)

SPRINGFIELDS
Grd: S.S.R.A. Spts Grnd, Dodney Drive, Lea, Preston (01772 726131)
Secretary: Mr T Threlfall (01772 718959).

THORNTON CLEVELEYS INTERNAT
Ground: Gamble Road, Thornton, Lancs
Secretary: D Stanborogh (01253 865814)

TURTON
Ground: Moorfield, Edgworth, Bolton
Secretary: E.Charnock (01204 852608)

WYRE VILLA
Ground: Stalmine Village, Nr Knott End. Lancs (01253 701468)
Secretary: Mr G Bradley (01253 810637).

DIVISION TWO CLUBS 1997-98

BARROW WANDERERS
Ground: Lesh Lane, off Abbey Rd, Barrow-in-F.
Secretary: M Sawyer (01229 871915).

BARNOLDSWICK UNITED
Ground: Victory Park, Barnoldswick.
Secretary: Mrs Lynn James (01282 815361)

BLACKPOOL ROVERS RESERVES
Ground: School Road, Marton, Blackpool
Secretary: P Kimberley (01253 349853)

BRITISH AEROSPACE CANBERRA
Ground: BAE Sports Club, Samlesbury (01772 464351)
Secretary: S P Halse (01254 772687).

BAC PRESTON
Ground: BAE Sports Club, Samlesbury (01772 464351)
Secretary: F Heaton, (01772 724751)

CARNFORTH RANGERS
Ground: Quarry Road, near town centre
Secretary: Mr K Webster (01524 735322).

CHORLEY MOTORS
Ground: Dawson Lane, Whittle-le-Woods, Chorley
Secretary: D Jolly (01257 270518).

GARSTANG
Ground: Riverside, off High St, Garstang
Secretary: S Freeman (01995 602514).

GLAXO
Ground: Nth Lonsdale Rd, Ulverston (01229 582261)
Secretary: M Simpson, (01229 870142)

HASLINGDEN ST MARY'S
Ground: Townsend Street, Haslingden (01706 221814)
Secretary: M Molloy (01706 229337)

HESKETH BANK
Ground: Hesketh Spts Field, Station Rd, Hesketh Bank
Secretary: D Hand (01772 813247).

LYTHAM St ANNES
Grd: Church Rd, Lytham St A. (01253 734137)
Secretary: Mr Perkins

MILNTHORPE CORINTHIANS
Ground: Strands Lane, Milnthorpe (01539 564640)
Secretary: C Davidson, (01595 62884)

NORCROSS & WARBRECK
Grd: Anchorsholme Lane, Thornton Cleveleys
Secretary: S Lee (01253 720363).

POULTON TOWN
Ground: Cottam Hall Grd, Blackpool Old Rd, Poulton
Secretary: D Sponder (01253 890284)

PRESTON WEST END
Ground: Close to Shawes Arms, London Rd, Preston
Secretary: S Robinson (01772 715907)

TEMPEST UNITED
Ground: Tempest Rd, Chow Moor Village, Lostock
Secretary: P Bennett (01942 810244).

VICKERS SPORTS CLUB
Ground: Hawcoat Lane, Barrow in Furness.
Secretary: Mrs B Knagg (01229 831785).

WHINNEY HILL
Ground: Clayton-le-Moors, Accrington
Secretary: D W Keely (01254 387938)

WIGAN COLLEGE
Ground: Christopher Park, Standish (01942 41140)
Secretary: D Thompson (01942 209425).

EAST LANCASHIRE FOOTBALL LEAGUE

President: F W Bullock

Chairman: M P Bibby

Secretary: J Constable, 66 Dukes Meadow, Ingol, Preston PR2 7AT (01772 727135)

DIVISION ONE
FINAL LEAGUE TABLE 1996-97

		P	W	D	L	F	A	Pts
1	Oswaldtwistle	22	17	1	4	79	22	52
2	Barnoldswick Utd	22	16	2	4	58	27	50
3	Whalley Rangers	22	12	3	7	64	54	39
4	Gargrave	22	12	2	8	44	31	38
5	Riminton	22	10	6	6	44	41	36
6	Worsthorne	22	10	4	8	50	41	34
7	Mill Hill St Peters	22	10	3	9	40	33	33
8	Crosshills	22	9	1	12	47	53	29
9	Trawden Celtic	22	7	7	8	35	41	28
10	Stacksteads S J	22	6	4	12	30	56	22
11	Settle United	22	3	4	15	29	56	13
12	Sabden	22	1	1	20	27	93	4

DIVISION TWO
FINAL LEAGUE TABLE 1996-97

		P	W	D	L	F	A	Pts
1	Hurst Green	26	22	2	2	87	22	68
2	Colne United	26	19	3	4	83	42	60
3	Langho	26	18	4	4	87	37	58
4	Earby Town	26	15	6	5	111	61	51
5	Rock Rovers	26	16	2	8	79	51	47
6	Whinney Hill	26	13	6	7	48	41	45
7	Barnoldswick P R	26	12	7	7	41	43	43
8	Colne	26	8	3	15	47	63	27
9	Oswaldtwistle Town	26	7	6	13	40	79	27
10	Nelson F O B	26	6	4	16	57	81	22
11	Read United	26	4	6	16	44	67	18
12	Chatburn	26	5	2	19	44	90	17
13	Pendle Forest	26	3	6	17	43	93	15
14	Ribchester Rovers	26	1	9	16	28	70	12

DIVISION ONE
RESULTS CHART 1996-97

		1	2	3	4	5	6	7	8	9	10	11	12
1	Barnoldswick United	X	2-1	3-2	5-2	0-1	2-2	4-2	4-1	4-1	2-1	1-2	1-0
2	Crosshills	0-6	X	3-1	0-2	0-1	3-2	1-4	2-3	3-2	4-0	5-2	3-1
3	Gargrave	3-0	1-0	X	1-3	1-1	1-2	3-5	2-1	2-1	0-0	1-0	2-0
4	Mill Hill St Peters	0-1	2-2	1-0	X	2-3	3-0	3-0	3-0	0-1	4-0	4-4	3-5
5	Oswaldtwistle	3-1	4-0	2-0	4-1	X	0-2	6-1	16-0	7-1	3-0	3-1	3-1
6	Rimington	2-4	4-2	2-6	0-0	1-0	X	5-2	3-2	4-1	2-3	2-2	0-0
7	Whalley Rangers	0-3	5-2	1-3	2-4	3-4	4-1	X	4-2	2-2	2-2	2-2	3-1
8	Sabden	0-2	2-6	2-6	0-1	1-7	1-2	1-4	X	2-4	0-3	4-5	1-3
9	Settle United	0-4	1-4	0-4	0-1	0-2	2-3	1-2	6-1	X	1-1	0-1	0-0
10	Stacksteads St J	0-4	2-0	1-4	1-3	0-6	0-0	2-7	4-1	4-3	X	5-2	1-3
11	Trawden Celtic	1-2	1-2	3-0	2-1	1-0	1-1	1-3	1-1	1-1	1-0	X	0-0
12	Worsthorne	3-3	5-4	0-1	2-0	5-3	2-4	4-6	4-1	4-1	4-0	3-1	X

DIVISION ONE
CLUB DIRECTORY 1997-98

BARNOLDSWICK UNITED

Secretary: Mrs L.James, 37 Long Inn Lane, Barnoldswick, Lancs BB8 6BJ (01282 815361).
Ground: West Close, Victory Park, Barnoldswick.
Colours: Blue & black/black/black **Change Colours:** Blue & yellow/blue/blue & yellow

COLNE UNITED

Secretary: Mr S Bannister, 26 Higgin St, Colne, Lancs.BB8 9RS (01282 711796)
Ground: Sough Park, Kelbrook, Earby, Colne.
Colours: Black and white/black/black **Change colours:** All claret

CROSSHILLS

Secretary: Mr P Smith, 72 North Parade, Skipton, N Yorks BD23 3SR (01756 799338)
Ground: Sutton Fields, Sutton-in-Craven, Keighley, West Yorkshire.
Colours: Red/black/red **Change colours:** All blue

GARGRAVE

Secretary: Mr P Watson, Saw Mill Cottage, Marton Road, Gargrave, Skipton N Yorks BD23 3NN (01756 749351)
Ground: Skipton Road, Gargrave
Colours: Claret & blue **Change Colours:** Blue & white

HURST GREEN

Secretary: Mr N Brown, 11 Chatburn Rd, Longridge, Preston, Lancs PR3 3FN (01772 785416)
Ground: off Smithy Row, Hurst Green
Colours: Black & white/black/black **Change colours:** Yellow & green/green/yellow

MILL HILL St PETERS

Secretary: Mr D Willacy, 15 Springfield Ave, Feniscowles, Blackburn, Lancs (01254 208347)
Ground: Mill Hill St Peters, Queen Victoria St, Mill Hill, Blackburn.
Colours: Blue & gold/black/black **Change colours:** Green & white

OSWALDTWISTLE TOWN

Ground: Heys Playing Field, Heron Way, Oswaldtwistle.
Secretary: Mrs M.Riley, 11A Polar Close, Oswaldtwistle, Lancs. BB5 3AY (01254 382830)
Colours: All green & yellow **Change colours:** All blue & black

RIMINGTON

Secretary: Mr L Whittaker, 2 Dorset Drive, Clitheroe, Lancs BB7 2BQ (01200 29112).
Ground: Coulthurst Jubilee Field, Back Lane, Rimington (behind Black Bull).
Colours: Tangerine/black/tangerine **Change colours:** Blue/red

SETTLE UNITED

Secretary: Mr J Dinsdale, 3 Goldielands Settle N Yorks (01729 823738)
Ground: Bridge End Ground, Goggleswick, Settle.
Colours: Yellow & black/black/black **Change Colours:** Black & white

STACKSTEAD ST JOSEPH'S

Secretary: Mr R Cronshaw, 16 Heathbourne Rd, Stacksteads, Bacup, Lancs (01706 873638)
Ground: Stacksteads Recreation Ground.
Colours: All Blue **Change Colours:** Yellow/black/black

TRAWDEN CELTIC

Secretary: M Timberlake, 191 Cotton Tree Lane, Colne, Lancs BB8 7BN (01282 868143)
Ground: Trawden Rec Ground, Rock Lane, Trawden
Colours: Black & white/black/black & white **Change colours:** Red & blue/blue/red

WHALLEY RANGERS

Secretary: Mrs J Charlesworth, 39 Thwaites Rd, West End, Oswaldtwistle BB5 4QT (01254 393386).
Ground: Queen Elizabeth Playing Field, Mitton Rd, Whalley.
Colours: Red & black/black/black **Change colours:** White & red/white/red

WORSTHORNE

Secretary: Mr J Carrington, 18 Rossendale Ave, Burnley, Lancs. BB11 5HF (01282 428273)
Ground: Bank Hall, Colne Rd, Burnley
Colours: Yellow & green/green/yellow **Change colours:** Claret & blue/claret/claret

NORTH WESTERN FOOTBALL LEAGUES

Final League Tables 1996-97

FRANK ARMITT LIVERPOOL COMBINATION

Division One

		P	W	D	L	F	A	Pts
1	Waterloo Dock	28	19	6	3	75	32	63
2	Stockbridge	28	17	4	7	60	34	55
3	St Dominics	28	17	3	8	75	47	54
4	Crawfords U B	28	15	8	5	76	37	53*
5	Ford Motors	28	15	4	9	64	54	49
6	Royal Seaforth	28	13	5	10	63	50	44
7	Electric Supply	28	11	8	9	44	38	41
8	Eldonians	28	11	7	10	55	54	40
9	Mossley Hill	28	11	4	13	62	61	37
10	Selwyn	28	10	6	12	47	50	36*
11	South Liverpool	28	7	11	10	43	48	32
12	York C T	28	8	5	15	50	67	29
13	GPT Plessey	28	8	4	16	50	70	25
14	Ayone	28	3	8	17	44	93	17
15	Lucas Sports	28	2	3	23	26	99	9

* Crawford v Selwyn, match awarded to Crawford 1-0

GEORGE MAHON CUP FINAL (1909-1997)

Sponsored by PETER COYNE LIMITED

Crawfords v Waterloo Dock 1-2

Division Two

		P	W	D	L	F	A	Pts
1	Crystal Villa	20	14	2	4	49	30	44
2	Bootle Res	20	13	3	4	50	22	42
3	B R N E S C	20	13	3	4	49	26	42
4	Cheshire Lines	20	10	5	5	40	23	35
5	Speke	20	10	3	7	58	39	33
6	Halewood Town	20	8	1	11	40	41	25
7	Avon Athletic	20	7	2	11	30	60	23
8	Maghull Res	20	6	4	10	28	46	22
9	Rainhill Town	20	6	2	12	48	44	20
10	Elec Supply Res	20	4	3	13	22	54	15
11	Mossley Hill Res	20	4	2	14	32	61	14
12	Beesix	Expelled - Record expunged						

ALTRINCHAM & DISTRICT SATURDAY LEAGUE (Cheshire FA)

Premier Division

		P	W	D	L	Pts
1	Partington Village	20	18	0	2	54
2	Broadheath Central	20	15	1	4	46
3	Timperley Wndrs	20	12	2	6	38
4	Wellgreen	20	12	1	7	37
5	Pelican Rovers	20	10	2	8	32
6	Atlantic	20	7	3	10	24
7	Knutsford	20	6	5	9	21
8	Old York Victoria	20	6	3	11	21
9	The Bowler	20	5	3	12	18
10	Timperley	20	4	2	14	14
11	Radbroke Hall	20	3	2	15	11

ALTRINCHAM & DISTRICT SUNDAY LEAGUE

Crossings Car Sales Premier Division

		P	W	D	L	Pts
1	Southern	20	14	4	2	46
2	Packet House	20	12	6	2	47
3	Stretford Trds & Lab	20	11	4	5	37
4	Bowdon Vale	20	9	8	3	35
5	Jackson's Boat	20	8	7	5	31
6	Brooklands Tap	20	8	6	6	27*
7	King William	20	6	4	10	22
8	Station (Flixton)	20	5	4	11	19
9	Stamford Lads	20	6	0	14	18
10	Unicorn Town	20	5	1	14	16
11	Lisbon	20	2	4	14	10

* Three points deducted

PERKINS SHROPSHIRE COUNTY LEAGUE

Premier Division

		P	W	D	L	F	A	Pts
1	Star Aluminium	24	18	2	4	66	23	56
2	Newport Town	24	16	3	5	48	24	51
3	Meole Brace	24	13	7	4	69	37	46
4	Hanwood Utd	24	13	5	6	51	37	44
5	Lt Drayton Rgrs	24	13	3	8	75	45	42
6	St Martins	24	11	3	10	42	43	36
7	Wellington Amt	24	8	6	10	44	49	30
8	Belle Vue OB	24	7	6	11	45	52	27
9	Hadley Keys	24	8	2	14	38	53	26
10	Wem Town	24	6	5	13	37	54	23
11	Belvidere	24	5	6	13	35	63	21
12	Oakengates Tn	24	5	4	15	29	57	19
13	Snailbeach W S	24	5	4	15	35	77	19

Division One

		P	W	D	L	F	A	Pts
1	Broseley	24	19	2	3	72	24	59
2	Shawbury Utd	24	18	3	3	95	30	57
3	Morda Utd Res	24	16	3	5	69	33	51
4	Donnington P R	24	14	3	7	48	50	45
5	Star Alum Res	24	12	6	6	55	41	42
6	Telford Juniors	24	10	8	6	55	41	38
7	Church Stretton	24	11	3	10	44	34	36
8	Whitchurch Utd	24	9	3	12	52	57	30
9	Brown Clee	24	5	4	15	32	56	19
10	Ellesmere Rgrs	24	5	4	15	40	80	19
11	Craven Arms	24	4	5	15	39	69	17
12	Maxell	24	5	1	18	40	82	16
13	Meole Brace Rs	24	5	1	18	38	80	16

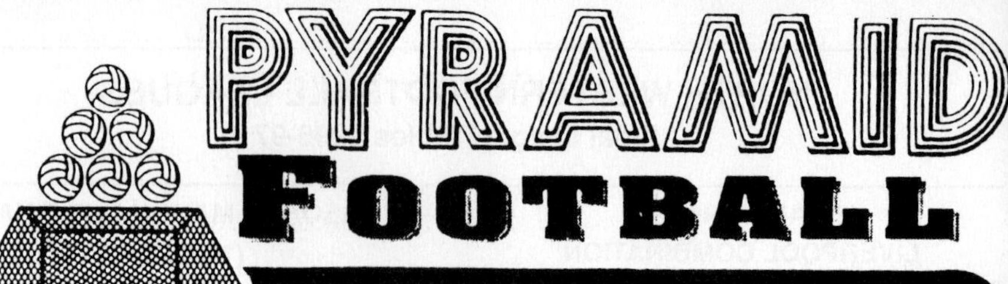
PYRAMID
FOOTBALL

NORTHERN COUNTIES (EAST) LEAGUE

FEEDER TO:
NORTHERN PREMIER LEAGUE

FOUNDED: 1982
(Amalgamation of Yorkshire League (founded 1920) and the Midland League (founded 1889))
President: H F Catt
Chairman: C Morris
Hon. Secretary: B Wood, 6 Restmore Ave., Guiseley, Leeds LS20 9DG (01943) 874558)

SECRETARY'S REPORT

My review of the 1996/97 Season opens with a look at the playing records of our clubs outlining the successes and failures throughout that time.

The promotion/demotion system between the NCE and the Unibond League at the end of the 95/96 season worked to the advantage of Stocksbridge PS who moved ahead in the Pyramid but we received no demoted club though Harrogate Town were in the danger zone for some time until changes in the Unibond set-up meant they won a reprieve. Incidentally, both our former clubs, Lincoln United and the 'Steelmen', completed successful seasons in the Unibond League.

Chief talking point in our Prem. Div. was whether Hatfield Main could continue their hold on the championship but managerial changes there soon indicated they would not. Vase holders, Brigg Town, with Belper Town took up the early running in the Division with Denaby United and Hallam pressing both the two leading clubs who leapfrogged each other to take top spot until the beginning of March. Glasshoughton Welfare were also enjoying one of their best seasons and North Ferriby United were on the edge of the leading pack though with games to make up because of their FA Vase successes.

Once Denaby United had reached first position they were in no mood to be pushed out and their final record of just three League defeats in the season was a measure of the quality of their football which saw them take the Premier Division title and their first major honour in 25 years. Their last match at home to Brigg Town was a 3-3 draw and the Championship Trophy was presented by League Chairman, Cliff Morris, to Manager David Lloyd's victorious team. Although Brigg themselves had been involved in the fight for Runners-up position with North Ferriby United and Belper Town, the crucial fixture, in fact, was at Ferriby's ground on Tuesday 22 April when Belper scored a priceless 2-1 away win which meant they gained 2nd place ahead of Brigg Town and North Ferriby.

Belper Town attack the Arnold goal in the top-of-the-table clash at the King George V ground. Match won by Arnold 2-1.
Photo MARTIN WRAY

A disappointment for the Champions was that their facilities failed to reach the standard required for promotion but Belper Town as Runners-up have gained promotion to the Unibond League and we wish them well. At the bottom of the Premier Division, Sheffield just escaped occupying a relegation position for a second season with a last match 4-3 victory at home to North Ferriby. Indeed, it proved to be their final game at the Owlerton Stadium where conditions have been far from ideal and their landlords obviously wished them to depart. For next season, 'Club' will return to the Don Valley Stadium. Ashfield United were the club who dropped to a relegation next-to-bottom position but they will not continue in the League as they have decided to cease playing at their Kirkby-in-Ashfield ground following a spate of vandalism attacks and we are very sorry at this turn of events. Bottom club Liversedge might have expected to be demoted to Div. 1 but this will not now happen due to the numbers required in the Division.

With Belper Town's promotion upwards to the Unibond League, a problem has arisen concerning the demoted club to the NCE and, although the Northern Joint Liaison Committee have decided that the agreed transfer rule should operate, the club involved — Curzon Ashton — are appealing to the Football Association at the date this report is written, and so we do not know the final outcome. If they join us the Prem. Div. will have 20 clubs — if not, it will operate with 19.

Promoted clubs from the Central Midlands League have always proved formidable opposition and newcomers, Glapwell, have certainly maintained that standard finishing in a very creditable 5th position. Eccleshill United, Garforth Town and Harrogate Railway were the three clubs fighting for honours in the latter stages of the Div. 1 campaign (Hall Road Rangers challenge had faded) with the Bradford and Leeds Clubs eventually confirming their superiority. Town had to win their final game at home to Louth United to push Eccleshill to a nail-biting finish but could gain only a 1-1 draw which meant that United's last home game against Glapwell (they won 3-0) crowned a very successful season and promotion to the Prem. Div. provided that satisfactory ground improvements are carried out very shortly. Garforth will not be promoted as work on their new ground complex has yet to begin. Basement clubs Brodsworth MW and Blidworth Welfare will be seeking re-election to the Division. Althougth not wishing to 'rub salt' into Brodsworth's wounds, I have to mention that this is the 4th successive season that the Miners must seek re-selection.

Another CML club is to join the Division next season. Staveley MW, former NCE members but now with a different and well-appointed ground, and we shall welcome them to our ranks.

Two new teams joined the Reserve Division — Selby Town Res and North Ferriby Utd Res — with the latter team proving the more successful. Points deducted from Middlesbrough in the Premer League have made an important difference to that club's final position and the same has happened to Farsley Celtic Res. where last season's champions would have taken the title again but for a 2pts deduction. They had to settle for second place behind the new champions, Ossett Albion Res. who have never won the title before in the NCE. North Ferriby Res., like their first team, just failed to gain honours in the Division. Both Hall Road Res. and Pontefract Colls. Res. are leaving the Division with Worsbrough Bridge MW Res being new applicants.

Hucknall Town have been the League's most successful Cup side in domestic competitions adding to their President's Cup 3-2 aggregate victory over Belper Town with a 3-1 win at Rotherham United against Pontefract Colls. in the League Cup Final — Matt Edwards scoring a hat-trick. The Wilkinson Sword Trophy was lifted by Garforth Town at the expense of Eccleshill United (on the away goals rule after a 1-1 aggregate) and Emley Res beat Thackley Res. 3-2 in the Res. Div. Final at Ossett Albion.

At the end of last season we were thrilled by the 3-0 victory of Brigg Town against Clitheroe in the FA Carlsberg Vase Final and it was a great advert for NCE football that North Ferriby United achieved a similar Wembley visit this year though not quite as successfully. Perhaps the omens were just a little against Ferriby with a replica of Captain Cook's sailing ship 'Endeavour' arriving at Whitby and taking the local headlines the very weekend the town team took its trip to the Twin Towers. It was United's 10th match in the competition in what has been an historic march to Wembley for our Premier Div. side.

There was a crowd of 11,098 at the grand old stadium with Ferriby's green and white favours well in evidence in the sunshine and heavy showers and manager, Tim Hotte, hadn some experienced players included in his side some of whom had already tasted the Wembley flavour. A strong point of Ferriby's play in the run-up to the Final had been the lack of goals conceded — just 4 in the 10 matches — 'keeper Paul Sharp being a dominant figure in that defence. Ironically, then they were to give away three goals in the Final which was a little surprising and, although there was plenty of attractive approach play by the United forwards, that elusive half chance rarely fell the Humbersider's way to give them a possibility of pulling back the 1-0 lead taken by Whitby Town at half-time.

That first strike by Whitby's David Logan was followed soon afterwards by a 'goal' by Andy Flounders but unfortunately he had strayed offside following a Kenny Harrison cross. United had to press in the second period but could not find a breakthrough and further goals were added by Town's Williams and Toman in the 61st and 75th minutes. So, although there was to be no happy ending for the East Riding team, they can be very proud of their wonderful achievement. It was a great cup run and the club were a credit to their supporters and the League with an added bonus of £6850 Carlsberg sponsorship cash available for the club's development. Very well done!

In the FA Cup we have had little success in recent years and it was North Ferriby United who were the team which reached the farthest point — the 3rd Qualifying Round. Incidentally, Ferriby played a total of 22 Cup games in various cup competitions last season. In County Competitions, Arnold Town and North Ferriby won the Notts and East Riding Senior Cups respectively whilst Armthorpe Welfare (West Riding County Cup) and Louth United (Lincs Senior 'A' Cup) were Runners-up. Finally, congratulations to Glapwell who won the Evans Halshaw Floodlit Cup.

As mentioned last year, entry to FA competitions is dependent on a satisfactory floodlighting system and it could be that some of our clubs will not be able to take part next season in those national cups. It is hoped that the recent successes of our teams in the Vase will spur any 'dimly lit' clubs to lighting improvements.

FINAL LEAGUE TABLES 1996/97

DIVISION PREMIER	P	W	D	L	F	A	Pts
Denaby United	38	25	10	3	82	33	85
Belper Town	38	24	7	7	78	41	79
Brigg Town	38	23	8	7	80	43	77
North Ferriby United	38	21	9	8	86	36	72
Ossett Albion	38	21	8	9	73	36	71
Hucknall Town	38	19	8	11	84	48	65
Hallam	38	17	7	14	56	69	58
Ossett Town	38	14	11	13	52	53	53
Arnold Town	38	12	15	11	48	43	51
Glasshoughton Welfare	38	13	12	13	58	58	51
Selby Town	38	14	9	15	63	69	51
Armthorpe Welfare	38	12	9	17	42	48	45
Thackley	38	12	9	17	43	58	45
Maltby Main	38	12	8	18	58	81	44
Pickering Town	38	11	8	19	45	72	41
Pontefract Collieries	38	8	11	19	44	73	35
Hatfield Main	38	8	10	20	40	75	34
Sheffield	38	7	11	20	50	70	32
Ashfield United	38	7	11	20	51	80	32
Liversedge	38	5	9	24	40	87	24

DIVISION ONE	P	W	D	L	F	A	Pts
Eccleshill United	28	21	4	3	81	30	67
Garforth Town	28	20	4	4	57	22	64
Harrogate Rail Ath	28	15	7	6	54	32	52
Yorkshire Amateur	28	15	4	9	52	52	49
Glapwell	28	14	4	10	52	41	46
Borrowash Victoria	28	12	6	10	47	39	42
Hall Road Rangers	28	12	5	11	48	46	41
Louth United	28	9	9	10	47	37	36
Rossington Main	28	10	6	12	44	46	36
Worsbrough Bridge MW	28	9	8	11	41	49	35
Parkgate	28	8	7	13	38	46	31
Winterton Rangers	28	7	9	12	39	51	30
Tadcaster Albion	28	4	10	14	20	51	22
Brodsworth MW	28	4	5	19	22	58	17
Blidworth Welfare	28	4	4	20	31	73	16

LEADING GOAL SCORERS – SEASON 1996/97

PREMIER DIVISION

A Ward	Brigg Town	30
P D Tomlinson	Hucknall Town	27
D A Morris	Ossett Albion	26
G J Cygan	Pontefract Collieries	24
P Collier	Selby Town	22
M Edwards	Hucknall Town	22
S Lowe	Ashfield United/Sheffield	19
D B France	North Ferriby United	17
A J Flounders	North Ferriby United	16
P A Gilbertson	Ossett Albion	14
S Roach	Brigg Town	14
C A Hodgson	Pontefract Collieries	13
J Horne	North Ferriby United	13

DIVISION ONE

R Beardshaw	Yorkshire Amateur	20
A Wilkinson	Eccleshill United	19
C Winfarrah	Louth United	19
S P Bambrook	Garforth Town	17
J Dickinson	Rossington Main	17
W Gamble	Glapwell	16
L J Collingwood	Hall Road Rangers	15
L Corbally	Eccleshill United	15
D Rushby	Eccleshill United	15
M J Taplin	Borrowash Victoria	15
K Farley	Garforth Town	14
G Page	Glapwell	14
R Blake	Louth United	12
D Spence	Harrogate Railway	12
G Ross	Winterton Rangers	11

RESERVE DIVISION

B L Duffy	Emley Res	23
D A Wilson	North Ferriby United Res	23
C Darvill	Harrogate Town Res	17
L Lambert	North Ferriby United Res	17
D I Botham	North Ferriby United Res	16
M P Dolan	Eccleshill United Res	15
P Davies	Ossett Albion Res	14
M Townend	Ossett Albion Res	14
I Ogilvie	Ossett Town Res	13
S G Polli	Ossett Town Res	13
R Trapps	Liversedge Res	12
M Wilkinson	Liversedge Res	12
C Wilcock	Ossett Albion Res	11

PREMIER DIVISION RESULTS CHART 1996–97

HOME TEAM	1	2	3	4	5	6	7	8	9	10	11	12	13	14	15	16	17	18	19	20
Armthorpe Welf	*	1-2	2-1	1-1	0-1	3-0	0-0	1-2	1-3	0-2	1-0	4-1	1-1	1-1	1-0	0-1	3-1	1-2	4-0	2-1
Arnold Town	1-0	*	1-1	2-1	0-1	0-2	2-1	1-2	3-1	0-0	4-1	1-0	1-1	1-2	1-0	1-1	0-0	2-2	0-1	0-1
Ashfield United	2-2	1-1	*	0-1	0-2	0-2	3-0	0-2	0-0	2-3	1-1	3-2	1-8	2-1	2-2	0-2	5-0	3-3	1-4	2-1
Belper Town	1-0	4-2	2-0	*	1-5	0-0	3-2	3-0	6-1	2-1	2-0	1-1	1-1	2-1	2-2	3-0	2-0	3-2	1-1	5-1
Brigg Town	1-0	1-1	6-2	4-2	*	3-1	4-1	7-0	3-0	1-0	3-2	2-3	0-4	1-1	1-2	3-1	2-4	1-4	2-0	3-0
Denaby United	1-0	2-1	3-1	1-0	3-3	*	3-1	5-0	2-1	1-1	4-0	7-0	3-1	0-0	0-0	1-1	1-1	2-1	1-0	1-1
Glasshoughton W	1-1	0-1	3-1	0-1	1-1	1-2	*	4-1	0-0	2-1	2-2	3-3	1-0	1-0	1-1	0-0	1-4	1-2	5-1	5-2
Hallam	0-1	0-2	2-2	1-2	1-0	1-2	1-1	*	3-0	1-2	1-0	3-2	0-3	1-4	1-0	2-1	1-1	2-1	4-2	2-1
Hatfield Main	2-0	3-3	1-5	0-1	0-3	0-1	0-3	2-3	*	1-3	1-0	0-1	0-4	2-1	0-2	0-2	1-1	1-1	2-1	1-0
Hucknall Town	3-1	2-0	4-1	5-1	0-2	1-2	2-3	1-1	1-4	*	4-0	0-0	1-5	1-1	0-1	1-1	7-0	6-0	3-0	2-1
Liversedge	3-0	0-0	2-2	1-4	0-1	0-4	1-2	2-2	3-0	1-4	*	0-2	2-2	1-3	1-1	4-2	1-0	3-3	1-2	1-1
Maltby MW	0-2	3-3	2-0	1-4	2-2	1-3	3-3	1-2	5-2	2-2	3-2	*	1-2	0-1	1-0	5-1	2-1	2-6	1-0	1-2
North Ferriby United	3-0	1-1	0-0	1-2	1-1	3-0	4-0	2-1	0-0	2-0	1-0	5-1	*	3-2	3-0	3-0	3-0	0-3	5-1	4-1
Ossett Albion	2-0	1-1	2-0	0-0	2-1	1-4	2-0	5-1	0-0	3-2	5-1	3-0	1-0	*	6-1	1-2	2-1	5-0	2-1	3-0
Ossett Town	5-0	2-3	4--0	1-0	2-2	1-5	0-2	2-2	1-0	1-4	3-2	3-1	1-1	2-1	*	2-2	1-0	1-2	2-1	0-1
Pickering Town	0-3	0-4	2-1	1-7	0-1	0-4	2-2	1-3	4-2	1-3	2-0	4-0	1-2	0-2	0-1	*	1-1	1-0	1-3	0-1
Pontefract Colls	0-0	2-1	2-1	0-2	0-2	0-0	0-0	0-2	3-3	2-5	7-0	1-2	2-1	1-3	1-3	2-3	*	2-0	2-2	1-1
Selby Town	1-3	0-0	3-2	1-0	1-2	1-1	3-0	1-1	2-2	1-3	3-0	2-3	0-3	1-3	2-1	3-2	0-1	*	2-0	1-1
Sheffield	1-1	1-1	1-1	1-4	0-1	1-2	0-3	2-3	2-2	1-1	5-0	0-0	4-3	0-0	1-1	1-2	6-0	1-2	*	1-3
Thackley	1-1	1-0	1-2	0-1	1-1	3-6	1-2	2-1	1-2	0-3	0-2	1-0	2-0	1-0	0-0	0-0	3-0	4-1	1-1	*

DIVISION ONE RESULTS CHART 1996–97

HOME TEAM	1	2	3	4	5	6	7	8	9	10	11	12	13	14	15
Blidworth Welf	*	3-1	0-1	2-3	0-0	1-6	1-2	0-5	1-2	1-4	0-2	0-1	0-3	6-3	0-1
Borrowash Vict	2-2	8	2-0	2-0	3-0	1-0	1-2	1-2	1-0	1-1	3-1	1-2	3-1	1-0	5-3
Brodsworth MW	2-0	0-3	*	3-4	0-3	0-1	1-1	2-5	1-1	0-0	1-2	1-0	1-4	1-2	0-1
Eccleshill United	1-0	3-0	4-0	*	3-1	3-0	0-0	4-1	1-4	2-1	4-1	6-0	6-1	3-2	3-0
Garforth Town	3-0	1-0-	2-0	2-2	*	1-0	1-0	3-2	1-1	2-1	3-0	1-0	4-0	3-0	2-1
Glapwell	5-0	1-0	5-1	1-5	1-3	*	3-2	0-1	2-1	1-0	0-0	1-1	5-1	2-1	1-3
Hall Road Rgrs	5-0	1-1	3-0	1-3	0-3	2-2	*	0-1	2-1	2-3	3-0	2-1	0-1	4-2	2-3
Harrogate Rlwy	2-1	1-1	1-0	1-2	0-2	4-0	2-2	*	1-4	2-0	5-0	-0-	3-0	2-1	4-1
Louth United	8-1	2-2	0-2	4-1	0-3	0-1	1-2	0-1	*	2-0	3-3	1-0	2-2	1-1	4-0
Parkgate	3-2	2-1	4-0	0-3	2-0	1-4	2-3	2-3	1-1	*	1-0	2-1	1-3	0-2	2-2
Rossington Main	1-1	3-1	4-1	2-3	0-2	1-2	6-1	2-2	1-2	3-1	*	0-1	3-0	1-0	4-1
Tadcaster Albion	1-4	1-1	0-0	0-7	2-2	1-1	1-2	1-1	2-0	1-1	1-1	*	0-3	0-1	1-2
Winterton Rgrs	3-1	1-3	1-1	0-0	0-1	4-0	2-4	0-0	1-1	2-2	0-2	1-1	*	0-1	2-2
Worsbrough Bdge	2-3	4-3	2-1	1-1	1-6	1-6	3-0	2-2	1-1	0-0	0-0	2-0	1-1	*	4-0
Yorks Amat	1-1	2-3	3-2	0-4	3-2	2-1	1-0	1-0	2-0	2-1	4-1	7-0	3-2	1-1	*

LEAGUE CUP 1996/97

ROUND ONE

Garforth Town	v	Winterton Rangers	3-1	Tadcaster Albion	v	Worsbrough Bridge MW	2-5
Parkgate	v	Brodsworth MW	0-3				

ROUND TWO

Ashfield United	v	Garforth Town	4-1	Hucknall Town	v	Arnold Town	3-0
Belper Town	v	Glasshoughton Welfare	2-3	Louth United	v	Eccleshill United	4-1
Blidworth Welfare	v	Hatfield Main	2-1	Pontefract Colls	v	Maltby Main	3-2
Brigg Town	v	Liversedge	4-1	Rossington Main	v	Borrowash Victoria	3-4
Brodsworth MW	v	Ossett Town	0-4	Sheffield	v	Armthorpe Welfare	0-2
Denaby United	v	Hallam	1-2	Thackley	v	North Ferriby United	0-2
Glapwell	v	Pickering Town	1-2	Worsbrough Bridge	v	Harrogate Railway	2-3
Hall Road Rangers	v	Selby Town	2-0	Yorkshire Amat	v	Ossett Albion	1-2

ROUND THREE

Armthorpe Welfare	v	Ossett Town	0-3	Hallam	v	Borrowash Victoria	5-0
Ashfield United	v	Glasshoughton Welfare	0-1	North Ferriby United	v	Louth United	1-3
Blidworth Welfare	v	Brigg Town	1-1, 4-5	Ossett Albion	v	Hucknall Town	0-2
Hall Road Rangers	v	Pickering Town	1-1, 0-2	Pontefract Collieries	v	Harrowgate Railway	3-3, 3-1

ROUND FOUR

Brigg Town	v	Glasshoughton Welfare	2-0	Pickering Town	v	Ossett Town	2-4
Louth United	v	Hucknall Town	2-2, 2-2	Pontefract Collieries	v	Hallam	3-2

(Hucknall won 4-3 on penalties)

SEMI-FINALS

Hucknall Town	v	Brigg Town	3-1	Pontefract Collieries	v	Ossett Town	2-1

FINAL

Hucknall Town	v	Pontefract Collieries	3-1

PRESIDENT'S CUP 1996/97

SEMI-FINALS

Belper Town	v	Pontefract Collieries	3-2	Hucknall Town	v	Brigg Town	1-0

FINAL

Belper Town	v	Hucknall Town (1st leg)	1-0	Hucknall Town	B	Belper Town (2nd leg)	3-1

(Hucknall Town won 3-2 on aggregate)

WILKINSON SWORD TROPHY 1996/97

SEMI-FINALS

Glapwell	v	Eccleshill United	2-4	Yorkshire Amateur	v	Garforth Town	1-4

FINAL

Garforth Town	v	Eccleshill United (1st leg)	0-0	Eccleshill United	v	Garforth Town (2nd leg)	1-1

(Garforth Town won on away goals)

RESERVE DIVISION CUP 1996/97

SEMI-FINALS

Ossett Albion Res	v	Emley Res	1-3	Selby Town Res	v	Thackley Res	0-2

FINAL

Emley Res	v	Thackley Res	3-2

ARMTHORPE WELFARE

Chairman: Alan Bell, Tel: 01302 832578 (H) **Vice Chairman:** James Houston
Secretary: Maureen Cottam, The Orchards, Whiphill Lane, Armthorpe, Doncaster DN3 3JP. Tel: 01302 832514 (H)
Manager: Carl Leighton **Asst Manager:** John McKeown **Coach:** Steve Taylor.
Physio: Joey Johnson **Comm. Manager:** Peter Camm **Press Officer:** Sharon Morgan.
Ground: Welfare Ground, Church Str, Armthorpe, Doncaster DN3 3AG (01302 831247)
Directions: M18 junc 4, A630, left at r'bout then proceed to next r'bout and turn right. Ground 400yds on left behind Plough Inn. Two and a half miles from Doncaster (BR). Buses A2, A3 & 181 pass ground.
Seats: 200 **Cover:** 400 **Capacity:** 2,500 **Floodlights:** Yes **Nickname:** Wellie **Founded:** 1926
Clubhouse: No. Refreshments on ground. Wheatsheaf Hotel used after matches. **Club Shop:** No
Colours: White/navy/white **Change colours:** Navy/white/navy **Club Sponsors:** Houston Transport
Programme: 24 pages **Editor:** John Morgan, 01302 834475 (H) **Midweek matches:** Tuesday
Previous League: Doncaster Senior **Record Att.:** 2,000 v Doncaster R., Charity match 85-86
Club record scorer: Martin Johnson **Club record appearances:** Gary Leighton.
Honours: Northern Co's East Lg R-up 87-88 (Lg Cup R-up 91-92, Div 1 R-up 83-84, East Central Div 1 84-85); Doncaster & Dist. Lg 82-83 (Div 1 81-82, Div 2 79-80, Div 3 78-79; Lg Cup 79-80 80-81 81-82 82-83; Challenge Cup 82-83); West Riding Chall. Cup 81-82 82-83; Goole & Thorne Dist. Cup 82-83

ARNOLD TOWN

President: Alan Croome **Chairman:** David Law **Vice-Chairman:** Roy Francis **General Manager:** Ray O'Brien
Secretary: Steve Shout, 11 Newholme Drive, Wilford, Nottm NG11 7FR (0115 981 5390).
Team Manager: Iain McCulloch **Asst Manager:** Bill Brindley **Physio:** John Scott
Ground: King George V Recreation Ground, Gedling Rd, Arnold, Notts (0115 926 3660).
Directions: From M1 jct 26, take A610 to B6004 (Stockhill Lane) 3 miles to A60, right at A60, immediate left (St Albans Rd), thru lights by Sainsburys, left at rear of Sainsburys, ground on right adjacent to market. From A1(M)/A614/A60 to lights (White Hart on right), 1st left thru lights, St Albans Rd then as above. Four miles from Nottingham Midland BR station. Buses 53, 55, 59 pass ground, buses 25, 40, 51 58, 90, 91 stop within 200yds.
Capacity: 3,400 **Seats:** 150 **Cover:** 950 **Floodlights:** Yes **Nickname:** Eagles **Founded:** 1989
Clubhouse: Licensed bar open matchdays & training night. Also tea-bar on matchdays. **Club Shop:** Yes
Programme: 44 pages, 60p **Editor:** Melvyn Draycott (0115 944 2654) **Sponsors:** Mapperley Sports
Colours: Yellow (blue trim)/blue/yellow **Change Colours:** All white (blue trim) **Midweek matches:** Tuesday
Reserves' Lge: Midland Reg. All. **Record Attendance:** 3,390, Arnold FC v Bristol R., FA Cup 1st Rd, 9/12/67.
Previous Leagues: Central Midlands 89-93. *Arnold FC: Bulwell & Dist, Nott Spartan, Notts Comb (pre 55), Central Alliance 55-63/ Midland 63-82/ Northern Co's East 82-86/ Central Mids 86-89. Kingswell: Notts Youth/ Notts Amateur/ Notts Spartan/ East Midlands Regional (pre'76)/Midland 76-82/ Northern Co's East 82-86/ Central Midlands 86-89.*
Player progressing to Football League: Devon White (Lincoln C 85), Chris Freestone (Middlesbrough 94)
96-97 Captain: Bryn Gunn **Top Scorer:** Steve Smith 12 **96-97 P.o.Y.: Players & Supporters:** Bryn Gunn
Club Record - Scorer: Peter Fletcher 100 **Appearances:** Neil Waters 269 **Managers:** Adrian Thorpe
Honours (as Arnold FC + Arnold Town FC): Central Mids Lg 92-93 (R-up 88-89, Lg Cup 87-88 (R-up 90-91), F/lit Cup 89-90); Northern Co's East Lg 85-86 (R-up 83-84,94-95, Div 1 94-95); Presidents Cup 94-95; Notts Snr Cup 60-61 64-65 65-66 68-69 70-71 92-93 95-96 96-97,(R-up 69-70 74-75 75-76 76-77 84-85); FA Cup 1st Rd replay 77-78; Central All 62-63; FA Tphy 2nd Rd replay 71-72; Midland Co's Lg R-up 70-71 75-76, Lg Cup 74-75 (R-up 68-69 70-71 80-81).

BRIGG TOWN

President: B Robins **Chairman:** David Crowder, Tel: 01724 864742 (H)
Secretary: Robert B Taylor, 'Highfield House', Barton Rd, Wrawby, Brigg, N Lincs DN20 8SH. Tel: 01652 652284 (H).
Match Sec: John Martin. Tel: 01652 654526 (H) **Manager:** Ralph Clayton **Coach:** John Kaye
Ground: The Hawthorns, Hawthorn Avenue, Brigg (01652 652767).
Directions: From M180 Junc 4 Scunthorpe East, A18 through Brigg leaving on Wrawby Rd, left into East Parade/Woodbine Ave, follow houses on right into Hawthorn Ave. One mile from Brigg (BR).
Seats: 250 **Cover:** 2 Stands **Capacity:** 4,000 **Floodlights:** Yes **Formed:** 1864
Clubhouse: Licensed club open matchdays
Colours: Black & white stripes/black/red **Change colours:** Orange shirts **Nickname:** Zebras
Programme: 16 pages **Editor:** Match Secretary **Midweek Matchday:** Wednesday
Record Attendance: 2,000 v Boston U. 1953 (at Brocklesby Ox).
Previous Leagues: Lindsey; Lincs 48-76; Midland Counties 76-82
Previous Grounds: Manor House Convent, Station Rd (pre 1939); Brocklesby Ox 1939-59
Honours: F.A. Challenge Vase 95-96; Northern Co's East Lg Presidents Cup R-up 91-92 92-93, R-up 95-96; Lincs Lg 49-50 53-54 73-74 75-76 (Div 1 68-69 69-70 70-71 71-72, Lg Cup 49-50 65-66 68-69 69-70 72-73); Mids Co's Lg 77-78 (Lg Cup 77-78); Lincs 'A' Snr Cup 75-76 76-77 94-95; Lincs 'B' Snr Cup 54-55 56-57 66-67 68-69 84-85.

CURZON ASHTON

Chairman: Harry Galloway **Chief Executive:** Harry Twamley **President:** Peter Mayo
Secretary: Graham Shuttleworth, 42 Southgate Road, Chadderton, Oldham, OL9 9PT. Tel: 0161 682 1137 (H)
Manager: Dave Denby **Physio:** Malcolm Liptrot. **Press Officer:** Barry Thorpe
Ground: National Park, Katherine Street, Ashton-under-Lyne OL7 6DA (0161 330 6033) **Directions:** Behind Ashton police station off Manchester Rd (A635), Ashton-under-Lyne, one and a half miles from Ashton-under-Lyne (BR).
Capacity: 5,000 **Cover:** 450 **Seats:** 350 **Floodlights:** Yes **Formed:** 1963
Clubhouse: Open every night. Food on matchdays. **Club Shop:** Yes, contact Roy Howe (0161 2208345)
Programme: 16pages 50p **Editor:** Robert Hurst (0161 775 3883) **Nickname:** Curzon
Colours: All blue **Change colours:** Yellow/green/yellow **Midweek matches:** Tuesday
PREVIOUS Leagues: Manchester Amateur; Manchester (until 1978); Cheshire Co. 78-82; North West Co's 82-87, Northern Prem. Lge. 87-97. **CLUB RECORDS - Attendance:** 1,826 v Stamford, FA Vase SF 1980. **Goalscorer:** Alan Sykes. **Appearances:** Alan Sykes 620. **BEST SEASON - FA Cup:** 3rd Qual. Rd replay 89-90 (1-3 at Mossley after 1-1 draw). **FA Vase:** Semi-Final 79-80. **FA Trophy:** 2nd Qual. Rd 82-83 84-85.
HONOURS: Cheshire Co. Lge Div 2 R-up 78-79 (Res. Div 81-82), Manchester Lge 77-78 (R-up 74-75 75-76, Lge Cup 77-78 (R-up 74-75 75-76), Murray Shield R-up 75-76, Res. Div 74-75 75-76 76-77 77-78), Manchester Amat. Lge 63-64 65-66 (R-up 64-65 79-80 (Res) 80-81 (Res)), Manchester Prem. Cup 81-82 83-84 85-86 86-87 89-90, Manchester Intermediate Cup 71-72 72-73 73-74 (R-up 70-71), Manchester Amat. Cup R-up 63-64, Ashton Chall. Cup 64-65 67-68, Philips F'lit Cup R-ups 77-78, N. W. C. Res. Div 82-83 84-85 (R-up 83-84, Lge Cup 84-85 (R-up 83-84 85-86)), Northern Comb. Supp. Cup 87-88 88-89, S.E. Lancs Lge Shield R-up 84-85.

DENABY UNITED

Chairman: Brian E Beckett **Vice Chairman:** David Hough **President:** Alan Wilson
Secretary: Derek Mower, 60 Windmill Crescent, Mexborough, S Yorks S64 0EB. Tel: 01709 329338 (H)
Manager: David Lloyd **Asst Manager:** Dennis Hobson **Physio:** John Carver
Ground: Tickhill Square, Denaby Main, Doncaster (01709 864042).
Directions: From Conisbrough take first left in Denaby along Wadworth St. From Mexborough take first right after Reresby Arms, left on to Bolton St. then left on to Wheatley Street. Rail to Conisbrough.
Seats: 250 **Cover:** 350 **Capacity:** 6,000 **Floodlights:** Yes
Clubhouse: None **Club Shop:** Yes **Nickname:** None **Founded:** 1895
Programme: 64 pages 60p **Editor:** David Green (01709 862319) **Reserves' League:** Beefeater Co. Sen.
Colours: Red & white stripe/black/black **Change colours:** White/blue/blue **Midweek matches:** Wednesday
Previous - Leagues: Sheffield Ass 1900-02 15-18 19-20 40-45; Midland 02-13 20-40 45-60 61-65; Doncaster & District 18-19; Central Alliance 60-61; Yorks 65-82. **Ground:** Denaby Recreation Ground 1895-1912.
Record attendance: 5,200 v Southport, FA Cup 1st Rnd 1927
Players progressing to Football League: Jack Barker (Derby & England), Keith Burkinshaw (Liverpool 1953), Andy Barnsley (Rotherham 1985), Chris Beaumont (Rochdale 1988), Jonathan Brown (Exeter 1990).
Honours: Yorks Lg R-up 67-68 (Div 2 R-up 66-67, Div 3 R-up 81-82, Lg Cup 71-72); Northern Counties East Div 1 South R-up 83-84; Midland Lg R-up 07-08; Sheffield & Hallamshire Snr Cup 32-33 35-36 86-87; Thorn EMI Floodlight Competition R-up 83-84; Sheffield Association Lg 40-41; Mexborough Montague Cup 14-15.

ECCLESHILL UNITED

Chairman: Keith Firth. Tel: 01274 787057 (H) **Secretary:** Ian Gardiner, 14 Tivoli Place, Little Horton, Bradford BD5 0PQ. Tel: 01274 226052 (H)
Manager: Barry Gallagher **Physio:** Gordon McGlynn **Press Officer:** Bill Rawlings (01274 635753).
Ground: Plumpton Park, Kingsway, Wrose, Bradford BD2 1PN (01274 615739).
Directions: M62 jct 26 onto M606, right on Bradford Ring Road A6177, left onto A650 for Bradford at 2nd r'bout. A650 Bradford Inner Ring Road onto Canal Rd, branch right opposite Woodheads Builders Merchants into Kings Rd, fork right after 30mph sign to junction with Wrose Rd, across junction - continuation of Kings Rd, 1st left onto Kingsway - ground 200 yds on right. 2 miles from Bradford (BR). Buses 686 or 687 for Wrose.
Seats: 225 **Cover:** 225 **Capacity:** 2,225 **Floodlights:** Yes **Founded:** 1948 **Nickname:** Eagles
Clubhouse: Open normal licensing hours. Bar, lounge, games room, kitchen (hot & cold snacks), committee room
Club Shop: Yes, selling range of souvenirs. Contact Roy Maule Snr, 01274 662428.
Colours: Blue & white stripes/blue/blue **Change colours:** All yellow **Reserves' Lge:** NCE Res. Div
Programme: 24-28 pages, 50p **Editor:** John Burgess (01274 585642) **Midweek matches:** Tuesday
Previous - Leagues: Bradford Amat; W Riding Co Amat. **Ground:** Myers Lane **Name:** Eccleshill FC
Club Records - Attendance: 600 v Bradford City 90-91 **Goalscorer:** Paul Viner **Appearances:** Paul Viner
Win: 7-1 v Yorkshire Main (H), N.C.E. Lge Div. 2 86-87. **Defeat:** 0-6 v Rossington Main (A), N.C.E. Lge Cup 2nd Rd 92-93, & v Gt. Harwood T. (A), FA Cup Prel. Rd 91-92.
Players progressing to Football League: Terry Dolan (Huddersfield, Bradford PA, Bradford City)
Honours: Northern Counties East Div 2 R-up 86-87 (Reserve Div 86-87 89-90 (R-up 87-88 94-95)); Bradford Amtr Lg Cup 61-62; Bradford & Dist. Snr Cup 84-85; Bradford & Dist. FA Snr Cup 85-86; West Riding County Amateur Lg 76-77

Arnold Town celebrate after retaining the Notts Senior Cup

L-R, Back Row: Bill Brindley (Ass. Man.), Kris Mudditon, Craig Clark, Ian McCulloch (Team Manager), Andy Elliott.
Middle Row: Neil Water, Pete Catling, John Scott (Physio), Calvin Plummer, Mark Clarke, Brett Williams, Lee Walshaw.
Front Row: Adam Scott (Mascot), Adrian Thorpe, Bryn Gunn, Gene Buxton, Stuart Hammonds, Darren Brogan.
Photo: Nottingham Post Group Ltd.

NORTH FERRIBY UNITED

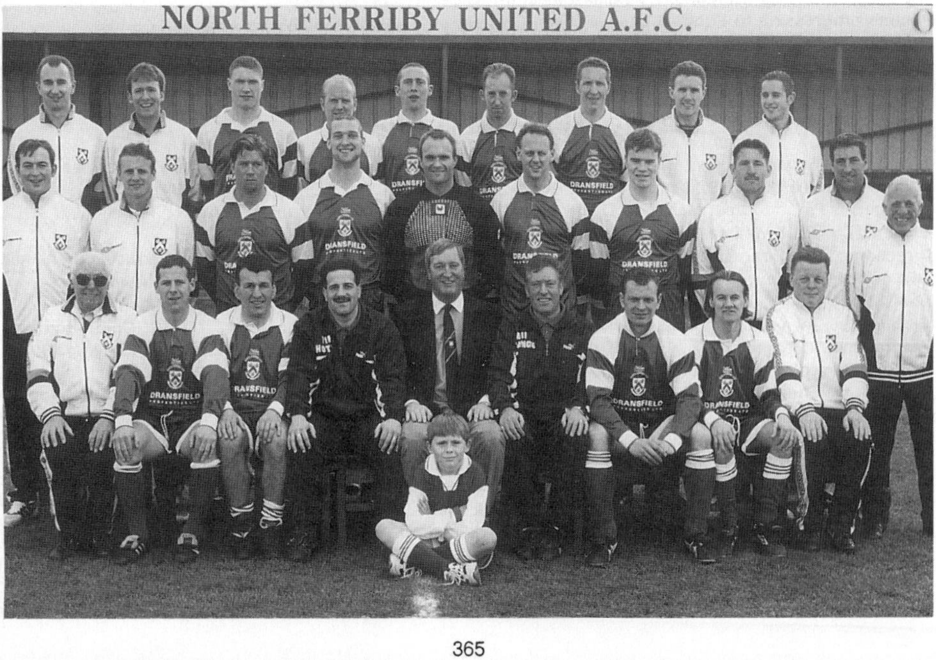

GLASSHOUGHTON WELFARE

President: R Rooker **Chairman:** Gordon Day, Tel: 01977 514178 (H)
Secretary: Eric Jones, 'Marrica', Westfields Ave, Cutsyke, Castleford WF10 5JJ. Tel: 01977 556257 (H)
Match Sec: Barry Bennett, Tel: 01977 682593 (H) **Manager:** Wayne Day **Asst Manager/Coach:** M Ripley
Ground: Glasshoughton Welfare, Leeds Rd, Glasshoughton, Castleford (01977 518981).
Directions: From M62 use either Junct. 31 or 32 towards Castleford. From Junction 32 the road comes into Glasshoughton. From Junction 31 turn right at 2nd roundabout at Whitwood Tech. College. The ground is on the left in Leeds Road. Car park on ground. 1 mile from Castleford (BR).
Seats: None **Covered:** 250 **Capacity:** 2,000 **Floodlights:** Yes **Founded:** 1964
Clubhouse: Bar & refreshment facilities. **Club Shop:** No
Club colours: Blue and white stripes/blue/blue **Change colours:** All yellow **Reserves' Lge:** N.C.E. Res. Div.
Programme: 20 pages, 20p **Programme Editor:** Nigel Lee (01977 516615) **Midweek Matchday:** Tuesday
Previous - League: West Yorkshire **Name:** Anson Sports 1964-76 **Ground:** Saville Park 1964-76
Honours: West Riding County Cup 93-94. **Record Att.:** 300 v Bradford C, 90

HALLAM

Chairman: Tony Scanlan, Tel: 01246 413548 (H) **Vice Chairman:** P Fuller **President:** A Cooper
Secretary: Richard L Groves, 22 Moorgate Crescent, Dronfield, Sheffield, S18 1YF. Tel: 01246 413548 (H)
Press Officer: Mark Radford, Tel: 0114 249 7287 (H) **Manager:** K Johnson **Physio:** A Jackson
Ground: Sandygate, Sandygate Road, Crosspool, Sheffield S10 (0114 230 9484)
Directions: A57 Sheffield to Glossop Rd, left at Crosspool shopping area signed 'Lodge Moor' on to Sandygate Rd. Ground half mile on left opposite Plough Inn. 51 bus from Crucible Theatre.
Seats: 100 **Cover:** 200 **Capacity:** 1,000 **Floodlights:** Yes **Club Shop:** Yes
Clubhouse: Licensed bar and meals in Plough Inn opposite. Hot & cold snacks on ground for matches.
Programme: Yes 30p **Editor:** Mark Radford (Press Off.) **Nickname:** Countrymen **Formed:** 1860
Colours: Blue & white hoops/white/blue **Change colours:** All red **Midweek Matches:** Wednesday
Local Press: Star, Green'Un, Sheffield Telegraph. **Club Sponsors:** Umbro, Bank of Scotland, S Peace & Son
PREVIOUS - Leagues: Yorks 52-82.
CLUB RECORDS - **Attendance:** 2,000 v Hendon, FA Amtr Cup 3rd Rd 59
(13,855 v Dulwich at Hillsborough, FA Amtr Cup 55)
Goalscorer: A Stainrod 46 **Appearances:** P Ellis 500+
Win: 7-0 v Hatfield Main (H) 92-93, & v Kiveton Park (H) 69-70.
Defeat: 0-7 v Hatfield Main (A) 88-89
Players progressing to Football League: Sean Connelly to Stockport County, 1992-93.
Honours: Northern Counties (East) Lg Div 1 R-up 90-91 94-95, Yorkshire Lg Div 2 60-61 (R-up 56-57), Sheffield & Hallamshire Snr Cup 50-51 61-62 64-65 67-68.

HATFIELD MAIN

President: B Speakman **Chairman:** A Jones **Vice Chairman:** B Speakman
Secretary: Bruce Hatton, 92 Ingram Rd, Dunscroft, Doncaster, Sth Yorks DN7 4JE (01302 841648).
Manager: D Fell **Asst Manager:** D Harding **Coach:** R Hunter, G Chapman **Physio:** Tommy Kirk
Ground: Dunscroft Welfare Ground, Dunscroft, Doncaster, Sth Yorks (01302 841326).
Directions: From Doncaster (A18) Scunthorpe Rd to Dunsville, left at Flarepath Hotel down Broadway. Ground half mile on right. Half mile from Stamforth & Hatfield (BR). Buses every fifteen minutes from Doncaster.
Seats: 200 **Cover:** 600 **Capacity:** 4,000 **Floodlights:** Yes **Founded:** 1936.
Clubhouse: Open during normal licensing hours. Hot & cold snacks available. **Club Shop:** Yes
Programme: 25 pages, 50p **Editor:** Tony Ingram (01302 842795) **Commercial Manager:** Barry Speakman
Colours: All red **Change:** All blue **Nickname:** The Main
Midweek matches: Tuesday **Reserves' League:** None **Club Sponsors:** F Cross & Son (Hatfield)
Previous League: Doncaster Dist, Yorkshire 55-82.
Club Records - **Attendance:** 1,000 v Leeds, A Jones testimonial. Competitive: 750 v Bishop Auckland, FA Amtr Cup
Appearances: Lal Dutt **Transfer fee received:** £1,000 for Mark Hall (York C.)
Players progresing to Football League: Mark Atkins (Scunthorpe, Blackburn), Mark Hall (York).
96-97 - Captain: Russ Harmer **Top Scorer:** Matt Cressey **P.o.Y.:** Russ Harmer
Honours: Northern Counties East Prem Div 95-96, R-up 88-89, Div One 94-95; Yorks Lge Div 1 R-up 65-66; W Riding Cup 61-62 63-64.

HUCKNALL TOWN

Chairman: John Coleman **Vice-Chairman:** John Beharall **President:** Andy Stewart
Secretary: Brian Scothern, 95 Brookfield Ave., Shortwood Estate, Hucknall, Notts NG15 6FF (0115 956 3151)
Manager: John Ramshaw **Assistant Manager:** Billy Millar **Physio:** Ken Burton.
Ground: Watnall Road, Hucknall, Notts NG15 7LP (0115 956 1253)
Directions: M1 jct 27, A608 to lights, right onto A611 to Hucknall, right at r'bout (new by-pass), over next r'bout, right at next r'bout into Watnall Rd - grd on right. From M1 jct 26 follow Nottm signs to lights on island, left onto A610, right at Three Ponds Pub onto B600 towards Watnall, 200 yds past Queens Head turn right signed Hucknall, follow over motorway and past Rolls Royce - ground on left. Nearest station Hucknall
Capacity: 3,000 **Seats:** 240 **Cover:** 1,100 **Floodlights:** Yes **Nickname:** The Town **Founded:** 1987
Clubhouse: Every night and weekend lunchtimes **Club Shop:** Yes **Sponsors:** Doff-Portland
Programme: 72 pages, 50p **Editor:** Simon Matters (0115 956 1336) **Midweek matches:** Tuesday
Colours: Yellow/black/black **Change colours:** All red **Reserve League:** Midlands Regional Alliance
PREVIOUS - Leagues: Bulwell & Dist. 46-59 60-65; Central All. 59-60; Notts Spartan 65-70; Notts All. 70-89; Central Midlands 89-92. **Ground:** Wigham Park 46-54 **Name:** Hucknall Colliery Welfare (until pit closure 1988)
Club Records - Attendance: 1,305 v Macclesfield, FA Cup 2nd Qual 26/9/92. **Appearances:** Ted Mullane
96-97 - Captain: Colin Thacker **P.o.Y.:** Dave McCarthy **Top Scorer:** P Tomlinson/M Edwards (30)
Hons: Northern Counties (East) Lg Div 1 R-up 92-93 (Lg Cup 93-94 96-97) Presidents Cup 96-97; Central Mids Lg(2) 89-91 (R-up 91-92, Lg Cup(3) 89-92); Notts All.Sen (4) 76-78 87-89, Div 1 Div 1 72-73 80-81 86-87 Div 2 70-71; Intermediate Cup 72-73 78-81 84-84; Lge Cup 78-79; Notts Snr Cup 84-85 90-91 (R-up 83-84 85-86 87-88 89-90); FA Vase QF 85-86.

LIVERSEDGE

Chairman: Robert Gawthorpe **Manager:** John Storey **Asst Mgr:** Tony Passmore
Secretary/Press Officer: Michael Balmforth, 2 Reform Street, Gomersal, Cleckheaton BD19 4JX (01274 862123).
Ground: Clayborn Ground, Quaker Lane, Hightown Rd, Cleckheaton, West Yorks (01274 862108).
Directions: M62 jct 26, A638 into Cleckheaton, right at lights on corner of Memorial Park, through next lights & under railway bridge, 1st left (Hightown Rd) and Quaker Lane is approx quarter mile on left and leads to ground. From M1 jct 40, A638 thru Dewsbury and Heckmondwike to Cleckheaton, left at Memorial Park lights then as above. Buses 218 & 220 (Leeds-Huddersfield) pass top of Quaker Lane.
Seats: 250 **Cover:** 750 **Capacity:** 2,000 **Floodlights:** Yes **Nickname:** Sedge **Founded:** 1910
Clubhouse: Matchdays, Tues, Thursday. Pool, TV. Pies + crisps **Club Shop:** No
Programme: 28 pages, 50p **Editor:** Secretary **Midweek Matches:** Tuesday
Colours: All blue **Change colours:** All red **Reserves League:** NCEL Res. Div.
PREVIOUS - Leagues: Spen Valley; West Riding County Amateur 22-72; Yorkshire 72-82.
Ground: Primrose Lane, Hightown. **Name:** None
Players progressing to Football League: Garry Briggs (Oxford), Martin Hirst (Bristol City).
96-97 - Captain: Paul Smith **P.o.Y.:** Mick Oddy **Top Scorer:** Paul Murphy
Honours: West Riding Co. Chal. Cup 48-49 51-52 69-70; West Riding County Cup 89-90; North Counties East Lg Div 1 R-up 89-90 (Div 2 R-up 88-89); West Riding Co. Amtr Lg(6) 23-24 25-27 64-66 68-69 (Lg Cup 57-58 64-65).

MALTBY MAIN

Chairman: G McCormick **Vice Chairman:** M Richardson **President:** H Henson
Secretary: Nick Dunhill, 10 Conrad Drive, Maltby, Rotherham, Sth Yorks S66 8RS (01709 815676).
Manager: Dave McCarthy **Asst Manager:** Kevin Eley **Physio:** G Hally
Ground: Muglet Lane, Maltby (01709 812462 match days)
Directions: Exit M18 at junct 1 with A631. Two miles into Maltby, right at traffic lights at Queens Hotel corner on to B6427 Muglet Lane. Ground 3/4 mile on left. Bus 101 from Rotherham stops at ground. Bus 287 from Sheffield to Queens Hotel, then follow as above.
Seats: 150 **Cover:** 300 **Capacity:** 2,000 **Floodlights:** Yes **Club Shop:** No
Clubhouse: No, Miners Welfare Club opposite.
Programme: 12 pages, 50p **Editor:** Secretary **Press Officer:** Secretary
Colours: Black & white/black/black **Change colours:** Yellow/blue/yellow
Sponsors: Jack Green Sports, RJB Mining. **Nickname:** Miners
Midweek matchday: Tuesday **Reserve League:** None
PREVIOUS - Name: Maltby Main 1916-65 (disbanded); Maltby Miners Welfare 1970-96. **Leagues:** Sheffield County Senior; Yorkshire 73-82.
CLUB RECORDS - Attendance: 1,500 v Sheffield Wed., June 91-92 (friendly) **Win:** 6-0
940 v Thackley, Yorks Lg Cup 77-78. (competitive) **Defeat:** 0-5
Players progressing to Football League: Michael Williams (Sheffield Wednesday) 1991-92.
96-97 - Captain: Rob Moorwood **Top Scorer:** Richard Coleman
P.o.Y. - Players: Tim Willis **Supporters:** Craig Pinder
Honours: Sheffield & Hallamshire Snr Cup 77-78, Northern Counties East Lg Presidents Cup 92-93 (SF 90-91), Mexborough Montague Cup 76-77 80-81 90-91, Yorks Lg R-up 77-78, Sheffield Wharncliffe Cup 80-81.

Goalmouth action from last season's match between Maltby Main (dark shorts) and Selby Town at Muglet Lane. The visitors ran out 6-2 winners. Photos: Martin Wray.
Above: Ian Noteman (Selby Town, No. 9) seems certain to score but his header goes just over the bar.
Below: All eyes on the ball as this Selby Town corner comes over.

NORTH FERRIBY UNITED

President: Jeff Frank **Chairman:** Les Hare **Vice Chairman:** Brian Sievewright
Secretary: Stephen Tather, 16 Peasholme, Heads Lane, Hessle, E Yorks HU13 0NY (01482 642046).
Press Officer: Roy Wallis **Manager:** Tim Hotte **Asst Mgr:** Brian France **Coach/Physio:** Colin Naylor
Ground: Grange Lane, Church Road, North Ferriby HU14 3AA (01482 634601).
Directions: Main Leeds-Hull road A63 or M62, North Ferriby is 8 miles west of Hull. Into North Ferriby, thru village past the Duke of Cumberland Hotel, right down Church Rd, ground half mile on left. One mile from North Ferriby (BR).
Seats: 250 **Cover:** 1,000 **Capacity:** 5,000 **Floodlights:** Yes **Nickname:** United **Founded:** 1934
Clubhouse: Bar, lounge, TV, pool – open every night **Club Shop:** Yes **Midweek matches:** Tuesday
Programme: 32 pages, 50p **Editor:** Jeff Frank (01482 633387). **Reserves League:** N Counties East Res Div
Colours: White & green/green/green **Change colours:** All yellow **Sponsors:** Dransfield Developments
Previous leagues: East Riding Church/ East Riding Amateur/ Yorks 69-82.
CLUB RECORDS - Attendance: 1,800 v Tamworth, FA Vase Semi-Final, 1989 **Goalscorer:** Mark Tennison **Appearances:** Richard Woomble, 1974-94. **Win:** 8-0 v North Newbald, E. Riding Sen. Cup 1992 **Defeat:** 1-7 v North Shields, N.C.E. Lge Prem. Div. 1991 **Transfer fee received:** £3,000 for Tim Hotte (Hull City, 1988).
Players moving to Football Lge: T Hotte (Hull) 88, I Ironside (Halifax) 88, D France, D Windass & M Matthews (Hull) 91.
96-97 Captain: Steve Brentano **96-97 P.o.Y.:** Paul Sharp **96-97 Top Scorer:** Darren France
Honours: FA Vase Finalist 96-97, SF 88-89 (QF 89-90, 5th Rd 87-88); Yorkshire Lg R-up 75-76 (Lg Cup 74-75, Div 2 70-71), Northern Co's East Div 1 85-86 (Lg Cup R-up) 90-91, Presidents Cup 90-91, Div 1 (North), R-up 82-83, Reserve Div R-up 90-91); East Riding Snr Cup 70-71 76-77 77-78 78-79 90-91 96-97; East Riding Church Lg 37-38.

OSSETT ALBION

President: Miss Helen Worth **Chairman:** Neville A Wigglesworth **Vice-Chairman:** S B Garside
Secretary: David Chambers, 109 South Parade, Ossett, Wakefield, WF5 0BE. Tel: 01924 276004 (H)
Manager: Jimmy Martin **Physio:** John Hirst **Coach:** Peter Eaton
Commercial Mgr: D Riley (01924 240247) **Press Officer:** Neville Wigglesworth (01924 275630).
Ground: Dimple Wells, Ossett (01924 273618-club, 01924 280450-grd)
Directions: M1 jct 40. Take Wakefield road, right at Post House Hotel down Queens Drive. At end right then second left down Southdale Rd. At end right, then first left down Dimple Wells (cars only). Coaches take second left following the road for 200yds bearing left twice. Four miles from both Wakefield and Dewsbury BR stations. Buses 116 and 117.
Seats: 200 **Cover:** 500 **Capacity:** 3,000 **Floodlights:** Yes **Nickname:** Albion **Founded:** 1944
Clubhouse: 3 bars + function room, open 7 days per week - catering available.
Club Shop: Yes, selling various souvenirs & programmes. Contact chairman. **Sponsors:** Arco.
Colours: Old gold/black/black **Change colours:** All white **Reserves' Lge:** NCEL Res Div
Programme: 44 pages, 50p **Editor:** N Wigglesworth (01924 275630). **Midweek matches:** Tuesday
Previous Leagues: Heavy Woollen Area 44-49; West Riding Co. Amtr 49-50; West Yorks 50-57; Yorks 57-82.
CLUB RECORDS - Attendance: 1,200 v Leeds Utd, floodlight opening 1986. **Goalscorer:** John Balmer **Appearances:** Peter Eaton, 800+ (22 yrs) **Win:** 12-0 v British Ropes (H), Yorkshire Lge Div. 2 6/5/59 **Defeat:** 2-11 v Swillington (A), W. Yorkshire Lge Div. 1 25/4/56
Honours: Yorks Lg 74-75 (R-up 59-60 61-62, Lg Cup 75-76, 76-77, Div 2 78-79, 80-81 (R-up 58-59)); Northern Co. East Div 1 86-87 (Lg Cup 83-84); West Yorks Lg 53-54 55-56 (Div 2 52-53, Lg Cup 52-53); West Riding County Cup 64-65 65-66 67-68; Wheatley Cup 56-57 58-59

OSSETT TOWN

President: Paul Jervis. **Chairman:** Graham Firth **Vice Chairman:** Bruce Saul
Secretary: Frank Lloyd, 27 Park Close, Mapplewell, Barnsley S75 6BY (01226 382415).
Manager: Trevor Best **Asst Manager:** Paul Murphy **Coach:** Mick Polli **Commercial Manager:** Peter Jessop
Ground: Ingfield, Prospect Road, Ossett, Wakefield WF5 8AN (01924 272960).
Directions: M1 jct 40, B6129 to Ossett, left into Dale Street, left again at lights opposite bus station on ring road, ground on left. Nearest stations Dewsbury or Wakefield Westgate - both three miles from. Buses 116, 117, 126 and 127 from Wakefield, buses 116, 126 and 127 from Dewsbury, buses 117, 118 or 216 from Leeds.
Seats: 360 **Cover:** 650 **Capacity:** 4,000 **Floodlights:** Yes **Founded:** 1936
Clubhouse: Open Fri & Sun lunchtimes, all day Sat and every evening. Pie & peas, chips, soup from tea bar.
Colours: All red **Change colours:** All sky **Midweek matches:** Tuesday **Sponsors:** Action Stations
Programme: 12 pages, 50p **Editor/Press Off.:** Bruce Saul, 01924 277652 **Reserves' League:** N.C.E. Res Div
PREVIOUS - Leagues: Leeds 36-39; Yorkshire 45-82 **Ground:** Fern House (pre-1958)
CLUB RECORDS - Attendance: 2,600 v Manchester Utd, friendly 1988 **Win:** 10-1 v Harrogate RA (H), N.C.E. Lge Prem. Div. 27/4/93 **Defeat:** 0-7 v Easington Colliery, FA Vase 8/10/83 **Transfer fee received:** £1,350 for Derek Blackburn (Swansea 1957) **Appearances:** Steve Worsfold **Goalscorer:** Dave Leadbeater
Players progressing to Football League: Simon Lowe (Barnsley) 83, Gary Chapman (Bradford C.) 88, Mick Norbury (Scarborough) 1989, Mike Williams (Sheffield W.) 90.
96-97 Captain: Lloyd Fellows **P.o.Y.:** Lloyd Fellows **Top Scorer:** R Sayer
Honours: N.C.E. - Lg Cup 89-90, Div 2 88-89, Res. Div 88-89, Res. Cup 87-88 88-89; W. Riding Co. Cup 58-59 81-82.

PICKERING TOWN

Chairman: Anthony Dunning, Tel: 01751 473697 (H) **President:** S P Boak
Secretary: Steve Adamson, 16 Overgreen View, Burniston, Scarborough, N Yorks YO13 0HZ. Tel: 01723 870930 (H)
Manager: Nigel Tate **Asst Manager/Physio:** Michael Hudson **Coach:** Robbie Goodwill
Ground: Recreation Club, Mill Lane (off Malton Rd), Pickering, North Yorkshire (01751 473317)
Directions: A169 from Malton. On entering Pickering take 1st left past Police Station and B.P. garage into Mill Lane, ground 200 yards on right.
Seats: 100 **Cover:** 500 **Capacity:** 2,000 **Floodlights:** Yes **Founded:** 1888 **Nickname:** Pikes
Clubhouse: Open 1.30pm for Saturday games, 6pm for midweek games. Food available from Football Club Kitchen at half-time and after games. **Club Shop:** No **Club Sponsors:** Flamingoland
Programme: 32 pages, 50p **Editor:** Anthony Dunning (Chairman) **Midweek matches:** Tuesday
Colours: Blue/white/blue **Change colours:** Amber/black/amber **Reserves' League:** York & Dist.
Local Press: Pickering Gazette & Herald, Yorkshire Evening Press, Mercury, Scarborough Evening News.
Record Gate: 1,412 v Notts County, friendly, August 1991.
Previous leagues: Beckett; York & District; Scarborough & District; Yorkshire 72-82.
Players progressing to Football League: Chris Short (Scarborough & Notts Co.)
Craig Short (Scarborough, Notts Co, Derby Co, Everton.)
Honours: Northern Co's East Lg R-up 92-93 (Div 2 1987-88, Div 1 R-up 91-92), Yorks Lg Div 3 73-74, North Riding Snr Cup R-up 93-94 94-95, North Riding County Cup 90-91.

PONTEFRACT COLLIERIES

Chairman: Roger Ripley, Tel: 01977 510980 (H) **Match Sec:** Mark Whitley, Tel: 01977 706469 (H)
Secretary: Alan Dean, 1 Scawthorpe Close, Pontefract, West Yorks WF8 2HT. Tel: 01977 796091 (H), 0973 482213 (M)
President: J Betts **Manager:** Jim Kenyon **Asst Mgr:** Frank Maclachlan **Physio:** Alan Dean
Ground: Skinner Lane, Pontefract, West Yorkshire (01977 600818)
Directions: M62 jct 32 towards Pontefract. Left at traffic lights opposite Racecourse entrance (travelling through Pontefract follow Racecourse/Leeds signs to traffic lights and turn right) - ground past Territorial Army unit. 1 mile from Monkhill (BR). All Leeds and Castleford buses stop near ground.
Seats: 300 **Cover:** 400 **Capacity:** 1,200 **Floodlights:** Yes **Nickname:** Colls **Founded:** 1958
Clubhouse: Fully licensed. Hot & cold snacks. Open before and after games **Club Shop:** No
Programme: 16 pages, 50p **Editor/Press Officer:** Secretary **Reserve League:** N.C.E. Res. Div.
Colours: Blue & black/black/black **Change Colours:** White/blue/blue **Midweek Matches:** Monday
Local Press: Pontefract & Castleford Express **Sponsors:** John Betts Quality Used Cars
PREVIOUS - Leagues: West Yorkshire 58-79; Yorkshire 79-82. **CLUB RECORDS - Goalscorer:** Gary Cygan
Appearances: John Brown **Attendance:** 1,000 v Hull City, floodlight opening 1985.
Players progressing to Football League: David Penney to Derby County, 1985.
Honours: Northern Co's East Lg Div 1 83-84 95-96 (Div 2 R-up 82-83); Floodlit Comp 87-88 88-89; Yorks Lg Div 3 81-82; West Riding Co. Cup R-up 87-88 90-91; Embleton Cup 82-83 86-87 95-96; Castleford FA Cup 82-83 86-87,94-95; Wilkinson Sword 95-96

SELBY TOWN

Chairman: Barry Walker, Tel: 01977 682736 (H) **Match Sec:** Paul Atkin, Tel: 01405 861829 (H)
Secretary: Keith Tiplady, 58A St Mary's Ave, Hemingbrough, Selby, N York YO8 7YY. Tel: 01757 638219 (H)
President: Stan Henry **Manager:** B Walker & T Carter **Asst Manager:** J Storey **Coach:** B Walker
Ground: Flaxley Road Ground, Richard Street, Scott Road, Selby, North Yorkshire YO8 0BS. (01757 210900)
Directions: From Leeds, left at main traffic lights in Selby down Scott Rd. then 1st left into Richard St. From Doncaster go straight across main traffic lights into Scott Road then 1st left. From York right at main traffic lights into Scott Rd, and 1st left. 1 mile from Selby (BR).
Seats: 220 **Cover:** 350 **Capacity:** 5,000 **Floodlights:** Yes **Nickname:** The Robins **Founded:** 1918
Clubhouse: Bar at ground open first and second team matchdays **Club Shop:** Yes
Programme: 30 pages, 50p **Editor:** Mark Fairweather, 01757 705376 (H) **Midweek Matches:** Wednesday
Colours: Red/black/black **Change colours:** All yellow **Sponsors:** Hazlewood Preserves
Reserves' League: N.C.E. Res. Div. **Players progressing to Football League:** Numerous
Previous - League: Yorkshire (1920-82) **Ground:** Bowling Green, James St. 1920-51
Record attendance: 7,000 v Bradford Park Avenue (FA Cup 1st Rnd 1953-54)
Best Season - FA Cup: Second Round Proper 54-55 **FA Vase:** Prel Round 89-90
Honours: Yorkshire Lg 32-33 34-35 35-36 52-53 53-54 (R-up 24-25 25-26 27-28 28-29 30-31 31-32 50-51 55-56, Div 3 R-up 74-75, Lg Cup 37-38 53-54 54-55 62-63); Northern Co. East Div 1 95-96, Div 2 R-up 89-90; West Riding Snr Cup 37-38; West Riding Co Cup 27-28 48-49; West Riding Chall. Cup 34-35 35-36

SHEFFIELD

Chairman: Peter Beal, Tel: 0114 258 6186 (H) **President / Press Officer:** Alan Methley
Secretary: Stephen Hall, 24 Crofton Ave., Sheffield S6 1WF. Tel: 0114 234 4553 (H), 01246 450255 (B).
Manager: John Pearson **Asst Manager:** Sam Saif **Commercial Manager:** John Pearson
Ground: Don Valley Stadium, Worksop Rd, Sheffield S9 3TL (0114 256 0607)
Directions: M1 Junc 33, turn onto dual carriageway sign City centre, take 2nd exit A57. Turn right at bottom of slip road, and at bottom of hill turn right again at lights. Left at lights at rear of Morrison's supermarket. Follow road passing under bridge, ground on right
Seats: 25,000 **Cover:** 13,000 **Capacity:** 25,000 **Floodlights:** Yes **Founded:** 1857 **Nickname:** The Club
Clubhouse: Licensed Bar **Club Shop:** No **Colours:** Red & black/black/red & black **Change:** All blue
Programme: 16 pages, 50p **Editor:** David Deans (0114 232 5901) **Club Sponsors:** Bumford Heating
PREVIOUS - League: Yorks 49-82 **Grounds:** Abbeydale Park, Dore (1956-1989); Sheffield Amateur Sports Club, Hillsborough Park 1989-91; Sheffield International (Don Valley) Stadium 1991-94; Sheffield Sports Stadium 94-97.
Record Gate: 2,000 v Barton Rovers, FA Vase SF 76-77. **Midweek matchday:** Wednesday
Player progressing to Football Lge: Richard Peacock, Hull 94-95.
96-97 Captain: J Eastwood **96-97 Top Scorer:** **96-97 P.o.Y.:** M Thomson
Honours: F.A. Amateur Cup 03-04; F.A. Challenge Vase Runners-up 76-77;
Northern Co's East Lg Cup 94-95 (Div 1 88-89 90-91); Yorkshire Lg Div 2 76-77.

THACKLEY

Chairman: John Myers **Treasurer:** Steven Paley **Press Officer:** Jamie Scott (01274 611520).
Secretary: Stewart Willingham, 3 Kirklands Close, Baildon, Shipley, West Yorks BD17 6HN (01274 598589).
Manager/Coach: John Boyle **Asst Manager:** Colin Smith. **Physio:** John Laider.
Ground: Dennyfield, Ainsbury Avenue, Thackley, Bradford (01274 615571). **Directions:** On main Leeds/Keighley A657 road, turn off at Thackley corner which is 2 miles from Shipley traffic lights and 1 mile from Greengates lights. Ainsbury Avenue bears to the right 200yds down the hill. Ground is 200yds along Ainsbury Avenue on the right. 3 miles from Bradford Interchange (BR), one and a half miles from Shipley (BR). Buses to Thackley corner (400 yds).
Seats: 300 **Cover:** 600 **Capacity:** 3,000 **Floodlights:** Yes **Founded:** 1930.
Clubhouse: Open Tue-Sun evenings, matchdays and w/e lunchtimes. Hot & cold snacks on matchdays.
Club Shop: Yes. Programmes, souvenirs. Metal badges available - £2.50 + s.a.e. Contact Jamie Scott (01274 61152).
Colours: Red & white/white/red **Change colours:** All white **Midweek matches:** Tuesday
Programme: 20 pages, 50p **Editor:** Secretary **Sponsors:** Diamond International Shipping
Previous - **Leagues:** Bradford Amateur, W. Riding County Amateur, W. Yorks, Yorks 67-82.
Name: Thackley Wesleyians 1930-39.
Record Attendance: 1,500 v Leeds Utd 1983 **Best FA Vase year:** 5th Rd 80-81 (01-2 v Whickham).
Players progressing to Football League: Tony Brown (Leeds, Doncaster, Scunthorpe, Rochdale), Ian Ormondroyd (Bradford City, Aston Villa, Derby, Leicester).
96-97 Captain: Warren Fletcher **96-97 Top Scorer:** Keith Sanderson **96-97 P.o.Y.:** Richard Wilson
Honours: Northern Co's (East) Lg R-up 94-95 (Lg Cup R-up 94-95), Yorks Lg Div 2 73-74, West Yorks Lg 66-67, West Riding Co. Amtr Lg 57-58 58-59 59-60, West Riding Co. Cup 73-74 74-75, West Riding Co. Chal. Cup 63-64 66-67,(R-Up 94-95) Bradford & Dist. Snr Cup(11) 38-39 49-50 55-56 57-60 65-67 78-79 87-88.94-95.

Arnold Town on the attack against Flixton in their FA Cup encounter at Gedling Road. Photo: A Singleton.

Belper Town (white shirts) attack the Arnold Town goal in the top of the table clash earlier this year in front of a packed crowd. Photo: Martin Wray.

Midfield action from Denaby United's FA Vase clash with Newcastle Town last season. Photo: M A Taylor.

DIVISION ONE CLUBS

BLIDWORTH WELFARE

Chairman: Richard Paterson. Tel: 01623 27470 (H). **President:** Ray Hilton **Comm. Manager:** Chris Jukes
Secretary: Darrel Bailey, 220 Wharf Road, Pinxton, Notts. Tel: 01773 813432 (H) **Press Officer:** Pete Craggs
Match Secretary: Bill Deakin, 220 Brick Kiln Lane, Mansfield, Notts NG19 6LR. Tel: 01623 454071 (H).
Manager: Andy Brown **Asst Manager:** John Miller **Coach:** Shaun Hird
Ground: Welfare Ground, Mansfield Rd, Blidworth, Mansfield (01623 793361).
Directions: On B6020, Rainworth side of Blidworth. From M1 jct 27 take A608 to Kirby and Annesley Woodhouse, at lights follow A611 to Kirby then take B6020 through Ravenshead to Blidworth - thru village and ground at top of hill on right. From A1 follow A614 and A617 to Rainworth, left at lights then 1st right on to B6020 to Blidworth - ground on left at top of hill. Served by Mansfield-Nottingham buses.
Capacity: 3,000 **Seats:** 200 **Cover:** 700 **Floodlights:** Yes **Founded:** 1980
Clubhouse: Welfare Social Club built 199. Normal matchday hours. **Club Shop:** No
Programme: 32 pages, 50p **Editor:** Andy Brown, Tel: 01773 861176 (H) **Midweek matches:** Tuesday
Colours: Orange/black/orange **Change colours:** All yellow **Nickname:** Hawks
Previous - Leagues: Notts All. 80-82; NCEL 82-86; Centrals Mids 86-94. **Grounds:** None
Club Records - **Attendance:** 400 v Shirebrook Colliery, C.M.Lge 89-90.
Scorer: Andy Locker **Appearances:** Dave Colley
Record win: 6-0 v Harworth Colliery Institute (H), League Cup 91-92.
Record defeat: 0-11 v Sheffield Aurora (A), Central Midlands League 90-91.
Honours: None to date.

BORROWASH VICTORIA

Chairman: Ian Anderson **Vice Chairman:** Peter Erwin **Founded:** 1911 **Reformed:** 1963
Sec./Press Officer: Ian Collins, 30 Margreave Road, Chaddesden, Derby DE21 6JD (01332 739437).
Manager/Coach: Kevin Smith **Asst Manager:** Kevin Harrigan **Physio:** Geoff Woolley
Ground: Asterdale Bowl, Borrowash Road, Spondon, Derby (01332 668656).
Directions: M1 jct 25, A52 towards Derby, 3rd left off by-pass into Borrowash Rd, ground 400 yds on left. 2 miles from Spondon (BR). Nottingham to Derby buses pass nearby.
Capacity: 5,000 **Seats:** No **Covered:** 500 **Floodlights:** Yes **Nickname:** Vics
Clubhouse: Normal pub hours. Hot & cold food. **Club Shop:** No **Midweek matches:** Tuesday
Colours: Red & white/black/black **Change Colours:** Yellow/sky/yellow **Club Sponsors:** St Ivel
Programme: 16 pages, 50p **Editor:** Secretary **Previous Ground:** Dean Drive, 11-84
Previous Leagues: Derby Sunday School & Welfare 52-57; Derby Comb.; Midland 79-82; Northern Co's East.
Club Records - **Win:** 11-1 **Defeat:** 3-8 **Goalscorer:** Paul Acklam **Appearances:** Neil Kellogg
Attendance: 2,000 v Nottingham Forest, floodlight opening 22/10/85.
Honours: Northern Co's East Lg Div 1 Sth 83-84 (R-up 84-85, Div 2 Sth R-up 82-83), Derby Comb. 77-78 (R-up(10) 65-66 68-74 75-77 78-79, Lg Cup 68-69 75-76 (R-up 63-64 66-67), Midland Co's Lg Div 80-81 (Div 1 Cup 80-81), Derbys Snr Cup R-up 90-91, Derbys Div. Cup 73-74 (R-up 70-71 72-73), Central Midlands Lg B E Webbe Cup R-up 88-89 (Reserves Cup 94-95), FA Cup 3rd Qual. Rd 91-92.

BRODSWORTH WELFARE

Chairman: Barry L Hogg, Tel: 01302 722501 (H) **Press Officer:** John Muldowney
Secretary: Robert Beswick, 75 Coniston Drive, Bolton-on-Dearne, Rotherham S63 8NE (01709 890913)
Manager: Neil Harle **Physio:** J Bedford **Match Sec:** John Muldowney, Tel: 01302 721274 (H)
Ground: Welfare Ground, Woodlands, Nr. Doncaster (01302 728380).
Directions: From A1 take A638 to Doncaster, take left after Woodlands Pub into Welfare Road, ground 50yds on left. Regular bus service from North Bridge Bus Station, Doncaster.
Seats: No **Cover:** 250 **Capacity:** 3,000 **Floodlights:** Yes **Founded:** 1912
Clubhouse: Yes, Matchday drinks and snacks
Colours: Green & yellow stripes/yellow/yellow **Change colours:** All yellow
Club Shop: No **Nickname:** Brody **Midweek home matchday:** Tuesday
Previous Name: Brodsworth Main **Previous Leagues:** Doncaster Snr/ Sheffield/ Yorks.
Programme: 20 pages, compiled Match Sec. **Editor:** Match Sec.
Record fee paid: Nil **Record fee received:** Barry Stobart, Wolves 60.
96-97 Captain: Paul Curtis **96-97 Top scorer:** Scott Horsefall (12)
Honours: Yorks Lg 24-25, Donc. & Dist. Lg 84-85 (Lg Cup 85-86, Div 2 78-79, Div 2 Cup 78-79), Sheffield Jnr Cup 83-84, Mexborough Montagu Cup 91-92 92-93.

GARFORTH TOWN

President: Norman Hebbron **Chairman:** Stephen Hayle.
Secretary: Paul Bracewell, 24 Coupland Rd, Garforth, Leeds LS25 1AD (0113 286 3314).
Manager/Coach: Dave Parker. **Asst Manager:** Dave Harrison **Physio:** Jack Coup
Ground: Brierlands Lane, Aberford Road, Garforth, Leeds (0113 2864083).
Directions: From South/East/North, A642 from A1 to Garforth, ground one and a half miles on left over brow of hill. From South West, M62 jct 30, A642 to Garforth (A63 to Garforth from Leeds), thru Garforth on A642, ground on right 1 mile on from lights just past new housing developement and Indian restaurant. Buses 18 & 83 from Leeds, alight at East Garforth Post Office - ground 500yds on right walking away from Garforth. By rail to Garforth (Leeds-York) line - cross over bridge to Safeways side and ground just under 1 mile down road.
Seats: None **Cover:** 400 **Capacity:** 2,000 **Floodlights:** Yes **Nickname:** The Miners **Founded:** 1965
Clubhouse: Open matchdays & training nights **Club Shop:** Yes **Sponsors:** DP Heating & Ventilation
Programme: 28 pages, 50p **Editor:** K Strangeway (0113 286 6500) **Press Officer:** Secretary
Colours: Red/black/red **Change colours:** All blue **Midweek matches:** Tuesday
Previous leagues: Leeds Sunday Combination; West Yorks; Yorks 78-82.
Previous names: Miners Arms 64-78, Garforth Miners 78-79
Club Records - Goalscorer: Vinnie Archer **Appearances:** Philip Matthews (82-93) **Attendance:** 817 v Leeds, friendly 1987 **Win:** 7-0 v Immingham T. (H), N.C.E. Div. 1 91-92 **Defeat:** 1-7 v Lincoln Utd (A), N.C.E. Div. 1 92-93
96-97 Captain: Darren Hamer **96-97 P.o.Y.:** Damien Holmes **96-97 Top Scorer:** Simeon Bambrook (19)
Honours: FA Vase QF 85-86; Northern Co's East Lg Div 1 R-up 96-97, Div 2 R-up 85-86; Yorks Lg Div 3 R-up 79-80; Barkston Ash Snr Cup 80-81 84-85 85-86 86-87 92-93 94-95; Wilkinson Sword Trophy 96-97.

GLAPWELL

Chairman: Ellen Caton, 111 The Hill, Glapwell, Chesterfield. S44 5LU. Tel: 01246 854648 (H)
Secretary: Lynne Winterton, 17 Park Avenue, Glapwell, Chesterfield, Derbys S44 5PZ. Tel: 01623 810043 (H)
Manager: Dave Waller
Ground: Hall Corner, Park Ave., Glapwell, Chesterfield, Derbyshire (01623 812213).
Directions: M1 Junc 29 A617 towards Mansfield, after Young Vanish Inn take filter lane left onto Bolsover Road, ground facing, use rear entrance next to garden centre
Colours: Black & white stripes/white/white **Change colours:** Red/black/black
Founded: 1980 **Floodlights:** Yes **Midweek matches:** Tuesday
Programme: 16 pages, 30p **Editor:** Paul Winterton, Tel: 01623 810043 (H)
Honours: Central Midlands Lg 93-94 (Floodlit Cup 93-94), Derbyshire Senior Cup SF 93-94.

HALL ROAD RANGERS

Chairman: Robert Smailes, 7 Cotterdale, Sutton Park, Hull, HU7 4AA. Tel: 01482 821354 (H)
Secretary: David J Simmons, 24 Gorton Road, Willerby. Hull HU10 6LT. Tel: 01482 658998 (H), 01482 224429 (B)
Manager: Mick Matthews **Asst Mgr:** Peter Smurthwaite **Coach:** Ian Davis
Ground: Dene Park, Dene Close, Beverley Rd, Dunswell, Nr Hull (01482 850101).
Directions: M62 to A63, turn left before Humber Bridge onto A164 to Beverley, after approx 5 miles turn right onto A1079. In 2 miles turn left at large roundabout to ground 20 yards on right.
Seats: 50 **Cover:** 750 **Capacity:** 1,200 **Floodlights:** Yes **Club Shop:** Yes
Clubhouse: Open all week for drinks and snacks. Bar snacks. Snooker, pool, darts.
Programme: 36 pages, 50p **Editor/Press Officer:** Brendon Smurthwaite (01482 441421) **Nickname:** Rangers
Colours: Blue & white hoops/blue/blue & white **Change colours:** Green & white hoops **Founded:** 1959
Midweek Matches: Wednesday **Reserve League:** East Riding Co. Lge. **Sponsor:** John Moore Security
Previous Leagues: East Riding; Yorks 68-82. **Previous Ground:** Hull Co-Op (until 1968)
96-97 - Top Scorer: Lee Collingwood **P.o.Y.:** Lee Collingwood **Local Press:** Hull Daily Mail
Club Records - Attendance: 400 v Manchester City Aug 93 **Scorer:** G James **Appearances:** G James
Players progressing to Football League: Gerry Ingram (Blackpool, Sheff Wed).
Honours: Northern Co's East Lg Div 2 90-91, Yorks Lg Div 3 72-73 79-80, East Riding Snr Cup 72-73 93-94.

HARROGATE RAILWAY ATHLETIC

President: J Robinson **Chairman:** Dennis Bentley **Commercial Mgr:** Wendy Rock (01423 883104)
Secretary: W Douglas Oldfield, 80 Stonefall Ave., Harrogate, Nth Yorks HG2 7NP (01423 540786).
Manager: A Vincent **Coach:** A Canham **Physio:** J Tope
Press Officer / Programme Editor: Craig Dinsdale, Tel: 01423 521815 (H)
Ground: Station View, Starbeck, Harrogate (01423 885539).
Directions: A59 Harrogate to Knaresborough road. After approx 1.5 miles turn left just before railway level crossing. Ground is 150 yds up the lane. Adjacent to Starbeck (BR). Served by any Harrogate to Knareborough bus.
Seats: 300 **Cover:** 600 **Capacity:** 3,000 **Floodlights:** Yes **Founded:** 1935
Clubhouse: Games, TV room, lounge, open during normal public house hours every day. Hot food available.
Club Shop: Yes **Midweek matchday:** Monday **Sponsors:** Crest Homes
Colours: Red & green/green/red **Change:** White/red/white **Nickname:** The Rail
Local Press: Yorkshire Post, Harrogate Herald & Advertiser, York Press
Previous leagues: West Yorkshire; Harrogate District; Yorkshire 55-73 80-82.
Record Attendance: 1,400; 1962 FA Amateur Cup
96-97 Top Scorer: A Spence **96-97 Captain:** G Edmunds **96-97 P.o.Y.:** S Hampson
Honours: Northern Co's (East) Lg Cup 86-87

LOUTH UNITED

Chairman: George Horton **Vice-Chairman:** Andrew Sylvester **President:** Dave Fairburn
Secretary/Press Officer: Albany Jordan, 20d Upgate, Louth, Lincs. LN11 9ET. Tel: 01507 600694 (H)
Manager: Steve Newby **Coaches::** Nigel Fanthorpe/D Cole **Physio:** Kenny Vincent
Ground: Park Avenue, Louth, Lincs (01507 607351).
Directions: A16 To Louth Market Place, exit via Eastgate/Eastfield Rd, to Fire Station turn right into Park Avenue. Ground at bottom of avenue of prefabricated bungalows.
Capacity: 2,500 **Seats:** None **Cover:** 400 **Floodlights:** Yes **Nickname:** The Lions **Founded:** 1947
Clubhouse: Weekdays 6.30-11.45, Sat 12-11.45. Full bar facilities. Snacks available. **Club Shop:** No
Programme: 50p **Editor/Press Officer:** Albany Jordan (Sec.) **Midweek matches:** Tuesday
Colours: Royal with white stripes/royal/red **Change:** Red & black stripes **Reserves League:** Lincolnshire
Previous - Leagues: Lincs 47-75 82-88; Central Midlands 88-93. **Names:** Louth Nats & Louth Town - merged
Grounds: None
Club Records - Goalscorer: Peter Rawcliffe 39 **Appearances:** Gary Smith 476
Attendance: 2,500
Transfer fee received: £10,000 for Martyn Chalk (Derby County, 1990).
Players progressing to Football League: Terry Donovan (Grimsby), Paul Bartlett (Derby), Brian Klug (Ipswich), Glen Cockerill (Lincoln, Watford, Southampton), Peter Rawcliffe & Peter Green (Grimsby), Martin Chalk (Derby).
Sponsors: Foxhall Plant Hire
Honours: Lincs Lg Prem 72-73 85-86 86-87 (Div 1 57-58 66-67 67-68; Lg Challenge Cup 73-74 86-87; Lg Charity Cup 55-56 56-57 67-68; Central Mids Lg Cup R-up 92-93; Wakefield F'lit Cup R-up 91-92; Lincs Snr 'A' Cup 77-78.

Shaun Blades of Winterton Rangers and Ricky Greenhof of Harrogate Railway Atghletic (dark shirts) almost collide (or maybe they're dancing) during last season's league match at Station View. Photo: N Thaler

Louth United score against Parkgate at Roundwood last season. Photo: M Taylor

PARKGATE

President: T L Dabbs **Chairman:** Albert T Dudill, Tel: 01709 524533 (H) **Vice Chairman:** Les Taylor
Secretary: Bruce Bickerdike, 2 Cardew Close, Rawmarsh, Rotherham S62 6LB (01709 522305 Fax: 01709 528583).
Press Officer: Secretary **Manager:** Gary Gillatt **Asst Manager:** Alan Smith **Physio:** Peter Wakefield
Ground: Roundwood Sports Complex, Green Lane, Rawmarsh, Rotherham (01709 826600).
Directions: From Rotherham A633 to Rawmarsh. From Doncaster A630 to Conisbrough, then A6023 through Swinton to Rawmarsh. Grd at Green Lane – right from Rotherham, left from Conisbrough at the Crown Inn. Grd 800yds right
Seats: 300 **Cover:** 300 **Capacity:** 1,000 **Floodlights:** Yes **Founded:** 1969
Clubhouse: Licensed bar, 2 lounges. Meals available lunchtime Mon-Sat. **Club Shop:** No.
Colours: All red **Change colours:** All sky **Nickname:** The Gate or The Steelmen **Midweek matches:** Tuesday
Programme: 20 pages, 50p **Editor:** Stuart Bisby (01709 817524) **Club Sponsors:** British Steel
Previous - Leagues: Rotherham Association; Whitbread County Senior; Yorkshire 74-82
Ground: None **Names:** BSC Parkgate (until mid-eighties); RES Parkgate (pre-1994).
Senior Honours: None **Record attendance:** v Worksop 1982

ROSSINGTON MAIN

Chairman: Stephen Tagg, Clematis Cottage, 52 High St., Collingham, Newark, NG23 7LB. Tel: 01636 892833 (H)
Secretary: Gerald Parsons, 15 Seaton Gardens, Rossington, Doncaster DN11 0XA. Tel: 01302 867542 (H)
Joint Managers: D Ridley & L Ostle **Physio:** J White
Ground: Welfare Ground, Oxford Street, Rossington, Doncaster (01302 865524).
Directions: Enter Rossington and go over the railway crossings. Pass the Welfare Club on right, Oxford Street is next right - ground is at bottom. 8 miles from Doncaster (BR).
Seats: 200 **Cover:** 500 **Capacity:** 2,000 **Floodlights:** Yes **Nickname:** The Colliery **Founded:** 1920
Clubhouse: Evenings & matchdays, Sandwiches, rolls, satillite TV, pool. **Club Shop:** No
Programme: 50p **Editor:** Chairman **Midweek matches:** Wednesday **Sponsor:** RJB Mining
Colours: All white **Change colours:** Blue & black **Reserve League:** Beefeater County Sen
Previous Leagues: Doncaster Sen, Yorkshire Lge, Sheffield County Sen, Cent Mids.
Club Records - Attendance: 864 v Leeds United 8/91. **Goalscorer:** Mark Illman **Appearances:** Darren Phipps
Players progressing to Football League: Jim Harkin (Shrewsbury, Mansfield, Doncaster Rov),Shaw Bothers (WBA, Doncaster), Joe Leiversly (Arsenal), Dennis Leiversly/Ken Hardwicke/Brian Makepease/Jack Teasdale/Gary Jones (Doncaster), Ronnie Spence (York City), Reg Brian (Blackpool), Bob Forest/Brian Taylor (Leeds Utd), Malcolm Webster (Arsenal/Southend/Cambridge).
Honours: Sen Lge 44-45, Cup 44-45, CMFL Prem Lge 84-85, Cup 83-84 84-85, DDSAL Shield 90-91 R-up 89-90.

STAVELEY MINERS WELFARE

Chairman: Henry Ireson, Tel: 01246 452475 (H) **Vice-Chairman:** Phil White
Secretary: John Wilmot, 12 Winster Rd, Staveley, Chesterfield, Derbyshire S43 3NJ. Tel: 01246 476875 (H)
Ground: Inkersall Road, Staveley, Chesterfield, Derbyshire (01246 471441).
Directions: M1 jct 30, follow A619 Chesterfield - Staveley is 3 miles from jct 30. Turn left at GK Garage in Staveley town centre into Inkersall Rd - ground 200yds on right at side of Speedwell Rooms. Frequent buses (47, 70, 72, 75, 77) from Chesterfield stop in Staveley town centre - 3 mins walk to ground.
Capacity: 5,000 **Cover:** 200 **Seats:** 200 **Floodlights:** Yes **Nickname:** The Welfare **Founded:** 1989
Clubhouse: The Staveley Miners Welfare, 500yds from ground, is open before and after games.
Club Shop: Yes, contact Craig Cousins, 01246 475068.
Colours: All red **Change colours:** Yellow/blue/yellow **Midweek matches:** Tuesday
Programme: 16 pages, 30p **Editor:** Henry Ireson (Chairman) **Reserves' League:** Central Midlands Res. Div.
Club Records - Attendance: 280 v Stocksbridge, Sheffield Snr Cup 22/1/94.
Goalscorer: Paul Nicholls **Appearances:** Shane Turner
Previous Leagues: Chesterfield & D. Amat 89-91; County Sen 91-93. **Honours:** County Sen Lg Div 2 92-93, Div 3 91-92, Chesterfield & D. Amat Lg R-up 89-90 90-91, Byron (Lge) Cup 89-90, R-up 90-91.

TADCASTER ALBION

Chairman: Michael R Burnett, Tel: 01937 832802 (H/Fax) **President:** Lord Edward Stourton
Secretary: Mrs Angela J Burnett, 6 Beech Grove House, Ouston Lane, Tadcaster LS24 8DP. Tel: 01937 832802 (H/Fax)
Manager: Ken Payne **Match Sec:** Howard Clarke, 01937 832887 (H/B)
Ground: The Park, Ings Lane, Tadcaster, LS24 9AY (01937 834119)
Directions: From West Riding and South Yorks, turn right off A659 at John Smith's Brewery Clock. From East Riding turn left off A659 after passing over river bridge and pelican crossing (New Street).
Colours: Blue & red/red/red **Change colours:** White/black/black **Midweek Matchday:** Tuesday
Programme: 20 pages **Programme Editor:** Mrs Angela Burnett (Sec.) **Founded:** 1936

WINTERTON RANGERS

President: J W Hiles **Chairman:** D Waterfall **Vice Chairman:** A Smith
Secretary/Press Officer: G Spencer, 2 Dale Park Ave., Winterton, Scunthorpe, Sth Humbs DN15 9UY (01724 732039).
Manager: Martin Jacklin **Asst Manager/Coach:** Peter Lea
Ground: West Street, Winterton, Scunthorpe, South Humberside (01724 732628).
Directions: From Scunthorpe take A1077 Barton-on-Humber road for 5 miles. On entering Winterton take second right (Eastgate), third left (Northlands Road) and first right (West Street). Ground 200yds on left
Seats: 200 **Covered:** 200 **Capacity:** 3,000 **Floodlights:** Yes **Founded:** 1930
Clubhouse: Open matchdays & evenings Mon-Sat, hot & cold food available on matchdays. Pool and snooker rooms.
Colours: Navy & white/navy/navy **Change colours:** All red **Nickname:** Rangers
Midweek matches: Wednesday **Sponsors:** Finaction Ltd **Club Shop:** No.
Programme: 28-36 pages, 50p **Editor:** M Fowler (01724 734570)
Local Press: Scunthorpe Evening Telegraph
Previous League: Scunthorpe & Dist. 45-65/ Lincs 65-70/ Yorkshire 70-82.
Previous Grounds: Watery Lane 1930-48.
Record attendance: 1,200 v Sheffield Utd – Official opening of floodlights, October 1978.
Record transfer fee received: £5,000 for Henry Smith (Leeds United, 1979).
Best FA Vase year: QF 76-77 **Best FA Cup year:** 4th Qual Rd replay 76-77 (lost 2-3 after 3-3)
Players progressing to Football League: Henry Smith (Leeds, Hearts), Keith Walwyn (Chesterfield, York, Carlisle), Rick Greenhough (Chester, York)
96-97 Captain: Steve Bell **96-97 P.o.Y.:** Tony McGrath **96-97 Top Scorer:** Grafme Ross
Honours: Lincs Jnr Cup 47-48 61-62; Lincs Snr 'B' Cup 69-70; Yorks Lg 71-72 76-77 78-79 (Lg Cup 80-81); Northern Co's East Lg Div 2 89-90; S'thorpe Lg & Cup many times; Philips National F'light 6-aside 76-77.

WORSBROUGH BRIDGE M.W. & ATHLETIC

Chairman: Mr J Wright **Press Officer:** Mr A Wright (01226 243418).
Secretary: Garry Wiggan, 9 Pantry Well, Worsbrough Bridge, Barnsley, S. Yorks S70 4SW (01226 247023)
Manager: K Paddon **Asst Manager:**
Ground: Park Road, Worsbrough Bridge, Barnsley (01226 284452).
Directions: On the A61 Barnsley-Sheffield road two miles south of Barnsley, 2 miles from M1 jnt 36 opposite Blackburns Bridge. Two and a half miles from Barnsley (BR). Yorkshire Traction run buses every 10 mins thru Worsbrough Bridge.
Seats: 175 **Cover:** 175 **Capacity:** 2,000 **Floodlights:** Due **Founded:** 1923
Colours: All red **Change colours:** Yellow/blue **Reformed:** 1947
Record attendance: 2,300 v Blyth Spartans, FA Amateur Cup 1971
Previous Leagues: Barnsley 52-61/ County Snr 62-70/ Yorks 71-82.
Midweek Matchday: Wednesday **Programme:** 20 pages, 20p
Honours: Northern Co's East Div 1 R-up 90-91 (Div 3 R-up 85-86); Sheffield Snr Cup R-up 72-73; County Snr Lg 65-66 69-70 (R-up 62-63, Lg Cup 65-66); Barnsley Lg 52-53 58-59 59-60, Lg Cup 56-57 58-59 (R-up 53-54), Beckett Cup 57-58.

YORKSHIRE AMATEUR

Chairman: William Ellis, Tel: 01405 839990 (H) **President:** Rayner Barker
Secretary: Charles Sharman, 44 Roxholme Place, Leeds LS7 4JQ (0113 293 8894 H) (0113 244 5596 B).
Manager: Kevin Smith **Coach:** Dave Holmes **Physio:** Terry Davies
Ground: The Bracken Edge Football Ground, Roxholme Road, Leeds LS8 4DZ (0113 262 4093).
Directions: From South M1 to Leeds, then A58 Wetherby Road to Fforde Green Hotel, left at lights and proceed to Sycamore Ave. (on right). From East A1 to Boot & Shoe Inn then to Shaftesbury Hotel, turn right into Harehills Lane, then to Sycamore Avenue. Two and a half miles from Leeds (BR). Buses 2, 3 & 20 from Briggate to Harehills Ave.
Seats: 200 **Cover:** 160 **Capacity:** 1,550 **Floodlights:** Yes **Club Shop:** Yes
Clubhouse: Bar, tea bar, games, lounge. Every night 8.30-11, Sat matchdays 12-11, Sun 12-3.
Programme: 12 pages, 50p **Editor:** Secretary **Midweek Matches:** Tuesday **Founded:** 1919
Colours: White/navy/red **Change colours:** All red **Sponsors:** Bridge Electrical **Nickname:** Ammers
Local Newspapers: Yorkshire Post/ Yorkshire Evening Post/ North Leeds Advertiser.
Previous League: Yorks 20-24 30-82. **Previous ground:** Elland Road 1919-20
Record Attendance: 4,000 v Wimbledon, FA Amateur Cup QF 1932.
Players progressing to Football League: Gary Strodder & Stuart Naylor (WBA), Peter Swan (Leeds), Brian Deane (Doncaster, Sheffield United, Leeds). **1996-97 Top Scorer:** R Beardsaaw (20)
Honours: FA Amtr Cup SF 31-32, West Riding Co. Cup(3), Yorks Lg 31-32 (Div 2 58-59 (R-up 52-53 71-72), Div 3 77-78, Lg Cup 32-33), Leeds & Dist. Snr Cup.

REDFERNS INTERNATIONAL REMOVERS CENTRAL MIDLANDS LEAGUE

FEEDER TO:
Northern Counties East League

Chairman & General Secretary:
F A Harwood, 103 Vestry Road, Oakwood, Derby DE21 2BN (01332 832372)

Public Relations Officer: S Wilton, 57 Main Road, Smalley, Derby DE7 6DS (01332 880199)

REVIEW OF THE SEASON

The season held a sting in the tail. It had, in many ways, been a memorable campaign, with many clubs reporting a greater interest in their activities and increases in attendances.

Heanor Town led the Supreme Division from day one and completed their second championship in three years on Easter Monday with a 5-0 success at Sandiacre Town, eventually winning the title by a massive seventeen points.

In an exciting race for runners-up spot, Dunkirk's magnificent finish to the season saw them pip likely contenders Staveley Miners Welfare by a point on the last day of the season. Once again Heanor's facilities were not of the required standard for Northern Counties East League football and promotion was denied both the Lions and Dunkirk, but Staveley Miners Welfare will be making the transition next season as the Central Midlands League continues their policy of support from the base of the Northern (UniBond) Pyramid.

In the Premier Division Clipstone Welfare also completed a second title in three seasons which, this time, will be accompanied by promotion to the Supreme Division along with the other candidates, Grimethorpe Miners Welfare, Rossington and Collingham.

For their pains in taking Clipstone Welfare all the way to the wire, Grimethorpe Miners Welfare ended a fine first season in the league by picking up the Cox League Cup with a 2-1 win over Heanor Town at Mansfield Town's Field Mill ground in a well-supported Final. Thus Heanor were denied a league and cup double for the second time in three seasons.

The sting in the tail came with the announcement that three of our clubs were to fold within days of completion of the season. Nuthall, Case Sports and Killamarsh Juniors all found the cost prohibitive and willing hands hard to come by.

Most of our clubs are faced with massive and costly building programmes if they are to achieve their ambitions of progress through the Northern Pyramid. It could well be that, with such high demands, yet more may fall by the wayside in the name of progress. A daunting thought indeed, which makes one wonder at this level of the Pyramid at least, if these demands are not too extravagant.

Derby Rolls Royce have resigned apparently to return to Junior football, but new recruits include Greenwood Meadows and Hucknall Rolls Royce from the Notts Alliance, Welfare from the Beefeater County Senior League, Selston from the Midlands Regional Alliance and Goole AFC – a club borne out of the ashes of the old Goole Town.

A bonus for the League is that four of the five new recruits boast floodlights.

Heanor Town F.C. The Lions from the Central Midlands League.

Dunkirk F.C. Team line up before their 1-0 splendid home victory vs Steveley M.W.

FINAL LEAGUE TABLES 1996/97

TRAVIS PERKINS SUPREME DIVISION

	P	W	D	L	F	A	Pts
Heanor Town	30	24	2	4	72	26	74
Dunkirk	30	17	6	7	66	35	57
Staveley M. Welfare	30	16	7	7	45	32	55
Gedling Town	30	16	6	8	59	44	54
Graham Street Prims	30	16	5	9	61	34	53
Mickleover Sports	30	12	12	6	62	40	48
Thorne Colliery	30	13	4	13	35	44	43
Nettleham	30	11	9	10	42	48	42
Nuthall	30	10	6	14	55	52	36
Long Eaton United	30	9	7	14	41	49	34
Shirebrook Town	30	8	9	13	32	51	33
Case Sports	30	7	10	13	38	62	31
Kimberley Town	30	8	6	16	45	53	30
South Normanton Ath.	30	7	9	14	32	51	30
Harworth Col. Ins.	30	5	7	18	28	57	22
Sandiacre Town	30	5	7	18	35	70	22

PREMIER DIVISION

	P	W	D	L	F	A	Pts
Clipstone Welfare	34	25	6	3	109	29	81
Grimethorpe M. Welfare	34	23	7	4	104	26	76
Rossington	34	22	3	9	92	50	69
Collingham	34	20	7	7	73	37	67
Killamarsh Juniors	34	19	6	9	89	51	63
Sheffield Hallam Univ.	34	18	6	10	74	53	60
Sneinton	34	17	6	11	61	37	57
Askern Welfare	34	17	4	13	76	57	55
Shardlow St James	34	15	4	15	72	63	49
Derby Rolls Royce	34	13	5	16	68	61	44
Sheepbridge	34	12	5	17	64	69	41
Hemsworth Town	34	13	5	16	52	63	41*
Radford	34	12	5	17	50	70	41
Stanton Ilkeston	34	9	9	16	53	75	36
Mexborough Athletic	34	8	7	19	48	104	31
Holbrook	34	8	4	22	46	98	28
Blackwell M. Welfare	34	3	5	26	24	130	14
Mickleover R.B.L.	34	3	4	27	22	104	13

SUPREME DIVISION RESULTS CHART 1996-97

HOME TEAM	1	2	3	4	5	6	7	8	9	10	11	12	13	14	15	16
1. Case Sports		0-4	2-4	0-5	0-3	0-2	0-2	2-1	4-1	1-0	3-5	2-2	3-0	2-2	0-4	0-0
2. Dunkirk	2-2		3-0	1-2	4-0	1-3	2-0	3-3	1-1	3-2	2-0	6-1	4-0	2-0	1-0	2-3
3. Gedling Town	2-3	0-1		1-3	6-1	2-3	2-1	2-2	1-1	3-4	2-1	4-2	0-2	4-2	2-1	1-0
4. Graham Street Prims	1-2	3-1	0-4		1-1	1-2	4-0	0-1	0-2	0-1	5-2	2-1	4-0	3-1	1-0	3-0
5. Harworth Colliery Inst	2-1	1-1	2-3	0-4		1-5	0-1	0-2	1-1	1-1	2-1	4-0	0-0	0-1	0-1	0-1
6. Heanor Town	5-0	2-1	3-1	3-1	2-1		3-1	2-0	2-2	2-2	3-2	4-1	6-1	0-1	1-2	1-0
7. Kimberley Town	2-3	1-3	0-1	2-2	4-2	0-2		2-0	1-1	2-3	1-1	2-3	1-2	0-1	2-3	3-0
8. Long Eaton United	0-0	0-1	0-0	3-2	4-2	0-1	0-0		2-5	0-1	3-2	3-2	2-3	3-1	0-2	0-0
9. Mickleover Sports	3-3	1-2	0-1	1-1	3-0	2-0	5-0	3-1		0-2	2-2	4-1	2-2	4-0	1-0	1-2
10. Nettleham	2-0	2-2	1-1	0-3	2-0	1-0	0-2	2-2	1-5		0-4	3-1	1-1	1-0	0-1	0-1
11. Nuthall	1-1	2-2	1-3	0-2	1-0	0-1	3-2	3-0	3-3	6-3		0-0	6-1	4-1	0-2	2-1
12. Sandiacre Town	4-2	1-4	1-3	0-2	1-2	0-5	2-2	1-0	1-2	1-1	0-2		0-1	3-3	3-0	2-1
13. Shirebrook Town	0-0	0-1	0-0	2-2	3-0	1-2	0-4	3-1	1-2	0-1	1-0	3-0		2-2	0-1	0-1
14. South Normanton Ath	0-0	0-4	1-2	1-1	1-0	1-3	1-1	2-1	1-1	2-2	2-0	0-0	2-0		0-1	2-4
15. Staveley Miners Wel	2-2	2-0	2-2	1-0	1-1	0-2	3-1	2-4	1-1	2-2	3-1	0-0	2-2	2-1		3-2
16. Thorne Colliery	1-0	3-2	1-2	1-3	1-1	0-2	1-5	0-3	3-2	2-1	1-0	3-1	1-1	1-0	0-1	

PREMIER DIVISION RESULTS CHART 1996-97

HOME TEAM	1	2	3	4	5	6	7	8	9	10	11	12	13	14	15	16	17	18
1. Askern Welfare		7-0	2-3	3-4	1-5	0-0	0-2	1-3	1-3	7-0	3-0	3-1	0-2	2-2	2-4	1-0	2-2	0-0
2. Blackwell M. Welfare	0-3		0-3	1-2	2-5	0-8	1-1	4-2	0-6	2-3	3-1	0-3	0-6	0-6	2-5	0-3	1-3	2-1
3. Clipstone Welfare	3-2	6-0		2-0	2-0	1-1	5-0	4-3	3-0	4-1	8-0	8-0	2-4	0-0	9-0	1-1	2-0	3-0
4. Collingham	4-3	0-0	0-3		3-2	1-1	4-0	4-0	2-2	6-2	5-0	0-0	2-1	1-0	3-0	2-1	3-1	5-1
5. Derby Rolls Royce	0-2	4-0	1-2	3-2		0-2	4-1	1-1	0-1	5-1	3-1	0-1	3-2	4-1	1-3	0-0	2-1	3-3
6. Grimethorpe M. W.	5-0	10-1	1-2	2-0	4-2		0-0	7-0	3-1	2-2	9-0	3-0	0-1	4-1	1-0	4-0	2-1	3-1
7. Hemsworth Town	5-2	5-1	1-1	0-1	1-1	1-3		4-1	3-2	6-0	4-2	1-0	1-5	2-1	1-0	1-2	1-2	1-2
8. Holbrook	1-3	2-1	0-5	2-7	0-6	0-5	2-1		2-1	1-1	4-2	4-1	1-2	5-1	1-3	0-6	0-2	0-1
9. Killamarsh Juniors	0-2	8-0	1-3	2-3	3-2	1-2	4-1	3-2		3-0	7-0	2-1	3-0	3-3	2-1	0-0	4-1	3-3
10. Mexborough Ath.	2-0	0-0	0-5	0-3	3-1	1-5	2-3	1-1	1-7		3-0	0-0	4-2	1-2	3-3	1-4	0-1	4-3
11. Mickleover R.B.L.	2-1	2-2	0-5	0-0	0-1	1-0	0-1	0-1	2-3	0-1		2-6	0-1	1-1	2-2	0-4	0-7	2-1
12. Radford	2-5	4-0	1-1	0-3	3-0	0-1	1-0	1-1	1-1	0-2	2-1		2-4	1-0	2-0	0-2	1-5	4-2
13. Rossington	1-3	6-0	2-2	1-1	4-2	3-0	4-2	3-2	0-0	6-0	4-0	2-3		3-2	4-1	1-0	1-0	8-1
14. Shardlow St James	1-2	4-0	2-1	1-0	4-1	1-5	7-0	5-1	0-3	3-2	1-0	6-3	2-3		2-3	5-1	0-4	3-0
15. Sheepbridge	0-1	3-0	1-3	0-1	1-1	2-4	1-0	1-2	2-4	6-2	3-0	6-2	2-3	0-2		5-1	0-2	0-1
16. Sheffield Hallam U.	0-3	3-0	4-2	1-0	5-3	0-5	1-0	2-0	4-0	9-3	3-0	2-1	4-2	1-3	1-1		1-1	2-2
17. Sneinton	0-1	1-1	0-1	2-1	1-0	0-0	0-1	2-1	2-3	3-1	2-0	2-1	2-0	5-0	1-1	3-1		1-1
18. Stanton Ilkeston	1-3	4-0	1-4	0-0	0-2	2-2	1-1	2-1	1-3	1-1	3-1	1-2	3-1	1-0	3-4	3-5	3-1	

COX CENTRAL MIDLANDS LEAGUE CUP

Holders: Killamarsh Juniors

Preliminary Round

Dunkirk	v	South Normanton A	1-0	Rossington	v	Graham Strt Pr	1-1 1-3

First Round

Case Sports	v	Blackwell Miners W	9-0	Graham Street Prims	v	Heanor Town	2-2 1-2
Grimethorpe Miners W.	v	Collingham	3-0	Harworth Colliery Inst	v	Sneinton	1-0
Killamarsh Juniors	v	Nettleham	4-4 2-4*	Hemsworth Town	v	Gedling Town	2-2 2-1*
Mexborough Athletic	v	Dunkirk	1-2	Mickleover Royal B. L.	v	Askern Welfare	1-3
Mickleover Sports	v	Derby Rolls Royce	2-0	Nuthall	v	Long Eaton U.	0-0 3-1
Sandiacre Town	v	Kimberley Town	0-2	Shardlow St James	v	Sheepbridge	1-0
Shirebrook Town	v	Radford	2-2 1-2	Sheffield Hallam Univ.	v	Clipstone Welfare	1-1 2-1
Stanton Ilkeston	v	Thorne Colliery	1-3	Staveley Miners Welfare	v	Holbrook	5-0

Second Round

Askern Welfare	v	Thorne Colliery	0-0 3-2	Case Sports	v	Radford	3-0
Dunkirk	v	Heanor Town	1-3	Harworth Colliery Inst.	v	Shardlow St J	1-1 0-4
Kimberley Town	v	Nettleham	0-2	Mickleover Sports	v	Grimethorpe MW	1-1 0-4
Nuthall	v	Sheffield Hallam Un.	7-2	Staveley Miners Welfare	v	Hemsworth Town	0-1

Third Round

Grimethorpe Miners W	v	Hemsworth Town	3-2	Nettleham	v	Heanor Town	1-2
Nuthall	v	Case Sports	1-1 4-3*	Shardlow St James	v	Askern Welfare	1-0

Semi-Finals

Heanor Town	v	Shardlow St James	3-0	Grimethorpe Miners W	v	Nuthall	3-2
(at Staveley Miners Welfare FC)				(at Staveley Miners Welfare FC)			

Final Tie

Grimethorpe Miners W v Heanor Town 2-1

(at Mansfield Town FC) Attendance: 392

*Denotes after extra time.

WAKEFIELD FLOODLIT CHALLENGE CUP

Group 'A'

Grimethorpe MW	v	Shirebrook Town	1-1	Grimethorpe MW	v	Staveley MW	1-1
Shirebrook Town	v	Grimethorpe MW	1-2	Shirebrook Town	v	Staveley MW	1-0
Staveley MW	v	Grimethorpe MW	1-2	Staveley MW	v	Shirebrook Town	0-1

	P	W	D	L	F	A	Pts
Grimethorpe MW	4	2	2	0	6	4	8
Shirebrook Town	4	2	1	1	4	3	7
Staveley MW	4	0	1	3	2	5	1

Group 'B'

Gedling Town	v	Nuthall	2-1	Gedling Town	v	Stanton Ilkeston	3-0
Nuthall	v	Gedling Town	0-4	Nuthall	v	Stanton Ilkeston	5-1
Stanton Ilkeston	v	Gedling Town	2-3	Stanton Ilkeston	v	Nuthall	2-3

	P	W	D	L	F	A	Pts
Gedling Town	4	4	0	0	12	3	12
Nuthall	4	2	0	2	9	9	6
Stanton Ilkeston	4	0	0	4	5	14	0

Group 'C'

Collingham	v	Nettleham	0-2	Collingham	v	Sandiacre Town	2-2
Nettleham	v	Collingham	1-2	Nettleham	v	Sandiacre Town	1-0
Sandiacre Town	v	Collingham	0-4	Sandiacre Town	v	Nettleham	1-1

	P	W	D	L	F	A	Pts
Collingham	4	2	1	1	10	3	7
Nettleham	4	2	1	1	5	3	7
Sandiacre Town	4	0	2	2	3	8	2

Group 'D'

Harworth CI	v	Heanor Town	1-7	Harworth CI	v	Kimberley Town	1-2
Heanor Town	v	Harworth CI	5-1	Heanor Town	v	Kimberley Town	1-1
Kimberley Town	v	Harworth CI	1-0	Kimberley Town	v	Heanor Town	2-4

	P	W	D	L	F	A	Pts
Henor Town	4	3	1	0	15	4	10
Kimberley Town	4	2	1	1	7	5	7
Harworth CI	4	0	0	4	3	15	0

Second Road			First Leg	Second Leg	Aggr Score
Nuthall	v	Collingham	1-2	4-1	5-3
Shirebrook Town	v	Heanor Town	1-3	0-4	1-7
Nettleham	v	Gedling Town	2-3	3-1	5-4
Kimberley Town	v	Grimethorpe Miners Welfare	0-1	1-3	1-4
Semi-Finals					
Nuthall	v	Heanor Town	5-1	1-4*	6-5
Grimethorpe Miners W	v	Nettleham	0-1	0-0	0-1
Final					
Nuthall	v	Nettleham	3-0	0-0	3-0

*Denotes after extra time

Holders: Harworth Colliery Institute

KEN MARSLAND INVITATION TROPHY

Group 1

Clipstone	v	Glapwell	5-0	Clipstone	v	Sheepbridge	5-0
Clipstone	v	Shirebrook	3-1	Clipstone	v	Staveley	2-2
Glapwell	v	Clipstone	3-1	Glapwell	v	Sheepbridge	3-2
Glapwell	v	Shirebrook	0-0	Glapwell	v	Staveley	0-2
Sheepbridge	v	Clipstone	2-2	Sheepbridge	v	Glapwell	3-0
Sheepbridge	v	Shirebrook	1-2	Sheepbridge	v	Staveley	1-15
Shirebrook	v	Clipstone	3-1	Shirebrook	v	Glapwell	1-0
Shirebrook	v	Sheepbridge	2-2	Shirebrook	v	Staveley	0-2
Staveley	v	Clipstone	2-2	Staveley	v	Glapwell	7-1
Staveley	v	Sheepbridge	1-0	Staveley	v	Shirebrook	4-1

	P	*W*	*D*	*L*	*F*	*A*	*Pts*
Staveley MW	8	6	2	0	35	7	20
Clipstone Welfare	8	3	3	2	21	13	12
Shirebrook Town	8	3	2	3	10	13	11
Glapwell	8	2	1	5	7	21	7
Sheepbridge	8	1	2	5	11	30	5

Group 2

Derby RR	v	Mickleover RBL	0-1	Derby RR	v	Mickleover Sports	1-3
Derby RR	v	Sandiacre Town	0-2	Derby RR	v	Shardlow	0-6
Mickleover RBL	v	Derby RR	0-3	Mickleover RBL	v	Mickleover Spts	0-6
Mickleover RBL	v	Sandiacre	1-3	Mickleover RBL	v	Shardlow	1-5
Mickleover Sports	v	Derby RR	0-2	Mickleover Sports	v	Mickleover RBL	4-0
Mickleover Sports	v	Sandiacre	1-2	Mickleover Sports	v	Shardlow	1-3
Sandiacre	v	Derby RR	2-3	Sandiacre	v	Mickleover RBL	7-1
Sandiacre	v	Mickleover Sports	2-4	Sandiacre	v	Shardlow	1-5
Shardlow	v	Derby RR	3-1	Shardlow	v	Mickleover RBL	6-1
Shardlow	v	Mickleover Sports	0-0	Shardlow	v	Sandiacre	4-0

	P	*W*	*D*	*L*	*F*	*A*	*Pts*
Shardlow St James	8	7	1	0	32	5	22
Mickleover Sports	8	4	1	3	19	19	13
Sandiacre Town	8	4	0	4	19	19	12
Derby Rolls Royce	8	3	0	3	10	17	6
Mickleover RBL	8	1	0	7	5	34	3

Group 3

Heanor	v	Kimberley	3-1	Heanor	v	Long Eaton	4-2
Heanor	v	Nuthall	2-1	Heanor	v	Stanton	2-0
Kimberley	v	Heanor	0-3	Kimberley	v	Long Eaton	2-0
Kimberley	v	Nuthall	4-1	Kimberley	v	Stanton	3-1
Long Eaton	v	Heanor	3-3	Long Eaton	v	Kimberley	2-6
Long Eaton	v	Nuthall	1-5	Long Eaton	v	Stanton	5-6
Nuthall	v	Heanor	3-0	Nuthall	v	Kimberley	1-2
Nuthall	v	Long Eaton	4-0	Nuthall	v	Stanton	2-3
Stanton	v	Heanor	0-6	Stanton	v	Kimberley	0-6
Stanton	v	Long Eaton	3-3	Stanton	v	Nuthall	3-1

	P	*W*	*D*	*L*	*F*	*A*	*Pts*
Heanor Town	8	6	1	1	23	11	19
Kimberley Town	8	6	0	2	24	11	18
Stanton Ilkeston	8	3	1	4	16	28	10
Nuthall	8	3	0	5	18	15	9
Long Eaton United	8	0	2	6	16	33	2

Group 4

Dunkirk	v	Gedling	1-1	Dunkirk	v	Long Eaton 'A'	4-0
Dunkirk	v	Radford	1-3	Gedling	v	Dunkirk	1-2
Gedling	v	Long Eaton 'A'	9-0	Gedling	v	Radford	4-1
Long Eaton 'A'	v	Dunkirk	0-3	Long Eaton 'A'	v	Gedling	0-2
Long Eaton 'A'	v	Radford	1-2	Radford	v	Dunkirk	0-2
Radford	v	Gedling	2-4	Radford	v	Long Eaton 'A'	3-2

	P	*W*	*D*	*L*	*F*	*A*	*Pts*
Gedling Town	6	4	1	1	21	6	13
Dunkirk	6	4	1	1	13	5	13
Radford	6	3	0	3	11	14	9
Long Eaton Utd 'A'	6	0	0	6	3	23	0

Semi-Finals

Heanor Town Reserves	v	Gedling Town Res	3-2	Shardlow St James Res	v	Staveley MW Res after extra time	3-2

Final

Heanor Town Reserves v Shardlow St James R 0-2 (at South Normanton Athletic FC)

SUPREME DIVISION CLUBS 1997-98

CLIPSTONE WELFARE

Secretary: Barry Clarke, 40 Church Road, Clipstone, Mansfield, NG21 9DG (01623 640829).
Manager: Carl Hanson **Midweek Matchday:** Tuesday or Wednesday
Ground & Directions: Clipstone Lido Ground Clipstone Road West, Mansfield, Notts (01632 655674). B6030 from Mansfield, between Forest Town & Clipstone, on left entering Clipstone.
Colours: Red & navy/navy/white **Change Colours:** Amber & navy/navy/amber
Honours: Notts Snr Cup 85-86 94-95, Notts Alliance 72-73 73-74 74-75 92-93 94-95 (Lg Cup 72-73 73-74 74-75 94-95 (R-up 92-93)), Notts I'mediate Cup 55-56.

COLLINGHAM

Secretary: Mr G Williams, 47 Dukes End, Collingham, Newark, Nottinghamshire NG23 7LD (01636 892189)
Manager: Paul Hyde **Midweek Matchday:** Tuesday
Ground & Directions: Collingham FC, Station Road, Collingham, Newark, Notts. (01636 892303) Take A46 Newark to Lincoln road (Newark bypass). Turn left into Collingham on the A1133 road. In village turn right at traffic lights. Ground 100 yards on left.
Colours: Amber & black/black/black **Change Colours:** Blue & white/blue/blue

DUNKIRK

Secretary: Steve Trossell, 24 Kingfisher Wharf, Castle Marina, Nottingham NG7 1GA (0115 947903)
Manager: John Humphreys **Midweek Matchday:** Tuesday
Ground & Directions: The Ron Steel Sports Ground, Trentside Farm, Clifton Bridge, Nottingham (0602 850803). Ring Road - Clifton Bridge (North End), Industrial Estate, Lenton Lane.
Colours: Red/white/red **Change Colours:** Black & white/black/red
Honours: Notts Alliance Div 1 84-85 (Div 2 82-83, Lg Cup R-up 84-85), Notts I'mediate Cup 83-84.

GEDLING TOWN

Secretary: Paul Dobson, 26 Chevin Gardens, Top Valley Estate, Nottingham NG5 9ES (0115 9274790)
Manager: Everton Marsh/Jamie Brodie **Physio:** Trevor Wells/Pete Tyers
Ground & Directions: Riverside Ground, rear Ferry Boat Inn, Stoke Inn, Stoke Bardolph, Gedling, Nottm (01159 402145). A612 Nottingham-Lowdham-Southwell road. just before Burton Joyce turn right into Stoke Lane to Ferryboat Public House. Approx 1 1/2 miles. Ground rear of Ferry Boat Inn.
Capacity: 2,000 **Seats:** None **Cover:** 500 **Floodlights:** Yes **Shop:** No
Clubhouse: Matchdays only. Hot & cold food. Licensed bar.
Programme: 32pages 50p **Editor:** Paul Dodson **Founded:** 1989 **Nickname:** None
Colours: Yellow & nvay/navy/yellow **Change colours:** All red
Record Attendance: 250 v Arnold Town. **Goalscorer:** Robbie Orton 31, **Apperances:** Gary Ball 125. **Win:** 11-0 v Radford 91-92. **Defeat:** 2-5 v Staveley MW 93-94.
Best season FA Vase: 3rd Rd 96-97 **Midweek Matchday:** Wednesday
96-97 Captain: John Flint **P.O.Y.:** Robbie Orton **Top Scorer:** Robbie Orton 31
Honours: Central Mids Lg Div 1 90-91 (Premier Div R-up 91-92, Wakefield Floodlit Trophy 92-93, Ken Marsland Cup(Res.) 93-94), Notts Amtr Lg 89-90 (Snr Cup R-up 89-90).

GRAHAM STREET PRIM.

Secretary: David Wright, 6 Athol Close, Sinfin Moor, Derby DE24 9L2 (01332 606837)
Manager: S Woodings **Midweek Matchday:** Tuesday
Ground & Directions: Carriage & Wagon Welfare Club, Longbridge Lane, off Ascot Drive, Derby (01332 571376) M1 Junc 25, take A52 to Derby, turn left onto A5111 ring road, Raynesway. Take left at next island Ascot Drive and first right into Longbridge Lane
Colours: Red (white trim)/black/red **Change Colours:** Yellow/black/black

GRIMETHORPE MINERS WELFARE

Secretary: Arthur Gill, 7 Duke Street, Grimethorpe, Barnsley, Yorks S72 7NJ (01226 712863)
Manager: Stewart Barrowclough **Midweek Matchday:** Tuesday or Wednesday
Ground & Directions: Grimethorpe Miners Welfare, Cemetery Road, Grimethorpe. (01226 711544), A1M to A635 Hickleton to Thurnscoe, turn right to Houghton, At Robin Hood, turn left to Grimethorpe M1 junc 36. A628 to Shafton traffic lights, turn right to Grimethorpe.
Colours: All Blue & black **Change Colours:** All red

HARWORTH COLLIERY INSTITUTE

Secretary: Tom Brogan, 30 Lindsey Road, Harworth, Doncaster, Sth Yorks DN11 8QH (01302 750132).
Manager: Alan Needham **Midweek Matchday:** Wednesday
Ground & Directions: Recreation Ground, Scrooby Rd, Bircotes, Doncaster (01302 750614). Off A1(M) at Blyth, head towards Bawtry for approx 2 miles, take third left, ground in village at top of hill on left. Or, from Doncaster to Bawtry then head for A1(M) and turn left after caravan site - ground at top of hill.
Colours: Amber & black/black/amber & black **Change Colours:** Red & blue/red/red
Honours: Wharncliffe Charity Cup 62-63 74-75, Central Midlands League 87-88 (Runners-up 86-87, Challenge Cup 86-87 87-88, F'lit Cup 91-92 (Runners-up 89-90)), Sheffield Senior League 64-65 74-75, Sheffield & Hallamshire Senior Cup SF 87-88

HEANOR TOWN

Secretary: Keith Costello, 45 Stainsby Avenue, Heanor, Derbyshire DE75 7EL (01773 719446).
Manager: Bill Fossey **Midweek Matchday:** Wednesday
Ground & Directions: The Town Ground, Mayfield Avenue, Heanor (01773 713742/715815). M1 (J26), take A610 onto A608, ground 200yds from Market Square
Colours: White/black/black **Change Colours:** All red or all blue
Honours: Central Midlands League Cup 94-95 (Runners-up 86-87 92-93, B E Webbe Removals Cup 88-89), West Midlands Reg. League Runners-up 72-73; Midland Co's League Runners-up 65-66 67-68; Derbys Senior Cup(9) 1892-94 1946-47 65-69 70-71 78-79; FA Cup 1st Rd 58-59 63-64.

KIMBERLEY TOWN

Chairman: George Giddens **Vice Chairman:** Reg Izzard **President:** Russell Penney
Match Secretary: Alan Jennings, 8 Watchwood Grove, Calverton, Nottingham NG14 6HX (0115 965 6100)
Manager: Andrew Freeman **Gen Manager:** Brian Harrison **Gen Secretary:** Stewart Brown
Ground & Directions: Stag Ground, Nottingham Road, Kimberley (0115 9382788). Through Nuthall from M1 jct 26 to Kimberley, ground entrance 150 yds after Stag Inn.
Seats: None **Cover:** 150 **Capacity:** 2,500 **Floodlights:** Yes **Nickname:** Stags
Clubhouse: Evenings (Except Sun) & matchdays. Hot & cold snacks available
Programme: 30 pages 50p **Editor:** George Brown **Midweek Matchday:** Tuesday
Colours: Blue & white/blue/red **Change colours:** Blue/white/blue
Honours: Notts Amateur Lg Div 1 54-55, Central Alliance Div 2 R-up 57-58.

LONG EATON UNITED

Chairman: J C Fairley **Vice Chairman:** B Webster
Secretary: David Hampson, 4 Airedale Close, Long Eaton, Nottingham. NG10 3HW (0115-9726343.
Manager: John Bartlett **Physio:**
Ground & Directions: Grange Park, Station Road, Long Eaton, Nottingham (01602 735700). M1 Junc 25, take A52 towards Nottingham, to island by 'Bardills Garden Centre', left onto B6003 to t/lights. Turn right A453 and take 2nd left into Station Rd. Entrance on left opposite the Speedway Stadium
Seats: None **Cover:** 500 **Capacity:** 5,000 **Floodlights:** Yes **Shop:** No
Clubhouse: Open matchdays, snacks available
Programme: 20 pages 50p **Editor:** G Whitehead **Press Officer:** Secretary
Sponsor: M C Builders **Nickname:** Blues **Founded:** 1956
Colours: Blue & black/black/black **Change colours:** Red & white/red/red
Midweek Matchday: Wednesday **Record Attendance:** 2,000 1973 FA Cup
Honours: Derbys Snr Cup 64-65 75-76, Midland Co's Lg R-up 76-77, Central Alliance Div South 58-59, Northern Co's (East) Div 1 South 84-85.

MICKLEOVER SPORTS

Secretary: Tony Shaw, 80 Onslow Road, Mickleover, Derbyshire DE3 5JB (01332 512826)
Manager: Mark Kelsey **Midweek Matchday:** Wednesday
Ground & Directions: Mickleover Sports Ground, Station Rd, Mickleover, Derby (01332 521167). Derby ring road A38 to A52, turn off at Markeaton Park Island. Take turn to Ashbourne A52, 2nd left into Radbourne Lane. Take 3rd left into Station Road, ground on corner.
Colours: White/black/black **Change Colours:** All blue

NETTLEHAM

Secretary: John Wilson, 21 Chancer Drive, Lincoln LN2 4LN (01522 884051).
Manager: Ian Musson **Midweek Matchday:** Tuesday
Ground & Directions: Mulsanne Park, Field Close, Nettleham (01522 750007). A46 approx. 3 miles north of Lincoln, right at Brown Cow Pub, proceed past Church 2nd turning on right, ground at end
Colours: Blue/blue/yellow **Change Colours:** All Red
Honours: Central Mids Lg Premier Division Cup R-up 87-88, Village Tphy, Nursing Cup, Kelly Read Cup, Blankney Hunt Cup, Lincoln & Dist. Amtr Cup R-up, Joe Miller Tphy(2).

ROSSINGTON

Secretary: Ian Wilson, 3 Hollin Close, Rossington, Doncaster DN11 0XX (01302 867221).
Manager: PaulHaywood **Midweek Matchday:** Wednesday
Ground & Directions: Welfare Ground, West End Lane, Rossington, Doncaster (01302 868272). M18 jct 1, A631 to Bawtry via Maltby/Tickhill, 1 mile out of Tickhill take B6463 to Rossington. In Rossington take road to colliery, over level crossing, ground on right after Sports Centre. 6 miles from Doncaster (BR)
Colours: White/navy/navy **Change colours:** Blue & black/black/blue.
Honours: Central Mids Lg Div 1 87-88 (Prem Div R-up 92-93, Div 1 Cup R-up 86-87 87-88, Res. Div 1 Cup 87-88, Res Div 1 R-up 94-95, Res. Div 2 Champs Cup R-up 86-87), Doncaster Snr Lg Div 2 R-up 85-86 (Div 1 Cup R-up 85-86), Sheffield & Hallamshire Jnr Shield 83-84, Bentley Lg 77-78 78-79 (Lg Shield 74-75 78-79).

SANDIACRE TOWN

Secretary: Mel Williams, 38 Pasture Road, Stapleford NG9 8GL (0115 939 2415)
Manager: Ged Le Blond **Asst Manager:** Trev Hammon
Ground & Directions: St Giles Park, Stanton Road, Sandiacre, Nottingham NG10 5EP (0115 939 2880). M1 jct 25, follow signs to Sandiacre passing Post House Hotel on right, straight over crossroads into Rushy Lane and towards Stanton Rd, 1st right after 1000yds into Stanton Rd, ground at bottom after another 1000yds.
Seats: None **Cover:** 250 **Capacity:** 2,000 **Floodlights:** Yes **Shop:** No
Clubhouse: Members Club 8-11pm. Sunday lunchtimes, Saturday 3.45-11pm. Snacks available
Programme: 44 pages 50p **Editor:** Secretary **Press Officer:** Mel Williams
Founded: 1978 **Nickname:** Saints **Midweek Matchday:** Tuesday
Colours: Red, white & navy/navy/red **Change colours:** Blue/sky/sky
96-97 Captain: Sean Smith **P.o.Y.:** Phil Baker **Top Scorer:** Ryan Pollard
Honours: Central Mids Lg Premier Div 92-93 (Lg Cup 92-93), Midlands Regional Alliance R-up 91-92, Central Mids Lge Cup R-up 95-96.

SHIREBROOK TOWN

Secretary: Steve Wall, 26 Carter Lane West, Shirebrook, Mansfield, Notts NG20 8NA (01623 747638).
Manager: S Greenwood, G Charlesworth **Midweek Matchday:** Tuesday
Ground & Directions: BRSA Sports Ground, Langwith Rd, Shirebrook, Mansfield (01623 742535). M1 jct 29, A617 to Mansfield, 2.5 miles, onto B6407 to Shirebrook, through town to Langwith Rd.
Colours: All Red & black **Change Colours:** Blue & black/blue/blue
Honours: Central Midlands League Reserve Prem Div 94-95 95-96.

THORNE COLLIERY

Secretary: Glyn Jones, Top Town Social, Frederick Street, Grimsby DN31 1RG (01472 350554)
Manager: Paul Morrell
Ground & Directions: Miners Welfare, Grange Road, Moorends, Thorne, Doncaster. (01374 996474), M18 Junc 6, in THorne, turnat lights to Moorends, go almost through village, Grange Road on right.
Seats: Yes **Cover:** Yes **Floodlights:** No **Club Shop:** No
Colours: Green/black/black **Change Colours:** Yellow/green/yellow
Programme: 44 pages £1 incl entry **Editor:** Stuart Robinson, (01405 814441)
Sponsors: National Deposit Friendly Society Ltd **Midweek Matchday:** Tuesday
Previous Leagues: Yorkshire, NCEL, Doncaster Sen.
Clubhouse: No, but refreshments available on matchdays. Use Red Bear in Thorne.

Staveley Miners Welfare FC; Team line-up before the top of the table clash and defeat at Dunkirk.
Photo - Martin Wray

Long Eaton United; Back Row (L-R); Steve Wells, John Barry, Steve Campbell, Paul Shipp, Martin Bestwick, Kevin Muir, Mark Byfield. Front Row; Martin Dick, Neil Lovell, Kevin Cresswell, Glyn Stacey, David Lymn, David Nead, Jim Fairley.

Staveley's keeper Andy Hall denies a Dunkirk attack *Photo - Martin Wray*

PREMIER DIVISION CLUBS 1997-98

ASKERN WELFARE

Secretary: Miss Lynn Sudworth, Hollycroft, Main St, Stillington, York YO6 1JU (01347 810038)
Manager: Ron Pounder **Midweek Matchday:** Wednesday
Ground & Directions: Askern Welfare Sports Ground, Doncaster Road, Askern, Doncaster (01302 700957). A1/A639 Pontefract. Follow sign for Askern/Campsall. At T-junction right. Left at Anne Arms, right at Supersave, ground on right.
Colours: White (navy trim)/navy/navy & white **Change Colours:** Orange/white/yellow

BLACKWELL MINERS WELFARE

Secretary: Robin Ward, 47 Gladstone Avenue, Blackwell, Alfreton, Derbys DE55 5JU (01773 811691).
Manager: Barrie Brady **Midweek Matchday:** Tuesday
Ground & Directions: Welfare Ground, Primrose Hill, Blackwell, Derbyshire DE55 5JE. (01773 811295). M1 Junc 28, A38 towards Mansfield, left onto B6406, left again at Hilcote Arms, ground 1 mile on left just past Miners Welfare.
Colours: Red & black stripes/black/red **Change colours:** Green/white/green

GOOLE AFC

Secretary: M E Norman, 10 High Ash Drive, Leeds LS17 8QY (0113 266 4900)
Manager: John Reed **Midweek Matchday:**
Ground & Directions: Victoria Pleasure Grounds, Marcus St, Goole (01405 762794). M62 JUnc 36 follow signs town centre. Turn right at 2nd lights into Boothferry Rd, 300 yards right again into Carter St, ground at end of road.
Colours: White with black trim/black/black & white **Change Colours:** Gold/black/gold & black

GREENWOOD MEADOWS

Secretary: Brain Hall, 34 Sullivan Close, Marmion Estate, St Ann's, Nottingham NG3 2HX (0115 958 2459)
Manager: G Walker **Midweek Matchday:**
Ground & Directions: Greenwood Meadows (0115 986 5913). M1 Junc 24 take A453 Nottingham-Clifton Bridge to Lenton Ind Estate. Left into Old Lenton Lane. Ground second on right on lane.
Colours: Green & white/green/green **Change Colours:** Red & black/black/black

HEMSWORTH TOWN

Secretary: Mike Pickering, 1 Sycamore Road, Hemsworth, Nr Pontefract, West Yorks WF9 4PD (01977 613974)
Manager: Sammy Waugh **Midweek Matchday:** Wednesday
Ground & Directions: Hemsworth Town FC, Sports Complex, Kirby Road, Hemsworth
Directions: M1 to M18 to A1M.North to A638 Wakefield Road, 3 miles turn off left. Signposted Langwaite Grange Ind Est (Netto). 2 miles on join B6422 Hemsworth. 2 miles further on in Hemsworth, ground 400 yards on left after Fina garage
Colours: Red/red/red & white **Change Colours:** All navy

HOLBROOK

Secretary: Stevan Broadhurst, 35 Laund Hill, Belper, Derbys. DE56 1FH (01773 821483)
Manager: Grant Woodside **Midweek Matchday:** Tuesday
Ground & Directions: The Welfare Ground, Shaw Lane, Holbrook, Derbyshire (01332 880259), From A38 take B6179 for Kilburn, turn left at lights for Belper. 1 mile on left at Bulls Head for Holbrook. 2 miles on turn right at Venture garage into Shaws Lane.
Colours: Blue & White/blue/blue & white **Change Colours:** Red & white/red/red

HUCKNALL ROLLS

Secretary: Peter Williams, 38 Tiverton Close, Hucknall, Nottingham NG15 6JT (0115 956 33691)
Manager: Roger Dawkins **Midweek Matchday:** Wednesday
Ground & Directions: Rolls Royce Sports & Social Club, Watnall Road, Hucknall Notts (0115 963 0134). M1 Junc 27. Follow sign A611 to Hucknall. Turn right on to by-pass. 2nd r/about turn right on to Watnall Road. Take 2nd left after fire station on R.R. Sports Ground
Colours: Blue & black/black/black **Change colours:** White/blue/white

MEXBOROUGH ATHLETIC (OAKHOUSE)

Secretary: Nev Wheeler, 15 Holmshaw Drive, Sheffield, South Yorkshire S13 8UJ (0114 2694142).
Manager: Nev Wheeler **Midweek Matchday:** Tuesday
Ground & Directions: Mexborough Athletic Club, New Oxford Road, Mexborough (01709 583426). M18 Junc 2, join A1 for 1 junc. Take Sheffield/Rotherham road to Conisborough, take right beside castle to Denaby. Go through Denaby to r/about at Mexborough, take right turn into Adwick Road, ground on left
Colours: All blue & white **Change colours:** Red and Navy/black/black.

MICKLEOVER ROYAL BRITISH LEGION

Secretary: Ray Taylor, 15 Inglwood Avenue, Mickleover, Derby DE3 5RT (01332 515047).
Manager: Kevin Morton **Midweek Matchday:** Tuesday
Ground & Directions: Mickleover RBL, Ypres Lodge, Western Road, Mickleover (01332 513548). On west side of Derby off A38, 1/2 mile from Mickleover Village centre.
Colours: Yellow/royal/royal **Change Colours:** Tangerine/black/black

RADFORD

Secretary: R W Thomas, 7 Warrener Grove, Heronbridge, Nottingham NG5 9BN (0115 955 3905)
Manager: Terry Lack **Midweek Matchday:** Tuesday
Ground & Directions: Radford Road, Radford, Nottm (0115 943250). M1 Junc 26, take A610 to Nottingham, at duel carriageway turn left. Move to right lane and go immediately right into Wilkinson St. At top turn right & right again at 2nd crossing.
Colours: Black & white/black/black **Change colours:** Blure & white/white/white

SELSTON

Secretary: Alan Jones, 6 Derwent Drive, Selston, Nott NG16 6QU (01773 580436)
Manager: Wayne Bradley **Midweek Matchday:**
Ground & Directions: Mansfield Hosiery Mills Sports Ground, Mansfield Road, Sutton in Ashfield, Notts (01623 552376). M1 junc 28, take A38 Mansfield, pass through 7 sets of lights to island (Kings Mill Hospital), ground oposite McDonalds on left
Colours: Black & white/black & blue/black & white **Change Colours:** Yellow & green/sky/yellow & green

SHARDLOW St JAMES

Secretary: Reg Symcox, 22 West End Drive, Shardlow, Derby DE7 2GY (01332 792733).
Manager: Dave Spencer **Midweek Matchday:** Wednesday
Ground & Directions: The Wharf, Shardlow, Derby. (01332 799135), M1 Junc 24, A6 Derby/Leicester, 6 miles out of Derby at Shardlow take next left after Shardlow church (on right), ground 100yds on left.
Colours: White & blue/white/white **Change colours:** Tangerine/black/tangerine

SHEEPBRIDGE

Secretary: D G Barnes, 22 Windsor Drive, Wingerworth, Chesterfield, Derbyshire S42 6TJ (01246 277445)
Manager: P Sindall/R Lilley **Midweek Matchday:** Wednesday
Ground & Directions: GKN Sports Ground, Newbold Road, Chesterfield, (01246 234282), M1 Junc 30, Follow signs to Chesterfield use bypass and on reaching island with Tesco store follow signs for Newbold. Ground on the Newbold Road.
Colours: Blue & white/blue/blue **Change colours:** Red & white/white/red

SHEFFIELD HALLAM UNIVERSITY

Secretary: Stephen Wright, 198 Holme Lane, Malin Bridge, Sheffield S6 4JZ (0378 481483)
Manager: John Warnock **Midweek Matchday:** Monday
Ground & Directions: Aurora Sports & Social Club, Bawtry Rd, Brinsworth, Rotherham (01709 372613), M1 junc 34, take A631 Bawtry Rd, ground 1 mile on right.
Colours: Red/black/red **Change Colours:** All blue

SNEINTON

Secretary: Albert Graves, 32 Shelford Road, Gedling, Nottingham NG4 4HW (0115 9878185)
Manager: Tom Brookbanks/Neil Cooper **Midweek Matchday:** Tuesday
Ground & Directions: Stoke Lane Gedling, Nottingham, A612 Nottingham to Southwell Road. Stoke Lane is situated off A612 between Gedling & Burton Joyce (signed Stoke Bardolph). Ground 200 yards on left over level crossing
Colours: Blue & black/black/black **Change Colours:** Green & white/white & green/white

SOUTH NORMANTON ATHLETIC

Secretary: Bob Ravenhall. 6 Carter Lane West, South Normanton, Alfreton, Derbyshire DE55 2DX (01773 8612363
Manager: **Midweek Matchday:** Wednesday
Ground & Directions: South Normanton Athletic FC, Lees Lane, South Normanton, Derby (01773 581491). M1 Junc 28, B6019 towards South Normanton, right after 1 mile (in South Normanton) at Mobil garage into Market Street, after quarter mile turn left immediately after The Clock pub into Lees Lane, ground at bottom
Colours: Yellow/navy/yellow **Change colours:** Black & white/black/black

STANTON ILKESTON

Secretary: Mrs S Smedley, 4 Queens Avenue, Ilkeston, Derbyshire DE7 4DL (0115 9323772)
Manager: J Smedley/C Trueman **Midweek Matchday:** Monday or Wednesday
Ground & Directions: Hallam Fields Sports Ground, Stanton Club, Hallam Fields, Nr Ilkeston, Derbys (0115 9323244), M1 (J26), take A52 Nottingham, then A6002 for Ilkeston. Follow road through t/lights, turn right at next lights. Follow road to Rutland Windows. Turn left into Thurman St, to top turn left ground 200 yds right.
Colours: Blue & white/blue/blue **Change Colours:** Yellow/blue/blue

POWERLEAGUE NOTTS FOOTBALL ALLIANCE

Established: 1894

General Secretary & Treasurer: Mr Godfrey Stafford
7 The Rushes, Gotham, Nottingham, NG11 0HY (0115 9830576)
Fixtures Secretary: Martin Lacey
28 Chaceley Way, Silverdale, Wilford, Nottingham NG11 7EE (0115 9812143)

Rainworth Miners Welfare, runners-up '94 and '95, Champions '96, retain the Championship for '97.

Last seasons promoted clubs Champions Ollerton Town just manage to stay up on goal difference from Awsworth Villa.

Relegated last term, G P T FC make a swift return, likewise in Division Two Radcliffe Olympic return after only one season down.

SENIOR DIVISION
FINAL LEAGUE TABLE 1996-97

		P	W	D	L	F	A	GD	Pts
1	Rainworth M W	30	22	5	3	88	32	56	71
2	Welbeck C W	30	18	7	5	75	39	36	61
3	Hucknall R R	30	16	10	4	53	37	16	58
4	Ruddington Utd	30	17	5	8	64	44	20	56
5	Boots Athletic	30	17	4	9	58	37	21	55
6	Pelican	30	13	9	8	61	51	10	48
7	Greenw'd Meadow	30	11	11	8	49	43	6	44
8	John Player	30	11	7	12	50	46	4	40
9	Notts Police	30	11	7	12	37	38	-1	40
10	Wollaton	30	9	7	14	35	51	-16	34
11	Cotgrave C W	30	8	8	14	37	55	-18	32
12	Southwell City	30	7	7	16	33	61	-28	28
13	Keyworth United	30	8	3	19	30	59	-29	27
14	Ollerton Town	30	4	11	15	28	52	-24	23
15	Awsworth Villa	30	5	8	17	46	77	-31	23
16	Thoresby C W	30	4	9	17	33	55	-22	21

FIRST DIVISION
FINAL LEAGUE TABLE 1996-97

		P	W	D	L	F	A	GD	Pts
1	Linby C W	30	24	4	2	69	26	43	76
2	G P T FC	30	20	3	7	76	40	36	63
3	Retford United	30	17	5	8	43	28	15	56
4	Attenborough	30	16	6	8	66	36	30	54
5	Teversal Grange	30	16	6	8	67	40	27	54
6	Basford United	30	13	8	9	46	38	8	47
7	Bilsthorpe C W	30	13	7	10	69	54	15	46
8	Bestwood M W	30	12	7	11	57	52	5	43
9	Beeston Town	30	12	6	12	53	49	3	42
10	Abacus	30	11	7	12	62	63	-1	40
11	W'ton Simpsons	30	11	5	14	61	67	-6	38
12	Boots Ath Res	30	9	4	17	45	60	-15	31
13	Clifton	30	6	6	18	38	72	-34	24
14	Gedling M W	30	6	6	18	37	74	-37	24
15	Rainworth MWRs	30	3	10	17	35	67	-32	19
16	City & Sherwood	30	4	4	22	29	86	-57	16

SECOND DIVISION
FINAL LEAGUE TABLE 1996-97

		P	W	D	L	F	A	GD	Pts
1	Kimberley M W	30	24	4	2	151	36	115	76
2	Radcliffe Olympic	30	18	6	6	64	33	31	60
3	Wollaton Reserves	30	18	5	7	69	42	27	59
4	Carlton D C	30	17	7	6	116	48	68	58
5	Ruddington U Res	30	16	8	6	84	64	20	56
6	Magdala Amateur	30	17	2	11	96	54	42	53
7	Southwell City Res	30	15	5	10	67	56	11	50
8	Grnw'd Meadows	30	15	4	11	60	42	18	49
9	Hucknall R R Res	30	12	5	13	61	60	1	41
10	John Player Res	30	10	6	14	57	74	-17	36
11	East Leake Athe	30	10	4	16	37	62	-25	34
12	Pelican Res	30	7	5	18	39	67	-28	26
13	Basford Utd Res	30	7	4	19	53	102	-49	25
14	W'ton Simpson R	30	6	6	18	34	93	-59	24
15	Thoresby C W Rs	30	6	3	21	37	89	-52	21
16	Calverton Tn 2	30	4	2	24	41	144	-103	12

LEAGUE CUP 1996-97

HOLDERS: PELICAN

FINAL

Thursday 8th May 1997, 6.15pm

Cotgrave C W v Boots Athletic 3-2 at John Player FC

SENIOR DIVISION 1997-98

ATTENBOROUGH

Secretary: Terry Allen, 3 Firth Close, Arnold, Nottingham NG5 8RU (0115 920 0698)
Ground & Directions: The Village Green, The Strand, Attenborough, Beeston, Nottingham. Midway between Beeston & Long Eaton on A6005 - adjacent to Nature Reserve (via Attenborough Lane).
Colours: All blue **Change cols:** White/black/black.

AWSWORTH VILLA

Secretary: Keith Slaney, 24 Attewell Road, Awsworth, Nottm NG16 2SY (0602 302514).
Ground: Shilo Park, off Attewell Road, Awsworth. **Colours:** Red & white & black/black

BOOTS ATHLETIC

Secretary: Ian Whitehead, 21 Rosthwaite Close, West Bridgford, Nottingham NG2 6RA (01159 812830).
Ground: Lady Bay, West Bridgford, Nottingham (01159 822392). **Colours:** White/black.
Hons: Notts Alliance Div 1 91-92 (Lg Cup 91-92), Notts Snr Cup R-up 93-94, Notts Inter R-up 91-92.

COTGRAVE COLLIERY WELFARE

Secretary: Kevin Whitehead, 51 Cross Hill, Cotgrave, Nottinham. (0115 9894043)
Ground: Cotgrave Welfare. **Colours:** Yellow/black.

KEYWORTH UNITED

Secretary: M Simpson, 25 Waddington Drive, Wilford Hill, West Bridgford, Nottm NG2 7GT (0115 923 2921)
Ground: Platt Lane, Keyworth (0115 937 5998) **Colours:** Green/black

LINBY COLLIERY WELFARE

Secretary: Frank Taylor, 6 Beech Avenue, Hucknall, Nottingham, NG15 7FH (0115 952 9633)
Ground: Church Lane, Linby **Colours:** Red/White

NOTTINGHAMSHIRE POLICE

Secretary: John Beeston, 17 Alandene Ave, Watnall, Nottingham NG16 1HH (0115 938 2110)
Ground: Police Training Centre, Epperstone, Notts. **Colours:** White/navy.
Hons: Notts Snr R-up 91-92, Notts All. Div 1 & Lge Snr Cup R-up 85-86, PAAN Nat. K-O Comp 63-64.

OLLERTON TOWN

Secretary: Jack Graham, 73 Petersmith Drive, New Ollerton, Mansfield, Notts NG22 9SD (01623 863127)
Ground: Walesby Lane, New Ollerton, Notts
Colours: Red & black/black

PELICAN

Secretary: Dave Eastwood, 42 Chetwin Road, Bilborough, Nottm NG8 4HN (01159 138345).
Ground: Brian Wakefield Sports Ground, Lenton Lane, Nottm (0115 986 8255)
Colours: All Blue. **Hons:** Notts Alliance Lg Cup 90-91 (R-up 91-92 93-94).

RAINWORTH MINERS WELFARE

Secretary: Alan Wright, 10 Faraday Road, Mansfield NG18 4ES (01623 24379).
Ground: Kirklington Road, Rainworth, Notts
Directions: On A617 Mansfield - Newark Road. **Colours:** All White
Hons: Notts Alliance 77-78 78-79 79-80 80-81 81-82 82-83 (R-up 93-94, Lg Cup 81-82), Notts Snr Cup 80-81 81-82 (R-up 82-83 92-93), FA Vase R-up 82-82, Thorn EMI F'lit Cup R-up 82-83 83-84 84-85.

RETFORD UNITED

Secretary: Jeff Lamb, 18 Northumbria Drive, Retford, Notts, DN22 7PR (01777 705833)
Ground: Oaklands Lane (Off London Road), Retford. **Colours:** Black & white stripes/black

RUDDINGTON

Secretary: John Fisk, 3 Savages Road, Ruddington, Nottm NG11 6EW (0115 984 2552).
Ground & Directions: The Elms Park Ground, Loughborough Road, Ruddington (01159 844976. On A60 Nottm to Loughborough, 5 miles out of Nottingham.
Colours: Red & blue stripes/blue. **Honours:** Notts Comb. Lg 79-80 (Lg Cup 70-71 76-77 80-81).

SOUTHWELL CITY

Secretary: P K Johnson, 63 The Ropewalk, Southwell, Notts NG25 0AL (01636 812594).
Ground: War Memorial Ground, Bishops Drive, Southwell, Notts, (01636 814386)
Colours: Black & white stripes/black

THORESBY COLLIERY WELFARE

Secretary: Brian Wathall, 29 First Ave., Edwinstowe, Nr Mansfield NG21 9NZ (01623 823885).
Ground: Thoresby Colliery, Fourth Avenue, Edwinstowe, Nr Mansfield. **Colours:** Blue/white.

WELBECK COLLIERY WELFARE

Secretary: Mr Ron Turner, 75 Hamilton Drive, Warsop, Mansfield, Notts NG20 0EY (01623 847738).
Ground: Elksley Road, Meden Vale (01623 842611) **Colours:** Black & yellow/black.
Hons: Notts Alliance Div 2 93-94 (Intermediate Cup 93-94), Chesterfield & District Lg 92-93.

WOLLATON

Secretary: Andrew Moon, 150 Wollaton Vale, Wollaton, Nottm NG8 2PL (0115 928 1215).
Ground: Wollaton Cricket & Sports Club, Wollaton Village, Nottm (0115 928 9748).
Colours: Sky/maroon **Hons:** Notts All. Div 1 R-up 92-93 (Div 2 91-92 (I'mediate Cup R-up 91-92)).

DIVISION ONE CLUBS 1997-98

ABACUS

Secretary: Stephen Bingley, 6 Brisbane Close, Mansfield Woodhouse NG19 8QZ (01623 23072).
Ground: Sherwood Colliery Sports Ground, Debdale Lane, Mansfield Woodhouse, Notts.
Colours: Black & white stripes.

BASFORD UNITED

Secretary: S Thompson, 2 Haddon Road, West Brdgford, Nottm NG12 6EQ (0115 914 1940)
Ground: Greenwich Avenue, Bagnall Road, Basford, Nottm (0115 942 3918).
Directions: M1 (J26) follow signs 'A610 Nottingham' then 'B6004 Arnold' into Mill Street.
Colours: Black, yellow & purple/black

BEESTON TOWN

Secretary: Andy Meakin, 26 Redland Drive, Chilwell, Nottingham NG9 5LE (0115 967 7520
Ground: University Ground, Nottingham **Colours:** All white

BESTWOOD MINERS WELFARE

Secretary: Mrs Alana Jackson, 9 Derwent Drive, Hucknall, Nottm NG15 6DS (0115 953 8561)
Ground: Bestwood Workshops, Park Rd, Bestwood **Colours:** Navy & red/navy

BILSTHORPE COLLIERY WELFARE

Secretary: Les Lee, 18 The Hollies, Rainworth, Mansfield, (01623 490053)
Ground: Eakring Road, Bilsthorpe, Notts **Colours:** Red/black

CARLTON DC

Secretary: Robert Huckerby, 30 Vernon Ave, Carlton, Nottingham NG4 3FX (0115 955 9120)
Ground: Carlton Hill Recreation Ground, Carlton, Nottingham **Colours:** Black & blue/black

CITY & SHERWOOD HOSPITALS

Secretary: Alan Bird, 72 Bilborough Rd, Nottm NG8 4DW (0115 928 5507)
Ground: M.O.D. Chilwell (0115 925 4811) **Colours:** All blue

CLIFTON

Secretary: Keith Elliott, 61 Greencroft, Clifton Est., Nottm NG11 8GJ (0115 921 5401)
Ground: Green Lane, Clifton Est., Nottm (0115 921 5113) **Colours:** All white

GEDLING MINERS WELFARE

Secretary: Mrs Maureen Chambers, 8 Fraser Road, Carlton, Nottm NG4 1NJ (0115 961 2994)
Ground: Gedling Colliery Welfare, Plains Road, Mapperley (0115 926 6300) **Colours:** Yellow & blue/blue

KIMBERLEY MINERS WELFARE

Secretary: Graham Rowley, 47 Noel Street, Kimberley, Nottingham NG16 2NF (0115 938 9151)
Ground: Didby Street, Kimberley, Nottingham **Colours:** Black & red/black

RADCLIFFE OLYMPIC

Secretary: C Johnson, 2 The Firs, Holme Pierrepoint, Nottingham NG12 2LT (0115 933 3791)
Ground: Wharf Lane, Radcliffe-on-Trent, Nottingham **Colours:** Blue/red

TEVERSAL GRANGE

Secretary: Kevin Newton, 8 Vere Ave., Sutton in Ashfield, Notts NG17 2ES (01623 511402).
Ground: Teversal Grange Country Inn, Carnarvon Street, Teversal, Notts **Colours:** Red & black/black

WORTHINGTON SIMPSONS

Secretary: Alan Allam, 11 Graham Close, Balderton, Newark, Notts NG24 3EW (01636 72430)
Ground: Lowfields Works, off Hawton Lane, Baldeton, Newark, Notts (01636 702672).
Colours: Yellow/black **Hons:** Notts Alliance Lg Cup (Intermediate Cup(res) 92-93 (R-up 93-94)).

This Division also includes the Reserve sides of: Boots Athletic, Rainworth MW, Wollaton.

It's not so easy to get penalties on this ground!

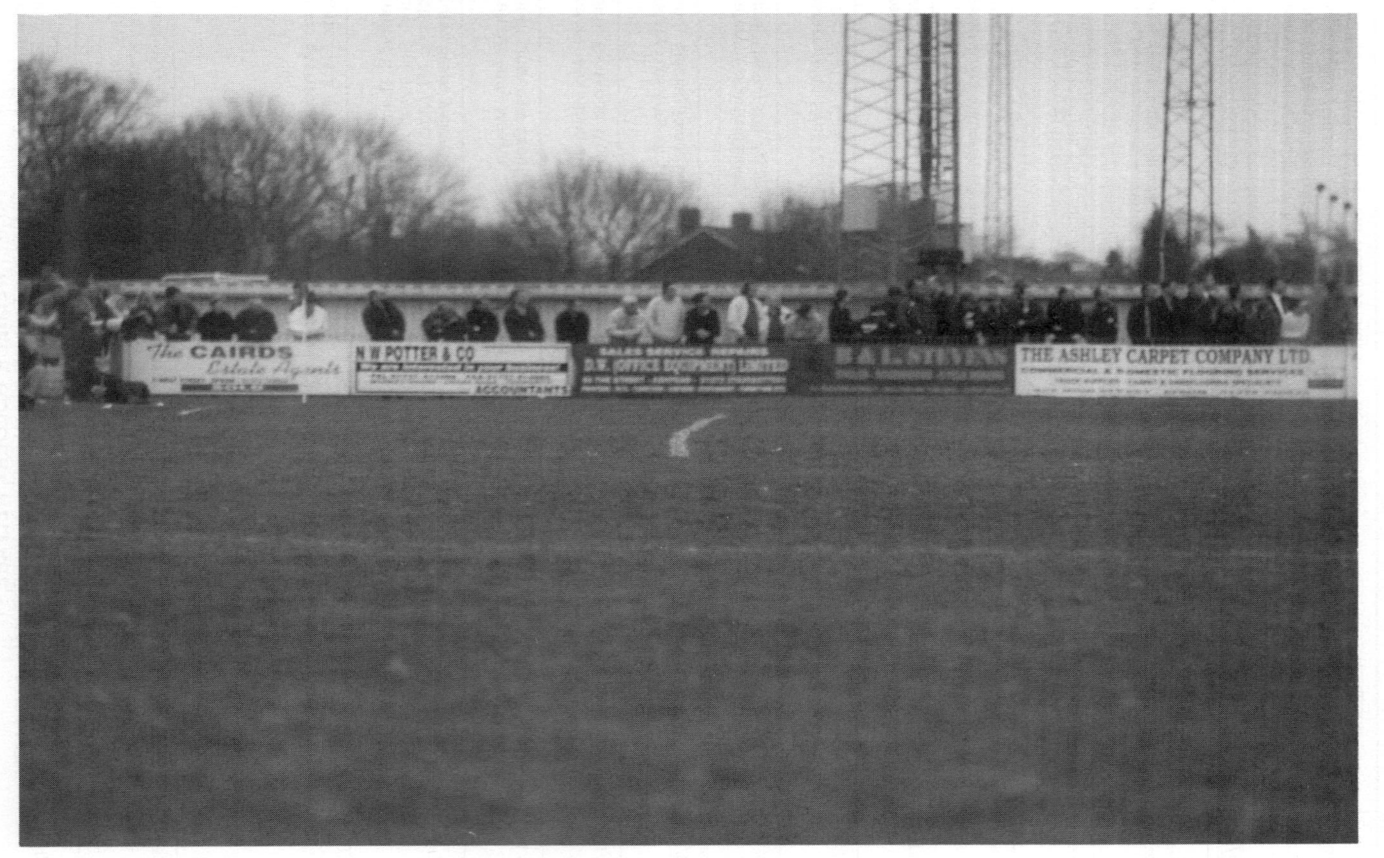

Photo: Graham Cotterill

MIDLANDS FOOTBALL LEAGUES

Final League Tables 1996-97

CAMBRIDGESHIRE LEAGUE

Premier Division

		P	W	D	L	F	A	Pts
1	Over Sports	28	23	3	2	94	21	73
2	Great Shelford	28	16	5	7	62	36	53
3	Girton United	28	14	10	4	39	19	52
4	Newmarket T Rs	28	14	9	5	66	50	51
5	Debden	28	15	5	8	52	42	50
6	Frixton	28	13	6	9	51	52	45
7	Steeple Bumpst'd	28	12	5	11	52	46	41
8	Waterbeach	28	10	7	11	63	50	37
9	Camberton Utd	28	11	3	14	48	52	36
10	Cottenham Utd	28	10	5	13	44	55	35
11	West Wraiting	28	9	3	16	38	49	30
12	Cherry Hinton	28	8	6	14	34	61	30
13	Godmanchester	28	6	7	15	39	60	25
14	Bassingbourn	28	6	6	16	37	74	24
15	Fulbourn Institute	28	2	2	24	21	73	8

Senior 'A'

		P	W	D	L	F	A	Pts
1	Hinton Res	28	21	2	5	85	34	65
2	Sawston Utd	28	19	3	6	100	46	60
3	Linton Granta	28	19	3	6	87	42	60
4	Ely City Res	28	16	5	7	61	42	53
5	Bluntisham Rgrs	28	15	6	7	74	39	51
6	Gt Shelford Res	28	12	4	12	54	57	40
7	Longstanton	28	12	2	14	55	54	38
8	Soham T Rgrs R	28	11	5	12	64	65	38
9	Ashdon Villa	28	10	4	14	59	64	34
10	Garnlingay Utd	28	8	10	10	41	47	34
11	Somersham T R	28	8	8	12	52	75	32
12	Whirtlesford Utd	28	9	3	16	47	92	30
13	Mildenhall T Rs	28	8	3	17	46	78	24
14	Balsham	28	5	3	20	41	91	18
15	Papworth	28	4	5	19	32	72	17

* Three points deducted

Senior 'B'

		P	W	D	L	F	A	Pts
1	Buckden	30	21	5	4	90	35	68
2	Brampton	30	20	6	4	79	35	66
3	Fordham	30	19	5	6	92	46	62
4	Hemingford Utd	30	19	5	6	68	30	62
5	Willingham	30	13	4	13	69	59	43
6	Dehden Res	30	13	4	13	54	59	43
7	Sawston Rovers	30	12	4	14	74	64	40
8	Haslingfield	30	12	4	14	53	64	40
9	Great Paxton	30	11	7	12	48	69	40
10	West Row Gun's	30	11	5	14	64	64	38
11	Waterbeach Res	30	10	7	13	54	54	37
12	Milton	30	10	6	14	49	65	36
13	Abington Utd	30	10	6	14	42	67	36
14	Haddenham Rvs	30	7	5	18	42	71	26
15	Fulbourne Inst R	30	7	4	19	44	75	25
16	Linton Granta Rs	30	5	3	22	36	100	18

Division One 'A'

		P	W	D	L	F	A	Pts
1	Hardwick	24	19	1	4	85	26	58
2	Inte Royston	24	18	1	5	70	32	55

Division One 'B'

		P	W	D	L	F	A	Pts
1	Fulbourn Hosp.	26	21	0	5	106	49	63
2	Enrith United	26	18	4	4	85	35	58

PEARL ASSURANCE PETERBOROUGH & DISTRICT LEAGUE

Premier Division

		P	W	D	L	F	A	Pts
1	Ortonians	30	23	5	2	75	25	74
2	Wisbech Tn Rs	30	21	2	7	80	32	65
3	Moulton Harrox	30	18	10	2	63	22	64
4	Hotpoint	30	15	8	7	67	46	53
5	Oundle Town	30	15	5	10	79	39	50
6	Perkins Sports	30	14	8	8	56	45	50
7	Ryhall United	30	15	3	12	55	55	48
8	Deeping Rangers	30	14	5	11	61	42	47
9	Pinchbeck Utd	30	11	10	9	55	49	43
10	Whittlesey Utd	30	12	5	13	35	42	41
11	Leverington Sp	30	10	9	11	45	46	36*
12	Brotherhoods	30	8	5	17	42	76	29
13	Eye United	30	7	4	19	40	92	25
14	Pearl Assurance	30	4	8	18	36	75	20
15	Stamford Belv.	30	3	5	22	25	75	14
16	March T Utd Res	30	2	4	24	19	72	7

* Three points deducted

Division One

		P	W	D	L	F	A	Pts
1	Alconbury	26	19	5	2	66	21	62
2	Ortonians Res	26	17	6	3	85	32	57
3	Deeping Rgrs Rs	26	17	3	6	61	33	54
4	Ontwell Swifts	26	15	3	8	66	35	48
5	Manea United	26	13	5	8	76	52	44
5	Kings Cliffe	26	13	5	8	76	52	44
7	Gedney Hill	26	12	4	10	65	48	40
8	Newage Ketton	26	10	5	11	62	65	35
9	Perkins Sp Rs	26	8	5	12	43	59	29
10	Hotpoint Res	26	5	10	11	43	61	25
11	Ketton	26	5	5	16	38	77	18
12	Leverington Rs	26	6	3	16	34	51	18
13	March Tn U 'A'	26	5	2	18	31	84	17
14	Holbeach Rs	26	3	2	20	30	86	-1*

*Twelve points deducted

Division Two

		P	W	D	L	F	A	Pts
1	Silver Jubilee	26	19	4	3	88	41	61
2	Stilton	26	17	6	3	70	24	57
3	Oakham Town	26	19	2	5	72	32	56
4	Ramsey Tn Res	26	17	4	5	67	24	55
5	Pinchbeck U Rs	26	14	6	6	54	34	48
6	ICA Juventas	26	12	6	8	48	35	42
7	Langtoft	26	9	6	11	48	53	33
8	Oundle Res	26	7	10	9	45	47	31
9	Deeping Rgrs A	26	8	6	12	41	46	30
10	Bell Walsoken	26	8	6	12	44	57	30
11	Pearl Assur'ce R	26	6	3	17	40	80	21
12	Whittlesey U Res	26	4	5	17	37	69	17
13	Chatteris Tn Res	26	3	7	16	31	84	16
14	Eye United Rs	26	1	5	20	25	84	8

Division Three

		P	W	D	L	F	A	Pts
1	Parson Drive	26	18	4	4	80	32	58
2	Hereward O B	26	16	7	3	68	25	55
3	Crowland	26	14	5	6	67	39	47
4	Whittlesey B Star	26	14	5	7	70	50	47

TRAVIS PERKINS NORTHANTS COMBINATION

Premier Division

		P	W	D	L	F	A	Pts
1	Towcester Town	28	22	5	1	78	30	71
2	Woodford Utd	28	21	3	4	95	41	66
3	Moulton	28	18	4	6	58	36	58
4	West Haddon	28	15	1	12	45	47	46
5	Heyford Athletic	28	14	3	11	69	50	45
6	Crick Athletic	28	12	6	10	56	41	42
7	Spralton	28	11	9	8	47	45	42
8	Milton	28	13	2	13	47	43	41
9	Harpole	28	10	6	12	55	54	36
10	Kislingbury	28	9	7	12	55	61	34
11	Northants Police	28	9	6	13	47	56	33
12	Brixworth All St	28	9	6	13	39	56	33
13	Bugbrook S M 'A'	28	5	5	18	51	74	20
14	Wilby	28	4	6	18	39	81	18
15	N'pton Gernco	28	2	3	23	32	98	9

Division One

		P	W	D	L	F	A	Pts
1	Pottersbury	26	23	1	2	146	25	70
2	Weedon	26	22	2	2	101	33	68
3	Earls Barton Utd	26	19	2	5	87	28	59
4	Grammarians	26	18	2	6	77	33	56
5	Woodford Utd Rs	26	14	3	9	55	59	45
6	Earls Barton	26	12	3	11	65	57	39
7	Spencer Utd	26	10	4	12	59	68	34
8	Cold Ashby Rvrs	26	11	1	14	44	63	34
9	Pattishall	26	10	3	13	47	63	32
10	Wollaston Vics	26	8	3	15	60	83	27
11	Wellingboro Nal.	26	7	5	14	50	82	26
12	Wellingboro Nuc.	26	6	2	18	40	97	20
13	Welford Victoria	26	5	0	21	26	95	15
14	Crick Ath Res	26	1	1	24	44	115	4

STAFFORDSHIRE COUNTY LEAGUE (NORTH)

		P	W	D	L	F	A	Pts
1	Alsager College	28	18	5	5	89	33	41
2	Weston United	28	15	7	6	55	25	37
3	Wolstanton Utd	28	16	5	7	60	32	37
4	Pittshill Victory	28	16	3	9	56	37	35
5	Congleton Vale	28	15	3	10	53	37	33
6	Meir Park	28	13	7	8	45	33	33
7	Redgate Clayton	28	10	10	8	39	31	30
8	Audley	28	11	5	12	44	43	27
9	Stone Old Alley	28	9	7	12	41	51	25
10	Abbey Hulton U	28	9	5	14	38	52	23
11	Eccleshall	28	7	8	13	33	62	22
12	Vale Juniors	28	6	9	13	37	70	21
13	Alsagers Bank	28	7	5	16	38	60	19
14	Oakamoor	28	6	7	15	30	68	19
15	Goldenhill Wand.	28	6	6	16	27	51	18

SPRINGBANK VENDING MIDLAND LEAGUE

Division One

		P	W	D	L	F	A	Pts
1	Norton United	24	20	2	2	67	25	62
2	Redgate Clayton	24	14	5	5	38	21	47
3	Baddeley Grn R	24	11	6	7	50	35	39
4	Brocton	24	10	9	5	49	40	39
5	Ball Haye Green	24	11	5	8	50	37	38
6	Milton United	24	10	5	9	34	28	35
7	Adderley Green	24	10	3	11	42	44	33
8	Audley	24	10	2	12	34	41	32
9	Eccleshall	24	6	9	9	47	55	27
10	Goldenhill Wand.	24	7	6	11	28	49	27
11	Hanford	24	5	5	14	31	45	20
12	Rists United	24	4	7	13	28	48	19
13	Stallington	24	3	6	15	25	55	15

Division Two

		P	W	D	L	F	A	Pts
1	Foley	24	17	3	4	91	47	54
2	Stone Dominoes	24	12	4	8	48	35	40
3	Cheadle Rovers	24	11	5	8	52	52	38
4	Kidswood Utd	24	12	4	8	47	40	33*
5	Cheadle O B	24	8	8	8	51	47	32
6	Featherstone	24	9	4	11	78	66	31
7	Knypersley Vics	24	7	3	14	37	60	24
8	Nantwich Town	24	5	7	12	44	67	22
9	Alsager	24	5	6	13	35	69	21

* Seven points deducted

LOVEWELL BLAKE ANGLIAN COMBINATION

Premier Division

		P	W	D	L	F	A	Pts
1	Mulbarton Utd	30	21	3	6	88	36	66
2	Madra United	30	19	7	4	89	27	64
3	Kirkley	30	18	7	5	66	45	61
4	Dereham Town	30	18	6	6	77	24	60
5	Stalham Town	30	14	6	10	69	59	48
6	Wroxham Res	30	13	9	8	54	46	48
7	Ashlea	30	11	8	11	40	45	41
8	Diss Town Res	30	11	7	12	49	53	40
9	Horsford Utd	30	12	3	15	50	56	39
10	Thorpe Village	30	12	3	15	37	52	39
11	Blofield United	30	9	7	14	45	53	34
12	Wymonham Tn	30	8	10	12	58	67	34
13	St Andrews	30	9	5	16	41	62	32
14	Lowestoft T Rs	30	8	7	15	40	52	31
15	Lakeford Rngrs	30	8	7	15	46	67	31
16	Lockton United	30	1	1	28	20	125	4

Division One

		P	W	D	L	F	A	Pts
1	Acle United	30	24	2	4	84	24	74
2	Attleborough Tn	30	21	4	5	88	31	67
3	Cotthishall H V	30	17	7	6	70	42	58
4	Beccles Town	30	15	9	6	72	50	54
5	Poringland Wndrs	30	16	4	10	62	46	52
6	Gorleston Res	30	13	7	10	54	41	46
7	Mattishall	30	13	6	11	56	58	45
8	Fakenham T Res	30	13	5	12	57	43	44
9	Anglian Windows	30	12	7	11	59	48	43
10	Wortwell	30	12	4	14	51	68	40
11	Brandon Town	30	11	6	13	72	67	39
12	North Walsham	30	10	4	16	52	58	34
13	Newton Flotman	30	8	8	14	30	54	32
14	Oulton Broad LR	30	7	6	17	53	73	27
15	Yarmouth T Res	30	5	3	22	40	90	18
16	Hellesdon	30	0	4	26	20	127	4

BEAUVALE MIDLANDS REGIONAL ALLIANCE

Premier Division

		P	W	D	L	F	A	Pts
1	Rowsley 86	32	21	7	4	64	28	70
2	Eastwood T Res	32	19	9	4	82	31	66
3	Belper United	32	20	6	6	79	36	66
4	Barrowash Vic	32	17	8	7	56	37	59
5	Littleover Irongate	32	16	7	9	75	59	55
6	Butterley Brick	32	16	7	9	66	55	55
7	Ilkeston T Res	32	15	6	11	73	48	51
8	Brailsford	32	14	3	15	60	57	45
9	Matlock Tn Res	32	11	11	10	47	41	44
10	Belper Tn Res	32	12	7	13	57	60	43
11	Arnold Tn Res	32	12	7	13	48	58	43
12	Wirksworth Tn	32	10	8	14	45	55	38
13	Holbrook St M	32	9	10	13	47	56	37
14	Selston	32	8	6	18	41	67	30
15	Hucknall Tn Res	32	5	11	16	38	56	26
16	Slack & Parr	32	5	6	21	35	73	21
17	Matlock United	32	1	3	28	24	120	6

EAST MIDLANDS SENIOR LEAGUE

(Formerly Derby Senior League)

Premier Division

		P	W	D	L	F	A	Pts
1	Melbourne D'mo	26	22	3	1	116	29	69
2	Belper St Johns	26	15	4	7	78	38	49
3	Ambergate	26	14	3	9	76	61	45
4	Qualcast	26	14	3	9	69	58	45
5	FC Napier	26	10	8	8	48	44	38
6	Alvaston & B'ton	26	10	7	9	69	58	37
7	Findern	26	10	6	10	56	54	36
8	Allestree FC	26	11	3	12	58	79	36
9	Grenville Ath	26	9	6	11	62	71	33
10	Hemington	26	7	8	11	69	68	29
11	TS Rail	26	7	8	11	55	57	29
12	Allenton Athletic	26	7	6	13	54	66	27
13	Aston	26	6	3	17	31	95	21
14	Stanley Common	26	3	6	17	40	103	15

BEDFORD & DISTRICT LEAGUE

Premier Division

		P	W	D	L	F	A	Pts
1	Caldecote	22	16	5	1	64	15	37
2	Woburn	22	14	5	1	60	24	33
3	White Horse	22	13	4	5	68	38	30
4	Henlow Italians	22	14	2	6	44	25	30
5	Riseley Sports	22	11	5	6	39	26	27
6	Marston Shelton	22	9	2	11	40	40	20
7	Blunham	22	8	3	11	42	48	19
8	Wootton Utd	22	7	5	10	30	39	19
9	Wilshamstead	22	7	3	12	36	58	17
10	Eaton Socon	22	5	6	11	26	48	16
11	Dunton	22	2	4	16	17	59	8
12	Campton	22	2	4	16	23	71	8

Division Two

		P	W	D	L	F	A	Pts
1	Cranfield Vlge	16	12	3	1	65	21	27
2	Bedford S A	16	9	6	1	17	22	24
3	Corinthians	16	8	4	4	51	27	20
4	Stevington	16	9	1	6	71	37	19
5	Bedford NE Ave	16	6	5	5	32	34	17
6	Caldecote Res	16	5	4	7	10	34	14
7	Marston-Shelt. R	16	5	2	9	13	50	12
8	USACLI	16	1	5	10	21	59	7
9	Dunton Reserves	16	1	2	13	15	71	4

Division One

		P	W	D	L	F	A	Pts
1	Bromham Utd	26	16	6	4	61	29	38
2	Sandy Albion	26	16	5	5	63	31	37
3	St Cuthberts	26	16	4	6	79	43	36
4	Sandy Town	26	15	4	7	53	36	34
5	Kempston Town	26	14	5	7	60	44	33
6	Kempston Rvr R	26	9	9	8	48	51	27
7	Hunting Athletic	26	10	6	10	48	47	26
8	The Bell	26	8	4	14	39	44	20
9	Biggleswade U R	26	6	8	12	46	53	20
10	Elslow Abbey	26	8	4	14	39	54	20
11	Rushden Rngrs	26	7	5	14	46	56	19
12	Ickwell & O Wdn	26	8	3	15	44	61	19
13	Lidlington Utd	26	8	2	16	30	64	18
14	Cranfield United	26	4	9	13	28	64	17

Refreshments in the 'Family Enclosure'

Photo: Eric Marsh

Founded
1889

The

NORTHERN LEAGUE

Founded
1889

FEEDER TO:
NORTHERN PREMIER LEAGUE
FOUNDED: 1889
(The World's Second Oldest League)

President: George Courtney
Chairman: M Amos

Hon. Secretary & Treasurer: A Golightly, 85 Park Road North, Chester-le-Street, Co Durham DH3 3SA

Talk about bitter-sweet. We should have sought sponsorship from Bourneville.

Whilst the Northern League had its most successful playing season for many years,everything else was overshadowed by the deaths in June of Ernest Armstrong and in February of Arthur Clark.

Ernest — former MP, Labour government minister, deputy Speaker of the House of Commons and vice-chairman of the Methodist Conference — had begun his Northern League involvement as a hard tackling wing half with Stanley United. Hard tackling, apparently, was putting it mildly.

President since 1981, Ernest stood down at the 1996 annual meeting to make way for his friend Arthur Clark, himself retiring after 21 years as League chairman. At his family's suggestion, the League has instituted a memorial trophy to be contested by four teams in Ernest's parliamentary constituency — Stanley United, Crook Town, Tow Law and Willington.

Earlier in 1996, Ernest and FA chief executive Graham Kelly had been among the speakers at a dinner to honour Arthur Clark's 50 years Northern League service, beginning with Crook CW, and 21 as chairman. Since 1980 he had also been a member of the FA Council.

His death, after a stroke, was a major loss to the League. His wisdom and experience were unequalled and his enthusiasm boundless. He had even rather taken to the title of Censor by the Sea, imposed by a League magazine editor occasionally put out by interference from above.

Back Row: Res. Keeper Mike Williams, Graeme Williams, Dave Logan, Mike Hall, Allan Martin, David Campbell (keeper), Graham Robinson, David Goodchild, Mitch Cook, Kenny Goodrick.
Front Row: Mascot, Paul Pitman, Ian Williams, Andy Toman, Neil Hodgson (capt.), Lawrie Pearson, John Borthwick, Mascot.

Following Arthur's passing, a memorial award was introduced for the person who in the League management committee's opinion had given the most meritorious service in the preceding season. It was won by Malcolm Smith, who despite a spinal illness, extended his duties as Willington's manager to become the club's saviour when a series of horrendous problems threatened its existence.

Almost unable to drive because of his illness, Malcolm stood down when a new 18-strong committee was in place, but returned at the end of the season to help save Murton, when in despair they resigned from the League.

Murton's problem was wreckers. Not vandals, out and out wreckers. By whatever name they remain our clubs' biggest danger — even greater than lack of money or bodies. Murton's ground, and its committee, had been devastated equally. It really had to be seen. Now they have decided to carry on, and have made an impressive start on the rebuilding. Pray God that the wreckers leave it alone.

There were, of course, very much better times than that. They culminated at Wembley on May 10 when Whitby Town, already League champions, lifted the Carlsberg FA Vase. The Seasiders had brought enormous credit both to themselves and to the League, had treasured the moment and brought a huge, pirate-hatted following.

Stone cold sober before the match, so he says, the new League chairman found himself drunk on euphoria by 4.45pm. They should bottle it instead of alcopops. But how Arthur Clark, and Ernest Armstrong, would have loved it, too.

Carried away with it all, we'd even dreamed of an all Northern League final but Guisborough Town lost in the semi-final to North Ferriby. Bedlington Terriers had also reached the last eight — North Ferriby again! — and will be among this season's favourites.

Both Whitby and Consett had reached the FA Cup first round proper, Whitby finally going out to Hull City after City's last minute equaliser brought the replay score to 4-4. The Tigers managed four more in extra time,.

Consett's progress was perhaps the more surprising, including a 1-0 win at Vauxhall Conference neighbours Gateshead before travelling to Mansfield in the first round. They, too, learned to treasure the moment and found a travelling army who chanted eternal allegiance. Where are the fair weather fans now?

It was, in any case, the first time for ten years that the Northern League had had two teams in the first round, and the first since North Shields in 1967 that we'd been to Wembley. The previous season, the NL had failed to progress a club past the Vase last 32. The 1996–97 Directory conceded that the embarrassment was 'real, but doubtless only temporary'. How prescient, how true!

So Whitby were champions, and very comfortably. Bedlington, third behind Billingham Synthonia, had the consolation of victory over the Synners in the League Challenge cup and over Morpeth in the Northumberland Senior Cup. That, too, was the first all Northern League final for ten years. Northallerton, impressive on and off the field, won the second division from Billingham Town, promoted at last. Newcomers Jarrow Roofing were also promoted and took the Craven Cup, for second division clubs, on a May night in a blizzard.

Then the bad news. Darlington Cleveland Social, who had become a virtual one man band, resigned from the League early in the season. Ferryhill Athletic, members for over 70 years, struggled without a ground of their own and with only one second division win all season. Without assurances from the club on future plans, the 1997 annual meeting reluctantly suspended Athletic's membership for the coming season. They will need a lot of help if they are to return.

The Federation Brewery, sponsors for four years, announced shortly after Whitby reached Wembley that their backing was to cease. It was a complete shock. Fortunately, the League was swiftly able to reach a handsome agreement over three years with Arnott Insurance, who so generously had sponsored Whitby Town — even down to the dinner suits for the post-Wembley do at the Cafe Royal.

Arnott promise to be a superb sponsor. Henceforth we are the Arnott Insurance Northern League.

Whitby, of course, were promoted. Penrith, Northern League members from 1948–82, return on transfer from the North West Counties League and will rekindle a lot of fond memories of the A66 to Southend Road. Marske United, finally with planning permission for floodlights, join the second division from the Vaux Wearside League, in which they were runner-up.

Northern Ventures Northern Gains, the occasionally acclaimed League magazine, will remain at 30p and has reached a production agreement with North of England Newspapers which should mean both an even better magazine and a generous sponsorship for the League.

JustSport, the Newcastle-based sports goods dealer, will also continue to sponsor both the team of the month award and the Fair Play league. Whitby won that, too; it was the SeaSiders' season.

George Courtney, familiar FIFA referee, has become League president. Mike Armitage, 25 years Shildon's secretary, succeeds Arthur Clark as the North-East divisional man on the FA Council. No one, for all that strength, believes that progress will ever again be easy at this level.

The Arnott Insurance Northern League nonetheless looks ahead confidently. The Vase final is on May 9 1998, and we anticipate a return. Mine, as ever, will be a Bourneville.

Mike Amos.

FEDERATION BREWERY NORTHERN LEAGUE 1996–97

DIVISION ONE	P	W	D	L	F	A	Pts
Whitby Town	38	32	3	3	130	36	99
Billingham Sythonia	38	28	6	4	109	46	90
*Bedlington Terriers	38	28	5	5	113	37	86
Durham City	38	19	11	8	69	50	68
Crook Town	38	19	9	10	88	56	66
Morpeth Town	38	20	6	12	73	56	66
Guisborough Town	38	17	9	12	68	54	60
Tow Law Town	38	14	11	13	76	70	53
South Shields	38	13	11	14	52	62	50
Murton	38	15	5	18	58	81	50
Consett	38	12	11	15	66	59	47
Dunston Federation	38	12	10	16	64	70	46
Shildon	38	13	7	18	73	87	46
Easington Colliery	38	12	8	18	56	74	44
RTM Newcastle	38	13	3	22	66	87	42
Seaham Red Star	38	7	14	17	50	83	35
Stockton	38	8	10	20	70	105	34
Chester-le-Street	38	7	12	19	53	86	33
Whickham	38	4	6	27	37	98	21
*West Auckland	38	6	3	29	43	117	18

*points deducted

DIVISION TWO	P	W	D	L	F	A	Pts
Northallerton	36	25	6	5	98	41	81
*Billingham Town	36	24	6	6	111	39	75
Jarrow Roofing	36	23	6	7	88	34	75
Ashington	36	22	5	9	70	38	71
Evenwood Town	36	21	4	11	84	46	67
*Horden C.W.	36	20	7	9	67	37	64
Prudhoe Town	36	18	10	8	73	47	64
*Shotton Comrades	36	20	6	10	91	42	63
Willington	36	19	6	11	78	53	63
Peterlee Newtown	36	16	7	13	55	56	55
Hebburn	36	16	3	17	66	61	51
Ryhope C.A.	36	12	5	19	50	70	41
*Norton & Stockton	36	11	7	18	47	58	37
Brandon United	36	10	7	19	64	75	37
*Alnwick Town	36	11	4	21	55	79	34
Eppleton C.W.	36	6	7	23	44	110	25
*Washington	36	6	7	23	42	79	22
*Esh Winning	36	4	12	26	44	100	21
Ferryhill Athletic	36	1	2	33	16	177	5

*3 points deducted

FEDERATION BREWERY NORTHERN LEAGUE 1996–97 — DIVISION ONE

HOME TEAM	1	2	3	4	5	6	7	8	9	10	11	12	13	14	15	16	17	18	19	20
Bedlington Terriers	*	2-2	5-0	6-2	2-2	3-2	0-0	4-1	0-1	2-0	3-0	3-1	4-1	3-2	0-1	1-1	2-1	11-0	5-0	2-3
Billingham Synthonia	3-0	*	4-0	2-0	3-2	4-2	7-1	1-0	4-3	3-2	1-1	5-1	1-1	3-0	4-1	4-2	3-3	6-0	5-0	1-3
Chester-le-Street	0-4	3-5	*	3-0	4-3	2-2	1-1	1-1	0-2	1-2	4-1	3-2	1-1	2-3	0-0	1-3	1-1	4-1	1-2	1-3
Consett	0-4	1-2	7-0	*	2-0	1-1	0-0	3-0	0-0	0-1	1-2	4-1	1-1	3-3	3-3	6-0	4-0	3-0	1-0	2-4
Crook Town	0-2	0-4	2-2	1-1	*	3-2	2-0	5-1	2-1	1-1	2-1	3-1	4-1	2-1	2-1	2-2	4-1	2-2	4-0	0-1
Dunston Federation	1-2	3-2	2-2	2-0	1-1	*	1-3	0-1	1-2	0-2	2-1	1-3	0-2	2-4	3-5	2-1	4-3	2-0	2-2	0-2
Durham City	0-3	0-2	2-0	2-1	5-2	0-0	*	3-3	0-0	2-3	1-2	2-1	1-1	3-1	1-0	5-1	0-0	2-1	5-0	0-0
Easington Colliery	3-2	0-1	2-2	2-2	0-1	1-1	0-2	*	1-3	0-3	0-3	1-0	2-1	2-0	3-3	1-1	0-1	6-2	5-2	3-2
Guisborough	1-3	0-3	3-3	0-0	3-1	2-1	2-3	1-1	*	2-1	1-2	4-0	2-2	2-4	2-1	2-4	3-1	3-0	1-0	2-4
Morpeth	0-2	1-1	1-0	3-0	0-0	1-1	0-2	1-2	2-1	*	3-1	3-4	3-1	3-1	0-1	4-1	2-1	5-0	2-0	0-4
Murton	1-2	0-2	3-1	1-1	2-0	2-1	1-2	3-1	1-5	2-5	*	2-3	0-0	4-1	4-0	5-2	0-2	1-2	3-1	0-10
RTM Newcastle	1-2	2-3	2-0	2-0	1-3	2-3	1-3	4-1	1-2	0-3	5-3	*	1-2	2-2	1-3	2-1	2-1	1-2	4-1	2-4
Seaham R.S.	1-8	3-3	0-1	1-5	0-4	1-2	2-4	1-0	2-1	0-1	0-0	0-1	*	3-3	1-1	2-0	2-3	2-2	5-2	0-2
Shildon	0-3	1-2	2-1	4-3	1-2	0-2	2-1	2-1	1-4	2-3	0-1	3-3	3-2	*	0-3	2-3	3-1	4-3	0-0	1-1
South Shields	0-1	0-1	2-3	1-1	0-6	0-2	1-1	4-1	1-1	3-0	1-1	4-0	1-1	0-4	*	2-1	2-0	1-0	2-0	1-4
Stockton	3-5	1-3	5-4	1-3	0-3	2-2	0-3	1-4	0-0	4-4	3-0	4-6	2-2	3-3	0-0	*	2-4	5-3	2-1	0-4
Tow Law Town	1-3	3-2	1-1	1-2	2-2	2-2	5-5	1-2	2-2	3-3	1-0	2-1	2-2	4-1	4-0	6-1	*	5-2	5-1	2-1
West Auckland	1-4	1-4	3-0	3-2	0-9	2-3	1-2	2-0	0-1	0-2	1-2	0-1	1-3	1-4	0-2	1-1	0-1	*	1-0	2-7
Wichham	0-4	0-1	0-0	0-1	2-4	0-4	0-1	1-2	0-2	4-2	1-2	1-1	6-0	2-5	1-1	0-6	0-0	4-2	*	3-2
Whitby Town	1-1	3-2	3-0	2-0	3-2	4-2	3-1	4-2	2-1	4-1	10-0	3-0	5-0	4-0	5-0	3-1	3-0	2-1	5-0	*

FEDERATION BREWERY NORTHERN LEAGUE 1996–97 — DIVISION TWO

HOME TEAM	1	2	3	4	5	6	7	8	9	10	11	12	13	14	15	16	17	18	19	20
Alnwick Town	*	1-6	1-5	3-2	*	4-1	1-3	1-0	10-0	1-3	3-1	2-5	1-3	2-1	1-2	2-2	0-1	1-1	2-2	0-5
Ashington	1-1	*	1-2	0-0	*	7-0	5-1	0-0	2-0	2-1	2-0	2-0	1-2	1-0	1-0	1-2	2-3	1-0	3-1	3-0
Billingham Town	5-0	3-0	*	6-0	*	1-0	5-1	5-2	10-0	2-1	1-2	0-2	3-3	2-1	4-0	1-1	4-0	1-3	6-1	0-1
Brandon United	0-1	3-4	3-4	*	*	6-2	0-1	1-0	1-1	4-1	2-2	4-2	1-3	3-0	2-2	0-1	2-3	0-5	2-2	0-1
Darlington CS	*	*	*	*	*	*	*	*	*	*	*	*	*	*	*	*	*	*	*	*
Eppleton	2-4	2-2	0-10	2-1	*	*	1-1	2-6	1-1	2-1	0-1	0-3	1-3	2-1	1-5	0-5	2-2	1-5	3-3	1-2
Esh Winning	3-0	1-2	0-2	3-3	*	2-4	*	0-2	2-3	6-1	1-4	0-1	0-2	1-3	0-2	2-4	1-3	0-6	1-6	0-3
Evenwood	3-1	0-2	1-4	3-1	*	2-0	2-0	*	10-0	4-0	0-3	2-1	1-2	3-0	2-0	0-0	3-1	4-2	2-1	5-1
Ferryhill	0-2	2-8	1-3	1-4	*	2-4	0-2	0-8	*	0-2	0-4	0-3	0-11	0-1	0-4	0-4	0-10	1-8	2-3	0-5
Hebburn	3-1	1-2	0-2	2-3	*	3-0	2-1	0-2	8-1	*	1-0	0-4	2-3	4-0	5-0	5-2	4-0	1-2	2-0	0-0
Horden	1-0	1-2	1-1	2-0	*	5-2	4-0	2-1	5-0	3-1	*	0-2	1-1	0-1	2-1	2-2	2-0	0-2	2-0	2-2
Jarrow Roofing	3-1	3-0	3-0	3-0	*	2-1	7-1	1-1	12-0	0-0	2-2	*	3-1	2-0	1-1	2-2	1-0	1-0	4-1	1-0
Northallerton 1994	3-2	1-1	2-1	1-2	*	0-1	3-0	2-1	3-0	5-1	1-1	4-1	*	3-1	0-1	3-1	5-1	1-2	2-1	5-1
Norton	1-0	0-1	1-1	1-0	*	1-1	4-3	4-3	6-0	1-2	0-1	0-2	3-3	*	1-0	2-2	0-1	1-0	1-2	0-0
Peterlee	3-0	3-1	1-5	0-4	*	3-2	2-1	1-3	6-0	1-0	2-0	1-1	1-5	1-3	*	1-0	1-1	1-4	1-1	3-2
Prudhoe	3-0	2-0	2-3	5-3	*	4-0	2-1	1-3	4-1	2-1	1-3	2-1	0-2	2-1	1-1	*	4-1	3-1	1-1	3-1
Ryhope CA	1-3	0-1	1-1	2-1	*	1-1	0-1	1-2	2-0	1-2	1-0	1-4	0-2	3-2	0-2	0-0	*	1-6	4-1	2-5
Shotton Comrades	1-0	0-2	1-1	1-2	*	4-1	10-0	1-1	1-0	1-2	1-3	3-1	2-2	3-1	1-1	1-1	4-1	*	4-3	3-0
Washington	1-0	0-1	1-4	2-2	*	1-0	1-4	0-2	3-0	0-1	1-3	0-4	1-4	2-2	0-1	0-1	0-1	0-1	*	0-3
Willington	2-3	2-1	2-3	4-2	*	6-1	0-0	5-0	5-0	3-3	0-2	2-1	1-2	2-2	1-1	2-1	2-1	3-1	4-2	*

It's seems like a long time since those halcyon days of the FA Amateur Cup, but the Northern League once again had a team at Wembley, and the fans enjoyed their day out!

Photo (above): Dennis Nicholson

Photo (below): Peter Barnes

FIRST DIVISION CLUBS

BEDLINGTON TERRIERS

Chairman: David Perry. **Manager:** Keith Perry **Assistant Manager:** Steven Locker.
Secretary: Eric Young, 6 Millbank Place, Bedlington, Northumberland NE22 5AT (01670 829196).
Coach: Tony Lowery **Physio:** John Nicholson. **Press Officer:** Secretary
Ground: Welfare Park, Park Rd., Bedlington, Northumberland (01670 825485).
Directions: Into Bedlington, turn left at 'Northumberland Arms' on Front St., then 2nd Right, ground on right 100 yds.
Seats: 150 **Cover:** 200 **Capacity:** 1,500 **Floodlights:** Yes **Formed:** 1949
Programme: 40 pages, 50p **Previous Leagues:** Northern Alliance. **Midweek Matches:** Wednesday
Colours: Red & white/white/white **Change colours:** All blue **Souvenir Shop:** No
Clubhouse: Open every evening, 11-11pm Sat. & Sun lunch. Pool, darts etc.
Record win: 11-0 v West Auckland, (H) Lge 96-97. **Record Attendance:** 1,013 v Blyth Spartans, Nth Lg 85-86.
Previous Names: Bedlington Mechanics 49-53/ Colliery Welfare 53-56/ Mechanics 56-61/ Bedlington United 61-65/ Bedlington Colliery 65-68/ Bedlington Town 68-74.
Club record scorer: John Milner 33
Honours: Northern League Div 2 94-95 (R-up 84-85), Northern Alliance 66-67 (R-up 67-68 69-70 71-72, Lg Cup 57-58 66-67 69-70 81-82, Lge Chall Cup 96-97, Northumberland Sen Cup 96-97.

BILLINGHAM SYNTHONIA

Chairman: Don Beattie **Vice Chairman:** Peter Lax **President:** Harry Davies
Secretary: Graham Craggs, 2 Ribble Close, Billingham, Cleveland TS22 5NT (01642 535856).
Manager: Stuart Coleby **Physio:** Tommy Cushley. **Coach:** Lenny Gunn
Ground: The Stadium, Central Avenue, Billingham, Cleveland (Press Box 01642 532348).
Directions: Turn off A19 onto A1027 signposted Billingham, Norton (this applies from either north or south), continue straigh on along Central Avenue, ground on left opposite office block. 1 mile from Billingham (BR).
Seats: 370 **Cover:** 370 **Capacity:** 1,970 **Floodlights:** Yes **Club Shop:** No.
Programme: 12 pages (+ads), 50p **Editor:** Nigel Atkinson (01642 342469) **Press Officer:** Secretary
Club colours: All white **Change colours:** All green
Nickname: Synners **Club Sponsors:** Teeside Park **Founded:** 1923
Midweek Matches: Wednesday **Previous Name:** Billingham Synthonia Recreation
Previous League: Teesside (1923-War). **Record Attendance:** 4,200 v Bishop Auck. 6/9/58.
Best FA Trophy season: Quarter-final replay 93-94 (lost 1-2 after 1-1 draw at Woking).
Best FA Cup season: 1st Rd 48-49 51-52 56-57 57-58 87-88 89-90.
Players progressing to Football League: Peter Atkinson & Ken Harrison (Hull 1947), Ernie Wardle & John Murray (M'boro 1948 & 49), Richard Mulvaney (Blackburn 1964), Mike Hodgson (Hartlepool 1964), David Hockaday (Blackpool 1975), Terry Gaffney (Hartlepool 1977), Aidan Davidson (Notts County 1988).
Clubhouse: 200yds across car park. Normal club hours.
96-97 Captain: Stephen Corkain **96-97 Top Scorer:** Andrew Fletcher **96-97 P.o.Y.:** Andrew Fletcher
Club record scorer: Tony Hetherington **Club record appearances:** Andy Harbron.
Honours: Northern Lg 56-57 88-89 89-90 95-96, R-up 49-50 50-51 51-52, Lg Cup 51-52 87-88 89-90, Div 2 86-87, Teesside Lg 36-37 (Lg Cup 34-35 38-39), Durham Challenge Cup 88-89 90-91, North Riding Snr Cup 66-67 71-72, North Riding Amateur Cup 38-39 56-57 62-63 63-64, FA Amateur Cup 4th Rd 48-49, FA Trophy QF replay 94-95.

BILLINGHAM TOWN

Chairman: Mr.P.Martin. **Hon.President:** Mr.F.Cook M.P. **President:** Mr G.A.Maxwell.
Secretary/Press Officer: Tom Donnelly, 36 Cumberland Crescent, Billingham, Cleveland TS23 1AY (01642 555332).
Manager: Trevor Arnold **Asst Manager/Coach:** Neal Granycome
Ground: Bedford Terrace, Billingham, Cleveland. (01642 560043)
Directions: Leave A19 on A1027 (signed Billingham). Turn left at 3rd r/bout, over bridge 1st left, 1st left again to grd.
Seats: 176 **Cover:** 600 **Capacity:** 3,000 **Floodlights:** Yes **Founded:** 1967
Colours: Blue/Blue/white **Change colours:** Yellow/green/yellow
Programme: 28 pages, 50p. **Editor:** Alex Matthews (01642 653621) **Souvenir Shop:** No
Clubhouse: Open matchdays. Hot & cold food. **Nickname:** The Social.
Record Attendance: 1,500 v Manchester City, FA Youth Cup 1985.
Midweek Matches: Tuesday **Previous Lges:** Stockton & Dist. 68-74/ Teesside 74-82.
Best FA Cup season: 1st Rd Proper 55-56. **Reserves' Lge:** Stockton & Dist Sunday
Players progressing to Football League: Gary Pallister (Middlesbrough & Manchester Utd), Gerry Forrest (Southampton), Dave Robinson (Halifax), Tony Barratt (Hartlepool), Mark Hine (Grimsby & Darlington), Tony Hall (Middlesbrough), Graham Hall (Arsenal).
Record scorer: Paul Rowntree 100 **Record appearances:** Darren Marsh, 250 in Northern League.
96-97 - Captain: Richard Cooper **Top Scorer:** Paul Rowntree (43) **P.o.Y.:** Paul Rowntree
Honours: Durham Amat Cup 76-77 77-78; Teesside Lg 77-78 81-82; Nth Riding Snr Cup R-up 76-77 81-82; Stockton & Dist Lg(3)

CONSETT

Chairman: Dave Struthers. **Vice Chairman:** I Hamilton. **President:** D McVickers
Secretary: Ian Hamilton, 29 Grange Street, Delves Lane, Consett, Co. Durham DH8 7AG (01207 509366).
Manager: Colin Carr **Physio:** Joe Darroch **Press Officer:** Andrew Pearson (01207 506194)
Ground: Belle Vue Park, Ashdale Road, Consett, County Durham (01207 503788)
Directions: Quarter of mile north of town centre - along Medomsley Rd, left down Ashdale Rd, ground 100m yards on left. Follow signs for Sports Centre and Baths.
Seats: 400 **Cover:** 1,000 **Capacity:** 4,000 **Floodlights:** Yes **Founded:** 1899
Colours: Red with black & white trim/black/red **Change colours:** Sky blue/dark blue/sky blue
Previous Leagues: Northern Alliance 19-26 35-37/ North Eastern 26-35 37-58 62-64/ Midland 58-60/ Northern Counties 60-62/ Wearside 64-70.
Programme: 16 pages, 30p **Programme Editor:** Colin French **Souvenir Shop:** No
Record Gate: 7,000 v Sunderland Reserves, first match at Belle Vue, 1950. **Nickname:** Steelmen
Best FA Cup season: 1st Rd 58-59 (lost 0-5 at Doncaster Rovers).
Players progressing to Football League: Tommy Lumley (Charlton), Alan Ellison (Reading), Laurie Cunningham (Barnsley), Jimmy Moir (Carlisle), Jackie Boyd (West Bromwich Albion).
Clubhouse: Matchdays, and evenings on request. Darts & pool. **Midweek Matches:** Wednesday
Honours: North Eastern Lg 39-40 (Div 2 26-27, Lg Cup 50-51 (jt) 53-54), Durham Challenge 5, (R-up 2), Northern Lg R-up 76-77 (Div 2 88-89, Lg Cup 78-79 80-81), Northern Counties Lg 61-62, Sunderland Shipowners Cup 67-68, Monkwearmouth Charity Cup 67-68, Wearside Lg R-up 68-69 69-70, FA Trophy 2nd Rd 78-79.

CROOK TOWN

Chairman: Wilf Dobinson **Vice-Chairman:** Bob Emerson **President:** Sir Tom Cowie O.B.E.
Secretary: Alan Stewart, The Wardens Flat, 47 Grasmere Grove, Crook, Co Durham DL15 8NX (01388 763425)
General Manager: Bill Worley **Manager:** Paul Watson **Physio:**Jimmy Vipond **Coach:** John Parnaby
Ground: Millfield Ground, West Road, Crook, County Durham (01388 762959).
Directions: 400 yds west of town centre on Wolsingham Road (A689). Nearest BR station is Bishop Auckland (5 miles). Buses 1A & 1B from Bishop Auckland or X46 & X47 from Durham.
Seats: 400 **Cover:** 300 **Capacity:** 3,500 **Floodlights:** Yes **Club Shop:** Yes
Programme: Yes **Editor:** Jeff Paterson (01388 450335) **Press Officer:** Secretary
Colours: Amber/black/amber **Change colours:** All White **Sponsors:** Vaux Breweries **Formed:** 1889
Midweek Matches: Wednesday **Reserve's League:** Auckland & Dist **Nickname:** Black & Ambers
Record Attendance: 17,500 v Walton & Hersham, FA Amateur Cup quarter-final 24/02/52.
Best FA Trophy season: 3rd Rd 76-77. **FA Vase season:** 2nd Rd 93-94, 95-96. **FA Cup season:** 3rd Rd (v Leicester) 31-32. 2nd Rd(4), 1sr Rd.(10).
Previous Leagues: Auckland & District 1894-96/ Northern 1896-28 29-30/ Durham Central 28-29/ North Eastern 30-36/ Wartime Durham & Northumberland League 40-41/ Durham Cen 41-45.
Players progressing to Football League: Since 1960; F Clark (Newcastle 62), K Bowron (Berwick 63), A Coates & W Rougnley (Q.o.t.S 63 64), P Garbutt (Carlisle 64), R Snowball (Darlington 64), W Hepplewhite (Carlisle 65), C Neal (Darlington 67), D Attlee (Seattle Sounders 75), T Turnbull (Hartlepool 76), G Whetter (Darlington 86).
Clubhouse: Lic Bar open matchdays. Hot & Cold Food available from Shop
96-97 Captain: Michael Vasey. **Top Scorer:** John Grady/Paul Atkinson 13 **P.o.Y.:** Ian McGraghan
Club Record Scorer: Ronnie Thompson 118, 52-62 **Club Record appearances:** Jimmy McMillan 505, 51-68
Honours: FA Amtr Cup 00-01 53-54 58-59 61-62 63-64 (SF 48-49 57-58 59-60), Northern Lg 5, (R-up 4), Lg Cup 3, (R-up 4). Durham Challenge Cup 26-27 31-32 54-55 59-60, Durham Benevolent Bowl 5.

DUNSTON FEDERATION BREWERY

Chairman: Malcolm James. **Vice-Chairman:** Fred Fowles **President:** Norman Rippon.
Secretary: Bill Montague, 12 Dundee Close, Chapel House, Newcastle-upon-Tyne NE5 1JJ (0191 2672250).
Manager: Peter Quigley **Asst Manager:** Steve Kendal **Physio:** Glen Martin.
Press Officer: Ian McPherson (0191 4205583) **Commercial Secretary:** Malcolm James.
Ground: Federation Park, Wellington Road, Dunston, Gateshead (0191 493 2935).
Directions: Dunston/Whickham exit off A1(M), ground 400 yds north along Dunston Rd on left. 1 mile from Dunston or Metrocentre stations. Buses from Gateshead & Metrocentre stop outside ground.
Seats: 80 **Cover:** 200 **Capacity:** 2,000 **Floodlights:** Yes **Founded:** 1975
Colours: All royal (white trim) **Change:** Green/white. **Nickname:** The Fed
Programme: 28 pages, 30p **Editor:** Ian McPherson (0191 420 5583) **Souvenir Shop:** No
Record Attendance: 1,550 - Sunderland Shipowners Cup Final 1/4/88.
Best F.A. Vase season: Quarter-Finals 92-93 (lost 0-2 at Gresley Rovers).
Best F.A. Cup season: 3rd Qualifying Rd 92-93 (lost 0-3 to Northallerton Town).
Previous Ground: Dunston public park 75-86
Sponsors: Federation Brewery **Clubhouse:** Matchdays only. Hot & cold snacks, darts, pool.
Midweek home matchday: Tuesday **Reserve team:** None.
Club record scorer: Paul King **Club record appearances:** Paul Dixon.

Hons: Northern Lg Div 2 92-93, Northern Amtr Lg 77-78 (R-up 2), Lg Cup 77-78 78-79 (R-up 75-76), Lg Shield 78-79 79-80), Wearside Lg 88-89 89-90 (R-up 90-91, Lg Cup 90-91), Northern Comb. 86-87 (R-up 3), Lg Cup 83-84 86-87 (R-up 3), Sunderland Shipowners Cup 87-88, Durham County Tphy 81-82 (R-up 2), Minor Cup 79-80 (R-up 78-79)), Gateshead Charity Cup 77-78 80-81, Heddon Homes Cup 80-81.

DURHAM CITY

Chairman: TBA **President:** G Newton. **Secretary:** Bon Major, 11 Sherwood Close, Glebe Village, Washington Tyne & Wear NE38 7RJ (0191 416 8679 H, 0191 477 1011 Ext 3105 B)
Vice Chairman: A Thompson
Commercial Manager: D Willis. **Press Officer:** Martin Haworth (01670 519477)
Manager: B Cruddas **Asst Manager/Coach:** T Harrison **Physio:** Joanne Dowson
Ground: New Ferens Park, Belmont Durham (0191 386 9616)
Colours: All Yellow with d/blue trim **Change colours:** Red/black/red. **Reformed:** 1949.
Programme: 30 pages **Editor:** Dave Asberry (0191 386 6469) **Nickname:** City
Midweek Matches: Wednesday. **Club Sponsors:** Key Windows
Previous Leagues: Victory 18-19/ N Eastern 19-21 28-38/ Football Lge 21-28/ Wearside 38-39 50-51.
Best FA Cup season: 2nd Rd 25-26 57-58 (Also 1st Rd 27-28 55-56).
Players progressing to Football League: Harry Houlahan (Newcastle 51), Derek Clark (Lincoln 51), Leo Dale & David Adamson (Doncaster 54/70), Stan Johnstone (Gateshead 54), Dennis Coughlan (Barnsley 57), John Wile (Sunderland 66), Brian Taylor (Coventry 68), Paul Malcolm (Rochdale 84).
Club record appearances: Joe Raine, 552.
Hons: Northern Lg 94-95 (R-up 70-71, Div 2 R-up 30-31 91-92), FA Vase QF 87-88, Durham Benevolent Bowl 55-56, FA Amtr Cup 2nd Rd rep. 57-58, FA Tphy 1st Rd 83-84, Durham Challenge Cup R-up(2).

EASINGTON COLLIERY

Chairman: F Wellburn **Vice-Chairman:** Charlie Dodds. **Manager:** Vin Pearson
Secretary: Alan Purvis, 12 Wark Crescent, Jarrow, Tyne & Wear, NE32 4SH (0191 489 6930)
Ground: Easington Colliery Welfare Ground, CW Park, Easington, Co Durham. (0191 527 3047)
Directions: A19 Easington turn-off, B1284 thru Easington till Black Diamond PH (next to zebra crossing), grd right
Seats: 175 **Cover:** 475 **Capacity:** 2,450 **Floodlights:** Yes **Club Shop:** No
Programme: Yes **Editor:** Charlie Dodds **Press Officer:** Alan Purvis
Colours: Green & white stripes/green/green **Change colours:** Yellow/black/yellow
Sponsors: None. **Nickname:** The Colliery. **Founded:** 1913 **Reserves:** None.
Midweek Matches: Tuesday **Record Attendance:** 4,500 v Tranmere Rovers, FA Cup 1st Round 1955.
Previous Leagues: Wearside 13-37 39-64 73-88. **Best FA Cup season:** 1st Round Proper 1955-56.
Players progressing to Football League: Ron Greener (Newcastle 1951), Frank Wayman (Darlington 1957), John Langridge (Hartlepool 1982).
Clubhouse details: Normal licensing hours. Pies, soup and sandwiches available.
96-97 Captain: John Bendelew **P.o.Y.:** John Bendelew **Top Scorer:** Andrew McKenna
Club record scorer: D Howard **Club record appearances:** D Howard.
Honours: Northern Lg Div 2 R-up 85-86, Wearside League 29-30 31-32 32-33 47-48 48-49 (R-up 28-29 46-47 73-74, Lg Cup 32-33 45-46 61-62), Monkwearmouth Cup 30-31 47-48 75-76, Sunderland Shipowners Cup 74-75 79-80, FA Trophy 2nd Qualifying Rd replay 88-89, FA Vase 4th Rd replay 82-83.

GUISBOROUGH TOWN

Chairman: Ron Ball **Vice Chairman:** Keith Watson **President:** Vacant
Secretary: Keith Smeltzer, 55 Thames Ave., Guisborough, Cleveland TS14 8AR (01287 638993).
Manager: Mark Forster **Asst Manager:** Steve Corden **Physio:** Steve Carter
Ground: King George V Ground, Howlbeck Rd, Guisborough, Cleveland (01287 636925). **Directions:** From west: bear left at 2nd set of lights, left into Howlbeck Rd after quarter mile, ground at end. Buses from Middlesbrough.
Seats: 150 **Cover:** 400 **Capacity:** 3,500 **Floodlights:** Yes **Club Shop:** Yes
Programme: 32 pages, 40p **Editor:** A Walton (01287 636232) **Press Officer:** A Robinson (01642 674996)
Colours: Red & white stripes/Black/Red. **Change colours:** Yellow
Sponsors: Henson Windows & Conservatories **Nickname:** Priorymen **Founded:** 1973.
Midweek home matchday: Wednesday **Reserve Team's League:** Teesside Strongarm.
Record Gate: 3,112 v Hungerford, FA Vase SF, 1980 *(at Middlesbrough FC - 5,990 v Bury, FA Cup 1st Rd 1988).*
Best FA Cup season: First Round Proper 1988-89 (lost 0-1 to Bury).
Previous Leagues: Middlesbrough & District/ South Bank/ Northern Alliance 77-80/ Midland Counties 80-82/ Northern Counties (East) 82-85.
Players progressing to Football League: Frank Harrison (Middlesbrough 1982), Steve Holmes (Preston 93).
Clubhouse: Evenings & weekends. Darts & pool. Hot & cold snacks and drinks from kitchen on matchdays.
96-97 Captain: Steve Corden **P.o.Y.:** Peter Quantrill **Top Scorer:** Shane Breckon
Club Record Goalscorer: Mark Davis 323 **Club Record Appearances:** Mark Davis 551
Honours: FA Vase R-up 79-80, Northern Lg Cup 87-88 (Div 2 R-up 86-87), Northern Alliance 79-80 (R-up 78-79, Lg Cup 78-79), North Riding Senior Cup 89-90 90-91 91-92 92-93 94-95, FA Trophy 1st Rd Proper 90-91 91-92 92-93. FA Vase Semi finalist 96-97.

Bedlington Terrier's Paul Evans beats Collier Row & Romford's Alec Norman to the ball Photo - Roger Turner

Durham's Vince Brand takes on Northwoods Eamon O'Connor. Photo - Alan Watson

JARROW ROOFING BOLDON C.A.

Chairman: Richard McLoughlin. **Press Officer/Treasurer:** Rose McLoughlin.
Secretary/Manager: Richard McLoughlin, 8 Kitchener Terrace, Jarrow NE32 5PU (0191 489 9825).
Coach: Kevin Arnott **Physio:** Fred Corner/Alan Leslie
Ground: Boldon CA Sports Ground, New Road, Boldon Colliery (0191 519 1391)
Seats: 150 **Cover:** 800 **Capacity:** 3,500 **Floodlights:** Yes **Club Shop:**Yes
Clubhouse: Open nights and weekend lunchtimes. Chips, hotdogs, burgers etc available from tea bar on matchdays.
Programme: 20 pages, free with entry **Editor:** Brian Marshall (0191 455 1190) **Nickname:** Roofing.
Colours: All Royal Blue with red trim **Change colours:** Claret & blue **Founded:** 1987.
Midweek matchday: Wednesday **Record Attendance:** 500 v South Shields
Previous Leagues: Mid-Tyne/ Tyneside Amtr 88-91/ Vaux Wearside **Sponsors:** Jarrow Roofing Co.
Club Record Appearances: Mick Haley **Club Record Goalscorer:** Lee Young
Honours: Wearside Lg Div 2 R-up 91-92 95-96; Sunderland Shipowners Cup R-up 93-94, 94-95; Tyneside Amtr Lg R-up 90-91, Chal. Shield 90-91 (R-up 89-90); Bill Dixon Cup 90-91; Mid-Tyne Lg 87-88; Fred Giles Cup R-up 87-88; Gateshead Charity Cup SF 90-91; Monkwearmouth Cup 94-95; Craven Cup 96-97:

MORPETH TOWN

Chairman: Ken Beattie. Tel.: 01670 515271 (H), 01670 520565 (B). **Press Officer:** Secretary
Secretary: Joe Hobin, 23 Princes Gardens, Malvins Close, Blyth, Northumberland. NE24 5HJ. (01670 360820).
Ground: Craik Park, Morpeth Common, Morpeth, Northumberland. (01670 513785).
Directions: Morpeth is signed off the A1 onto A197. Take the B6524, right at Mitford sign, then right after about a mile into the ground, next to Morpeth Common.
Colours: Yellow & black stripes/black/yellow. **Change colours:** All red with white trim.
Previous Leagues: Northern Alliance. (pre 1994). **Previous Ground:** Storey Park, Morpeth. (pre 1992).
Honours: Northern Alliance 83-84, 93-94 (R-up 37-38, 65-66, 73-74, 81-82, 84-85); Challenge Cup Winners 38-39, 85-86, 93-94 (R-up 36-37, 62-63, 73-74).

MURTON

Chairman: Tom Torrence **Vice Chairman:** J Hudson **President:** John Hellens.
Secretary: Tom Turnbull, 15 Dalton Terrace, Seaham, Co Durham SR7 9BZ (0191 526 6488 H, 0191 581 9874 B)
Manager: Jeff Cranson **Asst Mgr:** Brian Burlinson **Coach:** Richie Madden.
Physio: Vince Symmonds **Press Officer:** James Hudson (0191 526 0283) **Commercial Mgr:** T Carr.
Ground: Recreation Park, Church Lane, Murton, County Durham (0191 517 0814).
Directions: Exit A19 onto B1285 heading west into Murton - Church Lane on left opposite catholic church.
Seats: 100 **Cover:** 320 **Capacity:** 3,500 **Floodlights:** Yes **Founded:** 1904
Clubhouse: 'The International' 300 yards from ground on B1285. Normal pub hours. Restaurant upstairs. Function room for 100. Open plan downstairs with horse shoe bar. Matchday snacks at ground.
Programme: 12 pages, 30p **Programme Editor:** Stuart Upperton **Club Shop:** No.
Colours: All white with red trim **Change colours:** Red/black/red **Nickname:** Gnashers
Club Sponsors: John Hellyns **Midweek home matchday:** Wednesday
Record Gate: 3,500 v Spennymoor Utd, Durham Challenge Cup 1951.
Previous Grounds: Fatton Pasture 04-28. **Players progressing to Football League:** Numerous.
Previous Leagues: Wearside 13-46 51-88/ North East Counties 46-51.
Record win: 17-1 v Thornley **Record defeat:** 0-14 v South Shields (H).
Club record scorer: **Club record appearances:** Robert Welch 500 (1962-78).
Honours: Northern Lg Div 2 89-90, Wearside Lg 28-29 36-37 59-60 (Lg Cup 58-59 70-71), Sunderland Shipowners Cup 59-60 69-70 70-71, Monkwearmouth Charity Cup 21-22 28-29 34-35 35-36 63-64 70-71 87-88, Durham Chall. Cup 92-93, Durham Jnr Cup 50-51.

NORTHALLERTON

Chairman: Denis Cope **Vice Chairman:** Keith Alderson **President:** Ian Butler
Secretary: David Watson c/o Calvert Stadium, Ainderby Road, Northallerton, N Yorks
Manager: John Woods/Mike Sell **Physio:** Andrew Garson **Press Officer:** Secretary
Ground: Ainderby Rd, Romanby, Northallerton, North Yorks (01609 772418)
Directions: Leave A1 at Leeming Bar (A684) follow signs to Northallerton, approaching town take B1333 signed Romanby - ground 250yds on left.
Seats: 150 **Cover:** 500 **Capacity:** 3,000 **Floodlights:** Yes **Founded:** 1994
Clubhouse: Mon-Fri 7.30-11pm, Sat noon-7.30pm, Sun 12-2 & 7.30-10.30pm.
Midweek matchday: Wednesday **Club Shop:** Yes, Contact Mark Walker (01609 780837)
Colours: Black& white/black/white **Change colours:** Yellow/blue/yellow. **Nickname:** Town
Programme: 16 pages, 50p **Editor:** Ian Bolland
Club Sponsors: TBA **Record Gate:** 671 v Farnborough, FA Tphy 3rd Rd 20/2/93.
Best FA Cup year: 4th Qual. Rd 92-93 **Best FA Trophy year:** 3rd Rnd 92-93
Previous Leagues: Allertonshire (now defunct)/ Vale of Mowbray (defunct)/ Ripon & Dist./ Teesside/ North Yorks (defunct)/ Darlington & Dist./ Harrogate & Dist.
Players progressing to Football League: Andy Toman (Hartlepool, Darlington, Scarborough).
96-97 Captain: Wayne Lasien **P.o.Y.:** Jimmy Scot **Top Scorer:** John Woods
Club record scorer: John Woods **Club record appearances:** Lee Wasden.
Honours: Northern Lg Cup 93-94 (Div 2 R-up 89-90), North Riding Snr Cup R-up 83-84, Harrogate & Dist. Lg, Richmond Cup, Bedale Cup, Millbank Cup, Orde Powlett Cup, Harrogate Invitation Cup, Alverton Trophy.

PENRITH

Chairman: D Johnson **Vice Chairman:** M Robson
Secretary: John Balmer, 58 Castle Hill Road, Penrith, Cumbria (01768 866736)
Manager: Geoff Byers **Physio:** Les Cornwell.
Ground: Southend Road Ground, Penrith, Cumbria (01768 863212).
Directions: M6 Jct 40, onto dual carriageway to Appleby & Scotch Corner, turn first left at next r'bout, approx half a mile into Penrith on A6 into town, take 1st left for ground. Three quarters of a mile from Penrith (BR).
Seats: 200 **Cover:** 1,000 **Capacity:** 4,000 **Floodlights:** Yes **Club Shop:** No
Clubhouse: Open Thurs-Fri 9.30pm-2am, Sat 2-6pm & 9.30pm-2am, Wed match nights 6.30-10.30pm.
Programme: 24 pages, 50p **Editor/Press Officer:** J Bell (01768 63898) **Founded:** 1894
Colours: Blue/white/blue **Change colours:** White/red/white **Nickname:** Blues.
Sponsors: British Gypsum **Midweek Matches:** Wednesday **Reserve team:** None
Record Attendance: 2,100 v Chester 1981. **Best FA Cup season:** 2nd Rd 81-82
Previous leagues: Carlisle & Dist., Northern 48-82, NW Co's 82-87, 90-97, Northern Prem. 87-90.
Players progressing to Football League: K Sawyers, G Fell, G Mossop (all Carlisle).
96-97 Captain: Martin Kirkby **P.o.Y.:** Martin Kirkby **Top Scorer:** Tony Fyfe
Club Record Goalscorer: C Short **Club Record Appearances:** Lee Armstrong
Honours: Northern Lg R-up 61-62; NW Co's Lg R-up 83-84; NW Co's F/Light Trophy 95-96 96-97; Cumberland Snr Cup [12].

R.T.M. NEWCASTLE

Chairman: Tom Brash **Vice-Chairman:**
Secretary: Jim Anderson, 7 Whitbeck Rd, Statyford, Newcastle-upon-Tyne NE5 2XA (0191 243 1025)
Manager/Coach: Rob Atkin **Asst Manager:** T Mitchell **Physio:** T Mitchell
Ground: Wheatsheaf Sports Ground, Woolsington, Newcastle-upon-Tyne. NE13 8DF. (0191 286 0425).
Directions: From central station follow airport signs for 7 miles - ground next to Wheatsheaf Hotel on left, approximately 800yds before airport. Callerton Parkway metro station is 400yds from ground.
Seats: 300 **Cover:** 300 **Capacity:** 2,000 **Floodlights:** Yes **Club Shop:** Yes
Clubhouse: Matchdays only. Hotdogs, soup, sandwiches available.
Programme: 12 pages, 30p **Editor:** Secretary **Press Officer:** Secretary.
Colours: Blue/white/blue **Change colours:** Yellow & black stripes/black/yellow **Sponsors:** RTM
Nickname: 'Star' **Founded:** 1930 **Midweek matchday:** Monday **Reserve League:** None.
Record Attendance: 1,800 v Almondsbury Greenway, FA Vase SF 77-78.
Best season FA Cup: 1st Rd 84-85 (lost 0-2 York C.). **FA Trophy:** Qtr-finals 88-89 (lost 1-4 [H] Telford Utd). **FA Vase:** 77-78
Previous Leagues: Newcastle Business Houses 32-38/ North East Amateur/ Tyneside Amateur/ Northern Combination/ Wearside 75-85.
Players progressing to Football League: Ian Crumplin & Tony Robinson (Hartlepool 1976 & 1986), Barry Dunn (Darlington 1979), Ian McInerney (Huddersfield Town 1988).
Club Record Appearances & Record Goalscorer: Ian Crumplin.
Honours: Northern Lg R-up 87-88, Lg Cup 85-86 (R-up(1), Div 2 85-86; Wearside Lg (5), R-up (3), Lg Cup (5); Sunderland Shipowners Cup 82-83 84-85, Monkwearmouth Charity Cup (4); Northern Comb. 62-63 68-69, Lg Cup 66-67 71-72; Northumberland Snr Cup (4), R-up (3); Minor Cup 64-65; J R Cleator Cup 86-87.

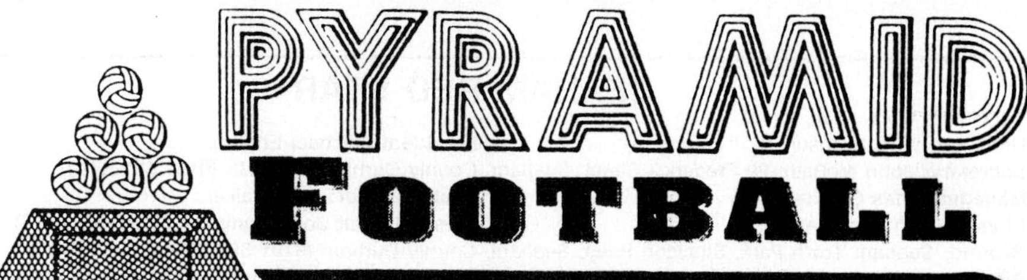
PYRAMID
FOOTBALL

SEAHAM RED STAR

Chairman: Reg Atkinson **President:** Michael English.
Secretary: John McBeth, 29 Frederick Street, Seaham, County Durham SR7 7HX (0191 581 5712).
Manager: Chris Copeland **Asst Manager:** Paul Walker.
Physio: Allan Jackson **Press Officer:** John Campbell (0191 581 4308).
Ground: Seaham Town Park, Stockton Road, Seaham, County Durham (0191 581 2540).
Directions: From Tyne Tunnel: A19 Teeside approx 8 miles; B1404 Seaham slip road, left at top of slip road. Right at traffic lights & first left past school into ground.
Seats: 60 **Cover:** 200 **Capacity:** 4,000 **Floodlights:** Yes **Year Formed:** 1973
Clubhouse: Mon-Sat 11am-11pm, Sun 12-2, 7-10.30pm. Large function room, snooker, pool, Restuarant & Bars.
Colours: All Red **Change colours:** All blue **Nickname:** The Star
Programme: 20 pages **Editor:** David Copeland (0191 581 8514) **Club Shop:** No.
Record Attendance: 1,500 v Guisborough, Wearside Lg/ v Sunderland, floodlight opener 1979.
Best season FA Vase: 5th Rd 78-79. **FA Trophy:** 2nd Rd 89-90
Previous Leagues: Sunday football/ Houghton & District 73-74/ Northern Alliance 74-79/ Wearside 79-83.
Previous Name: Seaham Colliery Welfare Red Star 78-87.
Previous Grounds: Deneside Recreation Recreation Park 73-75/ Vane Tempest Welfare 75-78.
Players progressing to Football League: Bobby Davison (Huddersfield 1980), Nigel Gleghorn (Ipswich 1985), Billy Stubbs (Nottm Forest 1987), Paul Nixon (Bristol Rovers (1989), Mick Smith (Hartlepool).
Midweek home matchday: Wednesday **Reserve team's League:** Banks Youth League.
96-97 Captain: **Top Scorer:** **P.o.Y.:**
Club record scorer: Tom Henderson **Club record appearances:** Michael Whitfield.
Honours: Northern Lg Cup 92-93, Phillips F'lit Tphy 78-79; Durham Chall Cup 79-80; Wearside Lg 81-82, Lg Cup 81-82, Div 2 R-up 87-88, Monkwearmouth Charity Cup R-up 79-80.

SHILDON

Chairman: Bill Aisbitt **Vice Chairman:** George Elliott **President:** John Atkinson.
Secretary: Mike Armitage, 22 Hambleton Ct, Byerley Park, Newton Aycliffe, Co. Durham DL5 7HR (01325 316322).
Manager: Ray Gowan **Asst Manager:** **Physio:** Jimmy Smalls
Ground: Dean Street, Shildon, County Durham (01388 773877).
Directions: In the town centre 1 mile from BR station and 300yds from Darlington-Bishop Auckland bus stop.
Seats: 400 **Cover:** 500 **Capacity:** 4,000 **Floodlights:** Yes **Club Shop:** No
Clubhouse: Open every evening 7.30-11pm (open earlier on matchnights), 1pm onwards on Saturday matchdays. Bar, pool & darts.
Programme: 48 pages, 40p **Editor:** Neil Bennett (01325 332310) **Press Officer:** Secretary
Colours: All red (white trim) **Change colours:** All blue. **Midweek Matches:** Wednesday
Sponsors: Atkinsons Stairs **Nickname:** Railwaymen. **Founded:** 1890
Record Attendance: 13,000 - Leeholme v Perkinsville, schoolboys game, 1920s. For Shildon game; 11,000 Shildon v Ferryhill Athletic, Durham Senior Cup 1922.
Best FA Cup season: 2nd Rd 36-37. Also 1st Rd 27-28 29-30 34-35 36-37 55-56 59-60 61-62. **FA Trophy:** 3rd Qual Rd 74-75. **FA Vase:** 1st Rd 86-87. **FA Amateur Cup:** 4th Rd 58-59
Previous Leagues: Auckland & District 1892-96/ Wearside 96-97/ North Eastern 07-32.
Players progressing to Football League: Ken Whitfield (Wolves 47), James Smith (Chelsea 51), Mike Peacock, Philip Shute, Nigel Bolton (Darlington 60, 84, 95), Kevin Stonehouse (Blackburn 79).
96-97 Captain: Bryan Liddue **P.o.Y.:** Neil Immerson **Top Scorer:** Nigel Bolton (32)
Club Record Appearances: Bryan Dale **Club Record Goalscorer:** Jack Downing, 61 (1936-37).
Honours: Northern Lg 33-34 34-35 35-36 36-37 39-40 (R-up 32-33 38-39, Lg Cup 33-34 34-35 37-38 38-39 39-40 52-53), Durham Challenge Cup 07-08 25-26 71-72, Durham Amateur Cup 01-02 02-03, Durham Benevelopment Bowl 24-25.

SOUTH SHIELDS

Chairman: John Rundle **Vice Chairman:** George Scott **President:**
Secretary/Press Officer: David Fall, 50 Basil Way, South Shields NE34 8UD (0191 426 2135)
Manager: Bobby Graham **Asst Manager:** Keith Tweddle **Physio:** Jim Wilkinson
Ground: Mariners Club, Filtrona Park, Shaftesbury Avenue, Jarrow, Tyne & Wear NE34 9PH.(0191 4279839)
Directions: From A1(M) take A194(M) to South Shields, A194 town centre road for 5 miles, ignore A1300 (Sunderland & coast) & turn left at next lights beside Co-op store into Simonside Ind. Est. (Shaftesbury Ave.), grd at bottom
Seats: 150 **Cover:** 400 **Capacity:** 2,500 **Floodlights:** Yes **Founded:** 1974

Clubhouse: Two function suites, club kitchen.
Colours: Claret/blue/white/white **Change:** All white **Nickname:** Mariners
Previous Leagues: Northern Alliance 74-76. **Previous Ground:** Jack Clarke Park 74-92.
Record Attendance: 1,500 v Spennymoor, Durham Challenge Cup Final 94-95
Best season FA Vase: Qtr Finals 75-76
Programme: 40p **Editor:** Steve Leonard **Club Shop:** Yes
Midweek matchday: Tuesday **Reserve team:** None.
96-97 Captain: M Irwin **Top Scorer:** **P.o.Y.:** Marc Irwin
Honours: Northern Lge Div 2 R-up 95-96; Northern Alliance 74-75 75-76; Wearside Lg 76-77 92-93 94-95; Monkwearmouth Charity Cup 86-87 (R-up 94-95); Shipowners Cup 92-93 (R-up 83-84); Durham Chall Cup 76-77, R-up 94-95.

STOCKTON

Chairman: Lol Lyons
Secretary: Peter Morris, 20 Wheatear Lane, Ingleby Barwick, Stockton-on-Tees, Cleveland TS17 0TB (01642 760779)
Manager: Alan Robinson **Asst Mgr:** Michael Watson. **Coach:** Peter May.
Press Officer: Gary Stephenson (01642 713355)
Ground: Teesdale Park, Acklam Road, Thornaby, Stockton-on-Tees TS17 8TZ (01642 606803).
Directions: A19 to Thornaby turn off, ground half mile on right. One mile from Thornaby BR station. Any Stockton-Middlesbrough bus - stop at Acklam Rd, Thornaby.
Seats: 150. **Cover:** 350. **Capacity:** 5,000 **Floodlights:** Yes **Formed:** 1980
Clubhouse: 150+ seater social club with concert room, pool/games room and bar. Open every night and Sunday lunchtimes and all day Saturday. Sandwiches available in bar, canteen in ground sells pies, burgers, soup, drinks etc.
Programme: 24 pages, 30p **Editor:** Alan Reddy (01642 585625). **Club Shop:** No.
Club colours: Red & black stripes/black/red **Change colours:** All sky.
Sponsors: T.B.A. **Reserves' Lge:** Teesside **Midweek Matches:** Tuesday.
Previous Leagues: Stockton & District 80-81/ Wearside 81-85.
Previous Names: Stockton Cricket Club 65-80.
Previous Grounds: Grangefield Youth & Community Centre, Stockton 80-82/ Tilery Sports Centre 82-83.
Best season FA Cup: 4th Qual. Rd replay 92-93 (lost 1-2 at home to Blyth after 1-1 draw). **FA Vase:** 2nd Rd. **FA Trophy:** 1st Rd
Record Attendance: 3,000 v Middlebrough, pre-season friendly August 1986.
Record win: 11-0 v Horden C.W.(H) Buchanan Cup 94-95.
96-97 Captain: **P.o.Y.:** **Top Scorer:**
Club record appearances: Michael Watson.
Hons: Northern Lg Div 2 87-88 91-92; Nth Riding Co. Cup 85-86; Inaugral winners of Craven Cup (Northern Div 2 clubs) 94-95.

TOW LAW TOWN

Chairman: John Flynn
Secretary: Bernard Fairbairn, 3 Coppice Walk, Mowden Park, Darlington, County Durham DL3 9DP (01325 350743).
Manager: Stuart Leeming **Assistant Manager:** Terry Kirkbride. **Press Officer:** John Flynn (01325 730525)
Ground: Ironworks Road, Tow Law, Bishop Auckland (01388 731443).
Directions: Just of High Street in Tow Law town centre.
Founded: 1890 **Seats:** 200 **Cover:** 300 **Capacity:** 6,000 **Floodlights:** Due
Clubhouse: Every evening 8.30 -10.30.
Colours: Black & white stripes/black/black & white **Change colours:** Red & white
Nickname: Lawyers. **Programme:** Yes. **Club Shop:** Yes
Midweek Matches: Tuesday **Record Gate:** 5,500 v Mansfield Town, FA Cup 1967.
Best season F.A. Cup: 2nd Rd replay 67-68. Also Competition Proper 68-69 84-85 89-90. **FA Trophy:** 2nd Rd replay 82-83. **FA Amateur Cup:** 3rd Rd replay 70-71
League Clubs defeated in F.A. Cup: Mansfield Town 67-68. **Previous leagues:** None
Players progressing to Football League: Reuben Cook & Ralph Guthrie (Arsenal 1951 & 53), Gordon Hughes & Terry Melling & Chris Waddle (Newcastle 1956 & 65 & 80), Eric Johnstone & Kevin Dixon (Carlisle 1963 & 83), Keith Adamson (Barnsley 1966), Tom Henderson (Bradford PA 1969), Vincent Chapman (Huddersfield 1988).
Honours: Rothmans National Cup 77; Northern Lg 23-24 24-25 Champions 94-95, R-up 28-29 88-89, Lg Cup 73-74; Rothmans Overseas Cup 76-77; Durham Chall Cup 1895-96; Durham Amtr Cup 1892-93

RTM Newcastle's defenders John Taylor, Terry Edwards & Roger Delgado block Sheffield's Kevin Lindsey from the goal.
Photo - Ray Pruden

Lee Armstrong of Penrith, who have returned to the Northern League, tackles Vauxhall's Neil Wenham
Photo - Alan Watson

SECOND DIVISION CLUBS

ALNWICK TOWN

Chairman: John Common **Press Officer:** Secretary
Secretary: R Miller, 2 Beech Grove, Alnwick NE66 1EB (01665 606169)
Manager: D Clark **Assistant Manager:** Dave Williamson.
Ground: St James' Park, Alnwick, Northumberland (01665 603162).
Directions: 35 miles north of Newcastle on A1, take the slip road to Alnwick, then first left. At roundabout turn left, ground is then on your left.
Seats: 100 **Cover:** 200 **Capacity:** 2,500 **Floodlights:** Yes **Founded:** 1879
Colours: Black & white stripes/black/black **Change colours:** All yellow
Midweek Matches: Tuesday **Reserve's League:** North Northumberland **Programme:** 20 pages, 25p
Previous - Leagues: Northern Alliance 35-39 46-64 64-82. **Names:** Alnwick United Services/ Alnwick United.
Record Attendance: 600 v Bedlington Terriers, Northern Alliance 1971.
Best season FA Cup: 3rd Qual. Rd 51-52 (3-4 at Blyth), 57-58 (4-6 at Easington Colliery). **FA Trophy:** 3rd Qualifying Rd 90-91.
Players progressing to Football League: George Turnbull (Grimsby 1950), Brian Pringle (1973).
Honours: Northern Lg Div 2 R-up 88-89; Northern Alliance 37-38 62-63 63-64 65-66 67-68 68-69 69-70 70-71 71-72 (R-up 59-60 61-62 66-67 72-73), Lg Cup 61-62 65-66 67-68 68-69 70-71, Subsidiary Cup 80-81; Durham Central Lg Cup 64-65; Northumberland Benevolent Bowl 86-87; Northumberland SNR Cup R-up 61-62; Northumberland Amtr Cup 71-72.

ASHINGTON

Chairman: T Reed **Joint Presidents:** Sir Bobby Charlton and Jackie Charlton OBE
Secretary: Brian Robinson, 80 Milburn Rd, Ashington, N/thumberland NE63 0PG (01670 852832 H, 01670 521212 B)
Manager: Keith Grant. **Asst.Manager:** Colin Stocks. **Physio:** Brian Hogg
Ground: Portland Park, Ashington NE63 9XG (01670 811991 Social Club)
Directions: 200 yds north at traffic lights in centre of town.
Seats: 350 **Cover:** 2,200 **Capacity:** 4,000 **Floodlights:** Yes **Club Shop:** No
Clubhouse: Open normal licensing hours in evenings & from 11.0 a.m. on Tuesdays (market days). Pool, darts, jukebox, snacks etc. Jumpers, baseball caps etc. available behind bar.
Programme: Yes, 50p **Editor:** A.Marchett (01670 854585) **Press Officer:** Brian Bennett (01670 856606)
Club colours: Black & white stripes/black/black & whit**Change colours:** Yellow with black trim.
Midweek Matches: Tuesday. **Sponsors:** Furst Renault Garage.**Formed:** 1883 **Nickname:** The Colliers.
Best F.A. Cup season: 3rd Rd 26-27. **League Clubs defeated in F.A. Cup:** Halifax Town 50-51.
Record Attendance: 13,199 v Rochdale, FA Cup 2nd Rd 9/12/50.
Previous Leagues: Northern Alliance 1892-93 1902-14 69-70/ Football League/ North Eastern 14-21 29-58 62-64/ Midland 58-60/ Northern Counties 60-62/ Wearside 64-65/ Northern Premier 68-69.
Players progressing to Football League: Tony Lowery (W.B.A./Mansfield T), Les Mutrie (Colchester), R Cummins (Aberdeen/Newcastle U). David Walton (Sheff Utd./Shrewsbury T.)
Honours: FA Amateur Cup SF 73-74; Northumberland Snr 20-21 32-33 38-39 49-50 55-56 56-57 61-62 66-67 79-80; Northumberland Challenge Bowl 12-13 21-22 22-23 23-24 25-26 33-34; Midland Lg 58-59; North Eastern Lg Cup 33-34 (jt with Sunderland Reserves) 39-40, Div 2 26-27 (Res); Northern Alliance 13-14 24-25(Res) 39-40(Res) 55-56(Res), R-up 05-06 10-11 11-12 22-23(Res) 54-55(Res) 56-57(Res), Lg Cup 47-48(Res).

BRANDON UNITED

Chairman: Neil Scott **Vice Chairman:** Joe Cutmore. **President:** Terry Jacques
Secretary: Brian Richardson, 108 Braunespath Estate, New Brancepeth, Durham DH7 7JF (0191 373 1304).
Manager: John Carey **Asst Mgr:** Roli Bell **Physio:** Bev Dougherty
Ground: Welfare Ground, rear of Commercial Street, Brandon, Durham (0191 378 2957).
Directions: A690 - 3 miles west of Durham City. Buses 49 & 49A from Durham.
Seats: 200 **Cover:** 300 **Capacity:** 3,000 **Floodlights:** Yes **Club Shop:** No
Clubhouse: Open every day, lunch & evening. Pool & juke box. Entertainment at weekends.
Programme: 40 pages, 30p. **Editor:** Keith Nellis (0191 378 0704) **Press Officer:** Secretary.
Colours: All red **Change colours:** All blue. **Founded:** 1968. **Nickname:** United
Sponsors: Shildon Sawmills. **Midweek Matches:** Wednesday **Record Gate:** 2,500, FA Sunday Cup SF.
Best season FA Cup: 1st Rd replay 88-89 (lost to Doncaster). Also 1st Rd 79-80. **FA Vase:** Qtr Finals 82-83, 83-84. **FA Trophy:** 3rd Qual Rd 87-88, 89-90.
Previous Lges: Durham & Dist. Sunday 68-77/ Northern All. 77-80/ Northern Amtr 80-81/ Wearside 81-83.
Players progressing to Football League: Bryan Liddle & Dean Gibb (Hartlepool 1984 & 86), Paul Dalton (Manchester Utd 1988), Neil Richardson (Rotherham).
Club Record Goalscorer: Tommy Holden **Club Record Appearances:** Derek Charlton.
Honours: FA Sunday Cup 75-76; Northern Lg Div 2 84-85 (Lg Cup R-up 92-93); Northern All (2) 77-79, R-up 79-80, Lg Cup 77-78 79-80 (R-up 78-79); Sunderland Shipowners Cup 81-82; Durham Co. Sunday Cup 73-74 75-76 76-77; Durham & Dist Sunday Lg(4) 73-77, Div 2 69-70, Div 3 68-69; Staffieri Cup 75-76.

CHESTER-LE-STREET TOWN

Chairman: John Tomlinson **Vice Chairman:** Jack Thornback **President:** John Holden.
Secretary: Melvin Atkinson, 1 St Marys Close, Chester-le-Street, Co Durham DH2 3EG (0191 388 3664).
Manager: Peter Mulcaster **Asst Mgr/Coach:** Joe Burlison. **Physio:** Joe Burlison.
Commercial Manager: Paul Days **Press Officer:** Jack Thornback (0191 3883554).
Ground: Moor Park, Chester Moor, Chester-le Street, County Durham (0191 388 3363).
Directions: Ground lies approx 2 miles south of town on A167 (C.-le-S. to Durham road). Regular buses from C.-le-S. and Durham pass ground. Railway station 2 miles distant in town centre.
Seats: 200 **Cover:** 600 **Capacity:** 2,000 **Floodlights:** Yes **Founded:** 1972
Clubhouse: Open matchdays, Wed, Thurs & Sun. Wed/Thurs 7-10.30pm, Sun 12-2pm, midweek matches 6.30-10.30pm, Sat 12-10.30pm.
Midweek Matches: Tuesday **Shop:** No, but old programmes available from editor.
Colours: Blue & white hoops/white/white **Change colours:** All yellow.
Programme: 32 pages, 30p **Editor:** Press Officer **Nickname:** Cestrians
Previous - Leagues: Newcastle City Amtr 72-75/ Washington 75/ Wearside 77-83. **Names:** Garden Farm 1972-78.
Grounds: Ravensworth Welfare, Low Fell 72-73/ Riverside Pk 73-78/ Sacriston Welfare 78-79.
Record Gate: 473 v Barrow, FA Cup 83-84 (3,000 for Sunderland v Newcastle, Bradford appeal match 1985).
Record win: 8-0 v Billingham T., FA Vase Preliminary Rd 6/10/84.
Record defeaat: 1-7 v Curzon Ashton, FA Vase Third Rd, 12/12/92.
Players progressing to Football League: Dave Atkinson (Sunderland 1986), Peter Ward (Huddersfield 1987).
Club record scorer: Colin Howey, 50 **Club record appearances:** Brian Wray, 148.
Honours: Northern Lg Div 2 83-84, Wearside Lg 80-81 (R-up 82-83), Monkwearmouth Cup 80-81 81-82, FA Vase 4th Rd 91-92, Washington Lg, Durham Minor Cup, Washington AM Cup.

EPPLETON COLLIERY WELFARE

Chairman: Ralph Lawson **Vice Chairman:** **President:** Mr F Hartis.
Secretary: John Gibson, Avondene, Houghton Road, Hetton-le-Hole, Tyne & Wear DH5 9PH (0191 526 3782)
Manager: Alan Hurst **Asst Manager:** Stuart Gooden **Commercial Mgr/Press Officer:** Secretary.
Ground: Eppleton Welfare Park, Park View, Hetton-le-Hole, Tyne & Wear (0191 5261048).
Directions: Situated behind Front Street Post Office & directly behind Hetton swimming baths, Hetton-le-Hole on A182. Buses 194, 535, 231, X5, X94 in Front Street. 8 miles from Durham BR statio; buses 154 and 254 from Durham.
Seats: 250. **Cover:** 500 **Capacity:** 2,500 **Floodlights:** Yes **Founded:** 1929.
Clubhouse: Bar & lounge on ground. Normal opening hours. Whitbread beers.
Club Shop: Club sweaters, polo shirts, metal lapel badges available
Colours: Black & sky/black/black **Change:** Yellow/green/green
Record Attendance: 1,250 - Monkwearmouth Charity Cup Final 1987-88.
Previous - Leagues: Wearside 51-65 74-92/ Houghton & District 65-74. **Grounds:** None. **Names:** None (merged with Natcobos, early 70's).
Programme: 16 pages, 20p **Editor:** **Nickname:** Welfare
Club Sponsors: E & N Ritchie **Midweek matchday:** Wednesday
Honours: Northern Lg Div 2 R-up 92-93, Wearside Lg 90-91 91-92 (Lg Cup 74-75 78-79 87-88, Sunderland Shipowners Cup 47-48 85-86 90-91 (R-up 91-92), Monkwearmouth Charity Cup 89-90 90-91 91-92), Durham Challenge Cup 89-90.

ESH WINNING

Chairman: Charles Ryan **Vice Chairman:** Billy Hall **President:** Jack Lumsden
Secretary: Robin Hinds, 158 Norburn Park, Witton Gilbert, Durham DH7 6SQ (0191 371 0204).
Manager: T.B.A. **Physio:** T.B.A.
Ground: West Terrace, Waterhouses, Durham (0191 373 3872).
Directions: Durham to Ushaw Moor, to Esh Winning; ground 1 mile further at Waterhouses.
Seats: 160 **Cover:** 160 **Capacity:** 3,500 **Floodlights:** Yes **Club Shop:** No
Clubhouse: Open daily. Snacks served
Programme: 20 pages, 50p **Editor/Press Officer:** Ian Fish (0191 373 0641)
Colours: Yellow with black trim/green/yellow & green **Change colours:** Purple & Black.
Club Sponsors: Renault Trucks (North East). **Formed:** 1967 **Nickname:** 'Esh'
Midweek Matches: Tuesday **Record Gate:** 900 v Liverpool Fantail, FA Sunday Cup 1982.
Record win: 9-0 v Langley Park (H) **Record defeat:** 0-8 v Dunston FB (A).
Record transfer fee paid: Nil **Received:** £400 for Derek Middleton (Easington Colliery).
Best FA Cup season: 2nd Qual Rd 90-91 **Best FA Vase season:** 2nd Round 83-84.
Previous - Leagues: Durham & Dist Sunday/ Northern Alliance 81-82. **Grounds:** None. **Names:** Esh Winning Pineapple (pre-1982).
Club Record Goalscorer: Paul Ward 31 **Club Record Appearances:** Paul Hewitson 40.
Honours: Durham & District Sunday Lg 78-79 79-80, Durham County Sunday Cup R-up 78-79, Staffieri Cup 74-75, Guards Cup 72-73, North Durham Youth Lg 94-95, Auckland Yth Lge 94-95.

EVENWOOD TOWN

Chairman: Matt Robinson **President:** N Colegrove
Secretary: Jim Coates, 19 Wellgarth, Evenwood, Bishop Auckland, Co Durham DL14 9QU (01388 833035)
Manager: Dr Graeme Forster **Press Officer:** G Forster (0191 373 5143)
Ground: Welfare Ground, Stones End, Evenwood, County Durham (01388 832281).
Directions: In village centre by Sports & Social club in Stones Rd.
Seats: 32 **Cover:** 200 **Capacity:** 3,500 **Floodlights:** Yes **Founded:** 1890
Clubhouse: Open lunch & evening every day.
Sponsors: C A Roofing **Midweek Matches:** Wednesday **Programme:** None
Club colours: All blue **Change:** Red (white sleeves)/white/red (white hoops).
Nickname: The Wood. **Best FA Cup season:** 1st Rd 1936.
Record Gate: 9,000 v Bishop Auckland, FA Amtr Cup 1931.
Previous Names: None **Players progressing to Football Lge:** Too numerous to record.
Previous Leagues: Barnard Castle & District 1894-95/ Auckland & District 1894-96 1903-04 08-23 28-31/ Wear Valley 1896-99 1904-06 24-25/ Gauntlett Valley 06-07/ South Durham 27-28.
96-97 Captain: **Top Scorer:** **P.o.Y.:**
Honours: Northern Lg 48-49 69-70 70-71 (Lg Cup 35-36); Durham Challenge Cup 69-70.

HEBBURN

Chairman: Bill Laffey **Vice-Chairman:** Brian Lowe.
Secretary: Tom Derrick, 63 Staneway, Felling, Gateshead, NE10 8LS. (0191 442 1563)
Manager: Tony Robinson **Assistant Manager:** Dennis Melia **Physio:**
Ground: Hebburn Sports & Social Ground, Victoria Road West, Hebburn (0191 483 5101).
Directions: On the main road through the town about 1 mile from railway station. Hebburn lies on the Metroline - excellent bus service from Heworth Metro.
Seats: 153. **Cover:** 420. **Capacity:** 2,000 **Floodlights:** Yes **Club Shop:** No
Clubhouse: Open 7-11pm weekdays, Sat 11am-1pm, Sun noon-2.30pm. Pool, darts etc.
Programme: 24 pages, 30p **Editor:** Steve Newton. **Press Officer:** Alan Armstrong (0191 430 0078).
Colours: Yellow & black trim/sky blue/yellow **Change colours:** All red
Midweek Matches: Wednesday **Nickname:** Hornets. **Founded:** 1912
Record Attendance: 503 v Darwen, FA Cup Preliminary Round replay 7/9/91.
Record win: 10-1 **Record defeat:** 3-10.
Best FA Vase season: 2nd Round 91-92.
Best FA Cup season: 2nd Qualifying Rd replay 89-90 (lost 0-3 at South Bank).
Previous Leagues: Jarrow & Dist. Jnr 12-14/ South Shields Comb. 19-22/ Tyneside Comb. 22-27/ Tyneside 27-39/ Northern Comb. 41-44 45-59/ North Eastern 44-45 59-60/ Wearside 60-89.
Previous Grounds: None **Previous Names:** Reyrolles/ Hebburn Reyrolles (pre-1988).
96-97 Captain: **P.o.Y.:** **Top Scorer:**
Club Record Goalscorer: Keith Carter **Club Record Appearances:**
Honours: Shields Gazette Cup 91-92; Wearside Lg 66-67, Monkwearmouth Charity Cup 68-69; Durham Challenge Cup 42-43 91-92; Tyneside Lg 38-39; Northern Comb. 43-44; Gateshead Charity Cup 35-36 37-38; Palmer Hospital Cup 27-28; Hebburn Aged Miners Cup 35-36; Heddon Homes Cup 42-43; Hebburn Infirmary Cup 35-36 36-37 37-38 38-39.

HORDEN COLLIERY WELFARE

Chairman: John McCoy **Press Officer:** Karl Henson (01915 842479)
Secretary: Robert Wood, 29 Morpeth Str., Horden, Peterlee, County Durham SR8 4BE (0191 586 8802).
Ground: Welfare Park Ground, Park Road, Horden, Peterlee, County Durham (0191 518 2692 Club)
Directions: A19 to Peterlee, signposted from there.
Seats: 300 **Cover:** 400 **Capacity:** 4,500 **Floodlights:** Yes **Reformed:** 1980
Clubhouse: Normal licensing hours. Hot & cold snacks, darts, pool.
Colours: Red with black & white/red/red **Change colours:** Blue/black/blue
Midweek Matches: Tuesday **Programme:** 10 pages, 20p **Nickname:** Colliers
Previous Lges: Wearside 07-35 63-75/ N. Eastern 35-58 62-64/ Midland (Co's) 58-60/ Northern Co's 60-62.
Best FA Cup year: 2nd Rd 38-39 (2-3 at home to Newport Co.). Also 1st Rd 25-26 52-53 53-54 54-55 81-82.
Previous Names: Horden Athletic. **Record Attendance:** 8,000 - FA Cup 1937.
Players progressing to Football League: Paul Dobson (Hartlepool United).
Honours: Durham Challenge Cup 35-36 63-64 80-81 81-82; Durham Benevolent Cup 33-34; Wearside Lg 11-12 12-13 13-14 33-34 64-65 67-68 69-70 70-71 71-72 72-73, Lg Cup 33-34 49-50; Monkwearmouth Charity Cup 12-13 23-24 32-33 69-70 72-73; Sunderland Shipowners Cup 65-66 72-73; North Eastern Lg 37-38 63-64 ('Non-Reserve' Medal 50-51).

Bedlington Terriers: Back Row (L-R); Mark Cameron, Don Peattie, Warren Teasdale, Andy Gowens, John Milner, Dean Gibb, Micky Cross, Tommy Ditchburn. Front Row; Brian Hayes, John Egan, Tony Burgess, John Sokoluk, Gary Hays, Gary Middleton, Micky Taylor, Steve Boon. *Photo - Roger Turner*

Whitby Town captain, Neil Hodgson, failed to connect with this acrobatic attempt, but he still managed to lead his side to a 5-1 victory over Mossley in the FA Vase quarter final. *Photo: Colin Stevens.*

MARSKE UNITED

Chairman: John Hodgson **Vice Chairman:** John Corner. **President:** Raymond Jarvis
Secretary: Ian Rowe, 19 High Row, Loftus, Saltburn By The Sea, Cleveland. TS13 4SA (01287 643440 H, 01642 230546 B, 01642 241273 Fax)
Manager: Charlie Bell **Asst Manager:** Stephen Dowling **Physio:** Barry Schollay
Coach: Charlie Bell/Stephen Dowling/Jackie O'Reilly
Commercial Manager: Chris Sharratt/Steve Davies
Ground: Mount Pleasant, Mount Pleasant Ave., Marske, Redcar (01642 471091).
Directions: From A19 take A174 exit marked Yarm, Teesport, Redcar, Whitby and head east towards Teesport until Quarry Lane r/about. Take 1st left exit (A1085) into Marske, take 1st right (Meadow Rd) then 1st left (Southfield Rd), then 1st left again Mount Pleasant Ave directly into carpark.
Seats: 169 **Cover:** 300 **Capacity:** 2,500 **Floodlights:** Yes **Founded:** 1956
Clubhouse: Open every night and weekend lunchtimes. Food served after all games.
Programme: 32 pages 50p **Editor:** John Hodgson (01642 484006).
Colours: Yellow/royal/white **Change:** Royal/sky/yellow
Sponsors: Arnott Insurance **Nickname:** The Seasiders.
Club Shop: Yes, contact Pat Hodgson (01642 484006) **Midweek matchday:** Tuesday
Previous Leagues: Cleveland, South Bank & Dist, Teesside, Vaux Wearside.
Record Win: 16-0 **Record Defeat:** 3-9
Club Record Goalscorer: Chris Morgan 212 **Club Record Appearances:** John Hodgson.
Honours: N Riding Sen Cup 94-95; N Riding County Cup 80-81 85-86; Teesside Lg 80-81 84-85; Wearside Lg 95-96, (R-up 93-94 94-95 96-97), Cup 92-93 94-95 95-96; M/mouth Charity Cup 93-94 95-96; Sunderland Ship. Cup 95-96 96-97.

NORTON & STOCKTON ANCIENTS

Chairman: Peter Mulcaster **President:** Barry Lee **Press Officer:** Secretary
Secretary: Stephen Warnes, 18 Siskin Close, Norton, Stockton-on-Tees, Cleveland TS20 1SG (01642 897145)
Ground: Station Road, Norton, Stockton-on-Tees, Cleveland (01642 530203).
Directions: Norton village 2 miles from Stockton centre, turn into Station Road on outskirts of village.
Seats: 200 **Cover:** Yes **Capacity:** 2,000 **Floodlights:** Yes **Formed:** 1959
Clubhouse details: Full bar facilities, 150 yds from ground.
Colours: Amber & black/black/amber & black **Change colours:** White with amber trim
Programme: 12 pages with entry **Editor:** **Nickname:** Ancients
Midweek Matches: Wednesday
Previous Leagues: Teesside (pre-1982). **Previous Name:** Norton & Stockton Cricket Club Trust.
Record Attendance: 1,430 v Middlesbrough, Friendly 88 **Best F.A. Cup season:** 1st Qual Rd(4) 88-89 90-93
Honours: Northern Lg Cup 81-82.

PETERLEE NEWTOWN

Chairman: Stan Summerill **Vice-Chairman:** Bill Burnett. **President:** David Brown
Secretary: Danny Cassidy, 23 Melbury Str, Seaham, County Durham SR7 7NF (0191 581 4591).
Manager: Tommy Smith **Asst Manager:** Eddie Freeman **Physio:** Ron Lamdrel.
Ground: Eden Lane, Peterlee, County Durham (0191 586 3004).
Directions: From town centre Fire Station, turn left into Edenhill Rd, then right into Robson Ave. Left at the next junction and ground is on the right.
Seats: 50 **Cover:** 200 **Capacity:** 6,000 **Floodlights:** Yes **Formed:** 1976
Clubhouse: Open normal licensing hours. Sandwiches etc available.
Colours: Sky/navy/sky **Change colours:** Yellow/black/yellow **Club Shop:** No.
Programme: 10 pages, 30p **Editor:** Secretary **Press Officer:** Ray Matthews (0191 587 0727)
Sponsors: Artix Ltd **Previous lges:** Northern Alliance 76-79/ Wearside 79-82.
Nickame: Newtowners. **Record Attendance:** 2,350 v Northern, Hillsborough Fund match 1989.
Midweek Matches: Wednesday. **Best FA Cup season:** 4th Qual. Rd replay 85-86
Players progressing to Football Lge: Keith Fairless (Scarborough) 1986, Brian Honour (Hartlepool) 1988).
96-97 Captain: **P.O.Y.:** **Top Scorer:**
Club record scorer: Keith Fairless **Club record appearances:** Keith Bendelow.
Honours: Northern Lg Div 2 82-83, North Eastern F'lit League, 4th Qual Rd FA Cup

PRUDHOE TOWN

Chairman: Alex Waters
Secretary: Brian Tulip, 12 Orchard Close, Prudhoe NE42 5LP (01661 833169).
Manager: Terry Hunter **Asst Manager:** Kenny Barton **Physio:** Ernie Goodfellow
Ground: Kimberley Park, Broomhouse Road, Prudhoe, Northumberland NE42 5EH (Tel/Fax: 01661 835900).
Directions: Approach Prudhoe along A695, turn right at 'Falcon' Inn, 200 yds down Eastwood Rd., turn left into Broomhouse Rd., ground on right.
Seats: 150 **Cover:** Yes **Capacity:** 5,000 **Floodlights:** Yes **Founded:** 1959
Clubhouse: Open every evening plus Sat/Sun lunchtimes
Colours: Purple & jade/purple/purple. **Change:** White & blue chevrons/navy/sky.
Programme: 8 pages, 20p **Editor:** J Smith **Press Officer:** Ken Barton (0191 273 4640)
Sponsors: Swinton Insurance **Midweek Matches:** Wednesday **Nickname:** Citizens
Previous Leagues: Hexham & Dist 59-69/ Newcastle & Dist 69-71/ N. Comb./ N. Amtr/ Northern All. 84-88.
Previous Names: Ovington 1969-75/ Prudhoe East End 75-94.
Previous Grounds: Farm field, Ovington 59-68/ Mickley Welfare 68-69.
Record Attendance: 2,500 v Blyth, Northumberland Snr Cup 1981.
96-97 - Captain: **Top Scorer:** **P.o.Y.:**
Honours: Hexham & Dist. Lg 68-69 (Lg Cup 68-69), Newcastle & Dist. Lg 69-70 70-71 (Lg Cup 69-70, Charity Shield 69-70 70-71), Northern Comb. 79-80, Northerm Amtr Lg 71-72, Clayton Charity Cup 68-69, Northumberland Minor Cup 78-79, Northumberland Benevolent Bowl 79-80, Heddon Homes Charity Cup 81-82.

RYHOPE COMMUNITY ASSOCIATION

Chairman: David Lawson **Press Officer:** Secretary
Secretary: Bob Lewins, 7 Belsay Gardens, St.Gabriels Estate, Sunderland. SR4 7SZ (01915 141725)
Ground: Meadow Park, Stockton Road, Ryhope, Sunderland (0191 523 6555)
Directions: From Sunderland follow signs for A19 South, ground adj to Cherry Knowle Hopital in Ryhope
Seats: 150 **Cover:** 200 **Capacity:** 2,000 **Floodlights:** Yes **Founded:** 1988.
Colours: Red & white/black & red/red & white **Change colours:** All Blue
Record Gate: 2,000; Ryhope Colliery Welfare v Workington, FA Cup 1967.
Previous Leagues: Sporting Club Vaux: Tyne & Wear/ North Eastern Amateur.
Previous Names: Ryhope Colliery Welfare (founded 1898, previously Ryhope Villa) merged with Sporting Club Vaux (founded in 1968 as Monkwearmouth, later Bishopwearmouth, South Hetton) in 1988/ Sunderland Vaux Ryhope Colliery Welfare 88-93.
Previous Grounds: Sporting Club Vaux: Glenesk Road (pre-1988)
Players progressing to Football League: Alan Harding (Lincoln, Darlington, Hartlepool), Kenny Ellis (Hartlepool, Darlington, Belgian clubs), Kenny Mitchell (prof. Icelandic club), Robert Malt (Leeds), Brian Smiles (Chelsea), Ron Robinson (Ipswich, Leeds), Nigel Staddington (Doncaster, Sunderland).
Honours *(Sporting Club Vaux hons italicised)* Wearside Lg 61-62 62-63 63-64 65-66 (Lg Cup 63-64 77-78), Durham Challenge Cup 77-78, Monkwearmouth Charity Cup 09-10 65-66 66-67, Sunderland Shipowners Cup 61-62 *86-87*, FA Cup 1st Rd Proper 67-68, FA Vase 1st Rd 81-82.

SHOTTON COMRADES

Chairman: J Maddison **Vice Chairman:** T.Robindon. **President:** G Taylor.
Secretary: Billy Banks, 47 St Mary's Drive, Church Green, Sherburn Village, Durham DH6 1RL (0191 372 1649)
Manager: B.Huntingdon. **Asst Manager:** **Physio:** W.Banks.
Ground: Shotton Recreational Ground, Station Road, Shotton Colliery, Co. Durham (0191 526 2859).
Directions: A19 to Peterlee to Shotton, right at War Mem. t-junction, follow round 800yds, ground on right.
Seats: 80 **Cover:** 400 **Capacity:** 1,700 **Floodlights:** No **Formed:** 1973
Club Shop: No **Clubhouse:** No. **Reserves' Lge:** Banks u-19 Yth
Colours: Black & white/black/black **Change colours:** All orange.
Sponsors: T.B.A. **Midweek matches:** Wednesday **Nickname:** Coms
Programme: 12 pages, 20p **Editor:** Mr E A Jones **Press Officer:** Secretary
Previous - Leagues: Peterlee Sunday 74-76/ Houghton & District 76-80/ Northern Alliance 80-83. **Grounds:** None
Record Attendance: 1,726 v Dennis Waterman XI. **Record transfer received:** £500 for G Gudlip (Shildon)
Rec. win: 8-0 v Bedlington Ter. (H), '92 **Rec. defeat:** 1-7 v Brandon Utd (A), F.A. Cup Prel. Rd 91-92.
Best F.A. Cup season: 2nd Qualifying Rd 85-86 (lost 0-2 at home to Wingate).
96-97 - Captain: **P.o.Y.:** J Cudlip **Top Scorer:** David Belwood
Club Record scorer: Keith Willets 50 **Club Record appearances:** J Cudlip.
Honours: Houghton & District Lg 78-79 (Lg Cup(2)), Northern Alliance Lg Cup SF, Hetton Charity Cup 78-79, Peterlee Sunday Lg 75-76 (Div 2 74-75), FA Vase 1st Rd 86-87 90-91, Durham Challenge Cup QF 78-79 (Minor Cup QF 78-79).Northern Lg.Div 2 Cup R-Up. 94-95.

WASHINGTON

Chairman: Derek Armstrong **Press Officer:** Ray Lish (0191 415 7071)
Secretary: George Abbott, 14 Grosvenor Street, Southwick, Sunderland SR5 2DG (0191 549 1384).
Ground: Albany Park, Spout Lane, Concord, Washington (0191 417 7779).
Directions: Ground situated behind the cinema opposite bus station.
Seats: 25 **Cover:** Yes **Capacity:** 3,000 **Floodlights:** No **Founded:** 1949
Clubhouse: Open normal licensing hours, with live entertainment, pool etc.
Programme: 8 pages, 10p **Editor:** Mr Bull (0191 4164618) **Club Shop:** No
Colours: All red **Change colours:** All blue **Midweek Matches:** Wednesday
Nickname: Mechanics **Previous Leagues:** Washington Amateur/ Northern Alliance 67-68/ Wearside 68-88.
Previous Ground: Usworth Welfare Park **Record Gate:** 3,800 v Bradford Park Avenue, FA Cup 1970.

WEST AUCKLAND TOWN

Chairman: Mr Norman Ayton
Sec/Press Officer: Allen Bayles, 11 Edith Terrace, West Auckland, Co.Durham. DL14 9JT (011388 833783).
Manager: Dale Swainston **Ass.Manager:** Paul Anderson **Coach:** Robin Gill
Ground: Darlington Road, West Auckland, Co.Durham (011388 834403). **Directions:** Leaving West Auckland take A68-ground on right before leaving village. Bus route via Bishop Auckland fron Newcastle or Darlington.
Seats: 250 **Cover:** 250 **Capacity:** 3,000 **Floodlights:** Yes **Founded:** 1892 **Shop:** No
Clubhouse: None-use local working mans club five minutes walk away. Thomas Lipton Trophy on display within). On ground reception room for visiting officials and snack bar
Colours: All white **Change Colours:** Black & amber/black/black **Nickname:** West
Midweek Matches: Tuesday **Sponsors:** Tenwick Transport,Hathaway Roofing,Southend Builders.
Previous - League: Auckland & Dist. **Names:** St Helens Utd (1919 only), West Auck Town.
Record Gate: 6,000 v Dulwich Hamlet, FA Amateur Cup 58-59. **Best F.A. Cup season:** 1st Rd 58-59,61-62.
96-97 - Captain: Gary Lowes **P.o.Y.:** **Top Scorer:** Paul Adamson
Honours: F.A.Amateur Cup Finalists 60-61 (QF 59-60) Northern League Champions 59-60,60-61 Div 290-91,Lg Cup 59-60,62-639r-UP;48-49,61-62,63-64) Durham Challenge Cup 63-64 Durham Benevolent Bowl 62-63 Best F.A.Trophy 3rd Rd.77-78 Sir Thomas Lipton Trophy 'First World Cup'(as featured in a television play 'The Captains Tale'1909,+1911

WHICKHAM

Chairman: Tommy Thompson **Manager:** Billy Hodgson **Press Officer:** Ray Graham (0191 477 3633)
Secretary: Harry Hodgson, 18 Deepdale Close, Whickham, Newcastle upon Tyne, NE16 6SN (0191 488 2493)
Ground: Glebe Ground, Rectory Lane, Whickham (0191 420 0186)
Directions: A692 (Consett) from A69. Left at r'bout signed Consett/Whickham. Up hill and right at mini-r'bout. Continue along & turn left into Rectory Lane (by Lloyds Bank) for about 500 yds, clubhouse on right
Seats: 100 **Cover:** Yes **Capacity:** 4,000 **Floodlights:** Due **Founded:** 1944
Clubhouse: Mon-Fri. 12-3 & 7-11, Sat.11-11, Sun. 12-2, 7.30-11
Colours: Black & white stripes/black/black & white hoops. **Change colours:** All white
Programme: 20p **Shop:** No **Midweek Matches:** Wednesday
Previous Leagues: Derwent Valley -55/ Northern Comb. 55-57 59-74/ Tyneside Amtr 57-59/ Wearside 74-88.
Record Gate: 3,165 v Windsor & Eton, F.A. Vase SF 81 **Best F.A. Cup season:** 1st Qual. 89-90
Players progressing to Football League: Nigel Walker (Newcastle 1977), David Norton (Hartlepool 1981), Mike Carroll (Chesterfield 1981).
Honours: FA Vase 80-81, Wearside Lg 77-78 87-88 (R-up 80-81 84-85, Lg Cup 86-87, Monkwearmouth Charity Cup 76-77, Sunderland Shipowners Cup 77-78 80-81), Northern Comb. 69-70 72-73 73-74 (Lg Cup 60-61 73-74).

WILLINGTON

Chairman: George Hedges **Vice-Chairman:** Jack Snowdon **President:** T B A
Secretary/Press Officer: Bob Nichols, 46 Cavendish Court, Brandon, Durham DH7 8UW
Player/Manager: Kevin Stonehouse **Asst.Mgr:** Ken Mitchell **Physio:** T B A
Ground: Hall Lane, Hall Lane Estate, Willington, County Durham (01388 746221).
Directions: Willington is on A690 7 miles west of Durham City & 2 miles east of Crook. Off main through road at 'The Black Horse Tavern' corner turn off Commercial St, then into Hall Lane after 100yds.
Seats: 350 **Cover:** 400 **Capacity:** 2,680. **Floodlights:** Yes **Programme:** 20 pages, 30p
Clubhouse: Open evenings 7-11pm at Saturday matchdays 1-11pm. Bar facilities. Tea shop on matchdays.
Colours: Blue & white stripes/blue/blue **Change colours:** Yellow/green/yellow.
Sponsor: Rackwood Park Drift Mine **Nickname:** Blue & Whites **Founded:** 1906.
Midweek Matches: Wednesday **Youth League:** Auckland & district League.
Record Attendance: 10,000 v Bromley, FA Amateur Cup 2nd Rd 24/1/53.
Best season FA Cup: 1st Rd replay 73-74 45-46 50-51. **FA Trophy:** 3rd Rd 75-76
Previous Leagues: Auckland & Dist. 1906-11.
Players progressing to Football League: George Tweedy (Grimsby 33), Andy Graver Brian Ronson (Fulham 53), Andy Graver/Martin Burleigh (Newcastle 47/69).
96-97 - Captain: David Taylor **Top Scorer:** Neil Hixon **P.o.Y.:** Andrew Robson
Club Record Goalscorer: J 'Boxer' Taylor 55-69. **Club Record Appearances:** S Rutherford 47-61.
Honours: FA Amateur Cup 49-50 (R-up 38-39, SF 27-28); Northern League 13-14 25-26 29-30 (R-up 12-13 57-58 75-76), Lge Cup (8); Durham Benevolent Cup 48-49 50-51 57-58.

VAUX
WEARSIDE LEAGUE

FOUNDED: 1892

FEEDER TO:
ARNOTT INSURANCE NORTHERN LEAGUE

President: J. C. Thomas **Chairman:** P. J. Maguire

Hon. Secretary & Treasurer: Bill Robson
12 Deneside, Howden-le-Wear, Crook, Co. Durham DL15 8JR

Boldon C.A. emerged as league champions for the first time since the mid seventies in a nail biting finish to the season when they held off the challenge of defending champions Marske United by a single point.

In a repeat of previous seasons the destination of the championship was not decided until the very last week of the season. Boldon despite a late attack of nerves clinched the title in emphatic fashion with a five goal win over local rivals Jarrow.

However, Marske were to obtain some consolation when after missing out on promotion via the Pyramid the previous season they moved on to the Northern League, thanks to a concerted effort in their last three months of the season to bring their ground and facilities up to the standard required to qualify for election to the Second Division.

Marske, after their grand slam performance in season 1995-6 failed to match their all conquering run but did retain their hold on the Sunderland Shipowners Cup with a comfortable victory over Jarrow in the Final.

In the League and Monkwearmouth Cups Nissan were to run out winners in both competitions following up their pulsating 3-2 win on Good Friday over South Tyneside Utd in the Monkwearmouth Cup with an equally thrilling lone goal win on Easter Monday over the holders Marske Utd in the Final of the League Cup.

While the League again failed to impress in the County Cup scene two of the minnows, Jarrow and Stanley Utd, had impressive runs in the Durham Challenge Cup.

With the League being firmly committed to the North East Section of the Pyramid it is feeling the cost of bringing grounds up to the standard required. Whereas in 1993-4 the league operated with a total of thirty five clubs, last season saw the membership falling to only nineteen teams with as a result Division Two having to be, it is hoped, temporally suspended.

Next season will again see one division. While Marske gained deserved promotion the membership of Washington Glebe Welfare was terminated by the member clubs at the A.G.M. following a series of suspensions placed on the club during the previous year by the Durham County F.A.

Two new sides, Gateshead Reserves and Horden C.W. Athletic were elected as Associate Members at the A.G.M. and although the league is still actively looking for the reformation of a Second Division at the earliest opportunity, with the present climate of financial restraint coupled with a lack of suitable grounds and facilities in the area, this would appear to be unlikely to be achieved much before the turn of the century.

Next season will see the Sunderland Shipowners Cup reaching its centenary. Following discussions with the league's sponsors, Vaux Breweries of Sunderland, along with the Officials of the Northern League, the decision was taken to open the competition for one year only to previous members of the league currently in membership of the Northern League.

Two players tied for the leading goalscorer award last season, Gary Davies of Boldon C.A. and Michael Cunningham of South Tyneside Utd, with 32 goals each while the Vaux Administration Award went to Dave DiMarco of Southbank 1995.

FINAL LEAGUE TABLES 1996/97

DIVISION 1	P	W	D	L	F	A	Pts
Boldon CA	34	25	6	3	105	33	81
Marske Utd	34	25	5	4	97	24	80
Birtley Town	34	21	9	4	74	33	72
Annfield Plain	34	19	8	7	83	52	62
Nissan	34	17	10	7	63	41	61
Windscale	34	17	8	9	65	40	59
Sth Tyneside	34	17	7	10	69	37	58
Kennek Roker	34	15	6	13	66	53	51
Wolviston	34	12	5	17	59	65	41
Harton/Westoe	34	11	5	18	63	68	38
Whitehaven Ams	34	10	8	16	50	81	38
Stanley Utd	34	10	6	18	58	88	36
Cleadon SC	34	9	6	19	47	72	33
North Shields Ath	34	8	9	17	44	70	33
Hartlepool BWOB	34	10	2	22	46	97	32
Ryhope CW	34	9	3	22	37	68	30
Southbank	34	5	9	20	34	90	24
Jarrow	34	6	8	20	36	84	23

PREMIER DIVISION RESULTS CHART 1996-97

HOME TEAM	1	2	3	4	5	6	7	8	9	10	11	12	13	14	15	16	17	18	19
1. Annfield Plain		2-2	0-1	6-2	7-1	0-7	0-0	2-0	3-0	2-0	3-1	4-1	1-1	3-2	7-2	3-2	1-0	2-0	0-0
2. Birtley Town	6-1		0-0	5-1	3-0	1-0	4-0	1-1	3-1	2-1	1-1	4-1	1-0	1-0	7-2	7-1	3-1	3-2	2-1
3. Boldon C.A.	1-0	1-2		4-0	1-1	2-1	9-1	8-2	5-1	5-1	1-0	3-1	1-1	4-2	4-0	3-1	0-0	5-2	1-2
4. Hartlepool	2-1	0-2	1-3		2-0	0-5	0-3	1-1	1-2	0-5	0-3	4-1	1-4	3-1	1-0	5-0	2-1	0-3	3-6
5. Jarrow	1-1	1-1	1-5	0-3		0-0	3-1	2-5	1-1	2-1	0-5	0-0	0-4	2-0	9-1	5-1	0-4	1-2	0-2
6. Marske Utd	0-0	3-3	1-3	3-0	6-0		3-0	3-0	5-1	3-0	2-0	4-0	3-2	4-1	11-0	4-0	2-1	3-1	4-0
7. North Shields A	0-3	1-3	0-3	7-1	1-1	0-2		5-3	4-2	5-1	2-2	1-0	1-2	3-0	5-0	1-2	0-5	1-1	1-1
8. Southbank	0-0	2-2	0-4	3-3	2-1	0-6	0-0		0-3	0-2	1-4	0-4	0-2	1-0	1-2	2-2	0-1	2-1	2-1
9. Cleadon SC	0-4	1-2	0-4	2-3	1-1	0-3	3-0	1-1		4-3	2-0	1-3	0-1	2-0	3-0	2-2	4-2	1-4	1-3
10. Harton & Westoe	1-3	2-1	1-2	10-2	1-2	2-3	2-2	4-1	2-1		1-2	1-1	2-1	3-1	2-2	3-2	2-2	2-3	1-1
11. S/Tyneside Utd	6-0	0-0	0-2	4-1	4-1	1-2	0-1	3-0	3-0	1-1		4-4	1-1	0-2	1-1	3-0	2-1	3-2	2-2
12. Stanley Utd	1-7	2-1	3-13	0-1	2-0	3-1	2-2	5-0	0-3	1-2	2-0		3-2	2-1	10-2	1-1	0-4	4-2	3-0
13. Kennek Roker	3-7	0-2	2-3	3-1	5-2	2-4	1-0	5-2	2-0	4-1	2-1	3-2		0-1	5-1	1-1	0-1	1-2	2-0
14. Ryhope CW	0-4	0-2	2-2	1-0	1-4	0-6	3-0	3-0	0-3	3-0	0-2	3-2	0-4		4-1	1-0	0-0	3-1	1-2
15. Wash Glebe	1-1	1-3	2-3	0-3	1-2	2-7	–	5-2	2-2	3-2	0-7	1-0	0-1	1-6		5-2	–	0-0	1-3
16. Whitehaven AMS	5-3	3-0	1-3	2-1	2-1	2-0	3-0	1-0	2-2	0-3	0-4	3-2	1-1	3-3	0-0		2-3	2-1	0-2
17. Windscale	2-3	3-2	1-1	3-1	6-2	1-2	2-1	4-0	2-0	2-1	0-2	2-2	3-1	1-0	–	1-1		1-1	1-1
18. Wolviston	3-6	0-2	0-1	0-1	1-0	0-0	0-0	4-1	2-2	2-0	0-3	4-2	4-2	2-1	4-1	4-0	1-3		1-2
19. Nissan	1-1	0-0	2-1	3-0	3-0	0-0	3-0	2-2	1-0	2-1	0-3	5-0	1-1	2-1	6-0	6-2	0-1	6-3	

SUNDERLAND SHIPOWNERS CUP

First Round

Hartlepool BWOB	v	Stanley United	1-6	Harton & Westoe	v	Birtley Town	1-2
Windscale	v	Southbank	5-0				

Second Round

Stanley United	v	Whitehaven AMS	3-0	Annfield Plain	v	Ryhope CW	6-2
North Shields Ath	v	Kennek Roker	1-2	Boldon CA	v	Cleadon SC	1-1 2-0
Nissan	v	Jarrow	1-2	Marske Utd	v	South Tyneside	3-1
Windscale	v	Birtley Town	1-0	Wolviston	v	Washington Glebe	4-1

Third Round

Wolviston	v	Jarrow	0-1	Annfield Plan	v	Stanley Utd	7-4
Marske Utd	v	Kennek Roker	2-0	Windscale	v	Boldon CA	1-0

Semi-Finals

Marske Utd	v	Annfield Plain	3-0	Windscale	v	Jarrow	2-2 0-1

Final

Marske Utd	v	Jarrow	3-0

LEAGUE CUP

First Round

North Shields Ath	v	Washington Glebe	0-3	Boldon CA	v	Southbank 1995	3-1
Nissan	v	Stanley Utd	1-0				

Second Round

Harton and Westoe	v	Ryhope CW	3-1	Hartlepool BWOB	v	Annfield Plain	2-3
Whitehaven AMS	v	Birtley Town	1-5	Marske Utd	v	Wolviston	2-1*
Kennek Roker	v	Boldon CA	3-2	Washington Glebe	v	Nissan	0-5
South Tyneside Utd	v	Cleadon SAC	3-1	Windscale	v	Jarrow	4-0

Third Round

Annfield Plain	v	Marske Utd	2-3*	Harton and Westoe	v	Birtley Town	0-2
Nissan	v	Kennek Roker	2-0	South Tyneside	v	Windscale	4-0

Semi-Finals

Marske Utd	v	Birtley Town	1-0	Nissan	v	South Tyneside	2-0

Final

Marske Utd	v	Nissan	0-1

MONKWEARMOUTH CUP

First Round

Kennek Roker	v	Birtley Town	2-0	Boldon CA	v	North Shields Ath	3-1
Windscale	v	Hartlepool BWOB	3-2				

Second Round

Wolviston	v	Cleadon SC	1-2	Harton & Westoe	v	Southbank	0-2
Windscale	v	Kennek Roker	2-2 3-2	Nissan	v	Jarrow	2-1
Annfield Plain	v	South Tyneside	1-2	Washington Glebe	v	Boldon CA	0-5
Stanley Utd	v	Marske Utd	0-1	Ryhope CW	v	Whitehaven AMS	5-1

Third Round

Southbank	v	South Tyneside	1-3	Marske Utd	v	Windscale	0-3
Ryhope CW	v	Cleadon SC	2-0	Nissan	v	Boldon CA	5-2

Semi-Finals

Ryhope CW	v	South Tyneside	0-2	Nissan	v	Windscale	3-0

Final

Nissan	v	South Tyneside	3-2

*After extra time.

DIVISION ONE CLUBS 1997-98

ANNFIELD PLAIN

Chairman: Frank Ross **Manager:** D Longstaff **Press Officer:** Frank Ross
Secretary: M Lawson, 24 Northgate, Anfield Plain, Stanley, Co. Durham DH9 7UY (01207 235879).
Ground: Derwent Park, Annfield Plain. **Directions:** On A693 road to Consett, 200 yds west of junction with A6067. Ground behind new housing estate. 6 miles from Durham (BR). Buses from Sunderland, Newcastle & Durham.
Seats: 20 **Cover:** 200 **Capacity:** 6,000 **Floodlights:** No **Founded:** 1890.
Colours: Claret/white/white **Change colours:** All blue. **Programme:** 16 pages, 20p
Hons: Wearside Lg 84-85 (Monkwearmouth Charity Cup 92-93), FA Cup 1st Rd 26-27 28-29 64-65.

BIRTLEY TOWN

Chairman: J Heslington **Vice-Chairman:** J Grainger. **Manager:** Barry Fleming
Secretary: Kevin McConnell, 8 Leyburn Place, Birtley, DH3 1PL (0191 4100495)
Asst Manager: David Smith **Coach:** Malcolm Thompson **Commercial Manager:** Ray Stafford.
Ground: Birtley Sports Complex. **Directions:** (From Durham) Off A1(M) signpsted for Chester-le-Street, take 2nd turn off r-bout signed Birtley, take last turn off next r-bout (still signed Birtley), after one and a half miles take 1st left after AEI Cables - ground at rear of sports complex.
Seats: None **Cover:** None **Capacity:** **Floodlights:** No. **Founded:** 1890
Colours: Green/white/white **Change colours:** Yellow/blue/red. **Reformed:** 1986
Midweek matches: Wednesday **Sponsors:** C & C Coachworks **Clubhouse:** Matchdays only
Hons: Wearside Lg 45-46 (Lg Cup 35-36), Northern Alliance 23-24 (R-up 13-14).

BOLDON COMMUNITY ASSOCIATION

Chairman: R A O Shepherd. **Vice Chairman:** G Smith **President:** A Brewster.
Sec./Press Off./Comm Mgr: George Pollard, 126 Horsley Hill Road, South Shields (0191 4546821).
Manager: Bill Newham **Asst Manager:** P Quinn **Coach:** Tommy Frazer.
Ground: Boldon Community Association, New Road, Boldon Colliery.
Directions: A19 to junc A184 Sunderland/Newcastle. Follow signs to Boldon Asda stores, then to North Road Social Club (SHACK). Ground behind. 800 yds from East Boldon (BR). Buses 533, 531, 319, 528.
Seats: 100 **Cover:** 400 **Capacity:** 3,500 **Floodlights:** No **Founded:** 1892.
Colours: Blue & white/blue/blue & white **Change:** Scarlet & black **Nickname:** Villa.
Clubhouse: Matchdays only. Bar snacks **Sponsors:** Tyne Dock Engineering Co., South Shields.
Hons: Wearside Lg 3, (Lg Cup 3), M/mouth Char Cup 2, Shipowners Cup 6.

GATESHEAD RESERVES

Chairman: John Gibson **Treasurer:** Walker Johnston **Press Officer:** Andy Wilson
Secretary: Mark Donnelly, c/o club
Ground: The International Stadium, Gateshead
Directions: Follow A1 north to A194M (Tyne Tunnel). At 1st r/about take left onto A184. Ground 3 Miles on right.
Colours: Black & white/black/white **Change Colours:** Yellow/blue/yellow

HARTLEPOOL BOYS WELFARE OLD BOYS

Chairman: Tom Harvey **Treasurer:** Derek Stephens
Secretary: Phillip Jordan, 473 Catcote Road, Hartlepool TS25 2RA (01429 870015)
Manager: Jimmy Costello **Asst Manager:** Wilf Constantine **Physio:** Tony Metcalfe.
Ground: Grayfields Enclosure, Jesmond Road, Hartlepool.
Directions: Leave A19 on A179 signed Hartlepool, right for Throston Grange at 1st r'bout, left at 1st lights into Jesmond Road, ground 400yds on left.
Seats: None **Cover:** No **Capacity:** **Floodlights:** No **Founded:** 1952.
Colours: All yellow **Change colours:** White/red/red **Nickname:** None.
Programme: 10 pages, 50p **Editor:** Secretary **Clubhouse:** No.
Hons: FA Vase 3rd Rd, Wearside Lg Div 2 92-93, Hartlepool Church Lg(2)(Lg Cup(3)), Hartlepool Mem. Shield, Durham Amat Cup 2, Hartlepool & Dist. Lg(3)(Lg Cup(3)), Teesside Lg 73-74 85-86 (R-up 3).

HORDEN C W ATHLETIC

Chairman: J P Hargrave **Treasurer:** A Fordy **Press Officer:** Karl Henson
Secretary: Alan Fordy, 29 Linacre Court, Peterlee, SR8 2NP (0191 586 6585)
Ground: Horden Colliery Welfare.
Directions: From Horden main street, turn down South Terrace. Ground on left next to Horden Workmans Club.
Colours: Red/black/red **Change Colours:** Green & yellow/green/yellow

JARROW

Chairman: Paul Thu **Treasurer:** Jimmy Kane
Secretary: Calum McAuley, 156 Beaconside, Cleadon Village, South Shields (0191 4555924).
Ground: Perth Green Community Centre. **Directions:** From A19 or A1(M) follow drections to South Shields, right onto John Reid Road. First slip road onto Brockley Whinns Estate, follow road past Red Hackle pub, third left left onto Inverness Road, then right into Perth Green Community Centre.
Colours: Blue & white/blue/blue **Change:** Green/black/green **Founded:** 1980.
Hons: Sth Tyne Lg & Lg Cup, Washington Lg R-up 89-90 (Lg Cup 90-91, Aged Peoples Tphy R-up 90-91), Gateshead Charity Cup 90-91, Durham Tphy R-up 90-91.

NORTH SHIELDS

Chairman: Alan Matthews. **Manager:** Bob Weir. **Coach:** Wilf Keilty.
Secretary: Dave Thompson, 38 Barnstable Road, North Shields, (0191 2590249)
Ground: Ralph Gardner Park, West Percy Rd., N.Shields, Tyne & Wear,NE29 OES
Directions: A19 northbound through Tyne Tunnel. Take 1st slip round to 1st r/about & take 3rd exit & over next r/about. Take 3rd exit again at next r/about into Waterville Rd. Over another r/about and 2nd left into Silkey's Lane. 1st right into West Percy Rd, grd on right.
Colours: All red **Change colours:** Blue & black/black/black
Sponsors: Wilkinson Stores **Nickname:** New Robins **Founded:** 1896 **Clubhouse:** None
Hons: Nthn Cnt E, Champ/Cup/Presidents Cup 91-92. FA Amt Cup 68-69, N Lge 68-69.

SOUTH BANK

Chairman: Peter Livingstone **Treasurer:** David Watson
Secretary: David L Di Marco, 146 Oxford Road, Linthorpe, Middlesbrough TS5 5EL (01642 871725)
Ground: Mannion Park, The Broadway, Trunk Road, Grangetown
Directions: There are three main routes leading to the club; A66 Middlesbrough bypass. A1085 Redcar Trunk Road and A174 Parkway signpost for Wilton I.C.I. west gate roundabout. Entrance is 200 metres from roundabout heading towards Grangetown
Colours: Red & white/white/white **Change colours:** Blue/red/red

SOUTH SHIELDS CLEADON SOCIAL CLUB

Chairman: Gordon Ferries **Vice-Chairman/Press Off./Manager:** David Wood (0191 4554607).
Secretary: Mr Charlie Appleby, 49 Tynedale Rd, South Shields (0191 454 5724).
Asst Manager: Steve Duguid **Commercial Manager:** Joan Wood **Coach:** Andy Wilkinson
Ground: Jack Clarke Park, South Shields.
Directions: Enter South Shields on A194 to r'bout taking you on to A1300 John Reid Rd. 2nd left at 3rd r'bout into King George Rd then Sunderland Rd, right at lights into Grosvenor Rd, left into Horsly Hill Rd. Ground on right
Colours: Amber/black/amber **Change:** All red **Club Shop:** No
Midweek matches: Wednesday **Sponsors:** Cleadon & Dist. Soc. Club **Nickname:** The Club
Clubhouse: Cleadon Social Club, Fulwell Avenue, South Shields. Normal pub hours except Saturday.
Hons: Wearside Lg Div 2 90-91, Shields & Dist. Lg, Washington Lg 77-78 84-85

SOUTH SHIELDS HARTON & WESTOE

Chairman: Ronald Wightman **Treasurer:** Steven Camm
Secretary: Graham Bass, 76 Stanhope Road, South Shields NE33 4BS (0191 4544798)
Ground: Harton Colliery Welfare.
Directions: A1M at Whitemare Pool take A194 to South Shields for 2 1/2 miles. At third roundabout turn right onto A1300. At 2nd roundabout turn left onto Boldon Lane. Ground 50 yards on right
Colours: Royal & white/royal/blue & white **Change colours:** All red

SOUTH SHIELDS COUNTY KITCHENS

Chairman: Barry Raper **Treasurer:** Susan Raper.
Secretary: Barry Raper, 59 Priestley Court, South Shields NE34 9NQ (0191 5363087)
Ground: Monkton Stadium, Dene Terrace, Jarrow. **Directions:** From A1 north straight onto Jarrow slip road, then left into York Ave, take 6th left into Dene Terrace. ground on left
Colours: All Yellow & black **Change colours:** Green & white/black/green & white

STANLEY UNITED

President: A Westgarth **Vice-President:** B Waiting.
Secretary: V Kirkup, 9 Brookes Rise, Regents Green, Langley, Durham DH7 8XY (0191 3780921)
Asst Manager/Coach: K Finnegan **Physio:** J Burn.
Ground: High Road, Stanley, near Crook (nicknamed Hill Top Ground).
Directions: Teeside on A689 to Bishop Auckland and onto Crook, turn left at Market Place then 1st right for Tow Law to Billy Row and Stanley, right at top of bank then 1st left, grd 250 yards on left.
Colours: Red & white stripes/black/red **Change colours:** Sky/navy/navy **Nickname:** The Nops
Sponsors: Company Cars Direct **Clubhouse:** Open matchdays. **Club Shop:** No
Honours: Northern Lg 3, R-up 62-63), Lg Cup 3, FA Cup 1st Rd 53-54, FA Amtr Cup SF 19-20.

SUNDERLAND KENNEK ROKER

Chairman: J Broadbent **Treasurer:** Keith Hunter **Press Officer:** Les Dodds
Secretary: Tom Clark, 55 Vicarage Close, New Silksworth, Sunderland SR3 1JF (0191 521 1242)
Ground: Silksworth Welfare Park. **Directions:** Behind Lord Seaham Public House. Blind Lane Silsworth
Colours: Red & white stripes/black/red **Change:** Navy & orange/navy & orange/navy
Hons: Wearside Lg Cup 91-92 (Shipowners Cup 89-90 (R-up 80-81), M/mouth Charity Cup R-up 80-81).

SUNDERLAND RYHOPE C W

Chairman: David Lawson **Press Officer:** Secretary
Secretary: George McKitterick, 8 Kilburn Close, Ryhope Village, Sunderland. SR2 0QU (0191 523 8436)
Ground: Ryhope Recreation Park, Ryhope Street, Ryhope, Sunderland (0191 521 2843).
Directions: Take A19 (3 miles south of Sunderland centre) to Ryhope village, at Village Green turn into Evelyn Terrace/Ryhope Street and carry on up bank past Presto's for 600 yds - ground appears on left. 3 miles from Sunderland Central (BR), bus every 10 minutes from Sunderland centre.
Seats: No **Cover:** No **Capacity:** 1,000 **Floodlights:** Yes **Founded:** 1988.
Colours: Yellow/black/black & red **Change colours:** Red/white/red & white
Honours: Wearside Lg 4, (Lg Cup 2), Durham Chall Cup 77-78, M/mouth Charity Cup 3, S/land Shipowners Cup 2.

WASHINGTON NISSAN

Chairman: A Hill **Treasurer:** P Bevington **Press Officer:** Secretary
Secretary: Harry English, 193 Newcastle Road, Fulwell Mill, Sunderland SR5 1NR (0191 548 7194)
Manager: Stan Fenwick **Assistant Manager:** Keith Robertson. **Coach:** Darren Ward
Ground: Nissan Sports Complex.
Directions: North along A1 (M) use A690 (sign post Sunderland) connect with A19, north on A19, after passing the A1231 turn off, plant on the left. Past plant & follow signs 'Nissan Offices'.
Colours: Blue & yellow/ blue/blue **Change colours:** Red & black/black/black **Founded:** 1988
Clubhouse: Open Mon-Fri 5-11pm, Sat 11am-11pm, Sun noon-3 & 7-10.30pm
Hons: Wearside Lg Div 1 93-94 (Lg Cup R-up 91-92, Div 2 Cup 92-93 93-94), Nissan European Tphy 3.

WHITEHAVEN AMATEURS

Chairman: D Polkey **Press Officer:** Secretary
Secretary: Harry Upton 14 Foxhouses Road, Whitehaven CA28 8AF (01946 61750)
Manager: Ian Green **Assistant Manager:** Ian Atkins.
Ground: Whitehaven County Ground, Coach Road, Whitehaven
Directions: Barrow on A595, ignore branch to town centre at B.P. garage turn right at t/lights on A5094. 1/2 mile turn left at Esso garage into Coach Rd. Narrow lane ent immed after l/ crossing to grd behind Rugby Lge Stadium.
Colours: Yellow/blue/blue **Change colours:** White/navy/white
Honours: Cumberland Cup 90-91, County League 87-88 88-89, Wearside Lg Div 2 Cup R-up 93-94.

WINDSCALE

Chairman: R Napier **Press Officer:** Secretary **Treasurer:** A Barwise
Secretary: Geoff Turrell, 65 Leathwaite, Loop Road South, Whitehaven, Cumbria CA28 7UG (01936 62229)
Ground: Falcon Field, Egremont. **Directions:** A66 to Bridgefoot. A595 Barrow, bottom of hill approaching Egremont take 3rd turn off island (signed) Smithfield/Gillfoot, grd in housing estate
Colours: Purple/navy/navy **Change:** Blue & white/royal/royal **Founded:** 1950
Hons: Furness Snr Cup 85-86

WOLVISTON

Chairman: Eddie Poole **Vice Chairman:** Derek Stockton **President:** Bob Smith
Sec./Press Officer: Keith Simpson, 14 Lodore Grove, Acklam, Middlesbrough TS5 8PB (01642 823734).
Manager: John Johnson **Asst Manager:** Kevin Smith **Coach:** Alan Lucas
Ground: Metcalfe Way, Wynyard Road, Wolviston, Billingham, Cleveland TS22 5NE.
Directions: On Wynyard Road between Thorpe Thewles & Wolviston. A19 onto A689 into Wolviston village, take Wynyard Road heading towards Thorpe Thewles, grd left before Sir John Halls Estate.
Seats: None **Cover:** 200 **Capacity:** 2,000 **Floodlights:** No **Founded:** 1910
Colours: Royal/white/white **Change:** Red & white/red/white **Nickname:** Wolves
Sponsors: R.C.I. Industrial Cleaners **Rec. Gate:** 500 v Middlesbrough 27/7/93 **Club Shop:** No.
Clubhouse: Licensed bar. Hot & cold meals. Open 11am-11pm on matchdays.
Hons: Wearside Lg Div 2 89-90 (Lg Cup R-up 92-93), Teesside Lg R-up 84-85 (R T Raine Cup 86-87), Durham FA Trophy R-up 89-90, Stockton & District Lg 3, (Lg Cup 3), Lg Charity Cup 79-80).

THE NORTHERN FOOTBALL ALLIANCE

Founded: 1890

FEEDER TO: FEDERATION BREWERY NORTHERN ALLIANCE

President: Sir John Hall **Chairman:** G F Dobbins
Secretary: J H McLackland, 92 Appletree Gardens, Walkerville
Newcastle upon Tyne NE6 4SX (0191 2621636)
Press Officer: Bill Gardner (0191488 3422)

PREMIER DIVISION

FINAL LEAGUE TABLE 1996-97

		P	W	D	L	F	A	Pts
1	Lemington United	32	25	4	3	84	25	79
2	Ponteland United	32	25	3	4	109	30	78
3	Middlesbrough	32	21	6	5	89	44	69
4	West Allotment	32	21	3	8	78	44	66
5	Carlisle City	32	19	5	8	71	41	59*
6	St Columbas	32	14	4	14	60	59	46
7	Hartlepool	32	13	6	13	56	56	45
8	Walker Ledwoodd	32	12	6	14	47	71	42
9	Seaton Delaval	32	11	8	13	43	51	41
10	Spittal Rovers	32	11	7	14	36	53	40
11	Gillford Park	32	10	5	17	57	65	35
12	Benfield Park	32	10	5	17	52	63	35
13	Winlaton	32	8	9	15	44	59	33
14	Walker Central	32	10	3	19	44	67	30*
15	Haltwhistle	32	8	6	18	40	76	30
16	Amble Town	32	5	6	21	46	82	21
17	Bohemians	32	3	6	23	32	102	15

* Points Deducted

DIVISION ONE

FINAL LEAGUE TABLE 1996-97

		P	W	D	L	F	A	Pts
1	Ryton	26	21	1	4	84	27	64
2	Reyrolle	26	19	3	4	65	23	60
3	Newbiggin	26	17	4	5	68	26	55
4	Shankhouse	26	16	3	7	65	38	51
5	Heddon Inst	26	14	4	8	72	49	46
6	Walbottle	26	14	4	8	77	53	43*
7	Percy Main	26	12	5	9	60	40	41
8	Hexham Swinton	26	10	3	13	38	61	33
9	Longbenton	26	6	3	17	46	75	21
10	Heaton Stann	26	8	3	15	42	79	21*
11	Swalwell	26	4	7	15	45	68	19
12	Procter & G	26	4	6	16	33	61	18
13	Ashington Hirst	26	4	6	16	45	86	18
14	Orwin	26	4	6	16	32	86	18

* Points Deducted

DIVISION TWO

FINAL LEAGUE TABLE 1996-97

		P	W	D	L	F	A	Pts
1	Northbank	26	20	4	2	107	23	64
2	N University	26	20	3	3	101	25	63
3	Coxlodge S C	26	18	3	5	1084557		
4	Wallington	26	12	9	5	80	54	45
5	Newcastle B T	26	11	6	9	63	49	39
6	Highfields Utd	26	12	3	11	56	56	39
7	Rutherford	26	9	10	7	48	44	37
8	Shieldfield S C	26	11	2	13	57	66	35
9	Morpeth 'A'	26	8	7	11	73	58	31
10	Hexham B C	26	10	1	15	61	97	31
11	Northern S C	26	8	6	12	56	61	30
12	Otterburn	26	8	4	14	49	55	28
13	Whitley Lodge	26	1	5	20	22	169	8
14	Wark	26	1	3	22	37	116	6

PREMIER DIVISION RESULTS CHART 1996-97

		1	2	3	4	5	6	7	8	9	10	11	12	13	14	15	16	17
1	Amble Town	X	3-3	1-2	7-1	2-3	2-5	1-5	1-3	3-2	1-2	0-3	2-0	0-1	2-3	2-3	3-2	3-0
2	Carlisle City	4-0	X	3-1	3-2	3-0	3-3	0-1	2-0	2-0	1-2	2-5	2-1	1-0	0-1	0-0	4-0	0-0
3	Gillford Park	5-0	0-3	X	4-0	2-3	0-1	0-0	0-2	1-1	1-1	2-5	3-4	2-0	1-1	5-1	3-2	1-2
4	Gos Bohemians	1-1	2-3	2-0	X	1-1	0-3	1-1	2-8	4-0	0-3	0-6	0-0	0-0	2-4	1-3	2-5	0-4
5	Haltwhistle C P	3-0	3-2	1-4	1-4	X	1-1	1-3	2-4	1-5	1-2	0-4	1-1	1-2	1-4	1-1	0-4	2-1
6	Hartlepool Utd	2-2	1-3	4-2	7-0	2-0	X	4-0	0-1	2-1	1-2	1-2	1-0	1-0	2-1	2-1	2-2	2-1
7	Lemington	2-0	1-3	4-0	1-0	3-0	10-1	X	5-2	0-1	5-2	3-1	2-2	1-0	2-0	3-0	2-0	3-1
8	Middlesbrough	5-0	1-3	4-1	2-1	4-1	1-0	2-5	X	4-0	6-2	2-2	4-0	1-1	3-2	0-0	1-1	3-3
9	N Benfield Park	2-0	2-1	1-3	4-0	1-2	1-1	0-2	1-5	X	0-2	0-3	1-1	0-1	4-2	4-0	0-1	2-2
10	N S St Columbas	3-1	1-2	3-5	5-0	1-2	2-1	1-2	0-2	1-4	X	0-4	1-3	5-1	1-2	1-3	2-2	5-0
11	Ponteland Utd	3-0	4-1	5-1	10-1	4-1	3-0	0-1	2-2	8-0	1-1	X	0-1	4-0	4-1	5-3	1-2	2-0
12	Seaton Delaval	2-2	0-2	2-0	2-1	3-1	1-1	1-3	1-2	2-1	1-2	1-3	X	0-1	3-1	2-2	0-2	0-4
13	Spittal Rovers	5-2	0-0	2-1	1-0	0-0	2-1	0-4	1-4	5-3	1-1	1-2	0-2	X	3-0	0-0	2-3	0-2
14	Walker Central	2-1	2-5	1-3	3-1	1-3	2-0	1-1	2-1	1-1	0-2	0-3	1-2	1-3	X	0-1	1-3	0-1
15	Walker Ledwood	1-1	2-5	2-1	2-1	3-2	4-3	0-3	1-6	3-2	2-0	0-4	1-3	4-1	1-2	X	0-5	1-0
16	West Allotment	3-2	3-2	2-1	6-0	3-0	3-0	0-2	1-2	0-5	3-1	2-3	3-1	6-1	3-0	2-0	X	2-1
17	Winlaton Hall	1-1	0-3	2-2	2-2	1-1	3-1	0-4	1-2	0-3	1-3	1-3	1-1	1-1	4-2	4-2	0-2	X

NORTHERN ALLIANCE
STAN SEYMOUR LEAGUE CUP 1996-97

First Round

Carlisle City	v	Newcastle University	5-0	Coxlodge S C	v	Rutherford	1-5
Gillford Park	v	Shieldfield S C	4-2	Highfields United	v	Lemington Social	1-4
Middlesbrough 'A'	v	Morpeth Town Res	1-1*	Benfield Park	v	Walker Ledwood	1-1, 1-4
Newcastle BT	v	Hartlepool United	2-4	Northern S C	v	Northbank	1-5
St Columbas	v	Gosforth Bohemians	6-1	Otterburn	v	Amble Town	2-3
Seaton Delaval	v	Hexham Border Co	11-0	Wallington	v	Ponteland United	0-5
Wark	v	West Allotment Celtic	0-7	Whitley Lodge	v	Spittal Rovers	2-4

** Tie awarded to Morpeth*

(Byes: All First Division clubs plus Haltwhistle and Winlaton of the Premier Division)

Second Round

Newbiggin C W	v	Heddon Institute	3-2	Rutherford	v	Hebburn Reyrolle	0-2
Lemington Social	v	Northbank	2-1	Spittal Rovers	v	Hartlepool Utd 'A'	1-4
N Sh St Columbas	v	Hexham Swinton	5-2	Gillford Park	v	Carlisle City	0-2
West Allotment	v	Percy Main	3-0	Swalwell	v	Winlaton Hallgarth	1-2 aet
Walker Central	v	Ryton	0-3	Ashington Hirst	v	Ponteland United	2-3
Shankhouse	v	Longbenton	3-1	Heaton Stannington	v	Haltwhistle	1-2
Walker Ledwood	v	Morpeth Town 'A'	0-3	Orwin	v	Forest Hall	w/o O
Walbottle Masons	v	Seaton Delaval	3-0	Amble Town	v	P & G Monkseaton	4-1

Third Round

Amble Town	v	Orwin	4-2	Morpeth Town 'A'	v	Shankhouse	4-3
N S St Columbas	v	Ponteland United	2-4	Carlisle City	v	Hebburn Reyrolle	2-1 aet
Lemington Social	v	Hartlepool United 'A'	5-1	Ryton	v	Winlaton Hallgarth	4-1
West Allotment Celtic	v	Newbiggin C W	1-2	Walbottle Masons	v	Haltwhistle C P	4-0

Fourth Round

Newbiggin C W	v	Morpeth Town 'A'	3-1	Carlisle City	v	Amble Town	-*
Ryton	v	Walbottle Masons	3-1	Ponteland United	v	Lemington Social	2-1

** Amble Town dismissed from competition*

Semi-Final

Newbiggin C W	v	Carlisle City	1-2	Ryton	v	Ponteland United	0-3

Final

Carlisle City	v	Ponteland United	2-0

The final played at Hexham's Wentworth Park was held up for three-quarters of an hour due to separate injuries sustained by Ponteland's player-manager Barrie Wardrobe and Carlisle's young keeper Stephen Bellas. Both players were taken to hospital.

Geoff Fell headed in a left wing cross from Mike Robinson to put the Cumbrians ahead just before Bella's injury on the stroke of half time. Wardrobe was then stretchered off in the second hald with a broken leg before Robinson volleyed home a perfect cross from Peter Harbach in the dying seconds.

The result left Ponteland with an unenviable record. They have yet to claim this particular trophy despite appearing in five finals in the last six seasons.

City striker Gary Milne posed a continuous threat to Ponteland's defenders and was named as man-of-the-match.

PREMIER DIVISION CLUBS 1997-98

CARLISLE CITY

Chairman: J Ewbank **Manager:** W Armstrong.
Secretary: D Ivison, 40 Skiddaw Road, Carlisle CA2 5OS (01228 31654).
Ground: The Sheepmount Sports Complex, Carlisle (01228 26569).
Directions: B6264 Brampton-Carlisle road & follow Workington signs, dual-c'way down hill (Carlisle Castle on right), where road intersects double back on yourself and take turning left just before castle, follow down hill keeping left until ground.
Colours: All Sky **Change colours:** White/red

CARLISLE GILLFORD PARK

Chairman: R Wilson **Manager/Coach:** R Rutherford/D Graham.
Secretary: Paul McMullen, 154 Blackwell Road, Currrock, Carlisle (01228 22983).
Ground: Gillford Park, Carlisle (01228 26649).
Directions: A69 to Rose Hill r'bout, straight over & 2nd left into Eastern Way, 1 mile to lights, left, 1st right Petrill Bank Rd, right at bridge, ground 200yds up this road.
Colours: All red **Change colours:** White/black.

HALTWHISTLE CROWN PAINTS

Chairman: Derek Pape **Manager/Coach:** TBA
Secretary: R Skeet, 14 Westgate, Haltwhistle, Northumberland NE49 9AF (01434 320703).
Ground: Bardon Mill Sports Ground, Bardon Mill, Northumberland
Directions: A69 to Bardon Hill 1st right under bridge, ground on the left
Colours: Yellow/black **Change colours:** All royal

HARTLEPOOL UNITED

Chairman: H Hornsey **Manager/Coach:** Mick Tait
Secretary: Maureen Smith, 2 North Drive, Hartlepool, (01429 277277)
Ground: Victoria Park, Clarence Road, Hartlepool, Cleveland (01429 222077). **Directions:** From Newcastle A19 south, turn off to A179 Hartlepool, follow signs for Marina into Clarence Rd.
Colours: Sky & White/blue **Change colours:** Red with white trim/red

HEBBURN REYROLLE

Chairman/Press Officer: Alan Graham **Manager/Coach:** Norman Dryden
Secretary: Gordon Taylor, 29 Crawley Avenue, Hebburn, Tyne & Wear NE31 2LT (0191 4834537)
Ground: Hebburn Sports Ground, Victoria Road West, Hebburn, Tyne & Wear.
Directions: From Newcastle & Gateshead via the Felling Bypass travel to Heworth r/about, take A195 signed Hebburn/Jarrow. Ground approx 2 miles on left.
Colours: Red & blue/blue **Change colours:** Green & navy/navy

LEMINGTON SOCIAL

Chairman: R Craven **Manager:** John Connolly
Secretary: R M Alsop, 11 Allerdene Close, West Denton Park, Newcastle, NE15 8RN (0191 267 5072).
Ground: Cowgate New Tavern Sports Ground, Ponteland Rd, Cowgate, Newcastle-upon-Tyne.
Directions: Kenton turn off A1, over Kenton r'bout & next 2 r'bouts, ground on right before garage and behind Co-op dairy.
Colours: Red & black/black **Change colours:** White/navy

NEWCASTLE BENFIELD PARK

Chairman: J Rowe **Manager:** Tom Sword
Secretary: Danny Gates, 5 Winship Terrace, Byker, Newcastle-upon-Tyne (0191 276 3049).
Ground: Benfield Park, Benfield Rd, Newcastle-upon-Tyne.
Directions: From Newcastle towards coast take 2nd exit after Corner House pub lights, right into Benfield Rd, ground on left opp. Walkergate Hosp. & adjacent to school.
Colours: Blue/white **Change colours:** White/blue

NORTH SHIELDS St COLUMBAS

Chairman: N Hooper **Manager/Coach:** J Wall.
Secretary: A J Baird, 23 Balkwell Ave., North Shields, Tyne & Wear NE29 7JN (0191 258 0833).
Ground: Purvis Park, St John's Green, Percy Main, North Shields.
Directions: From Tyne Tunnel take N Sdields road past Duke Of Wellington, after 1/2 mile take 2nd left, ground on right.
Colours: All white **Change colours:** Black & white/black

PONTELAND UNITED

Chairman: F W Smith **Manager:** B Wardrobe/S Baxter
Secretary: L McMahon, 1 Wardle Drive, Annitsford, Cramlingham NE23 7DB (0191 250 0463).
Ground: Ponteland Leisure Centre, Ponteland (01661 25441).
Directions: Left at lights entering Ponteland from N'castle, ground 100m on left adjacent to Leisure Centre.
Colours: Black & white stripes/black **Change colours:** All white.

RYTON

Chairman: Philip Hall **Manager/Coach:** Alan Patterson/Stephen Murray
Secretary: Les Robson, 31 Park View Gardens, Runhead, Ryton, Tyne & wear NE40 3JD (0191 413 7628)
Ground: Avenue Ground, Old Hexham Road, Swalwell, Tyne & Wear.
Directions: From Newcastle, cross the Tyne via Redheugh Bridge & take A1 Western bypass past the Metro Centre. Take the 1st left sliproad past the Metro Centre. Turn right at r/about and follow for half mile. Ground on right just past Fewsters.
Colours: Blue & black/black **Change colours:** Orange/black

SEATON DELAVAL AMATEURS

Chairman: T Ashburn **Manager/Coach:** I Watts
Secretary: V Donnelly, 6 Hollymount Square, Bedlington (01670 829464).
Ground: Wheatridge Park, Seaton Delaval.
Directions: A189 from Newcastle, at Annitsford r'bout A190 to Seaton Delaval, left at r'bout entering village, ground 450yds on right next to Deal Garage and behind Market Garden. 3 miles from Cramlington BR station. Bus 363 from Newcastle passes ground.
Colours: Sky/black **Change colours:** Yellow/blue

SPITTAL ROVERS

Vice Chairman: Paul Renton **Manager/Coach:** Steven Roughead
Secretary: G Burn, 7 Sea Road, Spittal, Berwick-on-Tweed TD15 1RN (01289 306049).
Ground: Newfields, Berwick-on-Tweed.
Directions: From south take Berwick by-pass to 3rd r'bout. Safeway Store on right - pitch reached by taking 2nd left on r'bout.
Colours: Black & white stripes/black **Change colours:** Red/black

WALKER CENTRAL

Chairman: R T McClellan **Manager/Coach:** A Bell.
Secretary: Mr B Mulroy, 31 Dalton Cres., Byker Wall, Newcastle-upon-Tyne NE6 2DA (0191 265 7803).
Ground: Monkchester Recreation Ground, Walker, Newcastle.
Directions: From City: Shields Rd to Union Rd, to Welbeck Rd, right into Monkchester Rd, left into pitch (between houses) opposite Norbury Grove.
Club colours: Blue & yellow/blue **Change colours:** Red & white/red

WALKER LEDWOOD FOSSE

Chairman: W A Callanan **Manager/Coach:** T Lunn.
Secretary: K Slade, 59 Moorland Cres., Walkergate, Newcastle-upon-Tyne NE6 4AT (0191 276 1519)
Ground: Miller's Dene, Walkergate, Newcastle-upon-Tyne.
Directions: Miller's Dene Fosseway from Newcastle, travel through Byker to the r'bout at the top of Shields Rd, turn right & continue to next r'bout, left at B & Q store & continue down Fosseway. The ground is the second one down the Fosseway past Fire Station on left.
Colours: All white **Change colours:** Green & black/black

WEST ALLOTMENT CELTIC

Chairman: J Mather **Manager/Coach:** Ken Scott
Secretary: J T Jackson, 4 Rosewood Crescent, Seaton Sluice, Whitley Bay NE26 4BL (0191 237 0416).
Ground: Hillheads Park, Whitley Bay
Directions: From Newcastle take A1058 to Tynemouth Baths, turn left roundabout on A192 to Foxhunters Pub. Turn right follow A191 to Ice Rink on right, ground beside.
Colours: Black & white stripes/black **Change colours:** Red/blue.

WINLATON HALLGARTH

Chairman: R Young **Manager/Coach:** K Rides/S Breen.
Secretary: Sid Batey, 6 Wylam View, Winlaton, Tyne & Wear NE21 4RJ (0191 414 7970).
Ground: Shibdon Park, Shibdon Road, Blaydon-on-Tyne, Tyne & Wear.
Directions: From north, over A1 Tyne Bridge to 1st slip road, take Swalwell and Consett road to r'bout, right, Blaydon Baths car park and ground 400yds on right.
Colours: Green & white/white **Change colours:** Yellow & black/black

TEESSIDE STRONGARM FOOTBALL LEAGUE

Founded: 1891

President: K P Moore **Chairman:** L Crossman
Secretary: R D Marsay, 12 Aislaby Court, Wilton Lane, Guisborough, Cleveland TS14 6TG (01287 637087)

FINAL LEAGUE TABLE 1996-97

		P	W	D	L	F	A	Pts	GD
1	Acklam Steelworks	30	21	5	4	88	29	68	59
2	Tees Components	30	21	4	5	97	32	67	65
3	Thornaby YC	30	19	9	2	88	29	66	59
4	Grangetown BC*	30	18	4	8	68	65	55	3
5	Richmond Town	30	14	9	7	51	30	51	21
6	BEADS FC	30	14	8	8	48	44	50	4
7	BSC Redcar	30	14	2	14	70	63	44	7
8	Fishburn Park	30	11	5	14	47	46	38	1
9	Dormans Athletic*	30	12	2	16	73	74	35	-1
10	Mannion Park*	30	10	7	13	60	59	34	1
11	Nunthorpe Athletic*	30	9	9	12	53	55	33	-2
12	Stokesley SC	30	9	6	15	45	68	33	-23
13	Stockton Supp*	30	10	4	16	48	69	31	-21
14	New Marske SC	30	5	5	20	43	89	20	-46
15	Loftus WR SC	30	5	5	20	54	103	20	-49
16	Guisborough Town Res	30	3	6	21	40	117	15	-77

* 3 points deducted

LEAGUE CHAMPIONS
Acklam Steelworks

RUNNERS UP
Tees Components

RE-ELECTION
Loftus WR & Guisborough Town Res

MACMILLAN BOWL FINAL
Acklam Steelworks 2-0 Beads FC

R T RAINE TROPHY FINAL
BSC Redcar 3-2 New Marske SC

NORTH RIDING COUNTY CUP FINAL
Acklam Steelworks 1-0 Kirbymoorside

J V MADDEN TROPHY
Acklam Steelworks 4-0 Fishburn Park

CLUB DIRECTORY

ACKLAM STEELWORKS

Secretary: Peter Conley, 53 Roseberry Road, Longlands, Middlesbrough, Cleveland TS4 2LJ (01642 224266)
Ground: Acklam Steelworks Club, Park Road South, Middlesbrough (01642 818717)
Directions: Marton Road A172, follow route to Middlesbrough centre, follow signs to County Sports Stadium, entrance opposite Sports Stadium.
Sponsor: Upsall Vending
Colours: Red/blue/red **Change Colours:** Blue & black/black/blue

B.E.A.D.S.

Secretary: Dave Kane, 27 Edgeworth Court, Hemlington, Middlesbrough, Cleveland TS8 9EP (01642 596559)
Ground: Beechwood & Easterside SC, Marton Road, Middlesbrough. (01642 311304)
Directions: Follow A172 into Middlesbrough centre down Marton Road, ground behind Social Club.
Sponsor: Classic Trophies UK
Colours: Red & black/black/black **Change Colours:** Yellow/blue/blue

BSC REDCAR

Secretary: David Collins, 23 Welland Road, Redcar, Cleveland TS10 1NR (01642 491547)
Ground: BSC Sports & Social Club, Dormanstown, Redcar (01642 486691)
Directions: Approaching Redcar from Middlesbrough, enter Dormanstown at BSC Steel House Works rounabout, turn 1st right then 1st left, ground behind club.
Sponsor: Area Electrical Projects
Colours: Sky/black/black **Change Colours:** White/black/black

CARGO FLEET SC

Secretary: M Coonorton, 84 Durham Road, Eston, Middlesbrough, Cleveland TS6 9LZ (01642 467327)
Ground: Pallister Park, Middlesbrough
Directions: Head towards M'bro (A171) Oremesby Bank, onto Cargo Fleet Lane, turn first left aftyer Cargo Fleet Club onto Homerton Rd, turn right at end of Homerton Road. Ground 100 yards on right.
Sponsor: Cargo Fleet Social Club/Sam Smiths Brewery.
Colours: Red & black/black/black. **Change Colours:** Navy/blue/yellow

CARLIN HOW WMC

Secretary: Neil Townend, 32 Westray Street, Carlin How, Saltburn, Cleveland TS13 4EL (01287 643741)
Ground: Kilton Lane, Carlin How.
Directions: From M'bro follow A173/174 towards Loftus. When entering Carlin How, turn right just before traffic lights/Loftus Bank, onto Maynard St. Follow road 200 yards, ground on right passed club.
Sponsor: Carlin How & Dist WMC Institute Ltd
Colours: All red **Change Colours:** Black & amber/black/black

DORMANS ATHLETIC

Secretary: Don Hall, 52 Westbourne Road, Linthorpe, Middlesbrough, Cleveland TS5 5BJ (01642 879603)
Ground: Dormans Athletic Club, Oxford Road, Middlesbrough. (01642 817099)
Directions: Follow the A1032 down Acklam Road towards Middlesbrough Centre, turn right onto Oxford Road, ground on right before the garage.
Sponsor: MSV Technics
Colours: Blue & black/black/black **Change Colours:** All red

FISHBURN PARK

Secretary: Karen Hutton, 24 Abbots Road, Whitby, N Yorks YO22 4EB (01947 602537)
Ground: Showfield Ground, White Leys Rd, Whitby
Directions: Follow A171 to Whitby, at 1st r/about turn left. End of road, fork right, ground 3rd right.
Sponsor: Saxonville Hotel/Landers Butchers
Colours: All green **Change Colours:** White/blue/blue

GRANGETOWN BOYS CLUB

Secretary: Kevin Larkin, 19 Braemar Grove, Teesville, Middlesbrough, Cleveland TS6 0AN (01642 452095)
Ground: Grangetown YCC, Trunk Road, Grangtown, Midlesbrough (01642 455435)
Directions: Follow the trunk road into Redcar from M'bro, ground on right after roundabout leading over bridge.
Sponsor: M & H Plant Hire
Colours: Black & Amber/black/black **Change Colours:** All royal blue

GUISBOROUGH TOWN RESERVES

Secretary: Keith Smeltzer, 55 Thames Avenue, Guisborough, Cleveland TS154 8AR (01287 638993)
Ground: King George V Playing Fields, Howlbeck Road, Guisborough (01287 636925)
Directions: Follow A171 into Guisborough, turn left at 2nd traffic lights opposite Moorcock Hotel, turn 3rd left follow signs for swimming baths. **Sponsor:** Hensons
Colours: Red & white/black/red **Change Colours:** All yellow

NEW MARSKE SPORTS CLUB

Secretary: Peter Whitaker, 28 High Street, Marske, Redcar, Cleveland TS11 7BE (01642 486770)
Ground: New Marske Sports Club, New Marske, Redcar (01642 479808)
Directions: From M'bro A174 to rounabout junc with Longbeck Lane turn right, ground on left.
Sponsor: Car Care
Colours: Yellow/blue/yellow **Change Colours:** White & red/black/black

NUNTHORPE ATHLETIC

Secretary: Kevin Levitt, 131 Burlam Road, Middlesbrough, Cleveland, TS5 5AX (01642 824332)
Ground: Recreation Ground, Guisborough Road, Nunthorpe (01642 313251)
Directions: Leaving Middlesbrough on A172, turn left into Nunthorpe ground 300 yards on right.
Sponsor: Val Reeve & Chis Elvin at Paws
Colours: Blue & black/black/black **Change Colours:** Red & white/blue/red & white

RICHMOND TOWN

Secretary: Linda Blackburn, 14 Westfields, Richmond, N Yorks DL10 4DD (01748 824919)
Ground: Earls Orchard Playing Fields, Sleegill, Richmond
Directions: Entering Richmond on A6108, over 2 roundabouts turn right at third, 2nd left follow downhill and cross Green Bridge on road to Hudswell village, ground on left immediately after bridge.
Sponsor: Property Management Services/Turf Hotel
Colours: Blue & yellow/blue/blue **Change Colours:** Blue & black/black/blue & black

STOKESLEY SC

Secretary: Peter Grainge, 77 Darnton Drive, Easterside, Middlesbrough, Cleveland TS4 3RF (01642 316691)
Ground: Stokesley Sports Club, Broughton Road, Stokesley (01642 710051)
Directions: Follow signs for Stokesley. Take B1257 to Great Broughton at roundabout junc A172/A173, ground on left next to cricket field.
Sponsor: The Stokesley Sports Shop
Colours: All red **Change Colours:** White & blue/blue/blue

TEES COMPONENTS

Secretary: Bryan Kitchen, 151 Guisborough Road, Nunthorpe, Middlesbrough, Cleveland TS7 0JQ (01642 311358)
Ground: Recreation Ground, Machine Lane, North Skelton.
Directions: Follow A173 into Skelton, then into North Skelton. Ground off North Skelton High Street, follow the lane between Esso garage and church
Sponsor: Tees Components Ltd
Colours: Yellow/navy/navy **Change Colours:** Blue & black/blue/blue

THORNABY FOOTBALL CLUB

Secretary: Susan Gardner, 25 Brotton Rd, Thornaby, Stockton, Cleveland TS17 8EP (01642 646032)
Ground: Teesdale Park, Acklam Road, Thornaby.
Directions: Leave A19 at Thornaby interchange, follow road through traffic lights towards Stockton centre, turn right when in dip at sign for Teesdale Park
Sponsor: Scott Bros
Colours: Claret/claret/sky **Change Colours:** Blue/black/black

THORNABY YOUTH CLUB

Secretary: Geoffrey Kirk, 9 Tipton Close, Thornaby, Stockton, Cleveland TS17 9QF (01642 676516)
Ground: Dene School, Baysdale Road, Thornaby.
Directions: Leave A19 at Thornaby interchange. turn left at the Roundel Pub onto Mitchell Ave, proceed towards Thornaby Town centre, turn right at Baysdale Road, follow road round to entrance.
Sponsor: Thornaby Youth Club/Market Tavern
Colours: Claret/white/white **Change Colours:** Blue & black/black/black

WHITBY TOWN RESERVES

Secretary: Charlie Woodward, 6 Westlands Avenue, Whitby, N Yorks YO21 3DZ (01947 602312)
Ground: Turnbull Ground, Upgang Lane, Whitby.
Directions: Entering Whitby by A169 or A171, take 1st fork and follow signs for West Cliff
Sponsor: Whitby Tanks Ltd/Harrison's Garage Ltd
Colours: All blue **Change Colours:** White/black/white

Brighouse Town, West Riding County Amateur League Premier Division, before the Premier Division Cup Final (Result: Brighouse Town 0 Storthes Hall 1)
Back Row (L-R): Tony Lyons (Manager), Darren Shaw, Leighton Armstrong, Andy Greenwood, Nick Delaney, Andy Moss, John Rose, Wayne Gibson, Kindy Singh, Chris Lister (Coach).
Front Row (L-R): Mark Wood, George Mulhall, Andy Stewart, Glen Lee, Craig Kenny, Andy Warnes.

Photo: G D & M Watsorr

NORTH EASTERN FOOTBALL LEAGUES

Final League Tables 1996-97

NORTH EAST CHRISTIAN FELLOWSHIP LEAGUE

Division One

		P	W	D	L	F	A	Pts
1	Whitley Bay Churches	18	14	3	1	54	23	45
2	Bethshan	18	12	1	5	57	36	37
3	Jesmond PC	18	7	8	3	48	34	29
4	Sunderland CC	18	7	6	5	49	33	27
5	St Georges	18	8	2	8	54	41	26
6	Emmanuel Yarm	18	7	4	7	39	29	25
7	Heaton Hearts	18	6	5	7	38	42	23
8	Crossroads	18	4	5	9	26	44	17
9	Lady Lourdes	18	3	2	13	38	67	11
10	Ryton Churches	18	3	2	13	31	75	11

Division Two

		P	W	D	L	F	A	Pts
1	Stranton Saints	18	13	2	3	78	32	41
2	Chowdene Chapel	18	12	3	3	84	41	39
3	Centenary Methodist	18	12	0	6	52	38	36
4	Athenians	18	9	5	4	53	25	32
5	Consett Methodist	18	10	2	6	56	59	32
6	Lanchester Chapel	18	7	4	7	59	49	25
7	Heworth CF	18	6	4	8	63	49	22
8	St Marys St Cuth	18	7	0	11	49	81	21
9	Westgate Road BC	18	3	0	15	47	80	9
10	Bethany	18	1	0	17	21	108	3

HETTON YOUTH LEAGUE

		P	W	D	L	Pts
1	Trimdon	26	24	0	2	72
2	Redby	26	22	1	3	67
3	Grove Coles	26	21	1	4	64
4	Horden	26	17	0	9	51
5	Springboard	26	14	1	11	43
6	Ryhope	26	12	4	10	40
7	Lumley	26	11	6	9	39
8	Burnmoor	26	10	3	13	33
9	Hylton	26	8	6	12	30
10	Dubmire	26	7	3	16	27
11	Herrington	26	6	7	13	25
12	Vane Tempest	26	7	3	16	24
13	Shiney Row	26	2	2	22	8
14	South Hetton	26	1	2	23	5

NORTHERN INTERMEDIATE LEAGUE (YOUTH TEAMS)

		P	W	D	L	F	A	Pts
1	Leeds	34	28	3	3	112	23	87
2	Sunderland	34	25	5	4	77	41	80
3	Barnsley	34	21	6	7	65	38	69
4	Middlesbrough	34	21	5	8	77	43	68
5	Sheffield United	34	17	7	10	74	46	58
6	Newcastle	34	15	10	9	69	40	55
7	Rotherham	34	15	10	9	60	47	55
8	Sheffield Wednesday	34	13	11	10	63	47	50
9	Hull	34	12	6	16	38	55	42
10	Huddersfield	34	10	10	14	44	50	40
11	Bradford City	34	11	7	16	39	47	40
12	Doncaster	34	12	2	20	51	63	38
13	Hartlepool	34	11	3	20	41	56	36
14	York	34	10	6	18	38	60	36
15	Scunthorpe	34	9	8	17	33	59	35
16	Darlington	34	8	8	18	37	76	32
17	Scarborough	34	5	9	20	29	79	24
18	Chesterfield	34	2	6	26	25	102	12

CLEVELAND LEAGUE

		P	W	D	L	F	A	Pts
1	Cargo Fleet	28	23	3	2	106	31	72
2	Carlin How	28	22	2	4	81	29	68
3	Grangetown	28	19	5	4	100	41	62
4	Whinney Banks	28	19	1	8	110	40	58
5	Great Ayton	28	18	2	8	84	49	56
6	New Marske FC	28	12	4	12	71	55	40
7	Staithes	28	11	6	11	70	66	39
8	Loftus	28	11	4	13	68	66	37
9	Boosbeck	28	11	2	15	60	72	35
10	Bellmangate	28	9	4	15	59	72	31
11	White Horse	28	7	5	16	42	100	26
12	Skelton	28	4	8	16	29	59	20
13	McKinley Park	28	5	5	18	44	98	20
14	New Marske FC	28	5	4	19	37	95	19
15	British Steel Club	28	4	5	19	37	125	17

EVENING NEWS SATURDAY LEAGUE (Scarborough League)

Division One

		P	W	D	L	Pts
1	Edgehill Mere	22	22	0	0	44
2	West Pier	22	16	2	4	34
3	Wards	22	14	3	5	31
4	K'moorside	22	14	2	6	30
5	Ryedale Sp	22	13	1	8	27
6	Filey Town	22	10	2	10	22
7	Flamborough	22	8	4	10	20
8	Scalby	22	6	4	12	16
9	Eastfield*	22	5	3	14	11
10	Cayton Cor	22	3	5	14	11
11	Whitby Arcs	22	2	6	14	10
12	FC Aberdeen	22	2	2	18	6

* 2 Points deducted

Division Two

		P	W	D	L	Pts
1	Rillington	24	16	5	3	37
2	Ayton	24	16	4	4	36
3	FC Ivanhoe	24	13	6	5	32
4	Hunmanby	24	13	5	6	31
5	Edgehill Reserves	24	11	5	8	27
6	North Riding	24	11	5	8	27
7	Eastfield Reserves	24	10	5	9	25
8	Fishburn Park	24	9	6	9	24
9	Stainsacre	24	7	5	12	10
10	Scholes Park	24	8	3	13	19
11	Barrowcliffe	24	4	5	15	13
12	Sherburn	24	5	3	16	13
13	West Pier Reserves	24	2	5	17	9

ROTHERHAM ASSOCIATION FOOTBALL LEAGUE (Sheffield & Hallamshire FA)

Premier Division

		P	W	D	L	F	A	Pts
1	Brinsworth Athletic	14	9	1	4	34	19	19
2	Thorpe Hesley	14	9	0	5	33	20	18
3	Jockey New Boys	14	7	4	3	32	22	18
4	Lord Conyers	14	8	1	5	33	31	17
5	New Life	14	6	2	6	29	26	14
6	Mexboro' Sportsman	14	5	3	6	21	31	13
7	BSM Drawbridge	14	3	3	8	26	34	9
8	Brinsworth WMC	14	2	0	12	16	41	4

Albion Road WMC, Eastwood View WMC withdrew

Division One

		P	W	D	L	F	A	Pts
1	Maltby Sheppey	21	14	3	3	75	34	33
2	Silverwood SC	21	14	4	3	88	39	32
3	Oak Tree '95	21	14	1	5	57	35	31
4	Queens Rawmarsh	21	10	2	8	54	30	20
5	Dinnington Snkr C	21	8	3	10	62	53	19
6	Langold Old Boys	21	8	1	8	41	52	17
7	Treeton Welfare	21	2	2	16	40	92	8
8	Sheffield Deaf	21	2	0	19	32	114	4

Rock Tavern withdrew

THE SHEFFIELD SPORTS AND ATHLETIC FOOTBALL LEAGUE (Sheffield & Hallamshire FA)

Premier Division

		P	W	D	L	F	A	Pts
1	Woodhouse W. End	16	14	1	1	70	17	43
2	Earl Fullflow	16	12	2	2	54	26	38
3	Melrite	16	8	2	6	43	41	26
4	Elm Lane Fisheries	16	7	1	8	46	52	22
5	Rose Inn	16	6	3	7	31	37	21
6	Sheff. Hallam U.S.	16	5	4	7	26	42	19
7	Jubilee Sports	16	4	2	10	37	44	14
8	Golden Plover	16	4	2	10	26	48	11*
9	Guest & Chrimes	16	3	1	12	30	56	10

* Three points deducted

Senior Division One

		P	W	D	L	F	A	Pts
1	Wincobank Barrow	18	14	2	2	75	26	41**
2	Arbourthorne	18	11	4	3	60	37	37
3	Norwich Union	18	9	4	5	51	39	31
4	Boynton Sports	18	9	4	5	49	44	31
5	Forgemasters	18	7	4	7	39	49	25
6	Catcliffe Plough A	18	7	3	8	49	47	24
7	Post Office	18	4	4	10	32	48	16
8	Wadsley Star	18	4	3	11	37	58	15
9	I E P Bramah	18	4	3	11	32	62	15
10	Whitbread Tinsley	18	3	5	10	30	44	13*

** Three points deducted
* One point deducted

DONCASTER SENIOR LEAGUE (Sheffield & Hallamshire FA)

Premier Division

		P	W	D	L	F	A	Pts
1	South Kirkby Coll.	26	21	4	1	110	20	67
2	Carcroft Vlge WMC	26	19	5	2	60	23	62
3	Hemsw'th St Patrick	26	17	2	7	84	39	53
4	Upton & Harewood	26	16	5	5	63	29	53
5	Scawthorpe Social	26	12	6	8	65	51	42
6	Plant Works	26	12	4	10	45	42	40
7	Skellow Grange	26	11	4	11	46	49	37
8	Sutton Rovers	26	11	2	13	53	49	35
9	Ackworth United	26	8	5	13	48	67	29
10	Northgate WMC	26	8	4	14	44	42	28
11	Hemsworth MW Rs	26	7	3	16	35	67	24
12	Askern Welfare	26	7	1	18	32	74	22
13	Kinsley Boys	26	5	2	19	28	89	17
14	Ings Lane	26	4	1	21	36	108	13

Division One

		P	W	D	L	F	A	Pts
1	Highfields MW	20	15	3	2	60	27	48
2	Edlington B. Legion	20	14	4	2	67	21	46
3	Tickhill Town	20	9	5	6	42	38	32
4	Edlington WMC	20	9	4	7	52	51	31
5	White Hart United	20	7	7	6	45	48	28
6	Lindholme	20	8	2	10	49	51	26
7	Rossington Res	20	7	4	9	43	37	25
8	Hemsw'th St Patrick	20	7	3	10	60	64	24
9	Yorkshire Main	20	6	2	12	43	62	20
10	Bentley Colliery	20	3	5	12	37	66	14
11	Lodge	20	3	5	12	24	57	14

Cantley Hawthorn withdrew

SOUTH YORKSHIRE AMATEUR LEAGUE
(Sheffield & Hallamshire FA)

Premier Division

		P	W	D	L	F	A	Pts
1	Burncross	16	14	2	0	59	19	44**
2	Market I	18	10	5	3	37	17	35
3	Hollinsend A	18	9	5	4	51	31	32
4	Oughtibridge	17	8	3	6	38	34	27*
5	Gate 13	18	7	3	8	39	35	24
6	Kings CH	18	6	5	7	32	34	23
7	D L Salle	18	6	4	8	25	30	22
8	Elm Tree	17	6	3	8	40	41	21*
9	Centralians	18	3	2	13	16	50	11
10	Phoenix A	18	1	4	13	30	76	7

** Plus 6 points for 2 games not played
* No points alteration for games not played
Midland Bank withdrew

Division One

		P	W	D	L	F	A	Pts
1	Hillsboro	16	15	0	1	56	16	45
2	S W D	16	12	1	3	48	19	37
3	Davy	16	7	5	4	36	29	26
4	Cumberland	16	7	3	6	32	41	24
5	S H Bankers	16	6	2	8	32	40	20
6	Medics A	16	5	2	9	30	37	17
7	The Retreat	16	4	2	10	34	43	14
8	Hollinsend	16	3	4	9	21	47	13
9	Castle Coll	16	3	1	12	27	44	10

CRAVEN LEAGUE
(West Riding FA)

Premier Division

		P	W	D	L	Pts
1	Skipton Bulldogs	22	21	0	1	42
2	Oxenhope Recreation	22	16	3	3	35
3	Cowling	22	11	5	6	27
4	Haworth	22	10	6	6	26
5	Cononley Sports	22	9	6	7	24
6	Embsay	22	10	4	8	24
7	Keighley Lifts	22	7	6	9	20
8	Cross Hills Res	22	6	6	10	18
9	Skipton LMS	22	6	4	12	16
10	Skipton Town	22	5	6	11	16
11	Rimington Res	22	3	4	15	10
12	Carleton	22	0	6	16	6

Division One

		P	W	D	L	Pts
1	Addingham	22	19	3	0	41
2	Colne Cricket Club	22	15	2	5	32
3	Rolls Royce	22	11	4	7	26
4	Oxenhope Rec Res	22	11	4	7	26
5	Kelbrook	22	11	3	8	25
6	Keighley Lifts Reserves	22	10	2	10	22
7	Gargrave Reserves	22	9	3	10	21
8	Intake	22	8	3	11	19
9	Grassington United	22	6	5	11	17
10	Grindleton	22	4	5	13	13
11	Bradley	22	5	3	14	13
12	Bronte Wanderers	22	2	5	15	9

BRADFORD GRATTAN FOOTBALL LEAGUE
(West Riding FA)

Premier Division

		P	W	D	L	F	A	Pts
1	Woodend Rangers	14	11	1	2	57	20	34
2	Dudley Hills SC FC	14	9	1	4	49	30	28
3	Fagley FC	14	6	2	6	35	24	20
4	Market Tavern FC	14	5	4	5	26	35	19
5	Wibsey FC 'A'	14	5	3	6	27	36	18
6	Mailcoach FC	14	4	2	8	28	30	14
7	K.S.C. 83 FC	14	4	2	8	19	46	14
8	U Save DIY	14	4	1	9	19	39	13

Thornton Utd, Holmewood Ath Reserves withdrawn

Division One

		P	W	D	L	F	A	Pts
1	Admiral Nelson	16	15	1	0	91	16	46
2	Royds Utd FC	16	13	1	2	53	22	40
3	Fagley Reserves	16	8	4	4	43	34	28
4	Wibsey Park Utd	16	8	0	8	40	46	24
5	Victoria Wands	16	6	2	8	50	45	20
6	Bierley United	16	5	2	9	40	57	17
7	New Inn FC	16	5	0	11	38	67	15
8	Ryecroft Rangers	16	4	2	10	29	59	14
9	One In Twelve FC	16	1	2	13	16	54	5

Woodend Rangers took the Premier Division title after losing out narrowly the previous season. League champions Thornton Utd made a last minute decision not to join the West Riding County Amateur League, but failed to complete their fixtures.

Runners up Dudley Mill Socialsist club heve changed their name to Dudley Mill Rangers and joined the West Riding County Amateur League

DRIFFIELD & DISTRICT LEAGUE
(West Riding FA)

Premier Division

		P	W	D	L	F	A	Pts
1	Bridlington Lab Club	20	16	2	2	72	25	34
2	Bridlington Tn Res	20	13	4	3	53	29	30
3	Hilderthorpe	20	12	4	4	55	27	28
4	Shiptonthorpe	20	7	8	5	37	27	22
5	Middleton Rovers	20	10	1	9	56	49	21
6	Crown A F C	19	9	3	7	48	43	21
7	Hornsea Town	20	7	2	11	45	57	16
8	Pack Horse	20	7	1	12	45	66	15
9	Driffield E I	20	5	3	12	24	54	13
10	Bridlington Rovers	20	3	3	14	21	56	9
11	Charles Dickens FC	20	3	3	13	27	60	7

* Two points deducted

Division One (Top 3)

		P	W	D	L	F	A	Pts
1	Globe	20	15	5	0	87	24	35
2	Nafferton	20	13	3	4	86	42	29
3	Bridlington George	20	12	5	3	53	30	29

SPEN VALLEY LEAGUE
(West Riding FA)

Premier Division	P	W	D	L	F	A	Pts
1 Yorkshire Rose	24	18	4	2	73	25	58
2 Howden Clough	24	18	2	4	117	41	56
3 White Rose Leisure	24	16	2	6	105	45	50
4 Savilletown Youth	24	14	2	8	67	46	44
5 White Horse FC	24	13	4	7	67	42	43
6 J Walker S & SC	24	13	2	9	73	59	41
7 Fountain Robertown	24	13	2	9	66	57	41
8 Hightown FC	24	11	3	10	64	49	36
9 Barclay's FC 'A'	24	8	3	13	55	62	27
10 Thornhill FC	24	4	4	16	32	56	16
11 Overthorpe SC Res	24	4	4	16	29	82	16
12 Mirfield Town FC	24	4	4	16	39	100	16
13 Scholes C C	24	2	0	22	40	163	6

Batley WMC resigned

Division One	P	W	D	L	F	A	Pts
1 Lord Nelson	26	23	3	0	117	24	72
2 Airedale Celtic	26	22	3	1	126	29	69
3 Ravensthorpe Rgrs	26	18	2	6	109	59	56
4 Barclays 'B'	26	15	4	7	82	59	49
5 White Rose Res	26	16	0	10	83	48	48
6 Albion Rangers	26	13	4	9	77	73	43
7 Birstall FC	26	11	3	12	80	67	36
8 Howden Clough Rs	26	10	3	13	73	71	33
9 Bull's Head Wesgate	26	8	6	12	48	76	30
10 British Oak	26	6	5	15	62	82	23
11 Longdale FC	26	5	5	16	36	107	20
12 J F Kennedy	26	5	2	19	60	92	17
13 Healey Carpets	26	4	2	20	50	119	14
14 Islamic FC	26	4	2	20	49	146	14

Bosnia FC & Scholes CC Reserves resigned

WAKEFIELD LEAGUE
(West Riding FA)

Premier Division	P	W	D	L	F	A	Pts
1 Nostell MW Res	21	13	7	1	63	34	46
2 Gardeners Arms	21	12	5	4	56	31	41
3 Shepherds Arms	21	10	4	7	53	49	34
4 Stanley United	21	9	3	9	52	40	30
5 Crofton Arms	21	8	4	9	44	45	28
6 Walton SSC	21	8	2	11	33	39	26
7 Fieldhead Hosp	21	7	1	13	27	48	22
8 Wrenthorpe	21	2	4	15	20	62	10

Division One	P	W	D	L	F	A	Pts
1 Waterloo	16	14	1	1	67	27	43
2 Bay Horse W	16	12	3	1	64	21	39
3 Snydale Athletic	16	11	2	3	61	31	35
4 Flanshaw Hotel	16	8	3	5	47	37	27
5 Normanton SJ	16	7	0	9	42	45	21
6 Horbury W'Pack	16	6	1	9	33	50	19
7 Eastmoor	16	5	1	10	27	43	16
8 Vine Tree	16	2	1	13	19	65	7
9 Kettlethorpe	16	1	0	15	22	63	3

HUDDERSFIELD & DISTRICT LEAGUE
(West Riding FA)

Division One

		P	W	D	L	F	A	Pts
1	Brackenhall	22	15	3	4	61	24	33
2	Honley	22	13	7	2	72	34	33
3	Kirkburton	22	11	6	5	57	36	28
4	Almondbury	22	11	5	6	61	40	27
5	Wooldale	22	11	3	8	33	32	25
6	Heywood Sp	22	10	4	8	43	34	24
7	Scholes	22	8	5	9	36	35	21
8	Hepworth	22	9	1	12	47	43	19
9	Storthes Hall Res	22	9	1	12	56	57	19
10	Skelmanthorpe	22	6	6	10	39	40	18
11	Kirkheaton	22	7	3	12	36	41	17
12	Bay Athletic Res	22	0	0	22	17	142	0

Division Two

		P	W	D	L	F	A	Pts
1	Britannia Sp	26	22	2	2	108	40	46
2	Slaithwaite	26	21	0	5	94	42	42
3	Netherton	26	17	4	5	60	38	38
4	Shepley	26	15	1	10	84	55	31
5	Marsden Res	26	12	1	13	47	49	25
6	Uppermill	26	11	2	13	62	57	24
7	Rawthorpe	26	11	2	13	66	71	24
8	Grange Moor	26	10	4	12	61	85	24
9	Sovereign Sp	26	8	6	12	50	61	22
10	Lepton	26	9	4	13	60	78	22
11	Meltham	26	9	3	14	38	66	21
12	Upperthong	26	8	3	15	49	61	19
13	Golcar Reserves	26	6	4	16	50	78	16
14	Cartworth Moor	26	3	4	19	34	82	10

SELBY & DISTRICT FOOTBALL LEAGUE
(West Riding FA)

First Division

		P	W	D	L	F	A	Pts
1	Stepping Stones	16	12	2	2	64	19	38
2	Kellingley Welfare	16	11	2	3	50	22	35
3	Redhill S S	16	10	2	4	48	27	32
4	Riccall Colliery	16	8	6	2	57	31	30
5	Normanton Cmrds	16	6	4	6	35	33	22
6	Kippax Welfare	16	6	2	8	35	42	20
7	Hensall Athletic	16	5	3	8	21	32	18
8	Altofts	16	2	1	13	14	64	7
9	Pollington	16	0	2	14	21	74	2

Barlby, Crimea Tavern, Kippax Utd resigned during season.

Second Division

		P	W	D	L	F	A	Pts
1	Fox Inn	26	22	2	2	116	30	68
2	Bradley Arms	26	17	6	3	89	52	57
3	Real Cliffe	26	17	3	6	109	47	54
4	Thorpe United	26	13	6	7	82	48	45
5	H R Selby	26	13	4	9	83	54	43
6	Drax P S	26	13	3	10	52	59	42
7	South Milford	26	11	5	10	67	71	38
8	Kippax Welfare Res	26	10	6	10	54	65	36
9	St Josephs	26	10	3	13	48	56	33
10	Eggborough P S	26	9	2	15	60	71	29
11	Wistow Wanderers	26	8	2	16	58	82	26
12	Monk Fryston Utd R	26	7	2	17	43	70	23
13	Fairburn AFC	26	5	4	17	42	73	19
14	Ferrybridge C	26	2	2	22	31	150	8

WEST RIDING COUNTY AMATEUR LEAGUE

Horton Print Group Premier Division

		P	W	D	L	F	A	Pts
1	Ovenden WR	26	17	5	4	56	32	39
2	Field	26	15	6	5	61	33	36
3	Storthes Hall	26	14	7	5	65	41	35
4	Marsden	26	13	5	8	57	42	31
5	Brighouse Town	26	13	5	8	40	38	31
6	Crag Road United	26	12	4	10	57	42	28
7	Tyersal	26	11	3	12	60	65	25
8	Wibsey	26	8	8	10	49	49	24
9	Halifax Irish	26	10	4	12	41	53	24
10	Altofts	26	9	3	14	42	57	21
11	Farnley WMC	26	8	5	13	46	69	21
12	Golcar United	26	8	3	15	38	52	19
13	Salts	26	7	2	17	41	54	16
14	Dudley Hill Athletic	26	4	6	16	38	64	14

Division One

		P	W	D	L	F	A	Pts
1	Hemsworth MW	30	21	6	3	112	38	48
2	Aberford Albion	30	20	6	4	75	25	46
3	Phoenix	30	16	8	6	65	26	40
4	Pontefract Borough	30	15	7	6	65	39	37
5	Campion	30	16	3	11	91	62	35
6	Eastmoor	30	15	5	10	70	46	35
7	Morley Town	30	13	6	11	54	51	32
8	Rawdon OB	30	12	5	13	70	65	29
9	Ardsley Celtic	30	11	6	13	66	68	28
10	Greetland	30	9	9	12	56	71	27
11	Lower Hopton	30	12	2	16	48	68	26
12	Otley Town	30	10	5	15	79	67	25
13	Ventus Yeadon	30	11	2	17	62	77	24
14	Overthorpe	30	9	5	16	55	78	23
15	Brighouse Res	30	9	4	17	56	84	22
16	Bowling Celtic	30	1	1	28	16	175	3

Division Two

		P	W	D	L	F	A	Pts
1	Bay Athletic	30	19	6	5	78	32	44
2	Pudsey Liberal	30	17	7	6	71	38	41
3	Littletown	30	17	5	8	88	62	39
4	Yorkshire Saints	30	17	4	9	82	50	38
5	Salt GSOB	30	12	13	5	57	29	37
6	Westbrook Wdrs	30	16	5	9	62	45	37
7	Wibsey Reserves	30	14	5	11	60	59	33
8	Holmewood Athletic	30	12	7	11	78	65	31
9	Steeton	30	12	4	14	50	58	28
10	Hall Green United	30	10	7	13	61	60	27
11	Ovenden Reserves	30	11	3	16	59	62	25
12	Heckmondwike	30	10	5	15	53	77	25
13	TS Harrison	30	10	4	16	50	80	24
14	Keighley Sh'	30	8	6	16	56	74	22
15	Campion Reserves	30	7	4	19	60	91	18
16	Trinity Athletic	30	4	3	23	49	124	11

WEST YORKSHIRE ASSOCIATION FOOTBALL LEAGUE

Premier Division		P	W	D	L	F	A	Pts
1	Carlton Athletic	32	22	4	5	91	36	50
2	Whitkirk Wanderers	32	22	4	6	97	52	48
3	Wakefield	32	21	3	7	80	36	47
4	Nestle Rowntrees	32	16	7	8	94	52	41
5	Knaresborough Tn	32	16	6	10	67	62	38
6	Beeston St Anthony's	32	16	5	11	69	36	37
7	Rothwell Athletic	32	17	3	12	58	55	37
8	Bardsey	32	17	2	13	83	58	36
9	Horbury Town	32	12	8	11	63	65	32
10	Barwick	32	11	9	12	53	58	31
11	York R I	32	13	3	16	52	58	29
12	Nostel M W	32	10	5	17	48	72	25
13	Magnet Sports	32	8	8	16	61	76	24
14	Robin Hood Ath	32	7	8	17	43	80	22
15	Swillington M W	32	9	3	19	66	99	21
16	G N Khalsa	32	6	4	21	47	99	16
17	Sherburn White Rose	32	3	4	25	45	123	10

Division One		P	W	D	L	F	A	Pts
1	Bramley	26	17	8	1	86	32	42
2	Armley Athletic	26	14	5	6	54	37	35
3	Pontefract Labour	26	13	8	5	69	41	34
4	Garforth WMC	26	13	7	6	51	37	33
5	Great Preston	26	10	9	7	50	42	29
6	Willowfield Celtic	26	11	6	9	54	46	28
7	Horsforth St Marg.	26	9	7	10	54	46	25
8	Featherstone Coll	26	8	9	9	40	43	25
9	Upper Armley OB	26	8	9	9	55	58	25
10	Selby R S S C	26	8	6	12	42	61	22
11	Whitkirk Wndrs Res	26	8	5	13	46	51	21
12	East End Park WMC	26	6	9	11	46	55	21
13	Wakefield Reserves	26	3	5	17	26	50	13
14	Rothwell Ath Res	26	5	1	18	26	100	9

YORKSHIRE OLD BOYS ASSOCIATION FOOTBALL LEAGUE (West Riding FA)

Senior Division A		P	W	D	L	F	A	Pts
1	Leeds Univ Union	22	17	1	4	60	27	52
2	Old Modernians	22	15	3	4	66	39	48
3	Yorkshire Bank	22	13	5	4	55	27	44
4	Ealandians	22	12	4	6	67	50	40
5	Wakefield City	22	10	7	5	39	31	37
6	Matthew Murray FP	22	8	5	9	42	56	29
7	Almondburians	22	7	3	12	47	56	24
8	Roundhegians	22	6	6	10	44	62	24
9	Old Centralians	22	7	3	12	32	42	24
10	Sandal Wanderers	22	6	5	11	38	48	23
11	Abbey Grange OB	22	3	4	15	34	58	13
12	Leeds Med's/Dent's	22	2	6	14	33	61	12

Senior Division B		P	W	D	L	F	A	Pts
1	Matthew Murray FP R	18	14	2	2	51	24	44
2	Yorkshire Bank Res	18	12	4	2	43	20	40
3	Old Batelians	18	11	2	5	59	39	35
4	St Bedes Old Boys	18	9	2	7	39	39	29
5	Old Modernians Res	18	9	1	8	46	42	28
6	Old Collegians	18	6	2	10	34	47	20
7	Wakefield City Res	18	5	2	11	33	50	17
8	Old Thornesians	18	4	3	11	37	50	15
9	Leeds Academicals	18	3	6	9	25	41	15
10	Wheelwright O B	18	4	2	12	40	55	14

TSW PRINTERS (Scunthorpe) LINCOLNSHIRE LEAGUE

Division One

		P	W	D	L	F	A	Pts
1	Barton Tn OB	38	31	3	4	108	32	96
2	Lincoln Utd Res	38	25	7	6	83	31	82
3	App Frod Ath	38	24	7	7	71	27	79
4	Wyberton	38	25	4	9	76	45	79
5	Limestone Rgrs	38	24	4	10	87	47	73
6	Lincoln Mrlands	38	21	8	9	93	43	71
7	Boston Utd Res	38	21	5	12	99	62	68
8	Grimsby Imm Am	38	18	10	10	72	46	64
9	Ruston Sports	38	17	10	11	79	50	68
10	Bottesford Town	38	17	8	13	71	51	61
11	Sleaford Town	38	16	10	12	88	70	54
12	Grantham T Rs	38	15	6	17	63	66	51
13	Louth Utd Amts	38	15	5	18	76	68	50
14	Skegness Town	38	11	7	20	55	86	40
15	Horncastle Town	38	9	7	22	51	80	37
16	Epworth Town	38	9	5	24	56	113	32
17	Hykeham Town	38	8	2	28	43	106	26
18	Louth Old Boys	38	5	6	27	48	124	24
19	BRSA Retford	38	4	8	26	42	103	20
20	Nettleham Res	38	1	6	31	30	141	9

LINCOLNSHIRE LEAGUE CUP Sponsored by HYKEHAM FORUM SUPPLIES

HOLDERS: Lincoln Moorlands

First Round

Horncastle Town	v	Nettleham Reserves	3-1
Hykeham Town	v	Limestone Rangers	2-4
Louth United	v	Skegness Town	2-5
Grimsby Imm Amt	v	Bottesford Town	3-1

Second Round

Grantham Town	v	Epworth Town	7-1
Lincoln Utd Res	v	Horncastle Town	7-1
Appleby Frod Ath	v	Louth Old Boys	6-1
BRSA Retford	v	Boston Utd Res	0-2
Grimsby Imm Amt	v	Barton Town	1-3
Lincoln Moorlands	v	Limestone Rangers	2-3
Ruston Sports	v	Skegness Town	2-1
Wyberton	v	Sleaford Town	3-4

Quarter Finals

Appleby Frod Ath	v	Boston Utd Res	0-1
Barton Town	v	Sleaford Town	2-0
Grantham Town	v	Ruston Sports	1-0
Limestone Rngrs	v	Lincoln United	3-1

Semi Final

Barton Town	v	Limestone Rangers	1-0
Grantham Town R	v	Boston United Res	2-1

Final

Barton Town	v	Grantham Town Res	3-1

J I G NETWORK DURHAM ALLIANCE (Ex Washington League)

Division One

		P	W	D	L	F	A	Pts
1	Cabplant S'oaks	22	16	4	2	97	33	53
2	Simonside	22	12	7	3	67	34	43
3	Easington CWM	22	13	4	5	55	29	43
4	Deneside WMC	22	10	6	6	68	39	36
5	Springwell SC	22	11	5	6	69	47	35
6	Washt'n Westw'd	22	11	2	9	64	44	35
7	Whitehill	22	9	6	7	57	40	33
8	Hartlepool B W	22	8	0	14	44	72	24
9	Belford House	22	6	4	12	64	20	22
10	Dawdon CWM	22	5	6	11	41	64	21
11	Washington Stps	22	5	3	14	37	75	18
12	Boldon Rossi	22	2	1	19	28	154	1*

* Six points deducted

Division Two

		P	W	D	L	F	A	Pts
1	Tribal Sports	26	22	1	2	110	23	67
2	Thorney Close	26	21	3	2	125	34	66
3	S Sh Black Prnce	26	17	3	6	95	64	51
4	Double Maxim	26	15	3	8	57	49	48
5	Shotton Pr Bish.	26	12	8	6	73	42	44
6	Hearts of Oak	26	13	4	9	69	55	43
7	Morriston Park	26	13	3	10	89	79	42
8	Seaham Mallard	26	11	3	12	90	58	36
9	Witton Gilbert	26	11	6	9	65	70	36
10	The Niteklub	26	7	2	17	45	78	23
11	Wearmouth C W	26	5	5	16	51	105	20
12	AFC Whitehouse	26	5	5	16	47	80	17
13	Boldon Sleepers	26	4	2	20	40	113	8
14	Easington Flag I.	26	1	0	25	37	143	3

THE "DEE JAYS" SCUNTHORPE SUNDAY FOOTBALL LEAGUE

Division One

		P	W	D	L	F	A	Pts
1	Bro'ton Town	14	13	0	1	69	11	26
2	Queen Bess	14	7	3	4	28	18	17
3	Britannia Inn	14	6	4	4	35	24	16
4	Ashby Star	14	6	3	5	31	32	15
5	Poachers	14	4	4	6	33	38	12
6	Burton Athletic	14	4	3	7	21	32	11
7	Kd/Alth Cl	14	3	2	9	19	45	8
8	Bro'ton FC	14	2	3	9	16	51	7

Division Two

		P	W	D	L	F	A	Pts
1	Beacon	18	13	4	1	63	15	30
2	George & Dragon	18	12	4	2	47	26	28
3	Kirton Town	18	10	4	3	61	21	24
4	Poachers Reserves	18	9	3	6	46	32	21
5	Brigg SMC	18	8	3	7	50	55	19
6	Brum H Ath	18	7	2	9	46	44	16
7	Comet Wanderers	18	5	4	9	40	49	14
8	Ashby Star Res	18	6	1	11	30	50	13
9	Sc Rd Mill	18	4	3	11	32	64	11
10	Wint Rovers	18	2	0	16	22	79	4

WYTHEMSHAWE & DISTRICT SUNDAY FOOTBALL LEAGUE (Manchester FA)

Premier Team

		P	W	D	L	Pts
1	Temple Inn	20	16	2	2	50
2	Farmers Arms	20	16	1	3	49
3	Irlam Catholic Club	20	15	2	3	47
4	Red Rose	20	7	4	9	25
5	AFC Park	20	8	1	11	25
6	Wythenshawe RBL	20	7	3	10	24
7	Piper FC	20	8	1	11	22*
8	Prince of Wales	20	6	4	10	22
9	Trafford Hawks	20	5	3	12	18
10	Wythenshawe Amts	20	6	2	12	17*
11	Royal Oak	20	4	1	15	13

* Three points deducted

First Team

		P	W	D	L	Pts
1	Yew Tree FC	22	21	1	0	64
2	Lantern Inn	22	14	4	4	46
3	Wheatsheaf	22	13	4	5	43
4	Stella Athletic	22	11	3	8	36
5	Eagle FC	22	10	3	9	33
6	OSC Smarts	22	10	2	10	32
7	St Peter's	22	8	3	11	27
8	Sale Moor	22	8	1	13	25
9	Greenwood Tree	22	7	3	12	24
10	Black Boy	22	5	4	13	19
11	Crown Strollers	22	5	4	13	16
12	Sylvan Athletic	22	3	2	17	11

* Three points deducted

LRP BRIGHOUSE SUNDAY LEAGUE

Division One

		P	W	D	L	F	A	Pts
1	Crown	18	15	0	3	71	25	30
2	Eland AFC	18	12	5	1	73	22	27*
3	Rastrick CC	18	11	5	2	66	32	27
4	Windmill	18	9	3	6	51	39	21
5	Greyhound	18	9	3	6	56	64	21
6	Top Club	18	6	3	9	41	43	15
7	Star	18	6	1	11	54	61	13
8	Holywell Green	18	6	1	11	52	62	11*
9	AFC Whitehall	18	1	4	13	28	70	6
10	Sun Inn Reserves	18	2	1	15	28	100	5

* Two points deducted

Division Two

		P	W	D	L	F	A	Pts
1	SC Northowram	16	11	3	2	64	20	25
2	Hove Edge	16	11	1	4	63	31	23
3	Pop Inn	16	10	3	3	35	19	23
4	Eastfield	16	9	2	5	59	33	20
5	Pond	16	9	1	6	50	35	19
6	Thornhill Briggs	16	8	0	8	42	39	16
7	Rastrick OB	16	3	2	11	28	61	8
8	Triangle	16	2	1	13	19	60	5
9	Travellers	16	1	3	12	18	74	5

WAKEFIELD EXPRESS SUNDAY LEAGUE (West Riding FA)

Premier Division

		P	W	D	L	F	A	Pts
1	Rocking Horse	20	16	2	2	74	18	50
2	Little Bull	20	14	3	3	52	22	45
3	Redoubt	20	13	4	3	62	33	43
4	Grove Park	20	10	2	8	55	45	32
5	Black Swan	20	9	3	8	47	43	30
6	Travellers	20	9	1	10	65	62	28
7	Boot & Shoe	20	4	8	8	37	52	20
8	Blue Light	20	5	5	10	53	74	20
9	Nightingale	20	5	2	13	34	59	17
10	Cliffe Tree	20	4	4	12	32	67	16
11	Poplar	20	3	2	15	31	67	11

Division One

		P	W	D	L	F	A	Pts
1	Old Halfway House	18	15	1	2	71	25	46
2	Netherton WMC	18	13	1	4	63	30	40
3	Crown	18	11	0	7	34	38	33
4	New Wheel	18	10	0	8	31	39	30
5	New Pot Oil	18	9	2	7	39	44	29
6	Jolly Sailor	18	7	3	8	37	36	24
7	Peacocks	18	7	2	9	36	56	23
8	Graziers MS	18	6	1	11	37	42	19
9	Grove Park A	18	3	4	11	36	49	13
10	Gardeners Arms	18	0	4	14	21	56	4

BEEFEATER COUNTY SENIOR FOOTBALL LEAGUE

Secretary: Bob Bowler, 1 Holbein Close, Dronfield, Woodhouse, Sheffield S18 6QH
(01246 410739)

Forty three teams started the 1996-97 League and League Cup campaign last September, the number being reduced by one with the mid-season withdrawal of Kiveton Sports FC. The Premier Division, consisting of 14 contenders, was won by Denaby & Cadeby MW FC who conceded only 19 goals in their 16 fixtures - the Championship being decided on the last day of Competition with a 1-0 victory over eventual runners-up ABM who can console themselves in being the Division's top goalscorers. League Cup winners Swinton Athletic FC also filled top spot in a 13 strong Division One, three points clear of Worksop Town FC. The Division Two contest proved to be a runaway of ten clear points for newcomers Wombwell Main FC whose 110 goals in 28 League games gave them leading goalscorer status, nine ahead of Sheffield Lane Top FC who were also in their debut season. We are sorry to see the departure of Worsbrough Bridge MW & Athletic FC to the newly-formed Reserve Division of the Northern Counties East Football League. We wish them well in their new environment.

The League Management Committee's selection policy was relatively successful with four of the League's five newcomers filling places in the top seven in the Division.

The Arnold Kettel Sporting Award was won by Penistone Church FC Reserves with the Hague & Ibbotson leading individual goalscorer award going to Andrew Ogden of Sheffield Lane Top FC who netted 33 of his team's total of 101 goals.

Congratulations are extended to all successful Clubs and individuals.

There were 2062 players registered in the League under the Sheffield & Hallamshire County FA's Central Registration of Players' system of whom 1458 actually played. The 590 matches fulfilled (548 League, 42 Cup) produced 569 cautions and 81 dismissals, an acceptable level in these days of referees' mandatory disciplinary instructions.

The 548 League fixtures resulted in the scoring of 2182 goals at an average of 3.98 per game. The Divisional breakdown saw 626 Premier Division goals at 3.44 per game, Division One 691 at 4.43 per match and Division Two 865 at 4.12.

At the conclusion of Beefeater's sponsorship, we now look forward to a long and lasting relationship with our new sponsors, British Industrial Reclamation, with whom a lucrative deal has been negotiated and officially agreed for a minimum period up to and including the millennium season.

PREMIER DIVISION
FINAL LEAGUE TABLE 1996-97

		P	W	D	L	F	A	Pts
1	Denaby & Cadeby	26	18	4	4	60	19	58
2	A.B.M.	26	16	4	6	62	33	52
3	Frecheville C.A.	26	15	6	5	60	37	51
4	Phoenix	26	12	9	5	57	36	45
5	High Green Villa	26	13	3	10	37	29	42
6	Ecclesfield R Rose	26	11	8	7	39	37	41
7	Stocksbridge P.S.	26	10	6	10	49	48	36
8	Mexborough Main St	26	10	5	11	38	37	35
9	Caribbean Sports	26	10	6	10	50	52	33*
10	Wombwell Town	26	8	6	12	40	51	30
11	Parkgate	26	8	5	13	43	54	29
12	Parramore Sports	26	8	4	14	41	67	28
13	Oughtibr WMSC	26	3	5	18	21	50	14
14	Worsbrough Bridge	26	2	5	19	29	76	11

* Three Points Deducted

DIVISION ONE
FINAL LEAGUE TABLE 1996-97

		P	W	D	L	F	A	Pts
1	Swinton Athletic	24	15	6	3	59	23	51
2	Worksop Town	24	15	3	6	67	42	48
3	Penistone Church	24	14	3	7	59	30	45
4	Wath Saracens Ath	24	13	6	5	65	40	45
5	Wickersley Old B	24	11	5	8	67	38	38
6	Hallam	24	12	4	8	51	41	37*
7	Sheffield Bankers	24	11	4	9	44	46	37
8	Treeton Welfare	24	10	5	9	53	49	35
9	The Wetherby	24	9	6	9	60	44	33
10	Thurcroft D Barrel	24	8	3	13	42	64	27
11	Grapes Nth General	24	6	5	13	64	68	23
12	Davy	24	4	4	16	38	67	16
13	Throstles Ridgeway	24	1	0	23	22	139	3

* Three Points Deducted

DIVISION TWO
FINAL LEAGUE TABLE 1996-97

		P	W	D	L	F	A	Pts
1	Wombwell Main	28	25	2	1	110	22	77
2	Avesta Sheffield	28	21	4	3	67	33	67
3	NCB Maltby MW	28	18	6	4	79	31	60
4	Sheffield Lane Top	28	17	7	4	101	25	58
5	Sheffield Centrals	28	17	6	5	59	31	57
6	Norton Woodseats	28	15	4	9	63	44	49
7	Queens Hotel	28	12	4	12	71	71	40
8	Elsecar Market Htl	28	10	7	11	50	41	37
9	Yorkshire Main	28	11	3	14	51	47	36
10	Rossington Main	28	6	6	16	37	61	24
11	Clifton Rovers	28	7	3	18	43	83	24
12	Old Edwardians	28	7	1	20	41	85	22
13	Sheffield	28	4	9	15	41	78	21
14	Penistone Ch Res	28	4	3	21	27	79	15
15	Harworth Coll Inst	28	2	3	23	25	134	9

PREMIER DIVISION RESULTS CHART 1996-97

		1	2	3	4	5	6	7	8	9	10	11	12	13	14
1	A.B.M.	X	5-0	2-1	2-2	2-2	0-3	0-2	3-1	3-0	3-2	2-0	2-0	2-1	1-2
2	Caribbean Sports	4-2	X	1-1	0-1	2-1	2-0	3-2	2-2	0-4	4-1	0-4	3-1	2-2	3-0
3	Denaby & Cadeby	1-0	2-0	X	3-0	3-0	1-0	0-0	1-0	3-1	8-0	1-4	2-0	4-1	3-0
4	Ecclesfield R Rose	2-2	2-1	2-1	X	0-2	2-1	1-3	4-2	0-0	2-2	0-0	2-3	3-1	2-0
5	Frecheville C.A.	0-2	4-3	1-0	1-0	X	0-1	3-3	4-1	5-1	2-1	1-1	6-0	3-2	5-4
6	High Green Villa	0-1	2-2	0-1	3-1	1-0	X	0-3	1-0	1-1	2-0	0-4	1-1	1-2	5-0
7	Mexborough Main St	0-1	0-3	1-1	2-0	1-3	0-2	X	2-0	0-1	1-2	1-1	0-2	2-1	5-0
8	Oughtibr W.M.S.C.	0-4	3-2	0-3	0-1	1-2	1-2	1-0	X	1-0	0-1	2-2	1-1	1-1	0-1
9	Parkgate	0-7	2-2	0-3	0-1	3-5	0-1	1-2	4-0	X	4-3	3-0	2-2	1-1	3-1
10	Parramore Sports	1-4	2-3	2-5	3-2	2-5	0-2	3-0	1-0	3-2	X	1-3	3-1	1-1	1-1
11	Phoenix	3-3	3-2	0-2	1-1	0-0	3-1	5-1	1-0	4-2	1-2	X	1-1	1-0	7-1
12	Stocksbridge P.S.	0-3	4-2	0-1	2-2	1-1	1-4	0-2	4-2	4-2	7-1	5-1	X	3-1	3-0
13	Wombwell Town	3-2	1-1	3-8	1-2	0-1	3-1	1-1	2-1	0-1	3-2	1-4	2-1	X	3-0
14	Worsbrough Bridge	3-4	1-3	1-1	1-3	1-3	0-2	2-4	1-1	2-5	1-1	3-3	1-2	2-3	X

BEEFEATER LEAGUE CUP 1996-97

First Round

High Green Villa v Caribbean Sports 5-1
Norton Woodseats v Worsbrough Bridge 2-1
Phoenix v Old Edwardians 6-2
Throstles Ridgeway v Denaby & Cadeby 0-4
Treeton Welfare v Sheffield 4-0
Wombwell Town v Ecclesfield Red Rose 4-1
Mexborough Main St v Hallam 1-0
Penistone Ch Res v Stocksbridge PS 0-3
The Wetherby v Parkgate 3-5
Thurcroft D Barrel v Wath Saracens Ath 2-0
Wickersley Old Boys v Worksop Town 1-5

Second Round

A.B.M. v Sheffield Lane Top 2-3
Clifton Rovers v Parkgate 4-5
Elsecar Market Hotel v Grapes Nth General 1-0
Harworth Coll Inst v Phoenix 0-8
Queen's Hotel v Mexborough Main St 1-8
Treeton Welfare v Sheffield Bankers 2-5
Wombwell Town v Rossington Main 5-0
Yorkshire Main v Oughtibridge WMSC 3-4
Avesta Sheffield v Sheffield Centralians 3-0
Davy v Stocksbridge PS 2-6
Frecheville CA v Parramore Sports 0-1
NCB Maltby MW v Penistone Church 3-2
Swinton Athletic v Norton Woodseats 3-2
Wombwell Main v Denaby & Cadeby 2-1
Worksop Town v High Green Villa 2-3

Third Round

High Green Villa v Avesta Sheffield 3-1
Parkgate v Parramore Sports 5-2
Swinton Athletic v NCB Maltby MW 3-0
Wath Saracens Ath v Sheffield Lane Top 3-1
Mexborough Main St v Stocksbridge PS 1-0
Phoenix v Oughtibridge WMSC 1-0
Treeton Welfare v Wombwell Main 1-2
Wombwell Town v Elsecar Market Hotel 2-1

Fourth Round

Parkgate v Wombwell Town 4-2
Wath Saracens Ath v High Green Villa 1-1
Swinton Athletic v Phoenix 2-0
Wombwell Main v Mexborough Main St 4-1

Semi-Final

Parkgate v Wath Saracens Ath 1-2
Wombwell Main v Swinton Athletic 2-3

Final

Swinton Athletic v Wath Saracens Ath 2-1 at Stocksbridge Park Steels FC, 2 April 1997

PREMIER DIVISION CLUBS 1997-98

A.B.M.

Secretary: Brian Wilks, 1 Roydfield Close, Sheffield S20 7NB (0114 247 0467)
Ground: Greenhill Main Road, Norton, Sheffield 8.
Sponsor: J McGuigan **Colours:** White/black/white

CARIBBEAN SPORTS

Secretary: Ashley Richards, 34 Louth Road, Sheffield S11 7AW (0114 268 5314)
Ground: The Common, Ecclesfield, Sheffield S30 3WL
Sponsor: Neville Roe **Colours:** All Red

DENABY UNITED RESERVES

Secretary: Barney Randall, 30 Tickhill Square, Denaby Main, Doncaster DN12 4AW (01709 866763)
Ground: Ticknell Square, Denaby Main, Doncaster
Sponsor: David's School of Motoring **Colours:** Black & white/black/black

ECCLESFIELD RED ROSE

Secretary: Alf Goodison, 202 High Street, Ecclesfield, Sheffield S35 9XF (0114 246 8286)
Ground: Civil Service Ground, Green Lane, Ecclesfield.
Sponsor: Windsor Frozen Foods **Colours:** All scarlet & black & white

FRECHEVILLE COMMUNITY ASSOCIATION

Secretary: David Taylor, 75 Gleadless Ave, Sheffield S12 3QG, (0114 264 9754)
Ground: Silkstone Road, Frecheville, Sheffield
Sponsor: E.S.P. **Colours:** Amber & black/black/amber

HIGH GREEN VILLA

Secretary: T Staples, 41 Woodburn Drive, Chapeltown, Sheffield S30 4YT (0114 246 8560)
Ground: High Green Playing Fields, Mortomley Close.
Sponsor: **Colours:** Amber/black/black

MEXBOROUGH MAIN STREET

Secretary: Tony Hough, 4 Cranswick Way, Conisborough, Doncaster DN12 3AY (01709 866479)
Ground: Hampden Road, Mexborough
Sponsor: Ideal Travel **Colours:** Claret & blue/claret/claret

PARKGATE RESERVES

Secretary: Fred Powell, 4 Landseer Court, Flanderswell, Rotherham S66 2NH (01709 548283)
Ground: Roundwood Sports Complex, Green Lane, Rawmarsh, Rotherham
Sponsor: **Colours:** White & black/black/black

PENISTONE CHURCH

Secretary: Mr D Hampshire, 36 Park Avenue, Penistone, Sheffield S30 6DN (01226 764689)
Ground: Church View Road, Penistone
Sponsor: Shearcut Engineering **Colours:** Black & white/black/black

PHOENIX

Secretary: Trevor Cottam, 41 Pleasant Road, Sheffield S12 2BD (0114 239 0897)
Ground: Phoenix Sports Complex, Brinsworth
Sponsor: Canada Life **Colours:** Green & white/green/green

STOCKSBRIDGE PARK STEEL RESERVES

Secretary: M Grimmer, 48 Hole House Lane, Stocksbridge, Sheffield S30 5BP (0114 288 6470)
Ground: Bracken Moor Lane, Stocksbridge, Sheffield
Sponsor: St Christopher Motor Co **Colours:** Yellow/blue/blue

SWINTON ATHLETIC

Secretary: Fred Bradshaw, 59 Piccadilly Road, Swinton, Mexborough S64 8LF (01709 582806)
Ground: Swinton Welfare, Park Road, Swinton
Sponsor: **Colours:** White & blue/black/black & white

WOMBWELL TOWN

Secretary: Gary Mallender, 1 Redcliffe Close, Redbrook, Barnsley S75 2RU (01226 236276)
Ground: Wombwell Sporting Centre, Station Road, Wombwell, Barnsley
Sponsor: **Colours:** All red

WORKSOP TOWN RESERVES

Secretary: Keith Ilett, 2 Mount Avenue, Worksop, Notts S81 7JL (Worksop 487934)
Ground: Sandy Lane, Worksop
Sponsor: DTH **Colours:** Black & amber/black/black

LRP BRIGHOUSE SUNDAY LEAGUE

Division One

		P	W	D	L	F	A	Pts
1	Crown	18	15	0	3	71	25	30
2	Eland AFC	18	12	5	1	73	22	27*
3	Rastrick CC	18	11	5	2	66	32	27
4	Windmill	18	9	3	6	51	39	21
5	Greyhound	18	9	3	6	56	64	21
6	Top Club	18	6	3	9	41	43	15
7	Star	18	6	1	11	54	61	13
8	Holywell Green	18	6	1	11	52	62	11*
9	AFC Whitehall	18	1	4	13	28	70	6
10	Sun Inn Reserves	18	2	1	15	28	100	5

* Two points deducted

Division Two

		P	W	D	L	F	A	Pts
1	SC Northowram	16	11	3	2	64	20	25
2	Hove Edge	16	11	1	4	63	31	23
3	Pop Inn	16	10	3	3	35	19	23
4	Eastfield	16	9	2	5	59	33	20
5	Pond	16	9	1	6	50	35	19
6	Thornhill Briggs	16	8	0	8	42	39	16
7	Rastrick OB	16	3	2	11	28	61	8
8	Triangle	16	2	1	13	19	60	5
9	Travellers	16	1	3	12	18	74	5

WAKEFIELD EXPRESS SUNDAY LEAGUE

(West Riding FA)

Premier Division

		P	W	D	L	F	A	Pts
1	Rocking Horse	20	16	2	2	74	18	50
2	Little Bull	20	14	3	3	52	22	45
3	Redoubt	20	13	4	3	62	33	43
4	Grove Park	20	10	2	8	55	45	32
5	Black Swan	20	9	3	8	47	43	30
6	Travellers	20	9	1	10	65	62	28
7	Boot & Shoe	20	4	8	8	37	52	20
8	Blue Light	20	5	5	10	53	74	20
9	Nightingale	20	5	2	13	34	59	17
10	Cliffe Tree	20	4	4	12	32	67	16
11	Poplar	20	3	2	15	31	67	11

Division One

		P	W	D	L	F	A	Pts
1	Old Halfway House	18	15	1	2	71	25	46
2	Netherton WMC	18	13	1	4	63	30	40
3	Crown	18	11	0	7	34	38	33
4	New Wheel	18	10	0	8	31	39	30
5	New Pot Oil	18	9	2	7	39	44	29
6	Jolly Sailor	18	7	3	8	37	36	24
7	Peacocks	18	7	2	9	36	56	23
8	Graziers MS	18	6	1	11	37	42	19
9	Grove Park A	18	3	4	11	36	49	13
10	Gardeners Arms	18	0	4	14	21	56	4

Promotion & Relegation 1997-98

LEAGUE

CLUBS JOINING (From)	CLUBS LEAVING (To)
GM VAUXHALL CONFERENCE	
Hereford United (Football League)	Macclesfield Town (Football League)
Cheltenham Town (Dr. Martens)	Bath City (Dr. Martens)
Yeovil Town (ICIS)	Bromsgrove Rovers (Dr. Martens)
Leek Town (Unibond)	Altrincham (Unibond)
UNIBOND PREMIER	
Radcliffe Borough (Promoted)	Witton Albion (Relegated)
Leigh (Promoted)	Buxton (Relegated)
Altrincham (GMVC)	Leek Town (GMVC)
	Knowsley United (Resigned)
UNIBOND DIVISION ONE	
Belper Town (NCEFL)	Curzon Ashton (NCEFL)
Trafford (NWCFL)	Warrington Town (NWCFL)
Whitby Town (Northern League).	Atherton LR (NWCFL)
NORTH WEST COUNTIES Division One	
Warrington Town (NWCFL)	Trafford (P Unbond First Division)
Atherton Laburnam Rovers (NWCFL)	Penrith (T Northern League)
Ramsbottom United (Promoted)	Bootle (Demoted)
Haslingden (Promoted)	Eastwood Hanley (Defunct)
NORTH WEST COUNTIES Division Two	
Fleetwood Wanderers (New Club)	
Woodley Sports (Prom. Manchester Lge 7th)	
NORTHERN COUNTIES EAST Premier Division	
Curzon Ashton (Rel. Unibond League)	Belper Town (Prom. Unibond)
Garforth Town (Promoted)	Ashfield United (Relegated)
Eccleshill United (Promoted)	Liversedge (Relegated)
NORTHERN COUNTIES EAST Division One	
Staveley MW (Central Midlands League)	
NORTHERN LEAGUE Division One	
Penrith (Transfer NWCFL)	Whitby Town (Prom. Unibond)
Northallerton (Promoted).	Chester Le Street Town (Relegated)
NORTHERN LEAGUE Division Two	
Billingham Town (Promoted)	Whickham (Relegated)
Jarrow Roofing (Promoted)	West Auckland Town (Relegated)
	Darlington Cleveland Social (Defunct)

LEAGUE CLUBS JOINING (From)	CLUBS LEAVING (To)
ICIS LEAGUE Premier Division	
Gravesend & Northfleet (T Dr. Martens)	Yeovil (GMVC)
Chesham United (Promoted)	Staines town (Relegated)
Basingstoke Town (Promoted)	Grays Athletic (Relegated)
Walton & Hersham (Promoted)	Chertsey Town (Relegated)
ICIS LEAGUE Division One	
Collier Row & Romford (Promoted)	Canvey Island (Relegated)
Leatherhead (Promoted)	Marlow (Relegated)
Wembley (Promoted)	Tooting & Mitcham United (Relegated)
ICIS LEAGUE Division Two	
Wealdstone (Promoted)	Ware (Relegated)
Braintree Town (Promoted)	Dorking (Relegated)
Northwood (Promoted)	Hemel Hempstead (Relegated)
ICIS LEAGUE Division Three	
Corinthian Casuals (Comb Counties)	
Ford United (Essex Sen. Lge)	
Croydon Athletic (Spartan)	
ESSEX SENIOR Premier Division	
Ford United (ICIS Div. Three)	
COMBINED COUNTIES Premier Division	
Chessington & Hook United	Corinthian Casuals (ICIS Div. Three).

MINERVA FOOTBALLS SPARTAN SOUTH MIDLANDS League

With the merger of the Spartan & South Midlands Leagues, the plan is for the Premier Divisions to continue running parallel with each other, as Premier Divisions North & South. At the end of this season the top dozen or so from each will join to form a more conventional size premier division with around 22/24 clubs. The present SSML Senior Division will become Premier Division Two absorbing the other clubs not in the above 22/24 clubs selected for the Premier Division.

The old SML Division One becomes Division One North, alongside a new Division One South formed by merging the old lower divisions of the Spartan League.

CLUBS JOINING (From)	CLUBS LEAVING (To)
SSM LEAGUE Premier Division South (Last season's Spartan Premier Division)	
	Croydon Athletic (ICIS Three)
	Tottenham Omada (W/d mid-season)
SSM LEAGUE Division One South (Last season's Spartan Division One and Two merged)	
Tottenham Omada (ex-Premier)	A.C.Milla (Disbanded Mid-season)
Crown & Manor	Catford Wanderers
Cheshunt Trojans (ex-Walthamstow)	Craven
Chingford Town (ex-United)	Clapham
	Crofton Albion
SSM LEAGUE Premier Div. North (Last season's South Midlands Premier Division) with the same 15 member clubs.	
SSM LEAGUE Senior Division (Last season's South Midlands' Senior Division)	
Biggleswade United (Promoted)	A.C.D. Triden
Coddington (Promoted)	
Shillington (Newly re-formed after missing the 1996-97 season)	
SSM LEAGUE Division One North (Last season's South Midlands' Division One)	
Greenacres (Hemel)	

LEAGUE

CLUBS JOINING (From)	CLUBS LEAVING (To)

DR MARTENS LEAGUE Premier Division

CLUBS JOINING (From)	CLUBS LEAVING (To)
Bath City (GMVC)	Cheltenham Town (GMVC)
Bromsgrove Rovers (GMVC)	Gravesend & Northfleet (Trans ICIS)
Tamworth (Promoted)	Sudbury Town (Trans Eastern Co)
Rothwell Town (Promoted)	Baldock Town (Relegated Southern)
Forest Green Rovers (Promoted)	Newport AFC (Relegated Southern)
St. Leonards Stamcroft (Promoted).	Chelmsford City (Relegated Southern)

DR MARTENS LEAGUE Midland Division

CLUBS JOINING (From)	CLUBS LEAVING (To)
Blakenwell (Midlands Alliance)	Leicester United (In Liquidation)
Wisbech Town (Eastern Counties Lge)	Dudley Town (Disbanded)
Brackley Town (Hellenic League)	

DR MARTENS LEAGUE Southern Division

CLUBS JOINING (From)	CLUBS LEAVING (To)
	Buckingham Town (United Counties)

EASTERN COUNTIES LEAGUE Premier Division

CLUBS JOINING (From)	CLUBS LEAVING (To)
Sudbury Town (Trans Dr. Martens)	Wisbech Town (Prom. Dr. Martens)
Ely City (Promoted)	Sudbury Town Res (Withdrawn)
Histon (Promoted)	

HELLENIC LEAGUE Premier Division

CLUBS JOINING (From)	CLUBS LEAVING (To)
Ardley United (Promoted)	Brackley Town (Dr. Martens)
Hallen (Promoted)	Highworth United (Relegated)
	Fairford Town (Relegated)

WINSTONLEAD KENT LEAGUE Division One

CLUBS JOINING (From)	CLUBS LEAVING (To)
VCD Athletic (Kent County)	
Swanley Furness (Previously known as Furness)	
Erith Town (Previously known as Woolwich Town)	

INTERLINK EXPRESS MIDLANDS ALLIANCE

CLUBS JOINING (From)	CLUBS LEAVING (To)
Wednesfield (Banks's Brewery)	Blakenall (Dr. Martens Midland)
Kings Norton Town (Mid. Comb.) previously Richmond Swifts	Hinckley Athletic (Amalgamated with Hinckley Town to form Hinckley United in (Dr. Martens Midland).

UNIJET SUSSEX Division One

CLUBS JOINING (From)	CLUBS LEAVING (To)
Littlehampton (Promoted)	Three Bridges (Relegated)
Chichester City (Promoted)	Oakwood (Relegated)
Redhill (Promoted).	Southwick (Relegated)

UNITED COUNTIES Premier Division

CLUBS JOINING (From)	CLUBS LEAVING (To)
Yaxley (Promoted)	Newport Pagnell Town (Relegated)
Buckingham Town (Dr. Martens)	

WESSEX LEAGUE

CLUBS JOINING (From)	CLUBS LEAVING (To)
AFC Newbury (P Hants Lge Premier)	Petersfield Town (Relegated Hants Lge)

SCREWFIX WESTERN LEAGUE Premier Division

CLUBS JOINING (From)	CLUBS LEAVING (To)
Melksham Town (Promoted)	Westury United (Relegated)
Keynsham Town (Promoted)	Elmore (Relegated)

BANKS'S BREWERY WEST MIDLANDS (Regional) League Premier Division

CLUBS JOINING (From)	CLUBS LEAVING (To)
Kington Town (Ch Promoted)	Wednesfield (P Midland Alliance)
Bustleholme (R\u Promoted)	Hill Top Rangers (18th Resigned)

ENDSLEIGH MIDLAND COMBINATION Premier Division

CLUBS JOINING (From)	CLUBS LEAVING (To)
GPT Coventry (Promoted)	Kings Norton Town previously Richmond Swifts (P Midland Alliance)
Continental Star (Promoted)	Shirley Town (Relegated)
Cheslyn Hay (4th Promoted)	West Midlands Fire Service (Relegated)
Dudley Sports (7th Promoted)	

It's certainly different and lucky 'Uncle Joe'!
but can you spot the deliberate mistake?

SOUTHERN LEAGUE

PYRAMID SECTION

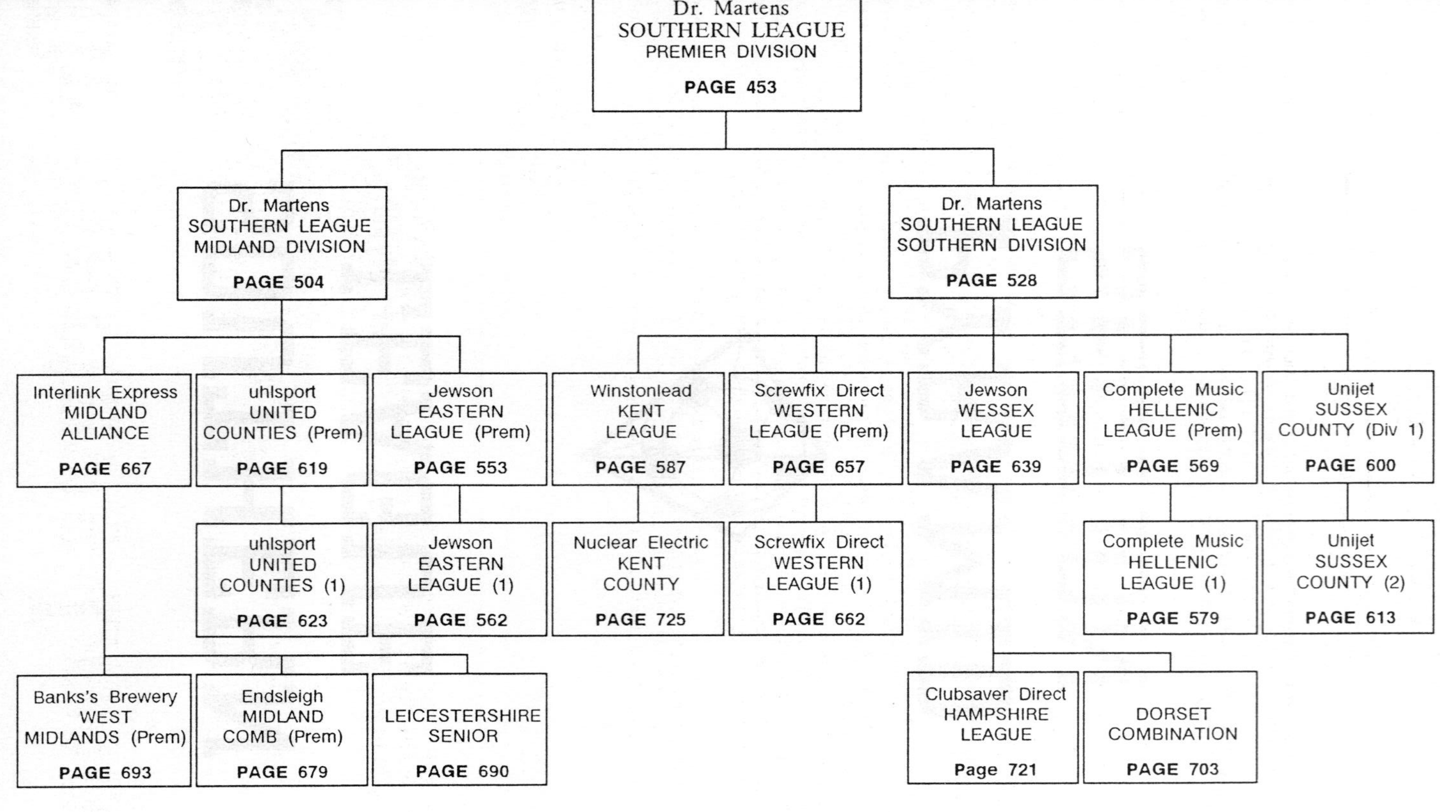

FEEDER & OTHER FEATURED LEAGUES

Anglian Combination - 734
Bedford & District - 692
Cambridgeshire - 729
Devon County - 717
Essex & Suffolk - 692
Gloucestershire County - 707
Northants - 691
Peterborough & Dist. - 729
Somerset Senior - 727
South Western - 711
Wiltshire County 736

Dr Martens League

President G E Templeman

Chairman D S R Gillard

Vice-Chairman K J Allen

Secretary & Treasurer D J Strudwick
11 Welland Close, Durrington, Worthing, West Sussex BN13 3NR
Tel: 01903 267788 (H) Fax: 01903 830500 Mob: 0860 445125

Where's Grisley?
Where's Grassley?
Where's Greesely?

Well, it is Gresley. And right now just about everybody in the football world knows exactly where it is. It is on the Southern Football League Championship Trophy alongside Brighton & Hove Albion, Headington United (now Oxford United), Ipswich Town, Portsmouth, Queens Park Rangers, Southampton, Tottenham Hotspur and Wimbledon. **Gresley Rovers** are the champions of the Southern Football League.

The Derbyshire outfit, superbly manipulated on the field by Paul Futcher and efficiently managed off the park by Garry Birtles, were never out of the top three all season. After breaking clear in August, only Gloucester City (for five weeks) and Halesowen Town (one week) topped the Rovers. Gresley regained the leadership of the Division from Halesowen on the 14th December, never looked back and ended the campaign eleven points clear.

The success of the Moatmen is all the more remarkable when it is remembered that as early as October the club conceded that it could not be promoted to the Football Conference. During the past two years the club's board of directors has concentrated much of its efforts on a relocation plan that will see Gresley leave their quaint but small Moat Street ground for a new purpose-built football stadium. It is a fine testimony indeed, therefore, that the Board (and in particular the team's management) kept the players' attention firmly focused on winning the Championship. Congratulations Gresley Rovers Football Club.

Despite losing only one match during the first half of their League programme,Gresley Rovers were never allowed to break away from the chasing pack. **Burton Albion, King's Lynn, Nuneaton Borough** and **Sudbury Town** (if they could have won their 'games in hand') all threatened to make an impact at the top. It was, however **Cheltenham Town, Gloucester City** and **Halesowen Town** who maintained a strangle-hold on the positions immediately behind the leaders. And here lies the perfect illustration of the frustrations and ironies of following football.

Halesowen watched Gresley win the League with 85 points, whilst they finished fourth with 73 points. Last year the Yeltz were runners-up with 92! Gloucester City finished third on 74 points. The eight points dropped in their final seven games, during an amazing fixture pile-up caused largely by City's fantastic run in the FA Trophy, left Gloucester just one point behind their nearest and fiercest rivals, Cheltenham Town. As Gresley Rovers were unable to benefit fully from the fruits of their success, it was the Robins who were promoted to the Football Conference. And, after finishing second four times in the past five years, surely nobody can really begrudge Cheltenham this twist of good fortune, outside of Gresley, Gloucester and Halesowen, that is!

At the foot of the table there was the annual 'dog fight' for points amongst a plethora of clubs towards the end of the season. **Cambridge City** who escaped relegation last year because the promotion/relegation cocktail with the Football Conference was not fully met by one of the Feeder Leagues, maintained its Premier place this year with an 'injury time' winning goal at **Merthyr Tydfil. Crawley Town, Dorchester Town** and **Hastings Town** all amassed points late in the season to ease the discomfort of their positions at the wrong end of the table. But, after just one season back in the Premier, **Ashford Town** finished nineteenth with only nine wins to their credit. The Nuts & Bolts have been saved from relegation, however, by the withdrawal of Sudbury Town. At the time of writing this report **Baldock Town, Newport A.F.C.** and **Chelmsford City** will all lose their Premier status. After hearing regular complimentary remarks about the strength and ability of the Chelmsford team, fellow clubs will clearly be surprised that City mustered only six League victories during the campaign. The team who achieved celebrity status via a sponsorship with a drinks company were shown the red card of defeat on 22 occasions. Only Baldock lost more League matches in the Division.

No adjective short of 'phenomenal' can describe **Tamworth's** performance in the Midland Division. The Lambs' opening day 2-0 win at new boys Raunds Town put them equal third in the table. By August Bank Holiday, nine days later, they were two points clear at the top. It was a lead they refused to relinquish throughout a campaign in which only three games were lost. The contest for second place was much closer. **Bilston Town, Bedworth United, Grantham Town, Ilkeston Town** (with a fine late run), **Moor Green, Rothwell Town** and **Solihull Borough** were all serious contenders for the second promotion spot. As the season drew to a close, with five games left, Grantham looked to be the favourites. But just when the nerve needed to be held under control, the Gingerbreads suffered under an injury crisis and only two of those last five matches were won. Rothwell, on the other hand, held firm. The Bones wrapped up their programme with a draw against Stafford Rangers and victories at **Sutton Coldfield Town** and **Raunds Town.** Seven out of the last nine points was enough to secure second place.

The first relegation spot from the Midlands Division was occupied as early as August. **Leicester United FC** was closed after just four fixtures. Sutton Coldfield Town, who only picked up one point from their first seven matches, Raunds Town and **V.S. Rugby** exchanged blows (metaphorically speaking) for the early part of the season. Raunds then pulled clear into the comfort zone leaving local rivals Corby Town to plummet to the bottom by January. The Steelmen were to remain at the foot until the final week when a 4-2 win against Raunds and a 2-2 draw against **Shepshed Dynamo** left Sutton Coldfield to lick their wounds following a 2-0 defeat at Ilkeston Town.

After thirteen matches in the Southern Division, **Havant Town** were undefeated and twelve points clear at the top. **Forest Green Rovers** had moved into second place comfortably clear of **St. Leonards Stamcroft** who had already begun to fall behind with their fixtures. By the third week of January. Havant Town, now under new management, had had their lead eroded and Forest Green had moved to the top. St. Leonards, at this stage were tenth in the table and eight games behind the leaders. Clevedon Town, Margate and Weston-super-Mare were now the most prominent challengers with **Newport I.O.W., Tonbridge Angels** and **Weymouth** on the fringe and capable of taking points from any team. As the season developed, **Fisher Athletic** had hauled themselves to the edge of the frame. At the 1st March, St. Leonards Stamcroft were twelfth in the Division and 21 games still to play! After completing the second half of their season in the final nine weeks of the campaign, the Southern Division freshmen had clawed themselves into runners-up spot. Havant finished third nine points adrift, but the Leigh Park club had recovered well from the spell that saw them toppled from top. Forest Green sustained the first place they took up in January. In athletics' terms they had timed their race perfectly.

At the opposite end of the table. Buckingham Town remained rooted on the bottom from week one. The club's first win of the season did not come until its thirteenth outing - a 2-1 win over **Waterlooville.** Only one other victory and eight draws were mustered from a disappointing season. After some early promise, Fleet Town joined the struggle with **Erith & Belvedere, Cinderford Town, Cirencester Town, Yate Town** and **Trowbridge Town** all flirting at the foot of the table. Fleet weighed anchor in the last couple of weeks and sailed out of the drop zone with three wins from their last four fixtures. They finished five points above Erith. Belvedere, though, had accumulated 37 points, a total that was to prove significant in saving the club from relegation despite finishing in 21st place for the second consecutive year.

The Dr. Martens Cup Final was contested by **Burton Albion**, who last won the trophy in 1964, and **Sudbury Town, winners 30 years later in 1994.** Albion, runners-up to Dartford in 1989, were cruising their home leg of the final 2-0, thanks to two goals from Martin Devaney, until Steven Greaves converted a penalty for Sudbury in the last minute. The tie was well set up for the second leg and, as the score would suggest, the match was tight. But John Barton's team skilfully dealt with Sudbury's early thrusts and Stephen Spooner put the contest beyond doubt with an 85th minute winner. Burton won the cup for the second time, 3-1.

The losing Semi-Finalists both came from the Regional Divisions. Weymouth, who defeated Forest Green Rovers in the Quarter Final, failed to score against Sudbury whilst conceding four goals over the two legs. **Racing Club Warwick** lost to the eventual winners, Burton Albion, 4-1 in both legs.

Sudbury's success in the League Cup was mirrored by the club's progress in the FA Cup. The Boro. were amongst twelve Dr. Martens League clubs in the Fourth Qualifying Round. They defeated **Canvey Island** 1-0 to move into the First Round Proper for the first time in the club's history. They were joined by **Ashford Town** (3-1 winners over **Kingstonian).** Cheltenham Town (4-1 replay victors over Bath City). Merthyr Tydfil (who defeated **Yeovil Town** 2-1) and Shepshed Dynamo (who beat **Bromsgrove Rovers** 2-0). Some formidable scalps were taken at this stage of the Competition.

In the First Round Proper, Merthyr Tydfil were squeezed out by Leyton Orient at Brisbane Road, 2-1. After holding **Peterborough United** to a 0-0 draw at the Posh's London Road ground, Cheltenham were beaten 3-1 at Whaddon Road. Shepshed who, like Sudbury, were in the First Round for the first time, were a little overwhelmed by promotion chasing **Carlisle United** 6-0. Ashford Town were held by **Dagenham & Redbridge** 2-2 and 1-1 before winning the tie 4-3 on penalties. **Brighton & Hove Albion** held on for a 0-0 draw at the Prior Ground and were then comfortably matched by Sudbury at the Goldstone Ground 1-1 before the Boro. won the tie 4-3 on penalties.

Sudbury received an excellent draw in the Second Round, a home tie with promotion contenders **Brentford** in a match staged at Layer Road, Colchester. Sudbury Town Secretary **David Webb** met the Bees Manager **David Webb** but the pleasantries ended there. Though Sudbury forced the pace and went a goal up, Brentford took control to win 3-1. Meanwhile, at Vicarage Road, despite spasmodic raids by Ashford on the Hornets goal, **Watford** were not seriously troubled and won the tie 5-0. Ashford and Sudbury had enjoyed great FA Cup runs, but both had ended just one hurdle short of the really big boys.

The Dr. Martens League was numerically strong in the latter stages of the FA Trophy and Gloucester City nearly went 'all the way'. Of the 16 clubs in the First Round, six reached Round Two. Dorchester Town defeated Salisbury City 3-2 in a replay; Gloucester convincingly beat Halifax 3-0, whilst the surprise package of the tournament, St. Leonards

Stamcroft, knocked out Dulwich Hamlet 2-1. Unfortunately, Grantham Town lost by the only goal of the game to Heybridge Swifts and Chelmsford City lost by the odd goal in three to the eventual finalists Dagenham & Redbridge.

In Round Three **Colwyn Bay** took three attempts to dispose of St. Leonards, 2-1. Eventual winners. Woking, scored twice in the last eight minutes to knock out Dorchester 3-2. Gloucester, though, enjoyed a great 3-1 win over **Runcorn** to move into the Semis. With Woking being drawn against Stevenage Borough, the Tigers must have thought that they had a super chance of reaching Wembley. No doubt Dagenham had the same thought on their own behalf. A 0-0 draw at Dagenham gave Gloucester the psychological advantage for their home encounter. But a 2-2 draw at Sunmeadow meant a reply on neutral territory. Sadly, despite amazing support for Gloucester at Slough, City lost 2-1. The Tigers had tried so hard in the memory of David Tuck.

With the exception of mentioning Steve Portway's record breaking achievement a few years ago, I have usually omitted any mention of the leading goal scorers in my Annual Report. This year I make another exsception, if only because the perennial strikers were at it again. Nuneaton's Robert Straw tied with Halesowen's Evran Wright at the top of the Premier Division chart with 28 goals. Incredibly, Evran's brother Henry, of **Bilston Town**, topped the Midland Division chart also with 28 goals, and another familiar name, Martin Buglione of **Margate** was joint top of the Southern Division register with 26 goals. Buglione had found his scoring knack again after spells with **St Johnstone** and **Sittingbourne**. Paul Hunt of Forest Green Rovers matched Buglione all the way.

No report on the physical side of the season would be complete without bidding farewell to the club being promoted to the Football Conference. Since aiding the formation of the Alliance (now the GMVC) in 1978, the Southern Football League has never failed to provide a promoted club. This is a record unrivalled by any other Football Conference Feeder League. Even now, at least nine of the Conference's 22 complement of clubs have their roots in the Southern League. This year, Cheltenham Town take a second bite at the top flight. Good luck, Cheltenham.

We welcome back from the Conference, Bath City and Bromsgrove Rovers. We hope that our great Competition will again provide you with the vehicle to progress.

It's good luck, too, to Forest Green Rovers, Rothwell Town, St. Leonards Stamcroft and Tamworth who have all won promotion to the League's Premier Division. Sadly, it's commiseratioins to Baldock Town, Chelmsford City and Newport A.F.C. who are all relegated.

The League bids farewell to Gravesend & Northfleet (transferred to the Isthmian League), Sudbury Town (resigned to play in the Eastern Counties League) and Buckingham Town (relegated to the United Counties League. We wish you all good fortune and hope that you will soon emulate again the feats you achieved whilst being members of the Southern Football League.

Three new clubs will be taking their place at this year's Annual General Meeting. To Blakenall (from the Midland Football Alliance) and Brackley Town (from the Hellenic League), welcome. To Wisbech Town (from the Eastern Counties League), welcome back. You are joining the best supported League outside of the Football Conference.

The top 50 best supported clubs is made up of 22 Football Conference clubs, nineteen Southern League clubs, five Isthmian League clubs and four Northern Premier League clubs. The next 50 comprises 20 from the Southern League, sixteen from the Northern Premier and fourteen from the Isthmian League. Gloucester City are the best placed Dr. Martens League club, in tenth position. The top nine include five clubs who have their origins in the Southern League. (Statistics taken from Non-League Newsdesk Turnstile League). If change is to come, it must be by evolutioin, not revolution. Furthermore, the strengths in our beautiful game should not be fragmented to cover weaknesses elsewhere. Hopefully, news of the above statistics will be good news for the Sponsors. Dr. Martens is tied up with at least the second best supported Football League in the country, outside the full-time game.

Talking of the sponsors, the help provided by Dr. Martens is invaluable. On behalf of the management committee and member clubs, I extend my appreciation to Max Griggs, Stephen Griggs and Andrew Borge. The company's investment in the member clubs this year, through the League, exceeds £150,000. Thank you.

Spalding Sports UK Ltd., again supplied every club with its Match Balls for the season. The Company has agreed to repeat the sponsorship next year, as well. Thank you.

So with a not insignificant cash injection and the financial worries of purchasing kit and footballs removed, at least some of the harsh commercial concerns of the clubs are taken care of by the League. Clubs are able, therefore, to concentrate their attentions on other areas of their business. In this respect I congratulate all clubs who have carried out tremendous ground improvments. On top of that Crawley Town and Salisbury City will commence the new season in new stadia. With similar projects in the pipeline at Dartford, Erith & Belvedere, Gresley Rovers, Paget Rangers, Solihull Borough and Trowbridge Town, the profile of the competition is being maintained at the highest level by its members.

Clubs also maintain the Southern League's position at the top of the hospitality league. It is commonly known that the Southern League is in the Premier Division when it comes to member clubs welcoming their guests, and at this point I must thank all the clubs that I have managed to visit last season for their generous vegetarian cuisine.

It is a great sadness, but regrettably a harsh reality, that during any year we may lose a friend along life's pathway. For everyone connected with the Southern Football League, this year was no exception. The League lost one of its greatest supporters. Laura Dellow, the widow of Bill, the League Secretary for 26 years between 1956 and 1982, passed away in January aged 89. Laura truly will be missed. But Laura had a wonderful and full life. For David Tuck, his life had only just begun. For David Coleman (former Salisbury City player) his life was in its prime. I think of these three people in rememberance of all the friends and acquaintances that football has lost this season.

DENNIS STRUDWICK

DR MARTENS LEAGUE - PREMIER DIVISION 1996-97

	P	Home W	D	L	F	A	Away W	D	L	F	A	Pts.	G.D.	Clean Sheets / Top Scorers		
														Clean Sheets - FA Cup & Trophy & League games only / **Top Scorers** (Competitions as listed in league bulletin)		
Gresley Rovers	**42**	12	5	4	38	20	13	5	3	37	20	**85**	35	18 Garner - 20	Marsden - 16	Allsop - 13
Cheltenham Town	**42**	11	5	5	33	19	10	6	5	43	25	**74**	32	14 Smith - 15	Boyle - 13	Howells - 11
Gloucester City	**42**	13	4	4	45	28	8	6	7	36	28	**73**	25	16 Watkins - 33	Mings - 14	Webb - 14
Halesowen Town	**42**	11	5	5	40	27	10	5	6	37	27	**73**	23	15 Wright - 30	Allsop, Crisp & Harrison - 10	
King's Lynn	**42**	12	2	7	36	28	8	6	7	29	33	**68**	4	11 Stringfellow - 24	McNamara - 16	Hudson - 12
Burton Albion	**42**	10	7	4	37	22	8	5	8	33	31	**66**	17	14 Nuttell - 18	Cotter - 16	Stride - 13
Nuneaton Borough	**42**	15	2	4	44	20	4	7	10	17	32	**65**	9	13 Straw - 30	Drewitt - 9	Simpson - 6
Sittingbourne	**42**	10	3	8	38	33	9	4	8	38	32	**64**	11	10 Walker - 19	Planck - 10	Searle - 10
Merthyr Tydfil	**42**	11	3	7	42	27	6	6	9	27	34	**60**	8	14 Evans - 19	Summers - 19	Rees - 11
Worcester City	**42**	10	6	5	32	23	5	8	8	20	27	**59**	2	10 Thomas - 17	Taylor - 12	Cottrill & Malloy - 8
Atherstone United	**42**	8	9	4	24	21	7	4	10	22	26	**58**	-1	16 Bennett - 11	Murphy - 9	Green - 8
Salisbury City	**42**	6	8	7	26	28	9	5	7	31	38	**58**	-9	11 Webb - 16	Boyce - 13	Harbutt - 12
Sudbury Town	**42**	9	3	9	34	33	7	4	10	38	39	**55**	-	9 Brown - 29	McLean - 22	Smith - 9
Gravesend & Northfleet	**42**	10	4	7	34	27	6	3	12	29	46	**55**	-10	10 Arter - 16	Newberry - 10	Munday - 9
Dorchester Town	**42**	10	4	6	36	29	4	5	12	26	37	**51**	-4	13 Pickard - 35	Killick - 9	Richardson - 9
Hastings Town	**42**	7	9	5	28	27	5	6	10	21	33	**51**	-11	9 Cuggy - 15	Parris - 9	Tuppenny - 6
Crawley Town	**42**	6	6	9	23	30	7	2	12	26	37	**47**	-18	10 Restarick - 18	Whittington - 9	Byrne - 6
Cambridge City	**42**	5	6	10	31	37	6	7	8	26	28	**46**	-8	12 Cambridge - 13	Harris - 12	Coe & Covey - 10
Ashford Town	**42**	4	12	5	30	32	5	6	10	23	47	**45**	-26	6 Dent - 18	Warrilow - 8	Wynter - 7
Baldock Town	**42**	6	4	11	24	41	5	4	12	28	49	**41**	-37	4 Fenton - 16	Small - 8	Atkinson - 7
Newport A.F.C.	**42**	6	5	10	26	33	3	8	10	14	27	**40**	-20	9 Brown - 12	Burton - 10	Evans - 8
Chelmsford City	**42**	5	7	9	31	34	1	7	13	18	36	**32**	-21	11 Docking - 16	Benjamin - 7	Southern - 7

Away Team Home Team	Ashf. 1	Ather. 2	Bald. 3	Burton 4	Camb. 5	Chelm 6	Chelt. 7	Crawl. 8	Dorch. 9	Glouc. 10	Graves 11	Gresl. 12	Hales. 13	Hast. 14	K.Lynn 15	Merth. 16	Newp. 17	Nune. 18	Salis. 19	Sitt. 20	Sudb. 21	Worc. 22
1. Ashford Town		**0-3** (461)	**2-2** (566)	**3-3** (596)	**2-2** (521)	**1-0** (688)	**1-1** (574)	**3-3** (567)	**2-1** (407)	**0-3** (648)	**1-1** (682)	**1-3** (615)	**1-1** (442)	**3-3** **(707)**	**4-0** (538)	**0-1** (660)	**1-1** (643)	**2-0** (659)	**0-1** (456)	**1-1** (552)	**2-2** (585)	**0-0** (462)
2. Atherstone United	**1-1** (258)		**1-3** (215)	**2-1** (606)	**1-0** (213)	**1-1** (217)	**0-0** (375)	**2-0** (303)	**2-1** (273)	**0-0** (315)	**0-0** (277)	**0-1** (588)	**0-5** (434)	**0-0** (262)	**1-1** (199)	**3-4** (206)	**1-0** (488)	**0-0** **(858)**	**4-0** (213)	**2-1** (256)	**1-0** (251)	**2-2** (276)
3. Baldock Town	**1-1** (210)	**0-2** (258)		**1-3** (348)	**0-3** **(416)**	**4-1** (380)	**1-0** (321)	**1-2** (283)	**2-1** (228)	**2-3** (301)	**0-5** (161)	**0-3** (323)	**0-1** (342)	**2-0** (303)	**1-1** (287)	**2-2** (315)	**1-0** (341)	**1-2** (184)	**1-1** (323)	**1-5** (168)	**3-2** (356)	**0-3** (245)
4. Burton Albion	**1-0** (775)	**1-2** (911)	**1-1** (822)		**3-3** (521)	**4-2** (656)	**0-0** (1142)	**2-0** (604)	**4-1** (745)	**3-1** (862)	**1-3** (713)	**2-3** **(2537)**	**0-0** (602)	**0-0** (568)	**4-1** (807)	**0-1** (675)	**3-0** (714)	**2-0** (1231)	**1-1** (724)	**1-0** (933)	**2-1** (662)	**2-2** (447)
5. Cambridge City	**4-0** (248)	**1-2** (237)	**1-1** (222)	**1-0** (267)		**1-0** (335)	**1-4** (227)	**4-0** (217)	**2-2** (214)	**0-1** (337)	**4-2** (334)	**2-3** (208)	**1-4** (278)	**1-3** (290)	**0-2** **(590)**	**2-2** (228)	**0-0** (454)	**2-2** (324)	**1-1** (213)	**1-3** (223)	**1-3** (351)	**1-2** (306)
6. Chelmsford City	**1-1** (802)	**0-1** (601)	**2-3** (537)	**2-2** (780)	**2-0** (705)		**2-4** (870)	**1-0** (470)	**1-1** (1012)	**1-3** (550)	**4-0** **(1114)**	**2-2** (811)	**3-0** (411)	**2-2** (769)	**0-2** (565)	**0-0** (824)	**1-1** (760)	**3-1** (763)	**1-2** (961)	**1-4** (917)	**1-3** (972)	**1-2** (550)
7. Cheltenham Town	**6-0** (854)	**2-0** (610)	**3-2** (761)	**3-3** (1066)	**1-0** (906)	**1-0** (763)		**1-2** (810)	**1-1** (536)	**1-1** **(3005)**	**0-1** (705)	**2-2** (1396)	**2-1** (747)	**1-0** (1009)	**1-2** (704)	**2-0** (801)	**0-0** (1565)	**2-0** (1068)	**0-2** (1017)	**2-0** (703)	**0-2** (867)	**2-0** (1009)
8. Crawley Town	**2-3** (419)	**2-0** (901)	**2-0** (534)	**0-2** (691)	**0-2** (602)	**1-2** (761)	**3-3** (448)		**2-0** (535)	**1-1** (534)	**0-2** (691)	**0-0** (672)	**0-3** (672)	**0-2** **(943)**	**0-0** (623)	**1-0** (506)	**1-3** (922)	**1-0** (757)	**2-2** (481)	**2-2** (631)	**1-2** (582)	**2-1** (618)
9. Dorchester Town	**0-2** (806)	**1-0** (190)	**3-2** (611)	**5-0** (480)	**0-2** (554)	**1-0** (606)	**1-3** (754)	**2-5** (593)		**2-2** (472)	**2-2** (623)	**1-3** (739)	**1-1** (631)	**1-1** (613)	**3-0** (638)	**2-0** (384)	**1-3** (486)	**2-0** (532)	**4-2** **(868)**	**2-0** (522)	**0-1** (787)	**2-0** (567)
10. Gloucester City	**6-1** (556)	**0-0** (927)	**3-1** (718)	**2-4** (861)	**2-0** (606)	**3-1** (816)	**2-1** **(2154)**	**2-1** (839)	**3-1** (1022)		**3-1** (804)	**1-2** (1552)	**0-3** (1132)	**2-0** (612)	**1-0** (752)	**6-3** (875)	**2-1** (816)	**1-0** (1055)	**1-3** (1863)	**1-1** (710)	**3-3** (732)	**1-1** (1082)
11. Gravesend & Northfleet	**1-3** (804)	**1-0** (539)	**1-2** (604)	**0-1** (488)	**1-1** (499)	**1-0** (857)	**1-3** (566)	**2-0** (517)	**1-3** (552)	**2-3** (696)		**2-1** (732)	**1-3** (610)	**2-0** (469)	**2-2** (601)	**0-0** (617)	**3-0** (575)	**1-1** (682)	**3-2** (608)	**3-0** **(1303)**	**4-2** (447)	**2-0** (570)
12. Gresley Rovers	**2-2** (709)	**1-1** (623)	**3-0** (679)	**1-0** **(1760)**	**3-1** (707)	**2-2** (754)	**2-0** (1010)	**2-0** (687)	**0-0** (589)	**3-1** (1376)	**2-0** (621)		**3-0** (854)	**3-0** (590)	**0-2** (664)	**0-2** (788)	**1-0** (788)	**1-4** (1420)	**5-0** (720)	**0-4** (642)	**1-1** (874)	**3-0** (693)
13. Halesowen Town	**3-1** (686)	**0-2** (701)	**6-0** (681)	**1-1** (859)	**3-1** (803)	**1-0** (718)	**1-5** **(1406)**	**2-2** (725)	**3-1** (482)	**5-4** (903)	**2-1** (690)	**1-1** (1109)		**1-2** (837)	**2-2** (827)	**1-2** (717)	**2-0** (916)	**2-0** (991)	**1-2** (833)	**2-0** (469)	**1-0** (562)	**0-0** (1256)
14. Hastings Town	**2-2** **(583)**	**0-0** (316)	**1-0** (435)	**2-1** (524)	**0-0** (466)	**1-0** (556)	**1-2** (412)	**1-0** (491)	**1-0** (403)	**0-2** (418)	**2-1** (444)	**1-2** (415)	**2-3** (421)		**2-2** (365)	**2-2** (394)	**2-2** (362)	**0-0** (442)	**2-3** (387)	**2-2** (569)	**4-3** (346)	**0-0** (362)
15. King's Lynn	**2-0** (856)	**2-1** (1156)	**4-2** (1103)	**2-0** (932)	**2-0** (1236)	**2-2** (1253)	**0-2** (1047)	**0-1** (928)	**0-4** (893)	**2-1** (786)	**5-1** (744)	**0-2** **(1476)**	**2-1** (732)	**1-4** (904)		**2-1** (1050)	**0-1** (792)	**4-0** (896)	**1-1** (888)	**3-2** (1079)	**2-1** (727)	**0-1** (982)
16. Merthyr Tydfil	**3-0** (605)	**3-2** (551)	**4-1** (711)	**0-1** (655)	**1-2** (432)	**2-0** (731)	**2-2** (543)	**3-1** (617)	**3-2** (572)	**1-0** (680)	**5-0** (462)	**0-2** (755)	**1-1** (851)	**0-0** (502)	**1-2** (679)		**2-0** **(1109)**	**5-1** (514)	**2-3** (610)	**1-4** (406)	**1-3** (505)	**2-0** (589)
17. Newport A.F.C.	**3-0** (504)	**2-0** (626)	**2-2** (617)	**0-3** (759)	**0-0** (560)	**2-2** (742)	**1-5** (511)	**0-1** (601)	**3-0** (650)	**0-4** (932)	**1-3** (432)	**0-1** (781)	**0-1** (775)	**0-2** (805)	**0-2** (562)	**3-1** **(944)**		**0-0** (635)	**3-1** (563)	**2-3** (504)	**3-1** (674)	**1-1** (788)
18. Nuneaton Borough	**3-0** (903)	**3-2** **(1607)**	**0-3** (940)	**2-1** (1007)	**3-1** (911)	**3-1** (732)	**1-0** (1241)	**1-2** (1333)	**3-0** (865)	**2-0** (824)	**3-0** (905)	**1-0** (1472)	**0-2** (1019)	**4-1** (1111)	**2-4** (930)	**1-1** (702)	**1-0** (1203)		**4-0** (830)	**4-0** (911)	**1-1** (1001)	**2-1** (977)
19. Salisbury City	**0-1** (421)	**3-2** (284)	**2-3** (212)	**1-1** (339)	**2-2** (257)	**1-1** (247)	**1-2** (310)	**1-0** (340)	**0-0** **(1024)**	**0-4** (487)	**4-1** (324)	**1-1** (289)	**1-2** (285)	**2-1** (281)	**2-0** (362)	**1-3** (167)	**0-0** (472)	**1-1** (460)		**0-1** (254)	**2-1** (170)	**1-1** (452)
20. Sittingbourne	**4-1** (1025)	**1-1** (691)	**1-0** (512)	**1-2** (676)	**0-2** (417)	**2-1** (714)	**1-0** (598)	**3-5** (758)	**1-3** (543)	**1-1** (593)	**1-3** **(1028)**	**2-0** (783)	**4-2** (597)	**2-0** (580)	**0-2** (693)	**3-1** (???)	**3-0** (656)	**2-2** (652)	**2-1** (584)		**4-5** (860)	**0-1** (537)
21. Sudbury Town	**2-2** (205)	**0-1** (214)	**4-0** (240)	**0-3** (295)	**0-2** (460)	**1-1** (550)	**1-4** (240)	**2-0** (440)	**2-4** (360)	**2-1** (361)	**2-0** (470)	**0-3** (206)	**4-2** (453)	**3-0** (348)	**5-1** **(650)**	**1-0** (350)	**1-1** (420)	**0-2** (502)	**0-1** (490)	**1-3** (254)		**3-2** (267)
22. Worcester City	**0-2** (644)	**3-0** (605)	**3-0** (662)	**2-1** (754)	**2-2** (618)	**1-1** (736)	**2-2** (1270)	**2-1** (649)	**1-0** (519)	**0-0** (770)	**4-2** (708)	**1-2** (721)	**1-1** **(1307)**	**3-0** (587)	**2-1** (696)	**2-1** (769)	**1-1** (963)	**0-1** (679)	**0-2** (746)	**0-2** (510)	**2-1** (632)	

CHALLENGE CUP 96-97

PRELIMINARY ROUND

Rothwell	1v3	King's Lynn
King's Lynn	0v0	Rothwell
Newport IOW	2v1	Dorchester Town
Dorchester Town	1v1	Newport IOW

FIRST ROUND

Yate Town	2v2	Merthyr Tydfil
Merthyr Tydfil	5v0	Yate Town
Witney Town	1v1	Clevedon Town
Clevedon Town	2v2	Witney
(AET & Witney win 4-2 on penalties)		
Stourbridge	1v1	Worcester City
Worcester City	3v1	Stourbridge
Shepshed Dynamo	2v2	R C Warwick
R C Warwick	1v1	Shepshed Dynamo
(RC Warwick win on away goals rule)		
Paget Rangers	3v2	Solihull Borough
Solihull Borough	1v2	Paget Rangers
Ilkeston Town	1v1	Gresley Rovers
Gresley Rovers	2v2	Ilkeston Town
(Ilkeston Town win on away goals rule)		
Evesham United	6v2	Dudley Town
Dudley Town	1v2	Evesham United
Sutton Coldfield	2v2	Moor Green
Moor Green	0v0	Sutton Coldfield
(Moor Green win on away goals rule)		
Corby Town	2v1	Grantham Town
Grantham Town	1v3	Corby Town
Raunds Town	0v1	King's Lynn
King's Lynn	1v2	Raunds Town
(Raunds Town win on away goal rule)		
Atherstone United	0v2	V.S. Rugby
V.S. Rugby	1v4	Atherstone United
Tamworth	3v0	Bedworth United
Bedworth United	1v4	Tamworth
Hinckley Town	1v2	Nuneaton Borough
Nuneaton Borough	2v2	Hinckley Town
Leicester United	v	Burton Albion
Leicester United withdrawn from the competition		
Redditch United	1v1	Bilston Town
Bilston Town	0v3	Redditch United
Halesowen Town	1v0	Stafford Rangers
Stafford Rangers	0v2	Halesowen Town
Buckingham Town	0v3	Cambridge City
Cambridge City	4v0	Buckingham Town
Sudbury Town	2v1	Fisher Ath. London
Fisher Ath. London	5v4	Sudbury Town
(Sudbury Town win on away goals rule)		
Hastings Town	1v2	St. Leonards Stamcroft
St. Leonards Stamcroft	3v0	Hastings Town
Erith & Belvedere	1v2	Margate
Margate	2v0	Erith & Belvedere
Gravesend & Northfleet	2v3	Sittingbourne
Sittingbourne	1v2	Gravesend & Northfleet
(Sittingbourne win on the away goals rule)		
Chelmsford City	0v1	Baldock Town
Baldock Town	2v1	Chelmsford City
Dartford	1v1	Crawley Town
Crawley Town	2v0	Dartford
Ashford Town	3v2	Tonbridge Angels
Tonbridge Angels	3v0	Ashford Town
Bashley	2v3	Salisbury City
Salisbury City	3v0	Bashley
Newport IOW	3v2	Havant Town
Havant Town	3v4	Newport IOW
Waterlooville	0v1	Fleet Town
Fleet Town	1v2	Waterlooville
(Waterlooville win on the away goals rule)		
Weymouth	4v1	Fareham Town
Fareham Town	3v3	Weymouth
Newport AFC	2v1	Cheltenham Town
Cheltenham Town	5v0	Newport AFC
Gloucester City	5v0	Cinderford Town
Cinderford Town	2v1	Gloucester City
Weston-super-Mare	0v2	Trowbridge Town
Trowbridge Town	0v0	Weston-super-Mare

SECOND ROUND

Merthyr Tydfil	2v2	Witney Town
(R) Witney Town	1v2	Merthyr Tydfil
Worcester City	1v1	R.C. Warwick
(R) R.C. Warwick	2v1	Worcester City
paget Rangers	0v3	Ilkeston Town
Evesham United	0v3	Moor Green
Corby Town	0v2	Raunds Town
Atherstone United	0v3	Tamworth
Nuneaton Borough	1v2	Burton Albion
Redditch United	0v3	Halesowen Town
Cambridge City	1v4	Sudbury Town
St. Leonards Stamcroft	3v2	Margate
Sittingbourne	0v2	Baldock Town
Crawley Town	1v2	Tonbridge Angels
Salisbury City	3v1	Newport IOW
Waterlooville	0v1	Weymouth
Cheltenham Town	1v0	Gloucester City
Trowbridge Town	1v1	Forest Green Rovers
(R) Forest Green R.	4v2	Trowbridge Town

THIRD ROUND

Merthyr Tydfil	0v2	R.C. Warwick
Ilkeston Town	2v1	Moor Green
Raunds Town	2v1	Tamworth
Burton Albion	1v0	Halesowen Town
Sudbury Town	1v0	St. Leonards Stamcroft
Baldock Town	3v4	Tonbridge Angels
Salisbury City	1v3	Weymouth
Cheltenham Town	0v1	Forest Green Rovers

FOURTH ROUND

R.C. Warwick	1v0	Ilkeston Town
Raunds Town	0v2	Burton Albion
Sudbury Town	3v2	Tonbridge Angels
Weymouth	2v0	Forest Green Rovers

SEMI-FINALS

R.C. Warwick	1v4	Burton Albion
Burton Albion	4v1	R.C. Warwick
Sudbury Town	1v0	Weymouth
Weymouth	0v3	Sudbury Town

FINAL

Burton Albion	2v1	Sudbury Town
Sudbury Town	0v1	Burton Albion

PREMIER DIVISION
10 YEAR RECORD

Dr MARTENS LEAGUE

No of Clubs Competing	87/8 (22)	88/9 (22)	89/0 (22)	90/1 (22)	91/2 (22)	92/3 (21)	93/4 (22)	94/5 (22)	95/6 (22)	96/7 (22)
Alvechurch	7	14	21	-	-	-	-	-	-	-
Ashford Town	12	18	19	-	-	-	-	-	-	19
Atherstone United	-	-	6	15	13	15	4	15	17	11
Aylesbury United	1	-	-	-	-	-	-	-	-	-
Baldock Town	-	-	-	-	-	-	-	-	18	20
Bashley	-	-	-	10	4	9	21	-	-	-
Bath City	-	9	2	-	-	-	-	-	-	-
Bedworth United	14	22	-	-	-	-	-	-	-	-
Bromsgrove Rovers	4	10	10	5	1	-	-	-	-	-
Burton Albion	16	8	4	7	10	8	11	3	16	6
Cambridge City	3	5	8	3	5	14	17	9	19	18
Chelmsford City	19	-	18	18	18	12	6	15	12	22
Cheltenham Town	-	-	-	-	-	2	2	2	3	2
Corby Town	10	16	20	-	14	3	9	22	-	-
Crawley Town	6	12	15	19	17	=6	5	11	9	17
Dartford	2	2	3	13	6	-	-	-	-	-
Dorchester Town	11	13	14	11	11	18	18	6	13	15
Dover Athletic	-	6	1	4	2	1	-	-	-	-
Fareham Town	9	19	-	-	-	-	-	-	-	-
Farnborough Town	-	-	-	1	-	-	1	-	-	-
Fisher Athletic	-	-	-	-	21	-	-	-	-	-
Gloucester City	-	-	9	2	12	13	10	4	4	3
Gosport Borough	15	7	22	-	-	-	-	-	-	-
Gravesnd & Northfleet	-	-	7	21	22	-	-	14	11	14
Gresley Rovers	-	-	-	-	-	-	14	8	5	1
Halesowen Town	-	-	-	8	8	10	3	13	2	4
Hastings Town	-	-	-	-	-	16	12	12	8	16
Hednesford Town	-	-	-	-	-	4	13	1	-	-
Ilkeston Town	-	-	-	-	-	-	-	-	20	-
Kings Lynn	-	-	-	-	-	-	-	-	-	5
Leek Town	-	-	-	-	-	-	-	7	-	-
Leicester United	8	20	-	-	-	-	-	-	-	-
Merthyr Tydfil	-	1	-	-	-	-	-	-	7	9
Moor Green	-	15	11	16	9	19	19	-	-	-
Newport A F C	-	-	-	-	-	-	-	-	14	21
Nuneaton Borough	21	-	-	-	-	-	22	-	-	7
Poole Town	-	-	-	17	20	-	-	-	-	-
Redditch United	18	21	-	-	-	-	-	-	-	-
Rushden Town	-	-	-	14	-	-	-	-	-	-
Rushden & Diamonds	-	-	-	-	-	-	-	5	1	-
Salisbury	-	-	-	-	-	-	-	-	15	12
Shepshed Charterhouse	13	-	-	-	-	-	-	-	-	-
Sittingbourne	-	-	-	-	-	-	8	20	-	8
Solihull Borough	-	-	-	-	-	=6	6	19	-	-
Stafford Rangers	-	-	-	-	-	-	-	-	21	-
Sudbury Town	-	-	-	-	-	-	-	18	10	11
Trowbridge Town	-	-	-	-	7	5	7	21	-	-
V.S. Rugby	17	3	5	9	3	20	-	17	22	-
Waterlooville	-	17	16	20	15	11	20	-	-	-
Wealdstone	-	11	12	12	19	-	-	-	-	-
Weymouth	-	-	17	22	-	21	-	-	-	-
Willenhall Town	20	-	-	-	-	-	-	-	-	-
Witney Town	22	-	-	-	-	-	-	-	-	-
Worcester City	5	4	13	6	16	17	15	10	6	10

ASHFORD TOWN

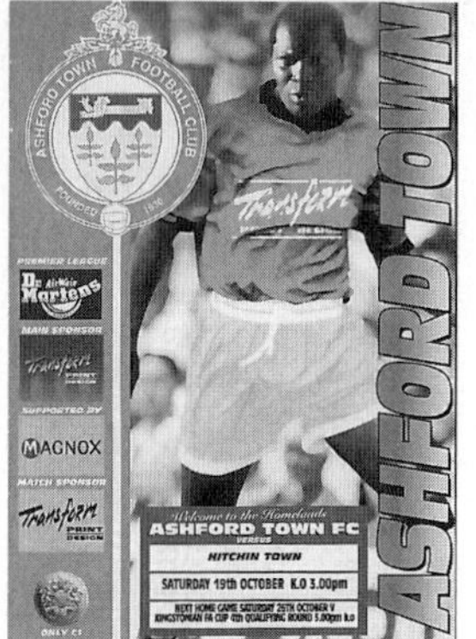

PROGRAMME DETAILS:
Pages: 32 **Price:** £ 1.00
Editor: Elaine Orsbourne

Formed: 1930 **Nickname:** Nuts & Bolts
Colours: All Green
Change colours: All White
Midweek home matchday: Tuesday
Reserve Team's League: No Reserve team for 1997-98.

Chairman: Doug Gillard **President:** Ashley M Batt
Secretary/Press Officer: A Lancaster, 128 Kingsnorth Rd, Ashford, Kent TN23 2HY (01233 621325). **Vice Chairman:** Roger West
Manager: Nigel Donn **Asst Manager:**
Coach: Nicky Sparks **Physio:** George Sargeant
Commercial Director: Ernie Warron, (01233 634125)
GROUND Address: The Homelands, Ashford Road, Kingsnorth, Ashford, Kent TN26 1NJ (01233 611838).
Directions: M20 jct 10, follow A2070 signs towards Brenzett & Lydd airport, dual carriageway to junction of old A2070, ground one mile on left through village of Kingsnorth. 4 miles south of Ashford
Capacity: 3,200 **Cover:** 1,250 **Seats:** 500 **Floodlights:** Yes
Clubhouse: Open matchdays and for special functions. Licensed bar, function room. Limited food - sandwiches & simple snacks.
Club Shop: Sells old progs, pennants, scarves, badges etc. Contact Alan Bird (01233 662680)
PREVIOUS - Names: Ashford United, Ashford Railway, Ashford F.C. **Leagues:** Kent 30-59. **Ground:** Essella Park, Essella Rd 30-87.
CLUB RECORDS - Attendance: 6,525 (at Essella Park, previous ground), v Crystal Palace, FA Cup 1st Rd 1959. 3,363 (at current ground), v Fulham FA Cup 1st Round 1994. **Goalscorer:** Dave Arter 197. **Appearances:** Paul McRobert 761. **Win:** 10-1 v Bury Town, February 1964. **Defeat:** 0-8 v Crawley Town, November 1964. **Fee Paid:** £7,000 for J Ross & D Arter (Sittingbourne, March 1994) £2,000 for Tim Hulme (Hythe Town, August 1988). **Fee Received:** £25,000 for Jeff Ross & Dave Arter (Hythe Tn, 90). *Individually: £20,000 for Lee McRobert (Sittingbourne, 93).*
Best Season - FA Trophy: Semi Final 72-73, 96-97 2nd Rd
FA Cup: 2nd Rd 61-62 (0-3 v QPR (H)), 66-67 (0-5 v Swindon [A]). 1st Rd 7 times. - **League clubs defeated:** None.
Players progressing to Football League: Ollie Norris (Rochdale 61), Howard Moore (Coventry 66), Tony Godden (WBA 75), Lee McRobert (Millwall 94)
96-97 Captain: Carlton Wynter **96-97 P.o.Y.:** Andy Pearson **96-97 Top scorer:** Nicky Dent 20
Local Press: Kentish Express **Local Radio:** Radio Kent, Invicta Radio
HONOURS: FA Trophy SF 72-73, Southern Lg Southern Div R-up 86-87 95-96, Kent Lg 48-49 (R-up 31-32, Lg Cup 38-39), Kent Senior Cup 58-59 62-63 92-93 95-96

Ashford Town *Photo - Keith Clayton*

Ashford Town

Match No.	Date	Venue H/A	Competition	Opponents	Result	League Pos.	Attendance	Goalscorers (Times if known)
1	Aug 17	H	DML	Gloucester City	Lost 0-3		648	
2	Aug 20	A	DML	Hastings Town	Drew 2-2		583	O'Brien 50, Wynter 87
3	Aug 24	H	DML	Newport County	Drew 1-1	14	643	Ross 7
4	Aug 26	A	DML	Gravesend & Northfleet	Won 3-1	9	804	Stanton 20, Wynter 24, Dent 45
5	Aug 31	A	DML	Burton Albion	Lost 0-1	18	775	
6	Sep 3	H	DML	Sudbury Town	Drew 2-2		585	Chambers 5 (pen), Dent 87
7	Sep 7	A	DML	Halesowen Town	Lost 1-3	18	701	Allon 67
8	Sep 14	H	DML	Nuneaton Borough	Won 2-0	13	659	Pearson 64, Parks 90
9	Sep 21	A	DML	Atherstone United	Drew 1-1	13	258	Dent 60
10	Sep 24	H	DML	Hastings Town	Drew 3-3	14	707	Dent 22, Carruthers 31, og 88
11	Oct 5	H	DML	Merthyr Tydfil	Lost 0-1	18	660	
12	**Oct 8**	**H**	**DMC**	**Tonbridge Angels**	**Won 3-2**		**401**	**Warrilow 38, 43, Wynter 77**
13	Oct 12	A	DML	Salisbury City	Won 1-0	12	421	Ross 12
14	Oct 15	H	DML	Gravesend & Northfleet	Drew 1-1	12	682	Morris 65 (pen)
15	**Oct 19**	**H**	**FAT 1 Q**	**Hitchin Town**	**Won 4-1**		**544**	**Allpress (og) 34, Dent 41, 80, Carruthers 79**
16	**Oct 26**	**H**	**FAC 4 Q**	**Kingstonian**	**Won 3-1**		**1089**	**White 20, Carruthers 41, 50**
17	**Oct 29**	**H**	**DMC**	**Tonbridge Angels**	**Lost 0-3**		**356**	
18	Nov 2	A	DML	Cheltenham Town	Lost 0-6	17	854	
19	**Nov 9**	**H**	**FAT 2 Q**	**Bishop's Stortford**	**Won 6-1**		**572**	**Dent 4, 47, 65, White 9, Parks 78, Chambers 89**
20	**Nov 16**	**H**	**FAC 1**	**Dagenham & Redbridge**	**Drew 2-2**		**1813**	**Warrilow 26, Dent 72**
21	Nov 23	H	DML	Burton Albion	Drew 3-3	18	596	Warrilow 8, 51, Dent
22	**Nov 25**	**A**	**FAC1**	**Dagenham & Redbridge**	**Drew 1-1⁺**		**2424**	**White 76**
23	**Nov 30**	**A**	**FAC 3 Q**	**Weymouth**	**Lost 0-2**		**849**	
24	**Dec 7**	**A**	**FAC 2**	**Watford**	**Lost 0-5**		**7590**	
25	Dec 14	H	DML	Dorchester Town	Won 2-1	18	407	White 51, Dent 59
26	Dec 21	A	DML	Chelmsford City	Drew 1-1	16	802	Dent 74
27	Jan 18	A	DML	Kings Lynn	Lost 0-2	19	856	
28	Jan 25	H	DML	Chelmsford City	Won 1-0	17	688	Ross 49
29	Jan 28	A	DML	Gresley Rovers	Drew 2-2	18	709	Dent 15, 47
30	**Feb 1**	**A**	**KSC**	**Fisher Athletic**	**Lost 0-1**		**130**	
31	Feb 3	A	DML	Crawley Town	Won 3-2		419	Dent 45, O'Shaughnessy 69, Morris 73 (p)
32	Feb 8	A	DML	Merthyr Tydfil	Lost 0-3	15	605	
33	Feb 15	H	DML	Gresley Rovers	Lost 1-3	16	615	Wynter 54
34	Feb 22	A	DML	Nuneaton Borough	Lost 0-3	19	903	
35	Feb 28	H	DML	Sittingbourne	Drew 1-1	17	551	Warrilow 75
36	Mar 1	H	DML	Worcester City	Drew 0-0	17	467	
37	Mar 8	A	DML	Atherstone United	Lost 0-3	18	461	
38	Mar 12	A	DML	Newport A.F.C.	Lost 0-3		504	
39	Mar 15	H	DML	Halesowen Town	Drew 1-1	17	442	Scott 59
40	Msr 18	A	DML	Gloucester City	Lost 1-6	17	556	Ross 3
41	Mar 22	A	DML	Baldock Town	Drew 1-1	17	210	Stanton 52
42	Mar 25	H	DML	Salisbury City	Lost 0-1	21	456	
43	Mar 29	H	DML	Crawley Town	Drew 3-3	21	567	White 30 (pen), Pearson 57, 90
44	Mar 31	A	DML	Sittingbourne	Lost 1-4	21	1025	Parkes 61
45	Apr 5	H	DML	Cambridge City	Drew 2-2	20	521	Taylor 16 (og), Warrilow 87
46	Apr 8	A	DML	Sudbury Town	Drew 2-2		215	Wynter 70, Lawrence 85
47	Apr 12	A	DML	Worcester City	Won 2-0	19	644	Chambers 58, Wynter 75
48	Apr 15	H	DML	Baldock Town	Drew 2-2		566	Wynter 56, Allon 78
49	Apr 19	H	DML	Cheltenham Town	Drew 1-1	20	574	Dent 23
50	Apr 22	A	DML	Cambridge City	Lost 0-4		248	
51	Apr 26	H	DML	King's Lynn	Won 4-0	19	538	Warrilow 15, Chambers 32, Ross 62, Dent 90
52	May 3	A	DML	Dorchester Town	Won 2-0	19	806	Scott 48, Lawrence 60

⁺ Won on Penalties

ASHFORD TOWN PLAYING SQUAD 1997-98

Goalkeepers: Maurice Munden (Sing Tao (HK), Dover, Welling, Folkestone, Charlton)
Defenders: Andy Pearson (Folkestone, Chatham, Maidstone), **Nigel Donn** (Dover, Maidstone, Leyton Orient, Gillingham), **Andy Morris** (Folkestone), **Tommy Warrilow** (Gravesend, Sittingbourne, Hythe, Crawley, Torquay, Kuopio ELO (Fin), Adelaide (Aust), Canterbury, Gravesend, Tonbridge Millwall), **Aaron O'Leary** (Youth team), **Paul O'Brien** (Dover)
Midfielders: Andy Allon (Margate, Hythe, Folkestone, Ashford, Folkestone, Dover, Folkestone), **Paul Chambers** (Folkestone Invicta, Dover, Folkestone Invicta), **Matt Carruthers** (Dover), **Carlton Wynter** (Hastings T, Sittingbourne, Ashford, Hastings T, Ashford, Bromley Green), **Stuart White** (Welling, Brighton, Gillingham, Charlton), **Jason Wheeler** (Herne Bay, Ashford, Hythe, Crawley, Maidstone), **Mark Stanton** (Hythe)
Forwards: Jeff Ross (Sittingbourne, Hythe, Ashford, Gravesend, Tonbridge, Herne Bay, Welling, Ashford), **Tom Parks** (Youth team), **Nicky Dent** (Sing Tao (HK), Dover, Poole, Yeovil, Bristol C, Bristol Manor Farm), **Scott McRobert** (Youth team)

PROGRAMME DETAILS:
Pages: 28 **Price:** 70p
Editor: Phil Bellinger

ATHERSTONE UNITED

Formed: 1979 **Nickname:** The Adders
Colours: Red & white stripes/red/red
Change colours: Yellow & blue/blue/blue
Midweek home matchday: Tuesday
Reserve's Lge: Midland Comb. Reserve Div.

Chairman: Stan Holland **President:** C Culwick
Vice Chairman: L Spencer **Secretary:** Neil Dykes, 18 Greendale Close, Atherstone, Warwickshire CV9 1PR, (01827 714326)
Manager: Ron Bradbury 01203 382548 **Asst Manager:** R Stockley
Physio: S Welch
Press Officer: T.B.A. **Commercial Manager:** M Steebleton

GROUND Address: Sheepy Road, Atherstone, Warwickshire. CV9 1HG. 01827 717829
Directions: Half mile north of town centre on B4116 Twycross/Ashby road.
Capacity: 3,500 **Cover:** 1,000 **Seats:** 373 **Floodlights:** Yes
Clubhouse: Open during normal licensing hours, all usual facilities.
Club Shop: Yes. Programmes, magazines, souvenirs etc. Contact Alan Hewitt, (01827 715799). **Metal Badges:** Yes
Club Sponsors: T.B.A.

PREVIOUS - Leagues: West Midlands 1979-87

CLUB RECORDS -
Attendance: 2,873 v V.S. Rugby, F.A. Cup 1st Round Proper 1987-88
Win: 12-2 v Tipton Town (H), West Midlands (Regional) League Premier Division 86-87.
Defeat: 1-7 v Rushden & Diamonds, Beazer League Premier Division 94-95.
Goalscorer: Alan Bourton **Appearances:** Lee Spencer
Fee Paid: £4,500 to Gloucester City for Gary Bradder, 1989.
Fee Received: £40,000 for Andy Rammell from Manchester United, September 1989.
Best Season - FA Cup: 2nd Rd Proper 1990-91 (lost 0-1 at Crewe Alexandra)
FA Trophy: 1st Round 88-89 91-92.
Players progressing to The Football League: Andy Rammell (Manchester United).
96-97 Captain: **96-97 P.o.Y.:** **96-97 Top scorer:**
Local Press: Tamworth Herald, Evening News, Atherstone Herald, Coventry Telegraph.
Local Radio: Mercia Sound, CWR.

HONOURS: Southern Lge Midland Div 88-89, West Midlands Lge 81-82 86-87 (Lge Cup 81-82, Premier Div Cup 86-87, Div 2 Cup (Reserves) 86-87), Walsall Senior Cup 83-84, Midland Combination Reserve Division 87-88, Birmingham Senior Cup R-up 89-90.

Atherstone United *Photo - Nuneaton & District Newspapers*

Atherstone United

Match No.	Date	Venue H/A	Competition	Opponents	Result	League Pos.	Attendance	Goalscorers (Times if known)
1	Aug 17	H	DML	Dorchester Town	Won 2-1		273	Bennett 53, Sinden 67
2	Aug 20	A	DML	King's Lynn	Lost 1-2		1156	Hawthorn (og) 60
3	Aug 24	A	DML	Halesowen Town	Won 2-0	9	686	Bennett 34, 55
4	Aug 26	H	DML	Gresley Rovers	Lost 0-1		588	
5	Aug 31	H	DML	Newport A.F.C.	Won 1-0	8	448	Green 13
6	Sep 3	A	DML	Cheltenham Town	Lost 0-2		610	
7	Sep 7	A	DML	Merthyr Tydfil	Lost 2-3	12	551	Bennett 34 (p), Middleton 86
8	**Sep 14**	**H**	**FAC 1 Q**	**Cogenhoe**	**Won 3-1**		**309**	**Bennett 55 (p), Sinden 57, Owen 9**
9	**Sep 17**	**A**	**BSC**	**Nuneaton Borough**	**Lost 0-2**		**808**	
10	Sep 21	H	DML	Ashford Town	Drew 1-1	11	258	Middleton 11
11	Sep 24	H	DML	King's Lynn	Drew 1-1	13	199	Murphy 81
12	**Sep 28**	**A**	**FAC 2 Q**	**Kettering Town**	**Drew 0-0**		**1278**	
13	**Oct 1**	**H**	**FAC 2 Q**	**Kettering Town**	**Lost 1-6**		**682**	**Middleton 4**
14	Oct 5	A	DML	Baldock Town	Won 2-0	10	258	Bennett 18, Murphy 63
15	**Oct 8**	**H**	**DMLC**	**V.S. Rugby**	**Lost 0-2**		**175**	
16	Oct 12	H	DML	Halesowen Town	Lost 0-5	14	434	
17	Oct 15	A	DML	Gresley Rovers	Drew 1-1	15	623	Bennett 81
18	**Oct 19**	**H**	**FAT 1 Q**	**Whitley Bay**	**Lost 0-2**		**218**	
19	Oct 20	H	DML	Cambridge City	Won 1-0	12	213	Oliver 90
20	**Oct 30**	**A**	**DMLC**	**V.S. Rugby**	**Won 4-1**		**205**	**Murphy 50, Oliver 51, 60, Dixon 87**
21	Nov 2	A	DML	Sittingbourne	Drew 1-1		691	Bennett 77
22	Nov 16	H	DML	Baldock Town	Lost 1-3	12	215	Green 45
23	Nov 23	H	DML	Merthyr Tydfil	Lost 3-4	16	206	Murphy 40, 69, Evans (og) 80
24	Nov 30	A	DML	Gravesend & Northfleet	Lost 0-1	15	539	
25	Dec 7	A	DML	Dorchester Town	Lost 0-1	15	190	
26	**Dec 10**	**H**	**DMC 2**	**Tamworth**	**Lost 0-3**		**717**	
27	Dec 14	H	DML	Chelmsford City	Drew 1-1		217	Green 31
28	Dec 26	A	DML	Nuneaton Borough	Lost 2-3	18	1607	Judd 13, Green 82
29	Jan 14	H	DML	Nuneaton Borough	Drew 0-0		858	
30	Jan 18	H	DML	Gravesend & Northfleet	Drew 0-0	17	277	
31	Jan 25	H	DML	Worcester City	Drew 2-2	18	276	Judd 45, Ellison 53
32	Jan 28	H	DML	Gloucester City	Drew 0-0		315	
33	Feb 1	A	DML	Cambridge City	Won 2-1	14	237	Bennett 62, Green 84
34	Feb 8	H	DML	Crawley	Won 2-0	14	303	Middleton 39 (p), Green 52
35	Feb 15	A	DML	Salisbury City	Lost 2-3	14	284	Percival 86, Ellison 90
36	Feb 22	H	DML	Sittingbourne	Won 2-1	14	256	Murphy 6, 74
37	Feb 26	A	DML	Hastings United	Drew 0-0	14	316	
38	Mar 8	A	DML	Ashford Town	Won 3-0	15	461	Murphy 21, Oliver 37, Middleton 85
39	Mar 11	H	DML	Cheltenham Town	Drew 0-0		375	
40	Mar 15	A	DML	Worcester City	Lost 0-3	15	605	
41	Mar 18	A	DML	Sudbury Town	Won 1-0		214	Oliver 45
42	Mar 22	H	DML	Hastings Town	Drew 0-0	14	262	
43	Mar 29	A	DML	Burton Albion	Won 2-1		911	Murphy 36, Middleton 44
44	Mar 31	H	DML	Burton Albion	Won 2-1	14	606	Judd 2, Ellison 6
45	Apr 9	A	DML	Newport AFC	Lost 0-2	14	626	
46	Apr 19	A	DML	Chelmsford City	Won 1-0	14	601	Ellison 76
47	Apr 22	H	DML	Salisbury City	Won 4-0		213	Bennett 30, 47, Green 51, 59
48	Apr 24	A	DML	Gloucester City	Drew 0-0		927	
49	Apr 26	A	DML	Crawley Town	Lost 0-2	12	901	

ATHERSTONE UNITED PLAYING SQUAD 1997-98

Goalkeepers : Richard Williams (Hednesford T, Atherstone U, Birmingham C)
Defenders: Leigh Everitt (Nuneaton B), **Lee Middleton** (Camb.U, Swindon, Coventry C), **Mark Allbrighton** (Nuneaton B), **Steve Woodfine** (Bedworth U, Nuneaton B), **Malcolm Randle** (Bedworth U, Hurley DM), **Matt Wileman** (Bedworth U, Atherstone U, Stoke)
Midfielders : Scott Blair (Stoke C), **David Hart** (Nuneaton B), **Robin Judd** (Solihull B, Atherstone U, Redditch U, Mile Oak R, Kidderminster H, Birmingham C), **Bobby Parker** (Bedworth U, Atherstone U, Bedworth U, Sutton C, Alvechurch, Tamworth, Atherstone U, Nuneaton B), **Robert Higgs** (Solihull B), **Paul Olner** (Hinckley T, VS Rugby, Gloucester, VS Rugby, Atherstone U), **Danny Martin** (Nuneaton B, VS Rugby, Nuneaton B, Stoke)
Forwards : Dave Bennett (Hinckley Ath, Nuneaton B, Swindon, Sheff. Wed, Coventry, Cardiff, Man.City), **Robbie Ellison** (Hednesford T, Atherstone U, Tamworth, Mile Oak R), **Dean Allbrighton** (Bolehall S, Bedworth U), **Kim Green** (VS Rugby,Solihull B, Hednesford T, VS Rugby, Atherstone U, Nuneaton B, VS Rugby, Coventry Sporting, MSA), **Jason Percival** (Hinckley T, Nuneaton B, Exeter, Stoke), **Chris Armeni** (Quorn, Notts Co (T))

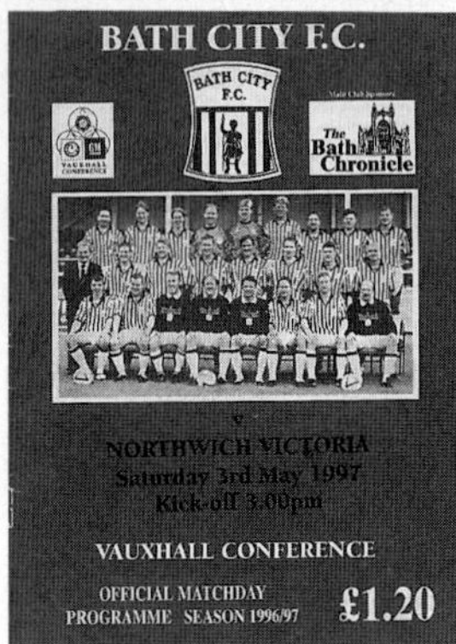

BATH CITY

Founded: 1889 **Nickname:** Romans
Club colours: Black/white striped shirts, black shorts & black/white socks.
Change colours: All sky blue
Midweek home matchday: Tuesday
Reserves' League: None

PROGRAMME DETAILS:
Pages: 36 **Price:** £1.20
Editor:
Jason Turner/Robert Twyford

Chairman: Raymond C Stock **Vice Chairman:** D Turner
Directors: I Prosser, L Kew, R C Twyford, O Newland
Secretary: Robert Twyford, c/o the club. 01179 325921 (H), 01225 423087 (B)
Commercial Manager: Jason Turner
Manager: Steve Millard **Asst. Man.:** Tony Gill
Coach: Shaun Penny **Physio:** Steve Tregale
GROUND Address: Twerton Park, Twerton, Bath Avon BA2 1DB. (01225 423087/313247 Fax: 01225 481391)
Directions: Twerton Park is situated on the A4/A36 Lower Bristol Road - on the Bristol side of Bath City Centre (Approx 2.5 miles). The area is serviced by J18 on the M4. From the centre of Bath the bus route is No.5 - Twerton High Street.
Capacity: 8,840 **Seated:** 1,017 **Covered Terracing:** 4,800
Clubhouse: Several bars open all week and full service with menu on match-days catering for up to 250 people.
Club Shop: Contact Mr K Sellick.

PREVIOUS Grounds: The Belvoir Ground, Lambridge - 1889-1932. **Leagues:** Beazer Homes (Southern League), Vauxhall Conference
CLUB RECORDS - **Attendance:** 18,020 v Brighton & Hove Albion, FA Cup.
Win: **Defeat:** 9-0 Yeovil Town 46-47
Career goalscorer: Paul Randall **Career appearances:** David Mogg (530)
Transfer fee paid: £15,000 for Micky Tanner from Bristol City.
Transfer fee received: £80,000 for Jason Dodd from Southampton.
BEST SEASON - **FA Cup:** 63-64, 93-94 **FA Trophy:** 89-90, 4th Rd
96-97 Captain: Nicky Brooks **96-97 Top scorer:** Mike Davis **96-97 P.o.Y.:** Mark Harrington
Past players who progressed to the Football League: Alan Skirton (Arsenal), Tony Book (Plymouth A.), Kenny Allen (Bournemouth), Peter Rogers (Exeter C.), R Bourne (Torquay), Dave Wiffil (Manchester C.), Stan Mortensen (Blackpool), Brian Wade (Swindon Town), Jeff Meacham (Bristol R.), Martin Hirst (Bristol C.), Paul Bodin (Swindon), Graham Withey (Coventry), Jason Dodd (Southampton), Paul Adcock (Torquay).
HONOURS: Southern League Champions 59-60, 77-78; R-up 29-33, 61-62, 89-90; Southern League Cup 78-79; Somerset Premier Cup 51-52, 52-53, 57-58, 59-60, 65-66, 69-70, 77-78, 80-81, 81-82, 83-84, 84-85, 85-86, 88-89, 89-90, 93-94, 94-95; Anglo-Italian Cup R-up 76-77, 77-78.

Bath City FC

Bath City

Match No.	Date	Venue H/A	Competition	Opponents	Result	League Pos.	Attendance	Goalscorers (Times if known)
1	Aug 17	A	VC	Northwich Victoria	Lost 0-1	18	769	
2	Aug 20	A	VC	Woking	Drew 2-2		2317	James 31, Wyatt 60
3	Aug 24	H	VC	Kettering Town	Lost 0-2	16	660	
4	Aug 26	H	VC	Dover Athletic	Won 2-1		544	Harrington 29, Penny 75
5	Aug 31	A	VC	Hednesford Town	Lost 0-2	17	1054	
6	Sep 3	A	VC	Slough Town	Lost 2-5		1032	Davis 30,76
7	Sep 7	H	VC	Gateshead	Won 3-0	17	465	Davis 7, Penny 36, Withey 67
8	Sep 9	A	VC	Stevenage Borough	Lost 1-2	18	2574	Penny 45
9	**Sep 14**	**A**	**FAC 1 Q**	**Devizes**	**Drew 2-2**		**300**	**Davis 32, Withey 90**
10	**Sep 17**	**H**	**FAC R**	**Devizes**	**Won 3-1**		**689**	**Harrington 43, Withey 51, Davis 65**
11	Sep 21	A	VC	Macclesfield Town	Drew 2-2	21	1091	Withey 29, Penny 36
12	Sep 24	H	VC	Kidderminster Harriers	Lost 0-3		571	
13	**Sep 28**	**H**	**FAC 2 Q**	**Newport AFC**	**Won 5-2**		**728**	**Davis (3) 4, 53, 84, Penny 46, Donovan og 71**
14	Oct 1	A	VC	Dover Athletic	Drew 2-2		1164	Wyatt 19, Davis 42
15	Oct 5	H	VC	Altrincham	Lost 1-2	21	619	Cross 42
16	**Oct 8**	**H**	**SCC**	**Welling United**	**Lost 0-2**		**237**	
17	**Oct 12**	**H**	**FAC 3 Q**	**Cirencester Town**	**Won 2-0**		**549**	**Davis 29, Penny 43**
18	Oct 15	A	VC	Telford United	Drew 1-1		549	Adcock 54
19	Oct 19	H	VC	Stalybridge Celtic	Lost 0-2	22	530	
20	**Oct 26**	**H**	**FAC 4 Q**	**Cheltenham Town**	**Drew 0-0**		**1088**	
21	**Oct 29**	**A**	**FAC 4 Q**	**Cheltenham Town**	**Lost 1-4***		**1018**	**Davis 36**
22	Nov 2	A	VC	Morecambe	Drew 1-1	22	917	Wyatt 1
23	Nov 9	H	VC	Halifax Town	Drew 0-0	22	567	
24	Nov 23	H	VC	Woking	Drew 1-1	21	1001	Paul 25
25	Nov 26	H	VC	Hednesford Town	Won 2-1		385	Davis 4, 41
26	Nov 30	A	VC	Rushden & Diamonds	Lost 1-4		1853	Pave 76
27	Dec 7	A	VC	Welling United	Lost 0-2	22	485	
28	Dec 14	A	VC	Gateshead	Lost 0-5	22	423	
29	Dec 21	H	VC	Stevenage Borough	Drew 0-0	22	587	
30	Dec 26	A	VC	Farnborough Town	Lost 1-4	22	807	Laight 76
31	Dec 28	A	VC	Kidderminster Harriers	Lost 0-6	22	3305	
32	Jan 4	A	VC	Southport	Lost 1-3	22	786	Penny 71
33	Jan 11	H	VC	Morecambe	Won 2-1	22	509	Paul 17, Wyatt 69
34	**Jan 18**	**H**	**FAT 1**	**Stevenage Borough**	**Drew 1-1**		**682**	**Penny 85**
35	**Jan 20**	**A**	**FAT 1 R**	**Stevenage Borough**	**Lost 1-6**		**1344**	**Brooks 89**
36	Jan 25	A	VC	Kettering Town	Lost 0-1	22	1444	
37	Feb 1	H	VC	Southport	Lost 0-2	22	531	
38	Feb 8	H	VC	Telford United	Lost 2-3	22	499	Davis 28, Walker 49
39	Feb 11	H	VC	Hayes	Won 3-1	21	377	Harrington 21, Davis 38, Hirons 40
40	Feb 15	A	VC	Halifax Town	Won 5-4	21	655	Harrington 31, Davis 41, 82, Brooks 43, Colbourne 86
41	Feb 22	H	VC	Macclesfield Town	Lost 0-3	21	955	
42	Mar 8	H	VC	Bromsgrove Rovers	Won 1-0	21	646	Hirons 22
43	Mar 15	A	VC	Altrincham	Won 3-1	21	648	Colbourne 14, France 22 (og), Mehew 24
44	Mar 29	H	VC	Slough Town	Drew 0-0		822	
45	Mar 31	A	VC	Bromsgrove Rovers	Lost 1-2	21	716	Colbourne 10
46	Apr 5	A	VC	Stalybridge Celtic	Drew 2-2	22	545	Hedges 58, Mehew 90
47	Apr 12	H	VC	Rushden & Diamonds	Won 3-2		960	Colbourne 7, Davis 78, Mehew 90
48	Apr 19	H	VC	Welling United	Won 3-1	19	831	Davis 50 (pen), 71, Colbourne 61
49	Apr 26	A	VC	Hayes	Won 1-0	20	1183	Colbourne 13
50	Apr 29	H	VC	Farnborough Town	Drew 1-1	20	1166	Davis 3
51	May 3	H	VC	Northwich Victoria	Won 3-2	20	1258	Towler 57, 75, Colbourne 59

* After Extra Time

BATH CITY PLAYING SQUAD 1997-98

Goalkeepers: Mark Hervin (Yeovil, Bristol R)
Defenders: Ian Hedges (AFC Bournemouth, Gloucester, Bristol Manor Farm), **Joe Davey** (QPR), **Colin Towler** (Yate, Mangotsfield), **Richard Crowley** (Gloucester, Bath, Cheltenham, Forest Green R, Bath, Frome)
Midfielders: Nicky Brooks (Clevedon, Mangotsfield, Barnstaple, Bristol C), **Mark Harrington** (Paulton R, Bristol C), **Danny Hazlehurst** (Southampton), **Stuart James** (Swindon), **Mike Wyatt** (Bristol R, Bristol C)
Forwards: Mike Davis (Bristol R, Yate), **Matt Walker** (Clevedon, Westbury U, Frome, Southampton), **Graham Colbourne** (Paulton R, Radstock), **Paul Hirons** (Taunton, Forest Green R, Yate, Clevedon, Cheltenham, Westbury U, Bath, Yeovil, Torquay, Bristol C), **Dave Mehew** (Weston-S-M, Yate, Walsall, Bristol R, Leeds), **Shaun Penny** (Weston-S-M, Gloucester, Forest Green R, Weymouth, Dorchester, Bath, KTP Kotkan (Fin), Bristol R, Bristol C), **Martin Paul** (Doncaster, Bristol R)

PROGRAMME DETAILS:
Pages: 40 **Price:** £1.20
Editor:
Brian Perry 0121 628 6009
Alan Saunders 01527 833838

BROMSGROVE ROVERS

Formed: 1885 **Nickname:** Rovers or Greens
Club colours: Green & white stripes/black/green.
Change colours: All red.
Midweek home matchday: Tuesday (7.45pm)
Reserves' league: Central Conference. **Newsline:** 0891 88 44 96.

Chairman: Keith McMaster **President:** Charles W Poole
Secretary: Eddie Million, c/o Bromsgrove Rovers FC
Commercial Manager: Rebecca O'Neill
Manager: Brian Kenning **Trainer:** Stewart Pinfold**Physio:** Paul Sunners
GROUND Address: Victoria Ground, Birmingham Road, Bromsgrove, Worcs, B61 0DR (01527 876949). **Directions:** Ground is situated on the north side of Bromsgrove on the Birmingham Road, off the A38 Bromsgrove by pass. The M5 and M42 join the A38 to the north of the town making it easy to get to the ground without having to go into town. The 144 Midland Red bus runs from New Street Station Birmingham and passes the ground.
Capacity: 4,893 **Seated:** 394 **Covered Terracing:** 1,344
Clubhouse: Victoria Club (01527 878260) - Serves hot & cold food. Big screen TV, pool table & darts. Open matchdays and week-day evenings.
Club Shop: Selling replica clothing & souvenirs. Contact Doug Bratt (01527 874997).
Sponsors: All Saints Masterfit (Bromsgrove).

PREVIOUS - Leagues: Birmingham Lge 1898-08, Birmingham Combination 1908-53, Birmingham 53-65, West Midlands 65-72, Southern League - Northern Div. 73-79, Midland Div. 79-1986, Premier Div. 86-92, GMVC 92-97.
Grounds: Old Station Road 1885-87, Recreation Ground 87-88, Churchfields 88-97, Well Lane 1897-1910.
CLUB RECORDS - Attendance: 7,389 v Worcester City - 1957. **Win:** 11-0 - v Hinckley Ath. 1970, v Halesowen Town 'A' 1939. **Defeat:** 0-12 v Aston Villa 'A' 1939. **Career goalscorer:** Chris Hanks 238, 1983-84. **Career appearances:** Shaun O'Meara 763, 1975-94. **Transfer fee paid:** £3,000 for Recky Carter (Solihull B.) 93-94. **Transfer fee received:** Undisclosed for Scott Cooksey (Peterborough) Dec. 93.
96-97 Captain: **96-97 Top Scorer:** **96-97 P.o.Y.:**
Past players who progressed to the Football League: M McKenna (Northampton 46), R Hartle (Bolton 52), A McLean (Bury 53), A Smith (A.Villa 54), M Deakin (C Palace 54), B Puster (Leicester 58), Tom Smith (Sheff Utd 1978), Malcolm Goodman (Halifax 1979), Steve Smith (Walsall 1980), Gary Hackett (Shrewsbury 1983), Bill McGarry, Martyn O'Connor (C Palace 1992), Scott Cooksey (Peterborough 1993), Steve Taylor (Crystal Palace 1995).
HONOURS: Vauxhall Conference R-up 92-93, Lge Cup 94-95 95-96; Bob Lord Trophy 94-95; Spalding Cup 95/96; Southern Lge Prem 91-92, R-up 86-87, Cup 92-93, R-up 86-87, Midland Div 85-86, Merit Cup 85-86, Cup 85-86, R-up 73-74 87-88; Bill Dellow Cup 85-86; Worcester Sen Cup (8), R-up (10); Birmingham Sen Cup 46-47, R-up 47-48 88-89; W Mid Lge R-up 67-70, Cup 67-68 70-71; Birminham Lge 59-60, R-up 04-05 56-57 60-61; Birmingham Comb 46-47, R-up 49-50 50-51; Hereford Charity Chall Cup 46-47, R-up 47-48.

Back Row (L-R); Paul Sunners (Physio), Craig Gaunt, Lee Young, Nick Clarke, Paul Haywood, Neil Olden, Colin Radburn, Stewart Randall, Reckey Carter, Stewart Pinfield. Front Row ; Brian Kenning (Mgr), Darren Grocutt, Andy Dale, Stuart Brighton, Kevin Richardson, Brendon Devery, Symon Burgher, Andy Powell, Mark Crisp, John Dyer (Asst Mgr).

Bromsgrove Rovers

Match No.	Date	Venue H/A	Competition	Opponents	Result	League Pos.	Attendance	Goalscorers (Times if known)
1	Aug 17	A	VC	Welling United	Won 2-1	7	501	Crisp 20, Wardle 58
2	Aug 20	H	VC	Telford United	Won 2-1		788	Crisp (2) 57, 68
3	Aug 24	H	VC	Southport	Lost 0-2		762	
4	Aug 26	A	VC	Northwich Victoria	Lost 0-1	10	722	
5	Aug 31	A	VC	Hayes	Lost 0-1	15	521	
6	Sep 3	H	VC	Kettering Town	Lost 1-2		898	Clarke 61
7	Sep 7	H	VC	Macclesfield Town	Lost 0-3	20	833	
8	Sep 9	A	VC	Hednesford Town	Lost 0-3		1276	
9	Sep 14	A	VC	Slough Town	Lost 0-2		1158	
10	Sep 17	H	VC	Altrincham	Won 4-0		562	Burgher 29, 56, Smith 37, Skelding 70 (p)
11	Sep 21	A	VC	Stevenage Borough	Lost 0-3	19	2552	
12	Sep 24	A	VC	Farnborough Town	Lost 1-2		529	Hunt 2
13	Sep 28	H	VC	Slough Town	Won 4-1	16	686	Crisp 16, Mainwaring 68, 76, Gardner 69
14	Oct 1	A	VC	Telford United	Lost 1-3		814	Burgher 8
15	Oct 5	H	VC	Gateshead	Drew 2-2	17	752	Taylor 39, Skeldington 60 (pen)
16	Oct 19	H	VC	Dover Athletic	Won 3-1		803	Dunphy 3, 69, Mainwaring 79
17	**Oct 26**	**A**	**FAC 4 Q**	**Shepshed Dynamo**	**Lost 0-2**		**969**	
18	Nov 2	A	VC	Stalybridge Celtic	Lost 0-3	16	585	
19	Nov 9	H	VC	Stevenage Borough	Drew 1-1	17	922	Gardner 8
20	**Nov 19**	**H**	**SCC**	**Northwich Victoria**	**Won 3-1***		**271**	**Grocutt 31, 104, Amos 115**
21	Nov 23	A	VC	Kettering Town	Lost 0-2	18	1578	
22	**Nov 26**	**H**	**WSC**	**Stourbridge**	**Lost 0-1**			
23	Nov 30	A	VC	Morecambe	Lost 2-3	19	652	Gardner 74, Amos 84
24	Dec 7	A	VC	Southport	Drew 0-0	20	741	
25	Dec 14	A	VC	Rushden & Diamonds	Won 2-1	18	2144	Taylor 25, Smith 60
26	**Dec 17**	**H**	**SCC**	**Macclesfield Town**	**Lost 0-1**		**347**	
27	Dec 21	A	VC	Farnborough Town	Drew 1-1		729	Hunt 49
28	Dec 26	A	VC	Kidderminster Harriers	Won 2-1		6081	Grocutt 71, Crisp 88
29	Dec 28	H	VC	Altrincham	Lost 1-3	17	727	Crisp 83
30	Jan 11	H	VC	Stalybridge Celtic	Lost 0-1	18	734	
31	**Jan 18**	**A**	**FAT 1**	**Merthyr Tydfil**	**Won 2-1**		**691**	**Hunt 67, Crisp 83**
32	Jan 25	A	VC	Morecambe	Lost 0-1	19	940	
33	Jan 28	H	VC	Halifax Town	Lost 0-1	19	608	
34	Feb 1	H	VC	Halifax Town	Won 3-0	18	686	Mainwaring 20, 45, Crisp 58
35	**Feb 8**	**H**	**FAT 2**	**Hyde United**	**Drew 1-1**		**971**	**Taylor 81**
36	**Feb 10**	**A**	**FAT 2 R**	**Hyde United**	**Drew 2-2**		**707**	**Taylor 65, Nesbitt 82**
37	Feb 15	A	VC	Dover Athletic	Lost 0-2	19	1023	
38	**Feb 17**	**H**	**FAT 2 R2**	**Hyde United**	**Lost 0-2**		**642**	
39	Feb 22	H	VC	Woking	Lost 0-3	20	881	
40	Mar 1	H	VC	Northwich Victoria	Lost 0-5	20	638	
41	Mar 8	A	VC	Bath City	Lost 0-1	22	646	
42	Mar 11	H	VC	Kidderminster Harriers	Lost 0-1	22	2548	
43	Mar 15	H	VC	Rushden & Diamonds	Lost 0-1	22	1109	
44	Mar 22	H	VC	Hayes	Drew 2-2	22	557	Taylor 26, Mainwaring 50
45	Mar 29	A	VC	Gateshead	Lost 0-1	22	614	
46	Mar 31	H	VC	Bath City	Won 2-1	22	716	Mainwaring 46, Davey 89 (og)
47	Apr 5	H	VC	Hednesford Town	Won 1-0	21	814	Taylor 78
48	Apr 8	A	VC	Woking	Won 3-1	20	2044	Taylor 2, Mainwaring 27, 81
49	Apr 26	A	VC	Macclesfield Town	Lost 0-4	21	3004	
50	May 3	H	VC	Welling United	Won 1-0	21	706	Brighton 25

* After Extra Time

BROMSGROVE ROVERS PLAYING SQUAD 1997-98

Goalkeepers: Chris Taylor (Solihull B, Moor Green, Evesham, Halesowen T, Bromsgrove)

Defenders: Kevin Richardson (Hednesford, Alvechurch, Sutton C, Worcester, Stafford R, Sutton C, Pelsall V), **Jimmy Skelding** (Worcester, Burton A, Bromsgrove, Wolves, Bilston), **Stewart Brighton** (Crewe), **Stuart Randall** (Evesham, Sutton C, Redditch, Coleshill, Tamworth), **Paul Wardle** (Gresley R, Bromsgrove, Belper, Denaby)

Midfielders: Darren Grocutt (Burton A, Evesham, Moor Green, Northfield), **Mark Crisp** (Macclesfield, Bromsgrove, Alvechurch, Bromsgrove, Redditch, Smethwick), **Robert Elms** (Boldmere, Northfield), **Steve Taylor** (Hednesford, Crystal Palace, Bromsgrove, Rushall O), **Jamie Petty** (Youth team), **Nick Amos** (Hornchurch)

Forwards: Andy Mainwaring (Cwmbran), **John Hunt** (Sutton C, Paget), **Chris Smith** (Stourbridge)

PROGRAMME DETAILS:
Pages: 48 **Price:** £1
Editor: David Twigg
(01283 562013)

BURTON ALBION

Formed: 1950 **Nickname:** Brewers
Colours: Yellow with black trim.
Change colours: Sky blue, black trim
Midweek matchday: Tuesday
Previous Ground: Wellington Street 50-57.

Chairman: C B Robinson 01283 813943 (H) **Vice Chairman:**
Secretary: Tony A Kirkland, 40 Hurst Drive, Stretton, Burton-on-Trent DE13 0ED 01283 536510 (H). 0374 102485 (Mobile)
Manager: John Barton **Assistant Manager:** John Newman
Commercial Man: Peter Alcock **Physio:** Matt Brown
Press Officer: David Twigg (01283 562013)

GROUND Address: Eton Park, Princess Way, Burton-on-Trent DE14 2RU (01283 565938. **Directions:** From south - M1 jct 22, A50 (Ashby) follow to Burton over Trent bridge, thru 3 sets of lights, right at mini-r'bout (Derby Turn Pub), left at next island - ground on left: From M42 - A38 (Lichfield), follow signs for Burton, take 2nd turn for Burton (A5121), right at island - ground on left: From M6 north - jct 15 and follow A50 for Stoke and Uttoxeter, follow A50 signs to Burton, continue under bypass, left into Shakespeare Rd after canal bridge (opp. Navigation Inn), ground at end.
Capacity: 4,500 **Cover:** 2,500 **Seats:** 400 **Floodlights:** Yes
Clubhouse: 'The Football Tavern' - open normal pub hours. Full hot & cold menu. **Steward:** Graham Frost
Club Shop: Yes **Metal Badges:** Yes **Sponsors:** B.I. Industries.

PREVIOUS Leagues: West Midlands 1950-58/ Southern 58-79/ Northern Premier 79-87

CLUB RECORDS - Attendance: 5,860 v Weymouth, Southern Lg Cup Final 2nd leg, 1964 *(22,500 v Leicester City, F.A. Cup 3rd Rd 1984 - played at Derby County F.C.).* **Goalscorer:** Ritchie Barker, 157. **Appearances:** Phil Annable, 567. **Fee Paid:** £21,000 to for R Jones and J Pearson (Kidderminster). **Fee Received:** £60,000 for Darren Carr (C Palace 89).
Best Season - FA Trophy: Runners up 86-87 (SF 74-75). **FA Cup:** 3rd Rd Proper 55-56/ 84-85. 1st Rd 9 times
Players progressing to Football League: L Green & T Parry & S Aston (Hartlepool 65/66), G Hunter (Lincoln 65), D Jones (Newport 68), R Barker & J Bourne & T Bailey (Derby 67/69/70), M Pollock & S Buckley (Luton 74), P Ward (Brighton 75), Tony Moore (Sheffield Utd 79), C Swan & G Clayton (Doncaster 80 & 86), R Jobson (Watford 82), P Haycock (Rotherham 86), A Kamara (Scarborough 87), P Groves (Leicester City 88), S Cotterill & J Gayle (Wimbledon 89), D Carr (Crystal Pal. 89), D Smith & D Roberts (Wolves 90 & 92).
96-97 Captain: S Redfern **96-97 P.o.Y.:** **96-97 Top scorer:** M Nuttell
Local Press: Burton Daily Mail (01283 43311) **Local Radio:** Radio Derby

HONOURS: Sth Lg Cup 63-64 96-97 (R-up 88-89), Div 1 (Nth) R-up 71-72 73-74; Nth Prem Lg Chall Cup 82-83 (R-up 86-87), Presidents Cup R-up 85-86 (SF 86-87); Birmingham Snr Cup 53-54 70-71 (R-up 86-87); FA Trophy R-up 86-87 (SF 74-75); GMAC Cup SF 86-87; Bass Charity Vase 81-82 85-86, Challenge Cup 84-85; Wt Mids Lg R-up 53-54; Staffs Sen Cup 55-56.

Burton Albion FC: Back Row (L-R); John Newman (Asst Mgr), Dave Titterton, Martin Devaney, David Holmes, Mark Blount, Emeka Ejiofor, Darren Acton, Matthew Smith, Darren Stride, Richard Smith, Charlie Palmer, Alex Hook, Steve Spooner, Matt Brown (Physio). Front Row; Tony Marsden, Alan Davies, Les Hornby, Pat Lyons, John Barton (Mgr), Simon Redfern, Nick Ashby, Dave Benton, Andy Marlow.

Burton Albion

Match No.	Date	Venue H/A	Competition	Opponents	Result	League Pos.	Attendance	Goalscorers (Times if known)
1	Aug 17	H	DML	Cambridge City	Drew 3-3		521	Hornby 19, Redfern 32, Spooner 42
2	Aug 20	A	DML	Halesowen Town	Drew 1-1		859	Cotter 60
3	Aug 24	A	DML	Sittingbourne	Won 2-1	5	676	Cotter 24, Nuttall 47
4	Aug 26	H	DML	Nuneaton Borough	Won 2-0	5	1231	Cotter 56, Devaney 65
5	Aug 31	H	DML	Ashford Town	Won 1-0	4	775	Stride 51
6	Sep 2	A	DML	Worcester City	Lost 1-2		754	Nuttell 20
7	Sep 7	H	DML	Sudbury Town	Won 2-1	4	662	Devaney 18, 53
8	**Sep 14**	**H**	**FAC 1 Q**	**Guisborough**	**Won 1-0**		**547**	**Nuttall 83**
9	Sep 21	A	DML	Hastings Town	Lost 1-2	6	524	Redfern 71
10	Sep 24	H	DML	Halesowen Town	Drew 0-0		602	
11	**Sep 28**	**H**	**FAC 2 Q**	**Stocksbridge Park**	**Won 2-1**		**680**	**Stride 3, 35**
12	Oct 5	A	DML	King's Lynn	Lost 0-2	8	932	
13	**Oct 12**	**A**	**FAC 3 Q**	**Southport**	**Lost 1-4**		**1078**	**Nuttall 36**
14	Oct 15	A	DML	Nuneaton Borough	Lost 1-2		1007	Cotter 9
15	Oct 19	A	DML	Merthyr Tydfil	Won 1-0	8	655	Nuttell 63
16	**Oct 22**	**H**	**BSC**	**Worcester City**	**Won 2-0**		**340**	**Nuttell 9, Cotter 13**
17	Oct 26	H	DML	Dorchester Town	Won 4-1	6	745	Redfern 7, Nuttell 14, Cotter 65, 74
18	Nov 2	H	DML	Gloucester City	Won 3-1	6	862	Stride 19, Cotter 51, Hornby 76
19	Nov 9	A	DML	Newport County	Won 3-0	5	769	Hornby 8, Spooner 47, Hadley 75
20	Nov 16	H	DML	Sittingbourne	Won 1-0	4	933	Hadley 10
21	Nov 23	A	DML	Ashford Town	Drew 3-3	4	596	Stride 14, Redfern 35, Nuttell 71 (p)
22	**Nov 30**	**A**	**FAT 3 Q**	**Ashton United**	**Lost 0-1**		**374**	
23	Dec 7	A	DML	Gloucester City	Won 4-2	4	861	Hornby 10, 55, Stride 13, Redfern 32
24	**Dec 11**	**A**	**BSC**	**Halesowen Harriers**	**Won 1-0**		**98**	**Marlowe 87 (pen)**
25	Dec 14	H	DML	Baldock Town	Drew 1-1	4	822	Cotter 68
26	**Dec 17**	**A**	**DMC**	**Nuneaton Borough**	**Won 2-1**		**513**	**Hassell 38 (og), Nuttell 75**
27	Dec 21	A	DML	Dorchester Town	Lost 0-5	5	480	
28	Dec 26	H	DML	Gresley Rovers	Lost 2-3	5	2537	Redfern 2, Nuttell 55
29	Dec 28	A	DML	Crawley Town	Won 2-0	5	691	Nuttell 8, 20
30	**Jan 14**	**H**	**DMC**	**Halesowen Town**	**Won 1-0**		**410**	**Spooner 9**
31	Jan 18	A	DML	Baldock Town	Won 3-1	5	348	Hornby 40, Devaney 56, Cotter 79
32	**Jan 21**	**H**	**BSC**	**Walsall**	**Won 3-2**		**260**	**Spooner 26, Keast 37, Stride 76**
33	Jan 25	H	DML	Salisbury City	Drew 1-1	5	724	Devaney 25
34	Feb 1	H	DML	Merthyr Tydfil	Lost 0-1	5	675	
35	**Feb 5**	**A**	**DMC**	**Raunds Town**	**Won 2-0**		**243**	**Stride 12, 45**
36	Feb 8	A	DML	Cambridge City	Lost 0-1	7	267	
37	Feb 10	H	DML	Worcester City	Drew 2-2		447	Redfern 64, Nuttell 90 (pen)
38	Feb 15	H	DML	Gravesend & Northfleet	Lost 1-3	6	713	Marlow 55
39	Feb 17	H	DML	Coventry City	Won 1-0		208	Devaney 22
40	**Feb 22**	**H**	**BSC**	**Newport A.F.C.**	**Won 3-0**	**6**	**714**	**Spooner 9, 75, Stride 50**
41	**Feb 25**	**A**	**DMC**	**R C Warwick**	**Won 4-1**		**533**	**Hornby 20, Nuttell 43, Devaney 86, Cotter 87**
42	Mar 1	H	DML	King's Lynn	Won 4-1	6	807	Cotter 12, 57, Devaney 20, Nuttell 45
43	Mar 4	A	DML	Gresley Rovers	Lost 0-1	6	1760	
44	Mar 8	A	DML	Salisbury City	Drew 1-1	6	339	Cotter 14
45	**Mar 11**	**H**	**DMC**	**R C Warwick**	**Won 4-1**		**313**	**Francis 21 (og), Nuttell 38, 44, Spooner 63, AOG 8-2**
46	Mar 15	H	DML	Chelmsford City	Won 4-2	6	656	Nuttell 14, 60 (pen), Redfern 25, Hornby 82
47	Mar 22	A	DML	Cheltenham Town	Won 3-3	6	1066	Devaney 18, Cotter 19, Redfern 45
48	Mar 29	H	DML	Atherstone United	Lost 1-2		911	Spooner 13
49	Mar 31	A	DML	Atherstone United	Lost 1-2	8	606	Stride 25
50	Apr 5	H	DML	Crawley Town	Won 2-0	7	604	Stride 8, Spooner 11
51	Apr 8	A	DML	Gravesend & Northfleet	Won 1-0		488	Marlow 63 (pen)
52	Apr 12	A	DML	Chelmsford City	Drew 2-2	6	780	Redfern 2, 72
53	**Apr 15**	**H**	**DMC F**	**Sudbury Town**	**Won 2-1**		**511**	**Devaney 6, 44**
54	Apr 19	H	DML	Hastings Town	Drew 0-0	7	568	
55	Apr 26	A	DML	Sudbury Town	Won 3-0	6	295	Cotter 9, Stride 77, Ejiofor 82
56	**Apr 29**	**A**	**DMC F**	**Sudbury Town**	**Won 1-0**		**495**	**Spooner 85**
57	May 3	H	DML	Cheltenham Town	Drew 0-0	6	1142	

BURTON ALBION PLAYING SQUAD 1997-98

Goalkeepers: Darren Acton (Telford U)

Defenders: Matthew Smith (Cork C, Plymouth, Derby), **Allan Davies** (Manchester C (T)), **Richard Smith** (Nottingham F (T)), **David Titterton** (Hednesford T, Wycombe W, Hereford, Coventry), **David Benton** (Worcester C, Kidderminster H, Birmingham), **Les Hornby** (VS Rugby, Yeovil T, Rothwell T, Desborough T, Spalding U, Desborough T, Northampton), **Charlie Palmer** (Walsall, Notts Co, Hull, Derby, Watford), **Pat Lyons** (WBA, Derby (T))

Midfielders: Simon Redfern (Local football), **Karl Payne** (Chesterfield), **Darren Stride** (Youth team), **Steve Spooner** (Rushden & D, Chesterfield, Blackpool, Mansfield, Rotherham, York, Hereford, Chesterfield, Halifax, Derby), **Andy Marlowe** (Moor Green, Bromsgrove R, Hednesford T, Bromsgrove R, Leyton Orient, Spurs (T))

Forwards: Mickey Nuttell (Rushden & D, Dag & Red, Kettering T, Boston U, Wycombe W, Cheltenham T, Peterborough), **Martin Devaney** (Gresley R, Leek T, Tamworth, Gresley R, Hanford, Ilkeston T), **Emeka Efiofor** (Youth team), **Micky Cotter** (Gravesend, Dover Ath, Erith & Belvedere, Welling U)

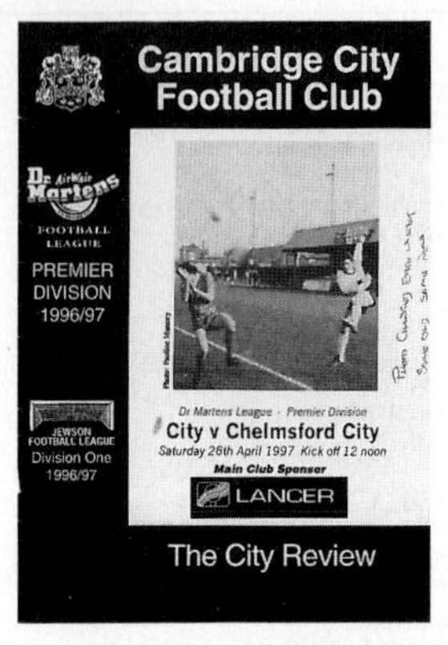

Cambridge City Football Club
Dr Martens Football League
PREMIER DIVISION 1996/97
Jewson Football League Division One 1996/97
Dr Martens League - Premier Division
City v Chelmsford City
Saturday 26th April 1997 Kick off 12 noon
Main Club Sponsor
LANCER
The City Review

PROGRAMME DETAILS:
Pages: 24 **Price:** £1.00
Editor: David Crane
(01223 233057)

CAMBRIDGE CITY

Formed: 1908 **Nickname:** Lilywhites
Colours: White & black halves/black/white & blck hoops
Change colours: All sky blue.
Midweek matchday: Tuesday
Reserve Team's League: Jewson Eastern Counties.

Chairman: Dennis Rolph**President:** Sir Neil Westbrook, CBE MA FRICS
Secretary: Stuart Hamilton, 55 Crowhill, Godmanchester, Huntingdon, Cambs (01480 382675).
Manager: Graham Daniels **Asst Manager:** Steve Low
Press Officer: Secretary **Physio:** John Aves, Collin Pettit
General Manager: W E Leivers

GROUND Address: City Ground, Milton Road, Cambridge CB4 1UY (0223 357973). **Directions:** 50 yards on left from start of A1309, Cambridge to Ely Rd. 30 mins walk Cambridge BR
Capacity: 5,000 **Cover:** 1,400 **Seats:** 400 **Floodlights:** Yes
Clubhouse: 11am-11pm Mon-Sat, 12-3pm & 7pm-10.30pm Sun. Bingo, Dances, Pool, Stag nights, Darts.
Club Shop: Sells programmes, club history, badges, scarves, pennants, replica shirts etc. Contact Neil Harvey (01223 235991).
Club Sponsors: Lancer UK

PREVIOUS - Name: Cambridge Town 1908-51. **Leagues:** Bury & Dist. 08-13 19-20, East Anglian 08-10, Southern Olympian 11-14, Southern Amateur 1913-35, Spartan 35-50, Athenian 50-58.

CLUB RECORDS - Attendance: 12,058 v Leytonstone, FA Amateur Cup 1st Rd, 1949-50. **Scorer:** Gary Grogan. **Appearances:** Mal Keenan. **Fee Paid:** £8,000 for Paul Coe (Rushden + Diamonds). **Fee Received:** £15,500 for Kevin Wilkin (Northampton Tn 91). **Best Season - FA Amateur Cup:** Semi Final 27-28. **FA Trophy:** 2nd Rd. 86-87 87-88. **FA Cup** 1st Rd; v Ashford 66, v Swindon 46, v Walthamstow Ave. 48, v Hereford 93.
Players progressing to Football League: K Wright (West Ham 46), A Gallego (Norwich 47), A Stokes (Watford 61), D Weddle (Middlesbrough 61), D Hicksen (Bury 62), B Harvey (Blackpool 62), R Whitehead (Darlington 62), G Cummins (Hull 62), R Pearce (Peterborough 63), A Banks (Exeter 63), T Carroll (Ipswich 66), Dominic Genovese (Peterborough 88), Roy Jones (Swindon), Winston Dubose (Oldham), K Wilkin (Northampton Tn 91), S Flack (Cardiff City 95), D Hedcock (Sheffield Wed 96).
96-97 Captain: Keith Lockhart **96-97 Top Scorer:** Neil Harris **96-97 P.o.Y.:** Andy Pincher
Local Press: Cambridge Evening News 35877 **Local Radio:** BBC Radio Cambridge

HONOURS: Southern Lg 62-63 (R-up 70-71, Southern Div 85-86, Div 1 R-up 69-70, Champ Cup 62-63; E Anglian Cup (9); Eastern Prof Floodlit Lg 65-66 72-73, Cambs Prof Cup (6); Cambs Invitation Cup (7); Spartan Lg 47-48 48-49 (R-up 49-50); Eastern Div Champs 45-46); Southern Amat Lg 20-21 27-28 28-29 30-31 31-32; Bury & Dist. Lg (4); E Anglian Lg (6); AFA Snr Cup 30-31 46-47 47-48(shared) 48-49 49-50; AFA Invitation Cup 50-51; Hunts Prem Cup 62-63 64-65; Suffolk Sen Cup 09-10; Addenbrookes Hosp Cup 87-88; The Munns Youth Cup 82-83 83-84 84-85; Chiltern Youth Lge Cup R-up 75-76; South Mids Lg Youth Trophy 82-83; Robinson Cup 87-88 89-90; Jim Digney 89-90; Essex & Herts Youth Lg 89-90.

Cambridge City FC: Neil Brindle, John Ashdjian, Andrew Nunn, Neil Harris, Andrew Jeffrey, Michael Cheetham, Nicky Smith, Daren Horn, Mark Reeder, Mark Adams, Simon Crow, Mark Shipp, Tom Austin. Middle Row; Martin Wilson, James Saddington, Peter Leete, Andrew Taylor, Jeremy George, Daniel Kelly, Barry White, Steve Gawthrop, Roscoe Hipperson, Keith Lockhart, Steve Callinan. Front Row; Trevor Ball, Aron Rutter, Andy Pincher, Brian Chapman (Kit Mgr), Keith Pybus (Res Coach), Graham Daniels (Mgr), Steve Low (Ast Mgr), Greg Reid (Physio), Richard Chattoe, Paul Byatt, Richard Innman Photo - Cambridge Newspapers

Cambridge City

Match No.	Date	Venue H/A	Competition	Opponents	Result	League Pos.	Attendance	Goalscorers (Times if known)
1	Aug 17	A	DML	Burton Albion	Drew 3-3		521	Pinchez 13, Leete 42, Tovey 45
2	Aug 20	H	DML	Gravesend & Northfleet	Won 4-2		334	Tovey 24, 65 (pen), Coe 79, Fowler 90
3	Aug 24	H	DML	Gloucester City	Lost 0-1	8	337	
4	Aug 26	A	DML	Baldock Town	Won 3-0	6	416	Cambridge 32, Tovey 49, Lockhart 60
5	Aug 31	A	DML	Halesowen Town	Lost 1-3	9	803	Tovey 61
6	Sep 3	H	DML	Sittingbourne	Lost 1-3		223	Leete 12
7	Sep 8	A	DML	Dorchester Town	Won 2-0	8	554	Coe 58, Cambridge 81
8	**Sep 14**	**H**	**FAC 1 Q**	**Diss Town**	**Won 6-1**		**328**	**Coe (5) 10, 12, 67, 72, 90, Goddard 65**
9	Sep 21	H	DML	Merthyr Tydfil	Drew 2-2	9	228	Cambridge 38, Coe 68
10	Sep 24	A	DML	Gravesend & Northfleet	Drew 1-1	10	499	Cambridge 25
11	**Sep 28**	**A**	**FAC 2 Q**	**Wrexham**	**Drew 1-1**		**286**	**Cambridge 42**
12	**Oct 1**	**H**	**FAC 2 Q**	**Wrexham**	**Won 2-0**		**307**	**Coe 2, Harrington 89**
13	Oct 5	A	DML	Gresley Rovers	Lost 1-3	15	707	Chattoe 90
14	**Oct 8**	**A**	**DMLC**	**Buckingham Town**	**Won 3-0**		**91**	**Coe 20, Pincher 50, Althorpe 80**
15	**Oct 12**	**H**	**FAC 3 Q**	**Canvey Island**	**Lost 0-3**		**461**	
16	Oct 15	H	DML	Baldock Town	Drew 1-1	16	222	Cambridge 18
17	**Oct 19**	**A**	**FAT 1 Q**	**Cirencester Town**	**Drew 2-2**		**127**	**Tovey 65, Lockhart 88**
18	**Oct 22**	**H**	**FAT 1QR**	**Cirencester Town**	**Won 6-5**		**195**	**Retallick 10, Beattie 33, Cambridge 39, Tovey 48, (Lockhart 58, Goddard 55**
19	Oct 26	A	DML	Atherstone United	Lost 0-1	17	213	
20	**Oct 29**	**H**	**DMLC**	**Buckingham Town**	**Won 4-0**		**133**	**Lockhart 20, Cambridge 24, Leete 26, Bearman 82**
21	Nov 2	H	DML	Hastings Town	Lost 1-3	20	290	Tovey 21 (pen)
22	**Nov 9**	**A**	**FAT 2 Q**	**Forest Green Rovers**	**Won 2-1**		**236**	**Cambridge 6, Tovey 48 (pen)**
23	Nov 16	H	DML	Crawley Town	Won 4-0	17	217	Cambridge 7, 79, Tovey 25, Lockhart 80
24	Nov 20	A	DML	Sittingbourne	Won 2-0	13	417	Howell 63, Pincher 68
25	Nov 23	A	DML	Cheltenham Town	Lost 0-1	13	906	
26	**Nov 30**	**H**	**FAT 3 Q**	**Newport A.F.C.**	**Drew 1-1**		**346**	**Retallick 25**
27	**Dec 4**	**A**	**FAT 3QR**	**Newport A.F.C.**	**Lost 1-4**		**414**	**Cambridge 6**
28	Dec 7	A	DML	Chelmsford City	Lost 0-2	14	932	
29	**Dec 10**	**H**	**DMC**	**Sudbury Town**	**Lost 1-4**		**162**	**Pincher 59**
30	Dec 14	H	DML	Gresley Rovers	Lost 2-3	17	208	Wallis 2, Pincher 7
31	Dec 21	H	DML	Worcester City	Lost 1-2	19	306	Taylor 73
32	Jan 11	A	DML	Worcester City	Drew 2-2	17	615	Chattoe 11, Leete 62
33	Jan 18	H	DML	Sudbury Town	Lost 1-3	18	351	Inman 30
34	Jan 25	A	DML	Gloucester City	Lost 0-2	20	606	
35	Jan 28	A	DML	King's Lynn	Lost 0-2	20	1236	
36	Feb 1	H	DML	Atherstone United	Lost 1-2	20	237	Harris 18
37	**Feb 4**	**A**	**CIC**	**Histon**	**Lost 1-2***		**102**	**Byatt 14**
38	Feb 8	H	DML	Burton Albion	Won 1-0	20	267	Cambridge 17
39	Feb 15	A	DML	Newport A.F.C.	Drew 0-0	20	560	
40	Feb 18	H	DML	Cheltenham Town	Lost 1-4		227	Harris 19
41	Feb 22	A	DML	Hastings Town	Drew 0-0	20	466	
42	Mar 1	H	DML	Halesowen Town	Lost 1-4	20	278	Ippolito 15
43	Mar 8	A	DML	Crawley Town	Won 2-0	19	602	Leete 48, 57
44	Mar 15	H	DML	Salisbury City	Drew 1-1	19	213	Calliman 77
45	Mar 22	A	DML	Salisbury City	Drew 2-2	19	257	Taylor 65, Harris 83
46	**Mar 11**		**EAC**	**Potton United**	**Drew 2-2***		**93**	**Cameron 26, 32 (Lost 3-4 Penalties)**
47	Mar 25	H	DML	Dorchester Town	Drew 2-2		214	Harris 20, Gawthrop 88
48	Mar 29	A	DML	Sudbury Town	Won 2-0		460	Harris 58, Pincher 80
49	Mar 31	H	DML	King's Lynn	Lost 0-2	17	590	
50	Apr 5	A	DML	Ashford Town	Drew 2-2	18	521	Harris 44, 53
51	Apr 8	H	DML	Nuneaton Borough	Drew 2-2		324	Bennett 19, Reilly 74
52	Apr 12	H	DML	Newport A.F.C.	Drew 0-0	18	454	
53	Apr 19	A	DML	Nuneaton Borough	Lost 1-3	21	911	Lockhart 89
54	Apr 22	H	DML	Ashford Town	Won 4-0		248	Harris (4) 19, 31, 50, 68
55	Apr 26	H	DML	Chelmsford City	Won 1-0	18	335	Garvey 30 (og)
56	May 3	A	DML	Merthyr Tydfil	Won 2-1	18	432	Taylor 70, Harris 90

* After Extra Time

CAMBRIDGE CITY PLAYING SQUAD 1997-98

Goalkeepers : Danny Kelly (Kettering T, Notts Co, Spurs (J)), **Barry Piggott** (Royston T, Cambridge C)

Defenders : Andy Beattie (Hendon, Cambridge C, Barnet, Maidstone U, Barnet, Cambridge U), **James Saddington** (Kettering T, Millwall, Cambridge C, Newmarket T), **Steve Gawthrop** (Youth team), **Andy Jeffrey** (Camb.U, Camb.C, Leicester C), **Andy Taylor** (Sudbury T, Bury T, Long Melford), **Richard Chattoe** (Baldock T, Weston-S-M, Bristol R), **Roscoe Hipperson** (King's Lynn, Thetford, Diss, Thetford)

Midfielders : Andy Pincher (Cambridge U (T)), **Wayne Goddard** (Soham Town R, Rushden & D, Cambridge C, Histon), **Keith Lockhart** (Sudbury T, Cambridge C, Hartlepool, Wolves, Cambridge U), **Chris Tovey** (Great Shelford, Cambridge C, Royston T, Cambridge C, Royston T, Letchworth GC), **John Fowler** (Kettering T, Camb.U), **Steve Callinan** (Sudbury T, Camb.C, Bury T, Norwich (J))

Forwards : Danny Howells (Barton R, Baldock T, Letchworth GC), **Peter Leete** (Potton U, Foxton), **Paul Byatt** (Gt.Shelford), **Nigel Wallis** (Diss, Braintree T, Sudbury T, Fleixstowe T), **Neil Cogger** (Haverhill R), **Neil Harris** (Maldon T, Gt.Wakering R)

CRAWLEY TOWN

Formed: 1896 **Nickname:** The Reds
Colours: All red
Change colours: Blue & black/black/black
Midweek matchday: Tuesday
Reserves' League: Suburban.

Chairman: John Maggs **President:** Ken Symons
Secretary: Dave Haining, 20 Irving Walk, Tilgate, Crawley RH10 5BQ (01293 535683).
Manager: Billy Smith **Asst Man:** John Broughton
Physio: Richard Massimo **Commercial Manager:** Andy Bell

GROUND Address: Broadfield Stadium, Brighton Road, Crawley RH11 9RX (01293 410000). **Directions:** M23 exit 11, 2nd exit off r/about, A23, towards Crawley, turn left at next r/about into ground.
Capacity: 4,800 **Cover:** 4,200 **Seats:** 1,080 **Floodlights:** Yes
Clubhouse: Weekdays 11-3 & 6-11pm, Sat 11-11pm, Sun noon-10.30pm, Bank Hols 11-11. Snacks available.
Club Shop: Sells programmes, metal badges, hats, scarves, mugs, replica kits.
Sponsors: Eurobell

PROGRAMME DETAILS:
Pages: 40 **Price:** £1
Editor: Ian Hands

PREVIOUS - Leagues: Sussex County 1951-56/ Metropolitan 56-63. **Grounds:** Malthouse Farm 1896-1914 38-40/ Victoria Hall + Rectory Fields 18-38/ Yetmans Field 45-49, Town Mead 49-53 54-97, Ilfield Rec Grd 53-54

CLUB RECORDS - Attendance: 4,104 v Barnet, FA Cup 2nd Round 4/12/93.
Goalscorer: Phil Basey 108.(68-72). **Appearances:** John Maggs 652.(63-73 75-79).
Win: 10-0 v Chichester United, Sussex County League Division Two 17/12/55.
Defeat: 0-10 v Arundel (A), Sussex County Lge 9/2/52.
Fee Paid: £5,000 for David Thompson (Wokingham, May 1992)
Fee Received: £50,000 for Craig Whitington (Scarborough 1993).
Best Season - FA Trophy: 2nd Rd 85-86 87-88.
FA Cup: 3rd Rd Proper 91-92 (lost 0-5 at Brighton). - **League Clubs defeated:** Northampton Town 91-92.
Players progressing to Football League: Ray Keeley, Graham Brown (Mansfield 68), Andy Ansah (Brentford 87), Craig Whitington (Scarborough 93).
96-97 Captain: **96-97 P.o.Y.:** Viv Jeffery **96-97 Top scorer:** Steve Restarick 18
Local Press: Crawley Observer, Crawley News, The Argus **Local Radio:** Fame 1521

HONOURS: Sussex Snr Cup (2) 89-91 (R-up 58-59 95-96); Sussex Intermediate Cup 26-27; Sussex Prof. Cup 69-70; Southern Lg Southern Div R-up 83-84; Merit Cup 70-71; Sussex Floodlit Cup (3) 90-93; Sussex Lg Div 2 R-up 55-56; Gilbert Rice Floodlit Cup 79-80 83-84; Southern Co's Comb. Floodlit Cup 85-86; Metropolitan Lg Chal. Cup 58-59; Mid-Sussex Snr 02-03; Montgomery Cup 25-26.

Crawley's Justin Gregory takes on a Hastings defender in the last Sussex derby to be staged at Town Mead, before moving to Broadfield Stadium. *Photo - Eric Buck, Crawley Observer*

Crawley Town

Match No.	Date	Venue H/A	Competition	Opponents	Result	League Pos.	Attendance	Goalscorers (Times if known)
1	Aug 17	H	DML	Halesowen Town	Lost 0-3		672	
2	Aug 21	A	DML	Salisbury City	Lost 0-1		340	
3	Aug 24	A	DML	Nuneaton Borough	Won 2-1		1333	Byrne 49, 61
4	Aug 26	H	DML	Chelmsford City	Lost 1-2	18	761	Byrne 72
5	Aug 31	H	DML	Worcester City	Won 2-1	14	618	Geddes 54, Byrne 62
6	Sep 3	A	DML	Dorchester Town	Won 5-2		593	Jeffery 6, Byrne 49, Restarick (3) 13, 76, 79
7	Sep 7	H	DML	Gresley Rovers	Drew 0-0	10	672	
8	**Sep 14**	**A**	**FAC 1 Q**	**Redhill**	**Won 1-0**		**929**	**Geddes 2**
9	Sep 21	A	DML	Sudbury Town	Lost 0-2	14	440	
10	Sep 24	H	DML	Salisbury City	Drew 2-2	15	481	Restarick 4, Geddes 88
11	**Sep 28**	**H**	**FAC 2 Q**	**Bromley**	**Lost 0-4**		**896**	
12	Oct 5	A	DML	Cheltenham Town	Won 2-1	11	810	Restarick 23, Geddes 32
13	**Oct 9**	**A**	**DMLC**	**Dartford**	**Drew 1-1**		**219**	**Restarick 47**
14	Oct 12	H	DML	King's Lynn	Drew 0-0	10	623	
15	Oct 15	A	DML	Chelmsford City	Lost 0-1		470	
16	Oct 19	A	DML	Gresley Rovers	Lost 0-2	14	687	
17	Oct 26	A	DML	Baldock Town	Won 2-1	10	283	Adam 36, Geddes 81
18	**Oct 29**	**H**	**DMLC**	**Dartford**	**Won 2-0**		**321**	**Restarick 51, 65**
19	Nov 2	H	DML	Newport A.F.C.	Lost 1-3	14	922	Whittington 87
20	Nov 9	A	DML	Gloucester City	Lost 1-2	14	839	Byrne 74
21	Nov 16	A	DML	Cambridge City	Lost 0-4	15	217	
22	Nov 23	H	DML	Sittingbourne	Drew 2-2	17	631	Restarick 21, Adam 39
23	**Nov 25**	**H**	**SSC**	**Brighton & Hove Albion**	**Lost 1-3**		**340**	**Restarick 10**
24	**Nov 30**	**H**	**FAT 3 Q**	**Chelmsford City**	**Lost 0-2**		**619**	
25	Dec 7	A	DML	Merthyr Tydfil	Lost 1-3	18	617	Restarick 13
26	**Dec 10**	**H**	**DMC**	**Tonbridge**	**Lost 1-2**		**277**	**Whittington 18**
27	Dec 14	H	DML	Cheltenham Town	Drew 3-3	16	448	Adam 27, Vansittart 49, Restarick 76
28	Dec 21	A	DML	Sittingbourne	Won 5-3	13	758	Whittington (3) 22, 33, 59, Restarick 63, Vansittart 89
29	Dec 28	H	DML	Burton Albion	Lost 0-2	14	691	
30	Jan 4	A	DML	Gravesend & Northfleet	Lost 0-2	16	517	
31	Jan 25	A	DML	Halesowen Town	Drew 2-2	16	725	Adam 32, Vansittart 90
32	Feb 1	H	DML	Baldock Town	Won 2-0	15	534	Restarick 65, Whittington 73
33	Feb 4	H	DML	Ashford Town	Lost 2-3		419	Restarick 11, Jeffery 25
34	Feb 8	A	DML	Atherstone United	Lost 0-2	17	303	
35	Feb 22	A	DML	Worcester City	Lost 1-2	17	649	Adam 25
36	Mar 1	A	DML	Newport A.F.C.	Won 1-0	16	601	Restarick 53
37	Mar 8	H	DML	Cambridge City	Lost 0-2	16	602	
38	Mar 15	H	DML	Gloucester City	Drew 1-1	16	534	Whittington 73
39	Mar 22	H	DML	Gravesend & Northfleet	Lost 0-2	16	691	
40	Mar 29	A	DML	Ashford Town	Drew 3-3		567	Restarick 13, 17, Jeffery 48
41	Mar 31	H	DML	Hastings Town	Lost 0-2	20	943	
42	Apr 5	A	DML	Burton Albion	Lost 0-2	21	604	
43	Apr 8	H	DML	Merthyr Tydfil	Won 1-0		506	Whittington 1
44	Apr 12	H	DML	Sudbury Town	Lost 1-2	21	582	Payne 70
45	Apr 15	H	DML	Dorchester Town	Won 2-0		535	Johanson 39, Jeffery 59
46	Apr 19	A	DML	King's Lynn	Won 1-0	17	928	Prosper 86
47	Apr 20	H	DML	Nuneaton Borough	Won 1-0		757	Warden 55
48	Apr 26	H	DML	Atherstone United	Won 2-0	16	901	Warden 13, Whittington 49 (pen)
49	Apr 29	A	DML	Hastings Town	Lost 0-1	17	491	

CRAWLEY TOWN PLAYING SQUAD 1997-98

Goalkeepers : Ian Chatfield (Dorking, Hayes, Chelsea (T), Redhill)
Defenders : John Mackie (Arsenal (T)), **John Crumplin** (Woking, Brighton, Bognor Regis T), **Tony Vessey** (Worthing, Steyning, Vasalund (Swe), Brighton), **Justin Gregory** (Hastings T, Worthing, Shoreham), **Mark Garland** (Kingstonian, CrystalPalace (T)), **Solomon Eriemo** (Hendon, Carshalton A, Aldershot T, Kingstonian, Wealdstone, Leyton-Wingate, Walthamstow Ave., Leytonstone & Ilf), **Marc Pullan** (Peacehaven & T), **Danny Foot** (Southend, Spurs (T))
Midfielders : Viv Jeffrey (Banstead Ath), **Paul Adam** (Molesey, Sutton U), **Mark Ford** (Sutton U), **Duncan Jones** (St.Leonards Stamcroft, Hastings T, Bexhill, Stamco), **Jon Warden** (Bromley, Kingstonian, Carshalton A, Tooting, Croydon), **Conrad Kane** (Bromley, Dulwich H, Kingstonian, Carshalton A, Dulwich H, Bromley, Dulwich H, Merstham), **Graham Harper** (Local football)
Forwards : Gavin Geddes (Brighton, Wick, Shoreham, Lewes), **Steve Restarick** (Dover A, Chelmsford C, Colchester U), **Rodney Prosper** (Horsham, Croydon, Molesey, Kingstonian, Carshalton A, Dulwich H, Tooting, Kingstonian, Horsham,Croydon A), **Craig Whitington** (Huddersfield, Scarborough, Crawley T, Worthing)

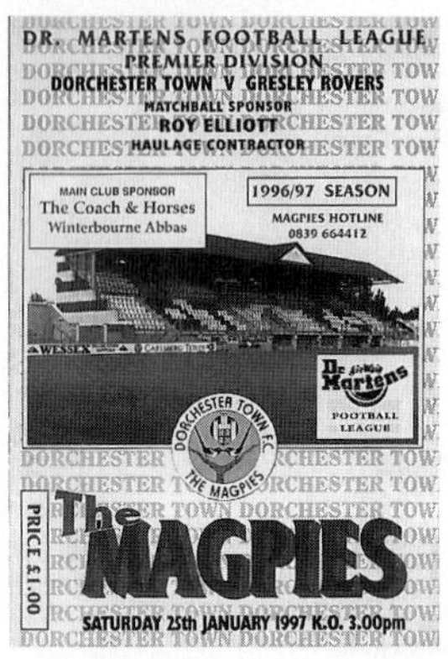

PROGRAMME DETAILS:
Pages: 32 **Price:** 80p
Editor: David Martin
(011305 264740)

DORCHESTER TOWN

Formed: 1880 **Nickname:** The Magpies
Colours: Black & white stripes/black/black
Change colours: Sky blue/white/sky blue
Midweek games: Tuesday **Newsline (Magpies Hotline):** 0839 664412.
Reserves' League: Dorset Comb

Chairman: C E Clark **President:**
Vice Chairman: K Mitchell **Comm Mgr:** Keith Kellaway (01305 262451)
Secretary: Albert Miller, 29 Shaston Crescent, Dorchester DT1 2EB (01305 264843)
Manager: Stuart Morgan **Physio:** Geoff Dine

GROUND Address: Avenue Stadium, Weymouth Avenue, Dorchester DT1 2RY (01305 262451). **Directions:** situated at the junction of the town bypass (A35) and the Weymouth road (A354). Nearest station: Dorchester South.
Capacity: 7,210 **Cover:** 4,000 **Seats:** 710 **Floodlights:** Yes
Clubhouse: Dorchester Lounge Club - access via main entrance to stadium. Cold food and snacks
Club Shop: Sells replica shirts, badges, mugs, etc.
Sponsors: Winterbourne Hospital

PREVIOUS - Grounds: Council Recreation Ground, Weymouth Avenue 1880-1929/ The Avenue Ground, Weymouth Avenue 29-90. **Leagues:** Dorset/ Western 1947-72.

CLUB RECORDS - Attendance: 4,000 v Chelsea, official ground opening 1990. Competitive: 3,027 v Weymouth, Southern Lge Prem Div 92. **Goalscorer:** Dennis Cheney 61 (in one season). **Appearances:** Derek (Dinkie) Curtis 458 50-66. **Win:** 7-0 v Canterbury (A), Southern Lge Southern Div 86-87. **Defeat:** 0-13 v Welton Rovers Western Lge 66. **Fee Paid:** £12,000 for Chris Townsend (Gloucester City, 1990). **Fee Received:** £35,000 for Trevor Senior (Portsmouth, 1981)
Best Season - FA Trophy: 3rd Rd replay 71-72, 96-97. **FA Cup:** 2nd Rd Replay 81-82 (1-2 v A.F.C. Bournemouth after 1-1 draw). 2nd Rd 54-55 57-58, 1st Rd 7 times.
Players progressing to The Football League: Len Drake (Bristol Rovers 57), David Noake (Luton 59), Mike Turner (Swindon 61), Trevor Senior (Portsmouth 81), David West (Liverpool 83), Mike Squire (Torquay 84), Jeremy Judd (Torquay 84), Anthony White (Bournemouth 85), Graham Roberts (Spurs, Chelsea, Rangers, England) who progressed via Weymouth. Darren Garner (Rotherham U, 95), Craig Taylor (Swindon).
96-97 Captain: Neil Coates **P.o.Y.:** Craig Taylor **Top scorer:** Owen Pickard
Local Press: Dorset Evening Echo, Western Gazette, Western Daily Press.
Local Radio: Two Counties Radio, Wessex FM .

HONOURS: Southern Lg 85-85, R-up 79-80 (Div 1 Sth R-up 77-78), Lg Cup 86-87 (R-up 91-92); Western Lg 54-55 (R-up 60-61, Div 2 R-up 49-50), Lge Cup 54-54; Dorset Snr Cup 50-51 60-61 67-68 68-69 71-72 93-94 94-95; Dorset Lg 37-38.

Dorchester Town FC.

Dorchester Town

Match No.	Date	Venue H/A	Competition	Opponents	Result	League Pos.	Attendance	Goalscorers (Times if known)
1	Aug 17	A	DML	Atherstone United	Lost 1-2		273	Pickard 60
2	Aug 20	H	DML	Cheltenham Town	Lost 1-3		754	Thorpe 58
3	Aug 24	H	DML	Baldock Town	Won 3-2		611	Thorpe 13, Richardson 45, Wilkinson 68
4	Aug 26	A	DML	Newport A.F.C.	Lost 0-3	20	729	
5	Aug 31	A	DML	Sittingbourne	Won 3-1	13	543	Crocker 71, Pickard 77, 79
6	Sep 3	H	DML	Crawley Town	Lost 2-5		593	Pickard 51, Killick 70
7	Sep 8	H	DML	Cambridge City	Lost 0-2	20	554	
8	**Sep 10**	**A**	**DMC Pr Lg**	**Newport I.o.W.**	**Lost 1-2**		**210**	**Richardson 74**
9	**Sep 14**	**A**	**FAC 1 Q**	**Clevedon Town**	**Lost 1-4**		**282**	**Pickard 47**
10	**Sep 17**	**H**	**DMC**	**Newport I.o.W.**	**Drew 1-1**		**316**	**Pickard 52**
11	Sep 21	A	DML	Gresley Rovers	Drew 0-0	19	589	
12	Sep 24	A	DML	Cheltenham Town	Drew 1-1	19	536	Pickard 17
13	Oct 5	H	DML	Sudbury Town	Lost 0-1	19	987	
14	Oct 12	A	DML	Gravesend & Northfleet	Won 3-1	19	551	Pickard 15, Richardson 55, Sullivan 73
15	Oct 15	H	DML	Newport A.F.C.	Lost 1-3		486	Pickard 25
16	**Oct 19**	**H**	**FAT 1 Q**	**Waterlooville**	**Won 1-0**		**408**	**Sullivan 40**
17	Oct 26	A	DML	Burton Albion	Lost 1-4		745	Coates 51
18	Nov 2	H	DML	Nuneaton Borough	Won 2-0	19	532	Pickard 61, 68
19	**Nov 9**	**A**	**FAT 2 Q**	**Billericay Town**	**Won 4-0**		**214**	**Pickard (3) 39, 77, 79, Lisk**
20	Nov 16	A	DML	Chelmsford City	Drew 1-1	20	1012	Richardson 14
21	Nov 23	H	DML	Gravesend & Northfleet	Drew 2-2	20	623	Pickard 37, Richardson 60
22	**Nov 30**	**A**	**FAT 3 Q**	**Sutton United**	**Won 2-0**		**397**	**Pickard 73 (og), 59**
23	Dec 7	H	DML	Ahterstone United	Won 1-0	16	190	Taylor 68 (pen)
24	Dec 14	A	DML	Ashford Town	Drew 1-1	19	407	Pickard 7
25	Dec 21	H	DML	Burton Albion	Won 5-0	14	480	Killick 16, 75, Pickard (3) 73, 82, 90
26	Dec 28	H	DML	Hastings Town	Drew 1-1	13	613	Richardson 1
27	Jan 11	H	DML	Sittingbourne	Won 2-0	13	522	Reeve 43, Pickard 68
28	**Jan 18**	**A**	**FAT 1**	**Slough Town**	**Drew 2-2**		**744**	**Lisk 68, Pickard 73**
29	**Jan 21**	**H**	**FAT 1 R**	**Slough Town**	**Drew 1-1**		**685**	**Taylor 39 (pen)**
30	Jan 25	H	DML	Gresley Rovers	Lost 1-3	15	739	Pickard 71
31	**Jan 27**	**A**	**FAT 1R2**	**Slough Town**	**Won 2-1**		**593**	**Pickard 35, Taylor 54**
32	Feb 1	A	DML	Worcester City	Lost 0-1	16	519	
33	**Feb 8**	**A**	**FAT 2**	**Salisbury City**	**Drew 1-1**		**727**	**Taylor 67**
34	**Feb 11**	**H**	**FAT 2 R**	**Salisbury City**	**Won 3-2**		**713**	**Wilkinson 21, Taylor 31 (p), Pickard 88**
35	Feb 15	H	DML	King's Lynn	Won 3-0	15	638	Wilkinson 30, Pickard 55, 59
36	Feb 22	H	DML	Chelmsford City	Won 1-0	15	606	Pickard 79
37	**Mar 1**	**H**	**FAT 3**	**Woking**	**Lost 2-3**		**2942**	**Killick 6, Pickard 67 (pen)**
38	Mar 4	H	DML	Merthyr Tydfil	Won 2-0	14	684	Wilkinson 61, Killick 86
39	Mar 8	A	DML	King's Lynn	Won 4-0	14	893	Pickard (3) 21, 35, 82, Redwood 16
40	Mar 9	A	DML	Baldock Town	Lost 1-2	14	228	Richardson 80
41	Mar 15	A	DML	Sudbury Town	Won 4-2	14	360	Wilkinson 31, Lisk 43, Pickard 57, Reeve 84
42	Mar 18	A	DML	Halesowen Town	Lost 1-3	15	482	Reeve 29
43	Mar 25	A	DML	Cambridge City	Drew 2-2		214	Reeve 27, 48
44	Mar 28	A	DML	Merthyr Tydfil	Lost 2-3		572	Reeve 33, Lovell 62
45	Mar 31	H	DML	Salisbury City	Won 4-2	15	868	Taylor 43, Killick 71, 86, Allsop 45
46	Apr 5	A	DML	Hastings Town	Lost 0-1	15	403	
47	Apr 12	H	DML	Halesowen Town	Drew 1-1	15	631	Taylor 27 (pen)
48	Apr 15	A	DML	Crawley Town	Lost 0-2		535	
49	Apr 19	H	DML	Worcester City	Won 2-0	15	567	Richardson 33, Killick 58
50	Apr 22	H	DML	Gloucester City	Drew 2-2		472	Killick 2, Pickard 32
51	Apr 26	A	DML	Nuneaton Borough	Lost 0-3	16	865	
52	Apr 29	A	DML	Gloucester City	Lost 1-3		1022	Killick 31
53	May 1	A	DML	Salisbury City	Drew 0-0		1024	
54	May 3	H	DML	Ashford Town	Lost 0-2	15	806	

DORCHESTER TOWN PLAYING SQUAD 1997-98

Goalkeepers : Kenny Veysey (Oxford U, Torquay, Arsenal), **Tony Oliver** (Bournemouth FC, Weymouth, Brentford, Portsmouth)

Defenders : Neil Coates (Yeovil T, Dorchester T, Yeovil T, AFC Bournemouth, Watford), **Toby Redwood** (Exeter), **Mark Sullivan** (Plymouth), **Mark Lisk** (Bashley, AFC Lymington, Eastleigh), **Darren Tallon** (Plymouth)

Midfielders : Steve Richardson (Poole T, Wimborne T, Ferryhill Ath, Hartlepool), **Jamie Reeve** (Hereford, AFC Bournemouth), **Rob Taylor** (Local football), **Andy Gater** (Christchurch), **Russell Coughlin** (Torquay, Exeter, Swansea, Blackpool, Plymouth, Carlisle, Blackburn, Manchester C), **Rob Taylor** (Local football) ,**Darren Reeks** (Wimborne, Poole, Hamworthy Engineering), **Dave Lovell** (Moreton, Puddleton), **Peter Conning** (Salisbury C, Trowbridge T, Yeovil T, Dorchester T, Bashley, Yeovil T, Weymouth, Altrincham, Rochdale)

Forwards : Tommy Killick (Wimborne T, Bashley, Wimborne T, Swanage, Poole T), **Paul Wilkinson** (Bashley, Wokingham T, Reading (T)), **Owen Pickard** (Hereford, Plymouth), **Marcus Crocker** (Torquay, Plymouth), **Andy Harris** (Weymouth, Bridport,Dorchester T, Bridport)

FOREST GREEN ROVERS

Formed: 1890 **Nickname:** Rovers
Colours: Black & white stripes/black/red
Change colours: All Yellow.
Midweek matchday: Wednesday
Youth League: Glos Co. Yth.

Chairman: Trevor Horsley **President:** E G Smith
Secretary / Managing Director: Colin Peake, Club Admin Office, Unit 14 Springfield Bus. Centre. Stonehouse, Gloucester GL10 3SX (01453 791232, Fax 791305)
Press Officer: Heather Cook (01453 823281, Mob 0385 940981)
Manager: Frank Gregan **Asst Manager:** Tommy Callinan
Physio: Dave Tyrrell

PROGRAMME DETAILS:
Pages: 36 **Price:** 80p
Editor: Julie Davis.

GROUND Address: 'The Lawn', Nympsfield Road, Forest Green, Nailsworth, Glos. GL6 0ET (01453 834860).
Directions: About 4 miles south of Stroud on A46 to Bath. In Nailsworth turn into Spring Hill off mini r'bout - ground approximately half mile up hill on left. The nearest BR station is Stroud.
Capacity: 3132 **Cover:** 980 **Seats:** 332 **Floodlights:** Yes
Clubhouse: (01453 833295). Bar and lounge, open every night.
Club Shop: Open matchdays. **Sponsors:** Daymac Graphics

PREVIOUS - **Leagues:** Stroud & Dist. 1890-1921, Glos Northern Snr 22-67, Glos Co. 67-73, Hellenic 73-82. **Name:** Stroud FC, 1989-92. **Ground:** None.

CLUB RECORDS - **Attendance:** 2,200 v Wolvers, floodlight inauguration 81.

BEST SEASON - **FA Cup:** 3rd Qual Rd 87-88. **FA Trophy:** 3rd Rd Proper 90-91. **FA Vase:** Winners 81-82.

Players progressing to Football League: G Rogers/K Gill (Newport Cnty 85), M England (Bristol Rov 85).

96-97 Captain: **P.o.Y.:** **Top scorer:**

Local Press: Stroud News & Journal, Gloucester Citizen.

Local Radio: Severn Sound, BBC Radio Gloucestershire.

HONOURS: FA Vase 81-82, Hellenic Lg 81-82, Gloucs Nthn Sen Lg 37-38 49-50 50-51, Gloucs Sen Cup 84-85 85-86 86-87, Gloucs Sen Amat Cup (N) 26-27 45-46 71-72 75-76 77-78, Gloucs Sen Prof Cup 84-85 85-86.

Forest Green Rovers celebrating the collection of the Southern Division Championship Shield.

Forest Green Rovers

Match No.	Date	Venue H/A	Competition	Opponents	Result	League Pos.	Attendance	Goalscorers (Times if known)
1	Aug 17	A	DML	Erith & Belvedere	Drew 0-0	13	106	
2	Aug 21	H	DML	Clevedon Town	Won 4-1	7	225	Callinan, Sykes (2), Watkins
3	Aug 24	H	DML	Fleet Town	Won 2-0	4	176	Tomlinson, Callinan
4	Aug 26	A	DML	Trowbridge Town	Lost 1-2	6	286	Sykes
5	Aug 31	H	DML	Weymouth	Won 2-0	2	236	Smith, Sykes
6	Sep 3	A	DML	Weston-Super-Mare	Drew 0-0	3	210	
7	Sep 7	H	DML	Margate	Won 2-1	2	171	Milsom, Sykes
8	**Sep 14**	**H**	**FAC**	**Torrington**	**Lost 4-5**		**146**	**Skidmore, Scott, Sykes (2)**
9	Sep 21	H	DML	Waterlooville	Won 3-2	2	160	Scott, Tomlinson, Moore
10	Sep 24	A	DML	Clevedon Town	Lost 0-3	3	161	
11	**Oct 1**	**H**	**GSCC**	**Cinderford Town**	**Won 2-0**		**151**	**Kilgour, Bayliss**
12	Oct 5	A	DML	Buckingham Town	Won 2-0	2	104	Moore (2)
13	**Oct 8**	**A**	**DMC 1**	**Cirencester Town**	**Drew 3-3**		**129**	**Bayliss (2), Moore**
14	Oct 12	H	DML	Fisher Athletic	Won 2-0	2	205	Moore (2)
15	Oct 16	H	DML	Trowbridge Town	Drew 1-1	2	151	Bayliss
16	**Oct 19**	**A**	**FAT 1**	**Buckingham Town**	**Won 1-0**		**88**	**Kilgour**
17	Oct 26	A	DML	Tonbridge Angels	Drew 1-1	2	383	Callinan
18	**Oct 29**	**H**	**DMC 1**	**Cirencester Town**	**Won 3-1**		**147**	**Smart, Bayliss, Moore**
19	Nov 2	A	DML	Bashley	Won 5-1	2	154	Smith (2), Bayliss (2), Sykes
20	**Nov 4**	**A**	**GSCC**	**Gloucester City**	**Lost 0-3**		**265**	
21	**Nov 9**	**H**	**FAT 2**	**Cambridge City**	**Lost 1-2**		**256**	**Bayliss**
22	Nov 13	H	DML	Weston-Super-Mare	Won 3-1	2	230	Smith, Moore
23	Nov 16	A	DML	Dartford	Drew 0-0	2	381	
24	Nov 23	A	DML	Waterlooville	Lost 0-2	2	101	
25	Nov 30	H	DML	Yate Town	Won 4-0	2	233	Kilgour, Cook, Hunt, Sykes
26	Dec 7	A	DML	Fleet Town	Won 2-1	2	151	Hunt, Bayliss
27	**Dec 10**	**A**	**DMC 2**	**Trowbridge Town**	**Drew 1-1**		**130**	**Cook**
28	Dec 14	H	DML	Fareham Town	Won 6-0	2	181	Smart (2), Bayliss (3), Hunt (3)
29	**Dec 17**	**H**	**DMC 2**	**Trowbridge Town**	**Won 4-2**		**138**	**Hunt (4)**
30	Dec 21	A	DML	Margate	Lost 0-2	3	233	
31	Dec 26	H	DML	Cinderford Town	Won 2-1	2	440	Smith, Hunt
32	Jan 11	H	DML	Havant Town	Won 3-2	2	371	Mitchell, Hunt, Sykes
33	**Jan 14**	**A**	**DMC 3**	**Cheltenham Town**	**Won 1-0**		**441**	**Smart**
34	Jan 18	A	DML	Fisher Athletic	Drew 3-3	2	131	Bayliss, Hunt, Sykes
35	Jan 25	H	DML	Bashley	Won 4-0	1	251	Smart, Bayliss, Hunt, Sykes
36	Feb 1	A	DML	Weymouth	Won 3-1	1	640	Smart, Bayliss, Hunt
37	**Feb 4**	**A**	**DMC 4**	**Weymouth**	**Lost 0-2**		**515**	
38	Feb 8	A	DML	Newport I.o.W.	Drew 1-1	1	367	Callinan
39	Feb 15	H	DML	Erith & Blevedere	Won 5-2	1	285	Smart, Bayliss, Hunt, Sykes, Scott
40	Feb 18	A	DML	Cirencester Town	Won 1-0	1	229	Smart
41	Feb 22	H	DML	Buckingham Town	Won 2-0	1	229	Mitchell, Smart
42	Mar 1	A	DML	Yate Town	Won 1-0	1	231	Sykes
43	Mar 10	H	DML	Witney Town	Drew 0-0	1	368	
44	Mar 15	H	DML	St Leonards Stamcroft	Won 2-1	1	364	Mitchell, Hunt
45	Mar 22	A	DML	Witney Town	Won 3-2	1	209	Mitchell, Hunt (2)
46	Mar 28	H	DML	Cirencester Town	Won 3-1	1	629	Smith, Smart, Bayliss
47	Mar 31	A	DML	Cinderford Town	Won 3-1	1	430	Bayliss, Hunt
48	Apr 5	H	DML	Newport I.o.W.	Won 2-1	1	354	Sykes (2)
49	Apr 12	A	DML	Havant Town	Drew 0-0	1	205	
50	Apr 19	H	DML	Dartford	Won 2-1	1	502	Bayliss, Hunt
51	Apr 26	A	DML	Fareham Town	Won 1-0	1	275	Kilgour
52	Apr 30	A	DML	St Leonards Stamcroft	Lost 1-2	1	600	Mitchell
53	May 3	H	DML	Tonbridge Angels	Drew 3-3	1	309	Bayliss (2), Mitchell

FOREST GREEN ROVERS PLAYING SQUAD 1997-98

Goalkeepers: Steve Book (Frome, Gloucester, Brighton, Bath, Frome, Weston-S-M, Welton R, Paulton R)

Defenders: Chris Tomlinson (Clevedon, Wokingham, Aldershot T, Canterbury, Aldershot), **Edwin Murray** (Swindon), **Mark Saunders** (Fairford, Gloucester), **Rob Skidmore** (Clevedon, Bristol C (T)), **Mike Kilgour** (Salisbury, Dorchester,Gloucester, Trowbridge, Stroud, Salisbury, Trowbridge, Melksham, Larkhall A, Bath), **Don Forbes** (Bath, Avon A), **Scott Crossey** (Westbury U, Cheltenham), **Nick Hendy** (Taunton, Mangotsfield, Forest Green R, Gloucester, Weymouth, Trowbridge, Bath, Bristol R)

Midfielders: Dave Mitchell (Trowbridge, Gloucester, Trowbridge, Mangotsfield, Clevedon, Yate, Trowbridge, Chippenham, Westbury U, Trowbridge), **Chris Smith** (Cinderford, Cirencester, Gloucester, Bath, Mangotsfield, Bristol R, Cheltenham, Cirencester), **Tommy Callinan** (Gloucester, Cinderford, Cheltenham), **Richard Ford** (Yate, Forest Green R, Cheltenham, Torquay, Nottingham F (T)), **John Scott** (Andover, Wokingham, Middlesbrough), **Rob Cook** (Shortwood U), **Gary Smart** (Mangotsfield, Bath, Cheltenham, Bristol R, Mangotsfield)

Forwards: Christian Moore (Leicester U, Belper, Gresley R, Nuneaton, Stockport, Leicester C), **Allan Kennedy** (Andover), **Karl Bayliss** (Gloucester, Stroud, Sharpness, Forest Green R, Cheltenham), **Alex Sykes** (Endsleigh, Cheltenham, Mansfield, Westfields), **Paul Hunt** (Cirencester, Brann (Nor), Bristol R, Cardiff, Charlton, Swindon)

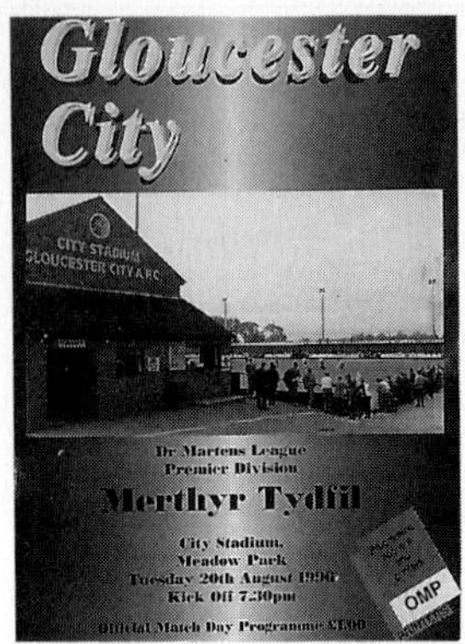

PROGRAMME DETAILS
Pages: 44 **Price:** £1
Editor: Mike Dunstan

GLOUCESTER CITY

Formed: 1889 **Nickname:** The Tigers
Colours: Yellow & black/black/black.
Change colours: Red & white/white/red
Midweek games: Tuesday

Chairman: Rob Thomas **President:** R F Etheridge
Vice-Chairman: Michael Tuck **Chief Executive:** Rob Thomas
Secretary: Ken C Turner, 24 Ladysmith Road, Cheltenham, Glos. GL52 5LQ. 01242 522514 (H) 0374 999839 (mobile).
Team Manager: Leroy Rosenior **Asst Manager:** Steve Ferguson
Press Officer: Jason Mills (01452 424189) **Physio:** Adrian Tandy
General Manager: Mike Billingham 01452 421400

GROUND Address: Meadow Park, Sudmeadow Road, Hempsted, Gloucester GL2 6HS (01452 421400. **Directions:** From North: A40 then then A4301 towards City Centre & Historic Docks, right into Severn Road over swingbridge, right into Llanthony Road/Hempsted Lane, 2nd right into Sudmeadow Road, ground 50yds on left.
Capacity: 5,000 **Cover:** 3,000 **Seats:** 560 **Floodlights:** Yes
Clubhouse: Meadow Park Sports & Social Club at entrance to ground. Normal licensing hours. Hot & cold food available.
Club Shop: Yes **Sponsors:** Hartland Renault

PREVIOUS - **Grounds:** Longlevens 1935-65, Horton Road 65-86. **Name:** Gloucester Y.M.C.A. **Leagues:** Bristol & Dist. (now Western) 1893-96, Gloucester & Dist. 97-1907, Nth Glos. 07-10, Glos. Nth Snr 20-34, Birmingham Comb. 1935-39.

CLUB RECORDS - **Attendance:** 4,000 v Dagenham & Redbridge, FA Trophy S-F 2nd Leg, 12.4.97. **Goalscorer:** Reg Weaver, 250. **Appearances:** Stan Myers & Frank Tredgett in 1950s. **Fee Paid:** £25,000 for S Fergusson (Worcester City), and D Holmes (Gresley R.) **Fee Received:** £25,000 Ian Hedges (AFC Bournemouth, 1990).

BEST SEASON - **FA Cup:** 2nd Rd 89-90. **FA Trophy:** Semi-Final 1996-97.

Players progressing to The Football League: Numerous including William Teague (61) & Rod Thomas (64) to Swindon, John Layton (Hereford 74), Ian Main (Exeter 78), Mike Bruton (Newport 79), Mel Gwinnett (Bradford C. 84), Steve Talboys (Wimbledon 91).
96-97 Captain: Chris Burns **96-97 P.o.Y.:** Simon Cooper **96-97 Top scorer:** Dale Watkins (35)
Local Press: Gloucester Citizen, Western Daily Press **Local Radio:** Severn Sound, BBC Radio Gloucestershire

HONOURS: Southern Lg R-up 90-91 (Lg Cup 55-56 (R-up 81-82), Midland Div 88-89), Glos Nth Sen Lg 33-34, Glos Sen. Cup 37-38 49-58 65-66 68-69 70-71 74-75 78-79 79-80 81-82 82-83 83-84 90-91 92-93, Sen Amat Cup (Nth) 31-32).

L-R, Back: Steve Fergusson, John McGrath (now Moor Green), Paul Milsom, David Coles, Adie Mings, David Holmes (now Burton Alb.), Jon Holloway. Middle: Mike Heather (Kit Man.), David Johnson, Don O'Riordan (now Manager Galway Utd.), Chris Burns, David Webb, Dale Watkins (now Cheltenham T.), Andy Kirkup (now Rothwell T.), Adrian Tandy (Physio). Front: Gary Thorne, Simon Cooper, Leroy Rosenior (Manager), Gary Kemp, Joe Roach (Asst. Man.), Ian Howell, Andy Tucker.

Gloucester City

Match No.	Date	Venue H/A	Competition	Opponents	Result	League Pos.	Attendance	Goalscorers (Times if known)
1	Aug 17	A	DML	Ashford Town	Won 3-0		648	Webb 18, 55, Mings 33
2	Aug 20	H	DML	Merthyr Tydfil	Won 6-3		875	Webb (3) 19, 46, 79, Watkins (3) 18, 67, 89
3	Aug 24	A	DML	Cambridge City	Won 1-0		337	Cooper 43
4	Aug 26	H	DML	Halesowen Town	Lost 0-3	2	1132	
5	Aug 31	H	DML	King's Lynn	Won 1-0	3	752	Mings 57
6	Sep 4	A	DML	Newport A.F.C.	Won 4-0		932	Watkins 31, Mings 59, 87, Holmes 85
7	Sep 7	H	DML	Baldock Town	Won 3-1	1	718	Holmes 41, 82 (pen), Mings 50
8	**Sep 14**	**A**	**FAC 1 Q**	**Basingstoke Town**	**Won 3-0**		**422**	**Watkins 4, Mings 39, Webb 62**
9	Sep 21	H	DML	Chelmsford City	Won 3-1	1	816	Watkins 14, 19, Mings 73
10	Sep 24	A	DML	Merthyr Tydfil	Lost 0-1	1	680	
11	**Sep 28**	**H**	**FAC 2 Q**	**Thatcham Town**	**Lost 1-3**		**701**	**Kemp 76**
12	Oct 5	A	DML	Sittingbourne	Drew 1-1	2	593	Holmes 75
13	**Oct 8**	**H**	**DMLC**	**Cinderford Town**	**Won 5-0**			**Kemp 4, Watkins 6, 30, Johnson 37, Rosenoir 88**
14	Oct 12	H	DML	Nuneaton Borough	Won 1-0	1	1055	Webb 77
15	Oct 15	A	DML	Halesowen Town	Lost 4-5	2	903	Holmes 13, Watkins (3) 15, 35, 61
16	Oct 19	H	DML	Hastings Town	Won 2-0	2	418	Milsom 24, Watkins 53
17	Oct 26	H	DML	Gresley Rovers	Lost 1-2		1552	Mings 20
18	**Oct 29**	**A**	**DMLC**	**Cinderford Town**	**Lost 1-2**		**192**	**Tucker 20**
19	Nov 2	A	DML	Burton Albion	Lost 1-3	2	862	Watkins 71 (pen)
20	Nov 9	H	DML	Crawley	Won 2-1	2	839	Chatfield 23, Ferguson 82
21	Nov 16	A	DML	Salisbury City	Won 4-0	2	489	Milsom 12, Watkins (3) 34, 39, 70
22	Nov 23	A	DML	King's Lynn	Lost 1-2	3	786	Adcock 70
23	Nov 25	H	DML	Newport A.F.C.	Won 2-1		816	Adcock 5, Ferguson 45
24	**Nov 30**	**H**	**FAT 3 Q**	**Kingstonian**	**Won 3-1**		**752**	**Webb 9, Watkins 49 (pen), 88**
25	Dec 7	H	DML	Burton Albion	Lost 2-4	3	801	Kemp 28, Watkins 45 (pen)
26	**Dec 10**	**A**	**DMC**	**Cheltenham Town**	**Lost 0-1**		**590**	
27	Dec 14	H	DML	Sittingbourne	Drew 1-1	3	710	Holloway 88
28	Dec 21	A	DML	Nuneaton Borough	Lost 0-2	3	824	
29	Dec 26	H	DML	Cheltenham Town	Won 2-1	3	2154	Watkins 75, 87
30	**Jan 18**	**A**	**FAT 1**	**Yeading**	**Won 3-0**		**245**	**Kemp 41, Nevin 85 (og), Burns 89**
31	Jan 25	H	DML	Cambridge City	Won 2-0	3	606	McGrath 24, Ferguson 80 (pen)
32	Jan 28	A	DML	Atherstone United	Drew 0-0	3	315	
33	Feb 1	A	DML	Sudbury Town	Lost 1-2	3	351	Kemp 61
34	**Feb 8**	**H**	**FAT 2**	**Halifax Town**	**Won 3-0**		**1118**	**Holmes 62, Watkins 66, 80**
35	Feb 15	H	DML	Hastings Town	Won 2-0	5	612	Tucker 73, Watkins 86
36	Feb 17	A	DML	Worcester City	Drew 0-0	3	770	
37	Feb 22	A	DML	Gravesend & Northfleet	Won 3-2	3	696	Burns 6, Kemp 37, Ferguson 63
38	**Mar 1**	**H**	**FAT 3**	**Runcorn**	**Won 3-1**		**1129**	**Burns 5, Kemp 35, Ellis 44 (og)**
39	Mar 8	H	DML	Sudbury Town	Drew 3-3	4	732	Burns 12, Johnson 31, Watkins 88
40	Mar 10	A	DML	Chelmsford City	Won 3-1		550	Webb 37, Tucker 48, Holmes 51
41	Mar 15	A	DML	Crawley Town	Drew 1-1	3	534	Mings 37
42	Mar 18	H	DML	Ashford Town	Won 6-1	3	556	Donn 12 (og), Mings 54, 56, Webb 70, 80, Holmes 83
43	**Mar 22**	**A**	**FAT Q F**	**Bishop Auckland**	**Drew 0-0**			
44	**Mar 25**	**H**	**FAT QF R**	**Bishop Auckland**	**Won 4-3**		**1829**	**Watkins 10, 56, Holmes 61, 74**
45	Mar 29	H	DML	Worcester City	Drew 1-1		1082	Watkins 73
46	Mar 31	A	DML	Cheltenham Town	Drew 1-1	3	3005	Webb 23
47	**Apr 5**	**A**	**FAT SF**	**Dagenham & Redbridge**	**Drew 0-0**		**2077**	
48	**Apr 12**	**H**	**FAT SF**	**Dagenham & Redbridge**	**Drew 2-2***		**4000**	**Watkins 38, Mings 116**
49	**Apr 16**	**N**	**FAT SF R**	**Dagenham & Redbridge**	**Lost 1-2**		**2053**	**Holmes 11**
50	Apr 19	H	DML	Gravesend & Northfleet	Won 3-1	3	804	Mings 64, 66, Watkins 82
51	Apr 22	A	DML	Dorchester Town	Drew 2-2		472	Watkins 11, Burns 29
52	Apr 24	H	DML	Atherstone United	Drew 0-0		927	
53	Apr 26	A	DML	Gresley Rovers	Lost 1-3	4	1376	Watkins 23
54	Apr 29	H	DML	Dorchester Town	Won 3-1		1022	Kemp 45, Webb 51, Kirkup 63
55	May 1	A	DML	Baldock Town	Won 3-2	3	301	Webb 64, Ferguson 84 (pen), Adcock 87
56	May 3	H	DML	Salisbury City	Lost 1-3	3	1863	Lovell 18 (og)

GLOUCESTER CITY PLAYING SQUAD 1997-98

Goalkeepers: David Coles (Yeovil T, Fulham, Aldershot, Brighton, Crystal Palace, HJK Helsinki (Fin), Aldershot)

Defenders: Don O'Riordan (Dorchester T, Torquay, Notts Co, Grimsby, Middlesbrough, Carlisle, Preston, Tulsa Roughnecks (USA), Derby), **Gary Kemp** (Almondsbury Picksons), **Dave Johnson** (Rushden & D, Northampton, Irthlingborough D, Kettering T), **Gary Thorne** (Swindon), **Andy Tucker** (Cheltenham T), **Jon Holloway** (Swindon), **John McGrath** (Worcester, Kidderminster, Worcester,Shrewsbury)

Midfielders: Simon Cooper (Cheltenham T), **Ade Adebowale** (Merthyr Tydfil, Chesham U, Bishop's Stortford, Hertford T, Balls Park), **David Webb** (TrowbridgeT, Gloucester C, Stroud, Devizes T, Wantage T, Supermarine), **Ian Howell** (Cheltenham T, Gloucester C, Trowbridge T, Hungerford T, Trowbridge T, Swindon Ath, Swindon), **Adie Mings** (Bath C, Chippenham T, Melksham T), **Steve Fergusson** (Worcester C, Telford U, Gloucester C, Worcester C, Redditch U, Alvechurch, Redditch U, Bromsgrove R), **Chris Burns** (Northampton, Swansea, Portsmouth, Cheltenham)

Forwards: Paul Milsom (Oxford U, Cardiff, Bristol C), **Dale Watkins** (Rushden & D, Grantham T, Peterborough C, Peterborough, Sheffield U (T)), **Paul Adcock** (Bath, Torquay, Bath, Plymouth), **Andy Kirkup** (Rushden & D, Wellingborough, Rushden, Corby, Rushden), **David Holmes** (Gresley R, Scarborough)

GRESLEY ROVERS
FOOTBALL CLUB
Main Club Sponsor
BM
Warehousing
Dr. Martens
Football
League
Premier
Division
Gresley Rovers
Versus
Burton Albion
Official
Matchday
Programme
£1

PROGRAMME DETAILS:
Pages: 36 **Price:** £1.00
Editor: Brian Spare
(01332 862812)

GRESLEY ROVERS

Formed: 1882 **Nickname:** The Moatmen
Colours: Red & white/red/red
Change colours: Light blue & navy/navy/navy
Midweek matchday: Tuesday
Reserves' League: Midland Comb (Res. Div.)

Chairman: Peter Hall **President:** Gordon Duggins
Vice Chairman: Dennis Everitt
Secretary / Press Officer: Neil Betteridge, 88 Midway Road, Midway, Swadlincote, Derbys DE11 7PG (01283 221881).
Manager/Coach: Garry Birtles **Asst Manager:** Andy Garner
Commercial Manager: Frank McArdle. **Physio:** Gordon Ford.
GROUND Address: Moat Ground, Moat Street, Church Gresley, Swadlincote, Derbys DE11 9RE (01283 216315).
Directions: To A444 via either the A5, A38, A5121 or M42 North to Appleby Magna. On reaching A444 head for Castle Gresley. Turn onto A514 to Derby; at island 2nd exit (Church St), then 2nd left (School St) then 1st left into Moat St. 5 miles Burton-on-Trent (BR). Buses from Swadlincote and Burton.
Capacity: 2,000 **Cover:** 1,200 **Seats:** 400 **Floodlights:** Yes
Clubhouse: Inside ground, open Mon, Tues & Thurs eves & matchdays.
Club Shop: Sells merchandise, programmes, metal badges etc. Contact Barrie Morton (01283 216315). **Sponsors:** BM Warehousing.

PREVIOUS - Leagues: Burton Lge 1892-95 97-01 09-10 43-45, Derbyshire Sen 1895-97 02-03, Leics Sen 1890-91 98-99 08-09 10-12 15-16 35-42 45-49, Notts 01-02, Midland 03-06, Central All 11-15 19-25 49-53 59-67, Birmingham Comb 25-33 53-54, Birmingham (now West Mids) 54-59 75-92, Central Comb 33-35, East Mids 67-75
Grounds: Mushroom Lane, Albert Village 1882-95, Church Str., Church, Gresley. 1895-1909.

CLUB RECORDS - Attendance: 3,950 v Burton Albion, Birmingham (now West Mids) Lg Division One, 57-58. **Win:** 23-0 v Holy Cross Priory, Leics Jun Cup 1889-90. **Defeat:** 1-15 v Burton Crusaders, 1886-87. **Career Goalscorer:** Gordon Duggins 306. **Career Appearances:** Dennis King 579. **Transfer fee received:** £30,000 for Justin O'Reilly (Port Vale 1996). **Transfer fee paid:**

BEST SEASON - FA Vase: Runners-up 90-91, (SF 92-93). **FA Trophy:** Qtr Finals 95-96. **FA Cup:** 1st Rd Proper: 30-31 (1-3 at York City), 94-95 (1-7 at Crewe Alex.) **League clubs defeated:** None.
Players progressing to Football League: Phil Gee (Derby County 85), Mark Blount (Sheffield Utd 94), Colin Loss (Bristol City 94), Justin O'Reilly (Port Vale 96)
96-97 Captain: Richard Denby **96-97 P.o.Y.:** Andy Garner **96-97 Top scorer:** Andy Garner (20)
Local Press: Derby Evening Telegraph, Burton Mail. **Local Radio:**

HONOURS: Southern Lge Champ 96-97; FA Vase R-up 90-91; West Mids Lg 90-91 91-92 (R-up 85-86 88-89); Lg Cup 88-89 R-Up. 86-87 91-92; Southern Lg Mid Div R-up 92-93; Derbys Snr Cup (7), (R-Up (2); Leics Snr Cup 1898-99 46-47 (R-Up 1899-90 45-46); Leics Sen Lg 00-01 46-47 47-48 R-Up (7); Coalville Charity Cup 46-47; Derby Senior Cup (S) (2) R-Up 00-01; Bass Vase (6); Cent All 64-65 66-67 R-Up (3) (Lg Cup 52-53); East Mids Reg Lg (2) R-Up (2); Dr.Martens (S Lge) Cup Fin 93-94.

Gresley Rovers: Back Row (L-R); Scott Gwyett, Kevin Allsop, Stuart Ford, Mack Wood, Gareth Jennings. Middle Row; Gordon Ford (Physio), Graeme Fowkes, Dave Fisher, Andy Garner, Stuart Evans, Mack Blaint, Tony Marsden, Brian Horseman, Alan Titterton (2 Mgr). Front Row; Paul Cox, Darren Turner, Paul Futcher (Pl/Mgr), Richard Denby, Gary Birtles (Asst Mgr), Richard Wardle, Gavin McAndrew.
Photo Derrick Kinsey

Gresley Rovers

Match No.	Date	Venue H/A	Competition	Opponents	Result	League Pos.	Attendance	Goalscorers (Times if known)
1	Aug 17	A	DML	Hastings Town	Won 2-1		415	Garner 65 (pen), 87
2	Aug 20	H	DML	Worcester City	Won 3-0		693	Allsop 5, 76, Blount 56
3	Aug 24	H	DML	Gravesend & Northfleet	Won 2-0	1	621	Mortley 10 (og), Walker 72 (og)
4	Aug 26	A	DML	Atherstone United	Won 1-0	1	588	Marsden 13
5	Aug 31	A	DML	Chelmsford City	Drew 2-2	1	811	Cunningham 5, Fowkes 55
6	Sep 3	H	DML	Halesowen Town	Won 3-0		854	Wardle 7, Fowkes 52, Allsop 62
7	Sep 7	A	DML	Crawley Town	Drew 0-0	3	672	
8	**Sep 14**	**H**	**FAC 1 Q**	**Chase Town**	**Won 2-1**		**506**	**Allsop 21, 42**
9	Sep 21	H	DML	Dorchester Town	Drew 0-0	2	589	
10	Sep 23	A	DML	Worcester City	Won 2-1	2	721	Castledine 33, Garner 81
11	**Sep 28**	**A**	**FAC 2 Q**	**Rushden & Diamonds**	**Lost 0-4**		**1875**	
12	Oct 5	H	DML	Cambridge City	Won 3-1	1	808	Hurst 38, Garner 59, Fowkes 61
13	**Oct 8**	**A**	**DMLC**	**Ilkeston Town**	**Drew 1-1**		**437**	**Castledine 63**
14	Oct 15	H	DML	Atherstone United	Drew 1-1	1	623	Fowkes 39
15	Oct 19	H	DML	Crawley Town	Won 2-0	1	687	Hurst 9, Garner 64
16	Oct 26	A	DML	Gloucester City	Won 2-1	1	1552	Marsden 48, 90
17	**Oct 29**	**H**	**DMLC**	**Ilkeston Town**	**Drew 2-2+**		**900**	**Hurst 5 (pen), Marsden 42**
18	Nov 2	A	DML	Baldock Town	Won 3-0	1	323	Marsden 26, Castledine 62, Hurst 79
19	Nov 9	H	DML	Sudbury Town	Drew 1-1	1	874	Garner 30 (pen)
20	Nov 23	H	DML	Chelmsford City	Drew 2-2	1	786	Marsden 6, Garner 10
21	Nov 30	A	DML	Halesowen Town	Drew 1-1	1	1109	Marsden 9
22	Dec 7	H	DML	Sittingbourne	Lost 0-4	2	642	
23	Dec 14	A	DML	Cambridge City	Won 3-2	1	208	Garner 30, Allsop 52, Marsden 76
24	Dec 21	H	DML	Hastings Town	Won 3-0	1	590	Blount 29, Allsop 59, 70
25	Dec 26	A	DML	Burton Albion	Won 3-2	1	2537	Allsop 59, Blount 64, Hurst 85
26	Jan 4	A	DML	Merthyr Tydfil	Won 2-0	1	755	Fowkes 29, Wardle 42
27	**Jan 18**	**H**	**FAT 1**	**Altrincham**	**Drew 3-3**		**927**	**Garner 6, 18, Wardle 43**
28	**Jan 21**	**A**	**FAT 1 R**	**Altrincham**	**Lost 0-1**		**573**	
29	Jan 25	A	DML	Dorchester Town	Won 3-1	1	739	Marsden 35, Fowkes 66, Castledine 80
30	**Jan 28**	**A**	**DSC**	**Borrowash Victoria**	**Won 1-0**		**358**	**Hurst 60 (pen)**
31	Feb 1	H	DML	Ashford Town	Drew 2-2	1	709	Allsop 49, Hurst 75
32	Feb 11	H	DML	King's Lynn	Lost 0-2	1	664	
33	Feb 15	A	DML	Ashford Town	Won 3-1	1	615	Hurst 10, Garner 65 (pen), Marsden 75
34	Feb 22	H	DML	Cheltenham Town	Won 2-0	1	1010	Fowkes 22, Garner 87 (pen)
35	Mar 1	A	DML	Gravesend & Northfleet	Lost 1-2	1	732	S Futcher 74
36	Mar 4	H	DML	Burton Albion	Won 1-0	1	1760	Garner 86 (pen)
37	Mar 8	H	DML	Newport A.F.C.	Won 1-0	1	788	Garner 44
38	Mar 15	H	DML	Baldock Town	Won 3-0	1	679	Cunningham 30, Garner 64, Fowkes 79
39	Mar 19	A	DML	Salisbury City	Drew 1-1	1	289	Marsden 74
40	Mar 22	H	DML	Merthyr Tydfil	Lost 0-2	1	788	
41	Mar 25	A	DML	Cheltenham Town	Drew 2-2	1	1396	Castledine 3, Garner 55
42	Mar 29	A	DML	Nuneaton Borough	Lost 0-1	1	1472	
43	Mar 31	H	DML	Nuneaton Borough	Lost 1-4	1	1420	Allsop 45
44	Apr 5	A	DML	King's Lynn	Won 2-0	1	1476	Horseman 12, Marsden 17
45	Apr 12	H	DML	Salisbury City	Won 5-0	1	720	Garner 2, 24, Marsden 19, 61, Cunningham 90
46	**Apr 15**	**H**	**DSC F**	**Matlock Town**	**Won 3-0**		**502**	**Jennings 30, Castledine 83, Fowkes 86**
47	Apr 19	A	DML	Newport A.F.C.	Won 1-0	1	781	Marsden 89
48	Apr 26	H	DML	Gloucester City	Won 3-1	1	1376	Blount 8, Marsden 16, Wardle 78
49	May 1	A	DML	Sudbury Town	Won 3-0	1	206	Cunningham 62 (pen), Allsop 84, 90
50	May 3	A	DML	Sittingbourne	Lost 0-2	1	783	

+ Lost on Away Goals

GRESLEY ROVERS PLAYING SQUAD 1997-98

Goalkeepers: Stuart Ford (Scarborough, Doncaster, Bury, Scarborough, Rotherham), **Nicky Goodwin** (Telford, Burton A, Corby, Kettering, Shepshed, Kettering, Graham St.Prims)

Defenders: Paul Futcher (Droylsden, Grimsby, Halifax, Barnsley, Derby, Oldham, Manchester C, Luton, Chester), **Brian Horseman** (Notts Co), **Mark Blount** (Peterborough, Sheffield U, Gresley R, Derby), **Scott Guyatt** (Brisbane C (Aust),Gresley R)

Midfielders: Gary Castledine (Oakham U, Cork C, Gainsborough T, Telford U, Mansfield T, Shirebrook MW), **Graeme Fowkes** (Weymouth, Birmingham (T)), **Tony Marsden** (Grantham T, Belper T, Burton A), **Darren Turner** (Notts Co), **Richard Wardle** (Tamworth), **Richard Denby** (Alfreton T, Huthwaite, Sutton T, Boston U, Chesterfield), **Steve Devine** (Hednesford, Corby, Hereford, Derby, Wolves), **Steve Futcher** (Wrexham)

Forwards: Mark Hurst (Leicester U, Grantham T, Huddersfield, Nottingham F), **Carl Cunningham** (Derby), **Andy Garner** (Blackpool, Derby), **Kevin Allsop** (Stapenhill, Harrstad (Nor), Hinckley T), **Gareth Jennings** (Hednesford T, Gresley R, Sutton Coldfield T, Stoke)

PROGRAMME DETAILS:
Pages: 44 **Price:** £1
Editor: R Pepper

HALESOWEN TOWN

Formed: 1873 **Nickname:** Yeltz
Colours: All Black & Yellow trim
Change colours: All Blue & White trim
Midweek home matchday: Tuesday
Reserve's League: None. **Newsline:** 0891 446882.

Chairman: Ron Moseley **President:** Laurence Wood
Vice Chairman: Nigel Pitt **Secretary:** Stewart Tildesley, 83 Bloomfield Street, Halesowen B63 3RF (0121 550 8443).
Manager: Stewart Hall **Asst Manager:** Colin Brookes
Physio: Gavin Blackwell **Commercial Manager:** Nigel Pitt
Press Officer: Paul Floud (0121 550 8999)

GROUND Address: The Grove, Old Hawne Lane, Halesowen, West Midlands B63 3TB (0121 550 2179). **Directions:** M5 jct 3, A456 (signed Kidderminster) to 1st island turn right (signed A459 Dudley), left at 2nd island (signed A458 Stourbridge), at next island take 3rd left into Grammar School Lane, then Old Hawne Lane - ground 400 yds on left.
Capacity: 5,000 **Cover:** 1,420 **Seats:** 420 **Floodlights:** Yes
Clubhouse: (0121 602 2210) 12-2.30 & 7-11pm daily (closes 10.30pm on Sundays). Cold snacks served.
Club Shop: Sells replica strips, T-shirts, waterproof tops, coats, scarves, programmes, badges etc.
Sponsors: Hamer Ford.
PREVIOUS Leagues: West Mids 1892-1905 06-11 46-86, Birmingham Comb. 11-39.

CLUB RECORDS - Attendance: 5,000 v Hendon F.A. Cup 1st Rd Proper 1954, *(18,234 v Southall, 1986 FA Vase Final at Wembley).* **Goalscorer:** Paul Joinson 369. **Appearances:** Paul Joinson 608. **Win:** 13-1 v Coventry Amateurs, Birmingham Senior Cup, 1956. **Defeat:** 0-8 v Bilston, West Midlands League, 7/4/62. **Fee Paid:** £7,250 for Stuart Evans (Gresley 1996) **Fee Received:** £40,000 for Jim Rodwell (Rushden & Diamonds 96)
Best Season - FA Vase: Winners 84-85, 85-86 R-up 82-83. **FA Cup:** 1st Rd 9 times: 54-55 then each season from 84-85 to 91-92. **FA Trophy:** 3rd Round Proper 94-95.
Players progressing to Football League: Arthur Proudler (Aston Villa), Cyril Spiers (Aston Villa), Billy Morris (Wolves), Dean Spink (Aston Villa), Stuart Cash (Nottm Forest), Andrew Pearce & Tim Clarke & Sean Flynn (Coventry), Dean Stokes (Port Vale), Frank Bennett (Southampton), Julian Alsop (Bristol Rovers).
96-97 Captain: John Snape **96-97 P.o.Y.:** Euran Wright **96-97 Top scorer:** Evran Wright (30)
Local Press: Sports Argus, Express & Star, Birmingham Mail, Halesowen News, Stourbridge & Halesowen Chronicle.
Local Radio: B.R.M.B., BBC West Midlands, Beacon.

HONOURS: Southern Lg Premier Div R-up 96, Southern Lg Midland Div 89-90, W Mids Lg(5) 46-47 82-85 85-86 (R-up 64-65, Lg Cup 82-83 84-85), Birmingham Snr Cup 83-84 (R-up 51-52 67-68), Staffs Snr Cup 88-89 (R-up 83-84), FA Vase(2) 84-86 (R-up 82-83), Worcs Snr Cup 51-52 61-62 (R-up 87-88), Midland Comb. Res Div 89-90.

Halesowen Town: Back Row (L-R); Graham De Val, Jeff Jones (Youth Mgr), Mark Hart, Matthew Clarke, Ross Collins, Kevin Harrison, Matthew Gardiner, Daniel McDonnell, Stuart Evans, Jason Owen, Adrian Cooper, Stuart Skidmore, Carlos Azevedo, Colin Brookes (Gen Mgr), Bob Glaze (Asst Youth Mgr), Ron Moseley (Chr). Front Row; Paul McClean, Lee Brown, Luke Yates, Mascot, John Snape (Capt), Mascot, Richard Crisp, Steven Piearce, Ryan Robinson-Little (Kit boy).

Halesowen Town

Match No.	Date	Venue H/A	Competition	Opponents	Result	League Pos.	Attendance	Goalscorers (Times if known)
1	Aug 17	A	DML	Crawley Town	Won 3-0		672	Shearer 27, Harrison 84, Crisp 88 (p)
2	Aug 20	H	DML	Burton Albion	Drew 1-1		859	Bradley 29
3	Aug 24	H	DML	Atherstone United	Lost 0-2		686	
4	Aug 26	A	DML	Gloucester City	Won 3-0	7	1132	Wright 12, 90, Crisp 89
5	Aug 31	H	DML	Cambridge City	Won 3-1	5	803	Crisp 18, Wright 43, Allsop 89
6	Sep 3	A	DML	Gresley Rovers	Lost 0-3		854	
7	Sep 7	H	DML	Ashford Town	Won 3-1	6	701	Wright (3) 56, 77 (2 pens), 80
8	**Sep 10**	**H**	**WSC**	**Paget Rangers**	**Won 2-1**		**284**	**Allsop 25, 89 (pen)**
9	**Sep 14**	**A**	**FAC 1 Q**	**Stourbridge**	**Lost 0-1**		**833**	
10	Sep 21	H	DML	Gravesend & Northfleet	Won 2-1	5	690	Crisp 5, Wright 28
11	Sep 24	A	DML	Burton Albion	Drew 0-0		602	
12	Sep 28	A	DML	King's Lynn	Lost 1-2	6	732	Shearer 53
13	Oct 5	H	DML	Newport A.F.C.	Won 2-0	4	916	Harrison 86, Coates 89
14	**Oct 8**	**H**	**DMLC**	**Stafford Rangers**	**Won 1-0**		**348**	**Colley 55**
15	Oct 12	A	DML	Atherstone United	Won 5-0	3	389	Allsop (3) 6, 13, 45, Crisp 87, Harrison 89
16	Oct 15	H	DML	Gloucester City	Won 5-4	3	903	Crisp (3) 9, 72 (p), 86 (p), Allsop 52, Harrison 82
17	Oct 19	H	DML	Salisbury City	Lost 1-2	3	833	Allsop 17
18	**Oct 29**	**A**	**DMLC**	**Stafford Rangers**	**Won 2-0**		**335**	**Bradley 57, Harrison 87**
19	Nov 2	A	DML	Sudbury Town	Lost 2-4	4	453	Wright 7, Allsop 29
20	Nov 9	H	DML	Chelmsford City	Won 1-0	3	716	Evans 83
21	**Nov 12**	**H**	**BSC**	**Halesowen Harriers**	**Drew 1-1**		**461**	**Harrison 43**
22	Nov 16	A	DML	Hastings Town	Won 3-2	3	421	Wright 26, 87, Harris 49
23	Nov 23	A	DML	Nuneaton Borough	Won 2-0	2	1019	Wright 22, 57
24	**Nov 25**	**A**	**BSC**	**Halesowen Harriers**	**Lost 0-1**		**450**	
25	Nov 30	H	DML	Gresley Rovers	Drew 1-1	3	1109	Owen 49
26	Dec 7	A	DML	Newport A.F.C.	Won 1-0	1	775	Owen 19
27	Dec 14	H	DML	King's Lynn	Drew 2-2	2	827	Harrison 12, Wright 58
28	**Dec 17**	**A**	**DMC**	**Redditch United**	**Won 3-0**		**228**	**Moran 52 (og), Crisp 55, Wright 89**
29	Dec 21	A	DML	Baldock Town	Won 1-0	2	342	Wright 75
30	Dec 26	H	DML	Worcester City	Drew 0-0	2	1256	
31	Dec 28	A	DML	Merthyr Tydfil	Drew 1-1	2	851	Harrison 70
32	**Jan 14**	**A**	**DMC**	**Burton Albion**	**Lost 0-1**		**410**	
33	**Jan 18**	**A**	**FAT 1**	**Southport**	**Drew 0-0**		**1005**	
34	**Jan 21**	**H**	**FAT 1 R**	**Southport**	**Lost 0-2**		**866**	
35	Jan 25	H	DML	Crawley Town	Drew 2-2	2	725	Harrison 3, Alsopp 88
36	**Jan 27**	**A**	**WSC**	**Kidderminster Harriers**	**Won 3-0**		**898**	Colley 1, 84, Wright 15
37	Feb 1	A	DML	Gravesend & Northfleet	Won 3-1	2	610	Wright 28, Crisp 80 (pen), Bradley 83
38	Feb 11	A	DML	Cheltenham Town	Lost 1-2	2	747	Knight 77 (og)
39	Feb 15	H	DML	Baldock Town	Won 6-0	2	681	Wright (4) 5, 52, 72 (p), 89, Bellingham 19, Coates 74
40	Feb 24	A	DML	Chelmsford City	Lost 0-3		411	
41	Mar 1	A	DML	Cambridge City	Won 4-1	2	278	Wright 22, 40, Bellingham 78, Harrison 86
42	Mar 8	H	DML	Hastings Town	Lost 1-2	4	83	Bellingham 61
43	Mar 15	A	DML	Ashford Town	Drew 1-1	4	442	Wright 62
44	Mar 18	H	DML	Dorchester Town	Won 3-1	4	482	Wright 2, Owen 3, Halsall 68
45	Mar 22	A	DML	Sittingbourne	Lost 2-4	4	597	Wright 7, 82
46	Mar 29	H	DML	Cheltenham Town	Lost 1-5		1406	Freeman 31 (og)
47	Mar 31	A	DML	Worcester City	Drew 1-1	5	1307	Wright 89
48	Apr 5	H	DML	Merthyr Tydfil	Lost 1-2	5	717	Hackett 57
49	**Apr 8**	**H**	**WSC**	**Solihull Borough**	**Lost 1-2**		**506**	**Wright 22**
50	Apr 12	A	DML	Dorchester Town	Drew 1-1	5	631	Sharpe 69
51	Apr 19	H	DML	Sudbury Town	Won 1-0	4	562	Wright 5
52	Apr 22	H	DML	Sittingbourne	Won 2-0		469	Evans 79, Sharpe 90
53	Apr 26	A	DML	Salisbury City	Won 2-1	3	285	Clark 45, Sharpe 60
54	May 3	H	DML	Nuneaton Borough	Won 2-0	4	991	Bradley 30, Owen 75

HALESOWEN PLAYING SQUAD 1997-98

Goalkeepers: Danny McDonnell (Lye T, Stourbridge, Lye T)

Defenders: Matthew Clarke (Halesowen H, Cradley T), **Phil Wood** (Pelsall V, Bilston T, Dudley T, Bilston T, Rushall O, Bilston T), **Jason Owen** (Stourbridge,Halesowen T, West Bromwich T), **Stuart Evans** (Gresley R, Wolves), **Matt Gardiner** (Stourbridge, Moor Green, Torquay)

Midfielders: Gary Hackett (Chester, Peterborough, WBA, Stoke, Aberdeen, Shrewsbury, Bromsgrove R), **John Snape** (Stourbridge, Northfield T, Bromsgrove R, WBA (A)), **Andy Bradley** (Tividale), **Richard Crisp** (Telford U, Aston Villa), **Mick Shearer** (Gloucester C, Nuneaton B, Kettering T, VS Rugby, Nuneaton B, Coventry Sporting, AP Leamington, Luton, Birmingham (A)),

Forwards: Kevin Harrison (Stourbridge, Tividale), **Evran Wright** (Bilston T, Stafford R, Barry T, Walsall, Halesowen T, Stourbridge, Oldbury U, Stourbridge, Springvale-Tranco), **Nick Colley** (Chasetown), **John Sharpe** (Exeter, Manchester C), **Mark Bellingham** (Cheltenham, Chelmsford, Gt.Wakering R, Stambridge)

PROGRAMME DETAILS:
Pages: 64 **Price:** £1
Editor: Tony Cosens
(01424 427867)

HASTINGS TOWN

Formed: 1894 **Nickname:** The Town
Colours: All white
Change colours: Red/black
Midweek matchday: Tuesday **Newsline:** 0891 664 356.
Reserves' League: Winstonlead Kent Div 2.

Chairman: David Nessling 01424 713339 (H).
Vice Chairman: **President:** David Harding
Secretary / Press Officer: R A Cosens, 22 Baldslow Road, Hastings TN34 2EZ 01424 427867 (H) 01424 444635 (B).
Team Manager: Garry Wilson 01424 755360.
Asst Manager: Peter Carman **Physio:** Ray Tuppen

GROUND Address: The Pilot Field, Elphinstone Road, Hastings TN34 2AX (01424 444635). **Directions:** From A21 turn left at 1st mini-r'bout into St Helens Rd, left after 1 mile into St Helens Park Rd, this leads into Downs Rd, at end of Downs Rd (T-junction) turn left, ground 200yds on right. From town centre take Queens Road (A2101). Right at roundabout into Elphinstone Road - ground 1 mile on right. One and a half miles from Hastings BR station - infrequent bus service from town centre to ground.
Capacity: 4,050. **Cover:** 1,750 **Seats:** 800 **Floodlights:** Yes
Clubhouse: Open matchdays and Tues, Thurs and Fri evenings from 7pm.
Club Shop: Sells replica kits, scarves, programmes, pens, key-rings, badges etc.
Sponsors: Croft Lodge Sports Club

PREVIOUS - **Leagues:** South Eastern 04-05, Southern 05-10, Sussex County 21-27 52-85, Southern Amateur 27-46, Corinthian 46-48.
Name: Hastings & St Leonards Amateurs **Ground:** Bulverhythe Rec. Gd. ('til c. 1976)

CLUB RECORDS - **Attendance:** 4,888 v Notts Forest, friendly 23/6/96.
Competitive: 1,774 v Dover Athletic, Southern Lge Prem. Div. 12/4/93.
Goalscorer: Dean White 28 **Appearances:**

Best Season - **FA Cup:** 4th Qual. Rd 85-86, 2-3 v Farnborough Town (A).
FA Amateur Cup: 3rd Rd. 38-39. **FA Vase:** 5th Rd. rep. 90-91.

Players progressing to Football League: Peter Heritage (Gillingham), Paul Smith (Nottm Forest)
96-97 Captain: **96-97 P.o.Y.:** **96-97 Top scorer:**
Local Press: Hastings Observer & News, Evening Argus. **Local Radio:** Radio Sussex, Southern Sound.

HONOURS: Southern Lg Southern Div 91-92 (Div 2 R-up 08-09 (Div 2(B) 09-10)), Sussex County Lg R-up 21-22 25-26 (Lg Cup 80-81, Div 2 79-80 (R-up 59-60), Div 2 Cup 79-80), Sussex Senior Cup 35-36 37-38 95-96, AFA Snr Cup 37-38, Gilbert Rice Floodlit Cup 89-90.

Hasting's Andy Larkin beats Crawley Town's goalkeeper Andy Harris, for Hasting Town's first goal at Town Mead.
Photo - Roger Turner

Hastings Town

Match No.	Date	Venue H/A	Competition	Opponents	Result	League Pos.	Attendance	Goalscorers (Times if known)
1	Aug 17	H	DML	Gresley Rovers	Lost 1-2		415	Willard 88
2	Aug 20	H	DML	Ashford Town	Drew 2-2		586	Cuggy 24, Playford 52
3	Aug 24	A	DML	Salisbury City	Lost 1-2		281	Emms 72 (og)
4	Aug 26	H	DML	Sittingbourne	Drew 2-2	21	569	Cuggy 16, 68
5	Aug 31	A	DML	Sudbury Town	Lost 0-3	21	348	
6	Sep 3	H	DML	Gravesend & Northfleet	Won 2-1	18	444	Cuggy 14, 42
7	Sep 7	A	DML	King's Lynn	Won 4-1	13	904	Playford 12, 33, Cuggy 20, Gregory 42
8	**Sep 14**	**H**	**FAC 1 Q**	**Burnham**	**Won 2-0**		**412**	**Cuggy 10, Calloway 20**
9	Sep 21	H	DML	Burton Albion	Won 2-1	10	524	Tuppenney 58, Lambert 82
10	Sep 24	A	DML	Ashford Town	Drew 3-3	11	707	O'Shaughnessy 15, 70, Tuppenney 76
11	**Sep 28**	**A**	**FAC 2 Q**	**Chertsey Town**	**Won 3-2**		**267**	**Parris 78, 90, Ball 88**
12	Oct 5	A	DML	Nuneaton Borough	Lost 1-4	5	1111	Gregory 1
13	**Oct 8**	**H**	**DMLC**	**St Leonards Stamcroft**	**Lost 1-2**		**1095**	**Simmonds 68 (pen)**
14	**Oct 12**	**H**	**FAC 3 Q**	**Molesey**	**Won 2-1**		**504**	**Cuggy 7, 26**
15	Oct 16	A	DML	Sittingbourne	Lost 0-2		580	
16	Oct 19	H	DML	Gloucester City	Lost 0-2	18	418	
17	**Oct 26**	**H**	**FAC 4 Q**	**Hendon**	**Drew 1-1**		**753**	**Simmonds 50 (pen)**
18	**Oct 29**	**A**	**FAC 4QR**	**Hendon**	**Lost 0-2**		**512**	
19	Nov 2	A	DML	Cambridge City	Won 3-1	15	290	O'Shaughnessy 64, Willard 83, Ullathorne 85
20	**Nov 6**	**A**	**DMLC**	**St Leonards Stamcroft**	**Lost 0-3**		**1102**	
21	Nov 9	H	DML	Merthyr Tydfil	Drew 2-2	15	394	Ferguson 55, Cuggy 72
22	Nov 16	H	DML	Halesowen Town	Lost 2-3	18	421	Simmonds 42 (pen), Tuppeney 67
23	Nov 23	A	DML	Worcester City	Lost 0-3	19	587	
24	**Nov 30**	**A**	**FAT 3 Q**	**Basingstoke Town**	**Won 1-0**		**348**	**Parris 43**
25	**Dec 7**	**H**	**SSC**	**Littlehampton**	**Lost 3-5**		**203**	**Parris 17, 75, Tuppeney 32 (pen)**
26	Dec 14	H	DML	Newport A.F.C.	Drew 2-2	20	362	Cuggy 21, Shearer 62
27	Dec 21	A	DML	Gresley Rovers	Lost 0-3	22	590	
28	Dec 28	A	DML	Dorchester Town	Drew 1-1	21	613	Parris 72
29	**Jan 17**	**H**	**FAT 1**	**Salisbury City**	**Lost 1-3**		**389**	**Ullathorne 30**
30	Jan 21	A	DML	Gravesend & Northfleet	Lost 0-2	21	469	
31	Jan 25	A	DML	Merthyr Tydfil	Drew 0-0	21	502	
32	Feb 1	H	DML	Nuneaton Borough	Drew 0-0	21	442	
33	Feb 8	A	DML	Baldock Town	Lost 0-2	21	303	
34	Feb 15	A	DML	Gloucester City	Lost 0-2	21	612	
35	Feb 22	H	DML	Cambridge City	Drew 0-0	21	466	
36	Mar 1	H	DML	Atherstone United	Drew 0-0	14	316	
37	Mar 4	H	DML	King's Lynn	Drew 2-2	16	365	Ferguson 13, Parris 87
38	Mar 8	A	DML	Halesowen Town	Won 2-1	20	83	Tuppeney 56, Playford 71
39	Mar 11	H	DML	Worcester City	Drew 0-0		362	
40	Mar 15	H	DML	Cheltenham Town	Lost 1-2	21	412	Yates 5
41	Mar 22	A	DML	Atherstone United	Drew 0-0	18	262	
42	Mar 25	H	DML	Sudbury Town	Won 4-3		346	Cuggy (3) 35, 43, 46, Larkin 17
43	Mar 29	H	DML	Chelmsford City	Won 1-0		556	Simmons 73 (pen)
44	Mar 31	A	DML	Crawley Town	Won 2-0	16	943	Larkin 53, Barham 90
45	Apr 5	H	DML	Dorchester Town	Won 1-0	16	403	Cuggy 27
46	Apr 7	A	DML	Chelmsford City	Drew 2-2		769	Ferguson 23, Behhamy 25 (og)
47	Apr 12	A	DML	Cheltenham Town	Lost 0-1	16	1009	
48	Apr 15	H	DML	Salisbury City	Lost 2-3		387	Ferguson 61, Cuggy 69
49	Apr 19	A	DML	Burton Albion	Drew 0-0	16	568	
50	Apr 26	H	DML	Baldock Town	Won 1-0	16	435	Playford 42
51	Apr 29	H	DML	Crawley Town	Won 1-0	16	491	Ferguson 56
52	May 3	A	DML	Newport A.F.C.	Won 2-0	11	805	Parris 63, 71

HASTINGS TOWN PLAYING SQUAD 1997-98

Goalkeepers : James Creed (Faversham T, Hastings T), **Peter Carman** (Ashford T, Herne Bay, Ashford T, Maidstone U)

Defenders : Lloyd Hume (Sittingbourne, Whitstable T, Chatham T, Tonbridge, Ashford T, Gillingham (A)), **Matt Ball** (Worthing, Bexhill T), **Phil Henderson** (Eastbourne T, Wivenhoe T, Northampton), **Paul Tuppenney** (Stamco, Hastings T), **Steve Willard** (Sidley U), **Danny Simmonds** (Brighton), **Andy Larkin** (Charlton)

Midfielders : Simon Beard (Sittingbourne, West Ham U (T)), **Liam Barham** (Wealdstone, Hastings T, Grays Ath, Kingstonian, VV Veendam (Holl), Dover Ath, Dunstable, Windsor & Eton, Dunstable, Hastings U, Brughton (A)), **Richard Calloway** (Tunbridge Wells, Yate T, Wokingham T, Chester, Bristol C), **Keiran O'Shaughnessy** (Local football), **Darrol Parris** (Youth team)

Forwards : Steve Cuggy (Margate, Dover Ath, Maidstone U, Blyth Spartans, Sunderland), **Stuart Playford** (Rye U), **Simon Ullathorne** (Gloucester C, Sittingbourne, Gravesend, Croydon, Cleator Moor Celtic, Workington, Windscale U), **Dave Benson** (Youth team)

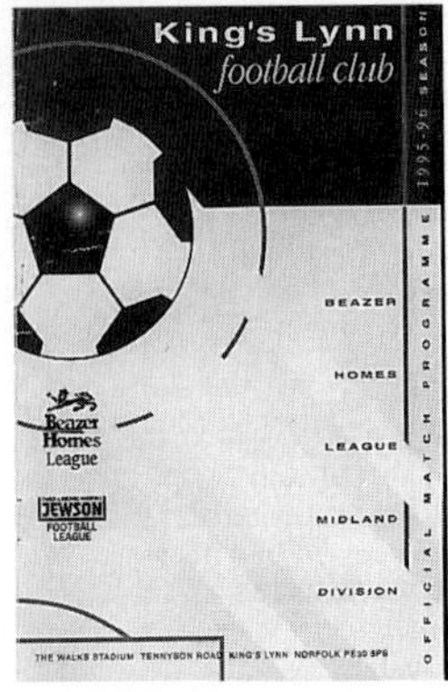

KING'S LYNN

Formed: 1879 **Nickname:** The Linnets
Colours: Royal Blue with gold trim/Blue/Blue & Gold hoops.
Change colours: All red
Midweek home matchday: Tuesday
Reserves' League: None

PROGRAMME DETAILS
Pages: 24 **Price:** £1
Editor: Gary Hart.

Chairman: John Scales. **President:** Jim Chandler.
Secretary: Martin Davis, 158 Lynn Road, Wisbech, Cambs PE13 3EB (01945 583567 H & B)
Manager: Peter Morris. **Asst Man/Coach:** N/A **Physio:** H Purvis
GROUND Address: The Walks Stadium, Tennyson Road, King's Lynn PE30 5PB (01553 760060). **Directions:** At mini r-about arriving from A10/A47 take Vancouse Avenue. Ground on left after a half mile. Quarter mile from King's Lynn (BR), half mile from bus station.
Capacity: 8,200 **Cover:** 5,000 **Seats:** 1,200 **Floodlights:** Yes
Clubhouse: Normal licensing hours, with extension on matchdays.
Club Shop: Sells metal badges and other merchandise
Club Sponsors: Eastern Group
PREVIOUS - Leagues: Norfolk & Suffolk/Eastern C'ties 35-39 48-54/UCL 46-48/Midland C'ties 54-58/ NPL 80-83. **Name:** Lynn Town. **Ground:** None.
CLUB RECORDS - Attendance: 12,937 v Exeter, FA Cup 1st Rd 50-51. **Career Appearances:** Mick Wright 1,152 (British Record).
Career Goalscorer: Malcolm Lindsay 321.
BEST SEASON - FA Cup: 3rd Rd 61-62 (0-4 at Everton). Competition Proper on 14 occasions; 05-06 37-38 49-50 51-52 58-63 64-65 68-69 71-72 73-74 84-85. **League clubs defeated:** Aldershot 59-60, Coventry 61-62, Halifax 68-69. **FA Trophy:** 2nd Rd 78-79. **FA Vase:** 5th Rd 94-95 (0-2 at Diss Town). **FA Amateur Cup:** R-up 1900-01.
Players progressing to Football League: N Rowe (Derby 1949), B Taylor & P Ward (Bradford P. A. 54 & 55), T Reynolds (Darlington 54), G Reed (Sunderland 55), P McCall (Bristol C 55), J Neal (Swindon 57), T Dryburgh (Oldham 57), J Hunter (Barrow 59), J Stevens (Swindon), G Catleugh (Watford), George Walters (Chesterfield 64), P McNamee (Notts County 1966), W Biggins (Burnley), Jackie Gallagher (Peterborough 80), Andy Higgins (Rochdale 83), Neil Horwood (Grimsby 86), Darren Rolph (Barnsley 87), Mark Howard (Stockport 88).
96-97 Captain: Colin Hoyle **96-97 P.o.Y.:** Ian Stringfellow **96-97 Top scorer:** Ian Stringfellow (24)
Local Press: Lynn News & Advertiser, Eastern Daily Press. **Local Radio:** KLFM
HONOURS: FA Amateur Cup R-up 1900-01, Southern Lg R-up 84-85 (Div 1 R-up 63-64), NPL Presidents Cup 82-83, Eastern Co's Lg 53-54 (R-up 49-50 52-53 (Lg Cup 53-54), Norfolk & Suffolk Lg(8)(R-up(6)), E Anglian Lg R-up(2), Norfolk Snr Cup(19)(R-up(20), Norfolk Invitation Cup 94-95, Norfolk Premier Cup 68-69(jt) 73-74, East Anglian Cup(4)(R-up(3), Eastern Prof Floodlit Lg 68-69, Southern Lg Midland R-up 95-96.

Kings Lyn: Back Row (L-R); Jamie Hawthorn, Lee Cooper, Andrew Stanhope, Craig Hopkins, H Purvis (Physio), Brett McNamara, Jason Pascoe, Darren Bloodworth, Robbie Curtis. Front Row; Mark Hales, Richard Skelly, Martin Matthews, Micky Gynn, Peter Morris (Mgr), Garry Harrison, Lee Hudson, Ian Stringfellow, Steve Lewis *Photo - Lynn News*

King's Lynn

Match No.	Date	Venue H/A	Competition	Opponents	Result	League Pos.	Attendance	Goalscorers (Times if known)
1	Aug 17	A	DML	Merthyr Tydfil	Won 2-1		679	Matthews 23, Pascoe 74
2	Aug 20	H	DML	Atherstone United	Won 2-1		1156	Gynn 49, Stringfellow 80
3	Aug 24	H	DML	Cheltenham Town	Lost 0-2		1253	
4	Aug 26	A	DML	Sudbury Town	Lost 1-5	12	650	Hudson 16
5	Aug 31	A	DML	Gloucester City	Lost 0-1	15	752	
6	Sep 3	H	DML	Chelmsford City	Drew 2-2		1047	Hudson 58, Stringfellow
7	Sep 7	H	DML	Hastings Town	Lost 1-4	17	904	Hudson 21
8	**Sep 10**	A	**DMC**	**Rothwell Town**	**Won 3-1**		**128**	**Hudson 43, Skelly 57 (p), Stringfellow 85**
9	**Sep 14**	A	**FAC 1 Q**	**Wrexham**	**Lost 2-3**		**378**	**McNamara 82, 87**
10	**Sep 17**	H	**DMC**	**Rothwell Town**	**Drew 0-0**		**550**	
11	Sep 21	A	DML	Salisbury City	Lost 0-2	20	362	
12	Sep 24	A	DML	Atherstone United	Drew 1-1		199	McNamara 2
13	Sep 28	H	DML	Halesowen Town	Won 2-1	16	732	Hoyle 20, McNamara 31
14	Oct 5	H	DML	Burton Albion	Won 2-0	12	932	McNamara 13, Hopkins 57
15	**Oct 9**	**A**	**DMLC**	**Raunds Town**	**Won 1-0**		**139**	**Hopkins 45**
16	Oct 12	A	DML	Crawley Town	Drew 0-0	11	623	
17	Oct 15	H	DML	Sudbury Town	Won 2-1	9	727	Harrison 21, Stringfellow 81
18	**Oct 19**	A	**FAT 1 Q**	**Yate Town**	**Won 3-1**		**168**	**Stringfellow (3) 54, 64, 70**
19	Oct 26	H	DML	Salisbury City	Drew 1-1	9	888	Dunlop 64
20	**Oct 29**	**H**	**DMLC**	**Raunds Town**	**Lost 1-2**		**491**	**Gynn 22**
21	Nov 2	A	DML	Gravesend & Northfleet	Drew 2-2	9	601	McNamara 57, 89
22	**Nov 9**	**A**	**FAT 2 Q**	**Staines Town**	**Won 1-0**		**292**	**Hudson 87**
23	Nov 16	H	DML	Newport A.F.C.	Lost 0-1	9	792	
24	Nov 19	A	DML	Chelmsford City	Won 2-0		565	Hudson 6, Dunlop 75
25	Nov 23	H	DML	Gloucester City	Won 2-1	8	786	McNamara 42, Stringfellow 63
26	**Nov 30**	A	**FAT 3 Q**	**St Albans City**	**Lost 1-3**		**535**	**Stringfellow 46**
27	Dec 7	H	DML	Nuneaton Borough	Won 4-0	8	896	Stringfellow 40, Hudson 56, Spencer 64, Skelly 77
28	Dec 14	A	DML	Halesowen Town	Drew 2-2	8	827	Stringfellow 48, McNamara 87
29	Jan 18	H	DML	Ashford Town	Won 2-0	7	756	Stringfellow 12, McNamara 26
30	Jan 25	A	DML	Nuneaton Borough	Won 4-2	7	930	McNamara 4, 5, Stringfellow 63, 76
31	Jan 28	H	DML	Cambridge City	Won 2-0	7	1236	Harrison 2, Skelly 31 (pen)
32	Feb 1	A	DML	Cheltenham Town	Won 2-1	6	704	McNamara 48, Hudson 83
33	Feb 5	A	DML	Baldock Town	Drew 1-1		287	McNamara 68
34	Feb 8	H	DML	Sittingbourne	Won 3-2	3	1079	Skelly 21, 78 (2 pens), Stringfellow 25
35	Feb 11	A	DML	Gresley Rovers	Won 2-0	3	664	Harrison 16, Hudson 87
36	Feb 15	A	DML	Dorchester Town	Lost 0-3	4	638	
37	Feb 22	H	DML	Merthyr Tydfil	Won 2-1	4	1050	McNamara 34, Pascoe 51
38	Feb 25	H	DML	Worcester City	Lost 0-1		982	
39	Mar 1	A	DML	Burton Albion	Lost 1-4	5	807	Stringfellow 86
40	Mar 4	A	DML	Hastings Town	Drew 2-2		365	Stringfellow 5, 79
41	Mar 8	H	DML	Dorchester Town	Lost 0-4	5	893	
42	Mar 15	A	DML	Newport A.F.C.	Won 2-0	5	562	Hudson 49, Stringfellow 58
43	Mar 22	A	DML	Worcester City	Lost 1-2	5	696	Stringfellow 61
44	Mar 29	H	DML	Baldock Town	Won 4-2		1103	Stringfellow 31, 39, Hudson 79, Hopkins 87
45	Mar 31	A	DML	Cambridge City	Won 2-0	4	590	Pascoe 54, Dunlop 86
46	Apr 5	H	DML	Gresley Rovers	Lost 0-2	4	1476	
47	Apr 12	A	DML	Sittingbourne	Won 2-0		693	Pascoe 4, Stringfellow 63
48	Apr 19	H	DML	Crawley Town	Lost 0-1		928	
49	Apr 26	A	DML	Ashford Town	Lost 0-4	7	538	
50	May 3	H	DML	Gravesend & Northfleet	Won 5-1	5	744	Hudson 12, Dunlop 50, 52, McNamara 73, Suter 89

KING'S LYNN PLAYING SQUAD 1997-98

Goalkeepers: Steve Lewis (Cambridge U), **Mark Hales** (Shirebrook T)

Defenders: Robbie Curtis (Northampton, Boston U, Shirebrook Coll), **Richard Skelly** (Northampton, Cambridge U, Newmarket T), **Darren Bloodworth** (Boston U, Kuitan (HK), King's Lynn, Kettering T, Bourne T, Holbeach U, Peterborough, Leicester C), **Colin Hoyle** (Notts Co, Bradford C, Barnsley, Arsenal)

Midfielders: Martin Matthews (Northampton, Derby (T)), **Garry Harrison** (Northampton, Aston Villa), **Gary Setchell** (Wisbech, King's Lynn), **Jason Pascoe** (Northampton, Boston U, Ashfield U, Worksop T, Sutton T, Oakham U), **Andy Stanhope** (Peterborough (T)), **Ian Stringfellow** (Dag & Red, Kettering T, Mansfield), **Simon Dunlop** (Hitchin, Boston T, Grimsby), **Kevin Lampkin** (Ilkeston, Mansfield, Huddersfield, Liverpool)

Forwards: Brett McNamara (Northampton, Stamford), **Lee Hudson** (Boston, SpaldingU, Moulton Harrox), **Craig Hopkins** (Shirebrook T), **Wayne Spencer** (Corby T, Buckingham T, Milton Keynes B, Dunstable, Leighton T)

PROGRAMME DETAILS:
Pages: 32 **Price:** £1.00
Editor: Anthony Hughes
(01685 359921)

MERTHYR TYDFIL

Formed: 1945 **Nickname:** The Martyrs
Colours: White & black/black/black
Change colours: All amber
Midweek home matchday: Tuesday
Reserves' League: None

Chairman: Ken Gunter **Football Secretary:** Peter Hunt.
Joint Presidents: The Archbishop of Cardiff, His Grace John Aloysious Ward, The Lord Bishop of Llandaff, The Right Rev. Roy Davies.
Manager: Colin Addison **Physio:** Ken Davey
Press Officer: Anthony Hughes **Commercial Manager:** Howard King.

GROUND Address: Penndarren Park, Merthyr Tydfil, Mid Glamorgan Tel: 01685 384102.
Directions: South A470 Express Way to Merthyr through Town Centre to Pontmorlais (traffic lights) turn left then first right, first right at Catholic Church and right again into Park Terrace to ground. North Heads of the Valley road to Town Centre, to Pontmorlais (traffic lights) turn right, then as above.
Capacity: 10,000 **Seats:** 1,500 **Cover:** 5,000. **Floodlights:** Yes
Clubhouse: Open Monday to Sunday 6.30 to 11.00pm. Two club cafes open on match days for hot food.
Club Shop: Sells replica kits, club souvenirs & programmes. Contact Mel Jenkins 01443 692336. **Sponsors:** Hoover PLC

PREVIOUS - Leagues: Southern League, Beazer Homes (Mid. Div.), Beazer Homes (Prem. Div.), G M Conference.

CLUB RECORDS - Attendance: 21,000 v Reading FA Cup 2nd Rnd 1949/50 **Win:** 11-0 **Defeat:** 9-2
Transfer fee paid: £ 10,000 to Cardiff City for Robbie James 1992
Transfer fee received: £12,000 for Ray Pratt from Exeter City 1981).

BEST SEASON - FA Trophy: 3rd Rd v Northwich Vic 95-96 **96-97 Top Scorer:** Paul Evans (19)

Past players who progressed to the Football League: Syd Howarth (Aston Villa), Cyril Beech, Gilbert Beech, Bill Hullet, Ken Tucker (Cardiff City), Nick Deacy (Hereford United), Gordon Davies (Fulham), Ray Pratt (Exeter City), Peter Jones, Paul Giles (Newport County).

HONOURS: Welsh FA Cup 48-49, 50-51, 86-87; Southern League 47-48, 49-50, 50-51, 51-52, 53-54; Southern League (Midland) 87-88; Southern League (Premier) 88-89; Southern League Cup 47-48, 50-51.

Tony Jenkins goes past Nick Amos of Bromsgrove Rovers in the FA Trophy match. Photo: Keith Clayton

Merthyr Tydfil

Match No.	Date	Venue H/A	Competition	Opponents	Result	League Pos.	Attendance	Goalscorers (Times if known)
1	Aug 17	H	DML	King's Lynn	Lost 1-2		679	Mitchell 88
2	Aug 20	A	DML	Gloucester City	Lost 3-6		875	Evans 42, 61, Summers 90
3	Aug 24	A	DML	Chelmsford City	Drew 0-0		824	
4	Aug 26	H	DML	Worcester City	Won 2-0	16	589	Evans 28, Wigley 89
5	Aug 31	A	DML	Baldock Town	Drew 2-2	17	315	Evans 49, Summers 82
6	Sep 3	H	DML	Salisbury City	Lost 2-3		610	Mardenborough 44, Rees 50
7	Sep 7	H	DML	Atherstone United	Won 3-2	14	551	Mitchell 6, Evans 25, Summers 88
8	**Sep 14**	**A**	**FAC 1 Q**	**St Blazey**	**Won 7-0**		**160**	**Rees (2), Evans (2), M'borough 70, Summers (2)**
9	Sep 21	A	DML	Cambridge City	Drew 2-2	16	228	Evans 43, Rees 64
10	Sep 24	H	DML	Gloucester City	Won 1-0	12	680	Summers 78
11	**Sep 28**	**H**	**FAC 2 Q**	**Torrington**	**Won 3-1**		**494**	**Evans 24, 90, Mitchell 33**
12	Oct 5	A	DML	Ashford Town	Won 1-0	9	660	Reeve 37
13	**Oct 8**	**A**	**DMLC**	**Yate Town**	**Drew 2-2**		**122**	**Abrahams 3, Rees 63**
14	**Oct 12**	**H**	**FAC 3 Q**	**Trowbridge Town**	**Won 1-0**		**594**	**Rees 48**
15	Oct 14	A	DML	Worcester City	Lost 1-2		769	Rees 65
16	Oct 19	H	DML	Burton Albion	Lost 0-1	11	655	
17	**Oct 26**	**H**	**FAC 4Q**	**Yeovil Town**	**Won 2-1**		**1514**	**Abrahams 28, Summers 82**
18	**Oct 29**	**H**	**DMLC**	**Yate Town**	**Won 5-0**		**362**	**Summers (3) 7, 60, 85, Gibbins 36, Jones**
19	Nov 2	H	DML	Chelmsford City	Won 2-0	12	731	**79**
20	Nov 9	A	DML	Hastings Town	Drew 2-2	10	394	Summers 28, Wigley 30
21	**Nov 16**	**A**	**FAC 1**	**Leyton Orient**	**Lost 1-2**		**4421**	Summers 56, Wimbleton 57
22	Nov 20	A	DML	Salisbury City	Won 3-1	10	167	**Evans 47**
23	Nov 23	A	DML	Atherstone United	Won 4-3	9	206	Pascoe 45, 73, O'Brien 70
24	Nov 30	H	DML	Baldock Town	Won 4-1	7	711	Evans (4) 1, 49, 66, 71
25	Dec 7	H	DML	Crawley Town	Won 3-1	5	817	O'Brien 7, Summers 19, Jones 83, Mardenborough 85
26	**Dec 10**	**H**	**DMLC**	**Witney Town**	**Drew 2-2**		**212**	Evans 9, O'Brien 18, Rees 75
27	Dec 14	A	DML	Sudbury Town	Lost 0-1	6	350	**Evans 22, Pascoe 88**
28	**Dec 17**	**A**	**DMLC**	**Witney Town**	**Won 2-1**		**74**	
29	Dec 21	A	DML	Cheltenham Town	Lost 0-2	7	801	**Jones 51, Evans 70**
30	Dec 26	H	DML	Newport A.F.C.	Won 2-0	6	1109	
31	Dec 28	H	DML	Halesowen Town	Drew 1-1	6	851	Jenkins 45, Evans 52
32	Jan 4	H	DML	Gresley Rovers	Lost 0-2	6	755	Mardenborough 81
33	**Jan 18**	**A**	**FAT 1**	**Bromsgrove Rovers**	**Lost 1-2**		**691**	
34	Jan 25	H	DML	Hastings Town	Drew 0-0	6	502	**Rees 27**
35	**Jan 28**	**H**	**DMLC**	**R.C. Warwick**	**Lost 0-2**		**200**	
36	Feb 1	A	DML	Burton Albion	Won 1-0	7	675	
37	Feb 8	H	DML	Ashford Town	Won 3-0	6	605	Mitchell 59
38	Feb 15	H	DML	Sudbury Town	Lost 1-3	8	505	Mitchell (3) 30, 33, 80 (pen)
39	Feb 18	A	DML	Nuneaton Borough	Drew 1-1	7	702	Summers 83
40	Feb 22	A	DML	King's Lynn	Lost 1-2	7	1050	Summers 3
41	Mar 1	H	DML	Cheltenham Town	Drew 2-2	10	543	Pascoe 31
42	Mar 4	A	DML	Dorchester Town	Lost 0-2		384	Williams 45, Summers 73
43	Mar 8	H	DML	Gravesend & Northfleet	Won 5-0	8	462	
44	Mar 15	H	DML	Sittingbourne	Lost 1-4	10	406	Bowen (5) 11, 56, 65, 74, 84
45	Mar 22	A	DML	Gresley Rovers	Won 2-0	10	788	Bowen 44
46	Mar 28	H	DML	Dorchester Town	Won 3-2		572	Mardenborough 56, Rees 83
47	Mar 31	A	DML	Newport A.F.C.	Lost 1-3	10	944	Pascoe 3, Mitchell 67, Summers 55
48	Apr 5	A	DML	Halesowen Town	Won 2-1	8	717	Thorpe 2 (og)
49	Apr 8	A	DML	Crawley Town	Lost 0-1		506	Wigley 51, Abraham 79
50	Apr 12	H	DML	Nuneaton Borough	Won 5-1	8	514	
51	Apr 19	A	DML	Sittingbourne	Lost 1-3	8		Bowen 31, Summers 39, 67, Reece 46, Jenkins 83
52	Apr 26	A	DML	Gravesend & Northfleet	Drew 0-0	9	617	
53	May 3	H	DML	Cambridge City	Lost 1-3	9	432	

MERTHYR TYDFIL PLAYING SQUAD 1997-98

Goalkeepers: Gary Wager (Bridgend T)

Defenders: Neil O'Brien (Inter Cardiff, Aberystwyth T, Llanelli), **Gareth Abraham** (Hereford, Cardiff), **David Barnhouse** (Swansea), **Samir Misbah** (Newport AFC, Cardiff), **Greg Downs** (Malvern, Bridgnorth, Forest Green R, Worcester, Merthyr, Redditch, Kettering, Raunds, Hereford, Birmingham, Coventry, Norwich)

Midfielders: Lee Jones (Inter Cardiff), **Paul Ramsey** (Torquay, Telford, St.Johnstone, Cardiff, Leicester C), **Phil Preedy** (Hereford), **Steve Mardenborough** (Gloucester, Newport AFC, Colchester, Stafford R, Lincoln, Darlington, Hereford, Cardiff, Newport Co, Swansea, Wolves, Coventry)

Forwards: Ian Mitchell (Chesham U, Hereford, Merthyr Tydfil, Newport Co), **Chris Summers** (Inter Cardiff, Barry T, Cardiff), **Tony Rees** (WBA, Grimsby, Barnsley, Birmingham, Aston Villa), **Sam Bowen** (Werstfields, Moor Green, Westfields), **Colin Pascoe** (Blackpool, Swansea, Sunderland, Swansea)

NUNEATON BOROUGH

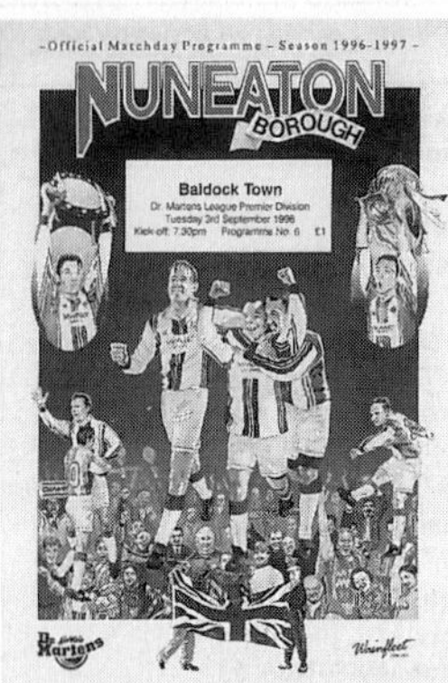

PROGRAMME DETAILS:
Pages: 40 **Price:** £1
Editor: Editorial team (contact Comm Mgr

Formed: 1937 **Nickname:** The Boro
Colours: All blue & white
Change colours: All yellow & green
Midweek matchday: Tuesday
Reserves' League: Ansells Midland Comb.

Chairman: Howard Kerry **Life President:** Alf Scattergood.
Secretary: Peter Humphreys, 29 Amington Rd, Shirley, Solihull, West Mids B90 2RF (0121 745 2031).
Press Officer: Gordon Chislett (01203 222106)
Commercial Manager: Phil Wright (01203 385738)
Manager: Brendan Phillips **Asst Man:** Colin We **Physio:** Richie Norman
GROUND Address: Manor Park, Beaumont Road, Nuneaton, Warks CV11 5HD (01203 342690/385738. Fax: 342690).
Directions: A444 to Nuneaton from M6 junction 3, 2nd exit at 1st roundabout, 2nd exit at 2nd r'about, left at 3rd r'bout, 2nd right into Greenmoor Rd, turn right at the end, grd on left. Parking 100 cars Manor Park Schl, Beaumont Rd, 50p each. Grd 1 mile Nuneaton Trent Valley (BR).
Capacity: 6,500 **Cover:** 3,500 **Seats:** 520 **Floodlights:** Yes
Clubhouse: Open every evening, weekend lunchtimes and matchdays (inc Reserve & Youth).
Club Shop: Sells souvenirs, progs & badges. Contact Andy Pace (01203 374043). **Sponsors:** Wainfleet Coaches

PREVIOUS - Leagues: Central Amateur 37-38/ B'ham Comb 38-52/ West Mids (B'ham) 52-58/ Southern 58-79 81-82/ GM Conference (Alliance Premier & Gola) 79-81 82-87.

CLUB RECORDS - Attendance: 22,114 v Rotherham, FA Cup 3rd Rd 1967
Transfer fee paid: £9,500 for Richard Dixey (Scarborough, 1981)
Transfer fee received: £60,000 for D Bullock (Huddersfield Tn 93)
Win: 11-1 (45-46 & 55-56) **Defeat:** 1-8 (55-56 & 68-69).
Goalscorer: Paul Culpin 201(Career) 55(Season - 92/93) **Career Appearances:** Alan Jones 545 (62-74)

BEST SEASON - FA Cup: 3rd Rd rep. 66-67. 1st Rd 19 times. **FA Trophy:** Qtr final 76-77(rep), 79-80, 86-87.
Players progressing to Football League: A Morton (Fulham 70), R Edwards Port Vale 72), K Stephens (Luton 78), T Peake (Lincoln 79), P Sugrue (Man City 80), M Shotton & T Smithers (Oxford 80), D Thomas (Wimbledon 81), P Richardson (Derby 84), P Culpin (Coventry 85), R Hill/T Morley/E McGoldrick/A Harris (Northampton 85/86), D Bullock (Huddersfield 93).
96-97 Captain: **96-97 Top Goalscorer:** Rob Straw (30) **96-97 P.o.Y.:**

HONOURS: Alliance Premier Lge R-up(2) 83-85, Southern Lg R-up 66-67 74-75, Sth Lg Cup Win 95-96, Midland Div 81-82 92-93, Champ 95-96, Lg Cup R-up 62-63, Merit Cup 92-93(joint)), Birmingham Lg 55-56 (Nth Div 54-55), Birmingham Comb. R-up 3; Birmingham Snr Cup 6, (R-up 3)

Nuneaton Borough AFC

Nuneaton Borough

Match No.	Date	Venue H/A	Competition	Opponents	Result	League Pos.	Attendance	Goalscorers (Times if known)
1	Aug 17	A	DML	Sudbury Town	Won 2-0		502	Straw 18, Drewitt 80
2	Aug 20	H	DML	Newport A.F.C.	Won 1-0		1203	Drewitt 75 (pen)
3	Aug 24	H	DML	Crawley Town	Lost 1-2		1333	Luby 2
4	Aug 26	A	DML	Burton Albion	Lost 0-2	10	1231	
5	Aug 31	A	DML	Salisbury City	Drew 1-1	10	460	Straw 7
6	Sep 3	H	DML	Baldock Town	Lost 0-3		940	
7	Sep 7	H	DML	Sittingbourne	Won 4-0	9	911	Dean 43, Statham 77, Straw 89, Drewitt 90 (p)
8	Sep 14	A	DML	Ashford Town	Lost 0-2	10	659	
9	**Sep 17**	**H**	**BSC**	**Atherstone United**	**Won 2-0**		**808**	**Straw 36, 89**
10	Sep 21	H	DML	Worcester City	Won 2-1	8	977	Simpson 34, Straw 65
11	Sep 25	A	DML	Newport A.F.C.	Drew 0-0	6	635	
12	Sep 28	H	DML	Gravesend & Northfleet	Won 3-0	6	905	Statham 18, Straw 43, 89
13	Oct 5	H	DML	Hastings Town	Won 4-1	5	1111	Simpson 5, Drewitt 56, Straw 73, Moss 75
14	**Oct 8**	**A**	**DMLC**	**Hinckley Town**	**Won 2-1**		**365**	**Drewitt 49, Straw 71**
15	Oct 12	A	DML	Gloucester City	Lost 0-1	5	1055	
16	Oct 15	H	DML	Burton Albion	Won 2-1	5	1007	Moss 60, Straw 84
17	**Oct 19**	**H**	**FAT 1 Q**	**Congleton Town**	**Lost 0-3**		**902**	
18	**Oct 26**	**A**	**FAC 4 Q**	**Colwyn Bay**	**Lost 0-1**		**1026**	
19	**Oct 29**	**H**	**DMLC**	**Hinckley Town**	**Drew 2-2**		**467**	**Simpson 67, Lake 84**
20	Nov 2	A	DML	Dorchester Town	Lost 0-2	8	532	
21	Nov 23	H	DML	Halesowen Town	Lost 0-2	10	1019	
22	**Dec 3**	**H**	**BSC**	**W.B.A.**	**Lost 1-2**		**442**	**Drewitt 30 (pen)**
23	Dec 7	A	DML	King's Lynn	Lost 0-4	11	896	
24	**Dec 17**	**H**	**DMC**	**Burton Albion**	**Lost 1-2**		**513**	**Straw 58**
25	Dec 21	H	DML	Gloucester City	Won 2-0	11	824	Straw 21, Mettioiu 75
26	Dec 26	H	DML	Atherstone United	Won 3-2	11	1607	Burr 7, 37, Straw 57
27	Dec 28	A	DML	Cheltenham Town	Lost 0-2	11	1068	
28	Jan 14	A	DML	Atherstone United	Drew 0-0	11	858	
29	Jan 18	A	DML	Sittingbourne	Drew 2-2	11	652	Mettioui 57, Straw 59
30	Jan 25	H	DML	King's Lynn	Lost 2-4	11	930	Mettioui 46, 52
31	Feb 1	A	DML	Hastings Town	Drew 0-0	12	442	
32	Feb 3	A	DML	Worcester City	Won 1-0	9	679	Straw 84,
33	Feb 8	H	DML	Sudbury Town	Drew 1-1	9	1001	Straw 14
34	Feb 11	A	DML	Baldock Town	Won 2-1	10	184	Straw 55, 70
35	Feb 18	H	DML	Merthyr Tydfil	Drew 1-1		702	Straw 46
36	Feb 22	H	DML	Ashford Town	Won 3-0	9	903	Williams 2, Mettioui 60, Bocketts 89
37	Mar 1	H	DML	Salisbury City	Won 4-0	8	830	Straw 56 (p), 90, Statham 80, Simpson 89
38	Mar 4	H	DML	Chelmsford City	Won 3-1		732	Straw (3) 11, 15, 82
39	Mar 15	A	DML	Gravesend & Northfleet	Drew 1-1		682	Drewitt 69
40	Mar 22	A	DML	Chelmsford City	Lost 1-3	11	763	Simpson 72
41	Mar 29	H	DML	Gresley Rovers	Won 1-0		1472	Straw 52
42	Mar 31	A	DML	Gresley Rovers	Won 4-1	6	1420	Drewitt 47, Yates 64, Stathem 83, Straw 87
43	Apr 5	H	DML	Cheltenham Town	Won 1-0	6	1241	Williams 3
44	Apr 8	A	DML	Cambridge City	Drew 2-2		324	Drewitt 52, Straw 72
45	Apr 12	A	DML	Merthyr Tydfil	Lost 1-5	7	514	Straw 32
46	Apr 19	H	DML	Cambridge City	Won 3-1	6	911	Simpson 1, Straw 19, Stanborough 48
47	Apr 20	A	DML	Crawley Town	Lost 0-1		757	
48	Apr 26	H	DML	Dorchester Town	Won 3-0	5	865	Donald 21, Drewitt 26, Yates 89
49	May 3	A	DML	Halesowen Town	Lost 0-2	7	991	

NUNEATON BOROUGH PLAYING SQUAD 1997-98

Goalkeepers : Paul Hayward (Bromsgrove R, Hednesford T, Bilston T, Blakenall, Redditch U, Kidderminster H, Worcester C, Paget R)
Defenders : Tom McGinty (VS Rugby, Moor Green, Coventry Sporting), **Gary Statham** (VS Rugby, Hinckley T, Shepshed A, Hinckley, Barlestone St.Giles, Barwell), **Barry Williams** (Redditch U, Ely C, Alvechurch), **Warren Donald** (Kettering T, Colchester, Northampton, West Ham), **Jon Hassall** (Stafford R, Chasetown, Northampton), **Nick Stanborough** (Hinckley A, Gresley R, Hinckley A, Hinckley, Earl Shilton), **Luke Yates** (Hednesford, Bilston, Sandwell B, Halesowen T, Nottingham F)
Midfielders : Dave Crowley (Stafford R, Bedworth U), **Craig Dean** (Hinckley T, Tamworth, Manchester U (T), **Ahmed Mettioui** (Hayes, Deportivo Braga (Port), Stafford R, Crewe, Faith Union (Morocco)), **Ray Woods** (Telford, Shrewsbury, Coventry, Wigan, Colne D, Caernarfon, Runcorn, Northwich V, Bangor C, Tranmere)
Forwards : Ian Drewitt (Stafford R, Merthyr Tydfil, Weymouth, Ton Pentre, Ferndale Ath), **Rob Straw** (Bedworth U, Tamworth, Bedworth U, Nuneaton B, Stafford R, Derby), **Tony Simpson** (Tamworth, Nuneaton B, Grantham T, Nottingham F), **Scott Darroch** (Bedworth)

ROTHWELL TOWN

Founded: 1895 **Nickname:** The Bones
Colours: Blue, red + white trim/blue/blue
Change Colours: Red, white trim/red/red
Midweek matchday: Tuesday **Newsline:** 0930 555 829.
Reserve Team's League: United Counties Lge Reserve Division.

Chairman: Stuart Andrews **Vice-Chairman:** Jeremy Freestone
President: Ken Cheney
Secretary: Roger Barratt, 18 Norton Street, Rothwell, Northants NN14 2DE (01536 507744).
Press Officer/Comm Mgr: Peter Bradley (01536 710925).
Manager: Jack Murray **Physio:** Graham Simmonds
Asst Manager: Graham Simmonds **Coach:** Kim Davies

PROGRAMME DETAILS:
Pages: 48 **Price:** 90p
Editor: Mark Southon
(01162 774877)

GROUND Address: Cecil Street, Rothwell, Northants NN14 2EZ (01536 710694). **Directions:** A14/A6 to Rothwell. At town centre roundabout turn into Bridge Street (right if northbound, left if southbound), take 3rd left into Tresham Street, ground is at top on left. Three miles from Kettering (BR); Rothwell is served by Kettering to Market Harborough buses.
Capacity: 3,500 **Seats:** 264 **Cover:** 1,264 **Floodlights:** Yes
Clubhouse: Rowellian Social Club, open every evening and weekend lunchtimes. Crisps and rolls available on matchdays (hot food and drinks available in ground). 'Top of the Town Ballroom', lounge seats 200.
Club Shop: Yes **Metal Badges:** Yes **Club Sponsors:** Forester Health

PREVIOUS - Leagues: Northants 1896-1911 21-33, Kettering Amateur 11-21 33-48, Leics. Senior 48-50, United Counties 50-56 61-94, Central Alliance 56-61. **Grounds:** Harrington Rd, Castle Hill. **Name:** Rothwell Town Swifts.

CLUB RECORDS - **Attendance:** 2,508 v Irthlingborough Diamonds, United Counties League 1971.
Win: 17-0 v Stamford, FA Cup Preliminary Round replay 1927.
Defeat: 1-10 v Coalville Town, Leicestershire Sen Lge 1949.
Transfer fee paid: Undisclosed for Andy Wright (Aylesbury 1992).
Transfer fee received: Undisclosed for Matty Watts (Charlton 1990).
BEST SEASON - FA Cup: Second Qualifying Round. **FA Trophy:** Second Round Proper 94-95. **FA Vase:** Fifth Round 92-93 (1-2 v Bridlington Town).

Local Press: Northants Evening Telegraph, Chronicle & Echo, Herald & Post.
Local Radio: BBC Radio Northants, KCBC.
Players progressing to Football League: Lee Glover (Nottingham Forest) 1987, Matty Watts (Charlton Ath.) 1990.
96-97 Captain: Kevin McDonald **96-97 Top Scorer:** Kevin McQuire **96-97 P.o.Y.:** K McQuire/Ben Lord

HONOURS: United Counties Lg 92-93 94-95 (R-up 69-70 70-71 87-88 89-90 90-91, KO Cup 55-56 70-71 71-72 91-92 92-93 (R-up 77-78 79-80 82-83), Div 2 52-53 53-54, Div 2 Cup 52-53 53-54, Benevolent Cup 92-93 94-95 (R-up 89-90 90-91)), Northants Lg 1899-1900 (R-up 1895-96 96-97 97-98), Northants Snr Cup 1899-1900 23-24 59-60 88-89 95-96 (R-up 24-25 71-72 87-88), Dr Martens Mid Div R-up 96-97.

Rothwell Town FC: Back Row (L-R); Graham Simmonds (Physio), Billy Hollywood (Asst Mgr), Dave Beazeley, Darren Vowden, Paul Beresford, John Coe, Marc Orton, Derek Brown, Simon Mason, Jack Meuuray (Mgr), Kim Davis (Coach). Front Row; Ashley Warner, Kevin McQuire, Nicky Anderson, Dean Foley, Kevin McDonald (Capt), Gary Torrance, Ben Lord.

Rothwell Town

Match No.	Date	Venue H/A	Competition	Opponents	Result	League Pos.	Attendance	Goalscorers (Times if known)
1	Aug 17	H	DML	Paget Rangers	Drew 0-0	11	152	
2	Aug 20	A	DML	Racing Club Warwick	Drew 1-1	12	100	Beazeley 89
3	Aug 24	H	DML	Stourbridge	Won 4-2	7	166	McDonald 33, Beazeley 55, Meeds 70 (p), Bone 83
4	Aug 26	H	DML	Corby Town	Won 3-0	4	367	Humphrey 60, McGuire 62, 83
5	**Aug 31**	**H**	**FAC Pre**	**Bourne Town**	**Won 5-1**		**135**	**Waite 8, Humphrey 44, 60, McGuire 78, 82**
6	Sep 4	A	DML	Solihull Borough	Lost 0-2	7	115	
7	Sep 7	A	DML	Ilkeston Town	Won 4-3	4	412	McGuire 22, 45, Humphrey 30, Bone 44
8	**Sep 10**	**H**	**DMC 1**	**King's Lynn**	**Lost 1-3**		**148**	**McGuire 42**
9	**Sep 14**	**H**	**FAC 1 Q**	**Spalding**	**Lost 2-3**		**137**	**Calvert 83, 87**
10	**Sep 17**	**A**	**DMC 2**	**King's Lynn**	**Drew 0-0**		**550**	
11	Sep 21	H	DML	Bedworth United	Lost 1-2	6	207	Calvert 34
12	Oct 5	H	DML	Redditch United	Won 4-0	4	172	Beazeley 17, McGuire 43, 57 (p), Meeds 89
13	Oct 12	A	DML	Stafford Rangers	Lost 1-2	6	448	McGuire 83
14	**Oct 16**	**A**	**NSC 1**	**Corby Town**	**Lost 1-4**		**110**	**Beazeley 63 (pen)**
15	Oct 19	H	DML	Ilkeston Town	Drew 2-2	10	192	Beazeley 35, McGuire 51
16	Oct 26	A	DML	Hinckley Town	Won 2-1	8	94	Meeds 52, Lord 63
17	Nov 6	H	DML	Racing Club Warwick	Won 2-0	6	148	Meeds 41 (pen), McDonald 66
18	Nov 9	H	DML	Dudley Town	Won 1-0	2	183	Meeds 33 (pen)
19	Nov 12	A	DML	Tamworth	Lost 0-3	2	655	
20	Nov 16	A	DML	Evesham United	Drew 1-1	2	114	Beazeley 39
21	Nov 23	H	DML	Hinckley Town	Won 3-2	2	142	Warner 25, Meeds 36 (pen), Beazley 78
22	Nov 26	H	DML	Solihull Borough	Won 3-0	2	157	Warner 13, Beazeley 71, 82
23	**Nov 30**	**H**	**FAT 3 Q**	**Workington**	**Lost 1-7**		**213**	**Meeds 57**
24	Dec 7	A	DML	Bilston Town	Won 4-0	2	119	McGuire 23, 80, 84, Warner 57
25	Dec 14	H	DML	Tamworth	Drew 2-2	2	420	Thompson 46, Orton 83
26	Dec 21	A	DML	Paget Rangers	Won 3-1	2	112	McGuire 21, 74, Thompson 60
27	Dec 28	H	DML	VS Rugby	Drew 2-2	2	260	Beazeley 28, 42 (2 pens)
28	Jan 18	H	DML	Shepshed Dynamo	Lost 3-4	2	178	Lord 34, Beazeley 36, McGuire 51
29	Jan 25	A	DML	Stourbridge	Lost 0-1	2	128	
30	**Jan 28**	**H**	**DCC 2**	**Cogenhoe United**	**Won 6-0**		**87**	**Beazeley 28, 60 (p), McDonald 33, 69, Anderson 68, Torrance 78**
31	Feb 1	A	DML	Moor Green	Drew 2-2	2	148	McGuire 33, Fletcher 90
32	Feb 8	H	DML	Evesham United	Won 6-1	2	201	McGuire 16, 22, 51, Meeds 20, 27 (2 pens), 64
33	Feb 15	H	DML	Moor Green	Lost 1-3	2	187	Warner 37
34	Feb 22	A	DML	Redditch United	Lost 2-5	3	182	Warner 32, Beazeley 59
35	Mar 1	A	DML	Bedworth United	Drew 1-1	6	283	McGuire 40
36	Mar 5	A	DML	Corby Town	Won 2-1	3	179	Beazeley 9, Foley 48
37	Mar 8	A	DML	Shepshed Dynamo	Won 2-1	2	210	Warner 10, Foley 84
38	Mar 15	A	DML	Dudley Town	Drew 1-1	3	133	Warner 48
39	**Mar 18**	**H**	**DCC 3**	**GPT (Coventry)**	**Won 4-1**		**56**	**Warner 1, Anderson 14, Beazeley 40 (p), Lord 63**
40	Mar 25	H	DML	Sutton Coldfield Town	Won 3-1	3	138	McDonald 33, Anderson 38, Warner 73
41	Mar 29	A	DML	Grantham Town	Lost 0-2	5	473	
42	Mar 31	H	DML	Raunds Town	Drew 2-2	5	527	McGuire 16, 25
43	Apr 5	A	DML	VS Rugby	Won 2-0	4	297	McGuire 6, Orton 87
44	Apr 8	H	DML	Grantham Town	Won 3-0	3	340	McGuire 6, Orton 77, Foley 89
45	Apr 12	H	DML	Bilston Town	Won 1-0	2	193	Beazeley 67
46	Apr 19	H	DML	Stafford Rangers	Drew 1-1	3	282	Beazeley 46
47	Apr 23	A	DML	Raunds Town	Won 4-0	3	130	Beazeley 10, Warner 55, 80, Torrance 80
48	Apr 26	A	DML	Sutton Coldfield Town	Won 3-2	3	177	Lord 13, Warner 21, McGuire 85

ROTHWELL TOWN PLAYING SQUAD 1997-98

Goalkeepers: Paul Beresford (Billericay T, Corby T), **Danny Liquorish** (Corby T, Wigston T, Anstey N, Friar Lane OB)

Defenders: Ben Lord (Higham T), **John Coe** (Rushden & D, VS Rugby), **Gary Torrance** (Desborough T, Corby T, Raunds T), **Darran Stephens** (Corby T, Leicester U), **Jason Meeds** (Rushden & D, Eynesbury R), **Andy Bullimore** (Grantham T, Melton T), **Darren Vowden** (Local Football)

Midfielders: Kevin McDonald (Corby T, Desborough T, Cottingham), **Marc Orton** (Leicester U, Friar Lane OB), **NickyAnderson** (Grantham T, Corby T, Hinckley T, Bedworth U, Nuneaton B), **Dean Foley** (Corby T, Raunds T, Desborough T, S&L Corby), **Simon Mason** (Corby T, Rushden & D, VS Rugby, Leicester U, Aylesbury U), **Doug Keast** (Burton A, Rushden & D, Corby T, Kettering T), **Andy Murfin** (Scunthorpe U), **Andy Kirkup** (Gloucester C, Rushden & D, Wellingborough T)

Forwards: Kevin McGuire (Raunds T, Northampton Spcr, Desborough T, Corby T), **Dave Beazley** (S & L, Corby, CorbyT), **Ashley Warner** (Corby T, Gloucester C, Telford U, Peterborough U), **Andy Evans** (Buckingham T, Wellingborough T, Cogenhoe U), **Ged Gribben** (Desborough T, S & L Corby)

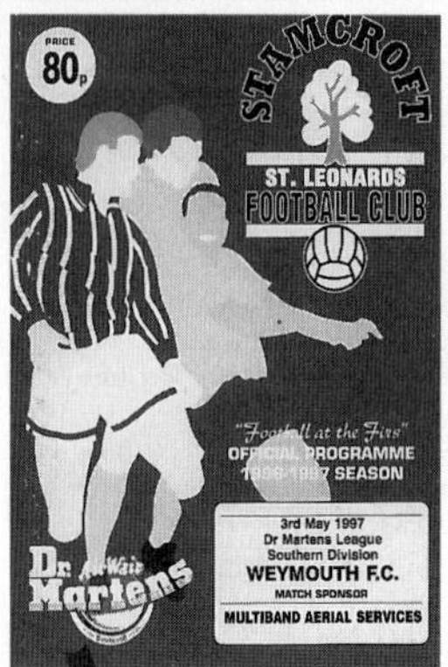

PROGRAMME DETAILS:
Pages: 60 **Price:** £1
Editor: Peter High
(01424 431482)

St LEONARDS STAMCROFT

Formed: 1971 **Nickname:** The Blues
Colours: Blue/white/blue
Change colours: White/navy/white
Midweek Matchday: Wednesday.
Reserves' League: Sussex County Res Sect
Clubcall Line: 0930 555 804

Chairman: Leon Shepperdson **President:** Mrs K Shepperdson
Vice-Chairman: Michael James
Secretary: Peter High, 1A Upper Maze Hill, St Leonards-on-Sea, East Sussex TN38 0LA (01424 431482).
Commercial Manager: John Huggett (01424 434755)
Press Officer: Tony Pankhurst (01424 751401) **Physio:** Mick James
Manager: Micky Reed **Asst Manager:** Andy Thomson

GROUND Address: The Firs, Elphinstone Road, Hastings, East Sussex (01424 434755). Matchday Office (01424 716362). **Directions:** From M25 & London approach Hastings on the A21. immediately after the junction with the A28 on the northern borough boundary, turn right into Junction Road. At T junction with B2093 turn right onto The Ridge. After 2 miles turn right, opposite the cemetary, into Elphinstone Road, ground 600yards down hill on left. Nearest station; Ore (Connex South East), one mile uphill (no bus or taxi). Hastings (Connex South East) 1.5 miles. Bus service from town centre to ground.
Capacity: 3,768 (Day), 3,015 (Even)**Seats:** 251 **Cover:** 1,000 **Floodlights:** Yes
Clubhouse: Licensed bar open normal pubhours. Breakfast Service 8-11.30 Sat. Hot food from tea bar.
Club Shop: Yes, selling leisure & sports wear, souvenirs & publications

PREVIOUS - **Leagues:** Eastbourne & Hastings 71-82, Southern Counties Comb 82-88, Sussex County 88-96. **Grounds:** Council pitches 71-73, Pannel Lane, Pett 73-93. **Names:** Stamco (71-96)

CLUB RECORDS - **Attendance:** 1,798 v Tiverton Town, FA Vase 4th Rd. 15/1/95. At old ground: 527 v Hastings Town, Sussex Senior Cup 2nd Round 5/12/93. **Record win:** 10-1 v Portfield (H), Sussex County League Division One 4/12/93. **Record defeat:** 1-6 v Hailsham Town (A) League Cup 23/9/92. **Career appearances:** Wayne Farrier (272). **Career goalscorer:** Dean Kewley (96 1992-95). **Transfer fee paid:** None. **Transfer fee received:** £1,500 for Peter Heritage (Margate)

BEST SEASON: **FA Cup:** 3rd Qual Rd 96-97. **FA Vase:** 5th Rd 94-95. **FA Trophy:** 3rd Rd 96-97
Local Press: Hastings Observer. **Local Radio:** BBC Southern Counties Radio, Southern FM
96-97 Captain: Tony Burt **96-97 Top Scorer:** Jon Magee **96-97 P.o.Y.:** Steve Gatting

HONOURS: Sussex Sen Cup 96-97; Sussex RUR Charity Cup R-up 94-95; Hastings Snr Cup 89-90 95-96 96-97, R-up 92-93; Dr Martens Lge Southern Div R-up 96-97, Merit Cup 96-97; Sussex County Div 1 R-up 94-95 95-96, Div 2 R-up 92-93, Cup R-up 89-90 90-91, Div Three R-up 88-89, Cup R-up 88-89

St Leonards Stamcroft FC: Back Row (L-R); N Phillips, T Burt, N Hall, Worthington, S Ilic, W Farrier, N Godden, J Magee, S Ferguson. Front Row; S Smith, P Ruddy, T Burgess, C Willard, Mascot, Wilson, P Baker, D Paine, D Jones.
Photo - Roger Turner

Salisbury City

Match No.	Date	Venue H/A	Competition	Opponents	Result	League Pos.	Attendance	Goalscorers (Times if known)
1	Aug 17	A	DML	Gravesend & Northfleet	Lost 2-3		601	Browne 21, Spencer 34
2	Aug 21	H	DML	Crawley Town	Won 1-0		350	Sandrey 64
3	Aug 24	H	DML	Hastings Town	Won 2-1		281	Chalk 1, Boyce 57
4	Aug 26	A	DML	Cheltenham Town	Won 2-0	4	1017	Harbutt 81, Lovell 87
5	Aug 31	H	DML	Nuneaton Borough	Drew 1-1	6	460	Boyce 28
6	Sep 3	A	DML	Merthyr Tydfil	Won 3-2		610	Boyce 65, Emms 76, 86
7	Sep 7	H	DML	Worcester City	Drew 1-1	5	452	Chalk 17
8	**Sep 14**	**H**	**FAC 1 Q**	**Godalming & Guildford**	**Drew 0-0**		**318**	
9	**Sep 17**	**A**	**FAC 1QR**	**Godalming & Guildford**	**Won 2-0**		**342**	**Browne 5 (pen), Webb 57**
10	Sep 21	H	DML	King's Lynn	Won 2-0	4	362	Harbutt 8, Webb 59
11	Sep 24	A	DML	Crawley Town	Drew 2-2	4	481	Chalk 29, Webb 48
12	**Sep 28**	**A**	**FAC 2 Q**	**Cheltenham Town**	**Lost 3-4**		**714**	**Boyce 7, Emms 25, Webb 61**
13	Oct 5	A	DML	Chelmsford City	Won 2-1	3	961	Boyce 6, Harbutt 34
14	**Oct 9**	**A**	**DMLC**	**Bashley**	**Won 3-2**		**122**	**Webb 31, 47, Emms 53**
15	Oct 12	H	DML	Ashford Town	Lost 0-1	4	421	
16	Oct 16	H	DML	Cheltenham Town	Lost 1-2		310	Harbutt 90
17	Oct 19	A	DML	Halesowen Town	Won 2-1	4	833	Lovell 53, Boyce 68 (pen)
18	Oct 26	A	DML	King's Lynn	Drew 1-1	4	888	Boyce 12
19	**Oct 29**	**H**	**DMLC**	**Bashley**	**Won 3-0**		**235**	**Webb 2, 75, Boyce 45 (pen)**
20	Nov 2	A	DML	Worcester City	Won 2-0	3	746	Harbutt 18, Webb 74
21	**Nov 9**	**H**	**FAT 2**	**Witney Town**	**Won 1-0**		**381**	**Lovell 40**
22	Nov 16	H	DML	Gloucester City	Lost 0-4	5	489	
23	Nov 20	H	DML	Merthyr Tydfil	Lost 1-3		167	Browne 65
24	Nov 23	A	DML	Baldock Town	Drew 1-1	6	323	Chalk 8
25	**Nov 30**	**A**	**FAT 3 Q**	**Harrow Borough**	**Drew 2-2**		**174**	**James 49 (og), Boyle 76 (pen)**
26	**Dec 2**	**H**	**FAT 3QR**	**Harrow Borough**	**Won 2-1**		**175**	**Emms 23, 33**
27	**Dec 11**	**H**	**DMC**	**Newport IoW**	**Won 3-1**		**189**	**Boyce 29, 35, Browne 90**
28	Dec 14	H	DML	Gravesend & Northfleet	Won 4-1	5	324	Harbutt (3) 6, 17, 81, Boyce 74 (pen)
29	Dec 28	A	DML	Sittingbourne	Lost 1-2	7	584	Webb 24
30	Jan 1	H	DML	Newport A.F.C.	Lost 1-3	7	563	Chalk 89
31	**Jan 15**	**A**	**FAT 1**	**Hastings Town**	**Won 3-1**		**389**	**Chalk 55, Emms 58, Webb 74**
32	**Jan 22**	**H**	**DMC**	**Weymouth**	**Lost 1-3**		**180**	**Boyle 53**
33	Jan 28	A	DML	Burton Albion	Drew 1-1	9	724	Webb 16
34	Feb 1	H	DML	Chelmsford City	Drew 1-1	10	247	Webb 32
35	**Feb 8**	**H**	**FAT 2**	**Dorchester Town**	**Drew 1-1**		**727**	**Browne 53**
36	**Feb 11**	**A**	**FAT 2 R**	**Dorchester Town**	**Lost 2-3**		**713**	**Chalk 33, Cranmer 38**
37	Feb 15	H	DML	Atherstone United	Won 3-2	12	284	Chalk 43, Emms 45, Lovell 58
38	Feb 22	A	DML	Sudbury Town	Won 1-0		490	Cranmer 72
39	Mar 1	A	DML	Nuneaton Borough	Lost 0-4	9	830	
40	Mar 8	H	DML	Burton Albion	Drew 1-1	12	339	Preston 90
41	Mar 15	A	DML	Cambridge City	Drew 1-1	13	213	Harbutt 85
42	Mar 19	H	DML	Gresley Rovers	Drew 1-1		289	Harbutt 35
43	Mar 22	H	DML	Cambridge City	Drew 2-2	13	257	Browne 33 (pen), Chalk 87
44	Mar 25	A	DML	Ashford Town	Won 1-0		456	Emms 14
45	Mar 29	H	DML	Newport A.F.C.	Drew 0-0		472	
46	Mar 31	A	DML	Dorchester Town	Lost 2-4	13	868	Sullivan 20 (og), Chalk 70
47	Apr 5	H	DML	Sittingbourne	Lost 0-1	13	254	
48	Apr 10	H	DML	Sudbury Town	Won 2-1		170	Sanders 39, Harbutt 45
49	Apr 12	A	DML	Gresley Rovers	Lost 0-5	13	720	
50	Apr 15	A	DML	Hastings Town	Won 3-2		387	Preston 4, Chalk 6, 84
51	Apr 19	H	DML	Baldock Town	Lost 2-3	13	212	Webb 9, Harbutt 83
52	Apr 22	A	DML	Atherstone United	Lost 0-4		213	
53	Apr 26	H	DML	Halesowen Town	Lost 1-2	14	285	Preston 81
54	May 1	H	DML	Dorchester Town	Drew 0-0		1024	
55	May 3	A	DML	Gloucester City	Won 3-1	12	1863	Webb 58, 87, Emms 80

SALISBURY CITY PLAYING SQUAD 1997-98

Goalkeepers: John Simpkins (Newport IOW, Bashley, Basingstoke T, East Cowes V(IOW))
Defenders: Roger Emms (Andover, Newbury T, Swindon Ath, Devizes T), **Simon Browne** (Dorchester T, Swanage, Weymouth), **Gavin Sandrey** (Fareham T, Weymouth, Dorchester T, Weymouth, Swindon T, Weymouth), **Matthew Lovell** (Cheltenham T, AFC Bournemouth), **Sandy Baird** (Bashley, Gosport B, Basingstoke T, Weymouth, Horndean, Fareham T, Horndean, Fareham T), **Danny Rofe** (Yate, Bristol R), **Barry Cranmer** (Downton, Poole, Salisbury, Basingstoke, Salisbury, Andover)
Midfielders: Robbie Harbut (Bashley, Southampton (T)), **Chris Shaw** (Poole T, Salisbury C, Weymouth, Salisbury C, Bath C, AFC Bournemouth), **Gary Fletcher** (Bashley, Wimborne, Poole, Wimborne, Salisbury, Brockenhurst, Bashley, Newbury, Basingstoke, Portals A), **Jon Preston** (Bournemouth Sports), **Paul Masters** (Havant, Dorchester, Southampton), **Mark Smith** (AFC Bournemouth), **Darren Middleton** (Youth team)
Forwards: Ian Chalk (Warminster T, Bemerton Ath, Swindon, Peterborough,Wrexham), **Matthew Guy** (Warminster T), **Lee Webb** (Poole T, Salisbury C, Westbury U, Trowbridge T, Westbury U, Devizes T), **Mickey Spencer** (Bath C, Yeovil T, Wokingham T, Bury)

SALISBURY CITY

Formed: 1947 **Nickname:** The Whites
Colours: White/black/white
Change colours: All Blue.
Midweek matchday: Wednesday
Reserve Team's League: None. **Club Line:** 0891 122 905

Chairman: P R McEnhill **Vice-Chairmam:** R Brocksom
Secretary: Sean Gallagher, 1 Tempest Road, Beamont Park, Amesbury, Wilts SP4 7UE (01980 626855 H & Fax).
Press Officer: David Macey (01264 773765)
Youth Dev. Off.: Simon Pickett **Commercial Manager:** Geoff Butler
Manager: Geoff Butler **Physio:** Kim Sturgess
GROUND Address: The Raymond McEnhill Stadium, Partridhe Way, Old Sarum, Salisbury SP4 6PU. **Directions:** The Stadium is situated off the main A345 (Salisbury - Amesbury) road on the northern edge of the city some two miles from the City centre.
Capacity: 4,000 **Cover:** 3,062 **Seats:** 450 **Floodlights:** Yes
Clubhouse: On ground
Club Shop: Sells replica shirts, memorabilia, programmes, scarves, metal badges, souvenirs. Contact Mr David Beavon (01747 828624).
Sponsors: M J Abbotts.

PROGRAMME DETAILS:
Pages: 48 **Price:** £1.20
Editor: Kevin Gover
(0585 293431)

PREVIOUS - **Leagues:** Western 47-68. **Name:** Salisbury FC, pre 92. **Ground:** Hudson Field 47-51, Victoria Park 51-97.

CLUB RECORDS - **Attendance:** 8,902 v Weymouth, Western League 1948. **Win:** 9-0 v Westbury United (H), FA Cup 1st Qual. Rd 72. **Defeat:** 0-7 v Minehead, Southern League 1975. **Career Goalscorer:** Royston Watts 180 (59-65). **Career Appearances:** Barry Fitch 713 (63-75). **Transfer fee paid:** £5,750 for Peter Loveridge (Dorchester Town, 1990). **Transfer fee received:** £16,000 for Ian Thompson (AFC Bournemouth, 1983).

BEST SEASON - **FA Trophy:** 2nd Rd 96-97 (lost to Dorchester Town). **FA Amateur Cup:** 2nd Rd 49-50 (lost to Hendon). **FA Cup:** 2nd Rd 59-60 (lost to Newport County)

Players progressing to Football League: Eric Fountain (Southampton 48), Cyril Smith (Arsenal & Southampton 48), Tony Alexander (Fulham 65), John Evans (Stockport County 67), Graham Moxon (Exeter 75), Eric Welch (Chesterfield 76), Ian Thompson (Bournemouth 83), Trevor Wood (Port Vale, Walsall, Hereford 88), Denny Mundee (B'mouth Brentford, Brighton 88), Matthew Carmichael (Lincoln 90), Shaun Brookes (Barnet & Orient 91).

96-97 Captain: Roger Emms **96-97 P.o.Y.:** John Simpkins **96-97 Top scorer:** Ian Chalk/Lee Webb (18)

Local Press: Salisbury Journal, Evening Echo & Sports Echo, Western Daily Press.

Local Radio: Wiltshire Sound, Spire F.M.

Honours: Southern Lg Southern Div Champ 94-95, R-up 85-86 92-93; Western Lg 57-58 60-61, R-up 58-59 59-60 61-62 67-68; Hants Senior Cup 61-62 63-64; Alan Young Cup 59-60 60-61 62-63; Wilts Premier Shield 56-57 59-60 61-62 66-67 67-68 70-71 77-78 78-79 95-96.

Salisbury City FC. Photo - Eric Marsh

Sittingbourne

Match No.	Date	Venue H/A	Competition	Opponents	Result	League Pos.	Attendance	Goalscorers (Times if known)
1	Aug 17	A	DML	Cheltenham Town	Lost 0-2		703	
2	Aug 21	H	DML	Sudbury Town	Lost 4-5		860	Walker 47, 77, Planck 73, Pearson 83
3	Aug 24	H	DML	Burton Albion	Lost 1-2		676	Lovell 89
4	Aug 26	A	DML	Hastings Town	Drew 2-2	22	569	Lovell 1, Walker 35
5	Aug 31	H	DML	Dorchester Town	Lost 1-3	22	543	Lovell 81
6	Sep 3	A	DML	Cambridge City	Won 3-1		223	Walker 18, Planck 78, Miller 87
7	Sep 7	A	DML	Nuneaton Borough	Lost 0-4	22	911	
8	**Sep 14**	**A**	**FAC 1 Q**	**Horsham YMCA**	**Won 3-2**		**176**	**Miller 35, Walker 57, Planck 89**
9	Sep 21	H	DML	Newport A.F.C.	Won 3-0	17	656	Planck 5, 49, King 60
10	Sep 24	A	DML	Sudbury Town	Won 3-1	17	254	English (og) 4, Planck 18, Searle 32
11	**Sep 28**	**H**	**FAC 2 Q**	**Tooting & Mitcham**	**Lost 4-5**		**717**	**Searle 45, Killer 46, Walker 62, Eeles 84**
12	Oct 5	H	DML	Gloucester City	Drew 1-1	17	593	Blondrage 79
13	**Oct 8**	**A**	**DMLC**	**Gravesend & Northfleet**	**Won 3-2**		**596**	**Eeles 45, Curns 78, Walker 90**
14	Oct 16	H	DML	Hastings Town	Won 2-0	16	580	M Miller 22, Walker 55
15	**Oct 19**	**H**	**FAT 1 Q**	**Fleet Town**	**Won 3-2**		**519**	**Blondrace 17, Searle 53, Walker 58**
16	Oct 26	A	DML	Chelmsford City	Won 4-1	11	917	Meade 2, 26, Walker 30, Searle 65
17	**Oct 30**	**H**	**DMLC**	**Gravesend & Northfleet**	**Lost 1-2+**		**610**	**Searle 47**
18	Nov 2	H	DML	Atherstone United	Drew 1-1	11	691	Meade 41
19	**Nov 9**	**A**	**FAT 2 Q**	**Aylesbury United**	**Drew 1-1**		**506**	**Searle 28**
20	**Nov 13**	**H**	**FAT 2 Q**	**Aylesbury United**	**Won 2-1**		**482**	**Meade 22, 26**
21	Nov 16	A	DML	Burton Albion	Lost 0-1	13	933	
22	Nov 20	H	DML	Cambridge City	Lost 0-2		417	
23	Nov 23	A	DML	Crawley Town	Drew 2-2	14	631	Meade 69, Miller 73
24	**Nov 30**	**H**	**FAT 3 Q**	**Yeading**	**Drew 0-0**		**474**	
25	**Dec 3**	**A**	**FAT 3QR**	**Yeading**	**Lost 1-3**		**142**	
26	Dec 7	A	DML	Gresley Rovers	Won 4-0	17	642	Walker (3) 21, 45, 80, Searle 27 (p)
27	**Dec 11**	**H**	**DMC**	Baldock Town	Lost 0-2		351	
28	Dec 14	A	DML	Gloucester City	Drew 1-1	11	710	Holliday 4
29	**Dec 17**	**A**	**KSC**	**Gravesend & Northfleet**	**Won 1-0**		**318**	**Brown 61 (og)**
30	Dec 21	H	DML	Crawley Town	Lost 3-5	14	758	Seager 19, Searle 31 (pen), Miller 51
31	Dec 28	H	DML	Salisbury City	Won 2-1	12	584	Meade 42, Lovell 83 (og)
32	Jan 11	A	DML	Dorchester Town	Lost 0-2	12	522	
33	Jan 18	H	DML	Nuneaton Borough	Drew 2-2	13	652	Pearson 73, Rutter 88
34	Jan 25	H	DML	Cheltenham Town	Won 1-0	12	598	Kimble 77
35	**Jan 29**	**A**	**KSC**	**Bromley**	**Lost 0-5**		**149**	
36	Feb 1	A	DML	Newport A.F.C.	Won 3-2	11	504	Rutter 7, Walker 42, Haylock 81
37	Feb 5	H	DML	Gravesend & Northfleet	Lost 1-3		1028	Kimble 17
38	Feb 8	A	DML	King's Lynn	Lost 2-3	13	1079	Walker 41, Kimble 49
39	Feb 15	H	DML	Worcester City	Lost 0-1	13	537	
40	Feb 22	A	DML	Atherstone United	Lost 1-2	13	256	Seager 67
41	Feb 25	A	DML	Ashford Town	Drew 1-1		552	Pearson 88
42	Mar 1	A	DML	Baldock Town	Won 5-1	13	168	Walker 7, Planck 14, 90, Hodge 53, Seager 75
43	Mar 8	H	DML	Chelmsford City	Won 2-1	13	714	Seager 11, Planck 45
44	Mar 15	A	DML	Merthyr Tydfil	Won 4-1		406	Walker 48, Rowland 49, Hodge 53, Searle 74
45	Mar 22	H	DML	Halesowen Town	Won 4-2	10	597	Miller 35, Rowland 48, 71, Searle 81
46	Mar 29	A	DML	Gravesend & Northfleet	Lost 0-3		1303	
47	Mar 31	H	DML	Ashford Town	Won 4-0	12	1025	Miller 10, 48, Hodge 33, Rowland 89
48	Apr 5	A	DML	Salisbury City	Won 1-0		254	Walker 79
49	Apr 9	H	DML	Baldock Town	Won 1-0	11	512	Planck 56
50	Apr 12	H	DML	King's Lynn	Lost 0-2	12	693	
51	Apr 19	H	DML	Merthyr Tydfil	Won 3-1	9		
52	Apr 22	A	DML	Halesowen Town	Lost 0-2		469	
53	Apr 26	A	DML	Worcester City	Won 2-0	8	510	Pavey 81, Sinden 88
54	May 3	H	DML	Gresley Rovers	Won 2-0	8	783	Smith 9, Walker 85

+ Won on Away Goals

SITTINGBOURNE PLAYING SQUAD 1997-98

Goalkeepers : Andy Hough (Sheppey U)
D efenders : Paul Haylock (Barnet, Shrewsbury, Maidstone U, Gillingham, Norwich), **Alan Walker** (Barnet, Mansfield, Plymouth, Gillingham, Millwall, Lincoln,Telford U, Bangor C, Stockport), **Scott Saunders** (Greenwich B, Charlton), **Ricky Pearson** (Margate, Ashford T, Erith & Belvedere, Fisher Ath, Ashford T, Gillingham), **Richard Ponsford** (From YTS), **Paul Holliday** (Youth team)
Midfielders : Steve Searle (Youth team), **Andy Blondrage** (Hastings T, Gravesend, Ashford T, Gravesend), **Tony Eeles** (Dover Ath, Gillingham), **Peter Overton** (Tonbridge, Faversham, Herne Bay), **Nick Miller** (Youth team)
Forwards : Tom Planck (Youth team), **Marc Seager** (Local football), **Tyrone King** (Youth team), **Raphael Meade** (Crawley, Brighton, Plymouth, Odense (Den), Ipswich, Luton, Dundee U, Sporting Lisbon (Port), Arsenal), **Linden Rowland** (Corby, Pontypridd, Sittingbourne), **Mark Miller** (Youth team)

PROGRAMME DETAILS:
Pages: 28 **Price:** £1
Editor: William Rickson
(c/o the club)

SITTINGBOURNE

Formed: 1881 **Nickname:** Brickies
Colours: Red & black stripes/black/red
Change colours: All yellow
Midweek matchday: Wednesday **Newsline:** 0891 333 027
Reserves' league: Winstonlead Kent

Chairman: B.Bright **President:** E H Bennett.
Secretary: Mrs M Bratton, c/o Sittingbourne F.C.
Manager: Alan Walker **Coach:** Paul Haylock **Physio:** Kevin Manser
Commercial Manager: Barry Bright

GROUND Address: Central Park, Eurolink, Sittingbourne, Kent ME10 3SB (01795 435077. Fax: 01474 814501).
Directions: Through Sittingbourne on main A2, club signposted clearly and regularly from both east and west. 1 mile from Sittingbourne BR station.
Capacity: 8,000 **Cover:** 3,300 **Seats:** 2,000 **Floodlights:** 420 lux
Clubhouse: The Cabin (Club's Tel No.)
Club Shop: Sells a wide selection of souvenirs etc. Open matchdays or contact Ann Morrison (01795 664436) or Clive Phillips (01795 477108).
Sponsors: Medway Galvanising.
PREVIOUS - Names: Sittingbourne United 1881-86. **Leagues:** Kent 1894-1905 09-27 30-39 46-59 68-91, South Eastern 05-09, Southern 27-30 59-67. **Grounds:** Sittingbourne Recreation Ground 1881-90, Gore Court Cricket Ground 90-92, The Bull Ground 1892-1990.
CLUB RECORDS - Attendance: 5,951 v Tottenham Hotspur, friendly 26/1/93. **Transfer fee paid:** £20,000 to Ashford Town for Lee McRobert, 1993. **Transfer fee received:** £210,000 from Millwall for Neil Emblen and Michael Harle, 1993.
BEST SEASON - FA Cup: 2nd Rd 25-26 (0-7 at Swindon Town), 28-29 (1-2 at Walsall), plus 1st Rd 26-27 30-31 62-63.
FA Trophy:
Players progressing to Football Lge: Jason Lillis (Walsall 93), Neil Emblen & Michael Harle & Steve Forbes & Lee McRobert (Millwall 93/93/94/95, Jimmy Case (Brighton 93), Lee Harper (Arsenal 94).
96-97 Captain: Ricky Pearson **96-97 P.o.Y.:** Paul Haycock **96-97 Top scorer:** Alan Walker
Local Press: East Kent Gazette, Kent Today, Kent Messenger Extra, Sittingbourne & Sheppy Adscene.
Local Radio: Invicta Supergold, BBC Radio Kent, Invicta FM.

HONOURS: Southern Lg Southern Div 92-93 95-96; Kent Lg 1897-98 1902-03 57-58 58-59 75-76 83-84 90-91 (Lg Cup 25-26 58-59 73-74 80-81, Div 2 Cup 54-55 57-58 83-84 86-87 87-88); Kent Senior Cup 01-02 28-29 29-30 57-58; Kent Senior Shield 25-26 27-28 53-54; Kent Senior Trophy 89-90; Thames & Medway Cup 55-56 58-59; Thames & Medway Comb 02-03 07-08 11-12 24-25 25-26; Chatham Charity Cup 03-04 19-20; Kent Midweek Lg(res) 91-92 (Lg Cup 90-91).

Sittingbourne FC. Back Row (L-R); Kevin Manser (Physio), Tyrone King, Marc Seager, Alan Walker (Play/Mgr), Andy Hough, Ricky Pearson, Steve Lovell, Mark Miller. Front Row; Mascot, Scott Saunders, Richard Ponsford, Tony Eeles, Paul Haylock, Tommy Planck, Damien Hodge, Garry Kimble.

St. Leonards Stamcroft

Match No.	Date	Venue H/A	Competition	Opponents	Result	League Pos.	Attendance	Goalscorers (Times if known)
1	Aug 17	A	DML	Waterlooville	Won 1-0		167	Magee
2	Aug 21	H	DML	Erith & Belvedere	Won 2-0		399	White, Magee
3	Aug 24	H	DML	Trowbridge Town	Won 3-0		433	Burt, N'Dumduna (2)
4	Aug 26	A	DML	Dartford	Lost 2-3		484	White, Baker
5	**Aug 31**	**H**	**FAC Pre**	**Metropolitan Police**	**Won 2-0**		**461**	**Ashworth, Miles**
6	Sep 4	A	DML	Havant Town	Lost 1-2		205	Miles
7	Sep 7	H	DML	Newport IoW	Drew 1-1		386	Smith
8	**Sep 14**	**H**	**FAC 1 Q**	**Arundel**	**Won 4-1**		**384**	**White, Magee, Miles (2)**
9	Sep 21	A	DML	Yate Town	Won 1-0		184	White
10	Sep 24	A	DML	Erith & Belvedere	Won 2-1		124	Magee, Miles
11	**Sep 28**	**A**	**FAC 2 Q**	**Croydon**	**Won 7-0**		**200**	**Farrier, White, Magee (3), Miles (2)**
12	Oct 5	H	DML	Weston Super Mare	Drew 2-2		415	White, Miles
13	**Oct 8**	**A**	**DMC 1-1**	**Hastings Town**	**Won 2-1**		**1095**	**Magee, Baker**
14	**Oct 12**	**A**	**FAC 3 Q**	**Bromley**	**Drew 1-1**		**630**	**Magee**
15	**Oct 16**	**H**	**FAC 3 Q R**	**Bromley**	**Lost 2-5**		**648**	**White, Phillips**
16	**Oct 19**	**A**	**FAT 1 Q**	**Gravesend & Northfleet**	**Drew 2-2**		**424**	**White (2)**
17	**Oct 23**	**H**	**FAT 1 Q R**	**Gravesend & Northfleet**	**Won 4-3**		**440**	**Baker, White, Magee, Phillips**
18	Oct 26	A	DML	Cirencester Town	Won 2-1		109	Magee, Baker
19	Nov 2	H	DML	Fisher Athletic	Won 2-1		388	Miles (2)
20	**Nov 6**	**H**	**DMC 1-2**	**Hastings Town**	**Won 3-0**		**1102**	**White, Magee, Smith**
21	**Nov 9**	**A**	**FAT 2 Q**	**Hampton**	**Won 1-0**		**225**	**Burt**
22	Nov 16	A	DML	Trowbridge Town	Won 4-1		272	Miles (3), Smith
23	Nov 23	H	DML	Witney Town	Lost 1-2		388	Phillips
24	**Nov 30**	**H**	**FAT 3 Q**	**Purfleet**	**Won 6-0**		**344**	**Magee (3), Miles, Smith (2)**
25	**Dec 7**	**H**	**SSC 2**	**Crowborough Athletic**	**Won 9-0**		**238**	**Jones, White, Magee (3), Miles, Smith, Baker (3)**
26	**Dec 11**	**H**	**DMC 2**	**Margate**	**Won 3-2**		**314**	**Magee, Miles, Willard**
27	Dec 14	A	DML	Fisher Athletic London	Lost 3-4		120	Smith (2), Baker
28	Dec 18	H	DML	Dartford	Won 3-1		380	Ashworth (2), Magee
29	Dec 26	A	DML	Margate	Won 2-1		404	White (2)
30	**Jan 18**	**H**	**FAT 1**	**Newport A.F.C.**	**Won 1-0**		**501**	**Miles**
31	**Jan 21**	**A**	**SSC 3**	**Hassocks**	**Won 4-1**		**203**	**Ruddy (2), White, Miles**
32	Jan 25	H	DML	Yate Town	Won 3-0		412	White (2), Ashworth
33	**Jan 28**	**A**	**DMC 3**	**Sudbury Town**	**Lost 0-1**		**190**	
34	Feb 1	A	DML	Fleet Town	Won 2-0		144	White, Miles
35	**Feb 8**	**H**	**FAT 2**	**Dulwich Hamlet**	**Won 2-1**		**776**	**White, Magee**
36	Feb 15	H	DML	Fleet Town	Drew 2-2		425	Willard, Ruddy
37	**Feb 20**	**A**	**SSC 4**	**Ringmer**	**Won 3-1**		**210**	**Magee (2), Miles**
38	Feb 22	A	DML	Clevedon Town	Drew 2-2		209	N'Dumduna, Ashworth
39	Feb 26	A	DML	Bashley	Drew 0-0		133	
40	**Mar 1**	**A**	**FAT 3**	**Colwyn Bay**	**Drew 2-2**		**555**	**Magee, Miles**
41	**Mar 5**	**H**	**FAT 3 R**	**Colwyn Bay**	**Drew 0-0**		**817**	
42	Mar 8	H	DML	Cirencester Town	Won 5-0		353	Baker (3), Farrier, Smith
43	**Mar 10**	**H**	**FAT 3R2**	**Colwyn Bay**	**Lost 1-2**		**1151**	**Ruddy**
44	Mar 12	H	DML	Havant Town	Won 4-2		297	Magee (3), Baker
45	Mar 15	A	DML	Forest Green Rovers	Lost 1-2		364	Ashworth
46	Mar 16	H	DML	Waterlooville	Won 2-0		441	Magee, Smith
47	Mar 19	H	DML	Clevedon Town	Won 4-1		315	Magee (2), Miles, Smith
48	Mar 22	H	DML	Bashley	Won 4-3		439	Willard, White (2), Magee
49	Mar 23	A	DML	Buckingham Town	Drew 0-0		184	
50	Mar 26	A	DML	Newport IoW	Won 2-1		296	Lambert (2)
51	Mar 29	A	DML	Tonbridge Angels	Drew 2-2		575	Ruddy (2)
52	Mar 31	H	DML	Margate	Drew 2-2		480	Magee (2)
53	**Apr 2**	**N**	**SSC SF**	**Portfield**	**Won 3-0**		**172**	**White, Magee (2)**
54	Apr 5	A	DML	Weston Super Mare	Won 2-0		312	Magee (2)
55	Apr 8	A	DML	Weymouth	Lost 0-1		515	
56	**Apr 10**	**A**	**HSC SF**	**Sidley United**	**Won 2-1**		**86**	**Godden, Pegman**
57	Apr 12	H	DML	Fareham Town	Won 6-0		457	Ruddy (2), White (2), Baker, Smith
58	Apr 13	H	DML	Cinderford Town	Won 4-1		389	Jones (3), White
59	Apr 16	H	DML	Tonbridge Angels	Won 1-0		524	Magee
60	Apr 19	A	DML	Witney Town	Lost 1-3		107	Miles
61	Apr 20	H	DML	Buckingham Town	Won 4-1		507	Miles (3), N'Dumduna
62	Apr 23	A	DML	Fareham Town	Drew 2-2		145	Burt, Magee
63	Apr 26	A	DML	Cinderford Town	Won 2-1		194	Miles
64	Apr 30	H	DML	Forest GReen Rovers	Won 2-1		601	White, Smith
65	May 3	H	DML	Weymouth	Won 4-1		482	Farrier, N'Dumduna, White, Miles
66	**May 5**	**N**	**SSC F**	**Saltdean United**	**Won 2-1**		**551**	**Miles, Smith**
67	**May 8**	**N**	**HSC F**	**Bexhill Town**	**Won 2-1**		**170**	**Farrier, Phillips**

ST. LEONARDS STAMCROFT PLAYING SQUAD 1997-98

Goalkeepers: Sacha Ilic (Radnicki (Yug), Partisan Belgrade (Yug))

Defenders: Wayne Farrier (Bexhill, Stamco, The Harrow), **Steve Gatting** (Charlton, Brighton, Arsenal), **Tony Burt** (Hastings T, Hastings U), **Steve Ferguson** (Hastings T), **Steve Smith** (Hastings T, Lewes, Hastings T, Southwick, Hastings T, Brighton (A)), **Peter Baker** (None), **Matt Jones** (Langney Sports, Eastbourne U)

Midfielders: Craig Willard (Bexhill), **Terry White** (Hastings T, Hythe, Hastings T, Bexhill, Millwall (J), Charlton (J)), **Nicky Hall** (Hastings T), **Paul Ruddy** (Youth team), **Brett Smith** (Sittingbourne, Slough, Chesham, Slough, Millwall), **Joe Lambert** (Hastings T), **Rob Stanley** (Youth team)

Forwards: Keith Miles (Langney Sports, Hastings T, Hailsham, Hastings T, Eastbourne U, Hastings U, Stamco), **Neil Phillips** (Bexhill, Hastings T, Bexhill), **John Magee** (Bangor (NI), Kettering, Burton A), **Danny Ashworth** (Langney Sports, Hastings T, Eastbourne U, Crawley), **Chris Scott** (Little Common A), **David N'Dunduma** (Brighton)

TAMWORTH

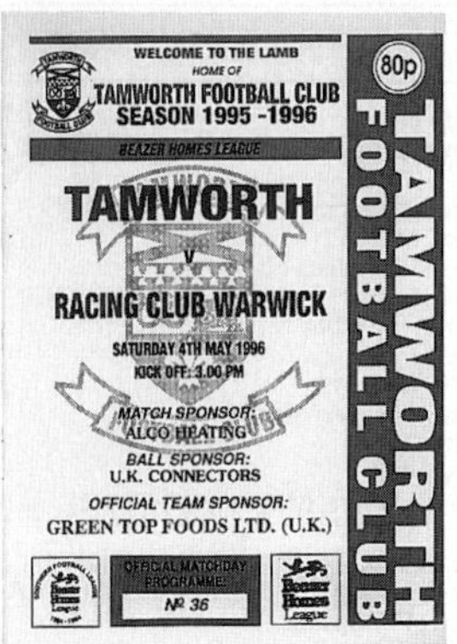

PROGRAMME DETAILS:
Pages: 28 **Price:** £1
Editor: Brian & Theresa Whitehouse

Formed: 1933 **Nickname:** Lambs or Town
Colours: Red/red/black
Change colours: White/black/white
Midweek home matchday: Tuesday
Reserves' League: Midland Comb. Res Div

Chairman: Bob Andrews **Vice Chairman:** Tony Reeves
President: Len Gendle. **Secretary:** Rod A Hadley, 38 Godolphin, Riverside, Tamworth B79 7UF (01827 66786 & Fax).
Manager: Paul Hendrie **Asst Man.:** Andy Dwyer **Physio:** Peter Smith
Press Officer: Mark Maybury **Commercial Manager:** Steve Shaw

GROUND Address: The Lamb Ground, Kettlebrook, Tamworth, Staffs B79 1HA (01827 65798). **Directions:** Follow the signs for Town Centre / Snowdome, then for Kettlebrook. The entrance to the ground and car parks is in Kettlebrook Road, 50yards from the traffic island by the railway viaduct.
Capacity: 3,000 **Cover:** 1,191 **Seats:** 400 **Floodlights:** Yes
Clubhouse: Club on ground - open matchdays, training nights and tote night (Monday) only.
Club Shop: Sells replica kit, scarves, stickers pens & metal badges.
Sponsors: Alco Heating

PREVIOUS - Leagues: Birmingham Combination 33-54, West Midlands (initially Birmingham Lg) 54-72 84-88, Southern 72-79 83-84, Northern Premier 79-83. **Grounds:** Jolly Sailor Ground 33-34.

CLUB RECORDS -
Attendance: 4,920 v Atherstone Tn, Birm Comb 48.
Win: 14-4 v Holbrook Institute (H), Bass Vase 34.
Defeat: 0-11 v Solihull (A), Birmingham Comb. 40.
Career Goalscorer: Graham Jessop 195
Season Goalscorer: Percy Vials 64 (36-37)
Career Appearances: Dave Seedhouse 869
Transfer fee paid: £5,000 for Steve Cartwright (Colchester Utd, 88).
Transfer fee received: £7,500 for Martin Myers (Telford Utd, 90).

BEST SEASON - FA Cup: 2nd Rd 69-70 (0-6 at Gillingham). **Trophy:** Qtr Final. **FA Vase:** Winners 88-89
Players progressing to Football League: P Hilton (WBA 49), A Godridge (Swansea 50), W Ealing (Doncaster), Higgins (Fulham), P Weir (Cardiff), S Fox (Wrexham), S Cartwright (Colchester 88), S Ryder (Walsall), D Williams (Brentford).
96-97 - Captain: Willie Batchelor **P.o.Y.:** Willie Batchelor **Top scorer:** Ian Bennett
Local Press: Tamworth Herald, Tamworth Times **Local Radio:** Radio WM, BRMB Radio, Extra AM.

HONOURS: FA Vase 88-89, West Mids Lg 63-64 65-66 71-72 87-88 (R-up(2) 67-69, Div 2 55-56, Lg Cup(5) 64-66 71-72 85-86 87-88 (R-up 70-71)), Birmingham Snr Cup 60-61 65-66 68-69 (R-up 36-37 63-64), Staffs Snr Cup 58-59 63-64 65-66 (R-up 55-56 66-67 70-71), Midland F'lit Cup R-up 71-72 72-73, Camkin Cup 71-72 (R-up 70-71),

Tamworth. Back Row (L-R); Derek Bond (Asst Mgr), Lee Wilson, Ian Bennett, Mark Harbottle, Willie Batchelor (Capt), Gary Smith, Mark Whitehouse, Ian Mitchell, Pete Smith (Physio). Front Row; Paul Hendrie (Mgr), Michael Crawford, Adrian Baddams, Chris Keogh, Darren Shaw, Tony Rowe, Paul Hunter, Jon Howard, David Foy, Ian Brown, Shaun Bedward, Andy Dwyer (Asst Mgr).

Tamworth

Match No.	Date	Venue H/A	Competition	Opponents	Result	League Pos.	Attendance	Goalscorers (Times if known)
1	Aug 17	A	DML	Raunds Town	Won 2-0		283	Howard, Harbottle
2	Aug 20	H	DML	Stourbridge	Won 1-0	4	609	Hunter
3	Aug 24	H	DML	Redditch United	Won 1-0	3	566	Harbottle
4	Aug 26	A	DML	Bedworth United	Won 1-0	1	484	Bennett
5	Sep 1	A	FAC	Dudley Town	Won 3-1		605	Shaw, Hunter (2)
6	Sep 3	H	DML	Evesham United	Won 3-1	1	661	Wilson (3)
7	Sep 7	A	DML	Moor Green	Won 2-0	1	457	Smith, Blackburn
8	Sep 14	H	FAC	Willenhall Town	Won 4-1		686	Foy, Hunter (3)
9	Sep 21	H	DML	Sutton Coldfield Town	Won 1-0	1	679	Batchelor
10	Sep 24	A	DML	Stourbridge	Won 2-1	1	234	Shaw, Batchelor
11	Sep 28	A	FAC	Racing Club Warwick	Won 5-0		380	Hunter (3), Whitehouse, Smith
12	Oct 1	A	SSC	Bushall Olympic	Won 5-0		150	Mulholland, Bennett, Baddams, Harbottle (p), Devaney
13	Oct 5	A	DML	Racing Club Warwick	Won 3-0	1	377	Batchelor, Foy, Smith
14	Oct 12	A	FAC	Hednesford Town	Lost 2-4		1298	Bennett, Smith
15	Oct 16	H	DML	Bedworth United	Won 3-0		400	Bennett, Hunter, Smith
16	Oct 19	H	FAT	Great Harwood Town	Drew 2-2		506	Bennett (2)
17	Oct 22	A	FAT	Great Harwood Town	Lost 0-1		196	
18	Oct 26	A	DML	Dudley Town	Won 4-0	1	444	Bennett (3), Smith
19	Oct 29	A	DMLC	Bedworth United	Won 4-1		131	Bennett, Smith (2), Hunter
20	Nov 2	H	DML	Raunds Town	Won 5-2	1	735	Bennett (4), Baddams
21	Nov 9	A	BSC	V S Rugby	Won 3-2		389	Bennett (2), Hunter
22	Nov 12	H	DML	Solihull Town	Won 3-0	1	655	Foy, Bennett (2)
23	Nov 16	H	DML	Bilston Town	Won 4-2	1	913	Batchelor, Smith (3)
24	Nov 20	A	DML	Evesham United	Won 3-2	1	153	Batchelor, Bennet, Hunter
25	Nov 23	H	DML	Paget Rangers	Won 3-1	1	654	Batchelor, Hunter (2)
26	Nov 26	H	DML	Hinckley Town	Drew 0-0	1	734	
27	Nov 30	H	DML	Racing Club Warwick	Won 6-0	1	777	Shaw, Smith, Baddams, Hunter, Wilson
28	Dec 3	A	BSC	Tividale	Won 2-1		82	Whitehouse, Wilson
29	Dec 7	H	DML	Moor Green	Won 3-1	1	626	Shaw, Foy, Hunter
30	Dec 10	A	DMLC	Atherstone United	Won 3-0		717	Baddams (2), 1 (og)
31	Dec 14	A	DML	Rothwell Town	Drew 2-2	1	420	Baddams, Hunter
32	Dec 28	H	DML	Stafford Rangers	Won 1-0	1	1334	Baddams
33	Jan 15	A	DMLC	Raunds Town	Lost 1-2		146	Foy
34	Jan 21	A	BSC	Bolmere St Michaels	Drew 3-3		360	Foy, Whitehouse, Hunter
35	Jan 25	A	DML	Solihull Borough	Lost 0-2	1	474	
36	Jan 29	A	DML	Corby Town	Won 3-0	1	266	Bennett, Hunter, Smith
37	Feb 3	A	SSC	Hednesford Town	Lost 0-2		2541	
38	Feb 8	A	DML	Redditch United	Won 3-2	1	643	Bennett (2), Wilson
39	Feb 11	H	DML	Grantham Town	Won 2-0	1	645	Hunter (2)
40	Feb 15	A	DML	Sutton Coldfield Town	Won 2-1	1	731	Batchelor, Wilson
41	Feb 18	H	BSC	Boldmere St Michaels	Won 4-1		591	Batchelor, Bennett (2), Wilson
42	Feb 22	H	DML	Corby Town	Won 2-0	1	802	Shaw (2)
43	Feb 26	A	DML	V S Rugby	Won 6-2	1	359	Shaw (2, 1 pen), Bennett, Howard, Hunter, Smith
44	Mar 1	A	DML	Hinckley Town	Won 1-0	1	430	Batchelor
45	Mar 4	H	DML	Ilkeston Town	Drew 0-0	1	701	
46	Mar 8	A	DML	Bilston Town	Drew 0-0	1	620	
47	Mar 15	A	DML	Grantham Town	Won 1-0	1	556	Howard
48	Mar 18	A	BSC	West Bromwich Albion	Won 3-0		1404	Shaw, Bennett (2)
49	Mar 22	H	DML	V S Rugby	Drew 0-0	1	1339	
50	Mar 25	A	HGT	Atherstone United	Drew 1-1		457	Baddams
51	Mar 29	A	DML	Bilston Town	Lost 0-1	1	977	
52	Mar 31	H	DML	Shepshed Dynamo	Won 4-0	1	1208	Bennett (2), Smith, Hunter
53	Apr 5	A	DML	Stafford Rangers	Won 5-0	1	884	Smith (3), Hunter (2)
54	Apr 12	A	DML	Paget Rangers	Won 3-0	1	622	Whitehouse (2), Hunter
55	Apr 15	H	DML	Bedworth United	Won 2-1	1	756	Hunter, Bennett
56	Apr 19	H	DML	Dudley Town	Drew 1-1		693	Baddams
57	Apr 24	H	BSC	Burton Albion	Lost 1-3*		1847	Whitehouse
58	Apr 29	H	HGT	Atherstone United	Won 3-0		557	Bennett, Shaw (2)
59	May 1	A	DML	Shepshed Dynamo	Won 3-0		354	Bennett (3)
60	May 3	H	DML	Solihull Borough	Lost 2-4		802	Smith, Hunter

* After Extra Time

TAMWORTH PLAYING SQUAD 1997-98

Goalkeepers: Tony Rowe (Monica Star, Halesowen T, Worcester, Northfield)

Defenders: Denis Mulholland (Redditch, Tamworth, Chelmsley, Kidderminster, Nuneaton, Solihull, Highgate, Sutton Coldfield, Paget, Moor Green, Grimsby), **Chris Keogh** (Hinckley T, Nuneaton, Sutton Coldfield, Tamworth, Sutton Coldfield, Nuneaton, Burton A, Redditch, Aston Villa), **Jon Howard** (Wolves), **Darren Shaw** (Wolves), **Willie Batchelor** (Barry, Inter Cardiff, Barry, Worcester, Highgate)

Midfielders: David Foy (Stafford R, Scunthorpe, Birmingham), **Adrian Baddams** (Stourbridge, Moor Green, Bedworth, Tamworth, Atherstone, Sandwell B), **Ian Brown** (Newport AFC, Tamworth, Solihull, Stourbridge, Stafford R, Aston Villa), **Brendan Devery** (Solihull, Bromsgrove, Moor Green, Birmingham), **Mick Williams** (Clipstone MW, Ilkeston, Telford, Mansfield), **Iam Mitchell** (Evesham, Barry, Solihull, Telford, Barry, Solihull, Banbury, King's Heath, Willenhall, Nuneaton, Highgate, Moor Green, Solihull), **Mike Crawford** (Local football)

Forwards: Paul Hunter (Barry, Merthyr, Inter Cardiff, Sandwell B, Barry, Telford, Barry, Cradley, Sutton Coldfield, Halesowen T, Paget), **Mark Whitehouse** (Worcester, Kettering, Telford, Bromsgrove, Kidderminster, Burton A, Worcester, Redditch, Tamworth, Oldbury, Moor Green), **Lee Wilson** (Dag & Red, Halifax, Telford, Mansfield), **Ian Bennett** (Leicester U, Paget, Armitage, Rushall O, Armitage, Bilston, Armitage, Bury), **Gary Smith** (Worcester, Sutton Coldfield, Paget), **Mark Harbottle** (Ilkeston, Tamworth, Ilkeston, Leicester U, Shepshed, Ilkeston, Burton A, Shepshed, Scarborough, Doncaster, Notts Co)

WORCESTER CITY

PROGRAMME DETAILS:
Pages: 32 **Price:** £1
Editor: Julian Pugh
(01905 25844)

Formed: 1902 **Nickname:** The City
Colours: Blue & white/black/white
Change colours: Red/white/red
Midweek matchday: Monday **Newsline:** 0898 884476
Reserve Lge: Skol Mid Comb/Central Conf

Chairman: Dr Michael Sorenson **Vice Chairman:** L Brown
Secretary: Steve Bond, 4 Ferry Close, Worcester, Worcs WR2 5PQ (01905 423120/25427).
Manager: George Rooney **Chief Coach:** Graham Selby
Physios: Peter O'Connell & Martin Obrey

GROUND Address: St Georges Lane, Barbourne, Worcester WR1 1QT (01905 23003 Fax: 26668)
Directions: M5 jct 6 (Worcester North), follow signs to Worcester, right at first lights, St Georges Lane is 3rd left. 1 mile from Foregate Street (BR) station.
Capacity: 4,749 **Cover:** 2,000 **Seats:** 1,223 **Floodlights:** Yes
Clubhouse: Open every evening and Saturday and Sunday daytime. Cold snacks available.
Club Shop: Sells programmes and souvenirs. Contact Mr Widdison c/oClub.
Sponsors: Banks's

PREVIOUS - Leagues: West Mids (Birmingham) 1902-38, Southern 38-79, Alliance Premier 79-85. **Names:** Worcester Rovers, Berwick Rangers. **Grounds:** Severn Terrace, Flagge Meadow.

CLUB RECORDS - Attendance: 17,042 v Sheff Utd (lost 0-2), FA Cup 4th Rd 24/1/59. **Win:** 18-1 v Bilston, Birmingham League 21/11/31. **Defeat:** 0-10 v Wellington, Birmingham League 29/8/20. **Career Goalscorer:** John Inglis 189 (1970-77). **Career Appearances:** Bobby McEwan 596 (1959-75). **Transfer fee paid:** £8,500 for Jim Williams (Telford United, 1981). **Tranmsfer fee received:** £27,000 for John Barton (Everton, 1979).

BEST SEASON - FA Cup: 4th Rd 58-59. 1st Rd (10) 05-06 25-26 28-29 50-51 57-58 60-61 78-79 82-84 87-88.

Players progressing to Football League: A Awford (Portsmouth 91), P King/K Ball/J Williams/M Gayle (Walsall 60/6579/91), J Fairbrother (Peterborough 65), D Tennant (Lincoln 66), R Davies (Derby 71), N Merrick (Bournemouth 74), J Barton (Everton 78), A Preece (Wrexham 90), D Lyttle (Swansea 92).

96-97 Captain: **96-97 P.o.Y:** **96-97 Top Scorer:** Anton Thomas (17)
Local Press: Berrows Journal, Worcester Evening News, W/ster Source.
Local Radio: Radio Wyvern & BBC Hereford & Worcester

HONOURS: Southern Lg 78-79 (Div 1 67-68, Div 1 Nth 76-77, Lg Cup R-up 45-46 59-60, Chal. Cup 39-40, Champs Cup 78-79), West Mids (B'ham) Lg(4) 13-14 24-25 28-30 (R-up(3) 31-34), Worcs Snr Cup(25) 07-14 28-30 32-33 45-46(jt) 48-49 55-59 60-61 62-63 64-65 69-70 77-78 79-80 81-82 83-84 87-88, B'ham Snr Cup 75-76, Staffs Snr Cup 76-77, Inter Lg Champs Cup 78-79, Welsh Cup SF 78-79, FA Tphy QF 69-70 73-74 80-81 81-82.

Worcester City FC: Back Row (L-R); Quentin Townsend, Chris Greenman, Richard Evans, Dave Richards, Anton Thomas, Paul Harding. Front Row; Paul Moore, Jason Burnham, Andy Power, Trevor Whittington, Carl Heeley.
Photo - Alan Coomes

Worcester City

Match No.	Date	Venue H/A	Competition	Opponents	Result	League Pos.	Attendance	Goalscorers (Times if known)
1	Aug 17	H	DML	Baldock Town	Won 3-0		662	Cottrill 5, Greenman 55 (p), Thomas 78
2	Aug 20	A	DML	Gresley Rovers	Lost 0-3		693	
3	Aug 24	H	DML	Sudbury Town	Won 2-1		632	Cottrill 30, Whittington 72
4	Aug 26	A	DML	Merthyr Tydfil	Lost 0-2	11	589	
5	Aug 31	A	DML	Crawley Town	Lost 1-2	12	618	Power 43
6	Sep 2	H	DML	Burton Albion	Won 2-1		754	Heeley 65, Scott 88
7	Sep 7	A	DML	Salisbury City	Drew 1-1	11	452	Scott 62
8	**Sep 14**	**A**	**FAC 1 Q**	**Fareham Town**	**Lost 1-2**		**195**	**Greenman 88 (pen)**
9	Sep 21	A	DML	Nuneaton Borough	Lost 1-2	15	977	Malloy 32
10	Sep 23	H	DML	Gresley Rovers	Lost 1-2	18	721	Heeley 82
11	**Sep 30**	**H**	**BSC**	**RC Warwick**	**Won 4-0**		**255**	**Thomas 29, 35, Cottrill 70, Norris 85**
12	Oct 5	H	DML	Gravesend & Northfleet	Won 4-2	13	708	Cottrill 34, 84, Thomas 57, Norris 78
13	**Oct 8**	**A**	**DMLC**	**Stourbridge**	**Drew 1-1**		**104**	**Cottrill 28**
14	Oct 14	H	DML	Merthyr Tydfil	Won 2-1		769	Norris 11, Taylor 84
15	Oct 19	H	DML	Chelmsford City	Drew 1-1	10	736	Heeley 55
16	**Oct 22**	**A**	**BSC**	**Burton Albion**	**Lost 0-2**		**340**	
17	Oct 26	A	DML	Newport A.F.C.	Drew 1-1	10	788	Taylor 3
18	**Oct 28**	**H**	**DMLC**	**Stourbridge**	**Won 3-1**		**205**	**Thomas 2, Cottrill 35, Molloy 75**
19	Nov 2	H	DML	Salisbury City	Lost 0-2	13	746	
20	Nov 9	H	DML	Cheltenham Town	Drew 2-2	12	1270	Thomas 85, Taylor 86
21	Nov 12	A	DML	Sudbury Town	Lost 2-3		267	Thomas 70, 75
22	Nov 23	H	DML	Hastings Town	Won 3-0		587	Cottrill 13, Norris 23, Healey 44
23	**Nov 30**	**A**	**FAT 3 Q**	**Bromley**	**Drew 1-1**		**345**	**Campfield 5 (og)**
24	**Dec 2**	**H**	**FAT 3QR**	**Bromley**	**Won 2-0**		**502**	**Taylor 22, Thomas 52**
25	Dec 7	A	DML	Baldock Town	Won 3-0	10	245	Malloy 21, Kaidler 36, 90
26	**Dec 9**	**H**	**DMC**	**RC Warwick**	**Drew 1-1**		**269**	**Guppy 43**
27	**Dec 17**	**A**	**DMC**	**RC Warwick**	**Lost 1-2***		**158**	**Taylor 17**
28	Dec 21	A	DML	Cambridge City	Won 2-1	10	306	Cottrill 43, 87
29	Dec 26	A	DML	Halesowen Town	Drew 0-0	10	1256	
30	Dec 28	H	DML	Newport A.F.C.	Drew 1-1	8	963	Malloy 19
31	Jan 11	H	DML	Cambridge City	Drew 2-2	8	615	Thomas 34, 36
32	**Jan 18**	**H**	**FAT 1**	**Heybridge Swifts**	**Lost 1-2**		**724**	**Molloy 57**
33	**Jan 20**	**H**	**WSC**	**Moor Green**	**Drew 2-2**		**247**	**Molloy 31, Thomas 70**
34	Jan 25	A	DML	Atherstone United	Drew 2-2	10	276	Greenham 20 (pen), Taylor 66
35	**Jan 28**	**A**	**WSC**	**Moor Green**	**Won 4-2**		**140**	**Taylor (3) 4, 104, 111, Molloy 62**
36	Feb 1	H	DML	Dorchester Town	Won 1-0	9	519	Greenman 61 (pen)
37	Feb 8	A	DML	Gravesend & Northfleet	Lost 0-2	10	570	
38	Feb 11	A	DML	Burton Albion	Drew 2-2		447	Harding 40, Thomas 49
39	Feb 15	A	DML	Sittingbourne	Won 1-0	9	537	Thomas 81
40	Feb 17	H	DML	Gloucester City	Drew 0-0	8	770	
41	Feb 22	H	DML	Crawley Town	Won 2-1	8	649	Thomas 33, 62
42	Feb 25	A	DML	King's Lynn	Won 1-0		982	Harding 82
43	Mar 1	A	DML	Ashford Town	Drew 0-0	7	467	
44	Mar 8	A	DML	Cheltenham Town	Lost 0-2	9	1009	
45	Mar 11	A	DML	Hastings Town	Drew 0-0		362	
46	Mar 15	H	DML	Atherstone United	Won 3-0	7	605	Hemstock 15, Cottrill 33, Whittington 66
47	Mar 22	H	DML	King's Lynn	Won 2-1	7	695	Taylor 68, 89
48	Mar 29	A	DML	Gloucester City	Drew 1-1		1082	Wittington 71
49	Mar 31	H	DML	Halesowen Town	Drew 1-1	7	1307	Greenman 12 (pen)
50	Apr 12	H	DML	Ashford Town	Lost 0-2	9	644	
51	**Apr 16**	**A**	**WSCF**	**Solihull Borough**	**Won 2-0**		**152**	**Harding 1, Power 72**
52	Apr 19	A	DML	Dorchester Town	Lost 0-2	10	567	
53	Apr 26	H	DML	Sittingbourne	Lost 0-2	10	510	
54	**Apr 28**	**H**	**WSCF**	**Solihull Borough**	**Drew 1-1**		**510**	**Evans 47**
55	May 3	A	DML	Chelmsford City	Won 2-1	10	550	Harding 43, Taylor 81

* After Extra Time

WORCESTER CITY PLAYING SQUAD 1997-98

Goalkeepers: Melvyn Watson (Upton T, Crewe (T)), **Paul Moore** (Barrow, Bangor C, Witton A, Worcester, Southport, Morecambe, Alvechurch, Worcester, Rhyl)
Defenders: Carl Heeley (Sutton C, Bilston T, Dudley T, Bilston T, Alvechurch, Great Wyrley), **Mark Burrow** (Youth team), **Chris Greenman** (Bromsgrove R, Peterborough, Coventry), **Trevor Whittington** (Redditch U, Solihull B, Evesham U, Telford U, Redditch U, Northfield T), **Dave Richards** (Walsall (T)), **Darren Williams** (Stoke (T)), **Andy Power** (Bromsgrove R), **Andy Blakeley** (Walsall (T)), **Jason Burnham** (Chester, Northampton)
Midfielders: Paul Molloy (Redditch U, Stafford R, Redditch U, Bromsgrove R), **Scott Morrell** (Shrewsbury (T)), **Paul Harding** (Cardiff, Birmingham, Notts Co, Barnet, Enfield), **Ian Cottrill** (Nuneaton, Worcester, Bromsgrove, Worcester)
Forwards: Keiran Hemstock (Youth team), **Steve Norris** (Chesterfield, Halifax, Carlisle, Scarborough, Telford U, VS Rugby, Long Buckby), **Anton Thomas** (Kettering T, Corby T, Leicester U, Bedworth U, Northampton), **Richard Evans** (Trowbridge T, Yeovil T, Bristol R, Weymouth), **Colin Taylor** (Bangor C, Runcorn,Telford, Wolves), **Paul Ashby** (Youth team)

MIDLAND DIVISION

LEAGUE TABLE 1996-97

	P	W	D	L	F	A	GD	Pts
Tamworth	40	30	7	3	90	28	62	97
Rothwell Town	40	20	11	9	82	54	28	71
Ilkeston Town	40	19	19	8	76	50	26	70
Grantham Town	40	22	4	14	65	46	19	70
Bedworth United	40	18	11	11	77	41	36	65
Solihull Borough	40	19	8	13	84	62	22	65
Bilston Town	40	18	10	12	74	57	17	64
Moor Green	40	18	7	15	88	68	20	61
Stafford Rangers	40	17	9	14	68	62	6	60
Raunds Town	40	16	11	13	61	66	-5	59
R. C. Warwick	40	16	10	14	70	72	-2	58
Shepshed Dynamo	40	14	12	14	64	65	-1	54
Redditch United	40	15	8	17	56	59	-3	53
Paget Rangers	40	13	9	18	42	55	-13	48
Dudley Town	40	12	10	18	70	89	-19	46
Hinckley Town	40	11	11	18	39	63	-24	44
Stourbridge	40	10	9	21	61	81	-20	39
Evesham United	40	9	12	19	55	77	-22	39
V. S. Rugby	40	9	9	22	49	81	-32	36
Corby Town	40	8	8	24	49	88	-39	32
Sutton Coldfield T.	40	7	9	24	29	85	-56	30

LEADING GOALSCORERS

28	H Wright (Bilston T.)
25	D Christopher (Redditch U.)
	K McGuire (Rothwell T.)
22	B Agar (R.C. Warwick)
	I Bennett (Tamworth)
	D King (Grantham T.)
	G Piggott (Dudley T.)
19	P Hunter (Tamworth)
	R Mitchell (Stafford R.)
18	L Dixon (Evesham U.)
	J Dowling (Solihull B.)
	S Keeble (Raunds T.)
17	T Burroughs (Paget R.)
	K Johnstone (Evesham U.)
16	D Beazeley (Rothwell T.)
	A Johnson (Stourbridge)
	M Moore (Moor Green)
	A Warner (Rothwell T.)
	G Smith (Tamworth)

RESULTS GRID 1996-97

HOME TEAM	1	2	3	4	5	6	7	8	9	10	11	12	13	14	15	16	17	18	19	20	21
1 Bedworth Utd.	*	0-2	3-1	5-0	2-0	4-1	1-0	2-0	1-0	3-0	1-3	2-2	1-1	1-1	2-0	2-0	1-1	7-0	6-0	0-1	3-1
2 Bilston Town	2-1	*	7-1	2-1	4-0	3-3	1-0	1-1	1-5	0-1	1-1	2-2	2-0	0-4	4-1	1-0	0-1	3-2	5-0	0-0	4-3
3 Corby Town	1-2	1-3	*	2-4	2-2	0-5	0-1	0-0	3-2	1-2	0-5	4-2	5-4	1-2	3-1	0-1	1-2	1-2	2-0	0-3	3-1
4 Dudley Town	1-1	3-2	1-3	*	1-1	3-2	0-1	3-2	1-2	2-2	3-0	1-5	1-2	1-1	1-1	3-2	3-3	3-3	0-0	0-4	1-4
5 Evesham Utd	0-0	2-2	0-0	3-1	*	0-2	1-2	2-4	1-2	1-0	2-2	1-2	1-0	1-1	3-2	2-1	1-2	1-3	0-1	2-3	2-2
6 Grantham Town	0-3	1-2	1-0	1-0	3-2	*	3-0	1-1	3-1	2-0	2-4	3-0	1-2	2-0	0-0	3-2	1-0	3-2	2-0	0-1	1-0
7 Hinckley Town	0-0	0-0	1-1	1-0	2-1	1-0	*	0-2	1-5	0-2	2-1	0-0	1-2	1-2	3-4	2-2	0-6	3-3	1-1	0-1	4-0
8 Ilkeston Town	1-1	2-1	1-2	2-2	3-4	3-1	4-0	*	2-1	1-1	3-0	2-0	1-0	3-4	4-2	1-4	3-2	4-2	2-0	1-0	1-0
9 Moor Green	1-4	1-1	2-2	5-3	3-1	0-1	3-1	2-2	*	1-2	1-2	4-1	1-2	2-2	3-0	0-1	5-2	2-1	4-1	0-2	2-2
10 Paget Rangers	3-2	2-3	4-0	1-2	0-2	0-1	4-1	1-2	1-0	*	0-0	0-1	1-2	1-3	0-0	2-1	0-2	2-1	0-1	0-3	1-0
11 R.C. Warwick	0-4	4-1	3-2	3-1	2-1	0-2	5-2	1-1	1-6	2-3	*	1-1	1-2	1-1	0-0	3-3	2-1	0-1	3-0	0-3	4-2
12 Raunds Town	2-1	1-4	0-0	1-3	2-1	1-3	0-0	3-2	2-1	2-2	1-0	*	1-0	0-4	0-0	3-1	3-1	0-3	2-2	0-2	3-0
13 Redditch Utd.	1-0	2-0	2-0	2-3	0-0	1-0	0-1	1-1	2-3	4-0	1-3	1-0	*	5-2	0-5	2-2	1-0	1-2	1-2	2-3	1-2
14 Rothwell Town	1-2	1-0	3-0	1-0	6-1	3-0	3-2	2-2	1-3	0-0	2-0	2-2	4-0	*	3-4	3-0	1-1	4-2	3-1	2-2	2-2
15 Shepshed D.	1-0	2-0	2-2	5-1	3-5	1-0	0-0	1-1	2-4	0-0	2-4	3-2	2-2	1-2	*	1-4	0-0	1-0	0-0	0-3	3-2
16 Solihull Bor.	3-2	2-1	3-3	5-1	5-1	0-1	0-1	1-1	5-2	3-1	1-2	1-1	2-2	2-0	3-2	*	4-1	1-3	2-0	2-0	1-1
17 Stafford R.	3-1	1-1	2-0	4-3	1-2	3-1	2-2	0-4	2-2	3-1	1-2	0-2	2-1	2-1	0-2	3-1	*	2-0	2-0	0-5	2-0
18 Stourbridge	2-2	0-3	4-1	1-4	0-0	0-4	1-2	1-3	2-2	0-0	3-3	1-3	1-1	1-0	0-1	2-4	2-2	*	3-0	1-2	1-2
19 Sutton Coldfield T	1-1	1-1	1-0	1-4	2-2	0-4	1-0	0-3	0-3	0-0	1-1	2-4	0-2	2-3	0-5	0-1	0-4	1-4	*	1-2	4-2
20 Tamworth	2-1	4-2	2-0	1-1	3-3	2-0	0-0	0-0	3-1	3-1	6-0	5-2	1-0	3-0	4-0	2-4	1-0	1-0	1-0	*	0-0
21 V.S. Rugby	2-2	0-2	2-1	2-4	1-0	1-1	1-0	2-0	1-2	0-1	2-1	1-2	1-1	0-2	0-4	1-4	2-2	2-1	0-2	2-6	*

MIDLAND DIVISION
10 YEAR RECORD

Dr MARTENS LEAGUE

No of Clubs Competing	87/8 (22)	88/9 (22)	89/0 (22)	90/1 (22)	91/2 (22)	92/3 (22)	93/4 (22)	94/5 (22)	95/6 (22)	96/7 (21)
Alvechurch	-	-	-	20	21	-	-	-	-	-
Armitage '90	-	-	-	-	-	-	22	22	-	-
Atherstone United	4	2	-	-	-	-	-	-	-	-
Banbury United	10	16	21	-	-	-	-	-	-	-
Barri (ex Barry Town)	-	-	5	6	4	4	-	-	-	-
Bedworth United	-	-	15	13	5	6	17	13	3	5
Bilston Town	17	13	17	14	12	14	8	13	12	7
Bridgnorth Town	11	17	12	17	17	16	12	5	22	-
Buckingham Town	12	-	-	-	-	-	-	6	9	-
Bury Town	-	-	-	-	-	-	-	-	21	-
Clevedon Town	-	-	-	-	-	-	5	-	-	-
Corby Town	-	-	-	2	-	-	-	-	20	20
Coventry Sporting	20	20	-	-	-	-	-	-	-	-
Dudley Town	8	9	9	19	22	17	14	11	10	15
Evesham United	-	-	-	-	-	15	10	14	19	18
Forest Green Rovers	9	12	10	18	19	19	15	18	-	-
Gloucester City	7	1	-	-	-	-	-	-	-	-
Grantham Town	3	5	14	9	13	13	11	21	14	4
Gresley Rovers	-	-	-	-	-	2	-	-	-	-
Halesowen Town	6	4	1	-	-	-	-	-	-	-
Hednesford Town	18	15	16	3	2	-	-	-	-	-
Hinckley Town	-	-	-	11	15	20	18	15	17	16
Ilkeston Town	-	-	-	-	-	-	-	2	-	3
King's Lynn	13	19	13	8	14	21	20	9	2	-
Leicester United	-	-	11	15	16	12	19	20	16	w/d
Merthyr Tydfil	1	-	-	-	-	-	-	-	-	-
Mile Oak Rovers & Youth	19	22	-	-	-	-	-	-	-	-
Moor Green	2	-	-	-	-	-	-	4	4	8
Newport AFC	-	-	-	7	10	5	4	1	-	-
Nuneaton Borough	-	6	3	5	6	1	-	7	1	-
Paget Rangers	22	-	-	-	-	-	-	-	5	14
Racing Club Warwick	-	-	19	16	18	22	13	10	18	11
Raunds Town	-	-	-	-	-	-	-	-	-	10
Redditch United	-	-	18	10	20	9	6	19	15	13
Rothwell Town	-	-	-	-	-	-	-	8	8	2
Rushden & Diamonds	-	-	-	-	-	3	1	-	-	-
Rushden Town	15	17	2	-	8	-	-	-	-	-
Sandwell Borough	-	14	22	-	-	-	-	-	-	-
Shepshed Dynamo	-	-	-	-	-	-	-	-	-	12
Solihull Borough	-	-	-	-	1	-	-	-	7	6
Spalding United	-	8	6	22	-	-	-	-	-	-
Stafford Angers	-	-	-	-	-	-	-	-	-	9
Stourbridge	21	18	8	1	9	7	9	16	11	17
Sutton Coldfield Town	5	10	7	12	3	8	16	17	13	21
Tamworth	-	3	4	4	7	10	7	3	6	1
Trowbridge Town	16	-	-	-	-	-	-	-	-	-
V S Rugby	-	-	-	-	-	-	2	-	-	19
Wellingborough Town	14	21	-	-	-	-	-	-	-	-
Weston Super Mare	-	-	-	-	-	11	3	-	-	-
Willenhall Town	-	11	20	21	-	-	-	-	-	-
Yate Town	-	-	-	-	11	18	21	-	-	-

PROGRAMME DETAILS:
Pages: 18 **Price:** £1
Editor: Jamie Home
(01203 354000)

BEDWORTH UNITED

Formed: 1947 **Nickname:** Greenbacks
Colours: Green & white/white/white
Change colours: Yellow & green.
Midweek matchday: Tuesday
Reserves' League: Midland Floodlit Youth League.

Chairman: Peter Randle **Vice Chairman:**
Secretary: Alan Aucott, 26 Hall Lane, Witherley, Nr Atherstone, CV9 3LT (01827 718736).
Press Officer: Jamie Home
Manager: Billy Hollywood **Asst Mgr:** None **Physio:** John Roberts.

GROUND Address: The Oval, Miners Welfare Park, Coventry Road, Bedworth CV12 8NN (01203 314302). **Directions:** M6 jct 3, into Bedworth on B4113 Coventry to Bedworth road, ground 200yds past past Bedworth Leisure Centre on this road. Coaches should park at this Leisure Centre. Buses from Coventry and Nuneaton pass ground.
Capacity: 7,000 **Cover:** 300 **Seats:** 300 **Floodlights:** Yes
Clubhouse: Social club open every day 7.30-11pm and weekend lunchtimes noon-3pm. Hot and cold bar food, pool, darts.
Club Shop: Selling a wide range of souvenirs & programmes. Contact Tom Ison-Jacques (01203 314884). **Sponsors:** 'D' Drill

PREVIOUS - **Leagues:** Birmingham Comb. 47-54; West Mids (at first Birmingham) Lg 54-72.
Name: Bedworth Town 47-68
Ground: British Queen Ground 11-39.

CLUB RECORDS - **Attendance:** 5,127 v Nuneaton Borough, Southern Lg Midland Division 23/2/82.
Win: 11-0 **Defeat:** 1-10
Career Goalscorer: Peter Spacey (1949-69)
Career Appearances: Peter Spacey
Transfer fee paid: £1,750 for Colin Taylor (Hinckley Town, 1991-92)
Transfer fee received: £30,000 for Richard Landon (Plymouth Argyle, January 1994).

BEST SEASON - **FA Trophy:** Second Round 80-81.
FA Cup: 4th Qualifying Rd 1983/89/90

Players progressing to Football League: Phil Huffer (Derby County 1953), Geoff Coleman (Northampton Town 1955), Ian Hathaway (Mansfield Town 1989), Richard Landon (Plymouth Argyle 1994).
Local Press: Heartland Evening News, Weekly Tribune, Bedworth Echo, Coventry Evening Telegraph
Local Radio: Mercia Sound, BBC CWR.

HONOURS: Birmingham Comb.(2) 48-50, Birmingham Snr Cup(3) 78-79 80-82, Midland Floodlit Cup 81-82 92-93.

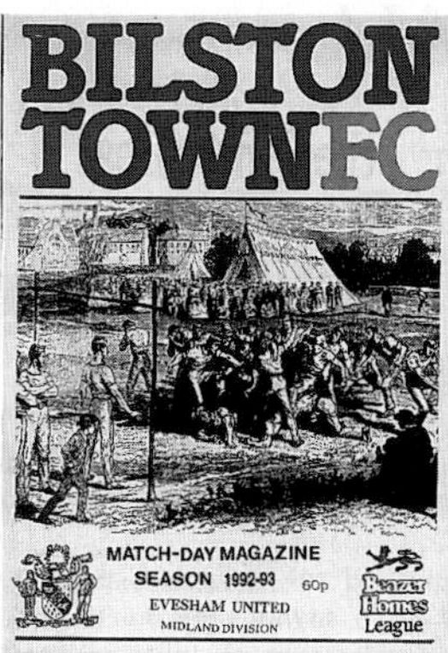

BILSTON TOWN FC
MATCH-DAY MAGAZINE
SEASON 1992-93
60p
EVESHAM UNITED
MIDLAND DIVISION
League

BILSTON TOWN

Formed: 1895 **Nickname:** Steelmen or Boro
Colours: Orange/white/white
Change colours: White/black/orange
Midweek matchday: Tuesday
Reserves' League: No reserve team

Chairman: I K Wymer **Vice-Chairman:** A K Hickman
President: Dennis Turner MP **Press Officer:** Mr A Owen.
Secretary: Jeff Calloway, 4 Mervyn Rd, Bradley, Bilston, West Midlands WV14 8DF (01902 491799).
Manager: Ian Painter **Asst Manager:** Alan Potts
Coach: I Painter/B Pope **Physio:** Reg Pickering
GROUND Address: Queen Street, Bilston WV14 7EX (01902 491498).
Directions: M6 junction 10, A454 towards Wolverhampton then pick up A563 towards Bilston and turn left into Beckett Street after a little over a mile, ground at bottom. 3 miles from Wolverhampton (BR), bus 45 from bus station passes ground. Buses 78 and 79 from Birmingham stop within quarter of a mile of ground.
Capacity: 4,000 **Cover:** 350 **Seats:** 350 **Floodlights:** Yes
Clubhouse: Open evenings and weekend lunchtimes (normal pub hours). Usual club activities.
Club Shop: Sells a range of souvenirs and programmes. Contact Paul Galloway, 4 Mervyn Rd, Bradley, Bilston, West Mids WV14 8DF.
Club Sponsors: Stowlawn Ltd and Second City.

PROGRAMME DETAILS:
Pages: 24 **Price:** 70p
Editor: Secretary
(01902 491799)

PREVIOUS - **Names:** Bilston Utd 1895-1932, Bilston. **Ground:** Pounds Lane 1895-1921.
Leagues: Birmingham Comb. 07-21 48-54, (Birmingham) West Mids 21-32 54-85.
CLUB RECORDS - **Attendance:** 7,500 v Wolverhampton Wanderers, floodlight opening 1953. *Competitive: 7,000 v Halifax Town, F.A. Cup First Round 1968.*
Win: 12-2 v Tipton Town **Defeat:** 0-8 v Merthyr Tydfil.
Career Goalscorer: Ron McDermott 78.
Career Appearances:
Transfer fee paid: for Steve Gloucester.
Transfer fee received: From Southend United for Ron Poutney, 1975.
BEST SEASON - **FA Trophy:** 2nd Round 70-71, 74-75. **FA Vase:** Quarter Finals 92-93.
FA Cup: 2nd Rd replay 72-73 (0-1 at Barnet after 1-1 draw). Also 1st Rd 68-69.
League clubs defeated: None.
Players progressing to Football League: R Ellows (Birmingham), James Fletcher (Birmingham 1950), Stan Crowther (A Villa 1955), Ron Pountney (Southend 1975), K Price (Gillingham), Campbell Chapman (Wolves 1984).
96-97 - Captain: **P.o.Y.:** **Top scorer:**
Local Press: Expess & Star, Evening Mail. **Local Radio:** Radio West Mids, WABC, Beacon, BRMB.

HONOURS: West Mids Lg 60-61 72-73 (R-up 22-23 70-71 73-74 74-75 75-76 84-85, Lg Cup 72-73 (R-up 65-66), Div 2 56-57), Birmingham Comb R-up 07-08 53-54, Staffs Senior Cup 57-58 59-60 60-61 61-62 (R-up 56-57 64-65 85-86), Birmingham Junior Cup 1895-96, Wednesbury Charity Cup 1981-81 81-82 82-83 84-85 (R-up 83-84).

Bilston Town:

BLAKENALL

Founded: 1946. **Nickname:** Nall.
Colours: Blue with white trim/white/blue with white trim
Change colours: Red & Black/black/black & white
Midweek Matchday: Tuesday

Chairman: P Langston **Vice Chairman:** D Cotterill
President: J Bridgett
Secretary: David Birch, 64 Wimperis Way, Great Barr, Birmingham B43 7DF (0121 360 3574)
Manager: Bob Green **Asst Manager:** Gary Webb
Coach: Brian Taylor **Commercial Manager:** Jeff Husted
Press Officer: Russell Brown (01902 822522)
GROUND Address: Red Lion Ground, Somerfield Rd, Leamore, Walsall, West Mids (01922 405835). **Directions:** M6 jct 10, follow signs for Walsall centre. At 1st lights turn left (about 200yds from Motorway junction) into Bloxwich Lane. Keep following this lane to the 'T' junction and turn right into Leamore Lane, at this island turn left into Somerfield Road. Ground is approx. 400yds on the right.
Seats: 250 **Cover:** 250 **Capacity:** 2,500 **Floodlights:** Yes
Clubhouse: Open 7-11 (Mon-Sun), 1-11 (Sat). Food available matchdays
Club Shop: No **Sponsor:** Castlemore Securities

PROGRAMME DETAILS:
Pages: 52 **Price:** 70p
Editor: Russell Brown
Tel: 01902 822522

PREVIOUS - Names: None. **Leagues:** Bloxwich Comb./ Staffs County/ Midland Comb. 60-79/ W Midlands Reg Lge 79-95/ Midland All 95-97

CLUB RECORDS - Attendance: 1,550 v Halesowen Town 85-86. **Win:** 11-0 v Bilston United 26/4/95.
Defeat: 0-7 v Macclesfield Town (Staffs Sen Cup) 31/1/95.
Fee Received: £10,000 for Darren Simkin (Wolverhampton Wanderers, 1992).

BEST SEASON - FA Trophy: FA Cup: FA Vase:
Players progressing to Football League: Darren Simkin (Wolverhampton Wanderers).
96-97 - Captain: Jason Minton **P.o.Y.:** Peter Duckett **Top scorer:** Ade Edwards (20)
Local Press: Express & Star, Walsall Chronicle, Walsall Advertiser, Walsall Observer, Sunday Mercury.
Local Radio: BBC West Midlands, BRMB, Beacon Radio.
Honours: Midland Football Alliance 96-97, R-up 95-96; Industrial Rewinds Lge Cup 95-96; Midland Invitation Triangular Cup 94-95; West Midlands Reg Prem Div 88-89, R-up 94-95, Prem div Lge Cup 94-95; Walsall Sen Cup 63-64 74-75 75-76 76-77 80-81 88-89 95-96; Midland Comb 76-77.

Blakenall FC after receiving the MFA Championship Shield from Mr Bernard Davies of league sponsors Interlink Express.

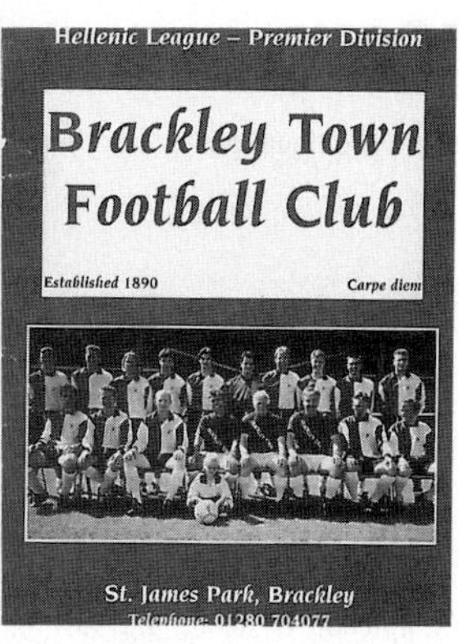

Hellenic League – Premier Division
Brackley Town
Football Club
Established 1890
Carpe diem
St. James Park, Brackley

BRACKLEY TOWN

Formed: 1890 **Nickname:** Saints
Colours: Red & white/black/white
Change colours: Yellow/blue/white
Midweek home matchday: Tuesday
Reserve Team's League:

Chairman: Kim Golding **President:** Miss C Billingham
Secretary/Press Officer: Pat Ashby, 17 Manor Rd, Woodford Halse, Daventry, Northants. NN11 3QP (01327 262955).

Vice Chairman:
Manager: Phil Lines **Asst Manager:**
Coach: Brian Robinson **Physio:** Charlie Busby
Commercial Director:
GROUND Address: St James Park, Churchill Way, Brackley, Northants NN13 7EJ (01280 704077).
Directions: Churchill Way, east off A43, south end of town
Capacity: 3,500 **Cover:** 150 **Seats:** 300 **Floodlights:** Yes
Clubhouse: Lounge & main hall. Open all week.

PROGRAMME DETAILS:
Pages: Price: £
Editor:

PREVIOUS - Names: None **Leagues:** Banbury & District/ North Bucks/ Hellenic 77-83/ United Counties 83-94/ Hellenic 94-97. **Ground:** Banbury Road, Manor Road, Buckingham Road (up to 1974).

CLUB RECORDS - Attendance: 600 v Kettering, Northants Senior Cup 1989

BEST SEASON - FA Trophy: FA Cup: League clubs defeated: None
Players progressing to Football League: Jon Blencowe (Leicester)

Local Press: Brackley Advertiser, Banbury Guardian, Herald & Post, Milton Keynes Citizen. **Local Radio:**
HONOURS: UCL R-up 88-89 (Div 1 83-84); N'hants Snr Cup R-up 88-89; Buck'ham Charity Cup (3); Hellenic Lg Prem 96-97, Div 1 Cup 82-83.

Back Row (L-R); Karlton Stratford, Phil Lines (Mgr), Jon Blencowe. Middle Row; Pat Lawrence (Comm), Pat Ashby (Sec), Justin Merritt, Darren Reynolds, Tim Williams, Cliff Cousins, Terry Muckleberg, Matthew Cresswell, Jason Allen, Rod Bush (Comm). Front Row; Kenn Nelson (Comm), James Foote (Kit); Phil Mason, Jess Mansfield, Charlie Busby (Physio), Kim Golding (Chr), Paul Spittle, Brian Robinson (Asst Mgr), Mark Thomas, Steve Jenkins, Alan Sleeman (Comm).

CORBY TOWN

Formed: 1948 **Nickname:** The Steelmen
Colours: White & black/black/white
Change colours: All yellow.
Midweek matchday: Wednesday
Reserves' League: United Counties Res Div

Chairman: James Kane **President:** H Hatterley.
Secretary: Roger Abraham, 68 Cornwall Rd, Kettering, Northants NN16 8PE (01536 522159).
Manager: Ian Benjamin **Coach:** Simon Mason
Physio: Mick Mackie.

GROUND Address: Rockingham Triangle Stadium, Rockingham Road, Corby NN17 2AE (01536 406640).
Directions: On northern outskirts of town at junction of A6003 and A6116, opposite entrance to Rockingham Castle grounds. One and a half miles from Corby (BR).
Capacity: 3,000 **Cover:** 1,150 **Seats:** 960 **Floodlights:** Yes
Clubhouse: VP Lounge open matchdays and during the week.
Club Shop: Sells badges, programmes etc. Contact C Woolmer (01536 260900). **Sponsor:** Commision for New Towns.

PROGRAMME DETAILS:
Pages: 32 **Price:** £1
Editor: C Smith
(01536 522159)

PREVIOUS - Leagues: United Counties 35-52, Midland 52-58.
CLUB RECORDS - Attendance: 2,240 v Watford, pre-season friendly 86-87. At Old Ground; 10,239 v Peterborough Utd, FA Cup 3rd Qual. Rd 52-53. **Win:** 14-0 v Gainsborough Trinity, 56-57. **Defeat:** 0-10 v Paget Rangers, 95-96. **Career Goalscorer:** David Hofbauer 141 (84-95). **Career Appearances:** Derek Walker 600 (78-92). **Transfer fee paid:** £2,700 for Elwyn Roberts (Barnet, 81). **Transfer fee received:** £20,000 for Matt Murphy (Oxford Utd 93).
BEST SEASON - FA Trophy: 3rd Rd, 1986-87. **FA Cup:** 3rd Rd 65-66 (lost to Plymouth). 1st Rd on five occasions; 54-55 63-66 67-68. - **League clubs defeated:** Luton Town 65-66.
Players progressing to Football League: A McCabe (Chesterfield 55), L Clalmers (Leicester City 56), K Brown (Nottm Forest 56), P Kearns (Aldershot 62), N Dean (Southampton 63), H Curran (Millwall 64), D McNeil/A McGowan/G Reilly (Northampton 69/75/76), P Chard (Peterborough 79), T Morley (West Ham), J Flower (Sheffield Utd, Aldershot), M Murphy (Oxford Utd 93), C McKenzie (Hereford 94).
Local Press: Northampton Evening Telegraph. **Local Radio:** BBC Radio Northampton, Hereward, KCBC.
HONOURS: UCL 50-51 51-52 (R-up 37-38), Midland Lg R-up 52-53, Southern Lg Midland Div R-up 90-91 (Merit Cup 63-64 90-91), Northants Snr Cup 6; Maunsell Cup 83-84, Daventry Charity Cup 94-95, Midland Floodlit Cup 74-75, Evans Halshaw F'lit Cup 91-92, Anglia Floodlit Trophy 68-69 72-73, Chelmsford Invitation Cup 63-64 64-65 65-66(joint), Kettering & Dist Samaritan Cup 60-61 (joint) 68-69, Wellingborough Charity Cup 50-51, Desborough Nursing Cup 48-49 50-51(joint), Bob Cumning Cup 6:

Corby Town FC:

DUDLEY TOWN

THE LAST TEAM PHOTOGRAPH 1997

L-R, Back Row: Richard Wilkes, Keith Brown, Andy dale, John Horne, Andy Crannage, Chris Jones, Nigel Richards, Dena Harrison, Steve Ingram. Front: Wayne Lloyd, Andy Burns, Gary Piggott, Mick Williams, Adrian Cooper, Toby Hall.
Photo: Marshall's (Birmingham) 01384 274877

THE 1996-1997 TEAM PHOTOGRAPH

L-R, Back Row: David Thoams (Trainer), Steve Shaw, Toby Hall, Donald Bailey, Chris Jones, Andy Crannage, Nigel Richards, Robert Grant, Mick Williams, Gary Piggott, Alan Moore (Coach). Front: Dean Harrison, Nick Henley, John Chambers (Manager), Richard Evans, Brian Agar, Curtis Barnes.

EVESHAM UNITED

Formed: 1945 **Nickname:** The Robins
Colours: Red & white/white/white
Change Colours: All blue
Midweek matches: Tuesday
Reserves' League: No reserve team.

Chairman: Stuart Reeves **Vice Chairman:** Jim Cockerton.
President: M E H Davis **Treasurer:** Dave Wright.
Secretary: Mike J Peplow, 68 Woodstock Rd, St Johns, Worcester WR2 5NF (01905 425993).
Press Officer: M Peplow (01905 425993) **Manager:** Chris Robinson
Asst Manager: Martin Bewell **Physio:** John Porter

PROGRAMME DETAILS:
Pages: 36 **Price:** 80p
Editor: Mike Peplow
(01905 425993)

GROUND Address: Common Road, Evesham, Worcestershire WR11 4PU (01386 442303).
Directions: From Evesham High Street turn into Oat St, and join one-way system, turn right between Willmotts factory called Conduit Hill into Common Rd, ground 200yds down on right just before railway bridge. 5 minutes walk from Evesham BR station.
Capacity: 2,000 **Seats:** 350 **Cover:** 600 **Floodlights:** Yes
Clubhouse: Open matchdays and training nights. Cold food available in club, and hot food from tea hut on matchdays.
Club Shop: Contact John Hawkins c/o the club. **Club Sponsors:** Safeway

PREVIOUS - **Leagues:** Worcester, Birmingham Combination, Midland Combination 51-55 65-92, West Midlands Regional 55-62. **Name:** Evesham Town **Ground:** The Crown Meadow (pre-1968).

CLUB RECORDS - **Attendance:** 2,338 v West Bromwich A., friendly 18/7/92 **Win:** 11-3 v West Heath United
Career Goalscorer: Sid Brain **Career Appearances:** Rob Candy **Defeat:** 7-2 v Tamworth
Transfer fee paid: £1,500; to Hayes for Colin Day, 1992.
Transfer fee received: £5,000 for Simon Brain (to Cheltenham Town).

BEST SEASON - **FA Vase:** Quarter Finals 1991-92. **FA Amateur Cup:** Runners-up 1923-24
FA Trophy: 3rd Qual Rd 96-97 **FA Cup:** 2nd Qual Rd 96-97

Players who have progressed to Football League: Billy Tucker, Gary Stevens (Cardiff 77), Kevin Rose (Lincoln 78), Andy Preece (Northampton 86), Simon Brain (Hereford, via Cheltenham Town), Billy Turley (Northampton Tn).
Top Scorer: Mark Davis **96-97 - Captain:** Kacey Johnstone **P.o.Y:** Richard Clark
Local Press: Evesham Journal, Worcester Evening News, Gloucester Echo.
Local Radio: Radio Wyvern, BBC Hereford & Worcester.

HONOURS: FA Amateur Cup R-up 23-24, Worcestershire Snr Urn(2) 76-78 (R-up 90-91), Midland Comb.(6) 52-53 54-55 65-66 67-69 91-92 (Chal. Cup 53-54 87-88 91-92 (R-up(5) 54-55 71-72 83-84 88-90)), Worcestershire Comb. 52-53 54-55; B'gham Combination R-up 30-31, Evesham Hosp. Cup 89-90, Tony Allden Mem. Cup 1973 1988 1992.

L-R, Back Row: Geoff Samuels (Coach), John Porter (Physio), Liam Dixon, Danny Finlay, Harvey Willetts, Richard Clark, Barry Rumble, Richard Holt, Eric Smith, Chris Robinson (Manager), Martin Bewell (Asst. Man.). Front: Mark Davis, Paul O'Brien, Marcus Hamill, Tim Wiggett, Mark Johnson, Craig Knight, Richard Beale, Steve Bartlett.

GRANTHAM TOWN

PROGRAMME DETAILS:
Pages: 36 **Price:** 70p
Editor: M Koranski

Formed: 1874 **Nickname:** Gingerbreads
Colours: Black & white stripes/black/black
Change colours: Blue/blue or black/blue or black
Midweek matchday: Tuesday
Reserves' League: Lincolnshire

Chairman: Alan Prince **President:** Baroness Thatcher of Kesteven.
Secretary: Mr Pat Nixon, 72 Huntingtower Road, Grantham, Lincs NG31 7AU (01476 564408).
Manager: Gary Mills **Asst Mgr:** Paul Buckthorpe **Physio:** Nigel Marshall

GROUND Address: The South Kesteven Sports Stadium, Trent Road, Grantham, Lincs (01476 562177)
Directions: Midway between A1 and A52 on edge of Earlesfield Industrial Estate; from A1 take A607 to Earlsfield Ind. Est and continue into Trent Rd.
Capacity: 7,500 **Cover:** 1,950 **Seats:** 750 **Floodlights:** Yes
Clubhouse: (01476 593506) Open evenings and weekends. Bar, darts, pool etc. Frequent live entertainment. Available for functions.
Club Shop: Sells programmes and a wide range of souvenirs. Contact Paul Wilson (01476 562177). **Sponsors:** Crystal Motors.
PREVIOUS - Leagues: Mid Amat All, Central All. 11-25 59-61, Midland Co's 25-59 61-72, Southern Lge 72-79, Northern Prem. 79-85.
Names: Grantham FC, pre-80. **Grounds:** London Road up to 90.

CLUB RECORDS - **Attendance:** 1,402 v Ilkeston Town, FA Cup Preliminary Rd 91-92
Win: 13-0 v Rufford Colliery (H), FA Cup Preliminary Rd 15/9/34.
Defeat: 0-16 v Notts County Rovers (A), Midland Amateur Alliance 22/10/1892.
Career Goalscorer: Jack McCartney 416 **Career Appearances:** Chris Gardiner 664
Transfer fee paid: £1,000 for Gary Jones (Doncaster Rovers, 1989)
Transfer fee received: £20,000 for Gary Crosby (Notts Forest 87)
BEST SEASON - **FA Cup:** 3rd Rd 1883-84 86-87 1973-74. Comp Proper on 23 occasions
FA Trophy: Quarter Final 1971-72
Players progressing to Football League: E Morris (Halifax 50), P Thompson/R Cooke (Peterborough 64/80), J Rayner (Notts County 64), D Dall (Scunthorpe 79), N Jarvis/H Wood (Scunthorpe 80), D White (Bristol Rvrs 86), T Curran (Grimsby 87), G Crosby (Nottm Forest 87), A Kennedy (Wrexham 87), R Wilson (Lincoln 87).
Local Press: Grantham Journal, Nottingham Evening Post, Melton & Grantham Trader, Grantham Citizen, Lincolnshire Echo. **Local Radio:** Radio Lincolnshire, Lincs FM.
HONOURS: Southern Lg R-up 73-74 (Div 1 Nth 72-73 78-79, Merit Cup 72-73), Midland Co's Lg(3) 63-64 70-72 (R-up 37-38 64-65 69-70, Lg Cup 68-69 70-71), Midland Amtr Lg 10-11 (Lg Cup R-up 10-11), Central All. 24-25 (Southern Div R-up 59-60), Lincs Snr Cup 1884-85 1936-37 (R-up(5) 34-36 39-40 45-47), Lincs Co. 'A' Cup(3) 53-54 60-62 (R-up 49-50 52-53 57-58), Lincs Co. Snr Cup 71-72 82-83 (R-up 80-81).

Dave King turns away after scoring against Corby Town away on Easter Monday. Photo: Dave Tilley

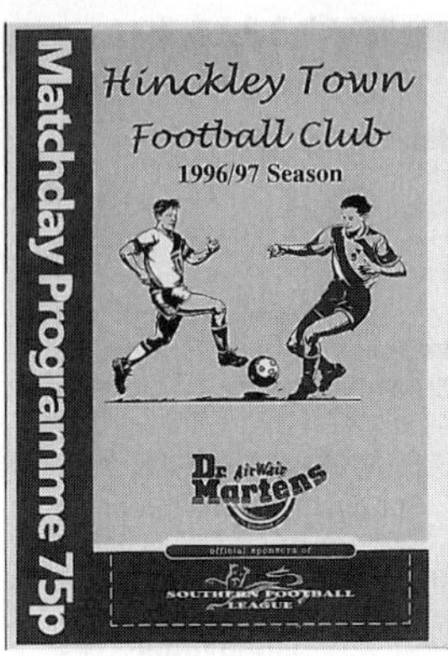

PROGRAMME DETAILS:
Pages: 44 **Price:** £1
Editor: Alan Mason

HINCKLEY UNITED

Formed: 1997
Colours: Red & blue/blue/red
Change colours: Amber & black/black/amber
Midweek matchday: Tuesday
Reserves' League: Endsleigh Mid Comb Res Div

Chairman: Kevin Downes **Vice Chairman:** Rob Mayne
Commercial Director: Mick Voce
Secretary: Stuart Millidge, 25 Elizabeth Rd, Hinckley, Leics. LE10 OQY (01455 635808) **Manager:** John Hanna/Dean Thomas **Coach:** Bill Nally.
Physio: Julie Hayton **Press Officer:** Andy Gibbs (01455 233483)

GROUND Address: Middlefield Lane, Hinckley, Leics. LE10 0RB 01455 613553/615012. **Directions:** From M69 junction 1 take A5 north to Dodwells Island, then A47 (sign Leicester). At 3rd r/about turn right (Stoke Road) then first right (Tudor Road), until crossroads. Turn left (Middlefield Lane), ground at end of lane on left.
Capacity: 5,000 **Cover:** 1,000 **Seats:** 320 **Floodlights:** Yes
Clubhouse: Social club with lounge, games room and concert hall.
Club Shop: Sells programmes, books, vidoes, badges, mugs.
Hinckley Town Records & *Hinckley Athletic Records*

PREVIOUS - Names: Westfield Rovers 58-66, Hinckley Town 66-97. **Grounds:** Westfield Playing Field 58-60/ Coventry Rd Rec Grd 60-68/ Leicester Rd 68-97. **Leagues:** Town; S Leicester & Nuneaton Amat, Leics Snr 72-86, Central Mids 86-88, West Mids 88-90. *Athletic; Leicestershire & Northants/ Leicestershire Senior/ Birmingham Combination 14-39 47-54/ West Midlands (Regional) 54-59 64-94/ Southern 63-64.*

CLUB RECORDS - Attendance: Town: 2,000 v Real Sociedad 86. *Athletic: 5,410 v Nuneaton Boro 49.* **Win:** Town; 10-0 v Kettering Tn Res, Central Mid Lge B.E. Webbe Cup. **Defeat:** Town: 0-10 v Barry Town, Southern Lge Mid Div. **Career Goalscorer:** Town: Paul Purser. *Athletic: M Hodgkins.* **Career Appearances:** *Athletic: Steve Markham 455 86-96.* **Fee paid:** Town: £1,600 for John Lane (V.S. Rugby). **Fee received:** Town: £1,750 for Colin Taylor (Bedworth Utd).

BEST SEASON - FA Vase: Town: Third Round 85-86. *Athletic: 5th Rd 89-90 93-94.*
FA Trophy: *Athletic: 1st Qual. Rd 69-70 72-73 73-74.*
FA Cup: Town: 4th Qual Rd v Welling 88-89. *Athletic: 2nd Rd v Queens Park Rangers 54-55*

Players progressing to Football League: *Athletic: John Allen (Port Vale), Keith Scott (Wycombe, Swindon, Stoke, Norwich), Gary Pick (Hereford), Mike Love (Wigan).* **Local Radio:** BBC Radio Leicester.
Local Press: Heartland Evening Echo, Hinckley Times, Leicester Mercury, Coventry Evening Telegraph

HONOURS: Town; West Midlands (Regional) Lg 89-90, Central Midlands Lg 86-87 (R-up 87-88, B E Webbe Cup R-up 86-87 87-88, Gerry Mills Cup R-up 87-88), Leics Senior Lg R-up 83-84 (Div 2 72-73, Div 2 Cup 72-73), Leicestershire Challenge Cup 89-90 (R-up 90-91 93-94), Leics Senior Cup (Jelson Holmes) R-up 87-88, Leics Senior Cup 88-89, Midland Floodlit Cup 88-89 (R-up 91-92 93-94). *Athletic; Leics Snr Cup 1899-1900 00-01 09-10 82-83, Leics Snr Lg 1896-97 97-98 99-1900 08-09 09-10 13-14, Birmingham Comb. 23-24 26-27 (R-up 22-23), West Mids (Reg.) Lg R-up 82-83, Birmingham Snr Cup 54-55(jt with Brush Sports), Leics Challenge Cup 57-58 58-59 59-60 60-61 61-62 67-68.*

L-R, Back Row: Jason Woodley, Rob Smith, Tony Hamilton, Scott Machin, Tommy Shelvin, Steve Choppen, Simon Williams, Clive Walker, Gerard Carr, Alex Irvine, Neil White, Jon Graham, Billy Nally (coach). Front: Ian Ruck (physio), Lorcan Costello, Paul Corden, Tim Warner, Jason Bindley, Craig Martin, Morton Titterton, John Hanna (Jt. manager), Dean Thomas (Jt. manager), Wayne Spencer, Nicky Platnauer, Mark Hodgkins, Ady Fitzhugh, Buster Kendall (kit manager). Photo courtesy of The Hinckley Times

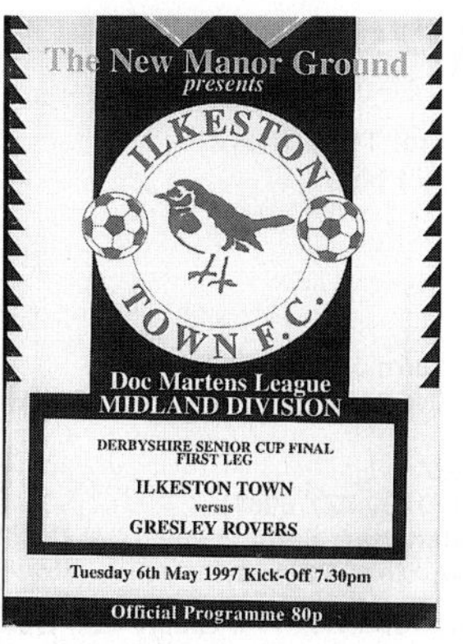

PROGRAMME DETAILS:
Pages: 32 **Price:** £1
Editor: Mic Capill
J.Shiels, D.Payne.

ILKESTON TOWN

Re Formed: 1945 **Nickname:** The Robins
Colours: Red/black/black
Change colours: All purple.
Midweek matchday: Tuesday
Reserves' League: Beauvale Mids Reg All.

Chairman: Paul Millership **President:** Robert Lindsay
Secretary: Tony Cuthbert, 8 Darwin Road, Long Eaton, Nottingham NG10 3NW (0115 9731531). **Commercial Manager:** Nicky Law
Manager / Coach: Keith Alexander **Asst Manager:** Gary Simpson

GROUND Address: New Manor Ground, Awsworth Rd, Ilkeston (0115 9324094). **Directions:** M42 to M1 junc 23A, continue on M1 to junc 26, exit left onto A610 towards Ripley, take 1st exit signed Awsworth and Ilkeston (A6096), follow bypass signed Ilkeston A6096. Turn right after 1/2 mile signed Cotmanhay. Ground 200 yards on left
Capacity: 3,500 **Seats:** 270. **Cover:** 1,100. **Floodlights:** Yes
Clubhouse: Open Wed-Fri 7-11pm, Sat-Sun noon-3 & 7-11pm, and Mon or Tue if there is a match. Snacks behind bar. Large tea bar open matchdays 2-5pm (6.30-9pm for night games).
Club Shop: Sells wide range of souvenirs & programmes + 'Team Talk'. Contact Manager (0115 9305 622) or club secretary
Sponsors: Ron Brooks Ilkeston Toyota

PREVIOUS - Leagues: Midland 1894-1902 25-58 61-71/Notts and Derby Senior Lg.1945-47/ Central Alliance 47-61/Midland CountiesLg.1961-71/Southern League 1971-73/ Midland Co.Lg.1973-82/ Northern Co.East Lg.1982-86/ Central Midlands 86-90/ West Midlands (Regional) 90-94. **Ground:** Manor Ground, Manor Rd (1945-92).

CLUB RECORDS - Attendance: 2,349 Kidderminster H (F.A.Trophy 3rd Rd) 94-95. **Win:** 14-2 v Codnor M.W 46-47: 13-0 v Swanwick OB 46-47. **Defeat:** 1-11 v Grantham T. 47-48: 0-10 v VS Rugby 85-86. **Career Goalscorer:** Jackie Ward 141. **Career Appearances:** Terry Swincoe 377. **Season Goalscorer:** Barry Jepson 62, 1952-53. **Transfer fee paid:** £7,000 for Paul Eshelby (Alfreton Tn 96-97). **Transfer fee received:** £11,750 for Chris Brookes (Luton Town, 1992).

BEST SEASON - FA Cup: 1st Round - 51-52 0-2 v Rochdale (H), 56-57 1-5 v Blyth Spartans (H). **FA Trophy:** 3rd Round 82-83 1-5 v Enfield, 94-95 2-2, 1-2 v Kidderminster H. **FA Vase:** 4th Round 88-89 1-2 v Tamworth.

96-97 - Captain: Nicky Law **Top Scorer:** Paul Eshelby **P.o.Y.:** David Robinson

HONOURS: Beazer Homes League, Midland Division 94-95, West Mids (Regional) Lg 93-94 (Div 1 91-92, Lg Cup 93-94 Div 1 Lg.Cup 91-92, Central Mids Lg Cup 87-88, Midland Lg 67-68 (R-up 1898-99), Midland Co.Lg.67-68, Central All. 51-52 52-53 53-54 54-55 (R-up 47-48 55-56).

Ilkeston Town FC

MOOR GREEN

MOOR GREEN FOOTBALL CLUB
Beazer Homes League Midland Division
Season 1995/96
MAIN SPONSOR
H. S. DATALINE LTD
TAMWORTH
80p

PROGRAMME DETAILS:
Pages: 52 **Price:** 80p
Editor: Peter Denham
(0121 777 3356)

Formed: 1901 **Nickname:** The Moors
Colours: Light & dark blue halves/navy/light blue
Change colours: Jade & lime/jade
Midweek matchday: Tuesday
Reserve League: No reserve team

Chairman: Geoff Hood **Vice-Chairman:** Ian Childs.
Secretary: Nigel Collins, 7 The Morelands, West Heath, Birmingham B31 3HA (0121 243 3661 H, 0121 475 0240 B)
Press Officer: Peter Clynes (0121 745 3262)
Commercial Manager: Commercial Dept.(0121 777 8961)
Manager: Bob Faulkner **Asst Manager:** Barry Powell
Coach: Doug Griffith **Physio:** Steve Shipway.
GROUND Address: 'The Moorlands', Sherwood Rd., Hall Green. B28 OEX. 0121 624 2727. **Directions:** Off Highfield Rd, which is off A34 (B'ham to Stratford). Hall Green & Yardley (BR) half mile.
Capacity: 3,250 **Cover:** 1,200 **Seats:** 250 **Floodlights:** Yes
Clubhouse: Two bars, dance floor. Open nightly & weekend lunch.
Club Shop: Selling scarves, mugs, stickers, programmes etc.
Sponsors: ????

PREVIOUS - **Leagues:** (friendlies only 1901-21) Birmingham & Dist. A.F.A. 1908-36/ Central Amateur 36-39/ Birmingham Comb 45-54/ West Mids 54-65/ Midland Comb 65-83.
Grounds: Moor Green Lane 1901-02/ numerous 02-22/ Windermere Road 1910-30.

CLUB RECORDS - **Attendance:** 5,000 v Romford, FA Amtr Cup 1951
Transfer fee paid: £1,000 for Adrian O'Dowd (Alvechurch)
Transfer fee received: £90,000 for In Taylor(Port Vale.

BEST SEASON - **FA Cup:** 1st Rd Proper 79-80 (lost 2-3 Stafford Rgs).

Players progressing to Football League: H Smith/R Jefferies (Aston Villa 47/50), F Pidcock (Walsall 53), P Woodward/B Mack (W B Abion 54), S Cooper (Birmingham City 83), K Barnes (Manchester City), P Brogan (Mansfield Town), I Taylor (Pt Vale 92), S Talbot (Port Vale 94).
Local Press: Solihull News, Solihull Times, Birmingham Post & Mail, Express & Star.
Local Radio: Radio WM, BRMB.
HONOURS: Sthn Lg Mid Div R-up 87-88, Mids Comb 80-81 (R-up(4) 74-76 79-80 82-83, Div 1 85-86, Presidents Cup(2) 66-68 78-79), Mids Comb Chall Cup 80-81 (R-up 69-70 82-83), Lord Mayor of B'ham Charity Cup 90-91, Mids F'lit Cup(2) 90-92, Tony Allden Tphy 81-82, B'ham Snr Cup 57-58, Worcs Snr Cup R-up 86-87, B'ham Jnr Cup 66-67, Worcs Jnr Cup 85-86, Solihull Charity Cup 85-86, Smedley Crook Memorial Cup 87-88, Cent Amat Lg 36-37 37-38 38-39, Verviers (Belg) Tphy 32-33 36-37, AFA Chall Cup 38-39, AFA Snr Cup 26-27 35-36, Mids F'lit Yth Lg Cup R-up 87-88, B'ham County Yth Lg Cup R-up 83-84.

Moor Green FC *Photo - Andrew Chitty*

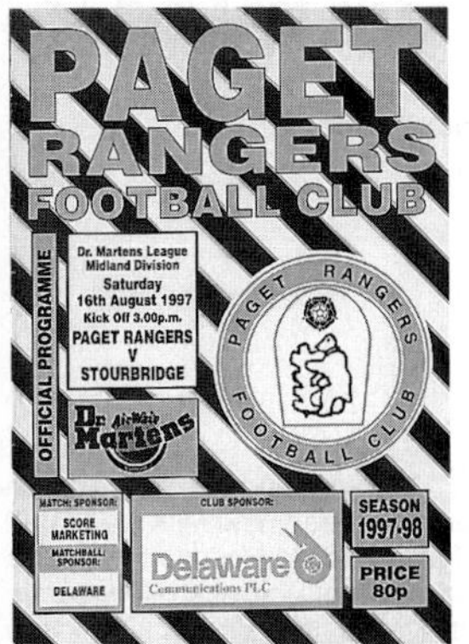

PROGRAMME DETAILS:
Pages: **Price:** 80p
Editor: Paul Vanes
Tel: 0121 770 9835

PAGET RANGERS

Formed: 1938 **Nickname:** The 'Bears'
Colours: Gold/black/gold.
Change colours: All red
Midweek matchday: Wednesday
Reserves' League: No reserve team

Chairman: R R Ruddick **Vice-Chairman:** Derek Culling
Secretary: Ian T Price, 80 Ward Grove, Lanesfield, Wolverhampton. WV4 6PQ (01902 679223)
Press Officer: Chris Inman
Commercial Manager: Rob Wilkinson (0121 686 3919)
Manager/Physio: Eddie Caulfield
Asst Manager: Paul Edwards **Coach:** Chris Sharpe

GROUND Address: Central Ground, Coles Lane, Sutton Coldfield B72 1NL. 0121 354 2997/0121 355 5475. **Directions:** A5127 into Sutton, right at Odeon cinema (Holland Road), then first right into Coles Lane - ground 150 yds on left. 10 mins walk from Sutton Coldfield (BR), bus 104 from Birmingham.
Capacity: 4,500 **Cover:** 500 **Seats:** 200 **Floodlights:** Yes
Clubhouse: Open daily, brick built lounge and concert room, fully carpeted and extensively decorated. Food available
Club Shop: No, metal badges available from chairman or secretary.
Sponsors: Delaware Communications

PREVIOUS - **Leagues:** Birmingham Suburban/Central Amateur/Midland Combination 50-81/Southern 86-88/West Midlands (Regional) 88-94/ Interlink Midland Alliance 94-95.
Grounds: Pype Hayes Park 38-46/ Springfield Road, Walmley 46-93

CLUB RECORDS - **Attendance:** 2,000 v Aston Villa, F'light opening 1971. **Win:** 24-1 v Evesham Town 1949. **Defeat:** 1-6 v Gloucester 87/Halesowen Town 87/Moor Green 88. **Career Appearances:** Gary Williams 512. **Career Goalscorer:** Unknown. **Transfer fee paid:** No transfer fee paid for any player. **Transfer fee received:** John Gittens (Southampton) £10,000

BEST SEASON - **FA Cup:** Third Qual Round 94-95. **FA Vase:** Fourth Rd 88-89, 0-1 v Wisbech. **FA Trophy:** First Rd 95-96, 0-2 v Winsford

Players progressing to Football League: John Gittens (Southampton)
96-97 Captain: **P.o.Y.:** **Top scorer:**
Local Press: Sutton Coldfield News, Sutton Observer. **Local Radio:** Radio WM, BRMB.

HONOURS: West Mids Lg R-up 91-92 (Lg Cup 91-92); Midland Comb.(6) 59-61 69-71 82-83 85-86 (R-up 77-78, Lg Cup 59-60 66-67, Div 1 Cup 70-71, Div 3 82-83(res)); B'ham Jnr Cup 51-52; Walsall Snr Cup 85-86; Midland Alliance 94-95; Lord Mayor Birmingham Charity Cup 94-95; Staffs Sen Cup R-up 94-95.

Back Row (L-R); Steve Scott, Rasheed Anifowose, Gary Knight, Stuart Tucker, Gary Price, Sean Small, Mick Chawner, Richard Brown. Front Row; Brendan McCarthy, Adam Smith, Stuart Clark, Trevor Borroughs, Paul Clarke, Marcus MacDonald, Ricky Marshall.

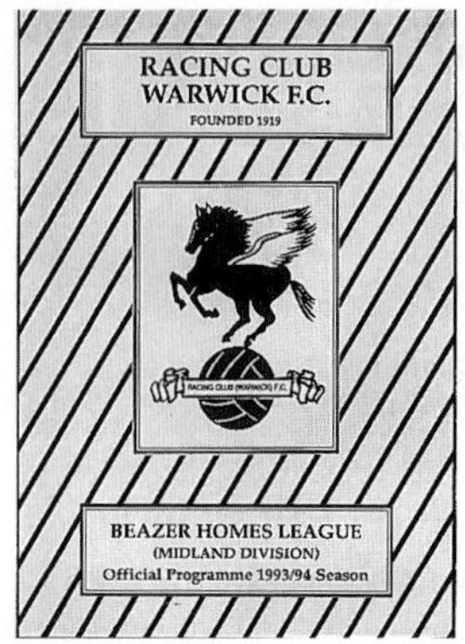

RACING CLUB
WARWICK F.C.
FOUNDED 1919
BEAZER HOMES LEAGUE
(MIDLAND DIVISION)
Official Programme 1993/94 Season

RACING CLUB WARWICK

Formed: 1919 **Nickname:** Racing
Colours: Gold/black/black (Ajax Style)
Change colours: Red/white/white
Midweek matchday: Wednesday
Reserves' League: No Reserve team.

Chairman: **Vice Chairman:** K Billington
Secretary:
Press Officer: Secretary
Commercial Manager: Robin Lamb
Manager: D Draper **Asst Manager:** K Billington
GROUND Address: Townsend Meadow, Hampton Road, Warwick CV34 6JP (01926 495786). **Directions:** On the B4095 Warwick to Redditch road (via Henley in Arden) next to owners' & trainers' car park of Warwick Racecourse. From M40 jct 15 (one and a half miles) take A429 into Warwick, left into Shakespeare Ave., straight over island, right at T-junction into Hampton Rd, ground 300yds on left. 2 miles from Warwick BR station.
Capacity: 1,000 **Cover:** 200 **Seats:** 250 **Floodlights:** Yes
Club Shop: Scarves, mugs, badges, programmes - contact Robin Lamb.
Clubhouse: 01926 495786 Open every evening & Fri, Sat, Sun & Mon lunchtimes. **Sponsors:** P & D Construction

PROGRAMME DETAILS:
Pages: 20 **Price:** 80p
Editor: Robin Lamb
Tel: 01926 774255

PREVIOUS - Leagues: Birmingham & West Midlands Alliance, Warwickshire Combination, West Midlands (Regional) 67-72, Midland Combination 72-89. **Name:** Saltisford Rovers 1919-68, Warwick Saltisford 68-70. **Grounds:** Coventry Road.

CLUB RECORDS - Attendance: 1,000 v Halesowen Town, FA Cup 1987. **Transfer fee paid:** £1,000 for Dave Whetton (Bedworth United). **Transfer fee received:** £2,000 for Ian Gorrie (Atherstone Utd). **Win:** 9-1 v Knowle. **Defeat:** 0-6 v Tamworth. **Career Goalscorer:** Steve Edgington 200. **Career Appearances:** Steve Cooper 600.

BEST SEASON - FA Vase: 4th Round 1977-78, **FA Cup:** 3rd Qual Rd 92-93.
Players progressing to the Football League: None

96-97 - Captain: K Sullivan **P.o.Y.:** Kerion Sullivan **Top scorer:** Brian Agar (25)
Local Press: Warwick Advertiser, Leamington Courier, Coventry Evening Telegraph.
Local Radio: BBC Radio Coventry.

HONOURS: Midland Combination 87-88 (R-up 88-89), Warwick Lg 33-34 34-35 35-36, Birmingham & West Mids Alliance 48-49, Birmingham & Dist Alliance Senior Cup 49-50, Leamington & Dist Lg 37-38 45-46 46-47 47-48, Leamington Hospital Cup 37-38 46-47, Warwick Cinderella Cup 35-36 36-37 37-38 38-39 46-47, T G John Cup 36-37, Leamington Junior Cup 38-39 46-47.

Back Row (L-R); Andy Green, Robert Gould, Ben Frost, Richard Anstiss, Kieran Sullivan, Matt Haywood.

Front Row; Richard Wade, Liam O'Neil, Barry Wilcox, Gary Hardwick, Mick Walker.

Photo - Keith Clayton

PROGRAMME DETAILS:
Pages: 68 **Price:** 50p
Editor: Mick Jones
(01933 625429)

RAUNDS TOWN FC

Formed: 1946 **Nickname:** Shopmates
Colours: Red & black
Change Colours: White.
Midweek matchday: Wednesday
Reserves' League: UCL Reserve Division One.

Chairman: George Hagan **President:**
Secretary: Mick Jones, 14 Welland Close, Raunds, Northants. NN9 6SQ. 01933 625429. **Press Officer:** Mick Jones (Secretary)
Commercial Manager: Ralph Maloney 01933 622036
Manager: Keith Burt **Asst Manager:** Glen Burdett

GROUND Address: Kiln Park, London Road, Raunds, Northants NN9 6EQ (01933 623351), Matchdays 01933 460941.
Directions: Take Raunds turning at roundabout on A45 and ground is first left. Nearest station; Wellingborough. Bus services local
Capacity: 3,000 **Seats:** 250 **Cover:** 600 **Floodlights:** Yes
Clubhouse: On ground, open every day
Club Shop: Yes Open matchdays, selling shirts, books programmes, contact Malc York, c/o club.
Sponsors: Jubilee Enterprises

PREVIOUS - Leagues: Rushden & District, Central Northants Combination, United Counties League Prem Div. **Grounds:** Greenhouse Field (until 1948), The Berristers (1948-91).

CLUB RECORDS - Attendance: 1,500 v Crystal Palace, ground opening 23/7/91. **Win:** 9-0 v Potton 95, 11-2 v Brackley 93. **Defeat:** 0-6 v Baldock 83, v Buckingham 84-85. **Career Goalscorer:** Shaun Keeble 184. **Career Appearances:** Martin Lewis 309 (+23 subs). **Transfer fee paid:** None. **Transfer fee received:** None

BEST SEASON - FA Cup: 3rd Qual Rd, 92-93 (0-4 at Nuneaton Borough), 93-94 (0-4 v Telford United). **FA Vase:** Semi-final v Arlesey Tn 94-5. **FA Trophy:** 1st Rd v Welling Utd 96-97

Players to progress to Football League: Greg Downs (Norwich, Coventry, Birmingham, Hereford).
Local Press: Northants Evening Telegraph, Wellingborough Post, Chronicle & Echo.
Local Radio: Northants Radio, KCBC

96-97 - Captain: Paul York **P.o.Y.:** John Flower **Top scorer:** Shaun Keeble (25)

HONOURS: UCL Prem Champions 95-96, UCL Div 1 82-83 (R-up 91-92, KO Cup 90-91 (R-up 83-84 93-94), Reserve Div 1 88-89 95-96 (R-up 86-87 87-88 89-90 90-91 91-92), Reserve KO Cup 84-85 88-89 93-94), Northants Snr Cup 90-91, Hunts Premier Cup R-up 92-93, Daventry Charity Cup R-up 83-84, Northants Jnr Cup 82-83 91-92(res) 92-93(res).

Raunds Town FC: Back Row (L-R); Paul Hill, Stan Hardy, Keith Francis, John Fowler, Kevin Fox, Darrell Page, Peter Green, Ashley Carr, Shaun Keeble. Front Row; Paul Wagstaffe, Mark Jameson, Paul York, Martin Lewis, Ian Pearce, Adrian Mann.

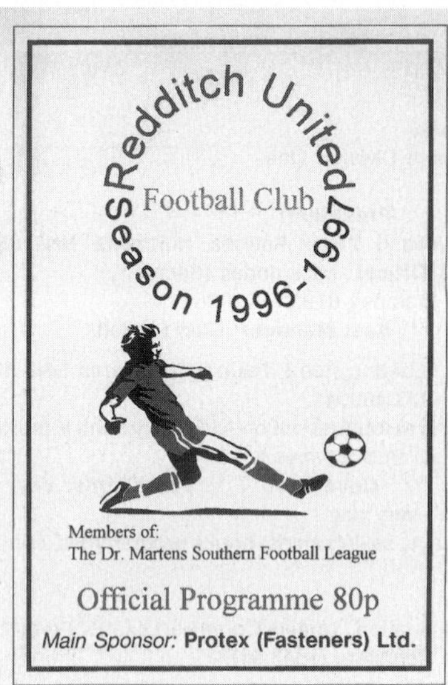

Redditch United
Football Club
Season 1996-1997
Members of:
The Dr. Martens Southern Football League
Official Programme 80p
Main Sponsor: Protex (Fasteners) Ltd.

REDDITCH UNITED

Formed: 1900 **Nickname:** The Reds
Colours: All red
Change colours: All royal blue
Midweek matchday: Tuesday
Reserves' League: Midland Comb. Res Div.

Chairman: Keith Broom **President:** Bob Thompson
Secretary: M A Langfield, 174 Harport Road, Redditch, Worcs B98 7PE (01527 526603)
Commercial Manager: Dave Roberts
Press Officer: R Newbold (0527 27516)
Manager: Mick Tuohy
Assistant Manager: Ivor Chambers
Physiotherapist: Ginger Jordan

GROUND Address: Valley Stadium, Bromsgrove Road, Redditch B97 4RN (0527 67450).
Directions: Access 7 on town centre ring-road takes you into Bromsgrove Road (via Unicorn Hill) - ground entrance 400yds past traffic lights on right. Arriving from Bromsgrove take first exit off dual carriageway. Ground 400 yds from Redditch BR station and town centre.
Capacity: 9,500 **Cover:** 2,000
Seats: 400 **Floodlights:** Yes

Clubhouse: Large clubroom and lounge boardroom. Open matchdays and for private hire. Food availsable on matchdays; hot dogs, burgers, chips etc.
Club Shop: No.

PROGRAMME DETAILS:
Pages: 48 **Price:** TBA
Editor: Roger Newbold
(01527 27516)

PREVIOUS - **Leagues:** Birmingham Combination 05-21 29-39 46-53, West Midlands 21-29 53-72, Southern 72-79, GMV Conference (then Alliance Premier League) 79-80.
Name: Redditch Town
Ground: HDA Spts Ground, Millsborough Rd.

CLUB RECORDS - **Attendance:** 5,500 v Bromsgrove, league match 54-55.
Transfer fee paid: £3,000 for Paul Joinson
Transfer fee received: £42,000 for David Farrell (Aston Villa, 1991).

BEST SEASON - **FA Cup:** 1st Rd replay 71-72 (lost 0-4 at P'boro after 1-1 draw). Also 1st Rd 71-72.
- League clubs defeated: None.
FA Trophy: 1st Round 1978-79

HONOURS: Southern Lg Div 1 Nth 75-76 (Midland Div R-up 85-86), West Mids (B'ham) Lg Southern Sect. 54-55, Birmingham Comb. 13-14 32-33 52-53 (R-up 06-07 14-15 51-52), Staffs Snr Cup 90-91, Birmingham Snr Cup 24-25 31-32 38-39 76-77, Worcs Snr Cup 1894-95 1930-31 74-75 76-77 (R-up 1888-89 1929-30 52-53 73-74), Worcs Jnr Cup 90-91

Players progressing to Football League: Hugh Evans (Birmingham 1947), Trevor Lewes (Coventry 1957), David Gilbert (Chesterfield 1960), Mike Tuohy (Southend Utd 1979), Neil Smith (Liverpool), David Farrell (Aston Villa 1992).

Local Press: Redditch Indicator, Redditch Advertiser, Birmingham Evening Mail, Redditch Weekly Mail.
Local Radio: BBC Hereford & Worcester.

SHEPSHED DYNAMO

Formed: 1890 **Nickname:** The Raiders
Colours: Black & white/black/black
Change colours: Blue/white/blue
Midweek matchday: Tuesday
Reserves' League: None

PROGRAMME DETAILS:
Pages: Price:
Editor:
Tel.

Chairman: Michael Voce **President / Vice Chairman:** TBA
Secretary: Peter Bull, 17 Welland Rd, Barrow-on-Soar, Leicestershire LE12 8NA (01509 413338).
Press Officer: Maurice Brindley (01509 267922)
Commercial Manager: Paul Mitchell
Manager: Mark O'Kane
Assistant Manager: Keith Milner **Physio:** John Watson

GROUND Address: The Dovecote, Butthole Lane, Shepshed, Leicestershire (01509 502684). **Directions:** M1 junction 23, A512 towards Ashby, right at first lights, right at garage in Forest Street, right into Butthole Lane opposite Black Swan. Five miles from Loughborough (BR).
Capacity: 5,000 **Cover:** 1,500 **Seats:** 209 **Floodlights:** Yes
Clubhouse: Accomodates 120 in main room, 50 in others.
Club Shop: No **Sponsors:** None

PREVIOUS - **Leagues:** Leicestershire Senior 07-16 19-27 46-50 51-81, Midland Counties 81-82, Northern Counties (East) 82-83, Southern 83-88, Northern Premier 88-93, Midland Combination 93-94.
Grounds: Ashby Road (pre-1897), Little Haw Farm.
Names: Shepshed Albion 1890-1975 91-94, Shepshed Charterhouse 75-91.

CLUB RECORDS - **Attendance:** 1,672 **Win:** Unknown **Defeat:** Unknown
Career Goalscorer: Jeff Lissaman **Career Appearances:** Austin Straker 300
Transfer fee paid: £2,000 for Doug Newton
Transfer fee received: £10,000 for John Deakin from Birmingham City

BEST SEASON - **FA Vase:** Semi-Finalists 78-79 **FA Trophy:** 1st Rd Replay 85-86 89-90.
FA Cup: 1st Rd 82-83 (lost 1-5 at Preston North End).

Players progressing to Football League: Neil Grewcock (Burnley 1984), Gordon Tucker (Huddersfield 1987), Devon White (Bristol Rovers 1987), John Deakin (Birmingham City).

HONOURS: Southern League Midland Division Runners-up 83-84, Northern Counties (East) League 82-83 (League Cup 82-83), Midland Counties League 81-82 (League Cup 81-82), Leicestershire Senior League 10-11 20-21 78-79 79-80 80-81 (Runners-up 21-22, Div 2 53-54 65-66 77-78, Div 2 Cup 77-78), Leicestershire Senior Cup 77-78 79-80 81-82 83-84 84-85 85-86 87-88, FA Vase SF 78-79, Loughborough Charity Cup 92-93.

L-R, Back: Melvyn Mole (physio), John Hayward, David Tonge, Chris Tonge, Lee Harriman, Richard Selby, Nick Stanborough, Tyrone Mintus, John Watson (physio), Mark O'Kane (manager), Mick Voce (chairman). Front: Darren Robinson, Jason Weafer, Jason Glover, Andy Beckford, Steve Burr (captain), Matthew Wallace, Steve Coleman, Lee McGlinchey, Ged Heyna, Mark Webster (coach).

PROGRAMME DETAILS:
Pages: 52 **Price:** £1
Editors: Jonathon Morgan & Clare Anker 0121 357 8878

SOLIHULL BOROUGH

Formed: 1951 **Nickname:** Boro
Colours: Red/white/red
Change colours: Yellow/black/yellow
Midweek matchday: Wednesday
Reserve's League: Midland Combination Reserve Division

Chairman: John Hewitson **President:** Joe McGorian
Vice Chairman: Trevor Stevens **Commercial Man.:** Roger Lucas
Secretary: John A France, 22 Swallows Meadow, Shirley, Solihull B90 4QB (0121 733 6584) **Press Officer:** Richard Crawshaw (01564 702746)
Manager: Paul Dyson **Reserve Manager:** Kevin Sweeney
Coach: Robert Hopkins **Physio:** Dave Smith

GROUND Solihull are groundsharing at Moor Green awaiting a stadium of their own. **Address:** 'The Moorlands', Sherwood Rd., Hall Green. B28 OEX. 0121 624 2727. **Directions:** Off Highfield Rd, which is off A34 (B'ham to Stratford). Hall Green & Yardley (BR) half mile. **Details;** as Moor Green F.C.
Clubhouse: The Borough Club, Tanworth Lane, Shirley. Open every night, Sunday and bank holiday lunchtimes. **Manager:** Mark Dumelow.
Club Shop: Yes **Sponsors:** Carling Black Label

PREVIOUS - **Leagues:** Mercian; Midland Combination 69-91.
Name: Lincoln FC **Grounds:** Widney Stadium, Solihull 65-88

CLUB RECORDS - **Attendance:** 1,360 v VS Rugby, FA Cup First Round 14/11/92. *At previous ground: 400 v Moor Green, Midland Combination Division Two, 1971.*
Win: 6-1 v Hednesford (H), Southern Lge Midland Div 91-92.
Defeat: 1-7 v VS Rugby (A), Birmingham Senior Cup.
Career Goalscorer: Chris Burton **Career Appearances:** Darrell Houghton
Transfer fee paid: £15,000 for Recky Carter, from Kettering Town
Transfer fee received: £30,000 for Andy Williams (to Coventry)

BEST SEASON - **FA Cup:** 1st Rd 92-93, 1-3 v VS Rugby (A) after 2-2
FA Vase: 5th Rd 74-75 **FA Trophy:** 3rd Qualifying Rd 92-93, 96-97

Players to Football League: Kevin Ashley (Birmingham C.), Andy Williams (Coventry C.), Geoff Scott (Leicester C.), Danny Conway (Leicester C.), Alan Smith (Leicester C.), Dean Spink (Aston Villa), John Frain (Northampton T.)
96-97 - Captain: Martin Myers **P.O.Y.:** Alan Byrne **Top scorer:** Joe Dowling
Local Press: Solihull Times, Solihull News, Sunday Mercury, Sports Argus. **Local Radio:** Radio WM, BRMB.
HONOURS: Southern Lg Midland Div 91-92, Midland Comb. R-up 90-91 (Chall. Cup R-up 74-75 90-91, Presidents Cup R-up 69-70), Lord Mayor of Birmingham Charity Cup 91-92 92-93 94-95 96-97, Worcs Senior Cup R-up 92-93 96-97.

L-R, Back Row: Willie Dunn, Dave Fearon, Tom McGann, Nicky Cross, Paul Hiles, Craig Gillett, Darrell Houghton, Steve Wilkinson, Gerald Murphy, Alan Cook, Brian Palgrave, John Muir. Front: Joe Dowling, Matt Coppin, Mark Beddowes, Shane Abell, Dave Latchford (Coach), Paul Dyson (Manager), Robert Hopkins (Player/coach), Mark Wolsey, Paul John, Martin Myers, Alan Byrne, Dave Smith (Physio).

STAFFORD RANGERS

PROGRAMME DETAILS:
Pages: 40 **Price:** £ 1.00
Editor: C & W Bedford
Tel. 01785 602430

Formed: 1876 **Nickname:** The Boro
Colours: White & black/black/black
Change colours: All blue
Midweek matchday: Tuesday
Reserves' League: No reserve team

Chairman: John Downing (Acting) **Vice-Chairmam:** TBA
Secretary: Peter Wall, c/o Stafford FC (01785 602430)
Press Officer: Chris Godwin **Commercial Manager:** George Berry
Manager: K Bowen **Physio:** B. Whittaker
GROUND Address: Marston Road Stafford ST16 3BX (01785 602430) (Fax 01785 602431) **Directions:** From M6 junction 14, A34 (Stone) to roundabout, straight over into Beaconside, take third right into Common Road, ground one mile ahead. From Town Centre, follow signs for B5066 (Sandon) turn left by Lotus shoe factory. Two miles from railway station.
Capacity: 6,000 **Cover:** 3,000 **Seats:** 426 **Floodlights:** Yes
Clubhouse: Yes - Open every day. Food available
Club Shop: Two shops, one old programmes and one souvenirs run by Jim & Irene Dalglish.
PREVIOUS - Leagues: Shropshire 1891-93, Birm 1893-96, 21-40, N Staffordshire 1896-1900, Cheshire 00-01, Birm Comb 00-12, 46-52, Cheshire Cnty 52-69, Nthn Prem 69-79, 83-85, Alliance Prem 79-83, GMVC 85-95.
Grounds: Lammascotes, Stone Rd, Newtown, Doxey (until 1896)

CLUB RECORDS - Attendance: 8,536 v Rotherham Utd FA Cup 3rd Rd 75
Win: 11-0 v Dudley Town FA Cup 6.9.58
Defeat: 0-12 v Burton Town Birmingham Lge 13.12.30
Career Goalscorer: M Cullerton 176 **Career Appearances:** Jim Sargent
Transfer fee paid: £13,000 for S Butterworth from VS Rugby 90
Transfer fee received: £100,000 for Stan Collymore from Crystal Palace 1990
BEST SEASON - FA Trophy: Winners 1971-72 & 78-79. R-up 75-76
Players progressing to Football League: include W Blunt (Wolves), G Bullock (Barnsley), K Mottershead (Doncaster), McIlvenny (WBA), S Collymore (C Palace), P Devlin (Notts County), R Price (Birmingham City).
96-97 - Captain: Paul Grainger **P.o.Y.:** Farrell Kilbane **Top scorer:** Richard Mitchell
Local Press: Staffordshire Newsletter, Express & Star, Evening Sentinel
Local Radio: Radio Stoke, Beacon Radio, Signal Radio.

HONOURS: Birm Comb Champions 12-13; Birm Lge Champ 25-26; Nthn Prem Lge Champ 71-72, 84-85; FA Trophy Win 71-72, 78-79, R-up 75-76; Bob Lord Trophy 85-86; Wednesday Charity Cup 20-21; Midland Floodlight Cup 70-71; NPL Champ Shield 84-85; Jim Thompson Shield 86-87; Staffs Sen Cup 54-55, 56-57, 62-63, 71-72, 77-78, 86-87, 91-92.

L-R, Back Row: Bill Petric (Physio), Paul Stephenson, Daren Bloor, Mark Wood, Neil Cartwright, Steve James, James Hunter, Mark Deegan, Andy Evans, Steve Round, Leighton Derry, Nathan Foster, Jamie Bates, Dr D A Dasgupta. Front: Allan Somerville, Keith Bertschin, Barrie Whittaker (Physio), Farrell Kilblane, Richard Mitchell, Steve Clifford, Kevin Bowen (Manager), Paul Grainger, Darren Boughey, Darren Oliver, Ken Jones (Coach), Paul Line, Ian Banks.

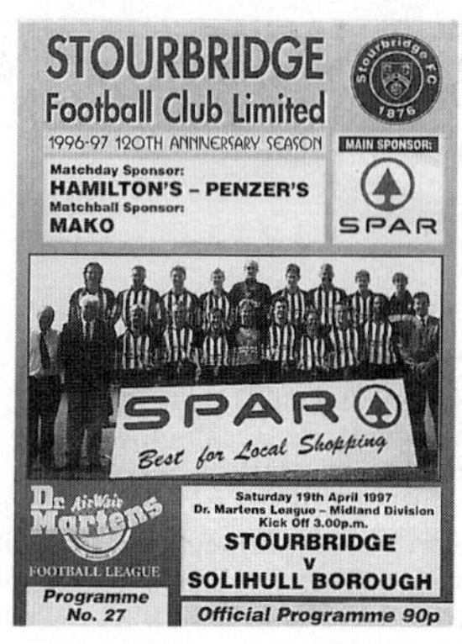

STOURBRIDGE

Formed: 1876 **Nickname:** The Glassboys
Colours: Red & white stripes
Change colours: Yellow & blue.
Midweek matchday: Tuesday
Reserves' League: ????

Managing Director: Nick Pratt **Chairman:** Morton Bartleet
Vice Chairman:
Secretary / Press Officer: Hugh Clark, 10 Burnt Oak Drive, Stourbridge, West Mids DY8 1HL (01384 392975).
Manager: Morton Bartleet **Coach:** **Physio:**
GROUND Address: War Memorial Athletic Ground, High Street, Amblecote, Stourbridge DY8 4EB (01384 394040).
Directions: Take A491, signposted Wolverhampton, from Stourbridge ring-road - ground 300yds on left immediately beyond traffic lights and opposite 'Royal Oak' pub. Buses 311, 313 from Dudley, and 256 from Wolverhampton, pass ground. One mile from Stourbridge Town (BR).
Capacity: 2,000 **Cover:** 1,250 **Seats:** 250 **Floodlights:** Yes
Clubhouse: Open every evening from 8pm and Sunday lunchtimes.
Club Shop: Programmes & souvenirs. Contact Nigel Gregg (01384 838334).
Sponsors: Spar, Wordsley Green

PROGRAMME DETAILS:
Pages: 28 **Price:** 90p
Editor: N Pratt
Tel. 01384 402881

PREVIOUS - Leagues: West Midlands (previously Birmingham) 1892-1939 54-71, Birmingham Combination 45-53. **Grounds:** None. **Name:** Stourbridge Standard

CLUB RECORDS - Attendance: 5,726 v Cardiff City, Welsh Cup final 1st leg 1974. **Career Goalscorer:** Ron Page 269. **Career Appearances:** Ron Page 427. **Transfer fee received:** £20,000 for Tony Cunningham (Lincoln C 79). **Transfer fee paid:**

BEST SEASON - FA Cup: 4th Qual Rd: v Arnold 67-68, v V.S. Rugby 84-85 & 85-86. **FA Trophy:** Qtr Final 70-71
Players progressing to Football League: P Clark (Stockport Cnty 65), K Ball (Walsall 72), P Freeman (W B A 68), C Bates/R Harwood (Shrewsbury Tn 74), L Lawrence (Shrewsbury Tn 75), S Cooper (Torquay 78), T Cunningham (Lincoln 79), M Gwinnet (Peterborough 81).
96-97 - Captain: Matt Gardiner **Top scorer:** Albert Johnson (18) **P.o.Y.:** Jason Smith
Local Press: Stourbridge News & County Express, Express & Star, Dudley Evening Mail.
Local Radio: Radio West Wids, B.R.M.B., Beacon.

HONOURS: Welsh Cup R-up 73-74; Southern Lg Midland Div 90-91 (Lg Cup 92-93), Div 1 North 73-74, Merit Cup 73-74; West Mids (prev. Birmingham) Lg 23-24 (R-up 4); Birmingham Comb. R-up 51-52; Birmingham Snr Cup 49-50 45-46 75-76 (R-up 3); Worcs Snr Cup 9, (R-up 12); Herefordshire Snr Cup 54-55; Camkin Cup R-up 69-70; Camkin Presidents Cup 70-71; Albion Shield 43-44; Keys Cup 37-38 62-63, Worcs Comb. R-up 27-28; Worcester Jnr Cup R-up 27-28; Tillotson Cup R-up 39-40, Brierley Hill Lg R-up 44-45 (Lg Cup R-up 44-45); Brierley Hill Yth Lg Coronation Cup 56-57.

Stourbridge FC: Back Row (L-R); Morton Bartleet (Mgr), Dave Trend, Justin Wood, Albert Johnson, Mark Hart, Danny Collier, Andry Wright, Scott Voice, Martin Thomas, Simon Ward. Front Row; Dale Band, Jason Smith, Alain Grainger, Adam Bastable, Matt Gardner, Calvin Hamilton, Mascot Adam Hyde. *Photo - Marshall's*

Sutton Coldfield Town
Football Club
Tamworth F.C.
80p

SUTTON COLDFIELD TOWN

Formed: 1897 **Nickname:** Royals
Colours: Blue & white/blue/blue & white
Change colours: Red & black/red/red & black
Midweek matchday: Tuesday
Reserves' League: No reserve team

Chairman: Kevin Holt
Secretary: Fred Rought, 25 Lebanon Grove, Chase Terrace, Burntwood, Staffs. WS7 8BE (01543 685029).
Press Officer: Brian Turner **Commercial Manager:** Peter Young.
Manager: Gary Bradder**Asst Man:** Alan Hampton **Physio:** Reg Brassington

GROUND Address: Central Ground, Coles Lane, Sutton Coldfield B72 1NL (0121 354 2997/0121 355 5475).
Directions: A5127 into Sutton, right at Odeon cinema (Holland Road), then first right into Coles Lane - ground 150 yds on left. 10 mins walk from Sutton Coldfield (BR), bus 104 from Birmingham.
Capacity: 4,500 **Cover:** 500 **Seats:** 200 **Floodlights:** Yes
Clubhouse: Brick built lounge and concert room, fully carpeted and extensively decorated. Open daily, food available.
Club Shop: Selling metal badges, scarves, hats, pens, rosettes, progs. Contact Paul Vanes (0121 770 9835).

PROGRAMME DETAILS:
Pages: 20 **Price:** 80p
Editor: Peter Young
Tel.

PREVIOUS - **Leagues:** Central Birmingham, Walsall Senior, Staffs County, Birmingham Combination 50-54, West Mids (Regional) 54-65 79-82, Midlands Combination 65-79.
Grounds: Meadow Plat 1879-89/ Coles Lane (site of current ambulance station) 90-1919.
Name: Sutton Coldfield FC 1879-1921.

CLUB RECORDS - **Attendance:** 2,029 v Doncaster Rovers, F.A. Cup 80-81 (Receipts £2,727).
Career Goalscorer: Eddie Hewitt 288 **Career Appearances:** Eddie Hewitt 465
Fee paid: £1,500 twice in 1991, for Lance Morrison (Gloucester) & Micky Clarke (Burton A.)
Fee received: £25,000 for Barry Cowdrill (WBAl 1979).

BEST SEASON - **FA Cup:** 1st Rd 80-81 (lost 0-1 to Doncaster), 92-93 (1-2 at Wanderers).
FA Trophy: 1st Round replay 1989-90 **FA Amateur Cup:** 2nd Round 1970-71.

Players progressing to Football League: Arthur Corbett (Walsall 1949), Paul Cooper (Manchester City), Noel Blake (Leeds), Steve Cooper (Barnsley), Peter Latchford (WBA & Celtic), Mark Smith (Wolves), John Barton (Everton), Barry Cowdrill (WBA 1979), Colin Dryhurst (Halifax 1979), Dale Belford (Notts County 1987), Ellis Laight (Torquay 1992).
Local Press: Sutton Coldfield News, Sutton Observer. **Local Radio:** BRMB, Radio WM.

HONOURS: Southern Lg Midland Div R-up 82-83, West Mids Lg 79-80 (Lg Cup 80-81 81-82), Midland Comb.(2) 77-79 (R-up(2) 69-71, Lg Cup 69-70), Walsall Senior Lg 46-47, Walsall Sen. Cup(3) 77-80 (R-up 80-81), Staffs Sen. Cup R-up 89-90 (SF 84-85 86-87), Lord Mayor of Birmingham Charity Cup 95-96, R-up 93-94, Worcs Sen. Cup SF 88-89, Walsall Challenge Cup R-up 46-47 47-48, Sutton Charity Cup 46-47 65-66 71-72 86-87 89-90 90-91, Express & Star Cup 44-45.

Back Row (L-R); Derek Kadua, Andy Biddle, Robert Bradley, Mark Cogent, Darren Brown, Cory Johnson, John Parsons, David Pierce, Ray Richardson, Dave Wright, Carl Brewster, Mark Swan. Front Row; Peter Burkes, Sam Adams, Adam Whitehouse, Andy Ling, Chris Wright, David Langston, Karl Morris, Mark Hodson, Mascot, Adam Holt
Photo - Marshalls Sport Service.

V.S. RUGBY

PROGRAMME DETAILS:
Pages: 36 **Price:** £1
Editor: Terry Coley
Tel: 0121 240 4521

Formed: 1956 **Nickname:** The Valley
Colours: Navy & sky/navy/sky
Change colours: All White
Midweek matchday: Wednesday **Club Newsline:** 0891 10 19 99
Reserves' League: No reserve team

Chairman: Peter Kilvert **Commercial Manager:** Ray Dickenson
Secretary: Doug Wilkins, 298 Rocky Lane, Great Barr, Birmingham B42 1NQ 0121 681 1544 H & Fax)
Press Officer: Alun Turner (01788 567181)
Manager: Alan Lewer **Coach:**
Asst Manager: Darren Heyes **Physio:** Alan Cooke

GROUND Address: Butlin Road, Rugby, Warks CV21 3ST (01788 543692).
Directions: The ground is situated off Clifton (B5414) on the north side of Rugby. 1 mile walk from the station.
Capacity: 6,000 **Cover:** 1,000 **Seats:** 240 **Floodlights:** Yes
Clubhouse: Open every night and weekend lunchtimes. Entertainment Saturday nights. Excellent facilities include Long Alley Skittles, darts and pool.
Club Shop: Yes
Sponsors: Jaymann Finance

PREVIOUS - **Name:** Valley Sports, Valley Sports Rugby.
Leagues: Rugby & District 1956-63, Coventry & Partnership, North Warks 63-69, United Counties 69-75, West Midlands 75-83

CLUB RECORDS - **Attendance:** 3,961 v Northampton FA Cup 1984
Win: 10-0 v Ilkeston Tn FA Trophy 4/9/85
Defeat: 8-0 v Shepshed, Midland F/Lit Lge 23/12/87
Career Goalscorer: Danny Conway, 124
Career Appearances: Danny Conway, 374
Transfer fee paid: £3,500 R Smith, I Crawley, G Bradder
Transfer fee received: £15,000 T Angus (Northampton)

BEST SEASON - **FA Cup:** 2nd round 87-88, plus 1st Rd 84-85 85-86 86-87 94-95
League clubs defeated: None

Players progressing to Football League: S Storer (Birmingham 1985), S Bicknell (Leicester), S Norris (Scarborough), T Angus (Northampton Town), Ashley Walker (Peterborough), Ian King (Stoke City).

96-97 - Captain: Michael Trotter
P.o.Y.: Darren Heyes
Top scorer: Andre Marsh

Local Press: Rugby Advertiser, Coventry Evening Telegraph, Rugby Observer
Local Radio: Mercia Sound, CWR

HONOURS: Southern Lg Midland Div 86-87 (R-up 94-95, Lg Cup 89-90), FA Vase 82-83, Midland F'lit Cup 84-85 89-90 (R-up 86-87), Birmingham Snr Cup 88-89 91-92, Utd Co's Lg Div 3 Cup 69-70. (all-time record FA Trophy win; 10-0 away to Ilkeston Town, Preliminary Rd 85-86).

Boyd Young (left) gets to grips with Mickey Turner of Crawley.
Photo: Andrew Chitty

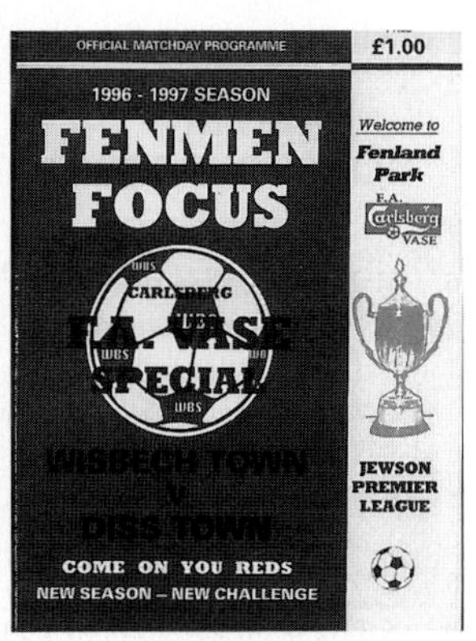

PROGRAMME DETAILS:
Pages: 40 **Price:** £ 1
Editor: Gordon Smith
Tel: 01945 581767

WISBECH TOWN

Founded: 1920. **Nickname:** Fenmen.
Colours: All red.
Change colours: Yellow/green/yellow
Midweek Matchday: Wednesday
Newsline: 0930 555 865.

Chairman: Eddie Anderson **Vice Chairman:** John Petch
President: J W A Chilvers
Secretary: John Petch, 34 Walton Road, Wisbech, Cambs PE13 3EN, (01945 584333 & Fax)
Manager: Ian Jones **Asst Manager:** S Shelton
Physio: P Ward **Press Officer:** R Green
GROUND Address: Fenland Park, Lerowe Road, Wisbech, Cambs (01945 584176).
Directions: Follow A47 bypass, take the dual carriageway into town, at Little Chef r/about, turn left into Lerowe Road after Volvo garage. Twenty minutes walk from town centre. Irregular bus services to Wisbech from Peterborough or March.
Seats: 258 **Cover:** 1,000 **Capacity:** 3,500 **Floodlights:** Yes
Clubhouse: Open every day. Matchday food & drink; Tea, coffee, cold drinks, confectionary, burgers, hotdogs, soup, sandwiches, rolls.
Club Shop: Yes, selling replica shirts, caps, pennants, pens, scarves etc. Contact Club Secretary.
PREVIOUS - Names: Leagues: Peterborough/ Utd Co's 35-50/ Eastern Co's 50-52 70-97/ Midland 52-58/ Southern 58-70. **Grounds:** Wisbech Park 20-21/ Waisoken Rectory 21-22/ Harecroft Road 22-47.
CLUB RECORDS - Attendance: 8,004 v Peterborough United, Midland League 25/8/57. **Goalscorer:** Bert Titmarsh 246 (31-37). **Appearances:** Jamie Brighty (731). **Win:** 18-1 v Rushden 45-46. **Defeat:** 1-10 v Brighton FA Cup 65-66. **Fee Paid:** None. **Fee Received:** £3,000.
Best Season - FA Cup: 2nd Rd 57-58. **FA Vase:** SF 84-85, 85-86.
League clubs defeated: Colchester
Players progressing to Football League: Chris Watts/Robert Taylor (Norwich City), Bryan Harvey/Terry Marshall (Newcastle), Jackie Callagher (Peterboro), Paul Scott (Blackpool), Peter Dobson (Ipswich).
96-97 Captain: Dave Massingham **96-97 P.o.Y.:** Andy Moore **96-97 Top scorer:** Peter Munns (47)
Local Press: Fenland Citizen, Wisbech Standard
Local Radio: Radio Cambridgeshire
Honours: Southern Lg Div 1 61-62; Utd Co's Lg (4) 46-48 49-50 61-62 (res) (R-up 48-49, Lg Cup 35-36 (R-up 46-47); Midland Lg R-up 57-58; Eastern Co's Lg 71-72 76-77 90-91 (R-up 70-71 73-74 83-84 92-93 96-97), Lg Cup 50-51 70-71 71-72 (R-up 73-74 76-77 86-87); Cambs Invitation Cup(8) 52-53 55-56 57-58 74-76 81-83 91-92; East Anglian Cup 87-88 (R-up 40-41 48-49); Peterborough Lg 24-25 27-28 28-29 31-32 32-33; Peterborough Snr Cup 32-33 76-77 89-90.

Wisbech Town FC:

SOUTHERN DIVISION

LEAGUE TABLE 1996-97

	P	W	D	L	F	A	GD	Pts
Forest Green Rovers	42	27	10	5	87	40	47	91
St. Leonards Stamcroft	42	26	9	7	95	48	47	87
Havant Town	42	23	10	9	91	49	32	79
Weston-super-Mare	42	21	13	8	82	43	39	76
Margate	42	21	9	12	70	47	23	72
Witney Town	42	20	11	11	71	42	29	71
Weymouth	42	20	10	12	82	51	31	70
Tonbridge Angels	42	17	15	10	56	44	12	66
Newport IOW	42	15	15	12	73	58	15	60
Fisher Athletic London	42	18	6	18	77	77	0	60
Clevedon Town	42	17	9	16	75	76	-1	60
Fareham Town	42	14	12	16	53	70	-17	54
Bashley	42	15	8	19	73	84	-11	53
Dartford	42	14	10	18	59	64	-5	52
Waterlooville	42	14	9	19	58	67	-9	51
Cirencester Town	42	12	12	18	50	68	-18	48
Cinderford Town	42	13	7	22	64	76	-12	46
Trowbridge Town	42	11	11	20	50	61	-11	44
Yate Town	42	12	8	22	55	87	-32	44
Fleet Town	42	12	6	24	47	91	-44	42
Erith & Belvedere	42	9	10	23	60	95	-35	37
Buckingham Town	42	2	8	32	27	107	-80	14

LEADING GOALSCORERS

26	M Buglione (Margate)
	P Hunt (Forest Green R)
22	D Laws (Weymouth)
	C Wilkins (Tonbridge Angels)
	S Tate (Waterlooville)
21	E Fearon (Newport IOW)
	J Magee (St Leonards S.)
20	D Tilley (Weston-s-Mare)
19	K Bayliss (Forest Green R)
	P Sykes (Margate)
	J Caffel (Witney Town)
18	P Gorman (Fisher A. London)
	P Sales (Bashley)
	C Soares (Newport IOW)
17	S Leigh (Havant Town)
	K Miles (St Leonards S.)
	S Portway (Erith & Belvedere)
	T White (St Leonards S.)
16	D Clarke (Yate Town)

RESULTS GRID 1996-97

HOME TEAM	1	2	3	4	5	6	7	8	9	10	11	12	13	14	15	16	17	18	19	20	21	22
1 Bashley	*	3-1	2-2	1-1	0-1	1-4	2-3	2-2	0-2	1-2	1-5	0-3	0-1	0-0	0-0	0-2	2-1	2-2	3-1	4-1	2-0	3-1
2 Buckingham T	0-9	*	0-2	1-3	1-2	1-1	3-0	1-1	0-2	0-0	0-2	0-2	1-2	0-0	0-0	0-1	1-3	2-1	0-1	0-5	1-2	1-3
3 Cinderford T	2-4	7-0	*	7-2	2-3	3-0	1-1	1-3	0-0	2-1	1-3	2-0	0-3	2-0	1-2	0-0	1-0	2-0	2-2	0-5	2-1	1-1
4 Cirencester	1-2	2-0	1-4	*	1-5	2-4	2-4	1-1	1-0	2-0	0-1	1-1	0-0	0-1	1-2	2-0	2-0	3-1	1-2	0-0	1-0	2-0
5 Clevedon T	5-2	2-2	4-1	4-2	*	0-6	5-0	0-1	2-0	5-2	3-0	2-3	1-1	4-3	2-2	1-1	2-1	1-4	0-0	2-2	0-3	3-1
6 Dartford	2-1	1-0	1-0	4-2	3-1	*	1-0	1-2	1-4	1-0	0-0	0-0	0-3	0-1	3-2	2-1	1-1	2-2	1-1	3-5	1-2	0-0
7 Erith & Belv	1-3	3-0	2-0	0-0	2-2	3-1	*	4-1	2-0	0-2	0-0	2-3	1-1	4-4	1-2	3-2	0-3	1-2	1-5	1-1	1-3	0-3
8 Fareham T	1-1	3-1	3-0	0-0	1-0	2-0	3-0	*	4-1	1-3	0-1	2-1	0-3	2-1	2-2	1-1	1-1	0-0	0-3	2-0	0-0	1-2
9 Fisher A Lon	3-1	4-2	3-3	1-3	2-0	1-0	3-2	5-3	*	2-3	3-3	2-4	2-3	0-1	4-3	1-2	2-1	2-2	1-3	1-2	1-2	0-1
10 Fleet Town	1-2	1-1	2-0	1-1	0-1	0-4	1-4	2-0	3-1	*	1-2	0-1	0-6	0-4	0-2	1-2	0-3	0-6	2-1	1-1	0-0	4-3
11 Forest Green R	4-0	2-0	2-1	3-1	4-1	2-1	5-2	8-0	2-0	2-0	*	3-2	2-1	2-1	2-1	3-3	1-1	3-2	3-1	2-0	0-0	4-0
12 Havant T	1-1	4-1	4-1	0-1	2-1	0-0	4-0	1-0	1-2	5-1	0-0	*	1-2	2-0	2-1	1-1	1-1	1-1	1-1	2-1	3-0	1-0
13 Margate	3-5	2-0	3-1	3-2	0-1	1-0	3-1	2-0	1-3	3-0	2-0	0-2	*	0-0	1-2	2-3	2-0	2-2	1-0	1-2	0-4	4-1
14 Newport IOW	3-1	2-0	1-3	0-0	3-2	1-1	3-3	2-4	2-3	2-3	1-1	2-3	1-1	*	1-2	1-1	4-3	3-2	2-2	2-1	0-0	7-0
15 St Leonards S	4-3	4-1	4-1	5-0	4-1	3-1	2-0	6-0	2-1	2-2	2-1	4-2	2-2	1-1	*	1-0	3-0	2-0	2-2	4-1	1-2	3-0
16 Tonbridge A	3-1	1-0	2-0	3-1	2-1	1-0	2-0	2-0	0-1	2-0	1-1	4-2	0-0	1-2	2-2	*	1-1	0-0	1-3	1-2	1-1	3-1
17 Trowbridge T	2-3	1-0	2-0	1-1	0-0	1-1	2-2	1-2	1-3	0-1	2-1	1-3	0-0	0-1	1-4	2-0	*	1-0	0-4	2-2	1-2	1-0
18 Waterlooville	1-0	5-3	2-1	0-1	3-0	2-3	2-1	1-0	1-3	3-1	2-0	1-2	0-1	0-3	0-1	0-0	1-4	*	1-2	1-0	2-2	0-4
19 Weston S M	6-0	1-1	1-0	0-0	2-3	2-0	5-2	5-1	2-2	3-1	0-0	3-3	2-0	1-0	0-2	3-1	2-0	2-0	*	1-2	2-0	0-1
20 Weymouth	0-1	5-0	2-3	3-1	5-1	2-1	2-0	1-1	6-2	5-0	1-3	2-0	2-0	1-1	1-0	0-0	2-0	5-0	0-3	*	0-2	1-1
21 Witney Town	0-1	9-0	2-1	2-1	0-0	5-1	2-2	1-0	1-3	4-0	2-3	1-2	2-1	1-1	3-1	0-1	2-1	0-1	1-1	1-1	*	4-1
22 Yate Town	6-3	3-1	2-1	1-1	2-1	3-2	4-1	2-2	1-1	1-5	0-1	1-5	1-3	1-5	0-1	1-1	0-3	1-2	1-1	0-2	0-2	*

SOUTHERN DIVISION
10 YEAR RECORD

Dr MARTENS LEAGUE

No of Clubs Competing	87/8 (21)	88/9 (22)	89/0 (22)	90/1 (21)	91/2 (22)	92/3 (22)	93/4 (22)	94/5 (22)	95/6 (22)	96/7 (22)
Andover	6	18	18	9	7	20	-	-	-	-
Ashford Town	-	-	-	5	9	8	6	5	2	-
Baldock Town	15	6	10	4	11	13	7	2	-	-
Bashley	-	-	1	-	-	-	-	7	16	13
Braintree Town	-	-	-	-	4	9	13	14	5	-
Buckingham Town	-	16	3	1	5	12	12	-	-	22
Burnham	8	5	11	11	10	16	16	22	-	-
Bury Town	9	4	9	12	17	22	22	18	-	-
Canterbury City	20	13	15	18	21	17	20	-	-	-
Chatham Town	21	-	-	-	-	-	-	-	-	-
Chelmsford City	-	1	-	-	-	-	-	-	-	-
Cinderford Town	-	-	-	-	-	-	-	-	14	17
Cirencester Town	-	-	-	-	-	-	-	-	-	16
Clevedon Town	-	-	-	-	-	-	-	11	17	11
Corinthian	18	22	21	21	-	-	-	-	-	-
Dartford	-	-	-	-	-	-	-	-	-	14
Dover Athletic	1	-	-	-	-	-	-	-	-	-
Dunstable	7	15	4	17	16	21	18	-	-	-
Erith & Belvedere	10	17	20	19	20	7	19	19	21	21
Fareham Town	-	-	12	20	19	15	14	21	20	12
Fisher 93	-	-	-	-	-	19	17	17	15	10
Fleet Town	-	-	-	-	-	-	-	-	19	20
Folkstone Town	17	11	17	w/d	-	-	-	-	-	-
Forest Green Rovers	-	-	-	-	-	-	-	-	8	1
Gosport Borough	-	-	-	15	22	-	-	-	-	-
Gravesend & Northfleet	4	2	-	-	-	4	1	-	-	-
Hastings Town	12	7	8	7	1	-	-	-	-	-
Havant Town	-	-	-	-	3	5	5	3	7	3
Hounslow	16	8	19	-	-	-	-	-	-	-
Hythe Town	-	-	6	8	13	-	-	-	-	-
Margate	5	20	16	10	14	10	9	13	11	5
Newport Isle of Wight	-	-	-	14	15	18	8	9	4	9
Poole Town	14	3	2	-	-	14	15	20	22	-
Ruislip	19	22	-	-	-	-	-	-	-	-
Salisbury	3	9	5	3	12	2	4	1	-	-
Sheppey United	11	19	22	-	-	-	-	-	-	-
Sittingbourne	-	-	-	-	6	1	-	-	1	-
St Leonards Stamcroft	-	-	-	-	-	-	-	-	-	2
Sudbury Town	-	-	-	13	8	6	2	-	-	-
Tonbridge Angels	13	21	-	-	-	-	11	12	18	8
Trowbridge Town	-	10	7	2	-	-	-	-	9	18
Waterlooville	2	-	-	-	-	-	-	4	3	15
Wealdstone	-	-	-	-	-	11	21	15	-	-
Weston Super Mare	-	-	-	-	-	-	-	6	13	4
Weymouth	-	-	-	-	2	-	10	8	6	7
Witney Town	-	14	14	16	18	3	3	10	12	6
Yate Town	-	-	13	6	-	-	-	16	10	19

BALDOCK TOWN

PROGRAMME DETAILS:
Pages: 48 **Price:** £1
Editor: TBA

Formed: 1889 **Nickname:** Reds
Colours: All red
Change colours: All white
Midweek home matchday: Wednesday
Reserve Team's League: No reserve team.

Joint Chairmen: Mike Watson-Challis & Ray Childerstone
Secretary: Cyril T Hammond, 2 Elmwood Court, High Str., Baldock, Herts SG7 6AY. 01462 894253 (H) 01462 895449 (B).
General Manager: B Williams
Team Manager: Robbie O'Keefe **Physio:** Fred Day.
Press Officer: David Hammond (01462 892797)

GROUND Address: Norton Road, Baldock, Herts SG7 5AU (01462 895449).
Directions: Off A1(M) at Letchworth/Baldock sign, left to 3rd island, A505 to Baldock, Norton Road is left off A505, left past Orange Tree pub, ground on right after railway bridge. From North or East turn left into town, Hitchin Street, right into Norton then proceed as above. From Baldock station (Kings Cross to Royston line) - left down Ickneild Way and right into Norton Road.
Capacity: 3,000 **Cover:** 1,250 **Seats:** 250 **Clubhouse:** Members' bar and separate function room. Food available.
Club Shop: No. **Metal Badges:** Yes
Supporters Club: Phil Rosendale (01462 223135)

PREVIOUS - Ground: Bakers Close (until 1982). **Leagues:** South Midlands 25-39 47-54 63-83, Parthenon 54-59, London 59-63, United Counties 83-87.

CLUB RECORDS - Attendance: 1,588 v Stevenage Boro. FA Cup 2nd Prelim 96-97
Goalscorer: Unknown. **Appearances:** Keith (Paddy) Stanton 550. **Fee Paid:** £2,000; for Colin Hull (Bishop's Stortford); for Glen Russell (Braintree 1993). **Fee Received:** £30,000 for Kevin Phillips (Watford F.C.).
Best Season - FA Vase: 5th Round 83-84. **FA Trophy:** 2nd Qual. Round 90-91. **FA Cup:** 4th Qual. Round replay (0-1 v Halesowen Town [A] after 1-1 draw) 91-92.
Players progressing to Football League: Ian Dowie (Luton & West Ham), Alan Stewart (Portsmouth), Kevan Phillips (Watford).
96-97 Captain: **96-97 P.o.Y.:** **96-97 Top scorer:**
Local Press: Comet, Gazette. **Local Radio:** Radio Bedfordshire, Chiltern.

HONOURS: United Counties Lg R-up 83-84 86-87, South Mids Lg 27-28 65-66 67-68 69-70 (R-up 53-54 82-83, Lg Cup 65-66 69-70, Div 1 49-50, Reserve Div 1 66-67), Herts Charity Cup 91-92 94-95, Herts Charity Shield 57-58 69-70, Wallspan Floodlit Cup 85-86, Hinchingbrooke Cup 86-87, TSI Floodlit Cup 88-89, Woolwich E.B.S. Cup 83-84, Herts Intermediate Cup 86-87. Southern Lge R-up 94-95. Southern Lge Cup Dr Martens 95-96

Baldock Town: Back Row (L-R); Brien Stein, Mick Small, Danny Power, Dean Mann, Matt Barnaby, Lee Graves, Darren Fenton. Front Row; Danny Howell, Grant Wedlock, Mark Phillips, Ray Kilby, Marcelle Bruce, Matthew Woolgar, Richard Chattoe.

Photo - Gordon Whittington

BASHLEY

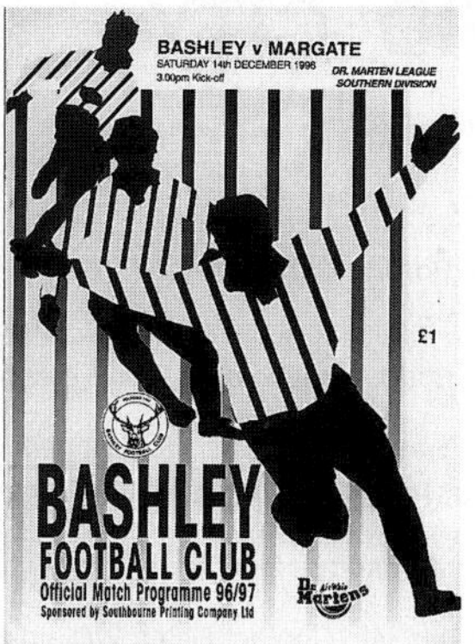

PROGRAMME DETAILS:
Pages: 36 **Price:** £1
Editor:

Formed: 1947 **Nickname:** The Bash
Colours: Yellow & black
Change colours: Blue & white.
Midweek matchday: Tuesday **Reserves' League:** Wessex Comb.

Chairman: R J Pinney **President:** Ian Hassell
Vice Chairman: Frank Whitman
Secretary: Ian Hassell, 35 Freshwater Road, Christchurch, Dorset BH23 4PD.
Commercial Manager: Mary Whitman
Press Officer: Terry Collett
Manager: Jimmy Case **Asst Manager/Coach:** Barry Blankney
Physio: Chris Lovegrove
GROUND Address: Recreation Ground, Bashley, Hampshire BH25 5RY. Tel: 01425 620280. **Directions:** A35 Lyndhurst towards Christchurch, turn left down B3058 towards New Milton, ground on left in Bashley village. Half hour walk from New Milton (BR) station
Capacity: 4,250 **Cover:** 1,200 **Seats:** 200 **Floodlights:** Yes
Clubhouse: Usual licensing hours. Snacks available.
Club Shop: Open matchdays - contact Anna Keegan
Club Sponsors: Jacksons Mercedes

PREVIOUS - Leagues: Bournemouth 50-83/ Hants 83-86/ Wessex 86-89.

CLUB RECORDS - **Attendance:** 3,500 v Emley, F.A. Vase S.F. 1st Leg 1987-88
Win: 21-1 v Co-operative (A), Bournemouth League, 1964.
Defeat: 2-20 v Air Speed (A), Bournemouth League, 1957.
Career Goalscorer: Colin Cummings (128)
Career Appearances: John Bone (829)
Transfer fee paid: £7,500 for J Stagg from Andover
Transfer fee received: £7,500 for Darren Powell from Weymouth 95

BEST SEASON - **FA Cup:** 2nd Rd Proper, 1994-95 (0-1 v Swansea City)
FA Vase: Semi Final 87-88, Qtr Final 88-89
FA Trophy: 2nd Round 91-92

Past Players who have progressed into The Football League: Wayne Brown (Bristol City, 1994).
97-98 Captain: Dave Morris **96-97 P.o.Y.:** Paul Sales **96-97 Top scorer:** Paul Sales
Local Press: Bournemouth Echo, Southern Pink, New Milton Advertiser. **Local Radio:** 2CR Solent, Ocean Sound.
HONOURS: Southern Lg Southern Division 89-90 (Lg Cup SF 89-90), Wessex Lg 86-87 87-88 88-89, Hants Lg Div 3 84-85, Hants Lg Combination 88-89, Russell Cotes Cup 88-89 90-91 92-93.

Bashley FC: *Photo - Andrew Chitty*

CHELMSFORD CITY

Formed: 1938 **Nickname:** City
Colours: Claret, white trim/claret/claret.
Change colours: Sky blue, claret trim/sky blue/sky blue.
Midweek home games: Tuesday
Reserve Team's League: Essex & Herts Border Comb.

Chairman: Trevor Wright (01245 356840 H, 0850 468403 Mob)
Secretary: David Gore, 18 Springfield Park Road, Chelmsford, Essex. CM2 6EB 01245 492750 (H).
Manager: Roy McDonough **Asst Manager:** Paul Roberts
GROUND Address: Wallace Binder Ground, Park Drive, Maldon CM9 5XX (01621 853762).
Seats: Yes **Cover:** Yes **Capacity:** 2,500
Floodlights: Yes **Sponsors:** Britvic UK
Club Shop: Sells progs, badges, scarves, mugs etc. Contact Helen Williams via club.

PROGRAMME DETAILS:
Pages: 32 **Price:** £1.20
Editor: Trevor Smith
(01245 353052)

PREVIOUS - Name: None (Brentwood Town were incorporated in 1968). **Leagues:** None. **Grounds:** New Whittle Street 38-97

CLUB RECORDS - Attendance: 16,807 v Colchester, Southern League 10/9/49. **Goalscorer:** Tony Butcher, 287 (1957-71). **Appearances:** Derek Tiffin, 550 (1950-63). **Win:** 10-3 v Billericay Town (H), Essex Senior Cup, 4/1/93. **Defeat:** 2-10 v Barking (A), FA Trophy, 11/11/78. **Fee Paid:** £10,000 for Tony Rogers (Dover Athletic, 1992). **Fee Received:** £50,000 for David Morrison (Peterborough 94).

BEST SEASON - FA Cup: 4th Rd, 1938-39 (v Birmingham City). 1st Rd 25 times.
Players progressing to Football League: G Merton (Watford 48), G Adams (Orient 49), W O'Neill (Burnley 49), B Farley/S McClellan/L Dicker/P Collins (Spurs 49/49/51/68), O Hold (Everton 50), R Marden (Arsenal 50), C McCormack (Barnsley 50), D Sexton (Luton 51), W Bellet & R Mason & A Nicholas (Orient 61 & 63 & 65), R Gladwin (Norwich 66), B King (Millwall 67), J O'Mara (Bradford City 74), N Spink (Aston 77), M Dziadulewicz (Wimbledon 79), M Cawston (Southend 84), P Coleman (Exeter 84), J Keeley & A Owers (Brighton 86 & 87), I Brown (Bristol C 93), D Morrison (Peterborough 94).
96-97 Captain: Robbie Garvey **Top Scorer:** Neal Docking (19) **P.o.Y:** Gary Bellamy
Local Press: Essex Chronicle, Chelmsford Weekly News, East Anglian Daily Times, Evening Gazette.
Local Radio: Essex Radio/Breeze AM, BBC Essex.

HONOURS: Southern Lg 45-46 67-68 71-72 (R-up 48-49 60-61 63-64 65-66), Southern Div 88-89, Lg Cup 45-46 59-60 (R-up 60-61); Merit Cup 71-72; Southern Lg War-Time (East) 39-40); Essex Prof Cup 5; Essex Snr Cup 85-86 88-89 92-93; Non-League Champs Chall Cup 71-72; E Anglian Cup 48-49; Eastern Co's Lg(3) 46-49 (Lg Cup 59-60); Eastern Floodlit Comp 6, (Cup 72-73 74-75); Metropolitan Lg 67-68, Lg Prof Cup 67-68, Autumn Shield 70-71; Essex Snr Lg Cup 84-85, Harry Fisher Memorial Tphy 88-89.

Back Row (L-R); Paul Smith (Physio), Jamie Reilly, Neal Docking, Gary Bellamy (Player/Mgr), Lee Ballard, Darren Oxbrow, Mark Pavey, Sean Campbell, Ian Butcher (Kit Mgr). Front Row; Garry Kimble, Liam Nash, Brett Girling, Chris Tovey, Colin Norman (Jt Mgr), Lee Guiver, Steve Farmer, John Rothon. *Photo - Simon Boulton*

CINDERFORD TOWN

Formed: 1922 **Nickname:** Town
Club colours: White & Black.
Change colours: All Red.
Midweek matchday: Tuesday.
Reserves' League: No reserve team

PROGRAMME DETAILS:
Pages: 50 **Price:** 80p
Editor: Mike Bradley
Tel: 01594 824566

Chairman: David Gettings **President:** S Watkins
Vice Chairman: Brian Cook
Secretary: Chris Warren, 9c Tusculum Way, Mitcheldean, Glos GL17 0HZ. 01594 543065 (H) 01594 542421 x 2360 (B)
Press Officer: B Cook
Manager: Brian Godfrey (01453 826901) **Physio:** Keith Marfell
Asst. Manager: Andy Beattie
GROUND Address: The Causeway, Hilldene, Cinderford, Glos (01594 827147 or 822039). **Directions:** From Gloucester take A40 to Ross-on-Wye, then A48 - Chepstow. In 8 miles turn right at Elton garage onto A4151 signed Cinderford, thru Littledean, up steep hill, right at crossroads, second left into Latimer Rd. Ground 5 mins walk from town centre.
Capacity: 2,500 **Cover:** 1,000 **Seats:** 250 **Floodlights:** Yes
Clubhouse: Open every day. 2 bars, kitchen, 2 skittle alleys, darts, dancehall, committee room. **Sponsors:** Thompson & Thompson
Club Shop: Souvenirs, club badges (£2.50), ties, mugs etc. Programme exchanges welcome - contact secretary.

PREVIOUS - **Leagues:** Glos Northern Snr 22-39 60-62, Western 46-59, Warwickshire Comb 63-64, West Midlands 65-69, Gloucestershire County 70-73 85-89, Midland Comb. 74-84, Hellenic 90-95.
Names: None **Grounds:** Mousel Lane, Royal Oak

CLUB RECORDS - **Attendance:** 4,850 v Minehead, Western League, 1955-56.
Win: 13-0 v Cam Mills 38-39. **Defeat:** 0-10 v Sutton Coldfield 78-79. **Career Appearances:** Russell Bowles 516. **Career Goalscorer:** Unknown.

BEST SEASON - **FA Cup:** 2nd Rd v Gravesend 95-96. **FA Trophy:** 2nd Qual Rd
FA Vase: 2nd Rd 91-92 **FA Amateur Cup:** 3rd Qual Rd 52

96-7 - Captain: Gareth Howells **Top Scorer:** Bradley Thomas **P.o.Y.:** Adie Harris

HONOURS: Hellenic Lg Premier Champions 94-95, Premier Lg.Cup 94-95, Floodlit Cup 93-94, Div 1 90-91; Glos Northern Snr Lg Div 1 38-39 60-61, R-up (6); Nth Glos Lg Div 1 38-39 60-61; Glos Snr Amtr Cup (Nth) (6), R-up (3); Western Lg Div 2 56-57; Warwickshire Comb. 63-64; W Mids Lg Prem Div Cup 68-69; Glos Jnr Cup (Nth) 80-81; Midland Comb. 81-82; Glos Co. Lg R-up 69-70 71-72 73-74; Glos FA Trophy R-up 92-93; Hungerford Cup 94-95.

Back Row (L-R); Brian Cook (Chr), Dave Stevenson, John Hamilton, Stuart Smith, Bradley Thomas, Gary Cornwall, Andy Beattie, Terry Stevenson, Peter Mason, Gareth Howells, Nick Jayne, Dean Threlfall, Clayton Hook, Tony Quoi, Keith Marfell (Physio), Dave Baldwin. Front Row; Bob Saunders (Kit), Steve Layer, Kevin Horsfall, Russell Wilton, Colin Peacey, Roy Dyke, Andy Watts, Phil Baker, Tony Goodwin, Paul Jenkins

Cirencester Town
Tuesday 10th October 1995
Cirencester Town
v
Shortwood United
Match Programme

CIRENCESTER TOWN

Founded: 1889 **Nickname:** Ciren
Colours: Red & black/ black/ red
Change colours: Blue/ black/ blue
Midweek Matchday: Tuesday
Reserves' League: Cirencester & District

Chairman: Stephen Abbley, 17 Dianmer Close, Hook, Swindon. SN4 8ER. Tel: 01743 853293 (H) 01793 884900 (B).
Secretary: Jim Saunders, 35 Chesterton Park, Cirencester, Glos. GL7 1XS 01258 659002 (H)
Commercial Manager: Margaret M **Press Officer:** Jim Saunders
Manager: Ray Baverstock 01242 260619
Coach: Mark Boyland **Physio:** Steve Slaughter
GROUND Address: The Stadium, Smithsfield, Chesterton Lane, Cirencester (01285 645783).
Directions: Follow signs on by-pass to Bristol & West. At roundabout where Sports Centre is situated, follow road 'up the hill' and take first left and then immediately right. 3 miles from Kemble (BR).
Seats: 236 **Cover:** 500 **Capacity:** 3,000 **Floodlights:** Yes
Clubhouse: Open Tuesday - Friday evenings & Saturday. Snacks are available on matchdays. **Club Shop:** None.
Club Sponsors: P.H.H. & Cheltenham Windows

PROGRAMME DETAILS:
Pages: Yes **Price:** £1
Editor: Margaret Marsh
Tel. 01258 645783

PREVIOUS - Leagues: Hellenic League **Names:** None. **Grounds:** None
CLUB RECORDS -
Attendance: 2,600 v Fareham 1969. **Win:** Unknown. **Defeat:** Unknown. **Career Goalscorer:** Unknown. **Career Appearances:** Unknown. **Transfer fee paid:** None. **Transfer fee received:** None.
BEST SEASON - FA Trophy: 1st Qual. Round 1996-97 (1st season in comp.) **FA Vase:** Never past the 1st Round. **FA Cup:** 3rd Preliminary Round, 1996-97
Players progressing to the Fooball League: None
96-97 - Captain: H Blackler **Top Scorer:** Mark Boyland **P.o.Y.:** Mark Teasedale
Local Press: Standard, Western Daily Press. **Local Radio:** BBC Radio Gloucester, Severn Sound.
HONOURS: Gloucestershire Senior Amateur Cup 89-90; Hellenic League Div One Challenge Cup 90-91; Hellenic League Prem Div 95-96, Legaue Cup 95-96; Gloucestershire County Cup 95-96.

Photo: Courtesy of The Cheltenham Newspaper Co. Ltd.

CLEVEDON TOWN A.F.C
Members of the Dr Martens League &
Somerset Youth Floodlit League
Clevedon Town A.F.C
v
Newport A.F.C
Tuesday 19th August 1997 - Kick-Off 7.30pm
OFFICIAL PROGRAMME - 80p
TODAYS MATCH SPONSOR: Bradshaw Microwave Ltd
MAIN CLUB SPONSOR: BRADSHAW GROUP

PROGRAMME DETAILS:
Pages: 14 **Price:** 80p
Editor: Steve Small
(c/o club)

CLEVEDON TOWN

Formed: 1880 **Nickname:** The Seasiders
Club colours: Blue & white hoops/blue/blue
Change colours: All yellow
Midweek Matches: Tuesday
Youth League: Somerset Youth F/Lit

President: **Chairman:** John Croft
Secretary: Mike Williams, 34 Robinia Walk, Whitchurch, Bristol BS14 0SH (01275 833835).
Manager: Steve Fey **Asst. Manager:**
Coach: Jeff Meacham **Physio:** T Banks
GROUND Address: Hand Stadium, Davis Lane, Clevedon (01275 341919 ground 341641 office).
Directions: M5 Jct 20 - follow signs for Clevedon Town Sports Complex; first left into Central Way (at island just after motorway), 1st left at mini-r'bout into Kenn Rd, 2nd left Davis Lane; ground half mile on right. Or from Bristol (B3130) left into Court Lane (opposite Clevedon Court), turn right after 1 mile, ground on left. Nearest BR station: Nailsea & Backwell. Buses from Bristol.
Capacity: 3,650 **Seats:** 300 **Cover:** 1,600 **Floodlights:** Yes
Clubhouse: Open every day and evening. Separate function suite & lounge bar. Hot food available. Matchday refreshment bar within ground sells confectionary, teas & hot food.
Club Shop: Sells all types of souvenirs, programmes and replica kit. Exchanges welcome. Contact J Anderson.
Club Sponsors:

PREVIOUS - **Leagues:** Weston & District, Somerset Senior, Bristol Charity, Bristol & District, Bristol Suburban, Western 74-93.
Grounds: Dial Hill (til early 1890's)/ Teignmouth Road (til 1991).
Names: Clevedon FC, Ashtonians (clubs merged in 1974).

CLUB RECORDS - **Attendance:** 1,295 v Tiverton Town, Western League Premier Division 17/4/93 *(At Teignmouth Road: 2,300 v Billingham Synthonia, FA Amateur Cup, 52-53).*
Win: 18-0 v Dawlish Town (H), Western League Premier Division 24/4/93.
Defeat: 13-3 v Yate YMCA (A), Bristol Comb 67-68

BEST SEASON - **FA Cup:** 3rd Qual. Rd 2nd replay 92-93 v Newport AFC, 2-4 after two 1-1.
FA Amateur Cup: 3rd Round Proper, 52-53.
FA Vase: 6th Round 87-88, v Sudbury (A). **FA Trophy:** 95-96

96-97 Captain: Steve Lester **P.o.Y.:** Steve Lester **Top scorer:** Darren Tilley (17)
Local Radio: Radio Bristol **Local Press:** South Avon Mercury
HONOURS: Western League 92-93 (R-up 91-92, League Cup R-up 92-93), Bristol Charity League, Somerset Snr Cup 01-02 04-05 28-29 76-77, Somerset Snr League Div 1(reserves) 92-93.

Clevedon Town AFC

DARTFORD

Formed: 1888 **Nickname:** Darts
Colours: White & black/black/white
Change colours: Red & white/white/red
Midweek home matchday: Wednesday.
Reserves' League:

Chairman: David Skinner **Vice-Chairman:** R W Mace
Secretary: Mike Brett-Smith, 83 Wellcome Avenue, Dartford, Kent DA1 5JL. Tel. 01322 277243.
Commercial Man.: **Press Officer:**
Manager: Gary Julians (01622 863409) **Coach:** Dave Wadhams
Assistant-Manager: Trevor Timms **Physio:** Terry Skelton

PROGRAMME DETAILS:
Pages: 36 **Price:** 50p
Editor: Mike Brett-Smith
Tel:

GROUND Address: Erith & Belvedere FC, Park View, Lower Road, Belvedere, Kent DA17 6DF (0181 311 4444).
Directions: From Dartford bridge follow signs for Crayford to Erith and follow A206. Ground half mile from Erith Blackwall tunnel: head for Abbey Wood and on to Belvedere. Entrance in Station Road, adjoining Belvedere (BR) station. Bus No.469.
Capacity: 1,500 **Cover:** 1,000 **Seats:** 500 **Floodlights:** Yes
Club Shop: Open matchdays. Mail Order: Norman Grimes 01474 815236.

PREVIOUS - **Leagues:** Kent 1894-96, 97-98, 99-1902, 09-14, 21-26, 92-96/ Southern Lg 1896-98, 99-1900, 27-81, 82-84, 86-92/ GMVC 1981-82, 84-86.

CLUB RECORDS - **Transfer fee paid:** £6,000 for John Bartley (Chelmsford 1988)
Transfer fee received: £25,000 for Andy Hessenthaler (Watford via Redbridge F).

BEST SEASON - **FA Trophy:** Runners-up in 1974. **FA Vase:** 1995/96
FA Cup: 3rd Round Proper 35-36 & 36-37. **- League clubs defeated:** Cardiff (1935), Exeter (1961), Aldershot (1968).

Players progressing to Football League: Fred Dall (West Ham 1936), Riley Cullum (Charlton 1947), Ted Croker (Charlton 1948), Frank Coombs (Bristol C 1949), James Kelly (Gillingham 1951), Tom Ritchie (Grimsby 1958), Dave Underwood (Watford 1960), Derek Hales (Luton 1972), Andy Hessenthaler (Watford via Redbridge F).

96-97 - Captain: **P.O.Y.:** **Top scorer:**
Local Press: Kentish Times, Kentish Independent **Local Radio:** Radio Kent, Radio Thamesmead.

HONOURS: Southern Lg 1930-31, 31-32, 73-74, 83-84, R-up 87-88, 88-89, Eastern Div 30-31, 31-32, Southern Div 80-81, Southern Lg Div 2 1896-97, Lg Cup 76-77, 87-88, 88-89, Championship Shield 83-84, 87-88, 88-89; Kent Lg 1995-96, Lg Cup 24-25, Kent Snr Cup 29-30, 34-35, 38-39, 69-70, Snr Trophy 95-96, Inter Lg Chall 1974; FA Trophy R-up 1974.

Dartford FC

ERITH &
BELVEDERE
F.C. LTD.
"PARK VIEW"
LOWER ROAD
BELVEDERE
KENT DA17 6DF
Tel: 081-311 4444
(Sheet Metal) Engineering Ltd.

PROGRAMME DETAILS:
Pages: 30 **Price:** 50p
Editor: Peter Bird
Tel: 0181 310 1086

ERITH & BELVEDERE

Formed: 1922 **Nickname:** Deres
Colours: Blue & white/blue/white
Change colours: All red
Midweek home matchday: Tuesday
Reserves' League: None.

Chairman: John McFadden **President:** L O'Connell
Vice Chairman: R E Cowley
Secretary: Miss Kellie Discipline, 30 Chatsworth Road, Dartford, Kent DA1 5AT. 01322 275766
Press Officer/Commecial Manager: Martin Tarrant
Manager: Mike Acland 01322 225594
Asst Manager / Coach: Dave Hough **Physio:** Rob Couldwell
GROUND Address: Park View, Lower Road, Belvedere, Kent DA17 6DF (0181 311 4444). **Directions:** From Dartford bridge follow signs for Crayford to Erith and follow A206. Ground half mile from Erith Blackwall tunnel: head for Abbey Wood and on to Belvedere. Entrance in Station Road, adjoining Belvedere (BR) station. Bus No. 469.
Capacity: 1,500 **Cover:** 1,000 **Seats:** 500 **Floodlights:** Yes
Club Shop: Sells programmes, badges and pens.
Clubhouse: Licensed social club open matchdays and weekends. Cold snacks available available, separate canteen provides hot food on matchdays.
PREVIOUS - Leagues: Kent 22-29 31-39 78-82, London 29-31, Corinthian 45-63, Athenian 63-78. **Names:** Belvedere & District FC (Formed 1918, restructured 1922)
CLUB RECORDS - Attendance: 5,573 v Crook Colliery Welfare Amt Cup 3rd Rd 1949. **Win:** 14-2 v Royal Marines, Kent Lge 18/11/33. (16-2 v RAF Friendly 4/9/41). **Defeat:** 0-15 v Ashford, Kent Lge 28/4/37. **Career Appearances:** Dennis Crawford 504, 56-71. **Career Goalscorer:** Colin Johnson 284, 61-71.
BEST SEASON - FA Amateur Cup: Runners-up 1923-24, 37-38. **FA Trophy:** Third Qualifying Round second replay 89-90. **FA Vase:** Third Round 76-77. **FA Cup:** 4th Qual Rd 1924-25 (Equiv to 1st Rd Prop). **League clubs defeated:** None.
Players progressing to Football League: John Coshall (West Ham 28), Fred Ford/Cyril Hammond/Keith Peacock (Charlton 36, 46, 62), Tommy Ord (Chelsea 72), Sean Devine (Barnet 95).
96-97 - Captain: Paul Foley **P.o.Y.:** Tim Bealey **Top scorer:** Steve Portway
Local Press: Kentish Times, Kentish Independant. **Local Radio:** Radio Kent, Radio Mellenium.
HONOURS: FA Amat Cup R-up 23-24 37-38; Athenian Lge Div 1 R-up 70-71 (Lge Cup 73-74), Memorial Shield 67-68; Corinthian Lge R-up 62-63, (Lge Cup 47-48 48-49 49-50); Kent Lge 81-82, (Lge Cup R-up 81-82); London Sen Cup 44-45 (R-up 38-39); Kent Amat Cup 6, (R-up 4); Kent F/lit Lge R-up 67-68; Kent Interm Cup R-up 90-91; Kent Jun Cup 67-68; Kent County Yth Lge 90-91; Kent Yth Cup 87-88. Bromley Hosp Cup 38-39; Essex & Herts Border Comb Cup 73-74;

Erith & Belverdere FC: Back Row (L-R); Bob Couldwell (Physio), Mike Acland (Mgr), Paul Foley, Stuart Staples, Danny Harwood, Steve Portway, Mickey Leslie, Steve Rutter, Libird Henry, Roger Lucifer (Asst Mgr). Front Row; Scott Liddle, Ray Aboagye, Tony Adlington, Graham Porter, Jason Mummery, Tim Bealy, Robert Bird.

Photo - Mr & Mrs Thaler

PROGRAMME DETAILS:
Pages: 36 **Price:** £1
Editor: Ian Tewson
Tel. 01329 662624

FAREHAM TOWN

Formed: 1947 **Nickname:** The Town
Colours: Red/black/red
Change colours: White/white/black
Midweek home matchday: Wednesday
Reserves' League: Hampshire Comb.

Chairman: Chris Solen 01329 847784 (H) 01329 844111 (B)
Director of Football: John Green **President:** Ken Atkins
Secretary: Tony Adams, 83 Murray Road, Horndean, PO8 9JQ (0370 62874).
Press Officer: M Willis **Commercial Manager:**
Manager: Mark Chamberlain (01705 327527) **Physio:** James McKay
General Manager: Tony Adams (01705 615931)

GROUND Address: Cams Alders, Highfield Avenue, Fareham, Hants PO14 1JA (01329 231151).
Directions: From junction 11 of M27, follow A27 towards Southampton. After passing Fareham station turn left at traffic lights (second left) into Redlands Avenue. Turn right at Redlands Inn then left into Highfields Avenue.
Capacity: 5,500 **Cover:** 500 **Seats:** 450 **Floodlights:** Yes
Clubhouse: Open every evening except Sundays. *Food available*
Club Shop: Sells programmes, scarves & fanzines.
Sponsors: Portsmouth Evening News

PREVIOUS - Name: Fareham FC. **Leagues:** Portsmouth 47-49, Hants 49-79. **Ground:** Bath Lane.

CLUB RECORDS - Attendance: 2,650 v Wimbeldon, FA Cup 1965. *(at Southampton F.C.; 6,035 v Kidderminster Harriers, FA Trophy Semi Final Second leg 86-87).* **Transfer fee paid:** £1,175 for Joe McCormack (Newport IOW). **Transfer fee received:** £43,000 for David Leworthy (Spurs).

BEST SEASON - FA Cup: 1st Rd replay 88-89 (2-3 at home to Torquay after 2-2). **FA Trophy:** Semi Final 86-87. **FA Amateur Cup:** Second Round 63-64 66-67 73-74

Players progressing to Football League: Ray Hiron (Portsmouth 64), John Hold (Bournemouth), David Leworthy (Spurs 84), Steve Claridge (Bournemouth 84), Darren Foreman (Barnsley), Kevin Bartlett (Cardiff City 86), Domenyk Newman (Reading 90).
96-97 Captain: Stuart Hensman **P.o.Y.:** Mark Gough **Top scorer:** Rob Semack
Local Press: Portsmouth Evening News, Southampton Evening Echo.
Local radio: Power FM

HONOURS: Hants Lg(8) 59-60 62-67 72-73 74-75 (R-up 55-56 60-61 67-68 71-72 76-77 78-79, Div 2 R-up 52-53, Eastern Div 24-25, Div 3 East 49-50), Hants Snr Cup 56-57 62-63 67-68 92-93, Russell Cotes Cup(6) 64-65 72-77, Gosport War Memorial Cup, SW Co's Cup(2), Pickford Cup(2),

Fareham Town FC *Photo - Andrew Chitty*

PROGRAMME DETAILS:
Pages: 32 **Price:** 70p
Editor: John O'Grady
Tel. 0171 237 6346

FISHER ATHLETIC (LONDON)

Formed: 1908 **Nickname:** The Fish
Colours: Black & white stripes/black/black.
Change colours: Blue/white/white
Midweek matchday: Tuesday
Reserves' League: Suburban

President: Barry Albin-Dyer **Life President:** Lord Mellish
Chairman: Chris Georgiou **Vice Chairman:** Dave Wilding
Secretary: M J Wakefield, 146 Layard Square, Drummond Rd, Bermondsey SE16 0JG (0171 237 2819).
Commercial Co-ordinator: C Stepton
Manager: Micky Stead **Coach:** Paul Collins **Physio:** Joe Miller

GROUND Address: The Surrey Docks Stadium, Salter Road, London SE16 1LQ (0171 231 5144. Fax: 0171 2520060).
Directions: 8 minutes walk from Rotherhithe (tube), 2 miles from London Bridge (main line). Buses 188, P11, P14.
Capacity: 5,300 **Cover:** 4,283 **Seats:** 400 **Floodlights:** Yes
Clubhouse: 0171 252 0590. Luxury clubhouse, Vice-President's club. Bar open 11am-3 & 5-11pm. Sandwiches & snacks available.
Club Shop: Open matchdays **Sponsors:** Alex O'Neil

PREVIOUS - **Leagues:** Parthenon, West Kent, Kent Amateur, London Spartan 76-82, Southern 82-87, GMV Conference 87-91.
Names: Fisher Athletic 08-93, Fisher'93 93-96. **Ground:** London Road, Mitcham.

CLUB RECORDS - **Attendance:** 4,283 v Barnet, GMV Conference 4/5/91.
Win: 7-0 v Lewes Sept 95, FA Cup **Defeat:** 0-6 v Salisbury, 21/8/93.
Career Goalscorer: Paul Shinners 205 **Career Appearances:** Dennis Sharp 720.
Transfer fee paid: £500 each for Sean Devine & Jamie Kempster (Erith & Belvedere 1995)
Transfer fee received: £45,000 for Paul Gorman (Charlton 1991)

BEST SEASON - **FA Cup:** 1st Rd 84-85 (0-1 at home to Bristol City), 88-89 (0-4 at Bristol Rovers).
FA Trophy: Third Round replay 87-88
FA Vase: Second Round replay 82-83

Players progressing to The Football League: John Bumstead (Chelsea), Trevor Aylott (Bournemouth), Paul Shinners (Orient 1984), Dave Regis (Notts County - via Barnet), Paul Gorman (Charlton 1991), Sean Devine (Barnet via Okonia Nicossia), George Barry (Leyton Orient).

96-97 - Captain: Paul Collins **P.o.Y.:** Marvin Samuels **Top scorer:** Paul Gorman (31)

HONOURS: Southern Lg 86-87 (R-up 83-84, Southern Div 82-83, Lg Cp 84-85, Championship Cup 87-88, Merit Cup), London Spartan Lg 80-81 81-82 (R-up 78-79, Senior Div 77-78, Div 2 R-up 76-77), Parthenon Lg 61-62 (Lg Cup 63-64 65-66), Kent Amateur Lg 73-74 74-75 (R-up 72-73), London Senior Cup 84-85 87-88 88-89, London Intermediate Cup 59-60 (R-up 75-76), Kent Senior Cp 83-84, Kent Senior Trophy 81-82 82-83, Surrey Intermediate Cup 61-62.

Back Row (L-R); Joe Miller (Physio), Ray Poer, Neil Thurgood, Wayne Curt, Paul Collins (Capt), Jason Peters, Gary Hutchinson, Trainer, Lee Williams (Coach). Front Row; Simon Dyer, Michael Robwerts, Paul Gorman, Danny Francis, Phil O'Neil, Paul Manning, John Brunning.

FLEET TOWN

PROGRAMME DETAILS:
Pages: 20 **Price:** 50p
Editor: Steve Beagley

Founded: 1890. **Formed:** 1947
Nickname: The Blues
Colours: Navy & sky/sky/navy & sky
Change colours: Yellow & red/yellow & red/yellow
Midweek Matches: Tuesday
Reserves' League: Suburban

Chairman: Anthony Cherry **President:** Les Hocking
Vice Chairman: Colin Sturgess
Secretary: Dave Grenham, 149 Aldershot Road, Church Crookham, Fleet, Hants GU13 0JS. Tel. 01252 623021
Manager: Trevor Norris **Assistant Manager:** Jess Bone
Coach: Clive Talentire **Physio:** Steve Hyde

GROUND Address: Calthorpe Park, Crookham Road, Fleet, Hants. Tel.: 01252 623804
Directions: Leave the M3 at Junction 4A. Follow signs to Fleet via A3013. At 5th roundabout (a T-junction), turn left over railway bridge. Carry on past 'Oatsheaf' pub on the right - ground is 1/4 mile further on right.
Capacity: 2,000 **Seats:** 200
Cover: 250 **Floodlights:** Yes
Clubhouse: Yes. Hot & cold food served.
Club Shop: Yes, contact Secretary
Sponsors: Hart Dist Council

PREVIOUS - Leagues: Wessex, Hants 61-77, Athenian, Combined Co's, Chiltonian.

CLUB RECORDS - Win: 7-0 **Transfer fee paid:** £1,500 to Farnborough, 1991
Career Goalscorer: John Smith **Career Appearances:** Steve Hodge / Paul Dear

1996-97 Top scorer: John Smith.

HONOURS: Wessex Lg 93-94, Lg Cup R-up 92-93, Hants Lg Div 2 R-up 61-62 (Div 1 R-up 60-61), Aldershot Snr Cup 92-93, Simpsonair Challenge Shield 1993, Hants Yth Lg Div 3 92-93.

Fleet Town FC: Back Row (L-R); Tony, Steve Hyde, Paul Woller, Kevin Betsy, Paul Mills, Andy Taylor, Vernon Pratt, Russ Watkinson, Neil Roberts, Jess Bone (Asst Mgr). Front Row; Jamie Horton, Mark Frampton, Chris Ferrett, Derek Holloway, Ricky Jones, Derek Traylen, Steve Kerbey

Photo - Andrew Chitty

HAVANT TOWN

Formed: 1958 **Nickname:**
Colours: Yellow & black/black/yellow
Change colours: Black & white/white/white
Midweek matchday: Wednesday
Reserves' League: Jewson Wessex Combination.

Chairman: Ray Stainton **President:** George Jones.
Directors: Derek Pope, Paul Cummins, Ian Craig, Trevor Brock.
Secretary: Craig Stainton, 4 Bridget Close, Horndean, Waterlooville, Hampshire. PO8 9NF (01705 359601)
Manager: Dick Semark **Physio:** Gary Buckner

GROUND Address: West Leigh Park, Martin Road, West Leigh, Havant PO9 5TH (0705 470918).
Directions: Take B2149 to Havant off the A27 (B2149 Petersfield Rd if coming out of Havant). 2nd turning off dual carriageway into Bartons Road then 1st right into Martins Road. 1 mile from Havant BR station.
Capacity: 6,000 **Cover:** 1,500 **Seats:** 240 **Floodlights:** Yes
Clubhouse: Open every day, lunchtime and evening. 2 bars, function suites, hot & cold food available.
Club Shop: Sells various souvenirs and programmes.
Sponsors: G A Day

PROGRAMME DETAILS:
Pages: 24 **Price:** 50p
Editor: Steve Cox
(0705 269072)

PREVIOUS - **Leagues:** Portsmouth 58-71/ Hants 71-86/ Wessex 86-91.
Names: Leigh Park/ Havant & Leigh Park.
Grounds: Front Lawn 1958-83.

CLUB RECORDS - **Attendance:** 3,500 v Wisbech Town, FA Vase QF 85-86.
Win: 10-0 three times; v Sholing Sports (H), FA Vase 4th Rd 85-86, v Portsmouth Royal Navy (H), Wessex League 90-91; v Poole Town, Southern League Southern Division 94-95.
Defeat: 1-7 v Camberley Town (H), FA Vase 3rd Rd 88-89.
Career Goalscorer: Unknown.
Career Appearances: Tony Plumbley.
Transfer fee paid: £5,750 for John Wilson (Bashley, 1990)
Transfer fee received: £7,000 for Steve Tate (Waterlooville, 1993).

BEST SEASON - **FA Cup:** Third Qualifying Round 92-93 (2-3 at Sittingbourne).
FA Vase: Quarter Final 1985-86

Players progressing to Football League: Bobby Tambling (Chelsea).
Local Press: News (Portsmouth) **Local Radio:** Ocean Sound, Radio Solent.

HONOURS: FA Sunday Cup 68-69, Wessex Lg 90-91 (R-up 88-89), Hampshire Lg Div 3 72-73 (Div 4 71-72), Hampshire Senior Cup R-up 91-92 94-95, Hampshire Intermediate Cup, Hampshire Junior Cup, Russell Cotes Cup 91-92, Portsmouth Senior Cup 83-84 84-85 91-92, Gosport War Memorial Cup 74-75 91-92 92-93 94-95, Southern Counties Floodlit Cup R-up 91-92, Hampshire Floodlit Cup 85-86, Portsmouth Lg.

Photo: Andrew Chitty

MARGATE

Formed: 1896 **Nickname:** The Gate
Colours: Blue & white/blue & white
Change colours: Maroon/white
Midweek matchday: Tuesday **Newsline:** 0891 800 665.
Reserves' League: Winstonlead Kent Lg. Div 2

Chairman: Keith Piper **President:** Mr R W Griffiths
Vice Chairman: Richard Piper **Press Officer:** Chairman
Secretary: K E Tomlinson, 65 Nash Road, Margate CT9 4BT (01843 291040).
Manager: Chris Kinnear

GROUND Address: Hartsdown Park, Hartsdown Road, Margate CT9 5QZ (01843 221769).
Directions: A28 into Margate, turn right opposite Dog & Duck P.H. into Hartsdown Road, proceed over crossroads and ground is on left. Ten mins walk from Margate (BR).
Capacity: 6,000 **Cover:** 3 sides **Seats:** 400 **Floodlights:** Yes
Clubhouse: Flexible hours, private functions, matchday facilities. Steward: Pam & Mark Weatherly.
Club Shop: Contact Paul Turner 01843 293056.
Sponsors: Link Music Limited

PROGRAMME DETAILS:
Pages: 44 **Price:** 80p
Editor: Keith Smith
Tel. 01843 293220

PREVIOUS - **Grounds:** Margate College/ Dreamland, Northdown Rd/ Garlinge. **Leagues:** Kent 11-23 24-28 29-33 37-38 46-59/ Southern 33-37. **Name:** Thanet Utd 1981-89

CLUB RECORDS - **Attendance:** 14,500 v Spurs, FA Cup 3rd Rd 1973.
Win: 8-0 v Tunbridge Wells (H) 66-67 & v Chatham Town (H) 87-88
Defeat: 11-0 v AFC Bournemouth (A), FAC 1st Rd. 20.11.71
Career Goalscorer: Dennis Randall 66 (season 1966-67).
Career Appearances: Bob Harrop.
Transfer fee paid: £5,000 for Steve Cuggy (Dover Athletic, 1993)
Transfer fee received: Undisclosed for Martin Buglione (St Johnstone 92-93).

BEST SEASON - **FA Trophy:** Third Round replay 78-79. **FA Amateur Cup:** Never entered
FA Cup: 3rd Rd 72-73 (0-6 to Spurs), 36-37 (1-3 at Blackpool).
League clubs defeated: Gillingham 29-30, Queens Park Rangers, Crystal Palace 35-36, Bournemouth & Boscombe Athletic 61-62, Swansea 72-73.

Players progressing to Football League: Over 40 including J Yeomanson (West Ham 47), D Bing/G Wright (West Ham 51), T Bing (Spurs 56), S Foster (C Palace 61), J Fraser (Watford 62), R Walker (Bournemouth 65), K Bracewell (Bury 66), T Jenkins/R Flannigan (Reading 69-70), M Blyth (Millwall 78), M Buglione (St Johnstone 92).
96-97 - Captain: Tony Dixon **P.O.Y.:** Bill Edwards **Top scorer:** Martin Buglione
Local Press: Isle of Thanet Gazette, Thanet Times, Thanet Extra. **Local Radio:** Radio Kent, Invicta Radio.
HONOURS: Southern Lg 35-36 (Lg Cp 67-68 (R-up 61-62 74-75), Div 1 62-63 (R-up 66-67), Div 1 Sth 77-78, East Div R-up 33-34, Merit Cp 66-67 77-78, Midweek Sect. 36-37), Kent Lg (4), (R-up 5, Div 2 4, Lg Cp 4), Kent Snr Cup (4), Kent Snr Shield (8), Kent F'lit Cp 62-63 66-67 75-76.

Action at Margate against St Leonards Stamcroft. *Photo - Martin Wray*

NEWPORT A.F.C.

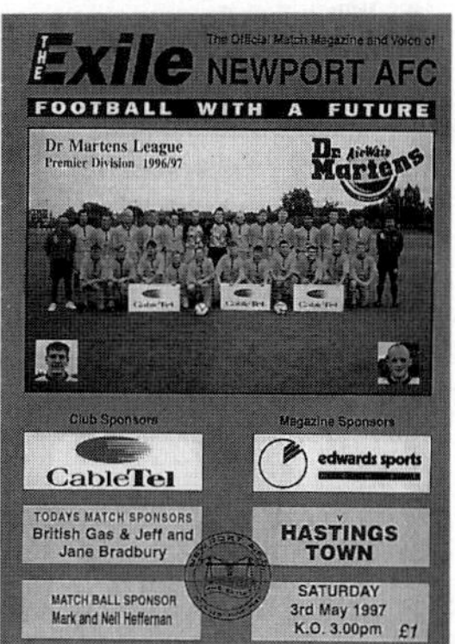

PROGRAMME DETAILS:
Pages: 42 **Price:** £1.00
Editor: Wallace Brown
(01633 265500)

Formed: 1989 **Nickname:** The Exiles
Colours: All Amber with black trim
Change colours: Green shirts, white shorts
Midweek matchday: Wednesday
Youth League: South West Counties Youth

Chairman: David Hando **President:** Brian Toms, MBE.
Vice-Chairman / Press Officer: Wallace Brown (01633 265500)
Secretary: Mike Everett, 66 Gibbs Rd, Newport. NP9 8AU (01633 280932)
Club Headquarters: The King, 76 Somerton Road, Newport. NP9 0JX (01633 662262 T/Fax). **Community Director:** Ray Taylor (01443 237545).
Manager: Tim Harris **Asst Manager:** Chris Hyde
Physios: T Gilbert & D Williams **Trainer:** David Williams
Football in the Community Off: Derek Brazil
GROUND Address: Newport Stadium, Spytty Park, Langland Way, Newport, South Wales. 01633 280802. **Directions:** From Severn Bridge on M4 take 1st exit signed Newport (jct 24), 1st left at r'bout follow signs for industrial area, left at r'bout after 2 1/2 miles, over 2 r'bouts, next left for ground. Ample free parking available at ground.
Capacity: 3,300 **Cover:** 1,236 **Seats:** 1,236 **Floodlights:** Yes.
Clubhouse: Club HQ is a pub less than 1 mile from stadium. Private members' club only at ground. Refreshments, hot & cold snacks available at ground.
Club Shop: Open matchdays, sells a wide selection of souvenirs & programmes. **Sponsors:** Cable Tel

PREVIOUS - **Leagues:** Hellenic 89-90.
Grounds: London Road, Moreton-in-Marsh 89-90; Somerton Park, Newport 90-92; Gloucester City FC 92-94 *(period in exile due to dispute with FAW over the League of Wales).*
Names: None. Newport AFC were formed after the demise of Newport County in 1988-89.

CLUB RECORDS - **Attendance:** 2,475 v Redditch United, Beazer (Midland) 24.8.94.
Win: 9-0 v Pontlottyn Blast Furnace (A), Welsh Cup First Round 1/9/90.
Defeat: 1-6 v Stafford Rangers (A) BHL 6/1/96
Career Goalscorer: Chris Lilygreen 93.
Career Appearances: Mark Price 274 (222 Lg + 52 cup)
Transfer fee paid: £3,700 for Mark Williams from Merthyr Tydfil
Transfer fee received: Not disclosed

BEST SEASON - **FA Cup:** 4th Qualifying Rd 92-93. **FA Trophy:** 2nd Rd Proper 95-96. **FA Vase:** N/A
96-97 - Captain: Paul Thorpe **P.O.Y.:** Leigh Hall **Top scorer:** Paul Burton
Local Press: South Wales Argus, South Wales Echo. **Local Radio:** Red Dragon.

HONOURS: Hellenic Lge Prem Div 89-90 (Lge Cup 89-90); Gloucs Sen Cup Winners 93-94; Beazer Homes Lge Mid Div Champ 94-95; Beazer Merit Cup Jnt Win 94-95; Gwent Sen. Cup Winners 96-97.

Back Row (L-R); Tony Gilbert (Physio), Mark Williams, Mark Tucker, Jason Donovan, Phil Coyne, Adriano Girslanni, Peter Mason, Jon Roberts, Jason Price, Derek Brazil (Football in Community Officer), Jayson Hoskins, Ryan Nicholls, Andy Evans, Darren Porretta, Graham Rogers (Youth Team Coach). Front Row; Steve Lowndes, Ray John, Linden Jones, Lee Powell, Todd Quarterley, Rob Ainley, Lee Brown, Ryland Morgans, Neil Smothers, Lee Relish, Danny Street.

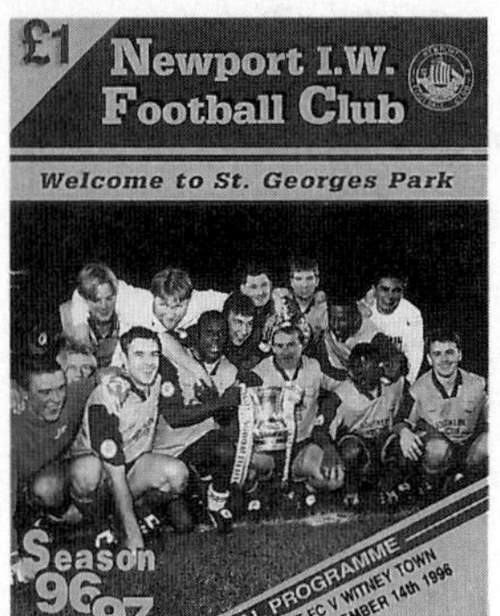

PROGRAMME DETAILS:
Pages: 28 **Price:** £1
Editor: Peter Ranger
(01983 526144)

NEWPORT I.O.W.

Formed: 1888 **Nickname:** The Port
Colours: Gold & royal blue trim/gold/gold & royal trim
Change colours: All Mauve.
Midweek matchday: Tuesday
Reserves' League: Isle of Wight League.

Chairman: Steve Mellor **Vice Chairman:** TBA
President: W H J Bunday. **Commercial Manager:** Dave Hiscock.
Secretary/Press Off.: Chris Cheverton, 127 Westhill Road, Ryde, Isle of Wight PO33 1LW (01983 567355).
Manager: Steve Mellor **Coach:** Dave Puckett
Co Manager: Tony Mount **Physio:** Lisa McKinney

GROUND Address: St George's Park, St George's Way, Newport, Isle of Wight PO30 2QH (01983 525027). **Directions:** Roads from all ferry ports lead to Coppins Bridge R-about at eastern extremity of town. Take Sandown/Ventnor exit, proceed to small r-about, St George's way is first exit (straight on), ground immediately visible on left. Five minute walk from Newport bus station; along Church Litten (past old ground), turn left then right at r-about.
Capacity: 5,000 **Cover:** 1,000 **Seats:** 300 **Floodlights:** Yes
Clubhouse: Open normal licensing hours. 2 bars, full range of hot and cold bar snacks. Buffet inside ground.
Club Shop: Sells clothes, programmes & sundries. Contact M Reader at ground.

PREVIOUS - Ground: Church Litten (previously Well's Field) 1888-1988. **Leagues:** Isle of Wight 1896-1928/ Hants 28-86/ Wessex 86-90.

CLUB RECORDS - Attendance: 2,217 FA Cup 1st Rd Nov 1994 v Aylesbury Utd, *(6,000 v Watford, FA Cup 1st Round 56-57, at Church Litten, old ground).* **Win:** 14-1, v Thornycroft Athletic (H), Hampshire League Division One, 22.12.45. **Defeat:** 2-10, v Basingstoke Town (H), Hampshire League Division One, 12.10.68. **Career Goalscorer:** Eddie Walder. **Career Appearances:** Jeff Austin 540 (69-87). **Transfer fee paid:** £3,000 for Stuart Ritchie (Bashley, May 1991). **Transfer fee received:** £2,250 for Mick Jenkins (Havant, March 1992).

BEST SEASON - FA Vase: Fifth Round 91-92, 93-94. **FA Cup:** 2nd Rd 35-36 45-46. 1st Rd another eight times; 45-46 52-55 56-59 94-95 95-96. - **League clubs defeated:** Clapton Orient 45-46.
Players progressing to Football League: Gary Rowatt (Cambridge City, Everton).
96-97 - Captain: Dave Puckett **P.o.Y.:** Graeme Gee **Top scorer:** Eurshell Fearon
Local Press: Portsmouth Evening News, I.O.W. County Press, Southampton Evening Echo.
Local Radio: Solent, Isle of Wight Radio, Ocean Sound.

HONOURS: Wessex Lg R-up 89-90, Comb. 91-92 (res.); Hants Lg (11), R-up(7), Div 2 R-up 70-71, Hants Snr Cup(7); Russell Cotes Cup (3); Pickford Cup (4); Isle of Wight Snr (Gold) Cup (31); Hants F'lit Cup 76-77 77-78; Isle of Wight Lg(4) 07-10 23-24; Hants I'mediate Cup 31-32 96-97; Hants Comb. Cup 38-39.

Newport IOW FC:

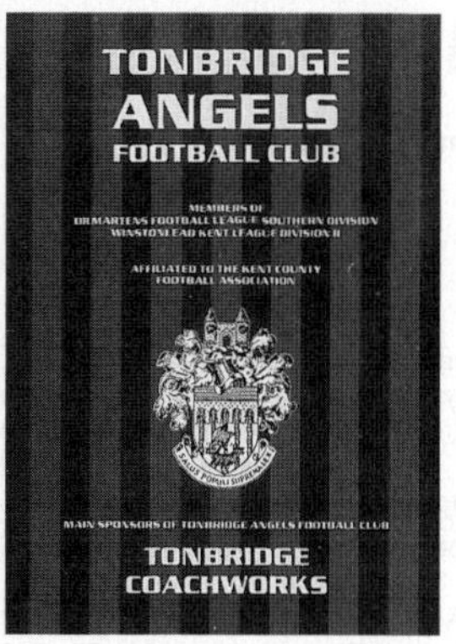

TONBRIDGE ANGELS

Founded: 1948 **Nickname:** The Angels
Colours: Black & blue/black/black
Change Colours: All green
Midweek matchday: Tuesday
Reserves' League: Winstonlead Kent Division Two.

Chairman: Nigel Rimmer **Vice Chairman:**
Secretary: Ken Jarrett, 8 Farraday Ride, Tonbridge, Kent. TN10 4RL. (01732 351856)
Press Officer: Simon Piper **Commercial Manager:** Mark Goodier
Manager: Bill Roffey **Physio:** Peter Battell/Chris Dunk

PROGRAMME DETAILS:
Pages: 38 **Price:** £1
Editor: Roger Alder
c/o Club

GROUND Address: Longmead Stadium, Darenth Avenue, Tonbridge, Kent TN10 3JW (01732 352417). **Directions:** From Tonbridge BR station, through High Street, north up Shipbourne Rd (A227 Gravesend road) to 2nd mini-r'bout ('The Pinnacles' pub), left into Darenth Avenue, ground at bottom of Avenue, far side of car park
Seats: 202 **Cover:** 400 **Capacity:** 5,000 **Floodlights:** Yes
Sponsors: Tonbridge Coachworks
Clubhouse: Open Mon-Sat evenings and Sunday lunchtimes. Hot food on matchdays from burger bar.
Club Shop: Yes, programmes, replica kits etc, contact Peter Jeffrey 01732 350692.

PREVIOUS - Leagues: Southern 48-89, Kent 89-93. **Ground:** The Angel 48-80. **Names:** Tonbridge Angels, Tonbridge F.C., Tonbridge A.F.C.

CLUB RECORDS - Attendance: 1,463 v Yeovil Town, FA Cup 4th Qualifying Round 26/10/91. *At the Angel Ground: 8,236 v Aldershot, FA Cup 1st Round 1951.*
Win: 11-1 v Worthing FA Cup 1951 **Defeat:** 2-11 v Folkstone, Kent Sen Cup 1949
Career Goalscorer: Unknown **Career Appearances:** Mark Gillham, 520 to date.
Transfer fee paid: **Transfer fee received:** £7,500 for Paul Emblen (Charlton Ath 97)

BEST SEASON - FA Cup: First Round (proper) 50-51 51-52 52-53 67-68 72-73.
Players progressing to Football League: R Saunders, M McMcDonald, T Burns, I Seymour, G Moseley, T Morgan, Neil Emblen.
96-97 - Captain: Alan Tutton **P.o.Y.:** Paul Emblen **Top scorer:** Craig Wilkins
Local Press: Kent Messenger, Courier, Sevenoaks Leader. **Local Radio:** Invicta, Radio Kent.

HONOURS: Kent League 94-95 (League Cup (2)), Southern League Cup Runners-up (2) (SF (1)), Kent Senior Cup 64-65 74-75 (Runners-up (2)), Kent Senior Shield 51-52 55-56 57-58 58-59 63-64.

Tonbridge Angels FC: Back Row (L-R); Graham Brenton, Craig Wilkins, Alan Tutton, Joe Radford, Adrin Le Moine, Brian Frampton, Paul Emblen, Bill Roffey (Mgr). Front Row; Grant Styles, Dave Forster, Jason Fenton, Danny Tingley, Matt Le Moine, Simon Colbran, Darren Walmsley, Phil Walker.

TROWBRIDGE TOWN

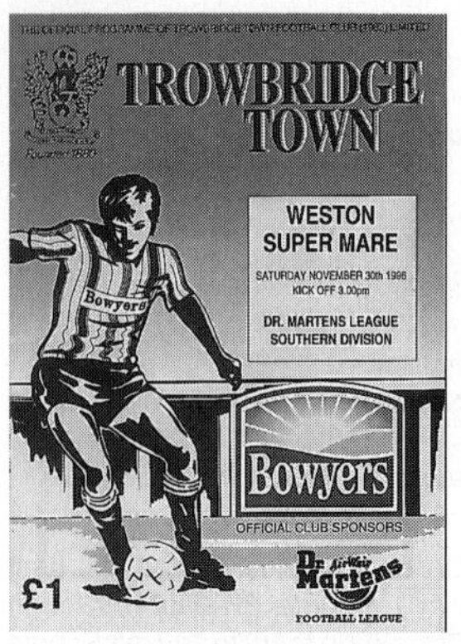

PROGRAMME DETAILS:
Pages: 48 **Price:** 80p
Editor: A Meaden
(01225 752076)

Formed: 1880 **Nickname:** The Bees
Colours: Old gold/black/black
Change colours: All white.
Midweek matchday: Tuesday.
Reserves' League: Wiltshire County.

Chairman: A I Moore **President:** A M Townley.
Vice Chairman: C Belcher **Secretary:** Colin Elliott, 40 Eastbourne Rd., Trowbridge, Wilts. BA14 7HW (01225 760619)
Press Officer: A Meaden (01225 755752) **Commercial Man.:** J Snell
Manager: J Murphy **Asst Man.:** B Hughes **Physio:** B Baird
GROUND Address: Twerton Park, Twerton, Bath Avon BA2 1DB. (01225 423087/313247 Fax: 01225 481391)
Directions: Twerton Park is situated on the A4/A36 Lower Bristol Road - on the Bristol side of Bath City Centre (Approx 2.5 miles). The area is serviced by J18 on the M4. From the centre of Bath the bus route is No.5 - Twerton High Street.
Capacity: 8,840 **Seated:** 1,017 **Covered Terracing:** 4,800
Clubhouse: Open before & after games. Hot & cold snacks.
Club Shop: Yes, selling souvenirs & programmes.
Sponsors: Bowyers (Wiltshire) Ltd.
PREVIOUS - Leagues: Somerset Senior, Trowbridge & Dist, Western 1892-98 1901-07 13-58, Wiltshire, Southern 58-81, Alliance Premier (GMV Conference) 81-84. **Grounds:** Timbrell Street 1880-87; Flower Show Field 87-1923; Bythesea Rd 23-34. **Name:** Trowbridge F.C.

CLUB RECORDS - Attendance: 9,009 v Weymouth, F.A. 4th Qualifying Rd 49-50. **Win:** 17-1 v Yeovil & Petters. **Defeat:** 0-10 v Barnet. **Transfer fee paid:** £7,000 for John Freegard (Gloucester City, 1991). **Transfer fee received:** £10,000 for Paul Compton (B'mouth),

BEST SEASON - FA Cup: 1st Rd replay (v Brighton) 47-48. 1st Rd 45-46 57-58 63-64. **FA Vase:** Semi Final 1990-91 **FA Trophy:** First Round replay 1983-84 **FA Amateur Cup:** Second Round 1930-31

Players progressing to Football League: A Eisentrager (Bristol C 50), D Townsend (Charlton 50), C Dixon (Cardiff 54), D Pyle/J Meacham (Bristol Rovers 55/87), E Weaver/K Skeen/B Wade (Swindon 61/64/85), P Compton (Bournemouth 80), J Layton (Newport 84), A Feeley (Leicester 84), R Cashley (Chester 85).M Fishlock (Hereford U).
Local Press: Wiltshire Times, Bath Evening Chronicle, Western Daily Press.
Local Radio: Radio Bristol, Wilts Radio, Wilts Sound.

HONOURS: Southern Lg Sthn Div R-up 90-91 (Lg Cup R-up 85-86), Western Lg(7) (R-up 4) Lg Cup 56-57), Wilts Lg Div 2 11-12 30-31 (jt)(R-up 5), Trowbridge & Dist Lg(3) 09-11 13-14, Wilts Snr Cup 1884-85 95-96(jt with Swindon T) 97-98 1921-22 25-26 33-34 37-38 (R-up 7), Wilts Prof. Shield(8), Wilts F'lit Lg Cup(3) 91-94, Bristol Charity Cup 25-26, Wilts Jnr Cup 10-11 12-13, Trowbridge & Dist Jnr Cup 19-20, Allen Palmer Cup 23-24 24-25(joint), Swanborough Cup 33-34 34-35 35-36(jt), Somerset Snr Lg 30-31 (R-up 11-12 33-34 35-36), Western Co's F'lit Lg Cup 80-81 85-86, Coronation Cup 92-93.

Darren Lush (white shirt) heads the ball clear of Hampton's Darren Smith during the FA Trophy game last season. Photo: Garry Letts.

WATERLOOVILLE
FOOTBALL CLUB LTD
WATERLOOVILLE FOOTBALL CLUB
Main Sponsors 1992-93
St. Christophers
Motor Group
50p
OFFICIAL MATCHDAY PROGRAMME SEASON 1992-93

PROGRAMME DETAILS:
Pages: 32 **Price:** 50p
Ed.: Universal Leisure Ltd
Tel.

WATERLOOVILLE

Formed: 1905 **Nickname:** The Ville
Colours: White & navy/navy/navy
Change colours: Yellow & green/green/yellow
Midweek matchday: Tuesday
Reserves' League: Wessex Combination.

President: M Hibberd **Chairman:** F P Faulkner
Vice Chairman: K L Ashman **General Manager:** D Armstrong
Secretary: P G Elley, 139 Chichester Rd, North End, Portsmouth, Hampshire PO2 0AQ (01705 665885).
Commercial Manager: Terry Diddymus (01705 230114).
Manager: Billy Gilbert **Physio:** Bill Pizey
Asst Manager/Coach: John Waugh

GROUND Address: Jubilee Park, Aston Road, Waterlooville PO7 7SZ (01705 263867). **Directions:** Turn right off town by-pass (B2150) at Asda r-about. Dual carriage to next island, & return back towards town (grd signposted). Aston Rd is 1st left. Nearest stations; Havant (4 miles), Cosham (5).
Capacity: 7,000 **Cover:** 1,500 **Seats:** 480 **Floodlights:** Yes
Clubhouse: Jubilee Club, open to all for all games (first team and reserves). Food available.
Club Shop: Sells usuals items. Contact Mrs B Tomkins.

PREVIOUS - **Leagues:** Waterlooville & District, Portsmouth 38-53, Hants 1953-71.
Grounds: Convent Ground 10-30, Rowlands Avenue Recreation Ground 30-63.

CLUB RECORDS - **Attendance:** 4,500 v Wycombe Wanderers, FA Cup 1st Rd 1976-77.
Transfer fee paid: £6,000 for Steve Tate (Havant Town, 1993)
Transfer fee received: £6,000 for Dave Boyce (Gravesend & Northfleet, 1993).

BEST SEASON - **FA Trophy:** Second Round 1976-77 **FA Amateur Cup:** First Round 1959-60
FA Cup: First Round 2nd replay 83-84, 0-2 v Northampton T. (A) after two 1-1 draws. Also 1st Rd 68-69 76-77 88-89.

Players progressing to Football League: Phil Figgins (Portsmouth 1973), Paul Hardyman (Portsmouth 1983), Guy Whittingham (Portsmouth via Yeovil Town 1988), Paul Moody (Southampton 1991).
Local Press: The News & Sports Mail. **Local Radio:** BBC Solent, Ocean Sound.

HONOURS: Southern Lg Div 1 Sth 71-72 (Lg Cup 86-87, R-up 82-83), Hants Lg R-up 69-70 (Div 2 59-60 64-65, Div 3 (East) R-up 53-54), Hants Snr Cup 69-70 72-73 84-85 (R-up 75-76 90-91), Russell Cotes Cup 88-89, Portsmouth Lg 49-50 50-51 51-52 (Div 2 46-47, Div 3 38-39), Portsmouth Snr Cup 68-69, Portsmouth Victory Cup 59-60 69-70

Dave Milkins and Neil Selby look on in disbelief as the ball just goes wide of the Erith & Belvedere post.
Photo: Andrew Chitty

WESTON-SUPER-MARE

Formed: 1899 **Nickname:** Seagulls
Club colours: White/blue/blue
Change colours: All yellow
Midweek matches: Monday
Reserves' League: None

President: D A Usher **Chairman:** Paul T Bliss
Secretary / Press Officer: Keith Refault, c/o Weston Super Mare FC, 01934 635665
Commercial Manager:
Manager: Len Ashurst **Asst Manager:** John Relish
Coach: **Physio:** Dave Lukins

PROGRAMME DETAILS:
Pages: 32 **Price:** £1
Editor: Secretary
Tel. 01934 635665

GROUND Address: Woodspring Park, Winterstoke Road, Weston-super-Mare BS23 2YG 01934 6355665/621618. **Directions:** M5 Jct 21. A370 along dual carriageway to 4th roundabout. First left and immediately right at roundabout, club on right. From South: M5 Jct 22, follow Weston signs for approx 7 miles, right at first r'bout (by Hospital), left at next r'bout, ground 1 mile on left. 20 mins. walk from Weston-super-Mare (BR).
Seats: 250 **Cover:** 1,000 **Capacity:** 2,000 **Floodlights:** Yes
Clubhouse: Mon-Fri 7-11pm, Sat 12-11pm, Sun 12-3 & 7-11pm. 2 skittle alleys, 2 bars. Bar meals and hot meals everyday.

Club Shop: Selling a wide range of souvenirs & programmes. Contact Mr Geoff Milsom, 12 Greenland Road, Milton, Weston-s-Mare BS22 8JP (01934 413059). **Sponsors:** Pioneer.

PREVIOUS - League: Western 1900-92. **Name:** Borough of Weston-super-Mare. **Grounds:** The Great Ground, Locking Road 48-55, Langford Road 55-83.

CLUB RECORDS - Attendance: 2,623 v Woking, FA Cup First Round Proper replay 23/11/93. *At Langford Road: 2,500 v Bridgwater Town, FA Cup First Round Proper replay 1961-62.* **Win:** 11-0 v Paulton Rovers. **Defeat:** 1-12 v Yeovil Town Reserves. **Career Goalscorer:** Matthew Lazenby, 180. **Career Appearances:** Harry Thomas, 740.
Transfer fee paid: None. **Transfer fee received:** None

BEST SEASON - FA Cup: 1st Rd Proper replay 61-62 (lost 0-1 after 0-0 draw at Bridgwater Town) 94-95 (lost 0-1 after 2-2 draw at Woking). **FA Vase:** Do not enter. **FA Trophy:** 1st Rd 86-87 89-90 92-93 93-94
Players progressing to Football League: Shaun Rouse (Carlisle United 94), Ian Maine, John Palmer.
96-97 - Captain: Paul McLoughlin **P.o.Y.:** Robbie James **Top scorer:** David Mehew
Local Press: Bristol Evening Post, Western Daily Press. **Local Radio:** Somerset Sound, Radio Bristol.

HONOURS: Somerset Snr Cup 23-24 26-27, Western Lg,Champions,91-92 (R-up 76-77, Lg Cup 76-77 (R-up 89-90), Merit Cup 76-77 77-78), Somerset Snr Lg (Reserves) Div 1 87-88 (R-up 90-91), Div 2 R-up 85-86, Div 3 84-85).

Weston Super Mare FC: Back Row (L-R); D Mehew, J Bowering, S Jones, D O'Hagan, W Brown, L Rogers, L White, K Madge. Front Row; R Souter, J Boulton, R James, P McLoughlin, L Jones, A Llewellyn, N Reeves

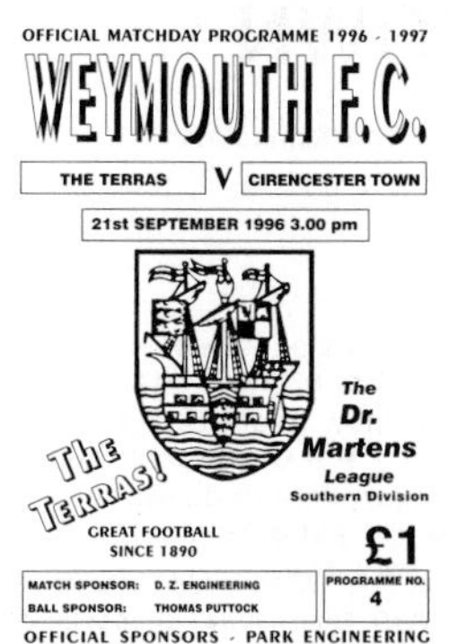

OFFICIAL MATCHDAY PROGRAMME 1996 - 1997
WEYMOUTH F.C.
THE TERRAS
V
CIRENCESTER TOWN
21st SEPTEMBER 1996 3.00 pm
The Dr. Martens League Southern Division
The Terras!
GREAT FOOTBALL SINCE 1890
£1
MATCH SPONSOR: D. Z. ENGINEERING
BALL SPONSOR: THOMAS PUTTOCK
PROGRAMME NO. 4
OFFICIAL SPONSORS - PARK ENGINEERING

PROGRAMME DETAILS:
Pages: 36 **Price:** £1
Editor: Ian White
(01305 785558)

WEYMOUTH

Formed: 1890 **Nickname:** The Terras
Colours: Claret & sky/claret & sky.
Change colours: Gold/claret trim.
Midweek matchday: Tuesday
Reserves' League: None

Chairman: Peter Shaw **Vice Chairman:** Matthew McGowan.
Secretary: Terry Northover, 2 Stoke Rd, Weymouth, Dorset DT4 9JF (01305 771480).
Manager & Director of Football: Matthew McGowan
Asst Manager: Terry Nutman **Physio:** Bob Lucas.
GROUND Address: Wessex Stadium, Radipole Lane, Weymouth, Dorset DT4 0TJ (01305 785558).
Directions: Arriving from Dorchester on A354, turn right following signs to Granby Industrial Estate at Safeway r'bout - ground on right as you enter estate.
Capacity: 10,000 **Cover:** All sides **Seats:** 900 **Floodlights:** Yes
Clubhouse: Matchdays & functions. Hot & cold food available.
Club Shop: Open matchdays only. During week contact Andrew Millar at 4 Franklin Rd, Weymouth DT4 0JR (01305 772743). Progs & souvenirs.
Sponsors: Park Engineering

PREVIOUS - Leagues: Dorset Lge, Western 1907-23 28-49, Southern 23-28 49-79, Alliance Premier 79-89. **Ground:** Recreation Ground (until 1987).

CLUB RECORDS - Attendance: 4,995 v Manchester Utd, ground opening, 21/10/87. **Career Goalscorer:** W Farmer, Haynes. 275. **Career Appearances:** Tony Hobson 1,076. **Transfer fee paid:** £15,000 for Shaun Teale (Northwich). **Transfer fee received:** £100,000 for Peter Guthrie (Spurs, 1988)

BEST SEASON - FA Amateur Cup: First Round 1900. **FA Trophy:** Fourth Round replay 1976-77. **FA Cup:** Fourth Round 61-62, 0-2 v Preston N.E. (A). 1st rd on 29 occasions. - **League clubs defeated:** Merthyr 24-25, Aldershot 49-50, Shrewsbury Town 56-57, Newport County 61-62, Cardiff City 82-83.
Players progressing to Football League: A Smith (Accrington 61), G Bond/T Spratt/A Donnelly/M Cave (Torquay 61/65/67/68), P Leggett (Swindon 62), R Fogg (Aldershot 63), B Hutchinson (Lincoln 65), A Wool (Reading 71), A Beer (Exeter 74), B Iles (Chelsea 78), G Roberts (Spurs 80), T Gulliver/R Hill/N Townsend/P Morrell/J Smeulders (Bournemouth 66/67/79/83/84), T Agana (Watford), A Townsend/D Hughes (Southampton), S Claridge (C Palace), B McGorry/S Teale (Bournemouth), T Pounder/R Evans (Bristol Rvrs), R Pethick (Portsmouth 93)

96-97 - Captain: Alex Browne **P.o.Y:** David Laws **Top scorer:** Paul Myers
Local Press: Dorset Evening Echo. **Local Radio:** Wessex FM.
HONOURS: All Prem Lg R-up 79-80 (Lg Cup 81-82); Prem Inter Lg Cup R-up 87-88 (QF 90-91); Sth Lg 64-65 65-66 (R-up 54-55 77-78), Lg Cup 72-73 (R-up 5), Sthn Div R-up 91-92; Wstn Lg 22-23, Div 2 33-34 36-37, (R-up 35-36 47-48); Dorset Sen. Cup (25); Mark Frowde Cup (12).

Weymouth FC: Back Row (L-R); Neil Housley, Tom Kelly, Lee Bradford, Darren Powell, Paul Mayers, Martin Shepherd, Richard Bartlett, Alex Brown. Front Row; John Waldock, David Laws, Nicky Limber, Ian Hutchinson.

Photo - Andrew Chitty

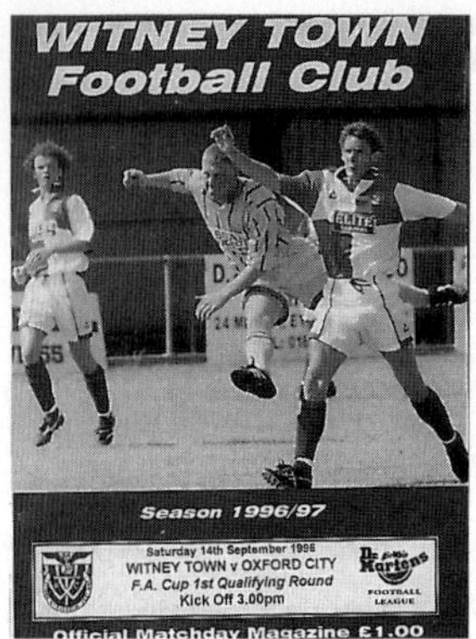

WITNEY TOWN
Football Club
Season 1996/97
Saturday 14th September 1996
WITNEY TOWN v OXFORD CITY
F.A. Cup 1st Qualifying Round
Kick Off 3.00pm
Official Matchday Magazine £1.00

WITNEY TOWN

Formed: 1885 **Nickname:** The Blanketmen
Colours: All Yellow
Change colours: Blue/white/white.
Midweek matchday: Tuesday
Reserves' League: None

Chairman: Brian Constable **President:** Sir Peter Parker
Vice-Chairman: Adrian Duns **Press Officer:** Kieran Bushnell 01993 703622
Secretary: Adrian Bircher, 13 Colwell Drive, Witney, Oxon. OX8 7NJ 01993 700634. **Commercial Man / P.R.O.:** Dermot Gallagher
Manager: Andy Lyne **Asst Manager:** Pete Bridgewater
Coach: Gary Ackling **Physio:** Roger Alder

GROUND Address: Marriott Stadium, Downs Rd, Witney, Oxon OX8 7LY. (01993 702549). **Directions:** From West on A40; take B4047 at island past Burford, follow signs for Witney West & N.W. Industrial Estates, thru Minster Lovell to West Witney, right into Downs Rd, ground on right. From the East on A40, 2nd turn off to Witney and follow signs for South & S.W. Industrial Estates, right at r'bout to traffic lights, left and proceed to r'bout, straight over, signs to West Witney Industrial Estate, left at lights onto B4047, left into Downs Rd, ground on right. Nearest BR station is Oxford 12 miles away.
Capacity: 3,500 **Cover:** 2,000 **Seats:** 280 **Floodlights:** Yes
Clubhouse: Members bar open seven days a week 6.30-11pm. Open all day Saturday. Hot food on matchdays.

PROGRAMME DETAILS:
Pages: 40 **Price:** £1
Editor:
A Bircher & K Bushnell
(01993 700634)

Club Shop: Selling programmes and souvenirs. Contact secretary. **Sponsors:** Regal (Witney) Ltd.

PREVIOUS - Name: Witney F.C. **Leagues:** Reading & Dist., Oxfordshire Senior, Hellenic 53-73.
Ground: Marriotts Close, Welch Way (pre-1992).

CLUB RECORDS - Attendance: 2,000 (approx) v Aston Villa, ground opening 1992. Competitive: 734 v Wealdstone 8/10/92. **Career Goalscorer:** Kenny Clarke 145. **Career Appearances:** Kevin Alder 402 (+6 sub). **Transfer fee paid:** £3,000 for Steve Jenkins (Cheltenham Town). **Transfer fee received:** £5,000 for John Bailey (Worcester City).

BEST SEASON - FA Trophy: Second Rd 78-79. **FA Amateur Cup:** Second Rd replay - 3 times, 66-67, 71-72, 72-73.
FA Cup: 1st Rd 71-72 (lost 0-3 at home to Romford).

Players progressing to Football League: Herbert Smith, Frank Clack (Birmingham City), Arthur Hall (Bristol Rovers 1959), David Moss (Swindon 1969), Jack Newman.
96-97 - Captain: Steve Tavinor **P.o.Y.:** Jason Caffel **Top scorer:** Jason Caffell (21)
Local Press: Witney Gazette, West Oxon Standard, Oxford Mail & Oxford Times.
Local Radio: Thames Valley FM, Fox (FM) Oxford.

HONOURS: Southern Lg Div 1 Nth 77-78; Hellenic Lg (8) 54-55 57-58 64-67 70-73 (R-up 53-54 67-68 69-70), Lg Cup (6), Prem Div Benevolent Cup 59-60 63-64; Oxon Snr Lg (5); Oxon Snr Cup (11).

Back Row (L-R); Tom Pegler, Kenny Clarke, Matt Timberlake, Andy Leach, Andy Martin, Gary Ackling (Coach). Front Row; Terry Merriman, Nigel Packer, Richard Bourne, Geoff Neville, Simon Anderson, Craig Dore.

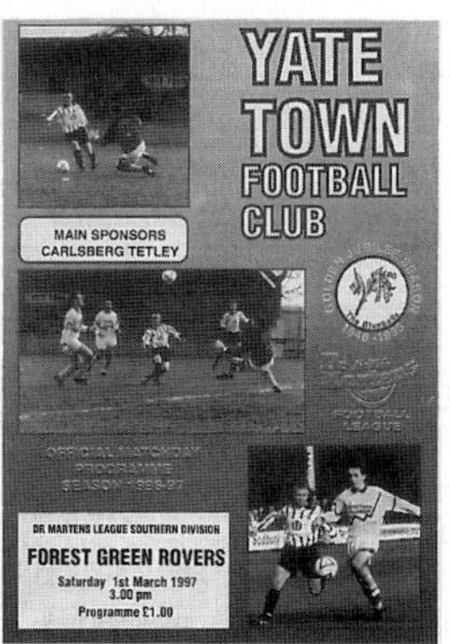

YATE TOWN

Formed: 1946 **Nickname:** The Bluebells
Colours: White/navy/navy.
Change colours: Tangerine/white/white
Midweek home matchday: Tuesday
Reserve Team's League: Bristol Suburban.

Chairman: R G Hawkins **President:** R Hewetson
Vice Chairman: D A Phillips
Secretary: Terry Tansley, 1 Tyning Close, Yate, Avon. BS17 4PN, 01454 324305
Press Officer / Commercial Manager: Bob Chester 01179 563674
Manager: John Freegard **Asst Manager:** Phil Purnell
Coach: Phil Purnell **Physio:** Steve Britton

PROGRAMME DETAILS:
Pages: 40 **Price:** £1
Editor: Bob Chester c/o Club

GROUND Address: Lodge Road, Yate, Bristol BS17 5LE (0454 228103).
Directions: M4 jct 18, A46 towards Stroud, then A432 to Yate. Turn right at top of railway bridge into North Road, first left past traffic lights. Five miles from Bristol Parkway BR main line station, half mile from Yate BR station. Buses 329, X68 and 328.
Capacity: 2,000 **Cover:** 236 **Seats:** 236 **Floodlights:** Yes
Clubhouse: Open every night and weekend lunchtimes. Skittles, darts, pool, live entertainment.
Club Shop: Selling programmes & usual souvenirs. Contact: Bob Chester 0117 956 3674
Sponsors: Homeworld.

PREVIOUS - Leagues: Gloucestershire County 68-83, Hellenic 83-89. **Name:** Yate YMCA 1946-70. **Grounds:** Yate Aerodrome 50-54, Newmans Field 54-60, Sunnyside Lane 60-84.

CLUB RECORDS - Attendance: 2,000 for Bristol Rovers v Bristol Rovers Past, Vaughan Jones testimonial 90. **Win:** 13-3 v Clevedon, Bristol Premier Comb 67-68. **Career Goalscorer:** Kevin Thaws. **Career Appearances:** Gary Hewlett. **Transfer fee paid:** None. **Transfer fee received:** £15,000 for Mike Davis (Bristol Rovers 93).

BEST SEASON - FA Vase: Fifth Round 1991-92
Players progressing to Football League: Richard Thompson (Newport County & Exeter City), Phil Purnell (Bristol Rovers), Darren Tilley (York City), Steve Winter (Walsall), Mike Davis (Bristol Rovers) 1993.
96-97 - Captain: Colin Towler **P.o.Y.:** Danny Iddles **Top scorer:** Dave Clarke
Local Press: Bristol Evening Post, Western Daily Press, North Avon Gazette. **Local Radio:** GWR, Radio Bristol.

HONOURS: Hellenic Lg(2) 87-89 (Div 1 R-up 84-85, Lg Skol Cup R-up 87-88), Glos Chal. Tphy 88-89 (R-up 78-79), Glos Snr Amtr Cup Sth 77-78 91-92(res) 92-93(res), Glos Snr Chal. Cup (Nth) R-up 89-90 92-93 94-95, Stroud Charity Cup R-up 74-75 81-82 84-85 (Sect. A Winners(6) 76-78 79-80 82-83 87-89), Berkeley Hosp. Prem. Cup(3) 73-75 80-81, S.W. Co's Sutton Vase 85-86.

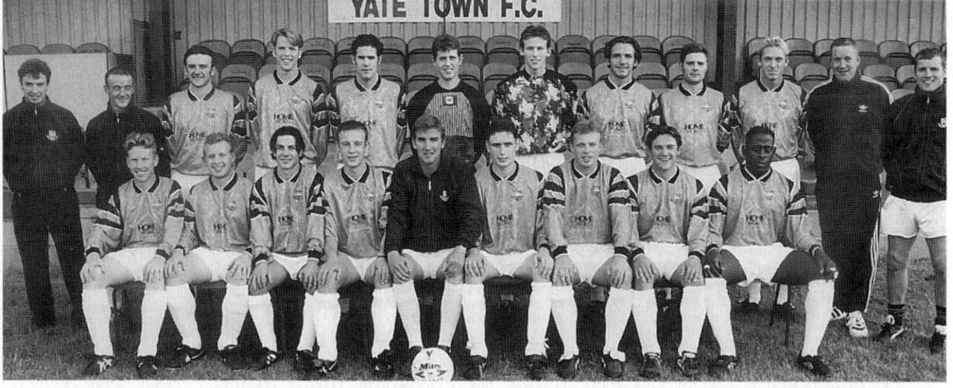

Back Row (L-R); Phil Purnell (Asst Mgr), Kriss Lee, Steve Tucker, Steve Peters, David Hope, Chris Bright, Shane Cook, Andy Hogg, Mark Madge, Paul Murgatroyd, Steve Britton (Physio), Marcus Bray (Coach). Front Row; Micky Airs, Marcus Jefferies, Alan Theobald, Danny Iddles, John Freegard (Player/Mgr), Mark Lippiatt, Alex Stocker, Darin Hunt, Kevin Thompson.

TIMBER & BUILDING MATERIALS

JEWSON

EASTERN COUNTIES LEAGUE

FEEDER TO: BEAZER HOMES LEAGUE

FOUNDED: 1935

Hon. Patron: Derek Needham **President:** Roger Pauley

Secretary: Colin Lamb, 3 Land Close, Clacton-on-Sea, Essex CO16 8UJ (01255 436398)

At the halfway point of the season the outcome appeared a foregone conclusion: but on the final weekend of an extraordinary year there were three teams in with at least a mathematical chance of the title.

For Wroxham this was their third championship of the decade and perhaps the hardest earned. It was sealed on the back of an unbeaten run that stretched from the end of September to the end of April, and included a 3-1 victory over the previous runaway leaders, Harwich, at the Royal Oak. A sign of their quality could be gleaned from their shock FA Cup victory over Doc Martens League high flyers King's Lynn, and star striker Paul Warne is believed to have been watched by Football League scouts.

The run of Wisbech to finish second, thus securing a place in the DML, was perhaps more remarkable as it contained lengthy runs in both the Vase and the FA Cup. For the second year running the Fenmen reached the First Round Proper of the Cup before going out to St Albans, the bigger disappointment being that they were not paired with a League club. They overcame a 22 point deficit on Harwich only in the final game of the entire Jewson League season - watched by a mammoth crowd of 932, they defeated Lowestoft 5-1 to ensure their promotion place.

One has to have some sympathy for Harwich supporters; at the end of January it seemed they could not lose the title race and the second half of the season must have seemed to them like some kind of unpleasant horror movie. They gained some compensation via the League Cup, beating First Division Haverhill Rovers 2-0 in the Rosemary Lane, Halstead final. To add to their woe manager Colin Hill resigned shortly after the end of the season.

In the First Division the battle for the promotion spots went the way of Ely City and Maldon. Ely clinched the title with something to spare and David Pinkowski's side will hope to emulate the example of Gorleston by challenging at the top after being promoted. Maldon's elevation to the Premier Division fully vindicates their decision to join the JECL from the Essex Senior League, and their sparkling ground (including enormous dug-outs!) will be a welcome addition. Elsewhere there were some intriguing sub-plots as a classic season drew to a close. Soham and Bury both reached the semi-finals of the inaugural Anglia TV 5-a-side tournament before being knocked out : Soham then defeated Bury in the third place play-off to win a cheque for £250. Gorleston's return to the top flight coincided with a resurgence for Yarmouth, and the pair indulged in a furious scrap for local honours, the Bloaters finishing ahead of the Greens.

And at Brewer's Green Lane the career of an undoubted legend came to a close. Bill Punton retired from management after a 7 year stint at Diss and brought the curtain down in appropriate style, his final home game being against Yarmouth, whom he managed for the previous 21 years. As a player he won honours at Norwich City, and as a manager he would take Diss to the FA Vase in 1994. Bringing the wheel full circle, Diss went straight back to Yarmouth and snapped up Paul Chick as Punton's replacement.

Jamie Hill

FINAL LEAGUE TABLES 1996 / 97

Premier Division

		P	W	D	L	F	A	Pts	GD
1	Wroxham	44	34	7	3	122	25	109	97
2	Wisbech Town	44	32	8	4	141	37	104	104
3	Harwich & P'ston	44	32	8	4	133	34	104	99
4	Diss Town	44	29	4	11	81	41	91	40
5	Gt Yarmouth Tn	44	26	7	11	87	51	85	36
6	Gorleston	44	26	5	13	86	54	83	32
7	Bury Town	44	23	10	11	101	54	79	47
8	Newmarket Tn	44	23	8	13	97	75	77	22
9	Lowestoft Tn	44	22	9	13	84	56	75	28
10	Stowmarket Tn	44	22	4	18	74	62	70	12
11	Tiptree United	44	19	8	17	64	59	65	5
12	Halstead Town	44	19	6	19	87	79	63	8
13	Soham Tn Rngrs	44	17	7	20	82	87	58	-5
14	Fakenham Town	44	15	11	18	78	80	56	-2
15	Warboys Town	44	15	10	19	62	72	55	-10
16	Woodbridge Tn	44	12	12	20	51	63	48	-12
17	Sudbury Wdrs	44	13	5	26	61	100	44	-39
18	Felixstowe Pt & Tn	44	11	6	27	56	103	39	-47
19	Watton United	44	10	6	28	49	106	36	-57
20	Sudbury Tn Res	44	7	7	30	46	96	28	-50
21	Clacton Town	44	7	5	32	43	156	26	-113
22	Hadleigh United	44	5	8	31	41	128	23	-87
23	March Town Utd	44	5	3	36	25	133	18	-108

First Division

		P	W	D	L	F	A	Pts	GD
1	Ely City	34	27	5	2	93	36	86	57
2	Histon	34	21	8	5	80	32	71	48
3	Ipswich Wdrs	34	21	6	7	86	35	69	45
4	Maldon Town	34	21	6	7	89	44	69	45
5	Needham Mkt	34	19	11	4	67	24	68	43
6	Swaffham Tn	34	13	14	7	63	43	53	20
7	Brightingsea Utd	34	13	14	7	50	39	53	11
8	Haverhill Rovers	34	15	7	12	54	46	52	8
9	Stanway Rovers	34	15	7	12	55	49	52	6
10	Whitton United	34	10	9	15	45	58	39	-13
11	Norwich United	34	10	8	16	48	61	38	-13
12	Cambridge City Rs	34	10	7	17	51	68	37	-17
13	Downham Town	34	9	4	21	45	88	31	-43
14	Thetford Town	34	7	9	18	34	66	30	-32
15	Mildenhall Town	34	7	8	19	35	61	29	-26
16	Cornard United	34	6	8	20	40	70	26	-30
17	Somersham Tn	34	5	10	19	23	69	25	-46
18	Chatteris Town	34	2	9	23	27	96	15	-69

JEWSON AWARDS 1996-97

	Premier Division Club of Month	First Division Club of Month	Good Behaviour Award
September	Stowmarket Town	Ely City	Stowmarket Town
October	Wisbech Town	Histon	Whitton United
November	Gt Yarmouth Town	Haverhill Rovers	Whitton United
December	Harwich & Parkeston	Stanway Rovers	Halstead Town
January	Tiptree United	Norwich United	Newmarket Town
February	Wroxham	Ipswich Wanderers	Sudbury Wanderers
March	Wisbech Town	Swaffham Town	Histon
April	Wroxham	Ely City	Swaffham Town

LEADING GOALSCORERS 1996-97

Premier Division

41	Peter Munns	Wisbech Town
34	John Kemp	Harwich & Parkeston
29	David Fleming	Harwich & Parkeston
	Ian Williams	Wisbech Town
28	Jackie Gallagher	Wisbech Town
27	Paul Warne	Wroxham
24	Stuart Jopling	Diss Town
23	Alistair Suddery	Newmarket Town
21	Carl Henry	Bury Town
	Andy Road	Lowestoft Town
	Colin Danby	Gorleston
20	Matthew Metcalf	Wroxham
	Andy Smiles	Sudbury Wanderers
19	Lee Sharp	Newmarket Town
	Dale Vince	Bury Town
	Mark Howard	Fakenham Town
	Paul Thompson	Gorleston
	Andy Morton	Soham Town Rangers
	Stephen Day	Sudbury Wanderers
	Simon Mead	Warboys Town

First Division

30	Glen Driver	Needham Market
24	Scott Witney	Maldon Town
22	Spencer Clay	Ely City
21	Ritchie Barker	Ipswich Wanderers
19	Stephen Card	Maldon Town
	Matthew Eden	Ely City
	Steve Buckle	Ipswich Wanderers
18	David Gipp	Cornard United
16	Steve McKenna	Ely City
	Neil Harris	Maldon Town
15	Stuart Vaughan	Brightlingsea United
	Mark Blockwell	Swaffham Town
14	John Harris	Downham Town
	Derrin Williams	Haverhill Rovers
	Neil Kennedy	Histon
	Tom Noble	Stanway Rovers

PREVIOUS CHALLENGE CUP WINNERS

1990-91 Histon beat Wroxham 2-1
1991-92 Norwich United beat Gorleston 6-2 in a replay after the initial match drawn 2-2
1992-93 Wroxham beat Cornard United 6-0
1993-94 Woodbridge Town beat Chattons Town 2-0
1994-95 Wisbech Town beat Newmarket Town 3-1 after extra time
1995-96 Halstead Town beat Fakenham Town 4-0
1996-97 Harwich & Parkeston beat Haverhill Rovers 2-0

CLUBS TO HAVE COMPLETED THE DOUBLE OF LEAGUE CHAMPIONSHIP AND LEAGUE CUP IN THE SAME SEASON

1936-36 Harwich & Parkeston (Joint Champions)
1951-52 Gillingham Reserves
1953-54 King's Lynn
1963-64 Bury Town
1965-66 Lowestoft Town
1966-67 Lowestoft Town
1971-72 Wisbech Town
1977-78 Lowestoft Town
1981-82 Tiptree United
1986-87 Sudbury Town
1988-89 Sudbury Town
1989-90 Sudbury Town
1992-93 Wroxham
1995-96 Halstead Town

PREMIER DIVISION CLUBS 1997-98

BURY TOWN

Chairman: Colin Hurley **Vice Chairman:** Brian Lafflin **President:** Cyril Elsey.
Secretary: Mrs Wendy Turner, 64 Winthrop Rd., Bury-St-Edmunds, Suffolk. IP33 3UF (01284 753688)
Manager/Coach: Tony Godden **Asst Manager:** Keith Vince **Physio:** John Chandler
Ground: Ram Meadow, Cotton Lane, Bury St Edmunds, Suffolk IP33 1XP, (01284 754721).
Directions: Leave A14 at sign to central Bury St Edmunds, follow signs to town centre at exit r'bout, at next r'bout 1st exit into Northgate St, left at 'T' junct (lights) into Mustow St, left immediately into Cotton Lane - grd 350 yds on right, through 'Pay & Display' car park. 10 mins from station.
Capacity: 3,500 **Cover:** 1,500 **Seats:** 300 **Floodlights:** Yes **Club Shop:** Yes
Clubhouse: Members'/Public Bars open at matchdays
Programme: 40 pages 80p **Editor:** Jason Wakeling **Press Officer:** Ron Kent
Colours: All blue **Change colours:** All red. **Sponsors:** The Flying Fortress
Midweek matchday: Tuesday **Formed:** 1872 **Nickname:** The Blues
Best Season - FA Cup: 1st Rd replay 68-69 (lost 0-3 at AFC Bournemouth after 0-0 draw). **FA Vase:** Qtr Finals 88-89. **FA Trophy:** 2nd Rd 70-71
Previous Lges: Norfolk & Suffolk/ Essex & Suffolk Border/ Eastern Co's 35-64 76-87/ Metropolitan 64-71.
Players progressing to Football League: D Lewis (Gillingham, Preston), L Carberry (Ipswich), T Bly (Norwich 56, Peterborough), T Pearce (Ipswich), G Stevens (Brighton, Spurs), S Milton (Ipswich 90)
96-97 - Captain: M Wales **P.o.Y.:** D Vince **Top scorer:** C Henry
Records - Goalscorer: Doug Tooley 58. **Appearances:** Doug Tooley. **Attendance:** 2,500 v Enfield, FA Cup 3rd Qualifying Rd 1986.
Honours: Eastern Counties Lg 63-64, R-up 37-38, Lg Cup 61-62 63-64; Metropolitan Lg 65-66, R-up 67-68 70-71, Lg Cup 67-68, Professional Cup 65-66; Suffolk Premier Cup (9); Suffolk Senior Cup 36-37 37-38 38-39 44-45 84-85.

CLACTON TOWN

Chairman: Ron Ayton **President:** **Manager:** John Herbert & David Lowe
Secretary: Mrs Sandra Harris, 57 Coopers Lane, Clacton-on-Sea, Essex CO15 2BY (01255 476133).
Ground: The Rushgreen Bowl, Rushgreen Road, Clacton-on-Sea (01255 432590).
Directions: A133 to Clacton, at r'bout right into St Johns Rd, 4th left Cloes Lane, 3rd right Rushgreen Rd, ground approximately half mile on right. From B1027 take main Jaywick turn off (Jaywick Lane), then 2nd left (after about a mile) into Rushgreen Rd. Ground 400 yds. 2 miles from Clacton (BR), buses 3, 5 or 5a to Coopers Lane/Rushgreen Rd.
Seats: 200 **Cover:** Yes **Capacity:** 2,500 **Floodlights:** Yes **Founded:** 1892.
Clubhouse: Licensed club. Open 7-11pm Mon-Sat, 12-3pm Sat-Sun. Refreshments & snacks available.
Colours: All Royal blue **Change colours:** All red **Shop:** Yes
Programme: 40 pages, 50p **Editor:** Larry Warren (01255 475182) **Nickname:** Seasiders.
Midweek Matches: Tuesday **Previous Leagues:** Eastern Co's 35-37 38-58/ Southern 58-64.
Players progressing to Football League: Vivian Woodward (Spurs, Chelsea, England), Mick Everitt (Arsenal, Northampton), Christian McLean (Bristol Rovers).
Record Attendance: 3,505 v Romford, FA Cup 1st Qualifying Rd 1952 (at Old Road).
Honours: Southern Lg Div 1 59-60; Eastern Co's Lg R-up 36-37 53-54 64-65 74-75 (Lg Cup 73-74); Eastern F/lit Cup 95-96; East Anglian Cup 53-54; Worthington Evans Cup 56-57 67-68 74-75; FA Cup 1st Rd (v Southend) 60-61.

DISS TOWN

Chairman: Des Tebble **President:** R A Gooderham **Treasurer:** Noel Mullenger.
Secretary: Richard Upson, Bamburgh House, Brewers Green Lane, Diss, Norfolk IP22 3QP (01379 642923).
Manager: Paul Chick **Asst Manager:** Donnie Pye **Physio:** Peter Etheridge
Ground: Brewers Green Lane, Diss (01379 651223).
Directions: Just off B1066 Diss-Thetford road, near Roydon School. One and a half miles from Diss (BR).
Seats: 280 **Cover:** Yes **Capacity:** 2,500 **Floodlights:** Yes **Club Shop:** Yes
Clubhouse: Open evenings (except Sunday), Sat/Sun lunchtimes, and matchdays.
Programme: 16 pages, 50p **Editor:** G Enderby (01953 455979)
Colours: Tangerine/navy/tangerine **Change colours:** White/navy/tangerine.
Founded: 1888. **Nickname:** Tangerines. **Sponsors:** Diss Fasteners
Midweek Matches: Tuesday **Reserve's League:** Anglian Combination.
Previous Leagues: Norwich & District/ Norfolk & Suffolk 35-64/ Anglian Combination 64-82.
Players progressing to the Football League: A Thurlow (Man City), M Cawston (Norwich), T Whymark (Ipswich), C Stafford, P Gibbs (Colchester)
96-97 - Captain: Garry Smith **Top Scorer:** Paul Smith **P.o.Y.:** Lee Bray
Record Attendance: 1,731 v Atherton LR, FA Vase SF 1st leg 19/3/94
Honours: FA Vase 94-95 (QF 91-92); Eastern Co's Lg Div 1 91-92; Anglian Comb. 76-77 78-79, R-up 74-75, Div 1 67-68 73-74, Lg Cup 67-68 79-80 81-82; Norfolk & Suffolk Lg R-up 55-56, Applegate Cup 56-57 57-58(jt), R-up 55-56; Norfolk Snr Cup 74-75 95-96; Jewson Prem Lge R-up 95-96.

ELY CITY

Chairman: Brian Jordan **Manager:** David Pinkowski & Tony Lyes
Secretary: Derek Oakey, 11 Frederick Talbot Close, Soham, Nr Ely, Cambs CB7 5EY (01353 722141).
Ground: Unwin Sports Ground, Downham Road (01353 662035).
Directions: A10 Ely by-pass turn off for Downham. 3 miles (approx) from Ely (BR).
Seats: 150 **Cover:** 350 **Capacity:** 1,500 **Floodlights:** Yes **Founded:** 1885
Clubhouse: Open matchdays, refreshments available
Colours: All red **Change colours:** Jade/black/jade **Nickname:** Robins
Programme: 20p **Editor:** John Lawson **Midweek Matches:** Tuesday
Previous Lges: Peterborough/ Central Alliance 58-60.
Record Gate: 260 v Soham, Eastern Co's Lg Div 1, 12/4/93. *At old ground: 4,260 v Torquay, FA Cup 56-57*
Honours: Cambs Snr Cup 47-48, Eastern Co's Lg R-up 69-70 (Lg Cup 79-80), FA Cup 1st Rd 56-56 (2-6 v Torquay).

FAKENHAM TOWN

Chairman: Tony Fisher **President:** B E Woodhouse **Manager:** Mark Barham
Secretary: Eddie Linnell, 40 Warren Avenue, Fakenham, Norfolk NR21 8NP (01328 855445).
Ground: Clipbush Lane, Fakenham (01328 856222).
Directions: Corner of A148 & Clipbush Lane
Seats: 264 **Cover:** 500 **Capacity:** 3,000 **Floodlights:** Yes **Founded:** 1884.
Clubhouse: Bar, TV. Refreshments available **Club Shop:** Yes.
Colours: Amber & black/black/black. **Change colours:** Red/white/red.
Programme: 32 pages, 50p **Editor:** John Cushion
Midweek Matchday: Tuesday. **Sponsors:** Wensum Lodge Hotel **Nickname:** Ghosts.
Previous Leagues: N Norfolk 1884-1910/ Norwich & Dist 10-35/ Norfolk & Suffolk 35-64/ Anglian Comb 64-87.
Reserves' League: Anglian Comb. **Record Gate:** 1,000 v Norwich City, floodlight inauguration.
Players progressing to the Football League: Nolan Keeley (Scunthorpe & Lincoln).
Honours: Norfolk Snr Cup 70-71 72-73 73-74 91-92 93-94 94-95; Eastern Co's Lg Div 1 R-up 91-92; Anglian Comb. Cup 78-79.

FELIXSTOWE PORT & TOWN

Chairman: Dave Ashford **Manager:** Paul Adams **Fixture Sec:** Mike Gosling (01394 279758)
Secretary: Steve Page, 11A Lonsdale Close, Ipswich, Suffolk IP4 4HB (01473 712613).
Ground: Dellwood Avenue, Felixstowe (01394 282917).
Directions: A45 to Felixstowe. Turn right at 3rd r'bout then 1st left - ground 100 yds on left. 5 mins from Felixstowe (BR) and town centre.
Seats: 200 **Cover:** 200 **Capacity:** 2,000 **Floodlights:** Yes **Founded:** 1890.
Clubhouse: Bar, snack bar, TV, darts, pool table. Snacks available
Colours: White/blue/gold. **Change:** Blue/white/yellow & blue **Nickname:** Seasiders.
Programme: 16 pages, 30p **Editor:** Phil Griffiths **Club Shop:** Yes
Prev. Leagues: Essex & Suffolk Border/ Ipswich & Dist. **Midweek Matches:** Wednesday
Record Attendance: 1,500 v Ipswich Town, floodlight inauguration 25/1/91.
Honours: Suffolk Senior Cup 66-67 74-75.

GORLESTON

Chairman: Kevin Antcliffe **President:** Jimmy Jones **Manager:** M.Hubble & Steve Foyster
Secretary: A Ottley, 60 Peterhouse Ave., Gorleston, Gt Yarmouth, Norfolk NR31 7PZ (01493 603353).
Ground: Emerald Park, Woodfarm Lane, Gorleston, Great Yarmouth (01493 602802).
Directions: On Magdalen Estate - follow signs to Crematorium, turn left and follow road to ground. Five and a half miles from Great Yarmouth Vauxhall (BR).
Seats: 250 **Cover:** 4,000 **Capacity:** 5,000 **Floodlights:** Yes **Club Shop:** Yes
Clubhouse: Bar, colour TV, pool table, darts, snacks. Matchday Tea, coffee, cold drinks, burgers, hotdogs, rolls.
Programme: 56/60 pages 70p **Editor:** Brian Bunn (01493 843114) **Nickname:** Greens.
Colours: All Green. **Change colours:** All white. **Founded:** 1884.
Midweek Matchday: Tuesday. **Record Attendance:** 4,473 v Orient, FA Cup 1st Rd 29/11/51.
Previous Leagues: Gt Yarmouth & Dist/Norfolk & Suffolk/ Anglian Comb.
Past players progressing to the Football League: J Joblins (Norwich), M Bailey (Wolves), D Stringer (Norwich), R Carter (Aston Villa), D Carter (Man City), A Brown (Charlton), S Morgan (Cambridge), P Gibbs (Colchester).
96-97 Captain: **96-97 P.O.Y.:** **96-97 Top Scorer:**
Honours: Eastern Co's Lg 52-53 72-73 79-80 80-81; Lge Cup 55-56; Norf. Snr Cup(13)(R-up 25); Anglian Comb. 68-69, Norf. & Suf. Lg (7); E Anglian Cup (3); Jewson Lge Div 1 95-96; FA Cup 1st Rd 51-52 57-58:

GREAT YARMOUTH TOWN

Chairman: Colin Smith **General Manager:** Dale Gordon **Manager:** Paul Tong
Secretary: Brian Benge, 48 Reynolds Avenue, Caister, Gt Yarmouth, Norfolk NR30 5QE
Ground: Wellesey Recreation Ground, Wellesey Road (01493 842936).
Directions: Just off Marine Parade, 200 yds north of Britannia Pier. Half a mile from Vauxhall (BR).
Seats: 500 **Cover:** 2,100 **Capacity:** 3,600 **Floodlights:** Yes **Club Shop:** No.
Clubhouse: (01493 8443373). Dancehall, Committee Room, darts, pool. Hot & cold food available
Programme: 20 pages, 50p **Editor:** Gerry Brown **Nickname:** Bloaters.
Colours: Amber & black stripes/black/black. **Change colours:** White/red/red.
Midweek Matches: Tuesday **Previous Leagues:** Norfolk & Suffolk **Founded:** 1897.
Players progressing to the Football League: R Hollis (Norwich), M Blyth & N Keeley (Scunthorpe), S Davy (West Ham), K Ready (Aston Villa), G Butcher (Blackburn).
96-97 - Captain: Mark Vincent **Top Scorer:** Ricky Martin **P.o.Y.:** Leighton Miller
Record Attendance: 8,944 v Crystal Palace, FA Cup 1st Rd 52-53.
Honours: Eastern Co's Lg 68-69 (R-up 56-57 67-68 77-78 78-79, Lg Cup 37-38 74-75 80-81), East Anglian Cup(3), Norfolk Snr Cup(12)(R-up(22)), Norfolk Premier Cup(twice shared), Norfolk & Suffolk Lg 13-14 26-27 27-28, FA Vase SF 82-83, FA Cup 2nd Rd(2)(1st Rd(1)), Anglian Comb. Cup 65-66(res), E Anglian Lg 56-57(res).

HALSTEAD TOWN

Chairman: Mick Coe **Vice-Chairman:** John Theedom **President:** Mr E J R McDowell
Secretary: Stephen Webber, 12 Ravens Ave, Halstead, Essex CO9 1NZ (01787 476959).
Manager: Steve Parnell **Physio:** B Dunster.
Ground: Rosemary Lane, Broton Ind Est, Halstead, Essex CO9 2HR (01787 472082). **Directions:** A131 Chelmsford to Braintree - follow signs to Halstead. In Halstead, 1st left after Police Station, then 1st right, and first left to ground.
Seats: 312 **Cover:** 400. **Capacity:** 2,000 **Floodlights:** Yes **Founded:** 1879.
Clubhouse: Open evenings and matchdays. **Midweek Matches:** Tuesday
Colours: White/black/white **Change colours:** Red/white/red **Programme:** 50p. **Editor:** Paul Downes
Previous Leagues: Nth Essex/ Halstead & Dist./ Haverhill/ Essex & Suffolk Border/ Essex Snr 80-88.
Players progressing to the Football League: Steve Allen (Wimbledon Physio).
Record Attendance: 4,000 v Walthamstow Avenue, Essex Senior Cup 1949.
Honours: Eastern Co's Lg 94-95 95-96, R-up 93-94 (Div 1 R-up 89-90), Cup 95-96; Essex Senior Trophy 94-95 96-97; Knight Floodlit Cup R-up 90-91; Essex & Suffolk Border Lg 57-59 77-78 94-95(res), (R-up 49-50 54-55 60-61), Div 1(res) 94-95); Essex Snr Lg Cup R-up 79-80; Essex Jnr Cup 01-02 46-47 (R-up 00-01).

HARWICH & PARKESTON

Chairman: Paul Revell **President:** J Whitmore **Manager:** Steve Wright/Jimmy Minter
Secretary: Andy Schooler, 21 The Vineway, Harwich, Essex CO12 4AX **Press Officer:** Carl Allan
Ground: Royal Oak, Main Road, Dovercourt, Harwich CO12 4AA (01255 503649).
Directions: On main road into Dovercourt. 600 yds from Dovercourt (BR).
Seats: 350 **Cover:** 1,000 **Capacity:** 5,000 **Floodlights:** Yes **Founded:** 1877.
Clubhouse details: Open every day. Dances, bingo, darts, pool, function room. **Club Shop:** Yes
Colours: White & black/black/black **Change colours:** Mauve & white/white/mauve **Nickname:** Shrimpers.
Programme: 28 pages, 40p **Editor:** Carl Allen **Midweek Matches:** Tuesday
Reserve Lge: Essex & Suffolk Border Prem. Div.
Previous Leagues: Eastern Co's 35-37 38-64/ Essex County 37-38/ Athenian 64-73 83-84/ Isthmian 73-83.
Players progressing to Football League: I Gillespie (C Palace, Ipswich), G Waites, K Sanderson, I Brown (Bristol C 91)
Record Attendance: 5,649 v Romford, FA Amat Cup 4th Rd 1938
Honours: FA Amateur Cup R-up 1898-99 52-53; FA Vase QF 90-91; Eastern Counties Lg 35-36(jnt) (Lg Cup 35-36 36-37 96-97); Essex County Lg 37-38; Athenian Lg Div 1 R-up 65-66 (Div 2 64-65, Lg Cup 64-65); Essex Senior Cup 1898-99 36-37; Essex Senior Trophy 89-90; AFA Senior Cup 35-36 36-37; Worthington Evans Cup 80-81.

HISTON

Chairman: Gareth Baldwin **President:** G P Muncey **Manager:** Simon Allen
Secretary: Gareth Baldwin, 5 Caxton Lane, Foxton, Cambridge CB2 6SR (01223 872246).
Ground: Bridge Road, Impington, Cambridge (01223 232301).
Directions: Leave A14 northern Cambridge bypass on B1049 (signposted Histon and Cottenham). Ground half a mile on right. 5 miles from Cambridge (BR). Bus No. 104.
Seats: 250 **Cover:** 200 **Capacity:** 2,250 **Floodlights:** Yes **Founded:** 1904.
Clubhouse details: Bar/lounge open Tues-Sun evenings, Sun lunctimes and matchdays. Snacks available
Programme: 16 pages, 30p. **Editor:** Gareth Baldwin. **Record Attendance:** 2,400 v K. Lynn, FA Cup.
Colours: Red and black/black/black. **Change colours:** All blue & white **Midweek Matches:** Tuesday
Previous Leagues: Cambridgeshire 04-48/ Spartan 48-60/ Delphian 60-63/ Athenian 63-65.
Honours: Eastern Co's Lg Div 1 R-up 96-97, Cup 90-91; Cambridge Invitation Cup 77-78 79-80 96-97 (R-up 50-51 52-53 53-54); Spartan Lg Div 1 (East) 50-51; Cambs Chall Cup; Cambs Lg Section; Kershaw Sen Lge A 96-97, Cup 96-97; Auto Trader Lge & Cup (U18) 96-97.

Fakenham Town's Simon Barnes (left) & Richard Dyer (right) in action against Watton United at Clipbush Park.
Photo - John Cushion

Histon FC: Back Row (L-R); Gareth Baldwin (Chr/Sec), Pat Jennings (Guest). Middle Row; Simon Allen (1st Team Mgr), Steve Low (Asst 1st team Mgr), Paul Sdadrack (Ass 2nd Team Mgr), Nacer Relizani (2nd Team Mgr). Front Row; Bobby Broom (Yth Mgr), Jerry Edwards (Asst Yth Mgr), Barry Ferdinando (Sponsor).

LOWESTOFT TOWN

Chairman: Roy Harper **President:** C Harrod **Manager:** Michael Chapman
Secretary: Terry Lynes, 156 Denmark Road, Lowestoft, Suffolk NR33 2EL (01502 564034).
Ground: Crown Meadow, Love Rd, Lowestoft (01502 573818). **Directions:** Just off A12, 10 mins from Lowestoft (BR).
Seats: 466 **Cover:** 500 **Capacity:** 1,850 **Floodlights:** Yes **Founded:** 1890.
Clubhouse: Pub hours, Snacks available **Club Shop:** Yes
Colours: Royal/white/royal **Change colours:** All red **Nickname:** Blues.
Programme: 20 pages, 60p **Editor:** Rachel Harrow **Midweek Matches:** Tuesday
Sponsors: SLP **Reserves' Lge:** Anglian Combination **Previous League:** Norfolk & Suffolk 1897-1935
Players progressing to Football League: Eddie Spearitt (Ipswich 1965), Nigel Cassidy (Norwich 1967), Richard Money (Scunthorpe 1973), Graham Franklin (Southend 1977).
Record - Attendance: 5,000 v Watford, FA Cup 1st Rd 67. **Goalscorer:** M Tooley 383. **Appearances:** C Peck 629.
Honours: Eastern Co's Lg(8) 35-36(joint) 37-38 62-63 64-65 67-68 69-71 77-78 (Lg Cup(7) 38-39 54-55 65-67 68-69 75-76 83-84), Norf. & Suffolk Lg(8) 1897-99 1900-04 28-29 30-31, Suffolk Prem. Cup(5) 66-67 71-72 74-75 78-80, Suffolk Snr Cup(10) 02-03 22-24 25-26 31-32 35-36 46-49 55-56, E Anglian Cup(10), FA Cup 1st Rd 26-27 38-39 66-67 77-78, Anglian Comb. (Reserves) 77-78 79-80 (Lg Cup 76-77), E Anglian Lg (Reserves) 57-58 63-64.

NEWMARKET TOWN

Chairman: Alf Collen **President:** M J Nicholas **Manager:** Richard Datson
Fixture Secretary: Terry Osborne, 1 Falmouth Street, Newmarket CB8 0LE (01638 601310).
Ground: Cricketfield Road, off New Cheveley Road, Newmarket (01638 663637).
Directions: 400 yds Newmarket (BR) - turn right into Green Rd, right at cr/rds New Cheveley Rd, grd at top on left
Seats: 144 **Cover:** 150 **Capacity:** 1,750 **Floodlights:** Yes **Founded:** 1877.
Clubhouse: Matchdays only. Refreshments available
Programme: 50p **Editor:** Tony Pringle (01638 669438) **Midweek Matches:** Tuesday
Colours: Yellow & navy/navy/navy **Change Colours:** Maroon & blue/maroon/maroon **Nickname:** Jockeys.
Previous League: Bury Snr/ Ipswich Snr/ Essex & Suffolk Border/ Utd Co's 34-37/ Eastern Co's 37-52.
Best F.A. Cup year: 4th Qualifying Rd 92-93 (lost 0-2 at home to Hayes).
Players progressing to the Football League: Mick Lambert (Ipswich), M Wright (Northampton), G Tweed (Coventry), R Fuller (Charlton), Colin Vowden (Camb.Utd.)
96-97 - Captain: Dave Brown **Top Scorer:** Ali Suddery **P.o.Y.:** Kevin Crisp
Record Attendance: 2,701 v Abbey Utd (now Cambridge Utd), FA Cup 1st Qualifying Rd 1/10/49.
Honours: Suffolk Snr Cup 34-35 93-94; Cambs Invitation Cup 58-59; Cambs Challenge Cup 21-22 26-27; Cambs Snr Lg, 19-20; Ipswich Snr Lg 30-31 31-32 32-33 33-34; Peterborough Lg 57-58; Suffolk Premier Cup 93-94 94-95 96-97.

SOHAM TOWN RANGERS

Chairman: M Robinson **President:** J Mann
Secretary: Mrs Wendy Gammon, 32 Broad Piece, Soham, Cambs CB7 5EL (01353 722139).
Manager: R Goodjohn **Coach:** Mick Drury
Ground: Julius Martins Lane, Soham, Cambs (01353 720732). **Directions:** A142 between Newmarket and Ely
Seats: 200 **Cover:** 1,500 **Capacity:** 2,000 **Floodlights:** Yes **Shop:** Yes
Clubhouse: General bar, Stud Bar, Lounge Bar. **Midweek Matchday:** Wednesday
Programme: 50p **Editor:** Graham Eley**Founded:** 1947. **Nickname:** Town or Rangers.
Colours: Green & white/white/white **Change colours:** Blue/black/black
Sponsors: Clark & Butcher & Able Acess Ltd **Reserves League:** Cambs Prem. B.
96-97 - Captain: **P.o.Y.:** P Braybrooke **Top Scorer:** A Morton
Record Attendance: 3,000 v Pegasus, FA Amateur Cup 1963. **Previous Leagues:** Peterborough & Dist.
Honours: Eastern Co's Lg Div 1 R-up 92-93; P'boro. Lg(3).

STOWMARKET TOWN

Chairman: Derek Barnard. **President:** John Bultitude **Fixture Sec:** Mrs Gillingham (01449 674507)
Secretary: Colin Davies, 15 Winchester Close, Stowmarket, (01449 615632)
Manager: Trevor Wardlaw **Coach:** David King **Physio:** John Chandler
Ground: Green Meadows Stadium, Bury Road, Stowmarket (01449 612533). **Directions:** About 800 yds from Stowmarket BR station - turn right at 1st lights and head out of town over r'bout into Bury Road - ground on right.
Seats: 200 **Cover:** 450 **Capacity:** 2,000 **Floodlights:** Yes **Club Shop:** Yes
Clubhouse: Bar open 6.30pm onwards Mon-Fri, weekends 12.0pm onwards. Matchday food available.
Programme: 20 pages, 50p **Editor:** John Gillingham (01449 674507). **Founded:** 1883.
Colours: Gold/black/black **Change colours:** All Red **Nickname:** Stow
Reserves' Lge: Essex & Suffolk Border **Record Attendance:** 1,200 v Ipswich Town, friendly July 1994.
Midweek Matches: Wednesday **Previous Leagues:** Ipswich & Dist./ Essex & Suffolk Border 25-52.
Players progressing to Football League: Craig Oldfield (Colchester), Les Tibbott, Ted Phillips & Brian Klug (Ipswich).
96-97 - Captain: Roger Aldis **P.o.Y.:** Nigel Vincent **Top Scorer:** Ian Gedny
Honours: Eastern Co's Lg R-up 91-92, Suffolk Premier Cup(4), Suffolk Snr Cup(10), Suffolk Jnr Cup.

SUDBURY TOWN

Chairman: Phil Turner **President:** H D J Yallop.
Secretary: David Webb, 6 Melford Road, Sudbury, Suffolk CO10 6LS (01787 372352).
Manager: Richie Powling. **Asst Mgr/Coach:** David Crown. **Physio:** Tony Brightwell
Ground: Priory Stadium, Priory Walk, Sudbury, Suffolk (01787 379095).
Directions: Take Friars Street from town centre, pass cricket ground and continue to the 'Ship & Star'. Left into Priory Walk and continue to ground. Half mile and three quarters of a mile from bus and rail stations respectively.
Capacity: 5,000 **Cover:** 1,000 **Seats:** 300 **Floodlights:** Yes **Founded:** 1885
Clubhouse: Open on matchdays and for functions. Pool, darts & dancehall. (01787 379095)
Colours: All yellow **Change colours:** Red & black/black/black **Shop:** Yes
Programme: 48 pages £1. **Editors:** Darren Witt/Kalvin Sargeant.
Sponsors: Fairview Homes & Wheelers (Timber & Building). **Nickname:** The Borough
Previous Leagues: Suffolk & Ipswich/ Essex & Suffolk Border/ Eastern Counties 55-90.
Midweek matchday: Tuesday **Record Attendance:** 4,700 v Ipswich Town, testimonial 1978.
Best Season - F.A.Vase: R-up 88-89. **F.A.Trophy:** 3rd Rd.Proper 95-96. **FA Cup:** 4th Qual Rd 5 times
Players progressing to Football League: Gilbert Dowsett (Tottenham Hotpur 52), John Taylor (Cambridge Utd 88), Steve McGavin (promoted with Colchester Utd 92).
Hons: Beazer Champ 93-94; Southern Lg Cup 93-94 (Southern Div R-up 93-94), Eastern Counties Lg (7), R-up (6), Lg Cup (6), Suffolk Premier Cup (13), R-up(7), Suffolk Senior Cup (5); East Anglian Cup 85-86 86-87 91-92, R-up 83-84 95-96; Essex & Suffolk Border Lg (5); E.S.B.L.Cup Winners 49-50, R-Up 46-47; Eastern Floodlit Group 93-94 94-95.

Sudbury Town, pictured after holding 3rd Division Brighton to a 0-0 draw in the FA Cup First Round at Priory Stadium. Photo - Andrew Chitty

SUDBURY WANDERERS

Chairman: Nick Smith **Manager:** Mick Mills.
Secretary: Brian Tatum, 4 Beaconsfield Close, Sudbury, Suffolk CO10 6JR (01787 375840).
Ground: Brundon Lane, Sudbury, Suffolk (01787 376213).
Directions: From Sudbury centre follow Halstead/Chelmsford signs for about 1 mile. Take 1st right after railway bridge at foot of steep hill, and 1st right after sharp lefthand bend.
Seats: 200 **Cover:** 150 **Capacity:** 2,500 **Floodlights:** Yes **Founded:** 1958
Clubhouse: Matchdays/ training nights.
Colours: Yellow/blue/blue **Change Colours:** All Red
Programme: With entry **Editor:** P Scott (01787 379123) **Nickname:** Wanderers
Midweek Matchday: Tuesday **Record Attendance:** 248 v Woodbridge Town, 20/4/93.
Honours: Eastern Co's Lg Div 1 92-93, Ess. & Suff. Border Lg(2) 89-91 (R-up 88-89), Suffolk Snr Cup 90-91.

TIPTREE UNITED

Chairman: Frederick Byles **President:** Len Foakes **Manager:**
Secretary: Peter G Fidge, 77 Chelmer Road, Chelmsford, Essex CM2 6AA (01245 353667)
Ground: Chapel Road, Tiptree, Essex (01621 815213).
Directions: Enter town on B1023 - Chapel Road is left at second crossroads, ground 200yds on left. 3 miles from Kelverdon (BR). Served by Eastern National Colchester to Maldon bus.
Seats: 150 **Cover:** 300 **Capacity:** 2,500 **Floodlights:** Yes **Founded:** 1933. **Shop:** No.
Clubhouse: Large bar, two snooker tables, pool, darts, netball, badminton, pigeon club, bingo. Dance hall seats 180, small hall seats 60. Open daily 7-11pm (all day Fri & Sat) and noon-2.30, 7-10.30 Sun.
Colours: Red/black/black **Change colours:** All white. **Nickname:** Strawberries.
Programme: 30 pages, 30p **Editor:** Secretary **Sponsors:** S Smith (Transport)
Previous Lges: Essex & Suffolk Border/ Essex Snr 78-84 **Reserves' League:** Essex & Herts Comb.
Midweek Matchday: Tuesday. **Record Attendance:** 1,210 v Spurs, floodlight inauguration Dec 1990.
Honours: Essex Snr Tphy 80-81, Eastern Co's Lg 81-82 (Lg Cup 81-82 84-85), Essex Snr Lg R-up 75-76 77-78, Harwich Charity Cup(4).

WARBOYS TOWN

Chairman: Richard Kelly. **President:** **Manager:** Robbie Cook.
Secretary: Brian Lewis, 29 Vinery Court, Ramsey, Cambs, PE17 1JZ (01487 710653)
Ground: Sports Field, Forge Way, off High Street, Warboys, Cambs (01487 823483).
Directions: Access through Forge Way, half way along south side of High Street.
Seats: 50 **Cover:** 200 **Capacity:** 2,000 **Floodlights:** Yes **Founded:** 1885.
Clubhouse: Bar, lounge, function hall. Open every evening & Sunday lunchtime. Entertainment, drinks & snacks
Colours: Red & white/black/red. **Change colours:** White/maroon/maroon. **Nickname:** Witches.
Programme: 12 pages, 40p **Editor:** Martin England **Midweek Matches:** Tuesday
Previous Leagues: Peterborough & District 46-48 56-88/ Utd Co's 50-56/ Huntingdonshire 48-50.
Past Players progressing to Football League: Alex Chamberlain (Ipswich, Everton, Colchester).
Record Attendance: 500 v Ramsey Town, Hunts Senior Cup Semi Final.
Honours: Utd Co's Lg Div 2 R-up 54-55, P'boro Lg R-up(2) 59-60 61-62, P'boro Snr Cup 63-64, Hunts Snr Cup 26-27 28-29 31-32 32-33,94-95. (R-up 92-93), Hunts Scott Gatty Cup 30-31. Reserves: Hunts Benevolent Cup 57-58, Hunts Junior Cup 24-25 27-28 52-53, Hunts Lower Junior Cup 75-76 77-78. .gap 5

WATTON UNITED

Chairman: Dick Jessup **Vice-Chairman:** Phil Scott **President:** Malcolm Warner.
Secretary: Lesley Barnard, 15 Churchill Close, Watton, Thetford, Norfolk IP25 6BB (01953 881337).
Manager: **Physio:** M Kay. **Fixture Sec:** Nigel Tilford (01953 881441)
Ground: Watton Sports Centre, Dereham Road, Watton, Norfolk (01953 881281).
Directions: On A1075 towards Dereham about half a mile from junction with B1108.
Seats: 50 **Cover:** 150 **Capacity:** 2,000 **Floodlights:** Yes **Founded:** 1888.
Clubhouse: Drinks, sweets & snacks **Club Shop:** No.
Colours: White/white/green **Change colours:** Green/black/green **Nickname:** Brecklanders.
Midweek Matchday: Tuesday. **Previous Lges:** East Anglian/ Anglian Combination.
Sponsors: Style Windows **Reserve's League:** Anglian Combination.
Programme: 25p **Editor:** Secretary
Players progressing to Football League: Chris Watts (Norwich), Robert Taylor (Leyton Orient, Brentford).
Record Gate: 1,200 v Norwich City, floodlight inauguration 1985.
Honours: Anglian Combination 66-67 67-68 85-86 (Lg Cup 66-67 69-70).

WOODBRIDGE TOWN

Chairman: Keith Dixon **President:** G Shemmings
Fixture Sec: John Bennett, (01394 385973)
Secretary: Eric Smy, 25 Queens Avenue, Woodbridge, Suffolk IP12 4AQ (01394 384213)
Manager: David Hubbick **Commercial Manager:** David Leech
Ground: Notcutts Park, Seckford Hall Road, Woodbridge, Suffolk (01394 385308)
Directions: Turning into Woodbridge off last r'bout from Lowestoft, or 1st r'bout from Ipswich. Take 1st turning left and 1st left again. Drive to ground at end of road on left.
Seats: 50 **Cover:** 200 **Capacity:** 3,000 **Floodlights:** Yes **Founded:** 1885.
Clubhouse: Visitors bar, lounge bar, function hall.Matchday Tea, coffee, cold drinks, hotdogs, soup, burgers, sandwiches, rolls. Also cooked meals after match.
Programme: 36p Free with entry **Editor:** D Crowley
Colours: Black & white/black/black **Change colours:** All blue
Sponsors: Posh Windows & Doors **Nickname:** The Woodpeckers. **Midweek Matcheday:** Tuesday.
Previous Leagues: Suffolk & Ipswich **Reserves League:** Essex & Suffolk Border
96-97 - Captain: Jason Burman **Top Scorer:** Simon Fryatt **P.o.Y.:** Mark Bailey
Record Attendance: 3,000 v Arsenal, floodlight opener 2/10/90.
Honours: Suffolk Sen Cup(4), Jun Cup (4); Eastern Co Lg Cup 93-94, Lge Div 1 R-up 93-94; Ipswich Sen Lge (2).

WROXHAM

Chairman: Ray Bayles **President:** L King
Secretary: Chris Green, 24 Keys Drive, Wroxham, Norfolk NR12 8SS (01603 783936).
Manager: Bruce Cunningham **Asst Manager:** Keith Robson **Physio:** G Christmas
Ground: Trafford Park, Skinners Lane, Wroxham, Norfolk (01603 783538)
Directions: Arriving from Norwich turn left at Castle PH and keep left to ground. One and a half miles from Wroxham+Hoveton (BR). Buses 722, 724 and 717.
Seats: 50 **Cover:** 250 **Capacity:** 2,500 **Floodlights:** Yes **Club Shop:** No.
Clubhouse: Bar, pool, darts, carpet bowls etc. Drinks, hot & cold food
Programme: 20 pages with entry **Editor:** Ray Bayles (01603 403555). **Press Officer:** Secretary
Colours: Royal & white/blue/blue **Change colours:** Red & black/black/red & black
Founded: 1892. **Nickname:** Yachtsmen.
Midweek Matchday: Tuesday. **Reserve Team's League:** Anglian Combination.
Players progressing to Football League: Matthew Metcalf (Brentford) 1993.
Previous Leagues: Norwich City/ East Anglian/ Norwich & Dist./ Anglian Comb. 64-88.
Records - Attendance: 1,011 v Wisbech Town, Eastern Counties League Premier Division 16/3/93. **Goalscorer:** Matthew Metcalf. **Appearances:** Mark Halsey.
Honours: Eastern Co's Lg 91-92 92-93 94-95, R-Up: 94-95.(Lg Cup 92-93 (R-up 90-91), Div 1 88-89), Norfolk Snr Cup 92-93, Anglian Combination (6)(Lg Cup(7)The reserves completed the double in 94-95.

Warboys Town's Simon Mead's effort is scrambled off the line by a Fakenham defender.

Photo - Richard Kelly

Sudbury Town FC: *Photo - Malcolm Dixon*

FIRST DIVISION CLUBS 1997-98

BRIGHTLINGSEA UNITED

Chairman: Graham Steady **Manager:** Frank Thompson.
Secretary: H J Beere, 108 Regent Road, Brighlingsea, Essex CO7 0NZ (01206 303122).
Ground: North Road, Brightlingsea, Essex (01206 304199).
Directions: B1027 Colchester-Clacton, B1029 from Thorrington Cross - follow Church Road into town, left into Spring Road, left into Church Road. Nearest station; Colchester then bus 78 to Brighlingsea.
Seats: 50 **Cover:** 250 **Capacity:** 2,000 **Floodlights:** Yes **Club Shop:** Yes.
Clubhouse: Open matchadays & every evening except Sunday. Matchday tea, coffee, & snacks
Colours: Red & white/red/red. **Change colours:** Blue & white/blue/blue. **Nickname:** Oystermen.
Programme: 24 pages, 30p **Editor:** M Cole (01206 304430) **Founded:** 1887
Previous Leagues: Tendring Hundred, Essex & Suffolk Border, Essex Senior 1972-90.
Record Gate: 1,200 v Colchester, friendly 68-69. **Midweek Matches:** Tuesday.
Honours: Essex Snr Lg 88-89 89-90 (Harry Fisher Mem. Tphy 89-90 (R-up 88-89), Lg Cup R-up 78-79), Eastern Co's Lg Div 1 R-up 90-91, Essex & Suffolk Border Lg Prem. Div Cup 71-72, Harwich Charity Cup 87-88, Worthington Evans Cup 76-77 77-78 78-79.

CAMBRIDGE CITY Reserves

Chairman: Dennis Rolph **President:** Sir Neil Westbrook, CBE MA FRICS
Secretary: Stuart Hamilton, 55 Crowhill, Godmanchester, Huntingdon, Cambs (01480 412266).
Manager: Andy Beattie/Steve O'Donohue **Asst Manager:** Michael Cook **Physio:** John Aves, Collin Pettit
Ground: City Ground, Milton Road, Cambridge CB4 1UY (0223 357973)
Directions: 50 yards on left from start of A1309, Cambridge to Ely Rd. 30 mins walk Cambridge BR
Capacity: 5,000 **Cover:** 1,400 **Seats:** 400 **Floodlights:** Yes **Club Shop:** Yes
Clubhouse: 11am-11pm Mon-Sat, 12-3pm & 7pm-10.30pm Sun. Bingo, Dances, Pool, Stag nights, Darts.
Colours: White/black/white **Change colours:** All blue **Formed:** 1908
Programme: Yes **Editor:** David Crane (01223 233057) **Nickname:** Lilywhites
Club Sponsors: Lancer UK **Midweek matchday:** Tuesday

CHATTERIS TOWN

Chairman: Jimmy Gill **President:** J Chambers **Manager:** Steve Taylor and Ian Edwards
Secretary: Jimmy Gill, 3 West End Close, Chatteris, Cambs PE16 6HW (01354 693690).
Ground: West Street, Chatteris (01354 692139).
Directions: Entering Chatteris on A141 from Huntingdon turn right into West Street after by-pass roundabout.
Seats: 250 **Cover:** 400 **Capacity:** 2,000 **Floodlights:** Yes **Founded:** 1920.
Clubhouse: Bar & tea bar. Matchday drinks & snacks available
Colours: White/blue/white **Change colours:** Red & black/black/black. **Nickname:** Lillies.
Previous League: Peterborough **Midweek Matches:** Wednesday
Programme: 12 pages, 20p **Record Gate:** 2,000 v March Town Utd, League 5/5/88.
Players progressing to Football League: Andy Rogers (Reading, Southend, Plymouth), Dave Gregory (Plymouth).
Honours: Eastern Counties Lg Cup 67-68, Peterborough Premier Lg(3).

CORNARD UNITED

Chairman: Chris Symes **Vice-Chairman:** Mike Ford **President:** Jim French
Secretary: Chris Symes, 22 Greenacres, Mile End, Colchester, Essex CO4 (01206 851489)
Manager: Chris Symes. **Asst Manager:** Jason Stacker **Physio:** Mike Ford.
Ground: Blackhouse Lane Sportsfield, Great Cornard, Suffolk (01787 376719).
Directions: Left off r'bout on A134 coming from Ipswich/Colchester into Sudbury, follow signs for Country Park - ground is immediately opposite along Blackhouse Lane.
Seats: 250 **Cover:** 500 **Capacity:** 2,000 **Floodlights:** Yes **Club Shop:** No.
Clubhouse: Open matchdays & Sunday lunchtimes. Matchday Tea, coffee, cold drinks, & snacks.
Programme: 16 pages **Editor:** Secretary
Colours: Blue & white/white/blue **Change colours:** White/navy/white
Sponsors: Angelo Smith. **Nickname:** Ards. **Founded:** 1964.
Midweek Matches: Tuesday **Reserve League:** Essex & Suffolk Border.
Previous - Leagues: Sudbury S/day 64-65/Bury St Edmunds & Dist 65-72/Colchester 71-78/ Essex Suffolk Bord 78-89. **Grounds:** Cornard Rec 64-71/ Great Cornard Upper School 71-85.
96-97 - Captain: Andy McLargin **Top Scorer:** Dave Gipp **P.o.Y.:** Bob Seivey
Record - Appearances: Malcolm Fisher. **Goalscorer :** Andy Smiles. **Attendance:** 330 v Sudbury Town, Eastern Floodlit League 4/2/92. **Win:** 18-2 v St Peters House, Colchester League 14/9/72. **Defeat:** 4-10 v Finningham, Bury League 7/2/68.
Honours: Eastern Co's Lg Div 1 89-90 (Lg Cup R-up 92-93), Essex & Suffolk Border Lg 88-89 (Lg Cup 88-89), Suffolk Snr Cup 89-90, Suffolk Jnr Cup R-up 84-85.

DOWNHAM TOWN

Chairman: John Fysh **President:** T G Barker **Manager:** Steve Tyres.
Secretary: F.Thorne, 6 Maple Rd., Downham Market, Norfolk, PE38 9PY. (01366 382563)
Ground: Memorial Field, Lynn Road, Downham Market, Norfolk (01366 388424).
Directions: One and a quarter miles from Downham Market (BR) - continue to town clock, turn left and ground is three quarters of a mile down Lynn Road.
Seats: None **Cover:** Yes **Capacity:** 1,000 **Floodlights:** Yes **Founded:** 1881.
Clubhouse: Open matchdays, refreshments & snacks available
Programme: Yes, with entry **Editor:** Steve Penny (01553 810392)
Colours: Red & white/red/red **Change colours:** Sky/Navy/sky. **Nickname:** Town
Midweek Matches: Wednesday. **Previous Leagues:** Peterborough
Record Attendance: 292 v Diss Town, Jewson League Division One 1991/92.
Honours: P'boro Lg(5) 62-63 73-74 78-79 86-88, Norfolk Senior Cup 63-64 65-66 (R-up(3) 66-69).

HADLEIGH UNITED

President: H Claireaux **Chairman:** Dave Petts **Manager:** Louis Newman
Secretary: Peter Hutchings, 3 Mowlands, Capel St Mary, Ipswich, Suffolk IP9 2XB (01473 311093).
Ground: Millfield, Tinkers Lane, Duke Street, Hadleigh, Suffolk (01473 822165).
Directions: Turn off A12 approx halfway between Ipswich & Hadleigh. Take B1070 & follow signs to Hadleigh. Duke Street is off the High Street - turn left by Library.
Seats: 250 **Cover:** 500 **Capacity:** 3,000 **Floodlights:** Yes **Founded:** 1892.
Clubhouse: Open matchdays, Fridays & Sunday lunchtimes.
Colours: White & navy/navy/red **Change colours:** All yellow **Nickname:** Brettsiders.
Programme: 12 pages, 50p **Editor:** Roger Rush (01473 828318) **Sponsors:** Willhire Ltd
Reserves' Lge: Essex & Suff. Border **Player progressing to Football Lge:** Perry Groves (Arsenal).
Midweek Matches: Tuesday. **Previous - Leagues:** Suffolk & Ipswich (prev. Ipswich & D.)(pre-1991).
Grounds: Grays Meadow, Ipswich Roa.
Records - Attendance: 518 v Halstead Town,F.A.Vase Replay 17.1.95. **Win:** 8-1 v Chatteris (A) 17/1/95. **Defeat:** 0-7 v Harwich & Parkston (H) 12/10/96, & Wisbech (H) 26/4/97
Honours: Ipswich & Dist./Suffolk & Ipswich Lg 53-54 56-57 73-74 76-77 78-79 (Mick McNeil Lg Cup 76-77 80-81 81-82 86-87)), Suffolk Senior Cup 68-69 71-72 82-83.Eastern Co.Lg Champions 93-94.

HAVERHILL ROVERS

Chairman: Terry McGerty **President:** N Haylock **Manager:** Derek Richardson.
Secretary: Chris Rice, 23 Ovington Place, Haverhill, Suffolk. CB9 0BA. (01440 712396)
Asst Mgr: Paul Gaffin. **Physio:** Chris Rice **Press Officer:** Ray Esdale
Ground: Hamlet Croft, Haverhill, Suffolk (01440 702137). **Directions:** Centre of Haverhill.
Seats: 200 **Cover:** 200 **Capacity:** 3,000 **Floodlights:** Yes **Founded:** 1886.
Clubhouse: Open matchdays and functions. Snacks available
Colours: All red **Change colours:** All blue **Nickname:** Rovers.
Programme: 24 pages, 40p **Editor:** Ray Esdale (01440 704670) **Midweek Matches:** Tuesday
Previous League: Essex & Suffolk Border. **Players progressing to Football League:** R Wilkins (Colchester).
Record Attendance: 1,537 v Warrington Town, FA Vase QF 86-87.
Honours: Eastern Co's Lg 78-79 (Lg Cup 64-65); E & S Border Lg 62-63 63-64; East Anglian Cup 90-91; Suffolk Sen Cup 96-97.

IPSWICH WANDERERS

Chairman: A.Haste. **President:** P.Emmerson. **Manager:** Alan Dilloway
Secretary: Martin Head, 246 Sidelate Lane, Ipswich, Suffolk. IP4 3DH (01473 273811)
Ground: Humberdoucey Lane, Ipswich, Suffolk (01473 728581).
Directions: Take Woodbridge Road out of Ipswich,then left fork into Playford Road.Take first left into Humberdoucy Lane Ground 300yds on right.
Seats: 50 **Cover:** Yes **Capacity:** 2,000 **Floodlights:** Yes **Founded:** 1983.
Clubhouse: Bar, Tea, coffee, cold drinks, confectionary, burgers, hotdogs, sandwiches, rolls.
Programme: Yes. **Editor:** Alan Haste (01473 711877) **Sponsors:** Car Glass & Trim.
Colours: Royal & white/blue/blue & white **Change colours:** Red & black/black/red & black
Midweek Matches: Wednesday **Previous Leagues:** Little David Sunday **Nickname:** Wanderers.
Record Attendance: 335 v Woodbridge, ECL Div 1 4/4/94.

MALDON TOWN

Chairman: Bob Large. **Manager:** Ben Embery.
Secretary: B D Lloyd, 46 Maldon Road, Great Totham, Maldon, Essex CM9 8PR (01621 893148)
Ground: Wallace Binder Ground, Park Drive, Maldon CM9 5XX (01621 853762).
Seats: Yes **Cover:** Yes **Capacity:** 2,500 **Floodlights:** Yes **Founded:** 1946.
Colours: Blue & white/blue/blue & white **Change colours:** Red & black/black/red
Programme: Yes **Editor:** T Wynne **Midweek Matchday:** Tuesday
Previous - Leagues: Eastern Counties, Essex & Suffolk Border. **Ground:** Fambridge Road (pre-1994).
96-97 - Captain: Simon Arnold **P.o.Y.:** Alex Fiddes **Top Scorer:** Scott Witney
Honours: Essex Snr Lg 84-85 (Sportsmanship Award 87-88,88-89,94-95, Reserve Shield 93-94), Reserve Cup:94-95, Essex & Suffolk Border Lg 55-56 (Cup 64-65), Essex Intermediate Cup 51-52, Tolleshunt D'Arcy Cup 93-94.

MARCH TOWN UNITED

Chairman: Geoff Allen. **President:** D Wilkinson **Manager:**
Secretary: R S Bennett, 47 Ellingham Ave, March, Cambs PE15 9TE (01354 653271)
Ground: GER Sports Ground, Robin Goodfellows Lane, March (01354 653073).
Directions: 5 mins from town centre, 10 mins from BR station.
Seats: 500 **Cover:** 2,000 **Capacity:** 4,000 **Floodlights:** Yes **Founded:** 1885.
Clubhouse: On ground, seating 150. Light refreshments available
Club colours: Yellow & blue/blue/yellow. **Change colours:** Black & white/black/black.
Programme: 30p **Editor:** R Bennett **Nickname:** Hares
Previous - Leagues: Peterborough/ Isle of Ely/ Utd Co's 48-54. **Ground:** The Avenue (prior to 1946).
Midweek Matches: Tuesday **Record Gate:** 7,500 v King's Lynn, FA Cup 1956.
Honours: Eastern Co's Lg 87-88 (Lg Cup 60-61), Utd Co's Lg 53-64, FA Cup 1st Rd 53-54 77-78, Cambs Invitation Cup 54-55, East Anglian Cup 53-54 (jt with Barking).

MILDENHALL TOWN

Chairman: Brian Brigden **Manager:** Steve Hubbard **Fixture Sec:** Colin Marchant (01842 812123)
Secretary: Brian Hensby, 14 Sanderling Close, Mildenhall, Suffolk IP28 7LE (01638 715772).
Ground: Recreation Way, Mildenhall, Suffolk (01638 713449).
Directions: Next to swimming pool/car, quarter of a mile from town centre.
Seats: None **Capacity:** 2,000 **Founded:** 1890. **Nickname:** Town or Yellows.
Clubhouse: Open matchdays & functions. Light refreshments available
Colours: Amber/black/black. **Change colours:** All white
Programme: Free with admission **Editor:** F Marshall **Midweek Matchday:** Tuesday
Previous Leagues: Bury & District/ Cambs Lg 2B, 1B & Premier.
Record Attendance: 350 v Norwich City, friendly 22/7/89.
Honours: Suffolk Junior Cup 1899-1900.

NEEDHAM MARKET

Chairman: P Coleman **Managers:** Jim Fitzgerald & Wayne Leggett
Secretary: D Bloomfield, 33 Quinton Road, Needham Market, Suffolk IP6 8DA (01449 720693)
Fixture Secretary: I Croft, (01449 676517)
Ground: Bloomfields, Quinton Road, Needham Market, Suffolk (01449 721000)
Directions: Quinton Road is off Barretts Lane which inturn is off Needham Market High Street.
Colours: All Green & White **Change Coloures:** White/navy/navy
Floodlights: Yes **Midweek Matchday:** Wednesday
Programme: Yes **Editor:** Alan Spivey (01449 775118)

NORWICH UNITED

Chairman: John Hilditch **Vice-Chairman:** J Cubitt **President:** Michael Miles
Secretary: M Barber, Plantation Park, Blofield, Norwich NR13 4PL (01603 716963)
Manager: S Rushbrook **Physio:** Mike Chapman.
Ground: Plantation Road, Blofield, Norwich, Norfolk NR13 4PL (01603 716963).
Directions: Half a mile from Blofield village - coming from Norwich on Yarmouth Rd turn left in Blofield at Kings Head pub & follow to Plantation Rd (grd on right after bridge over bypass). 1/2 hour Brundall BR (Norwich-Yarmouth line).
Seats: 100 **Cover:** 1,000 **Capacity:** 3,000 **Floodlights:** Yes **Founded:** 1903.
Clubhouse: Matchday food & drink: Tea, coffee, cold drinks, hotdogs, burgers, soup, sandwiches, rolls.
Programme: 24 pages, 50p **Editor:** Secretary
Colours: Yellow/blue/yellow **Change colours:** All red
Nickname: Planters. **Midweek Matches:** Tuesday
Previous Ground: Gothic Club, Heartsease Lane, Norwich (until end of 90-91).
Club Record Goalscorer: M Money **Club Record Appearances:** Tim Sayer.
Record Attendance: 401 v Wroxham, League match, 2/10/91.
Honours: Eastern Co's Lg Div 1 90-91 (R-up 89-89, Lg Cup 91-92), Anglian Combination 88-89.

SOMERSHAM TOWN

Chairman: Alan Bailey **Vice-Chairman:** Norman Burkett **President:** Jack Marjason
Secretary: Norman Burkett, 6 West Leys, St Ives, Cambs. PE17 4DS (01480 464695)
Managers: Norman Hudson **Coach:** Bob Barnett **Physio:** Alan Magnus
Ground: West End Ground, St Ives Road, Somersham, Cambs (01487 843384).
Directions: On A604 St Ives to Somersham on right as you enter town.
Seats: None **Cover:** 200 **Capacity:** 1,500 **Floodlights:** Yes **Club Shop:**
Clubhouse: Open Friday, Sat/Sun lunchtimes.
Programme: 76 pages, 30p **Editor/Press Officer:** Dave Hardy (01487 840441)
Colours: All old gold **Change colours:** Sky/maroon/sky
Sponsors: Rapidtech (UK) Ltd. **Nickname:** Westenders **Founded:** 1893.
Midweek Matchday: Tuesday. **Reserve League:** Kershaw Senior A.
96-97 Captain: Chris Bailey **96-97 Top Scorer:** Ian Boon (10) **96-97 P.o.Y.:** Chris Bailey
Record Attendance: 538 v Norwich City, f/light inauguration 91 **Previous League:** Peterborough & Dist.
Club Record Goalscorer & Appearances: Terry Butcher
Honours: Hunts Snr Cup 72-73 94-95, Peterboro Snr Cup 84-85, Hinchingbrooke Cup 53-54, Cambs Lg Premier B Div 94-95(reserves).

STANWAY ROVERS

Chairman: Brian Peachey. **President:** Colin Henson.
Secretary: Alan Brierley, 19 Barley Way, Stanway, Colchester, Essex CO3 5YD (01206 572439).
Manager: Phil Bloss. **Physios:** John Chandler/Barry Wreford.
Ground: 'Hawthorns', New Farm Road, Stanway, Colchester, Essex (01206 578187).
Directions: Take turn off marked Stanway off A12. Turn right and go over flyover to Tollgate r'bout, 1st right into Villa Rd, after 25 yards turn left into Church Rd, 200 yards on left into New Farm Rd, ground 400 yards on left. Nearest BR station is Colchester North.
Seats: None **Cover:** 200 **Capacity:** 1,500 **Floodlights:** Yes **Founded:** 1955
Clubhouse: 6.45-11pm evenings, noon-11pm Sats. Rolls, soup, tea, coffee etc available matchdays.
Colours: Gold/black/gold **Change colours:** White/gold/black **Shop:** Pennants & ties
Programme: 12 pages, 50p **Editor:** Alan Brierley
Midweek matchday: Wednesday **Sponsors:** Collier & Catchpole. **Nickname:** Rovers.
Previous - Leagues: Colchester & E Essex/ Essex & Suff. Border (pre-1992). **Ground:** Stanway Secondary School, Winstree Road (20 years).
Reserves' Lge: Essex & Suff. Border **Record Gate:** 156 v Hadleigh, ECL Division One 10/7/94.
Players progressing to Football League: Andy Farrell (Colchester,Burnley,Wigan)
Honours: Essex Intermediate Cup R-up 89-90 90-91, Essex & Suffolk Border Lg R-up 91-92 (Div 1 86-87, Div 2 81-81 85-86), Essex Junior Cup R-up 74-75 (QF 73-74).

SWAFFHAM TOWN

Chairman: Stephen Choppen. **President:** J Smith. **Manager:** Mick Simmons.
Secretary: David Ward, 2 Princes Street, Swaffham, Norfolk PE37 7BX (01760 722516).
Ground: Shoemakers Lane, Swaffham, Norfolk (01760 722700).
Seats: None **Cover:** **Capacity:** 2,000 **Floodlights:** Yes **Founded:** 1892.
Clubhouse details: Open Tuesday, Thursday, Saturday & Sunday lunchtimes & evenings. Drinks, sweets etc
Colours: Black & white/black/black. **Change:** Blue/blue/yellow. **Nickname:** Pedlars
Programme: 36 pages, 30p **Editor:** Secretary
Midweek Matchay: Tuesday. **Previous Leagues:** Dereham, Anglian Combination
Record Attendance: 250 v Downham Town, Jewson Eastern Co's League Cup 3/9/91.
Honours: Norfolk Snr Cup(2), Anglian Comb. 89-90 (Div 1 88-89).

THETFORD TOWN

Chairman: Michael Bailey **Vice-Chairman:** B Richards
Secretary: John Wordley, 4 Claxton Close, Thetford, Norfolk IP24 1BA (01842 762530).
Manager: Ben Moyle **Coach:** Stuart Williams
Ground: Mundford Road, Thetford, Norfolk (01842 766120).
Directions: Turn off bypass (A11) at A143 junction - ground 800yds next to sports ground
Seats: 400 **Cover:** 400 **Capacity:** 2,000 **Floodlights:** Yes **Founded:** 1884.
Clubhouse: Bar, teas, refreshments, light meals & snacks
Programme: 48p with entry **Editor:** Graham Mills (01480 385425). **Press Officer:** Mick Burgess.
Colours: Claret & blue/sky/blue **Change:** All yellow **Sponsors:** Sportscene
Midweek Matches: Wednesday **Reserves League:** Anglian Comb. **Club Shop:** No.
Players progressing to Football League: Dick Scott (Norwich City, Cardiff City), Kevin Seggie (Leeds United), Simon Milton (Ipswich Town).
Record Attendance: 394 v Diss Town, Norfolk Snr Cup 91 **Previous Leagues:** Norfolk & Suffolk
Honours: Eastern Co's Lg R-up 89-90, Norfolk & Suffolk Lg 54-55, Norfolk Snr Senior Cup 47-48 90-91.

WHITTON UNITED

Chairman: John Watkins **President:** Russell Woodward
Secretary: David Gould, 7 Karen Close, Ipswich, Suffolk IP1 4LP (01473 253838)
Manager: Colin Macrow **Fixture Sec:** Mark Woodward (01473 742805)
Ground: King George V Playing Field, Old Norwich Road, Ipswich, Suffolk. (01473 464030)
Directions: Turn off A14, junction A1156 approx 3 miles west of A12/A14 junction.
Seats: No **Cover:** 100 **Capacity:** 600 **Floodlights:** Yes **Club Shop:** No
Clubhouse: Licensed Bar. Hot & Cold Food available.
Programme: Yes **Editor/Press Officer:** Ian Vernau
Colours: Green & white/green/green **Change colours:** All orange
Sponsors: Lindacre **Formed:** 1926 **Nickname:** None
Midweek Matches: Tuesday **Youth's League:** U18 Eastern Jun Alliance
Previous Leagues: Suffolk & Ipswich **Players progressing to Football League:** None known
96-97 - Captain: Robert Bate **Top Scorer:** Micky Squirrell **P.o.Y.:** Graham Pooley
Record - Attendance: 528 v Ipswich Town 29/11/95; League 244 v Ipswich Wanderers 13/1/96.
Honours: Suffolk Senior Cup 58-59 62-63 92-93; Suffolk & Ipswich League 46-47 47-48 65-66 67-68 91-92 92-93, Jewson Fairplay Trophy 96-97.

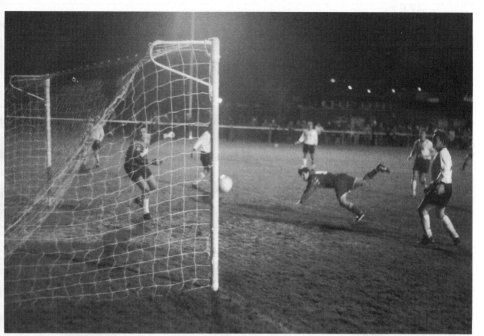

Wisbech's Peter Munns puts his team ahead with a diving header against Brache Sparta in their FA Vase 2nd Round match

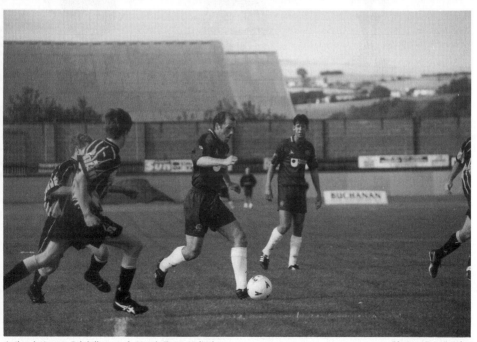

Action between Brightlingsea & March Town United. *Photo - Roy Pruden*

THE COMPLETE MUSIC HELLENIC FOOTBALL LEAGUE

FEEDER TO: BEAZER HOMES LEAGUE

Secretary: Brian King, 83 Queens Road, Carterton, Oxon OX18 3YF
((H)01993 843870 (W) 01793 464620)
Press Officer: T G Cuss

News from the Hellenic League

Brackley Town FC have been promoted to The Doc Martens Southern League.

Lambourn Sports FC have withdrawn from membership of the League and accordingly their First Team have vacated the Premier Division and their Reserve Team have vacated Reserve Division II.

The Division I Champions Ardley United are not to be promoted because they are unable to achieve a Premier Division Ground Grading for Season 1997/98. Attempts were made to enter into a Ground Sharing Agreement but this did not come to fruition.

Subject to achieving Ground Grading (no difficulties anticipated) Hallen FC who finished second in Division I and Harrow Hill FC who finished third in Division I will be promoted to the Premier Division. Both clubs are subject to a Bond Agreement to have available the appropriate Ground Grading for Premier Division Football.

Watlington FC who are Champions of the Oxfordshire Senior League are promoted to Division I under the Pyramid System.

An application for membership of Division I has been received from the Cirencester Football Academy. This application, supported by the League, was rejected by the Hellenic Football League Joint Liaison Committee Leagues on the grounds that this new club should start at the lowest level on the Pyramid. The club remain desirous of joining the League and have made an appeal to their County Association namely the Gloucestershire Football Association.

In view of the removal of two clubs from the Premier Division the clubs in the relegation positions namely Highworth Town and Fairford Town will remain in the Premier Division. The clubs in danger of relegation from Division I into Feeder Leagues namely Letcombe and/or Milton United (the League was already one short) and only Milton United would have been relegated, will remain within the League.

In Reserve Division I Cirencester Town Reserves have withdrawn and Banbury United FC and Readington Amateurs FC will be promoted from Reserve Division II, whilst in Reserve Division II Lambourn Sports Reserves have withdrawn and Highworth Town Reserves will be relegated from Reserve Division I.

The Premier Division will consist of 18 clubs, Division I will consist of 16 or 17 clubs, Reserve Division I will consist of 13 clubs and Reserve Division II will consist of 12 clubs.

The League Season will commence for Premier and Division I clubs on Saturday, August 16th 1997 and for Reserve Division I and Reserve Division II clubs on Saturday, August 30th 1997.

The Hungerford Cup, awarded to clubs who in the opinion of other clubs and officers and Committee Members of the League have made the most improvement on or off the field or both during the past season, was awarded to Abingdon United FC. Ardley United FC and Brackley Town FC were in equal second place.

The Premier Division Sportsmanship Award was won by Didcot Town FC. The Division I Sportsmanship Award was won by Wootton Bassett FC. The Club Linesmans Award was won by Eric Stott of Swindon Supermarine FC with John Osborne of Clanfield FC in second place.

The retiring Treasurer Mr Ken Loveday presented the accounts and balance sheet. He expressed concern that income from discipline offences had risen from £1,555 in 1995/96 to £2,813.40 in Season 1996/97. The new Honorary Treasurer will be Graham Osman.

Trevor Cuss, Hon. Press Liaison Officer

HELLENIC LEAGUE ROLL OF HONOUR 1996-97

Premier Division Champions	Brackley Town
Premier Division Runners Up	Abingdon United
Premier Division Challenge Cup Winners	Swindon Supermarine
Premier Division Challenge Cup Finalists	Kintbury Rangers
Division One Champions	Ardley United
Division One Runners Up	Hallen
Division One Challenge Cup Winners	Ardley United
Division One Challenge Cup Finalists	Harrow Hill
The Norman Matthews Cup Winners	Abingdon United
The Norman Matthews Cup Finalists	North Leigh
Hungerford Cup Winners	Abingdon United
Reserve Section	
Division One Champions	Swindon Supermarine
Division One Runners Up	Endsleigh
Division Two Champions	Banbury United
Division Two Runners Up	Headington Amateurs
Reserve Section Challenge Cup Winners	Swindon Supermarine
Reserve Section Challenge Cup Finalists	Cirencester United
Club Linesman of the Year	Eric Stott (Swindon Supermarine)
County Cups	
Berks and Bucks Senior Trophy Winners	Abingdon United
Wiltshire Premier Shield Winners	Swindon Supermarine
Oxfordshire Senior Cup Finalist	Carterton Town
Gloucestershire Senior Trophy Winners	Endsleigh Reserves

HELLENIC LEAGUE
FINAL LEAGUE TABLES 1996-97

Premier Division

		P	W	D	L	F	A	Pts
1	Brackley Town	34	25	6	3	79	2	81
2	Abingdon United	34	22	5	7	57	32	71
3	Burnham	34	20	9	5	67	34	69
4	Swindon Super.	34	21	5	8	72	40	68
5	North Leigh	34	17	7	10	56	39	58
6	Tuffley Rovers	34	16	8	10	62	43	56
7	Endsleigh	34	13	11	10	49	50	50
8	Banbury United	34	14	5	15	51	46	47
9	Didcot Town	34	13	7	14	42	52	46
10	Carterton Town	34	12	4	17	57	57	41
11	Shortwood Utd	34	11	6	17	53	60	39
12	Lambourn Sports	34	10	8	16	44	53	38
13	Bicester Town	34	10	7	17	31	53	37
14	Wantage Town	34	11	4	19	36	69	37
15	Almondsbury Tn	34	8	10	16	44	52	34
16	Kintbury Rangers	34	9	5	20	41	67	32
17	Highworth Town	34	8	5	21	40	73	29
18	Fairford Town	34	7	5	22	32	73	26

Division One

		P	W	D	L	F	A	Pts
1	Ardley United	32	24	7	1	76	21	79
2	Hallen	32	21	8	3	79	23	71
3	Harrow Hill	32	20	7	5	56	29	67
4	Cheltenham Scns	32	20	5	7	75	47	65
5	Purton	32	19	5	8	75	36	62
6	Kidlington	32	19	4	9	64	33	61
7	Pegasus Juniors	32	18	4	10	61	29	58
8	Headington Ams	32	14	6	12	49	47	48
9	Ross Town	32	13	7	12	56	47	46
10	Cirencester Utd	32	12	4	16	51	56	40
11	Wootton Bassett T	32	9	8	15	37	50	35
12	Clanfield	32	9	3	20	46	64	30
13	Bishops Cleeve	32	7	9	16	39	66	30
14	Yarnton	32	9	3	20	30	67	30
15	Easington Sports	32	5	5	22	34	78	20
16	Letcombe	32	4	4	24	26	97	16
17	Milton United	32	2	5	25	42	106	11

PREMIER DIVISION CUP

First Round

Fairford Town	v	Lambourn Sports	4-0	Wantage Town	v	Carterton Town	0-3

Second Round

Tuffley Rovers	v	Highworth Town	4-1	Bicester Town	v	Swindon Supermarine	0-2*
Didcot Town	v	Abingdon Utd	1-0	Brackley Town	v	Almondsbury Town	2-0
North Leigh	v	Carterton Town	1-2	Kintbury Rangers	v	Burnham	2-1
Endsleigh	v	Shortwood United	2-0	Fairford Town	v	Banbury United	4-0

Third Round

Kintbury Rangers	v	Brackley Town	2-0	Tuffley Rovers	v	Fairford Town	3-1
Carterton Town	v	Didcot Town	2-0	Swindon Supermarine	v	Endsleigh	1-0

Semi-Final

Tuffley Rovers	v	Kintbury Rangers	1-1/2-3
Carterton Town	v	Swindon S'marine	0-0/1-3

Final

Kintbury Rangers	v	Swindon Supermarine	0-1

DIVISION ONE CUP

First Round

Headington Amateurs	v	Kidlington	1-2

Second Round

Hallen	v	Milton United	w/o	Bishops Cleeve	v	Purton	2-3*
Clanfield	v	Yarnton	3-0	Cirencester United	v	Wootton Bassett	1-2
Cheltenham Saracens	v	Kidlington	3-1	Letcombe	v	Easington Sports	3-1*
Ross Town	v	Ardley United	0-2	Harrow Hill	v	Pegasus Juniors	2-0

Third Round

Clanfield	v	Wootton Bassett	1-4	Harrow Hill	v	Hallen	4-2*
Letcombe	v	Cheltenham Saracens	1-6	Ardley United	v	Purton	2-0

Semi-Final

Cheltenham Saracens	v	Ardley United	2-5/0-4	
Harrow Hill	v	Wootton Bassett	2-0/1-3	(4-3 on penalties)

Final

Ardley United	v	Harrow Hill	2-2*	(4-2 on penalties)

THE NORMAN MATTHEWS FLOODLIGHT CUP

First Round

Kintbury Rangers	v	Wantage Town	1-2/0-2
Swindon Supermarine	v	Carterton Town	2-1/1-3

Second Round

Banbury United	v	Brackley Town	1-0/1-3	Burnham	v	Lambourn Sports	1-4/1-0
Almondsbury Town	v	Fairford Town	3-1/2-0	Didcot Town	v	Abingdon United	0-1/0-1
North Leigh	v	Endsleigh	4-2/5-2	Bicester Town	v	Wantage Town	1-0/1-1
Highworth Town	v	Tuffley Rovers	1-1/1-0	Shortwood United	v	Carterton Town	0-4/0-6

Third Round

Brackley Town	v	Bicester Town	3-0/0-2	North Leigh	v	Highworth Town	1-0/6-3
Lambourn Sports	v	Abingdon United	0-4/0-4	Almondsbury Town	v	Carterton Tn	0-0/0-0(3-5p)

Semi-Final

Brackley Town**	v	Abingdon United	3-0/0-2	Carterton Town	v	North Leigh	1-4/1-2

** Struck out of competition

Final

Abingdon United	v	North Leigh	4-2

PREMIER DIVISION CLUBS 1997-98

ABINGDON UNITED

Chairman: John Blackmore **President:**
Secretary: Terry Hutchinson, 41 Austin Place, Dunmore Farm Estate, Abingdon, Oxon OX14 1LT (01235 559019)
Manager: R Hayward **Coach:** P Storey **Physio:** G Corcoran
Press Officer: W Fletcher (01235 203203)
Ground: Northcourt Road, Abingdon OX14 1PL (01235 203203).
Directions: From north (Oxford) leave A34 at Abingdon north sign & Northcourt Rd is 1st major turning after r'bout. From South/East/West leave Abingdon on A4183, turn left into Northcourt Rd after 1 mile. 2 miles from Redley (BR)
Seats: 52 **Cover:** 120 **Capacity:** 2,000 **Floodlights:** Yes **Founded:** 1946
Colours: All yellow **Change colours:** White/red or blue/white **Nickname:** The U's
Reserves' Lge: Hellenic Res section **Previous league:** North Berks **Prev. Grnds:** None
Programme: 30p **Editor:** W Fletcher, ACJI (0235 20255).
Midweek matchday: Tuesday **Record Gate:** 1,500 v Oxford Utd 1994.
Clubhouse: Two bars, food available. Open normal pub hours every day.
Club record appearances: D Webb.
Honours: N Berks Lg 53-54 (Lg Cup R-up 53-54), Charity Shield 52-53; Hellenic Prem R-up 96-97, F/Lit Cup 96-97, Div 1 R-up 76-77 81-82 (Lg Cup R-up 89-90), Div 1 Cup 65-66 81-82 (R-up 66-67, Reserve Cup R-up 93-94); Berks & Bucks Snr Cup R-up 83-84, Snr Tphy R-up 93-94 96-97.

ALMONDSBURY TOWN

Chairman: F David Pick **President:** Peter Howarth
Secretary: D W Winstone, 30 Cherington, Yate, Bristol BS17 4UZ (01454 323877)
Manager: Nick Tanner **Coach:** Nigel Hawkins **Physio:** Steve Watkins
Ground: Oakland Park, Almondsbury, Bristol (01454 612220).
Directions: Adjacent to M5 junction 16 - follow A38 Thornbury - ground first left. 4 miles from Bristol Parkway (BR). County bus services to Thornbury, Stroud and Gloucester.
Seats: None **Cover:** No **Capacity:** 2,000 **Floodlights:** Yes **Founded:** 1897
Colours: Sky/navy/navy **Change colours:** All yellow **Programme:** 20 pages 25p
Record Gate: Hellenic Cup Final replay 89-90.
Previous Leagues: Bristol Weslyan/ Bristol Suburban/ Bristol Premier Comb./ Glos Co.
Nickname: Almonds. **Midweek Matchday:** Tuesday
Clubhouse: 7 days, all sports, refreshments, function room, entertainment, skittles.
Honours: FA Vase R-up 78-79 (SF 77-78), Glos Co. Lg(4) 76-78 79-81 (R-up 75-76 81-82), GFA Chal. Tphy 78-79 (R-up 80-81), Avon Prem. Comb. 74-75, Glos Snr Amtr Cup 87-88, Hellenic Lg 83-84 (R-up 82-83, Lg Cup(2) 83-85).

BANBURY UNITED

Chairman: J Breslin **Vice Chairman:** B Kaye **President:** D K Jesson
Secretary: B Worsley, c/o Sol Systems, Unit 4 Mallorie Hse, Beaumont Rd, Banbury, OX16 7RH (01295 265638 H)
Manager: Ian Bowyer **Coach:** Tony Rose **Physio:** John Source
Ground: The Stadium, off Station Rd, Banbury, Oxon (01295 263354).
Directions: M40 jct 11, follow signs for Banbury then BR station, turn right down narrow lane before entering station forecourt; eastern end of town.
Seats: 50 **Cover:** 500 **Capacity:** 6,500 **Floodlights:** Yes **Club Shop:** Yes
Programme : 24 pages 60p **Editor:** Kevin Hicklin **Press Officer:** Barry Worsley.
Colours: Blue & white/blue/blue **Change colours:** Green/white/green
Midweek matches: Tuesday. **Reserves' Lge:** Hellenic Res. section **Nickname:** Puritans.
Founded: 1933 **Reformed:** 1965 **Club Sponsors:** Timms Homes.
Record Attendance: 7,160 v Oxford City, FA Cup 3rd Qualifying Round, 30/10/48.
Best FA Cup season: 1st Rd replay 73-74 (Also 1st Rd 47-48 61-62 72-73).
Best FA Trophy year: 3rd Rd 70-71 73-74.
Prev. Lges: Banbury Jnr 33-34/ Oxon Snr 34-35/ Birmingham Comb. 35-54/ W. Mids 54-66/ Southern 66-90.
Players progressing to Football League: Ollie Kearns (Reading), Kevin Wilson & Richard Pratley (Derby), Mick Kearns & Terry Muckleberg (Oxford), Martin Singleton (Coventry).
Clubhouse: Match days & week-ends. Mid-week on hire. Hot food available during aftermatches.
96-97 Captain: Martin Singleton **96-97 P.o.Y.:** Neil Sole **96-97 Top Scorer:** Darren Deeley (15)
Club Record Goalscorer: Dick Pike (1935-48), Tony Jacques (65-76) - both 222.
Club Record Appearances: Dave Matthews.
Honours: Oxon Snr Cup 78-79 87-88 (R-up 6); Birmingham Comb. R-up 47-48; Oxon Prof. Cup 52-53(jt) 70-71 (jt) 72-73 77-78 79-80(jt); Hellenic Lg.Cup R-Up 91-92; Birmingham Snr Cup R-Up 48-49 59-60 (S.F.46-47); Oxon Snr Lg. 34-35 39-40 47-48(res); Oxon Hosp. Cup 46-47 (R-up 45-46); Oxon Benev. Cup R-up 77-78 80-81 82-83; Daventry Charity Cup 88-90; Smiths Mem. Cup 68-70 (R-up 66-68); Hitchin Centenary Cup 68-69 (R-up 67-68); Leamington Charity Cup 51-52; Warks Comb. R-up 57-58 60-61, Presidents Cup R-up 60-61; Midland Floodlit Cup 67-68; Wallspan Comb. 85-86.

BICESTER TOWN

Chairman: Bill Hammond. **Vice Chairman:** Ray Honour. **President:** Mike Staniford.
Secretary/Press Officer: Phil Allen, 38 Bassett Avenue, Bicester OX6 7TZ (01869 252125).
Manager: Barry Grant **Coach:** Barry Grant **Physio:** Ray Huntley
Ground: Sports Ground, Oxford Rd, Bicester (01869 241936)
Directions: From Oxford; past Tescos on outskirts of Bicester - ground on right. From Aylesbury; turn left at first island on outskirts of Bicester onto bypass, right at next island, pass Tescos & ground on right.
Seats: 250 **Cover:** 550 **Capacity:** **Floodlights:** Yes **Founded:** 1876
Colours: Red & black/black/black **Change:** Green & white/green/green
Previous Lge: Oxon Senior **Reserve team's league:** Hellenic Lge Reserve Division.
Programme: With entry **Editor:** Secretary **Midweek Matchday:** Tuesday
Nickname: Foxhunters **Previous Name:** Slade Banbury Road (pre-1923).
Clubhouse: One bar **Record Attendance:** 955 v Portsmouth, floodlight inauguration 1/2/94.
Honours: Hellenic Lg 60-1 77-78 (Lg Cup 90-91 (R-up 92-93), Div 1 76-77).

BURNHAM

Chairman: Malcolm Higton **Vice Chairman:** M.A.Beavis. **President:**
Secretary: Alan King, 41 Underwood Road, High Wycombe, Bucks HP13 6YD (01494 523920)
Manager: Shane Chandler **Coach:** John Griffith **Physio:** Mark Green
Ground: The Gore, Wymers Wood Road, Burnham, Slough SL1 8JG (01628 602467/602697).
Directions: North west of village centre, 2 miles from Burnham BR station, 2 miles from M4 junction 7, 5 miles from M40 junction 2, 100yds north of Gore crossroads - fork right into Wymers Wood Rd and ground is immediately on right.
Capacity: 2,500 **Cover:** 250 **Seats:** 250 **Floodlights:** Yes **Club Shop:** Yes
Press Officer: Secretary **Programme:** 30 pages **Editor:** Cliff Sparkes
Colours: Blue & white/blue/white **Change colours:** Yellow/yellow/black
Midweek matchday: Tuesday **Reserve Team's Lge:** Suburban. **Sponsors:** Caflon International
Record Attendance: 2,380 v Halesowen Town, FA Vase 2/4/83.
Best FA Cup season: 3rd Qualifying Rd. **Best FA Trophy season:** Third Qualifying Rd replay 89-90.
Previous Leagues: Sth Bucks & East Berks/ Maidenhead Intermediate/ Windsor, Slough & Dist./ Gt Western Comb. 48-64/ Wycombe Comb. 64-70/ Reading Comb. 70-71/ Hellenic 71-77/ Athenian 77-84/ London Spartan 84-85.Southern 85-95.
Players progressing to Football League: D Hancock (Reading), R Rafferty (Grimsby Town, Portsmouth), D Payne (Barnet, Southend United, Watford, Peterborough Utd).
Clubhouse: Open every evening and weekend lunchtimes. Darts and pool, two bars, usual matchday food.
96-97 Captain: Jason Millar **96-97 P.o.Y.:** Jason Millar **96-97 Top Scorer:** Paul Coles (16)
Club Record Scorer: Fraser Hughes 65, 69-70
Honours: FA Vase SF 82-83 (QF 77-78), Athenian Lg R-up(2) 78-80, Hellenic Lg 75-76 (Div 1 R-up 72-73, Lg Cup 75-76, Div 1 Cup 71-72), London Spartan Lg 84-85 (Lg Cup 84-85), Reading Comb. Lg Cup 70-71 (All Champions Cup 70-71), Wycombe Comb. R-up(4) 65-67 68-70, various local cup competitions.

Burnham FC: Back Row (L-R); R Saunders (Treas), M Beavis (V/Chr), P Holden (Asst Mgr), S Bunce, J Weeks-Pearson, M Timberlake, P Brett, D Pritchard, W Holden, P Coles, J Beavis, M Green (Physio), M Broadley (Comm Mgr). Front Row; S Chandler, J Maciak, L Hyatt, M Higton (Chr), J Millar, A Lyne (Mgr), M Maciak, C Dore, M Potter.

CARTERTON TOWN

President: Mr G Fox **Chairman:** Mr G Maxwell **Match Secretary:** Glyn Yates
Secretary: Mrs Cath Bulley, 58 Ashfield Road, Carterton, Oxfordshire, OX18 (01993 842704).
Manager: Derek Beesley/ Dave Matzen **Physio:** Ady Cooper
Coach: Jim Flynn **Press Officer:** P King.
Ground: Kilkenny Lane, Carterton, Oxfordshire (01993 842410)
Directions: Enter Swinbrook Rd which off the Burford-Carterton road, proceed into Kilkenny Lane (one track road), ground car park 200yds on left before sharp corner. Hourly buses to Carterton from Oxford.
Seats: 50 **Cover:** 100 **Capacity:** 1,500 **Floodlights:** Yes **Founded:** 1922
Colours: Black & white/black/white **Change colours:** Yellow/blue/yellow **Reformed:** 1946/1983
Previous Leagues: Witney & District **Record Gate:** 600 v Oxford Utd, Oxon Snr Cup 93-94.
Programme: 20 pages with admission **Editor:** Jenny Maxwell (0993 841301).
Sponsors: **Reserve League:** Hellenic Reserve section.
Midweek matches: Tuesday **Club record goalscorer:** Tim Dorrington.
Clubhouse: Lounge & fully licensed bar open every day 7.30-11pm, Sat & Sun noon-2pm, Sat 4-6pm. Snacks & meals available.
Honours: Oxon Junior Shield 85-86; Oxon Snr Cup R-up 90-91 96-97; Witney & Dist. Lg 65-66 (Div 1 84-85 76-77); Hellenic Lg Div 1 89-90 93-94 (Reserve Div 1989-90 (R-up 93-94)); Oxon Intermediate Cup R-up 93-94(res.)

Carterton Town FC: Back Row (L-R); T Underwood (Asst Mgr), R Stephens (Physio), A Henry, G Brown, G Fisher, R Darvill, A Leach, W Jones, J Twiss, W Holden, C Panter, J Tompkins (Asst Mgr). Front Row; K Horsfall, M Townsend, A Roberts, A Sinnott (Mgr), G Maxwell (Chr), S Ovens, L Cozier, D Kew.

DIDCOT TOWN

President: **Chairman:** John Bailey
Secretary: N Bennett, 75 Churchill Road, Didcot, Oxon. OX11 7BU (01235 813016).
Manager: Robert Dodd **Coach:** Barry Cooper **Physio:** Mark Roberts
Ground: Station Road, Didcot (01235 813212).
Directions: Midway down Station Rd, Didcot, on right quarter mile from Railway Station towards town centre.
Seats: 50. **Cover:** 200 **Capacity:** 5,000 **Floodlights:**Yes. **Founded:** 1907
Colours: All red & white **Change colours:** All blue
Previous Leagues: Hellenic 53-57/ Metropolitan 57-63.
Nickname: Railwaymen. **Midweek Matchday:** Tuesday
Record Attendance: 550 v Wycombe Wanderers, 1956.
Programme: 50p **Editor:** Peter Swain.
Clubhouse: Every evenings and Sunday lunchtimes.
Honours: Hellenic Lg 53-54,Lg Cup 1965-66 66-67 92-93 Div 1 76-77,Div1 Cup 76-7

ENDSLEIGH

Chairman: Michael Alcock
Secretary: Graham Ayers, 7 Oakbrook Drive, The Reddings, Cheltenham, Glos GL51 6SB (01452 548556)
Manager: Mark Ratcliffe **Match Secretary:** Chris Hawkins (01242 692332) **Press Officer:** Sean Regan
Ground: Cheltenham Town FC, Whaddon Road, Cheltenham (01242 521974)
Directions: M5 Junc 10, follow signs to town, the A46 (Winchcombe & Broadway). Grd just off Prestbury Rd.
Capacity: 5,000 **Seats:** 1,000 **Cover:** 4,000 **Floodlights:** Yes **Formed:**
Colours: Blue/blue/white **Change colours:** All white. **Nickname:** Super Owls
Record Attendance: 83 v Bridgwater Town 95
Previous Ground: The Folley, Swindon Road, Cheltenham (pre-1993)
Previous Leagues: Glos Northern Snr (pre'93) **Midweek Matchday:** Wednesday
Honours: Glos Northern Snr Lg 92-93 (Div 1 91-92).

FAIRFORD TOWN

Chairman: M B Tanner **President:** B W Wall
Secretary: W Beach, 33 Park Cross, Fairford, GL7 4LF (01285 712136).
Ground: Cinder Lane, London Road, Fairford, Cirencester (01285 712071).
Manager: Gerry Kelly **Coach:** Rob Simpson **Physio:** C Tye
Directions: Entering Fairford on A417 from Lechlade turn left down Cinder Lane 150yds after 40mph sign. From Cirencester on same road, follow thru village and turn right down Cinder Lane 400yds after Railway Inn. Buses from Swindon, Lechlade and Cirencester.
Seats: 100 **Cover:** 150 **Capacity:** 2,000 **Floodlights:** Yes **Club Shop:** No.
Programme: 20 pages with admission **Editor/Press Officer:** Chairman
Colours: Red/white/red **Change colours:** White/blue/blue
Club Sponsors: Jewson **Founded:** 1891 **Nickname:** Town.
Midweek matchday: Wednesday **Reserve Team's League:** Hellenic Reserve section.
Record Attendance: 1,500 v Swindon Town, friendly 93
Previous Leagues: Cirencester & District (pre-1946)/ Swindon & District 46-70.
Previous Grounds: None
Clubhouse: Open each evening, weekend lunches & before and after all games
96-97 Captain: **96-97 Top Scorer:** **96-97 P.o.Y.:** Nigel Barry
Club Record Goalscorer: Pat Toomey. **Club Record Appearances:**
Record win: 9-0 v Moreton T.
Record defeat: 0-9 v Sharpness.
Honours: Glos Challenge Trophy 79-80 (R-up 82-83); Hellenic Lg R-up 78-79 79-80 90-91 94-95, (Premier Div Cup 78-79, Div 1 71-72, Div 1 Cup 71-72); Glos Jnr Cup 62-63; Swindon & Dist Lg 64-65 68-69.

HALLEN

Chairman: Barry Phillips **President:** Ken Naish
Secretary: Charmaine Phillips, 145A Station Road, Henbury, Bristol BS10 7LZ (0117 9501754)
Manager: Steve Brundson **Physio:** Tammy Mullan
Ground: Hallen Playing Fields, Moorhouse Lane, Hallen, Nr Bristol (0272 504610).
Directions: M5 jct 17, A4018 to Henbury r'bout, right, right again at junction, next right to Station Road, left into Avonmouth Road at r'bout. One mile to Hallen, ground first left, then right into lane to ground.
Seats: No **Cover:** No **Clubhouse:** Yes **Programme:** No **Founded:** 1949
Colours: Royal & black/black/black **Change Colours:** Green, black & red/red/red
Previous Names: Lawrence Weston Athletic (80's), Lawrence Weston Hallen (pre-1991).
Record Gate: **Midweek Matchday:** Wednesday
Previous Ground: Kings Weston (early 1980's) **Previous League:** Glos County (pre-1993)
Honours: Glos County Lg 92-93, Glos Snr Trophy 92-93.

HARROW HILL

Chairman: Reg Taylor **President:** Ken Jones **Manager/Coach:** R White
Secretary: Geoff Tuffley, 19 Westfield Court, Heywood Road, Cinderford GL14 2RU (01594 542421)
Match Sec: Roger Partridge, (01594 825360) **Physio:** R Taylor
Ground: Larksfield Road, Harrow Hill (01594 543873)
Directions: Take A40 west out of Gloucester, follow A40 for 8 miles then take A4136 to Longhope, pass by on the outskirts of Michealdean, up steep hill (plump Hill), then second turn on the right signed Harrow Hill. At phone box on the left turn right into Larksfield Road, ground on right at top of hill.
Colours: Claret & blue/sky/sky **Change Colours:** Black & white/black/black
Record Gate: 350 v Cinderford Town 92 **Midweek Matchday:** Tuesday **Nickname:** Harry Hill

North Leigh's Matthew Ellis attacks against Kintbury *Photo - Oxford Mail*

Action between Carterton & Banbury *Photo - Oxford Mail*

HIGHWORTH TOWN

President: Alan Vockins **Chairman:** Steven Leppard **Press Officer:** David Evans.
Secretary: Fraser Haines, 222 Windrush, Highworth, Swindon SN6 7EB (01793 861109).
Manager: Gary Goodwin **Coach:** Joe Matano **Physio:** Graham Ashby
Ground: Elm Recreation Ground, Highworth. (01793 766263)
Directions: Enter on A361 from Swindon, past Simpsons Garage, straight over island, next sharp left into Green by Vet's Surgery - ground & car park 60yds on left next to Sports Hall.
Seats: 50 **Cover:** 250 **Capacity:** 2,000 **Floodlights:** Yes **Founded:** 1894.
Colours: Red & white/black/red **Change colours:** Blue & white/black/blue **Club Shop:** No.
Programme: 16 pages, 60p **Editor:** Dave Evans (01793 764712)
Nickname: Worthians **Previous Leagues:** Wilts/Swindon & Dist.
Midweek matchday: Wednesday **Sponsors:** Smart Movers. **Reserves Lge:** Hellenic Reserve Div.
Record Attendance: 1,862 v QPR opening Floodlights
Clubhouse: Sat 12-2.30 & 4.30-11pm. Mon, Wed & Fri 7-11pm. Rolls & Hot food.
Club Record Scorer: Kevin Higgs **Club Record Appearances:** Rod Haines.
Record win: 12-0 v Beeches, Arthur Shipway Cup 1992.
Record defeat: 2-8 v Milton United, Hellenic League Division One, 1987.
Honours: Wilts Snr Cup 63-64 72-73 95-96 (R-up 88-89), Hellenic Div 1 Cup 88-89, Arthur Shipway Cup 88-89 93-94, Swindon & District Lg 63-64 64-65 65-66 68-69.

KINTBURY RANGERS

President: **Chairman:** A Keith Plank
Secretary: A K Plank, 26 Kennet Road, Kintbury, Hungerford, RG17 9XW (01488 658460).
Manager: Darren Angell **Coach:** D Ingram/J Smyth **Physio:** Gary Murphy
Ground: Recreation Ground, Inkpen Road, Kintbury (0488 57001).
Directions: Turn off A4 (signed Kintbury) between Newbury/Hungerford. 2nd left after level crossing into Inkpen Road, entrance 200yds on right by Jubilee Centre. Half mile from Kintbury (BR).
Seats: None **Cover:** No **Capacity:** 1,000 **Floodlights:** Yes **Founded:** 1890
Colours: Amber/black/amber **Change colours:** White/blue/white
Nickname: Rangers **Reformed:** 1943.
Reserves' Lge: Hellenic Res. sect. **Previous Leagues:** Newbury District/ Nth Berks.
Programme: 16 pages, 50p **Programme Editor:** Colin Godfrey (0635 874209)
Record Gate: 550 v Newport AFC, 1990. **Midweek Matchday:** Wednesday
Clubhouse: Open every nightl 7.30-11. Hot & cold meals matchdays.
Club record appearances: Nigel Llewellyn.
Honours: Nth Berks Lg 77-78 81-82, Hellenic Lg Div 1 R-up 87-88, Berks & Bucks I'mediate Cup 60-61 (R-up 87-88).

NORTH LEIGH

President: Mrs C Smith **Chairman:** Peter King. **Vice Chairman:** B.Shepperd.
Secretary: Mr P J Dix, 8 Windmill Close, North Leigh, Nr Witney, Oxon OX8 6RP (01993 881199).
Manager: A Buckingham/P Hutter **Asst Manager:** Mr P King **Physio:** Mr R Keen
Ground: Eynsham Hall Park Sports Ground, North Leigh, nr Witney, Oxon (0993 881427).
Directions: Ground is situated off A4095 Witney to Woodstock road 3 miles east of Witney. Entrance to ground is 300yds east of Main Park Entrance.
Seats: 100 **Cover:** 200 **Capacity:** 2,000 **Floodlights:** Yes **Club Shop:** No.
Programme: 20 pages, £1 with entry **Editor:** J Fogg **Press Officer:** B Norton (01993 881777).
Colours: Sky/navy/navy **Change colours:** White/navy/red
Club Sponsors: Various **Founded:** 1908 **Nickname:** None.
Midweek matches: Wednesday **Previous Leagues:** Witney & District 08-89.
Clubhouse: Bar open matches. Snacks available.
Club record scorer: P Coles **Club record appearances:** P King.
Honours: Hellenic Lg Div 1 R-up 92-93 (Reserves Cup 93-94), Oxon Jnr Shield 56-57 83-84, Oxon Charity Cup 84-85 88-89, Witney & Dist. Lg(13) 50-57 84-90 (Lg Cup(10) 47-48 51-52 53-55 56-57 81-82 85-89), Oxon Yth Cup 93-94 94-95, Oxon Yth u-17 Lg & Cup 93-94. Oxford Senior Cup R-Up 94-95. Marriott Cup 95-96.

SHORTWOOD UNITED

Chairman: Peter Webb **Vice C'men:** W Stratford, W Lewis **President:** R T Tanner
Secretary: Mark Webb, 1 The Bungalow, Shortwood, Nailsworth, Stroud, Glos GL6 0SD (01453 833204).
Manager: Simon Stroud **Coach:** Denzil Brizland **Physio:** Aide Brown & Mike Newman
Ground: "Meadow Bank", Shortwood, Nailsworth, Gloucestershire (01453 833936).
Directions: In Nailsworth turn into Spring Hill then first left. Continue past shop and and keep left past "Britannia" (signposted Shortwood) - continue to end for ground. 4 miles from Stroud (BR).
Seats: 50 **Cover:** 150 **Capacity:** 5,000 **Floodlights:** Yes **Club Shop:** No.
Programme: 18 pages, 30p **Editor:** Keith Sheppard **Press Officer:** Ashley Loveridge
Colours: All red **Change:** Blue/blue or white/blue or white
Sponsors: **Nickname:** The Wood. **Founded:** 1900
Midweek matchday: Wednesday **Reserves' League:** Glos Northern Snr
Record Attendance: 1,000 v Forest Green Rovers, FA Vase 5th Rd 81-82.
Previous Leagues: Stroud/ Glos Northern Snr/ Glos Co.
Previous Ground: Table Land, Wallow Green
Clubhouse: Mon-Sat 7-11pm, Sun noon-12 & 7-10.30pm. Crisps etc in bar, hot food kitchen on matchdays.
96-97 Captain: Clive Boulton **96-97 P.o.Y.:** Julian Freeman **96-97 Top Scorer:** Julian Freeman
Club Record appearances: Peter Grant. **Club Record Goalscorer:** Peter Grant
Record win: 11-0 **Record defeat:** 0-9
Record transfer fee received: Paul Tester (Cheltenham, 80-81).
Honours: Glos.Co.Lg 81-82 (R-up 80-81), Glos Tphy 83-84 91-92,94-95,(R-up 79-80), Hellenic Lg 84-85 91-92 (R-up 85-86 89-90 94-95, Div 1 R-up 83-84, Div 1 Cup 83-84), Prem Lge Cup R-up 95-96, Hungerford Merit Cup, Glos Snr Amtr Cup 85-86 (R-up 79-80), Stroud Charity Cup 91-92 92-93 94-95 (R-up 95-96), Stroud Lg 27-28 (Div 2 26-27 64-65(res), Div 3 25-26 49-50(res) 62-63(res)), Glos Northern Snr Lg R-up 67-68 91-92(res)(Div 2 62-63 80-81(res) 90-91(res)), Arthur Shipway Cup 78-79 79-80.

SWINDON SUPERMARINE

Chairman: Steve Moore **President:** Cliff Puffit
Secretary: Eric Stott, 43 Stanier Street, Swindon, Wilts SN1 5QU (01793 521301).
Manager: John Fisher **Coach:** Glynn Dubber **Physio:** Alan Jennings
Ground: Highworth Road, South Marston, Swindon (01793 824824)
Directions: On A361 Swindon/Highworth road, adjoining Marston Industrial Estate. 6 miles from Swindon (BR) - buses in direction of Highworth, Fairford & Lechdale. If lost ask for Vickers Sports Ground.
Seats: 75 **Cover:** 120 **Capacity:** 1,000 **Floodlights:** Yes **Founded:** 1992.
Colours: Blue & white/blue/blue **Change colours:** Yellow/navy/yellow **Programme:** Yes
Midweek Matchday: Wednesday **Previous Leagues:** Wilts.
Previous Names: Supermarine (prev. Vickers Armstrong 46-81), Swindon Athletic (prev. Penhill Yth Centre 70-84/ Penhill 84-84-89) amalgamated in 1992.
Previous Ground: Supermarine: Vickers Airfield (until mid-1960s), *Swindon Ath.: Merton 70-84/ 'Southbrook', Pinehurst Road 84-92.*
Honours: Wilts Snr Cup R-up 93-94, Hellenic Lg Reserve Section 93-94. As Supermarine: Wilts Snr Cup 85-86 (R-up 74-75 84-85), Hellenic Div 1 R-Up 82-83 (Res Section West R-up 84-85 (Challenge Cup 83-84), Wilts Comb Snr 75-76, Swindon & District Lg Div 3 55-56, Dr Elliott Cup(5), Faringdon Thursday Memorial Cup(3). *Swindon Ath.: Wilts Snr Cup 82-83 86-87 89-90 (R-up 83-84 85-86 90-91), Hellenic Lg Div 1 85-86 86-87, Wilts Co. Lg 82-83 83-84).*

TUFFLEY ROVERS

President: A W Purdy **Chairman:** Tony Newport
Secretary: Graham Moody, 50 Giles Cox, Quidgley, Gloucester GL2 4YL (01452 724083).
Manager: D Foxwell. **Coach:** C Gardner **Physio:** S Tracey
Ground: Glevum Park, Lower Tuffley Lane, Gloucester (01452 423402).
Directions: Follow Gloucester city ring-rd to r'bout signed M5 South & Bristol, take 4th exit signed Hempsted & city centre, after 200yds turn right (McDonalds on corner) into Lower Tuffley Lane, ground 400yds on left.
Seats: 50 **Cover:** Yes **Capacity:** **Floodlights:** Yes **Founded:** 1929
Colours: Claret & blue/white/claret **Change colours:** Yellow/claret/blue **Nickname:** Rovers
Previous Grounds: Stroud Rd, Gloucester/ Randwick Park, Tuffley. **Club Shop:** No.
Previous Leagues: Stroud/ Glos Northern Senior/ Glos County (pre-1991).
Midweek Matchday: Wednesday
Programme: approx 10 pages with entry **Editor:** Mr A Purdy, 43 Ermin Park, Brockworth.
Club Sponsors: Ermin Plant. **Reserve League:** Glos.Northern Senior Stroud Lge.
Clubhouse: 800 yds from ground. Open before & after matches, and normal pub hours at other times. Snacks.
96-97 Captain: **96-97 Top Scorer:** **96-97 P.o.Y.:**
Record Attendance: 150 v Cinderford Town 94-95
Honours: Hellenic Lg Div 1 92-93 (Div 1 Cup 92-93), Glos Co. Lge 90-91, Glos Snr Amtr Cup 87-88, Stroud Lg 72-73,94-95, Glos Northern Senior Lg. Div 1 87-88 Div2 79-80.

WANTAGE TOWN

Chairman: A Woodward **President:** Ernie Smart **Match Secretary:** Colin Blunsden
Secretary: Alan Parker, Little Orchard Road, Wantage, OX12 8DW. (01235 763842).
Manager: Derek Bint **Coach:** Kevin O'Hanlon **Physio:** Ian Howard
Ground: Alfredian Park, Manor Park, Wantage, Oxon (01235 764781).
Directions: Take Hungerford Road from Wantage, ground signposted on right oppsite recreation ground.
Seats: 50 **Cover:** 300 **Capacity:** 1,500 **Floodlights:** Yes **Club Shop:** No
Programme: 28 pages, 50p **Editor:** Andy Wells (01235 767291).
Colours: Green & white hoop/white/white **Change colours:** All White
Sponsors: Broadway Motors **Nickname:** Alfredians **Founded:** 1892
Midweek Matchday: Wednesday **Record Attendance:** 500 v Newport AFC 89
Previous Leagues: Swindon & Dist. 1901-12 30-35 47-56/ N Berks 12-22 38-40 46-47/ Reading & D. 22-30 35-38.
Previous Ground: Challow Park (pre-1922)
Players progressing to Football League: Roy Burton and Colin Duncan (both Oxford United).
Clubhouse: Mon-Fri 7.30-11pm, Sat noon-2.30, 4-7pm.
96-97 Captain: **96-97 P.o.Y.:** **96-97 Top Scorer:**
Club Record Goalscorer: A Rolls **Club Record Appearances:**
Record win: 11-1 v Amersham Town (A), Hellenic League 60-61.
Record defeat: 0-14 v Thame United (A), 20/1/62.
Honours: Hellenic Lg R-up 81-82, Div 1 80-81 (R-up 69-70 87-88 91-92 95-96), Div 1 Cup R-up 91-92; Oxon Snr Cup 82-83; Berks & Bucks Intermediate Cup 54-55; Swindon & District Lg 07-08 33-34 52-53 55-56.

DIVISION ONE CLUBS 1997-98

ARDLEY UNITED

Chairman: Norman Stacey **Match Secretary:** Alan Mitchell (01869 346854)
Secretary: Nigel Adams, 35 Forsythia Close, Bicester, Oxon, OX6 9GA (01869 325734)
Manager: Peter Foley **Coach:** **Physio:** Norman Stacey
Press Officer: Ron Jones (01869 246717)
Ground: Ardley Sports Ground (01869 346429)
Directions: M40 junc 10 take A43 towards Middleton Stoney on the right after 1/2 mile.
Colours: Sky/navy/sky **Change colours:** Yellow/black/black
Midweek matchday: Tuesday **Previous Leagues:** Oxon Snr (pre-1993)
Honours: Oxon Snr Lg R-up 92-93 (Pres. Cup R-up 90-91 91-92).

BISHOPS CLEEVE

President: John Davies **Chairman:** David Lewis
Secretary: Phil Tustain, 7 Dale Walk, Bishops Cleeve, Glos GL52 4PQ (01242 674968).
Manager: David Lewis **Coach:** G Samuels **Physio:** Philip Tustain
Ground: Stoke Rd, Bishops Cleeve (01242 676257)
Directions: 3 miles north of Cheltenham on A435. 3rd left in village into Stoke Rd - ground on right. 4 miles from Cheltenham (BR); served by Cheltenham to Tewkesbury buses.
Seats: None **Cover:** 50 **Capacity:** 1,500 **Floodlights:** No **Founded:** 1892.
Colours: Green & black/black/black **Change colours:** Blue/white/red.
Midweek Matchday: Wednesday **Nickname:** Skinners
Previous Leagues: Cheltenham, Nth Glos **Record Gate:** 1,000 v Newport AFC.
Previous Grounds: The Skiller (pre-1913), Village Field (pre-1950)
Clubhouse: Full facilities, bar, dance area **Honours:** Hellenic Lg Cup R-up 90-91.

Action from match between Wantage & North Leigh

Photo - Oxford Mail

Carterton's Chris Panther attacks through the midfield against North Leigh.

Photo - Oxford Mail

CHELTENHAM SARACENS

Chairman: J Utteridge **Manager:** Ian Ford
Secretary: R Attwood, 179 Arle Road, Cheltenham GL51 8LJ (01242 515855).
Match Sec: Terry Coates **Coach:** Kevin Barry **Physio:** Jim Utteridge
Press Officer: Terry Coates (01242 692320).
Ground: Petersfield Park, Tewkesbury Road, Cheltenham (01242 584134).
Directions: 1 mile from Cheltenham centre on A4019 Tewksbury Road (next to B & Q) - 1st left over railway bridge, 1st left and follow service road.
Seats: None **Cover:** 100 **Capacity:** 2,000 **Floodlights:** No **Founded:** 1964.
Colours: All blue **Change colours:** Black & white/black/black
Club Shop: No **Nickname:** Saras. **Midweek Matchday:** Wednesday
Prog.: 20 pages, 50p (Ed: Secretary) **Previous League:** Cheltenham 1964-86.
Reserve Team's League: Hellenic Reserve section.
Players progressing to Football League: S Cotterill (Wimbledon, B/mouth) 88, K Knight (Reading) 89.
96-97 Captain: Richard Alder **96-97 Top Scorer:** Clive Shatford **96-97 P.o.Y.:** Sean Stokes
Honours: Glos Snr Cup 91-92. **Clubhouse:** 2 mins away at 16-20 Swindon Rd, Cheltenham.

CIRENCESTER FOOTBALL ACADEMY

Chairman: Tony Bedwell **President:** **Press Officer:** Steve Slattery
Secretary: Keith Ryan, 11 Pinehurst Road, Swindon, Wilts SN2 1QE (01793 526059)
Manager: Pat Slattery **Coach:** John Freeth **Physio:** Steve Slattery
Ground: Tetbury Road, Cirencester (01285 654783)
Directions: Follow by pass towards Bristol. THe ground is on left approx 1/2 mile from town centre.
Colours: Red & black/black/red **Change colours:** Black & blue/blue/blue
Midweek Matchday: Variable **Nickname:** Academy **Record Attendance:**

CIRENCESTER UNITED

President: A Day **Chairman:** J Austin **Vice Chairman:** Paul King.
Secretary/Press Officer: G Varley, 95 Vaisey Rd, Cirencester, Glos GL7 2JW (01285 657836).
Manager: A Smith **Coach:** T Dryden **Physio:** P Messenger
Ground: Four Acres P.F., Chesterton Lane (01285 885460)
Directions: Dual carriageway towards Bristol, under footbridge, first left after Cirencester Town F.C., ground 200yds on left hand side.
Seats: None **Cover:** No **Programme:** Yes **Floodlights:** No **Founded:** 1970
Colours: Red & black/black/red **Change colours:** Green & yellow/green/green
Nickname: Herd. **Previous Grounds:** None **Previous Name:** The Herd (pre-1990)
Previous Leagues: Cirencester & District (4 years)/ Cheltenham (8 years).
Programme: 40 pages, 50p **Editor:** N Warriner (01285 656187) **Club Shop:** No.
Midweek Matchday: Wednesday **Sponsors:**
Clubhouse: Training nights & matchdays. Rolls & sundries available.
96-97 Captain: J Stratford **96-97 Top Scorer:** J Beard **96-97 P.o.Y.:** A Meredith
Club record scorer: M Day **Club record appearances:** A Smith.
Honours: Glos Snr Amtr Cup R-up 86-87 89-90; Cirencester Lg 72-73 74-75 (Div 2(3) 71-73 74-75, Lg Cup 74-75, Res. Cup 74-75); Cheltenham Lg 76-77 83-84 (Div 2 75-76, Lg Cup 83-84 (R-up 86-87), Snr Charity Cup 86-87); Stroud Charity Cup 86-87 (Section A 82-83 83-84); Arthur Shipway Cup 86-87 (R-up 87-88 92-93); Fairford Hospital Cup R-up(4) 83-85 90-91 92-93; Hellenic Res Div 95-96, Cup 96-97.

CLANFIELD

President: B Wallis **Chairman:** J Osborne
Secretary: J Osborne, 70 Lancut Road, Witney, Oxon OX8 5AQ (01993 771631).
Manager: Bill Pirie/Mark Light **Physio:**
Ground: Radcot Road, Clanfield, Oxon (01367 810314)
Directions: On A4095 8 miles west of Witney & 4 miles east of Faringdon on south side of Clanfield. Buses from Witney - contact Thames Transit for details.
Seats: No **Cover:** 300 **Capacity:** 2,000 **Floodlights:** No **Club Shop:** No.
Colours: Red & white **Change colours:** Yellow & Black/black/black
Programme: 8 pages, with admission **Editor:** Secretary
Sponsors: Morelands Brewery **Nickname:** Robins **Founded:** 1890
Previous Leagues: Nth Berks/ Witney & Dist. **Reserves' League:** Hellenic League Reserve section.
Clubhouse: Every evening & Sat/Sun lunch
96-97 Captain: J Court **96-97 Top Scorer:** D Hamill **96-97 P.o.Y.:** A Howard
Honours: Oxon Jnr Shield 32-33, Oxon I'mediate Cup 67-68, Witney & Dist. Lg 66-67 (Div 1 65-66, Div 2 64-65), Hellenic Lg Div 1 69-70 (Premier Div Cup 72-73, Div 1 Cup 69-70 85-86), Jim Newman Mem. Tphy 83-84 87-88, Faringdon Thursday Memorial Cup 69-70 71-72.

EASINGTON SPORTS

Chairman: Jim Hay **President:** Terry Horley
Secretary: Terry Horley, 65 Grange Road, Banbury, Oxon OX16 9AT (01295 254950).
Manager/Coach: Jim Hay **Physio:** Alan Gardner **Press Officer:** T Horley
Ground: Addison Road, Easington Estate, Banbury, Oxon (01295 257006).
Directions: From Oxford A423. After passing under flyover on the outskirts of Banbury take first turning left into Grange Road then third right into Addison Rd. Ground at top on left. One and a half miles from Banbury (BR).
Seats: 50 **Cover:** 100 **Capacity:** 1,000 **Floodlights:** No **Founded:** 1946
Colours: Red & white/black/black **Change colours:** Blue & white/blue/blue. **Programme:** Yes, 25p
Midweek Matchday: Wednesday **Record Gate:** 250 v Witney Town 68
Previous Ground: Bodicote. **Previous Leagues:** Banbury Jnr/ Oxon Snr/ Warkwick Combination.
Reserves' League: Hellenic Res. section **Clubhouse:** Changing rooms, showers, bar facilities and food.
Honours: Oxon Snr Cup R-up, Oxon Intermediate League & Cup, Oxon Snr Lg.

HEADINGTON AMATEURS

President: John Dunne **Chairman:** Donald Light **Press Officer:** Paul Sammons
Secretary: C Barrett, 6 Holland Place, Wood Farm, Headington, Oxford OX3 8QT (01865 750828).
Manager: J Light. **Coach:** B McCrae **Physio:** J Taylor
Ground: Barton Rec., Barton Village Road, Barton, Oxon (01865 60489).
Directions: From Green Rd r'bout, Headington, (on A40) take Barton/Islip exit (1st exit coming from Witney, last coming from London), turn left into North Way, follow road for half mile - ground at bottom of hill on left.
Seats: None **Cover:** None **Floodlights:** No **Founded:** 1949. **Nickname:** A's.
Colours: All red **Change:** Blue/blue/white
Midweek matchday: Tuesday **Previous Leagues:** Oxford City Junior 49-66/ Oxford Senior 67-88.
Programme: 8 pages, £1 with entry **Editor:** Stan Hawkswood (01865 65546) **Club Shop:** No.
Sponsors: Oxford Marquees **Reserves' Lge:** Hellenic Res. sect.
Player progressing to Football Lge: James Light (Oxford) 1970s.
Clubhouse: Open Tues & Thurs 6-11pm, Sat matchdays 4.45-11pm. Rolls, chips, burgers, hot dogs, sweets etc.
Club record scorer: Tony Penge **Club record appearances:** Keith Drackett.
Record win: 6-0 v Carterton (H) 1991 **Record defeat:** 1-8 v Banbury United (A), February 1994.
Honours: Oxon Snr League(4) 72-74 75-77 (R-up 71-72 74-75 77-78 81-82 84-85, Div 1 68-69, Presidents Cup(2) 72-74 (R-up 71-72 77-78 84-85)), Oxon Charity Cup 75-76 (Intermediate Cup 88-89), Hellenic League Div 1 R-up 87-88 (Res. Sect. 92-93, Res. Cup 91-92).

KIDLINGTON

President: Gordon Norridge. **Chairman:** Peter Walton.
Secretary: Peter Walton, 3 Azalea Ave, Kidlington, Oxon. OX5 1HQ (01865 377226)
Manager: K Grossman **Coach:** M O'Connell **Physio:** S Dickens
Ground: Yarnton Rd, Kidlington, Oxford (01865 375628)
Directions: From Kidlington r'bout (junction of A4260 & A34) A423 north to Kidlington; after 1st lights take 2nd left (Yarnton Road), ground is 200yds on the left.
Colours: Green & black/black/green **Change colours:** Red & black/black/red **Floodlights:** No
Programme: 20 pages, 20p **Editor:** M A Canning **Founded:** 1920
Midweek Matchday: Wednesday **Previous League:** Oxon Snr 47-54.
Record Attendance: 2500 v Showbiz XI 1973 **Clubhouse:** Two bars open after matches
Honours: Oxon Snr Lg 53-54 (R-up 47-48), Hellenic Lg Cup 74-75 (R-up 68-69 73-74 74-75, Div 1 R-up 63-64 78-79), Oxon Intermediate Cup 52-53 84-85 (R-up 68-69 73-74 74-75), FA Vase 5th last sixteen 76-77.

LETCOMBE

President: Dave McDowell. **Chairman:** Dennis Stock **Vice-Chairman:** G Delacoze
Secretary: Desmond Williams, 8 Larkdown, Wantage OX12 8HE (01235 764130).
Manager/Coach: Graham Foster **Commercial Manager:** R Stock.
Ground: Bassett Road, Letcombe Regis, Wantage, Oxon (012357 68685).
Directions: B4507 Swindon road from Wantage, left for Letcombe Regis, follow road thru Letcombe Regis; ground on right on far side of village.
Seats: No **Cover:** No **Floodlights:** No **Nickname:** None **Founded:** 1960.
Colours: Yellow/blue/yellow. **Change colours:** White/blue/blue **Midweek Matchday:** Wednesday
Sponsors: Autotype/ D McDowell **Previous Lges:** North Berks 60-90/ Chiltonian 90-93.
Programme: £1 with entry **Editor:** R.Stock (01235 762387) **Club Shop:** No.
Clubhouse: Open evenings except Monday. Rolls & hot food sold.
Record scorer: R Taylor **Record appearances:** P Davies. **Reserves' Lge:** Hellenic Res. sect.
96-97 Top Scorer: B Spiero **96-97 P.o.Y.:** M Delacoze **96-97 Captain:** P Allen
Honours: Chiltonian Lg Div 1 90-91, North Berks Lg 89-90 (Lg Cup 87-88, War Memorial Cup 89-90, A G Kingham Cup 89-90.

Ardley's Tony Blossom avoids the feet of Letcombe's Matty Spraggs *Photo - Oxford Mail*

Action from match between Wantage & North Leigh *Photo - Oxford Mail*

MILTON UNITED

Chairman: Mr K Tull **President:** Mr J Cannon **Match Secretary:** Sid Tindall
Secretary: Sue Walker, 122 High Street, Sutton Courtney, Abingdon, OX14 4AX. (01235 847158)
Ground: The Sportsfield, High Street, Milton, Abingdon, Oxon (01235) 832999
Directions: Use A34 bypass approx 10 miles north of M4 jct.13 & 10 miles south of Oxford. Leave A34 at Milton Hill roundabout and follow signs to Milton Park.
dabout follow road over railway bridge, take 1st left, ground immediately on left.
Capacity: **Seats:** None **Cover:** None **Floodlights:** No **Club Shop:** No.
Programme: Yes **Editor/Press Officer:** David Taylor(01235 816376)
Colours: Sky & maroon/white/white **Change colours:** All white
Sponsors: Morlands Brewery **Founded:** 1926
Midweek matchday: Tuesday **Reserve Team's League:** Hellenic Lge Res sect
Record Attendance: 500 v Almondsbury Picksons, Hellenic Lg 90-91.
Clubhouse: On ground, open matchdays.
96-97 Captain: **96-97 Top Scorer:** **96-97 P.o.Y.:**
Club Record Goalscorer: Nigel Mott **Club Record Appearances:**
Honours: Hellenic Lg 90-91 (Div 1 89-90 R-Up.94-95)), Nth Berks Lg(4) 85-86 87-89 (R-up 84-85 86-87, Lg Cup(3) 84-86 88-89, Div 2 80-81, Charity Shield(4) 84-86 87-89 (R-up 82-83), Nth Berks War Mem. Cup(3) 83-85 87-88, Berks & Bucks I'mediate Cup 90-91.

PEGASUS JUNIORS

President: Peter Hill **Chairman:** R W Pasley
Secretary: Brian James, 7 Loder Drive, Hereford HR1 1DS (01432 274982).
Manager/Coach: M.Williams. **Physio:** D Smith.
Ground: Essex Arms, Widemarsh St, Hereford. (0432 268705)
Directions: A49 Ross Road over Greyfriars Bridge, Victoria Street to end of Edgar Street, turn right, straight over mini-r/about, ground 50 yards on left.
Seats: None **Cover:** None **Capacity:** **Floodlights:** No. **Founded:** 1955
Programme: 50p **Editor:** K Bishop
Colours: All red. **Change colours:** Blue & white/blue/blue.
Previous Leagues: Leisure Centre.
Clubhouse: 48 Stowens Street. **Midweek Matchday:** Tuesday
Honours: Herefordshire Snr Amtr Cup 71-72, Herefordshire Co. Chal. Cup(5) 81-83 84-85 87-88 89-90 (R-up 93-94), Worcs Snr Urn 85-86, Hellenic Lg Div 1 84-85 (R-up 93-94, Div 1 Cup R-up 93-94).

PURTON

President: Graham Price **Chairman:** John Hayden **Press Officer:** Alan Eastwood
Secretary: Nick Webb, 4 Glevum Close, Purton, Swindon, Wilts SN5 9HA (01793 770242).
Ground: The Red House, Purton (01793 770262 - Saturday afternoons only).
Directions: Purton is on B4041 Wootton Bassett to Cricklade Road. Ground near village hall.
Seats: **Capacity** **Cover:** **Floodlights:** No **Founded:** 1923
Colours: All red **Change colours:** White & blue/blue/blue
Programme: 40 pagesp **Editor:** Alan Eastwood (01793 694036).
Sponsors: Courtoulds. **Nickname:** The Reds **Midweek Matchday:** Wednesday
Clubhouse: Open after matches
96-97 Captain: **96-97 Top Scorer:** **96-97 P.o.Y.:**
Honours: Wilts Lg 48-49 85-86 (Div 2 83-84, Div 3 86-87), Wilts Snr Cup(6) 38-39 48-49 50-51 54-55 87-89, Wilts Yth Cup 77-78 85-86 88-89, Fairford Hosp. Cup(3) 87-89 93-94.

ROSS TOWN

Patron: Dave Sexton **Chairman:** Geoff Jones **Press Officer:** Chris Parsons (01989 750691)
Secretary: Tim Barnard, Apsley House, Whitchurch, Ross-on-Wye, HR9 6DJ (01600 890722)
Manager: Phil Davies **Coach:** Martin Thomas **Physio:** Alan Bridges
Ground: Cinderford Town FC, Causeway Ground, Hilldene, Cinderford (01594 822039)
Directions: From Gloucester take A40 to Ross-on-Wye, then A48 - Chepstow. In 10 miles turn right at Elton garage onto A4151 signed Cinderford, thru Littledean, up steep hill, right at crossroads, second left into Latimer Rd. Ground 5 mins walk from town centre.
Capacity: 3,500 **Cover:** 1,000 **Seats:** 250 **Floodlights:** Yes
Colours: Red & white/red/red & white **Change colours:** Yellow & sky/black/yellow

Midweek Matchday: Various **Nickname:** Riversiders
Record Attendance: 147 v Harrow Hill 26/3/97
96-97 Captain: Chad Harris **96-97 Top Scorer:** Graham Jones **96-97 P.o.Y.:** Chad Harris
Honours: Hereford Lge 94-95, Charity Shield 95-96; Hereford FA Charity Bowl 94-95; Worcester & Dist Lge 95-96, Baylis Cup 95-96; Hereford FA County Chall Cup R-up 95-96; Pershore Hospital Charity Cup R-up 95-96.

WATLINGTON TOWN

Chairman: Bill Strong **President:** C Coles **Press Officer:** Kevin House
Secretary: Steven Muir, 91 Shirburn Street, Watlington, Oxford OX9 5BU (0411 132309)
Manager: Brian House **Coach:** Brian House **Physio:** Steven Muir
Ground: Shirburn Road, Watlington, Oxford.
Directions: From Oxford take A40/M40 east to junc 6, take B4009 towards Watlington. Ground is on right after 2 miles.
Colours: Red & black/black/red & black **Change colours:** Tangerine/white/tangerine
Midweek Matchday: Tuesday **Record Attendance:**

WOOTTON BASSETT TOWN

Chairman: Paul Harrison **President:** Keith Lodge
Sec./Press Officer: Mr R Carter, 14 Blackthorn Close, Wootton Bassett, Swindon, Wilts SN4 7JE (01793 851386).
Manager: Dave Warren **Coach:** Tony Lockyear **Physio:** Geoff Hawkins
Ground: Gerard Buxton Sports Ground, Rylands Way, Wootton Bassett, Swindon (0793 853880).
Directions: M4 jnct 16 to Wootton Bassett (A3102), left at 2nd r'bout (Prince of Wales pub on right), 2nd left into Longleaze (just after Mobil garage) and Rylands Way is 3rd right by shops, ground 100yds on right. Coming from Calne/Devizes proceed thru town centre and turn right into Longleaze after Shell petrol station on right - Rylands Ave. is 3rd left. Coming from Malmesbury take last exit off r'bout by Prince of Wales pub and Longleaze is 2nd left.
Seats: None **Cover:** 350 **Capacity:** 4,000 **Floodlights:** Due **Founded:** 1882
Colours: All Blue **Change colours:** All Red
Programme: 12 pages, free **Editor:** T.B.A. **Club Shop:** No.
Previous Grounds: None **Record Gate:** 2,103 v Swindon T., friendly 91.
Sponsors: Cathy Moore Recruitment **Previous Leagues:** Wilts (pre-1988).
Midweek matchday: Wednesday **Reserve team's League:** Wiltshire.
Clubhouse: Open every matchdays, usual opening hours. Usual type of bar food available together with filled rolls. Tea & coffee available over bar. Matchday refreshments - teas, coffees, soups with light snacks.
95-96 Captain: **95-96 Top Scorer:** **95-96 P.o.Y.:**
Record scorer: Brian (Toby) Ewing **Record appearances:** Steve Thomas.
Record win: 11-2 **Record defeat:** 0-9
Hons: Hellenic Lg Div 1 Cup 89-90 93-94, Wilts Lg 87-88 (Div 2 84-85, Subsidiary Cup 78-79), Wilts Snr Cup R-up 02-03 03-04 87-88, Ghia Snr 83-84, Ghia Jnr Cup R-up 88-89, FA Amateur Cup QF 26-27.

YARNTON

Chairman: Michael Staniford **President:** Susan Staniford
Secretary: Amanda Kirk, 11 Saw Close, Chalgrove, Oxon OX44 7TW (01865 891088)
Manager: Peter Wright **Coach:** David Hunt **Physio:** Adrien Cooper
Ground: Marsh Road Sports Ground, Yarnton, Oxon (01865 842037).
Directions: North of Oxford on A44 - head for Woodstock/Evesham. Ground situated behind The Grapes pub. Entrance on right before roundabout. Oxford-Woodstock buses stop near ground, Oxford-Kidlington stop 30mins walk from ground.
Seats: None **Cover:** None **Capacity:** Unknown **Floodlights:** No **Founded:** 1947
Colours: Royal & white/blue/blue **Change colours:** Yellow & green/black/black **Club Shop:** No.
Previous Grounds: None **Previous Lges:** Witney & Dist. 47-80/ Oxon Snr 80-91.
Programme: 12 pages, £1 with admission **Clubhouse:** No.
Midweek matchday: Tuesday **Sponsors:** Woodstock Felt Roofing & Red Lion, Yarnton
Record Gate: 150 v Kidlington 92
96-97 Captain: **96-97 Top Scorer:** **96-97 P.o.Y.:**
Honours: Oxford Jnr Shield 76-77, Witney & Dist. Lg Div 2 72-73 (Supplementary Cup 65-66), Oxon Snr Lg Div 1 80-81 (Ben Turner Cup 90-91), Oxon Jnr Chal. Cup 56-57 72-73, Fred Ford Mem. Cup 76-77, Burford Spts Cup 76-77.

Didcot's Simon Kelly gets above Abingdon's Tom Smith *Photo - Oxford Mail*

FEEDER TO:
BEAZER HOMES LEAGUE

President: D D Baker **Chairman:** P C Wager **Vice Chairman:** E V Ward
Hon. Secretary: A R Vinter, The Thatched Barn
Catt's Wood Road, Lower Hardress, Canterbury CT4 5PG (01227 700108)

"Three Steps to Heaven", the title words to the old Eddie Cochran and Showaddywaddy song might well be an apt way to describe the events which took place during the 1996/97 Season within the Winstonlead Kent League as Herne Bay won the League Championship, the League Cup and the Plaaya Kent Senior Trophy in an astounding season that saw them play sixty four competitive matches. The "treble", an achievement that has never been attained before, since the introduction of the Trophy, was secured on the final day of the season as Herne Bay won their final League game at Cray Wanderers, their third Championship success in six seasons. Ironically, Herne Bay only went top of the League for the first time throughout the season only twenty four hours beforehand when they defeated Thamesmead town, so, in racing terms, they came along the rails and finished with a flourish, a credit to Tommy Sampson, their manager, and his side.

Who would have thought that back in August, when the long season begun, we would have seen a season of football in Kent that had everybody talking week in week out. There was, each week, more twists and turns throughout the campaign which I found difficult, at times, to describe as the cliche's were all being used; for instance - "it will go to the wire", "more ups and downs than the rollercoaster at Dreamland, Margate", "the Wembley dream", etc, etc. At the start, the Winstonlead Kent League, who said goodbye to Dartford as they were promoted to the Dr Martens Southern League, welcomed two new sides into the fray in Lordswood, from the Nuclear Kent County League, and Woolwich Town, who had crossed from the London Spartan League, which gave us twenty one teams competing in Division One. Woolwich, after a few difficult first weeks when their ground was still being worked upon, found life hard to begin with and, unfortunately, for several weeks they found themselves looking at everyone else above them but with a good run of mid-season form, which included a Manager of the Month Award for Ian Birrell, their manager, they completed their campaign with a creditable seventeenth place. Lordswood, on the other hand, in their inaugural season faired a little better and their campaign of consolidation saw them complete their programme with a position of fifteenth.

the League Championship outcome was always going to be a difficult one to predict with many sides, this season, having strong squads with strong ambitions of the coveted Championship Trophy. Furness, the defending Champions and League Cup holders, were always going to be a contender, Deal Town, a side considered by many to take the crown, Chatham Town, after two third places and runners-up slot in their last three season were also in the running, and, of course, Herne Bay. Many of the pundits though were surprised by the resurgence of Ramsgate who began their season with six straight wins to become one of the first front runners. Unfortunately, they could not sustain that early promise as five consecutive defeats then followed which left the table wide open and throughout the campaign we have seen many sides perform well and above previously thought expectations. These sides include Canterbury City, who were second in the table on several occasions, Hythe United, after being re-elected produces some good results and maintained a mid-table position, and Folkestone Invicta, who after a poor start began to play with more purpose and, at one time, were an outside bet for the title.

Surprise results have been paramount in the League this season, for example: the rejuvenated Faversham Town, who last season ended with nineteen consecutive defeats and this campaign they started with seven straight losses, who defeated Ramsgate away by the odd goal in seven and then, at home, they accounted for Furness by five goals to one. Throughout the campaign, a forecast of a certain match outcome would have to be judged very carefully and it was, to no-ones surprise, going to be another season with a close finish which the sponsors, Winstonlead, the clubs and the supporters were all relishing.

After Christmas, a period which saw Kent under a blanket of snow and ice which caused three weeks of boredom, the League table began to look a little "topsy turvy" because of the various Cup commitments (featured later in the review) and the predictable postponements. Nevertheless, Ramsgate, Furness, Sheppey United, another side bidding for honours, Folkestone Invicta and Deal Town were all in good positions for the final months of the season. The shock results kept coming, Ramsgate lost at home to Beckenham Town and Cray Wanderers and Furness also lost at home to Thamesmead town. Herne Bay did not escape this syndrome entirely as they suffered setbacks at Cornithian and Hythe United. Meanwhile, Chatham Town, who had started the season poorly and after managerial changes, began to assert themselves and move up the table whilst Cray Wanderers, who had been a thorn in the side to many opponents during the campaign, began to slip towards the re-election zone. With regard to that region of the table, Woolwich Town, as previously stated, pulled themselves clear after many weeks at the foot only to be replaced by Corinthian and

Tunbridge Wells, two sides who, after a tough campaign, will have to seek re-election at the Annual General Meeting. for Corinthian, it will be their second such objective since joining the League six seasons ago whilst for Tunbridge Wells, it was their worst finish in the League for over fifteen years.

With the onset of Easter and springtime in the Garden of England, it became apparent that any one of the eight clubs could still lift the Championship crown but, as the weeks ticked by to the end, several fell by the wayside including Folkestone Invicta, Deal Town and Whitstable Town. It then became a "four horse race" between Ramsgate, Furness, Sheppey United and Herne Bay. Furness met Ramsgate, a "Championship decider", which the latter, who were bidding for their first Championship success in forty years, won by the odd goal in three to complete their campaign, it also set the target of seventy seven points for others to chase. Sheppey United, with three matches left, needed six points to overtake the 'Rams' but a defeat at Whitstable Town meant they had to win their last two matches, a draw with Cray Wanderers and then a loss at Chatham Town saw them finish fourth. Furness, mathematically, could still catch Ramsgate by winning their last three games, which they did, but unfortunately, their goal difference was inferior to the Isle of Thanet club. Meanwhile, Herne Bay, after an arduous campaign, were picking up the points, although they were held to draws against Woolwich Town. With three matches left, which were scheduled to be played inside four days, they were still six points behind the leading two but a home win against Crockenhill and then two one nil results at Thamesmead Town and Cray Wanderers saw Herne Bay lift that glorious Trophy. Herne Bay's run in had seen them take twenty four points from their last ten outings, they conceded only one goal in the League in their last eight, and with only six League defeats all season, their only loss at home was against Furness, who finished in third place. A word of consolation must be forwarded to Ramsgate and Jimmy Ward, their manager, for their performance throughout the year, they have the distinction of being runners-up, their best season since they were fourth in 1986/87, but the agonising wait for the outcome must have been terrible for all concerned.

In Division Two of the Winstonlead Kent League, Tonbridge secured their first Championship when they won the title by nine points from second placed Dartford, Sittingbourne were third. Tonbridge, unbeaten in the League since November, also attained the Kent Intermediate Cup when they beat Whitstable Town in the Final by three goals to nil at Chatham Town's Maidstone Road ground. In the Division Two Cup, Hastings Town were victorious for the first time in their history as they defeated Deal Town in a close fought affair at Dover Athletic's Crabble ground, the score one nil.

The Cup competitions, nationally and locally, provided the Winstonlead Kent League sides with much notoriety. In the F.A. Littlewoods Cup, Tunbridge Wells, Chatham Town, Whitstable Town, Folkestone INvicta and Herne Bay all progressed to the First Qualifying Round stage, unfortunately, Herne Bay were the only winners, after a replay, against Walton & Hersham. They then defeated Horsham before bowing out to Welling United of the GM Vauxhall Conference in the Third Qualifying Round. The F.A. Carlsberg Vase proved very interesting with, what can only be described as "Cup fever".

In early November, the Kent League had ten representatives in the First Round of the Vase and when it came to the next stage there was still a good contingent, seven clubs, left competing. Unfortunately, Beckenham Town, Chatham Town, Sheppey United and Slade Green departed at this venture which left Greenwich Borough, Herne Bay and Whitstable Town to carry the flag into the Third Round. Herne Bay defeated Saltash United, Whitstable Town had a good win at Burnham whilst Greenwich Borough succumbed to a defeat, after a replay, against Concord Rangers. Herne Bay then travelled to Arlesey Town where they won by the odd goal in five against a side who were previous winners whilst Whitstable defeated, after a replay, the conquerors of Greenwich Borough. The Fifth Round, the last sixteen in the country, there was talk of the Twin Towers at Wembley, it was also the first time that the Kent League had had two representatives at this stage of the competition. The two seaside clubs were in the public eye, six miles apart and great rivals, but both had difficult away matches if they were to progress to the latter stages. At Banstead Athletic, Herne Bay succumbed to a two nil defeat whilst Whitstable Town lost narrowly at North Ferriby United by the single goal. The Kent League were proud of their performances, they had surpassed even their own expectations by progressing further in the competition than they had ever done before.

In the Plaaya Kent Senior Trophy, Herne Bay and Greenwich Borough battled their way through the early Rounds to contest the Final at Welling United's ground. Herne Bay came through a tough Semi-Final encounter with Chatham Town that went to a penalty "shoot out" in the replay whilst Greenwich Borough recorded the biggest scoreline of the competition when they beat Canterbury City nine nil in the Third Round. In the Final, goals from Roly Graham and Scott Appleton secured the Trophy for Herne Bay in front of 742 spectators, their first success in the competition since 1978/79 and the first leg of their incredible "treble". In the Winstonlead Kent League Division One Cup, Herne Bay secured their second piece of silverware as they defeated Sheppey United in the Final by three goals to one at Folkestone Invicta's Cheriton Road ground. Sheppey, who were also last season's runners-up when they lost to Furness in the Final, accounted for themselves well in a keenly contested game but goals from Phil Miles, Peter Coupland and Roly Graham saw the Cup go to Herne Bay.

Attendances within the Winstonlead Kent League over the season have been down slightly, this is due mainly to the loss of Dartford to the Dr Martens Southern League but generally they have been good with Herne Bay the best supported club in the League, second were Folkestone Invicta.

Overall, the Winstonlead Kent League season has provided us with many talking points, excitement, thrills and much more that I cannot possibly describe. The achievements and disappointments are all part and parcel of a football season and I am proud to have been involved, I only hope the same sense of fulfilment will be apparent next season.

Paul Rivers, Winstonlead Kent League Press Office

FINAL LEAGUE TABLES 1996/97

DIVISION ONE

Attendances Home Matches												Attendances Total Matches	
Aggregate	*Average*			*P*	*W*	*D*	*L*	*F*	*A*	*Pts*	*GD*	*Aggregate*	*Average*
3673	183.7	1	Herne Bay	40	23	11	6	73	35	80	38	6447	161.2
2211	110.1	2	Ramsgate	40	24	5	11	82	47	77	35	4399	110
1479	74	3	Furness	40	23	8	9	66	38	77	28	3548	88.7
1220	61	4	Sheppey Utd	40	22	7	11	74	47	73	27	3278	81.9
2760	138	5	Deal Town	40	20	5	15	80	56	65	24	4726	118.2
3411	170.1	6	Folkestone Inv	40	19	7	14	66	57	64	9	5539	138.5
2858	142.9	7	Whitstable Tn	40	17	12	11	61	44	63	17	5150	128.8
2471	123.6	8	Chatham Town	40	16	11	13	60	52	59	8	4496	112.4
1393	69.7	9	Greenwich Boro	40	16	10	14	71	62	58	9	3158	79
1169	58.5	10	Faversham Tn	40	16	9	15	58	73	57	-15	3015	73.4
2371	118.6	11	Beckenham Tn	40	15	10	15	49	47	55	2	4056	101.4
836	41.8	12	Canterbury City	40	15	10	15	47	55	55	-8	2643	66.1
2211	110.1	13	Hythe United	40	15	8	17	70	76	53	-6	4124	103.1
1416	70.8	14	Thamesmead Tn	40	15	8	17	53	61	53	-8	3231	80.8
1933	96.7	15	Lordswood	40	14	8	18	57	72	50	-15	3733	93.3
1937	96.9	16	Slade Green	40	12	9	19	45	50	45	-5	3646	91.2
886	44.3	17	Woolwich Town	40	10	13	17	40	62	43	-22	2724	68.1
1884	94.2	18	Cray Wanderers	40	11	6	23	43	66	39	-23	3811	95.3
1854	92.7	19	Crockenhill	40	9	11	20	51	80	38	-29	3781	94.5
2053	102.7	20	Tunbridge Wells	40	8	10	22	44	76	34	-32	3816	95.4
961	48.1	21	Corinthian	40	8	6	26	37	71	30	-34	2653	66.3

DIVISION TWO

		P	*W*	*D*	*L*	*F*	*A*	*Pts*	*GD*
1	Tonbridge FC	38	28	6	4	103	41	90	62
2	Dartford*	38	26	6	6	100	46	81*	54
3	Sittingbourne*	38	24	7	7	108	57	76*	51
4	Furness	38	22	7	9	73	38	73	35
5	Hythe United	38	18	9	11	76	60	63	16
6	Deal Town	38	18	6	14	80	53	60	27
7	Herne Bay	38	18	6	14	63	54	60	9
8	Dover Athletic	38	18	6	14	62	66	60	-4
9	Lordswood	38	18	4	16	77	69	58	8
10	Margate*	38	16	8	14	64	66	53*	-2
11	Hastings Town	38	13	10	15	80	80	49	0
12	Crockenhill	38	15	4	19	67	82	49	-15
13	Thamesmead Tn*	38	13	9	16	59	65	45*	-6
14	Ramsgate	38	11	11	16	72	90	44	-18
15	Whitstable Town	38	10	9	19	56	68	39	-12
16	Chatham Town*	38	11	8	19	39	72	38*	-33
17	Beckenham Tn	38	11	5	22	61	97	38	-36
18	Folkestone Inv	38	9	6	23	48	100	33	-52
19	Corinthian	38	6	6	26	49	87	24	-38
20	Faversham Tn	38	6	5	27	75	121	23	-46

GOLDEN BOOT AWARD

DIVISION ONE

Steve Marshall	(Sheppey United)	31
Scott Appleton	(Herne Bay)	24
Simon Bryant	(Deal Town)	21

DIVISION TWO

Lee Young	(Lordswood)	27
Steve Hobbs	(Hythe United)	24
Danny Beal	(Hastings Town)	21

DIVISION ONE RESULTS CHART 1996-97

		1	2	3	4	5	6	7	8	9	10	11	12	13	14	15	16	17	18	19	20	21
1	Beckenham Town	X	1-2	0-1	1-1	1-0	1-2	2-0	1-1	1-1	1-2	1-3	1-4	4-0	3-3	0-1	0-3	2-1	1-2	0-0	1-1	2-2
2	Canterbury City	0-2	X	1-2	2-0	1-0	3-0	0-0	1-1	1-1	2-1	1-2	0-1	1-1	2-0	0-0	2-3	1-1	3-1	0-0	2-1	1-0
3	Chatham Town	2-0	1-3	X	1-1	2-0	2-0	3-1	4-3	1-1	0-0	2-2	0-2	1-2	0-2	0-1	2-1	1-2	3-0	3-2	0-3	1-1
4	Corinthian	0-1	0-3	1-0	X	1-1	2-1	0-4	2-1	0-1	0-1	0-1	2-1	2-2	1-2	0-2	4-2	2-3	0-0	2-1	0-1	1-3
5	Cray Wanderers	0-2	1-2	1-5	0-5	X	1-1	1-0	0-2	2-0	1-4	1-3	0-1	0-1	4-1	0-1	0-1	1-0	2-2	3-1	0-1	0-0
6	Crockenhill	0-0	3-0	2-1	5-1	3-3	X	0-1	1-1	1-2	1-1	2-4	2-1	1-2	1-4	3-1	0-3	1-3	1-0	0-0	0-2	0-3
7	Deal Town	4-2	1-0	2-2	3-2	3-2	6-2	X	5-0	2-0	0-2	2-3	0-0	3-1	3-1	3-5	3-2	7-1	1-0	2-0	4-1	6-1
8	Faversham Town	1-0	0-4	2-0	1-0	3-2	0-5	2-2	X	1-3	5-1	2-1	0-3	1-0	1-3	2-2	1-3	1-1	0-3	2-1	3-0	0-0
9	Folkestone Inv	0-2	3-0	2-1	3-1	1-3	3-1	1-0	2-2	X	0-1	0-1	2-4	1-1	2-1	1-2	2-3	3-1	0-3	4-1	0-0	3-1
10	Furness	0-1	5-1	2-2	3-0	1-2	7-1	1-0	3-1	2-0	X	2-1	3-1	2-2	1-0	1-2	1-0	1-0	0-1	2-2	2-0	1-3
11	Greenwich Boro	2-0	1-1	0-2	2-1	2-0	1-1	1-0	1-2	3-4	1-1	X	2-3	4-4	5-2	0-1	0-2	2-1	2-2	0-1	2-2	1-2
12	Herne Bay	1-0	4-0	0-0	3-0	2-0	4-0	3-2	2-2	4-0	0-1	1-1	X	5-1	2-2	2-2	2-2	1-0	3-2	2-0	2-2	1-1
13	Hythe United	1-2	3-4	1-2	2-1	3-2	4-3	5-0	1-2	0-1	0-1	3-0	2-0	X	3-1	3-3	1-1	1-5	3-1	2-1	0-2	5-1
14	Lordswood	1-1	0-0	2-5	2-1	2-1	4-1	0-2	2-0	2-3	0-0	2-5	0-0	4-2	X	0-2	2-1	1-2	2-0	1-2	0-1	0-0
15	Ramsgate	0-1	5-1	1-2	3-2	1-2	4-2	1-4	3-4	3-1	0-1	3-1	3-0	6-0	1-2	X	3-1	1-0	4-0	2-0	0-0	2-1
16	Sheppey Utd	1-0	2-1	0-0	3-0	0-0	0-0	2-1	1-2	2-0	2-1	3-2	0-3	1-0	5-0	1-0	X	1-0	3-2	7-0	3-3	2-1
17	Slade Green	0-2	4-0	0-0	0-0	3-0	1-2	2-0	0-1	0-2	1-0	0-0	0-1	1-1	0-1	2-0	1-1	X	0-1	1-1	1-4	2-1
18	Thamesmead Tn	0-0	1-0	3-1	1-0	0-2	1-1	1-3	2-0	0-2	3-4	3-6	0-1	3-0	1-0	0-2	2-1	3-2	X	2-2	2-2	0-0
19	Tunbridge Wells	2-3	3-0	1-1	2-0	1-2	1-1	2-0	1-4	1-6	0-2	1-0	0-1	2-1	3-3	1-3	2-4	1-0	1-2	X	0-2	1-1
20	Whitstable Town	1-2	0-1	1-2	4-0	3-1	2-0	0-0	5-1	0-3	0-0	1-1	0-2	0-2	5-0	2-1	2-1	0-0	3-1	3-2	X	0-1
21	Woolwich Town	1-4	0-0	3-2	0-1	0-2	0-0	2-0	2-0	2-2	1-2	0-2	0-0	1-4	0-2	1-5	1-0	1-3	0-2	2-1	1-1	X

MONTHLY AWARDS 1996-97

MANAGER OF THE MONTH

Aug/Sep	Fabio Rossi	(Crockenhill)
October	Ronnie Knox	(Furness)
November	Glen Cooper	(Cray Wanderers)
December	John Roseman	(Chatham Town)
January	No Award Given	
February	John Adams & Terry Hill	(Thamesmead Town)
March	Ian Birrell	(Woolwich Town)
April	Malcolm McKeown	(Tonbridge)

WINSTONLEAD GOALS OF THE MONTH

DIVISION ONE	DIVSION TWO
Deal Town	Sittingbourne
Sheppey United	Whitstable Town
Deal Town	Sittingbourne
Folkestone Invicta	Hythe United
Greenwich Borough	Hastings Town
Sheppey United	Furness & Sittingbourne
Ramsgate	Tonbridge FC
Sheppey United	Dartford

MISCELLANEOUS TRIVIA

DIVISION ONE

Highest Win

7-0	Sheppey Utd	v	Tunbridge Wells
7-1	Deal Town	v	Slade Green
7-1	Furness	v	Crockenhill
6-0	Ramsgate	v	Hythe United

Best Away Win

6-1 Folkestone Invicta at Tunbridge Wells

Highest Match Goals

9 Thamesmead Town 3 Greenwich Borough 6

Most Goalless Draws

7 Woolwich Town

DIVISION TWO

Highest Win

12-0	Faversham Town	v	Margate
9-0	Deal Town	v	Ramsgate

Best Away Win

7-1 Hastings Town at Chatham Town

Highest Match Goals

12 Faversham Town 12 Margate 0

Most Goalless Draws

5 Chatham Town

LEAGUE DIVISION ONE CUP 1996-97

HOLDERS: FURNESS

First Round

Lordswood	v	Crockenhill	2-1
Slade Green	v	Ramsgate	1-0
Greenwich Boro	v	Whitstable Town	1-0
Sheppey United	v	Faversham Town	5-1
Herne Bay	v	Chatham Town	3-1

Second Round

Lordswood	v	Sheppey United	1-3
Hythe United	v	Corinthian	4-0
Deal Town	v	Beckenham	3-0
Herne Bay	v	Woolwich Town	2-0
Canterbury City	v	Tunbridge Wells	0.1-0.5
Thamesmead Town	v	Cray Wanderers	1-2
Furness	v	Slade Green	1.0-1.0*
Greenwich Borough	v	Folkestone Invicta	6-0

* Slade Green won Second Round Replay against Furness 3-0 on penalties

Quarter-Final

Sheppey United	v	Tunbridge Wells	4-1
Deal Town	v	Slade Green	0.1-0.2
Hythe United	v	Cray Wanderers	0-2
Herne Bay	v	Greenwich Borough	3-1

Semi-Final

Sheppey United	v	Cray Wanderers	1.1(2)-0.1(1)
Slade Green	v	Herne Bay	2.0(2)-1.3(4)

Final

Sheppey United	v	Herne Bay	1-3

WINNERS: HERNE BAY

LEAGUE DIVISION TWO CUP 1996-97

HOLDERS: FOLKESTONE INVICTA

First Round

Beckenham Town	v	Chatham Town	1-2
Ramsgate	v	Dartford	3-1
Herne Bay	v	Faversham Town	2-1
Dover Athletic	v	Thamesmead Tn	4.1-4.1*

*Thamesmead Town won First Round Replay match against Dover Athletic 4-2 on penalties

Second Round

Whitstable Town	v	Corinthian	5-0
Herne Bay	v	Ramsgate	1.3-1.0
Thamesmead Town	v	Tonbridge FC	1-4
Crockenhill	v	Hythe United	1-0
Chatham Town	v	Margate	0-2
Lordswood	v	Deal Town	3.2*-3.1*
Sittingbourne	v	Furness	1-2
Hastings Town	v	Folkestone Invicta	5-2

*Deal Town reinstated to competition after Lordswood were expelled for irregularities in Second Round Replay

Quarter-Final

Whitstable Town	v	Margate	1-2
Tonbridge FC	v	Furness	1-3
Herne Bay	v	Deal Town	1-2
Crockenhill	v	Hastings Town	0-4

Semi-Final

Margate	v	Deal Town	1.1(2)-4.0(4)
Furness	v	Hastings Town	1.2(3)-1.6(7)

Final

Deal Town	v	Hastings Town	0-1

WINNERS: HASTINGS TOWN

BEST SUPPORTED MATCHES

393	Herne Bay	v	Whitstable Town
381	Folkestone Inv	v	Hythe United
379	Hythe United	v	Folkestone Inv
356	Whitstable Tn	v	Herne Bay
328	Cray Wndrs	v	Herne Bay
278	Lordswood	v	Chatham Town

TOP HOME ATT'NCES

183.7	Herne Bay
170.1	Folkestone Inv
142.9	Whitstable Tn
138.0	Deal Town
123.6	Chatham Tn

HIGHEST CUP ATTENDANCES

742	Welling United	v	Herne Bay (FAC 3Q)
504	Greenwich Boro	v	Herne Bay (KST F)
436	Herne Bay	v	Sheppey Utd (KL1 F)
338	North Ferr Utd	v	Whitstable Tn (FAV 5)
327	Arlesey Town	v	Herne Bay (FAV 4)
315	Whitstable Tn	v	Concord Rgrs (FAV

DIVISION ONE CLUBS 1997-98

BECKENHAM TOWN

Chairman: T.B.A. **Vice Chairman:** B Hollaway.
Secretary: Peter Palmer, 107 Wentworth Rd, West Croydon, Surrey CR0 3HZ (0181 689 2134).
Manager: Kevin Sugrue **Asst Manager:**J.Moore.
Ground: Eden Park Avenue, Beckenham, Kent (0181 650 1066).
Directions: M25, A21 to Bromley then follow signs to Beckenham. Ground 1 mile west of town off A214, 2 mins walk from Eden Park (BR) station - trains from London Bridge. Bus 264.
Seats: 120 **Cover:** 120 **Capacity:** 4,000 **Floodlights:** Yes **Reformed:** 1971. **Shop:** Yes
Clubhouse: All day opening at weekends. Hot & cold food, teas, etc. Bar & dance area. Pool & fruit machines.
Colours: Red & white/red/white **Change Colours:** Yellow/black/black. **Nickname:** Reds.
Record Gate: 720 v Berkhamstead F.A.Cup 94-95 **Prev. Ground:** Stanhope Grove, Beckenham (60 yrs)
Previous Leagues: South East London Amtr 71-73/ Metropolitan 73-75/ London Spartan 75-82.
Programme: 8 pages, 50p **Editor:** Bob Chilvers (0181 301 2624) **Midweek matchday:** Tuesday.
Record Scorer: Ricky Bennett **Record appearances:** Lee Fabian.
Honours: London Spartan Lg Cup R-up 77-78 78-79, Kent Snr Tphy R-up 81-82 93-94, Kent Lg Cup R-up 84-85 92-93 (Div 2 Cup R-up 90-91).

CANTERBURY CITY

Chairman: Paul Gladwish **Vice Chairman:** John Muddiman **President:** V H Heslop.
Secretary: Keith J Smith, 7 Knight Ave, London Rd Est, Canterbury, Kent CT2 8PZ (01227 456116).
Manager: Martin Farnie **Asst Manager:** Gary Allen. **Physio:** Brian Ball
Ground: Kingsmead Stadium, Kingsmead Road, Canterbury CT2 7PH (01227 457245)
Directions: A28 out of city centre into Military Road. At 1st r-about turn left into Tourtel Rd, proceed to next r-about and head straight over into Kingsmead Rd - stadium on right opposite Canterbury swimming pool. Half mile from Canterbury West (BR). Bus service 624 or 625 from Canterbury bus station
Capacity: 5,000 **Cover:** 200 **Seats:** 200 **Floodlights:** Yes **Club Shop:** Yes
Clubhouse: Lounge bar open on matchdays. Snack bar, burgers, hot-dogs, pies, chips, tea, coffee, etc
Programme: 32 pages, 50p **Editor:** Keith Smith (01227 456116) & Roy Twyman **Press Officer:** Roy Twyman
Colours: Green & white/white/green & white **Change:** Red & black/black/red
Nickname: The City. **Sponsors:** Gladwish Land **Founded:** 1947.
Midweek home matchday: Wednesday **Reserve Team's League:**
Best FA Cup season: 1st Rd 64-65 (lost 0-6 to Torquay), 68-69 (lost 0-1 to Swindon).
Previous - Leagues: Kent 47-59/ Metropolitan 59-60/ Southern 60-94. **Name:** Canterbury Waverley. **Grounds:** Wincheap Grove, Bretts Corner 47-58.
Players progressing to Football League: R Gawler (Southend 49), A Hughes (Grimsby 54), A Nugent (Darlington 56), J Richardson (Southport 56), T Horsfall (Cambridge Utd), J Murray (Wolves), K Hill, M Weatherley (Gillingham), T Norton (Brighton), P Hilton (Brighton 73), D Wiltshire (Gillingham 74), G Pugh (Torquay 84)
96-97 Captain: Julian Holmes **96-97 Top scorer:** Gary Pullen 14
96-97 P.o.Y.: Mark Rees **96-97 Supporters' P.o.Y.:** Sammy Spence
Records - Attendance: 3,001 v Torquay, FA Cup 1st Rd 64. **Goalscorer:** Wilf Heathcote 113 (48-51) **Appearances:** John Carragher 627 (60-70) **Win:** 10-0 v Deal Tn (H), Southern Lge 65. **Defeat:** 0-9 v Corby Tn (A), Southern Lge 63.
Fees - Paid: £2,000 for Graham Knight (Maidstone Utd) **Received:** £2,000 for Dave Wiltshire (Gillingham).
Honours: FA Trophy 2nd Rd replay 74-75; Kent Lg Cup 49-50, (Div 2 Res 90-91, Div 2 Cup (Res) 48-49, 89-90; Kent Senior Cup 53-54; Kent Senior Trophy 79-80; Kent Intermediate Cup 73-74; Kent Messenger Trophy 74-75; Frank Norris Memorial Shield 88-89 89-90; Kent League Div 2 Champ Res 90-91.

CHATHAM TOWN

Chairman: P Enright **President:**
Secretary: Brian Burcombe, 4 Hallwood Close, Parkwood, Rainham, Kent ME8 9NT (01634 363419).
Manager: John Adams **Asst Manager:**
Ground: Maidstone Road Sports Ground, Maidstone Road, Chatham, Kent (01634 812194).
Directions: M2, A229 Chatham turn-off, follow signs to Chatham, grd 1.5 miles on right opposite garage. 1 mile from Chatham (BR).
Seats: 500 **Cover:** 1,000 **Capacity:** 5,000 **Floodlights:** Yes **Founded:** 1882.
Colours: Red & black halves/black/black. **Change Colours:** Yellow & green **Nickname:** Chats.
Midweek matchday: Tuesday **Record Gate:** 5,000 v Gillingham, 1980.
Previous Lges: Southern (several spells)/ Aetolian 59-64/ Metropolitan 64-68/ Kent (Sev. spells).
Programme: 12 pages, 50p **Editor:** Trevor Busby **Sponsors:** Topps Scaffolding
Clubhouse: Matchdays and functions
Honours: Kent Lg(9) 1894-95 03-05 24-25 26-27 71-72 73-74 76-77 79-80 (R-up 02-03 23-24 25-26 70-71 74-75 80-81, Lg Cup 71-72 76-77 (R-up(3)), Thames & Medway Comb.(5) 1896-97 04-06 19-20 23-24, FA Cup QF (beat Nottm Forest 2-0 en route) 1888-89, FA Tphy 3rd Rd 70-71, Kent Snr Cup 1888-89 1904-05 10-11 18-19, Kent Snr Shield 19-20.

Canterbury City: Back Row (L-R); Brian Ball (Physio), Gary Allen (Asst Mgr), Steve Parlett, Mark Rees, Steve Clark, Micky Walsh, Barry Gethlin, Gary Pullen. Front Row; Martin Farnie (Mgr), Matt Jordan, Hannah Wiley (Mascot), Julian Holmes, Matthew Wiley (Mascot), Sammy Spence, Scott Drake.

Photo - Kentish Gazette

CORINTHIAN

Chairman: R J Billings **Manager:** Tony Sitford
Secretary: Dave Roff, 79 Edwin Street, Gravesend, Kent DA12 1EJ (01474 569457).
Ground: Gay Dawn, Valley Road, Fawkham, Nr Dartford, Kent DA3 8LZ (01474 707559/702335 fax:708431).
Directions: A2 off Longfield, take Fawkham Road - ground one mile on left. Or, A20 to Fawkham Green then ground one and a half miles on right. One and a quarter miles from Longfield (BR).
Seats: 134 **Cover:** 175 **Capacity:** 2,000 **Floodlights:** Yes **Club Shop:** Yes
Programme: 12 pages, 30p **Editor:** TBA **Press Officer:** Secretary
Colours: Green & white hoops/white **Change Colours:** Sky & white
Sponsors: None **Founded:** 1972. **Nickname:** None.
Midweek matchday: Tuesday **Players progressing to Football League:** Andy Hessenthaler (Watford).
Reserves' League: Wintonlead Kent Div 2 **Record Attendance:** 480 v Spurs, friendly 1979.
Clubhouse: Bar, cafeteria & restaurant
Club Record Appearances: Gavin Tovey **Club Record Goalscorer:** Lee Annett
Honours: Essex AFA Snr Cup 82-83, Kent Snr Tphy 83-84 86-87, Fort Lauderdale International Tournament 84-85, Kent Intermediate Cup 89-90 90-91.

CRAY WANDERERS

Chairman: Gary Hillman **President:** Bill Faulkner
Secretary: Mr Kerry Phillips, 15 Watling Street, Bexleyheath, Kent DA6 7QJ (01322 554108).
Director of Football: Frank Maloney **1st Team Manager:** John Roseman
Manager: Alan Hudson. **Asst Manager:** Charlie Pooley **Coach:** Peter Little
Ground: Oxford Road, Sidcup, Kent (0181 300 9201).
Directions: Between Sidcup High Street and Footscray High Street; from A20 turn off for Footscray, left at lights, Oxford Rd is 5th left. Three quarters of a mile from Sidcup (BR) station - buses 492 21 51 233 R11 stop at top of Oxford Rd
Seats: 106 **Cover:** 300 **Capacity:** 2,000 **Floodlights:** Due **Club Shop:** Yes
Programme: 24 pages, 50p **Editor/Press Officer:** Greg Mann (H 0181-318 9604) (W 0171 500 4493)
Colours: Amber & black **Change Colours:** Purple & white
Sponsors: N.Hillman & Sons **Founded:** 1860. **Nickname:** Wands.
Midweek matchday: Tuesday **Record Gate:** 1,523 v Stamford, F.A. Vase QF 79-80.
Previous Leagues: Kent 1894-1903 6-7 9-14 34-38/ W Kent 03-06 07-09/ London 20-34 51-59/ Kent Amtr 38-39 46-51/ S London All 43-46/ Aetolian 59-64/ Gtr London 64-66/ Metropolitan 66-71/ London Metropolitan 71-75/ London Spartan 75-78.
Clubhouse: Open pub hours (freehouse). Hot & cold food available.
96-97 P.o.Y.: Tonde Utsaja (23) **96-97 Captain:** Mark Turner **96-97 Top Scorer:** Mark Turner
Club Record Goalscorer: Ken Collishaw, 272. **Club Record Appearances:** John Dorey c500, 61-72
Honours: London Lg(2) 56-58 (Lg Cup 54-55), Aetolian Lg 62-63 (Lg Cup 63-64), Gtr London Lg 65-66 (Lg Cup(2) 64-66), Metropolitan Lg Cup 70-71 (Amtr Cup(2) 66-68), London Spartan Lg(2) 76-78, Kent Lg 01-02 80-81 (R-up 79-80 90-91, Lg Cup 83-84), Kent Snr Tphy 92-93, Kent Amtr Cup(4) 30-31 62-65.

CROCKENHILL

President: Mr H Miller **Chairman:** Chris Otterway **Vice-Chairman:** Brian Perfect
Secretary: Brian Perfect, 30 Tylers Green Road, Crockenhill, Swanley, Kent BR8 8LG (01322 663638)
Manager: Nick Elia **Asst Manager:** Carl Edyman **Coach:** Nick Elia
Ground: 'Wested', Eynsford Road, Crockenhill, Kent (01322 662097).
Directions: Just off M25 junction 3, B2173 towards Swanley, left after 200yds into Wested Lane, ground 1 mile on right (Ord. Survey grid Ref: 516669 sheet 177). Just over a mile from Swanley (BR) station - trains from Victoria. Kentish Bus 477 to Crockenhill - at village shops turn left at T-juntion - ground 1 mile up narrow lane on left.
Seats: 200 **Cover:** 200 **Capacity:** 2,000 **Floodlights:** No **Founded:** 1946. **Shop:** Yes
Clubhouse: Open matchdays, Sunday lunchtimes, many evenings. Wide range of food always available.
Colours: Red & white/black/black **Change Colours:** Black & white/black/black & blue **Nickname:** Crocks.
Programme: 8 pages + cover/ads **Editor:** Ruth Perfect **Midweek matchday:** Tuesday
Previous Leagues: Kent Amtr 46-59/ Aetolian 59-64/ Gtr London 64-68 **Reserve Lge:** Kent League Div 2
Players progressing to Football League: T Cascarino (Gillingham 82), Paul Gillcrest (Southampton)
96-97 Captain: Scan Cooney **96-97 Top Scorer:** Leroy Huggins **96-97 P.o.Y.:** Leroy Huggins
Record Gate: 800 v Maidstone, Kent Amtr Cup 1948.
Honours: Kent Lg 82-83 (R-up 84-85), Kent Snr Tphy 80-81, Kent Jnr Cup R-up 48-49, West Kent Amtr Cup 56-57, Sevenoaks Charity Cup 48-49, Kent Amtr Lg 56-57 (R-up 54-55, Prem Div 53-54 (R-up 52-53), Div 1 48-49 (R-up 46-47), Snr Div Cup R-up 56-57, Div 1 Cup R-up 46-47).

DEAL TOWN

Chairman: Roy Smith. **Vice-Chairman:**
Secretary: Mrs Lynne Fox, £2 Manor Road, Deal, Kent CT14 9BX (01304 361163).
Fixture Sec: Colin Adams (01304 372784) **Manager:** Dave Dadd. **Asst Manager:** Bob Finn
Ground: Charles Sports Ground, St Leonards Road, Deal, Kent (01304 375623).
Directions: A258 through Walmer, left into Cornwell Road, continue into Hamilton Road, veer left into Mill Rd, follow round to right into Manor Road, right into St Leonards Road, ground 100 yards on right. 1 mile from both Walmer and Deal BR stations. Local buses stop near ground.
Seats: 150 **Cover:** 500 **Capacity:** 2,000 **Floodlights:** Yes **Club Shop:** No
Programme: 28 pages, 50p. **Editor:** Colin Adams (01304 372784) **Press Officer:** Colin Adams
Colours: Black & white hoops/white/black & white hoops **Change Colours:** Yellow & Blue halves/blue/blue.
Founded: 1908. **Nickname:** Town. **Sponsors:**
Midweek matchday: Tuesday **Reserves' Lge:** Wintonlead Div 2
Record Gate: 4,000 v Billy Wright showbiz XI, Feb '61.
Previous Leagues: Kent 09-59/ Aetolian 59-63/ Southern 63-66/ Gtr London 66-71
Player progressing to Football Lge: Danny Wallace (Southampton)
Clubhouse: Matchdays & functions. Bar. Tea bar with hot & cold food.
96-97 Captain: Colin Gilmore **96-97 Top Scorer:** Simon Bryant 22 **96-97 P.o.Y.:** Tony Pearson
Club Record Scorer: Joe Brayne 175. **Club Record Appearances:** Alan Barrow 544 (recent times).
Honours: Kent Lg 53-54 (R-up 88-89, Lg Cup 57-58 81-82 (R-up 94-95, SF 88-89 89-90), Kent Snr Tphy 94-95 R-up 82-83 90-91, Gtr London Lg Cup 68-69, Aetolian Lg R-up 59-60.

ERITH TOWN

Chairman: Phillip Legg **Vice Chairman:** **President:**
Secretary: J R Kelly, 88 Hook Lane, Welling, Kent DA16 2DP (0181 303 8977)
Ground: Shared with Greenwich Borough, Harrow Meadow, Eltham Green Rd, Eltham, London SE9 (0181 850 3098).
Directions: South Circular (A205) to Yorkshire Grey pub, ground opposite. 1 mile from both Eltham and Kidbrooke BR stations.
Seats: 50 **Cover:** 50 **Capacity:** 2,500 **Floodlights:** Yes **Shop:**
Colours: Red & blue/black/black **Change Colours:** Yellow/black/black
Midweek matchday: Tuesday **Previous Ground:** Flamingo Park, Sidcup (pre 1994)
96-97 Captain: **96-97 P.o.Y.:** **96-97 Top Scorer:**

FAVERSHAM TOWN

Chairman: Sal Aisani **President:** Cris Aisani **Secretary:** Reg Parr,
Manager: John Glover **Coach:** Bob Mason **Commercial Mgr:** Terry Whitehead
Ground: New Stadium, Salters Lane, Faversham, Kent (01795 532738).
Directions: On A2 (Canterbury road) just west of town.
Seats: 350 **Cover:** 1,500 **Capacity:** 2,000 **Floodlights:** Yes **Founded:** 1901.
Clubhouse: Open matchdays (Sat/Sun/Tues) Wed/Thurs. Snacks sold.
Colours: White/blue/red **Change Colours:** Red/white/blue **Nickname:** Town.
Midweek matchday: Tuesday **Reserves' League:** Kent Lg Div 2
Programme: 16 pages, 40p **Editor:** Quiram Aisani
Previous - Leagues: Aetolian 59-64/ Metropolitan 64-71/ Athenian 71-76. **Grounds:** Ashford Rd 1901-46/Gordon Square 46-58
Records - Attendance: 1,400 v Sheppey Utd, 1949. **Win:** 8-0 v Greenwich B., Aug'89 **Defeat:** 0-9 v Sittingbourne, Jan '82. **Goalscorer:** Tony Rudd 43. **Appearances:** Bob Mason.
96-97 Captain: **96-97 Top Scorer:** **96-97 P.o.Y.:**
Honours: Kent Lg 69-70 70-71 77-78 89-90 (R-up 87-88, Lg Cup 70-71 90-91 (R-up 82-83)), Kent Snr Tphy 76-77 77-78 (R-up 87-88 88-89), Kent Amtr Cup 56-57 58-59 71-72 72-73 73-74.

FOLKESTONE INVICTA

Chairman: Tommy Guiver. **President:** Bill Hewson
Secretary: Neil Pilcher, 25 Pavilion Road, Folkestone, Kent. CT19 5RW (01303 245066)
Manager: Neil Cugley **Asst Manager:** Dave Williams
Ground: The New Pavilion, Cheriton Road, Folkestine, Kent CT20 5JU (01303 257461).
Directions: On the A20 behind Safeway foodstore, midway between Folkestone Central & West BR stations.
Seats: 900 **Cover:** 3,500 **Capacity:** 6,500. **Floodlights:** Yes **Founded:** 1936.
Colours: Amber & black strips/black/amber. **Change Colours:** Blue & green/green/blue.
Midweek matchday: Tuesday **Sponsors:** Eurotunnel(Le Shuttle).
Previous Lges: Kent County (pre-1991). **Record Gate:** 2,332 v West Ham Utd Friendly Nov 96
Programme: 60 pages, £1 **Editor:** Neil Pitcher.
Clubhouse: Yes, Strips Club & Invicta Club
96-97 Captain: Tom Dixon **96-97 P.o.Y.:** Tom Dixon **96-97 Top Scorer:** Steve Lawrence
Honours: (since joining Winstonlead Kent League) Plaaya Kent Senior Trophy R-Up 93-94,94-95.

GREENWICH BOROUGH

President: R Moore **Chairman:** P Meagan
Secretary: Ms Denise Richmond, 7 Castlecombe Rd, Mottingham, London SE9 6BA (0181 289 8956).
Manager: Dave Mehmet **Asst Manager:** R Dowling
Ground: Harrow Meadow, Eltham Green Rd, Eltham, London SE9 (0181 850 5360).
Directions: S Circular (A205) to McDonalds, grd opposite. 1 mile from both Eltham and Kidbrooke BR stations.
Seats: 50 **Cover:** 50 **Capacity:** 2,500 **Floodlights:** Yes **Founded:** 1928. **Clubhouse:** Yes.
Colours: All Red **Change Colours:** All black **Nickname:** Boro.
Midweek matchday: Tuesday **Record Gate:** 2,000 v Charlton, floodlight opening, 1978.
Sponsors: **Programme:** 16 pages, 50p **Editor:** Keith Harmer
Previous - Leagues: South London Alliance/ Kent Amateur/ London Spartan 77-84. **Ground:** Erith & Belvedere F.C. 92-93. **Name:** London Borough of Greenwich.
Honours: London Spartan Lg 79-80 (Lg Cup 82-83), Kent Lg 86-87 87-88 (Lg Cup 84-85 86-87), Kent Snr Tphy 84-85, FA Vase 5th Rd 89-90.

Herne Bay celebrate winning the Plaaya Kent Senior Trophy.

HERNE BAY

Chairman: M Todd **Vice Chairman:** A Kearney **President:** J Hodkinson
Secretary: T Sampson, 33 Sharp's Field, Headcorn, Kent TN27 9UF, (01622 891784)
Manager: Tom Sampson **Asst Manager:** Keith Lissenden **Physio:** J Hodkinson.
Ground: Winch's Field, Stanley Gardens, Herne Bay, Kent (01227 374156).
Directions: Leave A299 at Herne Bay r'bout, 2nd left, 1st left. Half mile from Herne Bay (BR); down Station Approach (half mile), 1st right (Spencer Road), 2nd right.
Seats: 250 **Cover:** 2,000 **Capacity:** 5,000 **Floodlights:** Yes **Founded:** 1886.
Clubhouse: Open evenings and matchdays.
Programme: 36 pages, 60p **Editor:** Doug Smith **Press Officer:** Tom Sampson
Colours: Blue & white . **Change Colours:** Red & black halves **Nickname:** The Bay.
Sponsors: ABIK Leisure/Waterways. **Midweek matchday:** Tuesday
Previous - Leagues: Kent Amtr/ Thanet/ East Kent/ Kent 53-59/ Aetolian 59-64/ Athenian 64-74. **Ground:** Memorial Park 1886-1953. **Reserve's League:** Kent Lge Div Two.
96-97 Captain: Terry Martin **96-97 P.o.Y.:** Scott Appleton **96-97 Top Scorer:** Scott Appleton 31
Record - Attendance: 2,303 v Margate, FA Cup 4th Qual. Rd 1970. **Win:** 12-0; v Betteshanger CW Res. and Whitstable Res. (A), both Kent Div 2 55-56. **Defeat:** 0-9 v Hounslow, Athenian Lge 1973-74. **Transfer fee received:** £3,000 for Mark Munday (Gravesend) 1994.
Honours: Kent Lg 91-92 94-95 96-97 (R-up 92-93, Div 2 62-63 63-64 (R-up 92-93(res) 94-95(res)), Lg Cup 96-97 R-up 78-79, Div 2 Cup 53-54), Kent Snr Tphy 78-79, Kent Amtr Cup 57-58 (R-up 58-59 63-64 68-69 72-73), Aetolian Lg Div 2 62-63 63-64 (Lg Cup R-up 62-63, Div 2 Cup 62-63 63-64), Athenian Lg Div 2 70-71 (Lg Cup 66-67), Kent Amtr Lg Cup 53-54 54-55, Thames & Medway Comb. Cup R-up 61-62, Plaaya Kent Sen Trophy 96-97, FA Cup 4th Cup Qual. Rd 70-71 86-87.

HYTHE UNITED (1992)

Chairman: Steve Walker **President:** Rt Hon Michael Howard QC
Secretary: A.Maycock, 86 Dymchurch Rd, Hythe, Kent. CT21 6LH (01303 268346)
Manager: Michael Dix **Asst Manager:** Dave Linstrem **Physio:** Reece McIntosh
Ground: Reachfields, Fort Rd, Hythe (01303 264932)
Directions: On A259 west out of Hythe, turn left after light railway lights (Fort Road), entrance at end
Capacity: 3,000 **Seats:** 400 **Cover:** 2,400 **Floodlights:** Yes **Club Shop:** No
Programme: Free with entry **Editor:** A J Maycock **Press Officer:** M R Giles
Colours: All Red **Change Colours:** Green. **Sponsor:** H V Wooding Ltd **Founded:** 1992
Midweek Matchday: Tuesday **Youth League:** Kent Youth
Record Attendance: 422 v Folkstone 1996 **Previous Leagues:** Nuclear Elec Kent Lge
Clubhouse: Bar open weekends/matchdays & training nights
96-97 Captain: Dave Ward **96-97 Top Scorer:** Andy Bennett **96-97 P.o.Y.:** Clive Barham
Honours: None as Hythe United

LORDSWOOD

Team line-up before 2-1 victory against Cray Wanderers. Photo - Martin Wray

Chairman: D Sims **Vice Chairman:** D Caulfield **Manager:** B Zilwood
Secretary: Steve Lewis, Sunnybrook, Gorsewood Road, Hartley, Longfield, Kent DA3 7DF (01474 708233 H)
Ground: Lordswood Sports & Social Club, North Dane Way, Walderslade, Chatham, Kent ME5 9XX (01634 669138)
Capacity: 425 **Seats:** 125 **Cover:** No **Floodlights:** No **Club Shop:** No
Colours: Orange/black/black **Change Colours:** All green **Founded:** 1968
Programme: Yes **Editor/Press Officer:** D Harman **Nickname:** Lords
Midweek Matchday: Tuesday/Thursday **Reserve or Youth League:** Both
Record Attendance: 386 **Previous Leagues:** Kent County Lge **Clubhouse:** Yes
96-97 Captain: K Carpenter **96-97 Top Scorer:** L Young **96-97 P.o.Y.:** G Cook

RAMSGATE

Chairman: R Lawson **Vice Chairman:** C Payne **President:** Tom Pendry
Secretary/Press Officer: Steve Lancaster. 66 Park Avenue, Birchington, Kent (01843 597703).
Manager/Coach: Lennie Lee **Asst Manager:** Dave Bostock **Physio:** John Burroughs
Commercial Manager: Martin Power (01843 597703).
Ground: Southwood Stadium, Prices Avenue, Ramsgate, Kent (01843 591662).
Directions: From London on A229, A253 into Ramsgate - left into Netherhill at r'bout, right into Ashburnham Rd, right into Southwood Rd. 15 mins walk from Ramsgate BR station; walk thru Warre Recreation Ground, along St Lawrence High Str., left at 'White Horse', follow Southwood Rd and turn right into Prices Avenue.
Seats: 400 **Cover:** 600 **Capacity:** 5,000 **Floodlights:** Yes **Founded:** 1946.
Clubhouse: Open matchdays & private functions. Two bars, two pool tables, darts. Hot & cold food on matchdays.
Colours: Red & white. **Change Colours:** White/blue/blue **Nickname:** Rams.
Midweek matchday: Tuesday **Sponsors:** Hoverspeed.
Reserve Team's League: Winstonlead Kent Div. Two.
Programme: 28 pages. **Editor:** Steve Redford (01843 596138). **Club Shop:** No.
Previous Leagues: Southern 59-75. **Previous Name:** Ramsgate Athletic
Records - Attendance: 5,200 v Margate, 56-57. **Goalscorer:** Mick Williamson. **Win:** 9-1 v Crockenhill, Kent League Cup 22/1/94.
96-97 Captain: **96-97 P.o.Y.:** **96-97 Top Scorer:**
Honours: Kent Lg 49-50 55-56 56-57 (Lg Cup 48-49 92-93 93-94 94-95)
Kent I'mediate Cup 54-55, Kent Snr Cup 63-64, Thames & Medway Cup 60-61, Kent Snr Shield 60-61, Kent Floodlit Tphy 69-70, Kent Snr Tphy(2) 87-89.

SHEPPEY UNITED

Chairman: Peter Sharrock **Manager:** Mal Watkins
Secretary: Mr Barry H Bundock, Dunedin, 104 Southsea Ave., Minster, Sheerness, Kent ME12 2NH (01795 876025) (0374 112834 Mobile)
Ground: Kingsmead Stadium, Canterbury, Kent (01227 457245).
Directions: A28 out of city centre into Military Road. At 1st r-about turn left into Tourtel Rd, proceed to next r-about and head straight over into Kingsmead Rd - stadium on right opposite Canterbury swimming pool. Half mile from Canterbury West (BR). Bus service 624 or 625 from Canterbury bus station
Seats: 200 **Cover:** 200 **Capacity:** 5,000 **Floodlights:** Yes **Founded:** 1890.
Colours: Red & white/white **Change colours:** Blue & black
Midweek matchday: Wednesday **Nickname:** Islanders or Ites.
Previous Name: Sheppey Athletic/Ites **Programme:** 20 pages, 50p
Previous Ground: Botany Road, St Georges Avenue, Sheerness (pre-1992).
Record Gate: 4,000 v Sittingbourne, Kent Senior Trophy 1927 (at Botany Road).
Previous Leagues: Southern 1894-1901 84-91/ Kent 01-27 32-59 72-84/ Aetolian 59-64/ Gtr London 64-65/ Metropolitan Lg 65-71.
Players progressing to Football League: E C Harper (England, Blackburn, Spurs, Preston).
Hons: Kent Lg(6) 05-07 27-28 72-73 74-75 78-79 94-95, (R-up 03-04 04-05 77-78 83-84, Lg Cup 75-76 78-79, Div 2(reserves) 32-33 84-85 (R-up 1894-95 1979-80); Thames & Medway Comb. 08-09 12-13 22-23 25-26 28-29 55-56; Kent Amtr Cup 45-46 51-52; Kent Snr Shield 77-78; Kent Snr Cup R-up(3); Gtr London Lg 64-65; FA Cup 6th Qual. Rd 19-20; FA Tphy 1st Rd Proper 85-86.

SLADE GREEN

Chairman: Brian Smith. **President:** William Dudley
Secretary: Bruce Smith, 15 Gumping Rd, Orpington, Kent BR5 1RX (01689 858782).
Joint Managers: M Watts/T Carley. **Coach:** Tony Pruce. **Physio:** Alan Martin.
Ground: The Small Glen, Moat Lane, Slade Green, Erith, Kent (01322 351077).
Directions: Off A206 between Erith & Dartford. 400 yards from Slade Green BR station. Buses 89 & B13.
Capacity: 3,000 **Seats:** 150 **Cover:** 400 **Floodlights:** Yes **Club Shop:**
Clubhouse: Yes; Hall, Directors Lounge & Canteen
Programme: 30 pages, with admission **Editor/Press Officer:** Robert Smith (01322 287982).
Colours: White & green **Change Colours:** All yellow
Sponsor: Kingsway Furniture **Founded:** 1946. **Nickname:** The Green
Midweek matchday: Tuesday **Reserve League:**
Previous - Leagues: Dartford 46-52/ Kent Amateur 52-62/ Greater London 62-70. **Name:** Slade Green Athletic 46-86.
Players pogressing to Football League: Roy Dwight (Nottm Forest), Alan Clark (Charlton), Fred Lucas (Charlton).
96-97 - Captain: Graham Hall **Top Scorer:** Peter Deadman **P.o.Y.:** Peter Deadman/Dean Lee
Records - Attendance: 3,000 v Millwall, friendly 25/7/92. **Goalscorer:** Colin Dwyer **Appearances:** Colin Dwyer. **Win:** 14-0 v Island Social, Kent Amtr Lge 1953. **Defeat:** 1-9 v Whitstable Greater London 64-65
Honours: Kent Snr Tphy 91-92 (R-up 80-81); Kent Lg Cup 82-83; Kent Amtr Lg 52-53 53-54 60-61 (Lg Cup 60-61); Kent Intermediate Cup 61-62; Kent Benevolent Cup 46-47; West Kent 60-61 65-66; Dartford Lg R-up 48-49 (Lg Cup 47-48 (R-up 46-47)); Erith Hospitals Cup 46-47 48-49; Gtr London Lg R-up 68-69; Plumstead Challenge Cup 48-49.

SWANLEY FURNESS

Furness, now Swanley Furness *Photo - Roger Turner*

Chairman: Alan Simmonds
Secretary: Richard Ayling, 22 Houston Rd, London SE23 2RN (0181 699 1052).
Manager: John Randall **Physio:** **Press Officer:** Martin Wiseman (01689 833083)
Ground: Green Court Road, Swanley, Kent BR8 8JG (01322 666442).
Directions: From junction of M25 & M20 follow signs for Swanley. Left at Crockenhill turning, then first right after motorway crossing. 500 yards from Swanley (BR).
Seats: 100 **Cover:** 200 **Capacity:** 1,500 **Floodlights:** No **Founded:** 1968.
Clubhouse: Matchdays and functions **Sponsors:**
Colours: All white **Change Colours:** All blue **Nickname:** None.
Record Gate: 1,150 v Dartford Kent Lge 95-96. **Midweek matchday:** Tuesday
Record win: 11-0 v Kent Police, Kent Lge 94-95.
Previous Leagues: Sidcup & Dist/ S.E London Amtr/ London Spartan 82-87 *Furness: Sth London All (pre-1991).*
Previous Names: Danson (Bexley Borough)(founded 1941) and Furness United merged in 1991. Danson Furness United 91-93, Furness 94-97
Previous Grounds: Randell Down Road 41-53/ Eltham Road 53-60/ Crook Log, Brampton Road 60-92.
Programme: 32 pages, 50p **Editor:** Secretary
Player progressing to Football League: Darren Adams (Cardiff 94-95).
96-97 Captain: Robert Gibbons **96-97 Top Scorer:** Dean Henry **96-97 P.o.Y.:** Michael Cloke
Honours: Kent Lg Div 1 95-96, R-up 94-95, Lge Cup 95-96; SE Amteur Lg Cup R-up 60-61.

THAMESMEAD TOWN

Chairman: Brian Morris. **Vice Chairman:** Keith Dunsmore. **President:**
Secretary: Albert Panting, 97 Sydney Road, Bexleyheath Kent DA6 8HQ (0181 303 1350)
Manager: Terry Hill. **Coach:** Keith Gurr. **Physio:** Shaun Edwards
Ground: Bayliss Avenue, Thamesmead, London SE28 8NJ (0181 311 4211).
Directions: From Abbey Wood (BR) north east along Harrow Manor Way, into Crossway at 3rd r'bout, Bayliss Av. is 3rd right (Bexley bus 272 stops in Crossway near Bayliss Av. By road: From Dartford tunnel A2 to London, exit Danson Interchange and follow signs for Thamesmead and Abbey Wood. From Blackheath tunnel exit on south side and follow signs to Woolwich, to Plumstead and then to Thamesmead.
Seats: 125 **Cover:** 125 **Capacity:** 400 **Floodlights:** Yes **Club Shop:**
Clubhouse: Mon-Fri 6-11pm, Sat 12-11pm, Sun 12-3 & 7-10.30pm. Double bar, lounge, dance-floor, children's games room, video machines, hot & cold food. New members Bar.
Programmes: Yes. 50p **Ediotor:** **Press Officer:** Matthew Panting.
Colours: Green & black **Change Colours:** All red
Sponsors: Courage Brewery **Nickname:** The Mead. **Founded:** 1970.
Midweek matchday: Tuesday. **Reserves League:** Winstonlead Kent D2
Previous Leagues: London Spartan 80-91. **Previous Ground:** Meridian Sports Ground, Charlton.
Club Record Appearances: Delroy D'Oyley. **Record win:** 9-0 v Kent Police, Kent League 19/4/94.
Record Attendance: 400 v Wimbledon, ground opening 1988.
Honours: Spartan Lg Div 3 79-80 (Lg Cup 84-85 86-87; I'mediate champs 85-86); Kent I'mediate Cup 83-84 94-95; 4 promotions, and 9 trophies (inc London FA and Kent FA Cups) in progress thru Spartan I'mediate Divs, 1980-87; Winstonlead Kent Div 2 94-95, Div 2 Cup 94-95.

TUNBRIDGE WELLS

Chairman: M Higgs **Vice Chairman:** P C Wager.
Secretary: P C Wager, 46 Mereworth Rd, Tunbridge Wells, Kent TN4 9PL (01892 524182).
Manager: Bill Tucker **Asst Manager:** **Coach:** Jack Whitely
Ground: Culverden Stadium, Culverden Down, Tunbridge Wells, Kent TN4 (01892 520517).
Directions: Leaving town on main Tonbridge rd (A26), turn left opposite 'Spanner in the Works' pub - grd half mile. 1 mile from Tunbridge Wells Central (BR). Served by any Tunbridge Wells-Tonbridge bus - to St Johns.
Seats: 350 **Cover:** 1,000 **Capacity:** 3,750 **Floodlights:** Yes **Club Shop:** Yes
Clubhouse: Open matchdays and as required.
Programme: 20 pages, 50p **Editor:** Secretary. **Press Officer:**
Colours: Red/White/Red. **Change Colours:** Yellow/navy/navy.
Sponsors: **Nickname:** Wells. **Founded:** 1886. **Reformed:** 1967.
Midweek Matchday: Tuesday **Reserve League:**
Prev. Names: None. *predecessors: T. Wells FC 1886-1910 47-50/ T. Wells Rgrs 03-09 63-67/ T. Wells Utd 51-62.*
Previous Grounds: Down Lane 1906/ Combley Park 06-10/ Swiss Cottage 06-14/Down Farm 19-39/ St Johns 47-50/ Eridge Road 50-51.
96-97 Captain: C Wells **96-97 P.o.Y.:** **96-97 Top Scorer:**
Club Record Goalscorer: John Wingate 151 **Club Record Appearances:** Tony Atkins 410.
Record Attendance: 967 v Maidstone United, FA Cup 1969.
Record win: 10-0 v Deal (H), May'86 **Record defeat:** 1-11 v Deal Town (H), 20/2/93.
Honours: Kent Lg 84-85 (R-up 68-69, Lg Cup 74-75 77-78 85-86 87-88), Kent Snr Tphy R-up 85-86 91-92.

VICKERS CRAYFORD, DARTFORD ATHLETIC

Secretary: Brian Norris 47 Oxenden Wood Road, Chelsfield Park, Orpington, Kent BR6 6HP (01689 854302)
Fixture Secretary: Mr Gary Dillon, 5 Ladds Way, Swanley, Kent BR8 8HN (01322 669057)
Ground: VCD Sports & Social Club, Oakwood, Old Road, Crayford, Kent (01322 524262)
Colours: Green & white/white/white **Change Colours:** Yellow/blue/blue
Midweek matchday: Tuesday **Previous Ground:** Flamingo Park, Sidcup (pre 1994)
96-97 Captain: **96-97 P.o.Y.:** **96-97 Top Scorer:**

WHITSTABLE TOWN

Chairman: Joe Brownett **Vice Chairman:** Peter Dale **President:** George Gifford.
Secretary: Mrs Sylvia J Davis, 5 Old Bridge Rd, Whitstable, Kent CT5 1RJ (01227 265646).
Manager: Wayne Godden **Asst Manager:** John Crabbe **Physio:** Micky West.
Ground: Belmont Road, Belmont, Whitstable, Kent (01227 266012).
Directions: From Thanet Way (A299), left at Tescos r'bout and down Millstrood Rd - ground at bottom of road, 400yds from Whitstable (BR) station. Car park at Grimshall Rd entrance.
Capacity: 2,000 **Cover:** 1,000 **Seats:** 500 **Floodlights:** Yes **Club Shop:** Yes
Clubhouse: Social & recreation purposes, open all matchdays. Bar. Hot food & drinks at tea-bar.
Programme: 48 pages, 50p **Editor/Press Officer:** Trevor Myhill (01227 277297).
Colours: Red/white/red **Change colours:** Yellow/blue
Sponsors: D & J Tyres **Nickname:** Oystermen, Reds, Natives **Founded:** 1885.
Midweek matchday: Tuesday
Record Gate: 2,500 v Gravesend & Northfleet, FA Cup 3rd Qualifying Rd, 19/10/87.
Previous Leagues: E. Kent 1897-1909/ Kent 09-59/ Aetolian 59-60/ Kent Amtr 60-62 63-64/ Seanglian 62-63/ Gtr London 64-67/ Kent Premier 67-68 (also in New Brompton, Thanet and Faversham & Dist. Lges over the years).
Prev. Names: Whitstable Utd (pre-1886)/ Whitstable Swifts 93-95/ Whitstable Town 95-1905/ Whitstable FC 08-66.
Prev. Grnds: Saddleston's Field 1885-94/ Westmeads (Cromwell Rd) 94-95/ Joy Lane 95-1908/ Church Rd 08-09.
96-97 Captain: **96-97 P.o.Y.:** **96-97 Top Scorer:**
Club Record Goalscorer: Barry Godfrey **Club Record Appearances:** Frank Cox 429 (1950-60).
Record win: 18-0 v Greenstreet (H), Faversham & District Lge 20-21.
Record defeat: 0-10 v Sittingbourne (A), FA Cup 1st Qualifying Round 1962-63.
Honours: Kent Lg Div 2 27-28 33-34 49-50 (Lg Cup 79-80 (R-up 89-90 91-92)), Kent Amtr Lg East 60-61, Kent Amtr Cup 28-29, Kent Snr Tphy R-up 78-79 89-90 92-93, Gtr London Lg Cup R-up 65-66, Kent Amtr Cup 28-29, Kent Midweek Lg Cup 92-93.

Deal Town FC: *Photo - Andrew Chitty*

Herne Bay's Scott Appleton in an aerial battle with Greenwich defender Jeff Hindmarch (No 5), during their 2-0 victory in the Plaaya Kent Senior Trophy.

UNIJET SUSSEX COUNTY LEAGUE

FEEDER TO: BEAZER HOMES LEAGUE

FOUNDED 1920

President: P H Strange **Chairman:** Peter Bentley

Secretary: Peter Wells, 37 Bewley Road, Angmering, BN16 4JL (01903 771146)

FINAL LEAGUE TABLES 1996-97

	DIVISION ONE	*P*	*W*	*D*	*L*	*F*	*A*	*W*	*D*	*L*	*F*	*A*	*Pts*	*GD*
1	Burgess Hill Tn	38	14	3	2	62	23	14	1	4	43	23	88	59
2	Wick	38	13	2	4	58	23	10	5	4	44	21	76	58
3	Peacehaven & Tels	38	11	5	3	38	13	11	3	5	37	28	74	34
4	Saltdean United	38	11	3	5	34	14	9	3	7	32	28	66	24
5	Ringmer	38	10	2	7	31	21	9	3	7	31	32	62	9
6	Langney Sports	38	9	3	7	38	27	7	7	5	34	29	58	16
7	Eastbourne Town	38	9	3	7	34	27	8	3	8	25	24	57	8
8	Horsham YMCA	38	8	4	7	36	27	6	5	8	22	26	51	5
9	Hassocks	38	8	4	7	27	24	6	4	9	20	29	50	-6
10	Pagham	38	9	4	6	25	28	5	3	11	34	39	49	-8
11	Shoreham	38	10	3	6	40	32	4	3	12	22	34	48	-4
12	Arundel	38	7	5	7	39	40	5	6	8	27	38	47	-12
13	Hailsham Town	38	6	6	7	25	26	5	7	7	41	41	46	-1
14	Portfield	38	8	6	5	33	29	5	0	14	28	52	45	-20
15	Selsey	38	7	3	9	29	31	6	3	10	20	39	45	-21
16	Mile Oak	38	7	3	9	28	38	5	6	8	19	36	45	-27
17	Whitehawk	38	9	2	8	25	39	5	1	13	21	41	45	-34
18	Three Bridges	38	5	3	11	24	40	7	5	7	29	29	44	-16
19	Oakwood	38	6	6	7	25	32	5	3	11	23	37	42	-21
20	Southwick	38	4	4	11	23	39	3	3	13	21	48	28	-43

	DIVISION TWO	*P*	*W*	*D*	*L*	*F*	*A*	*W*	*D*	*L*	*F*	*A*	*Pts*	*GD*
1	Littlehampton Tn	34	11	2	4	40	15	13	2	2	55	16	76	64
2	Chichester City	34	11	3	3	37	17	11	0	6	32	18	69	34
3	Redhill	34	14	1	2	54	19	6	6	5	34	23	67	46
4	Sidley United	34	9	5	3	45	18	9	5	3	35	20	64	42
5	Eastbourne Utd	34	10	6	1	36	15	8	3	6	39	28	63	32
6	East Preston	34	11	3	3	44	16	7	2	8	35	32	59	31
7	Withdean	34	9	3	5	34	28	8	5	4	36	18	59	24
8	Worthing United	34	8	4	5	47	28	8	6	3	36	23	58	32
9	East Grinstead	34	10	1	6	28	23	6	1	10	21	33	50	-7
10	Crawley Down Vlge	34	9	4	4	37	21	5	3	9	26	42	49	0
11	Bexhill Town	34	10	4	3	42	30	4	1	12	23	42	47	-7
12	Newhaven	34	8	3	6	38	27	5	4	8	29	35	46	5
13	Midhurst/E'bourne U	34	6	2	9	33	47	4	4	9	24	44	36	-34
14	Crowbrough Ath	34	7	1	9	25	38	3	4	10	21	43	35	-35
15	Lancing	34	5	5	7	26	31	3	1	13	19	42	30	-28
16	Broadbridge Heath	34	6	1	10	29	47	2	2	13	17	51	27	-52
17	Bosham	34	2	2	13	22	47	4	0	13	24	60	20	-61
18	Steyning Town	34	2	1	14	17	54	1	2	14	15	64	12	-86

	DIVISION THREE	*P*	*W*	*D*	*L*	*F*	*A*	*W*	*D*	*L*	*F*	*A*	*Pts*	*GD*
1	Sidlesham	30	11	4	0	38	10	12	1	2	53	14	74	67
2	Shinewater Assoc.	30	14	1	0	49	8	8	5	2	28	16	72	53
3	Franklands Village	30	9	4	2	47	19	8	2	5	22	24	57	26
4	Ansty Rangers	30	6	7	2	26	22	6	4	5	29	25	47	8
5	Hurstpierpoint	30	6	3	6	34	28	8	2	5	23	23	47	6
6	Lingfield	30	9	2	4	37	20	4	5	6	20	17	46	20
7	Sun Alliance	30	7	2	6	31	34	6	2	7	24	32	43	-11
8	Buxted	30	6	4	5	19	18	6	2	7	23	23	42	1
9	Storrington	30	8	2	5	28	16	3	5	7	19	41	40	-10
10	St Francis Hospital	30	6	3	6	23	24	4	4	7	27	35	37	-9
11	Uckfield Town	30	9	2	4	39	28	2	2	11	16	37	37	-10
12	Thomson Athletic	30	4	5	6	20	24	5	2	8	26	34	34	-12
13	Ifield	30	5	2	8	24	31	4	2	9	20	33	31	-20
14	Forest	30	2	3	10	14	28	4	5	6	17	26	26	-23
15	Haywards Heath Tn	30	2	2	11	15	36	5	3	7	19	29	26	-31
16	Seaford Town	30	1	4	10	14	31	0	4	11	11	49	11	-55

DIVISION ONE RESULTS CHART 1996-97

		1	2	3	4	5	6	7	8	9	10	11	12	13	14	15	16	17	18	19	20
1	Arundel	X	3-1	1-2	1-1	0-2	1-1	2-2	0-0	4-6	2-2	5-1	0-4	0-2	1-3	5-2	2-5	5-3	2-1	2-0	3-2
2	Burgess Hill Town	5-1	X	2-1	2-4	6-0	3-2	3-0	6-0	1-0	3-0	3-5	5-0	8-3	2-2	3-0	3-0	1-1	3-2	2-1	1-1
3	Eastbourne Town	4-1	0-3	X	2-2	4-1	0-1	0-1	2-2	0-0	4-3	1-2	5-3	4-0	1-3	2-0	1-0	1-0	0-2	2-0	1-3
4	Hailsham Town	6-2	1-2	0-3	X	0-1	1-1	2-1	0-0	0-0	1-1	2-2	1-0	1-1	0-2	1-2	2-1	3-1	0-1	4-0	0-5
5	Hassocks	3-0	2-4	2-0	3-0	X	0-0	1-3	0-0	3-2	0-6	2-0	2-1	0-1	1-2	0-1	0-0	4-1	1-2	2-0	1-1
6	Horsham YMCA	0-0	0-1	2-3	1-1	2-1	X	1-1	5-1	3-0	2-0	1-0	0-1	0-2	3-2	1-6	1-2	7-0	2-3	4-2	1-1
7	Langney Sports	2-3	1-2	0-0	1-3	2-1	0-3	X	1-1	1-3	2-0	5-1	5-2	1-2	3-2	0-1	1-1	3-0	5-0	3-2	2-0
8	Mile Oak	2-1	1-3	0-1	2-2	1-2	0-4	3-2	X	2-1	3-1	1-5	4-2	2-0	2-4	0-2	2-1	1-1	1-1	0-2	1-3
9	Oakwood	1-1	0-2	3-0	2-4	0-1	0-0	2-7	3-1	X	1-0	2-2	4-0	1-1	1-0	1-1	1-0	1-2	1-1	1-3	0-6
10	Pagham	0-0	1-3	1-3	3-2	0-0	1-0	0-0	2-1	2-1	X	0-1	1-0	0-4	2-1	1-1	3-2	3-0	2-1	1-4	2-4
11	Peacehaven & Tels.	2-2	0-0	3-1	1-1	0-2	2-0	1-1	0-0	0-1	5-0	X	2-0	0-2	2-0	4-0	5-0	3-0	3-1	3-1	2-1
12	Portfield	3-1	4-2	2-0	4-4	0-0	2-1	1-3	1-3	3-2	0-2	1-1	X	3-0	2-2	0-2	3-1	1-1	1-3	1-0	1-1
13	Ringmer	3-1	1-3	0-0	2-1	0-0	5-1	4-1	0-1	1-0	1-0	0-2	2-0	X	1-2	5-0	3-2	0-2	0-3	3-1	0-1
14	Saltdean United	1-0	2-0	2-0	1-0	3-0	3-0	1-3	0-1	5-0	3-1	1-3	3-0	0-1	X	4-0	0-0	1-0	1-1	2-2	1-2
15	Selsey	1-2	0-3	0-1	2-2	1-1	2-3	4-1	5-0	1-0	1-4	0-2	2-4	3-2	0-2	X	2-0	2-1	1-1	0-1	2-1
16	Shoreham	3-3	1-4	1-1	4-2	3-0	2-1	1-2	4-1	1-2	4-2	2-0	3-1	1-2	1-2	2-1	X	3-0	0-5	4-1	0-0
17	Southwick	0-2	0-3	1-4	2-5	0-2	1-2	1-1	0-4	0-2	3-3	1-2	3-1	2-1	0-0	5-0	1-2	X	1-1	1-0	1-4
18	Three Bridges	1-1	1-3	1-0	0-3	1-0	3-1	0-3	1-2	3-3	1-4	1-2	3-4	2-2	0-2	2-0	0-3	4-3	X	0-1	0-3
19	Whitehawk	1-5	4-2	0-4	1-0	3-2	0-0	0-0	2-0	1-0	0-4	0-3	1-5	1-4	2-1	2-0	2-1	2-3	1-0	X	2-5
20	Wick	0-1	1-2	3-1	7-4	3-2	0-1	2-2	4-1	6-0	3-1	0-3	6-0	3-1	4-0	1-1	2-1	3-2	4-0	6-0	X

DIVISION ONE ATTENDANCES CHART 1996-97

		1	2	3	4	5	6	7	8	9	10	11	12	13	14	15	16	17	18	19	20
1	Arundel	X	81	58	65	80	62	57	57	50	38	58	51	56	65	60	78	64	53	52	135
2	Burgess Hill Town	250	X	187	196	453	211	141	85	269	149	387	219	207	197	247	229	147	197	207	491
3	Eastbourne Town	126	101	X	395	72	112	248	107	105	151	151	110	121	78	92	97	89	72	94	120
4	Hailsham Town	178	156	294	X	195	165	295	155	195	198	198	145	237	179	185	100	220	146	225	260
5	Hassocks	81	610	133	178	X	94	96	92	80	71	161	72	142	95	92	156	104	215	133	107
6	Horsham YMCA	81	174	64	89	102	X	76	69	93	69	88	71	71	115	103	76	85	141	94	143
7	Langney Sports	141	225	411	302	121	134	X	168	174	162	244	151	188	172	142	128	154	176	171	378
8	Mile Oak	72	112	65	60	68	65	82	X	83	58	110	52	65	75	40	104	135	62	92	72
9	Oakwood	76	136	75	86	147	87	78	82	X	76	117	45	128	46	76	86	26	322	64	83
10	Pagham	127	130	81	85	60	81	85	69	72	X	120	62	81	101	135	55	147	103	35	165
11	Peacehaven & Tels.	132	201	121	104	119	84	109	131	91	134	X	105	112	208	93	162	142	121	154	172
12	Portfield	67	67	33	54	43	35	56	36	42	66	56	X	65	35	101	79	47	56	47	110
13	Ringmer	86	117	107	215	76	98	155	84	72	78	193	85	X	94	96	126	76	84	108	124
14	Saltdean United	123	163	91	149	169	119	151	94	89	106	293	109	103	X	83	153	103	121	136	173
15	Selsey	92	102	62	71	89	62	84	92	71	89	58	169	81	72	X	181	75	51	82	182
16	Shoreham	90	246	89	96	132	70	120	85	42	125	120	63	86	60	54	X	138	56	102	96
17	Southwick	70	131	76	149	139	101	131	102	94	52	86	81	126	119	60	144	X	72	135	107
18	Three Bridges	152	324	103	123	138	146	104	75	476	104	107	103	103	128	104	116	227	X	114	128
19	Whitehawk	38	150	50	175	75	50	75	75	40	50	175	30	57	133	55	170	55	50	X	55
20	Wick	147	282	121	140	153	153	125	96	118	162	173	172	136	151	166	188	134	92	137	X

DIVISION ONE MERIT TABLE 1996-97

		No of Games	Wins	Wins by 5 Goals +	Goals Against	Clean Games	Cautions	Send Offs	Total
1	Wick	38	115	35	50	120	-90	0	230
2	Hassocks	38	70	0	80	130	-70	0	210
3	Burgess Hill Town	38	140	25	70	110	-135	-20	190
=	Peacehaven & Tels	38	110	20	70	115	-85	-40	190
5	Eastbourne Town	38	85	5	60	135	-65	-40	180
6	Ringmer	38	95	10	60	100	-100	0	165
7	Horsham YMCA	38	70	10	60	120	-100	-20	140
8	Mile Oak	38	60	0	40	110	-105	0	105
9	Langney Sports	38	80	20	45	105	-135	-20	95
10	Oakwood	38	55	5	50	90	-115	-20	65
11	Shoreham	38	70	5	35	90	-115	-40	45
12	Pagham	38	70	5	45	85	-150	-20	35
13	Southwick	38	35	5	20	110	-130	-20	20
14	Hailsham Town	38	55	10	25	75	-140	-20	5
15	Portfield	38	65	5	30	95	-130	-80	-15
16	Arundel	38	60	20	30	70	-205	-20	-45
17	Saltdean Utd	38	100	5	75	45	-230	-60	-65
18	Three Bridges	38	65	5	40	85	-175	-100	-80
=	Whitehawk	38	70	0	50	80	-160	-120	-80
20	Selsey	38	65	10	35	55	-230	-120	-185

MERIT TABLE POINTS

5 POINTS
for every win

5 POINTS
for every win, scoring 5 goals or more

5 POINTS
for every game with no goals conceded

5 POINTS
for every game with no cautions or send offs

-5 POINTS
for every caution

-20 POINTS
for every sending off

JOHN O'HARA LEAGUE CHALLENGE CUP 1996-97

First Round

Eastbourne Town	v	Crowborough Athletic	1-2*
Oakwood	v	Bosham	4-0
Ringmer	v	East Grinstead	1-1, 2-1
Mile Oak	v	Newhaven	7-1
Pagham	v	Redhill	3-1
Three Bridges	v	Langney Sports	1-3

Second Round

Bexhill Town	v	Shoreham	1-5
Crawley Down Village	v	Arundel	0-8
Eastbourne United	v	Peacehaven & Tels.	3-3*, 0-2
Hassocks	v	Sidley United	2-0
Mile Oak	v	Langney Sports	3-1
Portfield	v	East Preston	3-3*, 2-4
Selsey	v	Broadbridge Heath	6-0
Whitehawk	v	Withdean	1-4
Burgess Hill Town	v	Midhurst & Easebourne	9-0
Crowborough Athletic	v	Pagham	1-3
Hailsham Town	v	Lancing	4-0
Horsham YMCA	v	Steyning Town	3-1
Oakwood	v	Ringmer	1-2
Saltdean United	v	Worthing United	3-1*
Southwick	v	Chichester City	1-2
Wick	v	Littlehampton Town	3-1

Third Round

Arundel	v	Selsey	3-3*, 1-2
Hailsham Town	v	Withdean	2-3
Peacehaven & Tels.	v	East Preston	2-1
Shoreham	v	Saltdean United	0-2
Burgess Hill Town	v	Horsham YMCA	4-0
Hassocks	v	Mile Oak	6-0
Ringmer	v	Pagham	2-2*, 2-0
Wick	v	Chichester City	2-1

Fourth Round

Burgess Hill Town	v	Ringmer	4-1
Saltdean United	v	Hassocks	0-1
Peacehaven & Tels.	v	Wick	1-2
Selsey	v	Withdean	4-2

Semi-Final

Burgess Hill Town	v	Ringmer	4-1
Hassocks	v	Wick	0-5

Final

Burgess Hill Town	v	Wick	0-0*, 2-3

WINNERS: WICK

P.G. CUNNINGHAM SPORTSMANSHIP TROPHY 1996-97

Club	Points
Sidley United	78.82
Hassocks	76.49
Crawley Down Village	75.76
Eastbourne United	75.59
Southwick	74.86
Horsham YMCA	74.47
Eastbourne Town	73.95
Wick	73.16
Withdean	72.65
Steyning Town	72.42
Broadbridge Heath	72.35
East Preston	72.06
Littlehampton Town	72.06
Langney Sports	71.58
Burgess Hill Town	71.35
Mile Oak	71.05
Hailsham Town	70.81
Newhaven	70.00
Peacehaven & Telscombe	69.46
Redhill	69.41
Worthing United	69.41
Chichester City	69.09
Ringmer	68.95
Whitehawk	68.68
East Grinstead	68.48
Arundel	67.89
Three Bridges	67.63
Crowborough Athletic	67.58
Shoreham	67.50
Oakwood	67.22
Lancing	66.76
Bosham	65.29
Saltdean United	65.00
Midhurst & Easebourne	64.24
Portfield	64.21
Pagham	63.61
Bexhill Town	63.44
Selsey	57.57

LEADING (LEAGUE) GOALSCORERS 1996-97

Ansty Rangers	Richard Tilford	15
Arundel	Eamonn Searle	25
Bexhill Town	Michael O'Callaghan	25
Bosham	Gavin Hodgkins	8
Broadbridge Hth	Damian Francis	12
Burgess Hill Tn	Paul Boxall	29
Buxted	Andy Payne	11
Chichester City	Dave Kelly	16
	Stuart Chandler	16
Crawley Down V.	Mark Aldred	19
Crowborough Ath	Adrian Smith	11
East Grinstead	Steve Banks	13
East Preston	Chris Jack	33
Eastbourne Tn	Steve Loughton	24
Eastbourne Utd	Nicholas Tattam	14
Forest	Gavin Pritchard	7
Franklands Vlge	Mark Ormanroyd	27
Hailsham Town	Howard Stevens	11
Hassocks	Robbie Kitchen	11
Haywards Hth Tn	Stewart Tippler	10
Horsham YMCA	Phil Churchill	22
Hurstpierpoint	Mark Stafford	10
Ifield	Kevin May	7
Lancing	Chris Georgiou	10
Langney Sports	Gary Callingham	11
Lingfield	Stewart Small	17
Littlehampton Tn	Steve Guille	24
Midhurst & Ebne	Jay Shepherd	11
Mile Oak	Neil Roberts	12
Newhaven	Fran Haren	16
	Micky Dorrill	16
Oakwood	Nigel Brake	10
Pagham	Lee Stevens	12
	Paul Smith	12
P'haven & Tels.	Jon Lockhart	21
Portfield	Hugh Howden	15
Redhill	Simon Cox	17
Ringmer	Darren Longley	17
Saltdean United	Marc Shaw	14
Seaford Town	Jason Bond	6
Selsey	Paul Stevens	13
Shinewater Ass.	Robbie Warner	25
Shoreham	Andy Agutter	14
Sidlesham	Darran Atkins	35
Sidley United	Peter Heritage	15
Southwick	Tony Ropke	10
St Francis Hosp.	Simon Hatton	23
Steyning Town	Adie Rowe	4
Storrington	Ben Whitby	17
Sun Alliance	Dean Lewis	20
Thomson Ath	Jamie Fiveash	5
	Simon Russell	5
Three Bridges	Zac Newman	9
Uckfield Town	Andy Potter	26
Whitehawk	Simon Pierce	11
Wick	Anton Romasz	44
Withdean	Dave Agnew	19
Worthing Utd	Nigel Waller	28

MANAGERS OF THE MONTH 1996-97

	DIVISION ONE	DIVISION TWO	DIVISION THREE
Aug	Alan Pook (Burgess Hill Town FC)	Paul Norland (Withdean FC)	Steve Marchant (Hurstpierpoint FC)
Sep	Steve Richardson (Langney Sports FC)	Lloyd Fowler (Langney Sports FC)	Neil Thornicroft (Buxted FC)
Oct	Jimmy Quinn (Wick FC)	Peter Burdett (Redhill FC)	Peter Cleverley (Sidlesham FC)
Nov	Alan Pook (Burgess Hill Town FC)	John Finneran (East Preston FC)	Chris Snelling (Franklands Vlge FC)
Dec	Jimmy Quinn (Wick FC)	Carl Stabler (Littlehampton Town FC)	Chris Snelling (Franklands Vlge FC)
Jan	Richie Reynolds (Portfield FC)	Graham Standen & Alan Watson (Crawley Down Village FC)	Alan Walsh (Shinewater Assn FC)
Feb	Jimmy Quinn (Wick FC)	Adrian Girdler (Chichester City FC)	Peter Cleverley (Sidlesham FC)
Mar	Peter Edwards (P'haven & Tels. FC)	Peter Burdett (Redhill FC)	Alan Walsh (Shinewater Assn FC)
Apr	Alan Pook (Burgess Hill Town FC)	Adrian Girdler (Chichester City FC)	Alan Walsh (Shinewater Assn FC)

DIVISION ONE CLUBS 1997-98

ARUNDEL

Arundel pictured before the Canterbury FA Cup tie. *Photo - Graham Cotterill*

Chairman: Michael Peters **Vice Chairman:** S Brennan.
Secretary: Doug Feest, 342 Goring Road, Worthing. BN12 4PD (01903 249276)
Manager: Mike Rowland
Ground: Mill Road, Arundel (01903 882548).
Directions: A27 from Worthing to Arundel over railway bridge to roundabout. Second exit into Queen Street to town centre, turn right over bridge. Car park leading to ground 100yards right.
Seats: 100 **Cover:** 200 **Capacity:** 2,200 **Floodlights:** 206 lux **Founded:** 1889
Clubhouse: 2 bars, kitchen, toilets, telephone, pool, darts, Sky TV. Normal pub hours. No food.
Colours: Red & white halves/white/red **Change colours:** Jade & black **Nickname:** Mulletts
Programme: 8 pages, free **Editor:** Secretary **Sponsors:** None
Midweek matchday: Tuesday. **Previous Lge:** West Sussex 1896-1975
Reserves' Lge: Sussex Co. Res Div (West) **Players progressing to Football League:** John Templeman (Brighton & Hove Albion 1966).
Records - Attendance: 2,200 v Chichester, League 67-68. **Goalscorer:** Paul J Bennett. **Appearances:** 537, Paul Bennett (goalkeeper). **Win:** 13-0 v Horsham YMCA (H), Sussex Co. Lge Div 1 21/12/85.
96-97 - Captain: Jon Tucker **P.o.Y.:** Eamon Searle
Honours: Sussex County Lg 57-58 58-59 86-87 (Lg Cup 86-87, Div 2 Cup 76-77, Reserve Section 78-79, Reserve Section Cup 78-79, Merit Table winners 80-81, Sussex Fives 1984 1987), Sussex RUR Charity Cup 68-69 72-73 78-79 79-80, Sussex Jnr Cup 07-08, West Sussex Lg (Reserves) 70-71 (Malcolm Simmonds Cup 70-71).

BURGESS HILL TOWN

Chairman: Jim Collins. **President:** Jack Lake **Manager:** Alan Pook
Secretary: Martin Waner, 26 Hamilton Close, Mile Oak, Brighton BN41 2WY (01273 439849) (Mobile 0378 148853)
Ground: Leylands Park, Burgess Hill, West Sussex RH15 8AW (01444 242429).
Directions: Turn east from A273 London Road into Leylands Road, take 4th left (signposted) Leyland Park. Nearest station Wivelsfield
Seats: 100 **Cover:** Yes **Capacity:** 2,000 **Floodlights:** Yes **Club badges:**Yes
Programme: Yes **Editor:** Paul Gardner **Sponsors:** None
Colours: Yellow/black/black **Change colours:** All red
Nickname: Hillians **Founded:** 1882 **Midweek matchday:** Tuesday
Record Gate: 600 v Carshalton A, FA Cup 3rd Qual 81 **Previous Lges & Grounds:** None
Clubhouse: Bar & social facilities. Tea bar.
96-97 Captain: Daren Newman **96-97 Top Scorer:** Mark Sheriff **96-97 P.o.Y.:** Adrian Downey
Honours: Sussex County Lg 75-76 96-97 (Div 2 74-75, Lg Cup 73-74 79-80 (R-up 90-91), Div 2 Cup 73-73, F/lit Cup 96-97, Reserve Section 76-77 77-78 91-92, Reserve Sect. East 77-78 82-83 84-85, Reserve Cup 82-83, Yth Sect. West 91-92 East 95-96, North 96-97, Sussex Fives 1980), Mid-Sussex Lg 00-01 03-04 39-40 46-47 56-57 (Div 2 03-04(res), Div 3 20-21 36-37, Div 4(res) 56-57, Mid Sussex Snr Cup 94-95 96-97, Montgomery Cup 39-40 56-57, Mowatt Cup 45-46, Sussex RUR Charity Cup 91-92, Sussex I'mediate Cup 76-77, Sussex Yth Lge 96-97, Cup 91-92.

Back Row; Richard Cheal, Ashley Carr, Paul Hammond, Tony Vessey, Derren Woods, Richard Waters. 2nd Row; Garry Newton (Comm Mgr), Ian Stevens (Physio), Steve Danahar (Sponsor), Stuart Warne, Adrian Downey, Jack Dineen, Graham Farmer, Stewart Holmes, Graham Russell (Asst), Geoff Pook (Asst). 3rd Row; Rene Duchossoy, Daren Newman, Paul Boxall, Alan Pook (Mgr), Mark Sheriff, Chris Brown, Richard Fernley, Bob Hitchcock (Asst). Front Row; Team Mascots with Unijet Sussex County League Championship Trophy & SCFA Floodlight Cup.

Photo - Steve Dennett

CHICHESTER CITY

President: **Chairman:** Tony Muncaster **Match Sec:** Peter Harding
Company Secretary: John F Hutter, 28 Stockbrigde Gdns, Donnington, Chichester, West Sussex PO19 2QT (01243 785839).
Manager: Adrian Girdler **Physio:** Roly Howley **Press Officer:** T Wallis (01705 464438).
Ground: Oaklands Park, Chichester (01243 785978).
Directions: Half mile north of city centre adjacent to Festival Theatre. Turn into Northgate car park from Oaklands Way and entrance is beside Tennis and Squash club. 1 mile from Chichester (BR) - walk north through city centre.
Seats: 50 **Cover:** 500 **Capacity:** 2,500 **Floodlights:** Yes **Founded:** 1873
Colours: White/black/white **Change colours:** All red **Nickname:** Lilywhites
Programme Editor: T Wallis **Club Shop:** No **Midweek matchday:** Wednesday
Previous Lgs: Chichester/ West Sussex 1886-1920 **Record Gate:** 2,500 v Dorchester, FA Cup 1960
Clubhouse: Licensed, open matchdays and some evenings. Tea bar & boadroom.
Club record scorer: David Green **Club record appearances:** Neal Holder.
Honours: Sussex Co. Lg(5) 59-61 67-68 72-73 79-80 Invitation Cup 47-48 54-55 56-57 63-64, Div 2 Cup 84-85 87-88 90-91, Sussex Snr Cup 25-26, Sussex RUR Charity Cup 60-61(jt with Brighton & HA) 63-64, Sussex I'mediate Cup 67-68.

EASTBOURNE TOWN

Chairman: Kevin Moore **Manager:** Rob Thorley/Pete Cherry
Secretary: Kevin Moore, 27 Chesterton Drive, Seaford. BN25 3RJ (01323 897369)
Ground: The Saffrons, Compton Place Road, Eastbourne, East Sussex (01323 723734).
Directions: Turn south west off A22 into Grove Road (opposite BR station), ground 1/4 mile on the right.
Seats: 100 **Cover:** Yes **Capacity:** 3,000 **Floodlights:** Yes **Founded:** 1882
Clubhouse: Fully licensed bar. Board room. Tea bar.
Colours: Yellow/blue/blue **Changes:** Blue & black/black/black
Programme Editor: Chris Backhurst (01323 505062) **Nickname:** 'Bourne'
Previous Leagues: Southern Amtr 07-46/ Corinthian 60-63/ Athenian 63-76.
Sponsors: Eastbourne Car Auctions **Record Gate:** 7,378 v Hastings U. 1953
Honours: Sussex County Lg 76-77, Sussex Snr Cup(12) 1889-91 93-95 98-1901 02-03 21-22 31-33 52-53, Sussex RUR Charity Cup 32-33 47-48 49-50, Southern Amtr Lg(2), AFA Snr Cup 21-22 24-25 (R-up 22-23 23-24), AFA Invitation Cup 69-70 (R-up 56-57 68-69 70-71).

HAILSHAM TOWN

President: J Whippy **Chairman:** Dave Challinor **Manager:** Neil Thornycroft
Secretary/Press Officer: Derek York, 59 Anglesey Avenue, Horsebridge, Hailsham BN27 3BQ (01323 848024).
Ground: The Beaconsfield, Western Road, Hailsham, East Sussex (01323 840446).
Directions: A22 to Arlington Road, turn east, then left into South Road - left into Diplocks Way until Daltons. Four miles from Polegate (BR - Brighton-Eastbourne line); regular bus service from Eastbourne.
Seats: None **Cover:** 300 **Capacity:** 2,000 **Floodlights:** Yes **Founded:** 1885
Programme: Yes **Editor:** Secretary **Midweek matchday:** Tuesday.
Colours: Green & yellow/green/yellow **Change colours:** All white
Record Gate: 1,350 v Hungerford, FA Vase Feb '89 **Previous League:** E Sussex, Southern Comb.
Clubhouse: Hot and cold snacks. Open every evening, matchdays and Sundays, tea bar.
96-97 Captain: M Cable **96-97 P.o.Y.:** P Stevens **96-97 Top Scorers:** H Stevens 24
Club Record Goalscorer: H Stevens 51, 95-96 **Club Record Appearances:** P Comber 600
Honours: FA Vase 5th Rd 88-89, Sussex County Lg Div 2 R-up 80-81, Southern Co's Comb. 74-75, Sussex RUR Charity Cup, Sussex I'mediate Cup, Hastings Snr Cup, Sussex Jnr Cup, E Sussex Lg Cup, Hailsham Charity Cup, John O'Hara Cup 95-96.

HASSOCKS

President: Maurice Boxall **Chairman:** Jim Goodrum
Secretary: Bob Preston, 65 Oakhall Park, Burgess Hill, West Sussex RH15 0DA (01444 245695).
Manager: Dave John **Press Off.:** Paul Elphick (01273 551968) **Physio:** Norman Dodds
Ground: The Beacon, Brighton Rd, Hassocks (01273 846040). **Directions:** Off A273 Pyecombe Road to Burgess Hill, 300yds south of Stonepound crossroads (B2116) to Hurstpierpoint or Hassocks.
Seats: None **Cover:** 100 **Capacity:** 1,500 **Floodlights:** Yes **Founded:** 1902
Clubhouse: Clubroom, bar, kitchen.
Colours: All Red with white trim **Change colours:** Yellow & blue
Programme: 24 pages, 50p **Editor:** Paul Elphick **Nickname:** The Robins
Sponsors: Tracmaster Ltd **Midweek Matchday:** Tuesday
Previous - Leagues: Mid Sussex/ Brighton Hove & Dist/ Southern Co's Comb. **Ground:** Adastra Park, (pre-92).
Record Gate: 610 v Burgess Hill Town, Sussex County Lge 96-97.
Honours: Sussex County Lg Div 3 91-92, Div 2 R-up 94-95, Res. Sect. East R-up 92-93; Southern Counties Comb. 76-77, Lg Cup R-up 79-80; Brighton Hove & Dist. Lg 71-72; Sussex Intermediate Cup 74-75 (R-up 80-81).

HORSHAM YMCA

Chairman: Robert Knight **Match Secretary:** Robin Bishop (01903 746332)
Secretary: Robin Bishop, 6 Brook Close, Storrington, RH20 3NT (01903 746332, 0996 202955)
Manager: John Suter **Asst Mgr:** **Physio:** Robin Bishop
Ground: Gorings Mead, Horsham (01403 252689). **Directions:** Approaching Horsham fron East on A281 Brighton Road, the ground is on left & signposted opposite Gorings Mead
Seats: 100 **Cover:** 200 **Capacity:** 800 **Floodlights:** Yes **Founded:** 1898
Colours: White/black/red **Change colours:** All Red **Nickname:** YM's
Sponsors: Principal Copiers **Midweek Matchday:** Tuesday
Previous Leagues: Horsham & Dist/Brighton & Hove/Mid Sussex **Record Attendance:** 600 v Horsham FA Cup
96-97 Captain: Daryn Benn **96-97 P.o.Y.:** Peter Durrant **96-97 Top scorer:** Phil Churchill
Honours: Sussex Co Lge Div 2 65-66 82-83 R-up 94-95 (Lg Cup 81-82, Invitation Cup 66-67 67-68, Div 2 Invit. Cup 59-60 61-62 94-95)

LANGNEY SPORTS

Chairman: Len Smith **President:** J Stonestreet **Manager:** Steve Richardson
Secretary: Mrs Myra Stephens, 7b Erica Close, Langney, Eastbourne, East Sussex BN23 6HY (01323 766050).
Ground: Langney Sports Club, Priory Lane, Eastbourne, East Sussex (01323 766265).
Directions: A22 to Polegate, A27 to Stone Cross, right onto B32104 to Langney Shopping Centre, then left and first right. One mile from Pevensey & Westham (BR). Buses from Eastbourne.
Seats: **Cover:** 1,000 **Capacity:** 2,500 **Floodlights:** Yes **Shop:** Yes
Programme: Yes **Editor:** Mike Spooner (01323 461003)
Colours: All red **Change:** Sky & navy/navy
Sponsors: Nobo Group Plc. **Nickname:** None **Founded:** 1966
Midweek Matchday: Tuesday **Previous League:** Eastbourne & Hastings
Record Attendance: 1,000+ v Crystal Palace, f'light opener 90-91.
Clubhouse: Open every evening & lunchtime with adjoining sports hall, board room, matchday tea bar.
96-97 Captain: Jason Morley **96-97 P.o.Y.:** Sean McFadden **96-97 Top Scorer:**
Club Record Goalscorer: Nigel 146 **Club Record Appearances:** Steve Dell 386.
Honours: Sussex Co. Lg R-up 91-92 (Div 2 87-88, Lg Cup 89-90, Div 3 86-87, Div 3 Cup 86-87, 5-aside comp. 1990), Sussex I'mediate Cup 85-86, Eastbourne Challenge Cup 85-86 86-87.

Chichester City FC: Back Row (L-R); Rowland Howley (Sports Therapist), Stuart Chandler, Chris Sibley, Chris Heath, Jason Watson, Alan Wilkinson, Paul Stevens, Andy Dolphin, John Stuart. Front Row; Jim Butlin, Dave Kelly, Adie Girdler, Billy Cole, Glen Bridgeman, Jason Warton

Eastbourne Town: Playing Squad; Steve Charman, Ben Austin, Richard Hughs, Darren Smith, Steve Lawrence, Lee Edwards, David Oakes, Jimmy Chater, Terry Donovan, Neil Townsend, Neal Ryan, Jimmy Hughes, Stuart Addems, Steve Laughton. *Photo - Andrew Chitty*

Hailsham Town. *Photo - Roger Turner*

LITTLEHAMPTON TOWN

President: Ian Cunningham **Chairman:** Ian Cunningham **Manager:** Carl Stabler
Secretary: John Savage, 66 Nelson Road, Worthing. BN12 6EN. (01903 502850)
Ground: The Sportsfield, St Flora's Road, Littlehampton (01903 713944)
Directions: 10 minutes walk from Littlehampton station (BR) - turn left along Terminus Rd, continue through High Street and Church Rd to junction with St Flora's Rd (left).
Seats: 260 **Cover:** 260 **Capacity:** 4,000 **Floodlights:** Yes **Founded:** 1894
Colours: Gold/black/black. **Change:** Blue/white/white **Nickname:** Marigolds
Programme Editor: M Bennett (01903 785371) **Midweek Matches:** Tuesday
Record Gate: 4,000 v Northampton, FA Cup 1st Rd Proper 90-91
Clubhouse: Sportsman (Private Club). Separate board room & tea bar.
Honours: FA Vase SF 90-91, FA Cup 1st Rd 90-91, Sussex Co. Lg 58-59(jt with Shoreham) 75-77 84-85 90-91 96-97, Sussex Snr Cup 73-74.

MILE OAK

Chairman: Geoff Kerly **President:** D Bean **Manager:** Tony Gratwicke
Secretary: Colin Brown, 19 The Crescent, Southwick, West Sussex BN42 4LB (01273 591346).
Ground: Mile Oak Recreation Ground, Graham Avenue, Mile Oak (01273 423854)
Directions: From A27 take Mile Oak Road or Locks Hill & Valley Road to Chalky Road, ground 500yds on right along Graham Avenue which runs up valley from centre of Chalky Road.
Seats: None **Cover:** Yes **Capacity:** **Floodlights:** Yes. **Founded:** 1960
Colours: Tangerine/black/tangerine **Change colours:** All white **Nickname:** The Oak
Programme: Yes **Editor:** C Tew (01273 416036) **Record Gate:** 186
Previous Leagues: Southern Counties Combination/ Brighton Hove & District
Clubhouse: Mile Oak Pavillion; Hall and tea bar. **Midweek Matchday:** Tuesday
Honours: Sussex Co.Lg.Div 2 Champions, Div 3 R-up 91-92 (Div 2 Cup R-up 92-93), Southern Counties Combination 86-87, Brighton Hove & District Lg 80-81, Vernon Wentworth Cup 85-86, Sussex Intermediate Cup R-up 88-89.

PAGHAM

Chairman: Graham Peach **Vice-Chairman:** N Dray **President:** A Peirce
Secretary: Alan Seal, 6 Greenlea Ave, Pagham, West Sussex PO21 3LH (01243 262944 Mobile: 0850 707932)
Manager/Coach: Graham Peach **Asst Manager:** S Booker **Press Officer:** Ken Randall (01243 555415)
Ground: Nyetimber Lane, Pagham, West Sussex (0243 266112).
Directions: Turn off A27 Chichester by-pass (signposted A259 Pagham). Ground in village of Nyetimber. Three miles from Bognor (BR). Buses 260 & 240.
Seats: 200 **Cover:** 200 **Capacity:** 2,000 **Floodlights:** Yes **Founded:** 1903
Clubhouse: Bar open matchdays and some evenings. Hot food, pool, darts, satellite TV. Tea bar.
Colours: White/black/black **Change colours:** Yellow/green **Nickname:** Lions.
Midweek Matchday: Tuesday **Reserve's League:** Unijet Sussex Co. Reserve Div.
Programme: 12 pages, 50p **Editor:** Secretary **Club Shop:** No.
Sponsors: City Saes Centre **Previous Leagues:** Chichester 1903-50/ West Sussex 50-69.
Records - Attendance: 1,200 v Bognor, 1971. **Goalscorer:** Mark Vickers/ R Deluca. **Win:** 10-1 v Seaford Town (A), Sussex County Lge Div 2, 70. **Defeat:** 0-7 v Newport IOW (H), FA Amat Cup, 1970s.
Honours: Sussex Co. Lg R-up 80-81 87-88 88-89 92-93 (Div 2 78-79 86-87, Lg Cup 88-89, Div 2 Cup 71-72 85-86, Res. Sect. West 80-81, Res Sect. Cup 80-81, Res Section Cup 77-78 80-81 87-88 88-89 90-91), Sussex F'lit Cup R-up 88-89, Sussex RUR Charity Cup 88-89 (R-up 93-94), West Sussex Lg 65-66 68-69 69-70, Malcolm Simmonds Cup 67-68, Sussex I'mediate Cup 66-67.

PEACEHAVEN & TELSCOMBE

Chairman: Jim Edwards **Manager:** Gerry Green **Match Sec:** Fred Parris
Secretary: Mrs Margaret Edwards, 87 Ambleside Ave, Peacehaven, E. Sussex BN10 7LN (01273 583022)
Ground: Piddinghoe Avenue, Peacehaven, East Sussex (01273 582471).
Directions: Arriving from Brighton on A259, cross r'bout and Piddinghoe Avenue is next left after 2nd set of lights - ground at end. From Newhaven Piddinghoe Avenue is first right after first set of lights. Three miles from Newhaven (BR). Peacehaven is served by Brighton to Newhaven and Eastbourne buses.
Seats: None **Cover:** 250 **Capacity:** 3,000 **Floodlights:** Yes **Founded:** 1923 **Nickname:** The Tye
Clubhouse: Bar open evenings and weekends, pool darts, hot and cold food available. Tea bar.
Programme: Yes **Editor/Press Officer:** Secretary **Midweek Matches:** Wednesday
Colours: All white **Change colours:** All sky **Sponsors:** Anchor Garage
Record Gate: 1,420 v Littlehampton, Lge 91 **Previous Leagues:** Lewes/ Brighton
Honours: FA Cup 4th Qual. Rd 90-91; FA Vase 5th Rd 92-93, Qtr Fin 95-96. Sussex Co. Lg 78-79 81-82 82-83 91-92 92-93 94-95 95-96, R-up 77-78 80-81 90-91, Lg Cup 91-92 92-93, Div 2 R-up 75-76, Div 2 Cup 75-76; Norman Wingate Tphy 82-83 91-92 92-93; Hayden Tphy 82-83 92-93; Sussex Snr Cup R-up 81-82 92-93; Sussex RUR Charity Cup 77-78 81-82 92-93, R-up 80-81 89-90 90-91 94-95 95-96); Brighton Charity Cup 91-92 92-93 93-94; Vernon Wentworth 91-92 92-93;

Mile Oak FC: *Photo- Andrew Chitty*

PORTFIELD

Players in Photo: Lloyd Patilla, Adam Moore, Steve Black, Kevin Shires, Shane Davies, Lee Bishop, Hun Evans, Hugh Howden, Jamiue Thorp, Paul Robertson, Steve Poulton, Andy Morris, Chris Rustell, Jamie Miller.
Photo - Andrew Chitty

President: S Kenny **Chairman:** Terry Rustell **Manager:** Richie Reynolds
Secretary: Gary Rustell, 102 Churchwood Drive, Tangmere, Nr Chichester, West Sussex PO20 6GB (01243 537978)
Ground: Church Road, Portfield, Chichester, West Sussex PO19 4HN (01243 779875)
Directions: A27 from Arundel to Chichester, take road to signposted city centre then 1st left (Church Rd) after supermarket r'bout. 1 mile from Chichester (BR).
Seats: 60 **Cover:** 200 **Capacity:** 2,000 **Floodlights:** Yes **Club Shop:** Badges
Programme: Yes **Editor:** TBA **Admission:** £2.00 & £1
Colours: Amber/black/amber. **Change colours:** All Blue
Sponsors: T.B.A. **Founded:** 1896 **Nickname:** Field.
Midweek Matchday: Tuesday **Record Attendance:** Unknown **Previous League:** West Sussex.
Clubhouse: 2 bars, pool, snooker, seating for 100, dance floor, darts, and tea bar selling hot & cold food.
96-97 Top Score: Hugh Howden 22
Honours: Sussex Co. Lg Div 2 72-73 83-84 91-92 (Div 2 Cup 70-71 72-73, Res Sect Prem Lge 94-95, Cup 91-92), W Sussex Lg 46-47 48-49 (Malcolm Simmonds Cup 46-47), Sussex Jnr Cup 45-46, Benevolent Cup 46-47.

REDHILL

Redhill FC: Promoted from Division Two. *Photo - Andrew Chitty*

Chairman: Nick Creasey **Vice-Chairman:** Alan Thurlbeck **President:** Malcolm Chatfield
Secretary: Neil Hoad, 2b Earlswood Rd, Redhill, Surrey RH1 6HE (01737 213847).
Manager: Peter Burdett. **Asst Manager:** Dave Gellatley. **Coach:** Ricky Kidd
Ground: Kiln Brow, Three Arch Road, Redhill, Surrey (01737 762129).
Directions: On left hand side of A23, two and a half miles south of Redhill.
Seats: 150 **Cover:** 150 **Capacity:** 2,000 **Floodlights:** Yes **Founded:** 1894
Shop: Yes, Contact Spencer Mitchell, 21 Colebrook Rd, Redhill RH1 2BL (01737 780634).
Clubhouse: Social club, bar, canteen, board room, club shop, tanoy, toilets.
Programme: 36 pages, 50p **Editor:** Neil Hoap **Press Officer:** Tim Reynolds
Colours: Red & white stripes/red/ **Change colours:** White/black. **Nickname:** Reds/Lobsters
Sponsors: McDonalds (Redhill) **Midweek matchday:** Tuesday. **Reserve League:** Unijet Sussex Co.Lg.
Previous Leagues: E & W Surrey/ Spartan 09-10/ Southern Sub/ London 21-23/ Athenian 23-84/ Spartan 84-88.
96-97 - Captain: Mark Endsleigh **Top Scorer:** Ricky Geddes **P.o.Y.:** Mark Endsleigh
Records - Attendance: 1,200 v Crystal Palace & All Star XI, Brian Medlicott Testimonial 1989. **Goalscorer:** Steve Turner 119. **Appearances:** Brian Medlicott 766. **Win:** 9-0; v Crown & Manor (H), London Spartan League 3/10/87; v Little Common Albion (H), Sussex County League Division Two 25/9/93. **Defeat:** 1-7 v Peacehaven & Telscombe (H), Sussex County League Cup 9/2/93.
Honours: FA Amtr Cup SF 25-25, FA Cup 1st Rd 57-58, Athenian Lg 24-25 83-84 (Lg Cup 69-70 70-71),East & West Surrey Lg. 1902-03,Southern Suburban Senior West Lg. 1902-03,, Surrey Snr Cup 28-29 65-66 , Gilbert Rice F'lit Cup 80-81, Sussex County Lg Div 2 Cup 91-92, Southern Co's Comb. Cup 90-91.

RINGMER

President: Sir G Christie **Chairman:** Richard Soan
Secretary: Chris Christoff, 17 Babylon Way, Ratton, Eastbourne, (01323 501618)
Manager: Gary Allen. **Press Officer:** Alan Harper (01323 764263)
Ground: Caburn Ground, Anchor Field, Ringmer (01273 812738).
Directions: From Lewes road turn into Springett Avenue opposite Ringmer village green. Anchor Field first left. Three miles from Lewes (BR).
Seats: 100 **Cover:** Yes **Capacity:** 1,000 **Floodlights:** Yes **Founded:** 1906.
Colours: Sky & navy/navy/navy **Change colours:** All yellow **Nickname:** None
Programme: Yes **Editor:** Martin BUrke (01797 260260). **Admission:** £2.50
Previous League: Brighton **Record Gate:** 1,200 in FA Cup **Midweek Matchday:** Tuesday
Clubhouse: 2 bars, function room, boardroom, tea bar.
Honours: FA Cup 1st Rd Proper 70-71; Sussex Co. Lg 70-71, Div 2 68-69, Invit Cup 66-67; Res. Sect. East 79-80 80-81 (R-up 89-90), Yth Section 87-88, Yth Section East 87-88; Sussex Snr Cup 72-73 (R-up 80-81); Sussex Jnr Cup 25-26; Sussex Express Sn Charity Cup 94-95.

SALTDEAN UNITED

Chairman: Mike Walker **Vice Chairman:** Rod Flavell **President:** Jim Bower
Secretary: Iain Fielding, 40 Rowan Way, Rottingdean, Brighton BN2 7FP (01273 304995).
Manager: Tommy Hamilton **Asst Manager:** Mark Hammond **Physio:** Keith Gray
Ground: Hill Park, Combe Vale, Saltdean, Brighton (01273 309898).
Directions: A259 coast road east from Brighton to Saltdean Lido, left into Arundel Drive West, and Saltdean Vale to bridle path at beginning of Combe Vale. Club 200yds along track.
Seats: 50 **Cover:** Yes **Capacity:** 2,000 **Floodlights:** Yes **Founded:** 1966.
Programme: Yes **Editor:** Bob Thomas (01273 309898) **Press Officer:** Julian Appleton.
Colours: Red & black/black/black **Change colours:** Blue & yellow **Nickname:** Tigers
Sponsors: Marat **Record Attendance:** 250 **Previous League:** Brighton Hove & Dist.
Clubhouse: Licensed bar, lounge, juke box, video games, board room, tea bar. Pool table.
Honours: Sussex Co. Lg Div 3 88-89, Div 2 95-96.

SELSEY

Chairman: Roger Slade **Manager:** John Davies/Dave Kew **President:** Roy Glew
Secretary: Denny Lee, 29 Malthouse Cottages, West Wittering, Chichester, W Sussex PO20 8QJ (01243 513788)
Ground: High Street Ground, Selsey, Chichester, West Sussex (01243 603420)
Directions: Through Selsey High Street to fire station. Take turning into car park alongside the station. Entrance is in the far corner. Regular buses from Chichester.
Seats: 50 **Cover:** Yes **Capacity:** 2,250 **Floodlights:** Yes **Founded:** 1923
Colours: Blue/white/blue **Change colours:** White/red/red **Nickname:** Blues
Programme Editor: Mrs D Hayers (0243 604013) **Press Officer:** Mr P Emms.
Record Gate: 750-800 v Chichester or Portfield, 50's **Midweek Matchday:** Wednesday
Sponsors: Allslade Welding & Fabrications Ltd **Previous Leagues:** Chichester & Dist./ West Sussex.
Clubhouse: Bar, hospitality room, lounge, toilets, kitchen.
Honours: Sussex Co. Lg R-up 89-90 (Div 2 63-64 75-76 (R-up 86-87), Div 2 Cup 86-87 (R-up 84-85), Div 2 Invitation Cup 63-64, Sussex 5-aside 88-89), Sussex Snr Cup R-up 63-64, Sussex I'mediate Cup 58-59, Sussex Jnr Cup(Reserves) 76-77, West Sussex Lg 54-55 55-56 57-58 58-59 60-61 (Malcolm Simmonds Cup 55-56 56-57 57-58 58-59).

SHOREHAM

President: Alf Bloom **Chairman:** John Bell.
Secretary: Mrs Anne Harper, 66 Willow Crescent, Worthing. BN13 2SX (01903 267672).
Manager: John Prees **Press Officer:** Michael Wenham (01273 596009).
Ground: Middle Road, Shoreham-by-Sea, West Sussex (01273 454261).
Directions: Half mile from Shoreham-by-Sea (BR) - east across level crossing, up Dolphin Road, ground 150yds on right. Or, A27 to Shoreham. At Southlands Hospital turn left down Hammy Lane, left at end, ground opposite.
Seats: 20 **Cover:** 1 stand **Capacity:** 1,500 **Floodlights:** Yes **Founded:** 1892
Colours: Blue/white/blue. **Change colours:** Red & white **Nickname:** Musselmen
Programme: Yes **Editor:** Michael Wenham **Record Gate:** 1,342 v Wimbledon (f/lt opening 86)
Previous League: West Sussex **Midweek Matchday:** Wednesday **Sponsors:** Len German Wholesalers.
Clubhouse: Seats 70. Bar, pool, darts, tea bar.
Honours: Sussex Co. Lg 51-53 77-78 (R-up 34-35, Div 2 61-62 76-77 84-85 93-94, Div 2 Cup 74-75 82-83, Invitation Cup 57-58), Sussex Snr Cup 01-02 05-06, Sussex F'lit Cup R-up 89-90, Sussex RUR Charity Cup 02-03 05-06, Vernon Wentworth Cup 86-87.

WHITEHAWK

President: Ron Wiltshire **Chairman/Comm Mgr:** Ken Powell **Match Sec:** Fred Moore
Secretary: John Rosenblatt, 25 Arundel Street, Brighton BN2 5TH (01273 680322).
Manager: Paul Hubbard **Asst Manager:** Vic Standen **Coach:** Paul Hubbard.
Ground: The Enclosed Ground, East Brighton Park (01273 609736).
Directions: Follow Brighton seafront road towards Newhaven, turn inland (Arundel Road) opposite Marina, 3rd right into Roedean Road, 1st left into Wilson Avenue. Three miles from Brighton (BR); take Newhaven, Eastbourne or Saltdean bus to Marina, then as above.
Seats: None **Cover:** 500 **Capacity:** 3,000 **Floodlights:** Yes **Founded:** 1945
Colours: All red **Change colours:** All blue **Nickname:** Hawks
Programme: £2 with admission **Editor:** Tony Kelly (0273 698203) **Midweek Matchday:** Wednesday
Previous League: Brighton Hove & Dist. **Sponsors:** Brighton Co-operative Society.
Record Gate: 2,100 v Bognor Regis Town, FA Cup 4th Qualifying Rd replay 88-89.
Clubhouse: Licensed bar, pool, darts. Board room. Tea bar.
Club record scorer: Billy Ford **Club record appearances:** Ken Powell 1,103.
Honours: Sussex Co. Lg 61-62 63-64 83-84 (Div 2 67-68 80-81, Lg Cup 82-83 93-94, Invitation Cup 60-61 69-70, Div 2 Cup 80-81), Sussex Snr Cup 50-51 61-62, Sussex RUR Charity Cup 54-55 58-59 90-91, Sussex I'mediate Cup 49-50, Sussex Jnr Cup 48-49 51-52, Brighton Charity Cup 51-52 59-60 61-62 82-83 87-88 88-89, Worthing Charity Cup 82-83, FA Vase 5th Rd 93-94.

WICK

Wick FC: Line up before John O'Hara Cup Final against Burgess Hill Town

Photo - Roger Turner

Chairman: Norman Cairns. **Vice-Chairman:** J Burnett **President:** B Wadsworth
Secretary: Paul Beard, 2 Van Gogh Place, North Bersted, Bognor Regis, West Sussex PO22 9BG (01243 822063).
Manager: Jimmy Quinn. **Asst Manager:** Jim Thompson
Ground: Crabtree Park, Coomes Way, Wick, Littlehampton, West Sussex (01903 713535).
Directions: A27 to Crossbush, left at traffic lights signed Littlehampton, after 1 mile cross level crossing, turn left into Coombes Way next to Locomotive PH - ground at end. One and a half miles from Littlehampton (BR).
Seats: 50 **Cover:** 200 **Capacity:** 2,000 **Floodlights:** Yes **Founded:** 1892
Programme: Yes **Editor/Press Officer:** Thomas Cairns (01903 501857)
Colours: Red & black/black/black **Change colours:** All white. **Nickname:** Wickers
Midweek Matchedays: Tuesday **Reserve League:** Unijet Sussex Co. Reserve Div.
Sponsors: Swandean **Record Attendance:** 900. **Previous League:** West Sussex
Clubhouse: First floor. Capacity 120. Tea bar.
96-97 Captain: P Williams **96-97 Top Scorer:** A Romasz **96-97 P.o.Y.:** S Hack
Honours: Sussex Snr Cup 92-93, Sussex Co. Lg 89-90 93-94 (Lg Cup 87-88 96-97 (R-up 93-94 94-95), Div 2 81-82 85-86, Div 2 Cup R-up 81-82, Norman Wingate Tphy 88-89 90-91, Res. Sect West 87-88 90-91 94-95,, Sussex 5-aside R-up 85-86), Sussex RUR Charity Cup 89-90, Gilbert Rice F'lit Cup R-up 80-81 81-82, Sussex Jnr Cup 59-60, Brighton Charity Cup 85-86.Sussex Floodlit Cop R-Up 94-95.

Saltdean United: *Photo - Roger Turner*

DIVISION TWO CLUBS 1997-98

BEXHILL TOWN

President: Barry Woodcock **Chairman:** Elwyn Hughes **Manager:** David Shearing
Secretary: Mrs Leigh Quinn, 37 Colebrook Road, Bexhill-on-Sea. TN39 3PX (01424 214197).
Ground: The Polegrove, Brockley Rd, Bexhill-on-Sea, East Sussex (01424 220732)
Directions: At Little Common r'bout take 3rd exit to Cooden Sea Rd, left into Cooden Drive for one and a half miles, Brockley Rd on the right. Three quarters of a mile from Bexhill Central (BR).
Seats: 250 **Cover:** 250 **Capacity:** 2,000 **Floodlights:** No **Founded:** 1926
Colours: Green & white/white/white **Change colours:** Black & white
Programme: Yes **Editor:** Mr G Sully **Nickname:** Green Machine
Record Gate: 2,000 **Clubhouse:** Clubroom and bar.
Honours: Sussex Co. Lg 56-57 65-66 (Invit. Cup 55-56), Sussex RUR Char. Cup 57-58 73-74, Hastings Challenge Cup 93-94, Sussex Midweek Cup 25-26.

BROADBRIDGE HEATH

Chairman: Keith Soane **President:** G W Manketelow **Managers:** Gary Croydon, Martin Gander
Secretary: Andy Crisp, 19 Church Rd, Broadbridge Heath, Horsham, West Sussex RH12 3LD (01403 252273).
Ground: Broadbridge Heath Sports Centre, Wickhurst Lane, Horsham (01403 265871).
Directions: Alongside A24, Horsham north/south bypass.
Seats: 300 **Cover:** 300 **Capacity:** 1,300 **Floodlights:** Not full **Founded:** 1919
Programme: Yes **Editor:** Roy Neilson(01403 218318) **Nickname:** Bears
Colours: All royal blue **Change colours:** All red
Sponsors: Mark Woodham, Painter & Decorator **Midweek matches:** Tuesday. **Record Attendance:** 240
Previous Leagues: Horsham, West Sussex, Southern Co's Comb.
Clubhouse: Bar. Kitchen serving meals, pool, darts, social club etc.

CRAWLEY DOWN VILLAGE

Chairman: Andrew Watkins **Manager:** Graham Standen, Alan Watson
Secretary: Stuart Frier, 30 Squires Close, Crawley Down, Surrey. RH10 4JQ (01342 714507 or 0181 667 2752 (B)).
Ground: The Haven Sportsfield, Hophurst Lane, Crawley Down. (01342 717140)
Directions: From B2028, follow signpost for village to War Memorial, turn left into Hophurst Lane, ground 100 yards on left. From A22, Felbridge, left into Crawley Down Road, ground 2 miles uphill on right.
Colours: All red

CROWBOROUGH ATHLETIC

President: Mr Peter Taylor **Chairman:** Barry J Sykes
Secretary: David Mackellow, 38 Eridge Drive, Crowborough,TN6 2TJ (01892 653122)
Manager: Tony Atkins. **Press Officer:** Peter Crisp (01892 655470).
Ground: Alderbrook Recreation Ground, Fermor Road, Crowborough (01892 661893).
Directions: Turn east off A26 at Crowborough. Cross traffic lights, through High Street, right into Croft Rd, continue into Whitehall Rd and Fermor Rd, Alderbrook is second right after mini-r'bout.
Seats: None **Cover:** 200 **Capacity:** 1,000 **Floodlights:** Yes. **Founded:** 1894
Colours: Blue & white/blue/blue **Change colours:** All red. **Nickname:** Crows.
Programme Editor: Bert Collick (01892 655565) **Sponsors:** Blackden Enterprises Ltd.
Previous League: Brighton **Midweek Matchday:** Tuesday
Clubhouse: Bar & tea bar matchdays **Record Gate:** 439 v Stamco, Sussex County Lge Div 2, 93.
Honours: Sussex Co. Lg Div 1 92-93 (Div 2 Cup 77-78, Div 3 R-up), Sussex Intermediate Cup 86-87.

EAST GRINSTEAD TOWN

Chairman: Paul O'Donnell **Vice-Chairman:** **President:** Colin Dixon
Secretary: How Roberts, 37 Parham Road, Ifield, Crawley, West Sussex RH11 0ET (01293 526805)
Manager: Kevin Moyse **Gen Manager:** **Physio:** Janette Brown
Ground: East Court, East Grinstead (01342 325885)
Directions: A264 Tunbridge Wells road (Moat Road) until mini-r'bout at bottom of Blackwell Hollow, turn immediately right by club sign then 1st left, ground 200yds down lane past rifle club on right.
Seats: None **Cover:** 400 **Capacity:** 3,000 **Floodlights:** Yes **Club Shop:** No
Programme: 36 pages, 50p **Editor/Press Officer:** Bruce Talbot (01293 543809).
Colours: Gold/black/black **Change colours:** Navy & L/blue
Sponsors: Rydon Group. **Nickname:** Wasps **Founded:** 1890
Midweek Matchday: Tuesday. **Reserves League:** Sussex County Reserve Div East
Record Attendance: 2,006 v Lancing, FA Amateur Cup 8/11/48
Previous Leagues: Mid-Sussex 1900-15 35-37/ Sussex County 20-32/ Southern Amateur League 32-35.
Players progressing to Football League: None
Clubhouse: Open 1.30-10.30 matchdays (6-11 midweek matches). Available for hire. Darts, pool, satellite TV. Hot food available Saturdays matcdays, hot snacks rolls etc available at midweek matches.
96-97 - Captain: Darren Hinton **Top Scorer:** Doug Cashman **P.o.Y.:** Derek Brown
Club record appearances: Guy Hill in 19 seasons - 1977-94.
Honours: Sussex RUR Charity Cup (R-up 74-75); Sussex Co. Lg Invitation Cup 51-52; Sussex Jnr Cup (jointly) 07-08; Sussex Youth Cup 86-87; Southern Amtr Lg Snr Div 3 31-32; Mid-Sussex Lg(6),Lg Cup(7); Brighton Lg(3),Lg Cup(3);

Crawley Down Village: Back Row (L-R); Alan Watson (Mgr), S Gregg, A Pearce, F Fleming, D Todman, M Baker, A Barker, G Standen, B Chambers, D Barker (Coach), M Green (Physio). Front Row; D Heath, S Rutter, B Willie, M Aldred, L Hanson, A Aylwood

EAST PRESTON

President: Greg Stanley **Chairman:** Brian Harwood **Vice-Chairman:** Don Pryke.
Secretary: Keith Freeman, 41 Ambersham Cres., East Preston, West Sussex BN16 1AJ (01903 771158).
Manager: Roger Kent **Asst Manager:** Steve May **Physio:** Larry Palmer
Ground: Roundstone Recreation Ground, East Preston, West Sussex (01903 776026).
Directions: Less than a mile from Angmering (BR) station. A259 from Worthing to Roundstone Hotel (6 miles), turn south over railway crossing, left past Centurion garage, right into Roundstone Drive.
Seats: None **Cover:** 40 **Capacity:** **Floodlights:** Yes **Reformed:** 1966
Colours: Black & white/black/black **Change:** Blue & black/white/white **Nickname:** None
Programme: Yes **Editor:** Andy Mott (01903 726097) **Sponsors:** Focus DIY
Previous Lges: Worthing / W Sussex **Reserve's League:** Sussex Co. Res. Div (Prem).
Clubhouse: Lic bar open Mon-Fri evenings, Sat noon-11pm, Sun noon-11pm. Snacks on matchdays.
Honours: Sussex Co. Lg Div 3 83-84, R-up 90-91, Div 3 Cup 87-88, R-up 89-90; West Sussex Lg 77-78 80-81 81-82 82-83, Malcolm Simmonds Cup 80-81 82-83, Div 2 Sth 81-82, Div 3 Sth 79-80, Div 4 Cup 86-87, Div 5 Sth 82-83, Chichester Cup 87-88; Boreham Tphy 77-78 90-91, R-up 93-94; Vernon Wentworth Cup 80-81 89-90; Worthing Lg 67-68; Benev. Tphy 66-67 68-69; Worthing Charity Cup 68-69.

EASTBOURNE UNITED

Chairman: I Botting **Vice-Chairman:** B Winter **President:** N Mansell.
Secretary: M Stevens, 21 Brookside Ave, Polegate, BN26 6DL (01323 484644)
Manager: M French **Asst Manager:** **Physio:** G Bishop
Ground: The Oval, Channel View Rd, Eastbourne, East Sussex (011323-726989)
Directions: To seafront and turn left. Turn left into Channel View Rd at Princess Park, ground 1st right.
Seats: 160 **Cover:** 160 **Capacity:** 3,000 **Floodlights:** Yes **Founded:** 1894
Programme: 36 pages **Editor:** R.Adcock. **Press Officer:** M Stevens
Colours: White/black/white **Change colours:** Blue/black/black **Nickname:** The 'Us'
Midweek Matchday: Tuesday **Reserve League:** Sussex County Res. Div. (East).
Previous Leagues: Sussex Co. 21-28 35-56/ Metropolitan 56-64/ Athenian 64-77/ Isthmian 77-92.
Players progressing to Football League: B Salvage, T Funnell, M French.
Clubhouse: Bar, lounge, dancefloor, stage, tea bar, board room.
96-97 Captain: Rob Knight **96-97 Top Scorer:** N Tattam **96-97 P.o.Y.:** G Sallows
Honours: Sussex Co. Lg 54-55; Sussex Snr Cup (5), R-up 89-90; Sussex I'mediate Cup 65-66 68-69; Sussex RUR Charity Cup 55-56; Metropolitan Lg Cup 60-61; Athenian Lg Div 2 66-67, Div 1 R-up 68-69.

Eastbourne United: *Photo - Roger Turner*

LANCING

Chairman: John Brown **President:** R G Steele **Match Sec:** Mike Peters
Secretary: J Chisnall, 15 Orchard Way, Lancing, West Sussex BN15 9ED (01903 763048).
Manager: Frank Phythian **Physio:** Peter Towell.
Ground: Culver Road, Lancing, West Sussex (01903 764398).
Directions: From A27 turn south at Lancing Manor r'about into Grinstead Lane, 3rd turning on right North Farm Rd. Turn left then immed. right into Culver Rd. From railway station take 3rd turning on left heading north.
Seats: 350 **Cover:** 350 **Capacity:** 2,400 **Floodlights:** Yes **Founded:** 1941
Programme: Yes **Editor:** John Rea (01903 521543) **Press Officer:** John Rea **Sponsors:** Gold Arts
Colours: Yellow/blue/yellow **Change colours:** All red **Nickname:** Yellows
Midweek Matches: Wednesday **Previous League:** Brighton Hove & Dist.
Record Attendance: 2,591 v Tooting, FA Amtr Cup 22/11/47. At Culver Road: 2,340 v Worthing 25/10/52.
Clubhouse: Open matchdays & training nights. Sep tea bar.
96-97 Captain: Steve Pickles **96-97 Top Scorer:** Chris Georgiou 16 **96-97 P.o.Y.:** Glenn Souter
Honours: Sussex Co. Lg R-up 49-50 64-65, Div 2 57-58 69-70, R-up 82-83, Div 2 Cup 81-82 92-93; Sussex RUR Charity Cup 65-66; Brighton Lg 46-47 47-48; Sussex Interm Cup 46-47; Brighton Charity Cup 83-84 84-85 86-87.

MIDHURST & EASEBOURNE

Chairman: Pat Perry **President:** Andy Robertson.
Secretary: Ted Dummer, 14 Nine Acres, June Lane, Midhurst, West Sussex GU29 9EP (01730 813887).
Manager: Ken Boxall **Assistant Manager:** Brian Turner **Press Officer:** Rex Lane (01730 812839).
Ground: Rotherfield, Dodsley Lane, Easebourne, Midhurst, West Sussex (01730 816557). **Directions:** Ground one mile out of Midhurst on London Road (A286) opposite BP Garage. Ample car parking. Buses pass ground every hour.
Seats: 60 **Cover:** 200 **Capacity:** 800 **Floodlights:** No **Founded:** 1946
Colours: All royal blue **Change colours:** Red/black/black **Nickname:** None
Programme: 8 pages, free **Editor:** Secretary **Club Shop:** No.
Reserves' Lge: Sussex Co. Res. sect. **Record Gate:** 300 in local Gingell Cup, 1989.
Previous Leagues: West Sussex 46-79/ Southern Co's Combination 79-81.
Players progressing to Football League: Colin Gibson (Aston Villa, Man Utd, Leicester).
Clubhouse: Clubhouse with canteen and bar. Open matchdays & training nights only.
Honours: Sussex Co. Lg Div 2 Cup 88-89, Div 3 94-95, Southern Co's Comb. Div 2 80-81 (Chal. Cup 80-81), W Sussex Lg 67-68 76-77 79-80 (Div 1 55-56 62-63 64-65, Malcolm Simmonds Cup 59-60 73-74 77-78 79-80, Bareham Tphy 70-71), Sussex I'mediate Cup(5) 54-57 62-63 77-78.

NEWHAVEN

Chairman: Mick Godden **Manager:** Martin Langley
Secretary: Frank D Dixon, 39 Southdown Avenue, Peacehaven, East Sussex BN10 8RX (01273 585514).
Ground: Fort Road, Newhaven, East Sussex (01273 513940).
Directions: A275 from Lewes, or A259 coast rd, to Newhaven 1-way system. 1 mile from Newhaven Town (BR).
Seats: 50 **Cover:** Yes **Capacity:** 4,000 **Floodlights:** Yes **Founded:** 1887
Colours: Red & amber/red/red. **Change colours:** Yellow/green **Nickname:** Dockers
Programme: Yes **Editor:** S.Cox. **Admission:** £1.50
Previous Leagues: None (founder members of SCFL) **Record Gate:** 3,000
Midweek Matchday: Tuesday **Clubhouse:** Being redeveloped **Sponsors:** Long Dis Cabs.
Honours: Sussex County Lg 53-54 (Div 2 71-72 90-91, Invitation Cup 48-49, Lg Cup R-up 92-93, Reserve Section East R-up 92-93), Sussex Snr Cup R-up 53-54, Sussex RUR Charity Cup 93-94.

OAKWOOD

Chairman: Alf Bridges
Secretary: Gerry Martin, Singlegate, Tinsley Green, Crawley RH10 3NS (01293 882400).
Manager: Bryn Marshall **Physio:** Ms S Widy **Press Officer:** Simon Milham
Ground: Tinsley Lane, Three Bridges, Crawley, West Sussex (01293 515742).
Directions: From A23 to Gatwick, take 1st set of lights into Manor Royal, pass next lights, over r'bout to warehouse marked Canon, turn right signposted Oakwood. Last clubhouse down lane. Two miles north of Three Bridges (BR).
Seats: 20 **Cover:** Yes **Capacity:** 3,000 **Floodlights:** Yes **Founded:** 1966
Colours: Red & black/black/black **Change colours:** Blue/black/black **Nickname:** Oaks
Programme: 24 pages **Editor:** Simon Milham (01293 615043) **Club Shop:** Yes
Previous Lgs: Crawley & Dist., Southern Co's Comb. **Previous Ground:** Park pitches.
Record Gate: 367 **Midweek Matchday:** Tuesday
Sponsors: Linden Plc. **Reserve's League:** Sussex County Reserve section.
Clubhouse: Pool tables, multidart boards, large bar area. Board room & tea bar.
Record appearances: Peter Brackpool
Honours: Sussex Snr Cup R-up 92-93, Sussex Co. Lg Div 2 R-up 89-90 (Div 2 Cup 89-90, Div 3 84-85), Southern Comb. Cup 83-84.

SHINEWATER ASSOCIATION

Chairman: John Pinyoun **Manager:** Alan Walsh
Secretary: Brian Dowling, 79 Harebeating Drive, Hailsham BN27 1JE (01323 442488)
Ground: Shinewater Lane (01323 765880)
Directions: A27, take B2104 to Eastbourne. At Stone Cross go under railway bridge, 1st right into Larkspur Drive, 1st left into Milfoil Drive, 3rd left into Shinewater Lane
Colours: Navy & sky/navy/navy

SIDLESHAM

Chairman: Roy Parker **Manager:** Petyer Cleverley
Secretary: Pete Turner, 64 Hawthorn Road, Bognor Regis, West Sussex PO21 2DD (01243 822860)
Ground: Sidlesham Recreation Ground, (01243 641538)
Directions: Signposted Hunston/Selsey B2145 from roundabout travel towards Selsey for 4 miles, ground on right between houses
Colours: Green & yellow/green/green

SIDLEY UNITED

President: Tibby Adams **Chairman:** Bryn Sayers **Manager:** Dickie Day
Secretary: Rob Green, 4 Robin Hill, Little Common, Bexhill-on-Sea, TN39 4QS (01424 846220)
Ground: Gullivers Sports Ground, Glovers Lane, Sidley, Bexhill-on-Sea (01424 217078).
Directions: From Brighton on A259 to Bexhill bypass traffic lights, left into London Road, continue into Sidley, right into Glovers Lane and 1st left into North Road. One mile from Bexhill (BR).
Seats: None **Cover:** 150 **Capacity:** 1,500 **Floodlights:** No **Founded:** 1906
Colours: Navy & sky/navy/navy & sky **Change colours:** All red **Nickname:** Blues
Programme: Yes **Editor:** Peter Snow **Sponsors:** J Burke
Previous Leagues: East Sussex/ Hastings & District
Record Attendance: 1,300 in 1959 **Midweek Matchday:** Tues/ Weds
Clubhouse: Large bar area & function room. Tea bar.
Honours: Suss. Co. Lg Div 2 58-59 64-65 (Div 2 Invit. Cup 57-58), Suss. I'mediate Cup 47-48, Suss. Jnr Cup 24-25.

SOUTHWICK

Chairman: Roy Pollard **Vice-Chairman:** Dave Cook **President:** Dr D W Gordon.
Secretary: Peter Hallett, 10 Hawkins Close, Shoreham-by-Sea, West Sussex BN43 6TL (01273 700474)
Manager: John Dedman **Asst Manager:** Dennis Nicholl **Coach:** Paul Croft
Ground: Old Barn Way, off Manor Hall Way, Southwick, Brighton BN43 4NT (01273 701010).
Directions: Five minutes walk from either Fishergate or Southwick BR stations. By A27 from Brighton take 1st left after 'Southwick' sign to Leisure Centre. Ground adjacent.
Seats: 220 **Cover:** 1,220 **Capacity:** 3,500 **Floodlights:** Yes
Programme: Yes **Editor/Press Officer:** Paul Symes (01273 594142).
Colours: Red & black stripes/black/red **Change Colours:** White/black/white
Sponsors: Guildcare Nursing Homes **Nickname:** Wickers **Founded:** 1882
Midweek matchday: Tuesday **Record Attendance:** 3,200 v Showbiz side 1971
Reserve League: Sussex Co. Res Div **Best FA Cup season:** 1st Rd Prop 74-75 (lost 0-5 Bournemouth)
Best FA Amtr Cup season: 3rd 28-29 **Best FA Vase season:** 3rd Rd 79-80 85-86
Previous Leagues: West Sussex 1896-1920/ Sussex County 20-52 54-84/ Metropolitan 52-54/ Combined
Players progressing to Football League: Charles & William Buttenshaw (Luton 1948).
Clubhouse: Weekdays noon-3 & 6-11pm, all day Saturday, normal hrs Sunday. Members bar & boardroom with bar. Snacks on matchdays from tea bar.
96-97 Captain: Steve Watts **96-97 P.o.Y.:** Steve Watts **96-97 Top Scorer:** Tony Ropke
Honours: Isthmian Lg Div 2 Sth 85-86, Sus. Co. Lg 25-26 27-28 29-30 47-48 68-69 74-75 (R-up(9) 23-24 28-29 36-37 39-40 70-71 76-77 78-80 82-83, Lg Cup 77-78, Div 1 Invit. Cup 65-66, Div 2 R-up 65-66), Combined Co's Lg R-up 84-85, Sus. Snr Cup 1896-97 1910-11 12-13 24-25 27-28 29-30 30-31 36-37 47-48 67-68, Sus. RUR Charity Cup(10) 1896-97 08-09 10-11 24-26 27-30 37-38 76-77, W. Sus. Lg 1896-97 97-98 1908-09 10-11, Sus. Jnr Cup 1891-92.

THREE BRIDGES

President: Jim Steele **Chairman:** Alan Bell
Secretary: Martin Clarke, 18 Mannings Close, Pound Hill, Crawley RH10 3TX (01293 883726), (0585 662940 Mob).
Manager: Barry Hunt **Match Sec:** Secretary **Press Officer:** Alf Blackler
Ground: Jubilee Field, Three Bridges, Crawley, West Sussex (01293 442000)
Directions: From West Three Bridges station, turn second right into Three Bridges Road and first left 75 yds down, opposite the Plough Inn.
Seats: None **Cover:** 400 **Capacity:** 3,500 **Floodlights:** Yes **Founded:** 1901
Colours: Amber & black/black/black **Change colours:** Blue & white/blue/white **Nickname:** Bridges
Programme: Yes **Editor:** Andy West (01293 883163) **Sponsors:** Canon
Previous Lgs: Mid Sussex/ Redhill & District **Midweek Matchday:** Tuesday
Clubhouse: Bar, dance floor, pool, darts **Record Gate:** 2,000 v Horsham, 1948
Honours: Sussex Co. Lg R-up 85-86 87-88 88-89 (Div 2 54-55, Invitation Cup 70-71, Div 2 Invitation Cup 62-63), Sussex RUR Charity Cup 82-83.

WITHDEAN

Chairman: Phil Bond **President:** Graham Spicer **Manager:** Paul Norland
Secretary: Simon Pattenden, 37 Stanmer Road, Brighton. BN1 7JL. (H 01273 507128 B 01273 541102)
Ground: Withdean Stadium, off Valley Drive, Brighton (01273 542100)
Directions: Off main London - Brighton road.
Seats: 100. **Cover:** 1,000. **Capacity:** 10,000 **Floodlights:** No **Founded:** 1984.
Colours: Green & black/black/black **Change Colours:** All white **Club Shop:** No.
Programme Editor: Dave Bull **Previous Leagues:** Brighton Hove & District
Sponsors: Computer & Network Consultants Ltd. **Clubhouse:** Pub on ground
Honours: Sussex Co. Lg Div 3 92-93 (Div 3 Cup 91-92).

WORTHING UNITED

President: Ken Higson **Chairman:** Len Killpatrick
Secretary: Malcolm Gamlen, 1 Westbourne Ave., Worthing, West Sussex BN14 8DE (01903 263655).
Manager: Tony Elliot **Press Officer:** Brian Woolmer.
Ground: The Robert Albon Memorial Grd, Lyons Way, Worthing (01903 234466)
Directions: From west past Hill Barn roundabout to 2nd set of lights, turn left into Lyons Way. From east 1st set of lights at end of Sompting bypass turn right into Lyons Way
Seats: 100 **Cover:** 500 **Capacity:** 1,000 **Floodlights:** No **Founded:** 1988
Colours: Sky & white/navy/white **Change colours:** All white **Nickname:** None
Programme: Yes **Editor:** N Woolmer (0903 772698) **Sponsors:** Tinsley Robor.
Record Gate: 180 v Northwood, FA Vase 3rd Rd 91-92.
Clubhouse: Bar (capacity 80), refreshment facilities (tea bar).
Honours: As Wigmore Athletic prior to 1988. Sussex Co. Lg Challenge Cup 74-75 (Invitation Cup 59-60, Div 2 52-53, Div 2 Invitation Cup 59-60, Div 3 89-90, Reserve Section West 92-93, 5-aside comp. R-up 1993), Sussex Jnr Cup 49-50.

DIVISION THREE CLUBS 1997-98

ANSTY RANGERS

Secretary: Tina Darbyshire, 6 Faulkners Way, Burgess Hill. RH15 8SB. (01444 233030)
Ground: Deaks Lane, Ansty (01444 454010)
Directions: Take A272 for Ansty/Haywards Heath, to Ansty prior to mini r/about turn left into Deaks Lane.
Manager: **Colours:** Red & black/black/black

BOSHAM

Secretary: Richard Doncaster, 61 Manor Way, Southborne, Emsworth, Hampshire. (01243 375184).
Ground: The Receation Ground, Walton Lane, Bosham, W. Sussex PO18 8QF (01243 574011).
Directions: West from Chichester on A259. Turn south at roundabout by White Swan & Swan Garage (Delling Lane), Continue to T junction by Berkley Arms, turn left into Walton Lane. Ground 50 yards left.
Manager: Steve Watson **Colours:** Red/white/red

BUXTED

Secretary: Peter J Durrant, 'Haven', Station Road, Isfield. TN22 5XB. (01825 750449)
Ground: Buxted Recreation Ground, Buxted. (01825 763593)
Directions: A272 to Buxted, 1st right, Framfield Rd., opposite Buxted Inn, ground 500 yds. on right.
Manager: Peter Coleman **Colours:** Red & Black/black/red & black.

FOREST

Secretary: Gill Hultquist, 117 Ifield Drive, Ifield. RH11 0EA. (01293 522846)
Ground: Roffey Sports & Social Club, Spooners Rd., Roffey. (01403 210221)
Directions: Spooners Rd. is off the main Crawley road, 100 yds from the 'Star' PH, towards Crawley.
Manager: Russell Pentecost. **Colours:** Claret/blue/white.

FRANKLANDS VILLAGE

Secretary: Mrs Linsey Worsfold, 151a Franklands Village, Haywards Heath. RH16 3RF. (01444 416475)
Ground: Hardy Memorial Playing Field, Franklands Village. (01444 440138)
Directions: A272 (Haywards H. to Uckfield). Left at Princess Royal Hosp. r'about. 2nd left & ground at rear of social club.
Manager: Chris Snelling **Colours:** All Royal blue

HURSTPIERPOINT

Secretary: Daniel Cleaveley, 10 St Christophers Road, Hurstpierpoint BN6 9UX (01273 835665)
Ground: Fairfield Recreation Ground, Cuckfield Road. ((01273 834783)
Directions: Hurstpierpoint crossroads, north into Cuckfield Rd, B2117 for 1km. Ground between houses 158 & 160.
Manager: Steve Marchant. **Colours:** Blue & black/black/blue.

IFIELD

Secretary: Robert Anderson, 1 Old Orchards, Church Rd, Worth, Crawley. RH10 7QA. (01293 886215).
Ground: Ifield Sports Club, Ifield Green, Rusper Road. (01293 536569). **Directions:** From A23 Crawley by-pass going north, left at r'about signed Charlwood. Third left into Ifield Green, first right past Royal Oak (PH) into Rusper Rd.
Manager: Alan Wormull **Colours:** Red/black/red.

LINGFIELD

Secretary: Ian Tomsett, 8 Orchard Cottage, St Piers Lane, Lingfield, Surrey. RH7 6PN. (01342 835089)
Ground: Godstone Road, Lingfield, Surrey. (01342 834269).
Directions: A22, 4 miles north of E Grinstead, to Mormon Temple r'about, take exit Lingfield (B2028) Newchapel Rd. for 1 1/2 miles. Left at T junction into Godstone Rd. (B2029) & ground 1/2 mile on left.
Manager: Ali Rennie **Colours:** Red & yellow/black/yellow

OVING SOCIAL CLUB

Secretary: Peter Hall, St Bruno, Prinsted Lane, Emsworth, Hants PO10 8HR (01243 372652)
Ground: Village Playing Fields, Highfield Lane, Oving, Nr Chichester
Directions: Into Oving past the Gribble Inn, turn left into housing estate. Ground sign posted.
Manager: Pail Gilbert **Colours:** Black & white/white/white

ROYAL & SUN ALLIANCE

Secretary: Steve Jenkins, 33 Owlcastle Close, Horsham RH12 5YA (01403 256697)
Ground: Sunallon Sports Club, North Heath Lane, Horsham (01403 253814). **Directions:** Heading into Horsham on Warnham road, turn left at 1st lights, over mini-r/about to North Heath Lane, grd on left
Manager: Dix Roberts **Colours:** Yellow/blue/blue

ST. FRANCIS HOSPITAL

Secretary: Colin Mansbridge, 9 Pinehurst, Burgess Hill. RH15 0DG. (01444 244197)
Ground: St. Francis Hospital, Colwell Lane, Haywards Heath. (01444 441881). **Directions:** Enter through main entrance of Princess Royal Hospital on Lewes road, A272 Haywards Heath. Follow signs to Sports Complex.
Manager: Mark Leaney **Colours:** Green & white/white/green.

STEYNING TOWN

Secretary: Gina Barnes, 36 Shooting Fields, Steyning BN44 3RQ (01903 815387)
Ground: The Shooting Field, Steyning (01903 812228). **Directions:** Entering Steyning from west, take 1st left into High St, follow into Shooting Field estate, ground is 4th rurn left.
Manager: Alf Ford **Colours:** Red /white/red

STORRINGTON

Secretary: Keith Dalmon, 4 End Cottages, Storrington Rd., Amberley. BN18 9LX. (01798 831887)
Ground: Recreation Ground, Storrington. (01903 745860).
Directions: Turn west on A283 (off A24). Ground opposite pond to west of village centre.
Manager: Malcolm MacMichael **Colours:** All blue.

THOMSON ATHLETIC

Secretary: Graham Fiveash, 15 Chanctonbury Way, Southgate, Crawley RH11 8TE (01293 419065)
Ground: Tinsley Lane, Crawley. (01293 442000). **Directions:** From south on 123, right at traffic lights (Manor Rd.), past traffic lights, r'about, then 1st right into Tinsley Lane. 1st entrance.
Manager: Ted Arnold **Colours:** Black & white/black/black.

UCKFIELD TOWN

Secretary: Craig Rome, Flat 3, 26 Newtown, Uckfield. TN22 5DD. (01825 764171)
Ground: Victoria Pleasure Grounds, Uckfield. (01825 769400). **Directions:** Take Eastbourne road (old A22) south of Uckfield town centre. Entrance to ground 1/2 mile on right (just after Police station).
Manager: George Nimmo **Colours:** Red/black/black.

WESTFIELD

Secretary: Mrs Jenny Drinkwater, 28 Churchfields, Westfield TN35 4SN (01424 754032)
Ground: Parish Field. Westfield (01424 751011). **Directions:** Off A21 onto A28 Ashford Road.
Manager: Steve Booth **Colours:** Yellow & green/black/black

uhlsport
UNITED COUNTIES LEAGUE

FEEDER TO: BEAZER HOMES LEAGUE

FOUNDED 1895

Chairman: Geoffery Paul

Hon. Secretary: R J Gamble, 8 Bostock Avenue, Northampton (01604 494121 (B))

Press Secretary: J Biggs (01780 63048, 01123 702917)

Another memorable season in the United Counties League, the first of the new Uhlsport sponsorship, ended with the domestic honours shared by two of the competition's longest serving members, plus relative newcomers Yaxley.

The last two season's Premier Division titles had been won on goal difference, but while this term's eventual champions Stamford had five points to spare over runners-up Spalding, the race this term proved the most open ever with as many as a dozen clubs in the hunt as late as February.

Three quarters of the way through the campaign there was a strong challenge from Lincolnshire, the eventual top two being joined in the leading group by Boston, 1996 runners-up Stotfold were still in with a shout despite being forced to rebuild their squad in the summer, while the Northants challenge featured surprise package Long Buckby, and favourites Desborough.

With nine games to go Desborough's challenge came off the rail in spectacular fashion, they collected just a single point on the run in, sliding down the table to ninth. The other contenders all kept plugging away, but it was the experienced Stamford club which displayed the most consistent form. They won their last eight matches, the seventh, a 1-0 success at St Neots, enough to collect their first title in 15 years and their seventh in all. The runners-up battle went to the final Saturday, Spalding clinching second with a 4-2 win at Northampton Spencer. Boston, who went into their final match with a chance of second slot, had to settle for fifth, their home defeat by Long Buckby in the final match saw Buckby go past them while the Station Road club themselves had to settle for fourth due to Stotfold's success at St Neots.

Stamford's championship was a triumph for their controversial manager Steve Evans, who has transformed the Daniels from also rans to champions in two and a half years. The signings of David Speedie, Dave Bennett and Micky Gynn kept Stamford in the headlines although the trio were to enjoy only brief spells at Wothorpe Road, and were long gone by the time Stamford\'s form peaked to give them the edge in the title race.

At the bottom of the table Newport Pagnell kicked off with two wins and ten goals in their first two matches but won just once thereafter, a final points tally of 15 left them 12 adrift of Holbeach whose bold policy of relying on local players brought a handful of highspots but little consistency. Holbeach finished four points behind Bourne, another side heavily reliant on local players.

In Division One the honours went to Yaxley, after a mid table finish in their first season, the Cuckoos kicked off the campaign with a new management team of ex-Hotpoint chief Dave Willis and assistant Dave Eldred, plus a virtually new playing squad. The changes paid off as Yaxley stormed to the title, although this too proved an exciting championship contest. If Yaxley had lost their last match at Higham they could still have missed out on promotion, instead they came from behind to beat the Lankies, themselves contenders after an impressive unbeaten run under the new management of one time Northampton Town star Andy Mann. Whitworths kept faith with their Junior Cup winning team from the previous season, the reward their best ever league placing, going into the last Saturday of the season the Flourmen were second but would slip to third if Bugbrooke slipped up at home to next to bottom Irchester. The Badgers had been promotion favourites for most of the season but had dropped points against several teams at the wrong end of the table. It was a familiar story as Bugbrooke could only manage a 0-0 draw, leaving them third, that gave Holbeach a reprieve from relegation as Whitworths lacked the facilities to improve their status, but there was to be no reprieve for Bugbrooke manager Nick Verity who was axed shortly after the end of the season.

The Knockout Cup gave Desborough some consolation for their league slump. Ar Tarn were in impressive form en route to the final, their victims including Stamford and Stotfold, final opponents Northampton Spencer's most notable victims being S&L and St Neots, the Millers too had produced a dismal end to the league season, leaving the final wide open. The first leg at the Waterworks Field saw Lee O'Connor's solo opener for Spencer cancelled out by Gary Kennedy's late leveller from the penalty spot. At Kingsthorpe Mill two goals late in the first half left Desborough in control, Paul Murphy, a past winner in the competition with Raunds and Rothwell, and Jamie Cunningham with an overhead effort, the marksmen. Spencer stepped up a gear after the break and Ian Mann's effort from distance gave them renewed hope, but Desborough held on for a 3-2 aggregate victory.

On other cup fronts there were two contenders for the cup team of the year accolade. Potton kicked off the season by winning the Jess Pigott Memorial Trophy, before contesting no fewer than five finals at the end of the season. Arlesey beat them in both the Beds Senior and Hinchingbrooke finals, but the Royals carried off the Hunts Premier and North Beds Charity Cups before winding up their season with a 2-0 win at league champions Stamford in the final of the East Anglian Cup, the first ever outright success in the competition by one of our clubs. Spalding didn't win any silverware but they did collect some famous scalps in cup football. En route to the last 16 of the FA Carlsberg Vase the Tulips claimed the scalps of Wealdstone, Wembley, Bridgnorth and Hucknall, all away from home, before going out at Taunton. They also ousted the reigning Vase holders Brigg from the Lincs Senior Cup 'A' and were 3-2 winners at Dr Martens League Rothwell in the FA cup.

Other cup achievements worthy of note, Cogenhoe and Stamford reached the FA Carlsberg Vase 4th Round, the Daniels were within two minutes of beating eventual finalists North Ferriby, before losing in a replay. Premier newcomers Ford Sports saw off higher grade pair Raunds and Corby to reach the Northants Hillier Senior Cup final at the first attempt, the Motormen lost 3-1 to Kettering after extra time. Huntingdon's return to Senior football saw them reach the Hunts Senior Cup final, losing to Ortonians, but the league notched up its 15th consecutive success in the Northants Junior Cup, Vanaid's 2-1 triumph against Oundle at Nene Park, their second in four years. Ford Sports' second string went one better than the seniors winning the Northants Lower Junior Cup.

Saddest news of the season was the demise of Ramsey before the turn of the year. For many years among the leading lights in Division One, the lack of suitable facilities at Cricketfield Lane prevented upward progression and the writing had been on the wall for the Cambridgeshire club for a year or so.

The new season will see the Premier Division up in number to 21 clubs, Buckingham Town returning to the ranks after eleven years at the higher level. A new face in the top flight will be Yaxley who stop up after their championship success in Division One, they exchange places with Newport Pagnell who must regroup in Division One after five seasons in the Premier.

Jeremy Biggs, Press Liaison Officer

FINAL LEAGUE TABLES 1996-97

PREMIER DIVISION

		HOME								AWAY								TOTAL							
		P	*W*	*D*	*L*	*F*	*A*	*Pts*	*GD*	*P*	*W*	*D*	*L*	*F*	*A*	*Pts*	*GD*	*P*	*W*	*D*	*L*	*F*	*A*	*Pts*	*GD*
1	Stamford	19	15	1	3	41	23	46	18	19	11	2	6	38	28	35	10	38	26	3	9	79	51	81	28
2	Spalding	19	12	3	4	42	16	39	16	19	11	4	4	36	21	37	15	38	23	7	8	78	37	76	41
3	Stotfold	19	12	4	3	50	20	40	30	19	10	3	6	40	28	33	12	38	22	7	9	90	48	73	42
4	Long Buckby	19	12	5	2	36	16	41	20	19	9	5	5	27	23	32	4	38	21	10	7	63	39	73	24
5	Boston	19	13	2	4	49	19	41	30	19	8	7	4	39	20	31	19	38	21	9	8	88	39	72	49
6	S & L	19	12	4	3	56	27	40	29	19	9	4	6	28	37	31	-9	38	21	8	9	84	64	71	20
7	Cogenhoe	19	9	5	5	46	29	32	17	19	11	1	7	44	33	34	11	38	20	6	12	90	62	66	32
8	Potton	19	8	6	5	29	24	30	5	19	10	2	7	28	25	32	3	38	18	8	12	57	49	62	8
9	Desborough	19	10	3	6	29	23	33	6	19	7	6	6	34	26	27	8	38	17	9	12	63	49	60	14
10	St Neots	19	11	5	3	51	24	38	27	19	5	6	8	30	34	21	-4	38	16	11	11	81	58	59	23
11	M Blackstone	19	10	2	7	37	28	32	9	19	6	3	10	31	37	21	-6	38	16	5	17	68	65	53	3
12	Ford Sports	19	6	3	10	32	34	21	-2	19	8	4	7	32	30	28	2	38	14	7	17	64	64	49	0
13	N Spencer	19	6	5	8	39	38	23	1	19	7	3	9	30	32	24	-2	38	13	8	17	69	70	47	-1
14	Eynesbury	19	6	6	7	31	28	24	3	19	6	5	8	21	28	23	-7	38	12	11	15	52	56	47	-4
15	Wellingborough	19	6	3	10	24	26	21	-2	19	4	3	12	28	46	15	-18	38	10	6	22	52	75	36	-20
16	Wootton	19	6	5	8	27	27	23	0	19	3	3	13	13	33	12	-20	38	9	8	21	40	60	35	-20
17	Kempston	19	5	3	11	18	38	18	-20	19	4	3	12	23	51	15	-28	38	9	6	23	41	89	33	-48
18	Bourne	19	3	3	13	25	53	12	-28	19	5	4	10	24	47	19	-23	38	8	7	23	49	100	31	-51
19	Holbeach	19	4	2	13	16	48	14	-32	19	3	4	12	27	53	13	-26	38	7	6	25	43	101	27	-58
20	N Pagnell	19	2	4	13	22	47	10	-25	19	1	2	16	15	68	5	-53	38	3	6	29	37	115	15	-78

DIVISION ONE

		HOME								AWAY								TOTAL							
		P	*W*	*D*	*L*	*F*	*A*	*Pts*	*GD*	*P*	*W*	*D*	*L*	*F*	*A*	*Pts*	*GD*	*P*	*W*	*D*	*L*	*F*	*A*	*Pts*	*GD*
1	Yaxley	17	11	2	4	40	15	35	25	17	12	3	2	41	10	39	31	34	23	5	6	81	25	74	56
2	Whitworths	17	10	7	0	37	13	37	24	17	9	5	3	35	15	32	20	34	19	12	3	72	28	69	44
3	Bugbrooke	17	10	5	2	32	16	35	16	17	10	3	4	28	14	33	14	34	20	8	6	60	30	68	30
4	Higham	17	12	4	1	36	16	40	20	17	6	6	5	23	26	24	-3	34	18	10	6	59	42	64	17
5	Huntingdon	17	10	2	5	49	28	32	21	17	9	0	8	38	29	27	9	34	19	2	13	87	57	59	30
6	Rothwell Cor	17	9	4	4	30	16	31	14	17	7	3	7	31	24	24	7	34	16	7	11	61	40	55	21
7	St Ives	17	10	2	5	28	14	32	14	17	6	5	6	24	20	23	4	34	16	7	11	52	34	55	18
8	Cottingham	17	9	1	7	30	30	28	0	17	8	2	7	26	29	26	-3	34	17	3	14	56	59	-3	
9	Thrapston	17	10	3	4	29	17	33	12	17	4	4	9	22	34	16	-12	34	14	7	13	51	51	49	0
10	N Vanaid	17	7	2	8	28	24	23	4	17	6	4	7	28	31	22	-3	34	13	6	15	56	55	45	1
11	Olney	17	8	3	6	21	23	27	-2	17	5	3	9	21	24	18	-3	34	13	6	15	42	47	45	-5
12	Harrowby	17	6	4	7	35	34	22	1	17	6	2	9	27	34	20	-7	34	12	6	16	62	68	42	-6
13	Daventry	17	5	3	9	21	40	18	-19	17	5	3	9	25	38	18	-13	34	10	6	18	46	78	36	-32
14	ON Chenecks	17	7	3	7	26	23	24	3	17	3	2	12	20	31	11	-11	34	10	5	19	46	54	35	-8
15	Burton PW	17	4	4	9	22	29	16	-7	17	5	3	9	28	35	18	-7	34	9	7	18	50	64	34	-14
16	Sharnbrook	17	5	1	11	17	46	16	-29	17	5	3	9	17	37	18	-20	34	10	4	20	34	83	34	-49
17	Irchester	17	4	4	9	16	30	16	-14	17	3	3	11	18	40	12	-22	34	7	7	20	34	70	28	-36
18	Blisworth	17	1	1	15	16	50	4	-34	17	4	1	12	12	42	13	-30	34	5	2	27	28	92	17	-64

PREMIER DIVISION RESULTS CHART 1996-97

		1	2	3	4	5	6	7	8	9	10	11	12	13	14	15	16	17	18	19	20
1	Boston	X	5-0	2-0	1-1	4-0	0-1	4-0	0-1	2-4	5-4	4-0	4-1	2-0	1-0	2-2	4-1	2-3	2-1	3-0	2-0
2	Bourne	1-1	X	0-7	2-4	1-5	1-2	2-2	2-3	0-1	0-3	6-0	1-1	2-3	3-2	0-6	1-2	1-2	0-4	0-4	2-1
3	Cogenhoe	2-2	1-1	X	2-0	5-0	1-3	2-2	6-1	1-2	3-1	2-2	3-1	2-3	4-3	1-2	3-2	1-3	1-1	3-0	3-0
4	Desborough	1-1	0-1	3-1	X	0-3	2-1	3-1	2-0	1-0	3-1	4-1	1-5	1-1	2-0	0-1	2-1	0-1	2-3	0-0	2-1
5	Eynesbury	0-1	0-1	1-2	0-0	X	1-1	2-2	1-2	1-2	0-3	6-1	4-2	2-1	5-2	0-0	0-0	1-3	3-2	3-2	1-1
6	Ford Sports	1-3	0-2	2-4	0-2	1-1	X	4-2	4-0	3-0	2-1	1-3	0-2	2-3	1-2	1-1	1-0	3-3	1-4	5-0	0-1
7	Holbeach	0-6	1-2	0-3	0-7	0-1	2-4	X	2-1	0-0	0-1	2-2	0-3	2-1	1-3	0-2	1-2	2-0	1-4	0-5	2-1
8	Kempston	0-4	0-3	0-3	0-2	2-0	1-0	1-3	X	0-3	1-1	3-1	0-4	1-1	0-3	1-2	0-2	1-1	3-1	1-2	3-2
9	Long Buckby	0-3	2-2	3-1	1-0	0-0	0-0	2-1	5-2	X	2-0	5-0	1-1	2-3	2-0	1-0	3-0	1-1	3-2	1-0	2-0
10	M Blackstone	0-3	5-1	2-6	1-5	1-1	2-0	5-0	4-1	1-0	X	3-0	3-2	1-2	1-1	1-0	1-2	4-0	0-2	2-1	0-1
11	Newport Pagnell	1-4	1-1	0-0	2-2	1-2	1-2	1-3	7-2	1-3	2-4	X	0-1	0-4	1-1	0-3	1-8	1-2	1-3	0-2	1-0
12	N Spencer	2-2	3-2	2-4	2-2	0-2	4-2	4-1	2-2	1-2	1-0	3-0	X	0-1	4-4	2-4	2-4	1-2	1-3	4-0	1-1
13	Potton	1-0	3-0	3-1	1-1	1-1	0-4	2-0	3-1	0-0	2-1	2-0	1-2	X	1-1	2-4	2-3	2-2	1-2	2-1	0-0
14	St Neots	1-1	7-2	3-1	4-1	1-0	4-1	3-2	2-2	2-2	1-1	5-1	2-2	3-0	X	1-2	0-1	5-2	2-3	4-0	1-0
15	Spalding	1-0	5-0	1-2	0-0	0-1	0-3	3-1	1-0	2-1	4-1	4-1	2-0	2-0	1-2	X	1-1	5-0	0-0	5-1	5-2
16	Stamford	2-1	4-3	1-2	2-1	3-1	2-1	0-1	3-2	1-1	4-2	4-2	3-0	1-0	1-0	3-2	X	0-1	2-0	4-3	1-0
17	S & L	3-3	3-1	3-4	3-5	2-0	0-0	5-0	1-0	4-1	3-1	7-0	3-0	2-0	3-2	0-0	1-3	X	4-4	5-3	4-0
18	Stotfold	3-1	2-0	4-1	4-0	1-1	3-3	4-2	5-1	1-2	1-2	3-0	2-1	0-1	0-0	5-2	3-0	4-0	X	3-3	2-0
19	Wellingborough	0-2	3-0	3-1	0-1	3-2	4-1	3-3	1-2	0-1	1-1	1-0	0-1	0-2	1-1	0-1	1-4	2-0	0-1	X	1-2
20	Wootton	1-1	2-2	0-1	1-0	2-0	2-3	3-1	0-0	2-2	2-3	3-1	2-1	0-2	2-3	1-2	1-2	1-2	1-0	1-1	X

MANAGER OF THE MONTH AWARDS 1996-97

	PREMIER DIVISION	DIVISION ONE
Aug/Sep	Steve Blades (Mirrlees Blackstone)	Dave Willis (Yaxley)
Oct	Steve Evans (Stamford)	Dai Hunt (Sharnbrook)
Nov	Alan Day (Spalding United)	Andy Rossi (Huntingdon United)
Dec	Dave Conlon (Cogenhoe United)	Nick Verity (Bugbrooke St Michaels)
Jan/Feb	Ian Allinson (Stotfold)	Mark Herring (Wellingborough Whitworths)
Mar	Kevin Flear/Richard Green (Ford Sports Daventry)	Rob Dunion (Cottingham)
Apr/May	Steve Evans (Stamford)	Mark Herring (Wellingborough Whitworths)

DIVISION ONE RESULTS CHART 1996-97

		1	2	3	4	5	6	7	8	9	10	11	12	13	14	15	16	17	18
1	Blisworth	X	2-3	2-4	1-6	0-3	2-4	1-3	1-5	2-2	1-2	1-4	1-0	0-4	0-2	0-1	1-2	0-2	1-3
2	Bugbrooke	0-0	X	3-2	1-0	2-2	7-1	0-0	3-2	0-0	3-2	2-0	4-2	3-1	0-0	0-1	2-0	1-3	1-0
3	Burton P.W.	4-1	0-2	X	0-2	0-1	1-1	0-1	5-2	1-2	0-2	2-1	1-1	0-5	1-1	0-1	6-3	0-2	1-1
4	Cottingham	2-1	0-1	3-2	X	3-2	2-4	2-0	2-3	5-2	2-4	2-1	0-2	2-0	0-0	1-0	4-2	0-4	0-2
5	Daventry	0-1	1-4	0-8	0-2	X	2-0	5-1	0-3	3-1	2-1	2-0	0-5	1-5	0-3	3-3	1-1	1-3	0-0
6	Harrowby	3-1	1-0	3-0	1-2	3-3	X	3-3	0-2	7-0	3-2	2-2	1-3	0-4	2-4	3-4	1-1	0-2	2-1
7	Higham	2-1	1-0	3-1	3-0	3-1	3-0	X	4-2	2-1	1-1	1-0	2-0	1-1	1-1	3-1	3-2	2-2	1-2
8	Huntingdon	5-0	1-2	1-2	0-1	3-1	3-2	1-4	X	5-2	7-5	2-0	2-2	1-1	4-0	6-2	4-0	3-1	1-3
9	Irchester	3-0	0-0	3-1	0-1	0-0	0-2	1-1	0-4	X	0-1	0-3	3-1	2-3	0-0	0-2	3-0	0-3	1-8
10	N Vanaid	0-2	0-3	6-0	1-4	0-2	3-1	1-1	3-1	1-3	X	2-0	0-1	0-1	3-2	5-0	1-1	2-1	0-1
11	O.N. Chenecks	2-0	0-0	1-3	1-1	1-4	2-3	1-2	1-0	1-1	3-0	X	2-0	4-0	2-1	4-0	1-2	0-2	0-4
12	Olney	3-0	0-2	1-1	2-1	2-0	0-2	2-1	3-2	2-0	1-3	2-1	X	0-2	1-0	0-0	1-4	1-1	0-3
13	Rothwell Cor	6-1	1-1	1-1	2-0	4-0	2-0	5-1	1-2	2-0	0-2	1-0	1-1	X	0-4	2-0	1-0	1-1	0-2
14	St Ives	5-1	0-1	0-1	1-1	4-2	3-0	1-2	2-1	0-1	3-0	1-1	2-0	2-1	X	2-0	1-0	1-0	0-2
15	Sharnbrook	0-1	0-7	1-0	5-1	0-2	0-6	1-2	0-5	2-1	0-0	4-2	0-2	3-2	1-4	X	0-2	0-5	0-4
16	Thrapston	0-1	2-0	2-0	0-2	3-0	2-0	0-0	1-3	3-1	3-1	4-2	1-0	2-0	2-0	2-2	X	2-2	0-3
17	Whitworths	3-1	4-0	1-1	5-2	4-0	0-0	1-1	2-0	2-1	0-0	2-1	3-1	1-1	2-0	3-0	2-2	X	2-2
18	Yaxley	4-0	1-2	4-1	6-0	6-2	2-1	1-0	1-2	2-0	2-2	1-2	1-0	2-0	1-2	3-0	2-0	1-1	X

uhlsport UNITED COUNTIES LEAGUE KNOCKOUT CUP 1996-97

Preliminary Round

Wootton	v	Desborough	1-5
Burton PW	v	St Ives	0-3
Higham	v	St Neots	0-4
Irchester	v	Blisworth	0-1
Kempston	v	Huntingdon	1-0
Harrowby	v	Northampton Vanaid	1-4
Stotfold	v	Cogenhoe	3-2

First Round

Potton	v	Ramsey	2-0
Eynesbury	v	Holbeach	5-0
Yaxley	v	Long Buckby	0-2
Kempston	v	Ford Sports	0-1
Stamford	v	Wellingborough	3-2
Olney	v	Northampton Vanaid	2-1
Daventry	v	Nothampton Spencer	1-4
Mirrlees Blackstone	v	Stewarts & Lloyds	0-1
*Replay: Thrapston	v	Cottingham	4-3
Spalding	v	Rothwell Corinthians	2-1
Blisworth	v	Stotfold	1-4
Sharnbrook	v	Boston	0-5
Bourne	v	ON Chenecks	6-2
Cottingham	v	Thrapston	1-1*
St Neots	v	Whitworths	3-1
Newport Pagnell	v	St Ives	1-3
Desborough	v	Bugbrooke	2-1

Second Round

Olney	v	St Ives	3-1
Stewarts & Lloyds	v	Thrapston	5-2
Eynesbury	v	Desborough	0-2
Boston	v	St Neots	2-2*
*Replay: St Neots	v	Boston	2-2 (4-1 pens)
Long Buckby	v	Spalding	1-2
Bourne	v	Northampton Spencer	1-3
Ford Sports	v	Stotfold	0-3
Potton	v	Stamford	0-2

Semi-Final

Desborough	v	Stotfold	2-1
*Replay: St Neots	v	Northampton Spencer	0-1
Northampton Spencer	v	St Neots	1-1*

Final

First Leg

Desborough v Northampton Spencer 1-1

Second Leg

Northampton Spencer v Desborough 1-2

uhlsport UNITED COUNTIES LEAGUE 1996-97

PREMIER DIVISION	PLAYER OF THE YEAR	MOST APPEARANCES		LEADING SCORERS	
Boston Town	Jason Callaby (S&P)	Dave Scotney	41	Dave Scotney	23
Bourne Town	Tony Joynes (M), Lee McAllen (S)	Ian Flavell	40	Jeff Potts	17
Cogenhoe United	Kevin Slinn (C)	Kevin Slinn	39	Kevin Slinn	40
Desborough Town	Jamie Cunningham (S), Bryan Jeffery (P)	Des Elliott, Gary Kennedy	43	Jamie Cunningham	18
Eynesbury Rovers	Mick McCreanor (C)	Howard Phillips	38	Howard Phillips	16
Ford Sports	Andrew Green (M), Darren Tank (P)	Darren Tank	40	Byron Miller	13
Holbeach United	Steve Barnes (P&M), Dean Stacey (S)	Darren Earth	36	Steve Thompson	11
Kempston Rovers	Mark Smith (C)	Maurice O'Donnell	39	Stuart Mann	10
Long Buckby	Paul Creaney (C), Robbie Harris (P)	Paul Creaney	39	Rod Williams	12
Mirrlees Blackstone	Gavin Smith (P), Derrick Nuttell (S)	Gavin Smith	37	Trevor Smith	13
Newport Pagnell Town	Andy Bailey (P), Des Cook (M)	Des Cook	38	Darren Lynch	12
Northampton Spencer	Ian Mann (M, P&S)	Ian Mann	45	Jon Inwood	24
Potton United	Clive Woodland (C), Gary Houghton (P), Tim Chapman (S)	Dean Chapman, Keeley Thake	37	Glen Crook	10
St Neots Town	Chris Price (S&M), Steve Kuhne (P)	Grant Ager	45	Steve Kuhne	28
Spalding United	Scott Kent (S), Milton Graham (P)	Glenn Beech	41	Ronnie Fortune	17
Stamford	Lee Crane (S), Milton Graham (P)	Lee Crane 40		Mark Drake	18
Stewarts & Lloyds	Dean McAlwane (C)	Brian Ure	40	Dave Torrance	24
Stotfold	Roy Boon (C), Dave Chellew (P)	Scott Beeke, Brad Gillham	41	Andy Chapman	20
Wellingborough Town	Paul James (M), Graham Knight (P)	Paul James	34	Dave Botterill	13
Wootton Blue Cross	Andrew Carey (P), Andy Watt (S)	Rod Griffiths	33	Darek Jozwiak	8

Midfield action from the new Sapley Park, home of Huntingdon United in their U.C.L. First Division match against Rothwell Corinthians (hooped shirts). The match ended in a 1-1 draw. Photo: Martin Wray

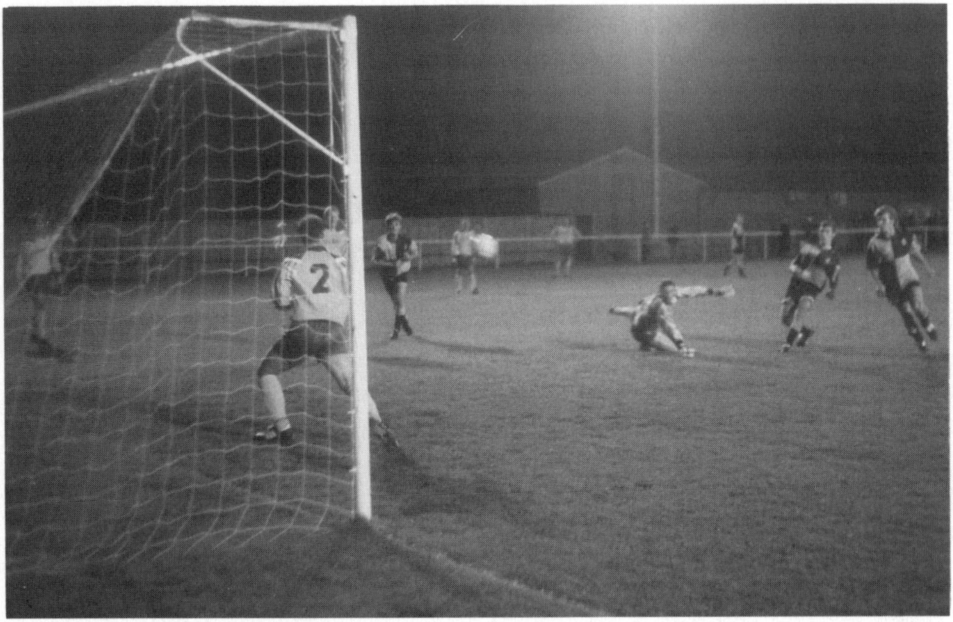

St. Neots Gary Clark (2nd from right) scores their final goal in the 5-2 win over S & L Corby in the U.C.L. Premier.
Photo: Gordon Whittington

Wayne Everdell (white shirt, centre of photo) scores from close range against Ramsey Town in St. Ives 5-1 victory in the U.C.L. First Division match last season.
Photo: Gordon Whittington

PREMIER DIVISION CLUBS 1997-98

BOSTON TOWN

Back Row (L-R); Bob Don-Duncan, Paul Martin, Paul Ward, Mark Collingwood, James Morgan, Richard Shaw, Lee Rippin, Ross Don-Duncan, Tom Watson, Andy Sandall, Shaughan Farrow. Front Row Andy Mundell, Stuart Burns, Jason Callatt, Ian Shooter, Shaun Hawket, Gary Walters, Simon Dunlop.

Chairman: Mick Vines **Vice Chairman:** J Rose. **Treasurer:** J Rose
Secretary: A Crick, Daisy Cottage, Shore Rd, Freiston, Boston, Lincs PE22 0LU (01205 760162. Fax:760162).
Manager: Bob Don-Duncan **Asst Manager:** Shaughan Farrow. **Physio:** Don Mitchell
Ground: Tattershall Road, Boston, Lincs (01205 365470).
Directions: A52 Grantham-Sleaford ,2nd left into Brotherton Rd.,Argyle St.to bridge,immediately over left into Tattersall road,ground 3/4 mile on left.
Capacity: 6,000 **Seats:** 450 **Cover:** 950 **Floodlights:** Yes **Club Shop:** Yes.
Programme: 40 pages, 50p **Editor/Press Officer:** Bob Whitaker (01205 368445)
Colours: Blue & white/blue/blue **Change:** All yellow
Sponsors: Tempests of Stickney/Keystone Fabricators **Nickname:** Poachers **Founded:** 1963.
Midweek Matchday: Tuesday **Reserves League:** None 94-95.
Record Attendance: 2,700 v Boston Utd, FA Cup 3rd Qual. Rd 1970.
Best Season - FA Cup: 1st Rd Prop 76-77 (lost 1-3 at Barnsley). **FA Trophy:** 2nd Rd 79-80 (lost 3-6 at Mossley after 0-0 draw). **FA Vase:** Semi-Finals 94-95 (lost 0-2 on agg to Taunton Tn).
Previous Leagues: Lincs 63-65/ Central Alliance 65-66/ Eastern Co's 66-68/ Midland 68-82/ Northern Co's East 82-87/ Central Midlands 87-91.
Players progressing to Football League: Julian Joachim (Leicester City), Neil Mann (Hull City).
Clubhouse: Open evenings (except Sunday), matchdays & functions. Bar & Lounge. Darts & pool.
Record Goalscorer (in a season): Carl Smaller 48, 1994-95.
Honours: Midland Co's Lg 74-75 78-79 80-81 (Lg Cup 76-77); Lincs Snr 'A' Cup (5) 73-74 79-82 89-90 (Snr 'B' Cup 65-66); Central Mids Lg 88-89; Central All 65-66; Lincs Lg 64-65; Hereward Spts Unt.Co.Lg.Prem Div Champ 94-95.

BOURNE TOWN

Chairman: Ivor Turner **Vice-Chairman:** Colin Notley **President:** Ray Ferrer
Secretary: Geoff McQueen, 9 Ancaster Road, Bourne, Lincs PE10 9HL (01778 394470)
Manager: Mick Bloodworth **Asst Manager:** Steve Blades **Physio:** Colin Notley
Ground: Abbey Lawn, Abbey Road, Bourne, Lincs (01778 422292). **Directions:** In market place take A151 Spalding Road, ground 500 yds on right. Public transport from Peterborough, Stamford and Grantham.
Capacity: 3,000 **Seats:** 300 **Cover:** 750 **Floodlights:** Yes **Club Shop:** Contact sec
Programme: 50 pages, 50p **Editor:** Chris Colvin **Press Officer:** Secretary
Colours: Maroon & sky/sky/maroon **Change Colours:** White & sky/white & sky/sky
Sponsors: Jaychem **Nickname:** Wakes **Founded:** 1883.
Midweek matchday: Wednesday **Reserves' Lge:** HSUCL Res Div 1
Previous Leagues: Peterborough/ UCL 47-56/ Central Alliance 58-61/ Midland Counties 61-63.
Players to progress to Football League: Peter Grummit (Nottm Forest), Shaun Cunnington (Wrexham, Grimsby, Sunderland), David Palmer (Wrexham).
Clubhouse: Small, open matchdays and specific events. Food, confectionary available.
Records - Attendance: 3,000 v Chelmsford, FA Tphy 1970. **Goalscorer:** David Scotney
Honours: Utd Co's Lg 68-69 69-70 71-72 90-91 (KO Cup 69-70, Benevolent Cup 90-91, Res Div 2 94-95), Lincs Snr 'A' Cup 71-72 (R-up 92-93), Central Alliance Division 1 South 59-60, Lincs Intermediate Cup 85-86.

BUCKINGHAM TOWN

Managing Director: Trevor Millington **Vice Chairman:** Bryn Pond
Secretary: Acting; Trevor Millington, Ford Meadow, Ford Street, Buckingham. (01280 816257)
Team Manager / Coach: Darren Wood **Assistant Manager / Physio:** Tim Chamberlain
Ground: Ford Meadow, Ford Street, Buckingham (01280 816257).
Directions: From town centre take Aylesbury (A413) road and turn right at Phillips Garage after 400yds. By public transport: train to Milton Keynes, then bus to Buckingham.
Capacity: 4,000 **Cover:** 420 **Seats:** 420 **Floodlights:** Yes **Club Shop:** Yes
Colours: All red **Change colours:** All white
Sponsors: Wipac. **Formed:** 1883 **Nickname:** The Robins
Midweek Matchday: **Reserves' League:** No reserve team
Previous Leagues: Aylesbury & Dist, Nth Bucks, Hellenic 53-57, Sth Mids 57-74, Utd Co's 74-86, Southern Lge 86-97.
Record Attendance: 2,451 v Orient, FA Cup 1st Rd 84-85.
Best Season FA Cup: 1st Round 1984-85, **FA Vase:** Quarter Finals 1990-91 & 92-93.
Programme: Yes **Editor:** Vic West
Clubhouse: Open evenings 6.30-11.00 (12.00-11.00 Sat & Sun) Rolls etc available on matchdays. Bingo, dominoes, darts & pool. Concert room with stage for hire, capacity 150.
96-97 Captain: Paul Lamb **96-97 P.o.Y.:** Robin Tucker **96-97 Top scorer:** Tony Hamilton
Honours: Southern Lg Southern Div 90-91; Utd Co's Lg 83-84 85-86, Div 1 R-up 75-76, Div 2 R-up 74-75, Lg Cup 83-84, Div 2 Cup R-up 74-75; Nth Bucks Lg (8); Aylesbury & Dist. Lg 02-03; Berks & Bucks Snr Cup 83-84, Berks & Bucks Jnr Cup (2), R-up (2), Berks & Bucks Minor Cup 32-33, Buckingham Snr Charity Cup (18) R-up (5)

COGENHOE UNITED

Chairman: Derek Wright **Vice Chairman:** Bob Earl **President:** Steve Brockwell
Secretary: Sue Wright, 6 Braefield Road, Cogenhoe, Northants NN7 1ND (01604 890737).
Manager: Dave Conlon **Asst Man.:** Stuart Robertson **Physio:** Ian Blair.
Ground: Compton Park, Brafield Rd, Cogenhoe, Northants (01604 890521).
Directions: Turn off A428 at Brafield-on-the-Green, first turn right to Cogenhoe or A45 to Billing Aquadrome. Carry on, take second Cogenhoe turn on left.
Capacity: 5,000 **Seats:** 100 **Cover:** 200 **Floodlights:** Yes **Founded:** 1967
Programme: 32 pages with Admission **Editor:** Gary Deer
Colours: All royal **Change:** All maroon **Club Shop:** No.
Midweek matchday: Tuesday **Nickname:** Cooks.
Sponsors: Supertrucking **Previous League:** Central Northants Combinatiom 1967-84.
Reserves' Lge: UCL Res. Div 1 **Record Gate:** 1,000 v Eastenders XI, Charity match 8/7/90.
Players to progress to Football League: Darren Bazeley (Watford 1989), Darren Harmon (Notts Co., Shrewsbury, Northampton 1989), Matt Murphy (Oxford Utd 1993), Gary Leonard (Northampton 1978).
Clubhouse: Open Tues-Fri 7-11pm, Sat 12-3 & 4-11pm, Sun 12-3 & 7-10.30pm. Snacks. Hot food on matchdays.
96-97 Captain: Neil Heslop
Record scorer & appearance: Tony Smith.
Hons: UCL Div 1 R-up 86-87 (Reserve Div 2 88-89), Knockout Cup 96-97; Daventry Charity Cup 91-92 95-96, (R-up 79-80); Central Northants Comb 80-81 82-83 83-84 (R-up 81-82, Prem Div Cup 82-83 (R-up 78-79), Div 1 Cup R-up 77-78, Charity Shield 82-83 83-84).

DESBOROUGH TOWN

Chairman: Bryan Walmsley **President:** Ernie Parsons.
Secretary: John Lee, 85 Breakleys Road, Desborough, Northants NN14 2PT (01536 760002).
Manager: Derek Maddox **Asst Manager:** Dave McHuchinson **Physio:** Paul Cunningham
Ground: Waterworks Field, Braybrooke Rd, Desborough (01536 761350).
Directions: Half a mile west of A6 following signs for Braybrooke.
Capacity: 8,000 **Seats:** 250 **Cover:** 500 **Floodlights:** Yes **Club Shop:**
Programme: 40 pages with entry **Editor:** Robert Bindley **Press Officer:** John Lee
Colours: Blue & whiteblue/blue **Change Colours:** Red & white/black/black **Previous Leagues:** None.
Sponsors: Wincanton Transport/R Fox **Nickname:** Ar Tarn **Founded:** 1896.
Midweek matchday: Tuesday **Record Attendance:** 8,000 v Kettering Town.
Players progressing to Football League: Wakeley Gage (Northampton, Chester, Peterborough and Crewe), Jon Purdie & Campbell Chapman (Wolves), Andy Tillson (Grimsby, QPR & Bristol Rvrs).
Clubhouse: Lounge & main hall, 2 bars, games room. Open every evening, weekend lunchtimes.
96-97 Captain: Paul Murphy **96-97 P.o.Y.:** Bryan Jeffrey **96-97 Top Scorer:** Jamie Cunningham
Honours: Utd Co's (Prev. Northants) Lg 00-01 01-02 06-07 20-21 23-24 24-25 27-28 48-49 66-67 (R-up 02-03 10-11 19-20 22-23 79-80), Div 2 10-11 (Res) 28-29 (Res), R-up 09-10 (Res) 26-27 (Res) 51-52 (Res), KO Cup 77-78 96-97; Northants Snr Cup 10-11 13-14 28-29 51-52.

Desborough Town celebrate their League Cup victory oner Northampton Spencer. *Photo - Gordon Whittington*

EYNESBURY ROVERS

Chairman: Brian Abraham **Vice Chairman:** Mike Preece **President:** Bill Stephenson
Secretary: Derek Irons, 12 Hadleigh Close, Bedford MK41 8JW
Manager: Peter Schofield **Asst Manager:** Steve White
Ground: Hall Road, Eynesbury, St Neots (01480 477449).
Directions: Approx 2 miles from A1, on South side of St Neots urban area, near Ernulf School.
Capacity: 3,000 **Seats:** 270 **Cover:** 270 **Floodlights:** Yes **Founded:** 1897
Programme: 24 pages, 30p **Editor:** Graham Mills **Club Shop:**
Colours: Royal blue & white **Change Colours:** All yellow. **Nickname:** Rovers.
Clubhouse: Large bar, capacity 150, committee room **Midweek matchday:** Tuesday
Sponsors: National Power **Reserve Team's League:** United Counties Reserve Div. One.
Record Gate: 5,000 v Fulham 1953 **Previous Lges:** Sth Mids 34-39/ UCL 46-52/ Eastern Co's 52-63.
Best FA Vase season: 2nd Rd 85-86 88-89 **Best FA Cup season:** 4th Qual. Rd 54-55 (1-3 at Camb. Utd)
Players to progress to Football Lge: Chris Turner (P'boro, Luton, Cambridge), Denis Emery (P'boro)
Hons: UCL Div 1 76-77, Hunts Snr Cup(12) 13-14 46-47 48-51 54-55 56-57 69-70 84-85 90-93, Hunts Premier Cup 50-51 90-91, Hinchingbrooke Cup(7) 46-47 48-52 57-58 66-67, Cambs Invitation Cup 61-62, E Anglian Cup R-up 90-91 91-92, Hunts Scott Gatty Cup 35-36 56-57 84-85 89-90 (R-up 93-94(res)), Hunts Jnr Cup 21-22 26-27, S Mids F'lit Cup 90-91(Res).

FORD SPORTS

Chairman: John Bailham **Vice Chairman:** Brian Sewell
Secretary: David Hitons, 53 Arnull Cres., Daventry, Northants NN11 5AZ (01327 871461).
Managers: Richard Green & Kevin Flear **Physio:** Dave Bull
Ground: Royal Oak Way South, Daventry, Northants (01327 709219).
Directions: Enter Daventry on A45 or A361 and follow signs for Royal Oak Way
Capacity: 1,000 **Seats:** Yes **Cover:** Yes **Floodlights:** Yes **Founded:** 1968
Programme: 12 pages **Reserves' Lge:** UCL Res Div 2 **Clubhouse:** Yes
Colours: Red & black/blue/blue **Change colours:** White & blue/blue/blue & white **Nickname:** Motormen
Prev. Lge: Central Northants Comb **Sponsors:** Ford Sports & Social Club
Player progressing to Football League: Martin Aldridge (Northampton).
96-97 Captain: Darren Tank **Top Scorer:** **P.o.Y.:**
Honours: UCL Div 1 92-93, 95-96, Benevolent Cup R-up 92-93; Highest Aggregate Goalscoring Trophy 92-93; Northants Sen Cup R-up 96-97.

HOLBEACH UNITED

Chairman: Anton Louth **President:** John King **Manager:** Yan Czarnecki
Secretary: Paul Beeken, Holbeach, Lincs PE12 7HA (01406 425355
Ground: Carters Park, Park Road, Holbeach (01406 424761. **Directions:** Second left at traffic lights in town centre, 220 yds down road on left. From King's Lynn; sharp right at traffic lights.
Capacity: 4,000 **Seats:** 200 **Cover:** 450 **Floodlights:** Yes **Founded:** 1929.
Programme: 44 pages, 50p **Editor:** Alan Wright **Club Shop:**
Colours: Old gold & black/black/black **Change Colours:** White/blue/blue **Nickname:** Tigers
Reserves' Lge: Peterborough **Clubhouse:** Large bar, lounge & kitchen, open every night.
Midweek matchday: Tuesday **Record Gate:** 4,094 v Wisbech 1954. **Sponsors:** Kings Quality Homes
Previous Leagues: Peterborough/ Utd Co's 46-55/ Eastern Co's 55-62/ Midland Co's 62-63.
Players progressing to Football League: Peter Rawcliffe (Lincoln).
Best FA Cup season: 1st Rd Proper 82-83 (lost 0-4 v Wrexham at Peterborough).
Best FA Trophy season: 2nd Qualifying Round 69-70 71-72.
Best FA Vase season: 5th Round 88-89 (lost 2-4 v Wisbech Town).
96-97 Captain: Rob Speechley **96-97 Top Scorer:** S Thompson **96-97 P.o.Y.:** S Barnes
Honours: Utd Co's Lg 89-90 (KO Cup 64-65 89-90, Benevolent Cup), Lincs Snr Cup 'A' 83-84 84-85 86-87 (Senior Cup 'B' 57-58)

KEMPSTON ROVERS

President: H Gilbert **Chairman:** Mark Salsbury **Vice-Chairman:** Russell Shreeves
Press Officer/Secretary: Alan Scott, 26 King William Rd, Kempston, Bedford MK42 7AT (01234 854875).
Manager: Mark Smith **Asst Manager:** Neil Simms
Ground: Hillgrounds Leisure, Hillgrounds Rd, Kempston, Bedford (01234 852346). **Directions:** M1 jct 13, A421 to Kempston, Hillgrounds Rd is off the B531 main Kempston-Bedford road. Entrance to Hillgrounds Road is opposite Sainsburys on the B531 - ground can be found just over twi miles from Sainsburys entrance. British Rail to Bedford Thameslink/Midland then bus No.103 from Bedford town centre stops outside ground.
Capacity: 2,000 **Seats:** 100 **Cover:** 250 **Floodlights:** Yes **Founded:** 1884.
Programme: 24 pages, 40p **Editor:** Alan Scott.
Colours: Red & white/black/black **Change Colours:** All yellow.
Nickname: Walnut Boys **Club record scorer:** Doug Jack.
Midweek matchday: Wednesday **Club Sponsors:** Audi Vindis Bedford
Record Attendance: unknown **Previous League:** Sth Mids 27-53.
Reserves's Lge: Bedford & Dist **Club Shop:** No, but old programmes available from clubhouse.
Players progressing to Football League: Ernie Fenn (WBA, Aston Villa), Matthew Woolgar (Luton 1994).
Clubhouse: Open 7-11pm every evening except Monday and weekend lunctimes noon-3pm. Sky TV, pool, fruit machines, hot pies & pasties.
Hons: Utd Co's Lg 73-74 (R-up 56-57 59-60 (Div 1 57-58 85-86, Div 2 55-56 (R-up 67-68), KO Cup 55-56 57-58 59-60 74-75 76-77), Beds Senior Cup 08-09 37-38 76-77 91-92 (R-up 92-93).

LONG BUCKBY

President: Alister Bruce **Chairman:** Ted Thresher
Secretary: Danny Derrig, 8 Manning Road, Moulton, Northampton NN3 7XE (01604 643037)
Manager: Mick Emms **Asst Manager:** Les Thurbon **Physio:** Mick Deacon
Ground: Station Rd, Long Buckby (01327 842682).
Directions: On Daventry - Long Buckby road. 400 yds from station (Northampton - Rugby line).
Capacity: 1,000 **Seats:** 200 **Cover:** 200 **Floodlights:** Yes **Founded:** 1945
Programme: 8 pages **Editor:** Rod Pryor. **Sponsors:** Northampton Elec Dist
Colours: All blue **Change colours:** All red **Nickname:** Bucks
Reserves' Lge: HSUCL Res Div 1 **Clubhouse:** Bar & concert room. Open matchdays.
Midweek matchday: Tuesday **Record Gate:** 750 v Kettering, Northants Snr Cup Final 1984.
Previous Leagues: Rugby & D./ Central Northants Comb. (pre-1968).
Previous Name: Long Buckby Nomads 1936.
Best FA Vase season: 2nd Rd 85-86 **Best FA Cup season:** 1st Qualifying Rd 92-93..
Players progressing to Football League:
Gary Mills (Nottingham Forest, Derby, Notts County, Leicester), Vince Overson (Burnley, Birmingham), Des Waldock (Northampton), Steve Norris (Scarborough, Carlisle, Halifax, Chesterfield).
Honours: UCL KO Cup 84-85, UCL Div 2 70-71 71-72, Div 2 KO Cup 71-72, Div 3 69-70; Northants Snr Cup R-up; Daventry Charity Cup 96-97.

MIRRLEES BLACKSTONE

President: Darren Laughton **Chairman:** Bill Sewell
Secretary: Derek Hall, 67 Ringwood, South Bretton, Peterborough PE3 9SR (01733 332074).
Manager: Dominic Genovese **Press Officer:** Kevin Boor.
Ground: Lincoln Road, Stamford (01780 757335).
Directions: A6121 Stamford to Bourne road, 2nd left past MB works.
Capacity: 1,000 **Seats:** 100 **Cover:** Yes **Floodlights:** Yes **Founded:** 1920.
Programme: 32 pages with entry **Editor:** Kevin Boor
Colours: Blue & black/black/black **Change Colours:** All Red
Clubhouse details: Open evenings, lunchtimes & matchdays.
Sponsors: Ideal Interiors **Midweek matchday:** Tuesday **Nickname:** Stones
Record Gate: 700 v Glinton. **Record win:** 11-0 v Brackley, 22/1/94 (A Dunn 6 goals).
Previous Leagues: Peterborough Works/ Peterborough/ Stamford & District.
Previous Names: Rutland Ironworks/ Blackstone (until 1975).
Players to progress to Football League: Craig Goldsmith (Peterborough, Carlisle), Alan Neilson (Newcastle & Wales).
Club record scorer (in one game): A Dunn; 6 v Brackley Town, 22/1/94.
Honours: UCL Div 1 R-up 87-88 (Benevolent Cup R-up), Lincs Snr Cup 'A' 92-93.

NORTHAMPTON SPENCER

President: P.A.Frost. **Chairman:** Graham Wrighting
Secretary: D Ling, 26 Pritchard Close, Rectory Farm, Northampton (01604 407124).
Manager: Gary Sargent **Asst Manager:** Keith Bowen
Ground: Kingsthorpe Mill, Studland Rd, Northampton NN3 1NF (01604 718898).
Directions: Turn off Kingsthorpe Rd at traffic lights into Thornton Rd, 1st right into Studland Rd, ground at end.
Capacity: 2,000 **Seats:** 100 **Cover:** 350 **Floodlights:** Yes **Founded:** 1936
Programme: 48 pages, 50p **Editor/Press Officer:** Andy Goldsmith (01604 412382)
Colours: Yellow/green/yellow **Change Colours:** All red **Nickname:** Millers
Midweek matchday: Wednesday **Clubhouse:** Lounge and bar, open normal licensing hours.
Club Sponsors: Doc Martens **Record Gate:** 800 v Nottm F., dressing-room opener 1993.
Previous League: Northampton Town 36-68 **Reserves' League:** HSUCL Res. Div. One
Previous Name: Spencer School Old Boys.
Previous Grounds: Dallington Park 1936-70, Duston High School 70-72.
Best FA Cup year: 1st Qual. Rd 93-94, 96-97. **Best FA Vase year:** 4th Round 87-88 (lost 1-2 v Gresley Rovers)
Players to progress to Football League: Paul Stratford (Northampton), Wakeley Gage (Northampton, Chester, Peterborough, Crewe)
Hons: United Counties Lg 91-92 (R-up 92-93, Div 1 84-85, KO Cup 88-89 93-94 (R-up 87-88 96-97), Benevolent Cup 91-92), Northants Snr Cup R-up 90-91 93-94.

POTTON UNITED

President: Peter Hutchinson. **Chairman:** Nigel Westhorp
Secretary/Press Officer: Derek Inskip, 3 Bellevue Close, Potton, Beds SG19 2QA (01767 260355).
Manager: Ken Davidson **Asst Manager:** Brian Chapman
Ground: The Hollow, Biggleswade Road, Potton (01767 261100).
Directions: Outskirts of Potton on Biggleswade Road (B1040). Three and a half miles from Sandy (BR). United Counties buses from Biggleswade.
Capacity: 2,000 **Seats:** 200 **Cover:** 250 **Floodlights:** Yes **Founded:** 1943
Clubhouse: Yes **Midweek matchday:** Tuesday
Programme: 28 pages, 50p **Editor:** Bev Westhorpe **Club Sponsors:** Darlows
Colours: Blue & white/blue/blue **Change Colours:** All yellow **Nickname:** Royals
Previous Leagues: Sth Mids 46-55/ Central Alliance 56-61
Previous Grounds: Recreation Grnd pre-1947
Reserves' Lge: UCL Res. Div. Two **Record Attendance:** 470 v Hastings Town, FA Vase 1989
Best FA Trophy year: 3rd Qualifying Round 71-72 72-73.
Best FA Vase year: 5th Round 89-90 (lost 1-2 to Billericay Town).
Best FA Cup year: 3rd Qualifying Round 74-75 (lost 1-2 to Bedford Town).
Hons: Utd Co's Lg 86-87 88-89, KO Cup 72-73, Benevolent Cup 88-89; Beds Snr Cup(5) 47-49 63-64 75-76 77-78 (R-up 94-95 96-97); Wallspan Floodlit Cup 87-88; Hinchingbrooke Cup 51-52 84-85 89-90 90-91 91-92; Hunts Premier Cup 89-90 91-92 94-95(joint) 96-97; Beds I'mediate Cup 43-44; Southern Comb. Cup 92-93; Nth Beds Charity Cup (12); East Anglian Cup 96-97; Jess Pigott Trophy 96-97.

ST NEOTS TOWN

Back Row (L-R); Gary Pilsworth (Mgr), Grant Agar, Chris Price, Steve Kuhne, Steve Young, Dave Baker, Gary Walker, Paul Newman, Steve McKnight, Phil Cavener, John Arundel. Front Row; Steve Scott, Shaun Gale, Andy Jakes, Ian Parr, Ned Stevenson, Paul Pescud.

Chairman: Bob Page **Press Officer:** Neil Holmes (01480 383382)
Secretary: Pat Page, 75 Shakespeare Road, Eaton Socon, St Neots, PE19 3HT (01480 215661)
Manager: Gary Pilsworth **Asst Manager:** Phil Cavener **Coach:**
Ground: Rowley Park, Cambridge Rd, St Neots, Cambs (01480 470012).
Directions: Through town centre, under railway bridge, 1st left.
Capacity: 3,000 **Seats:** TBA **Cover:** 250 **Floodlights:** Yes **Founded:** 1879
Programme: Yes **Editor:** Mike Birch **Nickname:** Saints
Reserves' Lge: UCL Res Div 2 **Clubhouse:** Built 1994. **Sponsors:** TBA
Club colours: Sky & navy/navy/navy **Change colours:** All yellow
Record Gate: 2,000 v Wisbech, 1966 **Best FA Cup year:** 1st Rd 66-67 (lost 0-2 at Walsall).
Best FA Vase year: 3rd Rd 78-78 **Best FA Trophy year:** Second Qualifying Round 69-70 72-73.
Previous Lges: South Midlands 27-36 46-49/ United Counties 36-39 51-56 66-69 73-88/ Metropolitan 49-51 60-66/ Central Alliance 56-60/ Eastern Counties 69-73/ Huntingdonshire 90-94.
Previous Ground: Shortsands **Previous Name:** St Neots & District 1879-1957.
Players progressing to Football League:
Frank Atkins (Cambridge), John Gregory (Aston Villa) and Matthew Oakey (Southampton).
Honours: Hunts Snr Cup(33), UCL 67-68 (KO Cup 67-68 68-69), Metropolitan Lg 49-50 (Lg Cup 79-80), South Midlands Lg 32-33, Huntingdonshire Lg 90-91 92-92 92-93 94-95.

SPALDING UNITED

Chairman: Rod Quinton **President:** John Chappell
Secretary: Jack Grimwood, 29 Moons Green, Moulton, Spalding, Lincs. PE12 6QW (01406 370698)
Manager: Alan Day **Asst Manager:** **Physio:** Todd
Ground: Sir Halley Stewart Field, Winfrey Avenue, Spalding (01775 713328).
Directions: Town centre off A16, adjacent to bus station. 250 yds from Spalding (BR) station.
Capacity: 7,000 **Seats:** 350 **Cover:** 2,500 **Floodlights:** Yes **Shop:** Yes
Programme: 36 pages, 50p **Editor:** Richard Sheldon & Richard Wa **Press Officer:** Ray Tucker
Colours: Tangerine & black/black/tangerine **Change:** All Blue
Sponsors: Foremost Supplies **Nickname:** Tulips **Founded:** 1921
Midweek matchday: Wednesday **Reserve League:** Utd Counties Lge Res Div Two.
Record Attendance: 6,972 v Peterborough, FA Cup 1952.
Previous Leagues: Peterborough/ Utd Co's 31-55 68-78 86-88/ Eastern Co's 55-60/ Central Alliance 60-61/ Midland Co's 61-68/ Northern Co's (East) 82-86/ Southern 88-91.
Best FA Cup year: 1st Round 57-58 (1-3 at Durham City), 64-65 (3-5 at Newport County).
Best FA Trophy year: 2nd Qualifying Round 69-70 70-71 71-72 74-75 76-77 81-82.
Best FA Vase year: Quarter-Finals 89-90 (lost 1-3 to Guiseley).
Players progressing to Football League: Carl Shutt (Sheffield Wednesday, Bristol City, Leeds).
Clubhouse: Open matchdays, and events.
96-97 Captain: Paul Langford **96-97 P.o.Y.:** Scott Kent **96-97 Top Scorer:** Ronnie Fortune
Honours: Utd Co's Lg 54-55 74-75 87-88 (R-up 50-51 51-52 52-53 72-73 75-76 96-97); KO Cup 54-55 94-95; Northern Co's East Lg 83-84; Lincs Snr Cup 52-53; Lincs Snr 'A' Cup 87-88; Snr 'B' Cup 50-51; Evans Halshaw F'lit Cup 89-90.

STAMFORD

A jubilant Stamford AFC with the League Chapionship Trophy: Back Row (L-R); Pat O'Keeffe (Player/Coach), Robbie Chapman, Paul Hill, Steve Collins, Dennis Rhule, Hamish Curtis, Trevor Quow, Milton Graham, Justin Osborne, Lee Crane, Mick Bennett, Mark Drake. Front Row; Paul Bryant, Gavin Dolby, Steve Evans (Mgr), Dean Elston, Arthur Twiddy (Chr), Jon Nottingham, Russell Pope, Michael Simpson, Gerard Evans (Physio).

Photo - Rutland & Stamford Mercury

Chairman: Arthur Twiddy **Vice-Chairman:** Bill Warrington **President:**
Secretary: Andrew Eason, 36 Queens Walk, Stamford, Lincs. (01780 754510)
Manager: Steve Evans. **Asst Manager:** P O'Keeffe **Physio:** Gerard Evans
Ground: Wothorpe Road, Stamford, Lincs (01780 763079).
Directions: Off A43 Kettering Rd, 1 mile east of A1. 200 yds from station.
Capacity: 5,000 **Seats:** 250 **Cover:** 1,250 **Floodlights:** Yes **Shop:** Yes **Founded:** 1896
Programme: 36 pages, 60p **Editor:** Andrew Eason **Press Officer:** Andrew Eason
Colours: All red **Change Colours:** Yellow/black/yellow **Nickname:** Daniels
Sponsors: Wilpave **Midweek matchday:** Wednesday **Reserves League:** UCL Res Div 2
Record Attendance: 4,200 v Kettering, FA Cup Third Qual. Rd 1953.
Previous Leagues: Peterborough/ Northants (UCL) 08-55/ Central Alliance 55-61/ Midland Co's 61-72.
Players to progress to Football League: R Chester (Aston Villa), T Tye (Chelsea), G Fell (Brighton, Southend, Torquay, York), C Chapman (Wolves), S Collins (Peterborough), K Alexander (Grimsby, Stockport, Lincoln), A Tillson (Grimsby, QPR, Bristol Rovers), B Stubbs (Notts Co.), D Genovese (Peterborough).
Clubhouse: Open matchdays, Sunday lunchtimes & evenings (bingo). Food available matchdays - hot and cold.
96-97 Captain: Dean Elston **96-97 P.o.Y.:** Lee Crane **96-97 Top Scorer:** Gavin Dolby
Honours: FA Vase 79-80 (R-up 75-76 83-84); Utd Co's Lg 75-76 77-78 79-80 80-81 81-82 96-97 (KO Cup 51-52 75-76 79-80 81-82 85-86); Northants Lg 11-12; Lincs Snr 'A' Cup 78-79 82-83; Lincs Snr 'B' Cup 51-52 53-54; Hinchingbrooke Cup, William Scarber Mem. Cup 70-71 82-83 85-86 88-89 94-95; Stamford Chal. Cup 89-90; Lincs Jnr Cup 48-49.

STEWARTS & LLOYDS

Chairman: Peter Webb **Vice Chairmen:** Gordon Hall, Harry Nelson
Secretary: Dave Foster, 29 Tettenhall Close, Corby, Northants NN198 9PJ (01536 742358)
Manager: Elwyn Roberts. **Asst Manager:** Andy McGowan **Physio:** Roger White
Ground: Recreation Ground, Occupation Road, Corby (01536 401497).
Directions: On Occupation Rd at rear of Stewart & Lloyds Leisure Club, next to old Corby Town F.C. ground.
Capacity: 1,500 **Seats:** 100 **Cover:** 200 **Floodlights:** Yes **Club Shop:**
Programme: 12 pages with admission **Editor/Press Officer:** Dave Foster **Nickname:** None
Colours: Yellow/blue/yellow **Change Colours:** Blue/white/blue **Formed:** 1935
Sponsor: Weldon **Midweek matchday:** Tuesday **Previous Leagues:** Kettering Amateur
Players to progress to Football League: Andy McGowan (Northampton), Willie Graham (Brentford)
Clubhouse: Licensed bar.
96-97 Captain: **96-97 P.o.Y.:** **96-97 Top Scorer:**
Club Record Goalscorer: Joey Martin 46 (92-93).
Honours: UCL R-up 85-86, Div 1(2) 73-75; UCL KO Cup, Prem 95-96, Div 1 Cup(2) 73-75, Div 2 KO Cup(2) 75-77)

STOTFOLD

Chairman: John Talbot **Vice Chairman:** Tom Peacock **President:** David Chellow
Secretary: W Clegg, 12 Common Rd, Stotfold, Hitchin, Herts SG5 4BX (01462 730421).
Manager: Ian Allinson **Asst Manager:** Ian Donnelly
Physio: Nobby Kearns **Press Officer:** Bill Clegg
Ground: Roker Park, The Green, Stotfold, Hitchin, Herts (01462 730765).
Directions: A507 from A1, right at lights, right at T-jct. A507 from Bedford via Shefford, left at lights, right at T-jct.
Capacity: 5,000 **Seats:** 300 **Cover:** 300 **Floodlights:** Yes **Nickname:** Eagles
Programme: 22 pages with entry **Editor:** John Talbot **Founded:** 1904.
Colours: Amber/black/black **Change Colours:** All Sky blue **Reformed:** 1945.
Midweek matchday: Tuesday **Reserve Team's League:** UCL Reserve Division One.
Club Sponsors: Motorola **Record Attendance:** 1,000 v Letchworth Town, FA Amtr Cup.
Previous Leagues: Biggleswade & District/ North Herts/ South Midlands 51-84.
Clubhouse details: Clubroom, bar, refreshment bar, dressing rooms, physio room.
Record scorer: Roy Boon **Record appearances:** Roy Boon/Dave Chellew.
Hons: Utd Co's Lg R-up 93-94, KO Cup R-up 91-92, Res Div 1 87-88; Sth Mids Lg 80-81 (R-up 55-56 57-58 58-59 59-60 63-64 65-66 77-78), Div 1 53-54, Chal. Tphy 81-82; Beds Snr Cup 64-65 93-94; Beds Premier Cup 81-82; Beds I'mediate Cup 58-59; Nth Beds Charity Cup 55-56 56-57 61-62 81-82 87-88 90-91; Beds Colts Lg 88-89; Southern Comb Cup 94-95 95-96 96-97.

WELLINGBOROUGH TOWN

Chairman: Corville Brown. **President:**
Secretary: Mike Walden, 5 Fernie Way, Wellingborough, Northants NN8 3LB (01933 279561).
Manager: Brian Knight. **Coach:** Joe Kiernan/Graham Felton **Physio:** Tif Felton
Ground: Dog & Duck, London Road, Wellingborough, Northants (01933 223536).
Directions: 200yds off A45 by-pass, by Dog & Duck PH. 1 mile from Wellingborough (BR).
Capacity: 5,000 **Seats:** 300 **Cover:** 500 **Floodlights:** Yes **Club Shop:** No
Programme: 16 pages 30p **Editor:** Secretary **Press Officer:** Secretary
Colours: Yellow/blue/blue **Change Colours:** All red.
Sponsors: Overstone Park School **Nickname:** Doughboys **Founded:** 1867
Midweek matchday: Tuesday **Reserve League:** HSUCL Res. Div. Two
Record Attendance: 4,013 v Kettering Town.
Best FA Cup season: 1st Round 28-29 (v Bristol Rovers) 65-66 (1-2 v Aldershot Town).
Best FA Trophy season: 1st Round 71-72 (lost 0-3 to Dartford after 1-1 and 0-0 draws).
Best FA Vase season: 95-96.
Previous Leagues: Midland 1895-97 98-1901/ Southern 01-05 71-89/ Northants (Utd Co's) 19-34 36-56 61-68/ Central Alliance 56-61/ Metropolitan 68-70/ West Midlands Regional 70-71.
Players progressing to Football Lge: Phil Neal (N'hampton, L'pool & Eng.), Fanny Walden (Spurs & Eng.)
Clubhouse: Full facilities. Open evenings & Sat lunchtimes.
96-97 Captain: Barrington Leslie **96-97 Top Scorer:** Dave Botterill **96-97 P.o.Y.:** Paul James
Club Record Goalscorer: S Hill **Club Record Appearances:** P Hayes 165, 1985-89.
Honours: Utd Co's Lg 10-11 62-63 64-65, Metropolitan Lge 69-70, Northants Snr Cup 1896-97 1901-02 02-03 33-34 47-48 49-50 81-82, Maunsell Cup 20-21 21-22.

WOOTTON BLUE CROSS

President: J Clarke. **Chairman:** D Peters
Secretary: Trevor Templeman, 3 Pollys Yard, Newport Pagnell, Bucks MK16 8YU
Manager: Shaun Staplehurst/Darren Marsh **Physio:** Trevor Templemen **Press Officer:** Secretary
Ground: Weston Park, Bedford Road, Wootton (01234 767662).
Directions: Four miles south of Bedford on main road through village at rear of Post Office.
Capacity: 2,000 **Seats:** 50 **Cover:** 250 **Floodlights:** Yes **Founded:** 1887
Programme: 24 pages **Editor:** Secretary. **Club Shop:**
Colours: All Blue **Change:** Yellow/blue/yellow **Sponsors:** Vision Blinds
Nickname: Blue Cross. **Reserve's League:** United Counties Reserve Div 2
Midweek matchday: Tuesday **Record Gate:** 838 v Luton, Beds Prem. Cup 1988.
Best FA Vase year: 3rd Rd 74-75 **Best FA Cup year:** 2nd Qual. Rd 50-51 (3-4 v Hitchin (H)).
Previous Leagues: Bedford & District/ South Midlands 46-55.
Previous Grounds: Recreation Ground, Fishers Field, Rose & Crown, Cockfield.
Players progressing to Football Lge: Tony Biggs (Arsenal).
Clubhouse details: Main hall, bar, darts, pool, bingo. Open every evening and weekend lunchtimes.
96-97 Captain: Shaun Staplehurst **P.o.Y.:** **Top Scorer:**
Honours: Utd Co's Lg Div 2 67-68 69-70 (KO Cup 82-83, Div 2 Cup 64-65), South Midlands Lg 47-48 (R-up 49-50), Beds Senior Cup 70-71, Hinchinbrooke Cup(5).

St Neots keeper Steve Young pulls off a dramatic penalty save to foil Olney's Alex Chaplin.

Stamford's Mick Bennett nets from point blank range to clinch the lead against Wootton Blue Cross

YAXLEY

President: John Dowse **Chairman:** Malcom Whaley **Vice Chairman:** Geoff Heathcote
Secretary: Malcom Larrington, 70 Main Street, Yaxley, Peterborough PE7 3DB (01733 243276)
Manager: Dave Willis **Coach:** Gary Clipston
Ground: Holme Road, Yaxley (01733 244928).
Directions: A1, then A15 at Norman Cross up to traffic lights, turn right then immediately right, follow road approx. 1 mile turn right into Holme Rd., ground approx. 200 yards on left.
Capacity: 1,000+ **Seats:** 150 **Cover:** Yes **Floodlights:** Yes **Founded:**
Programme: Yes **Editor:** Robin Peel **Sponsor:** Reads Removals
Colours: All tangerine **Change colours:** Blue & white/blue/blue & white **96-97 Captain:** Stuart Keir
Prev. Lge: Peterborough & District, Jewson Huntingdonshire, West Anglia.
Honours: UCL Div 1 96-97; Hunts Senior Cup (4); Peterborough League (2); Peterborough Senior Cup (2); West Anglia League; Scott-Gatty Cup.

DIVISION ONE CLUBS 1997-98

BLISWORTH

Chairman: Pete Edwards **President:** L Piggott.
Secretary: Mandy Inwood, 9 Northfield Way, Kingsthorpe, Northampton NN2 8AN (01604 590724).
Manager: Brian Oldham **Assistant Manager:** Gary Edwards/Steve Paul. **Physio:** Elaine Johnson
Ground: Blisworth Playing Field, Courteenhall Road, Blisworth (01604 858024).
Directions: Courteenhall Road off A43.
Capacity: 1,000 **Seats/Cover:** No **Floodlights:** No **Clubhouse:** Yes **Programme:** No.
Colours: White/black/black & white **Change colours:** Sky/navy/navy **Founded:** 1890.
Sponsors: Target Furniture, JB King Plant Hire **96-97 Captain:** Andy Johnson
Reserves' Lge: UCL Res. Div. 2 **Previous Lge:** Central Northants Combination 1978-87.
Player progressing to Football Lge: Dave Johnson (N'pton 83-84)
Hons: Northants Junior Cup 88-99

BUGBROOKE St MICHAELS

Chairman: Tom Treacy. **President:** John Curtis
Secretary: Roger Geary, 31 Kislingbury Rd, Bugbrooke, Northampton NN7 3QG (01604 831678).
Manager: Chris Goodchild **Asst Manager:** Mark Panter **Press Officer:** Rose Harris.
Ground: Birds Close, Gayton Road, Bugbrooke (01604 830707).
Directions: A45 Northampton to Daventry road, onto B4525 (Banbury Lane) at Kislingbury, left into Gayton Road, ground on left.
Capacity: 1,500 **Seats:** None **Cover:** Yes **Floodlights:** Yes **Founded:** 1929
Reserves' Lge: UCL Res. Div. 1 **Clubhouse:** Yes - normal licensing hours.
Programme: Eight pages. **Editor:** Rose Harris **Nickname:** Badgers
Club colours: Yellow & blue/blue/blue **Change colours:** All red **Record Gate:** 1,156
Previous Ground: School Close **Previous Lge:** Central Northants Combination 1952-87.
Players progressing to Football League: Kevin Slinn (Watford), Craig Adams (Northampton).
Sponsors: M C Builders. **96-97 Captain:** Dale Williams
Club Record Scorer: Vince Thomas **Club Record Appearances:** Jimmy Nord.
Hons: Northants Junior Cup 89-90, Central Northants Comb. 68-69 69-70 70-71 71-72 76-77 85-86, UCL Res Div 2 R-up 94-95.

BURTON PARK WANDERERS

Chairman: Bernard Lloyd **Vice Chairman:** Paul Clarke
Secretary: David Haynes, 125 Churchill Way, Burton Latimer, Northants NN15 5RT (01536 724871).
Manager: Colin Neill. **Asst Manager:** Jim Prior **Physio:** Nicky Mann
Ground: Latimer Park, Polwell Lane, Burton Latimer (01536 725841).
Directions: Entering Burton Latimer, turn off A6 Station Rd and right into Powell Lane; ground on the right.
Capacity: 1,000 **Seats:** 100 **Cover:** 150 **Floodlights:** No **Founded:** 1961
Colours: All blue **Change Colours:** Yellow & green/black/black
96-97 Captain: Nigel Buller **Sponsor:** Prescott Motors
Prog: 16 pages with entry **Nickname:** The Wanderers **Midweek matchday:** Tuesday
Previous Lge: Kettering Amateur **Record Attendance:** 253 v Rothwell, May 1989
Past Players to progress to Football League: Shaun Wills (Peterborough)
Honours: UCL Div 1 R-up, Benevolent Cup R-up

Burton Park Wanderers FC:

COTTINGHAM

Chairman: Mike Beadsworth **Vice Chairman:** Brian Tilley
Secretary: Lindsay Brownlie, 30 Bancroft Rd, Cottingham, Market Harborough LE16 8XA (01536 771009).
Manager: Rob Dunion. **Asst Manager:** Neil Burns.
Ground: Berryfield Rd, Cottingham (01536 770051). **Directions:** One and a half miles from Corby on A427 turn right to Cottingham. At junction of B670 turn left; Berryfield Road 200 yds on right.
Capacity: 1,000 **Seats:** None **Cover:** Yes **Floodlights:** No **Programme:** No
Reserves' Lge: UCL Res. Div. 2 **Clubhouse:** Bar & changing rooms
Colours: Yellow/green/yellow **Change colours:** Orange/black/black
Sponsors: B & J Decorators **96-97 Captain:** Neil Pask
Previous Leagues: Market Harborough/ Kettering Amateur/ East Midlands Alliance.
Honours: UCL Div 1 runners-up, Northants Junior Cup

DAVENTRY TOWN

Chairman: Ray Humphries **Vice Chairman:** Grant Hughes **President:** Paul Webster
Secretary/Press Officer: Cliff Farthing, 45 The Fairway, Daventry, Northants NN11 4NW (01327 72149).
Manager: Darren Foster, Terry O'Neill **Physio:** Tony Jackson
Ground: Elderstubbs Farm, Leamington Way, Daventry, Northants (01327 706286).
Directions: Adjacent to A45 by-pass at top of Staverton Road Sports Complex.
Capacity: 2,000 **Seats:** 250 **Cover:** 250 **Floodlights:** Yes **Founded:** 1886.
Programme: 4 Pages. **Editor:** Nigel Foster **Sponsor:** Campbell Estate Agents
Colours: Black & white/black/black **Change colours:** All red
Midweek Matchday: Tuesday **Reserve Team's League:** Central Northants Comb.
Clubhouse: Large bar/kitchen **Record Attendance:** 350 v Ford Sports 1991.
Best FA Cup year: Prel. Rd 94-95 **Best FA Vase year:** Preliminary Rd 91-92 94-95.
Previous Leagues: Northampton Town (pre-1987)/ Central Northants Combination 87-89.
Players Progressing to Football League: Martin Aldridge (Northampton).
Hons: UCL Div 1(2) 89-91 (Lg Cup R-up 92-93, Highest Aggregate Cup), Northants Junior Cup 36-37 60-61 91-92.

HARROWBY UNITED

Chairman: Paul Daglish **Vice Chairman:** Robert Wilson **Secretary:** Charlie Harvey, 64 Queensway, Grantham, Lincs NG31 9QD (01476 70255).
Manager: Barry Shaw **Asst Mgr:** Phil Drury **Coach:** Tony Cook **Physio:** Simon Shaw
Ground: Harrowby Playing Fields, Harrowby Lane, Grantham (01476 590822).
Directions: From A1 take B6403, go past A52 roundabout, past Ancaster turn and take road to Harrowby. Continue into Grantham, ground on right opposite Cherry Tree public house.
Capacity: 1,500 **Seats:** 100 **Cover:** 150 **Floodlights:** No **Founded:** 1949.
Programme: 12 pages **Clubhouse:** Large bar open normal licensing hours.
Colours: Blue & white/blue/blue **Change colours:** Red & white/white/red **Nickname:** Arrows.
Sponsor: Bailey Trailers **96-97 Captain:** Graham Drury
Reserves' League: Grantham **Best FA Vase season:** Preliminary Round 91-92.
Previous Leagues: Grantham/ Lincs/ East Mids Regional Alliance (pre-1990).
Players progressing to Football League: Richard Liburd (Middlesbrough).
Hons: Utd Co's Lg Div 1 91-92 (Benev. Cup R-up 91-92), Mids Regional All. 89-90 (Lg Cup 89-90), Lincs Snr 'B' Cup(2) 90-92.

HIGHAM TOWN

President: Vijay Patel **Chairman:** Richard Williams **Vice Chairman:** Brian Kirk
Secretary: Chris Ruff, 23 Queensway, Higham Ferrers NN10 8BU (01933 58862).
Manager: Adie Mann **Asst Mgr:** Matt Carroll **Coach:** Kevin Roberts **Physio:** Keith Bates.
Ground: Recreation Ground, Vine Hill Drive, Higham Ferrers (01933 53751).
Directions: From Kettering 1st right on A6 after A45 junction to St Neots. From Bedford, 3rd left after entering town on A6 from Rushden. Higham is served by London-Bedford-Corby United Counties Coachlines
Capacity: 1,000 **Seats:** Nil **Cover:** 100 **Floodlights:** No **Founded:** 1895.
Programme: 12 pages with entry **Editor:** Secretary **Reformed:** 1920 & 1946
Colours: Sky & navy/navy/navy **Change colours:** Black & white/black/black **Nickname:** Lankies.
Midweek matches: Tuesday **Reserves' Lge:** UCL Reserve Div. **Sponsors:** Higham News
Previous Lges: Wellingborough 20-21/ Northants (now Utd Co's) 21-36/ Rushden 46-50.
Record Attandance: 5,700 v Chesterfield, FA Cup final qualifying round replay 22-23.
Clubhouse: Open during season 8.30-11pm Tues, Thurs & Fri, after Saturday games & 12-1.30pm Sundays. Light refreshments available after Saturday games.
Record scorer: Stuart Sinfield 136 **Record appearances:** Brian Harbour 485. **96-97 Captain:** Neil Denny
Hons: UCL Div 1 R-up 70-71 71-72 92-93 94-95, Northants Lg 21-22 22-23 (R-up 23-24 26-27), Northants Snr Cup 21-22 (R-up 30-31 32-33), Maunsell Premier Cup 22-23 33-34.

HUNTINGDON UNITED

Huntingdon United FC: team line-up before their 1-1 draw with Rothwell Corinthians *Photo - Martin Wray*

Chairman: John Hope
Secretary: Stephen Thresh, 41 Maple Drive, Huntingdon, Cambs. PE18 7JE. (01480 417146)
Manager: Andy Rossi **Asst Manager:** Mitch Scarborough **Physio:** Sam Burrows
Ground: Sapley Park, Stoney Close, Huntingdon. (01480 41722).
Capacity: 750 **Covered:** 100 **Seating:** No **Floodlights:** No **Formed:** 1949
Colours: Green/red/red. **Change Colours:** Red & black/black/red & black
Programme: Yes **Editor:** Secretary **Nickname:** Green & Reds
Sponsor: Bowles Newsagents **Clubhouse:** Yes **Midweek matchday:** Tuesday
96-97 Captain: Martyn Ray **Top Scorer:** Mick Parak **P.o.Y.:** Peter Kelly
Past players progressing to Football League: Ernie Toseland (Coventry City 1928), George Webb (Manchester United 1936), Dave Ballard (Nottingham Forest 1958).

IRCHESTER UNITED

Chairman: Geoff Cotter
Secretary: Glyn Cotter, 26 Denford Way, Wellingborough, Northants NN8 5UB (01933 402514)
Manager: Andy Toon **Asst. Manager:** Roy Geeves **Physio:** Mick Howarth.
Ground: Alfred Street, Irchester (01933 312877).
Directions: Off Rushden Road to Wollaston Road, next to recreation ground.
Capacity: 1,000 **Seats:** None **Cover:** Yes **Floodlights:** No **Programme:** No
Colours: Red & white/black/red **Change colours:** Red/blue/blue **Clubhouse:** Yes
Reserves' Lge: UCL Res. Div. 2 **Previous Leagues:** Rushden & District 1936-69.
Best FA Cup year: Prel. Rd 34-35 **Best FA Vase year:** Preliminary Round 77-78.
Hons: Northants Lg Div 2 30-31 31-32, Northants Snr Cup 29-30 48-49 75-76, Rushden & District Lg 28-29 29-30 36-37 46-47 50-51 51-52 56-57.

NEWPORT PAGNELL TOWN

Back Row (L-R): Jim Shepherd (Physio), Terry Ashton (Jt Mgr), Jamie Williams, Andy Bailey, Tim Roberts, Chris Eva, Adam Peach, Darren Lynch, Danni Janes (Jt Mgr). Front Row; Liam Diggins, Neil Humphrey, Guy Stewart, Ian Halsall, Des Cook (Cpt), Paul Harrington, Victor Syminster.

Chairman: Charles Stanley **Vice Chairman:** Gerry Ward **President:** Ken Inch.
Secretary: John Anderson, 59 Willen Road, Newport Pagnell, Bucks MK16 0DE (01908 610440).
Manager: Terry Ashton/D Janes
Ground: Willen Road, Newport Pagnell (01908 611993).
Directions: Adjacent to A442 Newport Pagnell by-pass.
Capacity: 2,000 **Seats:** 100 **Cover:** 100 **Floodlights:** Yes **Club Shop:**
Programme: 56 pages **Editor:** Ernie Print
Colours: Green/white/green **Change colours:** Yellow & black
Sponsors: Brian Currie **Nickname:** Swans **Founded:** 1963.
Midweek Matchday: Tuesday **Reserve Team's League:** United Counties
Previous Leagues: Nth Bucks 63-71/ South Mids 71-73 **Best FA Vase year:** 2nd Rd 84-85
Clubhouse: Open every evening
96-97 Captain: Des Cook **P.o.Y.:** Des Cook **Top Scorer:** Darren Lynch
Honours: UCL Div 1 82-83 (R-up 91-92, Div 1 Cup 77-78), Daventry Charity Cup R-up 93-94.

NORTHAMPTON O.N. CHENECKS

Chairman: John Wilson **Vice Chairman:** Eddie Slinn **President:** Claude Hasdell
Secretary: Andrew Pell, 19 Codlin Close, Little Billing, Northampton NN3 9TG (01604 406810)
Manager: Neil McAllister **Asst Manager/Physio:** John Goodger
Ground: Billing Road, Northampton (0604 34045).
Directions: South ring road, exit A43 Kettering, left at lights, top of hill, ground 200 yds on right.
Capacity: 1,350 **Seats:** Yes **Cover:** Yes **Floodlights:** No **Founded:** 1946.
Prog.: 16 pages with entry **Editor:** Eddie Slinn **Clubhouse:** Yes
Colours: Blue & white/blue/blue **Change colours:** All red
Previous Leagues: N'pton Town (pre-1969) **Reserves' League:** UCL Res Div 1
Midweek Matchday: **96-97 Captain:** Amos Donnelly
Honours: UCL Div 1 77-78 79-80, Northants Jnr Cup R-up 93-94

NORTHAMPTON VANAID

Chairman: Rob Clarke **Vice Chairman:** Steve Tebbutt **President:** A Blundell
Director of Football: Dick Underwood
Secretary: Tony Loveday, 28 Rickyard Rd, The Arbours, Northampton NN3 3RR (0604 412502).
Manager: Adam Sandy **Asst Manager:** Steve Jelley **Physio:** Glen Botterill
Ground: Fernie Fields, Moulton, Northampton (0604 670366).
Directions: R'bout at Lumbertub pub take turn to Moulton, 1st right signposted.
Capacity: 700 **Seats:** 100 **Cover:** Yes **Floodlights:** **Founded:** 1968
Programme: Yes **Editor:** Tony Loveday **Clubhouse:** Large bar. Hot food/bar meals
Colours: Blue/blue/yellow **Change colours:** Yellow/black/yellow **Nickname:** Vans.
Previous League: N'pton Town (pre-1993) **Reserves' League:** UCL Res Div 2
Sponsors: Echo PLC **96-97 Captain:** Adam Sandy **Record Gate:** 78
Honours: UCL Div 1 93-94 (Benevolent Cup R-up 93-94), Northants Jnr Cup 93-94, Northampton Town Lg 88-89 89-90.

OLNEY TOWN

Back Row (L-R); Mark McCarthy, John Hammersly, Alex Chaplin, Paul Sawyer, Russell Ward, Mark Lancaster, Lee Bannister, Asa Aldridge, Alan Byron (Mgr). Front Row; Steve Raybould, Malcolm Thomas, Neil Baldwin, Simon Botterill, James Kinns, Tommy Wootton.

Chairman: Peter Shipton **President:** Andrew Soul
Secretary: Andrew Baldwin, 49 Midland Road, Olney, Bucks MK46 4BP (01234 711071)
Manager: Alan Byron **Asst Manager:** Keith Berry **Physio:** Peter Munting
Ground: East Street, Olney (0234 712227)
Directions: Enter Olney on A509 from Wellingborough, 100yds on left enter East St, ground 200 yds on left.
Capacity: 2,000 **Seats:** None **Cover:** Yes **Floodlights:** No **Founded:**
Programme: 32 pages **Editor:** Barry Simons **96-97 Captain:** Richard Large
Colours: Black &white/white/white **Change colours:** Yellow/black/black **Sponsors:** Cyclo Sports
Clubhouse: Yes **Previous Leagues:** Nth Bucks, Rushden & Dist.
Honours: UCL Div 1 72-73, Berks & Bucks I'mediate Cup 92-93

ROTHWELL CORINTHIANS:

Chairman: Brian Johnson **Vice Chairman:** May Clelland **President:** Terry Smith
Secretary: Bob Clelland, 5 Drake Close, Rothwell, Northants NN14 6DJ (01536 710134).
Manager: Rob Clark **Physio:** Mick Fox
Ground: Seargeant's Lawn, Desborough Road, Rothwell (01536 418688)
Directions: A6 towards Desborough, on right opposite Greening Road.
Capacity: **Seats:** 50 **Cover:** 100 **Floodlights:** No **Shop:** No
Programme: Yes **Editor:** Brian Johnson **Nickname:** Corinthians
Colours: Red & white/red/red **Change colours:** Green/black/black
Sponsor: Springfir Estates **Founded:** 1930's **96-97 Captain:** John Cairns
Club House: Yes **Previous Lge:** East Midlands Alliance
Honours: East Midlands Alliance (2).

St IVES TOWN

President: Alan Arkley **Chairman:** Michael DiSiena **Vice Chairman:** Alastair Robinson
Secretary: Jim Stocker, 23 Townsend Rd, Needingworth, St Ives, Cambs PE17 3SE (01480 492680).
Manager: Cliff Miles **Asst Manager:** Mick O'Donovan
Ground: Westwood Rd, St Ives, Cambs (0480 63207).
Directions: From Huntingdon: A1123 thru Houghton, right at 2nd lighs into Ramsey Rd, after quarter mile turn right opp. Fire Station into Westwood Rd. From A604: Follow Huntingdon signs past 5 r'bouts, left into Ramsey Rd at lights then follow as above.
Capacity: 5,000 **Seats:** 130 **Cover:** 300 **Floodlights:** Yes **Founded:** 1887.
Colours: White & black/black/red **Change colours:** Blue/red/blue **Club Shop:** No.
Sponsor: First Copy **96-97 Captain:** Tony O'Donovan **Nickname:** Saints
Reserves' Lge: UCL Res Div 2 **Clubhouse:** Bar and entertainment room. Normal licensing hours.
Midweek matchday: Tuesday **Record Gate:** 400 v Saffron Walden Town, FA Vase.
Previous Ground: Meadow Lane **Prev. Lges:** Cambs/ Central Amtr/ Hunts/ P'boro. & D. (pre-1985).
Honours: Hunts Snr Cup 00-01 11-12 22-23 25-26 29-30 81-82 86-87 87-88, Cambs Lg 22-23 23-24 24-25.

SHARNBROOK

Chairman: Peter Butler **President:** John Boyles
Secretary: Roy Boulton, 10 St Mary's Avenue, Rushden, Northants NN10 9EP (01933 315890)
Manager: Dai Hunt **Asst Manager:** Ali Woods **Physio:** Jim Donaldson
Ground: Lodge Rd, Sharnbrook (0234 781080). **Directions:** Second sign to Sharnbrook from Rushden on A6, under railway bridge, right at T-junction, left past church, right into Lodge Road.
Capacity: 1,000 **Seats:** None **Cover:** Yes **Floodlights:** No
Programme: 12 pages **Editor:** Ali Woods **Sponsor:** BC Cars
Colours: Yellow/black/yellow **Change colours:** White/maroon/maroon **Clubhouse:** Yes
Reserves' Lge: UCL Res Div 2 **Previous Leagues:** Bedford & Dist (pre-1968). **96-97 Captain:** Steve Denton
Hons: Beds I'mediate Cup 73-74 **Player progressing to Football Lge:** Matt Jackson (Luton, Everton)

THRAPSTON TOWN

President: Derek Barber **Chairman:** Dave Harris **Vice Chairman:** Barry Carter
Secretary: Bev Harrison, 23 Springfield Avenue, Tharpston, Northants NN14 4TJ (01832 732150)
Manager: Gary Petts **Asst Manager:** Barry Carter **Physio:** Nigel Gore
Ground: Chancery Lane, Thrapston, Northants (08012 732470).
Directions: Chancery Lane off A605 in town centre.
Capacity: 1,000 **Seats:** Yes **Cover:** Yes **Floodlights:** No **Founded:** 1960.
Programme: Yes **Editor:** Mrs A J Petts **Prev. Lge:** Kettering Amtr (pre-1978)
Colours: White/blue/blue **Change colours:** All yellow **Nickname:** Venturas
Sponsor: Hobbs Direct Mail **96-97 Captain:** Mark Buckby **Clubhouse:** Yes
Honours: Northants Junior Cup 87-88, Kettering Amateur Lg 70-71 72-73 73-74 77-78.

WELLINGBOROUGH WHITWORTHS

Chairman: Bob Jarvis **Vice Chairman:** Dave Woodley **President:** Terry Faulkner
Secretary: Brian Higgins, 1 Knightlands Road, Wellingborough NN9 5SU (01933 650031).
Manager: Mark Herring **Asst Manager:** John Reid **Physio:** Andrew King
Ground: London Road, Wellingborough, Northants (01933 227324).
Directions: Off London Road at Dog & Duck public house
Capacity: 700 **Seats:** None **Cover:** Yes **Floodlights:** No **Programme:** No
Colours: All yellow **Change colours:** Red & white/red/red **Reserves' Lge:** UCL Res Div 2
Sponsor: Whitworth Brothers **96-97 Captain:** Steve Grant
Clubhouse: Yes **Prev. Lges:** Rushden & Dist./ E. Mids All. (pre-1985).
Honours: Rushden & District Lg 76-77; Northants Jun Cup 96

Action from match between Huntingdon United & Rothwell Corinthians. *Photo - Martin Wray*

JEWSON
WESSEX LEAGUE

FEEDER TO: BEAZER HOMES LEAGUE

President/Chairman: Alf Peckham
Vice Chairman: Cyril Hurlock
Hon. Secretary: Trevor Brock, 2 Betula Close,
Waterlooville, Hampshire PO7 8EJ (01705 262367)

DIVISION ONE FINAL LEAGUE TABLE 1996-97

		P	*W*	*D*	*L*	*F*	*A*	*W*	*D*	*L*	*F*	*A*	*Pts*
1	A.F.C. Lymington	40	16	4	0	47	13	19	1	0	65	9	110
2	Wimborne Town	40	15	5	0	53	20	11	2	7	44	22	85
3	Thatcham Town	40	14	1	5	44	19	12	4	4	47	26	79*
4	Ryde	40	15	0	5	43	20	10	4	6	34	30	79
5	Bemerton Heath Hqn	40	13	5	2	43	22	10	4	6	26	23	78
6	Andover	40	11	5	4	51	19	8	7	5	29	23	69
7	Eastleigh	40	10	6	4	37	22	9	2	9	34	34	65
8	Downton	40	12	2	6	40	26	6	5	9	32	44	61
9	Cowes Sports	40	9	7	4	39	22	6	7	7	26	33	59
10	Portsmouth RN	40	13	2	5	42	28	3	2	15	23	51	51*
11	Gosport Borough	40	9	3	8	29	28	6	2	12	27	38	50
12	Aerostructures	40	8	4	8	31	37	5	5	10	14	29	48
13	Bournemouth	40	9	3	8	24	27	5	2	13	26	45	47
14	Brockenhurst	40	7	3	10	30	35	6	4	10	24	38	46
15	Whitchurch United	40	5	5	10	26	39	7	2	11	32	42	43
16	Christchurch	40	7	2	11	28	36	6	2	12	21	36	43
17	East Cowes Vics	40	4	3	13	25	39	6	4	10	28	33	37
18	Romsey Town	40	6	1	13	29	52	4	6	10	23	42	37
19	B.A.T.	40	4	4	12	21	34	4	5	11	22	40	33
20	A.F.C. Totton	40	4	6	10	31	40	4	2	14	23	47	32
21	Petersfield Town	40	6	3	11	26	38	2	2	16	16	54	29

*Thatcham Town deducted 4 points
Portsmouth RN deducted 1 point

FIRST DIVISION RESULTS CHART 1996-97

		1	2	3	4	5	6	7	8	9	10	11	12	13	14	15	16	17	18	19	20	21
1	AFC Lymington	X	1-0	0-0	1-1	2-1	2-0	3-1	5-1	3-1	2-0	2-0	2-0	2-2	2-0	3-1	2-1	5-1	1-1	3-2	4-0	2-0
2	AFC Totton	0-5	X	1-2	1-1	0-0	2-2	3-0	0-2	1-1	6-1	2-3	2-3	1-1	3-2	2-3	1-3	1-2	0-3	2-2	0-2	3-2
3	Aerostructures	1-5	3-0	X	0-2	0-1	3-1	2-0	1-1	2-1	1-3	1-1	2-5	1-0	1-4	3-2	2-1	2-2	1-4	0-2	5-2	0-0
4	Andover	0-1	2-0	3-0	X	1-1	0-1	3-2	2-0	4-0	1-1	2-2	5-1	2-3	2-2	5-0	2-0	1-2	5-1	6-0	1-1	4-1
5	B.A.T.	0-4	2-1	0-2	1-1	X	0-1	0-4	1-2	0-3	0-1	1-1	1-1	1-2	0-2	1-0	3-3	5-0	2-3	1-2	2-0	0-1
6	Bemerton HH	0-2	1-3	0-0	2-0	2-2	X	3-1	5-4	2-0	1-1	3-0	3-0	5-3	1-0	4-1	3-2	2-0	1-1	2-2	2-0	1-0
7	Bournemouth	0-3	1-0	1-0	0-2	1-4	0-2	X	0-1	2-0	1-1	3-1	1-0	2-3	2-1	3-0	3-0	0-0	0-1	3-2	1-1	0-5
8	Brockenhurst	0-1	0-0	4-1	0-0	0-2	0-1	1-2	X	4-2	2-0	3-1	2-2	0-2	2-3	2-1	1-2	3-1	3-1	1-4	2-3	0-6
9	Christchurch	0-7	2-1	0-2	1-2	1-1	1-2	0-3	2-0	X	1-2	4-0	1-1	0-3	3-1	0-1	6-1	3-1	2-3	0-1	1-0	0-4
10	Cowes Sports	0-2	4-1	0-0	2-2	1-1	3-0	7-1	2-0	1-1	X	5-1	0-0	2-0	2-1	2-1	1-2	1-1	0-0	1-5	4-0	1-3
11	Downton	0-1	4-0	4-0	1-2	4-0	1-2	3-1	3-3	1-0	0-3	X	3-2	3-1	1-0	4-1	2-0	2-2	1-0	0-6	1-2	2-0
12	East Cowes Vics	1-3	2-2	3-0	2-2	4-0	0-1	0-2	1-2	0-2	2-1	0-1	X	2-3	0-1	4-2	1-1	2-3	0-3	1-4	0-3	0-3
13	Eastleigh	0-3	3-0	1-1	0-2	4-1	1-1	3-2	0-1	0-1	0-0	3-1	2-0	X	2-2	3-0	4-1	1-1	3-1	1-1	3-1	3-2
14	Gosport Boro	1-7	3-1	0-1	0-1	3-1	1-0	0-0	2-0	2-5	4-0	2-3	0-1	0-1	X	1-0	2-1	2-2	2-0	2-2	2-1	0-1
15	Petersfield Town	2-4	1-2	1-3	1-1	1-3	0-2	1-0	1-1	0-1	3-1	3-2	2-1	1-4	1-2	X	3-0	3-1	0-1	0-3	0-4	2-2
16	Portsmouth RN	2-6	4-0	2-0	3-0	3-2	2-1	2-0	1-0	5-1	3-5	2-2	2-1	2-0	1-0	2-2	X	2-1	3-4	0-1	1-0	0-2
17	Romsey Town	0-2	1-4	2-1	0-4	3-1	3-3	1-3	1-3	1-0	1-2	2-6	0-3	1-4	3-2	4-0	3-2	X	0-1	0-1	2-5	1-5
18	Ryde	0-2	5-4	3-0	1-3	2-0	2-0	4-0	3-1	2-0	1-0	1-0	0-1	1-0	6-0	2-0	3-0	3-0	X	0-4	4-3	0-2
19	Thatcham Town	0-2	1-2	2-0	1-0	3-1	0-2	5-1	2-0	4-1	1-1	1-2	3-2	3-0	1-0	4-0	4-2	1-0	3-0	X	2-3	3-0
20	Whitchurch Utd	0-3	3-2	1-1	3-2	4-0	1-3	2-2	1-1	0-1	1-1	2-3	0-4	2-0	2-3	0-0	3-1	1-2	0-3	0-2	X	0-5
21	Wimborne Town	2-2	4-0	1-0	3-1	1-0	1-1	2-1	5-1	2-0	2-2	2-2	2-0	3-2	3-1	5-1	2-0	2-1	3-3	3-1	5-1	X

LEAGUE ATTENDANCES 1996-97

		Matches Played	*Highest Attendance*	*Lowest Attendance*	*Total Attendances*	*Average Attendance*
1	Wimborne Town	23	240	110	3,891	169
2	AFC Lymington	22	177	53	2,484	113
3	Andover	21	151	64	2,177	104
4	Romsey Town	21	318	51	2,155	103
5	Thatcham Town	23	150	50	1,885	82
6	B.A.T.	21	186	31	1,686	80
7	Cowes Sports	21	158	24	1,596	76
8	Gosport Borough	21	105	47	1,559	74
9	Brockenhurst	22	225	35	1.630	74
10	AFC Totton	21	148	31	1,534	73
11	Bournemouth	22	156	38	1,569	71
12	East Cowes Vics	21	153	33	1,428	68
13	Christchurch	21	135	40	1,373	65
14	Bemerton Heath	22	132	40	1,338	61
15	Whitchurch United	23	181	14	1,289	56
16	Eastleigh	22	86	20	1,199	55
17	Downton	22	107	6	1,167	53
18	Petersfield Town	22	119	25	1,156	53
19	Ryde	23	120	25	1,165	51
20	Aerostructure	22	89	22	1,039	47
21	Portsmouth RN	21	97	25	962	46
	TOTAL	457			34,282	75

Highest League Attendance:	318	Romsey Town	v	Eastleigh	26/8/96
Highest League Cup Attendance:	196	Wimborne Town	v	AFC Lymington	28/1/97
Lowest League Attendance:	14	Whitchurch Town	v	Bournemouth	1/2/97
Lowest League Cup Attendance:	6	Downton	v	Cowes Sports	16/10/96
League Cup Final Attendance:	400	Thatcham Town	v	Ryde	5/5/97

LEADING GOALSCORERS 1996-97

30	John Gomersall	Thatcham Town
27	John Wallsgrove	Portsmouth R.N.
25	Andy Sampson	AFC Lymington
22	Jamie Sturgess	Wimborne Town
20	Paul Clarkson	Whitchurch United

JEWSON WESSEX LEAGUE CUP 1996-97

First Round Aggregate Results

Aerostructures	v	Portsmouth RN	4-2
Downton	v	Cowes Sports	10-2
Whitchurch United	v	AFC Totton	6-4
Brockenhurst	v	BAT	5-0
Petersfield Town	v	Romsey Town	6-3

Second Round Aggregate Results

Bemerton Heath*	v	Aerostructures	1-1
Eastleigh	v	Gosport Borough	3-1
Ryde	v	Brockenhurst	1-0
Whitchurch United	v	Christchurch	5-3
Bournemouth	v	Andover	2-1
AFC Lymington	v	East Cowes Vics	4-1
Thatcham Town	v	Petersfield Town	3-1
Wimborne Town	v	Downton	6-3

*Won on away goals rule

Quarter-Final Aggregate Results

Bournemouth	walkover	Whitchurch United	
Thatcham Town	v	Bemerton Heath	2-1
Ryde	v	Eastleigh	5-4
Wimborne Town	v	AFC Lymington	4-3

Semi-Final Aggregate Results

Ryde	v	Bournemouth	3-1
Thatcham Town	v	Wimborne Town	8-3

Final at Eastleigh FC

Ryde	v	Thatcham Town	0-4

JEWSON WESSEX LEAGUE
FIRST DIVISION RECORD SINCE FORMATION

	86/7	*87/8*	*88/9*	*89/90*	*90/1*	*91/2*	*92/3*	*93/4*	*94/5*	*95/6*	*96/7*
Aerostructures	-	13	10	12	16	9	12	19	17	18	12
AFC Lymington	-	-	5	5	9	2	1	3	8	2	1
AFC Totton	3	8	14	6	14	17	16	21	9	14	20
Andover	-	-	-	-	-	-	-	2	7	9	6
Bashley	1	1	1	-	-	-	-	-	-	-	-
B.A.T.	-	-	-	3	8	16	18	9	13	15	19
Bemerton HH	-	-	-	8	18	8	3	7	5	8	5
Bournemouth	15	10	12	10	3	6	7	11	2	7	13
Brockenhurst	17	18	16	17	7	12	10	8	6	19	14
Christchurch	-	5	13	15	15	13	13	10	18	5	16
Cowes Sports	-	-	-	-	-	-	-	-	15	16	9
Downton	-	-	-	-	-	-	-	16	20	12	8
East Cowes Vics	-	9	8	13	13	14	20	14	16	10	17
Eastleigh	8	12	9	14	12	10	9	15	14	4	7
Fleet Town	-	-	-	18	10	11	8	6	1	-	-
Gosport Borough	-	-	-	-	-	-	5	5	10	11	11
Havant Town	5	2	2	11	1	-	-	-	-	-	-
Horndean	14	14	11	16	20	18	11	17	22	-	-
Lymington Town	10	19	-	-	-	-	-	-	-	-	-
Newport	4	4	3	2	-	-	-	-	-	-	-
Petersfield Town	-	-	-	-	-	-	-	18	21	20	21
Portals Athletic	12	-	-	-	-	-	-	-	-	-	-
Portsmouth RN	13	16	17	19	17	19	17	13	11	17	10
Romsey Town	16	3	7	1	4	4	21	-	-	-	18
R.S. Southampton	2	-	-	-	-	-	-	-	-	-	-
Ryde Sports	-	-	-	-	11	7	6	12	12	3	4
Sholing Sports	9	7	15	9	19	15	19	-	-	-	-
Steyning Town	11	17	-	-	-	-	-	-	-	-	-
Swanage Herston	-	-	-	-	2	5	14	20	19	21	-
Thatcham Town	6	11	4	7	6	3	4	4	3	1	3
Wellworthy Ath	7	15	-	-	-	-	-	-	-	-	-
Whitchurch United	-	-	-	-	-	-	15	22	-	13	15
Wimborne Town	-	6	6	4	5	1	2	1	4	6	2

LEAGUE CHAMPIONS

1986-87	-	Bashley
1987-88	-	Bashley
1988-89	-	Bashley
1989-90	-	Romsey Town
1990-91	-	Havant Town
1991-92	-	Wimborne Town
1992-93	-	AFC Lymington
1993-94	-	Wimborne Town
1994-95	-	Fleet Town
1995-96	-	Thatcham Town
1996-97	-	AFC Lymington

LEAGUE CUP CHAMPIONS

1986-87	-	Road Sea
1987-88	-	East Cowes Victoria Athletic
1988-89	-	AFC Lymington
1989-90	-	AFC Totton
1990-91	-	Thatcham Town
1991-92	-	Thatcham Town
1992-93	-	Gosport Borough
1993-94	-	Wimborne Town
1994-95	-	Thatcham Town
1995-96	-	Downton
1996-97	-	Thatcham Town

AEROSTRUCTURES SPORTS & SOCIAL CLUB

President: Al Tritten **Chairman:** Peter Mence **Gen. Mgr:** Nigel Kent
Secretary: Richard Phippard, 198 Butts Road, Sholing, Southampton SO19 1BP (01703 438413)
Manager: Sean Mallow **Reserve's Manager:**
Ground: Folland Park, Kings Avenue, Hamble (01703 452173).
Directions: M27 junction 8, then B3397 to Hamble. One and a half miles from Hamble (BR); turn right out of station, proceed for one mile then turn right into Queens Avenue. Ground 50 yards on right.
Midweek Matches: Wednesday, (Res Tuesday) **Reserve's League:** Wessex Comb.
Previous Name: Folland Sports (pre-1990).
Colours: All Maroon with sky pin stripe **Change colours:** White/white/red & white **Floodlights:** Yes
Record defeat: 1-10 v Andover (A), Wessex League 93-94.
Clubhouse: 300 capacity social club. Cricket & bowls
Honours: Hants Lg Div 3 80-81 (Div 4 79-80), Hants Intermediate Cup 79-90, Southampton Snr Cup 85 87 92

A.F.C. LYMINGTON

Chairman: John Mills **V-Chairmen:** Richard Millbery/Bob Philpott **President:** Jack Holliday
Secretary: John Osey, 9 Samphire Close, Lymington, Hants SO41 9LR (01590 676995).
Manager: Derek Binns **Asst Manager:** Kevin Green **Physio:** Alan Farrar
Ground: Lymington Sports Ground, Southampton Road, Lymington (01590 671305).
Directions: M27 jct 1, follow signs (A337) to Lymington via Lyndhurst and Brockenhurst, ground 250yds on left after 1st set of lights on entering town. 1 mile from Lymington Town BR station.
Seats: 200 **Cover:** 200 **Capacity:** 3,000 **Floodlights:** Yes **Club Shop:** Yes
Programme: 48 pages, 50p **Editor/Press Officer:** John Mills
Colours: Red & black/Black/Red. **Change colours:** Yellow & green/green/green.
Founded: 1988 **Nickname:** Linnets **Sponsors:**
Midweek Matches: Tuesday. **Reserve Team's League:** Jewson Wessex Combination.
Record Attendance: 2,900 v Karen Mills Memorial Day 12.3.95
Previous Name: Lymington Town (until 1988 when the club merged with Wellworthy Athletic).
Previous Ground: Ampress Ground (Wellworthy Athletic), until 1988 merger.
Best FA Cup season: 3rd Qualifying Rd 92-93 (lost 0-1 at home to Cheltenham).
Players progressing to Football League: Stuart Doling (Doncaster Rovers), Russell Perrett (Portsmouth).
Clubhouse: Sat 2-7pm training and match nights. Rolls, hot pies.
96-97 Captain: Graham Kemp **P.o.Y.:** Graham Kemp **Top Scorer:** Mike McDonnell 26
Club Record Scorer: Darren Pitter 197 **Club Record Appearances:** Glen Limburn 329.
Record win: 11-1 v Romsey Town (H), Wessex League 9/11/92.
Record defeat: 0-8 v Basingstoke Town (A), Hampshire Senior Cup 10/4/90.
Honours: Wessex Lg 92-93 96-97 (R-up 91-92 95-96), Wessex Lg Cup 88-89 (R-up 94-95), Wessex Comb. 92-93, Hants Snr Cup R-up 89-90, Texaco Cup 91-92, Bournemouth Snr Cup 92-93, (R-up 96-97), Russell Cotes Cup 93-94 94-95 (R-up 91-92 92-93), Pickford Cup R-up 92-93. *As Lymington Town: Russell Cotes Cup 35-36. Bournemouth Snr Cup 83-84 (R-up 69-71 84-85), Hants Lg Div 2 R-up 83-84, Hants Lg Div 3 67-68 (Div 2 R-up 82-83). As Wellworthy Ath: Bournemouth Snr Cup 87-88 (R-up 53-54), Hants Interm Cup 56-57 84-85, Pickford Cup 84-85, Bournemouth Lg 84-85, Hants Lg Div 3 R-up 85-86.*

A.F.C. Lymington.

AFC NEWBURY

Chairman: Gerry Hynes **Manager:**
Secretary: Jim Goslin, The Flat, Porch Farm, Newbury Road, Kingsclere, Newbury, Berks RG20 4SX (01635 298985)
Ground: Faraday Road, Newbury, Berks (01635 523222)
Directions: A34 to Robin Hood roundabout, then A4 towards Reading. Right at lights after 100 yards into Faraday Road. Ground at end of road.
Colours: Green & white/white/green & white **Change:** Red & white/red/red & white
Midweek Matches: Tuesday

A.F.C. TOTTON

Chairman: Bob Devoy **Vice Chairman:** Mr P Maiden **President:** Mr D Maton.
Secretary: Mrs Sheila Benfield, 35 Fishers Rd, Totton, Southampton SO40 9HW (01703 865421).
Manager: Ian Robinson **Press Officer:** Mr P Chilcott (01703 860453).
Ground: Testwood Park, Testwood Place, Totton, Southampton (01703 868981).
Directions: 5 mins walk from Totton station. Turn off r'bout in Totton centre into Library Rd, then 1st left & 2nd rd.
Seats: 200 **Cover:** 250 **Capacity:** 2,500 **Floodlights:** Yes **Founded:** 1886
Colours: White & blue/blue/white & blue **Change colours:** Red & white/red/red
Sponsors: Cap'n Cod **Midweek Matches:** Tuesday **Nickname:** Stags.
Record Gate: 600 v Windsor & Eton, F.A. Cup 4th Qualifying Rd 82-83.
Club Shop: No **Programme:** 30 pages 50p **Previous League:** Hants 1886-1986
Previous Name: Totton FC (until merger with Totton Athletic in 1979).
Previous Grounds: Downs Park/ Mayfield Park.
Clubhouse: Open for matches and training sessions. Burgers, sandwiches, tea, coffee, biscuits etc available.
96-97 Captain: **96-97 Top Scorer:** **96-97 P.o.Y.:**
Honours: Hants Lg(2)

ANDOVER

Chairman: Mick Burford **President:** R Coleman
Secretary: Chris Jeremy, 23 Stubbs Court, Artists Way, Andover, Hants SP10 3QR (01264 361973)
Manager: Ken Cunningham-Brown **Asst Manager:** Mike Burford **Physio:** Chris Burford
Ground: Portway Stadium, West Portway Industrial Estate, Andover SP10 3LF (01264 333052).
Directions: From the Andover By-pass A303 follow the signs to Portway Industrial estate. On exiting the A303 turn right at r/about and over bridge, bear off left at next mini r/about and after 150yards turn right onto estate. head straight on until you enter Hopkinson Way, ground on left 400/500 yards.
Capacity: 3,000 **Cover:** 250 **Seats:** 250 **Floodlights:** Yes **Club Shop:** No.
Programme: 50 pages, 50p **Editor:** **Metal Badges:** Yes.
Colours: Red & black/black/red **Change cols:** Blue & white/white/white
Founded: 1883. **Nickname:** The Lions. **Sponsors:**
Midweek matchday: Tuesday **Reserve Team's League:** None.
Record Attendance: 1,100 v Leicester, ground opening. *(3,484 v Gillingham at Walled Meadow, previous ground).*
Best FA Cup season: 1st Rd 62-63 (lost 0-1 to Gillingham). **Best FA Trophy season:** 3rd Qual Rd 69-70 70-71.
Best FA Vase season: 4th Rd 94-95 (lost 1-3 at Falmouth Town)
Prev. Lges: Salisbury & D./ Hants 1896-98 99-1901 02-62/ Southern 1898-99 1971-93/ Western 1962-71.
Players progressing to Football League: Keith Wilson (Soton 1959), Nigel Spackman (B'mouth 1980), Colin Court (Reading 1981), A Kingston (Soton), P Brown (Soton, Walsall), Emeka Nwajiobi (Luton).
Clubhouse: Open matchdays & private functions
Club Record Scorer: T Randall 73 **Club Record Appearances:** P Pollard 469
Honours: Wessex Lg R-up 94-95, Western Lg R-up 69-70 70-71, Hants Lg 13-14 24-25 33-34 44-45 48-49 50-51 61-62 (R-up 42-43, Northern Div 13-14, Div 2 R-up 37-38, Salisbury & Dist Lg 1894-95 95-96 96-97 99-1900 03-04 07-08 12-13, Hants Sen Cup 48-49 50-51 55-56 64-65, Russell Cotes Cup 23-24 31-32 37-38 44-45 52-53 58-59 60-61 61-62, Pickfords Cup 50-51, Hants Interm Cup 59-60 60-61, Hants Junior Cup 19-20 (R-up 1894-95 1910-11 12-13).

B.A.T. SPORTS

Chairman: Dixie Batt **Manager:** Eddie Harper & Paul Bishop
Secretary: M Geddes, 136 Regents Park Rd, Southampton SO15 8PD (01703 325224 H, 01703 793420 W)
Ground: BAT Sports Ground, Southern Gdns, off Ringwood Road, Totton (01703 862143).
Directions: Into centre of Totton, proceed up Ringwood Rd past small r'bout, 2nd left into Southern Gardens. Half mile from Totton (BR), bus X2 (Southampton-Bournemouth).
Seats: 150. **Cover:** 150. **Capacity:** 3,000 **Floodlights:** Yes **Founded:** 1925
Colours: Blue & yellow/blue/blue **Change:** Red & black/red/red
Programme: 20 pages, 30p **Midweek Matches:** Tuesday
Best FA Vase year: 2nd Rd 96-97
Clubhouse: Normal licensing hrs, all day for members' sports facilities. Darts, pool, CD player. Hot & cold snacks.

BEMERTON HEATH HARLEQUINS

Chairman: George Parker **President:** Peter Say. **Manager:** Steve Slade
Secretary: A.J.Hardwick, 2 Ashley Rd, Salisbury, Wilts. SP2 7BZ (01722 333015)
Ass.Manager: Kevin Franklyn. **Physio:** Andy Nash **Coach:** Gary Cross
Ground: Western Way, Bemerton Heath, Salisbury, Wilts (01722 331925).
Directions: Turn off A36 Salisbury-Bristol Rd at Skew Bridge (right turn if coming out of Salisbury), 1st left into Pembroke Rd for half mile, 2nd left along Western Way - ground quarter mile at end. 40 mins walk from Salisbury (BR) station. Bus 351 or 352 from city centre stops at junction of Pembroke Rd/ Western Way.
Seats: 155. **Cover:** 350 **Floodlights:** Yes **Founded:** May 1989 **Clubhouse:** Yes
Colours: Black & white/black/black & white **Change colours:** Yellow/white/white
Nickname: Quins **Programme:** 32 pages, 50p **Midweek Matches:** Tuesday
Record Gate:1,118 v Aldershot Town F.A.Cup Ist Qual.RD.Aug.94.
Previous Names: Bemerton Athletic, Moon FC & Bemerton Boys; all merged in 1989.
Previous Leagues: B'ton Ath.: Salis. & Wilts Comb., Moon: Salis. & Andover Sunday, B'ton Boys: Mid Wilts.
Honours: Wilts Snr Cup 92-93. *Wilts Lg(3) as Bemerton Athletic* **Club record appearances:** Keith Richardson.

BOURNEMOUTH

Chairman: V C Dominey **Vice Chairman:** J B Wood **President:** D Nippard
Secretary: Mrs Sandra Dominey, 26 Victoria Road, Parkstone, Poole, Dorset BH12 3BB (01202 737859 H)
Manager: Alex Pike **Asst Manager:** Nick Jennings **Coach:** Chris Weller
Physio: Irvin Brown **Comm. Manager:** Alex Pike **Press Officer:** Mark Willis.
Ground: Victoria Park, Namu Rd., Winton, Bournemouth, Dorset (01202 515123).
Directions: Any bus to Wimborne Road, Winton. 2 miles from Bournemouth Central (BR).
Seats: 250 **Cover:** 250 **Capacity:** 3,000 **Floodlights:** Yes **Founded:** 1875.
Colours: Red & white/red/red **Change colours:** Green & yellow/green/green
Programme: 58 pages, 50p **Editor:** Mark Willis **Club Shop:** No.
Nickname: Poppies. **Sponsors:** Chapel Carpets **Midweek Matches:** Tuesday
Previous Leagues: Hants. **Previous Ground:** Dene Park 1888-90
Previous Names: Bournemouth Rovers 1875-88/ Bournemouth Dene Park 1888-90.
Reserves' League: Jewson Wessex Comb.
Clubhouse: Open daily 7-11pm. Sandwiches & hot snacks (burgers, chips etc).
Club record scorer: B Head **Record fee rec.:** £1,500 for Chike Onourah (Wimborne 93-94)
Honours: Hants Lg 13-13 21-22, B'mouth Snr Cup 66-67 89-90, Texaco F'lit Cup R-up 91-92, Hant I'mediate Cup 49-50 69-70, Hants Yth Cup 54-55 57-58 67-68.

BROCKENHURST

Chairman: Brian Bidwell **Manager:** Mike Read
Secretary: Paul Christopher, 31 Brookside Road, Bransgore, Christchurch, Dorset BH23 8NE (01425 672012 H)
Ground: Grigg Lane, Brockenhurst, Hants (01590 623544).
Directions: 400 yds from Brockenhurst station, just off main shopping area.
Seats: 200 **Cover:** 300 **Capacity:** 2,000 **Floodlights:** Yes **Founded:** 1898
Colours: Blue & white/blue/blue **Change colours:** Red & white/red/red
Programme: 12 pages, 20p, **Editor:** C West (01590 623714)
Midweek Matches: Wednesday. **Previous League:** Hants 24-26 47-86
Clubhouse: Every evening plus Tues, Sat & Sun lunchtimes.
Honours: Hants I'mediate Cup 61-62, B'mouth Snr Cup 60-61, Hants Lg 75-76 (R-up 73-74 79-80, Div 2 70-71 (R-up 60-61), Div 3 59-60), F.A. Amateur Cup 2nd Rd 73-74.

CHRISTCHURCH

Chairman: Robin Osborne **Vice Chairman:** Jan Bridle. **President:** Dennis James.
Secretary: Mrs D Page, 87 The Albany, Manor Road, Bournemouth BH1 3EJ (01202 551977).
Manager: Ian Kelly. **Physio:** Brian Finch
Ground: Christchurch Sporting Club, Hurn Bridge, Avon Causeway, Christchurch (01202 473792).
Directions: A338 from Ringwood, turn off signed Hurn Airport on left. Before Airport use mini roundabout & take exit signed to Sopley and ground is immediately on the right. 3 miles from Christchurch (BR).
Seats: 215 **Cover:** 265 **Capacity:** 2,000 **Floodlights:** Yes **Founded:** 1885
Programme: 16 pages, 50p **Editor:** Phil Old **Press Officer:** Dennis James.
Colours: All royal blue (white trim) **Change colours:** Yellow/black/yellow & black **Nickname:** Priory
Sponsors: Franklin Transport **Midweek Matches:** Tuesday **Previous League:** Hampshire.
Previous Ground: Barrack Rd Recreation Ground (until 1984).
Players progressing to Football Lge: Jody Craddock (Cambridge Utd 1993), Dan West (Aston Villa, 1994).
Clubhouse: Normal pub hours. Cooked food at lunchtimes.
Club record appearances: John Haynes. **96-97 P.o.Y.:** Nick Carter
Honours: Hants Jnr Cup 1892-93 1911-12 20-21, Hants Int. Cup 86-87, Pickford Cup 1991, Hants Lg Div 2 37-38 47-48 85-86 (Div 3 56-57), B'mouth Snr Cup(5) 56-57 59-60 67-70, B'mouth Page-Croft Cup 94-95.

AFC Lymington celebrate after 1-0 victory at Downton to clinch the title

BAT's goal-line defence foiled Whitchurch this time, but went on to lose 0-4.

Gosport Borough's Kevin Nash causes havoc amongst Romsey Town's defence of Ron Chapman and keeper Michael Wisher.
Photo- Ray Pruden

COWES SPORTS

President: **Chairman:** Ray Sleep. **Manager:** Dale Young.
Secretary: Mr W G Murray, 53 Park Rd, Cowes, Isle of Wight PO31 7LY (01983 294445).
Ground: Westwood Park, Reynolds Close, off Park Rd, Cowes, Isle of Wight (01983 293793).
Directions: Take Park Road out of Cowes centre. Reynolds Close is a right turn half mile up hill.
Capacity: **Seats:** Yes **Cover:** Stand **Floodlights:** Yes **Founded:**
Colours: Blue & white stripes/black/blue **Change colours:** All red
Previous League: Hampshire (pre-1994) **Midweek Fixtures:** Wednesday
Best FA Cup season: Fourth Qualifying Round replay 57-58 (lost 1-4 at Trowbridge after 2-2 draw).
Honours: Hampshire Lg 93-94.

DOWNTON

Chairman: James Blake **President:** R Tanner
Secretary: Brian Trent 21 Fison Walk, Bishopdown, Salisbury, Wilts SP1 3JF (01722 323097)
Manager: M Savage **Coach:** C Huxford **Physio:** T Ship
Ground: Brian Whitehead Sports Ground, Wick Lane, Downton (01725 512162)
Directions: Travelling south from Salisbury on A338, 7 miles, turn right into Wick Lane, gr qtr mile on left.
Capacity: 1600 **Seats:** 250 **Cover:** Nil **Floodlights:** Yes **Club Shop:** No
Programme: Yes **Editor:** J Blake
Colours: Red/white/red **Change colours:** Yellow/blue/yellow
Sponsor: Lex Vauxhall Salisbury **Nickname:** The Robins **Founded:** 1905
Midweek Matchday: Wednesday **Youth League:**
Previous League: Bournemouth, Hants (pre-1993).
Clubhouse: Bar with kitchen facilities.
96-97 Captain: J Wood **96-97 Top Scorer:** D Miles **96-97 P.o.Y.:** M Savage
Honours: Wilts Sen Cup 79-80 80-81, (R-up 55-56 91-92 94-95); Wilts Jun Cup 49-50; Bournemouth Sen Lge 60 61 62 64 65 67 68, Sen Lge Cup 61-62 63-64 66-67, Cup 62-63 79-80; Wessex Lge Cup 95-96; Wessex Comb Cup (R-up 95-96); Russell Cotes Cup 95-96; Hayward Cup 64-65.

EAST COWES VICTORIA ATHLETIC

Chairman: Mick Everett **Vice-Chairman:** Lee Bray **Gen Manager:** Steve Stay
Secretary: Ray Fleming, Glenmead, Chilton Lane, Brighstone, I.O.W. PO30 4DR (01983 740113)
Manager: Tony Newman **Coach:** Steve Stay **Physios:** Mike Reed & Kevin Marsay
Ground: Beatrice Avenue Ground, East Cowes, I.O.W. (01938 297165).
Directions: From the ferry: 1 mile from town centre on lower main road to Newport or Ryde, near Whippingham Church adjacent to Osborne Middle School.
Seats: 250 **Cover:** 400 **Capacity:** 4,000 **Floodlights:** Yes **Founded:** 1968.
Colours: Red & white stripes/red/red **Change colours:** Green & white/green/green
Programme: 40 pages, 50p **Editor:** Alan Green (01983 296069)
Midweek Matches: Wednesday **Sponsors:** Bishops Insurance. **Club Shop:** No.
Nickname: Vics. **Previous Leagues:** (E.C. Vics): I.O.W. 1898-19 21-47/ Hants 14-21 47-87.
Previous Names: East Cowes Victoria (founded 1888) merged with East Cowes Athletic in 1968.
Midweek matchday: Wednesday **Reserve team's League:** Isle of Wight Lge.
Player progressing to Football League: Gareth Williams (Aston Villa, via Gosport Borough, 1987).
Clubhouse: Yes, open most evenings and matchdays. Crisps and confectionary available.
96-97 Top Scorer: John Beard **96-97 Captain:** Simon Jarvis **96-97 P.o.Y.:** Simon Butler
Club record appearances: Joe Reed.
Record Gate: 2,000 v Poole Town, FA Cup 1954
Record win: 9-0 v Brading Town (A), Hampshire Lg 86-87.
Record defeat: 0-10 v Andover (A), Wessex Lg 94-95.
Honours: (as East Cowes Vics pre-'68): Wessex Lg Cup 87-88, IOW Senior Gold Cup 79-80 81-82 82-83 83-84 84-85 85-86 88-89, Hants Lg 85-86 86-87 (Div 2 52-53 82-83, Div 3 63-64 71-72, Div 3 West 47-48), IOW Lg 1898-99 99-1900 30-31 34-35 78-79 82-83 86-87 87-88 94-95 (Div 2 1898-99 1904-05 06-07, Div 3 28-29 32-33, Comb Div 2 87-88 90-91,94-95 IOW Chal. Cup 1899-1900 00-01 01-02 19-20 47-48 50-51 51-52 52-53 80-81 84-85 87-88 90-91 91-92, IOW Mem. Cup 19-20 32-33 82-83 87-88 90-91, Brooklyn Cup 86-87 87-88 89-90 91-92, IOW Charity Cup 23-24 25-26, IOW Centenary Cup 89-90 91-92.

EASTLEIGH

Chairman: Roger Sherwood **President:** Phil Fernandez.
Secretary: Mr R G Kearslake, 10 Binsey Close, Millbrook, Southampton, Hants SO16 4AQ (01703 779545).
Manager: Ray Light **Asst Manager:** Dave Blandford **Physio:** Barry Wilkinson.
Ground: 'Ten Acres', Stoneham Lane, North Stoneham, Eastleigh SO50-9HT (01703 613361).
Directions: M27 to Jct 5, to r'bout - exit marked Stoneham Lane, ground on left but carry on to r'bout and come back down Stoneham Lane, turning right opposite Concord Club. Ground 400 yds on left. Three quarters of a mile from Southampton Parkway (BR). Bus 48 (Southampton-Winchester) to Stoneham Church stop.
Seats: 150 **Cover:** 210 **Capacity:** 4,300 **Floodlights:** Yes **Founded:** 1946.
Colours: All blue **Change colours:** White & blue/white/white
Programme: 32 pages with admission **Editor:** John Pothecary
Sponsors: Various **Nickname:** None. **Club Shop:** No.
Midweek matches: Wednesday **Previous Leagues:** Southampton Jnr & Snr 46-59/ Hants 50-86.
Previous Names: Swaythling Ath. 46-73/ Swaythling 73-80
Previous Grounds: Southampton Common 46-47/ Walnut Avenue, Swaythling 47-75.
Record Gate: 2,500 v Southampton, floodlight opener 30/9/75.
Clubhouse: Licence 11am-11pm Mon-Sat plus Sundays. Extensive facilities for weddings, parties, skittles and seminars. All catering undertaken.
96-97 Captain: **96-97 Top Scorer:** **96-97 P.o.Y.:**
Club record scorer: Johnny Williams, 177 **Club record appearances:** Ian Knight, 611.
Record win: 12-1 v Hythe & Dibden, home 11/12/48
Record defeat: 0-11 v Austin Spts, away 1/1/47.
Honours: FA Vase 4th Rd 90-91, Wessex Lg Cup R-up 91-92, Hants Lg Div 2 69-70 (R-up 54-55 60-61 62-63 64-65(Res), Div 3(W) 50-51 53-54 70-71(Res), Comb.(Res) 86-87)), Hants Midweek F'lit Cup 78-79, Soton Snr Lg(W) 49-50 (R-up 51-52(Res), Div 1 56-57(Res) 57-58(Res)), Russell Cotes R-up 76-77 80-81 89-90, Hants I'mediate Cup 50-51 56-57(Res) 74-75(Res)(R-up 73-74(Res)), Soton Snr Cup(Res) 74-75 78-79 87-88 (R-up(8) 55-56 57-59 60-61 66-67 71-72 80-81 87-88), Soton Jnr Lg Div 2 47-48(Res), Reg Mathieson Tphy(Res) 74-75 78-79 87-88.

GOSPORT BOROUGH

Chairman: I T Hay **President:** W J Adams.
Secretary: B V Cosgrave, 2 Cavanna Close, Rowner, Gosport PO13 0PE (01329 314117).
Manager: John Hawes. **Coaches:** Dave Pitt & Barry Cook. **Physio:** Dave Topliss
Ground: Privett Park, Privett Road, Gosport, Hants (01705 583986).
Directions: M27 junct 11, then A32 Fareham to Gosport, at Brockhurst r-about (after about 3 miles) right into Military Road passing thru H.M.S. Sultan, left into Privett Road at next r-about, ground 300 yds on left signed 'Privett Park Enclosure'. 2 miles from Portsmouth Harbour (BR) or Fareham (BR).
Capacity: 4,500 **Cover:** 500 **Seats:** 450 **Floodlights:** Yes **Club Shop:** No
Colours: Yellow/blue/blue **Change colours:** Red/Black/Black.
Programme: 20 pages, 50p **Editor:** Ian Hay (01329 314601)
Sponsors: Cougar Marine **Founded:** 1944. **Nickname:** The Boro'
Midweek matchday: Tuesday. **Reserve Team's League:** Jewson Wessex Combination.
Record Attendance: 4,770 v Pegasus, FA Amtr Cup 1951.
Best FA Trophy year: 1st Rd 88-89 **Best FA Amateur Cup year:** 3rd Rd 47-48 66-67
Best FA Vase year: 6th Rd rep 77-78 **Best FA Cup year:** 4th Qual. Rd 80-81 (lost to Windsor & Eton).
Previous Leagues: Portsmouth 44-45/ Hants 45-78/ Southern 78-92
Previous Name: Gosport Borough Athletic
Players progressing to Football League: P Harris (P'smouth, N'castle & Scotland), B Sherwood, D Dimmer, S Berry, R Blackman (Reading 47), R Pearson (P'smouth 49), A Mundy & M Barnard (P'smouth 51), P Smith (G'ham 54), A Grant (Brighton 56), B Gibbs (B'mouth 57), G Juryeff (P'smouth), R Carroll (Brentford 86), G Williams (A Villa 88).
Clubhouse: (01705 583986). Open matchdays from 1.30pm Saturday, 6.30pm Wednesday. Refreshment hut sells hot food and drinks.
96-97 Captain: **96-97 P.o.Y.:** **96-97 Top scorer:**
Club Record Scorer: Richie Coulbert 192 Mahoney 764. **Club Record Appearances:** Tony
Record Fees - Paid: £6,000 for Sandy Baird (Basingstoke Town, 1990)
Received: £30,000+ for Gareth Williams (Aston Villa, 1987).
Record win: 14-0 v Cunliffe-Owen, Hampshire Lg Div 1 45-46.
Record defeat: 0-9 twice; v Newport, Hants Lg Div 1 47-48. v Gloucester (A), Southern Lg Prem Div 89-90.
Honours: Wessex Lg Cup 92-93, Southern Lg Div 1 South R-up 84-85, Hants Lg 45-46 76-77 77-78 (Div 3 (Reserves) 70-71 75-76), Portsmouth Lg R-up 44-45, Hants Senior Cup 87-88, Russell Cotes Cup R-up 94-95, Hants Intermediate Cup 70-71, Portsmouth Senior Cup 61-62 69-70 70-71 94-95, South West Counties Pratten Challenge Cup 77-78.

PORTSMOUTH ROYAL NAVY

Chairman: Tony Miklinski
Secretary: Roy Newman, 8 Kimpton Close, Lee-on-Solent, PO13 8JY (01705 799198)
Manager: M Marsh **Physio:** F Cripps **Coach:** A Maher
Ground: The Navy Stadium, HMS Temeraire, Burnaby Road, West Portsmouth, (01705 724235).
Directions: From Portsmouth Harbour (BR), turn right onto The Hard, pass under the rail bridge and turn left into Park Road, after approx 200yards take 1st right into Burnaby Road. Entrance to ground 100 mtrs on the right.
Seats: 500 **Cover:** 500 **Capacity:** 1,500 **Floodlights:** Yes **Club Shop:** No
Programme: 50p **Editor:** Nicky Cooper **Press Officer:** Roy Newman
Colours: Royal & white/blue/blue **Change colours:** All Red
Club Sponsors: Federation Brewery **Formed:** 1962 **Nickname:** Sailors
Midweek Matches: Tuesday **Reserve Team's League:** Wessex Comb. Lge
Previous Leagues: Hampshire 62-86
Clubhouse: Open 1.5hrs before k.o. & 2hrs after game on matchdays and by arrangement only.
96-97 Captain: John Oliver **96-97 Top Scorer:** Jon Wallsgrove **96-97 P.o.Y.:** Jon Wallsgrove
Honours: Russell-Cotes Cup 67-68, Basingstoke Lg Div 2, Hants Lge Div 2 67-68 77-78 80-81.

ROMSEY TOWN

Chairman: Ken Jacobs
Secretary: Bill Clouder, 15 Malmesbury Road, Romsey SO51 8FS (01794 518556)
Manager: Dean Prince **Coach:** Martin Hall
Ground: The By-Pass Ground, South Front, Romsey (01794 512003)
Directions: Adjacent to roundabout at junction of A31 & A27, Romsey BR 3/4 mile.
Capacity: 1,500 **Cover:** Yes **Seats:** 250 **Floodlights:** Yes **Club Shop:** Yes
Colours: Yellow & black stripes/black & yellow/yellow **Change colours:** Red & black/red/red
Programme: Yes **Editor:** Andy Spreadbury (01703 739034)
Press Officer: Stuart Judd **Formed:** 1886 **Nickname:** The Town
Reserve Team's League: Wessex Lge Comb **Midweek Matchday:** Wednesday
Previous Leagues: HFC Bank Southampton Lge.
Clubhouse: Yes
96-97 - Captain: Guy Couch **Top Scorer:** Alan Bundy **P.o.Y.:** Nigel Cutler/Alan Bundy
Honours:

RYDE SPORTS

President: John Keynes **Chairman:** Ben Kennevin
Secretary: Mark Firmin, c/o Ground. (01983 615029 H)
Manager: Dennis Probee **Asst Manager:** Tony Newman. **Physio:** Tom Kennedy
Ground: Smallbrook Stadium, Ashey Rd, Ryde (01983 812906).
Directions: From the Pier Head follow directions to the Royal Isle of Wight Hospital, carry on past the hospital turning left at the Partlands Hotel - ground is one mile along Ashey Road. Not served by public transport.
Seats: 450 **Cover:** 1,500 **Capacity:** 5,000 **Floodlights:** 246 lux **Founded:** 1888.
Colours: All Red **Change colours:** All Blue **Metal Badges:** Yes.
Midweek Matches: Tuesday **Previous League:** Hants. **Club shop:** Yes
Programme: 20 pages, 50p. **Editor:** Mark Firmin (01983 812906) **Nickname:** The Reds.
Club Sponsors: Wight Sports/ Hoevertravel. **Reserve Team's League:** Isle of Wight League.
Best FA Vase season: Prel. Rd 90-91 **Best FA Cup season:** 3rd Rd Proper 35-36.
Record Gates: 3,100 v Aston Villa 17/12/90. 2,400 v Sheffield Wednesday 26/3/90.
Players pogressing to Football League: Roy Shiner (Sheff Wed), Keiron Baker & Kevin Allen (Bournemouth).
Clubhouse: Open everyday. 2 bars, function suite, balcony overlooking stadium, restaurant, fitness centre, gym, treatment room.Also Table Tennis Centre and Floodlit Astro Turf Football and Hockey pitch.
96-97 Captain: **96-97 Top Scorer:** **96-97 P.o.Y.:**
Current longest-serving player: Terry Pawling.
Honours: Hants Lg 1899-00 25-26 89-90 (Div 2 88-89, Div 3 64-65), Hants Snr Cup(8) 1899-00 03-04 25-26 34-39, IOW Gold Cup(7) 26-27 46-47 48-49 55-56 61-64, IOW Snr Challenge Cup 1898-99, IOW Gold Cup(7) 26-27 46-47 48-49 55-56 61-64, IOW Challenge Cup 27-28 80-81, P'mouth Snr Cup 1899-00 00-01 05-06 19-20 53-54 66-67 89-90, IOW Charity Cup(7) 18-22 44-47, Ryde & Dist Cup 89-90, Westwood Cup 84-85, IOW Lg 20-21 (Div 2 80-81), Memorial Cup 93-94.

Wimborne's Ryan Haigh jumps for joy.

Thatcham Town FC: *Photo - Eric Marsh*

Wimborne Town FC: *Photo - Andrew Chitty*

THATCHAM TOWN

Chairman: Phil Holdway **President:** **General Secretary:** John Haines
Football Secretary: Charles Heaver, 32 Baily Avenue, Thatcham, Berks RG13 3DU (01635 868179)
Manager: Jackie Stuart **Coach:** Ian Schofield
Ground: Waterside Park, Crookham Rd, Thatcham, Berks (01635 862016)
Directions: M4 junc 13, take A34 to Newbury, right onto A4 towards London. in Thatcham right towards railway station, ground on left beyond station, 2 mins walk from BR station.
Seats: 300 **Cover:** 300 **Capacity:** 3,000 **Floodlights:** Yes **Founded:** 1895
Colours: Blue & white/blue/blue **Change colours:** All red
Sponsors: Panasonic Gsm Mobile Phones **Club Shop:** Yes
Midweek Matches: Tuesday **Best FA Vase season:** 4th Qual Rd 96-97
Programme: 28 pages, 50p **Editor:** Dave Ware **Press Officer:** Dave Ware.(01635 861000)
Previous Ground: Station Road 46-52/ Lancaster Close 52-92. **Record Gate:** 1,400 v Aldershot ,F.A.Vase.
96-97 Captain: Richard Hayward **96-97 Top Scorer:** John Gomersall
96-97 Managers P.o.Y.: Glen Damen **96-97 Supporters P.o.Y.:** John Gomersall
Clubhouse: Open every evening & lunchtimes. **Honours:** Wessex Lg 95-96, Cup 90-91 91-92 94-95 96-97

WHITCHURCH UNITED

Chairman: Chris Rowland
Secretary: Debbie Case, 11 Falcon Close, Kempshott, Basingstoke RG22 5PP (01256 356645)
Ground: Longmeadow, Winchester Road, Whitchurch (01256 892493).
Directions: From Whitchurch (BR) station; turn left after Railway Inn, follow road to end, turn right into main road, arriving in town turn left along Winchester Road. Ground three quarters of a mile on left.
Seats: 200 **Cover:** Yes **Capacity:** **Floodlights:** Yes **Founded:**
Colours: Red & white/black/black **Change colours:** Blue/white/blue **Programme:** 24 pages
Previous Leagues: Hants (pre-1992). **Midweek Matches:** Thursday
Best FA Vase season: Extra-Preliminary Rd 93-94 (lost 1-3 at home to Peppard).
Clubhouse: Hot food on matchdays. Sports hall incorporating squash courts and indoor bowling green

WIMBORNE TOWN

Chairman: Steve Churchill **Vice Chairman:** Nick O'Hara **President:** Brian Maidment
Secretary: Mark Willis, 63 Victoria Close, Corfe Mullen, Wimborne, Dorset. BH21 3TX (01202 605089)
Manager: Alex Pike. **Coach:** Chris Weller **Physio:** Irvin Brown
Ground: The Cuthbury, Cowgrove Road, Wimborne, Dorset BH21 4EL (01202 884821).
Directions: Wimborne to Blandford Road, behind Victoria Hospital.
Seats: 275 **Cover:** 50 **Capacity:** 3,250 **Floodlights:** Yes **Club Shop:** Yes
Programme: 24 pages, 50p **Editor:** Secretary **Press Officer:** Secretary.
Colours: Black & white/black/black **Change colours:** Green/white/green
Club Sponsors: Fisks. **Nickname:** Magpies **Founded:** 1878
Midweek Matches: Tuesday **Reserve League:** Wessex Comb
Record Attendance: 3,250 v Bamberbridge FA Vase Semi-Final 28/3/92
Best FA Vase season: Winners 91-92 **Best FA Cup season:** 1st Rd Proper 82-83.
Previous Leagues: Dorset Lge, Dorset Comb, Western 81-86.
Clubhouse: Evenings 7-11pm, Sat noon-11pm, Sun noon-3pm & 7-10.30pm. Bar. Skittle alley.
96-97 Captain: Pete Howard **96-97 Top Scorer:** Jamie Sturgess **96-97 P.o.Y.:** Jamie Sturgess
Club Record Goalscorer: Jason Lovell. **Club Record Appearances:** Nicky Bridle
Honours: Wessex Lg 91-92 93-94 (R-up 92-93 96-97), Lg Cup 93-94 (R-up 90-91 95-96); Dorset Lg Div 1 80-81 81-82 (R-up 38-39 72-73), Div 2 31-32 34-35 36-37 (R-up 35-36), Lg Cup R-up(4) 72-74 80-82; Dorset Snr Cup 91-92 96-97, (R-up 80-82 85-86); Mark Frowde Cup 92-93 94-95; Dorset Snr Amateur Cup 36-37 63-64; Dorset Jnr Cup 31-32 36-37 (R-up 13-14 34-35); Dorset Minor Cup 12-13; Dorset Jnr Amateur Cup(3) 34-36 38-39; Bankes Charity Cup 89-90 94-95 95-96, Texaco F/Light Cup 90-91

Whitchurch United FC

SCREWFIX DIRECT WESTERN LEAGUE

FEEDER TO: BEAZER HOMES LEAGUE

President: Stan Priddle
Chairman: R J Webber **Vice Chairman:** Cyril Hurlock
Hon. Secretary: M E Washer, 16 Heathfield Road, Nailsea, Bristol BS19 1EB
(01275 851314)

For everyone connected with our League, this season was one of both optimism, and interest, since it heralded a new sponsor for our League. In that respect, we could have not bettered things, for in truth every hope was fulfilled both for them and for our Clubs. At our Presentation Weekend these thoughts were echoed by the Screwfix Direct owner Jon Goddard-Watts in what was a successful end to a successful season.

In most experts eyes, the season did not disappoint, inasmuch as Tiverton Town and Taunton Town fought hard and long, with Tiverton finally coming through deservedly to win another title, their third success in four years, and a fourth winning of the Les Phillips Cup in five years. To those who consider it all over before it starts every year, it is prudent to realise that after the four fixtures against these two, there are some 30 fixtures left, and only one club, Mangotsfield, won more than half the total games. Doesn't that suggest that reasons lay elsewhere? In the First Division, real interest was sustained until the final fixtures, with Melksham Town finally edging out Keynsham Town. Only the final couple of weeks saw the fading of Clyst Rovers, Exmouth Town and Bishop Sutton, who will benefit from the experience. For Melksham Town who only a couple of seasons ago, had resumed membership through the Pyramid structure, this was a tremendous effort well rewarded, and also a bonus point for the Pyramid structure despite its critics.

This year we welcome the addition of Bitton from the Gloucestershire County League, and Street from the Somerset Senior League, who are returning after a very long absence. Let us hope that both clubs will not find the going too hard and disparaging, for the gap in playing standards is very great indeed. We regretfully have been informed of the withdrawal of Amesbury Town, just prior to the season's start, and they will participate in the Salisbury League. This is very sad indeed, for the road back from this level is a long and arduous one. Although it is symptomatic of todays climate in football, one does begin to question the power being allowed to managers by clubs, and where management ends and control begins. All too often realisation comes too late.

So another season beckons and we hope that supporters and players both enjoy it, and that our standards will be maintained.

Maurice Washer, Secretary

FINAL LEAGUE TABLES 1996-97

PREMIER DIVISION

		P	W	D	L	F	A	Pts
1	Tiverton Town	34	31	1	2	103	20	94
2	Taunton Town	34	24	6	4	99	28	78
3	Mangotsfield U	34	19	8	7	75	44	65
4	Paulton Rovers	34	17	10	7	86	42	61
5	Chippenham Tn	34	12	12	10	58	52	48
6	Brislington	34	12	9	13	53	48	45
7	Calne Town	34	13	6	15	55	52	45
8	Torrington	34	11	11	12	54	54	44
9	Bridgwater Tn	34	12	8	14	53	55	44
10	Bridport	34	11	10	13	41	50	43
11	Odd Down	34	11	15	8	42	46	39*
12	Bideford	34	11	6	17	51	84	39
13	Barnstaple Tn	34	10	8	16	54	62	38
14	Bristol Man. Fm.	34	9	10	15	40	60	37
15	Backwell Utd	34	9	9	16	42	55	36
16	Chard Town	34	9	7	18	45	67	34
17	Westbury Utd	34	8	6	20	40	70	30
18	Elmore	34	4	4	26	30	132	16

* Points Deducted

FIRST DIVISION

		P	W	D	L	F	A	Pts
1	Melksham Tn	38	27	8	3	82	20	89
2	Keynsham Tn	38	27	7	4	77	21	88
3	Exmouth Town	38	23	7	7	77	42	76
4	Clyst Rovers	38	23	6	9	92	48	75
5	Bishop Sutton	38	21	7	10	96	52	70
6	Wellington	38	21	5	12	82	62	68
7	Devizes Town	38	18	11	9	75	39	65
8	Dawlish Town	38	18	9	11	66	36	63
9	Ilfracombe Tn	38	15	12	11	62	44	57
10	Welton Rovers	38	15	7	16	68	59	52
11	Minehead	38	16	4	18	61	56	52
12	Frome Town	38	12	11	15	45	60	47
13	Yeovil Town	38	12	8	18	66	77	44
14	Glastonbury	38	12	7	19	54	72	43
15	Crediton Utd	38	12	4	22	58	91	40
16	Warminster Tn	38	9	8	21	44	75	35
17	Larkhall Ath	38	7	13	18	51	92	34
18	Heavitree Utd	38	7	11	21	44	95	32
19	Pewsey Vale	38	5	4	29	26	105	19
20	Amesbury Tn	38	1	9	31	27	107	12

PREMIER DIVISION RESULTS CHART 1996-97

		1	2	3	4	5	6	7	8	9	10	11	12	13	14	15	16	17	18
1	Backwell Utd	X	4-0	2-3	1-2	0-2	2-1	1-1	3-1	0-0	1-0	4-1	1-0	2-2	0-4	1-2	0-5	1-1	3-0
2	Barnstaple Tn	3-2	X	1-2	1-2	2-2	2-3	0-0	1-2	1-0	1-1	7-0	1-2	1-1	2-2	1-4	1-3	1-2	0-0
3	Bideford	3-3	5-4	X	0-2	1-1	0-1	6-1	1-0	1-2	1-5	2-2	1-1	1-1	3-0	0-3	0-7	0-1	1-0
4	Bridgwater Tn	3-1	2-0	2-2	X	1-1	2-2	0-2	2-1	3-3	2-2	3-0	0-2	6-0	1-1	1-3	0-3	1-2	1-0
5	Bridport	1-1	0-1	1-0	3-0	X	2-2	2-1	1-0	0-1	5-3	2-0	0-2	0-2	1-1	1-3	0-1	2-4	2-0
6	Brislington	2-1	0-2	1-2	2-1	4-1	X	1-1	0-2	1-1	2-3	4-1	0-1	0-0	2-5	1-5	0-1	1-1	1-0
7	Bristol M Farm	1-1	1-3	2-0	0-2	3-0	0-2	X	1-1	4-1	2-1	2-2	1-3	1-2	1-1	0-6	2-5	1-0	2-3
8	Calne Town	1-0	5-2	2-1	3-1	0-1	2-1	2-0	X	1-1	0-3	6-0	2-3	0-0	1-0	0-2	0-2	1-3	2-3
9	Chard Town	1-2	1-2	0-2	2-1	2-0	1-3	0-0	1-0	X	0-2	3-0	1-1	2-3	0-5	1-2	0-1	2-2	1-2
10	Chippenham Tn	0-0	0-3	1-0	1-1	1-3	1-1	2-1	3-1	2-0	X	3-0	1-1	1-1	2-2	1-0	1-2	2-1	1-1
11	Elmore	1-0	2-1	2-6	1-4	1-3	1-7	1-2	0-6	0-4	2-2	X	0-3	2-2	0-5	0-6	1-7	2-0	2-1
12	Mangotsfield Utd	3-0	1-4	4-2	3-1	4-0	0-2	2-2	1-3	3-1	5-2	6-0	X	0-1	2-1	3-3	3-0	4-1	4-2
13	Odd Down	2-2	0-0	2-1	2-0	1-1	2-1	0-1	7-2	2-2	0-0	2-1	2-2	X	0-4	1-3	0-1	0-2	3-1
14	Paulton Rovers	2-0	7-1	12-0	3-2	0-0	1-0	1-0	2-2	4-2	2-2	6-2	5-2	0-0	X	2-3	1-2	1-0	1-4
15	Taunton Town	2-0	3-1	9-0	0-1	1-1	1-1	2-0	1-1	6-0	2-1	2-1	0-1	3-0	0-2	X	2-2	1-1	5-1
16	Tiverton Town	2-0	1-0	6-1	4-0	3-0	1-0	4-0	3-2	6-1	4-1	6-0	2-1	3-0	3-0	1-2	X	3-1	4-0
17	Torrington	1-2	2-2	1-0	1-1	3-1	1-1	2-2	2-2	4-3	4-3	9-0	1-1	0-0	1-2	0-6	0-2	X	0-1
18	Westbury Utd	1-1	0-2	2-3	3-2	1-1	1-3	1-2	0-1	1-4	1-4	6-2	1-1	0-1	1-1	0-6	0-3	2-0	X

FIRST DIVISION RESULTS CHART 1996-97

		1	2	3	4	5	6	7	8	9	10	11	12	13	14	15	16	17	18	19	20
1	Amesbury	X	1-6	2-4	0-2	0-0	1-2	0-1	2-3	2-7	0-3	0-4	0-4	2-2	0-3	0-1	0-1	0-1	3-3	3-3	1-1
2	Bishop Sutton	5-0	X	7-1	2-0	2-0	0-3	0-0	2-4	5-2	4-2	0-1	2-1	4-4	0-1	3-2	6-1	4-0	0-3	2-1	4-1
3	Clyst	5-1	3-1	X	6-1	1-0	1-1	2-1	0-0	3-1	5-0	2-2	1-2	3-0	2-1	3-2	11-0	5-2	4-1	0-1	3-1
4	Crediton	3-1	3-6	0-2	X	1-0	0-3	1-3	0-0	5-0	2-2	1-5	0-1	2-3	0-5	3-5	3-1	2-0	4-2	0-7	3-3
5	Dawlish	6-0	1-0	1-0	3-2	X	0-0	0-2	5-0	3-0	1-0	1-1	0-1	3-1	0-1	0-3	2-1	4-0	2-0	2-0	3-0
6	Devizes	0-0	0-0	1-2	0-1	1-3	X	1-1	3-0	1-1	8-1	0-0	0-2	3-1	0-1	2-1	2-2	5-1	3-2	2-0	3-3
7	Exmouth	4-1	2-0	2-0	2-0	3-3	1-3	X	3-1	3-0	1-0	1-1	0-2	1-3	0-2	3-0	2-1	0-1	2-1	2-2	3-1
8	Frome	2-0	1-2	3-1	2-1	1-4	0-1	0-2	X	2-1	1-1	1-0	0-2	2-2	0-0	1-1	1-2	1-1	4-1	2-1	0-3
9	Glastonbury	0-0	1-4	2-0	2-1	0-5	0-4	0-2	2-0	X	1-2	0-2	0-2	2-2	0-1	2-0	0-2	1-1	1-3	2-1	1-2
10	Heavitree	1-1	4-4	1-1	3-4	0-3	2-2	0-4	3-2	1-2	X	1-4	0-3	1-1	1-4	0-5	2-1	2-2	3-5	0-5	0-0
11	Ilfracombe	4-0	1-1	1-1	0-0	0-0	1-0	0-1	3-2	1-1	0-0	X	0-2	1-1	0-2	1-3	4-0	1-0	5-0	3-1	0-2
12	Keynsham	2-0	1-1	4-1	2-1	1-0	1-1	1-1	0-0	2-3	3-1	2-1	X	6-0	2-1	1-1	2-0	4-0	3-1	0-1	1-0
13	Larkhall	3-1	2-2	0-8	3-1	1-1	0-6	2-4	2-2	3-3	0-1	0-2	0-4	X	0-3	0-0	2-1	2-3	1-2	0-4	1-2
14	Melksham	5-1	1-0	1-1	2-0	1-1	1-0	1-3	2-0	1-0	1-0	2-2	1-1	4-0	X	1-0	2-0	1-1	3-0	2-2	6-1
15	Minehead	4-0	2-1	1-2	1-2	2-1	3-2	1-3	0-1	0-1	1-2	3-0	1-6	0-0	1-3	X	3-1	0-2	0-2	0-1	3-1
16	Pewsey Vale	0-1	0-3	0-1	1-4	0-0	1-4	0-2	1-1	1-4	1-2	1-0	0-1	2-1	0-8	1-5	X	1-5	0-4	0-4	1-2
17	Warminster	1-1	1-4	1-2	3-1	0-3	0-2	1-3	0-1	1-4	2-2	4-5	0-2	0-0	0-2	0-1	1-1	X	1-2	1-3	2-1
18	Wellington	2-1	0-1	3-1	5-1	4-0	2-0	0-5	4-1	2-1	3-0	3-2	1-0	2-1	1-1	2-3	4-0	2-1	X	2-2	7-1
19	Welton	4-1	1-4	0-2	0-1	1-3	4-2	3-1	1-2	0-3	3-0	0-3	1-1	1-2	0-3	1-0	2-0	0-3	1-1	X	2-2
20	Yeovil Res.	5-0	0-2	0-2	3-2	3-2	1-2	5-3	3-0	2-2	5-0	4-1	0-2	3-5	0-2	1-2	4-0	0-1	0-0	2-4	X

COMBINATION CHALLENGE CUP 1996-97

First Round

Crediton United	v	Tiverton Town	1-11
Ottery St Mary	v	Elmore	7-5
Exmouth Town	v	Barnstaple Town	9-3

Second Round

Chard Town	v	Bideford	11-1
Exmouth Town	v	Ottery St Mary	6-0
Dawlish Town	v	Wellington	1-8
Taunton Town	v	Tiverton Town	1-10

Semi-Final

Exmouth Town	v	Chard Town	1-2
Wellington	v	Tiverton Town	2-1

FINAL

CHARD TOWN	v	WELLINGTON	3-0

LES PHILLIPS CHALLENGE CUP 1996-97

First Round

Clyst Rovers	v	Wellington	2-1	Paulton Rovers	v	Yeovil Town	2-0
Barnstaple Town	v	Taunton Town	2-1	Larkhall Athletic	v	Keynsham Town	2-3
Chard Town	v	Bristol Manor Farm	2-1	Welton Rovers	v	Tiverton Town	0-5

Second Round

Odd Down	v	Amesbury Town	4-1	Tiverton Town	v	Torrington	4-0
Backwell United	v	Brislington	1-2	Minehead	v	Heavitree United	3-5
Bridgwater	v	Barnstaple	3-1	Pewsey Vale	v	Chard	1-3
Exmouth Town	v	Glastonbury	3-0	Bideford	v	Devizes Town	5-3
Elmore	v	Ilfracombe Town	1-2	Bridport	v	Chippenham Town	0-4
Melksham Town	v	Frome Town	2-1	Mangotsfield United	v	Clyst	2-0
Calne Town	v	Dawlish Town	4-0	Paulton	v	Bishop Sutton	2-1
Westbury United	v	Warminster Town	1-0	Crediton United	v	Keynsham	5-1*

*Ineligible player, Crediton removed

Third Round

Bideford	v	Tiverton Town	1-4	Melksham Town	v	Odd Down	4-3
Westbury United	v	Exmouth Town	1-2	Ilfracombe Town	v	Chard Town	0-1
Mangotsfield Utd	v	Bridgwater Town	2-0	Keynsham Town	v	Brislington	3-1
Paulton Rovers	v	Heavitree United	4-0	Calne Town	v	Chippenham Town	0-1

Quarter-Final

Mangotsfield United	v	Paulton Rovers	2-1	Tiverton Town	v	Melksham Town	1-0
Exmouth Town	v	Keynsham Town	0-1	Chippenham Town	v	Chard Town	2-1

Semi-Final

Mangotsfield United	v	Chippenham Town	0-1	Tiverton Town	v	Keynsham Town	4-0

FINAL

TIVERTON TOWN v CHIPPENHAM TOWN 1-0

REGISTRATION INFORMATION

	NUMBER OF PLAYERS REGISTERED	TRANSFERS ACTIONED
1995-96	1762	187
1994-95	1922	254
1993-94	1909	201
1992-93	2061	241

ATTENDANCE INFORMATION

PREMIER DIVISION

	AGGREGATE	AVERAGE GATE	GATES OVER 200
Backwell United	1970	115.8	2
Barnstaple Town	2565	150.8	2
Bideford	1909	112.3	1
Bridgwater Tn	5632	331.3	16
Bridport	2420	142.4	2
Brislington	1900	112	2
Bristol Manor Farm	8845	49.7	
Calne Town	1181	69.5	1
Chard Town	1783	104.8	1
Chippenham Town	1917	112.8	1
Elmore	2139	126	2
Mangotsfield Utd	2795	164.4	5
Odd Down	926	54.5	
Paulton Rovers	3059	180	5
Taunton Town	6247	368	17
Tiverton Town	7268	428	17
Torrington	1910	112.4	4
Westbury United	1393	82	
TOTAL	**47,859**	**165.6**	**77**

(289 Recorded Attendances)

DIVISION ONE

	AGGREGATE	AVERAGE GATE	GATES OVER 200
Amesbury Town	1307	69	
Bishop Sutton	1301	68.5	
Clyst Rovers	1070	56.3	
Crediton United	946	50	
Dawlish Town	866	46	
Devizes Town	1181	62	1
Exmouth Town	1301	68.5	
Frome Town	1138	60	
Glastonbury	727	38	
Heavitree United	785	41	
Ifracombe Town	1821	96	
Keynsham Town	1651	87	2
Larkhall Athletic	1192	62.7	
Melksham Town	2598	136.7	1
Minehead	880	46.3	
Pewsey Vale	920	48.4	
Warminster Town	2659	140	2
Wellington	1152	60.6	
Welton Rovers	1555	81.8	
Yeovil Town	1257	66.2	1
TOTAL	**26,307**	**72.8**	**7**

(361 Recorded Attendances)

OVERALL TOTALS

	Aggregate	Average Gate	Gates Over 200
650 Recorded Attendances	74,166	114.1	84

HIGHEST LEAGUE ATTENDANCES 1996-97

Taunton	v	Tiverton	1196	02.04.97
Bridgwater	v	Taunton	1112	26.08.97
Tiverton	v	Elmore	731	26.12.96
Tiverton	v	Taunton	680	16.04.97
Tiverton	v	Odd Down	618	19.04.97
Tiverton	v	Torrington	538	31.03.97
Bridgwater	v	Tiverton	516	22.04.97
Tiverton	v	Bridgwater	512	21.08.96
Melksham	v	Devizes	506	28.03.97

LEADING LEAGUE GOALSCORERS 1996-97

N Woon	Wellington	28
I Dixon	Welton	26
G Silverthorne	Keynsham	25
L Gould	Paulton	25
D Roberts	Clyst	25
B Murden	Melksham	23
P Everett	Tiverton	23
D Hall	Larkhall	21
S Day	Bishop Sutton	21
R McGahey	Clyst	21
S West	Exmouth	20

WESTERN FOOTBALL LEAGUE CHAMPIONS

PREMIER DIVISION

1995-96	Taunton Town
1994-95	Tiverton Town
1993-94	Tiverton Town
1992-93	Clevedon Town
1991-92	Weston-Super-Mare
1990-91	Mangotsfield United
1989-90	Taunton Town
1988-89	Saltash United
1987-88	Liskeard Athletic
1986-87	Saltash United
1985-86	Exmouth Town
1984-85	Saltash United
1983-84	Exmouth Town
1982-83	Bideford
1981-82	Bideford
1980-81	Bridgwater Town
1979-80	Barnstaple Town
1978-79	Frome Town
1977-78	Falmouth Town
1976-77	Falmouth Town
1975-76	Falmouth Town
1974-75	Falmouth Town
1973-74	Welton Rovers
1972-73	Devizes Town
1971-72	Bideford
1970-71	Bideford
1969-70	Glastonbury
1968-69	Taunton Town
1967-68	Bridgwater Town
1966-67	Welton Rovers
1965-66	Welton Rovers
1964-65	Welton Rovers
1963-64	Bideford
1962-63	Bristol City
1961-62	Bristol City
1960-61	Salisbury City
1959-60	Torquay United
1958-59	Yeovil Town
1957-58	Salisbury City
1956-57	Poole Town
1955-56	Trowbridge Town
1954-55	Dorchester Town
1953-54	Weymouth
1952-53	Barnstaple Town
1951-52	Chippenham Town
1950-51	Glastonbury

DIVISION ONE

1995-96	Bridgwater Town
1994-95	Brislington
1993-94	Barnstaple Town
1992-93	Odd Down
1991-92	Westbury United
1990-91	Minehead
1989-90	Ottery St Mary
1988-89	Larkhall Athletic
1987-88	Welton Rovers
1986-87	Swanage Town & Herston
1985-86	Portway-Bristol
1984-85	Portway-Bristol
1983-84	Bristol City Reserves
1982-83	Bristol Manor Farm
1981-82	Shepton Mallet
1980-81	Chippenham Town
1979-80	Melksham Town
1978-79	AFC Bournemouth Reserves
1977-78	Keynsham Town
1976-77	Saltash United
1960-76	Single Division
1959-60	Welton Rovers
1958-59	Bath City
1957-58	Poole Town
1956-57	Cinderford Town
1955-56	Torquay United
1954-55	Yeovil Town
1953-54	Bristol Rovers Colts
1952-53	Chippenham Town Reserves
1951-52	Bideford
1950-51	Stonehouse
1949-50	Barnstaple Town
1948-49	Chippenham United
1947-48	Salisbury City
1946-47	Clandown
1939-46	No Competition
1938-39	Trowbridge Town
1937-38	Weymouth
1936-37	Weymouth
1935-36	Swindon Town
1934-35	Swindon Town
1933-34	Weymouth
1932-33	Swindon Town
1931-32	Portland United
1930-31	Portland United
1929-30	Trowbridge Town

PREMIER DIVISION CLUBS 1997-98

BACKWELL UNITED

Chairman: Richard Cole. **Vice-Chairman:** Peter Higgins. **President:** John Southern
Secretary: Bill Coggins, 34 Westfield Road, Backwell, Bristol BS19 3ND (01275 463424).
Manager: Alan Pridham **Asst Manager:** Martin Finn. **Physio:** Ian Pinkney
Ground: Backwell Recreation Ground, West Town Rd, Backwell, Avon (01275 462612).
Directions: Near centre of Backwell on main A370 Bristol to Weston-super-Mare road. Buses from Bristol or Weston, or 20 mins walk from Nailsea & Backwell (BR) station; turn right out of station, right at traffic lights (half mile), ground quarter mile on right just past car sales.
Seats: 60 **Cover:** 150 **Capacity:** 1,000 **Floodlights:** Yes **Club Shop:** No.
Colours: All red **Change colours:** All Gold **Nickname:** Stags
Programme: 42 pages, 50p. **Editor:** Dick Cole (01275 463627) **Press Officer:** Peter Higgins.
Midweek Matches: Tuesday **Club Sponsors:** C W Jones Carpets. **Founded:** 1983
Record attendance: 487 v Brislington, Gt Mills Lg. 2/5/94.
Previous Lges: Clevedon & Dist/ Bristol Church of England/ Bristol Surburban (pre 1970)/ Somerset Snr 70-83
Clubhouse: Open 6-11pm weekdays, 12.30-11pm Sat. Snacks available.
96-97 Captain: **96-97 Top Scorer:** **96-97 P.o.Y.:**
Club Record Goalscorer: Steve Spalding **Club Record appearances:** Wayne Buxton.
Honours: Somerset Snr Lg 77-78 79-80 80-81 81-82 82-83 (Lg Cup 82-83 (R-up 79-80) Div 1 72-73); Somerset Snr Cup 81-82; SW Co.'s Sutton Transformer Cup 81-82. Gt.Mills Div 1 89-90 Champions,94-95 promoted in third place.

BARNSTAPLE TOWN

President: Wilf Harris **Chairman:** John Cann
Secretary: David Cooke, 51 Walnut Way, Whiddon Valley, Barnstaple, Devon. EX32 7RF (01271-326088)
Manager: Phil Lloyd **Asst Manager:**
Ground: Mill Road, Barnstaple, North Devon (01271 743469).
Directions: A361 towards Ilfracombe (from M5 Jct 26), in Barnstaple follow A361 Ilfracombe signs, second left after crossing small bridge is Mill Road.
Seats: 250 **Cover:** 1,000 **Capacity:** 5,000 **Floodlights:** Yes **Formed:** 1948
Colours: Red/white/red **Change colours:** Yellow/black/black **Nickname:** Barum.
Sponsors: J & A Cameras. **Midweek Matches:** Tuesday **Club Shop:** Yes
Programme: 40 pages, 50p **Programme Editor:** David Priscott (01271 328316).
Previous - Name: Pilton Yeo Vale. **Leagues:** Nth Devon, Devon & Exeter, S. Western. **Grounds:** Town Wharf (Pre 1920's); Highfield Rd, Newport (until 1935), Pilton Pk, Rock Pk.
Records - Attendance: 6,200 v Bournemouth, FA Cup 1st Rd, 54. **Win:** 12-1 v Tavistock (H), FA Cup Third Qualifying Round 1954. **Defeat:** 1-10 v Mangotsfield United (A), Western League Premier Division 90-91. **Transfer fee paid:** £4,000 for Joe Scott (Hungerford Town, 1980). **Received:** £6,000 for Ian Doyle (Bristol City).
Clubhouse: Full license. Bar snacks. **Club record appearances:** Trevor Burnell
Past players progressing to Football League: Len Pickard (Bristol Rovers 1951), John Neale (Exeter 1972), Barrie Vassallo (Torquay 1977), Ian Doyle (Bristol City 1978), Ryan Souter (Swindon 1994), Jason Cadie (Reading 1994).
96-97 Captain: Andy Rollason **96-97 P.o.Y.:** Darren Hawkins **96-97 Top Scorer:** Richard Hill
Honours: Western Lg 52-53 79-80 (R-up 80-81 81-82, Div 1 49-50 94-95, Merit Cup 74-75 83-84 84-85, Combination 92-93), FA Cup 1st Rd replay 51-52, Devon Professional Cup 62-63 64-65 67-68 69-70 71-72 72-73 74-75 76-77 77-78 78-79 79-80 80-81, Devon Lg, Devon St Lukes Cup 87-88, Devon Snr Cup 92-93, Devon Youth Cup 48-49 51-52.

BIDEFORD

President: C Prust **Chairman:** Jim McElwee
Secretary: Ron Ackland, Korna House, Shebbear, North Devon EX21 5RU (01409 281451).
Manager: Dean Edwards **Asst Manager:** Sean Joyce **Reserve Manager:** Steve Miller
Ground: The Sports Ground, Kingsley Road, Bideford (01237 474975).
Directions: A361 for Bideford - ground on right as you enter the town.
Seats: 120 **Cover:** 1,000 **Capacity:** 6,000 **Floodlights:** Yes **Founded:** 1949
Colours: Red/white/red **Change colours:** Yellow/white/yellow **Nickname:** Robins
Programme: 32 pages, 50p **Editor:** Ian Knight.
Previous Leagues: Devon & Exeter 47-49/ Western 49-72/ Southern 72-75
Midweek Matchday: Wednesday. **Record Gate:** 6,000 v Gloucester C., FA Cup 4th Qual. Rd 60
Players progressing to Football League: Shaun Taylor (Swindon Town, Bristol Rovers) Tony Dennis (Cambridge).
Clubhouse: 'Robins Nest' - on ground. Open lunchtimes and evenings, snacks and bar menu. Mgr: Mrs Sue Tyrell.
Record scorer: Tommy Robinson 259 **Record appearances:** Derek May 527.
96-97 P.o.Y: Ellis Laight **96-97 Captain:** Sean Joyce **96-97 Top Scorer:** Ellis Laight
Honours: Western Lg 63-64 70-71 71-72 81-82 82-83 (Div 1 51-52, Div 3 49-50, Lg Cup 71-72 84-85, Alan Young Cup 64-65 69-70, Merit Cup 68-69, Subsidiary Cup 71-72), Devon Snr Cup 79-80, Devon St Lukes Cup 81-82 83-84 85-86 95-96 (R-up 86-87 91-92 94-95), FA Cup 1st Rd 64-65(replay) 73-74 77-78 81-82.

BRIDGWATER TOWN '84

Chairman: Keith Setter. **President:** Tom Pearce
Secretary: Miss S A Wright, 37 Kidsbury Road, Bridgwater TA6 7AQ (01278 421189)
Manager: Alan Hooker. **Physio:** Mike Brown
Ground: Fairfax Park, College Road, Bridgwater (01278 446899 - matchdays only).
Directions: M5 jct 23, follow signs to Glastonbury (A39), turn right for Bridgwater (A39). Look for sign to Bridgwater College via College Way. One mile from Bridgwater (BR) station.
Seats: 150 **Cover:** Yes **Capacity:** 2,000 **Floodlights:** Yes **Club Shop:** Yes
Programme: Yes. **Editor:** G Nelson & R Heard **Press Officer:** G Nelson
Colours: Red/white/red **Change colours:** Blue/white/blue.
Sponsor: TMB Patterns **Founded:** 1984. **Nickname:** The Robins
Midweek Matchday: Tuesday **Youth Team's League:** U18 Floodlight
Previous League: Somerset Snr (pre-1994) **Clubhouse:** 'The Sportsman' Bath Road.
Honours: Somerset Snr Cup 93-94, Somerset Snr Lge 90-91 91-92, GMWL Div 1 95-96.

BRIDPORT

President: B Williams **Chairman:** David Fowler
Secretary: Keith Morgan, 95 Orchard Crescent, Bridport DT6 5HA (01308 425113).
Manager: Phil Simkin **Asst Manager/Physio:** Alan Newey.
Ground: The Beehive, St Mary's Field, Bridport, Dorset (01308 423834).
Directions: Take West Bay road from town centre, turn right immediately before Palmers Brewery.
Seats: 200 **Cover:** 400 **Capacity:** 2,000 **Floodlights:** Yes **Founded:** 1887
Colours: Red & black/black/red & black **Change colours:** Blue & black/blue/blue
Programme: 32 pages, 30p **Editor:** John Hallett (01308 868795). **Nickname:** Bees
Midweek Matches: Wednesday **Reserve's League:** Dorset Combination. **Club Shop:** Yes
Previous Leagues: Perry Street/ Western 61-84/ Dorset Combination 84-88.
Record Attendance: 1,150 v Exeter City, 1981; 3,000 v Chelsea, at Crown, 1950
Clubhouse: Yes, open matchdays and for functions. Hot and cold snacks available.
Club record scorer (in a season): Eric Hoole 36.
Honours: Western Lg Cup 70-71 72-73 77-78 (R-up 76-77, Div 1 R-up 94-95, Merit Cup 69-70 71-72 73-74); FA Vase 5th Rd 88-89; Dorset Comb.(3) 85-88 (Lg Cup 86-87 87-88); Dorset Snr Cup(8) 63-64 69-71 75-76 78-81 87-88; Dorset Snr Amtr Cup(6) 48-50 54-55 56-57 70-72; W. Dorset Chal. Bowl 07-08; Perry Str. Lg 22-23; Mark Frowde Cup 76-77 88-89

BRISLINGTON

President: C Elston **Chairman:** Paul Bishop **Vice-Chairman:** P K Brake
Secretary: Philip Rex, 27 Kings Head Lane, Bishopsworth, Bristol BS13 7DB (0117 987 9146 H)
Manager: Jamie Patch **Asst Manager:** Dave Payne **Physio:** Art Rowland/Dave Gould
Ground: Ironmould Lane, Brislington, Bristol (0117 977 4030)
Directions: Four miles out of Bristol on main A4 to Bath – turn left up lane opposite Garden Centre
Capacity: **Seats:** 144 **Cover:** 100 **Floodlights:** No **Club Shop:** No
Programme: 50p **Editor:** Laserset (0117 9695487). **Nickname:** Bris.
Colours: Red & black/black/black & white **Change colours:** All yellow & blue
Midweek matches: Wednesday **Reserve's League:** Somerset Senior **Sponsors:** Trade Windows.
Best FA Vase year: 3rd Rd 89-90 (lost 2-3 at Abingdon T.)
Clubhouse: Yes - on ground, open matchdays. **Previous League:** Somerset Senior (pre-1991).
Honours: Somerset Snr Cup 92-93 (R-up 93-94), Somerset Snr Lge, Les Phillips Cup SF 93-94 95-96, Prem Cup 95-96.

BRISTOL MANOR FARM

Chairman: F Wardle **Vice Chairman:** Brian Bartlett. **President:** Fred Wardle
Secretary: Steve Price, 19A Deans Mead, Lawrence Weston, Bristol BS11 0QX (0117 982 6952)
Manager: Geoff Bryant **Asst Mgr:** Barry Fry **Physio:** Alan Williams.
Ground: 'The Creek', Portway, Sea Mills, Bristol BS9 2HS (0117 968 3571)
Directions: M5 jct 18 (Avonmouth Bridge), follow A4 for Bristol - U-turn on dual carriageway by Bristol & West sports ground and return for half mile on A4 - ground entrance is down narrow lane on left (hidden entrance). Near to Sea Mills station (BR Temple Meads-Severn Beach line).
Seats: 84 **Cover:** 350 **Capacity:** 2,000 **Floodlights:** Yes **Club Shop:** No.
Programme: 28 pages, 50p **Editor:** Steve Price (0117 982 6952). **Sponsors:** Wardle Fencing.
Colours: Red & black stripes/red/red **Change colours:** All sky blue **Formed:** 1964
Midweek Matchday: Tuesday **Record Attendance:** 500 v Portway, Western Lg 1974.
Nickname: The Farm **Previous Leagues:** Bristol Suburban 64-69/ Somerset Snr 69-77.
Players progressing to Football League: Ian Hedges (Newport) 88-89, Gary Smart (Bristol Rovers).
Clubhouse: Lounge bar, entertainments, skittle alley, bar meals. Open every night and lunchtime Sat & Sun.
Club Record Goalscorer: Chris Rex, 222 **Club Record Appearances:** Paul Williams, 821.
Honours: Western Lg Div 1 82-83, Glos Tphy 87-88, Glos Amtr Cup 89-90, Somerset Snr Lg Div 1 (Lg Cup, Div 2).

Calne Town: Back Row (L-R); Steve Brown, Lester Foxall, Neil Rosslee, Nick Beaverstock, Martin Woodhouse, Ben Lang, Steve Davis, Mike Kendall, Sasha Fast, Tony Hammersley, James Stone. Front Row; Nick Tiley, Tommy Saunders, Terry Wells (Sponsor), Jamie Walters, Laurie Drake (Sec), Colin Bush, Wayne Townsend, Simon Bray, Matthew Berry. *Photo - Sunday Independent*

CALNE TOWN

President: Fred Rutty **Manager:** Tom Saunders. **Coach:** Colin Bush.
Secretary: Laurie Drake, 22 Falcon Rd, Calne, Wilts SN11 8PL (01249 819186).
Ground: Bremhill View, Lickhill Rd., North End, Calne (01249 816716).
Directions: From Bristol, on entering town keep left all the way taking slip road to North End, off main Swindon Road.
Seats: 78 **Cover:** 250 **Capacity:** 2,500 **Floodlights:** Yes **Club Shop:** No.
Programme: 20 pages, 50p **Editor:** Laurie Drake (01249 819186).
Colours: Yellow/blue/yellow **Change colours:** White/black/black
Sponsors: Calne Engineering **Nickname:** Lilywhites **Founded:** 1887.
Midweek Matcheday: Tuesday **Record Attendance:** 1,100 v Swindon, Friendly 25/7/1987.
Previous - League: Wilts Co. (pre-1986).
Clubhouse: Mon-Fri 7-11pm, Sat-Sun 12-11pm. Filled rolls, hot food, tea, coffee, sweets etc.
96-97 Captain: Jamie Walters **96-97 Top Scorer:** Steve Brown **96-97 P.o.Y.:** Paul Symonds
Club record scorer: Robbie Lardner **Club record appearances:** Gary Swallow, 259.
Honours: Western Lg Div 1 R-up 92-93, Wilts Snr Cup 12-13 34-35 84-85 (R-up 1894-95 94-95 1911-12 49-50), Wilts Lg 33-34 ('Ghia' Cup 8)1-81 85-86, Div 2 79-8)1, Div 3 85-86, Div 4 81-82).

CHARD TOWN

Chairman: Brian Beer **Vice Chairman:** Roy Goodland/John Glentworth
Secretary: John Rowswell, Edgehill, Church Lane, East Stoke, Stoke sub Hamdon, Somerset. (01935 823881)
Manager: Bob Russell **Coach:** Peter Smith. **Physio:** Peter Smith
Ground: Town Ground, Zembard Lane, Chard (01460 61402).
Directions: 150 yards from the town centre, off Combe Street. 8 miles from Crewkerne BR station.
Seats: 60 **Cover:** 200 **Capacity:** 1,500 **Floodlights:** Yes **Founded:** 1920
Programme: 24 pages with entry **Editor:** Ian Walker **Nickname:** Robins.
Colours: Scarlet/black/black **Change colours:** All white **Sponsors:** Annual Competition.
Midweek matches: Wednesday **Previous Leagues:** Somerset Snr 20-24 48-75/ Perry Street 25-48.
Clubhouse: Matchdays & most evenings. Snacks served
96-97 Captain: Stuart Smith **96-97 P.o.Y.:** Andy Bicknell **96-97 Top Scorer:** Andy Bicknell
Honours: Som. Snr Lg 49-50 53-54 59-60 67-68 69-70 (Lg Cup 61-62 71-72 76-77); Western Lg Div 1 R-up 83-84 87-88 95-96, (Merit Cup 82-83, Comb. Cup(Res) 91-92 (R-up 92-93)); Som. Snr Cup 52-53 66-67; S W Co's Cup 88-89; Western Com Lge 96-97, Cup 96-97:

CHIPPENHAM TOWN

Chairman: Malcolm Lyus **Vice-Chairman:** Andy Russell **President:** G W Terrell
Secretary: Chris Blake, 28 Sadlers Mead, Chippenham, Wilts SN15 3PB (01249 658212).
Manager: Vic Flippance **Physio:** John Palmer
Ground: Hardenhuish Park, Bristol Road, Chippenham (01249 650400).
Directions: M4 jct 17, A429 into Chippenham, follow signs for Trowbridge/Bath until r'bout, left onto A420 into town, ground 400yds on left. 5 mins walk from railway station on main A420 Bristol Road.
Seats: 100 **Cover:** 300 **Capacity:** 4,000 **Floodlights:** Yes **Formed:** 1873
Clubhouse: Yes, open matchdays. Food available. **Midweek matches:** Wednesday
Programme: 32 pages, 50p **Editor/Press Officer:** Ian Liversedge (01249 651290)
Colours: Blue/blue/burgundy **Change colours:** All yellow **Nickname:** The Bluebirds
Sponsors: Cifer Ltd, Kingston Smith, Supreme Video, Shoestrings Food Services, Vanitec Computers.
Record Gate: 4,800 v Chippenham Utd, Western Lg, 51. **Previous Lges:** Hellenic, Wiltshire Sen, Wiltshire Prem
96-97 Captain: Paul Rose **96-97 P.o.Y.:** Robbie Lardner **96-97 Top Scorer:** Barry Flippance
Club Record Goalscorer: Dave Ferris **Club Record Appearances:** Ian Monnery.
Honours: FA Cup 1st Rd 51-52, Western Lg 51-52 (Div 1 80-81, Div 2 52-53(Res) 80-81), Wilts Shield, Wilts Snr Cup, Wilts Snr League.

ELMORE

Chairman: A J Cockram **Vice Chairman:** P.J.Garnsworthy.
Secretary: Mrs A Freeman, c/o Elmore FC, (01884 258215)
Manager: Peter Buckingham **Asst Manager:** R Moore. **Physio:** M Crocker.
Ground: Horsdon Park, Tiverton, Devon EX16 4DE (01884 252341).
Directions: M5 Jct 27, A373 towards Tiverton, leave at 1st sign for Tiverton & Business Park, ground 500yds on right.
Seats: 200 **Cover:** **Capacity:** 2,000 **Floodlights:** Yes **Club Shop:** Yes.
Programme: 12 pages, 30p **Editor:** Richard Tapp(01884 252341)
Club Sponsors: Ken White Signs. **Nickname:** Eagles. **Founded:** 1947
Colours: Green & white/green/green **Change colours:** Red & black/black/black
Midweek matches: Tuesday **Reserve League:** None
Previous Leagues: Devon & Exeter 47-74/ South Western 74-78.
Record Attendance: 1,713 v Tiverton Town Fri.April 14th 95.
Clubhouse: 11am-11pm Mon-Sat. Full canteen service - hot & cold meals & snacks.
96-97 Captain: **96-97 P.o.Y.:** **96-97 Top Scorer:**
Club Record Appearances: P Webber. **Club Record Goalscorers:**
Hons: East Devon Snr Cup 72-73 75-76, Western Lg Cup 90-91,Les Philips(Lg Cup)94-95 (Div 1 R-up 90-91, Prem Div Merit Cup R-up 91-92, Div 1 Merit Cup 86-87 89-90 90-91), Devon St Lukes Cup R-up 90-91, Devon Snr Cup 87-88, Devon Intermediate Cup 60-61, Football Express Cup 60-61, Devon & Exeter Lg Div 2A 73-74 86-87(res)(Div 1A 76-77(res)), Devon Yth Cup 77-78.Great Mills Western League Runners Up 94-95.

KEYNSHAM TOWN

Chairman: Steve Nicholls **President:** Lester Clements
Secretary: Iain Anderson, 195 Mount Hill Road, Hanham, Bristol BS15 2SU (0117 9616426)
Manager: Barry Fry **Physio:** A Weaver
Ground: Crown Field, Bristol Road, Keynsham (0117 9865876).
Directions: A4 from Bristol to Bath, ground on left before entering village opposite Crown Inn. Bus service every 30 mins from Bristol passes ground. 10 mins walk from Keynsham BR station.
Seats: 120 **Cover:** 500 **Capacity:** 2,000 **Floodlights:** Yes **Club Shop:** No.
Clubhouse: Evenings & before & after games. Sunday lunch. Snacks.
Programme: 32 pages, 25p **Editor:** Mark Brown (0117 969 5487) **Press Officer:** D Brassington
Colours: Gold/black/gold **Change colours:** All white.
Sponsors: Ace Building Services Ltd. **Nickname:** K's. **Founded:** 1895
Midweek matchday: Monday **Reserve's League:** Somerset Senior.
Record Attendance: 3,000 v Chelsea, floodlight opening 88-89. Competitive: 2,160 v Saltash, Amateur Cup, Oct 1952.
Previous Leagues: Bristol District, Bristol Comb., Bristol Premier, Somerset Senior. **Grounds:** The Hams 1886-1910; Gaston 1910-25; Park Road 25-30; Charlton Rd 30-39.
96-97 Captain: Steve Clarke **96-97 Top Scorer:** Gary Silverthorne **96-97 P.o.Y.:** Steve Miles
Honours: Somerset Lg Div 1 77-78; Somerset Snr Cup 51-52 57-58; GFA Jnr Cup 25-26, Somerset & Avon (South) Premier Cup 79-80 (SF 93-94), FA Cup 4th Qualifying Rd.

MANGOTSFIELD UNITED

President: A J Hill **Chairman:** R Davis **Vice Chairman:** P Selway
Secretary: R Gray, 105 Chiltern Close, Warmley, Bristol BS15 5UW (0117 9616523).
Manager: Terry Rowles. **Asst Manager:** Andy Perrett **Physio:** Ken Dodd.
Ground: Cossham Street, Mangotsfield, Bristol BS17 3EW (0117 9560119).
Directions: M4 jct 19, M32 jct 1; A4174 marked Downend, through lights, over double mini-r'bout to Mangotsfield, left by village church onto B4465 signposted Pucklechurch, ground quarter mile on right. From central Bristol take A432 thru Fishponds, Staple Hill, to Mangotsfield and turn right by village church onto B4465.
Seats: 300 **Cover:** 800 **Capacity:** 2,500 **Floodlights:** Yes **Club Shop:** Yes
Programme: 32 pages, 50p. **Editor:** Bob Smale (0117 9401926). **Press Officer:** Secretary
Colours: Maroon/white/white **Change colours:** All white
Sponsors: Aaron Roofing Supplies **Nickname:** The Field **Founded:** 1950
Midweek matchday: Tuesday **Reserve League:** Somerset Senior.
Record Attendance: 2,386 v Bath City, FA Cup 77-78
Previous Leagues: Bristol & District 50-67/ Avon Premier Combination 67-72.
Players to progress to Football League: G.Megson, S.White, G.Penrice, P.Purnell, N.Tanner, M.Hooper.
Clubhouse: Open 11am-11pm. Snacks - hot food on matchdays. Lounge bar for official functions etc.
96-97 Captain: Dean Radford **96-97 P.o.Y.:** Gary Hewlett **96-97 Top Scorer:** Andy Perrett
Honours: FA Vase Semi-fin 95-96; Western Lg 90-91 (Lg Cup 73-74 (R-up 86-87) Div 1 R-up 82-83); Somerset Prem. Cup 87-88 (R-up 88-89 95-96); Glos Snr Cup 68-69 75-76; Glos FA Trophy 84-85 86-87 90-91 94-95 96-97; Hungerford Invitation Cup 74-75; Rothmans National Cup R-up 77-78; Hanham Invitation Charity Cup 84-85 85-86; Somerset Snr Lg(Reserves) Div 2 75-76 (Div 3 74-75); Somerset Comb. Cup 74-75; Glos Yth Shield 81-82 84-85 (R-up 82-83); Somerset Floodlit Yth Lg 81-82 82-83 83-84 84-85 87-88; Somerset Yth Shield 76-77.

Mangotsfield United: Back Row (L-R); Darrenn Welsh, Daniel Byrne, Mike Brooks, Scott Goozee, Ian Jones, Justin Claridge, Scott Hendy, Dean Radford, Tony Bennett. Front Row; Simon Winstone, Jeremy Christopher, Gary Hewlett, Wayne Morris, Justin Pritchard, Paul Cichy *Photo - Sunday Independent.*

MELKSHAM TOWN

President: H J Goodenough **Chairman:** Mike Perrin. **Manager:** Darren Perrin
Secretary: Paul Macey, 30 Wellington Square, Bowerhill, Melksham SN12 6QX (01225 706876).
Ground: The Conigre, Melksham (01225 702843). **Directions:** Just off main square ingrounds of Melksham House.
Capacity: 3,000 **Seats:** 100. **Cover:** 1,500 **Floodlights:** Yes **Founded:** 1876.
Colours: Gold/black/black **Change colours:** Blue & white/blue/blue
Previous Leagues: Wiltshire 1894-1974 93-94/ Western 74-93.
Midweek Matchday: Tuesday **Record Gate:** 2,821 v Trowbridge Town, FA Cup 57-58.
Clubhouse: Inside ground, open every evening & weekend lunchtimes.
Honours: Wilts Lg 03-04 93-94 (R-up 24-25 29-30 59-60 67-68 68-69 71-72), Western Lg Div 1 79-80, Wilts Snr Cup 03-04 69-70 77-78 (R-up 57-58 67-68 68-69), Wilts Shield 80-81 81-82 84-85 (R-up 86-87), FA Amateur Cup 1st Rd 68-69.

ODD DOWN ATHLETIC

President: P A L Hill **Chairman:** N Fenwick **Vice Chairman:** Mike Wilkins
Secretary: Mike Mancini, 36 Caledonian Rd., East Twerton, Bath BA2 3RD (01225 423293).
Manager: Steve Langley
Ground: Coombe Hay Lane, Odd Down, Bath (01225 832491).
Directions: On main Bath/Exeter road - leaving Bath turn left into Combe Hay Lane opposite Lamplighters Pub. 40 mins walk from Bath (BR).
Seats: 160 **Cover:** 250 **Capacity:** 1,000 **Floodlights:** Yes. **Founded:** 1901
Colours: Blue/white/blue **Change colours:** White/blue/white **Sponsors:** Crest Homes
Programme: 12 pages with admission **Editor:** Secretary **Shop:** No.
Prev. Lges: Wilts Premier, Bath & District, Somerset Senior **Midweek Matches:** Tuesday
Clubhouse: Yes, open noon-3 & 7-11pm. Hot & cold food available. **Reserve's League:** Somerset Senior
Record Scorer: Joe Matano 104 **Record Appearances:** T Mancini & T Ridewood, both 335.
96-97 Captain: Duncan Fear **96-97 P.o.Y.:** Ian Esihtrahge **96-97 Top Scorer:** Marit Brown (16)
Honours: Western Lg Div 1 92-93, Somerset Snr Cup 91-92.

PAULTON ROVERS

President: Mr T Pow **Chairman:** David Bissex **Vice Chairman:** Mr D Carter
Secretary: John Pool, 11 Charlton Park, Midsomer Norton, Avon BA3 4BP (01761 415190).
Manager: John Goss **Physio:** John Pool.
Ground: Athletic Ground, Winterfield Road, Paulton (01761 412907).
Directions: Leave A39 at Farrington Gurney (approx 15 miles south of Bristol), follow A362 marked Radstock for two miles, left at junction B3355 to Paulton, ground on right. Bus services from Bristol and Bath.
Seats: 138 **Cover:** 200 **Capacity:** 5,000 **Floodlights:** Yes **Founded:** 1881
Colours: White/maroon/maroon **Change colours:** Green & navy/navy/navy **Nickname:** Rovers.
Midweek matches: Tuesday **Previous Leagues:** Wilts Premier/ Somerset Snr.
Programme: 20 pages, 50p **Editor:** D Bissex (01761 412463). **Shop:** Yes
Sponsors: Barons Property Centre/Bass Breweries **Reserves' League:** Somerset Snr.
Clubhouse: 3 bars, lounge, skittle alley, dance hall. Capacity 300. Catering facilities.
Club record appearances: Steve Tovey **Club record scorer:** D Clark.
96-97 Captain: Lee Burns **96-97 Top Scorer:** Lee Gould **96-97 P.o.Y.:** Lee Burns
Honours: Western Lg Div 2 R-up 1900-01; Somerset Snr Cup 00-01 02-03 03-04 07-08 08-09 09-10 34-35 67-68 68-69 71-72 72-73 74-75; Somerset Snr Lg 00-01 03-04 04-05 70-71 71-72 72-73 73-74; Somerset F/Lit Youth Lge 96-97.

TAUNTON TOWN

Chairman: T F Harris **Vice Chairman:** **Treasuer:** Joan Ellis
Secretary: Tom Harris, C/O the club, (H 01823 333833)
Manager: Russell Musker. **Asst Manager:** Derek Fowler. **Physio:** David Williams
Ground: Wordsworth Drive, Taunton, Somerset TA1 2HG (01823 278191).
Directions: Leave M5 Jct 25, follow signs to town centre, at 2nd set of lights turn left into Wordsworth Drive; ground on left. 25 mins walk from Taunton (BR); turn left out of station and follow road right through town centre bearing left into East Reach. Follow road down and turn right into Wordsworth Drive shortly after Victoria pub.
Seats: 250 **Cover:** 1,000 **Capacity:** 4,000 **Floodlights:** Yes **Club Shop:** Yes
Clubhouse: Social club to accommodate 300, full bar facilities, separate bar & hall for private functions.
Programme: 28 pages, 50p **Editor:** Les Gill **Press Officer:** Joan Ellis
Colours: Sky & claret/claret/sky **Change colours:** Yellow/sky/yellow. **Formed:** 1947
Sponsors: Taunton Cider Co. **Newsline:** 0891 122 901 **Nickname:** Peacocks
Midweek matches: Wednesday **Reserve Team's League:** Great Mills Combination.
Best Season - FA Cup: 1st Rd Proper 81-82 (lost 1-2 at Swindon Town). **FA Trophy season:** 1st Rd Proper 80-81 (lost 1-5 v Hendon at Queens Park Rangers). **FA Vase season:** Finalists 93-94.
Players progressing to Football League: Charlie Rutter (Cardiff), Stuart Brace (Southend & Grimsby).
Previous Leagues: Western 54-77/ Southern 77-83. **Previous Grounds:** Several prior to 1953.
Record win: 12-0 v Dawlish Town (A), FA Cup Preliminary Rd, 28/8/93.
Record defeat: 0-8 v Cheltenham Town (A), FA Cup 2nd Qualifying Rd, 28/9/91.
96-97 - Captain: David Ewens **P.o.Y.:** David Ewens **Top Scorer:** Mark Loram
Club Record Appearances: Tony Payne **Club Record Scorer** (in a season): Reg Oram 67.
Honours: FA Vase R-up 93-94, Western Lg 68-69 89-90 (R-up 93-94, Les Phillips Cup R-up 93-94, Alan Young Cup 73-74 75-76(jt with Falmouth), Charity Challenge Cup 49-50 50-51), Somerset Snr Lg 52-53, Somerset Prem. Cup R-up 82-83 89-90 92-93.

TIVERTON TOWN

Tiverton Town FC

President: Dan McCauley **Chairman:** Dave Wright **Vice-Chairman:** Pete Buxton
Secretary: Ramsay Findlay, 35 Park Road, Tiverton, Devon EX16 6AY (01884 256341).
Manager: Martyn Rogers **Asst Manager:** Martin Grimshaw **Physio:** Alan Morgan
Ground: Ladysmead, Bolham Road, Tiverton, Devon EX16 8SG (01884 252397)
Directions: M5 Jct 27, west towards Tiverton on A373, continue to end of dual carriageway and turn left at r'about; ground entrance 300yds on right alongside BP petrol station.
Seats: 300 **Cover:** 1,200 **Capacity:** 3,500 **Floodlights:** Yes **Club Shop:** Yes
Clubhouse: Lunctimes, evenings. All day Sat during the season. 3 bars. Food (burgers, hot dogs, chips etc).
Programme: 40 pages, 60p **Editor/Press Officer:** Nigel Davis **Nickname:** Tivvy.
Colours: All Yellow **Change:** All white **Formed:** 1920
Midweek matches: Wednesday **Previous League:** Devon & Exeter
Previous ground: The Elms, Blundell Road 1920-39
Record Attendance: 3,000 v Leyton Orient, FA Cup First Round Proper 1994-95.
Players progressing to Football League: Jason Smith (Coventry City, 1993). Mark Saunders(Plymouth Argyle,1995).
96-97 - Captain: K Smith **Top Scorer:** P Everett **P.o.Y.:** S Daly
Honours: FA Vase R-up 92-93 (QF 94-95); FA Cup 1st Rnd 90-91 91-92 94-95; Western Lg 93-94 94-95 96-97 (R-up 92-93 95-96); Les Phillips Cup 92-93 94-95 95-96 96-97; Amateur Trophy 77-78 78-79, Div 1 R-up 88-89; Devon St Lukes Cup 90-91 91-92 92-93 94-95 96-97 (R-up 89-90); Devon & Exeter Lg 51-52 66-67 70-71 84-85; Devon Snr Cup 55-56 65-66; East Devon Snr Cup 35-36 37-38 52-53 55-56 60-61 62-63 66-67; North Devon Charity Cup 72-73 86-87.

TORRINGTON

President: Cyril Slade **Chairman:** Winston Martin
Secretary: David Priscott, 6 Highfield Terrace, Bishops Tawton, Barnstable EX32 0AN (01271 328316)
Manager: Geoff Evans **Asst Manager:** Mike Ford **Physio:** Albert Williams
Ground: Vicarage Field, School Lane, Great Torrington (01805 622853).
Directions: (From North, Barnstaple, Exeter, South Molton) In town centre turn left by parish church, turn right at swimming pool, ground behind swimming pool. Good parking. Red Bus from Bideford and Barnstaple (nearest BR station). Bus stop 300yds from ground.
Seats: 100 **Cover:** 1,000 **Capacity:** 4,000 **Floodlights:** Yes **Formed:** 1908
Midweek Matches: Tuesday **Club Sponsors:** Bideford Tool **Club Shop:** No.
Clubhouse: Weekdays 7-11pm, Sat & Sun 12-3. Two bars. Light snacks available.
Colours: Green & white hoops/green/green & white **Change colours:** Blue & white stripes/white/white
Programme: 48 pages, 50p **Editor:** Secretary **Best F.A.Vase Season:** 5th Rd 84-85.
Nickname: Torrie or Supergreens **Previous Leagues:** N Devon/ Devon & Exeter/ S Western 77-84.
96-97 - Captain: M Gilbert **Supporters P.o.Y.:** K Hill **P.o.Y.:** A Widger
Club record scorer: Trevor Watkins, 254 **Club record appearances:** Mike Gilbert 527
Honours: Western Lg R-up 90-91; Merit Cup 91-92 93-94 95-96; South Western Lg Cup 81; Devon St Lukes Cup R-up 95-96 96-97; Devon & Exeter Lg & Cup 73-74; Fest of Britain Cup 96-97; Les Phillips Cup R-up 91-92; Torridge Cup (13).

WESTBURY UNITED

Chairman: Phillip Alford **Vice Chairman:** Bert Back **President:** George Nicholls.
Secretary: Mrs Joy Bown, 23 Leighton Park Road, Westbury, Wilts. BA13 3RX (01373 823987).
Manager: Nigel Tripp **Asst Manager:** Phil Back **Physio:** Lee Webb
Ground: Meadow Lane, Westbury (01373 823409).
Directions: In town centre, A350, follow signs for BR station, Meadow Lane on right (club signposted). Ten mins walk from railway station (on main London-South West + South Coast-Bristol lines).
Seats: 150 **Cover:** 150 **Capacity:** 3,500 **Floodlights:** Yes **Formed:** 1921
Colours: Green & white/green/green **Change colours:** Sky & navy/blue/blue
Midweek Matches: Tuesday **Prev. Leagues:** Wilts Comb./ Wilts Co. (pre-1984)
Programme: 16 pages, 30p **Editor:** Mike Taylor (01373 826754).
Nickname: White Horsemen **Club Shop:** Yes **Reserve's league:** Trowbridge Lge.
Record Gate: 4,000 v Llanelli, FA Cup 1st Rd 37; 4,000 v Walthamstow Avenue F.A.Cup 37.
Players progressing to Football League: John Atyeo (Bristol City and England).
Clubhouse: Evenings 7-11pm, Fri, Sat & Sun lunctimes 12-3pm.
Honours: Western Lg Div 1 91-92, Wilts Senior Cup 31-32 32-33 47-48 51-52, Wilts Combination, Wilts Lg 34-35 37-38 38-39 49-50 50-51 55-56, Wilts Premier Shield R-up 92-93.

Keynsham Town. *Photo - Tim Lancaster*

FIRST DIVISION CLUBS 1997-98

BISHOP SUTTON

Chairman: **Vice Chairman:** Roy Penney **President:** Bob Redding.
Secretary: Roy Penney, 53 Ridgway Lane, Whitchurch, Bristol BS14 9PJ (01275 541392).
Manager: Chris Mountford **Coach:** Chris Stutt **Physio:** Vernon Ashton
Ground: Lakeview Football Field, Bishop Sutton (01275 333097).
Directions: On A368 at rear of Butchers Arms pub – Ground signposted on left entering village from the West.
Seats: None **Cover:** 200 **Capacity:** 1,500 **Floodlights:** No **Club Shop:** No.
Programme: Yes **Editor:** Mr G Williams **Press Officer:**
Colours: All blue **Change colours:** All red
Sponsors: Crown Insulation. **Nickname:** Bishops. **Founded:** 1977.
Midweek Matches: Tuesday **Youth team's League:** Somerset Mid Week **Record Attendance:** 410
Previous Leagues: Weston & Dist. Yth/ Bristol & Avon/ Somerset Snr (pre 1991)
Players progressing to Football League: David Lee (Chelsea), S Williams (Southampton), J French (Bristol Rovers).
Clubhouse: Open matchdays. Rolls, pies and usual pub food available.
Honours: Somerset Snr Lg R-up 89-90 (Div 1 83-84 (R-up 81-82), Div 2 82-83), Bristol & Avon Lg 80-81 (Div 2 79-80), Somerset Jnr Cup 80-81, Weston Yth Lg 77-78, Chew Valley KO Cup 83-84, Mid-Somerset Lg(Res) R-up 82-83 (Div 3 81-82).

BITTON

Chairman: David Venables **Manager:** Martyn Dyer
Secretary: Michael Hall, 14 Billingers Road, Kingswood, Bristol BS15 2DE (0117 960 3627)
Ground: The Recreation Ground, Bitton, (0117 932 3222)
Directions: M4 junc 18. Take A46 towards Bath, at first roundabout take A420 for Wick/Bridgeyate. On approach to Bridgeyate turn left at mini-roundabout onto A4175 and follow for 2.2 miles, then turn left for Bath on the A431. The ground is 100 yards on right.
Colours: Red & white/black/black **Change colours:** All yellow
Midweek Matches: Tuesday. **Previous Leagues:** Glos County

CLYST ROVERS

President: Mr P W Brown **Chairman:** Bob Chamberlain **Vice Chairman:** Colin Dadson
Secretary: Bob Chamberlain, Orchard Cottage, Clyst St George, Exeter EX3 0NZ (01392 873498)
Manager: R Wilson **Physio:** Bill Wreford.
Ground: Waterslade Park, Clyst Honiton, Devon (01392 366424)
Directions: A30 following signs for Exeter Airport. Coming from Exeter take 1st right after airport turning (ground signposted) up narrow 200yds past Duke of York Pub.
Seats: 130 **Cover:** 300 **Capacity:** 3,000 **Floodlights:** Yes **Founded:** 1926.
Programme: 32 pages, 30p **Editor:** Ray Dack (01392 215075)
Colours: Yellow/blue/yellow & blue **Change colours:** Blue/black/black
Reformed: 1951. **Nickname:** Rovers. **Sponsors:** Vantage Pharmacy, Paignton
Midweek Matches: Tuesday. **Club Shop:** Yes, Programmes, souvenirs etc.
Previous Leagues: Exeter & District 26-44 51-66/ Exeter & District Sunday 67-82/ South Western 81-92.
Record Gate: 768 v Tiverton, Devon St Lukes final 11/5/93.
Clubhouse: Open one and a half hours before kick off and after game. Excellent food available.
Honours: Devon St Lukes Cup R-up 92-93, Western Lg Cup SF 92-93.

CREDITON UNITED

Chairman: D.J.Blanchford **Vice Chairman:** C R Gillard **President:** W J Ash.
Secretary: A Sherriff, 17 Churchill Drive, Crediton, Devon, EX17 2DW, (01363 774002)
Manager: Norman Bye/Nick Thomas **Coach:** Dave Evans
Ground: Lord's Meadow Sports Centre, Crediton (01363 774671-club)
Directions: A377 to Crediton from Exeter, right onto A3072 (signposted Tiverton) at Crown of Crediton restaurant, turn right into Commercial Rd for Lord's Meadow Ind. Est.- Sports Centre car park 250 metres on left.
Seats: 150 **Cover:** 150 **Capacity:** 2,000 **Floodlights:** Yes **Club Shop:** No.
Programme: Yes **Editor:** C R Gillard **Press Officer:**
Colours: All blue **Change colours:** Red & black/black/red
Sponsors: Graphic Electronics **Founded:** 1946
Midweek Matches: Wednesday **Previous League:** Devon & Exeter (pre-1990)
Honours: Devon & Exeter Lg 87-88 (R-up 88-89, Harry Wood Trophy 88-89, Snr Div 1 62-63 66-67, Jnr Div 3 48-49(jt) 49-50, Snr Div 2b(res) 70-71, Snr Div 3(res) 86-87, Jnr Div 3(res) 56-57,Intermediate 1 Winners 94-95,I'mediate Div 3('A') 91-92, I'mediate Div 4 R-up('B') 92-93, I'mediate Div 5 R-up('B') 91-92), East Devon Snr Cup 33-34, Okehampton Challenge Cup 72-73 74-75, Whitbread Flowers Cup 78-79, Bill Rees Trophy 86-87, Geary Cup(res) 84-85 86-87, Liddon Cup('A') 84-85 86-87.

DAWLISH TOWN

Dawlish Town FC.

President: Bob Webster **Chairman:** Tony Darby
Secretary: Graham Jones, 133 Kingsdown Cres., Dawlish, Devon EX7 0HB (01626 866004).
Manager: Tony Bowker. **Assistant Manager:**
Ground: Playing Fields, Sandy Lane, Exeter Road, Dawlish (01626 863110).
Directions: Approx 1 mile from centre of town, off main Exeter road (A379).
Seats: 200 **Cover:** 200 **Capacity:** 2,000 **Floodlights:** Yes **Founded:** 1889
Programme: 34 pages, 30p **Programme Editor:** Roy Bolt.
Colours: Green & white/green/green **Change colours:** All white
Midweek home matchday: Tuesday **Previous League:** Devon & Exeter.
Record Gate: 1,500 v Heavitree Utd, Devon Prem. Cup Q-Final
Clubhouse: Open nightly, situated in car park opposite ground.
Honours: Western Lg Cup 80-81 83-84, Devon Premier Cup 69-70 72-73 80-81, Devon Snr Cup 57-58 67-68, Devon St Lukes Cup 82-83 (R-up 81-82), FA Vase Quarter Finals 86-87, Carlsberg Cup 96.

DEVIZES TOWN

Chairman: Alan Wallis **Manager:** Brian Newlands
Secretary: Chris Dodd, 69 Broadleas Park, Devizes, Wilts. SN10 5JG. (01380 726205)
Ground: Nursteed Road, Devizes. (01380 722817).
Directions: Off Nursteed Road (A342 signposted Andover); leaving town ground on right opposite Eastleigh Rd.
Seats: 130. **Cover:** 400 **Capacity:** 2,500 **Floodlights:** Yes **Founded:** 1883
Colours: Red & white stripes/black/red **Change colours:** Yellow & blue/blue/yellow.
Previous Name: Southbroom (until early 1900s) **Previous Ground:** London Rd (pre 1946)
Midweek Matchday: Tuesday **Previous Leagues:** Wilts Comb./ Wilts Premier.
Honours: Wilts Snr Cup 07-08 49-50 56-57 57-58 58-59 60-61 61-62 62-63 65-66 67-68 70-71 71-72 73-74 78-79.

EXMOUTH TOWN

President: Brian Bradley **Chairman:** P Marshall **Vice Chairman:** John Dibsdall
Secretary: John Edwards, 5 Pinn Lane, Pinhoe, Exeter EX1 3QX (01392 468633)
Manager: Robert Green. **Physio:** Julian Bennett
Ground: King George V Ground, Southern Road, Exmouth (01395 263348)
Directions: On right side of main Exeter to Exmouth road (A376). Half mile from Exmouth (BR) station.
Seats: 100 **Cover:** 250 **Capacity:** 2,500 **Floodlights:** Yes **Formed:** 1933
Colours: Blue & white/blue/blue **Change colours:** Green & yellow/green/yellow
Nickname: 'Town' or 'Blues' **Previous Lge:** Devon & Exeter 1933-73.
Programme: 36 pages, 30p **Editor:** J.Dibsdall.
Midweek matchday: Tuesday **Reserves' League:** Gt Mills Comb. **Sponsors:** None.
Club Shop: Yes **Record Gate:** 2,395 v Liverpool XI, friendly in 1987.
Clubhouse: Open every night and weekend lunchtimes. Snacks available.
Club Record Scorer: Mel Pym, 117 **Record Appearances:** Keith Sprague, Geoff Weeks 410 (Western Lg)
Honours: FA Vase SF 84-85; Western Lg 83-84 85-86 (R-up 86-87 88-89; Lg Cup 88-89; Div 1 R-up 81-82; Sportmanship Tphy 86-87 92-93); Devon Premier Cup 70-71 79-80; Devon St Lukes Cup 84-85 88-89 89-90; Devon Snr Cup 50-51; East Devon Snr Cup 50-51 82-83; Harry Wood Mem. Cup 81-82; Exmouth Chal. Cup [7]

FROME TOWN

President: Mr C W M Norton. **Chairman:** Colin Skirton **Vice Chairman:** Steve Porter, Geoff Norris
Secretary: Mrs S J Merrill, 11 Beaconsfield Way, Frome, Somerset BA11 2UA (01373 473820).
Manager: Simon Culliford **Coach:** **Physio:** Bob Stokes
Ground: Badgers Hill, Berkeley Road, Frome (01373 453643).
Directions: On the Westbury Road, 1 mile from town centre and Frome BR station
Seats: 250 **Cover:** 800 **Capacity:** 5,000 **Floodlights:** Yes **Founded:** 1904
Colours: All red **Change colours:** All purple **Programme:** 24 pages, 50p **Editor:** Secretary
Sponsors: Telewest Communications **Nickname:** Robins. **Club Shop:** No.
Previous League: Somerset Senior, Wilts League and Wilts Premier **Midweek matchday:** Wednesday
Record Attendance: 8,000 v Leyton Orient, F.A.Cup 1st Rd. 58. **Reserve's League:** Somerset Senior.
Best Season - F.A.Cup: 1st Rd Proper v L.Orient 54-55. **F.A.Trophy:** 2nd Rd Proper v Boston Utd (A) 84-85. **F.A.Vase:** 2nd.Rd.Proper v Paulton R (a) 1-2.
Clubhouse: Evenings & weekends. Cold food only.
96-97 Captain: D Piatt **96-97 Top Scorer:** J Burr **96-97 P.o.Y.:** J Burr
Honours: Wiltshire League 1909-10,1910-11,Western Lg 78-79 (Div 2 19-20, Div 2 R-up 54-55, Lg Cup 79-80 82-83, Merit Cup 82-83, Alan Young Cup 79-80, Subsidiary Cup 59-60), FA Cup 1st Rd 54-55, Somerset Premier Cup 66-67 68-69 82-83, Wilts Premier Lg 62-63, Western Co's F'lit Cup 83-84, Somerset Snr Cup 32-33 33-34 50-51, Somerset Snr Lg 06-07 08-09 10-11 (Div 1(res) 90-91, Div 3(res) 85-86, Lg Cup(res) 91-92).

GLASTONBURY

Chairman: Peter Watts **President:** Mr L R Reed **Life President:** Les Heal **Manager:** Simon Dovey.
Secretary: Leslie Heal, 2 Lowerside Road, Glastonbury, Somerset BA6 9BE (01458 832037)
Ground: Abbey Moor Stadium, Godney Road, Glastonbury, Somerset (01458 831460).
Directions: From Bristol take by-pass from Tin Bridge r/about turning right at Northload Bridge r/about, then 1st right. From Taunton take by-pass at 'B&Q' turning, left at Northload Bridge r/about, then 1st right.
Seats: 80 **Cover:** 300 **Capacity:** 1,500 **Floodlights:** Yes **Founded:** 1890.
Programme: 24 pages, 30p **Editor/Press Officer:** Les Heal (01458 832037)
Colours: Yellow/black/yellow **Change colours:** All red
Midweek Matches: Wednesday **Previous Leagues:** Bristol & District, Bristol Suburban
Clubhouse: Yes, on ground. Hot snacks from tea bar on matchdays.
Club Record scorer: Jim Allaway 42 **Club Record Appearances:** Brian Mortimer 496.
Honours: Western Lg 48-49 50-51 69-70 (R-up 47-48 51-52)Great Mills Div 1 94-95 Lg Cup 65-66 (SF 83-84), Alan Young Cup 67-68 (jt with Minehead) 70-71); Somerset Professional Cup 37-38 48-49; Somerset Snr Cup 35-36; Somerset Charity Cup 32-33; Somerset Jnr Cup 12-13 13-14; Somerset Lg 49-50 50-51

HEAVITREE UNITED

President: Mr E Drew **Chairman:** Barry Connaway **Vice Chairman:** Mr K Carpenter
Secretary: Keith Gilbert, 9 Dean Street, St Leonards, Exeter EX2 4HH (01392 438637)
Manager: **Asst Manager:** Nick Bibby **Physio:**
Ground: Wingfield Park, East Wonford Hill, Exeter, Devon (01392 73020).
Directions: Leave M5 at Exeter Granada Services, follow signs for City Centre/ Heavitree for approx. 3 miles and ground is situated on left at top of East Wonford Hill.
Seats: 150 **Cover:** 150 **Capacity:** 500 **Floodlights:** No **Founded:** 1885. **Shop:** No.
Clubhouse: 12am-12pm daily. Wide range of matchday hot food. **Programme:** 20 pages, 20p
Colours: Black & jade/black & jade/black **Change colours:** Black & white/black & white/black
Nickname: Heavies. **Sponsors:** Mortgage & Loan Centre **Midweek matchday:** Tuesday
Previous Lges: Exeter & Dist./ Devon & Exeter. **Record Gate:** 350 v Exeter City, friendly 1989.
96-97 Captain: T Wheatley **96-97 Top Scorer:** R Roberts/M Pepperell **96-97 P.o.Y.:** Mark Brown
Club record scorer: John Laskey **Club record appearances:** Alan Kingdom.
Honours: Exeter & Dist Lg 46-47 51-52 (Snr Div 2 56-57 59-60 60-61 67-68), Devon & Exeter Lg 70-71 76-77, Devon Snr Cup 46-47 60-61 70-71, E Devon Snr Cup 46-47 70-71 76-77, Wheaton Tphy 87-88.

ILFRACOMBE TOWN

Chairman: Mike Edmunds **Vice-Chairman:** Bob Martin. **President:** Bob Martin.
Secretary: Tony Alcock, 2 Worth Road, Ilfracombe, North Devon EX34 9JA (01271 862686).
Manager: Ian Cornish **Coach/Physio:** Eric Hayhurst
Ground: Marlborough Park, Ilfracombe, Devon (01271 865939).
Directions: A361 to Ilfracombe, 1st right in town after lights, follow Marlborough Rd to top, ground on left.
Seats: 60 **Cover:** 450 **Capacity:** 2,000 **Floodlights:** Yes **Club Shop:** No.
Programme: The Bluebird 8 pages, 40p **Editor:** Peter Bidgood (01271 864756) **Founded:** 1902
Colours: All Blue **Change colours:** Black & white/black/black **Sponsors:** Park View.
Midweek matchday: Tuesday **Nickname:** Bluebirds **Reserve's League:** North Devon.
Record attendance: 3,000 v Bristol City, Ground opening, 2/10/24
Previous Leagues: North Devon 04-14 20-22 60-84/ East Devon Premier 22-31/ Exeter & District 32-39 46-49/ Western 49-59/ South Western League (Reserves) 53-54.
Player progressing to Football Lge: Jason Smith (Coventry via Tiverton)
Clubhouse: Every night 7-11pm and weekend lunchtimes. Hot & cold meals on matchdays.
Club Record Goalscorer: Darren Bryant **Club Record Appearances:** Paul Jenkins 410.
Honours: East Devon Premier Lg 25-26 28-29 29-30, North Devon Senior Lg, North Devon Premier Lg 66-67 70-71 81-82 82-83, Western Lg Div 2 R-up 52-53.

Ilfracombe Town FC *Photo - Tim Lancaster*

LARKHALL ATHLETIC

President: Tony Rhymes **Chairman:** Jim McLay **Manager:** P Rankin/P Miles
Secretary: Mervyn Liles, 9 Eastbourne Ave., Claremont Rd., Bath BA1 6EW (01225 319427).
Ground: "Plain Ham", Charlcombe Lane, Larkhall, Bath (01225 334952).
Directions: A4 from Bath, 1 mile from city centre turn left into St Saviours Rd. In Larkhall square fork left, and right at junction, road bears into Charlcombe Lane. Ground on right as lane narrows.
Seats: None **Cover:** 50 **Capacity:** 1,000 **Floodlights:** No **Club Shop:**
Programme: Yes **Editor:** **Nickname:** Larks.
Colours: Royal & white/royal & white/royal **Change colours:** Red & white/red & white/red **Founded:** 1914
Midweek Matches: Tuesday **Previous League:** Somerset Snr
Honours: Som. Snr Cup 75-76, Som. Snr Lg, Western Lg Div 1 88-89 93-94 94-95(Div 1 Merit Cup(4) 83-86 87-88(jt with Yeovil Res).

MINEHEAD

Director of Football/Chairman/Secretary: Peter Bate, Meadow Cottage, Venniford, Minehead, Somerset. TA24 8ST. (01643 704063)
Manager: Chris Porter **Coach:** Charlie Kirk **Reserves Mgr:** Charlie Lewis
Ground: The Recreation Ground, Irnham Road, Minehead, Somerset (01643 704989).
Directions: Entering town from east on A39 turn right into King Edward Road at Police station, first left into Alexandra Rd and follow signs to car park; ground entrance within. Regular buses to Minehead from Taunton, the nearest railhead.
Seats: 350 **Cover:** 400 **Capacity:** 3,500 **Floodlights:** Yes **Founded:** 1889.
Colours: Blue & white/blue/blue **Change colours:** Yellow/Green/sky/yellow & green
Programme: 24 pages, 50p **Editor:** Dir of Football **Midweek Matches:** Tuesday.
Previous Leagues: Somerset Snr/ Southern 72-83. **Reserves League:** Combination League
Record Gate: 3,600 v Exeter City, FA Cup 2nd Rd, 77.
Honours: Southern Lg R-up 76-77 (Div 1 Sth 75-76, Merit Cup 75-76), Western Lg R-up 66-67 71-72 (Div 1 90-91, Alan Young Cup 67-68 (jt with Glastonbury), Somerset Premier Cup 60-61 73-74 76-77.

PEWSEY VALE

President: **Chairman:** Rob Thompson **Manager:** Graham Smith
Secretary: Mrs Barbara Flippance, 17 Slater Rd, Pewsey SN9 5EE (01672 563665).
Ground: Recreation Ground, Ball Rd, Pewsey (01672 562990).
Directions: On entering Pewsey from A345, at the Market Place proceed to end of High Street and turn right into Ball Rd, entrance to ground on right opposite pub. BR to Pewsey station.
Seats: **Cover:** Yes **Capacity:** **Floodlights:** No **Formed:**
Colours: Blue & white/blue/blue **Change colours:** All Red.
Previous League: Wiltshire County (pre-1993). **Midweek home matchday:** Wednesday
Honours: Wiltshire County League 92-93.

STREET

Chairman: Steve Bailey **Manager:** Simon White
Secretary: Mark Clarke, 1 Deerswood Gardens, Street, Somerset BA16 9PY (01458 442249)
Ground: The Tannery Ground, Middlebrooks, Street, Somerset (01458 445987)
Directions: Sign posted from both ends of A39 & B3151
Colours: All green & white **Change colours:** Red & black/black/black
Midweek home matchday: Tuesday

WARMINSTER TOWN

President: Bob Peaty **Chairman:** Peter Farrell **Vice-Chairman:** Rod Kitley.
Secretary: John Loftus. 34 George Street, Warminster, Wilts BA12 8QB (01373 832596).
General Manager: Derek Wesley **Manager:** Derek Graham
Ground: Weymouth Street, Warminster, Wilts BA12, (01985 217828).
Directions: Take A350 for Weymouth from lights at centre of town - ground on left at brow of hill.
Seats: 75 **Cover:** 150 **Capacity:** 2,000 **Floodlights:** Yes **Club Shop:** No.
Programme: 36 pages, 40p **Editor:** Chris Finch (01985 217326)
Colours: Red & black stripes/black/red **Change:** All white
Sponsors: Lyons Seafoods. **Nickname:** Red & blacks **Founded:** 1878
Midweek Matchday: Wednesday **Reserve League:** Wilthsire. **Previous League:** Wiltshire
Record Attendance: 1,500 for Ladies International, England v Wales, mid-1970s.
Clubhouse: Opened 22/7/94. Evenings/matchdays/as required
96-97 Captain: **96-97 P.o.Y.:** **96-97 Top Scorer:**
Honours: Wilts Snr Cup 1900-01 02-03 10-11 (R-up 09-10 26-27 32-33 53-54); Wilts Prem. Lg 56-57; Wilts Jnr Cup R-up 21-22 27-28 55-56 58-59; Central Wilts Lg 08-09

WELLINGTON

Chairman: Selwyn Aspin **Vice-Chairman:** Mike Bull **President:** Alan Shire
Secretary: Tony Brown, 6 Courtland Rd, Wellington, Somerset TA21 8ND (01823 662920).
Manager: Martin Darby. **Res. Manager:** Graham Aspin **Physio:** Ken Pearson.
Ground: Wellington Playing Field, North Street, Wellington, Somerset (01823 664810).
Directions: At town centre traffic lights turn into North St., then first left by Fire Station into the public car park that adjoins the ground.
Seats: None **Cover:** 200 **Capacity:** 3,000 **Floodlights:** Yes **Club Shop:**
Programme: Yes **Editor:** Jeff Brown
Colours: Tangerine/black/tangerine **Change colours:** Blue & claret stripes/blue/blue
Sponsors: A J Shire & Wadham Fencing **Nickname:** **Founded:** 1892
Midweek Matches: Wednesday **Reserves League:** Combination
Previous Leagues: Taunton Saturday, Somerset Senior
Players progressing to Football League: Nick Jennings (Plymouth).
96-97 Captain: Kevin Bryant **96-97 P.o.Y.:** Nick Woon **96-97 Top Scorer:** Nick Woon
Club Record Goalscorer: Ken Jones **Club Record Appearances:**
Honours: Western Lg Div 1 R-up 80-81 (Merit Cup 91-92); Western Comb Lge 95-96; Western Comb Lge KO Cup 95-96; Somerset Snr Lg Div 1 R-up; Rowbarton & Seward Cup;

WELTON ROVERS

Chairman: Rae James **President:**
Secretary: Geoff Baker, 6 Longfellow Road, Westfield, Radstock, Bath BA3 3YZ (01761 413742).
Manager: Malcolm Beck. **Asst Manager:** **Physio:** John Carver
Ground: West Clewes, North Road, Midsomer Norton, Somerset (01761 412097).
Directions: A367 Bath to Radstock – right at lights at foot of hill onto A362, ground on right.
Seats: 300 **Cover:** 300 **Capacity:** 2,400 **Floodlights:** Yes **Club Shop:** No.
Programme: 12 pages, 25p **Editor:** M Brown
Colours: Green & white/green/green **Change colours:** All Red
Sponsors: Norad Travel **Nickname:** Rovers. **Formed:** 1887
Midweek matchday: Monday **Reserve League:** Somerset Senior.
Record Attendance: 2,000 v Bromley, FA Amateur Cup 1963 **Previous Leagues:** None
Clubhouse: 7.30-11pm daily, Sat matchdays 1.30-2.45pm, Sun noon-2pm.
Club Record Appearances: **Club Record Goalscorer:** Ian Henderson, 51
Honours: Western Lg 11-12 64-65 65-66 66-67 73-74 (Div 1 59-60 87-88; Amateur Cup 56-57 57-58 58-59 59-60; Alan Young Cup 65-66 66-67 67-68(joint)); Somerset Snr Cup 06-07 11-12 12-13 13-14 19-20 24-25 25-26 60-61 61-62 62-63, Somerset I'mediate Cup 77-78, Somerset Jnr Cup 06-07(joint) 24-25 30-31, WBC Clares City of Wells Cup 78-79.

YEOVIL TOWN RESERVES

Chairman: John Fry **President:** S N Burfield
Secretary: Jean Cotton, c/o Club. (01935 428130 H)
Manager: Maurice O'Donnell/Tony Pounder **Physio:** Maurice O'Donnell
Ground: Huish Park, Lufton Way, Yeovil Somerset, BA22 8YF. (01935 23662, Fax 73956
Directions: Leave A303 at Cartgate roundabout and take A3088 signposted Yeovil. Take first exit at next roundabout and first exit at next roundabout into Lufton Way. Railway station - Yeovil Pen Mill (Bristol/Westbury to Weymouth) 2.5 miles from ground. Yeovil Junction (Waterloo to Exeter) 4 miles. Bus service from both stations on Saturday - matchdays.
Capacity: 8,720 **Seats:** 5,212 **Terracing:** 3,508 **Floodlights:** Yes **Metal Badges:** Yes.
Club Shop: Open on matchdays selling full range of souvenirs, match programmes, scarves, hats, replica kits *Team Talk Magazine* etc.
Colours: Green/white/green **Change colours:** All Yellow **Midweek matchday:** Wednesday
Clubhouse: Matchdays hot + cold food available. Meals can be ordered provided advance notice is given. All weather astro turf pitch available for bookings 9am-10pm.
96-97 Captain: Lee Collier **Top scorer:** Simon Gale **P.o.Y.:** Simon Gale

INTERLINK EXPRESS MIDLAND FOOTBALL ALLIANCE

FEEDER TO: BEAZER HOMES LEAGUE

President: Neville D Jeynes **Chairman:** P Fellows **Vice Chairman:** M W Lycett
General Secretary/Treasurer: Peter G Dagger, Alpins Cottage, 46 Banbury Road, Ettington, Warwickshire CV37 7SU ((H) 01789 740597 (Fax) 01789 740247)
Press/Publicity Officer: Kevin P Hurcombe, 17 Wigmore Close, Abbeymead, Gloucester GL4 5FF ((H) 01452 616406 (B) 01179 343524 (Fax) 01452 615565)

FINAL LEAGUE TABLE 1996-97

Premier Division

		P	W	D	L	F	A	Pts
1	Blakenall	38	23	11	4	84	39	80
2	Hinckley Athletic	38	22	10	6	77	44	76
3	Boldmere St M.	38	22	7	9	69	41	73
4	Willenhall Town	38	20	9	9	77	45	69
5	Barwell	38	17	10	11	65	51	61
6	Bridgnorth Town	38	18	4	16	76	67	58
7	Rocester	38	16	9	13	62	53	57
8	Stratford Town	38	15	10	13	53	48	55
9	Bloxwich Town	38	16	6	16	63	53	54
10	Oldbury United	38	14	11	13	50	43	53
11	Pelsall Villa	38	13	9	16	52	69	48
12	Knypersley Vic	38	11	12	15	42	53	45
13	Stapenhill	38	10	14	14	45	58	44
14	Shifnall Town	38	11	10	17	45	50	43
15	West Mids Police	38	10	11	17	37	60	41
16	Rushall Olympic	38	10	10	18	40	59	40
17	Sandwell Borough	38	9	13	16	48	69	40
18	Chasetown	38	9	12	17	44	65	39
19	Halesowen Harr.	38	8	12	18	44	67	36
20	Pershore Town	38	8	6	24	41	60	30

LIST OF HONOURS 1996-97

LEAGUE CHAMPIONSHIP

1994/95 Paget Rangers
Runners Up Hinckley Athletic
1995/96 Shepshed Dynamo
Runners Up Blakenall
1996/97 Blakenall
Runners Up Hinckley Athletic

INDUSTRIAL REWINDS LEAGUE CUP

1994/95
Sandwell Borough v Halesowen Harriers 2-0
1995/96
Blakenall v Oldbury United 1-0
1996/97
Willenhall Town v Bloxwich Town 1-1
(4-2 after penalties)

INTERLINK EXPRESS INVITATION CUP

1994/95
Blakenall v Shifnal Town 1-1
(4-3 after penalties)
1995/96
Pelsall Villa v Oldbury United 1-0
1996/97
Oldbury United v Bridgnorth Town 2-1

PAUL MITCHELL HOSPITALITY CUP

1994/95 Rushall Olympic
1995/96 Halesowen Harriers
1996/97 West Midlands Police

TRANISCON LTD PLAYER OF THE YEAR

1994/95 Anthony Smith Stratford Town
1995/96 Simon Hyden Rushall Olympic
1996/97 Adrian Horne Pelsall Villa

TOP GOALSCORER - THE GOLDEN BOOT

1994/95 John Bundred Knypersley Vic.
1995/96 Michael Biddle Knypersley Vic.
1996/97 Charlie Blackmore Willenhall Town

POLYMAC SERVICES BEST DISCIPLINARY AWARD

1994/95 Oldbury United
1995/96 Barwell
1996/97 Barwell

BEST PROGRAMME AWARD

1995/96 Boldmere St Michaels
1996/97 Pelsall Villa

MANAGER OF THE YEAR

1994/95 Eddie Caulfield Paget Rangers
1995/96 Mark OKane Shepshed D'mo
1996/97 Bob Green Blakenall

SPORTSLINE TEAM OF THE MONTH AWARD

Aug/Sep Hinckley Athletic
October Boldmere St Michaels
November Bridgnorth Town
December Willenhall
Jan/Feb Bloxwich Town
March Rocester
Apr/May Blakenall

BARWELL F.C.

The players celebrate after winning
the Jelson Homes Leicestershire Senior Cup on April 7th.

OLDBURY UNITED F.C.

The 1996/97 Interlink Express Invitation Cup winning squad.

CLUB DIRECTORY 1997-98

BARWELL

Chairman: David Laing. **Vice Chairman:** Ron Borman. **President:** Bob Gee
Secretary: Mrs Shirley Brown, 101 Eskdale Road, Hinckley, LE10 0NW (01455 619308)
Manager: Bill Moore **Asst Manager:** Paul Purser. **Physio:** Viv Coleman/Mark Moore
Ground: Kirkby Rd, Barwell, Leics (01455 843067).
Directions: M42 jct 10 (Tamworth Services), A5 towards Nuneaton. Remain on A5 for approx 11 miles, go straight on at traffic lights at the Longshoot Motel the 400 yards at r/about take 1st exit left sign A47 Earl Shilton, in 3 miles at traffic lights go straight ahead and in 1 mile at r/about take first left exit sign Barwell in village centre 1/2 mile go straight over mini r/about, 20 yards turn right into Kirkby Rd, ground 400 yards on right.
Capacity: 2,500 **Seats:** 140 **Cover:** 750 **Floodlights:** Yes **Club Shop:** No
Programme: 36 pages, 50p **Editor:** Mr Ron Boorman **Press Officer:** Merv Nash.
Colours: Yellow/green/yellow **Change colours:** Blue & white/blue/Blue. **Nickname:** Kirkby Roaders
Midweek matchday: Tuesday **Sponsors:** Leicester Windows **Founded:** 1992.
Previous Lges: Midland Combination 92-94. *Barwell Ath.: Leics Senior. Hinckley: Central Midlands 86-88.*
Previous Names: Barwell Athletic F.C., Hinckley F.C. - amalgamated in 1992.
Previous Ground: Barwell Athletic: None. Hinckley: groundshare at Hinckley Athletic (pre-1992).
Clubhouse: Evenings & lunchtimes. Snacks available.
96-97 Captain: **96-97 Top Scorer:** **96-97 P.o.Y.:**
Club Record Goalscorer: Scott Kempin **Club Record Appearances:** Kevin Johnson.
Honours: Barwell Athletic: Leics Snr Lg Tebbutt Brown Cup 91-92, Leics Sen Cup 96-97.

BLOXWICH TOWN

President: M M Ross **Chairman:** Veejay Thaper
Secretary: Kevin Edwards, 149 Coalpool Lane, Walsall WS3 1QL (01922 868608)
Manager: M Folland/P Knox **Coach:** Jim Skidmore. **Physio:** R.Pickering.
Ground: Abbey Park, Glastonbury Crescent, Bloxwich, Walsall. (01922 477640)
Directions: A34 Walsall-Bloxwich, then west onto A4124. Ground 2-3 miles on right, s.p. Mossley Estate.
Capacity: 1,000 **Seats:** 200 **Covered:** 400 **Floodlights:** Yes **Club Shop:** No.
Programme: 30 pages 50p **Editor:** Phil Bradburn **Founded:** 1972.
Colours: Blue & white/white/blue **Change Colours:** Red & Black/Black/Black.
Sponsors: Leamore Windows. **Nickname:** Kestrels **Midweek Matches:** Tues/Thurs
Players progressing to Football League: Martin O'Connor (Crystal Palace & Walsall).
96-97 Captain: Paul Wilde **96-97 Top Scorer:** Mark Holdcroft **96-97 P.o.Y.:** Ronnie Walker
Honours: Bloxwich Comb.(2), Staffs Co. Lg Div 1, Walsall Snr Cup 96-97 R-up 86-87, Invitation Cup 89-90, Midland Combination Premier Div. 95-96 R-Up.94-95. Midland Combination Div 1 89-90, Alan Peck Cup (3), Carlsberg Challenge Cup 95-96, Industrial Rewinds Lge Cup R-up 96-97.

BOLDMERE St MICHAELS

Manager: Alan Parsons
Secretary: Des Green, 4 Blandford Avenue, Castle Bromwich, Birmingham B36 9HX (0121 747 8404)
Ground: Church Road, Boldmere, Sutton Coldfield (0121 373 4435/0121 384 7531)
Directions: A38 & A5127 from City towards S. Coldfield, left at Yenton lights onto A452 (Chester Rd), Church Rd is 6th turning on the right. 400yds from Chester Road (BR).
Capacity: 2,500 **Seats:** 230 **Covered:** 400 **Floodlights:** Yes **Nickname:** Mikes.
Colours: Black & White stripes/black/black **Change Colours:** Yellow/green/yellow **Founded:** 1883
Programme: 32 pages, 75p **Editor:** Keith Fielding (0121 357 2901) **Sponsor:** Swift Forwarding
Midweek matches: Tuesday **Previous Leagues:** West Mids 49-63/ Midland Combination 63-94.
Clubhouse: Bar & lounge, every evening and four lunchtimes
Players who progressed to Football League: John Barton (Everton, Derby County), Kevin Collins (Shrewsbury), Jack Lane (Birmingham City, Notts Co.), John Lewis (Walsall), Don Moss (Cardiff, C Palace), Harry Parkes (Aston Villa), Wally Soden (Coventry).
Honours: Birmingham AFA 36-37; Birmingham AFA Snr Cup; Birmingham Jnr Cup, FA Amtr Cup SF 47-48; AFA Snr Cup 47-48; Central Amtr Lg 48-49; Midland Comb 85-86 88-89 89-90, Challenge Cup 77-78 89-90; Tony Allden Memorial Cup 78-79 88-89 91-92; Challenge Trophy 86-87; Sutton Charity Cup 96-97.

BRIDGNORTH TOWN

Chairman: Simon Bromley **Vice Chairman:** Ian Thomas **President:** Mike Williams
Secretary: Les Bristow, The Old Post Office, Eardington, Bridgnorth, WV16 5JT (01746 766187)
Manager: Ian Britton **Asst Manager:** Richus White **Physio:** Jenny Stretton
Ground: Crown Meadow, Innage Lane, Bridgnorth, Salop WV16 6PZ (01746 762747)
Directions: Follow signs for Shrewsbury (A458) over river bridge on by-pass, turn right for town centre at island, right at T junction, 1st left into Victoria Road, right at cross-road, follow road into Innage Lane, ground on left.
Capacity: 1,600 **Seats:** 250 **Cover:** 700 **Floodlights:** Yes **Club Shop:** Yes
Programme: 24 pages, 50p **Editor:** **Press Officer:**
Colours: Blue & white/white/blue **Change colours:** All red **Nickname:** The Town
Midweek matchday: Tuesday **Reserve's League:** Midland Comb Res Div **Founded:** 1946
Previous Lges: Kidderminster & Dist until 68; Midland Comb 68-83; Beazer Homes Midland 83-96
Clubhouse: Evenings & weekend lunchtimes. Dancehall, darts, pool, hot food on matchdays
96-97 Captain: **96-97 Top Scorer:** Martin Hallam (19) **96-97 P.o.Y.:**
Club Record Goalscorer: Roger Davies 157 **Club Record Appearances:** Kevin Harris 426
Record Attendance: 1,600 v South Shields FA Vase 5th Rd 1976
Players progressing to Football League: Roger Davies (Derby County), Paul Jones (Wolves)
Honours: FA Vase 5th Rd 75-76 94-95, Midland Comb 79-80 82-83 (R-up 76-77 80-81); Lg Cup 78-79, Tony Allden Mem Cup R-up, Kidderminster & Dist Lge, Shropshire Snr Cup 85-86; Shropshire County Cup 70-71 75-76 76-77 78-79 79-80; Welsh Amt Cup 70-71; Shropshire Jun Cup.

CHASETOWN

Chairman: G Rollins **Vice Chairman:** B Simpson **President:** A Scorey.
Secretary: P E Dixon, c/o Club
Manager: Cliff Painter **Asst Manager:** Brian Fox **Physio:** E Highfield.
Ground: The Scholars, Church Street, Chasetown (01543 682222/684609).
Directions: Follow Motorways M5, M6 or M42 and follow signs for A5. A5 to White Horse Road/Wharf Lane, left into Highfields Rd (B5011), left into Church Street at top of hill, ground at end just beyond church. Buses 394 or 395 W Mids Travel, 94 Chase Bus,from Walsall, 860 Midland Red from Cannock.
Seats: 112 **Cover:** 250 **Capacity:** 2,000 **Floodlights:** Yes **Club Shop:** Yes
Programme: 26 pages, 50p **Editor/Press Officer:** Mike Fletcher
Colours: All blue **Change Colours:** All Red.
Sponsors: Aynsley Windows **Nickname:** Scholars **Founded:** 1954.
Midweek matchday: Tuesday **Reserves League:** West Midlands
Record Attendance: 659 v Tamworth, FA Cup 2nd Qualifying Rd 1/10/88.
Previous Leagues: Cannock Yth 54-58/ Lichfield & Dist. 58-61/ Staffs Co. 61-72/ West Mids 72-94.
Previous Name: Chase Terrace Old Scholars 54-72.
Prev. Grnd: Burntwood Rec Cte (pre'83)
Clubhouse: Mon-Fri 7.30-11pm, Sat 11.30am-11pm, Sun 8-10.30pm. Basic snacks.
96-97 Captain: **96-97 Top Scorer:** **96-97 P.o.Y.:**
Club Record Goalscorer: T Dixon 172 **Club Record Appearances:** A Cox 469 (+15 sub).
Honours: West Mids Lg R-up 90-91 92-93 (Lg Cup 89-90 90-91, Div 1 77-78 (R-up 73-74 74-75 75-76 80-81 82-83), Div 1 Cup R-up 80-81 82-83, Div 2 R-up 87-88, Div 2 Cup R-up 86-87); Walsall Snr Cup 90-91 92-93; Staffs Snr Cup R-up 91-92.

HALESOWEN HARRIERS

Chairman: Derek Beasley **Match Secretary:** Malcolm Pearce.
Secretary: Mrs Christine Beasley, 43 Hawne Lane, Halesowen, West Midlands B63 3RN (0121 550 3788 H).
Manager: Dave Beasley **2nd Team Mgr:** Tony Gore **Physio:** Steve Ball/Dave Bowen
Ground: Hayes Park, Park Rd, Colley Gate, Halesowen (01384 896748. Club Newsline: 0891 66 42 52).
Directions: On A458 Birmingham to Stourbridge Rd (B'ham 10 miles, Stourbridge 4 miles). M5 Jct 3 (towards Kidderminster), right at 1st island (towards Dudley), turn left at island (towards Stourbridge), straight over next island then 3m to grd left side, 200yds past Park Lane. 1 mile Lye BR
Seats: 350 **Cover:** 500 **Capacity:** 4,000 **Floodlights:** Yes **Club Shop:** Yes
Programme: 24-28 pages **Editor:** Rob Shinfield (01384 850819) **Founded:** 1961
Colours: White/black/white **Change colours:** Yellow/Blue/Yellow **Nickname:** None
Sponsors: S Griffiths & Sons Ltd **Midweek matchday:** Tuesday or Wednesday.
Record Attendance: 750; friendlies v Walsall and Wolves in 1985. Competitive; 450 v Lye, Lge 1988.
Previous Leagues: Festival (Sunday)/ West Midlands (pre-1994).
Previous Grounds: Birmingham parks 61-70/ Halesowen Town FC 70-84 (both whilst in Sunday football).
Clubhouse: Open every evening. Limited range of hot snacks, but full cold snack kitchen.
96-97 Captain: Rob Shilvock **96-97 P.o.Y.:** Paul Probert **96-97 Top Scorer:** Mark Clark
Honours: West Mids Lg Div 1 85-86 (Div 2 84-85, Div 2 Cup 84-85), Inter City Bowl 67-68 68-69, Festival Lg(5)(R-up(9)), FA Sunday Cup SF 79-80, Midland Sunday Cup, Birmingham Sunday Cup.

Chasetown; Back Row (L-R); Simon Hyden, Steve Pemberton, Tony Dixon, Peter Perry, John Birt, Gary Jones, Mo Powis, Brian Fox. Front Row; Martin Leadbetter, Brendan Bird, Paul Berrow, Steve Neuchterlein, Graham Clegg, Graham Haddaway, Mascot Ross Perry

Halesowen Harriers; Back Row (L-R); Paul Probert, Rob Shilvock, Darren Owen, Neil Hitchman, Matthew Sidaway, Rob Tivey, Spencer Truelove, Andy Mitchell, Geoff Grosvenor. Front Row; Paul Davies, Mark Wilkinson, Ian Guise, Adrian Topley, Neil Wilson, Andy Arnett, Mark Clarke.

Photo - Marshall's Sport Service.

KINGS NORTON TOWN.

Chairman: M Rowley **Vice-Chairman:** S Sanders.
Secretary: Mike Rowley, 61 Derwent Drive, Priorslee, Telford, Shrops TF2 9QR (01952 200020)
Manager: Pete Dunbavin **Asst Manager:** **Coach:** Morris Gittens
Ground: The Valley Stadium, Bromsgrove Road, Redditch (01527 67450).
Directions: Access 7 on town centre ring-road takes you into Bromsgrove Road (via Unicorn Hill) - ground entrance 400yds past traffic lights on right. Arriving from Bromsgrove take first exit off dual carriageway. Ground 400 yds from Redditch BR station and town centre.
Capacity: 9,500 **Cover:** 2,000 **Seats:** 400 **Floodlights:** Yes **Founded:** 1994
Colours: White & red/black/red & white **Change colours** Green/white/black **Nickname:** Nomads
Programme: Yes **Commercial Manager/Press Office:** Fred Evans
Sponsors: Swift Personalised Products/ BGR Financial Consultants. **Midweek matchdays:** Tuesday.
Previous League: Midland Comb, Birmingham Works. *Richmond Amateurs: Birmingham AFA, pre-1994.*
Previous Names: Richmond Swifts, Swift Personalised Products (founded 1979)/ Richmond Amateurs - clubs merged in 1994. All historical entries below pertain to Swift PP except those *italicised.*
96-97 Captain: **96-97 P.o.Y.:** **96-97 Top Scorer:**
Club Record Scorer: A Dunkley (21, 93-94).
Honours: Midland Comb Div 1 95-96, Challenge Vase R-up 93-94, Kings Norton Lg Divs 1 + 2 & Lg Cup, J W Hunt Cup 95-96, Mercian Lg Div 1, Birmingham Works Lg, Birmingham Jnr Cup R-up, Birmingham Vase R-up 95-96.

KNYPERSLEY VICTORIA

Chairman: Philip Leese **Vice Chairman:** Peter Freeman **President:** G Quinn.
Secretary: J.A.Shenton, 27 Portland Drive, Biddulph, Stoke on Trent, ST8 6RY (01782 517962).
Manager: Dave Nixon **Coach:** Greg Clowes **Physio:**
Ground: Tunstall Road, Knypersley, Stoke-on-Trent, (01782 522737 club).
Directions: M6 Jct 15 join A500, 4th exit, pick up A527, follow through Tunstall, Chell, to Biddulph. Ground is situated on A527 just before Biddulph. From M6 jct 18 follow signs to Holmes Chapel then Congleton, A527 o Biddulph, continue thru lights, ground on left. Bus 61 Congleton-Tunstall passes ground.
Seats: 200 **Cover:** 200 **Capacity:** 1,200 **Floodlights:** Yes **Club Shop:** Yes
Programme: 40 pages, 50p. **Editor/Press Officer:** J A Shenton (01782 517962).
Colours: Claret & sky/claret/claret & sky. **Change Colours:** White & navy/navy/white.
Sponsors: KMF Precision Sheetmetal Ltd. **Nickname:** The Vics. **Founded:** 1969.
Midweek matchday: Tues/Thurs **Reserve League:** Staffs Senior.
Best FA Cup Season: 3rd Qual Rd 96-97 **Record Attendance:** 1,100 v Pt Vale, friendly 1989.
Previous Leagues: Leek & Moorlands 69-78/ Staffs Co. (North) 78-83/ Staffs Sen 83-90/ W Midland (Reg) 90-94.
Clubhouse: Open from 1pm on Saturdays and 7pm weekdays. Burgers, hot dogs, crisps etc at tea bar.
96-97 Captain: David Shallcross **96-97 P.o.Y.:** Rob Ponner **96-97 Top Scorer:** Paul James 18
Club Record Goalscorer: J Burndred 128 **Club Record Appearances:** David Shallcross 508
Honours: West Mids Lg Div 1 92-93, Staffs Snr Lg 84-85 (Lg Cup 84-85 85-86), Staffs Co. Lg R-up 79-80, Staffs FA Vase 83-84 86-87, Sentinel Cup 86-87, Leek & Moorlands Lg 72-73 (Div 2 71-72).

OLDBURY UNITED

Chairman: Roy Keeling. **Vice Chairman:** Ken Harris.
Secretary: Paul Charnoch, 27 Pennyhill Lane, West Bromwich, W.Mids B71 3RP (0121 588 8369)
Manager: Kevin Hadley. **Asst Mgr:** Paul Waddington **Physio:** Tony Dandy
Ground: The Cricketts, York Road, Rowley Regis, Warley, West Midlands (0121 559 5564).
Directions: M5 jct 2, follow Blackheath & Halesowen signs, first left at lights and fourth right into York Road (turning before motorway flyover), ground 200yds on left. One and a half miles from Sandwell & Dudley and Rowley Regis BR stations. Bus 404 from West Bromwich, Oldbury and Blackheath.
Seats: 300 **Cover:** 1,000 **Capacity:** 3,000 **Floodlights:** Yes **Founded:** 1958
Colours: Navy with sky trim/blue/blue **Change colours:** All amber **Club Shop:** No
Programme: 28 pages, 50p **Editor:** Football Secretary. **Press Officer:** Martin Scott
Record Gate: 2,200 v Walsall Wood, Walsall Snr Cup Final 1982. **Nickname:** Cricketts,The Blues.
Prev. Lges: Oldbury 58-62/ Warwick & W Mids All. 62-65/ Worcs (later Midland) Comb. 65-82/ Southern 82-86.
Players progressing to F'ball Lge: C Gordon, L Conoway, J Scott, R O'Kelly, G Nardiello, Dakin, T Reece.
Midweek matchday: Tuesday **Sponsors:** Beswick Paper Group, Oldbury.
Clubhouse: Mon-Fri 7.30-11pm, Sat-Sun 12-2.30 (12-11pm Sat matchdays). Snacks available on matchdays
96-97 Captain: Mick Guest **96-97 Top Scorer:** Neil Hesson **96-97 P.o.Y.:** Neil Hesson
Honours: West Mids Lg 92-93, Staffs Snr Cup 87-88, Midland Comb. R-up 78-79 (Presidents Cup 72-73(res), Div 3 R-up 82-83(res), Chal. Vase 82-83(res)), Walsall Snr Cup 82-83, B'ham Snr Amtr Cup, Oldbury Lg Div 2 61-62, Worcs Snr Urn 86-87, Sandwell Charity Cup 86-87, Interlink Invitation Cup 96-97.

PELSALL VILLA

Chairman: V Dolphin **Vice Chairman:** J H Gough **President:** B J Hill
Secretary: Gareth J Evans, 72 St Pauls Crescent, Pelsall, Walsall WS3 4ET (01922 693114).
Manager: Reg Priest **Asst Manager:** Kevin Gough. **Physio:** J.Lancaster.
Ground: The Bush, Walsall Road, Pelsall, Walsall (01922 682018 Club, 01922 692748 Ground)
Directions: M6 jct 7 A34 B'gham. Take A34 towards Walsall to 1st island, turn right (Ring Road), cross two islands. At large island at bottom of hill take last exit Lichfield, up hill, cross next island to lights. Continue to next set of lights and turn left (B4154 Pelsall). Go over railway bridge to Old Bush pub on right (next to Pelsall Cricket and Sports Club).
Seats: Yes **Cover:** 624 **Capacity:** 2,000 **Floodlights:** Yes **Club Shop:** Yes
Programme: 68 pages, 60p **Editor:** Secretary **Press Officer:** B J Hill
Colours: Red & black/black/black **Change colours:** Blue & white/blue/blue
Sponsor: Metelec **Nickname:** Villians **Reformed:** 1961.
Midweek home matchday: Tuesday. **Record Gate:** 1,800 v Aston Villa 28/11/91.
Best FA Cup season: 3rd Qualifying Rd 92-93 (lost 2-4 at Gainsborough Trinity).
Best FA Vase season: 5th Rd 92-93 (lost 0-1 at Buckingham Town).
Previous League: Staffs County (South) 61-81, West Midlands 82-96
Clubhouse: Mon-Fri 7.00-11pm, Sat noon-11pm, Sun noon-3 & 7.00-10.30pm. Hot & cold meals.
96-97 Captain: Adrian Horne **96-97 Top Scorer:** D Walters **96-97 P.o.Y.:** Mazlar Iqbal
Club Record Goalscorer: Dean Walters 231 **Club Record Appearances:** Kevin Gough 443.
Honours: West Mids Lg Div 1 Cup 88-89, R-up 89-90, Div 2 Cup R-up 83-84; Walsall Snr Cup R-up 89-90 92-93; Wednesbury Charity Cup 6, (R-up 7); D Stanton Shield (2), R-up 75-76; Sporting Star Cup 76-77, R-up 61-62; Rugeley Charity Cup 78-79 (R-up 69-70); Bloxwich Charity Cup(2); Edge Cup 83-84; Ike Cooper Tphy R-up 89-90; W Midlands Reg Lge Champions 94-95 (R-up 95-96) Div Cup 95-96; Midland Triangle Cup 95-96.

PERSHORE TOWN '88

Chairman: Anthony Broadstock **Vice Chairman:** C Brimmell.
Secretary: Ian Gill, 2 Sebright Close, Pershore, Worcs WR10 1QF (01386 554116 H).
Manager: Gary Aldington. **Asst Mgr:** Ricky Hooman. **Physio:** Rick Harber/Mark Palfrey
Ground: King George V Playing Fields, King Georges Way, Pershore, Worcs (01386 556902).
Directions: M5 jct 7, A44 to Pershore (8 miles) cross 1st lights in Pershore, at 2nd lights turn left & fold road round into King Georges Way, ground immediately on left.
Seats: 120 **Cover:** 120 **Capacity:** 4,000 **Floodlights:** Yes **Founded:** 1988.
Colours: All blue **Change colours:** Yellow/green/yellow.
Previous League: Midland Combination 90-94.
Programme: 20 pages, 50p **Editor:** Mr T S Conway (01386 554390) **Club Shop:** No
Reserves' Lge: Banks's W.Mid.Lg.Div.1. **Midweek matchday:** Tuesday **Nickname:** The Town
Best FA Cup season: 4th Qualifying Round 94-95 (lost 1-3 to Yeading).
Best FA Vase season: Preliminary Rd 92-93 (lost 0-1 at Stewarts & Lloyds).
Record Gate: 1,356 v Yeading, FA Cup 4th Qualifying Round 23/10/93.
Clubhouse: Bar open Tue-Thur 7.30-11pm, Fri 2-6 & 7.30-11pm, Sat noon-11pm, Sun noon-3 & 7-10.30pm. Coffee, tea, soup, hot pies and rolls available during matches.
Record scorer: Simon Judge 76. **Record appearances:** Ian Aldington, 192 + 5 sub.
Hons: Midland Combination 94-95 (Div 2 89-90), Worcs Jnr Cup 90-91, Robert Biggart Cup(2) 90-92 94-95 (R-up 89-90), Worcs Snr Urn R-up 92-93, Jack Mould Cup 90-91, Alfred Terry Cup 90-91, Martley Hosp. Cup('A') 90-91, Pershore Hosp. Cup(Res) 92-93 94-95, Evesham Hosp. Minor Cup R-up('A') 94-95.

ROCESTER

Chairman: A.Hawksworth.
Secretary: Mr Gilbert Egerton, 23 Eaton Road, Rocester, Uttoxeter, Staffs ST14 5LL (01889 590101).
Manager: Mick Collins. **Asst Mgr:** P.Fernihough. **Reserves' Mgr:** Mick Collins
Ground: The Rivers Field, Mill Street, Rocester, Uttoxeter, Staffs (01889 590463).
Directions: From A50 r'bout adjoining Little Chef restaurant at Uttoxeter take B5030 towards Rocester and Alton Towers, right into Rocester village after 3 miles over narrow bridge, in village centre bear right at sharp left-hand bend into Mill Str., ground 500yds on left just past former cotton mill.
Seats: 200 **Cover:** 500 **Capacity:** 4,000 **Floodlights:** Yes **Founded:** 1876
Colours: Amber/black/black **Change colours:** All blue **Nickname:** Romans
Programme: 32 pages, 50p **Editor:** Ian Cruddas (01889 564173). **Club Shop:** Yes
Players progressing to Football League: George Shepherd (Derby County), Mark Sale (Birmingham).
Record Gate: 1,026 v Halesowen Town, FA Vase 4th Rd January 1987 (at Leek Town FC).
Previous Lges: Ashbourne/ Leek & Moorland/ Cheadle & Distrist/ Uttoxeter Amateur/ Stafford 53-57/ Staffs County Nth 57-84/ Staffs Senior 84-87/ West Mids 87-94.
Reserves Lge: W Midlands **Midweek matchday:** Tuesday **Sponsors:** Stenson Bubble
Players progressing to Football League: Bert Carpenter (Manchester Utd), Joe Carpenter (Brighton), George Shepherd (Derby), Mark Sale (Birmingham, Torquay), Tony Hemmings (Wycombe (via Northwich)).
Clubhouse: On matchdays (normal licensing hours) and other special events. Hot drinks & snacks.
Club record scorer: Mick Collins **Club record appearances:** Peter Swanwick.
Hons: West Mids Lg R-up 89-90 (Div 1 87-88, Div 1 Cup 87-88), Staffs Snr Lg(2) 85-87, Staffs FA Vase 85-86 87-88.

Pelsall Villa; Back Row (L-R); Reg Priest, Neil Holmes, Mick Rawlins, Neil Coles, Neil Jones, Bryan Humphreys, Mazhar Iqual, Matt Cartwright, Ada Horne. Front Row; Ikbal Patel, Danny Donovan, Dean Walters, Steve Beech, Stuart Edwards, Chris Hodges, Steve Lyons, Paul Newman. Photo - Marshall's Sport Service

Sandwell Borough; Back Row (L-R); Mick Tuohy, Nick Hyde, Joe Clarke, Steve Moore, Matt Knight, Neil Martin, Andy Dean, Steve Morgan, Gary Webb, Nigel Conniff. Front Row; Paul Joinson, Lloyd Morrison, Wayne Burgess, Barry Young, Peter Bennett, Matt Richards, Lee Joinson. Photo - Marshall's Sport Service

Stapenhill FC; Back Row (L-R); Gary Hamson (Coach), K Hulland (Physio), S Warren, M Walton, J Cheetham, A Peaty, P Wood, A Coppinger, P Allum, J Wayte (Asst Mgr), B Sykes (Mgr). Front Row; L Stewart, P Thompson, S McGinty, D Carlin, J O'Hare, N Sykes, M Curry Photo - Burton Mail

RUSHALL OLYMPIC

Chairman: John Burks **Vice Chairman:** Trevor Westwood **President:** Brian Greenwood.
Secretary: Roy Turner, 18 Stanley Place, Rushall, WS4 1EL (01922 646198)
Manager: Mick Brookes **Asst Manager:** Mick Thurman **Physio:**
Ground: Dales Lane, off Daw End Lane, Rushall, Nr Walsall (01922 641021).
Directions: From Rushall centre (A461) take B4154 signed Aldridge. Approx., 1 mile on right, directly opposite Royal Oak Public House, in Daw End Lane. Grd on right. 2 miles Walsall (BR) station.
Seats: 200 **Cover:** 200 **Capacity:** 2,500 **Floodlights:** Yes **Club Shop:** No
Programme: 36 pages **Editor/Press Officer:** Darren Stockall (01922 379153).
Colours: Amber with black trim/black/black **Change colours:** White with red trim/red/red
Sponsors: WM Print **Founded:** 1951 **Nickname:** Pics.
Midweek matchday: Tuesday **Youth League:** West Mids (Reg.)
Record Attendance: 2,000 v Leeds Utd Old Boys, charity match 1982.
Previous Leagues: Walsall Amateur 52-55/ Staffs County (South) 56-78/ West Midlands (Regional) 78-94.
Players progressing to Football League: Lee Sinnott (Watford), Lee Palin (Aston Villa, Nottingham Forest, Bradford City), Stuart Watkiss (Walsall), Steve Taylor (Crystal Palace).
Clubhouse: Bar/lounge, open every night 8-11pm, Sat matchdays, Sunday noon-2.30pm.
96-97 Captain: Mark Wakefield **96-97 Top Scorer:** Steve Walker **96-97 P.o.Y.:** Dave Chapman
Club Record Goalscorer: Graham Wiggin **Club Record Appearances:** Alan Dawson (400+ apps).
Honours: West Mids League Div 1 79-80, Walsall Amtr League Div 1 55-56 (Div 2 52-53, Snr Cup 54-55 55-56, Jabez Cliff Cup 55-56), Staffs Co. League Div 1 60-61 61-62 62-63 64-65 (Div 2 56-57), Walsall Charity Cup 52-53, Walsall Chal. Cup 54-55 56-57, Walsall Memorial Charity Cup 55-56 56-57 57-58 58-59 59-60 60-61 61-62, W Preston Chal. Cup 56-57, Cannock & Dist. Charity Cup 56-57, Wednesbury Snr Cup 58-59 59-60 60-61, Sporting Star Cup 59-60 60-61 (joint) 64-65 65-66 67-68, J W Edge 62-63 66-67, Walsall Snr Cup 64-65, Lichfield Charity 64-65 66-67, Staffs Yth Cup 81-82.

SANDWELL BOROUGH

Chairman: Joe Owen **Manager:** Paul Molesworth. **Founded:** 1918.
Secretary: Bob Lawrence, 34 Woburn Crescent, Great Barr, Birmingham B34 6AX (0121 357 6396)
Ground: Oldbury Stadium, Newbury Lane, Oldbury (0121 544 4013).
Directions: Follow A4123 B'ham-Wolverhampton Rd, past island at jnt 2 M5, after half mile turn left into Newbury Lane and stadium is on the right. 2 miles from Sandwell & Dudley (BR).
Capacity: 3,000 **Seats:** 200 **Cover:** 600 **Floodlights:** Yes **Nickname:** Trees
Midweek matches: Wednesday **Previous Grnd:** Londonderry, Smethwick 18-81
Colours: All green **Change Colours:** Red/white/red
Record Gate: 950 v Halesowen T., FA Cup 1987
Programme: 12 pages 25p **Programme Editor:** R Unitt.
Previous Leagues: B'ham Suburban/ Central Amtr/ Worcs (Midlands Comb.) 48-88 90-94/ Southern 88-90.
Clubhouse: Licensed bar overlooking pitch. Open everyday
Players who have progressed to Football League: Andy Micklewright (Bristol Rov, Bristol City, Swindon, Exeter), Gary Bull (Southampton, Cambridge Utd)
Hons: Mids Comb. Chal. Cup R-up(5) 49-50 51-53 67-68 74-75, Chal. Tphy R-up 88-89, Pres. Cup 79-80 (R-up 76-77), Div 2 R-up 79-80), B'ham Jnr Cup.

SHIFNAL TOWN

Chairman: Mr L Jones **Vice Chairman:** R Owen **President:** R Arnold
Secretary: Glyn Davies, 30 Drayton Road, Shifnal, Shropshire, TF11 8BT (01952 460326 H).
Manager: Mervyn Rowe **Asst Manager:** M.Humphreys. **Physio:** Danny Wedge
Ground: Phoenix Park, Coppice Green Lane, Shifnal, Shropshire.
Directions: M54 jct 3, A41 towards Newport, 1st left for Shifnal (3 miles), in Shifnal take 1st right, and sharp right again up Coppice Green Lane, ground 800yds on left past Idsall School.
Seats: 104 **Cover:** 300 **Capacity:** 3,000 **Floodlights:** Yes **Club Shop:** No
Programme: 32 pages, 60p **Editor:** J.Wilson (01952 274855). **Press Off:** G Davies (01952 460326).
Colours: Red & white/black/red & white **Change colours:** Blue & white/white/blue & white
Sponsors: Associated Cold Stores & Transport Ltd. **Nickname:** None. **Founded:** 1964
Midweek matchday: Tuesday **Reserves' League:** None at present
Record Attendance: 1,002 v Bridgnorth Town, F.A. Vase 3rd Rd 83-84 (at Admirals Park).
Previous Leagues: Wellington (East Dist.) 64-69/ Shropshire County 69-77 85-93/ West Midlands 77-85/ Midland Combination 94-95.
Clubhouse: Not on ground but in Newport Rd, Shifnal. Open Mon-Fri 7.30-11pm, noon-11pm Sat matchdays, noon-2.30 & 7.30-11pm Sat non-matchdays, Sun noon-3 & 7.30-11pm.
96-97 Captain: **96-97 Top Scorer:** **96-97 P.o.Y.:**
Club Record Goalscorer: Steve Kelly 35. **Club Record Appearances:**
Honours: West Mids Lg 80-81 81-82 (Div 1 78-79), Shropshire Snr Cup 80-81 90-91 92-93.

STAPENHILL

Chairman: Tony Smith **Vice Chairman:** **President:** Fred Sleigh.
Secretary: Peter Begent, 22 Grasmere Close, Stapenhill, Burton-on-Trent DE15 9DS (01283 540583)
Manager: Bob Sykes **Asst Manager:** Garry Hamson **Physio:** Ken Hulland.
Ground: Edge Hill, Maple Grove, Stapenhill, Burton-on-Trent (01283 562471).
Directions: 3 miles from Burton on A444 Measham Rd, turn right (coming from Burton) at Copperhearth Pub Hse into Sycamore Rd, Maple Grove is 5th left. 3 miles from Burton-on-Trent (BR) buses 15, 16 from opposite station.
Capacity: 2,000 **Seats:** 100 **Covered:** 500 **Floodlights:** Yes **Club Shop:** No
Programme: 60p **Editor:** Secretary **Press Officer:** Secretary.
Colours: All red **Change Colours:** All blue
Sponsors: TAG Football Kits **Nickname:** Swans. **Founded:** 1947.
Midweek matcheday: Wednesday **Reserves League:** Midland Comb.
Previous League: Leics Snr 58-89/ Midland Combination 89-94.
Previous Name: Stapenhill Waterside Community Centre.
Clubhouse: In ground. Pub hours. Matchday tea bar.
96-97 Captain: David Carlin **96-97 Top Scorer:** Stephen McGinty **96-97 P.o.Y.:** Peter Thompson
Club Record Goalscorer: Brian Beresford 123 **Club Record Appearances:** Ian Pearsall 172.
Record Attendance: 2,000 v Gresley, Derbys Snr Cup final 88-89.
Record win: 11-0 v Alcester Town (H), Midland Combination Premier Division, 1992-93.
Record defeat: 0-7 v Bridgnorth Town, FA Vase.
Honours: Midland Combination R-up 92-93 (Div 1 89-90, Challenge Cup 92-93 93-94), Leics Snr Lg 59-60 86-87 88-89 (Tebbutt Brown Cup(2) 87-89), Leics Snr Cup 69-70 86-87, Derby Snr Cup R-up 88-89 91-92.

STRATFORD TOWN

Chairman: G Cutler **Vice-Chairman:** T.B.A. **President:** P Chatburn
Secretary: Leslie Welsh, 10 Ivy Lane, Ettington, Warwicks. CV37 7TD. (01789 740952)
Manager: S Dixon **Physio:** N Dixon **Commercial Mgr:** J Carruthers.
Ground: Masons Road, off Alcester Road, Stratford-upon-Avon, Warks (01789 297479).
Directions: Follow Alcester/Worcester A422 signs from town centre - Masons Rd is 1st right afterrailway bridge. 400 yards from Stratford-on-Avon (BR) station. Local buses for West Green Drive.
Capacity: 1,100. **Seat/Cover:** 200 **Floodlights:** Yes **Club Shop:** No.
Programme: 20 pages, 50p **Editor:**
Colours: Tangerine/black/tangerine **Change Colours:** White/white/black
Sponsors: Porters Precision Products **Nickname:** The Town **Founded:** 1944
Midweek Matches: Tuesday **Reserves' League:** Midland Comb. Reserve Division.
Record Attendance: 1,078 v Aston Villa, Birmingham Snr Cup, Oct 1996
Previous Leagues: W Mids 57-70/ Mid Com. 70-73 75-94/ Hellenic 70-75.
Players progressing to Football League: Martin Hicks (Charlton, Reading, Birmingham), Roy Proverbs (Coventry, Bournemouth, Gillingham), Richard Landon (Stockport Co.,Plymouth Argyle (via Bedworth Utd).
Clubhouse: Open every night except Sunday
96-97 Captain: **96-97 P.o.Y.:** **96-97 Top Scorer:**
Honours: Midland Comb 56-57 86-87; Chal. Cup 86-87 88-89 (R-up 55-56); Chal. Vase 81-82; Jack Mould Tphy 81-82; Tony Allden Mem. Cup 86-87; B'ham Snr Cup 62-63.

WEDNESFIELD

Chairman: Roger Thomas **Vice Chairman:** J Massey
Secretary: Trevor Highfield, 8 Greensway, Wednesfield, Wolverhampton. WV11 1BA (01902 733086)
Manager/Coach: Ken Hall **Physio:** M Andrews
Commercial Mgr: D Clayton **Press Officer:** J Massey (01902 781819).
Ground: Cottage Ground, Amos Lane, Wednesfield, Wolverhampton (01902 735506).
Directions: From Wolverhampton on the A4124 Wednesfield Rd. Stay on road right through Wednesfield until island. Leave island at 1st exit (Wood End Rd), left after 200yds into Amos Lane. Ground on right, approx. 400yds along. 3 miles Wolverhampton BR station. Bus 559 to Wood End or 560 to Red Lion.
Seats: 148 **Cover:** 250 **Capacity:** 1,000 **Floodlights:** Yes **Founded:** 1961.
Colours: Red & white/black/red & white **Change colours:** Yellow & blue/blue/blue & yellow
Programme: 50p **Editor:** TBA **Club Shop:** No. **Nickname:** Cottagers.
Sponsors: Ansells **Record Gate:** 480 v Burton Albion, FA Cup 1981.
Midweek matchday: Tuesday **Previous Ground:** St Georges PF 61-76
Previous League: Wolverhampton & District Amateur 61-76/West Midlands 77-97.
Previous Name: Wednesfield Social 61-89.
Clubhouse: Evenings 7-11pm. Food (burgers, chips etc) on 1st team matchdays.
96-97 Captain: **96-97 Top Scorer:** **96-97 P.o.Y.:**
Honours: West Mids Lg Div 1 76-77 (R-up 77-78).

WEST MIDLANDS POLICE

President: Chief Constable R Hadfield OBE
Chairman: Asst Chief Constable Anne Summers **Vice Chairman:** Jim Swingeford
Secretary: John Black, 57 Grosvenor Close, Sutton Coldfield, W.Mids. B75 6RP.(0121 308 7673)
Manager: Colin Brookes/Mark Fogarty
Commercial Manager: John Black. **Press Officer:** Tony Pearson.
Ground: Police Spts Ground, 'Tally Ho', Pershore Road, Edgbaston, Birmingham B5 7RN (0121 472 2944).
Directions: 2 miles south west of city on A441 Pershore Road. Ground is on the left 50yds past Priory Road lights (Warks County Cricket Ground). 3 miles from Birmingham New Street (BR) - buses 41, 45 & 47 from city.
Capacity: 2,500 **Seats:** 224 **Covered:** 224 **Floodlights:** Yes **Founded:** 1974
Midweek matches: Tues/Thurs. **Reserve's League:** Midland Combination.
Programme: 16 pages, 50p **Editor:** K Horrigan (0121 626 4020x6100) **Club Shop:** No.
Colours: Red & black stripes/black/black & red **Change Colours:** Yellow with blue trim/yellow/yellow
Record Gate: 1,072 v Sudbury Town, FA Vase QF 29/2/92.
Previous Leagues: B'ham Wednesday 28-38/ Mercian 46-53/ B'ham Works 53-69/ Mid Comb 74-94.
Clubhouse: Complex of 3 bars including snooker room, ballroom, kitchen. Hot & cold food. Open all day.
Honours: FA Vase QF 91-92, Mids Comb 90-91 (R-up 94-95, Chal. Cup 74-75 (R-up 85-86)), Tony Allden Mem. Cup 75-76 (R-up 91-92), B'ham Jnr Cup, Worcs Snr Urn 84-85 90-91 91-92 (R-up 81-82 85-86), National Police Cup(12) 61-65 66-67 69-70 73-76 80-81 87-88 91-92 (R-up(7) 67-68 70-72 76-78 88-89 94-95), Aston Villa Cup 60-61 64-65 65-66.

Willenhall Town FC, team line up before their 4-1 victory over Knypersley Victoria *Photo - Martin Wray*

WILLENHALL TOWN

President: Jack Williams **Chairman:** Don Crutchley **Vice Chairman:** David Homer.
Secretary: Malcolm Skitt, 52 Longwood Rise, Willenhall, West Midlands WV12 4AX (01902 632557).
Manager: Kenny Drakeford. **Asst Manager:** Phil Embury. **Physios:** Mike Andrews & Steve Hooper.
Ground: Noose Lane, Willenhall, West Midlands (01902 605132-club, 636586-office).
Directions: M6 Jnc 10 follow 'new' Black Country route and then 'Keyway'. On leaving 'Keyway' follow signs to Wolverhampton(A454). At 'Neachells' P H house right into Neachells Lane, and first right again into Watery Lane. At island turn left onto Noose Lane, ground is 200yds on left.
Seats: 324 **Cover:** 500 **Capacity:** 5,000 **Floodlights:** Yes **Club Shop:** Yes
Programme: 40 pages, 70p **Editor:** Bill Taylor (01902 843435). **Nickname:** Reds
Colours: Red & white/red/red **Change colours:** Blue & red **Founded:** 1953
Sponsors: Aspray Transport. **Midweek matchday:** Tuesday. **Reserves League:** Midland Comb.
Record Attendanc: 3,454 v Crewe Alexandra, FA Cup 1st Rd 1981.
Previous Leagues: Wolverhampton Amateur/ Staffs County/ West Mids 75-82 91-94/ Southern 82-91.
Players progressing to Football League: Sean O'Driscoll (Fulham & Bournemouth), Joe Jackson (Wolves), Stuart Watkiss (Wolves & Walsall), Tony Moore (Sheff Utd), Andy Reece (Bristol Rovers), Wayne O'Sullivan (Swindon).
Clubhouse: Open Mon-Thurs 12-3 & 7-11pm, Fri-Sat 11am-11pm, Sun 12-2 & 7-10.30pm. Snacks available.
96-97 Captain: Charlie Blakemore **P.o.Y.:** **Top Scorer:**
Club Record Goalscorer: Gary Matthews **Club Record Appearances:** Gary Matthews.
Honours: FA Vase R-up 80-81; West Mids Lg 78-79, Div 1 75-76, Prem. Div Cup 79-80, Div 2 Cup 78-79(res); Southern Midland 83-84; Birmingham Snr Cup R-up 82-83; J W Hunt Cup 73-74.

ENDSLEIGH INSURANCE
MIDLAND FOOTBALL COMBINATION

FEEDER TO: MIDLAND ALLIANCE

Chairman: Ian Johnson
Hon. Secretary: Norman Harvey, 115 Millfield Road
Handsworth Wood, Birmingham B20 1ED (01213 574172)

HONOURS LIST 1996-97

	Champions	Runners Up
PREMIER DIVISION	Richmond Swifts	Meir K.A.
DIVISION ONE	G.P.T. (Coventry)	Continental Star
DIVISION TWO	Feckenham	Fairfield Villa
DIVISION THREE	Swan Sports 1995	Studley BKL Res
RESERVE DIVISION	Bromsgrove Rvrs	Rushden & D
CHALLENGE CUP	Knowle	Kings Heath
PRESIDENTS CUP	G.P.T. (Coventry)	Monica Star
CHALLENGE VASE	Burntwood	Feckenham
CHALLENGE URN	Cradley Heath	Swan Sports 95
CHALLENGE TROPHY	Gresley Rovers	Bromsgrove R

FINAL LEAGUE TABLES 1996-97

PREMIER DIVISION

		P	*W*	*D*	*L*	*F*	*A*	*Pts*
1	Richmond Swifts	38	30	5	3	92	29	95
2	Meir KA	38	26	6	6	91	39	84
3	Coleshill Town	38	22	10	6	69	30	76
4	Studley BKL	38	22	6	10	100	49	72
5	Knowle	38	22	4	12	83	47	70
6	Worcester Athletico	38	20	7	11	85	60	67
7	Kings Heath	38	16	8	14	66	50	56
8	Massey Ferguson	38	15	11	12	62	61	56
9	David Lloyd AFC	38	14	11	13	54	57	53
10	Handrahan Timbers	38	15	6	17	46	54	51
11	Coventry Sphinx	38	14	8	16	51	74	50
12	Bilston Community Coll.	38	14	7	17	83	71	49
13	Bolehall Swifts	38	11	14	13	62	59	47
14	Southam United	38	13	8	17	53	62	47
15	Wellesbourne	38	12	5	21	62	89	41
16	Kenilworth Town	38	11	8	19	49	80	41
17	Highgate United	38	11	3	24	55	77	36
18	Alvechurch	38	9	5	24	46	82	32
19	Shirley Town	38	7	8	23	51	94	29
20	W. Midlands Fire Service	38	4	4	30	26	122	16

PREMIER DIVISION RESULTS CHART 1996-97

		1	2	3	4	5	6	7	8	9	10	11	12	13	14	15	16	17	18	19	20
1	Alvechurch	X	0-2	2-1	0-2	1-3	1-2	1-3	2-1	3-1	0-1	1-2	1-1	0-2	2-2	0-1	2-3	1-2	2-1	2-0	0-2
2	David Lloyd	1-1	X	1-5	1-1	1-1	0-0	2-0	1-1	1-1	2-0	2-1	2-0	3-3	0-1	1-2	2-0	0-2	2-1	0-0	3-0
3	Bilston Comm C	6-2	1-3	X	0-0	1-1	0-3	1-2	4-0	2-1	1-1	1-2	5-1	1-3	1-0	5-2	4-2	1-3	5-2	9-1	4-?
4	Bolehall Swifts	0-1	1-2	0-0	X	1-2	2-0	5-0	3-2	3-2	1-0	1-0	2-2	1-1	1-3	6-1	1-1	1-1	0-2	0-1	1-?
5	Coleshill Town	2-1	1-1	2-0	1-1	X	0-0	3-0	2-1	1-0	1-0	0-1	3-0	1-1	0-1	1-0	2-0	2-3	8-0	3-0	2-0
6	Coventry Sphinx	3-2	3-0	3-2	1-1	0-1	X	2-0	1-2	1-2	0-3	1-2	0-2	1-3	1-3	2-2	1-0	2-2	0-2	3-1	2-1
7	Handrahan Timb	3-0	2-0	3-0	1-2	0-0	2-3	X	2-3	1-0	2-3	2-1	2-1	2-1	1-2	1-0	0-1	0-1	0-3	0-2	1-1
8	Highgate United	0-1	3-1	6-2	2-2	1-2	1-2	1-2	X	3-1	2-5	2-3	1-3	2-3	1-3	1-1	3-1	1-3	2-3	0-1	3-2
9	Kenilworth Town	1-1	1-2	1-4	2-2	0-7	0-0	0-2	1-0	X	0-4	0-3	2-2	1-0	0-1	3-2	2-2	3-2	3-7	3-0	2-2
10	Kings Heath	5-0	3-1	2-0	3-0	0-2	4-1	1-1	1-2	2-0	X	1-2	0-1	0-1	1-2	2-0	1-1	1-1	3-1	2-0	2-2
11	Knowle	4-2	4-1	4-1	5-1	3-0	7-1	0-1	0-1	1-2	1-1	X	1-2	1-0	0-1	2-2	3-1	4-0	3-0	6-1	2-5
12	Massey Ferg.	4-4	1-0	4-1	0-1	1-1	2-3	2-2	1-0	3-1	2-1	2-2	X	1-1	0-2	4-2	2-1	3-1	6-2	2-0	0-2
13	Meir KA	3-0	2-1	0-0	3-1	1-1	7-2	3-1	3-0	6-1	5-2	2-1	4-0	X	2-1	7-2	2-0	2-1	2-1	4-0	0-3
14	Richmond Swifts	4-0	5-0	0-0	3-1	3-2	4-1	2-0	3-1	4-1	4-1	3-1	1-0	2-0	X	2-1	1-1	3-0	3-1	8-0	2-4
15	Shirley Town	0-1	0-4	1-4	3-3	1-2	3-0	0-0	2-0	1-3	1-1	0-2	1-1	0-5	0-2	X	3-0	1-5	2-2	7-3	1-4
16	Southam United	3-1	3-1	1-0	4-3	0-0	0-0	2-1	5-1	1-2	1-1	1-2	2-2	0-1	0-3	4-0	X	0-2	3-1	2-1	1-2
17	Studley BKL	6-1	2-2	2-0	3-2	0-2	7-0	0-1	3-0	3-2	2-3	1-2	4-1	2-3	2-2	3-0	4-1	X	7-0	6-0	2-0
18	Wellesbourne	1-0	1-1	2-2	1-1	1-2	0-2	1-2	1-0	1-2	1-2	1-3	3-0	1-2	0-2	4-2	2-3	2-2	X	4-0	1-5
19	W Mids Fire S	1-3	2-4	0-3	1-7	0-4	1-2	2-2	0-2	0-2	3-2	1-1	0-0	0-3	1-3	0-3	1-2	0-9	1-2	X	0-2
20	Worcester Ath	3-2	2-3	3-6	3-1	5-1	2-2	2-1	1-3	0-0	3-1	2-1	0-3	2-0	1-1	4-1	2-0	0-1	2-3	5-1	X

DIVISION ONE RESULTS CHART 1996-97

		1	2	3	4	5	6	7	8	9	10	11	12	13	14	15	16	17	18
1	Alveston	X	2-1	2-1	4-1	3-0	4-1	1-1	0-2	0-2	4-1	2-1	3-1	2-2	1-1	2-0	6-1	7-0	1-0
2	Barlestone St G	1-4	X	0-0	2-2	0-6	1-5	0-4	0-1	0-8	4-1	0-2	0-5	1-3	1-3	1-0	1-3	2-2	0-6
3	Brownhills Town	1-1	2-1	X	3-0	0-5	0-2	0-7	0-2	0-4	0-3	3-4	1-3	0-4	1-9	0-9	1-3	1-3	0-8
4	Chelmsley Tn 94	1-3	5-0	7-0	X	0-2	1-4	0-3	0-5	0-1	1-1	3-0	0-2	2-1	1-3	2-2	0-1	1-1	2-0
5	Cheslyn Hay	1-2	3-0	2-1	1-3	X	5-2	1-2	4-3	1-1	2-1	2-1	2-2	3-0	2-4	1-2	4-0	0-2	3-1
6	Colletts Green	1-2	1-1	4-0	1-1	1-2	X	1-0	1-0	2-1	5-2	0-1	2-1	1-0	0-0	1-1	1-1	4-1	6-0
7	Continental Star	2-2	5-2	8-1	3-2	5-1	3-1	X	0-1	2-0	2-1	3-1	0-0	1-1	2-1	1-1	1-1	8-0	2-1
8	Dudley Sports	1-1	3-0	6-2	2-1	1-2	1-0	0-0	X	0-1	3-1	1-1	1-2	2-1	1-1	2-1	7-0	4-0	1-1
9	GPT (Coventry)	1-2	7-0	2-2	6-0	4-1	3-0	3-0	5-0	X	5-0	0-2	3-0	3-0	4-0	0-0	3-0	5-0	0-1
10	Hams Hall	0-4	1-1	1-3	1-2	2-4	0-3	1-5	4-0	1-3	X	0-3	5-2	1-1	0-3	3-1	0-3	1-1	1-3
11	Holly Lane '92	3-1	2-2	0-0	1-1	0-2	2-1	0-3	2-2	0-1	2-1	X	4-1	3-0	0-0	1-4	2-5	1-0	3-0
12	Leicester YMCA	1-2	1-2	5-2	0-3	4-2	5-3	1-0	0-0	0-1	3-2	1-1	X	3-1	2-3	1-1	1-3	4-0	1-0
13	Monica Star	1-1	0-1	2-0	4-1	3-3	6-0	2-3	1-0	0-2	1-1	3-1	5-0	X	2-2	1-2	4-2	0-0	3-2
14	Newhall United	3-2	5-0	3-1	4-2	0-2	0-0	3-3	4-1	0-2	4-3	1-1	4-0	1-4	X	2-4	3-2	7-1	2-2
15	Northfield Town	3-2	3-0	3-0	1-3	4-4	0-1	3-2	3-2	1-2	2-1	2-0	1-0	2-0	3-0	X	0-1	3-0	2-1
16	Polesworth N W	1-2	1-0	0-1	2-1	2-3	2-1	2-4	2-3	0-1	3-2	1-4	8-2	2-0	1-1	0-0	X	4-1	1-3
17	Thimblemill Rec	0-2	0-1	1-1	0-1	0-7	1-2	1-4	1-5	1-3	4-1	1-1	3-2	2-1	0-5	2-3	2-2	X	1-4
18	Yardley	2-1	2-1	4-1															

PREMIER DIVISION REPORT 1996-97

TOTAL AMOUNT OR GOALS SCORED IN LEAGUE AND DIVISION CUP - 1376

LEADING GOALSCORERS IN DIVISION 1996-97

Brian Powell	Studley B.K.L.	37
Darren Tafft	Worcester Athletico	35
Junior McKeon	Richmond Swifts	28
	(7 Goals for Shirley Town)	
Mark Cartwright	Kings Heath	27
Peter Gocan	Bilston C.C.	24
Steven Bott	Meir K.A.	23
Mark McKinney	Wellesbourne21	
John Mitchell	Knowle	21

LEADING GOALSCORERS BY TEAM 1996-97

Alvechurch	Richard Anderson	8
Bilston C.C.	Peter Gocan	24
Bolehall Swifts	Simon Roberts	19
Coleshill Town	Mark Charnley	17
Coventry Sphinx	Kevin Curtis	8
David Lloyd AFC	Dean Wright	10
Handrahan Timbers	Paul Baker	13
Highgate United	Lee Martin	14
Kenilworth Town	Darren Howson	5
Kings Heath	Mark Cartwright	27
Knowle	John Mitchell	21
Massey Ferguson	Lee Lavery	13
Meir K.A.	Steven Bott	23
Richmond Swifts	Junior McKeon	21
Shirley Town	Tony Walton	8
Southam United	Alistar Innes	9
Studley B.K.L.	Brian Powell	37
Wellesbourne	Mark McKinney	21
West Midland Fire	Chris Glover	
	Lee Sketchley	6
Worcester Athletico	Darren Tafft	35

BEST DEFENCE IN DIVISION

Richmond Swifts 29 Goals

BEST ATTACK IN DIVISION

Studely B.K.L. 100 Goals

CLEMENT KEYS MANAGER OF THE MONTH 1996-97

August:	John Clarke & Tony Hudson	Kenilworth Town F.C.
September:	Kevin Johnson & Sid Gutteridge	Newhall United F.C.
October:	John Adams & Alan Scarfe	Studley BKL F.C.
November:	Tommy Owens & Peter Dunbavin	Richmond Swifts F.C.
December:	Ashley Alexander & Gez O'Neill	GPT (Coventry) F.C.
January:	Martin Sockett & Martin Smith	Coleshill Town F.C.
February:	Don Corrigan, Arthur Smith & Jim McGreevy	Alvis F.C.
March:	Dave Harris	David Lloyd F.C.
April:	Terry Greer	Meir K.A. F.C.

CLEMENT KEYS MANAGER OF THE YEAR 1996-97

Ashley Alexander & Gez O'Neill G.P.T. (Coventry) F.C.

THE FRED SHEPHERD MEMORIAL TROPHY 1996-97

Tony Rigsby	Continental Star	42
Brian Powell	Studley B.K.L.	37
Ian Evatt	G.P.T. Coventry	35
Darren Tafft	Worcester Athletico	35
Ian Morgan	Cheslyn Hay	31
Matthew Robbins	Hinckley Athletic	30
Junior McKeon	Richmond Swifts	28
Mark Cartwright	Kings Heath	27
Ian Pitt	Gresley Rovers	27
Kevin Joyce	Newhall United	26
Peter Gocan	Bilston C.C.	24
Richard Meadows	Alveston	24
Neil Pitkin	Polesworth N.Warwick	24
Steven Bott	Meir K.A.	23
Robert Colwell	Ledbury Town	23
Gary Muckley	Cradley Heath	23
Jason Fellows	Fairfield Villa	22
Billy Powell	Ledbury Town	22
Andy Underwood	Feckenham	22
Mark McKinney	Wellesbourne	21
John Mitchell	Knowle	21
Trevor Boot	Feckenham	20
Philip Harris	Dudley Sports	20
Dean Meyrick	Bromsgrove Rovers	20

PROGRAMME OF THE YEAR 1996-97

Sponsored by SPORTLINES

OVERALL WINNER: ALVECHURCH
Received £50, a silver salver and the shield

STAN MANSELL TROPHY

(Hospitality)
Voted on by Referees at every Combination game
JOINT WINNERS: GPT (COVENTRY) & BARWELL RESERVES

CHALLENGE CUP 1996-97

First Round

Bolehall Swifts	v	Monica Star	1-0
Knowle	v	Holly Lane '92	1-1, 5-4p
Worcester Athletico	v	Highgate United	2-6
Cheslyn Hay	v	Alvechurch	0-0, 4-2p
Shirley Town	v	Chelmsley Town '94	5-4
Barlestone St Giles	v	Continental Star	1-4

Second Round

David Lloyd	v	Kenilworth Town	2-2, 4-1p
Bilston Comm College	v	Kings Heath	1-3
Colletts Green	v	Coventry Sphinx	0-1
GPT (Coventry)	v	Northfield Town	3-4*
Leicester YMCA	v	Southam United	0-1
Polesworth N Warwick	v	Meir KA	1-2
Shirley Town	v	Wellesbourne	0-1
Thimblemill REC	v	Handrahan Timbers	0-3
Continental Star	v	Yardley	4-1
Bolehall Swifts	v	Alveston	1-0
Dudley Sports	v	Highgate United	4-1
Hams Hall	v	Cheslyn Hay	1-2
Newhall United	v	Massey Ferguson	3-2*
Richmond Swifts	v	Knowle	3-6*
Studley BKL	v	Brownhills Town	2-0
West Midlands Fire	v	Coleshill Town	2-5

Third Round

Studley BKL	v	Continental Star	2-1
Meir KA	v	Newhall United	5-2
Cheslyn Hay	v	Handrahan Timb.	0-0, 4-3p
David Lloyd AFC	v	Wellesbourne	2-3
Southam United	v	Bolehall Swifts	0-2
Coleshill Town	v	Dudley Sports	2-0
Kings Heath	v	Coventry Sphinx	2-1
Northfield Town	v	Knowle	0-4

Fourth Round

Bolehall Swifts	v	Kings Heath	0-3
Coleshill Town	v	Studley BKL	3-2*
Knowle	v	Cheslyn Hay	3-2
Wellesbourne	v	Meir KA	1-2

*After Extra Time

Semi-Final

Coleshill Town	v	Kings Heath	1-2
Meir KA	v	Knowle	2-2, 3-4p

FINAL

KINGS HEATH v KNOWLE 2-2, 4-5p

PRESIDENTS CUP 1996-97

First Round

Barlestone St Giles	v	Colletts Green	0-3
Alveston	v	Hams Hall	2-0

Second Round

Alveston	v	Yardley	3-0
Dudley Sports	v	Thimblemill REC	3-1
Holly Lane '92	v	Monica Star	2-2, 1-3p
Northfield Town	v	Cheslyn Hay	3-5*
Chelmsley Town '94	v	Colletts Green	1-2
GPT (Coventry)	v	Newhall United	4-2
Leicester YMCA	v	Continental Star	1-6
Polesworth N Wark	v	Brownhills Town	4-1

Third Round

Aveston	v	Polesworth N Warwick	2-3
GPT (Coventry)	v	Dudley Sports	4-0
Cheslyn Hay	v	Monica Star	1-4
Continental Star	v	Colletts Green	4-2

Semi-Final

GPT (Coventry)	v	Continental Star	2-1
Monica Star	v	Polesworth N Wark	6-1

FINAL

GPT (COVENTRY) v MONICA STAR 3-2* at Solihull Borough FC

CHALLENGE VASE 1996-97

First Round

Albright & Wilson	v	Earlswood Town	0-2	Badsey Rangers	v	Enville Athletic	3-5
Birmingham Vaults	v	Alvis	0-4	Blackheath Electro	v	Tipton Sports & Soc	0-1
Fairfield Villa	v	Cadbury Athletic	2-4	Feckenham	v	Archdale '73	6-1
Ledbury Town '84	v	Burntwood	1-4	Richmond Swifts R	v	West Mids Police R	5-1

Second Round

Earlswood Town	v	Burntwood	0-3	Cadbury Athletic	v	Alvis	1-0
Richmond Swifts Res	v	Envill Athletic	5-0	Feckenham	v	Tipton Sports & Soc	2-0

Semi-Final

Feckenham	v	Cadbury Athletic	0-0, 4-2p	Burntwood	v	Richmond Swifts R	2-0

FINAL

BURNTWOOD v FECKENHAM 2-1 at Bilston Community College FC

CHALLENGE URN 1996-97

First Round

Played in four groups

Second Round

Cradley Heath	v	Kenilworth	2-2, 4-2p	Dudley Sports Res	v	Swan Sports	0-3
Alvechurch Reserves	v	Tipton Town Res	1-4	Kenilworth Wardens	v	Mitchells & But.	1-1, 3-5p

Semi-Final

Mitchells & Butlers	v	Swan Sports	2-2, 8-9p	Tipton Town Res	v	Cradley Heath	0-1

FINAL

CRADLEY HEATH v SWAN SPORTS 3-1 at Northfield Town FC

CHALLENGE TROPHY 1996-97

First Round

Burton Albion v Barwell 4-1

Second Round

Bridgnorth Town	v	Nuneaton Borough	0-1	Bromsgrove Rovers	v	Boldmere St Michaels	3-0
Gresley Rovers	v	Solihull Borough	1-1, 8-7p	Hednesford Town	v	Stapenhill	1-2*
Hinckley Athletic	v	Atherstone United	2-3*	Rushden & Dia	v	Burton Albion	5-0
Tamworth	v	Stratford Town	4-1	Willenhall Town	v	Worcester City	0-1

Third Round

Stapenhill	v	Gresley Rovers	2-2, 5-6p	Atherstone United	v	Bromsgrove Rovers	1-1+
Nuneaton Borough	v	Rushden & Diamonds	0-1	Tamworth	v	Worcester City	1-1, 3-4p

+ (Atherstone expelled) 1-1 90 mins, Aban 96 mins fost

Semi-Final

Gresley Rovers	v	Worcester City	3-1	Bromsgrove Rovers	v	Rushden & Dia	2-2, 5-4p

FINAL

GRESLEY ROVERS v BROMSGROVE ROV 2-0

PREMIER DIVISION CLUBS 1997-98

ALVECHURCH VILLA

Manager: Keith Westwood/Stewart Anderson **Chairman:** Gordon Wilkie **Patron:** Roy Yardley
Secretary: Alan Deakin, 58 Chesterfield Close, Northfield, Birmingham, B31 3TR (0121 411 1745)
Ground: Lye Meadow, Redditch Rd, Alvechurch, Worcs (0121 445 2929).
Directions: M42 jct 2, follow signs to Redditch, taking dual carriageway. At island turn right (signed Alvechurch) ground approx one mile on right. Ground is actually on Redditch Road, just south of Alvechurch village.
Seats: 100 **Cover:** Yes **Capacity:** 3,000 **Floodlights:** Yes **Founded:** 1994
Colours: Gold/black/black **Change colours:** TBA
Sponsors: Centreprint **Nickname:** The Church. **Midweek matchday:** Wednesday
Previous Leagues: None **Best FA Cup year:** Not entered to date
Club record scorer: Dean Meyrick **Club record appearances:** Dean Meyrick/ Matthew Pugh
Hons: Mid Comb Chall Cup R-up 95-96, Smedley Crooke Cup R-up 94-95.

BILSTON COMMUNITY COLLEGE

Chairman: I K Wymer
Secretary: J Calloway, 4 Mervyn Rd, Bradley, Bilston, West Midlands WV14 8DF (01902 681660).
Manager: Gary Smith **Coach:** Ty Jones **Physio:** Andrew Kiddle
Ground: Queen Street, Bilston, West Midlands. (01902 491498)
Colours: Orange/white/white **Change:** White/black/orange. **Programme:** Yes
Previous League: Staffs County (South) (pre-1993)
Previous Ground: Springvale Spts & Social Club, Millfields Rd, Bilston (pre-1993).
Sponsors: Stowlawn Ltd **Nickname:** The College **Founded:** 1981
96-97 Captain: Mark Walker **96-97 Top Scorer:** Peter Gocan **96-97 P.o.Y.:** Conrad Warren
Honours: Midland Comb. Chall. Urn 93-94, Presidents Cup 94-95, Staffs Co. (Sth) Lg(5) 88-93, J W Hunt Charity Cup 90-91.

BOLEHALL SWIFTS

President: Mr Dennis Baker **Chairman:** Mr G Mulvey **Vice-Chairman:** Mr W Gould.
Secretary: Mal Tooley, 7 Ninefoot Lane, Belgrave, Tamworth, Staffs B77 2NA (01827 251973).
Manager: Ron Tranter **Player/Coach:** Mick Thurman. **Physio:** Barry Davis.
Commercial Mgr: Mike Fletcher. **Press Officer:** Mr L Bretherton/ Mr W Gould (01827 64530).
Ground: Rene Road, Bolehall, Tamworth (01827 62637).
Directions: A51 signs south to Bolebridge island, left under railway arches into Amington Rd, 4th left into Leedham Ave, fork right into Rene Rd, ground on right by school. From Tamworth BR station walk up Victoria Road for three quarters of a mile and catch No.3 or No.6 mini-bus to Bolehall. Alight at Leedham Avenue or Rene Road and follow as above.
Capacity: 2,000 **Seats:** 500 **Cover:** 600 **Floodlights:** Yes **Founded:** 1953
Midweek matches: Wednesday **Youth Team :** Play Sunday afternoons. **Nickname:** Swifts
Colours: Yellow/Black/Green. **Change Colours:** All green **Sponsors:** Walton Homes.
Programme: 32 pages, 70p **Editor:** W Gould (01827 64530).
Previous Leagues: Sutton Lge/ Staffs County 74-80/ Midland Combination 80-94. **Club Shop:** No.
Clubhouse: Large Social Club - 2 rooms. Open every evening (7-11) and lunchtimes. Entertainment Saturday nights. Cobs and crisps etc available.
Record Scorer: Billy Oughton **Record appearances:** Duane Mellors 196.
Hons: Midland Combination Div 2 84-85, F/Lit Cup R-up 96-97, Challenge Vase 84-85, Presidents Cup R-up 85-86; Fazeley Charity Cup 84-85 (R-up 85-86); Ernie Brown Memorial Cup R-up 89-90 90-91 91-92 92-93 94-95; Jack Mould Cup R-up 85-86.

CHESLYN HAY

Secretary: Daryl Oulton, 12 Brunslow Close, Willenhall, W Midlands WV13 2HN (01902 630336)
Ground: Wednesfield FC, Cottage Ground, Amos Lane, Wednesfield, Wolverhampton (01902 735506).
Directions: From Wolverhampton on the A4124 Wednesfield Rd. Stay on road right through Wednesfield until island. Leave island at 1st exit (Wood End Rd), left after 200yds into Amos Lane. Ground on right, approx. 400yds along. 3 miles Wolverhampton BR station. Bus 559 to Wood End or 560 to Red Lion.
Seats: 148 **Cover:** 250 **Capacity:** 1,000 **Floodlights:** Yes
Clubhouse: Evenings 7-11pm. Food (burgers, chips etc) on 1st team matchdays.
Colours: Orange/white/orange

COLESHILL TOWN

Manager: Martin Sockett
Secretary: Neil Hamilton, 31 Fourfields Way, New Arley, N Warwicks, CV7 8PX (01676 54088)
Ground: Pack Meadow, Packington Lane, Coleshill, Birmingham B46 3JQ (01675 63259).
Directions: A446 to A4117 towards Coleshill, Packington Lane forks from A4117, south of village and ground is 150 yds on right. M6 jct 4, 1 mile away.
Capacity: 3,000 **Seats:** 50 **Cover:** 50 **Floodlights:** Yes **Founded:** 1894.
Colours: All green. **Change Colours:** Green/white/green **Record Gate:** 1,000.
Programme: 30p, **Editor:** Mavis Gordon **Nickname:** Coalmen. **Midweek matches:** Tues/Thurs
Clubhouse: Bar open 7 nights a week. Bar manager resident.
Players who have progressed to Football League: Gary Shaw (Aston Villa, Walsall)
Honours: Mercian Lg 75-76, Walsall Snr Cup 82-83 (R-up 83-84), Midland Comb. R-up 83-84 (Div 2 69-70 (R-up 74-75), Invitation Cup 1970, Presidents Cup R-up(2) 67-69).

CONTINENTAL STAR

Secretary: Derek Stevens, Bungalow, Burbury Street South, Newtown, Birmingham B19 2JP (0121 523 3776)
Manager: Derek Stevens/ Lincoln Moses.
Ground: Colehill Town FC, Pack Meadow, Packington Lane, Coleshill, Birmingham B46 3JQ (01675 63259).
Directions: A446 to A4117 towards Coleshill, Packington Lane forks from A4117, south of village and ground is 150 yds on right. M6 jct 4, 1 mile away.
Capacity: 3,000 **Seats:** 50 **Cover:** 50 **Floodlights:** Yes
Colours: Yellow/Blue/Yellow
Clubhouse: Bar open 7 nights a week. Bar manager resident.
Honours: Midland Comb Div One R-up 96-97; Birmingham Vase.

COVENTRY SPHINX

Manager: Willie Knibbs
Secretary: K Whitehall, 34 Engleton Road, Radford, Coventry CV6 1JE (01203 598148).
Ground: Sphinx Drive, off Siddeley Avenue, Stoke Aldermoor, Coventry (01203 451361).
Colours: Sky blue & navy/Navy & sky blue/navy & sky blue.

DAVID LLOYD AFC

Ground: Rushall Olympic, Dales Lane, off Daw End Lane, Rushall, Nr Walsall (01922 641021).
Directions: From Rushall centre (A461) take B4154 signed Aldridge. Approx., 1 mile on right, directly opposite Royal Oak Public House, in Daw End Lane. Grd on right. 2 miles Walsall (BR) station.
Seats: 200 **Cover:** 200 **Capacity:** 2,500 **Floodlights:** Yes
Clubhouse: Bar/lounge, open every night 8-11pm, Sat matchdays, Sunday noon-2.30pm.

DUDLEY SPORTS

Secretary: John Lewis, 6 Hern Road, Brieley Hill, West Mids DY5 2PW (01384 895782)
Ground: High Ercal Avenue, Brierley Hill, West Mids (01384 826420).
Colours: Red+Blue/Blue/Red. **Change colours:** All blue

G.P.T. (COVENTRY)

Secretary: P Scanlon, 61 Norton Hill, Wyken, Coventry, West Mids CV2 3AX (01203 616576).
Ground: Coventry Sphinx FC, Sphinx Drive, off Siddeley Avenue, Stoke Aldermoor, Coventry (01203 451361).
Colours: White with blue trim/blue/blue. **Change colours:** All red
Honours: Midland Comb Div 1 96-97, Presidents Cup 96-97.

HANDRAHAN TIMBERS

Chairman: E J Smith **President:** W J Handrahan
Secretary: Robert Hopkins, Junction Road, Audham, Stourbridge, W Mids DY8 4JY (01384 838270)
Manager: Glen Taylor/Nigel Kirkham **Asst Manager:** Phillip McNally
Ground: The Mile Flat Sports Ground, Mile Flat, Wallheath, Kingswinford, West Mids (01381 484755).
Cover: 200 **Seats:** 40 **Floodlights:** No **Nickname:** Timbers **Founded:** 1982.
Colours: Red/black/black. **Change colours:** Sky/navy/navy **Club Shop:** No.
Programme: All games except outside cups). **Press Officer:** E J Smith (01384 295394).
Sponsors: W J Handrahan & Son **Previous Leagues:** Staffs County Lg (South) 82-86.
Clubhouse: Teas and refreshments. **Midweek matchday:** Wednesday
96-97 Captain: **96-97 Top Scorer:** **96-97 P.o.Y.:**
Club record scorer: Paul Baker **Club record appearances:** Jonathan Pole.
Honours: Midland Combination Div 1 R-up 93-94, Birmingham Challenge Vase R-up 93-94, Wednesbury Charity Cup 91-92, J W Hunt Cup 92-93 (R-up 93-94).Invitation Cup(Mid.Comb.Champios v Vup Winners)94-95.

HIGHGATE UNITED

Chairman: T G Bishop **Treasurer:** F H Drennan **Founded:** 1947.
Secretary: G Read, 23 Southam Rd, Hall Green, Birmingham B28 8DQ (0121-777-1786)
Manager: Jim Simms **Assistant Manager:** Steve Prost **Physio:** Richard Flynn
Ground: The Coppice, Tythe Barn Lane, Shirley, Solihull B90 1PH (0121 7444194).
Directions: A34 from City through Shirley, fork right B4102 (Tanworth Lane), half mile then right into Dickens Heath Rd, then first right and the ground is on the left. 100yds from Whitlocks End (BR).
Capacity: 5,000 **Seats:** 250 **Covered:** 750 **Floodlights:** Due 1996
Colours: All red **Change Colours:** All white **Nickname:** The Gate.
Midweek matches: Tuesday **Record Gate:** 4,000 v Enfield, FA Amateur Cup QF 1967.
Programme: 28 pages, 50p **Editor:** Terry Bishop (0676 22788). **Press Officer:** N C Sawyer.
Players progressing to Football League: John Gayle (W'ledon), Keith Leonard (A Villa, P Vale), Geoff Scott (Leic.)
Clubhouse: Members Club open Tues, Wed, Thurs, Sat & Sun. Light refreshments available at weekends.
96-97 Captain: **96-97 P.o.Y.:** **96-97 Top Scorer:**
Honours: Midland Comb.(3) 72-75 (Div 2 66-67 68-69 71-72, Lg Cup(5) 72-74 75-77 84-85 (R-up 78-79 92-93), Presidents Cup 70-71 85-86), Tony Allden Mem. Cup 74-75, Invit. Cup 68-69 71-72 85-86, West Mids All. 63-64, Birmingham Snr Cup 73-74 (SF 91-92).

KINGS HEATH

Manager: Clive Seeley
Secretary: Richard Johnson, 156 Station Road, Kings Norton, Birmingham B30 (0121 459 1386)
Ground: Highgate United FC, The Coppice, Tythe Barn Lane, Shirley, Solihull B90 1PH (0121 744 4194).
Directions: A34 from City through Shirley, fork right B4102 (Tanworth Lane), half mile then right into Dickens Heath Rd, then first right and the ground is on the left. 100yds from Whitlocks End (BR).
Capacity: 5,000 **Seats:** 250 **Covered:** 750 **Floodlights:** Due 1996
Colours: Gold stripes/black/gold **Change Colours:** All red **Nickname:** The Kings
Programme: 12 pages **Editor:** M Kite **Founded:** 1964.
Previous Names: Horse Shoe FC/ Kings Heath Amateur.
Previous Ground: Shirley Town (pre-1994).
96-97 Top Scorer: **96-97 Player P.o.Y.:**
96-97 Manager P.o.Y.: **96-97 Clubman:**
Players progressing to Football League: Geoff Scott (Stoke, Leicester, Birmingham).
Honours: Midland Combination Div 1 R-up 92-93, Div 2 R-up 82-83, Presidents Cup R-up 79-80 81-82 92-93; Birmingham Challenge Vase R-up 86-87; Worcester Sen Urn 96-97, Challenge Cup R-up 96-97.

MASSEY-FERGUSON

Chairman: Dave Malintel **Manager:** John Halford, Geoff Brassington
Secretary: Lee Thomas, 730 Broad Lane, Coventry, West Midlands CV5 7BB (01203 465476).
Coach: Carl Lascelles **Physio:** Joe Doolan
Ground: Massey-Ferguson Sports Ground, Banner Lane, Tile Hill, Coventry.(01203 694400)
Directions: A45 to Meridan turn (B4104). Over two traffic islands, turn right at 3rd island into Pickford Grange Lane, continue to Pickford Green Lane, & Hockley Lane, left into Broad Lane, right into Banner Lane, 3rd entrance right.
Seats: 70 **Cover:** 200 **Programme:** Yes
Previous League: Coventry Alliance (pre-1993). **Colours:** Red & Black,Black,Red.
Clubhouse: Not on ground
Honours: Midland Comb. Div 1 94-95, Div 2 93-94, Chall. Vase 93-94, Chall Cup 94-95, Presidents Cup 94-95; Coventry Evening Telegraph Cup 95-96.

MEIR K.A.

President: Peter Bott **Chairman:** Des Reaney **Vice Chairman:** Graham Lovatt.
Secretary: Graham Birks, 35 Greenacres Avenue, Blythe Bridge, Stoke on Trent ST11 9HY (01782 395647)
Manager: Terry Greer **Asst Manager:** **Coach:** Mark Bromley, Karl Wilcox
Ground: Stanley Park, Hilderstone Road, Meir Heath, Stoke-on-Trent (01782 388465)
Directions: M6 jct 14, A34 to Stone, A520 to Rough Close then Meir Heath, turn right (B5066) ground approx 1 mile on right. 3m Blythe Bridge (BR)
Capacity: 5,000 **Seats:** 200 **Cover:** 250 **Floodlights:** Yes **Founded:** 1976.
Colours: old Gold/black/black **Change colours:** Claret & blue/claret/white **Nickname:** Kings.
Programme: 32 pages 50p **Editor:** Steve Osbourne (01782 328[illegible]) **Press Officer:** Phil Bott (01782 317309)
Midweek matchday: Wednesday **Sponsors:**
Previous - Leagues: Staffs Alliance/ Staffs Snr 84-92. **Ground:** Normacot Rec. **Name:**'The Station'&'Shoulder of Mutton.'
Clubhouse: open matchdays. Hot food.
Club Record Scorer: W J Anderson 219 **Club Record Appearances:** David Preston, 547
Record win: 9-0 v Mile Oak Rovers (H), Midland Combination 15/1/94
Record loss: 0-9 v Wellesbourne (A) Midland Comb. 94-95.
96-97 Captain: **96-97 P.o.Y.:** Martin Wood **96-97 Top Scorer:** Steve Bott 26
Honours: Staffs Snr Lg 88-89, 90-91; Staffs FA Vase 93-94 95-96; Walsall & Dist Sen Cup 89-90; Mid Comb Prem Lge R-up 96-97.

STUDLEY B.K.L.

Chairman: D Robinson **Vice-Chairman:** Alec James
Secretary: Phil Summers, c/o club.
Manager: John Adams **Asst Manager:** Alan Scarfe. **Physio:** Derrick Mutton
Ground: 'Beehive', BKL Spts Ground, Abbeyfields, Birmingham Rd, Studley, Warks (01527 853817)
Capacity: **Seats:** None **Cover:** Yes **Floodlights:** No **Founded:** 1971.
Colours: Sky/navy/navy **Change colours:** White/red **Nickname:** Bees.
Sponsors: BKL Fittings **Clubhouse:** Yes, on ground **Reserve's League:** Skol Midland Comb Div 2
Programme: 30p **Editor:** Alec James **Press Officer:** Dave Chiswell.
Previous League: Redditch & South Warwickshire Sunday Combination 71-87.
Previous Name: BKL Works
Club record appearances: Lee Adams. **Club Record Scorer:** Kevin Rowlands.
Hons: Midland Comb. Div 1 91-92, Chall Cup R-up 91-92, Presidents Cup R-up 91-92, Div 2 Cup 87-88; Smedley Crooke Charity Cup 90-91 91-92; Birmingham Vase R-up 96-97.

WORCESTER ATHLETICO

Chairman: Bill Jones. **Vice Chairman:** Bill Jones **President:** Steve Goode.
Secretary/Press Officer: Don Roberts, 6 Gardens Close, Upton-on-Severn, Worcs WR8 0LT (01684 593439).
Manager: Dave Boddy **Coach:** G Wright **Physio:** A Pugh.
Ground: Nunnery Wood Sports Centre, Spetchley Road, Worcester, WR5 2NL (01905 357842)
Directions: M5 Junc 7, follow signs for Worcester, at 3rd roundabout turn right into Spetchley Road, ground 2nd left.
Seats: 200 **Cover:** 100 **Capacity:** 2,000 **Floodlights:** Yes **Founded:** 1904
Colours: Green & white **Change:** Red & black stripes **Nickname:** Emeralds
Programme: 16 pages, 50p **Editor:** Graham Hill (01905 351653) **Club Shop:** No.
Previous - Leagues: Malvern 04-71/ Worcester & Dist. 72-85/ Kidderminster 85-88. **Ground:** Old Street, Upton-on-Severn (pre'92) **Names:** Upton Town FC
Sponsors: The Bankhouse. **Midweek matchday:** Wednesday **Record Gate:** 350 v Colletts Green, 94
Clubhouse: Evenings 7.30-11pm, Saturday matchdays 12.30-11pm. Drinks & snacks available
96-97 Captain: G Burrow **96-97 P.o.Y.:** A Biggs **96-97 Top Scorer:** D Tafft (37)
Club record scorer: Paul Buckley **Club record appearances:** Keith Aingel.
Record win: 13-1 **Record defeat:** 0-17.
Honours: Midland Combination Div 2 89-90 (Jack Mould Tphy 89-90, Presidents Cup R-up 89-90), Worcs Jnr Cup 73-74 88-89 (R-up 74-75), Worcs Minor Cup 24-25 86-87.

DIVISION ONE CLUBS 1997-98

ALVESTON

Secretary: P Beese, 36 Bishops Close, Stratford-upon-Avon, Warks CV37 9ED (01789 267966).
Ground: Home Guard Club, Main Street, Tiddington, Stratford-upon-Avon.(01789 297718)
Colours: All Maroon and Sky Blue.

BARLESTONE St GILES

Secretary: John Farrington, c/o club.
Ground: Barton Road, Barlestone, Leics. (01455 291392)
Colours: Gold/black/black

CHELMSLEY TOWN '94

Secretary: Martin Smallwood, 244 Coleshill Heath Road, Marston Green, Birmingham B37 7HH (01926 493098)
Ground: The Pavilion, Coleshill Road, Marston Green, West Midlands (0121 779 5400).
Colours: Yellow & Green/Sky Blue/White.

COLLETTS GREEN

Secretary: Marg Coldicott, 3 Blagdon Close, St Peters, Worcester, (01905 767386)
Ground: Victoria Park, Pickersleigh, Malvern Link (01905 830442)
Colours: All green with white trim.

FAIRFIELD VILLA

Secretary/Press Officer: C W Harris, 7 Churchill Road, Catshill, Bromsgrove B61 0PE (01527 831049).
Ground: Recreation Ground, Stourbridge Road (B4091), Fairfield, Bromsgrove (01527 77049).
Colours: Red/Black/Black

FECKENHAM

Secretary: M G Hawkes 23 High Street, Astwood Bank, Redditch, Worcs (01527 893341)
Ground: Feckenham Playing Fields, Mill Lane, Feckenham
Colours: All green

HAMS HALL

General Mgr/Press Officer: Bob Ringrose, 6 Holly Drive, Hurley, Atherstone, Warks CV9 2JY (0827 872747).
Ground: Hams Hall Generating Station, Lea Marston, Sutton Coldfield B76 0BG (0370 936219).
Colours: White/black/black

HOLLY LANE '92

Secretary: R G Ashton, 19 Grange Road, Erdington, Birmingham B24 0DG (0121 350 2352).
Ground: Holly Sports & Social Centre, Holly Lane, Erdington, Birmingham B24 9LH.(01213 730979)
Colours: Yellow/green/green.

KENILWORTH TOWN

Secretary: R Butler, 52 Farmer Wardroad, Kenilworth, Warwicks (01926 857097)
Ground: Gypsey Lane (off Rouncil Lane), Kenilworth, Warks (01926 50851).
Colours: All Red with white trim.

KNOWLE

Secretary: George Phillips, 49 Circus Avenue, Chelmsley Wood, Birmingham B37 7NG (0121 770 9513).
Ground: Hampton Rd, Knowle, Solihull (01564 779807).
Colours: Red/white/red

LEICESTER YMCA

Secretary: Colin Chappell, 132 South Knighton Road, Leicester LE2 3LE (0116 247 8989)
Ground: YMCA Sports Ground, Belvoir Drive, Leicester, (0116247 8989)
Colours: Red & black/black/red & black

MONICA STAR

Secretary: A Blackwell, c/o club (0973 316647)
Ground: Sedgmere Sports & Social Club, Sedgmere Road, Yardley, Birmingham (0121 783 4380)
Colours: Red & Black Stripes/Red/Red.

NEWHALL UNITED

Secretary: David Wain, 26 Willow Drive, Newhall, Swadlincote, Derbys DE11 0NW (01283 225188 Business)
Ground: Hawfields Ground, St Johns Drive, Newhall, Swadlincote (01283 551029).
Colours: All Blue.

NORTHFIELD TOWN

Secretary: Monty Patrick, 38 Pensford Rd, Northfield, Birmingham B31 3AG (0121 475 2057).
Ground: Shenley Lane, Selly Oak, Birmingham B29 (0121 478 3900).
Colours: Yellow/blue/yellow

POLESWORTH NORTH WARWICK

Secretary: Phillip Dempster, 17 Stonehill Walk, Wilnecote, Tamworth, Staffs (01827 262543)
Ground: North Warwick Sports Ground, Hermitage Hill, Tamworth Road, Polesworth (01827 892482).
Colours: All Green.

SHIRLEY TOWN

Secretary: B Fox, 26 Claines Road, Northfield, Birmingham B31 2EE (0121 475 4465)
Ground: Shirley Stadium, Tile House Lane, Shirley, Solihull (0121 744 1560).
Colours: All maroon.

SOUTHAM UNITED

Secretary: R J Hancocks, 18 Warwick Road, Southam, Leamington Spa CV33 0HN (01926 813483).
Ground: Banbury Road Ground, Southam, Leamington Spa (01926 812091).
Colours: White & black/black/black

THIMBLEMILL R.E.C.

Secretary: Karl Young, 30 Moorpool Close, Harborne, Birmimgham (0121 427 2807)
Ground: Thimblemill Recreation, Thimblemill Road, Smethwick, Warley (0121 4292459).
Colours: White (blue trim)/white/navy blue

WELLESBOURNE

Secretary: Ted Forster (01926 494507)
Ground: The Sports Field, Loxley Close, Wellesbourne (01789 841878).
Colours: Blue & white halves/blue/blue

WEST MIDLANDS FIRE SERVICE

Secretary: Mr J Clarke, 51 Stonebury Ave., Eastern Green, Coventry CV5 7FW (01203 467997).
Ground: 'The Glades', Lugtrout Lane, Solihull (0121 705 8602).
Colours: Red with black pin stripe/Black/Black.

DIVISION TWO CLUBS 1997-98

ALBRIGHT & WILSON

Secretary: Andrew Such, 29 Bristnall Hall Road, Oldbury, Warley, West Midlands. B68 9TS (0121 552 8427)
Ground: Albright & Wilson Spts Club, Tat Bank, Oldbury, Warley (0121 552 1048).
Colours: Blue and Black Stripes/Black/Black.

ALVIS S.G.L.

Secretary: D A Leslie, 9 Stephenson Close, Milverton, Leamington Spa CV32 6BS (01926 336700).
Ground: Alvis Spts & Social Club, Green Lane, Finham, Coventry.(01203 692576)
Colours: Blue and White/White/Blue.

BIRMINGHAM VAULTS

Secretary: Kamaljit Rai, 89 Coopers Road, Handsworth Wood, Birmingham B20 (0956 833 990)
Ground: Bloxwich Town AFC, Abbey Park, Glastonbury Crescent, Bloxwich, Walsall
Colours: Red/black/black

BLACKHEATH ELECTRODRIVES

Secretary/Press Officer: G.Ellison, 12 Meadowhill Drive,Wordsley, West Midlands.DY8 5AF.(01384 836112)
Ground: Electrodrives Sports Ground, Cakemore Road, Rowley Regis, Warley (01215 599105 Social Club)
Colours: All red

BROWNHILLS TOWN

Secretary: Bernard Parr, 53 Poole Crescent, Brownhills, West Midlands (01543 370140)
Ground: Walsall Wood FC, Oak Park, Lichfield Road, Walsall (01543 361084)

BURNTWOOD

Secretary: Mervyn Ellis, 11 Green Meadows, Heath Hayes, Cannock, Staffs WS12 5YA (01543 271770)
Ground: Memorial Institute, Rugeley Road, Burntwood. (01543 675578)
Colours: Red and Blue /Blue/Red.

CADBURY ATHLETIC

Secretary: G.Boyle, 1 Greenway Gardens, Kings Norton, Birmingham B38 9RY (0121 628 6533)
Ground: Bournville Recreation Ground, Bournville Lane, Bournville, Birmingham. (0121 458 2000 Ext 3316)
Colours: Blue & white halves/white/blue.

EARLSWOOD TOWN

Secretary: Jim Jones, 22 Antony Road Shirley, Solihull, B90 2NX (0121 603 4436)
Ground: Malthouse Lane, Earlswood, near Solihull (015646 703989).
Colours: Red/black/red

ENVILLE ATHLETIC

Secretary: Gary Cooney, 16 The Dell, Wollaston, Stourbridge.
Ground: Hall Drive Ground, Hall Drive, Enville, Stourbridge (01384 872368).
Colours: Sky Blue/Maroon/Maroon.

LEDBURY TOWN '84

Secretary: M.Cluett, 55 Lawnside Rd, Ledbury, Herefordshire. HR8 2AE (01531 633182)
Ground: New Street, Ledbury (01531 6314630
Colours: White and Black/Black/Black.

MITCHELLS

Secretary: Alan Harwood, 54 York Road, Hall Green, Birmingham B28 8BB (0121 624 8992)

RICHMOND SWIFTS RESERVES

Secretary: Tony Moogan, 6 George Arthur Rd, Saltley, Birmingham B8 1LW (0121 328 9720).
Ground: Triplex Sports Ground, Eckershall Road, Kings Norton (0121 458 4570).
Colours: Red and White Halves/Red/White.

STOURBRIDGE COLLEGE & COMMUNITY

Secretary: David Hardie, 9 Chaffinch Road, Pedmore, Stourbridge DY7 9HT (01384 377883)
Ground: Stourbridge FC, High Street, Amblecote, Stourbridge DY8 4EB (01384 394040)

STUDLEY B.K.L. RESERVES

Secretary: Phil Summers, c/o club.
Ground: 'Beehive', BKL Spts Ground, Abbeyfields, Birmingham Rd, Studley, Warks (01527 853817)

SWAN SPORTS

Secretary: Tony Howell, 156 Westwood Road, Streetley, Sutton Coldfield B73 6UG (0121 605 2062)

TIPTON SPORTS & SOCIAL

Secretary: Bill Andrews, 42 Ambleside, Bradley, Bilston, West Midlands WV14 0SN (01902 497404)
Ground: Coneygre Leisure Centre.
Colours:

WEST MIDLANDS POLICE RESERVES

Secretary: Steve Tonks, 28 Charlotte Close, Tividale, W.Mids. (0121 557 4574)
Ground: Police Spts Ground, 'Tally Ho', Pershore Road, Edgbaston, Birmingham B5 7RN (0121 472 2944).
Colours: Red/black/black

EVERARDS BREWERY LEICESTERSHIRE SENIOR LEAGUE

FOUNDED: 1896
President: J M Elsom **Chairman:** P Henwood
Hon. Secretary: David Jemieson, 48 King George Road, Loughborough, Leics LE11 2PA (01509 267912)

PRESS REPORT

This season was the first that the league competed as part of the National League System, confirmation was received in early September '96, too late to be included in the league handbooks. The Premier division was set to kick off with 18 clubs, but was rocked before a ball was kicked, in the close season, by the resignation of Burbage Old Boys, due to continued ground problems.

At the start of the season 8 member clubs were given special permission to compete in the Premier division without floodlighting. At the end of the season, 2 of those clubs, Asfordby Amateurs and Newfoundpool, were unable to comply with the League rules and regulations concerning ground requirements and complete the 97/98 season in Division 1. Four clubs were given an extension to August '97 in order to complete installations, generally to follow the F.A. line of Vase entrants for 97/98. Two of the clubs, Barrow and Highfield Rangers have their facilities in order with Kirby Muxloe and Oadby to comply.

On the playing pitch, the Premier Division was won by Oadby Town, who romped home with a 22 point margin over 2nd place Friar Lane Old Boys. Last seasons champions St Andrews were pipped into 3rd spot, and Cottesmore Amateurs finished fourth, their leading goalscorer, Jon Neal heading the Premier division hotshots with 34 goals. In that total Neal scored twice as Cottesmore won the Beacon Bitter Cup (League Cup), 5-1 over Kirby Muxloe.

Division 1 was a much closer affair, with any of 2 of 6 clubs battling for the top 2 places. At the close of play Leicestershire Constabulary ran out winners by 3 points over 2nd placed Coalville, who held in their ranks, Simon Seal, the leagues' top scorer with a total of 44 league and league cup goals.

In the Premier division, Thringstone finished in 17th place but retained their premier status for the '97/98 season through the ground grading restructuring undertaken by the league management. To complete the 18 strong Premier division, division 1s' 2nd placed Coalville Town, together with 7th placed United Collieries and 12th placed Lutterworth Town were promoted. The division 1 champions, Leicestershire Constabulary, were unable to meet the premier division ground grading requirements for '97/98 season.

At the bottom end of division 1, Houghton Rangers finished in last spot, they have now finished in 1 of the last 2 places for the last 3 seasons will be relegated to the TMS Motor Group Leicester & District League – the first time the Junior Pyramid System WORKED both ways, Thurnby Rangers join the Senior League as their replacements.

In competitions outside the league St Andrews won the Westerby Cup, with a win over Shepshed Dynamo at Filbert Street, the home of Leicester City who they beat in the semi-final stage of the competiton. In the Jelson Homes Senior Cup (Leicestershire & Rutland County FA) Friar Lane Old Boys suffered a 1-0 defeat at the hands of Barwell Athletic.

Dave Lumley, Press Officer, 0116 277 8455 or mobile 0802 753957.

EVERARDS BEACON BITTER LEAGUE CUP

Semi-Finals

Cottesmore	v	Holwell	4-3	Syston	v	Kirby	1-2

Final Tie

Cottesmore (at Friar Lane Old Boys)	v	Kirby	5-1

CLUB DIRECTORY 1997-98

ANSTEY NOMADS **Colours:** Red & white stripes/black/white
Secretary: Mervyn Miles, 66 Charles Drive, Anstey, Leicester LE7 7BG (0116 236 2909)
Ground: Llimah International Park, Cropston Road, Anstey (0116 236 4868)

ANSTEY TOWN **Colours:** All blue
Secretary: Roger Sutherington, 47 Stadon Rd, Anstey, Leics (0116 235 0770)
Ground: Leicester Road, Thurcaston (0116 236 8231)

ASFORDBY AMATEURS **Colours:** Green/black/black
Secretary: C Barnard, 48 Sherwood Drive, Melton Mowbray. LE13 0LL (01664 67920)
Ground: Hoby Road Sports Ground, Asfordby, Melton Mowbray (01664 434545).

AYLESTONE PARK OLD BOYS **Colours:** Red & white/red/red
Secretary: Brendon Tyrrell, 7 Magnolia Close, Leicester Forest East, Leicester (0116 224 7186)
Ground: Dorset Avenue, Fairfield Estate, Wigston, Leics (0116 277 5307)

BARDON HILL **Colours:** Blue & white/blue/blue & white
Secretary: Adrian Bishop, 138 Bradgate Drive, Coalville, Leics LE67 4HG (01530 815560).
Ground: Bardon Close, Coalville, Leicester (01530 815569).

BARROW TOWN **Colours:** Red & black/black/red
Secretary: Alan Dawkins, 72 Beaumont Road, Barrow-on-Soar, Loughborough, Leics LE12 8PJ (01509 413288).
Ground: Riverside Park, Barrow Road, Quorn, Leics (01509 620650).

BIRSTALL UNITED **Colours:** White/navy/red
Secretary: Bob Garrard, 58 Halstead Rd, Mountsorrel, Leicester LE12 7HF (0116 237 6886)
Ground: Meadow Lane, Birstall (0116 267 1230)

BLABY & WHETSTONE ATHLETIC **Colours:** Navy/navy red & white trim
Secretary: Mrs S C Morris, 10 Winchester Road, Blaby, Leics LE8 3HJ (0116 277 3208)
Ground: Blaby & Whetstone Boys Club, Warwick Road, Whetstone (0116 286 4852)

COALVILLE **Colours:** White/black/black.
Secretary: Robert Brooks, 17 Ashland Drive, Coalville, Leics LE67 3NH (01530 833269).
Ground: Owen Street Sports Ground, Owen Street, Coalville (01530 833365)

COTTESMORE AMATEURS **Colours:** Green/navy/green.
Secretary: K Nimmons, 17 Redwing Close, Oakham, Rutland LE15 6DA (01572 724582).
Ground: Rogues Park, Main Street, Cottesmore, Rutland (01572 813486).

DOWNES SPORTS **Colours:** Tangerine/black/tangerine
Secretary: Stuart Millidge, 25 Elizabeth Rd, Hinckley, Leics LE10 0QY (01455 635808).
Ground: Leicester Rd, Hinckley (01455 615062)

EARL SHILTON ALBION **Colours:** Green & gold/green/green
Secretary: Adrian Knight, 19 Waverly Rd, Blaby, Leics LE8 3HH (0116 278 5042) **Ground:** Stoneycroft Park, New Street, Earl Shilton, Leics (01455 844277).

FOSSE IMPS **Colours:** Red & blue/blue/blue
Secretary: Ivan V Colbourne, 55 Harrowgate Drive, Birstall, Leics LE4 3GQ (0116 267 1424)
Ground: Co-op Ground, Birstall Rd, Leicester (0116 267 4059)

FRIAR LANE OLD BOYS **Colours:** Black & white stripes/black/black
Secretary: Martin Warner, 12 Oakenshawe Close, Leicester LE4 2RJ (0116 236 4443)
Ground: Knighton Lane East, Leicester (0116 283 3629)

HARBOROUGH TOWN IMPERIAL **Colours:** Red & black stripes/black/black
Secretary: John Chambers, 9 Meltham Close, Weston Favell, Northampton NN3 9QY (01604 785707)
Ground: Imperial Park, Northampton Road Sports Ground, Market Harborough, Leics.

HIGHFIELD RANGERS **Colours:** Yellow/navy/yellow
Secretary: Maurice Christian, 18 Blanklyn Avenue, Leicester LE5 5FA (0116 273 4002)
Ground: 443 Gleneagles Ave., Rushey Mead, Leicester (0116 266 0009)

HOLWELL SPORTS **Colours:** Green & gold/green/green
Secretary: Graham Parker, 25 Fernie Avenue, Melton Mowbray LE13 0HZ (01664 481008).
Ground: Welby Road, Asfordby Hill, Melton Mowbray, Leics (01664 812663)

HUNCOTE SPORTS & SOCIAL **Colours:** Blue & yellow/yellow/blue
Secretary: D Russell, 72 Sycamore Way, Littlethorpe, Leics LE9 5HU (0116 284 1952)
Ground: Enderby Lane, Thurlaston, Leics (01455 888430).

IBSTOCK WELFARE **Colours:** Red/black/red
Secretary: R A Wilkinson, 6 Valley Rd, Ibstock, Leicester LE67 6NY (01530 260744).
Ground: The Welfare, Leicester Road, Ibstock (01530 260656).

KIRBY MUXLOE S.C. **Colours:** Navy & sky/navy/navy
Secretary: Philip Moloney, 16 Church Lane, Ratby, Leics LE6 0JE (0116 239 2916)
Ground: Ratby Lane, Kirby Muxloe (0116 239 3201)

LEICESTERSHIRE CONSTABULARY **Colours:** Green & yellow/green/green & yellow
Secretary: Ian Leacy, 6 Lena Drive, Groby, Leicester LE6 0FJ (01530 243110).
Ground: Police HQ, St Johns, Enderby (0116 248 2198)

LOUGHBOROUGH DYNAMO **Colours:** Gold/black/black
Secretary: Max Hutchinson, 3 Wythburn Close, Loughborough, Leics LE11 3SZ (01509 266092).
Ground: Nanpanton Sport Ground, Loughborough (01509 612144).

LUTTERWORTH TOWN **Colours:** White/navy/navy
Secretary: Kevin Zupp, 14 Swiftway, Lutterworth, Leics LE17 4PB (01455 550358).
Ground: Hall Lane, Bitteswell, Lutterworth, Leics (01455 554046)

NARBOROUGH & LITTLETHORPE **Colours:** Yellow/green/green
Secretary: Mick Dodds, 24 Princess Street, Narborough, Leics LE9 5DH (0116 286 7042)
Ground: Ray Hurd Pavilion, Leicester Road, Narborough (Near M1 bridge) (0116 275 1855)

NEWFOUNDPOOL W.M.C. **Colours:** Green & yellow stripes/green/yellow
Secretary: Reg Molloy, 110 Wand Street, Leicester LE4 5BU (0116 266 5051)
Ground: Meadow Lane, Birstall (0116 267 3965)

NORTH KILWORTH **Colours:** Red & black/black/red & black
Secretary: Mrs H Cheney, 109 Queens Drive, Enderby, Leics LE9 5LL (0116 275 1460)
Ground: Rugby Road, North Kilworth, Lutterworth, Leics (01858 880890).

OADBY TOWN **Colours:** Red/white/black
Secretary: Lee Matts, 11 Stanhope Road, Wigston Harcourt, Leics LE18 3SJ (0116 288 8827)
Ground: Invicta Park, Wigston Road, Oadby, Leics (0116 271 5728)

QUORN **Colours:** Red/white/red
Secretary: W L Caunt, 64 Wood Lane, Quorn, Leics LE12 8DB (01509 414213).
Ground: Farley Way, Quorn, Leics (01509 620232)

SAFFRON DYNAMO **Colours:** Red/black/black
Secretary: Bob King, 14 Bramley Close, Broughton Astley, Leicester LE9 6QU (01455 284270).
Ground: Cambridge Road, Whetstone, (0116 284 9695)

SILEBY TOWN **Colours:** Red & white/black/black
Secretary: G Clarke, 123 Highgate Road, Sileby, Leics LE12 7PW (01509 813503).
Ground: Memorial Park, Seagrave Road, Sileby, Leics (01509 816104)

St ANDREWS SOCIAL CLUB **Colours:** Black & white/white/red
Secretary: Martin Wilson, 3 Ainsdale Rd, Western Park, Leicester LE3 0UD (0116 233 9872)
Ground: Canal Street, Old Aylestone, Leicester (0116 283 9872)

STONEY STANTON **Colours:** Navy/sky/navy
Secretary: Brian Chapman, 54 John Bold Avenue, Stony Stanton, Leicester LE9 4DN (01455 274295)
Ground: Highfields Farm, Huncote Road, Stoney Stanton, (01455 274295)

SYSTON St PETERS **Colours:** Black & white/black/red
Secretary: TBA
Ground: Memorial Ground, Necton Street, Syston, Leics (0116 269 8110).

THRINGSTONE MINERS WELFARE **Colours:** Blue & orange/blue/blue
Secretary: Paul Harley, 62 Henson Lane, Coalville, Leics LE67 8LH (01530 222810)
Ground: Homestead Road, Thringstone (01530 223367).

UNITED COLLIERIES **Colours:** Sky/navy/navy.
Secretary: John Meason, 29 Standard Hill, Coalville, Leics LE67 3HN (01530 810941)
Ground: 1 Terrace Rd, Ellistown, Coalville. (01530 230159)

THURNBY RANGERS **Colours:** Green & white/green/green
Secretary: Pat Darby, 83 Kinsdale Drive, Thurnby, Leics LE5 2PU
Ground: Dakyn Road, Thurnby Lodge, Leics

BANKS'S BREWERY WEST MIDLANDS (REGIONAL) LEAGUE

FEEDER TO: MIDLAND ALLIANCE

Hon. Secretary: Neil Juggins
14 Badgers Lane, Blackwell, Bromsgrove

The Premier Division produced the most one-sided contest for several years as reigning champions Wednesfield retained their title. They led the table at the start until cup games saw them fall behind with league fixtures, allowing Wolverhampton Casuals to be unlikely leaders throughout September and much of October. Having regained the lead Wednesfield pulled away from the rest, going 20 points clear at one stage and not suffering defeat until the 27th game of the season, ending a run of 34 unbeaten games stretching back from the tail end of the previous season. The championship was finally secured with two games remaining, courtesy of a 3-0 victory at Tividale, and four weeks later the double was secured at the same venue with victory over Westfields in the league cup final.

A whole batch of clubs were in contention for the Keys Cup, awarded to the runners-up, and eventually it was Stourport Swifts that took this honour for the second time in four seasons

At the bottom end of this section Hill Top Rangers were soon cast adrift and finished up some 14 points adrift of the pack. Their meagre total of 8 points was a record low total under "3 points for a win".

Division One had an unusual look to it in what was a transitional season. With just 27 clubs to be split between two sections the league cup competition was played on a group basis in order to supplement the fixture list. A month of league fixtures was followed by a month or so of league cup fixtures and so the season was well advanced before the leagues began to take shape. The northern section developed into a three horse race between Blakenall Reserves, Brereton Town (returning to the WMRL after an absence of 15 years) and Great Wyrley, and it was Great Wyrley who finished up as champions after 14 years of trying. Down at the bottom newcomers Sporting Khalsa endured a wretched season and only by taking 4 points from the last couple of games did they take their points tally into double figures.

In the southern section it was Smethwick Rangers that made the early running, only for another newcomer, Kington Town, to take a lead over Christmas which they comfortably held until the season's end. The final playing records of the eventual champions were amongst the best ever recorded at this level, whilst those of the wooden-spoonists were amongst the worst ever, reflecting the wide range in the standard of the clubs in these two sections. Despite their dominance neither Kington or Great Wyrley reached the league cup final, which was contested by Brereton Social and Bustleholme, the former winning on penalties.

Sadly none of the league's member clubs were able to make much impact on the national competitions. Only two clubs, Lye Town and Stourport Swifts, made it as far as the First Round Proper of the F.A. Vase and neither progressed further, making it the WMRL's least successful season ever in the competition. In the F.A. Cup only Wednesfield and Westfields reached the First Qualifying Round, though Wednesfield came close to eliminating Hednesford Town, holding them to a goalless draw at Amos Lane before being trounced 6-0 in the replay. Successes in the County F.A. Cup competitions were also in short supply. Ludlow Town beat Morda United (from a division below) in the final of the Shropshire County Cup, whilst Bromyard Town were winners of the Herefordshire County Cup.

For the 1997-98 season the following changes have taken place; Wednesfield have been promoted to the Midland Alliance though, once again, there will be no relegated club to take their place due to the Alliance's expansion. The Premier Division has, however, been expanded to 19 clubs following the promotion of Kington Town (who are having floodlights installed) and Bustleholme (who will be ground-sharing with Darlaston Town). The regionalised Divisions One North and South have been increased to 16 and 15 clubs respectively. The reserve sides of Chasetown, Oldbury United and Rushall Olympic have departed, along with Bilston United, who have dropped into local football. Newcomers include Birmingham College of Food (a new club), Hinton and Wellington (from the Herefordshire League), Lawson-Mardon Star and Newport (from the Shropshire League), Lucas Flight Controls (from local football) and the reserve sides of Brierley Hill Town, Halesowen Harriers, Malvern Town and Walsall Wood. Bridgnorth-based Bandon have switched from the South to the North Division. Several of these sides have previously been WMRL members, namely Hinton (1986-91), Lucas Flight Controls (as Aero Lucas 1983-89), Newport (1982-91), as have all of the reserve sides, ie. Brierley Hill Town (as Oldswinford Reserves 1982-87 & 1991-93), Halesowen Harriers (1991-94), Malvern Town (1979-85 & 1987-92) and Walsall Wood (1993-94). The youth section has been revamped, 28 clubs have been reduced to 23 and will operate in two sections instead of three.

FINAL LEAGUE TABLES 1996-97

PREMIER DIVISION

		P	W	D	L	F	A	Pts
1	Wednesfield FC	34	26	5	3	103	25	83
2	Stouport Swifts	34	24	5	5	103	34	77
3	Bloxwich Strollers	34	23	7	4	84	29	76
4	Lye Town	34	20	6	8	82	40	66
5	Brierley Hill Town	34	20	5	9	83	44	65
6	Stafford Town	34	17	9	8	57	40	60
7	Wolverhampton Casuals	34	17	7	10	72	69	58
8	Gornal Athletic	34	15	8	11	55	48	53
9	Ludlow Town	34	15	7	12	63	57	52
10	Westfields FC	34	13	8	13	50	53	47
11	Tividale FC	34	12	8	14	53	78	44
12	Darlaston Town	34	10	9	15	49	60	39
13	Ettingsall H T	34	8	7	19	42	81	31
14	Cradley Town	34	7	6	21	51	83	27
15	Malvern Town	34	6	8	20	47	70	26
16	Walsall Wood FC	34	6	6	22	35	72	24
17	Wolverhampton United	34	5	7	22	34	102	22
18	Hill Top Rangers	34	2	2	30	27	105	8

DIVISION ONE (NORTH)

		P	W	D	L	F	A	Pts
1	Great Wyrley FC	24	20	1	3	66	20	61
2	Blakenall Reserves	24	17	3	4	71	19	54
3	Brereton Town	24	15	5	4	61	31	50
4	Brereton Social	24	11	5	8	65	47	38
5	Morda United	24	11	4	9	50	45	37
6	Cannock Chase FC	24	11	3	10	56	57	36
7	Heath Hayes FC	24	9	5	10	38	49	32
8	Sikh Hunters	24	8	4	12	62	72	28
9	Corestone Services	24	7	7	10	36	59	28
10	Wolverhampton Casuals R	24	8	3	13	45	75	27
11	Rushall Olympic Res	24	7	2	15	32	55	23
12	Chasetown Reserves	24	6	2	16	43	54	20
13	Sporting Khalsa	24	2	4	18	24	66	10

DIVISION ONE (SOUTH)

		P	W	D	L	F	A	Pts
1	Kington Town	26	22	2	2	91	35	68
2	Bustleholme FC	26	16	4	6	62	32	52
3	Bandon FC	26	15	3	8	70	31	48
4	Smethwick Rangers	26	14	5	7	50	35	47
5	Bromyard Town	26	14	2	10	63	43	44
6	Leominster Town	26	12	4	10	70	58	40
7	Tipton Town	26	12	4	10	58	55	40
8	Bilston United	26	11	4	11	57	52	37
9	Oldbury Wanderers	26	10	7	9	44	42	37
10	Mahal FC	26	10	6	10	51	44	36
11	Cradley Town Reserves	26	6	4	16	43	73	22
12	Tividale Reserves	26	5	4	17	31	81	19
13	Pershore Town Reserves	26	3	6	17	27	78	15
14	Gornal Athletic Reserves	26	1	7	18	27	86	10

PREMIER DIVISION RESULTS CHART 1996-97

		1	2	3	4	5	6	7	8	9	10	11	12	13	14	15	16	17	18
1	Bloxhill Strollers	X	1-1	5-0	3-0	2-0	3-2	6-0	3-3	1-0	4-1	1-0	2-0	3-1	1-0	3-0	0-2	1-3	3-1
2	Brierley Hill Town	0-2	X	2-1	7-2	2-0	3-2	5-0	1-2	1-5	3-2	1-1	0-0	7-0	1-1	1-3	1-2	0-1	6-0
3	Cradley Town	0-4	0-4	X	2-2	0-1	4-0	3-1	4-1	0-5	5-3	0-1	1-1	3-1	0-2	1-3	1-1	3-4	4-0
4	Darlaston FC	0-3	0-1	2-1	X	1-1	1-2	4-0	0-2	1-2	4-2	1-2	0-2	1-2	2-0	2-2	2-0	4-1	1-1
5	Ettingshall Holy Trinity	1-1	0-3	2-1	2-4	X	1-2	3-0	2-3	1-2	1-1	2-1	2-8	2-2	1-5	1-6	4-1	1-6	2-2
6	Gornal Athletic	1-1	0-1	1-2	5-2	3-1	X	3-2	0-2	1-2	2-0	1-2	0-0	5-2	2-0	2-1	1-0	2-2	1-1
7	Hill Top Rangers	0-1	1-7	4-2	2-2	0-1	1-2	X	0-3	1-4	0-4	1-2	0-6	0-1	1-5	0-5	0-1	0-3	0-1
8	Ludlow Town	0-2	4-0	2-2	2-2	0-0	0-0	3-1	X	0-1	2-0	0-4	1-1	1-2	4-0	1-4	1-3	3-1	5-1
9	Lye Town	1-2	2-2	3-2	1-1	2-1	3-1	0-1	3-0	X	3-3	4-0	1-3	6-0	2-1	2-2	3-0	1-2	2-0
10	Malvern Town	4-6	1-2	5-1	0-1	4-0	0-1	1-0	1-3	2-4	X	0-0	1-2	2-2	0-0	0-1	0-4	1-1	2-1
11	Stafford Town	1-1	0-1	1-0	2-0	2-1	1-3	2-1	3-2	0-0	1-0	X	1-1	3-3	4-1	0-0	1-0	1-1	6-1
12	Stouport Swifts	4-0	4-5	4-0	3-4	5-1	3-0	6-3	2-0	2-0	2-1	0-3	X	4-1	3-1	2-1	2-0	5-0	7-0
13	Tividale FC	0-6	1-4	3-1	2-1	2-3	1-1	0-0	1-3	2-2	2-1	3-1	1-3	X	3-2	0-3	2-2	1-2	0-0
14	Walsall Wood FC	0-10	1-2	1-1	0-0	2-0	0-1	3-2	1-2	0-5	1-1	0-2	1-5	0-2	X	0-6	1-1	0-1	1-2
15	Wednesfield FC	0-0	2-0	4-1	1-0	2-0	3-1	5-1	5-0	2-0	4-1	1-1	2-0	5-0	2-0	X	2-0	4-1	4-1
16	Westfields FC	1-0	2-1	3-3	4-1	2-2	1-1	5-1	1-3	1-0	2-2	2-4	0-3	0-1	2-1	2-5	X	2-1	2-1
17	Woverhampton Casuals	2-2	0-1	4-2	0-0	4-0	1-1	5-3	5-4	3-7	4-1	3-2	0-4	1-3	1-0	1-6	1-0	X	3-3
18	Wolverhampton United	0-1	1-7	5-0	0-1	0-2	1-5	1-0	1-1	1-4	1-2	4-2	1-6	0-6	0-4	0-7	1-1	1-4	X

PREMIER DIVISION LEAGUE CUP 1996-97

First Round

Cradley Town	v	Gornal Athletic	2-1	Walsall Wood FC	v	Brierley Hill Town	0-1

Second Round

Bloxwich Strollers	v	Lye Town	3-2	Cradley Town	v	Wednesfield FC	0-9
Darlaston Town	v	Malvern Town	1-0	Ettingshall H T	v	Wolverhampton Cas	3-0
Hill Top Rangers	v	Ludlow Town	0-0, 1-3	Stafford Town	v	Westfields FC	0-2
Stourport Swifts	v	Brierley Hill Town	0-1	Tividale FC	v	Wolverh'ton Utd	2-2, 6-0

Third Round

Ettingshall H T	v	Bloxwich Strollers	0-3	Tividale FC	v	Ludlow Town	2-1
Wednesfield FC	v	Darlaston Town	4-2	Westfields FC	v	Brierley Hill Town	3-0

Semi-Final (Aggregate Scores)

Bloxwich Strollers	v	Westfields FC	2-4	Wednesfield FC	v	Tividale FC	7-1

FINAL

WEDNESFIELD FC v WESTFIELDS FC 4-0

DIVISION ONE LEAGUE CUP

FINAL

BRERETON SOCIAL v BUSTLEHOLME FC 3-3 Brereton Social won 3-2 on Penalties

BLOXWICH STROLLERS

Bloxwich Strollers: Back Row; Chris Fullelove, Musky Patel, Mark Perry, Scott Turbutt, Dave Pickstone, Neil Holmes, Carl Walwyn, Marc Lester. Front Row; Carl Yardley, Simon Archer, Michael Moseley, Dean O'Connor, Paul Tennant, Chris Marriott, John Bailey. Photo - Marshalls Sports Services

Chairman: Ronald Brant
Secretary: George A Llewellyn, 7 Birchover Road, Walsall WS2 8TU (01922 614595)
Manager: Leigh Taylor **Assistant Manager:** Gavin Stanton.
Ground: The Bush, Walsall Rd, Heath End, Pelsall, Walsall (01922 682018)
Directions: M6 jct 7 marked A34 B'gham. Take A34 towards Walsall to 1st island, turn right (marked Ring Road), cross two islands. At large island at bottom of hill take last exit marked Lichfield, up hill, cross next island to lights. Continue to next set of lights and turn left (B4154 Pelsall). Go over railway bridge to Old Bush pub on right
Colours: Black & white/black/black **Change colours:** Royal/white/royal **Founded:** 1888.
Programme: Yes **Editor:** Neil Morris.
Previous Leagues: Walsall/ Birmingham Combination 13-32/ West Mids 52-55/ Bloxwich Combination/ West Mids Metropolitan/ Staffs Co. (Sth)/ Midland Combination (pre-1988).
Hons: Birmingham Comb. 24-25 (R-up 22-23), West Mids Lg Div 2 R-up 92-93 (Div 2 Cup R-up 92-93), Staffs Co. Lg Sth, Edge Cup, Lg Shield 84-85, Walsall Challenge Cup 92-93, Walsall Charity Cup, Staffs Jnr Cup, Walsall Lg.

BRIERLEY HILL TOWN

Chairman: Anthony Purchase **Vice-Chairman:** Terry Baker.
Secretary: Bill Hughes, 13 Barnett Close, Kingswinford, West Midlands, DY6 9PW (01384 288855)
Manager: Richard Gwinnett **Asst Manager:** Steve Scott **Coach:** Chris Conway.
Ground: The Dell Sports Stadium, Bryce Rd, Pensnett, Brierley Hill, West Mids (01384 77289)
Directions: At lights in Brierley Hill High St turn into Bank St by Police Station. Over bridge into Pensnett Rd, ground 3/4 mile on left Paddy's Garage. Entrance 120yds in Bryce Rd.
Seats: 300 **Cover:** 300 **Capacity:** 5,000 **Floodlights:** Yes **Club Shop:** No.
Clubhouse: Open Mon, Wed & Fri. Hot foods & drinks on matchdays
Colours: Blue & white/blue/blue/ **Change colours:** All Yellow **Founded:** 1955
Programme: 20 pages, 50p **Editor:** Secretary **Sponsors:** Various
Previous - Leagues: Kidderminster (8 seasons)/ Staffs County (South)(7 seasons)/ West Midlands Regional (pre-94).
Name: Oldswinford F & SC 1955-93. **Grounds:** Field Lane/ Wollescote Park/ Swinford Common, Stourbridge 56-58/ South Road, Stourbridge 58-75/ Cottage Street (Brierley Hill Alliance FC) 75-77/ South Road, Stourbridge.
Midweek matchday: Mon or Wed. **Nickname:** Lions.
Record - Attendance: 800 v Wolverhampton Wdrs. **Transfer fee paid:** Nil. **Fee Received:** From Wolves for Neil Edwards.
Hons: West Mids Lg Prem. Div Cup R-up 84-85 (Div 1 80-81 (Div 1 Cup 80-81)).

BUSTLEHOLME

Chairman: Geoff Fellows
Secretary: Suzanne Glover, 15 Swann Hill, Hurst Hill, Coseley, Wolverhampton WV14 9UP (01902 659380)
Ground: Darlaston Town FC, Waverley Rd, Darlaston, W Midlands (0121 526 4423)
Directions: M6 jct 10, A454 Walsall/Willenhall. Take the A454 towards Willenhall. Turn left at traffic lights, outside the Lane Arms Public House into Bentley Road North. Follow road down hill, over railway & canal bridges to lights. Cross over lights into Richard Street & along Victoria Road. Take the first right into Slater Street, ground on left.
Seats: Yes **Cover:** Yes **Capacity:** **Floodlights:** Yes. **Club Shop:**
Colours: Yellow/green/green **Change colours:** White/green/green **Founded:** 1975.

CRADLEY TOWN

Chairman: Graham Taylor **Vice Chairman:** T Hetheridge **President:** W Forrest
Secretary: David Attwood, 4 Birch Coppice, Quarry Bank, Brierley Hill, W Midlands DY5 1AP. (01384 637430)
Manager: Trevor Davis **Asst Manager:** Trevor Thomas **Physio:** Martin Bennett
Ground: Beeches View, Beeches View Avenue, Cradley, Halesowen, Cradley Heath (01384 569658)
Directions: M5 jct 3, take A456, right at 2nd island, left into Rosemary Rd after Fox Hunt pub, Landsdown Rd, Dunstall Rd, left at T-junction, left again at next T-junction (Beecher Rd East), 1st left (Abbey Rd), right at end, ground 50yds on left. Nearest BR station is Cradley Heath.
Seats: 200 **Cover:** 1,500 **Capacity:** 3,000 **Floodlights:** Yes **Club Shop:** No.
Programme: Yes **Editor:** **Press Officer:** Trevor Thomas (01384 569658)
Colours: Red & black stripes/black/black **Change colours:** All blue
Sponsors: Allen Homes **Founded:** 1948 **Nickname:** Lukes
Midweek matchday: Tuesday **Reserve's League:** West Mids Lge Div One
Previous - Leagues: Metropolitan/ Brierley Hill/ Kidderminster/ West Mids Amtr/ Midland Comb. 71-82. **Name:** Albion Haden United. **Grounds:** None.
Players progressing to Football Lge: Alan Nicholls (Plymouth (via Cheltenham)), John Williams, Jon Ford, Andy McFarlane (all Swansea), Duane Darby (Torquay).
Clubhouse: Open all day every day. Food available.
96-97 Captain: Trevor Davis **96-97 Top Scorer:** Jason Marsden **96-97 P.o.Y.:** Steve Phillips/Dean English
Club Record Goalscorer: Jim Nugent **Club Record Apearances:** R J Haywood.
Record - Attendance: 1,000 v Aston Villa, friendly. **Win:** 9-1 v Wolverhampton United (H), West Midlands League 1990.
Defeat: 1-9 v Wednesfield (H) West Mids Lge Cup 96. **Transfer fee paid:** £1,000 for Darren Marsh (Oldswinford, 1992).
Received: £20,000 for John Williams (Swansea, 1991).
Hons: West Mids Lg Div 1 90-91, Midland Comb. Div 2 72-73 (R-up 75-76 77-78, Presidents Cup 74-75 75-76, Invitation 72-73), Metropolitan Lg 70-71, Wednesbury Charity Cup 90-91, Dudley Guest Hosp. Cup 71-72 72-73 75-76 90-91.

DARLASTON TOWN

Chairman: Gilbert Preece **Match Sec:** Neil Arrowsmith (01902 450612)
Secretary: Mrs Kath Abley, 42 Addenbrooke Street, Darlaston (0121 531 0487)
Manager: David Downing. **Assistant Manager:** Martin Seal. **Physio:**
Ground: City Ground, Waverley Rd, Darlaston (0121 526 4423).
Directions: M6 Jct 10, onto A454 towards Willenhall, left at lights outside 'Lane Arms' into Bentley Rd North, follow this down hill and over the railway and canal bridges to traffic lights. Cross over the lights into Richards St and along into Victoria Rd, 1st right into Slater St and ground on left but entrance is next left in Waverley Rd.
Seats: Yes **Cover:** Yes **Capacity:** **Floodlights:** Yes. **Club Shop:** Yes
Programme: Yes **Editor:** Dave Stevenson (0121 526 2465). **Press Officer:** Neil Chambers
Colours: Blue & white stripes/blue/blue **Change colours:** All yellow
Sponsors: Metafin Holdings **Nickname:** Blues. **Founded:** 1874
Midweek matcheday: Tuesday **Reserves League:**
Previous Leagues: Jun lges (inc Wednesbury League) pre-1908/ B'gham Comb. 08-11 28-54/ W Mids 11-28.
Players progressing to Football League: Jack Burkett (Nottingham Forest), Andy McFarlane (Swansea City).
Clubhouse: Open matchdays. Tues/Wed/Thur evenings & Sunday Lunch. Hot/cold drinks/snacks.
Honours: West Mids Lg Div 1 89-90 (R-up 91-92 92-93, Div 1 Cup Cup 89-90), Birmingham Snr Cup 72-73, Birmingham Vase 90-91 91-92, Birmingham Jnr Lg 07-08, Birmingham Comb. 10-11 37-38 45-46 (Tillotson Cup 36-37 37-38 38-39 45-46), Keys Cup 11-12), Wednesbury Lg(5) 1896-1901.

ETTINGSHALL HOLY TRINITY

Chairman: John O'Dell. **President:** David Gadd.
Secretary: Graham Mills, 27 Ashen Close, Sedgley, Dudley, West Mids DY3 3UZ (01902 66222)
Manager: Graham Mills. **Asst Manager:** **Physio:** Tony Kiddle.
Ground: Aldersley Stadium, Aldersley Road, Tettenhal, Wolverhampton (01902 751171)
Directions: From Wolverhampton take A41 Tettenhall Road, 1.5 miles turn right into Lower Street, then right into Aldersley Road, ground on right
Colours: All Green/white **Change colours:** Red & white/red/red **Nickname:** Trins.
Previous - League: Wednesbury Church & Chapel (early 1900s), Bilston Youth (1950s), Wolverhampton & District Amateur (1960s), Staffs County (South). **Grounds:** Compton Park (4 years(01/ Bilston Town FC 89-92/ Aldersley Stadium 92-94,Willenhall Town 94-95.
Programme: Yes **Editor:** John Edwards (01785 713458) **Founded:** 1920.
Midweek matchday: Wednesday **Club Sponsors:** DKB Electric/ John O'Dell
Honours: West Mids Lg Div 1 Cup R-up 85-86 (Div 2 R-up 84-85), Sporting Award 85-86, Staffs Co. Lg R-up 82-83 (Lg Shield 82-83 83-84), Ike Cooper Cup 82-84 83-84, Sporting Club Award 81-82, Wolverhampton & District Amateur Lg 80-81 (Div 1 65-66, Div 2 64-65), Div 1/2 Cup 64-65 65-66, A H Oakley Cup 80-81, J W Hunt Cup 82-83 83-84 (R-up 79-80), Wolverhampton Cup 83-84 (R-up 82-83).

GORNAL ATHLETIC

Chairman: Colin Worth
Secretary: Keith Birch, 24 Dursley Close, Willenhall, West Midlands WV12 4DE (01902 410784)
Manager: John Gwinnell **Coach:** Ian Clark/ Ross Hill. **Reserves' Manager:** Ian Davies
Ground: Garden Walk Stadium, Lower Gornal, Dudley, West Midlands (01384 252285).
Directions: From Dudley take A459 to Sedgley past the Burton Rd Hospital. 1st on left at the Green Dragon public house on the B4175 (Jews Lane). Follow the road until you come to the Old Bull's Head, turn left into Rednall Road, 2nd left to Garden Walk.
Seats: 100 **Cover:** 500 **Capacity:** 3,000 **Floodlights:** Yes **Founded:** 1945.
Colours: Yellow/green/green **Change colours:** Blue & black/blue/black **Club Shop:** No.
Previous League: Midland Comb. 51-63 **Nickname:** Peacocks
Sponsors: Jasper Steels **Reserve's League:** West Mids (Regional) Lge Res. Div.
Honours: West Mids Lg Div 1 R-up 83-84 (Div 1 Cup 92-93), Birmingham Vase 91-92.

HILL TOP RANGERS

Chairman: Joseph Scott
Secretary: Paul Allen, 14 Queen Street, Wednesbury, West Midlands WS10 7PT, (0121 502 5194)
Managers: P Allen **Asst Manager:** Dave Scott **Physio:** J Scott
Ground: Hadley Stadium, Wilson Road, Smethwick, West Midlands. (01902 609925)
Directions: M5 junc 1, take A4252 (Kendrick Way). Turn left at 2nd island into Tollhouse Way. Turn right at lights into High St (A4030), take right fork signed Bearwood, to lights. Turn left into Waterloo Rd. At tea saucer island go right, then right into Sycamore Rd, then right into Wilson Road. Car park at end
Clubhouse: Inside ground. Hot food from Sportsmans Bar. Snacks (crisps, chocolate) and hot and cold drinks available from tea bar at top of ground.
Colours: Yellow/black/yellow **Change Colours:** Red/navy/red **Club Shop:** No.
Previous - Leagues: West Bromwich & Dist. 80-84/ West Mids Metropolitan 84-86/ Mercian FA 86-88. **Grounds:** The Jesson 1980/ Hydes Rd 81-84/ Red House Park 84-87/ Darlaston FC 87-93/ Hadley Stadium, Sandwell 94-95.
Programme: With entry, or 50p **Editor:** Secretary **Founded:** 1980.
Midweek matchday: Tuesday **Record - Attendance:** 165 v Darlaston, W Mids Lg Div 1 12/4/94. **Win:** 15-0 v Ham Baker 7/1/84 (Cup) & v Minworth 18/10/86 (League). **Defeat:** 1-9 v West Bromwich Athletic 28/11/81 (Cup match, West Brom a Div higher). **Goalscorer:** Dean Cadman 175. **Appearances:** Dave Scott 399.
Players progressing to Football League: Andy Pearce (Coventry City, Sheffield Wednesday)
Honours: West Midlands (Regional) Lg Div 2 89-90, West Midlands Metropolitan Lg R-up 85-86, Mercian FA 86-87, West Bromwich District Charity Cup.

KINGTON TOWN

Chairman: William Mayglothing
Secretary: Karen Mayglothing, Wells Cottage, Stanner Road, Kington, Hereford HR5 3NL (01544 231151 H)
Ground: Park Road Ground, Mill Street, Kington, Hereford (01544 231007)
Directions: Follow signs for kington Town Centre, look for left turn between the Town Clock and the Burton Hotel. Carry on this road for 500 metres, ground on left as road bends.
Colours: Yellow & black/black/black **Change colours:** Maroon & white/maroon/maroon

Gornal Athletic: Back Row (L-R); Ron Evans, Gary Foster, Brian Carmichael, Steve Worley, Martin Barrowcliffe, Danny Adams, Mick Mansell. Front Row; Westley Felton, Terry Kettle, Dean Cadman, Dave Brookes, Stuart Benton, Fix Mafika.
Photo - Marshall's Sports Service

Hill Top Rangers: Back Row (L-R); Alan Cox, Lee Willis, John Dillon, Kevin Allen, Calvin Cranstone, Garry Moore, Steve Smith, Karl Freeth, Dave Scott. Front Row; Kevin Whitehurst, Dave Stone, Antone Allen, Simon Hampson, Mark Hampson, Mike Hope, Paul McAllister
Photo - Marshall's Sports Service

LUDLOW TOWN

Chairman: P.Gwilliam.
Secretary: Mr J Nash, 58 Hucklemarsh Road, Ludlow, Shropshire (01584 874337)
Manager: Martin MacKenzie **Asst Manager:** Jeremy Mulliner. **Coach:**
Ground: Riddings Park, Riddings Road, Ludlow, Shropshire (01584 875103).
Directions: From Kidderminster A4117; straight over r'bout into Henley Rd, 2nd left into Sandpits Rd, follow road for 1/4 mile until road bears round to the left into Ridding Rd - grd on right.
Seats: No **Cover:** 150 **Floodlights:** Yes **Clubhouse:** Yes **Programme:** No
Colours: Red & white/black/black **Change colours:** Blue & white/white/blue
Previous League: Kidderminster.
Honours: West Mids. Prem Lg.Cup, Finalists 94-95. Div 1 Cup 90-91; Shropshire County Challenge Cup 93-94,94-95 96-97; Presteigne-Otway Cup 90-91.94-95:

LYE TOWN

Chairman: Roy Pearson **President:** Ian Cole.
Secretary: Peter Timmins, Sports Ground, Stourbridge Rd, Lye, Stourbridge, West Midlands (01384 827471 H)
Manager: David Beasley. **Coach:** Alan Moore **Physio:** Harry Hill.
Ground: Sports Ground, Stourbridge Road, Lye (01384 422672).
Directions: On A458 Birmingham-Stourbridge road about 400yds after lights/crossroads at Lye. From M5 jct 3 take road marked Kidderminster as far as lights at bottom of Hagley Hill, right at island, 3rd turn off at next island,turn off left at crossroads/lights, ground about 400yds on left. Quarter mile from Lye (BR).
Seats: 200 **Cover:** 600 **Capacity:** 5,000 **Floodlights:** Yes **Founded:** 1930.
Colours: Blue & white/white/blue **Change Colours:** Red/black/red **Nickname:** Flyers.
Programme: 24 pages, 40p **Editor:** J.Galloway. **Clubhouse:** Yes (01384 822672).
Previous Leagues: Midland Combination 31-39. **Record Gate:** 6,000 v Brierley Alliance.
Honours: West Mids Lg R-up 76-77 78-79 79-80 80-81 (Prem. Div Cup 75-76), Midland Comb. 35-36 (R-up 32-33 34-35 37-38), B'ham Snr Cup R-up 80-81.

MALVERN TOWN

Chairman: Paul Carter **President:** R H Mann **Manager:** Martyn Day
Secretary: Glynne Knapper, 27 Alexandra Lane, Malvern, Worcs WR14 1JF (01684 574861).
Ground: Langland Stadium, Langland Avenue, Malvern, Worcs (01684 574068).
Directions: From Worcester take main road to Malvern. When reaching Malvern turn left at 1st lights into Pickersleigh Ave., follow to Langland Arms Pub on left, left into Madresfield Rd, 2nd left into Langland Ave., ground 100yds on right. 1 mile from Malvern (BR).
Seats: 140 **Cover:** 310 **Capacity:** 4,000 **Floodlights:** Yes **Founded:** 1947.
Colours: Claret/white/sky **Change colours:** White/black/maroon
Programme: 12 pages 20p (special matches) **Editor:** Dave Liley **Previous League:** Midland Comb. 55-79.
Clubhouse: 2 bars, large dance area **Record Gate:** 1,221 v Worcester, FA Cup
Honours: Worcester/ Midland Comb. 55-56.

STAFFORD TOWN

Chairman: Graham Hollingshead **President:** T Logan
Secretary: Dave Rowley, 32 Lodge Road, Brereton, Rugely, Staffs WS15 1HG (01889 583000)
Manager: Chris Curtiss **Press Officer:** David Howard (01785 222686).
Ground: Stafford Rangers FC, Aston Fields Rd, Stafford
Directions: From M6 junction 14, Take 3rd left to Red Hill Roundabout and follow signs for Aston Fields Ind Est along Beaconside. Aston Fields is sign posted 3rd right along Common Road, over railway bridge, ground on right
Capacity: 6,000 **Cover:** 3,000 **Seats:** 426 **Floodlights:** Yes **Founded:** 1974
Programme: 28 pages, 50p **Editor:** David Howard (01785 222686)
Colours: All red **Change colours:** Blue/navy/navy
Nickname: Reds or Town **Midweek matches:** Mon/Wed **Club Shop:** No
Previous Leagues: Staffs County (North) 74-77 82-84/ Midland Combination 77-82/ Staffs Senior 84-93.
Honours: WMRL Div 1 93-94, Staffs Snr Lg R-up 91-92, Midland Comb. Div 2 78-79, Staffs Vase 84-85 92-93 (R-up 87-88), Bourne Sports Trophy 84-85, Walsall Senior Cup SF 91-92.

STOURPORT SWIFTS

Chairman: Chris Reynolds **Vice Chairman:** Trevor Roberts **President:** Roy Crowe.
Secretary: John McDonald, 65 Princess Way, Stourport-on-Severn (01299 822088).
Managers: Rod Brown **Coach:** Gary Whild **Physio:**
Ground: Walshes Meadow, Harold Davis Drive, Stourport-on-Severn (01299 825188).
Directions: Follow one-way system through Stourport sign posted Sports Centre. Go over River Severn Bridge, turn left into Harold Davies Drive. Ground is at rear of Sports Centre. Nearest rail station is Kidderminster.
Seats: 250 **Cover:** 150 **Capacity:** 2,000 **Floodlights:** Yes **Club Shop:** No.
Clubhouse: Clubhouse open matchdays. Hot snacks available. Licensed bar.
Programme: 40 pages, 50p **Editor/Press Officer:** Dave Watts (01299 823349).
Colours: Yellow & black/black/black **Change colours:** All Red
Club Sponsors: M.I.P. Halesowen **Founded:** 1882. **Nickname:** Swifts.
Reserve's League: Kidderminster. **Midweek matchday:** Tuesday
Previous - Leagues: Kidderminster/ Worcester/ Midland Combination. **Grounds:** Bewdley Rd/ Moor Hall Park/ Feathers Farm/ Olive Grove/ Hawthorns.
96-97 - Captain: Tony Davies **Top Scorer:** Curtis Barnes **P.o.Y.:** Curtis Barnes
Record - Attendance: 4,000 v Birmingham, charity match. **Win:** 10-0. **Defeat:** 1-7. **Goalscorer:** Gary Crowther. **Appearances:** Ian Johnson
Honours: West Mids Prem Div R-Up 94-95 96-97, Lg Div 1 R-up 87-88, (Prem Div Cup 92-93, Div 2 Cup R-up 82-83); Worcs Snr Urn 92-93 93-94 94-95; Worcs Infirmary Cup 94-95 95-96.

TIVIDALE

Chairman: Donald Ashton **President:** Lord Peter Archer.
Secretary: Paul Boswell, 34 Princes Rd, Tividale, Oldbury, W Mids. B69 2LR (0121 532 4023)
Press Officer: T Clark **Manager:** Paul Madders **Asst Manager:** Ron Blackwood **Physio:** John Cotton
Ground: The Beeches, Packwood Rd, Tividale, Warley, West Midlands B69 1UL (01384 211743).
Directions: Dudley Port Station to Burnt tree, left towards Birmingham, ground 1 mile on right. Or, M5 jct 2, follow Dudley signs A4123, after approx 2 miles turn left into Regent Rd and left again into Elm Terraces, first left into Birch Crescent. Packwood Rd is second left - ground at end of cul-de-sac.
Seats: 200 **Cover:** 1,000 **Capacity:** 3,500 **Floodlights:** Yes **Nickname:** Dales **Founded:** 1954
Clubhouse: Mon-Fri 8-11pm, Sat 12-11pm, Sun 12-3 & 8-10.30. Rolls & sandwiches available. **Club Shop:** No
Programme: 40 pages, 60p **Colours:** Yellow/yellow/blue **Change colours:** All red **Newsline:** 0891 66 42 52
Midweek matchday: Tuesday **Reserves League:** Div. One. **Sponsors:** Midland & North Security Consultants
Previous - Leagues: Handsworth & District 56-60/ inactive 60-62/ West Mids Alliance 62-66. **Ground:** City Road.
Record - Attendance: 2,400 v Telford United, FA Cup. **Transfer fee received:** £3,000 for Leroy May (Hereford, 1993).
Players progressing to Football League: G Hughes, L May.
96-97 - Captain: Scott Taylor **Top Scorer:** Kieron Jackson **P.o.Y.:** Scott Taylor
Honours: W Mids Lg Div 1 72-73 (Prem. Div Cup 76-77, Div 1 Cup 72-73), Wednesbury Charity Cup 76-77.

WALSALL WOOD

Chairman: Robert Thomas **Manager:** Michael Speake
Secretary: John Rousell, 19 Kinver Avenue, Short Heath, Willenhall, West Midlands, WV12 4LS (01902 637711)
Ground: Oak Park, Lichfield Rd, Walsall (01543 361084).
Directions: Off A461 Walsall-Lichfield Rd, 4 miles from Walsall town centre and 100yds south of junction with A4152 Aldridge-Brownhills. If travelling via M6/M5 exit motorway at jct 7 (Post House) and continue on A34 towards Walsall before joining A4148 which connects with the A461. 4 miles from Walsall (BR) station - regular buses pass ground.
Capacity: 3,000 **Seats:** 400 **Cover:** 400 **Floodlights:** Yes **Founded:** 1926
Colours: Red/black/red **Change colours:** All blue **Programme:** Yes
Previous Leagues: Mids Comb. 51-92/ Staffs Snr 92-93. **Record Gate:** 800 v Aston Villa, 1980.
Clubhouse: Evenings, matchdays and Sunday lunchtimes. Darts, pool. Hot snacks on matchdays.
Honours: Midland Comb. 51-52 (R-up 53-54 54-55 57-58 58-59 60-61, Lg Cup 54-55 60-61 (R-up 56-57 58-59)), B'ham Jnr Cup 76-77. *Walsall Sportsco: Mids Comb. Lg Cup 79-80.*

WESTFIELDS

Chairman: Alan Dunsford **Vice Chairman:** Neil Preece **President:** Graham Preece.
Secretary: Andrew Morris, 17 Fayre Oaks Green, Kings Acre, Hereford HR4 0QT (01432 264711)
Manager: Gary Stevens **Coach:** Sean Edwards/Phil Dean **Physio:** Peter Boulton
Ground: Thorn Lighting, Holme Lacy Rd, Rotherwas, Hereford (01432 268131)
Directions: Proceed 1.5 mile south from Hereford on A49, left in Home Lacy Rd at Broadleys Inn, proceed 1 mile to Thorn Lighting Rotherwas, ground on the right on Rotherwas Ind. Estate. 2 miles from Hereford (BR).
Seats: 100 **Cover:** 150 **Capacity:** 2,000 **Floodlights:** Yes **Founded:** 1966 **Nickname:** The Fields
Clubhouse: 'Gamecock Inn' Holme Lacey Rd. Hereford (1/2 mile from ground). **Club Shop:** Yes
Programme: Yes **Editor:** Andy Morris **Press Officer:** Secretary **Sponsors:** Hereford Times
Colours: Maroon & sky/sky/sky **Change colours:** Sky/white/sky & maroon
Midweek matchday: Tuesday **Youth team's League:** W Midlands Youth Lge Floodlite
Previous Leagues: Herefordshire Sunday 66-74/ Herefordshire 72-74/ Worcester & Dist. 74-77.
Club Records - Goalscorer: Paul Burton **Appearances:** Phil Powell & Mark Tabb **Attendance:** 518 v Rushden & Diamonds FA Cup 96 **Players progressing to Football League:** Alex Sykes (Mansfield T. 92), Gary Bowyer (Nottm Forest 89), John Layton (Hereford U. 74)
96-97 - Captain: Steve Higgins **Top Scorer:** Gary Stevens **P.o.Y.:** Anthony Rivett
Honours: West Mids Lg Div 1 86-87, Div 2 R-up 83-84 (Div 2 Cup 79-80 83-84), Herefordshire Snr Cup 85-86 88-89 91-92 95-96 (Yth Cup 92-93 95-96), Kington Chall. Cup 83-84 85-86 86-87 89-90 91-92, Kington Invit. Cup 84-85 85-86 86-87 95-96, Presteigne Ottway Cup 78-79 81-82 84-85 93-94, Worcs Jnr Cup 79-80, Wye Guild Cup 74-75 77-78, Hereford Sunday Lg Prem 75-76 76-77 (Div 1 71-72, Div 2 76-77, Div 3 75-76, Prem Div Cup 75-76 76-77, Div 1 Cup 73-74 74-75, Div 3 Cup 72-73), Smart Brown Cup 67-68, Fair Play Cup 67-68. Dennis Hartland Mem Tphy 95-96, Robert Biggart Tphy 95-96.

WOLVERHAMPTON CASUALS

Chairman: Barry Austin **President:** Clive Hammond **Manager:** Gary Walters
Secretary: Michael Green, 63 St Phillips Avenue, Pennfields Wolverhampton WV6 7ED (01902 333677)
Ground: Brinsford Lane, Coven Heath, Wolverhampton (01902 783214). **Directions:** Onto M54 from M6 North, at Junc 2 turn right (A449 to Stafford). Ground half a mile, turn right into Brinsford Lane. Billbrooke (BR) 2 miles.
Seats: 50 **Cover:** 50 **Capacity:** 2,000 **Floodlights:** No. **Founded:** 1896.
Colours: White & green/green/green **Change colours:** Gold/black/gold
Programme: 28pages 30p **Editor:** G Smith
Previous Name: Staffs Casuals (pre 81) **Previous Ground:** Aldersley Stadium
Players progressing to Football League: David Heywood (Wolves), Chris Lewis (Leicester C), Des Lyttle (Nott F)
Clubhouse: Bar & snacks, open Tues/Wed/Thurs/Sat/Sun & alternate Mondays
Honours: WMRL Div 1 94-95, R-up (3) 85-88, Div 1 Cup 85-86.

WOLVERHAMPTON UNITED

Chairman: Brian Vaughan **President:** Geoff Parker **Vice Chairman:** Ken Boothe
Match Secretary: Cliff Dulstone, 34 Broadway, Finchfield, Wolverhampton (01902 753644).
Manager: Dave Downing **Club Sec:** John Lee **Commercial Manager:** Graham Jones
Match Secretary: Cliff Dulstone, 34 Broadway, Finchfield, Wolverhampton (01902 753644).
Ground: Cannock Sports Stadium, Pye Green Road, Cannock.
Directions: M6 Junc 11, follow signs to Cannock. At island turn left (down the ringway), at next island follow sign for A34, then take first turn on right. ground 9th turn on right.
Seats: 300 **Cover:** Yes **Capacity:** 5,000 **Floodlights:** Yes **Founded:** 1976
Colours: Gold with black trim/black/gold **Change colours:** All blue
Programme: 28 pages, 50p **Editor:** Graham Jones
Clubhouse: Wolverhampton, open every evening, Sat, Sun
Honours: W Mids Lg Div 1 B Champ 76-77, R-up 81-82 95-96, Cup 76-77 93-94 R-up 79-80 81-82; Walsall Sen Cup R-up 81-82 84-85; Wednesbury Sen Charity Cup 84-85 94-95.

Stourport Swifts: Back Row; Rod Brown, Colin Fulloway, Tony Davies, Jamie Wood, David Dale, Trevor Kerby, Chris Thomas, Mark Morris, John Jordon. Front Row; Paul Parker, Curtin Barnes, Steve Brain, Andy Yapp, Bill Morris, Bob Blakeny, Gary Whild, Steve Cookson, Danny Phiulpotts. Photo - Marshall's Sport Service

Westfields FC: Back Row (L-R); Peter Boulton (Physio), Gary Stevens (Player/Mgr), Steve Radjowski, David Howes, Mark Priday, Peter Harrison, Anthony Rivett, Matt McLean, Steve Higgins, Andy Morris (Ch Ex). Front Row; Ashley Botwood, Jerry Griffiths, Marvin Village, Kevin Jinks, Darren Lynch, Steven Griffiths.

KEYLINE
DORSET COMBINATION LEAGUE

FOUNDED: 1957

President: A P Humphries
Chairman: R E Maidment
Hon. Secretary: G A Theobold
41 South Road, Corfe Mullen, Wimborne, Dorset BH21 3HZ (01202 697994)

The early running for the 1996-97 League Championship was made by Gillingham Town FC, who won their first nine matches and in fact keeping clean sheets in their first seven League games. In early October Shaftesbury Football Club replaced their North Dorset rivals on top of the table and remained there for the rest of the season, winning the Championship by 12 points.

The Runners-up position was not decided until virtually the last game of the season, with Bournemouth Sports FC taking the honours from last season's League Champions, Hamworthy Engineering FC.

At the other end of the table things were just as tight, three clubs going into their final match with the prospect of finishing in bottom place and relegation to the Dorset League, Sherborne Town FC's victory over Parley Sports ensured their survival. Whilst a 1-0 defeat by Wareham Rangers, not only left Bridport FC Reserves in the basement position and relegation, but also meant that Westland Sports FC would be playing Combination football next season.

The Combination Cup Final, played at Wimborne Town FC, was contested by Bournemouth Sports and Hamworthy Engineering Football Clubs. Despite the inclement weather a good crowd turned up to witness Bournemouth Sports, playing in their first ever Combination Cup Final, narrowly defeat their local rivals by 3-2 after extra time.

In the Dorset Senior Cup the Combination League provided three of the four semi-finalists, Bournemouth Sports, Hamworthy Engineering and Wareham Rangers. Wareham Rangers FC progressed to the final losing 2-0 to Wimborne Town FC from the Wessex League.

Sherborne Town Football Club were the Combination League's only representative in this season's FA Challenge Vase, losing to Abingdon United by 5-0 in the Preliminary Round. Unfortunately this will be Sherborne Town's last appearance in the competition as new Rules being introduced for next season state that participating clubs must have floodlights.

The Representative team under manager Pat Notley (Hamworthy Engineering FC) lost its annual fixture with the Wiltshire League by 5-3 on penalties. The match against the Clubsaver Hampshire League due to be played in December had to be postponed and unfortunately another suitable date could not be found.

As stated earlier Bridport FC Reserves will be relegated to the Dorset League and their place in the Combination League will be taken by Lytchett Red Triangle Football Club, who finished the season as Dorset League Division One Champions.

The Trevor Williams Fair Play Trophy was won by Portland United FC and once again the Runners-up spot going to Bournemouth Sports.

The League have now secured a 3-year Sponsorship deal with Keyline Builders Merchants, who have depots throughout the country, and will be known as the Keyline Dorset Combination League. League fixtures, results and news can now be found on the Internet where it has its own website. The internet address is: hrrp://www.btinternet.com/-dtcomb

Geoff Theobald, Hon Secretary

FINAL LEAGUE TABLE 1996-97

		P	*W*	*D*	*L*	*F*	*A*	*Pts*
1	Shaftesbury	36	28	4	4	90	40	88
2	Bournemouth Sports	36	24	4	8	100	52	76
3	Hamworthy Engineering	36	23	6	7	95	41	75
4	Dorchester Town	36	22	5	9	73	40	71
5	Flight Refuelling	36	19	7	10	57	43	59
6	Weymouth Sports	36	15	14	7	57	43	59
7	Gillingham Town	36	18	5	13	63	52	59
8	Portland United	36	16	9	11	70	55	57
9	Sturminster Marshall	36	17	6	13	75	63	57
10	Allendale	36	13	8	15	68	74	47
11	Sturminster Newton	36	12	10	14	52	64	46
12	Hamworthy United	36	11	10	15	44	51	43
13	Blandford United	36	10	8	18	55	58	38
14	Wareham Rangers	36	9	8	19	58	86	35
15	Swanage Tn & Herston	36	9	6	21	54	73	33
16	Parley Sports	36	9	4	23	54	91	31
17	Sherborne Town	36	8	5	23	53	91	29
18	Westland Sports	36	8	4	24	56	115	28
19	Bridport	36	6	7	23	37	83	25

RESULTS CHART 1996-97

		1	2	3	4	5	6	7	8	9	10	11	12	13	14	15	16	17	18	19
1	Allendale	X	0-2	2-3	3-1	3-4	2-3	0-3	0-5	1-1	1-2	6-2	0-6	3-2	1-1	0-1	4-0	3-2	2-2	3-3
2	Blandford United	0-1	X	0-1	5-0	0-1	2-3	0-1	2-3	3-0	3-0	0-4	1-3	1-0	1-4	0-3	1-2	4-2	7-0	1-1
3	Bournemouth Sports	4-0	3-1	X	5-2	1-1	4-1	2-0	1-2	4-3	1-5	2-3	2-4	8-2	4-1	4-0	3-1	4-1	7-0	4-2
4	Bridport	1-2	1-1	0-4	X	2-2	0-3	0-2	3-0	1-1	2-1	2-2	2-1	4-1	1-2	1-2	1-4	0-1	3-2	0-1
5	Dorchester Town	2-0	1-1	1-2	0-0	X	0-1	4-0	2-0	1-2	2-0	1-1	2-0	4-2	0-1	3-0	3-2	1-0	4-1	2-0
6	Flight Refuelling	0-2	0-0	1-0	3-0	3-2	X	2-0	0-1	3-2	0-2	2-1	1-2	2-1	2-1	1-1	2-1	1-0	4-0	0-1
7	Gillingham Town	2-0	0-2	4-2	6-0	0-2	1-0	X	0-6	1-0	4-0	1-2	1-1	4-0	2-1	2-0	2-1	6-3	4-0	2-2
8	Hamworthy Engineering	4-2	5-1	2-2	4-0	2-0	2-0	3-0	X	3-0	1-1	0-1	1-1	8-1	2-1	4-1	1-0	7-2	3-2	1-0
9	Hamworthy United	0-0	1-0	0-1	5-1	3-1	2-1	0-1	1-0	X	1-0	0-0	0-3	2-0	1-1	3-0	1-1	2-2	3-3	0-0
10	Parley Sports	0-4	2-0	1-3	1-3	0-3	5-0	4-0	1-6	0-2	X	0-2	2-2	2-3	1-7	3-1	7-2	1-1	4-0	1-3
11	Portland United	1-0	4-4	1-2	2-0	0-1	0-6	3-2	3-1	4-1	5-1	X	1-2	1-1	0-2	6-2	3-0	2-2	4-0	1-1
12	Shaftesbury	2-4	3-2	3-1	1-0	4-2	1-1	2-1	3-1	4-1	4-2	2-0	X	2-1	4-1	1-0	2-1	1-0	4-0	5-4
13	Sherborne Town	2-6	0-0	1-1	3-0	1-3	0-3	1-2	1-1	2-1	5-0	1-5	0-2	X	2-2	1-2	3-1	3-1	3-0	1-2
14	Sturminster Marshall	6-2	1-3	1-5	2-2	2-3	1-1	1-0	2-1	3-2	2-1	1-0	2-1	7-2	X	3-0	2-2	3-1	5-1	1-0
15	Sturminster Newton	1-1	2-0	1-2	2-2	0-2	1-1	1-1	3-3	1-2	1-1	4-0	0-2	1-0	3-0	X	2-1	4-3	1-0	3-3
16	Swanage Town & H	0-1	2-2	2-1	5-2	2-3	0-0	2-1	0-2	0-0	7-1	3-0	0-2	3-1	2-1	1-1	X	1-4	1-2	0-3
17	Wareham Rangers	2-2	1-1	0-2	1-0	0-6	0-3	0-2	1-4	2-1	6-1	1-1	0-4	4-1	3-2	2-2	3-1	X	4-3	1-2
18	Westland Sports	2-5	0-3	1-3	2-0	3-2	1-3	3-3	2-5	1-0	2-1	0-4	3-5	2-5	5-1	4-5	4-3	3-0	X	0-2
19	Weymouth Sports	2-2	3-1	2-2	1-0	1-2	0-0	2-2	1-1	2-0	2-0	1-1	0-1	1-0	2-1	1-0	2-0	2-2	2-2	X

COMBINATION CUP 1996-97

First Round

Hamworthy Eng.	v	Bridport Reserves	1-1, 3-2

Second Round

Allendale	v	Shaftesbury	0-2	Bournemouth Sports	v	Flight Refuelling	2-1
Dorchester Town R	v	Gillingham Town	1-0	Hamworthy Eng	v	Westland Sports	6-1
Portland United	v	Sturminster Marshall	3-2	Sherborne Town	v	Sturminster Newton	0-3
Swanage T & H	v	Blandford United	3-0	Wareham Rangers	v	Parley Sports	2-3

Third Round

Bournemouth Sports	v	Dorchester Town R	7-0	Hamworthy Eng	v	Shaftesbury	2-1
Portland United	v	Parley Sports	4-0	Sturminster Newton	v	Swanage T & H	1-4

Semi-Final

Bournemouth Sports	v	Swanage T & H	3-0	Portland United	v	Hamworthy Eng	0-1

FINAL

BOURNEMOUTH SP v HAMWORTHY ENG 3-2 After Extra Time

ALLENDALE F.C.

Chairman: E Case (01202 887920 H, 01258 857191 B)
Secretary: Rod Pope, 51 Dalkeith Road, Corfe Mullen Wimborne, BH21 3PQ (01202 602922 H, 01929 424601 B)
Ground: Redcotts Recreation Ground, School Lane, Wimborne
Colours: White/blue/blue
Change Colours: All red

BLANDFORD UNITED

Chairman: M Bellman **Secretary:** Martin Holdaway, 13 Damory Court, Blandford Forum, Dorset DT11 7RN (01258 454733).
Ground: Recreation Ground, Park Lane, Blandford Forum, Dorset. (HQ Tel: 01258 456374).
Colours: All Royal Blue
Change colours: Green & white/white & green/green
Cover: No
Programme: Yes
Clubhouse: No

BOURNEMOUTH SPORTS CLUB

Chairman: T Bloor.
Secretary: John Field, 33 Stanton Road, Ensbury Park, Bournemouth, BH10 5DS (01202 388486)
Ground: Chapel Gate, East Parley, Christchurch, Dorset BH23 6BD (01202 581933).
Colours: Gold/black/gold
Change colours: All red
Cover: No
Programme: Yes
Clubhouse: Yes

DORCHESTER TOWN RESERVES

Chairman: C E Clarke
Secretary: Albert Miller, 29 Shaston Crescent, Dorchester DT1 2EB (01305 264843)
Ground: The Avenue Stadium, Dorchester. (01305 262451)
Colours: Black & white/black/black
Change: Sky/white/sky
Cover: Yes
Floodlights: Yes
Programme: Yes
Clubhouse: Yes

FLIGHT REFUELLING

Chairman: A Miles
Secretary: Harry W Doyle, 39 Towers Way, Corfe Mullen, Wimborne, BH21 3UA (01202 604640).
Ground: Merley Park, Merley, Wimborne, Dorset (01202 885773).
Colours: Blue & black stripes/black/blue
Change colours: All yellow
Cover: No
Programme: Yes
Clubhouse: Yes

GILLINGHAM TOWN

Chairman: E Murphy.
Secretary: David J Ayles, 37 Sylvan Way, Bay Road, Gillingham SP8 4EQ (01747 822065).
Ground: Hardings Lane, Gillingham (01747 823673).
Colours: Tangerine/black/black
Change colours: Yellow & green/green/green
Cover: Yes
Programme: Yes
Clubhouse: Yes

HAMWORTHY ENGINEERING

Chairman: M Robson.
Secretary: Ray Willis, 52 Heckford Rd, Poole BH15 2LY (01202 773290).
Ground: Hamworthy Rec. Club, Magna Rd, Canford Magna, Wimborne, Dorset BH21 3AE (01202 881922).
Colours: Green & white/green/green
Change colours: Blue & white/navy/navy
Cover: No
Programme: No
Clubhouse: Yes

HAMWORTHY UNITED

Chairman: D.Manmuel
Secretary: Peter Gallop, 51A Symes Road, Hamworthy, Poole, Dorset BH15 4PR (01202 670792).
Ground: The County Ground, Blandford Close, Hamworthy, Poole, Dorset (01202 674974).
Colours: Maroon & sky/maroon/maroon
Change colours: Green & black stripes/black/black
Cover: Yes
Floodlights: Yes
Programme: Yes
Clubhouse: Yes

LYTCHETT RED TRIANGLE

Chairman: G Horlock
Secretary: Graham Legg, 122 Sandy Lane, Upton, Poole, BH16 5LX (01202 623350)
Ground: Sports Field, High Street, Lytchett, Matravers, (01202 624298)
Colours: White with red trim/red/red
Change Colours: Blue/white/blue

PARLEY SPORTS

Chairman: P Vass
Secretary: Mrs Shirley Jones, 10 Heath Farm Way, Ferndown. BH22 8JR (01202 872924)
Ground: Parley Sports Club, Christchurch, West Parley, Bournemouth, Dorset (01202 573345).
Colours: Yellow/blue/yellow
Change colours: Blue/burgundy/burgundy
Cover: No
Clubhouse: Yes

PORTLAND UNITED

Chairman: P.Laming
Secretary: David M Camp, 23 Four Acres, Weston, Portland DT5 2LG (01305 821816).
Ground: New Grove Corner, Grove Road, Portland (01305 861489)
Colours: All blue.
Change colours: White/black/red.
Cover: Yes
Programme: Yes
Clubhouse: Yes

SHAFTESBURY

Chairman: A P Humphries.
Secretary: Mrs S White, 5 The Venn, Shaftsbury (01747 853376)
Ground: Cockrams, Coppice Street, Shaftesbury (01747 853990).
Colours: Red & white/red/red
Change colours: Yellow/black/black
Cover: Yes
Floodlights: Yes
Clubhouse: Yes

SHERBORNE TOWN

Chairman: F Henderson.
Secretary: Malcolm Bartlett, 5 Wessex Road, Stallbridge DT10 2PF (01963 362880)
Ground: Raleigh Grove, The Terrace Playing Fields, Sherborne (01935 816110).
Colours: White & black/white/white
Change colours: Tangerine/black/black
Cover: Yes
Programme: Yes
Clubhouse: Yes

STURMINSTER MARSHALL

Chairman: R Copeland
Secretary: David Miller, 8 Blaney Way, Corfe Mullen, Wimborne BH21 3HG (01202 602366)
Ground: Churchill Close, Sturminster Marshall, Wimborne
Colours: Jade/black/jade
Change: Yellow/navy/yellow

STURMINSTER NEWTON UNITED

Chairman: D Walters
Secretary: Richard Frear, 44 Green Close, Sturminster Newton DT10 1BL (01258 473036)
Ground: Barnetts Field, Honeymead Lane, Sturminster Newton, Dorset. (01258 471406)
Colours: All red
Change colours: All green
Cover: Yes
Programme: Yes
Clubhouse: No

SWANAGE TOWN & HERSTON

Chairman: Leonard Marsh
President: Mayor of Swanage
Fixture Secretary: Eric Webster, 24 James Day Mead, Ulwell Road, Swanage BH19 1NQ (01929 423522)
Ground: Days Park, off De Moulham Road, Swanage, Dorset (01929 424633).
Colours: White/black/black.
Change colours: Red/white/red
Cover: Yes
Floodlights: Yes
Programme: Yes
Clubhouse: Yes

WAREHAM RANGERS

Chairman: A.White
Secretary: Mrs Carol White, 18 Folly Lane, Wareham, Dorset BH20 4HH (01929 551765).
Ground: Wareham Recreation Ground, Worgret Rd, Wareham, Dorset.
Colours: Amber & black/black/black
Change colours: All sky blue
Cover: No
Programme: Yes
Clubhouse: No

WESTLAND SPORTS

Chairman: M Murley.
Secretary: Mike Mock, 67 Yew Tree Close, Yeovil BA20 2PB (01935 426219)
Ground: Westland Sports Ground, Westbourne Close, Yeovil (01935 703810).
Colours: Blue & Black stripes/Black/Black.
Change colours: Red/white/red.
Cover: No
Programme: Yes
Clubhouse: No

WEYMOUTH SPORTS

Chairman: A Burt
Secretary: Steve Walker, 48 Jestrys Avenue, Weymouth DT3 5NN (01305 813566)
Ground: Weymouth College, Cranford Ave., Weymouth, Dorset (01305 208859/208860).
Colours: Yellow & black stripes/black/black
Change: Blue & white/blue/blue
Prev. Lge: Dorset (champs 1993)

GLOUCESTERSHIRE COUNTY LEAGUE

FOUNDED: 1968

Chairman: A C Barrett **Vice Chairman:** J D Hart
Hon. Treasurer: P T McPherson, 36 St Andrews Road
Avonmouth, Bristol BS11 9EU (0117 982 7035)
Hon. Secretary: D J Herbert, 8 Fernhurst Road
St George, Bristol BS5 7TQ (0117 951 7696)

FINAL LEAGUE TABLE 1996-97

		P	*W*	*D*	*L*	*F*	*A*	*Pts*	*GD*
1	Old Georgians	34	19	13	2	58	27	70	31
2	Bitton	34	19	10	5	68	38	67	30
3	Frampton Athletic	34	17	10	7	81	54	61	27
4	Henbury O B	34	16	10	8	66	44	58	22
5	Cadbury Heath	34	16	9	9	64	44	57	20
6	Dursley Town	34	15	11	8	44	33	56	11
7	Brockworth	34	15	4	15	47	46	49	1
8	D.R.G.	34	12	11	11	63	47	47	16
9	Broad Plain House	34	13	8	13	52	57	47	-5
10	Oldland	34	12	7	15	51	73	43	-22
11	Patchway Town	34	10	11	13	43	51	41	-8
12	Pucklechurch Sports	34	11	7	16	45	52	40	-7
13	Stapleton	34	10	9	15	46	59	39	-13
14	Broadwell Amateurs	34	8	11	15	54	61	35	-7
15	Wotton Rovers	34	9	8	17	40	63	35	-23
16	Totterdown P.O.B.	34	9	6	19	36	58	33	-22
17	Ellwood	34	8	7	19	39	57	31	-18
18	St Marks C.A.	34	9	4	21	40	73	31	-33

RESULTS CHART 1996-97

		1	2	3	4	5	6	7	8	9	10	11	12	13	14	15	16	17	18
1	Bitton	X	0-1	2-0	2-0	1-2	3-3	2-4	2-1	0-0	3-3	0-2	1-0	0-0	2-0	2-0	4-0	2-0	4-0
2	Broad Plain House	1-1	X	2-2	0-1	2-1	0-3	1-2	3-1	0-1	3-0	0-3	0-4	0-0	4-1	3-3	3-2	1-2	4-1
3	Broadwell Amateurs	3-4	3-2	X	3-1	5-2	0-5	2-0	0-2	0-3	1-1	0-0	4-0	1-1	2-2	5-3	5-0	1-2	2-1
4	Brockworth	0-3	0-4	1-0	X	2-2	1-0	1-2	1-2	0-1	1-1	1-4	1-2	2-0	1-2	2-0	0-1	0-1	1-0
5	Cadbury Heath	1-2	1-2	4-2	0-4	X	2-1	2-1	1-0	3-1	0-0	1-1	4-1	5-0	4-1	3-0	0-2	1-1	1-2
6	D.R.G.	1-2	2-3	1-1	1-2	2-2	X	2-1	3-2	5-2	3-2	2-2	2-1	1-2	3-1	5-2	4-0	0-0	4-1
7	Dursley Town	0-3	1-2	1-1	3-1	1-0	0-0	X	0-0	0-2	0-2	1-1	1-1	3-1	2-1	3-0	3-0	2-1	2-1
8	Ellwood	1-2	1-1	1-1	1-2	0-3	2-0	1-2	X	2-3	0-4	1-1	2-3	3-0	0-3	3-1	0-2	1-0	2-3
9	Frampton Athletic	1-2	3-2	2-1	1-1	2-2	4-3	1-1	1-1	X	1-4	1-1	5-0	5-4	2-0	5-2	0-1	8-2	6-1
10	Henbury O.B.	4-2	3-1	3-2	1-2	0-0	1-0	1-1	4-0	5-0	X	0-1	2-0	1-1	1-0	2-1	5-2	3-1	2-2
11	Old Georgians	4-4	4-1	2-1	3-0	0-3	0-0	0-0	3-1	0-0	1-0	X	2-0	3-1	3-0	3-0	1-1	3-1	1-1
12	Oldland	2-2	1-1	3-2	0-3	4-3	2-2	0-0	2-2	2-9	3-1	1-2	X	3-2	1-2	3-2	2-2	2-1	2-0
13	Patchway Town	1-1	1-1	1-1	1-0	2-3	0-0	1-1	2-1	2-2	3-0	0-1	1-2	X	2-0	2-3	1-5	3-0	1-0
14	Pucklechurch Sports	1-1	3-2	3-0	1-2	1-1	2-0	1-1	1-0	3-4	1-1	3-0	0-1	0-2	X	0-1	4-1	2-0	1-2
15	St Marks CA	0-3	0-2	1-0	0-1	0-0	1-3	0-2	0-0	0-3	2-2	0-1	3-1	1-3	3-1	X	2-1	0-3	1-0
16	Stapleton	1-1	0-1	2-2	3-5	1-2	0-0	0-2	3-0	0-0	4-0	1-2	3-0	1-2	1-1	0-3	X	1-0	1-1
17	Totterdown P.O.B.	0-1	1-2	0-0	3-1	1-4	2-1	1-0	0-2	2-1	1-3	1-1	4-2	0-0	1-2	0-2	3-3	X	1-2
18	Wotton Rovers	1-4	1-1	3-1	2-2	0-1	1-1	0-1	0-3	2-2	1-4	0-2	2-0	1-0	1-1	6-3	0-1	1-0	X

LEADING GOALSCORERS 1996-97

K Morse	Bitton	24
M Cushley	Frampton Athletic	23
A Dibble	Old Georgians	19
A Bateman	Broad Plain	16
J Healey	D.R.G.	16
D Thacker	Brockworth	16
T Moore	Frampton Athletic	16
J Cook	Henbury O.B.	15
I Day	Cadbury Heath	15
D Trinder	Dursley Town	15
P Bartley	Henbury O.B.	14
A Williams	Bitton	14

GLOUCESTERSHIRE COUNTY LEAGUE RECENT WINNERS

Season	Winners	Runners Up
1990-91	Tuffley Rovers	Cadbury Heath
1991-92	Patchway Town	Cadbury Heath
1992-93	Hallen	Old Georgians
1993-94	Cadbury Heath	Endsleigh
1994-95	Henbury Old Boys	Harrow Hill
1995-96	D.R.G.	Cadbury Heath
1996-97	Old Georgians	Bitton

CLUBS DIRECTORY 1997-98

BROAD PLAIN HOUSE

Secretary: Larry Hartrey, 11 Smythe Croft, Whitchurch, Bristol BS14 0UB (01275 835247)
Ground: Filwood Playing Fields, Creswicke Road Knowle, Bristol.
Colours: Red & black/black/black **Change colours:** Yellow/blue/blue

BROADWELL AMATEURS

Secretary: Glyn Barnes, Orchard Cottage, Maze Walk, Christchurch, Coleford, Glos. GL16 7AN (01594 832523)
Ground: The Hawthorns, Poolway Road, Broadwell, near Coleford (01594 837347).
Directions: B4228 to Coleford then B4028 out of Coleford, B4226 into Broadwell ground on right.
Colours: Claret & blue/blue/blue **Change colours:** Yellow/blue/yellow
Prev. Lge: Glos Northern Snr (pre-1994) **Honours:** Glos Northern Snr Lg 93-94 (R-up 92-93).

BROCKWORTH (1958)

Secretary: Geoffrey Bick, 18 The Wend, Longhope, Gloucester GL17 0QR (01452 830889)
Ground: Brockworth Rugby & Assc. Football Club, Mill Lane, Brockworth Glos.
Colours: Black & white/black/black. **Change colours:** Red & blue/blue/blue

CADBURY HEATH

Secretary: C Thomas, 73 Ridgeway Rd, Fishponds, Bristol BS16 3ED (01179 518097).
Ground: 'Springfield', Cadbury Heath Rd, Warmley, Bristol (01179 675730).
Directions: A420 from Bristol through Kingswood, across new r'bout, right into Tower Rd North, past school, right into Cadbury Heath Rd, ground immediately on right down alley.
Colours: Red/red & black/red & white **Change Colours:** Yellow/black/black.
Hons: Glos Co. Lg 70-71 71-72 72-73 73-74 93-94 (R-up 74-75 90-91 91-92), Glos Amtr Cup Sth(3), FA Vase QF.

D.R.G.

Secretary: Robert Wakefield, 101 Wellsway, Keynsham, Bristol. BS18 1HZ (0117 9865516)
Ground: DRG Sports Ground, Carson Road, Mangotsfield, Bristol (01179 560390).
Directions: M4 jct 19 onto M32, off at jct 1 onto A4174 follow signs for Downend then Mangotsfield. Continue through town, road becomes Carsons Road, ground on right after factory.
Colours: Maroon & sky/maroon/sky **Change Colours:** Yellow/black/black
Previous Name: R.W.P. (pre-1986) **Previous Ground:** St Johns Lane 62-66. **Clubhouse:** Yes.

DURSLEY TOWN

Secretary: Phil James, 8 Meadow Vale, Tilsdown, Dursley, Glos. GL11 6HJ (01453 547413).
Ground: Memorial Ground, Kingshill Road, Dursley, Glos. (01453 546122) **Founded:** 1893.
Colours: Red & black/black/black **Change Colours:** Blue & black/black/black

ELLWOOD

Secretary: Ian Edwards, 24 Forest Road, Milkwall, Coleford, Glos Gl16 7LB (01594 833585)
Ground: Bromley Rd, Ellwood, Coleford, Glos (01594 832927).
Directions: B4234 to Parkend then B4431 up hill to next crossroads, turn left - ground half mile on left.
Colours: Blue/black/black **Change Colours:** Red/black/black

FRAMPTON ATHLETIC

Secretary: Keith Potter, 117 Goldcrest Road, Chipping Sodbury, Bristol BS17 6XN
Ground: Beesmoor Road, Frampton Cotterill, Bristol
Colours: Red/black/red **Change colours:** Black & white/black/black

HENBURY OLD BOYS

Secretary: C B Barron, 126 Charlton Rd, Westbury-on-Trym, Bristol BS10 6NL (01179 504002).
Ground: Arnall Drive Playing Fields, Henbury, Bristol (01179 590475). **Founded:** 1962
Directions: M5 jct 17, down Cribbs Causeway, into Station Road, left into Henbury Rd, ground on left.
Colours: Amber & black/black/amber & black **Change Colours:** Red & black/black/red & black.
Hons: Avon Combination 82-83 (Lg Cup 83-84), Glos Snr Amtr Cup South, Fry Club Cup 92-93.

OLD GEORGIANS

Secretary: B M Latchem, 87 Vicarage Rd, Whitehall, Bristol BS5 9AQ (01179 556292).
Ground: St George's School PF, Johnsons Lane, Whitehall, Bristol (01179 516888).
Directions: M32 jct 2, left, left, right at lights, right behind Kings Head. Buses 6 or 7 from central Bristol. One mile from Stapleton Road (BR).
Colours: Azure & navy/navy/navy **Change Colours:** Red/red/white
Hons: Glos Co. Lg 82-83 84-85 (R-up 83-84 92-93), Glos Chal. Tphy, Glos Snr Amtr Cup Sth, FA Vase QF 83-84.

OLDLAND

Secretary: Reg Hamblin, 152 Stockwood Lane, Stockwood, Bristol BS14 8TA (01275 8352033)
Ground: Aitchinson Playing Field, Castle Road, Oldland Common, (0117 932 8263)
Founded: 1898.
Colours: Blue & white/blue/blue **Change Colours:** Yellow & blue/blue/yellow

PATCHWAY TOWN

Secretary: R Stewart, 22 Arlingham Way, Patchway, Bristol, BS12 5NQ (01179 792983).
Ground: 'Scott Park', Coniston Rd, Patchway, Bristol (01179 691203)
Directions: M5 jct 16, A38 towards Bristol, right into Coniston Road, ground signposted Scott Park.
Colours: Black & white stripes/black/black **Change Colours:** Red/white/black
Hons: Glos County Lg 91-92

PUCKLECHURCH SPORTS

Secretary: R B Savage, 54 Shortwood Rd, Pucklechurch, Bristol BS17 3RN (01179 373972).
Ground: Recreation Ground, Pucklechurch, Bristol (01275 822102).
Directions: M32 jct 1 follow A4174 through Downend to Mangotsfield, left signposted Pucklechurch, continue to village, turn right, ground on left.
Seats: No **Cover:** None **Clubhouse:** Yes **Prog:** 32 pages,40p **Editor:** M Dowse.
Colours: All green **Change Colours:** White/white/green.
Hons: Avon Comb. 77-78 78-79 87-88 (Div 2 66-67, Lg Cup 77-78 78-79 87-88), Glos Jnr Cup 65-66 82-83, Bristol & District Lg 72-73.

STAPLETON

Secretary: Steve Rose, 60 Ormonds Close, Bradley Stoke, Bristol BS12 0DX (01454 9555962)
Ground & Directions: Frenchay Park Playing Field, Frenchay, Bristol. M32 jct 1, A4174, follow signs to Frenchay Hospital - ground opposite. Or M32 jct 2, follow signs for Frenchay through Stapleton, ground on left.
Seats: No **Cover:** No **Clubhouse:** Yes **Programme:** Yes **Founded:** 1932.
Colours: Red/black/black. **Change Colours:** Blue & black/black/black

TOTTERDOWN P.O.B.

Secretary: Brian Truman, 10 Elmore Road, Patchway, Bristol BS12 5LL (0117 976 0386)
Ground: City & Port of Bristol Sports Ground, Nibley Rd, Shirehampton, Bristol.
Directions: 5 mins walk from Shirehampton (BR) station (Temple Meads-Severn Beach line).
Colours: Red/navy/navy. **Change Colours:** Yellow/blue/blue.
Prevous Names: Totterdown Ath., Port of Bristol - clubs merged 1994. *Notes below apply to Totterdown.*
Prev. Lge: Bristol & Suburban (pre'93) **Hons:** Bristol & Suburban Lg R-up 92-93.
Previous Ground: Bristol & West Indian Cricket Ground, Gordon PF, Gordon Rd, Whitehall, Bristol (pre-1994).

VINEY ST SWITHINS

Secretary: Alex Thomas, 28 Allaston Road, Lydney, Glos GL15 5ST (01594 843634)
Ground: Viney Sports & Social Club, Viney Hill, Lydney, Glos.
Colours: Red & black/black/red **Change colours:** Blue & white/blue/blue

WINTERBOURNE UNITED

Secretary: John Lloyd, 9 Stanford Close, Frampton Cotterill, Bristol BS17 2DG (01454 775841)
Ground: The Rec, Parkside Road, Winterbourne, Bristol
Colours: White with blue trim/black/black **Change colours:** Blue & black/black/blue

WOTTON ROVERS

Secretary: M P Excell, 94 Bearlands, Wotton-under-Edge, Glos. GL12 7SB (01453 845178).
Ground: Synwell Playing Field, Synwell Lane, Wotton-under-Edge (01453 842929).
Directions: From Wotton war memorial down hill and follow Synwell Lane. Ground on left.
Seats: None **Cover:** No **Capacity:** 2,000 **Clubhouse:** Yes **Founded:** 1959.
Colours: All royal **Change Colours:** White/black/red
Record Gate: 2,000 **Programme:** 20 pages, 50p
Previous Names: Synwell Rovers (pre-1959)/ Wotton-under-Edge FC.

THE JEWSON SOUTH WESTERN LEAGUE

FOUNDED: 1951

Chairman: Mr Tristan Scott

Secretary: Mr M Goodenough, Rose Cottage, Horrels Ford, Milton Damerel, Holsworthy, Devon EX22 7NU (01409 261402)

Final League Table 1996-97

		P	W	D	L	F	A	Pts
1	Falmouth Town	30	24	0	6	91	27	72
2	Truro City	30	22	6	2	68	25	72
3	Porthleven	30	20	6	4	70	27	66
4	Bodmin Town	30	16	6	8	60	34	54
5	Saltash United	30	15	8	7	62	42	53
6	Penzance	30	14	7	9	62	37	49
7	Liskeard Athletic	30	13	7	10	39	32	46
8	Torpoint Athletic	30	11	9	10	52	49	42
9	Tavistock	30	11	4	15	48	70	37
10	Newquay	30	10	6	14	44	63	36
11	Holsworthy	30	8	8	14	28	43	32
12	St Blazey	30	9	5	16	51	68	32
13	St Austell	30	8	4	18	38	59	28
14	Millbrook	30	5	7	18	32	70	22
15	Wadebridge Tn	30	4	6	20	21	49	18
16	Launceston	30	4	3	23	26	94	15

LEAGUE CUP

HOLDERS: NANPEAN ROVERS

FINAL

Nanpean Rovers v St Blazey Rs 5p3, 1-1, 0-0

Truro City's Darren Redding clears from Ian Kilpatrick of Banstead Athletic in their FA Carslberg Vase tie at Merland Rise. Dennis Nicholson

CLUB DIRECTORY 1997-98

BODMIN TOWN

Chairman: C.Hooper. **Vice-Chairman:** P.Lee. **President:** A.Gynn.
Secretary: Martin Mullis, 24 Jubilee Terrace, Bodmin PL31 2QE (01208 77685).
Manager: Ricky Cardew. **Asst Manager:** Phil Brown. **Physio:** Jim Brewer
Ground: Priory Park (01208 78165) - Just off town centre in large park complex, at rear of town car park.
Capacity: **Cover:** Grandstand **Seats:** Yes **Floodlights:** Yes **Founded:** 1889
Colours: Yellow/black & yellow/yellow **Change colours:** All sky
Programme: 20 pages, 30p **Programme Editor:** Secretary **Club Shop:** No.
Sponsors: Gynn Construction **Nickname:** Black & Ambers
Midweek home matchday: Tuesday **Reserve team's League:** East Cornwall Premier.
Clubhouse: Mon-Fri 6.30-11pm (matchdays 6-11), Fri-Sat noon-11pm, Sun noon-3 & 7-10.30pm (except when Sky matches are on then 12 noon-10.30 p.m.). Bar snacks available most times.
Honours: South Western Lg 90-91 93-94 (R-up 76-77,92-93,94-95,Lg Cup 93-94 (R-up 77-78 88-89 94-95), Cornwall Snr Cup R-up 93-94, Cornwall Charity Cup 86-87 89-90.Cornish Guardian E.C.P.L.Supplimentary Cup 91-92 (R-Up. 93-94),Gordon Sweet Cup 90-91,92-93.

FALMOUTH TOWN

Chairman: Malcolm Newland **Vice Chairman:** Paul Ashburn **President:** Seb Coe.
Secretary: David Woon,Llamedos,Mount Stephens Lane,Falmouth,Cornwall TR11 2LJ (01326 315151(H)
Manager: Ray Nicholls **Asst Manager:** Dave Ball. **Coach:** Keith Barker
Ground: Bickland Park, Bickland Vale, Falmouth, Cornwall (01326 375156).
Directions: Follow A39 to Tregoniggie Industrial Estate - will pass ground on left. One and a half miles from Penmere Halt (BR) on Falmouth-Truro branch line. Bus service from town centre.
Seats: 300 **Cover:** 1,200 **Capacity:** 6,000 **Floodlights:** Yes **Club Shop:** TBA
Programme: 16 pages, 30p **Editor/Press Officer:** Mike Odgers (01209 715766).
Colours: Amber/black **Change colours:** Red/white.
Nickname: Town **Club Sponsors:** Stralfors/ Diadora. **Founded:** 1949.
Midweek home matchday: Tues/Wed **Reserve team's League:** Jollys Cornwall Comb.
Record Gate: 6,300 v Oxford United, FA Cup 1st Round 3/11/62.
Best FA Cup season: 1st Round 62-63 (lost 1-2 v Oxford United) 67-68 (lost 2-5 at Peterborough Utd).
Best FA Vase season: Quarter-Final replay 86-87 (lost 0-1 after 1-1 draw at St Helens Town).
Best FA Trophy season: 2nd Round proper 77-78.
Previous Leagues: Cornish Snr 50-51/ South Western 51-74/ Western 74-83.
Players progressing to Football League: Roy Carter (Hereford 1975), Joe Scott (Bournemouth 1978), Tony Kellow (Exeter 1976), John Hodge (Exeter 1991).
Clubhouse: Mon-Fri 7-11pm, Sat 12-11pm, Sun 12-3 & 7-10.30pm. Meals available.
Club Record Scorer: Joe Scott 198, 72-78 **Club Record Appearances:** Keith Manley 580 (appr) 70-83.
Honours: Cornish Snr Cup(10) 61-62 64-66 67-68 70-71 73-74 75-79 (R-up(7) 66-67 72-73 81-83 89-92), Western Lg(4) 74-78 (Lg Cup 74-75, Alan Young Cup 74-75 75-76 77-78(joint)), South Western Lg(12) 61-62 65-66 67-68 70-74 85-87 88-90 91-92 (R-up 58-59 64-65 69-70 87-88, Lg Cup(10) 57-59 61-63 67-68 70-71 85-86 90-92 (R-up(5) 59-60 71-72 86-88 92-93)), Pratten Cup 73-74, Cornwall Charity Cup 59-60 94-95, Cornwall Comb.(res) 83-84 (Supplementary Cup 93-94 (R-up 90-91)).

HOLSWORTHY

Manager: Peter England. **Assistant Manager:** Alan Mayes.
Secretary: Rob Moores, Rydon View, Central Avenue, Holsworthy, EX22 6DB (01409 253982).
Ground: Upcott Field (01409 254295) **Nickname:** The Magpies. **Cover:** Yes **Floodlights:** No.
Programme:28 pages, £2 with entry **Editor:** Terry Trewin.& Bob Thomson.
Colours: Black & White/Black/black & white **Change colours:** Gold/white/gold. **Nickname:** Magpies
Hons: Devon Snr Cup 53-54 (Prem. Cup 71-72 78-79),Devon Junior Cup 38-39.

LAUNCESTON

Chairman: D Redstone **Vice Chairman:** D Heard **President:** D Viggers.
Secretary: Chris Martin, 3 Tavistock Road, Launceston, Cornwall PL15 9HA (01566 776175).
Manager: Roger Fice **General Manager:** Keith Ellacott.
Physio: D James **Ground:** Pennygillam, Launceston (0566 773279)
Directions: Follow signs to Pennygillam Industrial Est., just off main A30 - ground 400yds on left.
Programme: Yes **Seats:** 150 **Cover:** 150 **Floodlights:** Yes **Nickname:** Clarets
Cols: Claret & blue/blue/claret **Change:** Sky/Sky/claret
Midweek matchday: Tues/Wed **Club Shop:** No.
Sponsors: D Viggers Coal **Reserve team's League:** Plymouth & Dist.
Clubhouse: Open after every game. Bar meals.
Hons: S. Western Lg R-up 84-85, Cornish Snr Cup 1899-1900 00-01 82-83 (R-up 92-93, Charity Cup R-up 88-89).

LISKEARD ATHLETIC

Chairman: David Hick **Vice Chairman:** Dave Rawlings **President:** R.D.Burt.
Secretary: Adrian Wilton, Martina, Dawes Close, Dobwalls, Liskeard, Cornwall PL14 6JD (01579 20980).
Manager: Phil Sullivan. **Asst Manager:** Geof Battams. **Physio:**
Ground: Lux Park, Liskeard, Cornwall (01579 42665).
Directions: Take Tavistock Road (A390) from town centre, after 1/2 mile turn left on St Cleer Road (following signs to Lux Park Sports Complex) and the ground is 200 yards on left. Half mile from Liskeard BR station.
Seats: 100 **Cover:** 300 **Capacity:** 2,000 **Floodlights:** Yes **Club Shop:** No.
Programme: 40 pages, 50p **Editor:** D.J.Rawlings.
Colours: Blue & White/blue/blue & white **Change colours:** All white.
Sponsors: Aviation C.B.International/ Gilbert Outfitters. **Nickname:** Blues. **Formed:** 1889
Midweek matchday: Tuesday
Previous Leagues: East Cornwall Premier, Plymouth & District, South Western 66-79, Great Mills 79-95.
Players progressing to Football League: Bradley Swiggs.
Clubhouse: (01579 342665) Normal licensing hours. Hot & cold food available.
96-97 Captain: **96-97 Top Scorer:** **96-97 P.o.Y.:**
Club Record Goalscorer: Not known **Club Record Appearances:** Brian Bunney, 500+.
Hons: South Western Lg 76-77 78-79 (R-up 75-76 77-78; Lg Cup 76-77 78-79) Western Lg 87-88 (R-up 85-86 89-90, Merit Cup 80-81); Cornwall Snr Cup 04-05 83-84 84-85 85-86 88-89 89-90 93-94 (R-up 70-71 75-76 76-77 78-79 94-95); Cornwall Charity Cup 21-22 79-80, Cornwall Jnr Cup 05-06 13-14 26-27; SW Pratten Cup 78-79; E Cornwall Prem RAOB Cup 67-68, Plymouth & Dist. Lg 60-61 (Div 1 59-60 (R-up 54-55 73-74), Div 2 76-77(Res)), Victory Cup 60-61, Charity Cup 59-60), E Cornwall Prem. Lg (Reserves) 84-85 92-93 93-94(Lg.Cup 88-89 93-94).

MILLBROOK

President: Mrs E Weekes **Chairman:** Mr J Weekes **Vice Chairman:** Mr K Townsend.
Secretary: Bob Bell, 15 Carew Close, Crafthole, Cornwall PL11 3EB (01503 230953)
Manager: Mr J Bennett **Asst Manager:** Mr S Matthews **Press Officer:** Mr W Linney.
Ground: Mill Park, Millbrook, Cornwall (0752 822113)
Directions: From Torpoint Ferry - 3 miles to Antony on A374, fork left, after 1 mile turn left again and follow B3247 to Millbrook (3 miles), take road marked 'Town Centre Southdown', right at mini-r'bout after quarter mile, ground clearly visible. From Tamar Bridge - follow signs for Torpoint, 2 miles after Polbathic take right turning marked Millbrook, 5 miles to Millbrook then proceed as above.
Capacity: **Seats:** None **Cover:** 200 **Floodlights:** Yes **Founded:** 1973.
Colours: White & Black/black/red **Change colours:** Sky/white/white **Nickname:** The Brook
Previous Leagues: Plymouth Comb.(8yrs)/ Plymouth & Dist.(6yrs).
Programme: 20 pages, 10p **Editor:** Mr J Weekes (0752 822637) **Club Shop:** No.
Sponsors: Plymouth Boat Cruises Ltd.
Midweek matchday: Tuesday **Reserve's League:** Plymouth & District.
Clubhouse: Weekdays 7-11pm, Sat 11am-11pm, Sun noon-3 & 7.30-10.30. Hot food (chips, burgers etc) available during and after matchdays.
Club record scorer: Unknown **Club record appearances:** John Horne 215.
Hons: South Western Lg R-up 81-82, Cornwall Snr Cup R-up 83-84 (Charity Cup 84-85, Jnr Cup 75-76), Plymouth & District Lg 80-81 (Div 1 R-up 76-77).

NEWQUAY

Chairman: A Kendall **Vice-Chairman:** J.Lugg. **President:** J L Parker
Secretary: John Hawkey, 16 Higher Tower Rd, Newquay, Cornwall.TR7 1QL (01637 871884)
Mgr/Coach: Graham Nicholls **Asst Manager:** Andy Mattock **Physio:** Ross McOpie
Ground: Mount Wise, Newquay (01637 872935)
Directions: 1/2 mile from Newquay BR, follow 1-way system for 1/2 miles - grd signed on left before Windsor Hotel.
Seats: 250 **Cover:** 500 **Capacity:** 4,000 **Floodlights:** Yes **Club Shop:** No
Programme: 16 pages, 30p **Editor:** M Lowry **Press Officer:**
Colours: Red & white stripes **Change colours:** Sky & navy
Sponsors: Studs Sports **Nickname:** Peppermints **Founded:** 1890.
Midweek Matchday: **Reserve League:** Cornwall Combination.
Previous Leagues: West Cornwall/ Plymouth & District 21-27/ Cornish Senior 31-51.
Players progressing to Football League: Chris Morris (Sheffield Wednesday, Celtic & Eire), David Philp (Plymouth Argyle), Kevin Miller (Exeter City,Birmingham C,Watford), John Hodge (exeter City,Swansea).
Clubhouse: 7-11pm w/days, 12-11pm Sat, 12-3 & 7-10.30pm Sun. Hot & cold snacks after matchs.
96-97 Captain: **96-97 P.o.Y.:** **96-97 Top Scorer:**
Hons: FA Vase 3rd Rd 90-91, Cornish Snr Cup 34-35 52-53 54-55 56-57 91-92 (R-up(9) 05-07 08-09 25-26 33-34 35-36 57-58 69-70 84-85), S. Western Lg(7) 58-60 77-78 79-80 81-82 83-84 87-88 (R-up 57-58 85-86 94-95, Lg Cup 55-56 88-89 (R-up(4) 56-58 79-81), Cornish Charity Cup(13) 06-07 08-09 53-56 57-59 62-63 69-70 74-75 76-78 88-89 (R-up(9) 07-08 20-21 56-57 60-61 73-74 75-76 81-82 84-86), W. Cornwall Lg 06-07 (R-up(2) 07-09), Cornish Snr Lg Herald Cup 34-35 (R-up(7) 33-34 35-36 49-51 55-57 58-59).

PENZANCE

President: Len Stanbury **Chairman:** Jim Dann
Secretary: Jim Dann, Carthew Farm, Newbridge, Penzance, Cornwall, TR20 8QL (01736 62749)
Manager: Martin Smith **Coach:** T.B.A. **Trainer:** Ken Prowse.
Ground: Penlee Park (0736 61964) **Floodlights:** Yes **Seats:** Yes **Founded:** 1888.
Directions: Seafront road past harbour, after amusement arcade turn right at r'bout (Alexander Rd), ground second right. Fifteen minutes walk from Penzance (BR); directions as above.
Colours: Black & white/black/black **Change colours:** All yellow **Nickname:** Magpies.
Clubhouse: Yes **Reserve team's league:** Cornwall Comb.
Players progressing to Football League: Gerry Gazzard (Brentford), Tony Kellow (Exeter).
Hons: Cornish Snr Cup 1892-93 95-96 97-98 98-99 1903-04 07-08 47-48 60-61 72-73 80-81 (R-up 1896-97 99-1900 00-01 04-05 48-49 49-50 54-55 56-57 74-75), South Western Lg 55-56 56-57 74-75 (Lg Cup R-up 60-61), Cornwall Charity Cup 47-48 48-49 (R-up 21-22 63-64), Cornwall Snr Lg Div 2 57-58 (Div 2 Cup 53-54 54-55), Cornwall Comb. R-up 65-66 (Lg Cup 69-70 (R-up 81-82)), Cornwall Jnr Cup (West) 03-04 04-05 05-06 07-08 09-10.

PORTHLEVEN

President: Mr W O Allen **Chairman:** Mr W Tearney **Vice Chairman:** Mr L Williams
Secretary: Vidal James, 11 Primrose Close, Weeth Park, Camborne, TR14 7HS (01209 710618) 561160).
Manager: Trevor Mewton **Coach:** Paul Christie **Comm. Mgr:** Mr V James.
Ground: Gala Parc, Mill Lane, Porthleven (0208 574754).
Directions: From Penzance on A394, B3304 into Porthleven, ground on left immediately before town. From Helston on B3304 ground on right as you exit town. Buses from Helston and Penzance.
Capacity: **Seats:** None **Cover:** Yes **Floodlights:** No. **Programme:** 20p
Colours: Amber/black **Change colours:** All blue **Nickname:** Fishermen
Previous Leagues: West Penwith/ Cornwall Snr/ South Western 66-77/ Cornwall Combination 77-89.
Reserves' Lge: Cornwall Comb. **Previous Grounds:** Treza Downs/ Sunset Farm.
Clubhouse: Mon-Fri 7-11pm, Sat 11am-8pm, Sun 11am-3 & 7-10.30pm. Full food menu.
Hons: Sth Western Lg R-up 72-73, Cornwall Comb.(6),(Lg Cup(6), Cornwall Charity Cup 70-71, Cornwall Snr Cup R-up 68-69, George Evely Cup 64-65 65-66 83-84 86-87, West Penwith Lg, Penzance Hosp. Cup, Penzance Charity Cup.

SALTASH UNITED

President: P Skinnard **Chairman:** M Howard **Manager:** Phil Towl
Secretary: P J Gammage, 23 Spire Hill Park, Saltash, Cornwall, PL12 4SR (01752 844046).
Ground: Kimberley Stadium, Callington Road, Saltash, Cornwall (01752 845746).
Directions: First left after crossing Tamar Bridge, through town centre, at top of town fork right at mimi r'bout, ground 400 yds ahead on left.
Seats: 250 **Cover:** 250 **Capacity:** 3,000 **Floodlights:** Yes **Formed:** 1945.
Programme: 40 pages, 40p **Editor:** Marian Gammage.
Colours: Red/Black/Black **Change:** Black & white stripes/black/black
Nickname: The Ashes **Midweek Matcheday:** Wednesday
Previous Leagues: Cornwall Snr/Sth Western 51-59 62-76/E Cornwall Prem 59-62/Gt Mills West 76-95.
Clubhouse: Club attached to stand and caters for dancing and club activities.Saphire Lounge caters for wedding receptions,quiz nights and private functions etc.
Hons: Cornwall Snr Lg 49-50 50-51, Western Lg 84-85 86-87 88-89 (R-up 83-84 87-88, Lg Cup 86-87 87-88 (R-up 88-89), Div 1 76-77, Merit Cup 79-80 87-88), Sth Western Lg 53-54 75-76 (R-up 3), Lg Cup 3, Cornwall Snr Cup 6.

St AUSTELL

Chairman: Colin Marshall **Asst Chairman:** Derek Silk
Secretary: Peter Beard, 24 Alexandra Rd, St Austell, Cornwall PL25 4QP (01726 64138).
Manager: John Peters **Asst Manager:** Colin Bunney **Physio:** N McKenna
Ground: Poltair Park (0726 77099). **Directions:** 5 mins walk north of St Austell (BR).
Seats: 200 **Cover:** 300 **Capacity:** 8,000 **Floodlights:** No **Founded:** 1890.
Colours: White/black/black **Change colours:** Blue/black/blue.
Previous Leagues: Rocky Park (1890s) **Record Gate:** 15,000 v Penzance, Senior Cup 49.
Hons: S West Lg 68-69 (R-up 4), Lg Cup 64-65 71-73 87-88 (R-up 4), Cornish Snr Cup(11)

St BLAZEY

Vice Chairman: Mr P Clemow. **President:** K.Cocks. **Chairman:** Mr H Cooke
Secretary: Martin Richards, 14 Landreath Place, St Blazey, Par, Cornwall PL24 2JX (01726 817419).
Manager: Kenny Cook. **Coach:** Gareth Lobb. **Physio:** T.B.A.
Ground: Blaise Park, Station Road, St Blazey (01726 814110).
Directions: A390 Liskeard-St Austell road, turn into Station Road at lights in St Blazey village; ground 100 yards on left. One and a half miles from Par (BR).
Seats: 200 **Cover:** 700 **Capacity:** 3,500 **Floodlights:** Yes **Founded:** 1896.
Colours: Green/black **Change colours:** All white **Nickname:** Saints
Programme: 24 pages, 30p **Editor:** M.Newcombe(011726 815964) **Club Shop:** No.
Sponsors: Express Joinery **Record Gate:** 6,500 v St Austell, Cornwall Snr Cup 48-49.
Midweek matchday: Tues/Wed **Reserve's League:** East Cornwall Premier.
Clubhouse: Mon-Thurs 11am-3pm & 7-11pm, Fri-Sat 11-11.45pm, Sun noon-3pm & 7-11pm. Bar snacks.
Club record scorer: B Tallamy **Club record appearances:** W Isbell.
Hons: South Western Lg 6, (R-up 9), Lg Cup 5, (R-up 5), Cornish Snr Cup 8, Cornish Charity Cup 35-36 56-57 83-84, Cornwall Snr Lg Cup (Herald Cup) 35-36 48-49.

TAVISTOCK

President: **Chairman:** R A Fenner **Vice Chairman:** D R D Pethick
Secretary: Philip Lowe, 1 Bainbridge Court, Colebrook, Plympton, PL7 4HH (01752 335273).
Manager: Steve Metters **Asst Manager:** Jerry Collins. **Coach:** Les Mewton.
Physio: Les Mewton **Press Officer:** Chairman.
Ground: Langsford Park, Crowndale Rd, Tavistock (01822 614447)
Directions: A386 from Plymouth, left after Ford garage into Crowndale Rd, ground half mile on left.
Capacity: 2,000 **Seats:** 200 **Cover:** 200 **Floodlights:** Yes **Founded:** 1888.
Colours: Red & Black/black/black. **Change colours:** All Blue
Programme: 32 pages, with entry **Editor:** Secretary **Club Shop:** No.
Sponsors: Dave Carter Spts, Plymouth **Record Gate:** 5,000 v Calstock, Bedford Cup final 1952.
Midweek matchday: Wednesday. **Reserve's League:** Plymouth & Dist **Nickname:** 'Tavy' or 'Lambs'
Players progressing to Football League: Peter, Neil Langman (Plymouth, 51 53).
Clubhouse: Open all day Saturday and evenings 6.30-10.30 or 11pm. Hot & cold food
Club record appearances: A Pethick 1,000+.
Hons: Devon Premier Cup 90-91 (R-up 94-95), Devon Snr Cup 1889-90 1968-69 77-78 81-82, South Western Lg Cup 68-69 (R-up 76-77 83-84), Bedford Cup on numerous occasions.

TORPOINT ATHLETIC

Manager: Phil Cardew
Secretary: Vic Grimwood, 43 Henerdon Heights, Plympton PL7 3EY (01752 81344).
Ground: Mill Field (01752 812889)
Directions: Bear left from Torpoint ferry, ground down hill on left after half a mile.
Clubhouse: Yes **Programme:** Yes **Seats:** Yes **Cover:** Yes **Floodlights:** No
Colours: Gold & black stripes/black/gold **Change colours:** White & Black/White/White.
Previous League: Plymouth & District League.(Premier)
Best FA Vase season: 4th Round 93-94 (lost 0-3 at home to Diss Town, eventual winners).
Hons: South Western Lg 64-65 66-67 (Lg Cup R-up 65-66), Cornish Snr Cup 8.

TRURO CITY

Manager: Leigh Cooper.
Secretary: Roy Rowe, 5 Alverton Gardens, Truro, Cornwall TR1 1JA (01872 78853).
Ground: Treyew Road, Truro, Cornwall (01872 78853) **Seats:** Yes **Floodlights:** Yes.
Directions: On A39 by-pass south of city. 10 mins walk from BR station; up hill and left at junction.
Colours: Red & black/black/black **Change colours:** White/Black/Black.
Reserve Team's League: Jolly's Cornwall Combination.
Hons: South Western Lg 60-61 69-70 92-93 (R-up 54-55 62-63 66-67 67-68 70-71, Lg Cup 59-60 66-67(joint) 92-93 (R-up 54-55 58-59 67-68 93-94)), Cornish Snr Cup 12, Cornish Charity Cup 7, Cornish Snr Lg 31-32 32-33, Cornwall Comb.

WADEBRIDGE TOWN

Manager: Robbie Black.
Secretary: Barry Cudmore, 3 Marine Terrace, Wadebridge, Cornwall PL27 7AJ (0208 813826).
Ground: Bodieve Park (0208 812537) **Seats:** Yes **Cover:** Ample **Floodlights:** No
Directions: At junction of A39 and B3314 to east of Wadebridge. **Nickname:** Bridgers.
Colours: Red & White/red/red **Change colours:** All blue.
Reserve Team's League: East Cornwall Premier.
Hons: South Western Lg R-up 68-69 78-79 79-80 (Lg Cup 5), (R-up 3), Cornish Snr Cup 79-80, Cornish Charity Cup 8,

WESTWARD DEVELOPMENTS DEVON COUNTY LEAGUE

Chairman: Brian Williams

Hon. Secretary: Roger Lowe, Panorama
Lamerton, Tavistock, Devon PL19 8SD (01822 613516)

FINAL LEAGUE TABLE 1996-97

		P	W	D	L	F	A	Pts	GD
1	Stoke Gabriel	38	25	10	3	95	39	85	56
2	Dartmouth United	38	24	6	8	88	45	78	43
3	Willand Rovers	38	22	7	9	101	52	73	49
4	Topsham Town	38	21	9	8	87	51	72	36
5	Budleigh Salterton	38	22	4	12	82	47	70	35
6	Appledore BAAC	38	21	5	12	116	49	68	67
7	Cullompton Rangers	38	22	2	14	77	60	68	17
8	Buckfastleigh Rangers	38	18	7	13	79	61	61	18
9	Newton Abbot	38	16	12	10	77	62	60	15
10	Plymouth Parkway	38	18	4	16	88	58	58	30
11	Plymouth Command	38	17	6	15	78	62	57	16
12	Ottery St Mary	38	15	9	14	88	78	54	10
13	Alphington	38	15	8	15	62	80	50+	-18
14	Newton Abbot Spurs	38	14	6	18	87	71	48	16
15	Weston Mill Oak Villa	38	12	6	20	76	87	42	-11
16	Elburton Villa	38	10	7	21	59	81	37	-22
17	Newton St Cyres	38	9	6	23	54	99	33	-45
18	Plymstock United	38	7	5	26	51	129	26	-78
19	Ivybridge Town	38	8	1	29	52	152	25	-100
20	Teignmouth	38	4	0	34	40	174	3*	-134

* 9 Points Deducted   + 3 Points Deducted

WESTWARD DEVELOPMENTS DEVON LEAGUE HONOURS

	Champions	Runners Up
1992-93	Buckfastleigh	Newton Abbot
1993-94	Newton Abbot	Stoke Gabriel
1994-95	Stoke Gabriel	Alphington
1995-96	Budleigh Salterton	Stoke Gabriel
1996-97	Stoke Gabriel	Dartmouth United

DEVON COUNTY LEAGUE CUP HONOURS

	Winners	Runners Up
1992-93	Newton Abbot	Willand Rovers
1993-94	Alphington	Willand Rovers
1994-95	Elburton Villa	Weston Mill Oak V
1995-96	Topsham Town	Newton Abbot
1996-97	Topsham Town	Dartmouth United

DEVON COUNTY LEAGUE OTHER HONOURS

CHARITY SHIELD

1994	Alphington & Newton Abbot (Shared)
1995	Stoke Gabriel
1996	Budleigh Salterton & Topsham Town (Shared)

HOSPITALITY SHIELD

1995	Willand Rovers
1996	Budleigh Salterton
1997	Ottery St Mary

SPORTSMANSHIP CUP

1993	Newton St Cyres
1993	Stoke Gabriel
1995	Stoke Gabriel
1996	Plymouth Command
1997	Plymouth Command

PROGRAMME AWARD

1993	Plymstock United
1993	No Contest
1995	No Contest
1996	Stoke Gabriel
1997	Newton Abbot Spurs

The south-west ground hop was a great success, and here we see Phil Hiscox (hop organiser and Devon League secretary) giving one of many press interviews.

Budleigh Salterton FC.

CLUB DIRECTORY 1997-98

ALPHINGTON

Secretary: S Mann, 8 Mount Wear Square, Countess Wear, Exeter EX2 7BN (01392 875765)
Ground: The Chronicles, Church Road, Alphington (01392 279556)
Directions: From M5/A30/A38 follow signs for Marsh Barton
Colours: Amber/black/amber
Change colours: Blue/black/blue.
Previous League: Devon & Exeter.
Hons: Devon County Lg Cup 93-94.

APPLEDORE & BIDEFORD AAC

Secretary: Eddie Nichols, 14 Alexandra Terrace, Bideford, EX39 2PL (01237 475493)
Ground: Marshford, (01237 477099). **Directions:** From Bideford the ground is on the A386
Colours: Yellow & black/black/black
Change: All Blue

BUCKFASTLEIGH RANGERS

Secretary: Bob Haskell, 41 Moorland Gate, Heathfield, Newton Abbott TQ12 6TX (01626 835386)
Ground: Duckspond Playing Fields, Buckfastleigh, Devon
Directions: On east side of A3380, just off main A38, to south of Buckfastleigh village centre.
Colours: Green/black/black
Change colours: Yellow/blue/blue
Hons: Devon County Lg 92-93.

BUDLEIGH SALTERTON A.F.C.

Secretary: Nick Pannell, 33 Armytage Road, Budleigh Salterton, Devon, EX9 6SD, (01395 445877).
Ground: Greenway Lane, Budleigh Salterton (01395 443850). **Directions:** Immediately before Budleigh turn left to Knowle Village, 2nd right (Bedlands Lane), left at school then right into Greenway Lane.
Colours: All Red
Change colours: All blue

CULLOMPTON RANGERS

Secretary: K Richards, 4 Carlton Rd, Exeter EX2 5NR (01392 211450)
Ground: Speeds Meadow, Duke Street, Cullompton, Devon.
Directions: M5 jct 28, head for town centre, turn left, through thru town centre for 1 mile, left into Meadow Lane, past sports centre, right at T-junction, left after 100yds and follow signs.
Colours: Red/black/red
Change colours: Yellow/blue/blue
Nickname: Rangers
Hons: Devon & Exeter Lg 61-62 63-64, Snr Div 59-60 78-79; East Devon Snr Cup 83-84; Devon Premier Cup R-up 84-85; Axminster Hosp. Cup 92-93.

DARTMOUTH UNITED F.C.

Secretary: Debbie Smith, 3 Archway Drive, Dartmouth, Devon, TQ6 9TE, (01803 833791)
Ground: Longcross, (01803 832902). **Directions:** From Totnes ground is on road into Dartmouth, after Mobil garage take next right (Milton Lane), the 1st right.
Colours: Black & white/black/white
Change colours: Blue/white/black

ELBURTON VILLA

Secretary: Yvonne Westcott, 4 Gara Close, Elburton, Plymouth PL9 8UN, (01752 405474).
Ground: Haye Road, Elburton, Plymouth. (01752 480025). **Directions:** From Plymouth take dual-carriageway to Elburton. Left at 2nd r/about, ground 50 yards left.
Colours: Red/white/black
Change colours: Yellow/blue/white.

IVYBRIDGE TOWN

Secretary: Garfield Goodwin, 36 Longwood Close, Plympton, Plymouth PL7 2HD (01752 344364)
Ground: Erme Playing Fields, Ivybridge (01752 892584).
Directions: Coming from Plymouth on A38 take Ivybridge turn, double back over A38 and take 1st left - ground entrance quarter mile on right after Industrial Estate.
Colours: Yellow/green/yellow
Change colours: Red & white/black/red & black

NEWTON ABBOT

Secretary: Mr Roy Perkins, 21 Prospect Terrace, Newton Abbot, Devon, TQ12 2LN (01626 61596).
Ground: The Playing Fields, Coach Rd, Newton Abbot (01626 335011).
Directions: Half mile off the Torquay Road leading to Newton Abbot centre, past Ford Park tennis courts.
Colours: Red & black/black/black
Change colours: Black & white/white/white
Hons: Devon Co. Lg 93-94 (R-up 92-93, Lg Cup 92-93), Devon Prem. Cup R-up 82-83 87-88 (Snr Cup R-up 90-91.

NEWTON ABBOTT SPURS

Secretary: Mark Hayman, 9 Shapley Way, Liverton, Newton Abbott TQ12 6PN (01626 821839)
Ground: Recreation Ground, Newton Abbott (01626 65343)
Directions: After racecourse take 1st exit at next roundabout, 200 yards turn right at signpost Rec Trust.
Colours: Blue/white/blue
Change Colours: Red/black/red

NEWTON St CYRES

Secretary: Roger Dymond, 12 New Estate, Newton St Cyres, Devon (01392 851719).
Ground: The Recreation Ground, Station Rd, Newton St Cyres, (01392 851546). **Directions:** A377 from Exeter towards Crediton, on reaching Newton Cyres proceed to village centre, turn right (signposted station) - grd 1/2 mile on right.
Colours: Blue & white/blue/blue
Change: Yellow/blue/white **Nickname:** Saints
Hons: Devon Prem Cup 88-89, Snr Cup 74-75, I'med Cup 72-73; Devon & Exeter Lg 88-89 (Cup 88-89), E Devon Snr Cup (4).

OTTERY St MARY

Secretary: Paul Grisedale, 15 The Signals, Feniton, Honiton, Devon EX14 0UP (01404 851059)
Ground: Washbrook Meadows, Butts Road, Ottery St Mary, Devon EX11 1EL (01404 813539).
Directions: From main town square, turn left following road around church, 2nd right into Butts Rd. Or, B3177 to Ottery from A30 Honiton by-pass - ground on left past Otter workshops.
Colours: Blue/blue/white
Change colours: Red/white/red
Nickname: The Otters
Hons: East Devon Snr Cup, Devon & Exeter Lg, Western Lg Div 1 89-90

PLYMOUTH COMMAND FC

Secretary: M.A.Launce, 57 Chaucer Way, Brake Farm, Plymouth, PL5 3EQ, (01752 700168)
Ground: HMS Drake (01752 555257). **Directions:** Follow signs for Naval Base (Weston Mill Entrance), report to gate.
Colours: Red/black/red
Change colours: Yellow & green/green/yellow

PLYMOUTH PARKWAY

Secretary: S Cadmore, 25 Dudley Gdns, Plymouth, Devon PL6 5PE (01752 782661).
Ground: Parkway Sports Club, Tamar Vale, Ernesettle Lane, Plymouth (01752 363080). **Directions:** Take Ernesettle exit off A38 & follow signs to Ernesettle Industrial Estate - ground on right halfway down steep hill.
Colours: Yellow.blue/white
Change: Tangerine/black/tangerine
Hons: Plymouth & Dist. Lg Div 2 90-91 (Div 4 Cup 88-89 (R-up 91-92(res)), Div 3 Cup R-up 89-90 84).

PLYMSTOCK UNITED

Secretary: Dave Baskwill, 334 Fort Austin Avenue, Crownhill, Plymouth PL6 5TG (01752 706284)
Ground: Deans Cross, Plymstock, Plymouth, Devon (01752 406776).
Directions: A38 Ernesettle junc, follow signs for Ind Est. ground half way down hill on right
Colours: All red
Change colours: Black & white/black/black
Nickname: Reds.
Hons: Plymouth & Dist Lg (3), R-up (3); Devon Snr Cup R-up 87-88, Victory Cup (4), R-up (6)

STOKE GABRIEL

Secretary: Barry Prowse, 33 Pilmuir Avenue, Chelston, Torquay TQ2 6AL (01803 606513)
Ground: G J Churchward Mem. Grnd, Broadley Lane, Stoke Gabriel, (01803 78223)
Directions: Turn right into Broadley Lane just before Four Crosses crossroads approaching from Paignton.
Colours: All navy
Change colours: Red & black/black/black
Hons: Devon Premier Cup 93-94 (R-up 91-92), Devon County Lg R-up 93-94, Torbay Herald Cup 83-84 88-89, South Devon Lg 87-88 88-89 (Belli Cip 90-91),

TEIGNMOUTH

Secretary: Mrs M Leggett, 3 Nelson Close, Teignmouth TQ14 9NH (01626 778356)
Ground: Coombe Valley, Lower Combe Lane, Teignmouth, Devon (01626 776688).
Directions: From Newton Abbot: Turn left into Mill Lane 100yds past lights at Shaldon Bridge, right after 100yds into Fourth Ave., 2nd right, car park down hill on left.
Colours: White/black/black
Change colours: Red/black/red
Nickname: Teigns
Hons: Torbay Herald Cup 58-59 79-80 80-81, Sth Western Lg Cup R-up 85-86, Sth Devon Lg Div 1 85-86(res) 89-90, Devon County Lg Cup SF 93-94.

TOPSHAM TOWN

Secretary: Sue Bulled, 207 Topsham Road, Exeter EX2 6EN (01392 421703)
Ground: Coronation Field, Exeter Road, Topsham (01392 873678). **Directions:** B3182 Exeter Topsham Rd, Ground is 3/4 mile after Countess Wear r/about.
Colours: All Blue
Change colours: All red

WESTON MILL OAK VILLA

Secretary: Mr John Davey, 74 Molesworth Road, Plympton, Plymouth, PL7 4NU (01752 348301)
Ground: WMOV Sports Ground, Ferndale Rd, Weston Mill, Plymouth (01752 363352). **Direction:** A38 Devenport junc, at 1st lights turn left, ground 100 yards left.
Colours: Green & black/green/green
Change colours: Red/black/black
Hons: Devon County Lg Cup SF 93-94

WILLAND ROVERS

Secretary/Press Officer: Andrew Jarrett, 2 College Court, Uffculme, Cullompton Devon, EX15 3EQ (01884 841210).
Ground: Silver Street, Willand, nr Cullompton, Devon (01884 33885).
Directions: Ground situated on east side of B3181, halfway between M5 jcts 27 & 28.
Colours: White/black/black
Change colours: All blue
Nickname: Rovers
Hons: Devon Snr Cup 85-86, I'med Cup 66-67; Devon Co. Lg Cup R-up 92-93 93-94, Exeter & Dist. Lg Snr Div 1 70-71, Jnr Div 1 67-68, Div 2 64-65, Div 3 65-66, Prem Lg Cup 79-80; East Devon Snr Cup 72-73 91-92 93-94.

CLUBSAVER HAMPSHIRE LEAGUE

FOUNDED: 1896

Chairman: N White

League Secretary: J Moody, 13 Tadfield Crescent, Romsey Hampshire SO51 5AN (01749 514073)

Division One

		P	W	D	L	F	A	Pts
1	Moneyfields	40	32	3	5	140	37	99
2	AFC Newbury	40	26	6	8	111	41	84
3	Blackfield-Lang.	40	23	5	12	105	56	74
4	Colden Common	40	23	4	13	76	49	73
5	New Street	40	20	7	13	94	57	67
6	Lock's Heath	40	21	3	16	77	55	66
7	Netley Central	40	20	5	15	72	60	65
8	Fleetlands	40	19	7	14	70	56	64
9	Hayling United	40	19	6	15	65	59	63
10	Horndean	40	19	5	16	76	67	62
11	Stockbridge	40	18	8	14	70	75	62
12	Poole Town	40	17	7	16	73	59	58
13	Liss Athletic	40	16	8	16	79	64	56
14	Winchester City	40	17	5	18	59	88	56
15	Bishopstoke	40	13	6	21	56	82	45
16	Pirelli General	40	12	7	21	62	83	43
17	A C Delco FC	40	11	5	24	57	116	38
18	Bass Alton Town	40	10	7	23	58	70	37
19	New Milton	40	10	6	24	43	94	36
20	Malshanger	40	7	7	26	45	156	28
21	Overton United	40	7	3	30	39	103	24

Division Two

		P	W	D	L	F	A	Pts
1	Mayflower	34	25	5	4	86	39	80
2	Brading Town	34	24	6	4	82	37	78
3	Otterbourne	34	22	6	6	83	53	72
4	Yateley Green	34	19	7	8	79	45	64
5	Fleet Spurs	34	19	4	11	69	39	61
6	St Marys	34	17	7	10	78	54	58
7	Tadley	34	16	6	12	67	59	54
8	Hilsea Club	34	14	8	12	83	63	50
9	V Thorneycroft	34	13	5	16	59	73	44
10	Paulsgrove	34	10	11	13	60	58	41
11	Hythe & Dibden	34	10	9	15	47	71	39
12	Esso Fawley	34	10	8	16	43	57	38
13	Verwood Town	34	8	13	13	54	72	37
14	Ludgershall Sp	34	10	6	18	52	70	36
15	Broughton	34	8	8	18	57	66	32
16	Ringwood Town	34	7	9	18	51	69	30
17	B Waltham T	34	6	3	25	50	112	21
18	Hedge End	34	5	5	24	54	117	20

Division Three

		P	W	D	L	F	A	Pts
1	Hamble Club	38	24	7	7	84	37	79
2	Winchester Cstle	38	23	9	6	108	39	78
3	Moneyfields Res	38	22	6	9	104	52	75*
4	AFC Basingstoke	38	21	8	7	76	32	74**
5	Awbridge	38	20	9	9	60	38	69
6	Queens Keep	38	19	8	11	91	55	65
7	Netley Central Rs	38	17	11	10	69	47	62
8	Covies	38	15	14	9	72	51	59
9	W'chester C Rs	38	16	9	13	66	49	57
10	Bass Alton T Rs	38	17	7	14	59	67	57
11	Laverstock-Ford	38	15	9	14	66	65	54
12	Fleetlands Res	38	16	5	15	65	69	50**
13	Four Marks	38	12	8	17	71	68	44*
14	Braishfield	38	12	8	18	43	65	44
15	AFC Aldermaston	38	10	9	19	58	69	39
16	Swanmore	38	11	6	21	47	95	39
17	Overton United	38	11	5	22	43	81	38
18	Basing Rovers	38	8	7	23	55	82	31
19	Compton	38	7	6	25	43	105	27
20	Sherborne St J	38	4	3	31	40	172	15

* Division Three clubs Moneyfields Reserves and AFC Basingstoke are both awarded three points each.
Bass Alton Town Reserves as well as the one point they were deducted earlier in the season were also deducted one goal.
Fleetlands Reserves have three points awarded, six points deducted, and 18 goals deducted.
The asterisks refer to un-played fixtures, hence the points deductions and awards etc.

DIVISION ONE CLUBS 1997-98

A.C. DELCO

Secretary: Brian Cook, 17 Hickory Gardens, West End, Southampton.SO30 3RN (01703 613334)
Ground: AC Delco Spts Ground, Stoneham Lane, Eastleigh (01703 613334).
Colours: Royal Blue & white stripes/black/blue. **Change:** Red & Black stripes/White/Black.
Programme: No **Midweek home matchday:** Wednesday.

AFC NEWBURY

Secretary: Damien Hayden, 10 Nideggen Close, Thatcham, Berkshire RG19 (01635 826540)
Ground: Faraday Road, Newbury.
Colours: Green & white/green/green **Change:** White/navy/white.
Programme: Yes **Midweek home matchday:** Tuesday or Wednesday.

BASS ALTON TOWN

Secretary: A J M Hillman, 19a Beechwood Rd, Alton, Hants GU34 1RL (01420 87103).
Ground: Bass Spts Ground, Anstey Rd, Alton (01420 82465).
Colours: Black & red/black/black **Change:** Blue & Yellow/Blue/Blue.
Programme: No **Midweek home matchday:** Any.

BISHOPSTOKE SOCIAL

Secretary: Tony Boland, 34 Fryern Close, Chandlers Ford, Hants SO50 2LF (01703 262763).
Ground: Chicken Hall Lane, Bishopstoke, Eastleigh, Hants (01860 612038).
Colours: Green & Black/Black/Black. **Change:** All Blue.

BLACKFIELD & LANGLEY

Secretary: Ian Hore, 5 Foxhayes Lane, Blackfield, Southampton, Hants SO45 2QD (01703 893325).
Ground: Gang Warily Rec., Newlands Rd, Blackfield, Southampton, Hants (01703 893603).
Colours: All Green. **Change:** Yellow/blue/blue
Programme: Yes **Midweek home matchday:** Wednesday.

COLDEN COMMON

Secretary: M.Budden, 44 Orchard Close, Colden Common, Winchester, Hampshire.SO21 1ST (01962 713813)
Ground: Colden Common Recreation Ground, Main Road, Colden Common (01962 712365).
Colours: Red & white/black/red **Change:** All yellow
Programme: Yes **Midweek home matchday:** Wednesday.

FLEETLANDS

Secretary: David Bell, 72 White Hart Lane, Portchester, Hants. PO16 9BQ.(01705 321781)
Ground: Lederle Lane, Gosport, Hants (01329 239723).
Colours: Red & black/white/white **Change:** All white.
Programme: Yes **Midweek home matchday:** Any.

HAYLING UNITED

Secretary: Mrs S Westfield, 14 Harold Road, Hayling Island, Hants PO11 9LT (01705 463305).
Ground: Hayling Park, Hayling Island, Hants.
Colours: Red & navy/navy/navy **Change:** Blue & white/blue/blue
Programme: No **Midweek home matchday:** Tuesday.

HORNDEAN

Secretary: Mrs Gladys Berry, 74 Five Heads Road, Horndean PO8 9NZ (01705 591698).
Ground: Five Heads Park, Five Heads Road, Horndean (01705 591363).
Colours: Black & Red/black/black **Change colours:** Navy & white/white/navy.

LISS ATHLETIC

Secretary: W.E.Moseley, 3 Yew Tree Place, Liss, Hants. GU33 7ET (01730 894631)
Ground: Newman Collard PF, Hill Brow Rd, Liss, Hants (01730 894022).
Colours: All Blue & White. **Change:** All yellow
Programme: No **Midweek home matchday:** Thursday.

LOCKSHEATH

Secretary: Michael Harrison, 30 Whitebeam Road, Hedge End, Southampton, Hants. SO30 OPZ (01489 784470)
Ground: Locksheath Rec, Warsash Rd, Titchfield Common, Eastleigh (01489 600932).
Colours: Red/black/black. **Change:** All white

MALSHANGER

Secretary: Fred Norris, 9 Goddards Firs, Oakley, Basingstoke, Hants. RG23 7JL (01256 781697)
Ground: The Sportsfield, Malshanger, Basingstoke (01256 780285).
Colours: Tangerine/Black/Tangerine. **Change:** Purple/Purple/White.
Programme: **Midweek home matchday:** Tuesday.

MONEYFIELDS

Secretary: Peter Shires, 242 Grafton Street, Mile End, Portsmouth, (01705 645813)
Ground: Moneyfields Sports Ground, Moneyfield Avenue, Copnor Road, Portsmouth, Hampshire.
Colours: Yellow/blue/blue. **Change:** Jade & white/jade/jade

NETLEY CENTRAL SPORTS

Secretary: Mr R W Crompton, 47 Station Rd, Netley Abbey, Southampton SO31 5AE (01703 452049).
Ground: Netley Rec, Station Rd, Netley Abbey, Southampton (01703 452267).
Colours: Royal & white/royal/royal **Change:** All red
Programme: Yes **Midweek home matchday:** Wednesday.

NEW MILTON TOWN

Secretary: Malcom Smith, 4 Kestral Drive, Mudeford, Christchurch Dorset BH23 4DE (01425 277565)
Ground: Fawcetts Spts Ground, Christchurch Rd, New Milton, Hants BH25 6QF (01425 628191).
Colours: Yellow & blue/black/yellow **Change:** White/navy/navy.
Programme: Yes **Midweek home matchday:** Wednesday.

NEW STREET

Secretary: Mrs F J Waterman, 'Jorin Bay' 2 Pine Walk, Andover, Hants SP10 3PW (01264 362751)
Ground: Foxcotte Park, Charlton Down, Andover.(01264 358358)
Colours: Green & black/black/green **Change colours:** Red/white/red.
Programme: Yes **Midweek home matchday:** Tuesday or Wednesday.

OVERTON UNITED

Secretary: Mrs A Wheeler, 3 Lordsfield Gardens, Overton, Hants RG25 2EW (01256 771241).
Ground: Recreation Centre, Bridge Street, Overton (01256 770561).
Colours: Blue & white stripes/white/blue **Change:** Green & purple/purple/purple
Programme: No **Midweek home matchday:** Tuesday or Thursday

PETERSFIELD TOWN

Secretary: M Nicholl, 49 Durford Rd, Petersfield, Hants GU31 4ER (01730 300518).
Ground: Love Lane, Petersfield, Hants (01730 233416).
Colours: Red & Black/Black/Black. **Change cols:** White/blue/white
Programme: Yes **Midweek Matches:** Wednesday.

PIRELLI GENERAL

Secretary: Miss Bernice Fox 31 Spring Close, Fair Oak, Eastleigh, Hants SO50 7BB (01703 693537).
Ground: Jubilee Spts Ground, Chestnut Ave., Eastleigh (01703 612721).
Colours: Blue & white/white/white **Change:** Yellow/black/yellow
Programme: Yes **Midweek home matchday:** Tuesday.

POOLE TOWN

Secretary: Bill Read, 15 Addison Close, Romsey, Hants SO51 7TL (01794 517991)
Ground: Petersham Lane, Gants Common, Holt, Wimborne, Dorset (01258 840379)
Colours: Red & white/red/white **Change Colours:** Yellow & black/blue/yellow

STOCKBRIDGE

Secretary: Graham Howard, 1 Moat Cottages, Longstock,Stockbridge, Hants.SO20 6EP (01264 810753)
Ground: The Recreation Ground, High Street, Stockbridge, Hants.
Colours: All red **Change:** All blue

WINCHESTER CITY

Secretary: Geoffrey Cox, 9 Burnetts Gdns, Horton Heath, Eastleigh, Hants SO5 7BY (01703 693021).
Ground: Hillier Way, Abbotts Barton, Winchester (01962 863553).
Colours: Red & white/black/red **Change:** White/green/green

DIVISION TWO CLUBS 1997-98

BISHOPS WALTHAM TOWN

Secretary: Mrs Margaret Weavil, 69 Oak Road, Ridgemede, Bishops Waltham, Hants SO32 1ER (01489 894952)
Ground: Priory Park, School Hill, Bishops Waltham (01489 892179).
Colours: Amber/Black/Black & Amber. **Change:** Blue/Blue/Blue & White.

BRADING TOWN

Secretary: Mick Edmondston, Seawinds, Nunwell St., Sandown.I.O.W. PO36 9DE (01983 404770)
Ground: Vicarage Lane, Brading, Isle of Wight (01983 405217).
Cols: All red. **Change:** All blue **Programme:** Yes

BROUGHTON

Secretary: A R Hammerton, 19 Plough Gdns, Broughton, Stockbridge, Hants SO20 8AF (01794 301495).
Ground: The Sports Field, Buckholt Rd, Broughton, Stockbridge, Hants.
Colours: Blue & white /blue/blue. **Change:** All Green.

ESSO (FAWLEY)
Secretary: Mr A Haws, 40 Hollybank Rd, Hythe, Southampton, Hants SO45 5FQ (01703 843402).
Ground: Esso Recreation Club, Long Lane, Holbury, Southampton, Hant (01705 893750).
Colours: White/blue/red **Change:** Red/white/white

FLEET SPURS
Secretary: C R Filkins, 5 Byron Close, Fleet, Hants GU13 9QD (01252 627385).
Ground: Ancells Farm, Fleet, Hants.
Colours: Red & black/black/red **Change:** Blue or green or purple/turqu/white.

HEDGE END
Secretary: M J Oliver, 25 Blossom Close, Botley, Southampton, Hants SO3 2FR (01489 786308).
Ground: Norman Ridaway Playing Fields, Heathouse Lane, Hedge End, Southampton.
Colours: Black & white/black/black **Change:** Blue & white/blue/blue.

HILSEA CLUB
Secretary: Mr Terry Harwood, 147 Manners Rd, Southsea, Hants PO4 0BD (01705 785140).
Ground: Portsmouth Sailing Centre, Eastern Rd, Portsmouth PO3 5LY (01705 670119).
Colours: Yellow/blue/white **Change:** Blue/blue/white

HYTHE & DIBDEN
Secretary: Mr A Moyst, 105 Hobart Drive, Hythe, Southampton, Hants SO40 6FD (01703 847335).
Ground: Ewart Rec Ground, Jones Lane, Hythe, Southampton (01703 845264 - matchdays only).
Colours: Green/green/yellow **Change:** Blue & white stripes/blue/black.

LUDGERSHALL SPORTS CLUB
Secretary: Steve Winstone, 57 Wood Park, Ludgershall, Andover, Hants SP11 9NS (01264 791193).
Ground: Astor Cres., Ludgershall (01264 398200).
Change Colours: Yellow/green/green **Colours:** All maroon

MAYFLOWER
Secretary: Mr C J Papadatos, 5 Albion Close, Porchester, Fareham, Hants PO16 9EW (01329 510623)
Ground: Clarence Gardens, Southsea (01705 824246 - FAX 01705 727273)
Colours: Blue & black stripes/black/black **Change:** Yellow & green/green/yellow

NOMADS
Secretary: Ken Walker, 5 Panton Close, Emsworth, Hants PO10 7XW (01243 379141)
Ground: Farlington Sports Ground, Eastern Road, Farlington
Colours: Red & black hoops

OTTERBOURNE
Secretary: R J Broom, 249 Passfield Rd, Eastleigh, Hants SO5 5DE (01703 328992).
Ground: Oakwood Park, off Oakwood Ave., Otterbourne (01962 714681).
Colours: Red/white/red & white **Change:** Blue & white/blue/blue.

PAULSGROVE
Secretary: S J Cox, 22 Alameda Road, Purbrook, Waterlooville, Hants. PO7 5HD (01705 785110)
Ground: The Grove Club, Marsden Rd (off Allaway Avenue), Paulsgrove, Portsmouth (01705 324102).
Colours: Red & black stripes/black/red **Change:** Blue & white/blue/black

PORTSMOUTH CITY

RINGWOOD TOWN
Secretary: Mrs S Crewe, 278 Windham Rd, Bournemouth, Dorset BH1 4QU (01202 398975).
Ground: Long Lane, Ringwood, Hants (01425 473448).
Colours: Red & white stripes/black/red **Change:** All blue

TADLEY
Secretary: Mike Miller, Meadow View, West Heath, Baughurst, Hants RG26 5LE (01256 850700).
Ground: The Green, Tadley, Hants.
Colours: Blue & maroon stripes/maroon/maroon **Change:** Yellow/blue/blue

VERWOOD TOWN
Secretary: Mrs J A Fry, 19a Noon Hill Rd, Verwood, Dorset BH31 7DB (01202 822826).
Ground: Pottern Park, Pottern Way, Verwood, Dorset.
Colours: All red **Change:** All blue

VOSPER THORNYCROFT
Secretary: Peter Prin, 454 Bursledon Road, Sholing, Southampton, Hants. SO19 8QQ (01703 403829)
Ground: Vosper Thornycroft Spts Ground, Portsmouth Rd, Sholing, Southampton (01489 403829).
Colours: All royal **Change:** Red & black/black/black

YATELEY GREEN
Secretary: Alan Baynes, 7 Borderside, Yateley, Camberley Surrey GU17 7LJ
Ground: Yateley Recreation Ground, Reading Road, Yateley, Camberley, Surrey
Colours: Green/black/black **Change:** Red/black/black

NUCLEAR ELECTRIC KENT COUNTY LEAGUE

President: Bill Manklow

Chairman: C T C Windiate

Press Officer: J C Mugridge, 14 Cherry Tree Road Tunbridge Wells, Kent TN2 5QA (01892 521578)

A total of seven teams resigned from the League during the 1996-97 season, first to go were Bishopsbourne Reserves who went immediately after the Annual General Meeting. However Rye United Reserves had made a late application and were accepted into the competition. Nomads were next then Knockholt, Aylesford, Swanscombe United, Platt United Reserves and Maidstone United (96) Reserves followed close behind leaving a number of Divisions depleted. Teynham & Lynsted, AFC Egerton, Sevenoaks Town and Thames Polytechnic all took part in the Kent Senior Trophy and both AFC Egerton and Sevenoaks progressed to the second round, AFC Egerton with a 4-1 win over Folkestone Invicta and Sevenoaks winning 4-0 against Thames Poly. Sevenoaks' rejoicing was short lived as they were eliminated from the competition as a result of playing an ineligible player. AFC Egerton's opponents in round two were the all conquering Herne Bay and it is to their credit that they only went out by the odd goal in three in a match lost in the last twenty minutes at Herne Bay. Unfortunately the competition is unlikely to see as many, if any sides, included in the Kent Senior Trophy in future as the Kent County Football Association has ruled that clubs' facilities must be of a standard appropriate for the Competition. A decision that has disappointed the winners of the Kent Intermediate Challenge Shield, the Premier Division of the Kent County League and the winners of Group A of the Kent Junior Cup. Lydd Town made it to the final of the Kent Intermediate Challenge Shield only to be beaten 3-2 in extra time at Tunbridge Wells by AFC Blackheath. Bearsted winners of Division One West showed that they will be a force to be reckoned with next season when they beat Milton Athletic, third in the Premier Division, by 2-1, again in extra time in the Inter Regional Challenge Cup. Simon Walsh and Brian Palmer in the closing minutes of extra time scored for Bearsted with Mark Clements netting for Milton. Two Western based sides worth a mention are Second Division Otford United and Third Division Wickham Park. Otford won their Division in the last few games ousting Hawkenbury who had been at in first place for most of the season and then went on to win Group A of the Kent Junior Cup. Wickham Park not only won their Division losing only one game on the way and scoring exactly 100 goals but also took the West Kent Challenge Shield from the holders First Division Phoenix Sports when they beat them 2-1 at Chatham. Whereas the most successful club in the Eastern Section was Rye United, with the first team winning Division One, the Les Leckie Cup and the Weald of Kent Charity Cup with their reserves being beaten finalists in the Eastern Junior Cup.

Premier Division sides VCD Athletic and Knatchbull applied for senior status and the Winstonlead Kent League during the season. Both these clubs worked hard on their grounds and facilities and in a very short timescale achieved a standard which earned them senior status. With the pyramid of football now activated between the two Leagues VCD, having won the Premier Division, had their application to the Winstonlead Kent League accepted. However, Knatchbull despite all their efforts ended in the bottom two of the Premier Division and their application to join the Winstonlead Kent League was not supported by either League.

The competition had a first when three of its lady referees, Linda Bailey, Anne Smart and Karen Ford, were appointed to Broomfield United and University of Kent last October. This created much media interest and many of you will have seen the ladies on Meridian Tonight being interviewed by Geoff Clarke - what you won't have seen is Geoff Clarke conducting the interview in his stockinged feet!

Four teams Beauwater, Snodland, Bearsted and Rye United applied to join the Premier Division but only the top team in First Division East and West are normally promoted and this year was no exception with both Rye United and Bearsted, who will be ground sharing with Oakwood, being promoted.

At the Leagues' Annual General Meeting held on Monday 16 June, Otford United FC scooped prize money of £400. Their first team won £100 and the Reserves £50 for having good disciplinary records in their Divisions and the first team added a further £250 for having the best disciplinary record in the whole of the League. This also won them the Fair Play award and to complete their evening Manager Dave Dugay won the Aford Manager of the Year Award. Other Clubs in the money were Platt United, Bishopsbourne, Broomfield United Reserves, Wickham Park, Stansfeld Oxford & Bermondsey Club Reserves, and Chislehurst who all won £100 each. Winners of £50 each were New Romney, Halstead, Walmer Rovers, Leaves Green and Bearsted Rovers.

New Clubs elected into the Competition are AFC Blackheath from the South London Alliance, Smarden from the Maidstone League, Brenchley Wanderers from the Tonbridge League, Guru Nanak from the Gravesend League and Larkfield and New Hythe from the Maidstone League. Two new reserve sides have come into the competition which are Old Bexlians Reserves and Halls Reserves.

John Mugridge, Press Officer, indicated his intention to resign during the season and Mrs Julie Connan has taken over from him, all other officers were re-elected en bloc.

CLUB DIRECTORY 1997-98

Premier & Division One East & West

A.C. EGERTON

Secretary: Mr D Pask, 1 Lewis Cottages, Leydenhatch Lane, Swanley, Kent BR8 7PU (01322 669539)
Ground: St Marys Cray Rec Grd, Park Rd, St Marys Cray **Founded:** 1971
Colours: Royal/royal/white **Change Colours:** Green & white/white/green & white

A.F.C. BLACKHEATH

Secretary: Dave Wilson, 74 Shroffold Road, Bromley, Kent BR1 5PF (0181 698 1192)
Ground: Huntsman Sports, Manor Way, Blackheath, London SE3 (0181 852 3602) **Founded:** 1983
Colours: All red **Change Colours:** Green/navy/navy

AYLESFORD PAPER MILL

Secretary: Mrs L Casey, 41 Cobdown Close, Ditton, Aylesford, Kent ME20 6SZ (01732 849476)
Ground: Cobdown, Station Road, Ditton, Nr Maidstone (01622 717771) **Founded:** 1979
Colours: Black & white/black/black **Change Colours:** Red green yellow

BEARSTED

Secretary: J Scannel, 24 Fauchons Lane, Bearsted, Maidstone, Kent ME14 4AH (01622 739072)
Ground: Honey Lane, Otham, Maidstone. (0860 302086) **Founded:** 1895
Colours: White/blue/blue **Change Colours:** Navy & green/navy/navy

BEAUWATER

Secretary: Mr R Taylor, 24 Sun Lane, Gravesend, Kent DA12 5HG (01474 332208)
Ground: Beauwater Leisure Club, Nelson Road, Northfleet (01474 336456) **Founded:** 1927
Colours: Yellow & blue/blue/blue **Change Colours:** Navy & red/navy/red

BISHOPSBOURNE

Secretary: Colin Smith, 39 Bridge Down, Bridge, Canterbury, Kent CT4 5AZ (01227 830537)
Ground: Canteen Meadow, The Street, Bishopsbourne, Nr Canterbury, Kent **Founded:** 1963
Colours: Royal/white/royal & white **Change Colours:** Red & white/black/black

BROMLEY GREEN

Secretary: Mr Haig Miles, 34 Crundale Close, Ashford, Kent TN23 2RP (01233 631354 B)
Ground: The Swan Centre, South Willesborough, Ashford, Kent **Founded:** 1930
Colours: All green **Change Colours:** White/green/green

BROOMFIELD UNITED

Secretary: Mr R Cork, Flat 17, Francis Court, 117 High Street, Herne Bay, Kent CT6 5LA (01227 742480)
Ground: Bridge Rec Ground, Patrixbourne Road, Bridge, Nr Canterbury **Founded:** 1925
Colours: Azure & black/black/black & azure) **Change Colours:** Red/red/white

Ex BLUES

Secretary: Mr M Harvey, 29 Crown Lane, Bromley, Kent, BR2 9PG (0181 464 4815)
Ground: Coney Hall, Recreation Ground, Church Drive, Coney Hall, Hayes, Kent **Founded:** 1945
Colours: Yellow & blue/blue/blue **Change Colours:** Red & black/black/black

EYNESFORD

Secretary: Mr E Walking, 76 Pollyhaugh, Eynesford, Nr Dartford, Kent DA4 0HF (01322 863673)
Ground: Harrow Meadow, Rear of Castle Hotel, Bower Lane, off Eynesford High Street. **Founded:** 1894
Colours: Black & white/black/black **Change Colours:** All purple

GREENWAYS

Secretary: Mr W Miller, 14 Cygnet Gardens, Northfleet, Kent DA11 7DN (01474 560913)
Ground: Beauwater Leisure Centre, Nelson Road, Northfleet, (01474 359222) **Founded:** 1965
Colours: All green **Change Colours:** Orange/black/orange

HAWKENBURY

Secretary: Malcolm Foy, 2 Chieveley Drive, Tunbridge Wells, Kent TN2 5HF (01892 533679)
Ground: Hawkenbury Rec Ground, Hawkenbury Rd, Tunbridge Wells. **Founded:** 1919
Colours: Amber/black/black **Change Colours:** Blue & black/black/black

IDEN

Secretary: Mr G Say, 18 Parkwood, Iden, Rye, East Sussex TN31 7XE (01797 280495)
Ground: Iden Playing Field, Iden, Rye, East Sussex **Founded:** 1965
Colours: Tangerine/white/tangerine **Change Colours:** Black & white/black/black

KENNINGTON

Secretary: Kevin Hayden, 33 Grosvenor Road, Kennington, Ashford, Kent TN24 9PA (01233 627826)
Ground: Kennington Cricket Club Pav. Ulley Road, Kennington, Ashford, Kent **Founded:** 1888
Colours: Yellow & sky/yellow/yellow **Change Colours:** Red/black/black

KNATCHBULL

Secretary: Mr D Howle, 13 Charminster, Washford Farm, Ashford, Kent TN23 2UH (01233 611207)
Ground: Hatch Park, Off A20, Mersham, Nr Ashford, (01585 663171) **Founded:** 1981
Colours: Claret & blue/white/white **Change Colours:** All white

LYDD TOWN & Reserves

Secretary: Mr P Sisley, 21 The Fairway, Littlestone, Romney Marsh, Kent TN28 8PJ, (01797 366101)
Ground: The Rype, Manor Road, Lydd. **Founded:** 1885
Colours: Red & green/green/green **Change Colours:** All green

MAIDSTONE UNITED

Secretary: Mr G Gray, 6 Morella Walk, Lenham, Maidstone, Kent ME17 2JX (01622 859964)
Ground: The Athletic Ground, London Road, Maidstone. **Founded:** 1992
Colours: Gold/black/black **Change Colours:** Blue & white/white/blue

MILTON ATHLETIC

Secretary: Mr P Duffin, 18 Hales Road, Tunstall, Sittingbourne, Kent ME10 1SR (01795 471260)
Ground: UK Paper Sports Ground, Gore Court Road, Sittingbourne, Kent **Founded:** 1926
Colours: White & navy/navy/navy **Change Colours:** Red & white/black/black

NEW ROMNEY

Secretary: Mr D Masters, 44 Fernbank Cres, Folkstone, Kent CT19 5SF (01303 253961)
Ground: Station Road, New Romney **Founded:** 1895
Colours: All blue **Change Colours:** Yellow/blue/blue

OAKWOOD

Secretary: Mr P Mannering, 24 Ellenswood Close, Otham, Maidstone Kent ME15 8SG (01622 862482)
Ground: Honey Lane, Otham, Maidstone **Founded:** 1924
Colours: All Red **Change Colours:** White/black/black

OTFORD UNITED

Secretary: Mrs M Smith, 13 Rye Lane, Otford, Kent TN14 5LU (01959 522927)
Ground: Otford Recreation Ground, High Street, Otford, Kent **Founded:** 1900
Colours: Amber/black/amber **Change Colours:** Blue/green/yellow

PHOENIX SPORTS

Secretary: Mr M Cole, 91 Hurst Road, Northumberland Heath, Erith, Kent DA8 3EW (01322 350750)
Ground: Phoenix Sports Club, Mayplace Road East, Bexleyheath, Kent DA7 6JT **Founded:** 1935
Colours: Red & white/black/red **Change Colours:** Yellow/black/black

RUSTHALL

Secretary: Mr M Mace, 28 Allan Close, Rusthall, Tunbridge Wells, Kent TN4 8PL (01892 540634)
Ground: Jockey Farm, Nellington Road, Rusthall, Tunbridge Wells **Founded:** 1899
Colours: All green **Change Colours:** Blue & marron/blue & marron/blue

RYE UNITED

Secretary: Mr B Goodsell, 15 Spring Hill, Northian, Nr Rye, East Sussex TN31 6PX (01797 253028)
Ground: Sydney Allnut Pav. Rye Cricket & Football Salts, Rye, East Sussex **Founded:** 1938
Colours: White & red & black/black/white **Change Colours:** Yellow/blue/yellow

SEVENOAKS TOWN

Secretary: Mr E Diplock, 23 Holly Bush Lane, Sevenoaks, Kent TN13 3TH (01732 454280)
Ground: Greatness Park, Seal Road, Sevenoaks, (01732 741987) **Founded:** 1883
Colours: Azure & black/azure & black/black **Change Colours:** Navy & scarlet/navy/navy

SNODLAND

Secretary: Mr T Reeves, 136 Townsend Road, Snodland, Kent ME6 5RN (01634 240076)
Ground: Potyn's Field, Paddlesworth Road, Snodland **Founded:** 1940
Colours: Sky & navy/sky/sky **Change Colours:** White/royal/royal

SNOWDOWN COLLIERY WELFARE

Secretary: Ernest Travers, 21 Bell Grove, Aylesham, Kent CT3 3AT (01304 842680)
Ground: Spinney Lane, Aylesham, Canterbury CT3 3AF **Founded:** 1907
Colours: Black & white/black/black **Change Colours:** All green

St MARGARETS

Secretary: Mr W Hay, 28 The Freedown, St Margarets at Cliffe, Nr Dover, Kent CT15 6BD (01304 852386)
Ground: The Alexander Field, Kingsdown Road, St Margarets at Cliffe, Nr Dover **Founded:** 1993
Colours: Yellow & black/black/black **Change Colours:** Blue & black/black/black

STANSFELD OXFORD & BERMONDSEY CLUB

Secretary: Mr E Ellis, 40 Tilbrook Road, Kidbrooke, London SE3 9QE (0181 319 0903)
Ground: St James Squash & Leisure Club, 35 Marvels Lane, Grove Park, SE12. **Founded:** 1897
Colours: Yellow/blue/yellow **Change Colours:** All red

SUTTON ATHLETIC

Secretary: Mr J Willis, 6 Somerset Road, Dartford, Kent DA1 3DP (01322 222540)
Ground: The Roaches, Parsonage Lane, Sutton at Hone, Nr Dartford. **Founded:** 1904
Colours: Yellow & green/green/green **Change Colours:** All red

TENTERDEN ST MICHAELS UNITED

Secretary: Mr S Stevens, Kent House, Ashford Road, St Michaels, Tenterden, Kent TN30 6PY (01580 762703)
Ground: Recreation Ground, Tenterden High Street, Tenterden **Founded:** 1890
Colours: Blue & white/blue/blue **Change Colours:** Red & white/white/red

TEN EM BEE

Secretary: Mrs Maureen Deacon, 29 Stembridge Road, Anerley, London SE20 7UE (0181 778 9455)
Ground: Old Bromley Road Playing Fields, Old Bromley Rd, Downham BR1 4JY **Founded:** 1975
Colours: All blue & gold **Change Colours:** Yellow/blue/blue

TEYNHAM & LYNSTED

Secretary: Mr C Page, 2 Foxgrove, Milton Regis, Sittingbourne, Kent ME10 2DW (01795 426675)
Ground: Central Park, Eurolink Way, Sittingbourne. **Founded:** 1961
Colours: Yellow & blue/blue/yellow **Change Colours:** White/black/black

THAMES POLYTECHNIC

Secretary: Mrs S Jarvis, 31 Monkton Road, Welling, Kent DA16 3JU (0181 854 5509)
Ground: Thames Polytechnic, Kidbrooke Lane, Eltham, London SE9 **Founded:** 1888
Colours: Green & yellow/green/yellow **Change Colours:** All blue

UNIVERSITY OF KENT

Secretary: Mrs I Simmonds, Sports Federation, Sports Centre, University of Kent Canterbury, Kent CT2 7NL
Ground: The Playing Fields, University of Kent, Canterbury **Founded:** 1967
Colours: Black & white/black/black **Change Colours:** Red & black/black/black

WALMER ROVERS

Secretary: Bernard Skinner, 131 Downs Road, Deal, Kent CT14 7TF (01304 361832)
Ground: Marke Wood Recreation Ground, Dover Road, Walmer. **Founded:** 1959
Colours: All blue **Change Colours:** All red

WESTERHAM

Secretary: Mr D Sayers, 16A The Green, Westerham, Kent TN16 1AX (01959 563163)
Ground: King George V Playing Fields, Costells Meadow, Westerham **Founded:** 1888
Colours: Red/black/black **Change Colours:** Green/black/black

WOONESBOROUGH

Secretary: Mr G Hunt, Hillcross Farm, Eastry, Sandwich, Kent CT13 0NY (01304 611311)
Ground: Hillborough, Woodnesborough Road, Eastry **Founded:** 1962
Colours: Red/black/black **Change Colours:** All blue

SOUTH WESTERN FOOTBALL LEAGUES

Final League Tables 1996-97

SOMERSET SENIOR LEAGUE

Premier Division	P	W	D	L	F	A	Pts
1 Street	34	23	9	2	77	26	78
2 Westland Utd	34	19	7	8	64	31	64
3 Portishead	34	19	6	9	66	36	63
4 Shirehampton	34	18	9	7	65	52	63
5 Nailsea United	34	19	5	10	64	38	62
6 Clevedon Utd	34	17	8	9	62	44	59
7 Fry's Club	34	16	7	11	74	54	55
8 Bridgwater T Rs	34	15	9	10	71	48	54
9 Burnham Utd	34	15	7	12	64	44	52
10 Peasedown Ath	34	14	7	13	56	43	49
11 Brislington	34	13	7	14	61	51	46
12 Hengrove Ath	34	13	3	18	52	60	42
13 Shepton Mallet T	34	10	9	15	56	48	39
14 Longwell Grn A	34	9	10	15	38	55	37
15 Wells City	34	9	6	19	54	55	33
16 Winscombe	34	9	5	20	38	67	32
17 Clevedon Town	34	9	4	21	45	69	31
18 Keynsham Cr	34	0	0	34	18	203	0

Second Division	P	W	D	L	F	A	Pts
1 Worle	34	26	3	5	107	28	81
2 Timsbury Ath	34	23	5	6	104	29	74
3 Watchet Town	34	23	4	7	78	32	73
4 Cleeve West Tn	34	18	6	10	75	31	60
5 Larkhall Ath Res	34	17	9	8	71	53	60
6 Cheddar	34	19	3	12	78	62	60
7 Long Ashton	34	17	5	12	69	43	56
8 Paulton Rvrs Rs	34	15	5	14	46	44	50
9 Hengrove Ath Rs	34	11	8	15	55	77	41
10 Welton Rvrs Res	34	11	5	18	64	80	38
11 Keynsham T Res	34	11	4	19	42	69	37
12 Frome Tn Res	34	10	7	17	52	82	37
13 Clandown	34	7	15	12	43	66	36
14 Blackbrook	34	10	6	18	54	83	35*
15 Glastonbury Rs	34	11	5	18	49	78	35*
16 Shepton M Tn Rs	34	9	7	18	52	85	34
17 Churchill Club 70	34	6	7	21	45	103	25
18 Wells City Res	30	8	4	22	38	87	21*

* Blackbrook one point deducted;
Glastonbury Reserves three points deducted;
Wells City Reserves seven points deducted.

First Division	P	W	D	L	F	A	Pts
1 Radstock Town	34	24	8	2	70	30	80
2 Imperial FC	34	19	8	7	61	38	65
3 Weston St John	34	18	5	11	64	49	59
4 Robinsons	34	15	13	6	60	37	58
5 Portishead Res	34	14	11	9	55	42	53
6 Ilminster Town	34	16	5	13	66	54	53
7 Long Sutton	34	12	10	12	50	56	46
8 Castle Cary	34	12	9	13	61	55	45
9 Stockwood Grn	34	11	11	12	49	43	44
10 Odd Down Res	34	12	8	14	58	60	44
11 Weston S M R-	34	13	6	15	46	49	44*
12 Westland Utd Rs	34	11	10	13	49	63	43
13 Backwell Utd Rs	34	11	9	14	52	57	42
14 Bristol M Fm Rs	34	12	4	18	49	65	40
15 Bishop Sutton Rs	34	10	8	16	56	68	38
16 Saltford	34	11	5	18	48	70	38
17 Congresbury	34	7	7	20	33	59	28
18 Mangotsfield U R	34	7	5	22	37	68	26

* One point deducted

Third Division	P	W	D	L	F	A	Pts
1 Clevedon U Res	34	22	7	5	94	37	73
2 P'sedown Ath Rs	34	21	8	5	95	38	71
3 Nailsea Utd Res	34	21	7	6	107	45	70
4 Burnham Utd Rs	34	21	6	7	91	40	69
5 Wrington-Redhill	34	19	9	6	94	54	66
6 Robinsons Res	34	18	5	11	76	60	59
7 Tunley Athletic	34	17	7	10	82	63	58
8 Dundry Ath '82	34	17	2	15	95	80	53
9 St George E in G	34	13	8	13	63	53	47
10 Fry's Club Res	34	14	5	15	75	90	47
11 Yatton Athletic	34	11	10	13	83	70	43
12 Banwell	34	10	8	16	58	67	38
13 Clotton	34	11	5	18	58	95	38
14 Temple Cloud	34	10	6	18	48	81	36
15 Nailsea Town	34	9	4	21	53	82	30
16 Weston St J Rs	34	5	8	21	60	95	23
17 Imperial FC Rs	34	5	8	21	32	103	23
18 Cheddar Res	34	5	1	28	31	143	16

BRISTOL PREMIER COMBINATION

Premier Division	P	W	D	L	F	A	Pts
1 Winterbourne U	30	23	4	3	95	35	73
2 Hambrook	30	23	1	6	79	31	70
3 Sun Life	30	21	3	6	106	59	66
4 Highridge United	30	18	3	9	81	48	57
5 R O St George	30	15	7	8	77	49	52
6 Hartcliffe	30	15	5	10	63	47	50
7 Sea Mills Park	30	12	7	11	55	50	43
8 St Philips MAS	30	13	6	11	57	51	42*
9 Nicholas Wndrs	30	11	6	13	45	65	39
10 Bristol 5 O B	30	10	7	13	59	64	37
11 Haynes Roofing	30	10	7	13	59	69	37
12 Thornbury Town	30	11	3	16	59	60	36
13 Longwell Grn Sp	30	8	6	16	59	70	30
14 Hanham Athletic	30	6	7	17	30	70	25
15 Iron Acton	30	3	1	26	40	116	10
16 Shibury Crusade	30	2	5	23	31	104	9

* Three points deducted

Division One	P	W	D	L	F	A	Pts
1 Hallen Res	30	19	5	6	75	35	62
2 Olveston Utd	30	18	6	6	68	30	60
3 Lawrence Rvrs	30	18	6	6	92	62	60
4 Urban Windows	30	13	10	7	47	44	49
5 Greyfriars Ath	30	13	5	12	69	62	44
6 AEK Rangers	30	13	3	14	57	57	42
7 DRG (FP) Res	30	11	8	11	56	63	41
8 Bristol Union	30	11	6	13	51	71	39
9 Pucklech Sp Rs	30	10	8	12	36	42	38
10 Billfields O B	30	11	4	15	54	56	37
11 Henbury O B Rs	30	10	7	13	50	63	37
12 Crosscourt Utd	30	9	9	12	41	51	36
13 Shirehampton Rs	30	11	3	16	54	77	36
14 Bristol University	30	10	3	17	66	71	33
15 Chipping S'bury	30	9	4	17	49	61	31
16 Staplehill	30	7	7	16	32	55	28

'SKURRAYS' WILTSHIRE LEAGUE

Division One

		P	W	D	L	F	A	Pts
1	Shrewton Utd	22	14	3	5	38	16	45
2	Corsham Town	22	14	2	6	49	22	44
3	Aldbourne	22	10	5	7	30	28	35
4	Devizes Town Rs	22	8	8	6	38	28	32
5	Biddestone	22	10	2	10	32	23	32
6	Bradford Town	22	7	10	5	22	22	31
7	Tisbury United	22	8	6	8	35	35	30
8	Southbrook Wal.	22	7	8	7	27	25	29
9	Wroughton	22	7	8	7	33	37	29
10	Melksham Tn Rs	22	6	10	6	34	34	28
11	Purton Res	22	5	1	16	22	59	16
12	Burmah Castrol	22	2	5	15	23	52	11
13	Sanford	Resigned Record - Expunged						

Division Two

		P	W	D	L	F	A	Pts
1	Raychem	27	21	1	5	70	24	64
2	Marlborough Tn	27	15	7	5	48	28	52
3	Malmesbury Vics	27	14	4	9	53	38	46
4	Warminster T Rs	27	13	6	8	38	27	45
5	Chippenham T R	27	10	11	6	49	30	41
6	G P S	27	12	5	10	45	41	41
7	Dunbar Athletic	27	12	4	11	66	49	40
8	Bromham	27	6	7	14	40	52	25
9	Amesbury T Res	27	2	7	18	30	79	13
10	Pewsey Vale Rs	27	3	2	22	20	91	11

BIDEFORD TOOL LEAGUE

Premier Division

		P	W	D	L	F	A	Pts
1	Shamwickshire	34	27	3	4	153	48	84
2	Fremington	34	27	3	4	146	44	84
3	Braunton	34	22	4	8	100	32	70
4	Bradworthy	34	19	6	9	76	52	63
5	Appledora/BAAC	34	18	9	7	54	38	63
6	Ilfracombe	34	18	8	8	83	42	62
7	Combe Martin	34	17	8	9	90	56	59
8	Barnstaple AAC	34	14	5	15	70	71	47
9	Torrington Admrls	34	12	7	15	61	77	43
10	Torrington Res	34	12	7	15	58	77	43
11	Morwenstow	34	12	6	16	63	80	42
12	Kilkhampton	34	10	8	16	63	98	38
13	Holsworthy Res	34	8	10	16	58	73	34
14	Chittlehampton	34	8	8	18	45	75	32
15	Putford	34	10	1	23	45	94	31
16	Georgeham	34	8	5	21	61	104	29
17	Northam Lions	34	7	3	24	40	79	24
18	Dolton	34	5	3	26	30	153	18

Premier Division

		P	W	D	L	F	A	Pts
1	South Molton	30	23	5	2	142	29	74
2	Braunton FP	30	23	4	3	106	32	73
3	Lynton-Lynmouth	30	21	5	4	103	50	68
4	Shebbear	30	20	4	6	81	29	64
5	Golden Lion	30	17	5	4	90	48	56
6	Ebberley Arms	30	13	4	13	65	59	43
7	Mortehoe	30	14	1	15	83	88	43
8	Bridgerule	30	12	4	14	38	61	40
9	Bratton Fleming	30	12	2	16	75	91	38
10	Combe Martin	30	12	2	16	73	93	38
11	North Molton	30	9	8	13	65	81	35
12	Appledore BAAC	30	9	4	17	59	78	31
13	Bradworthy	30	9	2	19	39	88	29
14	Bude	30	7	7	16	57	78	28
15	Hartland	30	3	6	21	44	119	14
16	Rolle Quay	30	1	5	24	32	130	8

TAUNTON SUNDAY LEAGUE

Division One

		P	W	D	L	F	A	Pts
1	Staplegrove	20	12	1	2	88	24	52
2	Bathpool	20	11	4	5	45	29	37
3	Wagon Rock	20	11	4	5	59	44	37
4	Kings Arms	20	11	1	8	72	60	34
5	Deane Rangers	20	10	3	7	54	48	33
6	Britania Inn	20	8	3	9	54	58	27
7	TYCC	20	8	3	9	34	46	27
8	Clavel	20	7	3	10	50	51	24
9	B/Lydeard	20	7	2	11	49	71	23
10	Milverton	20	3	5	12	39	83	14
11	Wiveliscombe	20	1	3	18	16	75	6

Division Two

		P	W	D	L	F	A	Pts
1	Linden City	18	12	1	5	57	23	37
2	Westgate	18	11	2	5	45	26	35
3	Kings Utd	18	11	2	5	43	31	35
4	Kings Pk Rngrs	18	9	2	7	40	42	29
5	Blackbrook	18	8	1	9	37	37	25
6	Ash Rangers	18	7	2	9	30	42	23
7	Alma Sparta	18	6	3	9	31	40	21
8	Crown & Sc	18	6	2	10	28	52	20
9	Williton Rkts	18	6	3	10	28	37	18
10	Sampford Blues	18	6	2	11	38	49	17

Division Three

		P	W	D	L	F	A	Pts
1	Curry Rivel	22	21	1	0	121	27	64
2	Norton Fitz.	22	16	3	3	90	28	51
3	W/S Wanderers	22	12	1	9	52	61	37
4	Trull Rovers	22	11	1	10	54	58	34
5	Vivery Rovers	22	10	3	8	74	55	33
6	White Lion	22	10	2	10	61	63	32
7	Blues Bros	21	9	3	9	67	64	30
8	Dolphin Inn	22	9	2	11	73	76	29
9	Blue Waves	22	7	4	11	58	72	25
10	Dunster	21	8	0	13	56	63	24
11	Linden Colts	22	2	6	14	37	96	12
12	Red Rock	22	2	2	18	38	118	8

Division Four

		P	W	D	L	F	A	Pts
1	Wyvern Fts	22	20	2	0	138	21	62
2	Albion*	21	17	2	2	149	31	53
3	North Curry	22	14	4	4	58	37	48
4	Ship's Rest	22	12	4	6	65	51	40
5	Inter Royal	22	11	2	9	85	78	35
6	Debenhams	22	9	2	11	71	68	29
7	CS Mariners	22	8	4	10	50	66	24
8	Royal Crown	22	8	2	12	61	83	26
9	Cavalier	22	7	0	15	49	102	21
10	Cherrygrove	22	7	0	15	50	103	21
11	C/Fm Celtic	21	4	3	14	53	99	15
12	Parrton Rgs	22	1	1	20	30	133	4

* Albion disqualified for misconduct

'CORNISH GUARDIAN'
EAST CORNWALL PREMIER LEAGUE

		P	W	D	L	F	A	Pts
1	Nanpean Rovers	36	29	4	3	120	31	91
2	Torpoint Ath Res	36	24	7	5	98	41	79
3	Camelford	36	21	8	7	73	32	71
4	Bodmin Tn Res	36	20	6	10	80	50	66
5	Padstow United	36	19	8	9	89	48	65
6	Saltash Utd Res	36	17	10	9	60	49	61
7	Liskeard Ath Res	36	17	9	10	81	59	60
8	St Blazey	36	18	4	14	63	66	58
9	St Dennis	36	16	8	12	72	57	56
10	Wadebridge T Rs	36	14	6	16	68	64	48
11	Callington Town	36	14	6	16	61	70	48
12	Roche	36	10	12	14	54	59	42
13	Bude Town	36	9	7	20	51	81	34
14	St Cleer	36	8	10	18	55	86	34
15	Bugle	36	8	9	19	32	60	33
16	St Breward	36	7	10	19	30	74	31
17	Foxhole Stars	36	7	7	22	51	106	28
18	St Austell Res	36	8	3	25	43	94	27
19	Sticker	36	5	8	23	35	88	23

'JOLLYS'
CORNWALL COMBINATION

		P	W	D	L	F	A	Pts
1	Perranwell	38	29	5	4	109	48	92
2	Penryn Ath	38	29	4	5	101	23	90
3	Truro City Rs	38	29	2	7	124	42	86
4	St Ives Town	38	28	2	8	99	46	86
5	Helston Ath	38	25	7	6	119	42	82
6	Falmouth Tn Rs	38	22	9	7	102	53	75
7	Penzance Res	38	19	7	12	84	67	64
8	Mousehole	38	18	6	14	63	57	60
9	Newquay Res	38	15	9	14	87	88	54
10	RNAS Culdrose	38	14	8	16	65	76	50
11	St Agnes	38	14	7	17	72	80	49
12	Troon	38	14	5	19	59	86	47
13	Porthleven Res	38	12	6	20	51	73	42
14	Goonhavern	38	11	8	19	58	70	41
15	St Just	38	10	7	21	68	93	37
16	Mullion Res	38	9	10	19	55	89	37
17	Illogan RBL	38	9	7	22	45	97	34
18	Ludgvan	38	7	5	26	54	98	26
19	Pendeen Rovers	38	3	7	28	39	115	16
20	Murazion Blues	38	0	5	33	24	136	5

'JOLLYS'
CORNWALL COMBINATION

HOLDERS: PENRYN ATHLETIC

PRELIMINARY ROUND

Mullion	v	Porthleven	3-1
RNAS Culdrose	v	Illogan RBL	2-0
Penryn Athletic	v	Ludgvan	8-0
Truro City Rs	v	St Agnes	0-0, 2-1

FIRST ROUND

Falmouth Town Rs	v	Mousehole	2-8
Marazion Blues	v	Penzance Reserves	0-1
Perranwell	v	Newquay Reserves	3-2
St Just	v	Troon	3-0
Helston Athletic	v	Pendeen Rovers	10-0
Mullion	v	St Ives Town	2-1
RNAS Culdrose	v	Goonhavern Athletic	2-4
Truro City Res	v	Penryn Athletic	1-2

QUARTER-FINALS

Goonhavern Ath	v	St Just	5-1
Penryn Athletic	v	Helston Athletic	0-1
Mullion	v	Falmouth T R	0-0, 1-1, 0-3
Penzance Res	v	Perranwell	1-5

SEMI-FINALS

Helston Athletic	v	Perranwell	2-3
Falmouth Tn Res	v	Goonhavern Athletic	6-1

FINAL

FALMOUTH TN RS v PERRANWELL 3-0 at Penzance FC

SOUTHERN FOOTBALL LEAGUES

Final League Tables 1996-97

PORTSMOUTH NORTH END LEAGUE

Division One

		P	W	D	L	F	A	Pts
1	Royal British Leg.	12	12	0	0	67	11	36
2	Grant Thornton	12	6	2	4	35	32	20
3	Old Portmuthians	12	5	2	5	29	43	17
4	Kingston Pris. Arr.	12	5	1	6	43	39	16
5	George & Dragon	12	3	5	4	18	20	14
6	Old House at H.	12	4	2	6	25	48	14
7	Old House (Pgve)	12	1	0	11	19	43	3

MEON VALLEY LEAGUE

Division One

		P	W	D	L	F	A	Pts
1	Sportique	16	12	3	1	52	19	39
2	Clanfield	16	12	1	3	60	86	37
3	Fareham Sac. H	16	7	2	7	47	49	23
4	Wickham Utd	16	7	1	8	39	43	22
5	Wickham D'mo	16	6	2	8	48	47	20
6	Soberton W D	16	6	2	8	30	34	20
7	Buccaneer	16	5	4	7	43	37	19
8	CPK	16	5	2	9	42	58	17
9	Inter Noalham	16	3	1	12	31	69	10

WINCHESTER DISTRICT LEAGUE

Division One

		P	W	D	L	GD	Pts
1	King Alfred Yth C	16	12	3	1	40	27
2	Highcliffe	16	11	4	1	31	26
3	Castle Res	16	9	4	3	31	22
4	Hurm Cans	16	7	3	6	2	17
5	Twyford	16	6	4	6	10	16
6	Sutton Scotney	16	6	1	9	-11	13
7	Littleton	16	5	2	9	-12	12
8	Hyde	16	4	1	11	-24	9
9	Compton Res	16	1	0	15	-67	2

TONBRIDGE LEAGUE

Premier Division

		P	W	D	L	F	A	Pts
1	Brenchley Wds	20	19	1	0	97	14	39
2	Town Malling	20	14	3	3	58	27	31
3	Pembury	20	13	3	4	62	26	29
4	Dowgate	20	10	3	7	44	34	23
5	High Brooms Cs	20	10	3	7	45	36	23
6	Atcost	20	9	4	7	43	34	22
7	Woodlands	20	9	4	7	44	56	22
8	Goudhurst	20	5	1	14	44	55	11
9	Horsmorden	20	4	1	15	38	69	9
10	Barden Cardinals	20	2	3	15	29	78	7
11	Blackham Ash	20	0	4	16	27	102	4

KENT BLAXILL ESSEX & SUFFOLK BORDER LEAGUE

Premier Division

		P	W	D	L	F	A	Pts
1	Gas Recreation	30	17	10	3	78	32	61
2	West Bergholt	30	18	7	5	76	32	61
3	Little Oakey	30	17	6	6	71	44	55
4	St Johns (Clac)	30	15	6	9	63	38	51
5	Halstead Tn Res	30	14	9	7	54	41	51
6	Harwich & P Rs	30	14	7	9	52	43	49
7	Long Melford	30	14	5	11	61	41	47
8	Haverhill Res	30	12	8	10	40	34	44
9	Alresford C R	30	11	9	10	50	44	42
10	Rowhedge	30	11	5	14	54	68	38
11	Stowmarket Rs	30	9	8	13	48	47	35
12	Sudbury Wd Rs	30	10	2	18	40	76	32
13	Mistley United	30	8	7	15	39	62	31
14	Dedham O B	30	8	5	17	37	64	29
15	Stanway Rvs Rs	30	7	3	20	35	79	24
16	Felixstowe Res	30	5	4	21	27	80	19

Division One

		P	W	D	L	F	A	Pts
1	Ipswich Wdrs Rs	30	20	4	6	73	32	64
2	Royal London	30	18	9	3	72	34	63
3	Earls Colne	30	17	6	7	81	40	57
4	Kelvedon Social	30	13	11	6	70	35	50
5	Weeley Athletic	30	15	4	11	62	57	49
6	West Bergholt R	30	14	5	11	66	62	47
7	Hadleigh Utd Rs	30	13	6	11	59	58	45
8	Mersea Island	30	11	10	9	42	34	43
9	Sudbury Luc Ath	30	10	10	10	42	37	40
10	Stanway Rovers	30	11	4	15	50	55	37
11	Boxted Lodgers	30	19	3	17	42	62	33
12	Foxash Social	30	9	6	15	40	77	33
13	Bramston CML	30	9	5	16	61	80	32
14	Gas Rec Res	30	7	7	16	53	84	28
15	Silver End	30	7	5	18	51	79	26
16	Cornard Utd Res	30	7	3	20	40	77	

WEST SUSSEX LEAGUE

Premier Division

		P	W	D	L	F	A	Pts
1	Oving Social Club	20	16	3	1	50	18	57
2	Apt Swan	20	16	2	2	51	20	50
3	South Gershed	20	13	3	4	54	24	42
4	North Holmwood	20	9	5	6	45	30	32
5	Cowgold	20	6	6	8	20	30	24
6	Ferring	20	7	3	10	35	47	24
7	Alfold	20	7	2	11	27	30	23
8	Lancing WD	20	6	3	11	30	47	21
9	Milland	20	5	3	12	28	42	18
10	Rossey	20	3	4	13	27	45	13
11	Rustington	20	1	6	13	18	66	9

BRITISH SUGAR SUFFOLK & IPSWICH LEAGUE

Senior Division

		P	W	D	L	F	A	Pts
1	Haughley U	30	23	5	2	85	32	61
2	Framlingham	30	21	6	3	73	32	48
3	Brontham & St A	30	19	7	4	64	28	45
4	Grundisburgh	30	14	10	6	74	40	38
5	Walton United	30	17	3	10	78	71	37
6	Ipswich Athletic	30	15	6	10	66	57	35
7	Stonham Aspal	30	14	5	11	66	53	33
8	Fonnereau	30	12	6	12	57	55	30
9	Kesgrave	30	12	5	13	45	51	29
10	Walsham	30	11	5	14	49	60	27
11	East Bergholt	30	8	5	17	41	64	21
12	BT Research	30	9	1	3	48	73	21
13	Achilles	30	8	4	13	42	70	20
14	Westerfield U	30	5	6	19	41	71	16
15	Nichollans	30	3	9	13	44	83	15
16	Halesworth T	30	5	4	21	28	59	14

COLCHESTER & EAST ESSEX LEAGUE

Premier Division

		P	W	D	L	F	A	Pts
1	Birch Pk Royals	18	14	3	1	61	30	45
2	8 Ash Green	18	13	3	2	61	25	42
3	West End	18	12	1	5	55	30	37
4	Tollesbury U	18	11	3	4	50	25	36
5	University	18	9	0	9	62	48	27
6	Nayland Rgrs	18	6	4	8	42	50	22
7	Colne Engame	18	5	2	11	31	48	17
8	Stoke	18	5	2	11	38	82	17
9	Feering W	18	2	2	14	26	58	8
10	Clarendon	18	2	2	14	32	82	8

SOUTH LONDON FOOTBALL FEDERATION

Premier Division

		P	W	D	L	F	A	Pts
1	Continental Star	14	12	1	1	44	16	23*
2	Downham Ath	14	10	2	2	53	20	22
3	AFC Blackh'th R	14	7	2	5	46	32	16
4	Wagoners	14	7	0	7	36	29	16**
5	Staveley	14	4	3	7	31	50	11
6	Marshall	14	4	2	8	34	48	10
7	Umojah	14	3	3	8	30	37	9
8	Catford Wdrs R	14	2	1	11	11	53	5

* Two points deducted

** Two points awarded

First Division

		P	W	D	L	F	A	Pts
1	Footzies	20	15	4	1	83	18	34
2	Ethelred Ath	20	13	4	3	56	36	30
3	Nite Life	20	11	2	7	55	40	24
4	Churchdown	20	10	2	8	71	46	22
5	Regal	20	10	1	9	49	44	21
6	Eltham Town	20	7	6	7	45	51	20
7	Locksley	20	8	3	9	52	65	19
8	Elliott Sports	20	5	4	11	40	80	14
9	Eltham Palace R	20	5	3	12	35	57	13
10	KC Athletic	20	5	3	12	34	61	13
11	Agricola	20	3	4	13	32	54	10

Federation Challenge Cup Final

Footzies 3-0 AFC Black Heath Res

Senior Challenge Cup Final

Footzies 4-1 Churchdown

Junior Challenge Cup Final

BKT Wdrs 4-0 Hilly Fields

SOUTH LONDON FOOTBALL ALLIANCE

Premier Division

		P	W	D	L	F	A	Pts
1	AFC Blackheath	22	15	3	4	69	32	48
2	Keyworth	22	13	7	2	64	27	46
3	Avery Hill College	22	14	4	4	62	25	46
4	Johnson & Phil.	22	13	5	4	56	36	44
5	R.A.C.S.	22	12	5	5	60	28	41
6	Drummond Ath	22	10	5	7	56	34	35
7	Cambridge U M	22	8	5	9	40	51	29
8	Segas (Syd'ham)	22	7	3	12	37	55	24
9	Bickley Town	22	6	3	13	28	53	21
10	R A S R A	22	5	5	12	39	45	20
11	Wilmington	22	2	4	16	28	69	10
12	Eagle	22	1	3	18	32	116	6

Queen Mary Cup Final

Metrogas 1-4 R.A.C.S.

Elizabeth Jaques Cup Final

Bexley 2-2 Samuel Montague Res

(after extra time, 2-4 penalties)

SOUTHERN SUNDAY FOOTBALL LEAGUES

Final League Tables 1996-97

GOSPORT/FAREHAM SUNDAY LEAGUE

Division One		P	W	D	L	F	A	Pts
1	Junction	18	13	2	3	62	27	41
2	Salterns WMC	18	11	1	6	53	37	34
3	Rowner Rec	18	11	1	6	44	36	34
4	Down End	18	9	1	8	39	36	28
5	Turnpilke (Sun)	18	6	6	6	31	30	24
6	AFC New Inn	18	8	0	10	41	44	24
7	Wallington	18	6	3	9	34	40	21
8	Locks Heath	18	6	1	11	41	62	19
9	Locks Hth WMC	18	4	5	9	26	41	17
10	Wheatsheaf	18	5	2	11	38	54	17

HAVANT SUNDAY LEAGUE

Senior Division		P	W	D	L	F	A	Pts
1	Pop Inn	16	12	3	1	75	19	39
2	Ensinger	16	11	2	3	53	18	35
3	Heroes	16	11	1	4	40	25	34
4	Dresden	16	8	2	6	43	34	26
5	Rowlands Castle	16	8	0	8	34	50	24
6	Cricketers	16	4	6	6	38	33	18
7	Court House	16	5	2	9	30	52	17
8	KJC Carphones	16	2	4	10	18	57	10
9	Solent Div	16	0	2	14	21	68	2

CITY OF PORTSMOUTH SUNDAY LEAGUE

Premier Division		P	W	D	L	F	A	Pts
1	Pickwick	20	14	2	4	58	28	44
2	Silearer	20	13	3	4	64	31	42
3	Devonshire	20	10	5	5	58	47	35
4	Harvest Home	20	10	3	7	52	51	33
5	Wymering	20	8	6	6	59	38	30
6	Havant Rovers	20	7	6	7	50	50	27
7	Brynwell	20	8	3	9	40	46	27
8	Wicor Mill	20	7	3	10	35	42	24
9	Burlington V	20	5	6	9	37	38	21
10	Manor Court	20	5	3	12	47	57	18
11	Mainline Taxis	20	2	2	16	27	99	8

BOGNOR & DISTRICT SUNDAY PROMOTIONAL LEAGUE

Division One		P	W	D	L	F	A	Pts
1	Barley Mow	22	21	1	0	116	28	64
2	Eastergate WO	22	19	0	3	125	25	57
3	Belmont Park	22	14	4	4	84	45	46
4	Chichester H B	22	13	4	5	57	24	43
5	Waterlooville	22	12	1	9	97	62	37
6	Rainbow Inn	22	9	5	8	69	56	32
7	General Henry	22	9	5	8	62	61	32
8	Woodmancote A	22	6	4	12	52	49	22
9	West Hampnett	22	6	1	15	35	71	19
10	AFC Tangmere	22	5	1	16	36	88	16
11	Arun FC	22	2	2	18	27	98	8
12	West Meads	22	1	2	19	22	170	5

WINCHESTER DISTRICT SUNDAY LEAGUE

Premier Division		P	W	D	L	GD	Pts
1	Rising Sun	20	18	1	1	59	37
2	Bakers	20	16	0	4	39	32
3	Ocean	20	15	1	4	30	31
4	Bell Keema	20	12	4	4	41	28
5	Castle	20	7	4	9	-8	16*
6	Rising Sun CC	20	6	3	11	-7	15
7	Winton	20	5	4	11	-17	14
8	Old House	20	5	3	12	-20	13
9	Worthies	20	6	1	13	-25	13
10	St James	20	6	0	14	-44	12
11	TKF	20	3	1	16	-48	7

* Two points deducted

MEDWAY AREA SUNDAY LEAGUE

Facit Senior Section Sponsored by Facit

		P	W	D	L	F	A	Pts
1	Quested	24	22	0	2	121	33	44
2	Snodland WMC	24	16	4	4	84	29	36
3	Cavaliers	24	17	2	5	92	39	36
4	Old Oak	24	14	0	10	77	37	28
5	Rainham Sports	24	13	2	9	65	52	28
6	Sheerness East	24	10	8	6	55	43	28
7	Bly Spartans	24	11	4	9	52	43	26
8	Cliffe Woods Clts	24	10	1	13	43	49	21
9	Ship (Frindsbury)	24	8	4	12	47	39	20
10	Portland Arms	24	9	2	13	51	74	20
11	Strood Athletic	24	6	2	16	32	98	14
12	Red Dog	24	4	2	18	29	97	10
13	St Regis Sports	24	1	0	23	15	130	1

Premier Division		P	W	D	L	F	A	Pts
1	Utd Serv. (R'ham)	26	19	2	5	72	25	40
2	Warren Wood S	26	18	3	5	87	44	39
3	Strood Rangers	26	17	5	4	65	34	39
4	Hempstead	26	17	3	6	69	41	37
5	ABC Sports	26	16	1	9	62	28	33
6	Parkwood 79	26	12	4	10	64	53	28
7	Rainham 84	26	10	7	9	56	50	27
8	Eagles	26	10	6	10	52	50	26
9	M2 Tune	26	9	6	11	56	65	24
10	Gillingham C	26	8	7	11	50	58	23
11	Old Bordenians	26	8	2	16	37	55	18
12	Knights Place R	26	4	5	17	27	71	13
13	Fulston Zebras	26	4	2	20	22	96	10
14	Cliffe	26	2	3	21	24	73	7

Division One Sponsored by C H Keeble & Sons

		P	W	D	L	F	A	Pts
1	Ship Athletic	26	23	2	1	100	33	48
2	Istead Utd Yth	26	16	4	6	73	42	36
3	Palm Cottage	26	16	2	8	67	42	34
4	Gillingham FC SC	26	12	9	5	56	41	33
5	Dewdrop	26	14	3	9	51	46	31
6	Kemsley Arms	26	11	6	9	53	50	28
7	Woodcombe Soc	26	11	6	9	48	44	28
8	Sherwood D'mo	26	9	3	14	70	74	21
9	Sportos	26	8	5	13	53	58	21
10	Lloyds S & SC	26	8	5	13	58	66	21
11	Anchorians	26	7	7	12	38	51	21
12	Dixwell	26	7	4	15	50	60	18
13	Green Lion	26	4	6	16	47	78	14
14	Woodstock	26	3	4	19	28	105	10

MALDON SUNDAY LEAGUE

Division One

		P	W	D	L	F	A	Pts
1	Burnham Sports	18	13	3	2	51	20	39*
2	S C Mayland	18	11	3	4	67	28	36
3	Great Totham	18	10	3	5	55	30	33
4	Latchingdon	18	9	2	7	57	50	32[3]
5	East Hanningfield	18	9	2	7	53	30	29
6	Tolleshunt D'Arcy	18	7	3	8	44	45	25[1]
7	Cobra	18	6	4	8	44	49	21**
8	Purleigh	18	6	5	7	38	43	20*
9	Mayland	18	4	1	13	46	61	13
10	Brush United	18	2	0	16	15	114	9[3]

* Three points deducted ** One point deducted
[3] Three points awarded [1] One point awarded

Division Two

		P	W	D	L	F	A	Pts
1	Tollegion	16	11	3	2	58	22	36
2	Bradwell United	16	12	0	4	74	41	36
3	Pyramids	16	9	2	5	40	26	29
4	Maldon Saints	16	8	4	4	43	38	28
5	Directa Hotspur	16	5	7	4	33	36	22
6	Althorne	16	6	3	7	27	40	21
7	Woodham Radars	16	4	4	8	21	36	16
8	Quay Sports	16	1	5	10	27	58	8
9	Chelmsford Police	16	1	2	13	24	50	5
10	Rees Sports	Withdrawn						

EAST LONDON SUNDAY LEAGUE

Division One

		P	W	D	L	F	A	Pts
1	The Drum	14	9	2	3	40	23	29
2	Star Anchor	14	8	3	3	35	20	27
3	Clarendon	14	8	3	3	38	27	27
4	Stanford	14	6	3	5	39	36	21
5	Paddington Rdrs	14	5	3	6	26	28	18
6	Mile End Raiders	14	4	3	7	21	26	15
7	Meath United	14	4	1	9	29	51	13
8	The George	14	1	4	9	19	36	7
9	Forest Gate Egls	14	1	1	10	18	59	0

KENT YOUTH LEAGUE
Final League Tables 1996-97

Under 18 Northern Section

		P	W	D	L	F	A	Pts
1	Corinthian	24	18	4	2	75	26	40
2	Furness	24	16	3	5	60	29	35
3	Sittingbourne	24	15	4	5	67	28	34
4	Tonbridge (N)	24	13	3	8	50	36	29
5	Maidstone Utd	24	13	3	8	43	37	29
6	Catford Wndrs	24	9	7	8	55	56	25
7	Fisher Athletic	24	11	3	10	50	51	25
8	Thamesmead T	24	10	4	10	46	45	24
9	Erith & Belvedere	24	8	3	13	51	49	19
10	Phoenix Sports	24	7	1	16	52	82	15
11	Bromley	24	7	1	16	33	69	15
12	Dartford	24	6	2	16	37	50	14
13	Tan Em Bee	24	2	4	18	45	109	8

Under 18 Southern Section

		P	W	D	L	F	A	Pts
1	Gravesend & N	30	26	2	2	109	16	54
2	Margate	30	20	4	6	80	34	44
3	Lordswood	30	20	3	7	82	28	43
4	Chatham Town	30	18	5	7	71	36	41
5	Herne Bay	30	19	2	9	64	26	40
6	Hastings Town	30	13	9	8	57	49	35
7	Ashford Town	30	13	7	10	72	34	33
8	Faversham Town	30	11	7	12	65	50	29
9	Teynham & L	30	12	5	13	72	67	29
10	Whitstable Town	30	11	5	14	55	69	27
11	Folkestone Inv	30	10	7	13	52	66	27
12	Aylesford P Mills	30	9	5	16	44	88	23
13	Tonbridge (S)	30	8	6	16	51	56	22
14	Knatchbull	30	5	7	18	46	83	18
15	Hythe Town	30	5	0	25	27	137	10
16	Sheppey United	30	1	4	25	25	128	6

Under 16 Division

		P	W	D	L	F	A	Pts
1	Furness	30	24	5	1	122	18	53
2	Catford Wndrs	30	24	1	5	119	19	49
3	Lordswood	30	21	3	6	87	34	45
4	Ten Em Bee	30	18	4	8	92	46	40
5	Dover Athletic	30	18	4	8	88	66	40
6	Chatham Town	30	16	5	9	84	53	37
7	Margate	30	14	7	9	105	58	35
8	Hastings Town	30	14	6	10	87	51	34
9	Bearsted	30	15	2	13	66	62	32
10	Sittingbourne	30	12	6	12	81	50	30
11	Faversham Town	30	11	4	15	56	52	26
12	Snowdown CW	30	11	2	16	72	89	22
13	Herne Bay	30	10	2	18	52	74	22
14	Whitstable Town	30	2	2	26	34	129	6
15	Maidstone Utd	30	2	1	27	25	164	5
16	Deal Town Rngrs	30	1	2	27	23	217	4

Under 14 Division

		P	W	D	L	F	A	Pts
1	Maidstone Utd	21	15	2	4	82	32	32
2	Lordswood	21	13	5	3	63	23	31
3	Furness	21	13	3	5	58	31	29
4	Catford Wndrs	21	10	5	6	44	27	25
5	Folkestone Inv.	21	9	7	7	31	29	23
6	Bearsted	21	7	4	10	45	45	18
7	Dover Athetic	21	2	3	16	12	56	7
8	Herne Bay	21	1	1	19	8	97	3

TEAM

TALK

RESERVE TEAM FOOTBALL 1996-97

OPTIMUM INTERIORS CAPITAL FOOTBALL LEAGUE
FINAL LEAGUE TABLE 1996-97

		P	W	D	L	F	A	Pts
1	Peterborough Utd	25	19	2	4	69	18	59
2	Brentford	25	16	6	3	57	23	54
3	Wycombe Wndrs	25	17	3	5	56	28	54
4	Rushden & Diam.	25	12	7	6	45	36	43
5	Cambridge Utd	25	12	6	7	49	47	42
6	Gillingham	25	12	5	8	53	34	41
7	Colchester Utd	25	12	5	8	46	34	41
8	Southend Utd	25	12	4	9	55	41	40
9	Northampton Tn	25	12	3	10	40	31	39
10	Fulham	25	10	6	9	47	32	36
11	Reading	25	10	6	9	49	41	36
12	Stevenage Boro	25	8	5	12	35	51	29
13	Barnet	25	8	4	13	36	52	28
14	Welling United	25	6	5	14	23	44	23
15	Leyton Orient	25	5	6	14	36	55	21
16	Crawley Town	25	6	2	17	28	61	20
17	Woking	25	6	2	17	33	75	20
18	Sutton United	25	2	3	20	20	74	9

OPTIMUM INTERIORS CENTRAL CONFERENCE
FINAL LEAGUE TABLE 1996-97

		P	W	D	L	F	A	Pts
1	Worcester City	16	9	5	2	24	14	32
2	Hereford United	16	9	3	4	31	18	30
3	Stoke City	16	8	3	5	30	24	27
4	Gloucester City	16	7	5	4	38	31	26
5	Cheltenham Town	16	7	4	5	26	26	25
6	Kettering Town	16	6	4	6	28	40	22
7	Kidderminster H	16	5	3	8	37	33	18
8	Hednesford Town	16	3	3	10	27	32	12
9	Bromsgrove Rov.	16	2	2	12	19	42	8

LANCASHIRE FOOTBALL LEAGUE
FINAL LEAGUE TABLES 1996-97

Division One

		P	W	D	L	F	A	Pts
1	Manchester Utd A	28	22	4	2	108	30	70
2	Stoke City A	28	18	5	5	57	24	59
3	Crewe Alex Res	28	17	4	7	64	34	55
4	Everton A	28	13	7	8	58	46	46
5	Liverpool A	28	14	4	10	46	36	46
6	Oldham Ath A	28	13	5	10	41	42	44
7	Tranmere Rov A	28	13	4	11	40	48	43
8	Wrexham A	28	13	3	12	49	45	42
9	Burnley A	28	12	3	13	44	49	39
10	Bury A	28	10	4	14	26	47	34
11	Blackburn Rov A	28	9	6	13	44	40	33
12	Bolton Wndrs A	28	6	4	18	38	52	22
13	Marine Reserve	28	5	7	16	28	68	22
14	Preston N End A	28	6	3	19	26	65	21
15	Morecambe Res	28	6	3	19	31	74	21

Division Two

		P	W	D	L	F	A	Pts
1	Manchester Utd B	32	20	4	8	89	53	64
2	Manchester City A	32	19	7	6	56	29	64
3	Liverpool B	32	19	3	10	67	39	60
4	Crewe Alex A	32	17	6	9	72	63	57
5	Chester City A	32	15	7	10	49	44	52
6	Everton B	32	14	7	11	74	58	49
7	Burnley B	32	15	3	14	55	51	48
8	Oldham Ath B	32	12	10	10	54	46	46
9	Blackburn Rov B	32	12	9	11	53	40	45
10	Stockport Co A	32	12	6	14	52	62	42
11	Blackpool A	32	11	7	14	50	49	40
12	Tranmere Rov B	32	11	7	14	60	62	40
13	Carlisle Utd A	32	11	7	14	50	60	40
14	Wigan Ath A	32	10	9	13	49	58	39
15	Rochdale A	32	10	5	17	43	64	35
16	Bury B	32	8	5	19	40	69	29
17	Marine Youth	32	2	6	24	29	95	12

RESERVE TEAM FOOTBALL 1996-97

SUBURBAN LEAGUE
FINAL LEAGUE TABLES 1996-97

PREMIER DIVISION

		P	W	D	L	F	A	Pts
1	Kingstonian	26	18	4	4	58	29	58
2	Basingstoke Tn	26	14	7	5	57	35	49
3	Slough Town	26	12	5	9	47	34	41
4	Farnborough Tn	26	12	5	9	49	41	41
5	Sutton United	26	11	7	8	57	42	40
6	Whyteleafe	26	10	9	7	47	49	39
7	Marlow	26	10	6	10	44	56	36
8	Bromley	26	10	4	12	41	47	34
9	Dulwich Hamlet	26	8	8	10	44	36	32
10	Thame United	26	9	4	13	43	63	31
11	Aldershot Town	26	7	7	12	54	63	28
12	Wembley	26	8	4	14	43	57	28
13	Carshalton Ath	26	6	6	14	45	54	24
14	Molesey	26	6	6	14	29	52	24

NORTH DIVISION

		P	W	D	L	F	A	Pts
1	Hayes	24	16	6	2	71	25	54
2	Uxbridge	24	17	2	5	55	24	53
3	Leighton Town	24	14	6	4	61	31	48
4	Staines Town	24	13	7	4	63	33	46
5	Yeading	24	12	6	6	65	28	42
6	Hendon	24	11	7	6	54	37	40
7	Kingsbury Town	24	10	5	9	47	41	35
8	Northwood	24	11	2	11	50	50	35
9	Wingate & Finch.	24	6	3	15	38	68	21
10	Hillingdon Boro	24	7	0	17	42	77	21
11	Ruislip Manor	24	5	4	15	37	69	19
12	Egham Town	24	4	4	16	23	61	16
13	Feltham	24	2	4	18	38	100	10

SOUTH DIVISION

		P	W	D	L	F	A	Pts
1	Met Police	24	16	4	4	56	35	52
2	Fisher A (London)	24	16	2	6	64	30	50
3	Corinthian Cas.	24	12	7	5	50	35	43
4	Leatherhead	24	13	4	7	53	40	43
5	Walton & Hersh.	24	12	2	10	46	42	38
6	Hampton	24	10	4	10	61	56	34
7	Tooting & Mitcham	24	9	5	10	45	41	32
8	Banstead Athletic	24	9	5	10	47	49	32
9	Epsom & Ewell	24	9	4	11	37	45	31
10	Croydon	24	8	5	11	40	54	29
11	Croydon Athletic	24	5	7	12	46	65	22
12	Chipstead	24	5	6	13	37	50	21
13	Raynes Park Vale	24	3	3	18	31	71	12

WEST DIVISION

		P	W	D	L	F	A	Pts
1	Oxford City	26	18	4	4	75	32	58
2	Maidenhead Utd	26	17	4	5	85	39	55
3	Thatcham Town	26	15	5	6	60	47	50
4	Abingdon Town	26	15	3	8	66	37	48
5	Flackwell Heath	26	14	2	10	56	46	44
6	Bracknell Town	26	13	2	11	67	43	41
7	Wokingham Tn	26	12	5	9	72	51	41
8	Fleet Town	26	11	3	12	56	59	36
9	Camberley Town	26	10	5	11	42	44	35
10	Windsor & Eton	26	9	4	13	60	74	31
11	Hungerford Town	26	7	5	14	31	44	26
12	AFC Newbury	26	6	4	16	40	79	22
13	Burnham	26	5	5	16	36	78	20
14	Cove	26	2	5	19	26	99	11

SUBURBAN LEAGUE CHALLENGE CUP SHIELD

FINAL

Abingdon Town v Sutton United 3-4

SUBURBAN LEAGUE CHALLENGE

FINAL

Basingstoke Town v Kingstonian 0-1 aet

ESSEX & HERTS BORDER COMBINATION LEAGUE
FINAL LEAGUE TABLES 1996-97

EASTERN DIVISION

		P	W	D	L	F	A	Pts
1	Dag/Redbridge	36	28	5	3	110	25	89
2	Purfleet	36	26	8	2	102	32	86
3	Canvey Island	36	23	6	7	94	48	73
4	Heybridge Swifts	36	22	6	8	80	52	72
5	East Thurrock Utd	36	20	5	11	86	61	65
6	Tilbury	36	18	7	11	90	61	61
7	Billericay Town	36	16	10	10	58	44	58
8	Concord Rangers	36	16	8	12	73	65	56
9	Maldon Town	36	17	4	15	60	56	55
10	Tiptree United	36	13	8	15	52	53	47
11	Braintree Town	36	12	10	14	61	49	46
12	Chelmsford City	36	10	13	13	57	59	43
13	Aveley	36	11	9	16	63	81	42
14	Great Wakering R	36	11	6	19	57	94	39
15	Hornchurch	36	8	6	22	54	88	30
16	Bowers United	36	7	7	22	45	87	28
17	Southend Manor	36	5	8	23	27	102	23
18	Burnham Ramblers	36	3	12	21	31	85	21
19	Witham Town	36	6	2	28	43	101	20

WESTERN DIVISION

		P	W	D	L	F	A	Pts
1	Leyton Pennant	32	23	6	3	77	19	75
2	Collier Row & R	32	20	4	8	68	42	64
3	Norwich City	32	19	4	9	59	37	61
4	Enfield	32	18	6	8	63	47	60
5	Ford United	32	14	8	10	58	41	50
6	Harlow Town	32	16	2	14	45	41	50
7	Bishops Stortford	32	13	7	12	57	48	46
8	Waltham Abbey	32	13	5	14	49	44	44
9	Hoddesdon Town	32	11	11	10	39	43	44
10	Berkhamsted Tn	32	11	8	13	60	54	41
11	Stevenage Town	32	13	2	17	51	68	41
12	Barkingside	32	11	6	15	36	57	39
13	Sawbridgeworth T	32	10	8	14	44	51	38
14	Hertford Town	32	10	4	18	44	89	34
15	Hemel Hemstead	32	8	5	19	40	58	29
16	Ware	32	6	8	18	45	71	26
17	Clapton	32	7	4	21	52	77	25

ISTHMIAN LEAGUE

PYRAMID SECTION

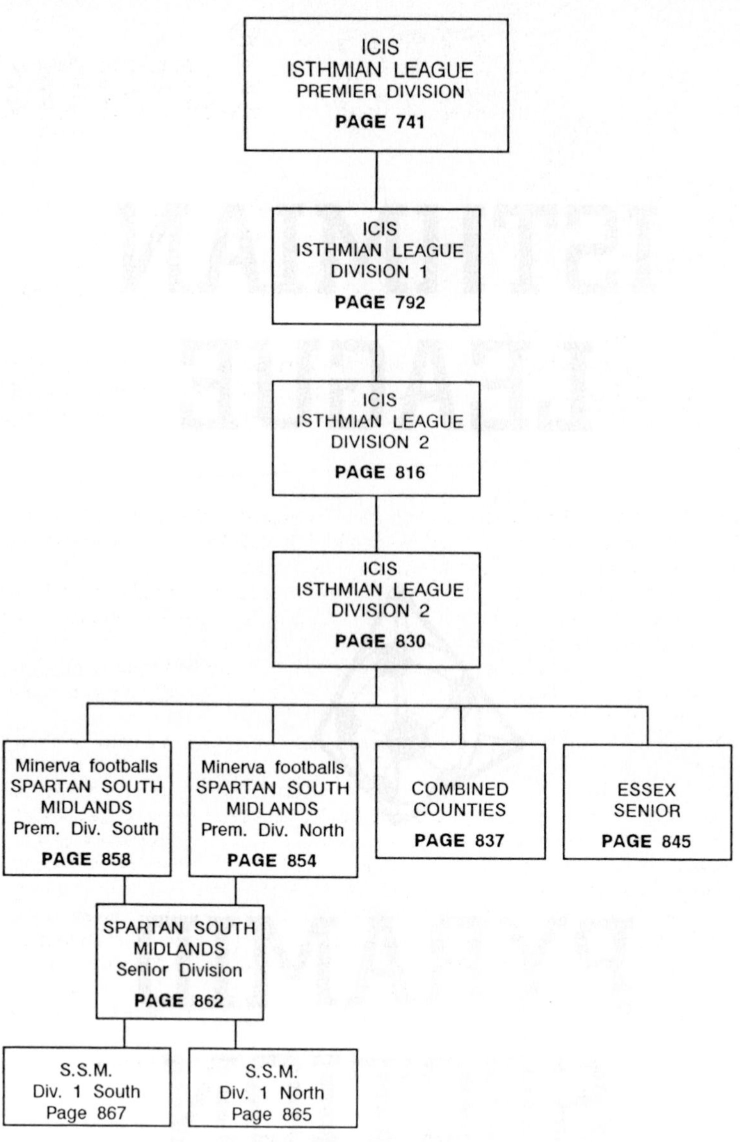
ICIS
ISTHMIAN LEAGUE
PREMIER DIVISION
PAGE 741
ICIS
ISTHMIAN LEAGUE
DIVISION 1
PAGE 792
ICIS
ISTHMIAN LEAGUE
DIVISION 2
PAGE 816
ICIS
ISTHMIAN LEAGUE
DIVISION 2
PAGE 830
Minerva footballs
SPARTAN SOUTH
MIDLANDS
Prem. Div. South
PAGE 858
Minerva footballs
SPARTAN SOUTH
MIDLANDS
Prem. Div. North
PAGE 854
COMBINED
COUNTIES
PAGE 837
ESSEX
SENIOR
PAGE 845
SPARTAN SOUTH
MIDLANDS
Senior Division
PAGE 862
S.S.M.
Div. 1 South
Page 867
S.S.M.
Div. 1 North
Page 865

FEEDER AND OTHER FEATURED LEAGUES

ICIS League

Chairman A C F Turvey, MCIM
'Ladymead', 18 Apple Way, Old Basing,
Basingstoke, Hants RG24 7HA
Tel: 01256 461789 Mobile: 0836 251368

Secretary & Treasurer N R Robinson, FCIArb
226 Rye Lane, Peckham, London SE15 4NL
Tel: 0181 409 1978 (H) 0171 639 5726 (B) 0836 241666 (M)

Following a thrilling finish to the previous season when four clubs had a chance of the championship on the last Saturday, the three remaining sides - Enfield, Yeovil Town and Boreham Wood - were obviously favourites to continue the chase for Conference football.

There was also the presence of Dagenham & Redbridge, relegated from above, and the emerging Heybridge Swifts who had been promoted, while St. Albans City, Dulwich Hamlet, Sutton United, Carshalton Athletic and Aylesbury United were expected to challenge.

As it turned out 'The Daggers' soon lost touch with games in hand and a great FA Cup run and it became obvious that regular challengers Enfield and Graham Roberts' newly built West Country side at Yeovil were in a different class.

Enfield drew first blood with a 3-0 home victory against their rivals but at the New Year it was purely a two club race with Yeovil soon edging ahead.

Enfield had enjoyed another excellent FA Cup run as had St. Albans City and Boreham Wood, but the serious challengers for the title seemed to disappear out of the two League Cup competitions fairly quickly. A superb effort by Maidenhead United, who included Yeovil, Sutton and Aylesbury amongst their victims to win the Full Members Cup, is probably a sign of other successes to come.

Boreham Wood just beat newcomers Braintree Town to win the Challenge Cup and Leighton Town prevented Wealdstone achieving a 'double', with another close win in the Associate Members Cup final.

A very tight battle in Division One saw an excellent Chesham United emerge as champions ahead of Basingstoke Town and Walton & Hersham who just pipped Hampton and Billericay Town for promotion.

New club Collier Row & Romford (now Romford) won another thrilling battle with Leatherhead at the top of Division Two by one point despite the brilliant goalscoring record of Steve Lunn who recorded 44 for 'The Tanners' out of an amazing total of 116 goals.

The two newcomers from the Southern League, Wealdstone and Braintree Town, moved confidently up to Division Two while at that level Banstead Athletic and Northwood brought much credit to the league in the FA Carlsberg Vase.

The League Representative side was well administered by Graham Roberts and recorded a memorable 1-0 victory over an FA XI full of potential England players from the Conference.

But back at the top of the Premier Division as Yeovil Town and Enfield continued to slug it out, a new personality emerged. Howard Forinton had signed for Yeovil from Oxford City and by the end of the season recorded 24 goals in 22 games to inspire the Somerset club's championship success. His six doubles in the last seven games was quite outstanding as his club pulled away under incredible pressure, to record a massive 101 points. The clubs' support was also very special as the 8,007 for the visit of Enfield underlined.

Poor Enfield were unbeaten away from home, had the best goal difference and conceded least goals but they will be back, and this season's championship with Dagenham & Redbridge and Kingstonian their main challengers should be a thriller.

GUARDIAN INSURANCE LEAGUE CUP 96-97

PRELIMINARY ROUND

Tring Town	1v6	Braintree Town
Egham Town	0v2	Collier Row & R
Flackwell Heath	1v4	Bedford Town
Lewes	0v2	Dorking
Hungerford Town	2v1	Met. Police
Epsom & Ewell	3v2	Wivenhoe Town
Southall	0v1	Tilbury
Hemel Hempstead	5v2	Barking
Banstead Ath.	1v0	Camberley Town
Northwood	2v1	Windsor & Eton
Wealdstone	1v0	Kingsbury Town
Cheshunt	1v3	Horsham
East Thurrock U	1v0*	Clapton
Witham Town	0v1	Wingate & Finchley
Ware	0v2	Aveley
Leatherhead	2v2	Harlow Town
(R) Harlow Town	2v3*	Leatherhead
Chalfont St. Peter	0v1	Leighton Town
Wembley	1v0	Bracknell Town
Hertford Town	1v2	Edgware Town

ROUND ONE

Carshalton Athletic	6v0	Whyteleafe
Aylesbury United	1v4	Braintree Town
Billericay Town	2v1	Basingstoke Town
Collier Row & R	4v3*	Bromley
Barton Rovers	0v1	Bedford Town
Oxford City	2v3*	Chertsey Town
Dorking	1v0	Hitchin Town
Maidenhead United	1v2	Heybridge Swifts
Hungerford Town	0v1	Walton & Hersham
Grays Athletic	1v0	Hornchurch
Chesham United	3v3	Epsom & Ewell
(R) Epsom & Ewell	1v2*	Chesham United
Thame United	4v1	Hampton
Leyton Pennant	1v4	Purfleet
Canvey Island	1v2	Sutton United
Dulwich Hamlet	0v1	Yeading
Yeovil Town	6v1	Molesey
Kingstonian	2v1	Tilbury
Hemel Hempstead	1v0	Abingdon Town
Banstead Athletic	3v1	Northwood
Wealdstone	4v2*	Horsham
Wokingham Town	2v1	Bishop's Stortford
Worthing	0v3	Tooting & Mitcham U
Bognor Regis T	6v2*	East Thurrock U
Staines Town	1v0	Uxbridge
Wingate & Finchley	1v6	St Albans City
Aveley	5v1	Leatherhead
Berkhamsted Town	5v6	Harrow Borough
Aldershot Town	0v3	Enfield
Croydon	0v1	Leighton Town
Hendon	1v0*	Wembley
Boreham Wood	3v2*	Edgware Town
Dagenham & Redbr.	3v0	Marlow

ROUND TWO

Carshalton Athletic	1v2	Braintree Town
Billericay Town	1v1*	Collier Row & R
(R) Collier Row & R	4v3*	Billericay Town

Collier Row removed from competition for rule infringement

Bedford Town	1v0	Chertsey Town
Dorking	0v4	Heybridge Swifts

Match ordered to be replayed

Heybridge Swifts	8v0	Dorking
Walton & Hersham	0v3	Grays Athletic
Chesham United	3v2*	Thame United
Purfleet	3v6	Sutton United
Yeading	1v1*	Yeovil Town
(R) Yeovil Town	0v1	Yeading
Kingstonian	3v2*	Hemel Hempstead
Banstead Athletic	6v0	Wealdstone
Wokingham Town	3v0	Tooting & Mitcham
Bognor Regis Town	2v1	Staines Town
St. Albans City	3v1	Aveley
Harrow Borough	3v2	Enfield
Leighton Town	1v0	Hendon
Boreham Wood	1v0	Dagenham & Redbr.

ROUND THREE

Braintree Town	3v1	Billericay Town
Bedford Town	2v1*	Heybridge Swifts
Grays Athletic	1v2	Chesham United
Sutton United	3v2	Yeading
Kingstonian	2v1*	Banstead Athletic
Wokingham Town	1v2	Bognor Regis T

Bognor removed from competition for rule infringement

St. Albans City	2v4	Harrow Borough
Leighton Town	0v2	Boreham Wood

ROUND FOUR

Braintree Town	2v1*	Bedford Town
Chesham United	2v1	Sutton United

Chesham removed from competition for rule infringement

Kingstonian	2v0	Wokingham Town
Harrow Borough	1v3	BorehamWood

SEMI-FINALS

Braintree Town	1v0	Sutton United
Sutton United	1v2	Braintree Town
Kingstonian	1v1	Boreham Wood
Boreham Wood	3v2*	Kingstonian

FINAL

Braintree Town	0v1	Boreham Wood

at Dagenham & Redbridge F.C.

FULL MEMBERS CUP 96-97

ROUND ONE

Croydon	1v0*	Carshalton Athletic
Molesey	3v1	Worthing
Hampton	2v1	Bromley
Oxford City	2v1*	Aldershot Town
Chertsey Town	3v1	Wokingham Town
Hendon	3v1	Berkhamsted Town
Thame United	0v1	Yeading
Marlow	2v1	Staines Town
Aylesbury United	1v0	Boreham Wood
Barton Rovers	0v3	Canvey Island
Grays Athletic	1v0	Leyton Pennant

ROUND TWO

Yeovil Town	2v0	Carshalton Athletic
Bognor Regis T	1v0*	Dulwich Hamlet
Kingstonian	4v4*	Walton & Hersham
Walton & H won 5-3 on penalties		
Molesey	0v2	Maidenhead United
Sutton United	2v2*	Hampton
Sutton won 5-3 on penalties		
Oxford City	2v3	Whyteleafe
Basingstoke Town	2v1	Tooting & Mitcham
Chertsey Town	0v3	Abingdon Town
Dagenham & Redbr.	2v2*	Hendon
Dagenham won 5-4 on penalties		
Purfleet	3v2	Hitchin Town
Uxbridge	0v3	Bishop's Stortford
Yeading	4v0	Marlow
Aylesbury United	2v1	Canvey Island
Billericay Town	2v1	Harrow Borough
Grays Athletic	0v0*	Chesham United
Grays won 7-6 on penalties		
Heybridge Swifts	0v1	Enfield

ROUND THREE

Yeovil Town	3v2	Bognor Regis T
Walton & Hersham	0v1	Maidenhead United
Sutton United	4v0	Whyteleafe
Basingstoke Town	1v0	Abingdon Town
Dagenham & Redbr.	0v1	Purfleet
Bishop's Stortford	1v2	Yeading
Aylesbury United	3v0	Billericay Town
Chesham United	3v3*	Enfield
Chesham won 3-1 on penalties		

ROUND FOUR

Yeovil Town	0v3	Maidenhead United
Sutton United	5v3	Basingstoke Town
Purfleet	0v2	Yeading
Aylesbury United	3v0	Chesham United

SEMI-FINALS

Maidenhead United	3v1	Sutton United
Yeading	2v2*	Aylesbury United
(R) Aylesbury United	1v0	Yeading

FINAL

Maidenhead United	3v0	Aylesbury United
at Marlow F.C.		

ASSOCIATE MEMBERS TROPHY 96-97

ROUND ONE

Leatherhead	5v3	Northwood
Chalfont St. Peter	0v2	Banstead Athletic
Wembley	4v1	Hertford Town
Dorking	0v7	Wealdstone
Epsom & Ewell	2v0	Lewes
Cheshunt	0v3	Ware
Aveley	2v2*	Barking
Barking won 4-2 on penalties		

ROUND TWO

Leatherhead	3v1*	Banstead Athletic
Wembley	4v1	Tilbury
Windsor & Eton	1v2	Hungerford Town
Tring Town	4v4*	Southall
Southall won 4-2 on penalties		
Camberley Town	0v3	Horsham
Flackwell Heath	0v1	Egham Town
Wealdstone	3v1	Bracknell Town
Metropolitan Police	2v0	Epsom & Ewell
Collier Row & R	3v1	Ware
Wivenhoe Town	2v0	Edgware Town
East Thurrock U	2v3	Witham Town
Kingsbury Town	1v1	Wingate & Finchley
(R) Wingate & Finchley	3v0	Kingsbury Town
Hemel Hempstead	0v1	Leighton Town
Clapton	1v6*	Braintree Town
Barking	2v0	Harlow Town
Hornchurch	1v2*	Bedford Town

ROUND THREE

Leatherhead	1v0	Wembley
Hungerford Town	4v2*	Southall
Horsham	2v3	Egham Town
Wealdstone	4v2	Metropolitan Police
Collier Row & R	3v4	Wivenhoe Town
Witham Town	1v2	Wingate & Finchley
Leighton Town	2v1*	Braintree Town
Barking	2v2*	Bedford Town
Bedford Town win on penaties		

ROUND FOUR

Leatherhead	6v2	Hungerford Town
Egham Town	1v2	Wealdstone
Wivenhoe Town	2v1	Wingate & Finchley
Leighton Town	1v1*	Bedford Town
Leighton Town win 4-1 on penalties		

SEMI-FINALS

Leatherhead	0v0*	Wealdstone
(R) Wealdstone	3v0	Leatherhead
Wivenhoe Town	0v2	Leighton Town

FINAL

Wealdstone	0v1	Leighton Town
at Hitchin Town FC		

ICIS PROMOTION & RELEGATION 1997

LEAGUE	NEW CLUBS	DEPARTING CLUBS
PREMIER	Gravesend & Northfleet (DM P)	Yeovil Town (Champions)
	Chesham United (ICIS 1)	Staines Town (20th)
	Basingstoke Town (ICIS 1)	Grays Athletic (21st)
	Walton & Hersham (ICIS 1)	Chertsey Town (22nd)
DIVISION 1	Staines Town (ICIS Prem)	Chesham United (Champions)
	Grays Athletic (ICIS Prem)	Basingstoke Town (R-up)
	Chertsey Town (ICIS Prem)	Walton & Hersham (3rd)
	Collier Row & Romford (ICIS 2)	Canvey Island (20th)
	Leatherhead (ICIS 2)	Marlow (21st)
	Wembley (ICIS 2)	Tooting & Mitcham Utd (22nd)
DIVISION 2	Canvey Island (ICIS 1)	Collier Row & R. (Champions)
	Marlow (ICIS 1)	Leatherhead (R-up)
	Tooting & Mitcham (ICIS 1)	Wembley (3rd)
	Wealdstone (ICIS 3)	Ware (20th)
	Braintree Town (ICIS 3)	Dorking (21st)
	Northwood (ICIS 3)	Hemel Hempstead (22nd)
DIVISION 3	Ware (ICIS 2)	Wealdstone (Champions)
	Dorking (ICIS 2)	Braintree Town (R-up)
	Hemel Hempstead (ICIS 2)	Northwood (3rd)
	Croydon Athletic (Spartan)	
	Ford United (Essex Senior)	
	Corinthian Casuals (Combined Counties)	

A jubilant Wealdstone after clinching the Division Three title at Northwood. Photo: Graham Smith

PREMIER DIVISION
10 YEAR RECORD

ICIS LEAGUE

	87/8	88/9	89/0	90/1	91/2	92/3	93/4	94/5	95/6	96/7
No of clubs competing	(22)	(22)	(22)	(22)	(22)	(22)	(22)	(22)	(22)	(22)
Aylesbury United	-	-	3	3	7	10	12	4	11	7
Barking	19	10	20	21	-	-	-	-	-	-
Basingstoke Town	22	-	8	18	14	11	21	-	-	-
Bishop's Stortford	13	7	9	13	22	-	-	19	12	19
Bognor Regis Town	16	9	19	17	21	22	-	-	-	-
Boreham Wood	-	-	-	-	-	-	-	-	3	10
Bromley	2	14	21	-	12	17	15	6	19	18
Carshalton Athletic	9	4	10	9	8	4	6	12	6	13
Chertsey Town	-	-	-	-	-	-	-	-	15	22
Chesham United	-	-	-	-	4	1	4	20	-	-
Croydon	18	22	-	-	-	-	-	-	-	-
Dagenham	-	18	6	14	9		(see Dagenham & Redbridge)			
Dagenham & Redbridge	-	-	-	-	-	-	-	-	-	4
Dorking	-	-	-	-	-	-	20	-	-	-
Dulwich Hamlet	20	16	22	-	-	14	16	11	5	12
Enfield	-	-	-	2	2	3	2	1	2	2
Farnborough Town	9	8	2	-	-	-	-	-	-	-
Grays Athletic	-	5	5	6	15	6	14	18	17	21
Harrow Borough	12	19	18	20	18	8	9	10	9	17
Hayes	6	8	14	8	19	9	13	3	1	-
Hendon	10	12	12	15	17	11	11	17	14	16
Heybridge Swifts	-	-	-	-	-	-	-	-	-	9
Hitchin Town	21	-	-	-	-	-	8	5	18	14
Kingstonian	14	6	4	5	10	13	10	13	8	11
Leytonstone-Ilford	4	1						(see Redbridge Forest)		
Leyton-Wingate	17	15	7	22	-	-	-	-	-	-
Marlow	-	20	17	7	6	15	3	21	-	-
Molesey	-	-	-	-	-	-	18	8	20	-
Oxford City	-	-	-	-	-	-	-	-	-	15
Purfleet	-	-	-	-	-	-	-	16	16	8
Redbridge Forest	-	-	11	1	-		(see Dagenham & Redbridge)			
St Albans City	15	17	15	16	13	2	7	7	7	6
Slough Town	3	3	1	-	-	-	-	2	-	-
Staines Town	-	-	16	19	20	20	-	-	-	20
Stevenage Borough	-	-	-	-	-	7	1	-	-	-
Sutton United	-	-	-	-	3	5	5	15	10	3
Tooting & Mitcham United	11	21	-	-	-	-	-	-	-	-
Walton & Hersham	-	-	-	-	-	-	-	14	21	-
Windsor & Eton	7	13	13	12	11	21	-	-	-	-
Wivenhoe Town	-	-	-	10	16	18	22	-	-	-
Woking	-	-	-	4	1	-	-	-	-	-
Wokingham Town	5	11	2	11	5	16	19	22	-	-
Worthing	-	-	-	-	-	-	-	-	22	-
Yeading	-	-	-	-	-	19	17	9	13	5
Yeovil Town	1	-	-	-	-	-	-	-	4	1

ICIS LEAGUE - PREMIER DIVISION

		Home					Away							Clean Sheets - FA Cup & Trophy & League games only
	P	**W**	**D**	**L**	**F**	**A**	**W**	**D**	**L**	**F**	**A**	**Pts.**	**G.D.**	**/ Top Scorers** (Competitions as listed in league bulletin)
Yeovil Town	**42**	17	3	1	49	17	14	5	2	34	17	**101**	49	25 Patmore - 30; Forinton - 26; Birkby - 16; Gill - 15; Turner - 12
Enfield	**42**	14	4	3	50	17	14	7	0	41	12	**95**	62	22 West - 23; May - 14; Moran - 12; Marshall - 10
Sutton United	**42**	10	7	4	43	31	8	6	7	44	39	**67**	17	5 Hynes - 23; Vansittart -23; Feltham - 14; Jones & Pearce - 10
Dagenham & Redbridge	**42**	11	3	7	32	21	7	8	6	25	22	**65**	14	21 Naylor - 18; John - 14; Stimpson - 9; Rogers - 8
Yeading	**42**	10	6	5	30	15	7	8	6	28	31	**65**	11	15 Kellman - 19 Pickett - 11 Gell & Allen - 9
St Albans City	**42**	7	7	7	31	32	11	4	6	35	23	**65**	10	15 Clark - 29; Haworth - 15; Daly -12; Howell - 10
Aylesbury United	**42**	11	5	5	39	27	7	6	8	25	27	**65**	10	15 Swaysland - 21 Carmichael - 20 Davies - 12
Purfleet	**42**	8	9	4	37	30	9	2	10	30	33	**62**	4	12 Cobb - 34; Carthy - 9; Odegbami - 9; Cavell - 5
Heybridge Swifts	**42**	9	7	5	32	30	7	7	7	30	32	**62**	0	16 Caldon - 20 Springett - 13 Jones - 8
Boreham Wood	**42**	9	7	5	34	22	6	6	9	22	30	**58**	4	9 A Samuels - 23 Robbins - 18 D Samuels & Shaw - 6
Kingstonian	**42**	10	4	7	46	34	6	4	11	33	45	**56**	0	4 Darlington - 23 Akuamoah - 20 Deadman - 7
Dulwich Hamlet	**42**	9	3	9	30	24	5	10	6	27	33	**55**	0	12 Whitmarsh - 18 Holness - 9 Lillington & McKimm - 8
Carshalton Athletic	**42**	10	5	6	34	21	4	6	11	17	35	**53**	-5	13 Salako - 17 Vines - 10 Kingsford & Bolton - 7
Hitchin Town	**42**	10	3	8	38	33	5	4	12	29	40	**52**	-6	6 Dellar - 15 Hall -11 Parker - 10 Bates - 5
Oxford City	**42**	8	5	8	34	32	6	5	10	32	51	**52**	-16	4 Forinton - 17 Herbert - 12 Fontaine - 9 Charles - 8
Hendon	**42**	8	5	8	29	31	5	7	9	24	28	**51**	-6	13 Lewis - 15 Richardson - 8 Banton & Kelly - 7
Harrow Borough	**42**	8	7	6	30	26	4	7	10	28	37	**50**	-4	8 Xavier - 13 Court - 7 James & Jones - 6
Bromley	**42**	10	5	6	37	25	3	4	14	30	47	**48**	-5	11 Tompkins - 20; Warden - 10; Wordsworth - 9; Rawlings & Sharman - 8
Bishops Stortford	**42**	7	7	7	28	28	3	6	12	15	36	**43**	-21	12 Cooper - 13; Walker - 5; Abekola, Forbes & Henry - 3
Staines Town	**42**	6	6	9	28	31	4	2	15	18	40	**38**	-25	7 Gasson - 8 Williams - 8 Jones & Mitchell - 7
Grays Athletic	**42**	3	6	12	19	32	5	3	13	24	46	**33**	-35	6 Southon - 7; Wilson - 6; Deleon, Goldstone, Ray & Risley - 4
Chertsey Town	**42**	4	5	12	21	51	4	2	15	19	47	**31**	-58	6 Peters - 6 Pearce - 5 Hippolyte & Ravenscroft - 4

Home Team / Away Team	Ayles. 1	Bish.S. 2	Boreh. 3	Brom. 4	Carsh. 5	Chert. 6	D & R 7	Dulw. 8	Enfi. 9	Grays 10	Harr. 11	Hend. 12	Heyb. 13	Hitch. 14	Kings. 15	Oxfo. 16	Purf. 17	St.Alb. 18	Stain. 19	Sutt. 20	Yead. 21	Yeov. 22
1. Aylesbury United		2-2 (453)	2-0 (515)	1-1 (485)	3-1 (470)	2-1 (766)	0-1 (578)	2-0 (502)	1-3 (1118)	3-0 (534)	2-0 (453)	1-2 (429)	1-0 (502)	2-1 (655)	2-5 (491)	6-1 (874)	0-2 (434)	2-1 (535)	2-1 (758)	3-3 (394)	2-2 (404)	0-0 (864)
2. Bishops Stortford	2-0 (389)		0-0 (412)	4-3 (294)	2-1 (324)	3-1 (312)	2-0 (344)	0-1 (367)	1-3 (765)	0-0 (269)	0-1 (221)	2-1 (476)	0-0 (420)	1-2 (381)	2-2 (410)	2-2 (322)	2-3 (334)	1-1 (431)	1-0 (348)	2-5 (421)	1-1 (363)	0-1 (466)
3. Boreham Wood	1-1 (306)	4-1 (253)		2-2 (251)	3-0 (219)	1-2 (242)	3-1 (114)	2-2 (217)	1-1 (782)	2-1 (203)	2-0 (281)	1-2 (412)	0-0 (153)	4-0 (359)	0-0 (303)	3-2 (202)	0-1 (177)	0-2 (472)	3-0 (211)	1-0 (261)	1-1 (137)	0-3 (333)
4. Bromley	0-2 (402)	2-1 (313)	2-0 (325)		2-0 (487)	5-1 (225)	1-0 (313)	0-0 (628)	0-2 (551)	1-2 (354)	1-2 (325)	2-2 (341)	1-1 (303)	3-2 (283)	2-2 (216)	3-0 (320)	2-1 (276)	1-1 (354)	1-2 (284)	2-1 (344)	5-1 (241)	1-2 (979)
5. Carshalton Athletic	2-0 (289)	1-0 (244)	1-2 (371)	3-2 (402)		2-0 (216)	0-0 (352)	0-0 (315)	0-1 (607)	6-0 (293)	2-1 (349)	0-2 (207)	4-1 (211)	1-2 (255)	1-3 (554)	1-1 (349)	2-1 (272)	2-0 (289)	2-0 (401)	3-3 (1460)	0-0 (358)	0-1 (603)
6. Chertsey Town	0-0 (464)	0-3 (232)	1-1 (175)	3-1 (252)	2-3 (247)		0-3 (225)	0-2 (320)	1-1 (669)	0-6 (201)	2-2 (246)	1-0 (311)	3-5 (353)	0-5 (212)	0-3 (326)	2-4 (377)	0-1 (215)	0-5 (291)	3-2 (323)	1-1 (417)	2-1 (278)	0-2 (452)
7. Dagenham & Redbridge	0-2 (421)	3-0 (690)	2-1 (661)	0-2 (751)	0-1 (552)	2-1 (353)		1-1 (671)	0-2 (1062)	2-1 (420)	3-1 (551)	1-1 (448)	3-0 (622)	1-1 (406)	2-0 (757)	4-2 (534)	2-0 (743)	0-1 (471)	3-0 (704)	2-1 (653)	1-2 (516)	0-1 (1181)
8. Dulwich Hamlet	1-1 (341)	2-0 (307)	2-1 (407)	2-1 (468)	4-1 (413)	3-0 (270)	0-2 (206)		0-1 (444)	3-0 (274)	0-0 (263)	2-1 (227)	1-3 (297)	2-2 (311)	1-2 (418)	0-1 (348)	2-1 (302)	1-2 (320)	0-2 (307)	0-1 (361)	0-1 (341)	4-1 (711)
9. Enfield	3-0 (876)	1-1 (1219)	3-0 (673)	4-3 (560)	2-0 (608)	5-0 (714)	0-1 (631)	2-3 (678)		4-0 (542)	1-0 (850)	2-2 (733)	1-2 (1048)	1-0 (347)	3-0 (865)	3-3 (852)	3-0 (936)	1-0 (851)	4-0 (860)	3-1 (1012)	1-1 (1069)	3-0 (1349)
10. Grays Athletic	2-0 (242)	0-1 (244)	2-4 (142)	1-0 (289)	0-1 (179)	0-3 (210)	0-3 (429)	1-1 (258)	0-2 (451)		3-2 (170)	0-0 (244)	0-1 (263)	2-2 (254)	1-1 (253)	1-1 (189)	0-1 (256)	1-2 (179)	1-2 (183)	1-1 (298)	1-2 (191)	2-3 (385)
11. Harrow Borough	0-0 (164)	1-1 (162)	2-0 (308)	2-0 (153)	1-1 (221)	1-0 (202)	1-0 (285)	2-1 (255)	1-1 (502)	1-0 (146)		2-2 (323)	3-3 (162)	3-1 (220)	1-2 (277)	2-3 (145)	3-1 (162)	0-2 (291)	0-2 (217)	2-1 (328)	0-1 (204)	2-3 (447)
12. Hendon	0-3 (405)	3-1 (232)	1-2 (334)	4-1 (370)	2-2 (251)	1-0 (243)	2-1 (203)	2-2 (297)	0-3 (847)	0-1 (268)	2-1 (302)		1-1 (287)	1-0 (245)	2-1 (275)	2-0 (179)	2-3 (259)	0-2 (265)	1-1 (232)	1-2 (411)	1-1 (261)	1-3 (372)
13. Heybridge Swifts	1-3 (272)	0-0 (387)	0-2 (236)	4-3 (212)	0-2 (329)	4-1 (182)	4-1 (412)	1-1 (305)	0-0 (530)	3-0 (194)	0-0 (312)	1-1 (274)		2-1 (221)	2-1 (347)	2-1 (335)	1-3 (312)	2-1 (323)	2-1 (246)	3-3 (366)	0-5 (212)	0-0 (875)
14. Hitchin Town	2-1 (373)	3-0 (265)	1-2 (329)	5-2 (188)	3-2 (328)	2-1 (356)	0-0 (361)	0-0 (349)	0-3 (703)	0-2 (350)	2-4 (278)	1-2 (376)	1-2 (268)		4-1 (411)	4-2 (212)	2-0 (334)	1-1 (291)	2-1 (328)	2-5 (182)	3-1 (232)	0-1 (537)
15. Kingstonian	0-1 (448)	0-1 (442)	5-1 (433)	1-1 (436)	1-1 (514)	2-0 (344)	2-3 (455)	4-2 (413)	0-1 (619)	5-2 (323)	4-4 (391)	2-1 (350)	1-0 (295)	3-1 (407)		4-1 (372)	3-2 (270)	0-1 (492)	3-3 (434)	2-3 (1009)	4-2 (437)	0-3 (676)
16. Oxford City	3-2 (464)	4-1 (261)	0-0 (151)	2-3 (218)	1-1 (214)	0-2 (216)	2-2 (267)	1-1 (259)	1-4 (382)	1-1 (251)	2-1 (327)	2-0 (282)	1-2 (179)	5-1 (212)	3-1 (257)		1-2 (217)	3-2 (311)	1-0 (191)	1-3 (323)	0-1 (247)	0-2 (869)
17. Purfleet	0-1 (122)	3-0 (128)	1-1 (193)	2-0 (207)	2-0 (215)	2-0 (162)	2-2 (401)	1-4 (207)	1-3 (428)	2-4 (285)	2-0 (119)	0-0 (153)	3-3 (152)	1-1 (136)	3-2 (229)	2-2 (179)		2-2 (127)	2-0 (131)	3-2 (306)	2-2 (193)	1-1 (347)
18. St. Albans City	0-0 (412)	1-1 (346)	0-2 (462)	0-3 (189)	0-0 (378)	4-5 (478)	0-2 (651)	2-2 (356)	1-4 (812)	4-2 (489)	2-2 (398)	1-0 (401)	4-2 (445)	2-1 (520)	2-0 (454)	0-1 (405)	2-1 (502)		3-0 (453)	1-1 (552)	0-0 (305)	2-3 (851)
19. Staines Town	3-1 (288)	0-0 (182)	2-1 (214)	3-0 (235)	2-0 (318)	0-0 (607)	0-0 (265)	1-3 (215)	0-2 (252)	3-1 (201)	1-1 (200)	0-3 (240)	2-2 (206)	1-2 (282)	2-1 (376)	1-2 (151)	1-3 (185)	1-2 (171)		2-3 (309)	2-3 (194)	1-1 (510)
20. Sutton United	3-3 (469)	2-1 (554)	1-1 (469)	2-2 (720)	2-0 (1106)	4-2 (537)	2-1 (589)	2-0 (717)	1-1 (829)	1-1 (503)	3-3 (579)	3-1 (574)	0-2 (310)	4-3 (536)	5-2 (853)	1-2 (601)	0-0 (737)	2-3 (579)	2-0 (489)		3-0 (506)	0-3 (1281)
21. Yeading	0-1 (165)	3-0 (142)	2-1 (187)	1-0 (160)	0-0 (164)	0-0 (165)	1-1 (237)	3-0 (131)	1-1 (430)	3-0 (66)	1-2 (284)	2-1 (231)	1-0 (125)	0-1 (145)	5-1 (247)	4-1 (131)	1-1 (212)	0-3 (284)	1-0 (204)	1-2 (266)		0-0 (409)
22. Yeovil Town	3-2 (2011)	1-0 (2628)	0-0 (3195)	1-0 (1810)	3-0 (1846)	4-0 (6013)	0-0 (2255)	6-1 (1707)	2-2 (8007)	2-0 (2184)	2-1 (2116)	2-0 (1904)	1-0 (2101)	1-0 (2004)	2-3 (2242)	4-1 (3275)	4-3 (3004)	3-1 (2168)	3-1 (2804)	3-2 (2803)	2-0 (2283)	

AYLESBURY UNITED

PROGRAMME DETAILS:
Pages: 36 **Price:** £1.50.
Editor: Dave Gamage
(01844 342308)

Formed: 1897 **Nickname:** The Ducks
Colours: Green & white qtrs/green/green
Change colours: Amber & black
Midweek home matchday: Tuesday **Newsline:** 0891 446 824
Reserve Team's League: None

Chairman: K Mistry **President:** K T Arnold
Vice Chairman:
Secretary / Press Officer: Tony Graham c/o the club. 01296 - 88178 (H) 436350
Manager: **Coach:** Gary Phillips
Football Development Manager: **Physio:** Paul Thawley
GROUND Address: The Stadium, Buckingham Road, Aylesbury HP20 2AQ (01296 436350/436891). **Directions:** On A413 to Buckingham, just off ring road opposite Horse & Jockey PH. Arriving from Buckingham ground is on left - from all other directions follow Buckingham signs and ground on right. Half hour walk from Aylesbury rail and bus stations.
Floodlights: Yes **Capacity:** 4,500 **Cover:** 1000 **Seats:** 400
Clubhouse: Pub hours, but shut during matches. Function room available for hire (01296 436891). Bar snacks available.
Club Shop: Sells programmes, magazines, leisurewear, badges etc. Contact Debbie Gamage c/o The Club. **Club Sponsors:**

PREVIOUS - **Leagues:** Bucks Contiguous 1897-1903, South Eastern 03-07, Spartan 07-51, Delphian 51-63, Athenian 63-76, Southern 76-88, GMV Conference 88-89
Grounds: Printing Works Ground 1897-1935, Sports Stadium, Wendover Rd (ground name changed to The Stadium, Turnfurlong Lane) 35-85, shared grounds 85-86.
Name: Night School, Printing Works (merged in 1897).

CLUB RECORDS - **Attendance:** 6,000 v England 1988 *(at old ground: 7,500 v Watford, FA Cup 1st Rd 1951).* **Career goalscorer:** Cliff Hercules. **Career appearances:** Cliff Hercules. **Transfer fee paid:** £15,000 for Glenville Donegal (Northampton, 1990). **Transfer fee received:** £35,000 for Glenville Donegal (Maidstone Utd, 1991)
BEST SEASON - **FA Trophy:** Quarter-Final replay 80-81.
FA Cup: 2nd Rd 88-89 89-90 91-92. **- League clubs defeated:** Southend Utd 89-90.
Players progressing to Football League: Ray Mabbutt (Bristol Rovers), Phil Barber (Crystal Palace 1986)
96-97 Captain: Mike Danzey **96-97 P.o.Y.:** Matt Hayward **96-97 Top scorer:** Mick Swaysland (26)
Local Press: Bucks Herald, Bucks Advertiser, Herald & Post.
Local Radio: Three Counties Radio, Chiltern Radio, Fox FM, Mix 96.

HONOURS: Southern Lg 87-88 (Mids Div R-up 84-85, Sth Div R-up 79-80); Athenian Lg Div 2 R-up 67-68; Delphian Lg 53-54 (R-up 52-53, Lg Cup 59-60); Spartan Lg 08-09 (R-up 52-53), West Div 28-29 (R-up 45-46), Div 1 38-39 (R-up 34-35); Berks & Bucks Snr Cup 13-14 85-86 96-97; Isthmian League Cup 94-95, Isthmian Charity Shield 95-96.

Aylesbury United: Back Row (L-R); Paul Thawley (Physio), Alex Adam, Gary Smith, Gary Simpson, Mick Swaysland, Matt Carmichael, Micky Danzey, Matt Hayward, Carl Hoddle, Peter Scott, Kevin Davies, Peter Wright (Community Officer), Ron Schmidt (Kit). Middle Row; Gary Phillips (Coach), Kevin Green (Man Dir), John Durban (Dir), Terry Arnold (Chr), Tim Salter (Dir), Tony Graham (Sec), Mark Newson. Front Row; Ricky Sullivan, Danny Power, Stacy Joseph, Justin Skinner, Matt Timberland, Kieran Gallagher, Robert Sharpe, Eddie Denton.

Aylesbury United

Match No.	Date	Venue H/A	Competition	Opponents	Result	League Pos.	Attendance	Goalscorers (Times if known)
1	Aug 17	A	IL	Hitchin Town	Lost 1-2		373	Carmichael
2	Aug 20	H	IL	Bromley	Drew 1-1		485	Adedeji (og)
3	Aug 24	H	IL	Carshalton Athletic	Won 3-1	9	470	Danzey, Carmichael 2 (1 pen)
4	Aug 27	A	IL	Kingstonian	Won 1-0	8	448	Sullivan
5	Aug 31	A	IL	Chertsey	Drew 0-0		464	
6	Sep 7	H	IL	Dagenham & Redbridge	Lost 0-1	18	578	
7	**Sep 10**	**H**	**GIC**	**Braintree Town**	**Lost 1-4**			
8	**Sep 14**	**A**	**FAC 1 Q**	**Welwyn Garden City**	**Won 4-1**		**341**	**Carmichael 3 (1 pen), Longman**
9	Sep 21	A	IL	Grays Athletic	Lost 0-2	15	240	
10	Sep 23	H	IL	St Albans City	Won 2-1	12	535	Sullivan, Gallagher
11	**Sep 28**	**H**	**FAC 2 Q**	**Boreham Wood**	**Lost 0-3**		**573**	
12	Oct 5	H	IL	Staines Town	Won 2-1	10	758	Newson 30, Carmichael 62
13	Oct 12	A	IL	Bishop's Stortford	Lost 0-2	11	389	
14	Oct 16	A	IL	Harrow Borough	Drew 0-0	10	164	
15	**Oct 19**	**A**	**FAT 1 Q**	**Tonbridge Angels**	**Won 2-0**		**438**	**Hayward, Carmichael**
16	Oct 22	H	IL	Boreham Wood	Won 2-0		515	Carmichael, Davies
17	Oct 26	A	IL	Oxford City	Lost 2-3	8	464	Carmichael, Danzey
18	Nov 2	H	IL	Yeovil Town	Drew 0-0	8	864	
19	**Nov 9**	**H**	**FAT Q 2**	**Sittingbourne**	**Drew 1-1**		**506**	**Davies**
20	**Nov13**	**A**	**FAT 2QR**	**Sittingbourne**	**Lost 1-2**			**Swaysland**
21	Nov 16	H	IL	Heybridge Swifts	Won 1-0	9	502	Swaysland
22	Nov 23	A	IL	Enfield	Lost 0-3	11	876	
23	Nov 30	H	IL	Chertsey Town	Won 2-1	8	766	Gallagher, Swaysland
24	Dec 7	A	IL	Dulwich Hamlet	Drew 1-1	9	341	Davies
25	Dec 14	H	IL	Yeading	Drew 2-2		404	Protheroe (og), Swaysland
26	Dec 20	A	IL	Purfleet	Won 1-0	8	122	Carmichael
27	Jan 18	H	IL	Hitchin Town	Won 2-1	7	655	Davies, Gallagher (pen)
28	Jan 25	A	IL	Bromley	Won 2-0	6	402	Swaysland, Davies
29	Feb 1	H	IL	Kingstonian	Lost 2-5	8	491	Carmichael (2)
30	**Feb 4**	**H**	**IL FMC**	**Boreham Wood**	**Won 1-0**			
31	Feb 15	H	IL	Grays Athletic	Won 3-0	8	534	Swaysland (2), Davies
32	Feb 22	A	IL	Boreham Wood	Won 1-0		306	Joseph
33	**Feb 25**	**H**	**IL FMC**	**Canvey Island**	**Won 2-1**			
34	Mar 1	H	IL	Bishop's Stortford	Drew 2-2	8	453	Shuttleworth (og), Carmichael
35	**Mar 4**	**H**	**IL FMC**	**Billericay Town**	Won 3-0			
36	Mar 8	A	IL	Staines Town	Lost 1-3	10	288	Davies
37	Mar 10	A	IL	Carshalton Athletic	Lost 1-3		256	Newson
38	Mar 15	H	IL	Harrow Borough	Won 2-0	11	453	Swaysland, Hayward
39	**Mar 18**	**H**	**ILFMC**	**Chesham United**	**Won 2-0**			
40	Mar 22	A	IL	Yeovil Town	Lost 2-3	11	2011	Swaysland (2)
41	Mar 24	A	IL	Dagenham & Redbridge	Won 2-0		421	Swaysland, Denton
42	Mar 28	H	IL	Oxford City	Won 6-1		874	Swaysland (4), Denton, Danzey
43	Mar 31	A	IL	Hendon	Won 3-0	7	405	Swaysland (2), Gallagher
44	Apr 3	A	IL	Sutton United	Drew 3-3		469	Carmichael (2), Swaysland
45	Apr 5	H	IL	Purfleet	Lost 0-2	7	434	
46	Apr 12	A	IL	Heybridge Swifts	Won 3-1	7	272	Davies, Swaysland, Carmichael (pen)
47	Apr 15	H	IL	Hendon	Lost 1-2		429	Davies
48	**Apr 17**	**A**	**FMC SF**	**Yeading**	**Drew 2-2***			**Davies, Carmichael**
49	Apr 19	H	IL	Enfield	Lost 1-3	7	1118	Denton
50	Apr 22	A	IL	St Albans City	Drew 0-0		412	
51	**Apr 24**	**H**	**FMC SF R**	**Yeading**	**Won 1-0**			**Carmichael**
52	Apr 26	A	IL	Yeading	Won 1-0	6	165	Danzey
53	Apr 29	H	IL	Sutton United	Drew 3-3		394	Power, Denton (pen), Swaysland
54	May 3	H	IL	Dulwich Hamlet	Won 2-0	7	502	Carmichael, Davies
55	**May 7**	**A**	**FMC F**	**Maidenhead United**	**Lost 0-3**		**778**	

AYLESBURY UNITED PLAYING SQUAD 1997-98

Goalkeepers: Gary Phillips (Barnet, Reading, Brentford, Barnet, WBA, Brighton)

Defenders: Matt Hayward (Thame, Pitstone & Ivinghoe, Aylesbury), **Mark Newson** (Barnet, Fulham, AFC Bournemouth, Maidstone, Charlton), **Justin Skinner** (Wimbledon), **Danny Power** (Barton R, Baldock, Luton), **Gary Simpson** (Luton), **Steve Gallen** (Dundalk, Doncaster, QPR), **Michael Danzey** (Camb.U, St.Albans, Peterborough, Nottingham F)

Midfielders: Gay Smith (Barnet, Welling, Wycombe, Enfield, Colchester, Fulham), **Luke Longman** (Wimbledon (T)), **Robert Sharpe** (Luton, QPR (J)), **Ricky Sullivan** (Hertford Heath), **Carl Hoddle** (Enfield, Woking, Barnet, Leyton O, B.Stortford), **Eddie Denton** (Abingdon T, Chesham, Newbury, Watford, Oxford U), **Peter Scott** (Hayes, Barnet, AFC Bournemouth, Fulham), **Chris Martin** (Risborough R, Aylesbury), **Jim Meara** (Doncaster, Watford)

Forwards: Mick Swaysland (London Colney, Evergreen), **Kevin Davies** (Chesham, Harrow, Chalfont St.Peter, Leighto, Marlow, Aylesbury, Marlow, Chesham, Tring, Kingstonian, Aylesbury, Luton), **Matt Carmichael** (Darlington, Scunthorpe, Lincoln, Basingstoke, Army), **Stacy Joseph** (Leyton O, Wimbledon)

BASINGSTOKE TOWN

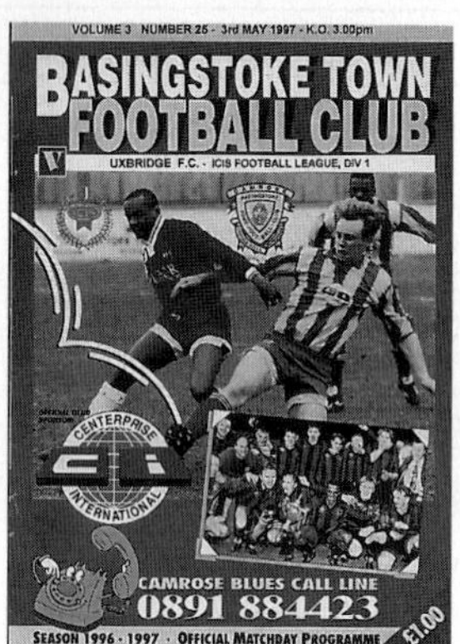

PROGRAMME DETAILS:
Pages: 40 **Price:** £1
Editor: Michael Edwards

Formed: 1896 **Nickname:** Stoke
Colours: Blue & gold stripes/blue/blue
Change colours: Red & black stripes/black/black
Midweek home matchday: Tuesday
Reserve Team's League: Suburban (Prem Div)

Chairman: David Knight **President:** Rafi Pazzak
Secretary: Richard Trodd, 5 Lemar Close, Brighton Hill, Basingstoke RG22 4HT (01256 413076)
Manager: Ernie Howe **Asst Manager:** Pete Peters
Coach: Steve Richardson **Physio:** Paul Bell
Press Officer: John Gray
Commercial Manager: Chris Richardson.

GROUND Address: Camrose Road, Western Way, Basingstoke RG24 6HW (01256 325063).
Directions: Exit 6 off M3 and follow A30 west, ground off Winchester Road. Two miles from bus and rail stations.
Capacity: 6,000 **Cover:** 1,500 **Seats:** 651 **Floodlights:** Yes
Clubhouse: Open every day (incl. lunchtime) (01256 464353).
Steward: Cheryl Fox
Club Shop: Selling programmes, books, scarves, shirts etc. Contact Neil Tysoe. **Metal Badges:** Yes
Sponsors: Centerprise International & McDonalds
PREVIOUS - Leagues: Hants 1900-40 45-71/ Southern 71-87. **Ground:** Castle Field 1896-1947.
CLUB RECORDS - Attendance: 4,091 v Northampton, FA Cup 1st Rd 1971. **Win:** 10-0 v Chichester City (H), FA Cup 1st Qualifying Round, September 1976. **Defeat:** 0-8 v Aylesbury United, Southern League, April 1979. **Goalscorer:** Paul Coombs **Appearances:** Billy Coombs. **Fees - Paid:** £4,750 for Steve Ingham (Gosport Borough). **Received:** £6,750 for Steve Ingham (Bashley)
Best FA Cup season: 2nd Rd 89-90 (lost 2-3 at home to Torquay). Also 1st Rd 71-72.
League clubs defeated in FA Cup: None.
Players progressing to Football League: Tony Godfrey (Southampton 1958), John Neale (Exeter 1972), Mike Doherty (Reading 1982), Micky Cheetham (Ipswich 1988), Matt Carmichael (Lincoln), Tony Franklin (Exeter), Steve Welsh (Peterborough 1990).
96-97 Captain: Steve Richardson **96-97 P.o.Y.:** Steve Harris **96-97 Top scorer:** Paul Coombs
Local Newspapers: Basingstoke Gazette (461131).
Local Radio Stations: Radio 210 (01734 413131)
HONOURS: Southern Lge Southern Div 85-86; Isthmian League Div 1 R-up 88-89 96-97; Hants League 67-68 69-70 70-71 (R-up 65-66 66-67 68-69, North Div 11-12 19-20); Hants Senior Cup 70-71 89-90 95-96 96-97.

Basingstoke Town FC. Taken the night they retained the Hants Senior Cup at the Dell, home of Southampton FC

Basingstoke Town

Match No.	Date	Venue H/A	Competition	Opponents	Result	League Pos.	Attendance	Goalscorers (Times if known)
1	Aug 17	H	IL	Thame United	Won 3-0	1	258	Joseph, Stairs, Coombs
2	Aug 20	A	IL	Wokingham Town	Drew 2-2	2	179	Carroll, Stairs
3	Aug 24	A	IL	Whyteleafe	Drew 1-1	5	187	Coombs
4	Aug 27	H	IL	Molesey	Drew 2-2	7	298	Bass, Carroll
5	Aug 31	H	IL	Bognor Regis	Drew 2-2	5	312	Carroll, Tydeman
6	Sep 7	A	IL	Leyton Pennant	Won 6-1	3	149	Carroll (2), Coombs (3), Terry
7	**Sep 10**	**A**	**GIC**	**Billericay**	**Lost 1-2**	**4**	**192**	**Stairs**
8	**Sep 14**	**H**	**FAC**	**Gloucester City**	**Lost 0-3**	**4**	**422**	
9	Sep 21	H	IL	Tooting & Mitcham	Won 1-0	3	286	Coombs
10	Sep 24	A	IL	Canvey Island	Drew 1-1	4	349	Stairs
11	Sep 28	H	IL	Maidenhead United	Won 2-0	1	365	Carroll, Coombs
12	Oct 5	A	IL	Worthing	Drew 1-1	2	401	Bass
13	Oct 12	H	IL	Barton Rovers	Won 3-0	2	338	Line, Mancey, Coombs
14	**Oct 23**	**H**	**HSC**	**Cowes Sports**	**Won 2-1**	**2**	**109**	**Carroll, Tydeman**
15	Oct 26	A	IL	Croydon	Won 2-0	2	148	Carroll, Coombs
16	Oct 29	A	IL	Berkhamsted Town	Won 3-1	2	163	Brown, Joseph, Coombs
17	Nov 2	H	IL	Marlow	Won 6-1	2	388	Huxford, Joseph, Coombs (3), Mancey
18	**Nov 9**	**A**	**FAT**	**Oxford City**	**Won 6-1**	**2**	**363**	**Brown, Harris, Carroll (2), Joseph, Mancey**
19	Nov 12	A	IL	Walton & Hersham	Won 2-0	1	185	Mancey (2)
20	Nov 16	H	IL	Hampton	Lost 0-2	1	501	
21	Nov 23	A	IL	Abingdon Town	Drew 1-1	2	264	Coombs
22	**Nov 30**	**H**	**FAT**	**Hastings Town**	**Lost 0-1**	**2**	**348**	
23	**Dec 3**	**A**	**HSC**	**Aldershot Town**	**Won 2-0**	**2**	**1029**	**Mancey, Coombs**
24	Dec 7	A	IL	Uxbridge	Drew 2-2	2	167	Harris, Coombs
25	Dec 14	H	IL	Leyton Pennant	Won 2-1	1	292	Brown, Mancey
26	Dec 21	A	IL	Billericay	Drew 1-1	1	320	Coombs
27	Dec 26	H	IL	Aldershot Town	Won 2-0	1	1814	Line, Coombs
28	Jan 1	A	IL	Bognor Regis	Won 2-0	1	331	Carroll, Mancey
29	**Jan 7**	**H**	**FMC**	**Tooting & Mitcham**	**Won 2-1**	**1**	**118**	**Manneh (2)**
30	Jan 11	H	IL	Whyteleafe	Won 4-1	1	390	Brown, Mancey, Coombs, o.g.
31	Jan 18	A	IL	Thame United	Won 2-1	1	174	Joseph, Tydeman
32	**Jan 21**	**A**	**HSC**	**Ryde Sports**	**Won 1-0**	**1**	**80**	**Tydeman**
33	Jan 25	H	IL	Wokingham	Lost 0-2	1	495	
34	Feb 1	A	IL	Molesey	Won 2-1	1	161	Harris (2)
35	**Feb 4**	**H**	**FMC**	**Abingdon Town**	**Won 1-0**	**1**	**116**	**Brown**
36	Feb 8	H	IL	Canvey Island	Won 2-1	1	425	Mancey, Carroll
37	Feb 11	H	IL	Chesham United	Won 4-0	1	820	Turton, Tydeman, Carey (2)
38	Feb 15	A	IL	Tooting & Mitcham	Won 4-0	1	219	Line, Mancey (3)
39	Feb 22	H	IL	Berkhamsted Town	Won 2-0	1	503	Carey (2)
40	Mar 1	A	IL	Barton Rovers	Won 4-1	1	150	Ferrett, Mancey, Carey, Joseph
41	**Mar 4**	**A**	**HSC**	**Farnborough Town**	**Won 2-1**	**1**	**471**	**Huxford, Carroll**
42	Mar 8	H	IL	Worthing	Drew 1-1	1	576	Line
43	Mar 15	A	IL	Maidenhead United	Drew 1-1	1	305	Tydeman
44	**Mar 20**	**A**	**FMC**	**Sutton United**	**Lost 3-5**	**1**	**303**	**Turton, Joseph (2)**
45	Mar 22	A	IL	Marlow	Lost 0-1	1	331	
46	Mar 29	H	IL	Croydon	Won 2-1	1	425	Carey, Coombs
47	Mar 31	A	IL	Aldershot Town	Lost 0-1	1	2263	
48	Apr 5	H	IL	Billericay Town	Drew 2-2	1	535	Mancey, Coombs
49	Apr 8	H	IL	Walton & Hersham	Drew 0-0	1	1061	
50	Apr 12	A	IL	Hampton	Lost 0-1	2	377	
51	Apr 19	H	IL	Abingdon Town	Won 3-0	2	628	Carroll, Mancey, Coombs
52	Apr 26	A	IL	Chesham United	Lost 1-2	2	1134	Mancey
53	**Apr 28**	**A**	**HSC F**	**Waterlooville**	**Won 2-0**	**2**	**2104**	**Carroll, Coombs**
54	May 3	H	IL	Uxbridge	Lost 0-2		220	

BASINGSTOKE TOWN PLAYING SQUAD 1997-98

Goalkeepers: Dean Beale (Worthing, Poole, Newport IOW, Basingstoke, Andover, Pirelli General, Sunderland, Southampton)

Defenders: Steve Richardson (Newbury, Reading, Southampton), **Andy Morley** (Poole), **Clive Huxford** (Salisbury, Eastleigh, Poole, Gosport B, Fareham, Waterlooville, Fareham, AFC Totton, Waterlooville), **Steve Harris** (Aldershot T, Farnham, Aldershot), **Simon Line** (Wokingham, Chertsey, Kingstonian, Brentford, Crystal Palace), **Brian Mundee** (Downton, Salisbury, Bashley, Basingstoke, Salisbury, Weymouth, Maidstone, Camb.U, Northampton, AFC Bournemouth, Hungerford)

Midfielders: Bruce Tydeman (Whitchurch U), **Chris Ferrett** (Fleet, AFC Bournemouth, Portsmouth (J)), **Alan Carey** (Bromley, Reading), **Tony Brown** (Aldershot T), **Robbie Carroll** (Salisbury, Bashley, Crawley, Worthing, Woking, Yeovil, Fareham, Brentford, Gosport B, Southampton), **Dave Osgood** (Bracknell, Aldershot T, Maidenhead, Burnham, Newbury, Basingstoke, Windsor, Maidenhead, Windsor)

Forwards: Paul Coombs (Farnborough, Aldershot), **Abdou Mennah** (Sukuta (Ghana), **Ian Mancey** (Local football), **Peter Terry** (Farnborough, Basingstoke), **Gary Joseph** (Worthing, Gosport B, Eastleigh, Basingstoke, Sholing Sports, Newport IOW), **David Prior** (Wokingham, Hampton, Wokingham)

BISHOP'S STORTFORD

Formed: 1874 **Nickname:** Blues
Colours: White & blue stripes/blue/blue
Change colours: Yellow/white/yellow.
Midweek matchday: Tuesday
Reserve League: Essex & Herts Border Comb.

Chairman: Gordon Lawrence **President:** B W A Bayford
Vice-Chairman: Mick Hancock **Secretary:** Graeme Auger, 58 Braziers Quay, South Street, Bishop's Stortford, Herts. CM23 3YW. (01279 465998)
Gen Manager: John Radford **Team Manager:** Dave Edwards
Coach: Ray Wickenden. **Physio:** Micky Stevens
Press Officer: Martin Stone (01376 510162).

GROUND Address: George Wilson Stadium, Rhodes Ave., Bishop's Stortford CM23 3JN (01279 654140) **Directions:** M11 jct 8, A1250 towards town centre, left at crossroads into London Rd (A1184), right at mini-r'bout and cross railway bridge, right at next island (by garage), Rhodes Ave is 2nd left (5-10 mins from M11). By rail: BR W Anglia Line (London Liverpool Str.-Cambridge)
Capacity: 6,000 **Cover:** 1,770 **Seats:** 270 **Floodlights:** Yes
Clubhouse: Open matchdays & Mondays (bingo). Available for hire.
Club Shop: Full stock inc. scarves, badges and other souvenirs. Massive stock of programmes and books etc. Contact Gareth Stephens (01279 501046)

PROGRAMME DETAILS
Pages: 48 **Price:** £1.20
Editor: Mick Hooker
(01279 817097)

PREVIOUS - Leagues: East Herts 1896-97 02-06 19-21/ Stansted & Dist. Lg 06-19/ Herts County 21-25 27-29/ Herts & Essex Border 25-27/ Spartan 29-51/ Delphian 51-63/ Athenian 63-73.

CLUB RECORDS - Attendance: 6,000 v Peterborough Utd, FA Cup 2nd Rd 1972 & v Middlesbrough FA Cup 3rd Rd replay, 1983 **Win:** 11-0: Nettleswell & Butntmill, Herts Jun Cup 2nd Rd 1911 **Defeat:** 0-13 v Cheshunt (H), Herts Sen. Cup 1st Rd 9/1/26. **Fee Paid:** £1,500 for Phil Hopkins (Walthamstow Ave., 84). **Fee Received:** £10,000 for Carl Hoddle (Leyton O., 89) **Scorer:** (Since 29) Jimmy Badcock 123 **Appearances:** Phil Hopkins 543.
Best Season - FA Amateur Cup: Winners 73-74. **FA Trophy:** Winners 80-81.
FA Cup: 3rd Rd rep. 82-83 (above) - **League clubs beaten:** Reading 82-83.
Players progressing to Football Lge: P Phelan (Southend) 61, M Hollow (Orient 62), P Phillips (Luton 69), T Baker (Colchester) 86, T Sorrell (Maidstone, Colchester, Barnet) 88, C Hoddle (Leyton O., Barnet) 89, T English (Colchester) 89.L Fortune-West (Gillingham) 95, L Braithwaite (Exeter City) 96.
96-97 Captain: Kevin Jordan **96-97 P.o.Y.:** Will Cooper **96-97 Top scorer:** Will Cooper
Local Press: B.Stortford Gazette, Herts & Essex Observer, Herald & Post.
Local Radio: BBC Essex, Essex Radio, Breeze AM, 1017.

HONOURS: Isthmian Lg Div 1 80-1 94-5 (Lg Cup 88-9, Full Mem. Cup 90-1), Prem. Inter Lg Cup 89-90; Athenian Lg 69-70 (R-up 66-7, Div 1 65-6, Div 2 R-up 64-5); Delphian Lg 54-5; London Snr Cup 73-4; Herts Snr Cup 58-9 59-0 63-4 70-1 72-3 73-4 75-6 86-7; E Anglian Cup 81-2; Herts Charity Cup 62-3 65-6 73-4 81-2 82-3 84-5 87-8 96-7; Herts Charity Shield 54-5; Herts I'mediate Cup(res) 94-95; Eastern F'lit Cup 84-5; Essex F'lit Cup 67-8; Essex & Herts Border Comb(W) 81-2 88-9 (R-up(2) 92-4); Fred Budden Tphy R-up 78-9 90-1 92-3.

Back Row (L-R): Ian Hollamby, Barry Fox, Karl Shuttlewood, Gavin King, Steve Moss, Richard Thomas, Richard Blake. Front Row; Lee Burns, Bradley Quinn, Kevin Jordan, Kevin Riley, Andy Walker, Will Cooper.

Bishop's Stortford

Match No.	Date	Venue H/A	Competition	Opponents	Result	League Pos.	Attendance	Goalscorers (Times if known)
1	Aug 17	A	IL	Oxford City	Lost 1-4		261	Hollomby
2	Aug 20	H	IL	Grays Athletic	Drew 0-0		269	
3	Aug 24	H	IL	St Albans City	Drew 1-1	17	431	Cooper
4	Aug 27	A	IL	Dulwich Hamlet	Lost 0-2		307	
5	Aug 31	A	IL	Bromley	Lost 1-2	21	313	Cooper
6	Sep 7	H	IL	Chertsey Town	Won 3-1	18	312	Cherry, Hollomby, Cooper
7	**Sep 10**	**A**	**GIC**	**Wokingham Town**	**Lost 1-2**			
8	**Sep 14**	**H**	**FAC 1 Q**	**Bedford Town**	**Won 2-0**		534	**Walker (pen), Forbes**
9	Sep 21	A	IL	Hendon	Lost 1-2	21	232	Cooper
10	Sep 24	H	IL	Dagenham & Redbridge	Won 2-0	19	344	Booker (2)
11	**Sep 28**	**A**	**FAC 2 Q**	**Boston United**	**Lost 0-3**		**977**	
12	Oct 5	H	IL	Heybridge Swifts	Drew 0-0	18	420	
13	Oct 12	H	IL	Aylesbury United	Won 2-0	14	389	Shuttlewood 70, Ravenscroft 85
14	**Oct 19**	**H**	**FAT 1 Q**	**Croydon**	**Won 3-0**		**337**	**Henry, Cooper, Walker (pen)**
15	Oct 21	A	IL	Dagenham & Redbridge	Lost 0-3		690	
16	Oct 26	H	IL	Enfield	Lost 1-3	18	765	Henry
17	Nov 2	A	IL	Sutton United	Lost 1-2	21	554	Benstead
18	**Nov 9**	**A**	**FAT 2 Q**	**Ashford**	**Lost 1-6**		**572**	**Ravenscroft**
19	Nov 11	A	IL	Purfleet	Lost 0-3	18	128	
20	Nov 16	A	IL	Kingstonian	Won 1-0	17	442	Henry
21	Nov 23	H	IL	Staines Town	Won 1-0	15	348	Adekola
22	Dec 7	H	IL	Carshalton Athletic	Won 2-1	12	324	Lebithan 27, Shuttlewood 32
23	Dec 14	A	IL	Hitchin Town	Lost 0-3	15	265	
24	Dec 21	H	IL	Yeovil Town	Lost 0-1	16	466	
25	Dec 26	A	IL	Boreham Wood	Lost 1-4	17	253	Hayter
26	Jan 18	H	IL	Oxford City	Drew 2-2	17	322	Cooper, Adekola
27	**Jan 19**	**A**	**IL FMC**	**Uxbridge**	**Won 3-0**			
28	Jan 25	A	IL	Grays Athletic	Won 1-0	16	244	Forbes
29	Feb 1	H	IL	Dulwich Hamlet	Lost 0-1	16	367	
30	Feb 8	A	IL	Chertsey	Won 3-0	15	232	Cooper, Adekola, Lebithan
31	Feb 15	H	IL	Hendon	Won 2-1	13	476	Cooper (2)
32	Feb 22	H	IL	Yeading	Drew 1-1	15	363	Burns
33	Mar 1	A	IL	Aylesbury United	Drew 2-2	15	453	Walker (pen), Burns
34	Mar 4	H	IL	Harrow Borough	Lost 0-1		221	
35	Mar 8	A	IL	Heybridge Swifts	Drew 0-0	16	387	
36	Mar 11	H	IL	Yeading	Lost 0-3		142	
37	Mar 15	H	IL	Purfleet	Lost 2-3	17	334	Cooper, Blake
38	Mar 22	H	IL	Sutton United	Lost 2-5	18	421	Riley, Walker (pen)
39	Mar 25	A	IL	St Albans City	Drew 1-1		346	Cooper
40	Mar 29	A	IL	Enfield	Drew 1-1		1219	Adekola
41	Mar 31	H	IL	Boreham Wood	Drew 0-0	18	412	
42	Apr 5	A	IL	Yeovil Town	Lost 0-1	18	2626	
43	Apr 9	A	IL	Harrow Borough	Drew 1-1		162	Walker
44	Apr 12	H	IL	Kingstonian	Drew 2-2	18	410	Forbes, Walker
45	Apr 19	A	IL	Staines Town	Drew 0-0	19	182	
46	Apr 22	H	IL	Bromley	Won 4-3		294	Fox (2), Cooper, Barnaby
47	Apr 26	H	IL	Hitchin Town	Lost 1-2	19	381	Cooper
48	May 3	A	IL	Carshalton Athletic	Lost 0-1	19	244	

BISHOP'S STORTFORD PLAYING SQUAD 1997-98

Goalkeepers: Gavin King (Cheshunt)
Defenders: Kevin Jordan (Southend, Tottenham (T)), **Karl Shuttlewood** (Worthing, Saffron Walden T, Sawbridgeworth T, B Stortford, Stansted, Saffron Walden T), **Stuart Wardley** (Saffron Walden T), **David Crate** (Ware, Hertford, Ware), **Richard Thomas** (Worthing, Leyton O, West Ham U (T)), **Barry Fox** (Boreham Wood, Grays, Millwall), **Steve Moss** (Worthing, Dulwich H, Worthing, Enfield, Worthing, Shoreham, Worthing, Walton & H, Basingstoke, Carshalton, Worthing, Woking, Camberley, Woking, Southampton), **Matt Barnaby** (Ware, Baldock, B.Stortford, Stevenage), **Mayin Sedgewick** (Harlow, Ware, Saffron Walden, Ware, B.Stortford)
Midfielders: Scott Forbes (Youth team), **Will Cooper** (Dag & Red), **Andy Walker** (Saffron Walden T, B Stortford, Stevenage B, Harlow T, Boreham Wood, Grays A, Harlow T, San Diego Sockers (USA), Harlow T), **Lee Burns** (Harlow, Hitchin,B.Stortford, Harlow, Stevenage, B.Stortford, Stevenage, Hertford, Harlow, Sawbridgeworth), **Kevin Riley** (Enfield)
Forwards: Ian Hollamby (Clavering, B Stortford), **David Adekola** (Brighton, Pruessain Koln (Ger), B.Stortford, Camb.U, Bath, Halifax, Bury), **Richard Blake** (St.Albans, Saffron Walden, Enfield), **Sean Junor** (C.Row & Romford, Clapton, Barking, Ford U, Romford, Aveley)

WOOD
BOREHAM WOOD FOOTBALL CLUB
SATURDAY 8th FEBRUARY 1997
v STEVENAGE BOROUGH
(F.A. Umbro Trophy 2nd Round) KICK OFF: 3.00PM

BOREHAM WOOD

Formed: 1948 **Nickname:** The Wood
Colours: White/black/red
Change colours: Amber & black
Midweek home matchday: Tuesday

Chairman: Phil Wallace **President:** W F O'Neill.
Secretary: Bob Nicholson, 56 Newcombe Road, Shenley, Radlett, Herts WD7 9EJ (01923 856077).
Manager: Bobby Makin **Asst Manager:** Alan Carrington
Coach: Billy Harrigan **Physio:** Dave Dickens
Press Officer: John D Gill (0181 723 6407)

PROGRAMME DETAILS:
Pages: 32 **Price:** £1.
Editor: John Gill
(0181 723 6407)

GROUND Address: Meadow Park, Broughinge Road, Boreham Wood, Herts WD6 5AL (0181 953 5097). **Directions:** A1 towards London from M25, 1st turn off for Boreham Wood, head for town centre, into Brook Rd at r'bout before town centre, Broughinge Rd is 1st left. 1 mile from Elstree & Boreham Wood station (Thameslink), then bus 292 or 107 to Red Lion (5 minutes walk).
Capacity: 4,502 **Cover:** 1,568 **Seats:** 500 **Floodlights:** Yes
Clubhouse: (0181 953 5097). Open during normal licensing hours. Snacks available. Function room (250) available for hire.
Club Shop: Sells good selection of souvenirs & programmes. Contact: Dell Ward 0181 363 7345. **Sponsors:** L & M Foods / Wansons

PREVIOUS - **Ground:** Eldon Avenue 1948-63. **Leagues:** Mid Herts 48-52, Parthenon 52-57, Spartan 56-66, Athenian 66-74. **Names:** Boreham Wood Rovers and Royal Retournez, amalgamated in 1948

CLUB RECORDS - Attendance: 2,500 v St Albans, F.A. Amateur Cup 70-71. **Goalscorer:** Micky Jackson, 208. **Appearances:** Dave Hatchett, 617. **Transfer Fee Received:** £10,000 from Barnet for Dean Samuels 1996

Best Season - FA Amateur Cup: 3rd Rd. replay 70-71. **FA Trophy:** Quarter Finals 1995-96. Replay at Chorley 3-4. **FA Cup:** 2nd Round v Luton Town 1996-97. 1st Rd 77-78, 73-74.

Players progressing to Football League: Colin Franks (Watford & Sheff Utd), Charles Ntamark (Walsall), Dean Samuels (Barnet 96)

96-97 Captain: Billy Harrigan **96-97 P.o.Y.:** Tony Samuels **96-97 Top scorer:** Tony Samuels (32)
Local Press: Boreham Wood Times, Watford Observer, Herts Advertiser. **Local Radio:** Chiltern Radio.

HONOURS: Isthmian Lg. Div I 94-95, Isthmian Lg Div 2 76-77 (Yth Cup R-up 80-81), Isthmian Lge. Cup 96-97; Athenian Lg 73-74 (Div 2 68-69, Div 1 R-up 69-70), Spartan Lg R-up 65-66, Herts Senior Cup 71-72 (R-up 66-67 74-75 79-80 87-88), Herts Junior Cup 51-52, Parthenon Lg 55-56 (R-up(2) 53-55 56-57, Herts Charity Shield 64-65, Herts Intermediate Cup 69-70, Herts Charity Cup(5) 80-81 83-84 85-86 88-90 (R-up 71-72 84-85 86-87 90-91 91-92 92-93), London Senior Cup R-up 89-90, London Intermediate Cup 70-71, Neale Trophy 69-70, Essex & Herts Border Comb 72-73 (Lg Cup 72-73, Western Div R-up 82-83 89-90), Mithras Cup 76-77, Middx Border Lg 81-82 (Lg Cup 79-80), Wallspan Floodlit 86-87.

Back Row (L-R); Alan Hamlet, Dave Hatchett, Steve Heffer, Tony Samuels, Barry Fox, Simon Sheppard, Garry Nisbet, Andy Lomas, Dean Samuels, Steve Daly, Nicky Ironton, Terry Harris (Coach). Front Row; Marc Liburd, Andy Prutton, Tony Joyce, Jason Shaw, Terry Robbins, Matthew Howard, Billy Harrigan, Rob Hollingdale.

Photo - Clive Butchins.

Boreham Wood

Match No.	Date	Venue H/A	Competition	Opponents	Result	League Pos.	Attendance	Goalscorers (Times if known)
1	Aug 17	A	IL	Kingstonian	Lost 1-5		433	Fox
2	Aug 20	H	IL	Hitchin Town	Won 4-0		359	Robbins (2), D Samuels (2)
3	Aug 27	A	IL	Bromley	Lost 0-2		325	
4	Aug 31	A	IL	Hendon	Won 2-1	13	334	T Samuels (2)
5	Sep 7	H	IL	Grays Athletic	Won 2-1	9	203	T Samuels, Hatchett
6	**Sep 14**	**H**	**FAC 1 Q**	**Tring Town**	**Won 8-1**		**187**	**Miles (2), D S'uels, Shaw, R'bins, N'bet, T S'uels, L'urd**
7	Sep 21	A	IL	Carshalton Athletic	Won 2-1	7	371	T Samuels, Liburd (pen)
8	Sep 24	H	IL	Chertsey Town	Lost 1-2	9	242	T Samuels
9	**Sep 28**	**A**	**FAC 2 Q**	**Aylesbury United**	**Won 3-0**		**573**	**T Samuels, Robbins (2)**
10	Oct 5	A	IL	Dulwich Hamlet	Lost 1-2	12	407	Robbins (pen)
11	**Oct 12**	**H**	**FAC 3 Q**	**Edgware Town**	**Won 3-2**		**422**	**T Samuels 6, D Samuels 8, Robbins 89**
12	Oct 19	H	IL	Kingstonian	Drew 0-0	15	303	
13	Oct 22	A	IL	Aylesbury United	Lost 0-2	16	515	
14	**Oct 26**	**H**	**FAC 4 Q**	**Thatcham**	**Won 5-0**		**522**	**Robbins 27, 78, 83, Nisbet 37, Liburd 69**
15	Nov 2	A	IL	Staines Town	Lost 1-2	19	214	Robbins
16	**Nov 5**	**H**	**GIC**	**Dagenham & Redbridge**	**Won 1-0**		**126**	**1 og**
17	Nov 9	H	IL	Harrow Borough	Won 2-0	12	281	Robbins 81, D Samuels 90
18	Nov 12	H	IL	Yeovil Town	Lost 0-3		333	
19	**Nov 16**	**H**	**FAC 1**	**Rushden & Diamonds**	**Drew 1-1**		**1567**	**Robbins 9**
20	Nov 23	A	IL	Heybridge Swifts	Won 2-0	12	236	Joyce (2)
21	**Nov 26**	**A**	**FAC 1 R**	**Rushden & Diamonds**	**Won 3-1**		**2619**	**Heffer, A Samuels, D Samuels**
22	Nov 30	H	IL	Hendon	Lost 1-2	14	412	Robbins
23	**Dec 7**	**A**	**FAC 2**	**Luton Town**	**Lost 1-2**		**5332**	**Robbins**
24	Dec 14	H	IL	St Albans City	Lost 0-2	17	472	
25	**Dec 17**	**A**	**GIC**	**Leighton Town**	**Won 2-0**			
26	Dec 21	A	IL	Enfield	Lost 0-3	18	673	
27	Dec 26	H	IL	Bishop's Stortford	Won 4-1	16	253	A Samuels (3), Brown
28	Jan 11	A	IL	Dagenham & Redbridge	Lost 1-2	16	661	Prutton 40
29	**Jan 18**	**A**	**FAT 1**	**Enfield**	**Won 3-1**		**693**	**Samuels (2), Nisbet**
30	Jan 25	A	IL	Hitchin Town	Won 2-1	14	329	Shaw, Bunce (og)
31	**Jan 29**	**A**	**GIC**	Harrow Borough	Won 3-1			
32	Feb 1	H	IL	Bromley	Drew 2-2		251	Samuels, Shaw
33	**Feb 3**	**A**	**IL FMC**	**Aylesbury United**	**Lost 0-1**		**1242**	
34	**Feb 8**	**H**	**FAT2**	**Stevenage Borough**	**Lost 0-1**			
35	Feb 11	A	IL	Oxford City	Drew 0-0		151	
36	Feb 15	H	IL	Carshalton Athletic	Won 3-0	14	219	Liburd, Robbins, Prutton
37	Feb 22	H	IL	Aylesbury United	Drew 1-1	16	306	Samuels
38	Mar 1	A	IL	Sutton United	Drew 1-1	16	469	P Shaw
39	Mar 8	H	IL	Dulwich Hamlet	Won 2-1	17	217	Robbins, Samuels
40	**Mar 11**	**H**	**GIC**	**Kingstonian**	**Won 3-1**		**209**	**(BW won 4-3 on agg.) Nisbet (2), T Samuels**
41	Mar 15	A	IL	Yeovil Town	Drew 0-0		3195	
42	Mar 18	H	IL	Dagenham & Redbridge	Won 3-1		114	T Samuels (2), Woodsford
43	Mar 22	H	IL	Staines Town	Won 3-0	15	211	Daly, Woodsford, T Samuels
44	Mar 25	H	IL	Sutton United	Won 1-0		261	Shaw
45	Mar 29	A	IL	Harrow Borough	Lost 0-2		308	
46	Mar 31	A	IL	Bishop's Stortford	Drew 0-0	14	412	
47	Apr 2	A	IL	Yeading	Lost 1-2		187	Heffer
48	Apr 5	H	IL	Enfield	Drew 1-1	20	782	Nisbet
49	Apr 8	A	IL	Chertsey Town	Drew 1-1		175	T Samuels
50	Apr 12	A	IL	Purfleet	Drew 1-1	14	193	Heffer
51	Apr 15	H	IL	Yeading	Drew 1-1		137	P Shaw
52	Apr 19	H	IL	Heybridge Swifts	Drew 0-0	14	153	
53	Apr 22	A	IL	Grays Athletic	Won 4-2		142	Prutton (3), Hollingdale
54	Apr 26	A	IL	St Albans City	Won 2-1	10	462	S Daly, T Samuels
55	Apr 29	H	IL	Purfleet	Lost 0-1		177	
56	May 3	H	IL	Oxford City	Won 3-2	10	202	Heffer, Nisbet, Robbins (pen)
57	**May 8**	**H**	**GILC**	**Braintree Town**	**Won 1-0***		**473**	**T Samuels**

* After Extra Time

BOREHAM WOOD PLAYING SQUAD 1997-98

Goalkeepers: Martin Taylor (B Stortford, Epping T, Woodford T, Hendon, Jyderup (Den), Charlton, Arsenal)

Defenders: Tony Joyce (Stevenage B, Staines T, Woking, Aldershot, QPR), **Gary Nisbet** (Collier Row, Walthamstow Pennant, Collier Row), **Steve Daly** (Wembley, Chalfont St.Peter, Ruislip Manor), **Billy Harrigan** (B Stortford, Chesham U, Leyt & Ilf, Walthamstow Ave, B Stortford, Camb.U), **Dave Hatchett** (Enfield), **Paul Ferry** (Edgware T)

Midfielders: Andy Prutton (Harrow B, Dartford, Cheshunt, Wormley R), **Jason Shaw** (Harrow B, Dartford, Redbridge F, West Ham), **Steve Heffer** (Hendon, Grays A, Swindon, Southend, West Ham), **Paul Jordan** (Watford), **Rob Hollingdale** (Wembley), **Ross Outram** (Aveley), **Mark Brown** (Exeter)

Forwards: Marc Liburd (Millwall, Watford (T)), **Tony Samuels** (Leyton, Collier Row, Bromley, Leyton-Wingate, Leyt & Ilf), **Terry Robbins** (Barnet, Welling U,Crawley T, Maidstone U, Gillingham, Tottenham), **Jamie Woodsford** (Luton)

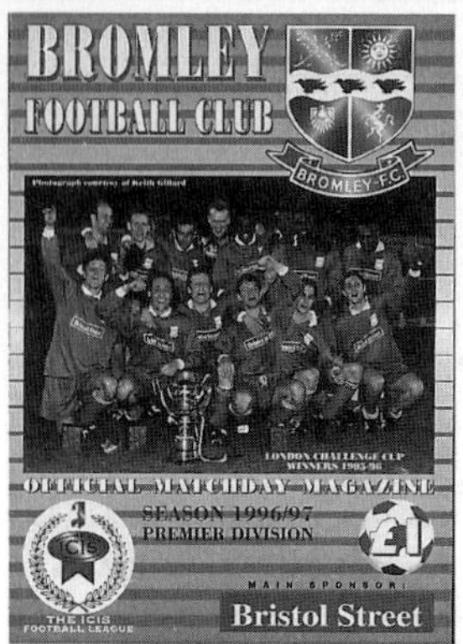

BROMLEY

Formed: 1892 **Nickname:** The Lilywhites
Colours: White/black/black.
Change colours: All blue
Midweek home matchday: Tuesday **Newsline:** 0930 555 838
Reserve Team's League: Suburban
Youth League: Southern Youth

Chairman: Glyn Beverly **Managing Director:** Eddy Davies
Secretary: Kerry Phillips, 15 Watling Street, Bexleyheath, Kent. DA6 7QJ. (01322 554108/529682, Fax 550543)
Manager: George Wakeling **Coach:** John Kane
Physio: John De Palma

PROGRAMME DETAILS:
Pages: 32 **Price:** £1
Ed: John Self.
(0181 402 2391)

GROUND Address: Hayes Lane, Bromley, Kent BR2 9EF (0181 460 5291 or 0181-313-3992).
Directions: One mile from Bromley South (BR). Buses 316, 146 and 119 pass ground. Junction 4 off M25, then A21 towards London.
Capacity: 5,000 **Cover:** 2,500 **Seats:** 1,300 **Floodlights:** Yes
Clubhouse: Open matchdays. Food available.
Club Shop: Yes. contact Jack Freeman

PREVIOUS - Leagues: South London - 1894/ Southern 94-96/ London 96-98 99-1901/ West Kent 01-04/ Southern Suburban 04-07/ Kent 1898-99 11-14/ Spartan 07-08/ Isthmian 08-11/ Athenian 19-52. **Grounds:** White Hart Field Cricket Ground, Widmore Rd (pre-1904)/ Plaistow Cricket Field 1904-37/ Hayes Lane 06-37/ Present Hayes Lane 38 to date

CLUB RECORDS - Attendance: 12,000 v Nigeria, 1950. **Goalscorer:** George Brown 570 (1938-61) **Appearances:** George Brown **Win:** 12-1 v Chertsey FA Cup 75. **Defeat:** 1-11 v Cray Wands 33. **Fees - Paid:** Unknown **Received:** £50,000 for Jon Goodman (from Millwall 90)

Best Season - FA Amateur Cup: Winners 10-11, 37-38, 48-49. **FA Trophy:** Second Round 91-92. **FA Cup:** 2nd Rd replay v Scarborough 37-38, Lincoln 38-39, Watford 45-46.

Players progressing to Football League: Roy Merryfield (Chelsea), Stan Charlton (Arsenal 52), Ron Heckman (Orient 55), John Gregory (West Ham 51), Bill Lloyd (Millwall 56), Brian Kinsey (Charlton 56), Harold Hobbs (Charlton & England), Matt Carmichael (Lincoln 90), Leslie Locke (QPR 56), Jon Goodman (Millwall 90).

96-97 Captain: Frank Coles **96-97 P.O.Y.:** Keith Sharman **96-97 Top Scorer:** Mark Tompkins
Local Press: Bromley Times. **Local Radio:** Radio Kent, Bromley Hospital Radio, Bromley Local Radio.

HONOURS: Isthmian League(4) 08-10 53-54 60-61 (R-up 52-53 55-56 87-88), Div 1 R-up 79-80 85-86 90-91, Prince Phillip 5-a-side Cup 1979; Athenian League 22-23 48-49 50-51 (R-up 35-36); London League Div 2 1896-97; Spartan League 07-08; London Snr Cup 09-10 45-46 50-51; Kent Senior Cup 49-50 76-77 91-92 96-97; Kent Amateur Cup(12) 07-08 31-32 35-37 38-39 46-47 48-49 50-51 52-53 53-55 59-60; London Challenge Cup 1995-96.

Bromley FC: Back Row (L-R); Ricky Antoine, Ian Rawlings, Keith Sharman, David Wietecha, Steve Campfield, Ollie Adedeji, Marcel Dennis, Aggreyobonyo Obiero. Front Row; Dean Francis, Frank Coles, Jon Warden, Alan Carey, Tim Griggs, David May.

Bromley

Match No.	Date	Venue H/A	Competition	Opponents	Result	League Pos.	Attendance	Goalscorers (Times if known)
1	Aug 17	H	IL	Staines Town	Lost 1-2		284	Coles
2	Aug 20	A	IL	Aylesbury United	Drew 1-1		485	Brown
3	Aug 24	A	IL	Yeovil Town	Lost 0-1	19	1811	
4	Aug 27	H	IL	Boreham Wood	Won 2-0		325	Wordsworth (2)
5	Aug 31	H	IL	Bishop's Stortford	Won 2-1	10	313	Rawlings, Wordsworth
6	Sep 7	A	IL	Sutton United	Drew 2-2	12	720	Wordsworth (pen), Antoine
7	**Sep 10**	**A**	**GIC**	**Collier Row & Romford**	**Lost 3-4***			
8	**Sep 14**	**H**	**FAC 1 Q**	**Viking Sports**	**Won 4-0**			**Tompkins (3), Campbell**
9	Sep 21	H	IL	Yeading	Won 5-1	8	241	Rawlings (2), Antoine, Wordsworth (2)
10	Sep 25	A	IL	Harrow Borough	Lost 0-2	8	153	
11	**Sep 28**	**A**	**FAC 2 Q**	**Crawley**	**Won 4-0**	8	**896**	**Tompkins (2), Rawlings, Wordsworth**
12	Oct 5	H	IL	Carshalton Athletic	Won 2-0		487	Campfield, Wordsworth
13	**Oct 12**	**H**	**FAC 3 Q**	**St Leonards Stamcroft**	**Drew 1-1**		**638**	**Magee**
14	**Oct 16**	**A**	**FAC 3QR**	**St Leonards Stamcroft**	**Won 5-2**		**648**	**Tompkins (2), Wordsworth, Coles, Antoine**
15	**Oct 19**	**H**	**FAT 1 Q**	**Uxbridge Town**	**Won 1-0**		**400**	**Tompkins**
16	**Oct 26**	**H**	**FAC 4 Q**	**Sutton United**	**Won 1-0**		**1063**	**Sharman 72**
17	Nov 2	A	IL	Grays Athletic	Lost 0-1	17	289	
18	**Nov 9**	**A**	**FAT 2 Q**	**Maidenhead United**	**Won 3-1**		**217**	**Coles (2), Sharman**
19	**Nov 16**	**H**	**FAC 1**	**Enfield**	**Lost 1-3**		**2709**	**Kane 9**
20	Nov 23	A	IL	Oxford City	Won 3-2	16	218	Tompkins, Rawlings, Kane
21	Nov 26	H	IL	Chertsey Town	Won 5-1		225	Tompkins (2), Coles, Kane, Dennington
22	**Nov 30**	**H**	**FAT 3 Q**	**Worcester City**	**Drew 1-1**		**345**	**Warden**
23	**Dec 2**	**A**	**FAT 3QR**	**Worcester City**	**Lost 0-2**		**502**	
24	Dec 14	H	IL	Hendon	Drew 2-2	13	341	Warden (2)
25	**Dec 17**	**A**	**IL FMC**	**Hampton**	**Lost 1-2**			**Dennington**
26	Dec 21	A	IL	Heybridge Swifts	Lost 3-4	15	212	Campfield, Antoine, Sharman
27	Dec 26	H	IL	Dulwich Hamlet	Drew 0-0	14	628	
28	Jan 18	A	IL	Staines Town	Lost 0-3	14	235	
29	Jan 25	H	IL	Aylesbury United	Lost 0-2	17	402	
30	Jan 27	A	IL	Purfleet	Lost 0-2		207	
31	Feb 1	A	IL	Boreham Wood	Drew 2-2	18	251	Dennington 65, Obieio 81
32	Feb 8	H	IL	Harrow Borough	Lost 1-2	19	325	Sharman 47
33	Feb 11	A	IL	Enfield	Lost 3-4		560	Adedeji, O'Connor, Warden
34	Feb 15	A	IL	Yeading	Lost 0-1	19	160	
35	Feb 18	A	IL	Hitchin Town	Lost 2-5	19	188	Rawlings, Sharman
36	Feb 22	A	IL	Dagenham & Redbridge	Won 2-0	19	751	Tompkins (2)
37	Feb 25	A	IL	St Albans City	Won 3-0		189	Warden (2), Coles
38	Mar 1	H	IL	Enfield	Lost 0-2	18	551	
39	Mar 4	H	IL	Kingstonian	Drew 2-2		216	White, Tompkins
40	Mar 8	A	IL	Carshalton Athletic	Lost 2-3	18	402	Tompkins, Rawlings
41	Mar 15	H	IL	Hitchin Town	Won 3-2	18	283	Tompkins, Coles, Griggs
42	Mar 18	H	IL	Sutton United	Won 2-1		344	Sharman White
43	Mar 22	H	IL	Grays Athletic	Lost 1-2	16	354	Tompkins
44	Mar 25	H	IL	Purfleet	Won 2-1		276	Warden, Griggs
45	Mar 29	A	IL	Kingstonian	Drew 1-1		436	Warden
46	Mar 31	A	IL	Dulwich Hamlet	Lost 1-2	16	468	Tompkins
47	Apr 2	H	IL	Bromley	Won 1-0		313	Rawlings
48	Apr 5	H	IL	Heybridge Swifts	Drew 1-1	16	303	Tompkins
49	Apr 12	A	IL	Chertsey Town	Lost 1-3	16	252	Charman
50	Apr 19	H	IL	Oxford City	Won 3-0	16	320	Francis, Tompkins, Sharman
51	Apr 22	A	IL	Bishop's Stortford	Lost 3-4		294	Tompkins (2), Dennington (pen)
52	Apr 26	A	IL	Hendon	Lost 1-4	16	370	Dennis
53	Apr 29	H	IL	Yeovil Town	Lost 1-2		979	Tompkins
54	May 3	H	IL	St Albans City	Drew 1-1	18	334	Dennis

* After Extra Time

BROMLEY PLAYING SQUAD 1997-98

Goalkeepers: Dave Wietecha (Millwall)

Defenders: Keith Sharman (Barking, Leyton O, Clapton), **Dean Francis** (Youth team), **Ollie Adedeji** (Boreham Wood, Bromley, Finchley), **Ian Rawlings** (Leyton-Wingate, Leyton O), **Paul Campbell** (Charlton), **David May** (Enfield, Barking, KTPTipples), **Danny Woods** (Youth team), **Mark Loveday** (Youth team), **Wes O'Connor** (Slough)

Midfielders: Bobby Dennington (Tooting & Mitcham U, Bromley, Tooting & MitchamU, Bromley, Leyton-Wingate), **Frank Coles** (Enfield, Leyton-Wingate, Leyt & Ilf, Dagenham, Leyt & Ilf, Charlton), **David Gray** (Youth team), **Matthew Motton** (Chertsey, Carshalton, Chertsey)

Forwards: Micky Brown (Sutton U, Bromley, Wealdstone, Tooting & Mitcham U, Dulwich Hamlet, Croydon), **Mark Tompkins** (Tooting & Mitcham U, Fisher A, Corinthian, Dulwich Hamlet, Darenth Heathside, AFC Eltham), **Steve White** (Youth team), **Tim Griggs** (Youth team)

PROGRAMME DETAILS:
Pages: 14 **Price:** 80p
Editor: Andy Hill.
(0181 647 6288)

CARSHALTON ATHLETIC

Formed: 1903 **Nickname:** Robins
Colours: White, maroon trim/maroon/white.
Change colours: Maroon/white.
Midweek matchday: Tuesday **Newsline:** 0891 446849.
Reserve League: Suburban.

Chairman: Mike Dawes. **Jt-Presidents:** W Stephenson & B Plumbridge
Vice Chairman: Keith Dawes. **Secretary:** Vic Thompson, 11 Poulton Avenue, Sutton, Surrey. SM1 3PZ. 0181 644 6402 (H)
General Manager: Fred Callaghan. **Manager:** Chris Kilby
Coach: Tommy Mason **Physio:** Alan McCreeney
Press Officer: Roger Fear **Comm. Man.:** John Carpentiere.

GROUND Address: War Memorial Sports Ground, Colston Av, Carshalton SM5 2PW (0181 642 8658). **Directions:** Turn right out of Carshalton BR Station, and Colston Avenue is first left. Entrance 150 yards on right. London Transport bus 151 from Morden to Wrythe Green Lane.
Capacity: 8,000 **Cover:** 4,500 **Seats:** 240 **Floodlights:** Yes
Clubhouse: Open every evening and lunchtime. Licenced bar, pool, darts, machines, discos on Saturday. Separate function hall (bookings taken). Food: sandwiches, rolls, burgers, hot dogs, teas, coffees and soft drinks. (0181 642 8658). **Club Sponsors:** Mile Train
Club Shop: Sells hats, scarves, T-shirts, badges, programmes etc.

PREVIOUS - **Grounds:** Wrythe Recreation Ground 1907-14/ Culvers Park 19-20. **Leagues:** Southern Sub (pre-1911), Surrey Snr 22-23, London 23-46, Corinthian 46-56, Athenian 56-73

CLUB RECORDS - **Attendance:** 7,800 v Wimbledon, London Senior Cup. **Career goalscorer:** Jimmy Bolton. **Career appearances:** Jon Raffington and Jon Warden. **Transfer fee paid:** £2,000 for Jimmy Bolton, 1990. **Transfer fee received:** £15,000 for Curtis Warmington (Enfield). **Win:** 13-0 v Worthing, Loctite Cup Third Round 28/2/91.

BEST SEASON - **FA Trophy:** 3rd Rd 80-81 (lost 0-3 at home to Mossley, eventual Runners-up).
FA Cup: 2nd Rd 82-83, lost 1-4 at Torquay. - **League clubs defeated:** None.

Players progressing to Football League: Roy Lunnes (Crystal Pal. 1960), Les Burns (Charlton 1967), Ron Walker (Watford), Nobby Warren (Exeter), Gus Caesar (Arsenal), Darren Annon (Brentford) 1994, Ian Cox (Crystal Pal.) 1994.

96-97 Captain: Mark Harmsworth **96-97 P.o.Y.:** Eddie Saunders **96-97 Top scorer:** Andy Salako (17)
Local Press: Wallington & Carshalton Advertiser, Carshalton Herald. **Local Radio:** Capital.

HONOURS: Isthmian League Div 2 Runners-up 76-77, Corinthian League 52-53 53-54, Surrey Senior League Runners-up 22-23, Surrey Senior Cup(3) 88-90 91-92, Surrey Senior Shield (Runners-up(2)), London Challenge Cup 91-92.

Back Row (L-R); Adrian Blake, Andy Salako, Paul Clark, Mark Harmsworth (Capt), Eddie Saunders, Danny Bower, Simon Bassey, John Ugbath. Front Row; Martin Chester, Matt Hanlan, Francis Vines, Gary Bowyer, Barry Kingsford, Sean Davy.
Photo - K Rolfe

Carshalton Athletic

Match No.	Date	Venue H/A	Competition	Opponents	Result	League Pos.	Attendance	Goalscorers (Times if known)
1	Aug 17	H	IL	Enfield	Lost 0-1		607	
2	Aug 21	A	IL	Harrow Borough	Drew 1-1		221	Salako
3	Aug 24	A	IL	Aylesbury United	Lost 1-3	14	470	Saunders
4	Aug 26	H	IL	Staines Town	Won 2-0	12	401	Kingsford, Williams
5	Aug 31	H	IL	Yeading	Drew 0-0	16	358	
6	Sep 7	A	IL	Heybridge Swifts	Won 2-0		329	Salako, Williams
7	**Sep 9**	**H**	**GIC**	**Whyteleafe**	**Won 6-0**			**Kingsford (2), Vines (2), Salako (2)**
8	**Sep 14**	**H**	**FAC 1 Q**	**Tunbridge Wells**	**Won 6-0**		**298**	**Pitcher (3), Saunders, Salako, Vines**
9	Sep 17	A	IL	Yeovil Town	Lost 0-3		1846	
10	Sep 21	H	IL	Boreham Wood	Lost 1-2	16	371	Bower
11	**Sep 28**	**A**	**FAC 2 Q**	**Farnborough Town**	**Lost 2-3**		**655**	**Salako, Williams**
12	Sep 30	H	IL	Hitchin Town	Lost 1-2		255	Bowyer
13	Oct 5	A	IL	Bromley	Lost 0-2	21	487	
14	Oct 12	H	IL	Purfleet	Won 2-1	18	272	Saunders 18, Vines 28
15	Oct 15	A	IL	Grays Athletic	Won 1-0		179	Kingsford
16	Oct 19	H	IL	Dagenham & Redbridge	Drew 0-0	11	352	
17	Nov 2	A	IL	Kingstonian	Drew 1-1	12	514	Hanlon
18	**Nov 4**	**H**	**IL C**	**Braintree Town**	**Lost 1-2**			**Vines**
19	Nov 16	H	IL	Oxford City	Drew 1-1		349	Ugbah
20	Nov 23	A	IL	Dulwich Hamlet	Lost 1-4	17	413	Salako (pen)
21	Nov 25	H	IL	Heybridge Swifts	Won 4-1		211	Vines (2, 1 pen), Clark, Salako
22	**Nov 30**	**H**	**FAT 3 Q**	**Heybridge Swifts**	**Lost 0-3**		**202**	
23	**Dec 2**	**A**	**IL FMC**	**Croydon**	**Won 4-1***			
24	Dec 7	H	IL	Bishop's Stortford	Lost 1-2	14	324	Clark 30
25	Dec 17	A	IL	Chertsey Town	Won 3-2		247	Vines, Daley
26	Dec 21	A	IL	Hendon	Drew 2-2	12	251	Ugbah (2)
27	Dec 26	H	IL	Sutton United	Drew 3-3	12	1460	Vines, Salako, Clarke
28	Jan 18	A	IL	Purfleet	Lost 0-2		215	
29	Jan 25	H	IL	Harrow Borough	Won 2-1	12	349	Butler (og), Salako
30	Feb 1	A	IL	Staines Town	Lost 0-2	12	318	
31	Feb 8	H	IL	Yeovil Town	Lost 0-1	13	603	
32	Feb 10	H	IL	Chertsey Town	Won 2-0		216	Kingsford, Salako
33	Feb 15	A	IL	Boreham Wood	Lost 0-3	12	219	
34	Feb 22	H	IL	Grays Athletic	Won 6-0	12	293	Bolton (3), Salako (2), Argent
35	Mar 1	A	IL	St Albans City	Drew 0-0	13	378	
36	Mar 8	H	IL	Bromley	Won 3-2	12	402	Bolton, Bassey, Salako
37	Mar 10	H	IL	Aylesbury United	Won 3-1		256	Daly, Kingsford, Newson (og)
38	Mar 15	A	IL	Dagenham & Redbridge	Won 1-0	10	552	Kingsford
39	Mar 18	A	IL	Enfield	Lost 0-2		608	
40	Mar 22	H	IL	Kingstonian	Lost 1-3	12	554	Salako
41	Mar 25	A	IL	Yeading	Drew 0-0		164	
42	Mar 29	A	IL	Hitchin Town	Lost 2-3		328	Salako, Saunders
43	Mar 31	A	IL	Sutton United	Lost 0-2	13	1106	
44	Apr 5	H	IL	Hendon	Lost 0-2	15	207	
45	Apr 12	A	IL	Oxford City	Drew 1-1		214	Bolton
46	Apr 14	H	IL	St Albans City	Won 2-0		289	Bolton, Salako
47	Apr 19	H	IL	Dulwich Hamlet	Drew 0-0	12	315	
48	May 3	H	IL	Bishop's Stortford	Won 1-0	13	244	Bolton

CARSHALTON ATHLETIC PLAYING SQUAD 1997-98

Goalkeepers: Adrian Blake (Chertsey T, Kingstonian, Walton & H, Yeading, Feltham, Walton & H)

Defenders: Eddie Saunders (Civil Service FC), **Dave Argent** (Epsom, Whyteleafe, FC Menden (Ger), Chipstead), **Dave Stevens** (Kingstonian, Carshalton, Crystal Palace), **Jim Wenlock** (Whyteleafe, Molesey, Ditton, Leatherhead, Kingstonian), **Paul Clark** (Kingstonian, St.Albans, Carshalton, Molesey, Walton & H, St.Albans, Camb.U)

Midfielders: Sean Daly (Sutton U, Croydon), **Gary Bowyer** (Kingstonian, Carshalton A, Bromley, Whyteleafe, Carshalton A, Crystal Palace (T)), **Robin Beste** (Warlingham, Dulwich Hamlet, Chelsea (A)), **Simon Bassey** (Charlton (T)), **Mark Harmsworth** (Molesey, Yeading, Walton & H, Yeading, Hayes, Fisher A, Hampton, Kingstonian, Hampton, Epsom & Ewell), **Neil Robson** (Molesey, Carshalton A, Dorking, Sutton U, Epsom & Ewell, Sutton U), **Phil Dawson** (Chipstead, Molesey, Carshalton, Woking, Carshalton, Sutton U, Chipstead)

Forwards: Andy Salako (Bromley, Tonbridge, St.Albans C, Croydon, Welling U, Charlton), **Barry Kingsford** (Youth team), **Jimmy Bolton** (Hendon, Kingstonian, Carshalton, Harrow, Farnborough, Kiruna (Swe), Farnborough, Tooting, Farnborough, Wimbledon, Hillingdon, Tottenham H), **Noel Frankum** (Leatherhead,Tooting, Kingstonian, Burnley)

CHESHAM UNITED

Formed: 1886 **Nickname:** The Generals
Colours: Blue & orange
Change colours: All Yellow & green
Midweek home matchday: Tuesday
Reserve Team's League: Suburban North

President: Bill Wells **Chairman:** David Pembroke
Secretary: Ronald Campion c/o Chesham United FC. Tel: 01494 837494 (H) 01494 783964 (B).
Manager: Andy Thomas **Assistant Manager:** Tony O'Driscoll
Physio: Michael Burgess **Commercial Manager:** Peter Wright
Press Officer: Jim Chambers
GROUND - Address: The Meadow, Amy Lane, Amersham Road, Chesham, Bucks. HP5 1NE (01494 783964 - ground clubhouse. 01494 791608 - fax. 0891 884580 - match information service). **Directions:** M25 junction 18, A404 to Amersham, A416 to Chesham - go down to r-about at foot of Amersham Hill, then sharp left. 10 mins walk from Chesham station (Metropolitan Line).
Capacity: 5,000 **Cover:** 2,500 **Seats:** 284 **Floodlights:** Yes
Clubhouse: Open every evening & matchdays. Bar snacks. Available for hire (business training meetings, weddings etc).
Club Shop: Open matchdays
Metal Badges: Yes **Sponsors:** MFI.

PROGRAMME DETAILS:
Pages: 52 **Price:** £1
Editors: J & S Chambers
(01494 775490 [H])

PREVIOUS - Leagues: Spartan 17-47/ Corinthian 47-63/ Athenian 63-73.

CLUB RECORDS - Attendance: 5,000 v Cambridge Utd, FA 3rd Rd 5/12/79. **Goalscorer:** John Willis. **Appearances:** Martin Baguley (600+). **Record Fees - Paid & Received:** Undisclosed (club policy).
Best FA Cup season: 3rd Rd 79-80. 1st Rd 66-67 68-69 76-77 82-83.
Best FA Trophy season: 3rd Rd 92-93 (1-3 v Sutton United [H])
Players progressing to Football League: Bill Shipwright & Jimmy Strain (Watford 53 & 55), Stewart Scullion (Charlton 65), John Pyatt (L'pool 67), Brian Carter (Brentford 68), Kerry Dixon (Spurs 78), Tony Currie (Torquay 84).
96-97 - Captain: Martin Gurney **P.o.Y.:** Trevor Argrave **Top Scorer:** John Lawford
Local Newspapers: Bucks Examiner, Bucks Advertiser, Bucks Free Press.
Local Radio Stations: Three Counties

HONOURS: FA Amtr Cup R-up 67-68, Isthmian Lg 92-93 (Div 1 90-91 96-97), Div 2 Nth 86-87, Associate Members Cup R-up 90-91, Charity Shield 94-95; Athenian Lg Div 1 Cup 63-64 68-69; Corinthian Lg R-up(2) 60-62 (Lg Cup 60-61); Spartan Lg(4) 21-23 24-25 32-33 (R-up 26-27 29-30 33-34); Berks & Bucks Snr Cup 21-22 25-26 28-29 33-34 47-48 50-51 64-65 66-67 75-76 92-93 (R-up 94-95).

Back Row (L-R); David Stephenson, Ian Hazel, Kevin Mitchell, Richard Peirson, Mike Burgess (Physio). Middle Row; Andy Thomas (Mgr), Tony O'Driscoll (Asst Mgr), John Lawford, Nathan Beckett, Youress Nabil, Trevor Argrave, Andy Reeder, Gary Fisher, Brian Harding (Asst Physio), Mickey Stamp (Dressing Room). Front Row; Allan Pluckrose, John Caesar, Matthew HGoward, Martin Gurney (Capt), Johnson Hippolyte, Chris McGuire, David Nolan

Chesham United

Match No.	Date	Venue H/A	Competition	Opponents	Result	League Pos.	Attendance	Goalscorers (Times if known)
1	Aug 17	A	IL	Walton & Hersham	Won 2-1		285	Lawford (2)
2	Aug 21	H	IL	Worthing	Won 2-1		486	Nolan, Lawford
3	Aug 24	H	IL	Aldershot Town	Lost 1-3		953	Caesar
4	Aug 27	A	IL	Hampton	Drew 1-1		243	Fisher
5	**Aug 31**	**A**	**FA**	**Berkhamsted**	**Won 3-2**		**372**	**Clifford, Lawford, Beckett**
6	Sep 3	A	IL	Maidenhead	Lost 1-2		244	Knight
7	Sep 7	H	IL	Marlow	Won 3-0		405	Lawford, Williams, Cesar
8	**Sep 9**	**H**	**G**	**Epsom & Ewell**	**Drew 3-3**		**132**	**Shea, Hobbs (2)**
9	**Sep 14**	**H**	**FA**	**Barking**	**Won 3-1**		**341**	**Fisher, Caesar, Lawford**
10	**Sep 18**	**A**	**G R**	**Epsom & Ewell**	**Won 2-1**		**101**	**Nolan, Lawford**
11	Sep 21	A	IL	Abingdon Town	Won 1-0		266	Lawford
12	Sep 25	H	IL	Barton Rovers	Won 4-0		313	Lawford (4)
13	**Sep 28**	**A**	**FAC**	**Potters Bar**	**Won 4-0**		**287**	**Clifford, Gurney, Lawford (2)**
14	Oct 5	H	IL	Uxbridge	Won 1-0		501	Hobbs
15	Oct 8	H	IL	Thame United	Won 3-2		310	Nolan, Caesar, Hobbs
16	**Oct 12**	**A**	**FAC**	**Hayes**	**Lost 0-1**		**683**	
17	Oct 15	A	IL	Billericay	Won 2-1		225	Nolan, Shea
18	**Oct 19**	**H**	**FAT**	**Walton & Hersham**	**Drew 1-1**		**418**	**Lawford**
19	**Oct 22**	**A**	**FAT R**	**Walton & Hersham**	**Won 3-1**		**235**	**Pluckrose (2), Nolan**
20	Oct 26	H	IL	Leyton Pennant	Won 2-1		459	Caesar (2)
21	Nov 2	A	IL	Whyteleafe	Won 3-1		210	Caesar, Lawford (2)
22	**Nov 6**	**H**	**G**	**Thame United**	**Won 3-2**		**213**	**Clifford, Pluckrose, Lawford**
23	**Nov 9**	**A**	**FAT**	**Aldershot**	**Lost 0-3**		**1943**	
24	Nov 16	A	IL	Berkhamsted	Drew 2-2		285	Nolan, Hippolyte
25	Nov 23	H	IL	Canvey Island	Won 4-0		503	Pluckrose, Stephenson, Hippolyte, Fisher
26	**Nov 28**	**A**	**G**	**Grays**	**Won 2-1**		**93**	**Caesar, Lawford**
27	Dec 7	H	IL	Croydon	Drew 2-2		434	Gurney, Hippolyte
28	Dec 9	A	IL	Bognor Regis Town	Lost 1-4		453	Hobbs
29	Dec 14	A	IL	Marlow	Lost 0-2		375	
30	Dec 21	H	IL	Molesey	Won 4-0		383	Pluckrose (2), Gurney, Lawford
31	Jan 11	A	IL	Aldershot Town	Drew 2-2		1474	Gurney (2)
32	**Jan 14**	**A**	**B&B**	**Aylesbury**	**Lost 1-3**		**374**	**Lawford**
33	Jan 18	H	IL	Walton & Hersham	Drew 1-1		445	Hazell
34	**Jan 21**	**A**	**FMC**	**Grays Athletic**	**Drew 0-0**		**80**	
35	Jan 25	A	IL	Worthing	Won 3-2		323	Fisher, Hobbs, Hippolyte
36	**Jan 29**	**H**	**G**	**Sutton**	**Won 2-1**		**259**	**Pluckrose (2)**
37	Feb 1	H	IL	Hampton	Won 1-0		408	Argrave
38	Feb 5	H	IL	Maidenhead	Won 2-1		372	Caesar (2)
39	Feb 8	A	IL	Barton Rovers	Won 1-0		185	Caesar
40	Feb 11	A	IL	Basingstoke Town	Lost 0-4		820	
41	**Feb 13**	**H**	**FMC**	**Enfield**	**Drew 3-3+**		**195**	**Knight, McGuire (2)**
42	Feb 15	H	IL	Abingdon Town	Won 2-1		444	Argrave, Lawford
43	Feb 22	H	IL	Billericay Town	Lost 1-2		468	Fisher
44	Mar 1	A	IL	Thame United	Lost 2-3		172	Argrave, Nabil
45	Mar 8	A	IL	Uxbridge	Drew 0-0		254	
46	Mar 11	H	IL	Tooting & Mitcham	Won 4-0		338	Fisher, Lawford (2), Nabil
47	Mar 15	H	IL	Bognor Regis Town	Won 1-0		416	Hippolyte
48	**Mar 18**	**A**	**FMC**	**Aylesbury United**	**Lost 0-2**		**314**	
49	Mar 22	H	IL	Whyteleafe	Lost 0-1		420	
50	Mar 28	A	IL	Leyton Pennant	Won 2-1		235	Hippolyte, Hazel
51	Mar 31	H	IL	Wokingham Town	Won 2-0		460	Stephenson, Lawford
52	Apr 5	A	IL	Molesey	Won 1-0		139	Argrave
53	Apr 8	A	IL	Tooting & Mitcham	Won 4-0		162	Peirson, Argrave, Caesar, McGuire
54	Apr 12	H	IL	Berkhamsted	Won 5-2		611	Caesar (2), McGuire (2), Nabil
55	Apr 19	A	IL	Canvey Island	Won 3-0		334	Argrave (2), McGuire
56	Apr 26	H	IL	Basingstoke Town	Won 2-1		1458	Pluckrose, Lawford
57	Apr 29	A	IL	Wokingham Town	Lost 1-2		168	Argrave
58	May 3	A	IL	Croydon	Won 1-0		96	Argrave

+ Won 3-1 on Penalties

CHESHAM UNITED PLAYING SQUAD 1997-98

Goalkeepers: Kevin Mitchell (Marlow, Windsor, Slough, Leatherhead, Woking,Windsor, Egham, Reading)

Defenders: Nathan Beckett (Leyton O), **Rochard Pierson** (Oxford C), **Mark Knight** (Berkhamsted), **Dave Stephenson** (Hendon, Malden V, Croydon, Tooting, Dorking, Croydon), **Colin Ferguson** (Marlow, Burnham, Maidenhead, Reading), **Matt Howard** (Boreham Wood, St.Albans, Hayes, Aylesbury, St.Albans, Brentford, Boreham Wood)

Midfielders: Ian Hazel (Carshalton, Aylesbury, Slough, Maidstone, Bristol R, Wimbledon), **Dave Nolan** (Enfield, Marlow, Northwood, Harrow, Hendon), **GaryFisher** (Whyteleafe, Carshalton), **Andy Reeder** (Uxbridge, Wycombe), **Allan Pluckrose** (Aylesbury, St.Albans, Slough, Aylesbury, SV Viktoria Goch (Ger), Torquay, Falmouth), **Martin Gurney** (St.Albans, Wokingham, Redbridge F, Harrow, St.Albans)

Forwards: John Lawford (Berkhamsted, Harrow, Wokingham, Aylesbury, Hayes, B.Stortford, Luton), **John Caesar** (Aylesbury, Marlow, Flackwell H, Oakridge), **Trevor Argrave** (Sutton U, Chertsey, Burnham, Chertsey), **Youness Nabil** (Chertsey, FAS (Morocco), **Johnson Hippolyte** (Chertsey, Yeading, Wealdstone, Chalfont St.Peter, Uxbridge, Hounslow), **Chris Maguire** (Havant, Witney, Lossiemouth, RAF)

PROGRAMME DETAILS:
Pages: 36 **Price:** £1.20
Editor: John Hillier

DAGENHAM & REDBRIDGE

Formed: 1992 **Nickname:** Reds or Daggers
Club colours: Red/blue/red
Change colours: All yellow
Midweek home matchday: Monday
Reserve's League: Essex & Herts Border Comb.
Match Reports: 0891 884434

Chairman: Dave Andrews **President:** Barry East
Secretary: Derek Almond, 149 Kings Head Hill, Chingford, London E4 7JG (0181 524 2689)
Manager: Ted Hardy **Asst Manager:** Dennis Moore
Safety Officer: David Simpson **Physio:** John Stannard
Press Officer: Paul Mullender (0181 553 1653)

GROUND - Address: Victoria Road, Dagenham RM10 7XL. (0181 592 7194. Fax: 0181 593 7227).
Directions: On A112 between A12 & A13. Buses 103 & 174 or, exit Dagenham East tube station, turn left and after approximately 500 yards take 5th turning left into Victoria Road.
Capacity: 6,000 **Seated:** 700 **Covered:** 3,000 **Floodlights:** Yes
Clubhouse: Open 11am-11pm on match days. Hot & cold food available.
Club Shop: Yes, open matchdays, contact Steve Thompson 0181 592 1549
Club Sponsors: Barking & Dagenham Post

PREVIOUS - Names: Ilford FC (1881-1979) and Leytonstone (1886-1979) merged to form Leytonstone-Ilford. This new club merged with Walthamstow Avenue (1900-88) to become Redbridge Forest who in turn merged with Dagenham (1949-92) to become Dagenham & Redbridge. All details refer to the club since the amalgamation in 1992
Grounds: None **Leagues:** None

CLUB RECORDS - Attendance: 5,300 v Leyton Orient - FA Cup 1st Rnd - 14.11.92. **Career goalscorer:** Paul Cavell - 47; Ian Richardson - 31; Jason Broom - 26. **Career appearances:** Paul Watts - 174; Steve Corner - 210; Jason Broom - 160. **Win:** 8-1 v Woking (A), GMV Conference 19/4/94. **Defeat:** 0-5 v Stalybridge Celtic (A), GMV Conference 31/4/94, 0-5 v Northwich Victoria, GMV Conference 3/9/94. **Transfer fee paid** £30,000 to Boston United for Paul Cavell & Paul Richardson - 1991. **Transfer fee received:** £85,000 from Watford for Andy Hessenthaler - 1991.
Best Season - FA Cup: 1st Round 96-97 **FA Trophy:** R-up 96-97
Past players progressed to the Football League: Juan Mequel DeSouza/Ian Richardson (Birmingham City 94,95), Terry Hurlock (Southampton 97), A Hessenthaler (Watford 91), Trevor Morton (Bournemouth 78)
Local Press: Dagenham Post, Waltham Forest Gazette,, Ilford Recorder
Local Radio: Breeze AM, BBC Radio Essex, Capital Radio.
96-97 - Captain: Glyn Creaser **Top scorer:** Courtney Naylor (19) **P.o.Y.:** Steve Conner

HONOURS: F.A. Trophy Runners-up 96-97

Dagenham & Redbridge

Dagenham & Redbridge

Match No.	Date	Venue H/A	Competition	Opponents	Result	League Pos.	Attendance	Goalscorers (Times if known)
1	Aug 17	H	IL	Harrow Borough	Won 3-1		551	Davidson, Parratt, Broom
2	Aug 20	A	IL	Yeovil Town	Drew 0-0		2255	
3	Aug 26	H	IL	Purfleet	Won 2-0	6	743	John, Davidson
4	Aug 31	H	IL	Enfield	Lost 0-2	9	1062	
5	Sep 7	A	IL	Aylesbury United	Won 1-0	7	578	Broom
6	**Sep 9**	**H**	**GIC**	**Marlow**	**Won 3-0**			**Simpson (2), Barnett**
7	**Sep 14**	**A**	**FAC 1 Q**	**Brackley**	**Drew 1-1**		**325**	**Cullerhouse**
8	**Sep 16**	**H**	**FAC 1QR**	**Brackley**	**Won 1-0**		**365**	**Conner**
9	Sep 21	H	IL	Staines Town	Won 3-0	4	704	Johnson, Barnett, John
10	**Sep 28**	**H**	**FAC 2 Q**	**Harrow Borough**	**Drew 0-0**		**527**	
11	**Oct 2**	**A**	**FAC 2QR**	**Harrow Borough**	**Won 2-0**		**262**	**Double, Conner**
12	Oct 5	H	IL	Kingstonian	Won 2-0	5	757	John 53, Barnet 84
13	**Oct 12**	**H**	**FAC 3 Q**	**Uxbridge Town**	**Won 3-0**		**593**	**Pickering 41, John 54, Bird 72**
14	Oct 19	A	IL	Carshalton Athletic	Drew 0-0		352	
15	Oct 21	H	IL	Bishop's Stortford	Won 3-0	7	690	Double, John, Barnett
16	**Oct 26**	**A**	**FAC 4 Q**	**Newport (IoW)**	**Won 4-1**		**924**	**Pratt 7, John 52, Davidson 63, Naylor 78**
17	Nov 2	A	IL	Hitchin Town	Drew 0-0		361	
18	**Nov 5**	**A**	**GIC**	**Boreham Wood**	**Lost 0-1**		**126**	
19	Nov 9	A	IL	St Albans City	Lost 2-0	6	651	Parratt 29, Naylor 67
20	**Nov 16**	**A**	**FAC 1**	**Ashford Town**	**Drew 2-2**		**1813**	**Simpson 15, Creaser 67**
21	Nov 18	H	IL	Dulwich Hamlet	Drew 1-1	6	671	Pratt
22	Nov 23	A	IL	Yeading	Drew 1-1	7	237	Double
23	**Nov 25**	**H**	**FAC 1 R**	**Ashford Town**	**Drew 1-1***		**2424**	**Rogers**
24	**Nov 30**	**A**	**FAT 3 Q**	**Aldershot**	**Won 3-1**		**1656**	**Naylor (2), Double**
25	Dec 7	A	IL	Sutton United	Lost 1-2	7	589	Conner 64
26	Dec 14	H	IL	Oxford City	Won 4-2	7	534	Smith (og), Rogers, Simpson, Naylor
27	Dec 21	A	IL	Chertsey Town	Won 3-0	7	225	Pratt, Rogers, Double
28	Dec 26	H	IL	Heybridge Swifts	Won 3-0	4	622	Naylor (2), Rogers (pen)
29	Jan 11	H	IL	Boreham Wood	Won 2-1	3	661	Creaser 70, Double 78
30	**Jan 13**	**H**	**IL FMC**	**Hendon**	**Drew 2-2***			**Culverhouse, Stimpson**
31	**Jan 18**	**A**	**FAT 1**	**Dover Athletic**	**Won 2-0**		**783**	**Stimpson, Naylor**
32	Jan 25	H	IL	Yeovil Town	Lost 0-1	4	1181	
33	Feb 1	A	IL	Purfleet	Drew 2-2	4	401	Naylor 4, 44
34	**Feb 8**	**H**	**FAT 2**	**Chelmsford City**	**Won 2-1**		**1351**	**Garvey (og) 28, Broom 38**
35	Feb 10	H	IL	Hendon	Drew 1-1		448	Conner
36	Feb15	A	IL	Staines Town	Drew 0-0	5	265	
37	**Feb 17**	**H**	**IL FMC**	**Purfleet**	**Lost 0-1**			
38	Feb 22	H	IL	Bromley	Lost 0-2	5	751	
39	**Mar 1**	**A**	**FAT 3**	**Morecambe**	**Drew 0-0**		**972**	
40	**Mar 3**	**H**	**FAT 3 R**	**Morecambe**	**Won 2-1**		**788**	**Naylor 85, 107**
41	Mar 8	A	IL	Kingstonian	Won 3-2	6	455	Rogers, Stimpson, Double
42	Mar 10	H	IL	St Albans City	Lost 0-1		471	
43	Mar 15	A	IL	Carshalton Athletic	Lost 0-1	9	552	
44	Mar 18	A	IL	Boreham Wood	Lost 1-3	10	114	Naylor
45	**Mar 22**	**H**	**FAT Q F**	**Ashton United**	**Won 1-0**		**1281**	**Rogers**
46	Mar 24	H	IL	Aylesbury United	Lost 0-2		421	
47	Mar 26	A	IL	Harrow Borough	Drew 1-1		285	Naylor (pen)
48	Mar 29	A	IL	Grays Athletic	Won 3-0		429	John (3)
49	Mar31	A	IL	Heybridge Swifts	Lost 1-4	12	412	Davidson
50	Apr 2	A	IL	Bromley	Lost 0-1	12	313	
51	**Apr 5**	**H**	**FAT SF**	**Gloucester City**	**Drew 0-0**		**2008**	
52	**Apr 12**	**A**	**FAT SF**	**Gloucester City**	**Drew 2-2**		**4000**	**Conner, Pratt**
53	**Apr 16**	**N**	**FAT SF**	**Gloucester City**	**Won 2-1**		**2053**	**Stimpson (2) 29, 61**
54	Apr 17	H	IL	Hitchin Town	Drew 1-1		406	Bird
55	Apr 19	H	IL	Yeading	Lost 1-2	13	516	Stimpson
56	Apr 22	A	IL	Dulwich Hamlet	Won 2-0		206	John, Naylor
57	Apr 24	A	IL	Enfield	Won 1-0		631	Stimpson
58	Apr 26	A	IL	Oxford City	Drew 2-2	9	267	Conner, Rogers
59	Apr 28	H	IL	Grays Athletic	Won 2-1		420	John, Stimpson
60	Apr 30	A	IL	Hendon	Lost 1-2		203	Hewes
61	May 1	H	IL	Chertsey Town	Won 2-1		353	John (2)
62	May 3	H	IL	Sutton United	Won 2-1	4	653	Naylor, John
63	**May 17**	**N**	**FAT F**	**Woking**	**Lost 0-1**			

DAGENHAM & REDBRIDGE PLAYING SQUAD 1997-98

Goalkeepers: Paul Gothard (Grays A, Chelmsford C, Colchester)

Defenders: Steve Conner (Dartford, Tilbury, East Thurrock U), **Glyn Creaser** (Rushden & D, Wycombe W, Barnet, Wolverton T, Kettering T, Milton Keynes C, Wolverton T), **Craig Davidson** (Chelmsford C, Southend, Aldershot), **Dave Culverhouse** (Maidstone U, Southend, Tottenham), **Bartholomew Mas** (Billericay T, Barking, Dag & Red, Maidstone U), **David Jacques** (Billericay, Romford, Chelmsford, Dag & Red, Maidstone, Enfield, Dartford, Leyt & Ilf), **Tim Cole** (Leyton Pennant, Walthamstow Pennant), **Lee Fowler** (C.Row & Romford, Barking, Bromley, Dag & Red, Leyton O)

Midfielders: John Stimson (Aveley, Dag & Red, Leyt & Ilf), **Jason Broom** (Billericay T, Eton Manor), **Darren Barry** (Wembley, B Stortford, Cork C, Nottingham F), **Dean Parratt** (B Stortford, Purfleet, Dag & Red, Wimbledon, Arsenal), **Warren Oakley** (West Ham U), **Gary Howard** (Billericay, Gt.Wakering R, Chelmsford, Brighton, Grays, Enfield, Stambridge, Gt.Wakering R), **Lee Double** (Youth team)

Forwards: Matthew Bird (Leyton O), **Vinnie John** (Clapton, Wimbledon (T)), **Tony Rogers** (Crawley, Dover, Chelmsford, Dover, Maidstone, Barking, Dartford, Tilbury, Leyt & Ilf, Basildon), **David Pratt** (SK Vard (Nor), Leyton Pennant, Leyton O, West Ham U (T)), **Courtney Naylor** (Local football), **Nigel Hewes** (Heybridge S, Dag & Red, Northampton (T)), **Lee Parrish** (Barking, C.Row, Ford U, Billericay, Ford U, Barking)

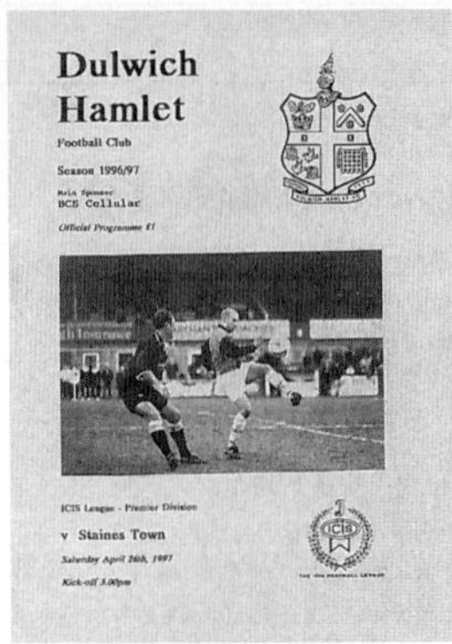

DULWICH HAMLET

Formed: 1893 **Nickname:** The Hamlet
Colours: Navy blue & pink stripes/navy/navy
Change colours: Green & white stripes/white/white
Midweek matchday: Tuesday
Reserve League: Suburban

Chairman: Martin Eede. **President:** Tommy Jover
Vice Chairman: Vacant **Secretary:** Martyn Cole, c/o Ground. Tel. 0181 398 1751.
Managers: John Ryan/Mick Browne **Commercial Manager:**
Physio: Danny Keenan. **Press Officer:** John Lawrence (0171 733 6385)

GROUND Address: Champion Hill Stadium, Edgar Kail Way, East Dulwich, London SE22 8BD (0171 274 8707). **Directions:** East Dulwich station, 200yds. Denmark Hill station, 10 mins walk. Herne Hill station then bus 37 stops near ground. Also buses 40 & 176 from Elephant & Castle, 185 from Victoria.
Capacity: 3,000 **Cover:** 1,000 **Seats:** 500 **Floodlights:** Yes
Clubhouse: Open 7 days a week, 3 bars. Function rooms and meeting room available for hire. Gymnasium, squash courts (0171 274 8707).
Club Shop: Sells programmes, pennants, badges, scarves, baseball caps, replica shirts (by order only). Contact Mishi D Morath at club.
Sponsors: South London Press

PROGRAMME DETAILS:
Pages: 36 **Price:** £1
Editor: John Lawrence

PREVIOUS - Grounds: Woodwarde Road 1893-95/ College Farm 95-96/ Sunray Avenue 96-1902/ Freeman's Ground, Champion Hill 02-12/ Champion Hill (old ground) 1912-92/ Sandy Lane (groundshare with Tooting & Mitcham F.C.) 91-92. **Leagues:** Camberwell 1894-97/ S/thern Sub 1897-1900 01-07/ Dulwich 00-01/ Spartan 07-08.

CLUB RECORDS - Attendance: 20,744, Kingstonian v Stockton, FA Amateur Cup Final 1933 *(at refurbished ground: 744 v Hendon, 3/10/94).* **Career Goalscorer:** Edgar Kail 427 (1919-33) **Career Appearances:** Reg Merritt 571 (50-66). **Fee Paid:** T Eames, G Allen **Fee Received:** E Nwajiobi (Luton). **Win:** 13-0 v Walton-on-Thames, 37-38. **Defeat:** 1-10 v Hendon, 63-64. **Best Season - FA Amateur Cup:** Winners 19-20 31-2 33-4 36-7. **FA Trophy:** Quarter Final 79-80. **FA Cup:** 1st Rd replay 30-31 33-34. 1st Rd on 13 occasions; 25-31 32-38 48-49.
Players progressing to Football League: W Bellamy (Spurs), A Solly (Arsenal), J Moseley & E Toser (Millwall), G Pearce (Plymouth), G Jago (Charlton 51), R Crisp (Watford 61), J Ryan (Charlton 63), E Nwajiobi (Luton 83), A Gray (Crystal Palace 84), C Richards (Bournemouth), P Coleman (Millwall 86), A Perry (Portsmouth 86).
96-97 Captain: Russell Edwards **96-97 P.o.Y.:** Steve McKimm **96-97 Top scorer:** Paul Whitmarsh
Local Press: South London Press, Southwark News

HONOURS: Isthmian League 19-20 25-26 32-33 48-49 (R-up(7) 21-22 23-24 29-31 33-34 46-47 58-59, Div 1 77-78), London Senior Cup 24-25 38-39 49-50 83-84 (R-up 05-06 07-08 20-21 27-28), Surrey Senior Cup(16) 04-06 08-10 19-20 22-23 24-25 27-28 33-34 36-37 46-47 49-50 57-59 73-75 (R-up(6) 11-12 31-33 37-38 50-51 67-68), London Chal. Cup R-up 91-92, London Charity Cup(12) 10-11(jt) 19-21 22-23 23-24(jt) 25-26 27-29 30-31(jt) 47-48 56-58, Surrey Senior Shield 72-73, Surrey Centen. Shld 77-78, Sth of the Thames Cup(4) 56-60, Southern Comb Cup 73-74.

Dulwich Hamlet FC: *Photo - Andrew Chitty*

Dulwich Hamlet

Match No.	Date	Venue H/A	Competition	Opponents	Result	League Pos.	Attendance	Goalscorers (Times if known)
1	Aug 17	H	IL	Yeading	Lost 0-1		341	
2	Aug 19	A	IL	Purfleet	Won 4-1		207	Odegbami, Whitworth, Lillington (2)
3	Aug 24	A	IL	Enfield	Won 3-2	8	678	Whitmarsh (2, 1 pen), McKimm
4	Aug 27	H	IL	Bishop's Stortford	Won 2-0		307	Whitmarsh (2)
5	Aug 31	H	IL	Yeovil Town	Won 4-1	3	711	Whitmarsh (2), McKimm, Odegbami
6	Sep 7	A	IL	Harrow Borough	Lost 1-2	4	255	Odegbami
7	**Sep 10**	**H**	**GIS**	**Yeading**	**Lost 0-1**			
8	**Sep 14**	**H**	**FAC 1 Q**	**Ashford Town (Mid'x)**	**Won 2-0**		**324**	**Lillington, Hewitt**
9	Sep 21	H	IL	Heybridge Swifts	Lost 1-3	5	297	Smart
10	**Sep 28**	**A**	**FAC 2 Q**	**Welling United**	**Lost 1-2**		**721**	**Whitmarsh**
11	Oct 5	H	IL	Boreham Wood	Won 2-1	7	407	Holness (2)
12	Oct 12	A	IL	Kingstonian	Lost 2-4	8	413	Patullo, Holness
13	Oct 15	H	IL	Hendon	Won 2-0		227	Holness, Lillington
14	Oct 19	A	IL	Sutton United	Lost 0-2	6	717	
15	Oct 22	A	IL	St Albans City	Drew 2-2		356	Anderson, Lillington
16	Oct 26	A	IL	Chertsey Town	Won 2-0	5	320	Lillington, Anderson
17	Nov 2	H	IL	Oxford City	Lost 0-1	6	348	
18	Nov 9	H	IL	Kingstonian	Lost 1-2	7	418	Whitmarsh 65
19	Nov 16	A	IL	Hitchin Town	Drew 0-0		349	
20	Nov 18	A	IL	Dagenham & Redbridge	Drew 1-1	7	671	Akers (pen)
21	Nov 23	H	IL	Carshalton Athletic	Won 4-1		413	Ferney, Anderson, Whitmarsh, McKimm
22	**Dec 4**	**A**	**FAT 3 Q**	**Dartford**	**Drew 0-0**		**286**	
23	Dec 7	H	IL	Aylesbury United	Drew 1-1	6	341	Anderson 32
24	**Dec 9**	**H**	**FAT 3QR**	**Dartford**	**Won 3-1**		**273**	**Mitchell (2), Akers**
25	Dec 14	A	IL	Staines Town	Won 3-1	4	215	Holness, McKimm, Akers (pen)
26	Dec 21	H	IL	Grays Athletic	Won 3-0	4	274	Whitmarsh (2), Holness
27	Dec 26	A	IL	Bromley	Drew 0-0	5	628	
28	**Jan 13**	**A**	**IL FMC**	**Bognor Regis Town**	**Lost 0-1***			
29	**Jan 18**	**A**	**FAT 1**	**Cheltenham Town**	**Won 2-1**		**703**	**Lillington, Whitmarsh**
30	Jan 25	H	IL	Purfleet	Won 2-1	5	302	Edwards, Holness
31	Feb 1	A	IL	Bishop's Stortford	Won 1-0	3	251	Holness
32	**Feb 8**	**H**	**FAT 2**	**St Leonards Stamcroft**	**Lost 1-2**		**776**	**Jones 45 (og)**
33	Feb 15	A	IL	Heybridge Swifts	Drew 1-1	4	305	Chin
34	Feb 18	A	IL	Yeading	Lost 0-3		131	
35	Feb 22	A	IL	Hendon	Drew 2-2	4	297	McKimm (2)
36	Mar 1	H	IL	Harrow Borough	Drew 0-0	4	263	
37	Mar 4	A	IL	Yeovil Town	Lost 1-6		1707	Anderson
38	Mar 8	A	IL	Boreham Wood	Drew 2-2	5	217	McKimm, Lillington
39	Mar 11	H	IL	Enfield	Lost 0-1		494	
40	Mar 15	H	IL	St Albans City	Lost 1-2	7	320	Whitmarsh
41	Mar 22	A	IL	Oxford City	Drew 1-1	8	259	Whitmarsh
42	Mar 29	H	IL	Chertsey Town	Won 3-0		270	Whitmarsh (2), Haynes
43	Mar 31	H	IL	Bromley	Won 2-1	8	468	Haynes, Holness
44	Apr 5	A	IL	Grays Athletic	Drew 1-1		258	Tootes (pen)
45	Apr 12	H	IL	Hitchin Town	Drew 2-2	8	311	McKimm, Haynes
46	Apr 15	H	IL	Sutton United	Lost 0-1		361	
47	Apr 19	A	IL	Carshalton Athletic	Drew 0-0	8	315	
48	Apr 22	H	IL	Dagenham & Redbridge	Lost 0-2		206	
49	Apr 26	H	IL	Staines Town	Lost 0-2	11	307	
50	May 3	A	IL	Aylesbury United	Lost 0-2	12	502	

* After Extra Time

DULWICH HAMLET PLAYING SQUAD 1997-98

Goalkeepers: Dave Hudson (Molesey, Banstead, Hendon, Malden V, Chalfont St.Peter, Wealdstone, Wimbledon)
Defenders: Matthew Middleton (Chesham U, Millwall), **Russell Edwards** (Barnet, Crystal Palace), **Dave Pattulo** (Molesey, Sutton U, Molesey, Sheen A), **Micky Rootes** (Molesey, Tooting, Woking, Wimbledon), **Tony Chin** (Youth team)
Midfielders: Lee Akers (Tonbridge, Croydon, Erith & B, Croydon, Dulwich Hamlet, Malden Vale, Dulwich Hamlet, Bromley, Greenwich B, Bromley, Dulwich Hamlet, Arsenal), **Gary Hewitt** (Erith & B, Bromley, Margate, Bromley, Gravesend, Hendon, Dulwich Hamlet, Erith & B, Gateway), **Ben Kamara** (Hampton, Dulwich H), **Luke Anderson** (Kingstonian, Horsham, Dulwich Hamlet), **Paul Kember** (Chipstead, Whyteleafe, Croydon, Dulwich H, Molesey, Whyteleafe), **Otis Hutchins** (Molesey, Tooting, Walton & H, Chelsea)
Forwards: Paul Whitmarsh (Stevenage B, Doncaster, West Ham), **Dean Holness** (Bromley), **Steve McKimm** (Molesey, Hendon, Malden V), **Phil Gallagher** (Molesey, Hendon, Malden V), **Simon Mitchell** (Kingstonian, Dorking, Croydon Ath)

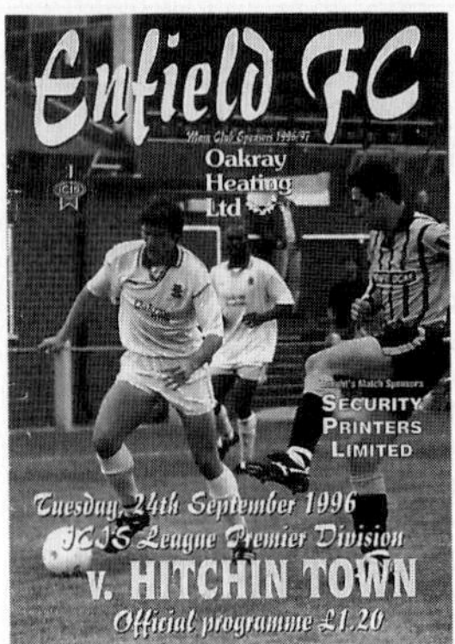

ENFIELD

Formed: 1893 **Nickname:** The E's
Colours: All White with blue trim
Change colours: Red & green/white
Midweek matchday: Tuesday **Newsline:** 0930 555845
Reserve's League: Essex & Herts Border Comb.

Chairman: A Lazarou **President:** T F Unwin
Secretary: Roger Reed, 16 College Gardens, Enfield, Middx EN2 0QF (0181 350 4064).
General Manager: Dee Curran. **Manager:** George Borg
Coaches: **Physio:** Phil Sheddon
Press Officer: John Jefferson Tel. 0181 3636273.
Marketing Manager: Jonathon Moreland.
GROUND Address: The Stadium, Southbury Road, Enfield EN1 1YQ (0181 292 0665). **Directions:** At junction of A10 & A110. 800 yards from Southbury Road station. Buses from town centre.
Floodlights: Yes **Capacity:** 8,500 **Cover:** 3,500 **Seats:** 820
Clubhouse: Sportsmans Lounge, open every lunch & evening. Snacks. Starlight nightclub, cabaret, dinner & dance.
Club Shop: Yes, contact Dave Hicks 01992 769156.
Sponsors: Oakray Heating **Metal Badges:** Yes

PROGRAMME DETAILS:
Pages: 24 **Price:** £1.20.
Editor: Lee Harding
(0181 887 0560)

PREVIOUS - Leagues: Tottenham & Dist 1894-95/Nth Middx 96-1903/ London 03-13 20-21/Middx 08-12 19-20/ Athenian 12-14 21-39 45-63/Herts & Middx Comb 39-42/ Isthmian 63-81/ GMV Conference 81-90. **Name:** Enfield Spartans 1893-1900. **Grounds:** Baileys Field 1893-96/ Tuckers Field 96-1900/ Cherry Orchard Lane 1900-36.

CLUB RECORDS - Attendance: 10,000 (10/10/62) v Spurs, floodlight opener. **Fee Paid:** for Gary Abbott (Barnet) **Fee Received:** for Paul Furlong (Coventry City) **Scorer:** Tommy Lawrence. **Appearances:** Steve King 617
Best Season - FA Amateur Cup Winners 66-7 69-70 R-up 63-4 71-2. **FA Trophy:** Winners 81-2 87-8. **FA Cup:** 4th Rd replay 80-81 (0-3 to Barnsley at Spurs (Att 35,244) after 1-1 draw). **- League clubs beaten:** Wimbledon, Northampton 77-78, Hereford, Port Vale 80-81, Wimbledon 81-82, Exeter 84-85, Orient 88-89, Aldershot 91-92, Cardiff City 94-95, Torquay Utd 94-95.
Players progressing to Football League: Terry McQuade (Millwall 61), Roger Day (Watford 61), Jeff Harris (Orient 64), Peter Feely (Chelsea 70), Carl Richards & Jon Bailey (B'mouth 80 & 95), Paul Furlong (Coventry 91), Andy Pape (Barnet 91), Greg Heald (Peterborough 94), Lee Marshal (Norwich City 97).
96-97 Captain: Paul Horan **P.o.Y.:** Steve McGrath **Top Scorer:** Steve West (23)
Local Press: Enfield Gazette, Enfield Advertiser, Enfield Independent, Enfield Town Express.

HONOURS: Alliance Premier League 82-83 85-86 (R-up 81-82, Lg Cup R-up 81-82), Isthmian Lg(8) 67-70 75-78 79-80 94-95 (R-up(7) 64-65 71-72 74-75 80-81 90-92 95-96, Lg Cup(2) 78-80 (R-up 91-92 94-95)), Athenian Lg(2) 61-63 (R-up 34-35), London Lg Div 1 11-12 (R-up 04-05 06-07, Middx Snr Cup(13) 13-14 46-47 61-62 65-66 68-71 77-81 88-89 90-91 (R-up(12) 10-11 20-21 47-48 51-52 57-60 62-63 66-67 72-73 75-76 84-85), London Snr Cup(6) 34-35 60-61 66-67 71-73 75-76 (R-up 63-64 67-68 70-71), Middx Lg (West) 09-10 (R-up 10-11), European Amtr Cup Winners Cup 69-70.

Back Row (L-R); Lee Marshal, Steve Terry, Steve Cox, Jim Carstairs, Gary Fitzgerald, Steve West, John Richardson, Martin St Hikaire, Dominic Gentle. Front; Justin Gentle, Paul Underwood, Shaun Marshall, David May, Matt Edwards, Paul Moran, Joe Francis, Shaun Flemming.

Enfield

Match No.	Date	Venue H/A	Competition	Opponents	Result	League Pos.	Attendance	Goalscorers (Times if known)
1	Aug 17	A	IL	Carshalton Athletic	Won 1-0		607	Moran
2	Aug 20	H	IL	Hendon	Drew 2-2		733	Marshall, Moran
3	Aug 24	H	IL	Dulwich Hamlet	Lost 2-3	10	678	West (2)
4	Aug 27	A	IL	St Albans City	Won 4-1	6	812	Marshall (2), West (2)
5	Aug 31	A	IL	Dagenham & Redbridge	Won 2-0	4	1062	Terry, J Gentle
6	Sep 7	H	IL	Oxford City	Drew 3-3	5	852	Marshall, J Gentle, West
7	**Sep 10**	**A**	**GIC**	**Aldershot**	**Won 3-0**		**1246**	**West, D Gentle (2)**
8	Sep 21	A	IL	Chertsey Town	Drew 1-1	6	669	West
9	Sep 24	H	IL	Hitchin Town	Won 1-0		347	St Hilaire
10	Sep 28	H	IL	Sutton United	Won 3-1	3	1012	Moran (2, 1 pen), Terry
11	Oct 5	A	IL	Yeading	Drew 1-1	3	430	D Gentle
12	Oct 19	A	IL	Purfleet	Won 3-1	3	428	Underwood (2), Marshall
13	Oct 26	A	IL	Bishop's Stortford	Won 3-1	2	765	D Gentle, Marshall, Francis
14	Nov 1	H	IL	Heybridge Swifts	Lost 1-2	4	1048	Tucker
15	**Nov 6**	**A**	**GIC**	**Harrow Borough**	**Lost 2-3**		**279**	**St Hilaire, Marshall**
16	Nov 9	H	IL	Yeovil Town	Won 3-0	3	1349	Moran (2, 2 pens), St Hilaire
17	**Nov 16**	**A**	**FAC 1**	**Bromley**	**Won 3-1**		**2709**	**West (3) 18, 26, 67**
18	Nov 19	A	IL	Staines Town	Won 2-0	2	252	Moran (pen), Annon
19	Nov 23	H	IL	Aylesbury United	Won 3-0	2	876	Gentle, West (2)
20	Nov 30	A	IL	Hitchin Town	Won 3-0	1	703	Annan, Moran, Gentle
21	**Dec 7**	**H**	**FAC 2**	**Peterborough United**	**Drew 1-1**		**2847**	**Marshall**
22	Dec 14	A	IL	Kingstonian	Won 1-0	2	619	West
23	**Dec 17**	**A**	**FAC 2 R**	**Peterborough United**	**Lost 1-4**		**3997**	**St Hilaire**
24	Dec 21	H	IL	Boreham Wood	Won 3-0	2	673	J Gentle, D Gentle, West
25	Dec 26	A	IL	Harrow Borough	Drew 1-1	2	502	St Hilaire
26	**Jan 18**	**H**	**FAT 1**	**Boreham Wood**	**Lost 1-3**		**693**	**Annan**
27	**Jan 21**	**A**	**IL FMC**	**Heybridge Swifts**	**Won 1-0**			
28	Jan 25	A	IL	Hendon	Won 3-0	2	847	May (2), West
29	Jan 28	H	IL	Grays Athletic	Won 4-0	2	542	May (3), Carstairs
30	Feb 1	H	IL	St Albans City	Won 1-0	2	851	West
31	Feb 11	H	IL	Bromley	Won 4-3	2	560	Endersby, Marshall, Moran (p), Terry
32	**Feb 13**	**A**	**IL FMC**	**Chesham United**	**Drew 3-3***			
33	Feb 15	H	IL	Chertsey Town	Won 5-0	1	714	Annan (p), May (2), Edwards, Tucker
34	Feb 22	H	IL	Purfleet	Won 3-0	1	936	Underwood, Edwards, Moseley (og)
35	Mar 1	A	IL	Bromley	Won 2-0	1	551	Endersby, May
36	Mar 8	H	IL	Yeading	Drew 1-1	2	1069	Moran
37	Mar 11	A	IL	Dulwich Hamlet	Won 1-0	2	494	Terry
38	Mar 15	A	IL	Sutton United	Drew 1-1	2	829	McGrath
39	Mar 18	H	IL	Carshalton Athletic	Won 2-0	2	608	May (2)
40	Mar 25	A	IL	Yeovil Town	Drew 2-2	2	8007	Moran (2, 1 pen)
41	Mar 29	H	IL	Bishop's Stortford	Drew 1-1	2	1219	Marshall
42	Mar 31	H	IL	Harrow Borough	Won 1-0	2	850	May
43	Apr 5	A	IL	Boreham Wood	Drew 1-1	2	782	Tucker
44	Apr 11	H	IL	Staines Town	Won 4-0	2	860	West (2), May, St Hilaire
45	Apr 15	A	IL	Heybridge Swifts	Drew 0-0	2	530	
46	Apr 19	A	IL	Aylesbury United	Won 3-1	2	1118	McGrath, Endersby (2)
47	Apr 24	H	IL	Dagenham & Redbridge	Lost 0-1	2	631	
48	Apr 26	H	IL	Kingstonian	Won 3-1	2	865	West (2), May
49	Apr 29	A	IL	Oxford City	Won 4-1	2	382	West (3), Pape (pen)
50	May 3	A	IL	Grays Athletic	Won 2-0	2	451	Underwood, May

* After Extra Time

ENFIELD PLAYING SQUAD 1997-98

Goalkeepers: Andy Pape (Barnet, Enfield, Harrow B, Feltham, Charlton, Crystal Palace, Ikast (Den), QPR), **Darryl Trigg** (Colchester)
Defenders: Steve Terry (Walton & H, Aylesbury U, Northampton, Hull, Watford), **Jim Carstairs** (Stockport, Camb.U, Arsenal), **Gary Fitzgerald** (Yeading, Watford), **Steve McGrath** (Yeading, Shamrock FC)
Midfielders: Jason Tucker (Aldershot T, Chertsey, Yeading, Aldershot), **Lee Endersby** (Harrow, Wembley, Brimsdown R), **Paul Moran** (Peterborough, Tottenham H), **Matt Edwards** (Walton & H, Kettering, Brighton, Tottenham H)
Forwards: Justin Gentle (Chesham U, Colchester, Luton, Boreham Wood, Cockfosters, Swindon, Wimbledon), **Martin St.Hilaire** (Yeovil T, Enfield, Harrow B, Harlow T, Chesham U, Aveley), **Steve West** (Concord R, Aveley, East Thurrock U, Tilbury, Aveley, Tilbury, Purfleet, Arsenal (T)), **Leroy May** (Kettering, Kidderminster, Stafford R, Walsall, Altrincham, Tividale, Hereford, Tividale), **Darron Annon** (Kingstonian, Brentford, Carshalton), **Shaun Marshall** (Stevenage, Hithin, Stevenage), **Dominic Gentle** (Grays, Boreham Wood, Cockfosters, ICL Letchworth)

GRAVESEND & NORTHFLEET FC
v
BALDOCK TOWN
Dr Martens League - Premier Division
Saturday 5th April 1997 - 3.00pm K.O.
1996/97 SEASON - OFFICIAL MATCHDAY PROGRAMME £1.20

PROGRAMME DETAILS:
Pages: 32 **Price:** £1.20
Editor: Lionel R H Ball (01474 569985)

GRAVESEND & NORTHFLEET

Formed: 1946 **Nickname:** The Fleet
Colours: Red/white/red
Change colours: White/black/black
Midweek home matchday: Tuesday
Reserves' League: Kent Midweek League

Chairman: Peter Dean
Vice Chairman / Chief Executive: David Stevens
Secretary: Mr D Joy, The Cottage, St Columba's School, Halcot Avenue, Bexleyheath, Kent DA6 7QB (01322 525824)
Press Officer: Lionel R H Ball (01474 569985)
Manager: Steve Lovell **Physio:** Micky Ward
GROUND Address: Stonebridge Road, Northfleet, Kent DA11 9BA (01474 533796). **Directions:** From A2 take Northfleet/Southfleet exit (B262), follow to Northfleet then B2175 (Springhead Rd) to junc A226, turn left (The Hill, Northfleet), rd becomes Stonebridge Rd, grd on right at bottom of steep hill after 1 mile - car parking for 400-500. 2 mins from Northfleet BR station.
Capacity: 3,300 **Cover:** 2,200 **Seats:** 400 **Floodlights:** Yes
Clubhouse: Fleet Social Centre open matchdays only. Hot and cold food available at tea bars on matchdays.
Club Shop: Sells progs, hats, scarves, badges etc, & other memorabilia. Contact Mick Hills or Angela Still. **Sponsors:** Mister Ham Man.

PREVIOUS - Names: Gravesend Utd, Northfleet Utd (merged 1946). **Leagues:** Kent (Gravesend Utd), Southern 46-79, Alliance Prem. 79-80. **Ground:** Central Avenue (Gravesend Utd) *(Northfleet Utd always played at Stonebridge Rd).*

CLUB RECORDS - Attendance: 12,036 v Sunderland, FA Cup 4th Rd 62-63. **Goalscorer (career):** Bert Hawkins. **Goalscorer (2 seasons):** Steve Portway 113 (92-94). **Appearances:** Ken Burrett 537. **Win:** 8-1 v Clacton Tn, Sth Lge 62-63, 7-0 Godalming 95-96 FAC. **Defeat:** 0-9 v Trowbridge Tn, Southern Lge Prem Div 91-92. **Fee Paid:** £8,000 for Richard Newbery (Wokingham 96). **Fee Received:** £17,500 for Steve Portway (Gloucester C 94).
Best Season - FA Cup: 4th Rd Replay 1963, 2-5 v Sunderland (A), 1-1 (H). **FA Trophy:** 3rd Rd 88-89.
Players progressing to Football League: Several incl. most recently:
K Baron (Aldershot 60), R Dwight (Coventry 62), R Cameron (Southend 63), R McNichol (Carlisle 65), A Humphreys (Mansfield 64), B Thornley (Brentford 65), P Jeavons (Lincoln 66), B Fry (Orient 66), B Gordine (Sheffield Utd 68), T Baldwin (Brentford 77), L Smelt (Nottm Forest 80), T Warrilow (Torquay 87)
96-97 Captain: James Jackson **96-97 P.o.Y.:** Mark Munday **96-97 Top scorer:** David Arter
Local Press: Gravesend & Dartford Reporter, Kent Evening Post, Gravesend Extra, Leader
Local Radio: Invicta Radio, Radio Kent, RTM.

HONOURS: Southern Lg 57-58 (Southern Div 94-95, Div 1 Sth 74-75 (R-up 70-71 88-89), Lg Cup 77-78 (R-up 57-58), Champ Cup 77-78), Kent Sen Cup 48-49 52-53 80-81 (R-up 47-48 76-77 90-91), Kent Floodlit Cup 69-70 (R-up 72-73), Kent Sen Shield R-up 47-48 51-52, Kent Interm Cup R-up 87-88, Kent Midweek Lg 95-96, R-up 92-93 93-94 94-95. Kent Youth Lg Cup 82-83 86-87, Kent Youth Lg 95-96, John Ullman Cup 82-83.

Gravesend & Northfleet FC 1997 *Photo Alan Coomes*

Gravesend & Northfleet

Match No.	Date	Venue H/A	Competition	Opponents	Result	League Pos.	Attendance	Goalscorers (Times if known)
1	Aug 17	H	DML	Salisbury City	Won 3-2		601	Powell 32, Munday 78, 79
2	Aug 20	A	DML	Cambridge City	Lost 2-4		334	Munday 63, Jackson 74
3	Aug 24	A	DML	Gresley Rovers	Lost 0-2		621	
4	Aug 26	H	DML	Ashford Town	Lost 1-3	19	804	Arter 68
5	Aug 31	H	DML	Cheltenham Town	Lost 1-3	20	566	Munday 50
6	Sep 3	A	DML	Hastings Town	Lost 1-2	19	444	Newbery 36
7	Sep 7	H	DML	Newport A.F.C.	Won 3-0	19	575	Gibbs 70, Jackson 71, 90
8	Sep 21	A	DML	Halesowen Town	Lost 1-2	21	690	Newbury 6
9	Sep 24	H	DML	Cambridge City	Drew 1-1	21	499	Munday 90 (pen)
10	Sep 28	A	DML	Nuneaton Borough	Lost 0-2	21	905	
11	Oct 5	A	DML	Worcester City	Lost 2-4	21	708	Munday 35 (pen), Lovell 58
12	**Oct 8**	**H**	**DMLC**	**Sittingbourne**	**Lost 2-3**		**596**	**Arter 32, 69**
13	Oct 12	H	DML	Dorchester Town	Lost 1-3	22	552	Jackson 45
14	Oct 15	A	DML	Ashford Town	Drew 1-1	22	682	Mortley 45
15	**Oct 19**	**H**	**FAT 1 Q**	**St Leonards Stamcroft**	**Drew 2-2**		**424**	**Lovell 57, Arter 85**
16	**Oct 22**	**A**	**FAC 1QR**	**St Leonards Stamcroft**	**Lost 3-4**		**440**	**Powell 1, 79, Newbery 90**
17	**Oct 26**	**H**	**FAC 4Q**	**Stevenage Borough**	**Lost 1-5**		**1330**	**Lovell 20**
18	**Oct 30**	**A**	**DMLC**	**Sittingbourne**	**Won 2-1+**		**610**	**Arter 25, Newbery 38**
19	Nov 2	H	DML	King's Lynn	Drew 2-2	22	601	Newbery 23, Arter 86
20	Nov 23	A	DML	Dorchester Town	Drew 2-2	22	623	Newbery 35, 47
21	Nov 30	H	DML	Atherstone United	Won 1-0		539	Arter 80
22	Dec 7	A	DML	Cheltenham Town	Won 1-0	21	705	Newbury 64
23	Dec 14	A	DML	Salisbury City	Lost 1-4	22	324	Powell 64
24	**Dec 16**	**H**	**KSC**	**Sittingbourne**	**Lost 0-1**		**318**	
25	Dec 21	H	DML	Sudbury Town	Won 4-2	20	447	Arter (3) 21, 56, 64, Newbery 39
26	Dec 26	H	DML	Chelmsford City	Won 1-0	15	857	Arter 73
27	Jan 4	H	DML	Crawley Town	Won 2-0	13	517	Kearns 48, Powell 58
28	Jan 18	A	DML	Atherstone United	Drew 0-0		277	
29	Jan 21	H	DML	Hastings United	Won 2-0	12	469	Newbery 9, 48
30	Jan 25	A	DML	Sudbury Town	Lost 0-2	13	470	
31	Feb 1	H	DML	Halesowen Town	Lost 1-3	13	610	Arter 21
32	Feb 5	A	DML	Sittingbourne	Won 3-1		1028	Robinson 16, Munday 42, Newbury 64
33	Feb 8	H	DML	Worcester City	Won 2-0	10	570	Gooding 27, Robinson 82
34	Feb 15	A	DML	Burton Albion	Won 3-1	11	713	Robinson 4, 28, Lovell 30
35	Feb 22	H	DML	Gloucester City	Lost 2-3	12	696	Lovell 5, 45
36	Feb 26	A	DML	Newport A.F.C.	Won 3-1		432	Lovell 39, Jackson 45, Arter 60
37	Mar 1	H	DML	Gresley Rovers	Won 2-1	11	732	Mortley 7, Robinson 21
38	Mar 8	A	DML	Merthyr Tydfil	Lost 0-5	11	462	
39	Mar 12	A	DML	Baldock Town	Won 5-0		161	Arter (3) 2, 36, 80, Munday 39, Robinson 63
40	Mar 15	H	DML	Nuneaton Borough	Drew 1-1	9	682	Arter 45
41	Mar 22	A	DML	Crawley Town	Won 2-0	8	691	Kearns 27, Arter 66
42	Mar 29	H	DML	Sittingbourne	Won 3-0		1303	Arter 35, 58, Lovell 70
43	Mar 31	A	DML	Chelmsford City	Lost 0-4	9	1114	
44	Apr 5	H	DML	Baldock Town	Lost 1-2	10	609	Lovell 22
45	Apr 8	H	DML	Burton Albion	Lost 0-1	12	488	
46	Apr 19	A	DML	Gloucester City	Lost 1-3	12	804	Gooding 71
47	Apr 26	H	DML	Merthyr Tydfil	Drew 0-0		617	
48	May 3	A	DML	King's Lynn	Lost 1-5	14	744	Munday 37

+ Lost on Penalties

GRAVESEND & NORTHFLEET PLAYING SQUAD 1997-98

Goalkeepers: Paul Sansome (Southend, Millwall, Crystal Palace)
Defenders: Ian Gibbs (Youth Team), **Matt Gubbins** (Ashford Town, Canterbury), **Peter Mortley** (Sittingbourne, Erith, Ipswich), **David Walker** (Dover, West Ham), **Mark Leahy** (Hitchin, B Stortford, Gravesend, Gillingham, Ashford), **Alan Tutton** (Tonbridge, Dartford, Erith, Boreham Wood, Margate, Dartford, Maidstone, Alma Swanley, Erith)
Midfielders: Jimmy Jackson (Charlton), **Mark Robinson** (Whitstable), **Clint Gooding** (Ashford), **Ian Docker** (Sittingbourne, Instant Dict (HK), Bromley, Kettering, Redbridge F., Gillingham), **David Powell** (Sheppey U., Hastings T., Margate, Bromley)
Forwards: Steve Lovell (Sittingbourne, Hastings, St Albans, Braintree, Sittingbourne, Gillingham, Millwall, Crystal Palace), **Dave Arter** (Ashford, Sittingbourne, Hythe, Ashford, Tonbridge, Herne Bay, Ashford), **Richard Newbery** (Wokingham, Woking, Wokingham, Hampton, Staines, Farnborough), **Andy Kearns** (Sittingbourne)

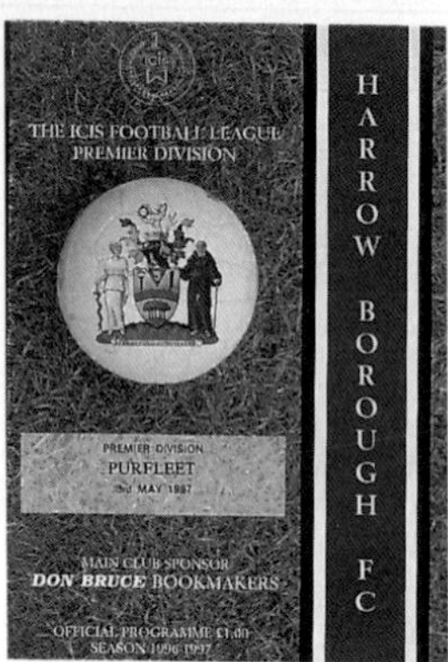

HARROW BOROUGH

Formed: 1933 **Nickname:** The Boro
Colours: Red with white trim/white/red & white hoops
Change colours: Black & white stripes/black/black
Midweek matchday: Tuesday

Chairman: Jim Ripley **President:** Jim Rogers
Secretary/Press Officer: Peter Rogers, 21 Ludlow Close, South Harrow, Middx HA2 8SR (0181 248 8003)
Manager: Bob Dowie **Asst Manager:** Alan Paris
Physio: Andy McDade. **Coach:**
Commercial Manager: Bill Porter c/o the club.

GROUND Address: Earlsmead, Carlyon Avenue, South Harrow, Middx HA2 8SS (0181 422 5989/5221).
Directions: Underground to Northolt (Central Line) then 140 or 282 bus, or to South Harrow (Piccadilly Line) then 114 or H10. By road leave A40 at Macdonalds roundabout towards Northolt station (A312 north), left at lights, right at next island, ground 5th turning on right.
Floodlights: Yes **Capacity:** 3,070 **Cover:** 1,000 **Seats:** 350
Clubhouse: Open every day with normal licensing hours. Four bars, games room, varied entertainment venue for major sporting and social events. Hot and cold food available, buffets by prior request.
Club Shop: Sells programmes, scarves, badges, T-shirts, etc. Contact Tony Trowbridge c/o club. **Sponsors:** Don Bruce Bookmakers.

PROGRAMME DETAILS:
Pages: 28 **Price:** £1
Editor: Jim Rogers
(0181 248 8003)

PREVIOUS - Leagues: Harrow & Dist 33-4/ Spartan 34-40,45-58/ W Middx Comb 40-1/ Middx Sen 41-5/ Delphian 58-63/ Athenian 63-75/ Isthmian 75-to date. **Names:** Roxonian 1933-8/ Harrow Town 38-66. **Ground:** Northolt Road 33-4.
CLUB RECORDS - Attendance: 3,000 v Wealdstone, F.A. Cup 1st Qualifying Round 1946. **Scorer:** Dave Pearce, 153. **Appearances:** Steve Emmanuel 522 (1st team only), Les Currell 582, Colin Payne 557. **Fee Paid:** To Dagenham for George Duck & Steve Jones. **Fee Received:** £15,000 for Chris Hutchings (Chelsea) **Win:** 13-0 v Handley Page (A), Middlesex Snr Lg 18/10/41. **Defeat:** 0-8 5 times: Wood Green T. (A) Middx Lge 40, Met Police (A) Spartan Lg 52, Briggs Spts (A) Spartan Lg 53, Hertford T. (A) Spartan Lge 53, Hendon (A) Middx Snr Cup 65.
Best Season - FA Trophy: Semi final 82-83. **FA Cup:** 2nd Rd 83-84 (1-3 at home to Newport Co).
Players progressing to Football League: M Bottoms (QPR 60), C Hutchings (Chelsea 80), R Holland (Crewe 85), J Kerr (Portsmouth 87), D Howell, A Pape & E Stein (Barnet), D Byrne (Gillingham), R Rosario (Norwich), D Kemp (Crystal Palace), M Doherty (Reading), D Bassett (Wimbledon), G Borthwick (Bournemouth), B Laryea (Torquay).
96-97 Captain: Several **96-97 P.o.Y.:** Jason Court **96-97 Top scorer:** Mark Xavier
Local Press: Harrow Observer.

HONOURS: Isthmian Lg 83-84 (Div 1 R-up 78-79), Athenian Lg Div 2 R-up 63-64, Spartan Lg R-up 57-58, Spartan Lg R-up 57-58 (Div 2 West 38-39 (R-up 37-38)), Middx Senior Cup 82-83 92-93, Harrow & Dist. Lg Div 1 R-up 33-34, Middx Charity Cup 79-80 92-93 (R-up 78-79), Middx Intermediate Cup 55-56, Middx Premier Cup 81-82.

Back Row (L-R): Andy McDade (Physio), Alan Paris, Jason Court, Glynn Hooper, David Hook, Brian Jones, Paul Benning, Dwain Clarke. Front Row; Kenny Webster, Gary Issott, Christian Metcalfe, Bob Dowie (Player/Mgr), David Cooper, Mark Xavier, Zan Rutherford.

Harrow Borough

Match No.	Date	Venue H/A	Competition	Opponents	Result	League Pos.	Attendance	Goalscorers (Times if known)
1	Aug 17	A	IL	Dagenham & Redbridge	Lost 1-3		551	Hurlock
2	Aug 21	H	IL	Carshalton Athletic	Drew 1-1		221	Metcalfe
3	Aug 24	H	IL	Kingstonian	Lost 1-2	21	277	Xavier
4	Aug 27	A	IL	Grays Athletic	Lost 2-3	22	170	Xavier, Jones
5	Aug 31	A	IL	Oxford City	Lost 1-2	22	327	Endersby
6	Sep 7	H	IL	Dulwich Hamlet	Won 2-1	19	255	James, Court
7	**Sep 10**	**A**	**GIS**	**Berkhampstead Town**	**Won 6-5**		**150**	**Ekoku (3), Issott, Xavier, Jones**
8	**Sep 14**	**H**	**FAC 1 Q**	**Stowmarket Town**	**Won 4-1**		**195**	**Xavier (3), James**
9	Sep 21	A	IL	Hitchin Town	Won 4-2	17	278	Ekoku, Issott, Witter (2)
10	Sep 25	H	IL	Bromley	Won 2-0		153	Endersby, Xavier
11	**Sep 28**	**A**	**FAC 2 Q**	**Dagenham & Redbridge**	**Drew 0-0**		**527**	
12	**Oct 2**	**H**	**FAC 2QR**	**Dagenham & Redbridge**	**Lost 0-2**		**262**	
13	Oct 5	A	IL	Yeovil Town	Lost 1-2	16	2116	James (pen)
14	Oct 12	A	IL	Heybridge Swifts	Drew 0-0	17	312	
15	Oct 16	H	IL	Aylesbury United	Drew 0-0		164	
16	Oct 19	H	IL	Staines Town	Lost 0-2	18	217	
17	Nov 2	H	IL	Hendon	Drew 2-2	18	323	Xavier, Ekoku
18	**Nov 6**	**H**	**GIS**	**Enfield**	**Won 3-2**		**230**	**Jones (2), Xavier**
19	Nov 9	A	IL	Boreham Wood	Lost 0-2	19	281	
20	Nov 16	H	IL	Yeading	Lost 0-1	19	204	
21	Nov 23	A	IL	Sutton United	Drew 3-3	21	579	James (pen), Court, Hooper
22	Nov 27	H	IL	Exford City	Lost 2-3		145	Stevens, Jones
23	**Nov 30**	**H**	**FAT 3 Q**	**Salisbury City**	**Drew 2-2**		**175**	**Metcalfe, Hooper**
24	**Dec 4**	**A**	**FAT 3QR**	**Salisbury City**	**Lost 1-2**			**Hooper 50**
25	Dec 7	A	IL	Purfleet	Lost 0-2	22	119	
26	Dec 14	H	IL	Chertsey Town	Won 1-0	20	202	Endersby
27	**Dec 17**	**A**	**GIC**	**St Albans City**	**Won 4-2**			
28	Dec 21	A	IL	St Albans City	Drew 2-2	19	398	Rutherford, Xavier
29	Dec 26	H	IL	Enfield	Drew 1-1	19	502	James (pen)
30	Jan 11	A	IL	Kingstonian	Drew 4-4	19	391	Hooper 18, 75, Butler 81, Court 84
31	Jan 25	A	IL	Carshalton Athletic	Lost 1-2	20	349	Rutherford
32	**Jan 29**	**H**	**GIC**	**Boreham Wood**	**Lost 1-3**			
33	Feb 1	H	IL	Grays Athletic	Won 1-0	19	146	Rutherford
34	**Feb 3**	**A**	**IL FMC**	**Billericay Town**	**Lost 1-2**			
35	Feb 8	A	IL	Bromley	Won 2-1	17	325	Rutherford, Court
36	Feb 15	H	IL	Hitchin Town	Won 3-1	16	220	James, Hooper, Butler
37	Feb 22	A	IL	Staines Town	Drew 1-1	17	200	Paris
38	Mar 1	A	IL	Dulwich Hamlet	Drew 0-0	17	263	
39	Mar 4	A	IL	Bishop's Stortford	Won 1-0		221	Xavier
40	Mar 8	H	IL	Yeovil Town	Lost 2-3	15	447	Issott, Webster
41	Mar 12	H	IL	Heybridge Swifts	Drew 3-3		162	Issott, Clarke, Webster
42	Mar 15	A	IL	Aylesbury United	Lost 0-2	15	453	
43	Mar 22	A	IL	Hendon	Lost 1-2	17	302	Xavier
44	Mar 26	H	IL	Dagenham & Redbridge	Drew 1-1		285	Butler
45	Mar 29	H	IL	Boreham Wood	Won 2-0		308	D Clarke, Butler
46	Mar 31	A	IL	Enfield	Lost 0-1	17	850	
47	Apr 5	H	IL	St Albans City	Lost 0-1	17	291	
48	Apr 9	H	IL	Bishop's Stortford	Drew 1-1		162	Court
49	Apr 12	A	IL	Yeading	Won 2-1	17	284	Rotherford, Court
50	Apr 19	H	IL	Sutton United	Won 2-1	17	328	D Clarke, Xavier
51	Apr 26	A	IL	Chertsey Town	Drew 2-2	17	246	Court, Jones
52	May 3	H	IL	Purfleet	Won 3-1	17	162	James, Issott, Metcalfe

HARROW BOROUGH PLAYING SQUAD 1997-98

Goalkeepers: David Hook (Hampton, Feltham)

Defenders: Dave Clarke (Eastwood T, Notts Co), **Sean James** (Bedfont), **Bob Dowie** (Leighton T, Enfield, Aylesbury U, Hendon, St.Albans C, Hendon, St.Albans C, Hertford T, Cheshunt, Hatfield T, B Stortford), **Jason Court** (Leverstock Green, Harrow B, Hayes, Leverstock Green, Hayes, Boreham Wood, Chalfont St. Peter, St.Albans C), **Kenny Webster** (Stevenage, Peterborough, Arsenal), **Ricky Antoine** (Dulwich H, Bromley, Charlton), **Steve Butler** (Berkhamsted, Wycombe)

Midfielders: Frank Appiah (Hayes, Charlton), **John Hurlock** (Droylsden, Altrincham, Nuneaton B, Bedworth U, Stockport), **Brian Jones** (Bedfont, Yeading), **Mark Witter** (Yeading, Wembley, Egham, Wembley, Millwall), **Paul Benning** (Chesham, Sutton U, Aylesbury, Chesham, Hungerford, Hayes, Peterborough, Gosnells C (Aust), Hayes), **David Cooper** (Hitchin, Exeter, Luton), **Gerry Solomon** (Dulwich, Carshalton, Harrow, Walton & H, Wealdstone, Hayes, Enfield, St.Albans, Harrow, Hendon, Wealdstone, Leyton O), **Colin Day** (Moreton T, Evesham, Hayes, Thorn EMI), **Neil Fraser** (Hayes, Harrow)

Forwards: Nko Ekoku (Hampton, Malden Vale, Sutton U), **Mark Xavier** (Hendon, Ruislip Manor, Hendon), **Christian Metcalfe** (Chelsea (T)), **Gary Issott** (Luton), **Ian Rutherford** (Berkhamsted, Hitchin, Hendon, Baldock, St.Albans, Crewe, Luton), **Glyn Hooper** (Porthleven, Liskeard, Falmouth)

HENDON

Formed: 1908 **Nickname:** Dons or Greens
Colours: Blue & white/blue/blue & white
Change: Green & white/green/green & white
Midweek matchday: Tuesday
Reserve League: Suburban (North)

Chairman: Ivor Arbiter. **President:**
Secretary: Graham Etchell, c/o Hendon FC. 0181 201 9494(Club)
Manager: Frank Murray **Asst Manager:**
Coach: **Press Officer:** David Ballheimer
Physio: **Commercial Manager:** T.B.A.

GROUND Address: Claremont Road, Cricklewood, London NW2 1AE. 0181 201 9494 Fax: 0181 9055966. **Directions:** From Brent Cross station (Northern Line) to the east take first left after flyover on North Circular - Claremont Rd is then left at 3rd mini-r'bout. Buses 102, 210, 226 and C11 pass ground.
Capacity: 8,000 **Cover:** 5,119 **Seats:** 381 **Floodlights:** Yes
Clubhouse: (0181 458 0489 - contact Noel Morgan). Two bars and two function halls open licensing hours 7 days a week. Hot & cold food, pool, darts, bingo, members club, satelite TV, entertainments. Available for hire.
Club Shop: (Contact Derek Furmedge 01814 552219 (shop), 01814 592042(H) Sells kit, bags, badges, pens, mugs, scarves, ties, programmes and other football souvenirs. **Sponsors:** Fender Guitars.

PROGRAMME DETAILS:
Pages: 64 **Price:** £1.20p
Editor: Secretary

PREVIOUS - Leagues: Finchley & Dist. 08-11, Middx 10-11, London 11-14, Athenian 14-63. **Names:** Christ Church Hampstead to 08, Hampstead Town to 26, Hampstead to 33, Golders Green to 46. **Grounds:** Kensal Rise 08-12; Avenue Ground, Cricklewood Lane 12-26.

CLUB RECORDS - Attendance: 9,000 v Northampton, FA Cup 1st Rd 1952. **Goalscorer:** Freddie Evans 176 (1929-35). **Appearances:** Bill Fisher 787 (1940- **Defeat:** 2-11 v Walthamstow Ave. (A), Athenian Lge 9/11/35. **Win:** 13-1 v Wingate (H), Middx Senior Cup 2/2/57. **Fee Paid:** £5,000 twice. **Fee Received:** £30,000 for Iain Dowie (Luton).
Best Season - F.A. Cup: 3rd Rd replay 73-74 (1-4 to Newcastle at Watford after 1-1 [A]). **FA Amateur Cup:** Winners 59-60 64-65 71-72. R-up 54-55 65-66. **FA Trophy:** 3rd Rd replay 76-77, 77-78.
Players progressing to Football League: Peter Shearing (West Ham 60), Iain Dowie (Luton 88), Peter Anderson (Luton), Jeff Harris (Orient), Phil Gridelet (Barnsley 90), Gerry Soloman (Leyton Orient 91), Junior Hunter & Micah Hyde (both Cambridge 94-95), Simon Clark (Peterborough 94-95).
96-97 Captain: Curtis Warmington **96-97 P.o.Y.:** Simon Clarke **96-97 Top scorer:** Junior Lewis
Local Press: Hendon Times, Willesden & Brent Chronicle. **Local Radio:** Capital, GLR, LBC.

HONOURS: European Amtr Champions 72-3; Isthmian Lg 64-5 72-3 (R-up 63-4 65-6 73-4, Lg Cup 76-7 (R-up 86-7), Full Members Cup 94-5), Premier Inter-Lge Cup R-up 86-7; Middx Lge 12-3 13-4; Athenian Lg 52-3 55-6 60-1 (R-up 28-9 32-3 47-8 48-9 51-2); London Lg Div 1 R-up 12-13 (Amtr Div 13-4); Finchley & Dist. Lg 10-1; London Snr Cup 63-4 68-9 (R-up 35-6 50-1 54-5 58-9 71-2); Middx Snr Cup (11) (R-up 83-4), Middx Interm 64-5 66-7 72-3, Middx Charity Cup(14); London Interm Cup 64-5 72-3 75-6 79-80 (R-up 63-4 68-9); Suburban Lg 92-3 (R-up 84-5).

Hendon FC. *Photo - Pisces Photography*

Hendon

Match No.	Date	Venue H/A	Competition	Opponents	Result	League Pos.	Attendance	Goalscorers (Times if known)
1	Aug 17	H	IL	Sutton United	Lost 1-2		411	Banton
2	Aug 20	A	IL	Enfield	Drew 2-2		733	Banton, White
3	Aug 24	A	IL	Yeading	Lost 1-2	18	231	Banton
4	Aug 27	H	IL	Heybridge Swifts	Drew 1-1	20	287	Duffield (pen)
5	Aug 31	H	IL	Boreham Wood	Lost 1-2	20	334	Banton
6	Sep 7	A	IL	Yeovil Town	Lost 0-2	22	1904	
7	**Sep 10**	**H**	**GIC**	**Wembley**	**Won 1-0***			
8	**Sep 14**	**H**	**FAC 1 Q**	**Croydon Athletic**	**Won 2-0**		**204**	**Dawber, Banton**
9	Sep 21	H	IL	Bishop's Stortford	Won 2-1	20	232	Banton, Richardson
10	Sep 23	A	IL	Purfleet	Drew 0-0		153	
11	**Sep 28**	**H**	**FAC 2 Q**	**Fisher 93**	**Drew 0-0**		**249**	
12	**Oct 1**	**A**	**FAC 2QR**	**Fisher 93**	**Won 1-0**		**205**	
13	Oct 5	A	IL	Chertsey Town	Lost 0-1		311	
14	**Oct 12**	**A**	**FAC 3 Q**	**Dover Athletic**	**Won 1-0**			**Kelly**
15	Oct 15	A	IL	Dulwich Hamlet	Lost 1-2	22	227	Lewis
16	**Oct 19**	**H**	**FAT 1 Q**	**Thame United**	**Drew 1-1**		**162**	**Lewis**
17	**Oct 22**	**A**	**FAT 1QR**	**Thame United**	**Drew 1-1***		**126**	**Richardson**
18	**Oct 26**	**A**	**FAC 4 Q**	**Hastings Town**	**Drew 1-1**		**753**	Darlington 12
19	**Oct 29**	**H**	**FAC 4QR**	**Hastings Town**	**Won 2-0**		**512**	Richardson 32, Darlington 34
20	Nov 2	A	IL	Harrow Borough	Drew 2-2	22	323	Darlington (2)
21	**Nov 4**	**A**	**FAT 1QR**	**Thame United**	**Won 3-0**			**Richardson, Lewis, Kelly**
22	**Nov 9**	**H**	**FAT 2 Q**	**Sutton United**	**Lost 1-3**		**402**	**Murphy**
23	Nov 12	H	IL	Oxford City	Won 2-0	22	179	Bolton, Brown (og)
24	**Nov 16**	**A**	**FAC 1**	**Cardiff City**	**Lost 0-2**		**2592**	
25	Nov 23	H	IL	Hitchin Town	Won 1-0	22	245	Bolton
26	**Nov 26**	**A**	**GIC**	**Leighton Town**	**Lost 0-1**			
27	Nov 30	A	IL	Boreham Wood	Won 2-1	18	412	Bolton, A Kelly
28	**Dec 3**	**H**	**IL FMC**	**Berkhamstead Town**				
29	Dec 7	H	IL	Staines Town	Drew 1-1	18	232	Richardson 87 (pen)
30	Dec 14	A	IL	Bromley	Drew 2-2	18	341	Lewis, Bolton
31	Dec 21	H	IL	Carshalton Athletic	Drew 2-2	17	251	Richardson (2)
32	Jan 11	H	IL	Yeading	Drew 1-1	18	261	Lewis 17
33	**Jan 13**	**A**	**IL FMC**	**Dagenham & Redbridge**	**Drew 2-2***			
34	Jan 18	A	IL	Sutton United	Lost 1-3	18	574	Bolton
35	Jan 25	H	IL	Enfield	Lost 0-3	19	847	
36	Feb 1	A	IL	Heybridge Swifts	Drew 1-1	20	274	Kelly
37	Feb 8	H	IL	Purfleet	Lost 2-3	19	259	Kelly, Dawber
38	Feb 10	A	IL	Dagenham & Redbridge	Drew 1-1		448	Ugbah
39	Feb 15	A	IL	Bishop's Stortford	Lost 1-2	20	476	Dawber
40	Feb 17	H	IL	Kingstonian	Won 2-1		275	Lewis (2)
41	Feb 22	H	IL	Dulwich Hamlet	Drew 2-2	20	297	Lewis, Clarke
42	Mar 1	A	IL	Kingstonian	Lost 1-2	20	350	Lewis
43	Mar 8	H	IL	Chertsey Town	Won 1-0	20	243	Ugbah
44	Mar 11	H	IL	Yeovil Town	Lost 1-3		372	Lewis
45	Mar 15	A	IL	Oxford City	Lost 0-2	20	282	
46	Mar 18	H	IL	St Albans City	Lost 0-2		265	
47	Mar 22	H	IL	Harrow Borough	Won 2-1	19	302	Stevens, Lewis
48	Mar 25	A	IL	Grays Athletic	Drew 0-0		244	
49	Mar 29	A	IL	St Albans City	Lost 0-1			
50	Mar 31	H	IL	Aylesbury United	Lost 0-3	19	405	
51	Apr 5	A	IL	Carshalton Athletic	Won 2-0	19	207	Richardson, Lewis
52	Apr 8	H	IL	Grays Athletic	Lost 0-1		268	
53	Apr 15	A	IL	Aylesbury United	Won 2-1		429	Murphy, Clarke
54	Apr 19	A	IL	Hitchin Town	Won 2-1	18	376	Lewis, Nugent
55	Apr 26	H	IL	Bromley	Won 4-1	18	370	Ugbah, Nugent, Richardson (pen), Lewis
56	Apr 30	H	IL	Dagenham & Redbridge	Won 2-1		203	Lewis, P Kelly
57	May 3	A	IL	Staines Town	Won 3-0	16	240	Darlington (2), Banton

* After Extra Time

HENDON PLAYING SQUAD 1997-98

Goalkeepers: Scott Ashcroft (Berkhamsted T), **Gary McCann** (Dulwich H, Sutton U, Chesham, Walton & H, Enfield, Sutton U, Fulham), **Jan Wagenaar** (Vitesse Arnhem(Holl), NEC Nijmegan (Holl)

Defenders: Dean Murphy (St.Albans C, Wokingham T, Barnet, Harpenden T), **Steve Smart** (Aylesbury, Sutton U, Wealdstone, Barnet, Tottenham H), **Curtis Warmington** (Kingstonian, Walton & H, Hendon, Enfield, Carshalton, Yeovil, Dulwich H, WestHam U), **John Ugbah** (Carshalton, Stevenage, Carshalton, Fisher A, Faweh), **Richard Nugent** (Kettering, Yeovil, Stevenage, Woking, Barnet, St.Albans, Barnet, Hitchin, Stevenage, Royston)

Midfielders: Jonathan Price (Aylesbury U, Chesham U, Walton & H, Chertsey T, Berkhamsted T, Staines T, Sutton U, Staines T, Wycombe W, Watford), **Simon Clarke** (Kettering T, West Ham), **Mark Dawber** (Chertsey T, Sutton U, Chesham U, Staines T, Wycombe W, Woking, Virginia Water), **John White** (Watford), **John Richardson** (Enfield, Slough, Chesham, Papatoetoe (NZ), Chalfont St.Peter, Chesham, Amersham), **Paul Kelly** (Chertsey, Chesham, Fulham), **Steve Heard** (Aylesbury, Eynesbury R, Rushden & D, Silkeborge (Den), Camb.U), **Neal Stevens** (Hayes, Brook House, Mavericks)

Forwards: Micky Banton (Walton & H, Chesham U, Barnet, Windsor & Eton, Hellenic (SA)), **Tony Kelly** (Hayes, Wealdstone, Hayes, Harefield U, Hillingdon, Wealdstone), **Jermaine Darlington** (Dover, Charlton, Watford, Chelsea, TottenhamH), **Junior Lewis** (Hayes, Dover, Fulham, Brentford), **Youssef Sakhraoui** (Wembley)

HEYBRIDGE SWIFTS

PROGRAMME DETAILS:
Pages: 40 **Price:** £1
Editor: Peter Fenn
(01621 740878)

Formed: 1880 **Nickname:** Swifts
Colours: Black & white stripes/black/black
Change colours: All Red
Midweek home matchday: Tuesday
Reserve Team's League: Essex & Herts Border Comb.

Chairman: Michael Gibson **President:** Ronnie Locker.
Vice Chairman: Paul Wilkinson **Secretary:** Dennis Fenn, 31 Saxon Way, Maldon, Essex CM9 7JN (01621 854798).
Manager: Garry Hill **Asst Man.:** Mick Loughton **Physio:** Barry Anthony
Press Officer: Tim Huxtable **Treasurer:** Chris Deines

GROUND Address: Scraley Road, Heybridge, Maldon, Essex (01621 852978).
Directions: Leave Maldon on the main road to Colchester, pass through Heybridge then turn right at the sign to Tolleshunt Major (Scraley Road). The ground is on the right. Six miles from nearest station (Witham). By bus via Chelmsford and Maldon.
Capacity: 3,000 **Cover:** 1,200 **Seats:** 550 **Floodlights:** Yes
Clubhouse: Two bars open every night. Games room, boardroom, kitchen (on matchdays).
Club Shop: Open matchdays, selling club sweaters, shirts, scarves, baseball hats, enamel badges, old programmes etc. Contact Chris Fenn, 40 Drake Avenue, Mayland CM3 6TY (01621 740878).
Sponsors: Balham Electrical Wholesalers

PREVIOUS - Leagues: Essex & Suffolk Border, North Essex, South Essex, Essex Senior 1971-84.

CLUB RECORDS - Attendance: 2,477 v Woking FA Trophy 97. **Goalscorer:** Julian Lamb 115 (post war), Dave Matthews 112 (Isthmian). **Appearances:** Hec Askew 500+, Robbie Sach 358 (Isthmian). **Fee Paid:** None. **Fee Received:** £35,000, Simon Royce (Southend Utd)

Best Season - FA Trophy: Qtr finals v Woking 22/3/97 (lost 0-1). **FA Cup:** First round 0-2 v Gillingham 11/11/94.
League clubs defeated: None
Players progressing to Football League: Simon Royce (Southend United), Peter Cawley & Ben Lewis (Colchester Utd), Alan Hull (Leyton Orient), Jonathan Hunt (Birmingham City), Dominic Naylor (Leyton Orient), Haken Hayrettin (Doncaster Rovers), Derek Payne & Tom Meredith (Peterborough Utd), Ben Barnett, Eddie Stein & Tim Alexander (Barnet).
96-97 Captain: Keith Bain **P.o.Y.:** Mark Keen **Top scorer:** Gary Caldon (30)
Local Press: Maldon & Burnham Standard (01621 852233).
Local Radio: BBC Essex, Essex FM.

HONOURS: Isthmian Lg Div 1 R-up 95-96, Div 2 North 89-90; Essex Senior Lg 81-82 82-83 83-84, Lg Cup 82-83, Trophy 81-82; JT Clarke Cup 82-83; Thorn EMI National Floodlit Competition R-up 82-83; Eastern Floodlit Cup 93-94; East Anglian Cup 93-94 94-95; Essex & Suffolk Border Lge 31-32; Essex Jun Cup 31-32; North Essex Lge 46-47.

Heybridge Swifts FC 97; Back Row (L-R); Liam Cutbush, Kirkm Game, John Pollard, Wayne Adcock, Mark Keen, Kingsley Banks, Ashley Vickers, Steve Harding. Front Row; Mitchell Springett, Megan Creasy (Mascot), Tom Meredith, Danny Hall, Mark Cranfield, Keith Bain (Capt), Matt Jones, Gary Caloon.

Photo - Garry Letts

Heybridge Swifts

Match No.	Date	Venue H/A	Competition	Opponents	Result	League Pos.	Attendance	Goalscorers (Times if known)
1	Aug 17	A	IL	Chertsey Town	Won 5-3		353	Cash (og), Caldon, Hughes, Springett (2 p)
2	Aug 20	H	IL	St Albans City	Won 2-1		323	Springett (2, 1 pen)
3	Aug 24	H	IL	Oxford City	Won 2-1	4	335	Caldon, Cranfield
4	Aug 27	A	IL	Hendon	Drew 1-1		287	Game
5	Aug 31	A	IL	Grays Athletic	Won 1-0	2	263	Caldon
6	Sep 7	H	IL	Carshalton Athletic	Lost 0-2	2	329	
7	**Sep 10**	**A**	**GIS**	**Maidenhead United**	**Won 2-1**			**Caldon, Hewes**
8	**Sep 14**	**A**	**FAC 1 Q**	**Bury Town**	**Drew 0-0**		**297**	
9	**Sep 16**	**H**	**FAC 1QR**	**Bury Town**	**Won 3-0**		**332**	**Pollard, Southgate, Springett**
10	Sep 21	A	IL	Dulwich Hamlet	Won 3-1	3	297	Springett, Caldon, Keen
11	Sep 24	H	IL	Kingstonian	Won 2-1	2	347	Jones, Matthews
12	**Sep 28**	**H**	**FAC 2 Q**	**Chelmsford City**	**Drew 1-1**		**1244**	**Springett**
13	**Oct 1**	**A**	**FAC 2QR**	**Chelmsford City**	**Lost 1-2**		**1684**	**Springett**
14	Oct 5	A	IL	Bishop's Stortford	Drew 0-0		420	
15	Oct 12	H	IL	Harrow Borough	Drew 0-0	2	312	
16	**Oct 19**	**A**	**FAT 1 Q**	**Canvey Island**	**Won 1-0**	3	**361**	**Adcock**
17	Oct 26	H	IL	Purfleet	Lost 1-3		312	Caldon
18	Oct 29	H	IL	Yeading	Lost 0-5	6	212	
19	Nov 1	A	IL	Enfield	Won 2-1		1048	Springett, Jones
20	**Nov 5**	**A**	**GIC**	**Dorking**	**Won 4-0**	5		
21	**Nov 9**	**H**	**FAT 2 Q**	**Grays Athletic**	**Won 2-1**		**270**	**Hewes, Jones**
22	Nov 12	H	IL	Staines Town	Won 2-1		246	Keen, Hewes
23	Nov 16	A	IL	Aylesbury United	Lost 0-1		502	
24	Nov 23	H	IL	Boreham Wood	Lost 0-2	5	236	
25	Nov 25	A	IL	Carshalton Athletic	Lost 1-4	6	211	Southgate
26	**Nov 27**	**H**	**GIC**	**Dorking**	**Won 8-0**			
27	**Nov 30**	**A**	**FAT 3 Q**	**Carshalton Athletic**	**Won 3-0**		**202**	**Jones, Caldon, Springett (pen)**
28	Dec 7	H	IL	Hitchin Town	Won 2-1		221	Caldon, Springett
29	Dec 14	A	IL	Yeovil Town	Lost 0-1	5	2101	
30	**Dec 17**	**A**	**GIC**	**Bedford Town**	**Lost 1-2***	6		
31	Dec 21	H	IL	Bromley	Won 4-3		212	Caldon (3), Francis
32	Dec 26	A	IL	Dagenham & Redbridge	Lost 0-3	6	622	
33	**Jan 18**	**A**	**FAT 1**	**Worcester City**	**Won 2-0**	7	**724**	**Keene, Cranfield**
34	**Jan 21**	**H**	**IL FMC**	**Enfield**	**Lost 0-1**			
35	Jan 25	A	IL	St Albans City	Lost 2-4	8	445	Jones (2)
36	Feb 1	H	IL	Hendon	Drew 1-1	9	274	Cranfield
37	**Feb 8**	**A**	**FAT 2**	**Grantham**	**Won 1-0**		**1223**	**Adcock**
38	Feb 15	H	IL	Dulwich Hamlet	Drew 1-1	10	305	Keen
39	Feb 18	A	IL	Staines Town	Drew 2-2		206	Hale (2)
40	Feb 22	H	IL	Sutton United	Won 3-0		194	Caldon (2), Cherry
41	Feb 25	H	IL	Grays Athletic	Drew 3-3	10	366	Game, Harding, Springett (pen)
42	**Mar 1**	**H**	**FAT 5**	**Kidderminster Harriers**	**Won 3-0**		**1187**	**Caldon (2), Harding**
43	Mar 4	H	IL	Chertsey Town	Won 4-1		182	Harding (2), Caldon, Game
44	Mar 8	H	IL	Bishop's Stortford	Drew 0-0	7	387	
45	Mar 12	A	IL	Harrow Borough	Drew 3-3		162	Caldon, Jones, Springett
46	Mar 15	A	IL	Yeading	Lost 0-1	8	125	
47	**Mar 22**	**H**	**FAT Q F**	**Woking**	**Lost 0-1**		**2477**	
48	Mar 25	A	IL	Kingstonian	Lost 0-1		295	
49	Mar 29	A	IL	Purfleet	Drew 3-3		152	Cherry, Jones, Ansah
50	Mar 31	H	IL	Dagenham & Redbridge	Won 4-1	11	412	Caldon, Cherry, Pollard, Ansah
51	Apr 5	A	IL	Bromley	Drew 1-1	11	303	Ansah
52	Apr 8	A	IL	Oxford City	Won 2-1		179	Ansah, Francis
53	Apr 12	H	IL	Aylesbury United	Lost 1-3	10	272	Caldon
54	Apr 15	H	IL	Enfield	Drew 0-0		530	
55	Apr 19	A	IL	Boreham Wood	Drew 0-0	9	153	
56	Apr 22	A	IL	Sutton United	Won 2-0		310	Caldon, Ansah
57	Apr 26	A	IL	Yeovil Town	Drew 0-0	8	875	
58	May 3	A	IL	Hitchin Town	Won 2-1	9	268	Caldon, Harding

* After Extra Time

HEYBRIDGE SWIFTS PLAYING SQUAD 1997-98

Goalkeepers: Kingsley Banks (Witham T, Barking, Enfield, Basildon U, Dartford, Gillingham, Tottenham)

Defenders: Mark Cranfield (Braintree T, Brightlingsea U), **Kirk Game** (Great Wakering R, Stambridge, Chelmsford C, Homburg (Ger), Colchester, Southend), **David Rolfe** (Baldock T, Braintree T, Chelmsford C, Eton Manor), **Ashley Vickers** (Worcester C, Sheffield U, Sheffield Wed), **Keith Bain** (Wivenhoe T, Sudbury T, Wivenhoe T, Tiptree U, Wivenhoe T), Wayne Adcock (Witham T, Braintree T, Chelmsford C, Eton Manor), **Mark Keen** (Chelmsford, Enfield, Dartford, Witham)

Midfielders: Matt Jones (Chelmsford C, Southend, Arsenal (T)), **Barry O'Dea** (Melbourne U (Aust), Witham T, Chelmsford C), **Adam Gillespie** (Local football), **Gary Popham** (Burnham Ramblers), **Dean Caldon** (Maldon T), **Bradley Roast** (Grays, Hitchin, Dag & Red, Aldershot T, Tottenham H)

Forwards: Mitchell Springett (Wivenhoe T, Bury T, Chelmsford C, Braintree T, Wivenhoe T, Braintree T, Halstead T, Camb.U), **John Pollard** (Bury T, Colchester), **Gary Caldon** (Maldon T, Basildon U, Billericay T), **Andy Ansah** (Bromley, Hayes, Leyton O, Gillingham, Peterborough, Southend, Brentford, Crystal Palace), **Keith Glynn** (Burnham Ramblers), **Steve Harding** (Burnham Ramblers, Maldon T, Heybridge S), **Richard Cherry** (B.Stortford, Canvey Is, Bromley, Grays, Purfleet, Enfield, Hendon, Kingstonian, Redbridge F, Grays, Barking, Woodford, Colchester, Gillingham)

HITCHIN TOWN

Formed: 1928 **Nickname:** The Canaries
Colours: Yellow/green/green
Change colours: Black & white/black/black
Midweek matchday: Tuesday **Clubcall Line:** 0891 122 934
Reserves League: None

Chairman: Terry Barratt
Secretary: Roger Austin, 22 St Katherine's Close, Ickleford, Hitchin, Herts. SG5 3XS (01462 457811).
Fixture Sec: Alan Sexton (Tel. ?????)
Press Officer: Bary Swain (01462 455096).
Manager: Andy Melvin **Physio:** Peter Prince.
Asst Mgr: David Moseley **Coach:** Tony Martin
GROUND Address: Top Field, Fishponds Road, Hitchin SG5 1NU (01462 459028-matchdays only).
Directions: On A505 near town centre opposite large green. 1 mile from Hitchin (BR).
Capacity: 3,800 **Cover:** 1,250 **Seats:** 400 **Floodlights:** Yes
Clubhouse: (01462 434483). Members bar, Function Hall (hireable). Open every day. Steward: Eamonn Watson/ Nigel Collins
Club Shop: Yes, contact Medwyn Williams
Sponsors: TBA

PROGRAMME DETAILS:
Pages: 48 **Price:** £1
Editor: Barry Swain
Tel: 01462 455096

PREVIOUS - **Leagues:** Spartan 28-39, Hert & Middx 39-45, Athenian 39,45-63.

CLUB RECORDS - Attendance: 7,878 v Wycombe Wanderers, FA Amateur Cup 3rd Rd 18/2/56. **Win:** Spartan Lge 29-30 13-0 v Cowley, 13-0 v RAF. **Defeat** (Isthmian Lge): 0-10 v Kingstonian (A) 65-66, v Slough T. (A) 79-80. **Career** (Isthmian Lge) **appearances:** Paul Giggle 950+ 67-88. **Career** (Isthmian Lge) **goals:** Paul Giggle, 129. **Transfer fee paid:** £2,000 for Ray Seeking (Potton United, July 1989). **Transfer fee received:** Undisclosed

BEST SEASON - **FA Trophy:** 3rd Round (rep) 76-77. **FA Amateur Cup:** Semi Final 60-61, 62-63
FA Cup: 2nd Rd - v Swindon 1-3 (A) 76-77, v Boston Utd, 0-1 (A) 73-74, v Wycombe Wand. 0-5 (H) 94-95, v Gillingham lost 0-3 (A) 95-96

Players progressing to Football League: R Smith (Millwall & England), L Garwood (Spurs 46), C J Walker, W Odell, S Foss, R Stevens, T Clarke, G Goodyear, L Harwood, P Burridge, R Kitchener (Chelsea 54), D Bumstead, M Dixon, D Pacey (Luton 56), M Dixon & B Whitby (Luton 57), K Abiss (Brighton 57), D Hille, G Ley, R Morton, L Payne (Newcastle & Reading), M Small (Brighton), R Nugent (Barnet), Chris McMenamin (Coventry 96).
96-97 Captain: Mark Burke **P.o.Y.:** Adam Parker **Top scorer:** Barry Dellar (19)
Local Presss: Hitchin Gazette/Hitchin Comet, Hitchin Herald & Post **Local Radio:** Chiltern, Three Counties

HONOURS: Isthmian Lge R-up 68-69 (Div 1 92-93); Spartan Lge 34-35; AFA Sen Cup 30-31; Herts Snr Cup (19-record); London Sen Cup 69-70 (R-up 72-73); E Anglian Cup 72-73; Herts Charity Cup(16), Herts I'mediate Cup(8); Woolwich Trophy 82-83; Televised Sport International Cup 88-89 90-91; Southern Comb. Senior Floodlit Cup 90-91.

Hitchin Town FC *Photo - Clive Butchins*

Hitchin Town

Match No.	Date	Venue H/A	Competition	Opponents	Result	League Pos.	Attendance	Goalscorers (Times if known)
1	Aug 17	H	IL	Aylesbury United	Won 2-1		373	Ingram, Dellar
2	Aug 20	A	IL	Boreham Wood	Lost 0-4		359	
3	Aug 24	A	IL	Sutton United	Lost 3-4	16	536	Dellar, Coley, Anderson
4	Aug 26	H	IL	Yeovil Town	Lost 0-1	16	537	
5	Aug 31	H	IL	Purfleet	Won 2-0		334	Dellar, Bone
6	Sep 3	A	IL	Staines Town	Won 2-1	10	282	Coley, Dellar
7	**Sep 10**	**A**	**GIS**	**Dorking**	**Lost 0-1**			
8	Sep 14	A	IL	Kingstonian	Lost 1-3	12	407	1 og
9	Sep 21	H	IL	Harrow Borough	Lost 2-4	14	278	Allpress, Hazard (pen)
10	Sep 24	A	IL	Enfield	Lost 0-1		347	
11	Sep 27	A	IL	Oxford City	Lost 1-5	17	212	Scott
12	Sep 30	A	IL	Carshalton Athletic	Won 2-1		255	Allpress, Dawson (og)
13	Oct 5	A	IL	Grays Athletic	Drew 2-2	11	254	Cooper 10, Hall 68
14	Oct 12	H	IL	Chertsey Town	Won 2-1	7	356	Cooper, Parker
15	**Oct 19**	**A**	**FAT 1 Q**	**Ashford Town**	**Lost 1-4**		**544**	**Bone 44**
16	**Oct 26**	**H**	**FAC 4 Q**	**Wisbech Town**	**Lost 1-2**		**942**	**Coley 30**
17	Nov 2	H	IL	Dagenham & Redbridge	Drew 0-0	10	361	
18	Nov 9	A	IL	Purfleet	Drew 1-1	11	136	Dellar 8
19	Nov 16	H	IL	Dulwich Hamlet	Drew 0-0		349	
20	Nov 23	A	IL	Hendon	Lost 0-1	13	245	
21	Nov 30	H	IL	Enfield	Lost 0-3	15	703	
22	**Dec 3**	**A**	**IL FMC**	**St Albans City**	**Won 4-0**			
23	Dec 7	A	IL	Heybridge Swifts	Lost 1-2	16	221	Cooper 25
24	Dec 14	H	IL	Bishop's Stortford	Won 3-0	12	265	Cooper, Coley, Dellar
25	Dec 21	A	IL	Yeading	Won 1-0	11	145	Bone
26	Jan 18	A	IL	Aylesbury United	Lost 1-2	13	655	Woodford
27	Jan 25	H	IL	Boreham Wood	Lost 1-2	15	329	Parker
28	Jan 28	H	IL	St Albans City	Drew 1-1	15	291	Bates
29	Feb 1	A	IL	Yeovil Town	Lost 0-1	15	2004	
30	**Feb 3**	**A**	**IL FMC**	**Purfleet**	**Lost 2-3**			
31	Feb 8	H	IL	Staines Town	Won 2-1	12	328	Dellar, Allpress
32	Feb 15	A	IL	Harrow Borough	Lost 1-3	17	220	Dellar
33	Feb 18	H	IL	Hitchin Town	Won 5-2		188	Hall (4), Bates
34	Feb 22	H	IL	Kingstonian	Won 4-1	11	411	Scott (3), Parker
35	Mar 1	A	IL	Chertsey Town	Won 5-0	11	212	Parker (3), Bone, Dellar
36	Mar 4	H	IL	Oxford City	Won 4-2		212	Dellar (2), Parker (2, 1 pen)
37	Mar 8	H	IL	Grays Athletic	Lost 0-2	11	350	
38	Mar 15	A	IL	Bromley	Lost 2-3		283	Bates, Dellar
39	Mar 29	H	IL	Carshalton Athletic	Won 3-2		328	Bates, Hall (pen), Dellar
40	Mar 31	A	IL	St Albans City	Lost 1-2	15		Allpress
41	Apr 5	H	IL	Yeading	Won 3-1	13	232	Burke, Parker, Williams
42	Apr 12	A	IL	Dulwich Hamlet	Drew 2-2		311	Bates, Parker
43	Apr 17	A	IL	Dagenham & Redbridge	Drew 1-1		406	Dellar
44	Apr 19	H	IL	Hendon	Lost 1-2	15	376	Hall
45	Apr 24	H	IL	Sutton United	Lost 2-5		182	Hall (2, 2 pens)
46	Apr 26	A	IL	Bishop's Stortford	Won 2-1	13	381	Dellar, Hall (pen)
47	May 3	H	IL	Heybridge Swifts	Lost 1-2	14	268	Hall

HITCHIN TOWN PLAYING SQUAD 1997-98

Goalkeepers: Gerald Sylvester (Eynesbury R, Haverhill R, Northampton)
Defenders: Ken Gillard (Chesham U, Northampton, Luton), **Mark Burke** (Luton, QPR (A)), **Jon Bone** (Baldock T, Hitchin T, Luton), **Lee Henry** (Youth team), **Gavin Covington** (Wycombe W, Hitchin T, Barnet, Dunstable), **Tim Allpress** (Enterprise(HK), Hitchin, Colchester, Bayer Uerdingen (Ger), Luton), **Danny Swale** (West Ham U), **Luke Parker** (Welwyn GC, Hatfield T, Stevenage)
Midfielders: Ian Scott (St.Albans C, Aylesbury U, Luton), **Sam Turner** (Luton), **Dave Drury** (Stotfold, Langford, Stotfold), **Adam Turner** (Youth team), **Mark McGonagle** (Barton R, Hitchin, Baldock, Luton), **Chris McMenamin** (Brache Sparta, Luton OB)
Forwards: Barry Dellar (Arlesey, Langford), **John Coley** (Stotfold, Langford), **Rudi Hall** (Ware, Wealdstone, West Ham U), **Carl Williams** (Carshalton, C.Row & Romford, Fulham), **Corey Donaghue** (Hayes, Sittingbourne, Welling)

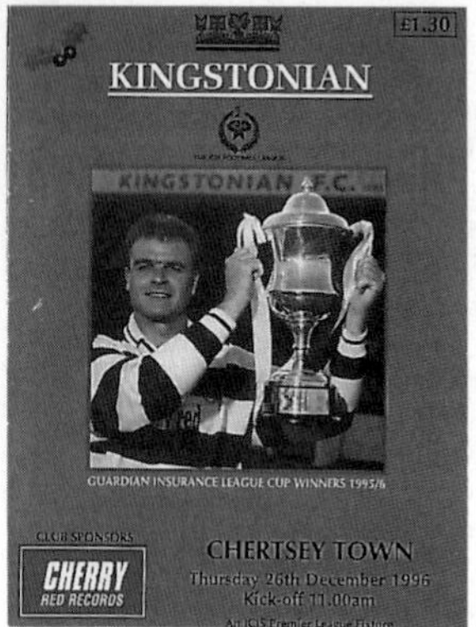

PROGRAMME DETAILS:
Pages: 28 **Price:** £1.50
Editor: Brian Giffard
(0181 940 6448)

KINGSTONIAN

Formed: 1885 **Nickname:** The K's
Colours: Red & white hoops/black/black
Change colours: Azure & black stripes
Midweek matchday: Tuesday **Reserve League:** Suburban.
Newsline: 0660 666 300. **G Chapples Buzz Line:** 0660 666 333

Chairman: G M Child **Vice Chairman:** Peter Gellard.
President: J Webster. **Managing Director:** Chris Kelly.
Football Secretary: W R McNully, 71 Largewood Ave., Tolworth, Surbiton KT6 7NX (0181 391 4552).
Manager: Geoff Chapple **Asst Man.:** J Broughton **Coach:** Colin Lippiatt
Press Officer: B P Frawley (0181 541 5250) **Physio:** James Pearce
Comm. & Admin. Man.: Chris Kelly (0181 547 3335)

GROUND Address: Kingsmeadow Stadium, Kingston Road, Kingston-on-Thames KT1 3PB 0181 547 3335. **Directions:** From town centre - Cambridge Rd on to Kingston Rd (A2043) to Malden Rd. From A3, turn off at New Malden, turn left on to A2043 - grd 1 mile on left. Half mile from Norbiton (BR)
Capacity: 9,000 **Cover:** 3,500 **Seats:** 690 **Floodlights:** Yes
Clubhouse: Banqueting centre, open 7 days. 3 bars capacity 400. Contact C Kelly (0181 547 3335). Banquets & Conf Mgr R Rodriques (0181 974 5712)
Club Shop: Sells programmes, shirts, badges, Contact Mrs Ann Dickinson (0181 747 3336). **Club Sponsors:** The Emporium Club.

PREVIOUS - Leagues: Kingston & Dist., West Surrey, Southern Suburban, Athenian 1919-29. **Names:** Kingston & Surbiton YMCA 1885-87, Saxons 87-90, Kingston Wanderers 1893-1904, Old Kingstonians 08-19. **Grounds:** Several to 1921; Richmond Rd 21-89.

CLUB RECORDS - Attendance: 4,582 v Chelsea (Friendly) 22.7.95. **Goalscorer:** Johnny Whig 295 **Appearances:** Micky Preston 555. **Win:** 15-1 v Delft, friendly 5/9/51 (competitive: 10-0 v Hitchin (H), Isthmian Lge 19/3/66). **Defeat:** 0-11 v Ilford (A), Isthmian Lge 13/2/37. **Fee Paid:** £10,000 for R Cherry (Redbridge Forest 91) **Fee Received:** £10,000 for D Harlow Farnborough 95.

Best Season - FA Amateur Cup: Winners 32-33 R-up 59-60. **FA Cup:** 2nd Rd Proper 94-95 (v Aylesbury U) 95-96 (v Plymouth A.). **League clubs defeated:** Brighton & H.A. 94-95 1-0.

Players progressing to Football League: C Nastri (C Palace), H Lindsay (Southampton 65), G Still (Brighton 79), D Byrne (Gillingham 1985), J Power (Brentford 87), Jamie Ndah (Torquay).

96-97 - Captain: Terry Evans **P.o.Y.:** Edward Akuamoah **Top scorer:** Edward Akuamoah
Local Press: Surrey Comet (0181 546 2261). **Local Radio:** County Sound.

HONOURS: Isthmian Lg 33-34 36-37 (R-up 47-48 62-63, Div 1 R-up 84-85), Icis Lg Cup winners 95-96; Athenian Lg 23-24 25-26 (R-up 26-27); London Snr Cup 62-63 64-65 86-87 (R-up 5); Surrey Snr Cup(9),(R-up 90-91).

Kingstonian FC. *Photo - Andrew Chitty*

Kingstonian

Match No.	Date	Venue H/A	Competition	Opponents	Result	League Pos.	Attendance	Goalscorers (Times if known)
1	Aug 17	H	IL	Boreham Wood	Won 5-1		433	Akuamoah (2), Bolton, Darlington, 1 og
2	Aug 20	A	IL	Staines Town	Lost 1-2		376	Annon
3	Aug 24	A	IL	Harrow Borough	Won 2-1	7	277	Darlington, Bolton
4	Aug 27	H	IL	Aylesbury United	Lost 0-1	12	448	
5	Aug 31	H	IL	Sutton United	Lost 2-3		1009	Akuamoah, Riley (pen)
6	Sep 7	A	IL	Purfleet	Lost 2-3	16	229	Ravenscroft, Brooker
7	**Sep 10**	**H**	**GIC**	**Tilbury**	**Won 2-1**			
8	Sep 14	H	IL	Hitchin Town	Won 3-1	9	407	Jones, Brooker, Bolton
9	Sep 21	H	IL	Yeovil Town	Lost 0-3	11	676	
10	Sep 24	A	IL	Heybridge Swifts	Lost 1-2		347	Bolton
11	Oct 5	A	IL	Dagenham & Redbridge	Lost 0-2	17	757	
12	Oct 12	H	IL	Dulwich Hamlet	Won 4-2	12	413	Darlington, Jones (2), Thomas
13	Oct 15	H	IL	Purfleet	Won 3-2		270	Luckett, Darlington, Akuamoah (p)
14	Oct 19	A	IL	Boreham Wood	Drew 0-0	8	303	
15	**Oct 22**	**A**	**IL CS**	**Hayes**	**Lost 2-4**			**Luckett, Darlington**
16	**Oct 26**	**A**	**FAC 4 Q**	**Ashford Town**	**Lost 1-3**		**1089**	**Darlington 90**
17	Nov 2	H	IL	Carshalton Athletic	Drew 1-1	10	514	Akuamoah (pen)
18	**Nov 5**	**H**	**GIC**	**Hemel Hempstead**	**Won 3-2***			
19	Nov 9	A	IL	Dulwich Hamlet	Won 2-1	8	418	Darlington 54, Akuamoah 78
20	Nov 12	H	IL	Grays Athletic	Won 5-2		323	Kruszynski (2), Luckett, Darlington, Lavender
21	Nov 16	H	IL	Bishop's Stortford	Lost 0-1	7	442	
22	Nov 23	A	IL	St Albans City	Lost 0-2	8	454	
23	**Nov 30**	**A**	**FAT 3 Q**	**Gloucester City**	**Lost 1-3**		**752**	
24	Dec 7	A	IL	Yeading	Lost 1-5	11	247	Akuamoah 45 (pen)
25	Dec 14	H	IL	Enfield	Lost 0-1	11	619	
26	**Dec 17**	**H**	**GIC**	**Banstead United**	**Won 2-1***			
27	Dec 21	A	IL	Oxford City	Lost 1-3	13	257	Thompson
28	Dec 26	H	IL	Chertsey Town	Won 2-0	11	344	Corbett, Thompson
29	**Jan 7**	**H**	**IL FMC**	**Walton & Hersham Utd**	**Drew 4-4+**			
30	Jan 11	H	IL	Harrow Borough	Drew 4-4	11	391	Akuamoah 38, 69 (p), Pitcher 40, Deadman 46
31	Jan 25	H	IL	Staines Town	Drew 3-3	11	434	Darlington, Akuamoah, Deadman
32	**Jan 28**	**H**	**GIC**	**Wokingham Town**	**Won 2-0**			
33	Feb 2	A	IL	Aylesbury United	Won 5-2	11	491	Evans, Pitcher, Biggins, Akuamoah, Darlington
34	Feb 8	A	IL	Sutton United	Lost 2-5	11	853	Akuamoah 43 (pen), 72
35	Feb 15	A	IL	Yeovil Town	Won 3-2	11	2242	Darlington (2), Evans
36	Feb 18	A	IL	Hendon	Lost 1-2		275	Akuamoah
37	Feb 22	A	IL	Hitchin Town	Lost 1-4	13	411	Akuamoah
38	Mar 1	H	IL	Hendon	Won 2-1	12	350	Darlington, Deadman
39	Mar 4	A	IL	Bromley	Drew 2-2		216	Darlington, Akuamoah
40	Mar 8	H	IL	Dagenham & Redbridge	Lost 2-3		455	Darlington, Luckett
41	Mar 15	A	IL	Grays Athletic	Drew 1-1	14	253	Darlington
42	Mar 22	A	IL	Carshalton Athletic	Won 3-1	13	554	Akuamoah (2), Darlington
43	Mar 25	H	IL	Heybridge Swifts	Won 1-0		295	Darlington
44	Mar 29	H	IL	Bromley	Drew 1-1		436	Akuamoah (pen)
45	Mar 31	A	IL	Chertsey Town	Won 3-0	10	326	Darlington (2), Akuamoah
46	Apr 5	H	IL	Oxford City	Won 4-1	9	372	Darlington (2), Deadman, Carruth
47	Apr 12	A	IL	Bishop's Stortford	Drew 2-2	9	410	Deadman, Thompson
48	Apr 19	H	IL	St Albans City	Lost 0-1	10	492	
49	Apr 26	A	IL	Enfield	Lost 0-3	12	865	
50	May 3	H	IL	Yeading	Won 4-2	11	437	Darlington, Carruth, Deadman, Luckett

* After Extra Time   + Walton won 5-3 on Penalties

KINGSTONIAN PLAYING SQUAD 1997-98

Goalkeepers: Richard Morgan (Carshalton)

Defenders: Andy Fisher (Carshalton, Dulwich Hamlet, Dorking, Molesey, Leatherhead, Carshalton), **John Finch** (Fulham, Dorking, Molesey, Leatherhead, Chelsea), **Matt Elverson** (Walton & H), **Gavin Nebbeling** (Preston, Fulham, Crystal Palace, Arcadia Shepherds (SA)), **Danny Lavender** (Hampton), **Danny Kirk** (Youth team), **Erskine Smart** (St.Albans, Dulwich H, St.Albans, Enfield, Hendon, Kingsbury, Watford), **Simon Sobihy** (Youth team), **Paul Carruth** (Tooting, Met. Police, Queen's Park, St.Mirren), **Richard Thompson** (Youth team)

Midfielders: Scott Corbett (Hampton), **Danny Brooker** (Sutton U, Dorking, Wimbledon (T)), **John Deadman** (Purfleet, Hendon, Grays), **Colin Luckett** (Millwall), **Mark Biggins** (Hampton, Hendon, St.Albans, Harrow, Wealdstone, Aldershot T, Woking, Windsor, St.Albans, Maidenhead, Feltham, Hanwell, Hampton)

Forwards: Steve Darlington (Wokingham T, Staines T, Windsor & Eton, Chalfont St.Peter, Hounslow), **Eddie Akuamoah** (Carshalton), **Geoff Pitcher** (Carshalton, Watford, Millwall), **Richard Evans** (Staines, Marlow, Sutton U, Windsor, Harrow, Wokingham, Reading)

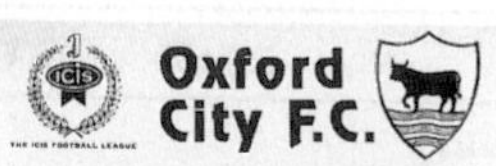

CITY CELEBRATE
DIVISION ONE CHAMPIONSHIP
OFFICIAL PROGRAMME
Club Sponsors
UNIPART DCM
DEMAND CHAIN MANAGEMENT
£1

PROGRAMME DETAILS:
Pages: 60 **Price:** £1
Editor: Laurie Simmons

OXFORD CITY

Formed: 1882 **Nickname:** City
Colours: Blue & white hoops/white/white.
Change colours: All yellow
Midweek Matchday: Tuesday
Reserve's League: Suburban Lge Prem Div

Chairman: M Woodley **President:** J Grosvenor
Vice Chairman: R Holt **Press Officer/Secretary:** John Shepperd, 20 Howe Close, Wheatley, Oxford OX33 1SS (01865 872181 & Fax).
Manager: Andy Thorne. 01865 882456 (H)
Asst Manager: Kevin Brock **Physio:** G Bowerman.

GROUND Address: Court Place Farm, Marsh Lane, Marston, Oxford. OX3 0NQ. Tel: 01865 744493. 01865 742394 (Clubhouse).
Directions: From London M40/A40, ring-road to North, take 1st slip road, follow signs to John Radcliffe hospital, ground on left after leaving flyover. From the north same ring-road.
Capacity: 3,000 **Seats:** 300 **Cover:** 400 **Floodlights:** Yes
Clubhouse: Open matchdays, most refreshments available.
Club Shop: Yes, open matchdays, selling souvenirs. Contact Paul Cotterell.
Sponsors: Unipart D.C.M.

PREVIOUS - Grounds: The White House 1882-1988/ Cuttleslowe Pk 90-91/ Pressed Steel, Romanway 91-93. **Leagues:** Isthmian 07-88/ South Midlands 90-93.

CLUB RECORDS - Attendance: 9,500 v Leytonstone, FA Amateur Cup 1950. **Win:** 9-0 v Harlow Town, Isthmian League 9/10/76. **Defeat:** 0-8 v Wycombe Wanderers, Isthmian League - date unknown. **Scorer:** John Woodley. **Appearances:** John Woodley. **Fee Paid:** £3,000 for S Adams (Woking). **Fee Received:** £17,500 for H Forinton (Yeovil T. 1.97)
Best Season - FA Amateur Cup: Winners 05-06 R-up 02-03 12-13. **FA Vase:** R-up 94-95. **FA Cup:** Second Round 69-70 (lost 1-5 at home to Swansea Town). **FA Trophy:** 1st Rd Prop 1996 v Merthyr Tydfil
Players progressing to Football League: A Blakeman (Brentford 1946), C Holton (Arsenal 1950), K Savin (Derby 1950), E Wilcox (WBA 1948), R Adams (Blackpool 1948), A Jeffries (Brentford 1949), P James (Luton 1949), D Gordon (WBA 1947), V Mobley (Sheffield Wednesday 1963), J Varney (Hull 1950), P Lee (Hereford 1973), H Poole (Port Vale 1955), G Parker (Luton 1981), M Keown (Arsenal 1984), D Meeson (Wolves 1952).
96-97 - Captain: Jon Muttock **Top scorer:** Howard Forinton (17) **P.o.Y.:** Martin Brown
Local Press: Oxford Mail, Oxford Journal **Local Radio:** Radio Oxford Thames Valley FM, Fox FM.

HONOURS: FA Amateur Cup 05-06 (R-up 02-03 12-13), F.A. Vase R-Up 94-95, Isthmian Lg R-up 34-35 45-46 (Div 1 R-up 77-78), Icis Lg Div 1 Champions 95-96, South Midlands Lg 92-93, Oxon Senior Cup - 27 times.

Back Row (L-R); Alan Thorne (Asst Mgr), Andy Smith, Martin Brown, David Summer, Graham Bowerman (Physio), Mick Torres, Andy Martin, Richard Peirson, Andy Thomas (Player/Mgr). Front Row; Stuart Beavon, Liam Herbert, Steve Fontaine, Neil Greig, Stewart McCleary, Kurt Douglas, Mark Hewitson, Howard Kemp

Oxford City

Match No.	Date	Venue H/A	Competition	Opponents	Result	League Pos.	Attendance	Goalscorers (Times if known)
1	Aug 17	H	IL	Bishop's Stortford	Won 4-1		261	Smith, Charles, Thomas, Forinton
2	Aug 20	A	IL	Yeading	Lost 1-4		132	Forinton
3	Aug 24	A	IL	Heybridge Swifts	Lost 1-2	14	335	S Fontaine
4	Aug 27	H	IL	Sutton United	Lost 1-3		323	Forinton
5	Aug 31	H	IL	Harrow Borough	Won 2-1	14	327	Forinton (2)
6	Sep 7	A	IL	Enfield	Drew 3-3	15	852	Fontaine, Martin, Sharkey
7	**Sep 11**	**H**	**GIC**	**Chertsey Town**	**Lost 1-3**			**Forinton**
8	**Sep 14**	**A**	**FAC 1 Q**	**Witney Town**	**Drew 1-1**		**288**	**Forinton**
9	**Sep 17**	**H**	**FAC 1QR**	**Witney Town**	**Lost 2-3***		**402**	**Charles (2)**
10	Sep 21	H	IL	Purfleet	Lost 1-2	19	217	Forinton
11	Sep 24	A	IL	Staines Town	Won 2-1		151	Morrisey, Herbert
12	Sep 27	H	IL	Hitchin Town	Won 5-1	6	212	Forinton (3), Herbert, Monamara
13	Oct 4	H	IL	St Albans City	Won 3-2		311	Thomas, Charles, Herbert
14	Oct 12	H	IL	Grays Athletic	Drew 1-1	5	251	Forinton
15	Oct 19	A	IL	Chertsey Town	Won 4-2	5	377	Morrisey, Smith, S Fontaine, Forinton (og)
16	Oct 26	H	IL	Aylesbury United	Won 3-2	4	464	Brown, Herbert, Sharkey
17	Nov 2	A	IL	Dulwich Hamlet	Won 1-0	3	348	Forinton
18	**Nov 9**	**H**	**FAT 2 Q**	**Basingstoke**	**Lost 1-6**		**325**	**Forinton**
19	Nov 12	A	IL	Hendon	Lost 0-2	4	179	
20	Nov 16	A	IL	Carshalton Athletic	Drew 1-1	4	349	Forinton (pen)
21	Nov 23	H	IL	Bromley	Lost 2-3	5	218	Martin, Herbert
22	Nov 27	A	IL	Harrow Borough	Won 3-2	4	145	Herbert, Smith, S Fontaine
23	Dec 7	A	IL	Grays Athletic	Drew 1-1	4	189	Fontaine 26
24	Dec 14	A	IL	Dagenham & Redbridge	Lost 2-4	5	534	S Fontaine, Herbert
25	**Dec 17**	**H**	**IL FMC**	**Aldershot Town**	**Won 2-1***			**S Fontaine, McClearey**
26	Dec 21	H	IL	Kingstonian	Won 3-1	5	257	Forinton, S Fontaine, Herbert
27	Jan 18	A	IL	Bishop's Stortford	Drew 2-2	6	322	S Fontaine (2)
28	**Jan 21**	**H**	**IL FMC**	**Whyteleafe**	**Lost 2-3**			**Pearson, Martin**
29	Jan 25	H	IL	Yeading	Lost 0-1	7	247	
30	Feb 1	A	IL	Sutton United	Won 2-1	6	601	Greig 39, Herbert 52
31	Feb 11	H	IL	Boreham Wood	Drew 0-0		151	
32	Feb 15	A	IL	Purfleet	Drew 2-2	6	179	Mutlock, Greig
33	Feb 22	H	IL	Chertsey Town	Lost 0-2	7	216	
34	Mar 4	A	IL	Hitchin Town	Lost 2-4		212	McLeary (2)
35	Mar 8	A	IL	St Albans City	Won 1-0	9	405	Herbert
36	Mar 15	H	IL	Hendon	Won 2-0	6	282	Brock, Herbert
37	Mar 22	H	IL	Dulwich Hamlet	Drew 1-1	6	259	Herbert
38	Mar 25	H	IL	Staines Town	Won 1-0		191	Charles
39	Mar 28	A	IL	Aylesbury United	Lost 1-6		874	Charles
40	Mar 31	H	IL	Yeovil Town	Lost 0-2	9	869	
41	Apr 5	A	IL	Kingstonian	Lost 1-4	11	372	Fisher (og)
42	Apr 8	H	IL	Heybridge Swifts	Lost 1-2		179	McCleary
43	Apr 12	H	IL	Carshalton Athletic	Drew 1-1	11	214	McDonnell
44	Apr 19	A	IL	Bromley	Lost 0-3	11	320	
45	Apr 22	A	IL	Yeovil Town	Lost 1-4		3275	Charles
46	Apr 26	H	IL	Dagenham & Redbridge	Drew 2-2	14	267	McDonnell, Charles
47	Apr 29	H	IL	Enfield	Lost 1-4		382	Concannon
48	May 3	A	IL	Boreham Wood	Lost 2-3	15	202	McCleary, McDonnell

* After Extra Time

OXFORD CITY PLAYING SQUAD 1997-98

Goalkeepers: Mick Torres (Local football), **Ian Moores** (Didcot)
Defenders: Terry Morrissey (Wokingham T, Oxford U), **Andy Smith** (Local football), **Jon Muttock** (Thame U, Carterton T, Oxford C, Wycombe W, Oxford U), **Martin Brown** (Abingdon T), **Andy Wallbridge** (Abingdon T, Marlow, Abingson T, Worcester, Fulham, Oxford U), **Neil Greig** (Abingdon T, Oxford U (T))
Midfielders: Justin Lee (Abingdon T, Arsenal), **Roger Charles** (Abingdon T, Oxford U (T)), **Liam Herbert** (Abingdon T, Oxford C, Abingdon T, Bicester T, Banbury U, Bicester T, Abingdon T, Thame U), **Andy Martin** (Abingdon T, Bicester T, Woodstock T), **Lee Sharkey** (Quarry Nomads), **Kevin Brock** (Rushden & D, Yeovil, Newcastle U, QPR, Oxford U), **Mark Hewitson** (Local football)
Forwards: Chris Fontaine (Abingdon T, Oxford C, Abingdon U), **Stuart McCleary** (Local football), **Steve Fontaine** (Abingdon U, Oxford C), **Matt McDonnell** (Marlow, Chesham, Aylesbury, Newbury, Shrewsbury, Oxford U)

PURFLEET

Founded: 1985 **Nickname:** Fleet
Colours: Green & yellow/green/yellow
Change colours: Claret/blue.
Midweek home matchday: Monday
Reserve's League: Essex & Herts Border Combination.

Chairman: Grant Beglan **President:** Keith Parker.
Vice Chairman: Ken Worrall
Secretary: Tony Perkins 48 Saltash Road, Hainault, Essex IG6 2NL (0181 500 3092) **Match Secretary/Press Officer:** Norman Posner
Commercial Manager: Bob Andrews (01268 415149).
Manager: Colin McBride **Asst Manager:** Chris King
Coach: Trevor Moore **Physio:** Bob Johnson.

PROGRAMME DETAILS:
Pages: 44 **Price:** £1
Editor: Norman Posner
Tel: 01708 458301 H

GROUND Address: Thurrock Hotel, Ship Lane, Grays, Essex (01708 868901) (Fax 01708 866703)
Directions: M25 or A13 to Dartford tunnel r'bout. Ground is fifty yards on right down Ship Lane. Nearest station is Purfleet, two miles from ground.
Capacity: 4,500 **Cover:** 1,000 **Seats:** 300 **Floodlights:** Yes
Clubhouse: 10am-11pm every day. Snooker, squash, weights room, aerobics, a-la carte restaurant, steam room. Three Bars. 56 Bedroom Hotel.
Steward: Tommy South.
Club Shop: Yes, selling programmes and magazines. Contact Tommy South (01708 868901).

SPONSORS: Main: Mann Enterprises. **Team:** Scantruck Ltd. **Prog:** London Container Services
PREVIOUS - League: Essex Senior 85-89. **Grounds:** None.

CLUB RECORDS - **Attendance:** 950 v West Ham United, friendly 1989.
Goalscorer: Terry Bellamy, 59. **Appearances:** Colin McBride, 234.
Win: 10-0 v Stansted (H) 86-87, v East Ham Utd (A) 87-88 (both Essex Senior League).
Defeat: 0-5 v Kingsbury Town (H), Isthmian Lge Division One 89-90.
BEST SEASON - **FA Cup:** Third Qualifying Rd 94-95 (lost 1-2 at home to Yeading).

Players progressing to Football League:
Paul Cobb & Lee Williams (Leyton O.)
96-97 - Captain: **P.o.Y.:** **Top scorer:** Paul Cobb (34)
Local Press: Thurrock Recorder, Thurrock Gazette.
Local Radio: Essex Radio, BBC Radio Essexx.

HONOURS: Isthmian Lg Div 2 91-92 (Div 1 R-up 93-94, Div 2 Nth R-up 88-89, Associate Members Tphy 91-92), Essex Snr Lg 87-88 (Lg Cup(2) 86-88), Stanford Charity Cup 87-88 (R-up 85-86). Essex Thames-Side Trophy 1994-95. Loctite Trophy 91-92. Essex Bus Houses Sen L/Cup 93-94. F Budden Trophy 94-95. Essex & Herts Border Comb R-up 94-95.

Purfleet FC *Photo - Mr P Barnes*

Purfleet

Match No.	Date	Venue H/A	Competition	Opponents	Result	League Pos.	Attendance	Goalscorers (Times if known)
1	Aug 17	A	IL	St Albans City	Lost 1-2		502	Deadman
2	Aug 19	H	IL	Dulwich Hamlet	Lost 1-4		207	Cobb
3	Aug 24	H	IL	Chertsey Town	Won 2-0	15	162	Carthy, Rees
4	Aug 26	A	IL	Dagenham & Redbridge	Lost 0-2		743	
5	Aug 31	A	IL	Hitchin Town	Lost 0-2	15	334	
6	Sep 7	H	IL	Kingstonian	Won 3-2	17	229	Donovan, Cobb, Rees
7	**Sep 10**	**A**	**GIC**	**Leyton Pennant**	**Won 4-1**			**Cobb (2), Cooper, Schneider**
8	**Sep 14**	**H**	**FAC 1 Q**	**Hornchurch**	**Won 5-1**		**103**	**Carthy (2), Donovan, Deadman, Cooper**
9	Sep 21	A	IL	Oxford City	Won 2-1	12	217	Cobb (2)
10	Sep 23	H	IL	Hendon	Drew 0-0		153	
11	**Sep 28**	**A**	**FAC 2 Q**	**Sudbury Town**	**Lost 1-2**	14	**313**	**Cavell**
12	Oct 5	A	IL	Sutton United	Drew 0-0	14	737	
13	Oct 12	A	IL	Carshalton Athletic	Lost 1-2	19	272	Carthy
14	Oct 15	A	IL	Kingstonian	Lost 2-3		270	Cobb (2)
15	Oct 19	H	IL	Enfield	Lost 1-3	20	428	Cavell
16	Oct 26	A	IL	Heybridge Swifts	Won 3-1	15	312	Carthy, Cobb, Odegbami
17	Nov 2	H	IL	Yeading	Drew 2-2	15	193	Cobb, Odegbami
18	**Nov 4**	**H**	**GIC**	**Sutton United**	**Lost 3-6**			**Cobb (3, 2 pens)**
19	Nov 9	H	IL	Hitchin Town	Drew 1-1	15	136	Cobb
20	Nov 11	H	IL	Bishop's Stortford	Won 3-0		128	Carthy, Moseley, Cavell
21	Nov 16	A	IL	Staines Town	Won 3-1	10	185	Odegbami, Carthy, Cooper
22	Nov 23	H	IL	Yeovil Town	Drew 1-1	9	347	Cobb (pen)
23	**Nov 30**	**A**	**FAT 3 Q**	**St Leonards Stamcroft**	**Lost 0-6**		**344**	
24	Dec 7	H	IL	Harrow Borough	Won 2-0	8	119	Cobb (2, 1 pen)
25	Dec 20	H	IL	Aylesbury United	Lost 0-1	10	122	
26	Jan 11	A	IL	Chertsey Town	Won 1-0	9	215	Cobb 35
27	Jan 18	H	IL	Carshalton Athletic	Won 2-0	9	215	Cobb, Cavell
28	Jan 25	A	IL	Dulwich Hamlet	Lost 1-2	9	302	Williams
29	Jan 27	H	IL	Bromley	Won 2-0	7	207	Cooper, Cobb
30	Feb 1	H	IL	Dagenham & Redbridge	Drew 2-2	7	401	Cobb (2, 1 pen)
31	**Feb 3**	**H**	**IL FMC**	**Hitchin Town**	**Won 3-2**			
32	Feb 8	A	IL	Hendon	Won 3-2	6	259	Odegbami 48, Cooper 77, Rees 89
33	Feb 15	H	IL	Oxford City	Drew 2-2	7	179	Williams, Cobb
34	Feb 22	A	IL	Enfield	Lost 0-3		936	
35	Mar 1	H	IL	Staines Town	Won 2-1	5	131	Odegbami, Cavell
36	Mar 3	H	IL	St Albans City	Drew 2-2		127	Cobb, Williams
37	Mar 8	H	IL	Sutton United	Won 3-2	3	305	Cobb (2, 1 pen), Williams
38	**Mar 13**	**H**	**ILFMC**	**Yeading**	**Lost 0-2**			
39	Mar 15	A	IL	Bishop's Stortford	Won 3-2	3	334	Moseley (2), Carthy
40	Mar 18	A	IL	Grays Athletic	Won 1-0		256	Cobb
41	Mar 22	A	IL	Yeading	Drew 1-1	3	212	Cobb
42	Mar 25	A	IL	Bromley	Lost 1-2		276	Cobb
43	Mar 29	H	IL	Heybridge Swifts	Drew 3-3		152	Cobb (pen), Odegbami, Carthy
44	Mar 31	H	IL	Grays Athletic	Lost 2-4	4	285	Cobb, Morley
45	Apr 5	A	IL	Aylesbury United	Won 2-0		434	Odegbami, Cobb
46	Apr 12	H	IL	Boreham Wood	Drew 1-1	5	193	Matthews
47	Apr 19	A	IL	Yeovil Town	Lost 3-4	6	3004	Cobb (2), Odegbami
48	Apr 26	A	IL	Boreham Wood	Won 1-0		177	Cavell
49	May 3	A	IL	Harrow Borough	Lost 1-3	8	162	Odegbami

PURFLEET PLAYING SQUAD 1997-98

Goalkeepers: Micky Desborough (Canvey Is, Dag & Red, Braintree, Chelmsford, Purfleet, Aveley, Hornchurch, Clapton)
Defenders: Graham Daly (Aveley, Walthamstow Ave, Woodford), **Steve Dickinson** (QPR (T)), **Steve Mosely** (Dover, Chelmsford, Enfield, Dartford, Barking, Billericay, Stambridge), **Lee Matthews** (Southend), **Martin Carthy** (Erith & B, Fisher, Erith & B), **Ray Taylor** (Chelmsford, Billericay, Charlton), **Ian Gredley** (Hornchurch)
Midfielders: John Rees (Aveley), **Danny Snowsill** (Youth team), **Paul Donovan** (Dagenham, Fulham (T)), **Sam Cooper** (Dag & Red, Peterborough), **Robbie Bourne** (Boreham Wood, Brimsdown R, Finchley, Brimsdown R)
Forwards: Paul Cavell (Macclesfield, Gateshead, Dag & Red, Boston U, Stafford R, Goole, Worksop), **Paul Cobb** (Enfield, Purfleet, Leyton O, Purfleet), **Joseph Odegbami** (Dulwich H, St. Polten (Aust), Paralimon (Cyp), EPA Larnaca (Cyp), Leventis U (Nig), Aaron Wright (Hornchurch), **Lee Williams** (Leyton O, Purfleet)

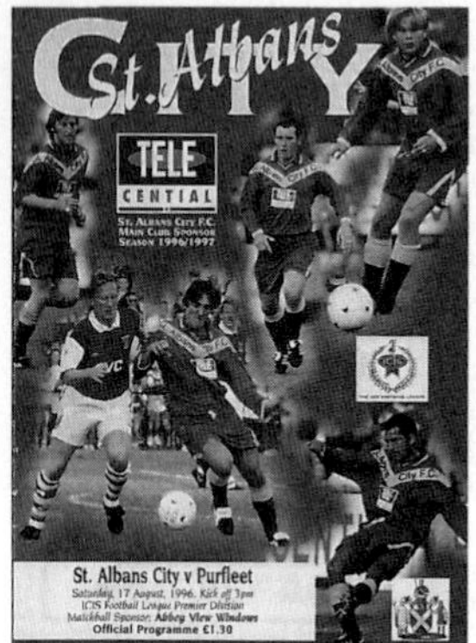

ST ALBANS CITY

Formed: 1908
Nickname: The Saints
Colours: Blue/broad yellow band
Change colours: Orange & black
Midweek home matchday: Tuesday **Newsline:** 0891 664354

Chairman: Bernard Tominey **President:** Cllr Malcolm MacMillan
Vice Chairman: Barry Nevill
Secretary: Steve Trulock, 42 Heath Road, St Albans AL1 4DP (01727 834920).
Manager: Jimmy Neighbour **Physio:** Judith Monteath
Press Off.: David Tavener (01582 401487, 0410 980542)
Managing Director: Graham McDougall (01727 864296/866819).

PROGRAMME DETAILS:
Pages: 40 **Price:** £1.30
Editor: Ray Stanton
(0181 561 6830)

GROUND - Address: Clarence Park, York Rd, St Albans, Herts AL1 4PL (01727 866819). **Directions:** Left out of St Albans station - Clarence Pk 200yds ahead across Hatfield Rd. M25, jct 21 to Noke Hotel island, straight on thru Chiswell Green towards St Albans, straight over 2 mini-r'bouts and one larger island, thru 2 sets of lights and right at island at far end of city centre (St Peters St.) into Hatfield Rd, over mini-r'bout, left at 2nd lights into Clarence Rd, ground on left.
Capacity: 6,000 **Cover:** 1,900 **Seats:** 904 **Floodlights:** Yes
Clubhouse: Open matchdays and available for functions. Manager: Ray McCord (01727 837956). Tea bar within ground serves hot food.
Club Shop: Large selection of club merchandise & League & non-League progs, magazines, videos & badges etc. Managers: Terry Edwards 01727 833685 & Ray Stanton.

PREVIOUS - Leagues: Herts County 08-10/ Spartan 08-20/ Athenian 20-23.
CLUB RECORDS - Attendance: 9,757 v Ferryhill Ath., FA Amtr Cup QF 27/2/26. **Appearances:** Phil Wood 900 (62-85) **Goalscorer:** W H (Billy) Minter 356 (top scorer for 12 consecutive seasons 1920-32). **Win:** 14-0 v Aylesbury United (H) Spartan Lge 19/10/12. **Defeat:** 0-11 v Wimbledon (H), Isthmian Lg 9/11/46. **Fee Paid:** £4,500 for Martin Duffield (Sutton United, March 1992) **Fee Received:** £92,750 for Dean Austin (Southend 90/Spurs 92).
Best Season - FA Amateur Cup: Semi final 22-23 24-25 25-26 69-70. **FA Trophy:** 2nd Rd 81-82 92-93 96-97. **FA Cup:** 2nd Rd replay 68-69 (1-3 at Walsall after 1-1 draw), 80-81 (1-4 at Torquay after 1-1 draw), 96-97 (9-2 at Bristol City).
Players progressing to Football League: A Grimsdell (Spurs 11), R Burke (Man Utd), J Meadows (W'ford 51), M Rose (Charlton 63), J Kinnear (Spurs 65), J Mitchell (Fulham 72), A Cockram (Brentford 88), D Austin (Southend 90), T Kelly (Stoke 90), M Danzey (Cambridge 92), D Williams (Brentford 93), G Edmonds (Wolves).
96-97 - Captain: Kevin Mudd **P.o.Y.:** Jon Daly **Top scorer:** Steve Clark (41)
Local Press: St Albans & District Observer, Herts Advertiser. **Local Radio:** BBC Three Counties, Chiltern Radio.
HONOURS: Isthmian Lg 23-24 26-27 27-28 (R-up 54-55 92-93), Div 1 85-86, Div 2 R-up 83-84, Lg Cup R-up 89-90, Res. Sect. R-up 48-49 60-61 61-62; Athenian Lg 20-21 21-22 (R-up 22-23); Spartan Lg 11-12 (R-up 12-13, East Div 09-10); Herts Co. Lg 09-10 (West Div 08-09, Aubrey Cup(res) 61-62); London Snr Cup 70-71 (R-up 69-70); AFA Snr Cup 33-34 (R-up 30-31 32-33 34-35); E Anglian Cup 92-93; Herts Snr Cup(12) (R-up 10), Herts Snr Tphy 86-87, Herts Charity Cup(25) (R-up(18); Mithras Cup 64-65 71-72 (R-up 76-77); Wycombe F'lit Cup(2) 68-70; St Albans Hosp Cup 45-46; Hitchin Centenary Cup 70-71 (R-up 71-72); Victory Cup 25-26 27-28, Liege Cup 26-27; Billy Minter Invit. Cup (3) 90-93.

Back Row (L-R); Gary Cobb, Richard Evans, Andy Polston, Kevin Mudd, Rob Haworth, Jon Daly, Steve Clark. Front Row; Gareth Howells, Erskine Smart, Greg Howell, Peter Risley, Naseem Bashir, Tony Kelly, Jay Thomas.
Photo - Garry Letts

St Albans City

Match No.	Date	Venue H/A	Competition	Opponents	Result	League Pos.	Attendance	Goalscorers (Times if known)
1	Aug 17	H	IL	Purfleet	Won 2-1		502	Howell, Haworth
2	Aug 20	A	IL	Heybridge Swifts	Lost 1-2		323	Clark
3	Aug 24	A	IL	Bishop's Stortford	Drew 1-1	11	431	Haworth
4	Aug 27	H	IL	Enfield	Lost 1-4		812	Cobb (pen)
5	Aug 31	H	IL	Staines Town	Won 3-0	11	453	Haworth (2), Clark
6	Sep 7	A	IL	Yeading	Won 3-0	6	284	Bashir (2), Daly
7	Sep 10	A	GIC	Wingate & Finchley	Won 6-1		120	Clark (3), Haworth (2), Martin
8	Sep 14	A	FAC 1 Q	London Colney	Drew 0-0*		757	
9	Sep 17	H	FAC 1QR	London Colney	Won 4-1		568	Cobb, Clark (2), Haworth
10	Sep 21	H	IL	Sutton United	Drew 1-1	9	552	Howell
11	Sep 23	A	IL	Aylesbury United	Lost 1-2		535	Cobb
12	Sep 28	H	FAC 2 Q	Yeading	Drew 1-1		397	Howell
13	Oct 1	A	FAC 2 R	Yeading	Won 1-0		220	Daly
14	Oct 4	A	IL	Oxford City	Lost 2-3	13	311	Adebowale, Howell
15	Oct 12	H	FAC 3 Q	Stansted	Won 5-0			Daly 2, Humphries 40, Howell 44, 69, Clark 80
16	Oct 15	A	IL	Staines Town	Won 2-1		171	Blackman, Clark
17	Oct 19	H	IL	Yeovil Town	Lost 2-3	13	851	Haworth, Daly
18	Oct 22	H	IL	Dulwich Hamlet	Drew 2-2	11	356	Clark, Bashir
19	Oct 26	A	FAC 4 Q	Witney Town	Won 4-0		606	Martin 48, Phillips 60 (og), Bashir 62, Daly 73
20	Nov 2	H	IL	Chertsey Town	Lost 4-5	14	478	Clark (2), Daly, Haworth
21	Nov 5	H	GIC	Aveley	Won 3-1			
22	Nov 9	H	IL	Dagenham & Redbridge	Lost 0-2	16	651	
23	Nov 16	A	FAC 1	Wisbech Town	Won 2-1		2509	Howell, Clark
24	Nov 23	H	IL	Kingstonian	Won 2-0	14	454	Clark (2)
25	Nov 30	H	FAT 3 Q	King's Lynn	Won 3-1		535	Dalby (2), Haworth
26	Dec 3	H	IL FMC	Hitchin Town	Lost 0-4			
27	Dec 7	A	FAC 2	Bristol City	Lost 2-9		7136	Clark, Daly
28	Dec 14	A	IL	Boreham Wood	Won 2-0	14	472	Blackman, Clark
29	Dec 17	H	GIC	Harrow Borough	Lost 2-4			
30	Dec 21	H	IL	Harrow Borough	Drew 2-2	15	398	Clark, Daly
31	Dec 26	H	IL	Heybridge Swifts	Won 4-2	13	445	Clark (2), Coleman, Haworth
32	Dec 28	A	IL	Hitchin Town	Drew 1-1	13	291	Clark
33	Jan 18	H	FAT 1	Weymouth	Won 2-0		506	Kelly, Clark (pen)
34	Feb 1	A	IL	Enfield	Lost 0-1	13	851	
35	Feb 8	H	FAT 2	Woking	Drew 1-1		2015	Howell (pen)
36	Feb 11	A	FAT 2 R	Woking	Lost 1-3		1907	Howell (pen)
37	Feb 15	A	IL	Sutton United	Won 3-2	15	579	Clark, Cobb (pen), Daly
38	Feb 18	A	IL	Grays Athletic	Won 2-1		179	Clark, Gentle
39	Feb 22	A	IL	Yeovil Town	Lost 1-3	14	2168	Clark
40	Feb 25	H	IL	Bromley	Lost 0-3		189	
41	Mar 1	H	IL	Carshalton Athletic	Drew 0-0	14	378	
42	Mar 3	A	IL	Purfleet	Drew 2-2		127	Clark, Mudd
43	Mar 8	H	IL	Oxford City	Lost 0-1	14	405	
44	Mar 10	A	IL	Dagenham & Redbridge	Won 1-0		471	Mudd
45	Mar 15	A	IL	Dulwich Hamlet	Won 2-1	13	320	Kelly, Gentle (pen)
46	Mar 18	A	IL	Hendon	Won 2-0		265	Gentle, Clark
47	Mar 22	A	IL	Chertsey Town	Won 5-0	7	291	Haworth (2), Adams, Gentle, Clark
48	Mar 25	H	IL	Biship's Stortford	Drew 1-1		346	Daly
49	Mar 29	H	IL	Hendon	Won 1-0			White (og)
50	Mar 31	H	IL	Hitchin Town	Won 2-1	6		Gentle (pen), Daly
51	Apr 5	A	IL	Harrow Borough	Won 1-0	6	291	Gentle
52	Apr 8	H	IL	Yeading	Drew 0-0		305	
53	Apr 12	H	IL	Grays Athletic	Won 4-2	3	489	Gentle (2), Daly, Haworth
54	Apr 14	A	IL	Carshalton Athletic	Lost 0-2		429	
55	Apr 19	A	IL	Kingstonian	Won 1-0	3	492	Mudd
56	Apr 22	H	IL	Aylesbury United	Drew 0-0		412	
57	Apr 26	H	IL	Boreham Wood	Lost 0-2	5	462	
58	May 3	A	IL	Bromley	Drew 1-1	6	354	Clark

* At St Albans

ST ALBANS CITY PLAYING SQUAD 1997-98

Goalkeepers: Gareth Howells (Dorking, Hellenic (SA), Torquay, Tottenham)
Defenders: Andy Polston (Hendon, Brighton, Tottenham), **Peter Risley** (Dagenham, B Stortford, Ware, Hoddesdon), **Darren Coleman** (Chesham, Edgware, Kingsbury, Finchley, Forest U), **Kevin Mudd** (Sittingbourne, St.Albans, Harrow, Finchley, Enfield, St.Albans, Mount Grace)
Midfielders: Greg Howell (Enfield, Stevenage, Southend, Tottenham (T)), **Gary Cobb** (Aylesbury, Chesham, Fulham, Luton), **Jon Daly** (Kingstonian, Hendon, Dulwich H, Whyteleafe, Croydon, Tooting, Croydon, Crystal Palace), **Tony Kelly** (Leyton O, Bury, Stoke, St.Albans, Enfield, Cheshunt, Dulwich H, Bristol C), **Geoff Cooper** (Harlow, Bognor Regis, Happy Valley (HK)l, Barnet, Wycombe, Brighton, Bognor Regis), **Jay Thomas** (Arlesey, Luton)
Forwards: Steve Clark (Wivenhoe, Saffron Walden, Stansted), **Barry Blackman** (Kingstonian, Hendon, Dulwich H, Gloucester, Wealdstone, Yeovil, Tooting, Edsbro (Swe), Croydon, Uppsala (Swe), Charlton (A)), **Naseem Bashir** (Aylesbury, Chesham, Chalfont St.Peter, Slough, Reading), **Rob Haworth** (Aylesbury, Kettering, Millwall, Fulham), **Richard Evans** (Barnet)

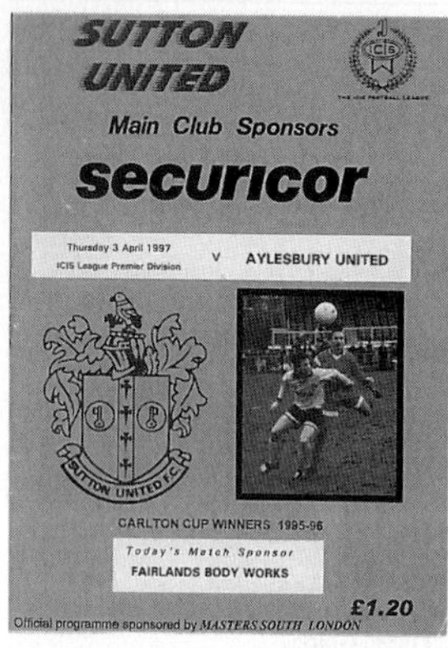

SUTTON UNITED

Formed: 1898 **Nickname:** The U's
Colours: Amber & chocolate/chocolate/amber & chocolate
Change colours: All white (chocolate trim)
Midweek matchday: Tuesday **Reserve League:** Suburban.
Local Newspapers: Sutton Herald, Sutton Guardian.
Chairman: Bruce Elliott **President:** Andrew W Letts.
Secretary: Brian Williams, 49 Panmure Rd, Sydenham, London SE26 6NB (0181 699 2721).
Manager: John Rains **Asst Manager:** Tony Rains
Coach: Bobby Mapleson **Commercial Manager:** Mike Baker
Press Officer: Tony Dolbear (0171 782 8644 daytime)
GROUND - Address: Borough Sports Ground, Gander Green Lane, Sutton, SM1 2EY (0181 644 4440 Fax: 5120). **Directions:** Gander Green Lane runs between A232 (Cheam Road - turn by Sutton Cricket Club) and A217 (Oldfields Road - turn at 'Gander' PH lights). Ground opposite 'The Plough' 50 yards from West Sutton BR station. Bus 413 passes ground.
Capacity: 6,200 **Cover:** 1,800 **Seats:** 765 **Floodlights:** Yes
Clubhouse: Open every day, food. Available for hire.
Club Shop: Open matchdays selling full range of souvenirs, etc, contact Tony Cove via club. **Sponsors:** Securicor.

PROGRAMME DETAILS:
Pages: 48 **Price:** £1.20
Editor: Tony Dolbear

PREVIOUS - Leagues: Sutton Jun, Southern Sub 10-21, Athenian 21-63, Isthmian 63-86, GMVC 86-91. **Names:** Sutton Association, Sutton Guild Rovers.

CLUB RECORDS - Attendance: 14,000 v Leeds United, FA Cup 4th Rd 24/1/70. **Scorer:** Paul McKinnon. **Appearances:** Larry Pritchard 781 (1965-84) **Fee Paid:** to Malmo FF for Paul McKinnon. **Fee Received:** For E Ekoku (Bournemouth) **Best Season - FA Amateur Cup:** R-up 62-63 68-69 SF 28-29 36-37 67-68. **FA Trophy:** R-up 80-81. SF 92-93. **FA Cup:** 4th Rd 69-70 88-89.

Players Progressing to Football Lge: Numerous incl the following since 1980 - M Robinson (C Palace 84), P McKinnon (Blackburn 86), R Fearon (I'wich 87), P Harding (Notts Co), E Ekoku (Bournemouth 91), M Golley (Maidstone), A Barnes (C Palace 91), P Rogers (Sheff U 92), S Massey (C Palace 92), A & R Scott (Sheff U 93), O Morah (Cambridge 94), M Watson (West Ham 95).

96-97 - Captain: **P.o.Y.:** **Top scorer:** Mark Hynes & Joff Vansittart (23)

HONOURS: Bob Lord Trophy 90-91, Isthmian Lg(3) 66-67 84-86 (R-up 67-68 70-71 81-82, Lg Cup(3) 82-84 85-86 (R-up 79-80), Loctite Cup 91-92), Athenian Lg 27-28 45-46 57-58 (R-up 46-47, Lg Cup 45-46 55-56 61-62 62-63, Res Sec 61-62 (R-up 32-33)), Anglo Italian Semi-Pro Cup 79 (R-up 80 82), London Snr Cup 57-58 82-83, London Charity Cup 69-70 (R-up(3) 67-69 72-73), Surrey Snr Cup(13) (R-up(9), Surrey Intermediate Cup (4) (R-up (6), Surrey Jnr Cup R-up 09-10, Surrey Snr Charity Shield(3) (R-up (6), Surrey Interm Charity Cup 31-32 (R-up 34-35 38-39), Dylon Charity Shield 84 (R-up 80 82 83 85), Groningen Yth tournament 83 85 (R-up 79 81 89 91), John Ullman Invit. Cup 88-89, Carlton Cup 95-96

Back Row (L-R); Gwynne Berry, Murray Jones, Bradley Pratt, Andy Harris, Nigel Golley, Joff Vansittart, Steve Watson, Barry Laker. Front Row; Jimmy Dack, Steve Payne, Dominic Feltham, Clive Gartell, David Everitt, Trevor Argrave, (Mascots Matthew Nock & David Watts).

Photo - Andrew Chitty

Sutton United

Match No.	Date	Venue H/A	Competition	Opponents	Result	League Pos.	Attendance	Goalscorers (Times if known)
1	Aug 17	A	IL	Hendon	Won 2-1		411	Everitt, Jones
2	Aug 20	H	IL	Chertsey Town	Won 4-2		537	Vansittart (2), Jones, Feltham
3	Aug 24	H	IL	Hitchin Town	Won 4-3	3	536	Feltham, Pratt, Payne, Vansittart
4	Aug 27	A	IL	Oxford City	Won 3-1		323	Jones (2), Everitt
5	Aug 30	A	IL	Kingstonian	Won 3-2	1	1009	Vansittart, Jones, Hynes
6	Sep 7	H	IL	Bromley	Drew 2-2	1	720	Jones, Watson (pen)
7	**Sep 10**	**A**	**GIC**	**Canvey Island**	**Won 2-1**			**Watson, Hynes**
8	Sep 21	A	IL	St Albans City	Drew 1-1	2	552	Everitt
9	Sep 28	A	IL	Enfield	Lost 1-3	4	1012	Hynes
10	Oct 5	H	IL	Purfleet	Drew 0-0	4	737	
11	Oct 12	A	IL	Yeading	Won 2-1	2	266	Vansittart (2)
12	Oct 19	H	IL	Dulwich Hamlet	Won 2-0	2	717	Vansittart (2)
13	**Oct 26**	**A**	**FAC 4 Q**	**Bromley**	**Lost 0-1**		**1063**	
14	Nov 2	H	IL	Bishop's Stortford	Won 2-1	2	554	Riley, Pearce
15	**Nov 4**	**A**	**GIC**	Purfleet	Won 6-3			Pearce (3), Hynes (2), Feltham (2)
16	**Nov 9**	**A**	**FAT 2 Q**	**Hendon**	**Won 3-1**		**402**	**Hynes (2), Feltham**
17	Nov 16	A	IL	Yeovil Town	Lost 2-3	3	2803	Tyler (og), Riley
18	Nov 23	H	IL	Harrow Borough	Drew 3-3	3	579	Pearce (2), Laker
19	Nov 30	A	IL	Dorchester Town	Lost 0-2	3	512	
20	Dec 7	H	IL	Dagenham & Redbridge	Won 2-1	3	589	Pearce 22, Riley 71 (pen)
21	Dec 14	A	IL	Grays Athletic	Drew 1-1		298	Dack
22	**Dec 17**	**H**	**GIC**	**Yeading**	**Won 3-2**	3		**Dack, Pearce, Hynes**
23	Dec 21	H	IL	Staines Town	Won 2-0	3	489	Riley, Hynes
24	Dec 26	A	IL	Carshalton Athletic	Drew 3-3	3	1460	Hynes (2), Feltham
25	Jan 18	H	IL	Hendon	Won 3-1	3	574	Riley (2), Hynes
26	Jan 25	A	IL	Chertsey Town	Drew 1-1		417	Laker
27	**Jan 29**	**A**	**GIC**	**Chesham United**	**Lost 1-2**	4		**Jones**
28	Feb 1	H	IL	Oxford City	Lost 1-2	3	601	Hynes 45
29	Feb 8	H	IL	Kingstonian	Won 5-2		853	Jones (2), Hynes (2, 1 pen), Everitt
30	**Feb 11**	**H**	**IL FMC**	**Hampton**	**Drew 2-2***	3		**Vansittart, Hynes**
31	Feb 15	H	IL	St Albans City	Lost 2-3	3	579	Coleman (og), Hynes
32	Feb 22	A	IL	Heybridge Swifts	Drew 3-3		366	Gartell, Vansittart, Pearce
33	**Feb 27**	**H**	**IL FMC**	**Whyteleafe**	**Won 4-0**	3		**Dack, Feltham, Hynes, Pearce**
34	Mar 1	H	IL	Boreham Wood	Drew 1-1	4	469	Hackett (og)
35	Mar 8	A	IL	Purfleet	Lost 2-3		305	Hynes, Vansittart
36	Mar 15	H	IL	Enfield	Drew 1-1	5	829	Riley (pen)
37	Mar 18	A	IL	Bromley	Lost 1-2		344	Jones
38	**Mar 20**	**H**	**IL FMC**	**Basingstoke Town**	**Won 5-3**			**Feltham (2), Vansittart, Pearce (2)**
39	Mar 22	A	IL	Bishop's Stortford	Won 5-2	5	421	Hynes (2), Vansittart (3)
40	Mar 25	A	IL	Boreham Wood	Lost 0-1		261	
41	Mar 29	H	IL	Yeading	Won 3-0	4	506	Vansittart (2), Hynes
42	Mar 31	H	IL	Carshalton Athletic	Won 2-0	3	1106	Feltham, Green
43	Apr 3	H	IL	Aylesbury United	Drew 3-3	3	469	Feltham, Payne, Jones
44	Apr 5	A	IL	Staines Town	Won 3-2	3	309	Riley, Feltham, Vansittart
45	**Apr 8**	**A**	**IL FMC**	**Maidenhead United**	**Lost 1-3**		**250**	**Vansittart**
46	Apr 12	H	IL	Yeovil Town	Lost 0-3	3	1281	
47	Apr 15	A	IL	Dulwich Hamlet	Won 1-0		361	Hynes
48	Apr 19	A	IL	Harrow Borough	Lost 1-2	4	328	Hynes
49	Apr 22	H	IL	Heybridge Swifts	Lost 0-2		310	
50	Apr 24	A	IL	Hitchin Town	Won 5-2		182	Hynes (2), Feltham, Vansittart, Burke (og)
51	Apr 26	H	IL	Grays Athletic	Drew 1-1	3	503	Feltham
52	Apr 29	A	IL	Aylesbury United	Drew 3-3		394	Vansittart, Hynes (2)
53	May 3	A	IL	Dagenham & Redbridge	Lost 1-2	3	653	Vansittart

* After Extra Time Won 5-3 on Penalties

SUTTON UNITED PLAYING SQUAD 1997-98

Goalkeepers: Les Cleevely (Carshalton, Yeovil, Welling, Carshalton, Epsom, Farnborough, Wealdstone, Kingsbaka (Swe), Crystal Palace, Southampton), **Kevin Robbins** (Redhill),

Defenders: Barry Laker (Banstead A, Wimbledon), **Gwynne Berry** (Welling, SuttonU, Woking, Sutton U, Whyteleafe), **Andy Riley** (Kingstinian, Carshalton, Leatherhead, Whyteleafe, Malden V), **Dave Everitt** (Leyton O, Walton & H), **Carl Procopi** (Hendon, Malden V)

Midfielders: Jimmy Dack (Carshalton A, Crawley T, Sutton U, Epsom & Ewell), **Steve Watson** (Croydon, Whyteleafe), **Warren Pritchard** (Youth team), **Clive Gartell** (Dulwich H, Molesey, Dulwich H, Molesey, Leatherhead, Epsom), **Matt Hanlon** (Carshalton, Molesey, Dorking, Farnborough, Dorking, Wycombe, Sutton U), **Steve Fowler** (Banstead, Carshalton, Tooting, Sutton U)

Forwards: Joff Vansittart (Crawley T, Brighton), **Dominic Feltham** (BaltimoreBlasts (USA), Chelsea), **Mark Hynes** (Whyteleafe, Fisher A, Croydon A, Merstham, Croydon, Brentford (T)), **Steve Payne** (Crawley T, Ringmer, Ware), **David Pearce** (Chertsey, Hayes, Kingstonian, Hayes, Kingstonian, Wokingham, Dagenham, Barnet, Harrow, Wealdstone, Millwall), **Warren Burton** (Tooting, Banstead, Molesey, Hampton, Molesey, Banstead, Egham, Epsom)

PROGRAMME DETAILS:
Pages: 36 **Price:** £1
Editor: Mark Massingham
Tel: 01932 244967

WALTON & HERSHAM

Formed: 1896 **Nickname:** Swans
Colours: White with red band/white/red.
Change colours: Yellow/Blue/White.
Midweek home matchday: Tuesday
Reserve Team's League: Suburban.

Chairman: TBA **President:** Mick Brown
Secretary: Mark Massingham, 7b Sidney Rd., Walton-on-Thames, Surrey. KT12 2NP (01932 885814).
Manager: Laurie Craker **Asst Manager:** Mark Hill
Physio: Ian Goodall. **Press Officer:** Mervyn Rees (01932 245756)
GROUND Address: Sports Ground, Stompond Lane, Walton-on-Thames (01932 245263-club).
Directions: From North: Over Walton Bridge & along New Zealand Ave., down 1-way street and up A244 Hersham Road - ground 2nd right. From Esher: Down Lammas Lane then Esher Rd, straight over 1st r'bout, 4th exit at next r'bout (West Grove) 2nd left at end of Hersham Rd and Stompond Lane is half mile on left. Ten minutes walk fron Walton-on-Thames (BR). Bus 218 passes ground.
Capacity: 6,500 **Cover:** 2,500 **Seats:** 500 **Floodlights:** Yes
Clubhouse: (01932 244967). Open most nights. Bar, TV, darts, pool, refreshments on matchdays.
Club Shop: Open matchdays. Contact Richard Olds, c/o the club.
Metal Badges: Yes. **Sponsors:** T.B.A.
PREVIOUS Leagues: Surrey Senior/ Corinthian 45-50/ Athenian 50-71.
CLUB RECORDS - Attendance: 6,500 v Brighton, FA Cup First Round 73-74. **Scorer:** Brian Jenkins. **Appearances:** Terry Keen. **Win:** 10-0 v Clevedon, FA Amateur Cup 1960. **Transfer fee paid:** £6,000. **Transfer fee received:** £5,000.
Best FA Cup season: 2nd Rd 72-73 (v Margate), 73-74 (v Hereford). **FA Amateur Cup:** Winners 72-73, (SF 51-52 52-53). **League clubs defeated in FA Cup:** Exeter 72-73, Brighton 73-74.
Players progressing to Football League: Andy McCulloch (QPR 1970), Mick Heath (Brentford 1971), Paul Priddy (Brentford 1972), Richard Teale (Queens Park Rangers 1973), Steve Parsons (Wimbledon 1977), Stuart Massey (Crystal Palace), Ross Davidson (Sheffield Utd).
96-97 - Captain: Trevor Baron **P.o.Y.** Brian Lee **Top Scorer:** Ansil Bushay
Local Newspapers: Surrey Herald, Surrey Comet.
Local Radio Stations: County Sound, BBC Southern Counties.
HONOURS: Isthmian Lg R-up 72-73, Barassi Cup 73-74; Athenian Lg 68-69 (R-up 50-51 69-70 70-71, Lg Cup 69-70); Corinthian Lg 46-49 (R-up 49-50), Premier Midweek F'lit Lg 67-69 70-71 (R-up 71-72); Surrey Snr Cup 47-48 50-51 60-61 61-62 70-71 72-73 (R-up 46-47 51-52 59-60 69-70 71-72 73-74); London Snr Cup R-up 73-74; Southern Comb. Cup 82-83 88-89 91-92; Surrey Comb. Cup 49-50 91-92; John Livey Memorial Trophy 91-92.

Back Row (L-R): Neil Cordice, Tim Alexander, Ansil Bushay, David Lay, Delroy Preddie, Mark Wiggins, Trevor Baron. Front Row; Grant Hutchinson, Brian Lee, Andy Sayer, Alan Dowson, Gary Powell, Barry Rake, Curtis Johnson.

Photo - Garry Letts

Walton & Hersham

Match No.	Date	Venue H/A	Competition	Opponents	Result	League Pos.	Attendance	Goalscorers (Times if known)
1	Aug 17	H	IL	Chesham United	Lost 1-2	16	273	
2	Aug 20	A	IL	Billericay Town	Lost 1-2	21		Stone
3	Aug 24	A	IL	Uxbridge	Lost 1-2	21	180	Rake
4	Aug 27	H	IL	Whyteleafe	Won 2-1	21		Spittal, Bushay
5	Aug 31	H	IL	Tooting & Mitcham	Won 4-0	11	208	Bushay, Sayer, Dunwell
6	Sep 7	A	IL	Canvey Island	Drew 0-0	10		
7	**Sep 10**	**A**	**GIC**	**Hungerford Town**	**Won 1-0**	**10**		**Dunwell**
8	**Sep 14**	**H**	**FAC**	**Herne Bay**	**Drew 1-1**	**11**	**184**	**Sayer**
9	**Sep 17**	**A**	**FAC**	**Herne Bay**	**Lost 0-1**	**11**	**284**	
10	Sep 21	H	IL	Bognor Regis	Won 3-0	8	210	Bushay, Lay (2)
11	Sep 24	A	IL	Leyton Pennant	Drew 2-2	7		Bushay, Blackman
12	Sep 28	H	IL	Wokingham Town	Lost 0-3	8	210	
13	Oct 5	H	IL	Aldershot Town	Won 3-1	7	1030	Lay, Sayer (2)
14	Oct 8	A	IL	Abingdon Town	Drew 0-0	7	151	
15	Oct 12	H	IL	Worthing	Won 4-0	3	237	Bushay (2), Dunwell (2)
16	Oct 15	A	IL	Barton Rovers	Won 1-0	3		Baron
17	**Oct 19**	**A**	**FAT**	**Chesham United**	**Drew 1-1**	**3**		**Baron**
18	**Oct 22**	**H**	**FAT R**	**Chesham United**	**Lost 1-3**	**3**	**237**	**Blackman**
19	Oct 26	H	IL	Thame United	Lost 0-2	3	170	
20	**Oct 29**	**H**	**SSC**	**Camberley Town**	**Won 6-0**	**3**	**88**	**Bushay (3), Lay, Blackman, Hutchinson**
21	Nov 2	A	IL	Hampton	Drew 0-0	3		
22	**Nov 6**	**H**	**GIC**	**Grays Athletic**	**Lost 0-3**	**3**	**102**	
23	Nov 12	H	IL	Basingstoke Town	Lost 0-2	4	185	
24	Nov 16	A	IL	Croydon	Drew 3-3	6		Bushay, Garner, Sayer
25	Nov 23	H	IL	Maidenhead United	Drew 2-2	6	194	Cordice, Hutchinson
26	Nov 30	A	IL	Marlow	Won 2-0	4		Bushay (2)
27	**Dec 3**	**H**	**Friendly**	**Crystal Palace**	**Lost 2-5**	**4**		**Bushay, Lay**
28	Dec 14	A	IL	Tooting & Mitcham	Won 3-2	6		Bushay, Cordice, Sayer
29	**Dec 17**	**H**	**SSC**	**Woking**	**Won 3-2**	**6**	**433**	**Blackman (2), Lay**
30	Dec 21	H	IL	Berkhamsted Town	Won 2-1	4	115	M Alexander, Rake
31	Dec 26	A	IL	Molesey	Won 4-1	4		Bushay, Hutchinson, Lay
32	**Jan 7**	**A**	**FMC**	**Kingstonian**	**Won 5-3+**	**4**	**146**	**Lee (2), Sayer (2), J Pearson**
33	Jan 11	H	IL	Uxbridge	Lost 0-3	6	180	
34	Jan 18	A	IL	Chesham United	Drew 1-1	6	455	Lay
35	**Jan 21**	**H**	**SSC**	**Carshalton Athletic**	**Lost 1-2**	**6**		**Cordice**
36	Jan 25	H	IL	Billericay Town	Won 2-1	5	175	Lee, Bushay
37	Feb 1	A	IL	Whyteleafe	Won 2-1	4		Baron, Cordice
38	Feb 8	H	IL	Leyton Pennant	Lost 1-2	5	205	Bushay
39	**Feb 11**	**H**	**FMC**	**Maidenhead United**	**Lost 0-1**	**6**		
40	Feb 15	A	IL	Bognor Regis	Drew 0-0	6		
41	Feb 22	H	IL	Barton Rovers	Won 5-0	5	140	Bushay (3), Johnson, Rake
42	Mar 1	A	IL	Worthing	Won 2-1	5		Sayer, Rake
43	Mar 8	A	IL	Aldershot Town	Drew 1-1	5		Johnson
44	Mar 11	H	IL	Canvey Island	Won 2-0	3	147	Bushay, Johnson
45	Mar 15	H	IL	Abingdon Town	Won 2-0	3	158	Lay, Blackman
46	Mar 22	H	IL	Hampton	Won 1-0	3	310	Baron
47	Mar 29	A	IL	Thame United	Drew 1-1	3		Lay
48	Mar 31	H	IL	Molesey	Won 1-0	3	337	Sayer
49	Apr 5	A	IL	Berkhamsted Town	Drew 1-1	3		Wiggins
50	Apr 8	A	IL	Basingstoke Town	Drew 0-0	3		
51	Apr 12	H	IL	Croydon	Won 2-1	3	245	Bushay, Sayer
52	Apr 19	A	IL	Maidenhead United	Drew 1-1	3		Johnson
53	Apr 26	H	IL	Marlow	Won 2-1	4		Baron, Cordice
54	May 3	A	IL	Wokingham Town	Won 2-0	5		Cordice, Sayer

+ Won on Penalties

WALTON & HERSHAM PLAYING SQUAD 1997-98

Goalkeepers: Delroy Preddie (Slough, Northampton)
Defenders: Alan Dowson (Gateshead, Slough, Darlington, Bradford C, Millwall), **Trevor Baron** (Woking, Slough, Woking, Slough, Marlow, Windsor, Slough, Windsor, Chertsey, Burnham, Marlow), **Sean Norman** (Chesham, Lowestoft, Chertsey, Papatoetoe (NZ), Chesham, Wealdstone, Wycombe, Colchester, Lowestoft), **Tim Alexander** (Bromley, Dag & Red, Woking, Brentford), **Matt Alexander** (Egham,Windsor, Walton & H), **Gary Powell** (Staines), **Brian Lee** (Slough, Millwall)
Midfielders: David Lay (Chesham, Marlow, Dunstable, Chesham, Reading), **Neil Cordice** (Chesham, Yeovil, Wealdstone, Yeovil, Wycombe, Northampton, Flackwell H), **Paul Byrne** (Slough, Chalfont St.Peter, Marlow, Flackwell H), **Garfield Blackman** (Slough, Marlow, Northwood, Welwyn GC), **Barry Rake** (Slough, Chesham, Slough, Millwall), **Jamie Pearson** (Youth team)
Forwards: Andy Sayer (Enfield, Slough, Leyton O, Fulham, Wimbledon), **Ansil Bushay** (Slough, St.Albans, Woking, Marlow, Chalfont St.Peter, Beaconsfield U, Flackwell H, Marlow), **Martin Stone** (Slough, Marlow, Chalfont St.Peter, Uxbridge), **Curtis Johnson** (Worthing, Chesham, Worthing, Kingstonian), **Grant Hutchinson** (Staines, Walton & H, Woking, Aldershot, Chelsea), **Mark Wiggins** (Molesey, Carshalton, Kingstonian, Carshalton, Epsom, Carshalton), **Wedi Okita** (Youth team)

YEADING

Formed: 1965 **Nickname:** The Dinc
Colours: Red & black stripes/black/black
Change colours: All white.
Midweek matchday: Tuesday
Reserve League: Suburban Lge

Chairman: Philip Spurden **President:** Mr R Carter
Vice Chairman: Steve Perryman **Secretary:** Peter Bickers, 140 Hercies Rd, Hillingdon, Middlesex (01895 203562).
Manager: Steve Cordery. **Asst Manager:** Leo Morris
Coach: T Choules. **Physio:** Edward Cole.
Commercial Manager:
Press Officer: Peter Bickers (as above)

PROGRAMME DETAILS:
Pages: 32 **Price:** £1
Editor: David Low.

GROUND Address: The Warren, Beaconsfield Road, Hayes, Middx (0181 848 7362/7369. Fax: 0181 561 2222).
Directions: Two miles from Hayes (BR) - take Uxbridge Road and turn right towards Southall, right into Springfield Road and then left into Beaconsfield Road. Bus 207 stops half mile from ground.
Capacity: 3,500 **Cover:** 1,500 **Seats:** 250 **Floodlights:** Yes
Clubhouse: Open normal pub hours. Social Secretary: William Gritt.
Club Shop: Planned **Metal Badges:** Yes **Sponsors:** Heineken.

PREVIOUS - Leagues: Hayes & District Yth, Uxbridge, S W Middx 1967-74, Middx 74-84, Spartan 1984-87.
CLUB RECORDS - Attendance: 3,000; v Hythe Town, FA Vase SF 1990; v Tottenham Hotspur, friendly.
Goalscorer: Dave Burt 327 **Appearances:** Norman Frape
Fee Paid: Unknown **Fee Received:** £45,000 for Andrew Impey (QPR).
Best Season - FA Cup: Third Qualifying Round 90-91. **FA Vase:** Winners 89-90.
Players progressing to Football League: Andrew Impey (QPR & England u-21).
96-97 - Captain: **Top Scorer:** **P.o.Y.:**
Local Newspapers: Hayes Gazette.

HONOURS: Isthmian League Div 2 Sth 89-90 (Div 1 R-up 91-92); Spartan League 86-87 (R-up 85-86, Senior Div R-up 84-85, League Cup 85-86 86-87); Middlesex Snr League(6) 71-73 74-76 81-82 83-84 (R-up 73-74 74-75 78-79, League Cup(6) 72-73 75-76 79-83); South West Middlesex League(2) 69-71; Middlesex Snr Cup 89-90 91-92, Middlesex Prem. Cup 80-81, Middlesex I'mediate Cup(5) 70-72 74-76 77-78, Middlesex Jnr Cup(4) 68-69 70-72 74-75; Uxbridge League 66-67; Middlesex Border League Cup 86-87 (AJA Cup 86-87); Suburban League Nth 87-88; Allied Counties Yth League 89-90 (League Cup 89-90).

Back Row (L-R); Steve Cordery (Mgr), Matt Flitter, Ross Pickett, Phil Dicker, Danny Honey, Steve McGrath, David Kellman, Mark Woods, Steve Graham, Tony Choules (Asst Mgr). Front Row; Tony Houghton, Andre Delisser, Lee Protheroe, Richard Gell, Martin Carter, Bruce Sewell, Paddy McCarthy.

Photo - Andrew Chitty

Yeading

Match No.	Date	Venue H/A	Competition	Opponents	Result	League Pos.	Attendance	Goalscorers (Times if known)
1	Aug 17	A	IL	Dulwich Hamlet	Won 1-0		341	Allen
2	Aug 20	H	IL	Oxford City	Won 4-1		132	Gell, Allen, Kellman (2)
3	Aug 24	H	IL	Hendon	Won 2-1	2	231	Graham, McGrath
4	Aug 27	A	IL	Chertsey Town	Lost 1-2		278	Dicker
5	Aug 31	A	IL	Carshalton Athletic	Drew 0-0	5	358	
6	Sep 7	H	IL	St Albans City	Lost 0-3	8	284	
7	**Sep 10**	**A**	**GIC**	**Dulwich Hamlet**	**Won 1-0**			
8	**Sep 14**	**H**	**FAC 1 Q**	**Bowers United**	**Won 6-0**		**92**	**Gell (2), Kellman, Holman, Graham, Allen**
9	Sep 21	A	IL	Bromley	Lost 1-5	10	241	Kellman
10	Sep 24	H	IL	Grays Athletic	Won 3-0	7	66	Pickett, Dicker, Holman
11	**Sep 28**	**A**	**FAC 2 Q**	**St Albans City**	**Drew 1-1**		**397**	**Kellman**
12	**Oct 1**	**H**	**FAC 2QR**	**St Albans City**	**Lost 0-1**		**220**	
13	Oct 5	H	IL	Enfield	Drew 1-1	9	430	Gell
14	Oct 12	H	IL	Sutton United	Lost 1-2	10	266	Flitter
15	**Oct 19**	**A**	**FAT 1 Q**	**Whyteleafe**	**Won 1-0**		**84**	**Pickett**
16	Oct 22	A	IL	Yeovil Town	Lost 0-2	14	2283	
17	Oct 29	A	IL	Heybridge Swifts	Won 5-0		212	Carter, Kellman, Gell, Pickett (2)
18	Nov 2	A	IL	Purfleet	Drew 2-2	9	193	Pickett (2)
19	**Nov 5**	**H**	**GIC**	**Yeovil Town**	**Drew 1-1**			
20	**Nov 8**	**A**	**FAT 2 Q**	**Chertsey Town**	**Drew 1-1**		**222**	**Gell**
21	**Nov 12**	**H**	**FAT 2 Q**	**Chertsey Town**	**Won 3-1**			**Gell, Kellman (2)**
22	Nov 16	A	IL	Harrow Borough	Won 1-0	11	204	Day (og)
23	Nov 23	H	IL	Dagenham & Redbridge	Drew 1-1	10	237	Pickett
24	**Nov 26**	**A**	**GIC**	**Yeovil Town**	**Won 1-0**		**906**	**Kellman**
25	**Nov 30**	**A**	**FAT 3 Q**	**Sittingbourne**	**Drew 0-0**		**474**	
26	**Dec 3**	**H**	**FAT 3QR**	**Sittingbourne**	**Won 3-1**			**Gell, Pickett, Kellman**
27	Dec 7	H	IL	Kingstonian	Won 5-1	10	247	Pickett (3) 5, 20, 54, Flitter, Lavender (og)
28	Dec 14	A	IL	Aylesbury United	Drew 2-2	9	404	Kellman (2 pens)
29	**Dec 17**	**A**	**GIC**	**Sutton United**	**Lost 2-3**			
30	Dec 21	H	IL	Hitchin Town	Lost 0-1	9	145	
31	Jan 11	A	IL	Hendon	Drew 1-1	10	261	Carter 89
32	Jan 25	A	IL	Oxford City	Won 1-0	10	247	Allen
33	**Jan 28**	**A**	**IL FMC**	**Thame United**	**Won 1-0**			
34	Feb 1	H	IL	Chertsey Town	Drew 0-0	10	165	
35	Feb 8	A	IL	Grays Athletic	Won 2-1	9	191	Kellman, Delisser
36	**Feb 11**	**H**	**IL FMC**	**Marlow**	**Won 4-0**			
37	Feb 15	H	IL	Bromley	Won 1-0	9	160	Kellman
38	Feb 18	H	IL	Dulwich Hamlet	Won 3-0		131	Sewell, Kellman, Gell
39	Feb 22	A	IL	Bishop's Stortford	Drew 1-1	6	363	Kellman (pen)
40	Mar 1	H	IL	Yeovil Town	Drew 0-0	6	409	
41	Mar 8	A	IL	Enfield	Drew 1-1	8	1069	Delisser
42	Mar 11	H	IL	Bishop's Stortford	Won 3-0		142	Allen (2), Delisser
43	**Mar 13**	**A**	**IL FMC**	**Purfleet**	**Won 2-0**			
44	Mar 15	H	IL	Heybridge Swifts	Won 1-0	4	125	Atkins
45	Mar 18	A	IL	Staines Town	Won 3-2		194	Allen (2), Atkins
46	Mar 22	H	IL	Purfleet	Drew 1-1	4	212	Taylor (og)
47	Mar 25	H	IL	Carshalton Athletic	Drew 0-0		164	
48	Mar 29	A	IL	Sutton United	Lost 0-3	5	506	
49	Apr 2	H	IL	Boreham Wood	Won 2-1		187	Sibanda (2)
50	Apr 5	A	IL	Hitchin Town	Lost 1-3	5	232	Protheroe
51	Apr 8	A	IL	St Albans City	Drew 0-0		305	
52	Apr 12	H	IL	Harrow Borough	Lost 1-2	5	284	Kellman
53	Apr 15	A	IL	Boreham Wood	Drew 1-1	5	137	Joyne (og)
54	**Apr 17**	**H**	**FMC SF**	**Aylesbury United**	**Drew 2-2**			**Delisser, Carter**
55	Apr 19	A	IL	Dagenham & Redbridge	Won 2-1	5	516	Sewell, Kellman
56	Apr 22	H	IL	Staines Town	Won 1-0	4	204	Gell
57	**Apr 24**	**A**	**FMC SF R**	**Aylesbury United**	**Lost 0-1**		**310**	
58	Apr 26	H	IL	Aylesbury United	Lost 0-1	4	165	
59	May 3	A	IL	Kingstonian	Lost 2-4	5	437	Allen, Kellman

YEADING PLAYING SQUAD 1997-98

Goalkeepers: Danny Honey (Aylesbury U, Newbury T, Reading (T))

Defenders: Matthew Flitter (Hayes, Brentford), **Tony Houghton** (Brentford (T)), **Phil Dicker** (St.Albans C, Southall, Harrow B, Hanwell T, Brentford), **Mark Woods** (Basingstoke T, Farnborough T, Windsor & Eton, Walton & H, Tooting & Mitcham U, Windsor & Eton, Addlestone, QPR), **Steve Atkins** (Cheshunt), **Lee Protheroe** (Ruislip M, St. Margaretsbury, Walthamstow Pennant), **Andre Delisser** (Northwood,Southall)

Midfielders: Paddy McCarthy (Chertsey T, Yeading, Chesham U, Farnborough T, Yeovil T, Weymouth, Wealdstone, Chelsea), **Steve Cordery** (Chesham U, Windsor & Eton, Egham T, Maidenhead U, Hayes, Feltham, Southall, Hillingdon B), **Richard Gell** (Wycombe, Chelsea), **Lee Holman** (Hayes, QPR), **Ben Hobson** (Wycombe), **Bruce Sewell** (Purfleet, C.Row, E.Thurrock, Ford U, Billericay, C.Row, Basildon)

Forwards: Dave Kellman (Hayes, Harlow T, Stevenage B, Willesden Hawkeye), **Eben Allen** (Dulwich H, Hampton, Marlow, Staines, Goadalming & G, WBA, Arsenal), **Ross Pickett** (Hayes, Slough, Hayes, Denham), **Hakan Altinok** (Hendon, Istanbul Sports (Turkey), **Martin Carter** (Hayes), **Antony Sibanda** (B.Stortford, Barking, Stansted, Saffron Walden, C.Row, Kingsbury, Yeading, Hendon, C.Row, Cobh Ramblers)

DIVISION ONE

LEAGUE TABLE 1996-97

		P	Home W	Home D	Home L	Away W	Away D	Away L	F	A	Pts
1	Chesham United	42	16	2	3	11	4	6	80	46	87
2	Basingstoke Town	42	13	5	3	9	8	4	81	38	79
3	Walton & Hersham	42	14	1	6	7	12	2	67	41	76
4	Hampton	42	13	5	3	8	7	6	62	39	75
5	Billericay Town	42	12	6	3	9	6	6	69	49	75
6	Bognor Regis Town	42	12	5	4	9	4	8	63	44	72
7	Aldershot Town	42	10	7	4	9	7	5	67	45	71
8	Uxbridge	42	7	12	2	8	5	8	65	48	62
9	Whyteleafe	42	8	3	10	10	4	7	71	68	61
10	Molesey	42	4	6	11	13	3	5	50	53	60
11	Abingdon Town	42	10	6	5	5	5	11	44	42	56
12	Leyton Pennant	42	8	8	5	6	4	11	71	72	54
13	Maidenhead United	42	9	5	7	6	5	10	57	57	*52
14	Wokingham Town	42	6	5	10	8	5	8	41	45	52
15	Thame United	42	9	5	7	4	5	12	57	69	49
16	Worthing	42	6	5	10	5	6	10	58	77	44
17	Barton Rovers	42	7	7	7	4	4	13	31	58	44
18	Croydon	42	7	4	10	4	6	11	40	57	43
19	Berkhamsted Town	42	8	4	9	3	5	13	47	66	42
20	Canvey Island	42	5	8	8	4	6	11	52	71	41
21	Marlow	42	7	4	10	4	2	15	41	84	39
22	Tooting & Mitcham Utd.	42	4	4	13	4	4	13	40	85	32

* - 3 pts deducted - ineligible player

RESULTS GRID 1996-97

	HOME TEAM	1	2	3	4	5	6	7	8	9	10	11	12	13	14	15	16	17	18	19	20	21	22
1	Abingdon	*	0-0	2-0	1-1	3-1	2-1	0-3	2-2	0-1	1-0	0-1	2-1	0-0	2-1	0-1	0-0	1-0	6-0	0-0	0-1	2-1	4-1
2	Aldershot	3-1	*	3-1	1-0	0-0	1-1	1-0	1-2	2-2	1-0	1-1	2-2	3-0	0-1	1-3	1-0	2-2	2-0	1-1	5-2	1-0	0-2
3	Barton R	0-0	0-0	*	1-4	1-0	0-0	0-3	2-0	0-1	0-1	3-1	2-1	2-1	0-1	1-1	0-0	3-1	2-1	0-1	0-1	0-0	1-1
4	Basingstoke	3-1	2-0	3-0	*	2-0	2-2	2-2	2-1	4-0	2-1	0-2	2-1	2-0	6-1	2-2	3-0	1-0	0-2	0-0	4-1	0-2	1-1
5	Berkhamsted	1-1	0-3	1-0	1-3	*	2-0	2-0	1-4	2-2	0-2	0-4	2-3	0-3	1-0	2-1	3-0	0-1	4-1	1-1	1-1	1-0	0-2
6	Billericay	2-1	2-2	1-1	1-1	3-0	*	0-0	2-0	1-2	2-0	0-0	4-3	2-2	0-2	0-1	2-0	4-1	2-1	2-1	2-1	3-1	4-0
7	Bognor Regis	2-2	0-5	0-1	0-2	1-0	4-1	*	1-0	4-1	1-0	1-1	2-0	1-0	3-0	0-1	2-2	3-0	2-1	0-0	2-2	3-0	2-1
8	Canvey Is.	1-0	0-1	1-2	1-1	2-2	1-3	1-1	*	0-3	3-0	1-0	1-2	4-2	2-2	0-1	3-3	2-1	0-0	0-0	1-4	0-1	2-2
9	Chesham	2-1	1-3	4-0	2-1	5-2	1-2	1-0	4-0	*	2-2	1-0	2-1	2-1	3-0	4-0	3-2	4-0	1-0	1-1	0-1	2-0	2-1
10	Croydon	2-0	1-1	1-0	0-2	1-0	2-0	0-5	2-2	0-1	*	0-2	2-2	0-2	2-1	0-1	3-0	3-1	0-3	3-3	1-2	1-2	0-1
11	Hampton	2-1	1-1	3-2	1-0	1-1	3-1	3-0	3-1	1-1	2-1	*	4-3	3-4	1-0	1-2	2-1	0-2	2-2	0-0	1-0	2-0	2-0
12	Leyton P.	1-0	4-2	4-0	1-6	0-5	2-2	3-0	1-1	1-2	0-0	0-0	*	1-1	5-0	2-3	2-4	4-1	1-1	2-2	2-1	1-1	2-0
13	Maidenhead	0-1	1-1	1-0	1-1	2-0	0-1	3-0	1-1	2-1	1-2	1-2	2-0	*	2-3	0-2	1-0	1-1	1-0	1-1	4-3	4-0	1-3
14	Marlow	0-1	3-1	1-1	1-0	0-2	1-3	0-2	2-1	2-0	1-1	2-1	0-1	2-0	*	0-2	2-2	1-1	1-7	0-2	1-2	0-2	3-1
15	Molesey	0-1	0-2	1-3	1-2	2-1	1-2	0-1	1-2	0-1	2-1	1-1	1-1	1-2	4-2	*	3-2	0-2	1-1	1-4	1-1	0-0	1-1
16	Thame U	0-3	0-2	2-0	1-2	3-2	2-2	1-1	1-0	3-2	3-1	1-2	2-1	1-0	6-1	0-2	*	1-0	0-3	1-1	0-3	1-1	1-1
17	Tooting & M	1-1	0-1	4-0	0-4	1-0	1-3	0-3	3-1	0-4	1-1	0-1	1-2	1-5	0-0	0-1	1-3	*	0-1	2-3	0-5	1-1	2-1
18	Uxbridge	0-0	3-3	1-1	2-2	1-0	1-1	1-0	1-1	0-0	0-0	1-1	2-2	2-0	4-0	2-2	4-2	5-0	*	2-1	1-3	0-2	1-1
19	Walton & H	2-0	3-1	5-0	0-2	2-1	2-1	3-0	2-0	1-2	2-1	1-0	1-2	2-2	2-1	1-0	0-2	4-0	0-3	*	2-1	0-3	4-0
20	Whyteleafe	0-2	1-0	0-0	1-1	3-3	0-1	0-3	4-2	1-3	1-0	1-0	2-1	1-2	3-1	2-0	2-0	2-5	1-3	1-2	*	1-2	3-4
21	Wokingham	3-0	0-1	0-1	2-2	0-1	0-1	1-2	1-2	2-1	0-0	1-1	2-3	0-0	2-0	1-2	1-0	1-0	0-1	0-2	1-1	*	2-0
22	Worthing	1-0	2-5	1-0	1-1	1-1	1-2	2-3	3-3	2-3	1-2	0-3	2-0	4-0	3-1	1-0	1-4	2-2	0-0	1-2	4-5	1-2	*

DIVISION ONE
10 YEAR RECORD

No of Clubs Competing	87/8 (22)	88/9 (21)	89/0 (22)	90/1 (21)	91/2 (22)	92/3 (21)	93/4 (22)	94/5 (22)	95/6 (22)	96/7 (22)
Abingdon Town	-	-	-	-	6	6	7	10	16	11
Aldershot Town	-	-	-	-	-	-	-	4	5	7
Aveley	-	-	-	4	21	21	-	-	-	-
Barking	-	-	-	-	12	19	14	15	22	-
Barton Rovers	-	-	-	-	-	-	-	-	18	17
Basildon United	7	21	-	-	-	-	-	-	-	-
Basingstoke Town	-	2	-	-	-	-	-	7	9	2
Berkhamsted Town	-	-	-	-	-	-	18	19	17	19
Billericay Town	20	-	-	-	-	8	6	5	6	5
Bishop's Stortford	-	-	-	-	-	5	1	-	-	-
Bognor Regis Town	-	-	-	-	-	-	12	18	7	6
Boreham Wood	4	11	7	14	4	11	10	1	-	-
Bracknell Town	19	20	-	-	-	-	-	-	-	-
Bromley	-	-	2	-	-	-	-	-	-	-
Canvey Island	-	-	-	-	-	-	-	-	-	20
Chalfont St Peter	-	16	11	11	13	18	20	-	-	-
Chertsey Town	-	-	-	-	-	-	-	3	-	-
Chesham United	18	14	10	1	-	-	-	-	12	1
Collier Row	-	19	-	-	-	-	-	-	-	-
Croydon	-	-	17	17	18	17	22	-	-	18
Dorking	-	-	6	10	11	3	-	22	-	-
Dulwich Hamlet	-	-	-	12	3	-	-	-	-	-
Grays Athletic	2	-	-	-	-	-	-	-	-	-
Hampton	9	17	19	-	-	-	-	-	-	4
Harlow Town	-	-	8	13	17	-	-	-	-	-
Heybridge Swifts	-	-	-	18	19	16	5	16	2	-
Hitchin Town	-	4	4	5	8	1	-	-	-	-
Kingsbury Town	14	8	22	-	-	-	-	-	-	-
Leatherhead	10	12	20	-	-	-	-	-	-	-
Lewes	16	6	15	20	-	20	-	-	-	-
Leyton Pennant	-	-	-	-	14	13	9	14	4	12
Maidenhead United	-	-	-	16	-	12	17	12	14	13
Marlow	1	-	-	-	-	-	-	-	8	21
Metropolitan Police	-	13	9	21	-	-	-	-	-	-
Molesey	-	-	-	8	10	2	-	-	-	10
Newbury Town	-	-	-	-	-	-	-	20	-	-
Oxford City	12	-	-	-	-	-	-	-	1	-
Purfleet	-	-	21	-	-	4	2	-	-	-
Ruislip Manor	-	-	-	-	-	-	19	17	21	-
Southwick	11	15	3	19	-	-	-	-	-	-
Staines Town	5	1	-	-	-	-	11	6	3	-
Stevenage Borough	21	-	-	1	-	-	-	-	-	-
Thame United	-	-	-	-	-	-	-	-	13	14
Tooting & Mitcham United	-	-	12	6	7	7	4	8	19	22
Uxbridge	17	9	18	16	15	15	15	13	10	8
Walthamstow Avenue	15	-	-	-	-	-	-	-	-	-
Walton & Hersham	8	7	5	7	9	10	3	-	-	3
Wembley	6	10	16	15	5	9	13	9	20	-
Whyteleafe	-	-	14	9	20	14	16	11	15	9
Windsor & Eton	-	-	-	-	-	-	21	-	-	-
Wivenhoe Town	-	5	1	-	-	-	-	21	-	-
Woking	3	3	2	-	-	-	-	-	-	-
Wokingham Town	-	-	-	-	-	-	-	-	11	-
Wolverton Town	22	-	-	-	-	-	-	-	-	-
Worthing	13	18	13	22	-	-	8	2	-	16
Yeading	-	-	-	3	2	-	-	-	-	-

ABINGDON TOWN

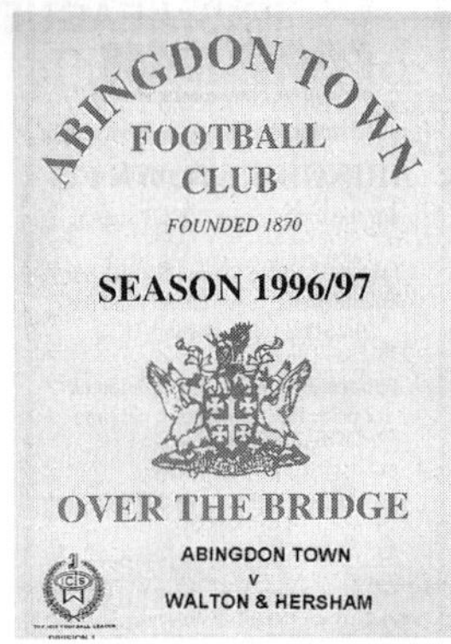

ABINGDON TOWN
FOOTBALL
CLUB
FOUNDED 1870
SEASON 1996/97
OVER THE BRIDGE
ABINGDON TOWN
v
WALTON & HERSHAM

PROGRAMME DETAILS:
Pages: 40 **Price:** 80p
Editor: Simon Element
(01235 202164)

Formed: 1870 **Nickname:** Over The Bridge
Colours: Yellow & green/green/green
Change colours: Black & white
Midweek home matchday: Wednesday
Reserve Team's League: Suburban (West).

Chairman: Phil Evans **President:** Dr Tim Reynolds
Vice Chairman: Craig Norcliffe **Secretary:** Ted Quail, 107 Park Lane, Thatcham, Newbury, Berks RG18 3BZ (01635 868967).
Press Officer: Simon Element (01235 202164)
Manager: Paul Lee **Asst Manager:** Roger Nicholls.
Physio: Ian Maskell. **Coach:** Kelvin Alexis.

GROUND Address: Culham Road, Abingdon OX14 3BT (01235 521684).
Directions: On A415 road to Dorchester-on-Thames half a mile south of town centre. Nearest rail station is Culham. Main line: Didcot Parkway or Oxford. Bus service from Didcot and London.
Capacity: 3,000 **Cover:** 1,771 **Seats:** 271 **Floodlights:** Yes
Clubhouse: (01235 521684). 7.30-11pm. 6pm matchdays. 12.30-2.30, 4-11 on Saturdays. Hot food on matchdays. Pool, darts, jukebox, canteen.
Club Shop: Yes, selling programmes, magazines, scarves, badges.
Metal Badges: £2 **Sponsors:** Morlands.

PREVIOUS - Name: Abingdon FC (merged with St Michaels in 1899). **Leagues:** Oxford & District, West Berks, Reading Temperance, North Berks, Reading & Dist. 1927-50, Spartan 50-53, Hellenic 53-88, London Spartan 88-89.

CLUB RECORDS - Attendance: 1,400 v Oxford City, FA Cup September 1960.
Career appearances: John Harvey-Lynch.
BEST SEASON - FA Cup: 4th Qual. Rd 60-61 0-2 v Hitchin, 89-90 1-3 v Slough (H), 92-93 1-2 v Merthyr T. (A) after 0-0.
FA Vase: 5th Round replay 89-90.
Players progressing to Football League: Maurice Owen (Swindon Town), George Buck (Stockport County & Reading), Sammy Chung (Reading, Norwich City, Watford & Wolverhampton Wanderers).
96-97 - Captain: **P.o.Y.:** **Top scorer:**
Local Press: Oxford Mail, Oxford Times, Abingdon Herald, South Oxon Guardian.

HONOURS: Berks & Bucks Senior Cup 58-59 (R-up 88-89 92-93); Isthmian League Div 2 (Sth) 90-91 (Associate Members Tphy R-up 90-91); London Spartan League 88-89 (League Cup SF 88-89); Hellenic League(4) 56-57 58-60 86-87, R-up(3) 70-72 87-88, League Cup 57-58 70-71 81-82 (R-up 83-84 86-87), Div 1 75-76, Div 1 Cup 75-76, Res. Div(3) 69-71 86-87, Res. Div Cup 70-71 85-86, Res. Div Suppl. Cup 74-75; Oxford & District League(3) 1898-1901; Reading & District League 47-48; Berks & Bucks Jnr Cup 06-07; Abingdon Centenary Cup 58-59; Joan Lee Memorial Cup 69-70 70-71 86-87.

Abingdon Town FC: *Photo - Eric Marsh*

PROGRAMME DETAILS:
Pages: 40 **Price:** £1
Editor: Karl Prentice/ Graham Brookland

ALDERSHOT TOWN

Formed: 1992 **Nickname:** The Shots
Colours: Royal & red/white & red/white & red
Change colours: White & black/black/black & white
Midweek matchday: Tuesday **Club Newsline:** 0891 446 834.
Reserve Team's League: Suburban.

Chairman: Terry Owens **Vice Chairman:** Karl Prentice
Company Secretary: Graham Brookland, c/o Aldershot Town FC.
Manager: Steve Wigley. **Press Officer:** Nick Fryer.
Asst Manager: **Physio:** Clare Eastland
GROUND Address: Recreation Ground, High Street, Aldershot, Hants GU11 1TW (01252 20211. Fax: 24347).
Directions: Ground situated on eastern end of High Street next to large multi-storey B.T. building. From M3 (jct 4) take A325 to Aldershot. After five miles at r'bout take 1st exit marked town centre (A323) into Wellington Ave. At Burger King r'bout take 2nd exit into High Street - ground on left, large car park adjacent. 5 mins walk from Aldershot (BR).
Capacity: 7,500 **Cover:** 6,850 **Seats:** 1,800 **Floodlights:** Yes
Clubhouse: 7-11pm every evening and matchdays except Wednesday. Pool, darts, satellite TV & skittles alley. Steward: Wally Clarke 01252 338426.
Club Shop: Range of souvenirs, programmes, replica kits. Open matchdays or contact Janet Guess (01252-20211) for mail order.
PREVIOUS - Leagues: None. **Sponsors:** Datrontech plc

CLUB RECORDS - Attendance: 5,961 v Farnborough Town, Hants Senior Cup SF 16/3/93. *Ground record: 19,138 Aldershot FC v Carlisle United, FA Cup 4th Rd replay 28/1/70.* **Win:** 8-1 v Merstham, FA Cup 14/9/96. **Defeat:** 1-5 v Gloucester City, FA Trophy Nov 1995. **Scorer:** Mark Butler 131. **Appearances:** Mark Butler 264. **Transfer Fees - Paid:** £5,000 to Basingstoke Tn.for Paul Chambers 94-95. **Received:** £5,000 for Jason Tucker from Enfield 96
BEST SEASON - FA Cup: 4th Qual Rd 95-96
FA Trophy: 3rd Qual Rd 94-95 95-96 96-97.
FA Vase: Quarter Final 93-94
96-97 - Captain: Paul Chambers **Top scorer:** Roy Young (15) **P.o.Y.:** Jimmy Sugrue
Local Press: Aldershot News, Farnham Herald
Local Radio: County Sound (203m m/w, 1476 khz), BBC Radio Surrey (104.6 fm), Radio 210 (210m m/w).
HONOURS: Isthmian League Div 3 92-93; Simpsonair Trophy 92-93; Skol Invitation Trophy 92-93; Hants Senior Cup SF 92-93; Suburban Lge Western Div champions 94-95; Allied Counties Youth Lge Champions 1994-95; Guradian Insurance Lge Cup R-up 95-96.

Aldershot Town: *Photo - Ian Morsman*

PROGRAMME DETAILS:
Pages: 64 **Price:** £1
Editor: Nick Rhodes
(01582 881865)

BARTON ROVERS

Formed: 1898 **Nickname:** Rovers
Colours: All royal blue
Change colours: All red
Midweek Matchday: Tuesday
Reserves' League: None

Chairman: Stephen J Harris **President:** P Howarth
Vice Chairman: T Capon **Secretary:** Owen Clark, 108 Manor Road, Barton-le-Clay, Bedford MK45 4NS (01582 882398).
Press Officer: Nick Rhodes (01582 881865)
Manager: Gordon Brown **Asst Manager:** Richard Camp
Coach: Gordon Brown **Physio:** Mick Clark
GROUND Address: Sharpenhoe Road, Barton-le-Clay, Bedford MK45 4SD (01582 882607). **Directions:** M1 Jct 12, from London exit turn right, take 2nd right through Harlington and Sharpenhoe. Ground on right entering village. Four and a half miles from Harlington (BR), 6 miles from Luton (BR), good bus service from Luton.
Capacity: 4,000 **Seats:** 160 **Cover:** 1,120 **Floodlights:** Yes
Clubhouse: Noon-3pm weekends (no football), noon-11pm (matchdays), 7-11pm weekdays. Real ale, hot & cold snacks, pool, darts, gaming machines.
Club Shop: Yes **Sponsors:** SRC Contractors

PREVIOUS - Grounds: Church Pitch 1898-1912; Barton Cutting 1912; Sharpenhoe Rd 12-33; Faldo Rd 33-38; Barton Rec. 46-75. **Leagues:** Luton & Dist. 47-54, Sth Midlands 54-79.

CLUB RECORDS - Attendance: 1,900 v Nuneaton, FA Cup 4th Qual. Rd 1976. **Win:** 17-1 v Flitwick Athletic (H), S Midlands Lge Div 1 55-56. **Defeat:** 1-11 v Leighton United (H), S Midlands Lge Prem Div 62-63. **Scorer:** Richard Camp 144, 1989-96. **Appearances:** Bill Goodyear 475, 1982-93. **Fees - Paid:** £1,000 for B Baldry (Hitchin Town, 1980). **Received:** £1,000 for B Baldry (Bishop's Stortford, 1981).
BEST SEASON - **FA Cup:** 1st Round 1980-81, 0-2 v Torquay United (A).
FA Vase: Runners-up 77-78 (SF 76-77 81-82, QF 75-76 78-79),
FA Trophy: 1st Qual Rd 96-97

Players progressing to Football Lge: Kevin Blackwell (Huddersfield, Torquay, Notts Co., Scarborough, Plymouth).
Local Press: Luton News, Herald, Beds on Sunday.
Local Radio: Radio Chiltern, Radio Beds.
96-97 - Captain: Danny Turner **P.o.Y.:** Steve Hunt **Top scorer:** Gordon Guile
HONOURS: Sth Mids Lg(8) 70-73 74-79 (R-up 67-68), Div 1 64-65 (R-up 55-56), Div 2 54-55, Lg Shield 57-58 60-61 68-69, Chal. Tphy 71-72 74-75 77-78 78-79; Beds Snr Cup (5) 71-73 80-82 89-90, R-up (5); Beds Premier Cup 95-96, R-up 81-82 83-84 88-89, Beds Intermediate Cup 53-54; Luton & Dist. Lg Div 3 47-48; North Beds Charity Cup 72-73 74-75 76-77 77-78 79-80 80-81 (R-up 70-71); Isthmian Lg Associate Members Tphy R-up 92-93; Isthmian Div 2 R-Up 94-95.

Back Row (L-R); Gordon Brown (Mgr), Jamie Pace, Adrian Headley, Frank Thompson, Tony McNally, Gary Turner, Kevin Wheeler, Steve Hunt, Stuart Endacott, Paul Seaman, Mick Clark (Physio), Owen Clark (Sec). Front Row; John Coley, Colin McGill, Richard Wilcox, Danny Turner (Cpt), Richard Camp (Asst Mgr), Danny Howell, Scott Turner.

BERKHAMSTED TOWN

Formed: 1895 **Nickname:** Lilywhites
Colours: White/black/black
Change Colours: Green & white halves.
Midweek Matchday: Tuesday
Reserve Team's League: Essex & Herts Border Combination.

Chairman: Brian McCarthy. **President:** Dennis Wright
Secretary: Mrs Susan Beddall, 26 St Edmunds, Berkhamsted, Herts HP4 2HT (01442 874514 H & B).
Press Officer: Bob Sear (01442 864547 H & B)
Manager: Gordon Taylor **Match Sec:** Lee Whybrow
Coach: Howard Cowley. **Physio:** Kevin Burke.

PROGRAMME DETAILS:
Pages: 32 **Price:** 70p
Editor: Steve Hamilton (01442 69237)

GROUND Address: Broadwater, Lower Kings Road, Berkhamsted, Herts HP4 2AA (01442 862815).
Directions: Adjacent to Berkhamsted station (Euston-Birmingham line). A41 to Berkhamsted town centre traffic lights, left into Lower Kings Road.
Capacity: 2,000 **Seats:** 120 **Cover:** 200 **Floodlights:** Yes
Clubhouse: Open 7 days a week. Pool & darts.
Club Shop: Old programmes and club scarves, ties, boot bags, and baseball hats available. See Graham Hastie.
Sponsors: C D Wright Electrical Wholesalers.

PREVIOUS - **Grounds:** Sunnyside Enclosure 1895-1919, Sports Ground 1919-83.
Leagues: W Herts & Herts Co. 95-22, Spartan 22-51 66-75, Delphian 51-63, Athenian 63-66 83-84, London Spartan 75-83.

CLUB RECORDS - **Attendance:** 1,163 v Barnet, FA Cup 3rd Qual. Rd 1987.

BEST SEASON - **FA Cup:** 3rd Qualifying Round 87-88

Players progressing to Football League: Frank Broome, Maurice Cook, Keith Ryan (Wycombe).
96-97 - Captain: **Top scorer:** **P.o.Y.:**
Local Press: Berkhamsted Herald, Berkhamsted Gazette.
Local Radio Stations: Chiltern Radio, Radio Beds.

HONOURS: Hertfordshire Senior Cup 52-53, London Spartan League 79-80 (Div 2 26-27), Herts Charity Shield 73-74 79-80 84-85 90-91 50-51 (jt), Herts Senior County League Aubrey Cup 52-53, St Marys Cup(12), Apsley Senior Charity Cup(9), Wallspan Southern Combination 84-85 (Floodlit Cup 84-85).

Berkhamstead Town FC:

BILLERICAY TOWN

BILLERICAY TOWN
FOOTBALL CLUB
SEASON 1997 - 1998
IMATION
Sponsored by
IMATION
and
SPALL SPORTS
matchday magazine £1.00
Visit our Internet Web Site • Sponsored by Millennia Publishing
http://www.millennia.co.uk/billericay-tfc/

PROGRAMME DETAILS:
Pages: 60 **Price:** £1
Editor: Steve Lewis.
(01277 625679)

Formed: 1880 **Nickname:** The Town
Colours: All Royal Blue with white trim.
Change colours: All white with red trim.
Midweek Matches: Tuesday.
Reserves' Lge: Essex & Herts Border Comb.

Chairman: Rod Moore **Vice Chairman:** John Bennewith, Tony Thake
President: Barry Spall **Secretary:** Len Dewson, 14 Graham Close, Billericay, Essex CM12 0QW (01277 622375).
Press Officer: Phil Heady (01277 626560)
Manager: John Kendall
Coach: Ken Varney **Physio:** Colin Masterson
GROUND Address: New Lodge, Blunts Wall Road, Billericay CM12 9SA (01277 652188). **Directions:** From Shenfield (A129) right at 1st lights then 2nd right. From Basildon (A129) over 1st lights in town, then left at next lights and 2nd right. Half mile from Billericay (GER) station (London Liverpool St. - Southend line). Ground 5 mins walk from buses 222, 251, 357, 255, 551.
Capacity: 3,500 **Seats:** 424 **Cover:** 600 **Floodlights:** Yes
Clubhouse: Open every evening 8-11pm (except Monday)(1pm-11pm Sat) and weekend lunchtimes noon-2.30pm. Discos, live entertainment.
Club Shop: Open matchdays for souvenirs, metal badges, old progs, programme swaps. Nigel Harris (01268 558114). **Sponsors:** Imation

PREVIOUS - Grounds: Laindon Road (pre-1971). **Leagues:** Romford & Dist. 1890-1914/ Mid Essex 18-47/ South Essex Comb. 47-66/ Essex Olympian 66-71/ Essex Snr 71-77/ Athenian 77-79.

CLUB RECORDS - Attendance: 3,841 v West Ham Utd, Floodlight opener 77. Comp match: 3,193 v Farnborough Tn, FA Vase SF 1st leg 76. **Win:** 11-0 v Stansted (A), Essex Senior League 5/5/76. **Defeat:** 3-10 v Chelmsford City (A), Essex Senior Cup 4/1/93. **Goalscorer:** F Clayden 273. **Appearances:** J Pullen 418. **Fees - Paid:** Undisclosed. **Received:** £22,500 for Steve Jones (West Ham, Nov. 1992).

BEST SEASON - FA Cup: 4th Qual Rd 77-78. **FA Vase:** Winners - 75-76, 76-77 & 78-79.
FA Trophy: 1st Rd Prop 93-94. **FA Amateur Cup:** 3rd Qual Rd 73-74

Players progressing to Football League: D Westwood (QPR) 75, A Hull, D Carter (Peterborough, Orient), D Cass (Orient) 88, D Ludden (Orient) 92, S Jones (West Ham Utd) 92.
96-97 - Captain: Gary Howard/Dave RootY.: Danny Hazle **Top scorer:** Leon Gutzmore 26
Local Press: Evening Echo, Billericay Gazette. **Local Radio:** BBC Radio Essex, Essex Radio, Essex FM

HONOURS: Essex Snr Lg 72-73 74-75 75-76, R-up 71-2 73-4, Lg Cup 71-74 76-77 (R-up 74-5), Challenge Cup 72-73; Isthmian Lg Div 2 79-80 (Div 1 R-up 80-1); Athenian Lg 77-79 (Lg Cup 77-78); East Anglian Cup R-up 79-80 84-5; Essex Snr Cup 75-76 (R-up 85-6 93-4 94-5 95-6); Essex Snr Tphy 77-78 79-80; Essex Thameside Tphy 86-87 91-92 (R-up 90-1); Essex F'lit Tphy 77-78; Phillips F'lit Tphy 76-77; Rothmans Merit Award 1978.

Billericay Town's ground. *Photo - Daniel Bridge*

BOGNOR REGIS TOWN

PROGRAMME DETAILS:
Pages: 36 **Price:** £1
Editor: Maurice Warner
Tel: 01243 822325

Founded: 1883 **Nickname:** The Rocks
Colours: White (green trim)/green/white
Change colours: All yellow
Midweek home matchday: Monday
Reserve's League: None.

Chairman: Jack Pearce **President:** S Rowlands
Secretary: Brian Pitchford, c/o The Club
Comm. Manager: Maurice Warner **Gen. Manager:** Jack Pearce
Manager: Jack Pearce. **Press Officer:** Kevin Seal, c/o the Club
Asst Manager: Neil Hider **Physio:** Steve Robinson

GROUND Address: Nyewood Lane, Bognor Regis PO21 2TY (01243 822325).
Directions: West along seafront from pier, past Aldwick shopping centre, and right into Nyewood Lane.
Capacity: 6,000 **Cover:** 3,800 **Seats:** 243 **Floodlights:** Yes
Clubhouse: Open every night, matchdays and Sunday lunchtimes. Hot food available.
Club Shop: Selling programmes and normal club items.
Sponsors: Butlins South Coast World

PREVIOUS - Leagues: W Sussex Lge 1896-1926, Brighton, Hove & District Lge 26-27, Sussex County Lge 27-72, Southern Lge 72-81

CLUB RECORDS - Attendance: 3,642 v Swansea FA Cup 1st Rd replay, '84. **Goalscorer:** Kevin Clements. **Appearances:** Mick Pullen, 914. **Record Fees - Paid:** None. **Received:** £10,500 for John Crumplin & Geoff Cooper (Brighton & Hove Albion, 1987) & Simon Rodger (Crystal Palace, 1989).
BEST SEASON - FA Cup: 2nd Rd 84-85 2-6 v Reading (A), 85-86 1-6 v Gillingham (A), 88-89 0-1 v Cambridge (H), 95-96 0-4 v Peterborough (A). **League clubs beaten:** Swansea 84-85, Exeter 88-89.
FA Amateur Cup: 1st Round 71-72 **FA Trophy:** 3rd Round 95-96
Players progressing to Football League: E Randall (Chelsea 50), J Standing (Brighton 61), A Woon (Brentford 72), J Crumplin & G Cooper (Brighton 87), Simon Rodger (C Palace 89).
96-97 - Captain: Michael Birmingham **P.o.Y.:** Paul Thomas **Top scorer:** Adie Miles
Local Press: Bognor Regis Journal & Guardian, Bognor Observer, Brighton Argus, Portsmouth News.
Local Radio: Radio Sussex, Ocean Sound, Radio Solent, Southern Sound, Spirit FM.
HONOURS: Isthmian Lg Div 1 R-up 81-82, (Lg Cup 86-87), Southern Lg R-up 80-81 (Lg Cup R-up 80-81, Merit Cup 80-81), Sussex Lg 48-49 71-72 (R-up 38-39 51-52, Div 2 70-71, Invitation Cup 40-41 49-50 62-63 71-72), Brighton Lg R-up 26-27, W Sussex Lg(5) 20-25 (R-up 1896-97, 25-26), W Sussex Jnr Lg 10-11 13-14, Southern Co's Comb 78-79, Sussex Snr Cup(9) 54-56 79-84 86-87 94-95 (R-up 51-52 58-59 84-85), Sussex Prof. Cup 73-74, Sussex RUR Cup 71-72, Sussex I'mediate Cup 52-53, Littlehampton Hosp. Cup 29-30 33-34, Bognor Charity Cup(8) 28-29 30-31 32-33 37-38 47-48 58-59 71-73, Gosport War Mem. Cup(2) 81-83 (R-up 86-87), Snr Midweek F'lit Cup R-up 74-75.

Adie Miles, Bognor's top goalscorer last season, about to shoot. *Photo: Peter Lirettoc.*

CHERTSEY TOWN

Formed: 1890 **Nickname:** Curfews
Colours: Blue & white stripes/white/white
Change colours: All red.
Midweek Matchday: Tuesday
Reserves League:

Chairman: Alan McKane **President:** Cllr Chris Norman
Vice Chairman: Nick Keel **Press Officer/Secretary:** Chris Gay, 23 Richmond Close, Frimley, Camberley, Surrey GU16 5NR (01276 20745).
Manager: Colin Payne. **Physio:** Julia Richards
Asst Manager: Roger Goodhind **Coach:** Steve Stairs
Commercial Manager: John Cox

GROUND Address: Alwyns Lane, Chertsey, Surrey KT16 9DW (01932 561774).
Directions: Alwyns Lane is off Windsor Street at north end of shopping centre. 10 mins walk from Chertsey (BR). London Country bus.
Capacity: 3,000 **Seats:** 250 **Cover:**1000 **Floodlights:** Yes
Clubhouse: Open weekday evenings and weekend lunchtimes.
Club Shop: Open matchdays, selling club & football souvenirs. Contact Steve Maughan.
Sponsors: Hayes Express Services.

PROGRAMME DETAILS:
Pages: 36 **Price:** £1.20.
Editor: Chris Gay
(01276 20745)

PREVIOUS - Leagues: West Surrey (pre-1899), Surrey Jnr 1899-1920, Surrey Intermediate 20-46, Surrey Snr 46-63, Metropolitan 63-66, Gtr London 66-67, Spartan 67-75/ London Spartan 75-76, Athenian 76-84, Isthmian 84-85, Combined Counties 85-86. **Grounds:** The Grange (pre-World War 1), The Hollows (pre-1929).

CLUB RECORDS - Attendance: 2,150 v Aldershot, Isthmian Lge Division Two 4/12/93.
Goalscorer: Alan Brown 54, 1962-63.
Win: 10-1 v Clapton (H), Isthmian Lge Division Three, 91-92.
Defeat: 1-12 v Bromley (H), FA Cup Preliminary Rd, 82-83. **Transfer fee received:** £56,500.
Best Season - FA Vase: Quarter Final 87-88 91-92. **FA Cup:** 3rd Qualifying Rd 92-93 (lost 1-3 at home to Kingstonian). **FA Trophy:** 2nd Qual Rd 95-96. **FA Amateur Cup:** 3rd Qual Rd 61-62.
Players progressing to Football League: Rachid Harkouk (Crystal Palace, Queens Park Rangers & Notts County), Peter Cawley (Wimbledon 1987), Lee Charles (Queens Park Rangers 1995).
96-96 P.o.Y.: Chris Sparks
Local Press: Surrey Herald. **Local Radio:** BBC Southern Counties, County Sound.
HONOURS: Isthmian League Cup 94-95 (Associate Members Trophy 94-95), Div 2 R-up 94-95, Div 3 R-up 91-92; Surrey Snr League 59-60 61-62 62-63 (League Cup 59-60 61-62); Combined Co's League R-up 85-86 (Concours Tphy 85-86); Surrey Snr Cup R-up 85-86; Spartan League & League Cup R-up 74-75.

L-R, Back: Steve Scott, Jason Watmore, Steve Stairs, Michael Whittaker, Alan Hamlet, Paul Holland, Steve Toms, James Keen, Colin Payne (Player/manager), Roger Goode, Alan McKane (Chairman), Joe Searle (committee), Nick Keel (Vice Chairman). Front: Billy Banks (Treasurer), Bill Dennett (Kit & Groundsman), Colin Davis, Terry Flaherty, Mark Turner, John Jones, Rob McKane, Keith Cooper, Alan Mills, Richard McDonough, Julia Richards (Physio), Mike Bashford (committee).

PROGRAMME DETAILS:
Pages: 28 **Price:** 70p
Editor: Russell Chandler
(0181 406 4573 H)

CROYDON

Formed: 1953 **Nickname:**
Colours: Sky & navy quarters/navy & sky/navy & sky
Change colours: All red
Midweek home matchday: Monday
Reserve Team's League: Suburban.

Chairman: Ken Jarvie
Secretary: Mrs Jacqueline Jarvie, 2 Spa Close, London SE25 6DS. 0181 653 7250 (H), 0181 654 8555 (B).
Press Officer: Russell Chandler, 26 Dartnell Road, Croydon, Surrey. CR0 6JA. 0181 406 4573 (H) 0181 654 8555 (B).
Manager: Ken Jarvie **Match Sec:** Gordon Tennant
Coach: Dave Ndjie **Physio:** Stewart Wilbey/Bobby Childs

GROUND Address: Croydon Sports Arena, Albert Road, South Norwood, London. SE25 4QL 0181 654 3462/8555. **Directions:** Train to East Croydon or Norwood Junction, then bus 12 to either Belmont or Dundee Road. Walk down either - ground at bottom. 5 mins walk from Woodside (BR).
Capacity: 8,000 **Cover:** 450 **Seats:** 450 **Floodlights:** Yes
Clubhouse: Open every evening and lunchtime, holds 250, snacks available. Dancing, discos, bingo. Lounge bar available for private hire.
Club Shop: Yes
Sponsors: Philips.

PREVIOUS - Leagues: Surrey Senior 53-63/ Spartan 63-64/ Athenian 64-74. **Name:** Croydon Amateurs 1953-74.

CLUB RECORDS **Attendance:** 1,450 v Wycombe, FA Cup 4th Qualifying Rd 1975.
Career appearances: Alec Jackson (400+).
Transfer fee paid: Steve Brown
Transfer fee received: Peter Evans (to Sutton Utd)

BEST SEASON - **FA Cup:** 2nd Round replay 79-80 (2-3 v Millwall after 1-1)
FA Trophy: 2nd Round 81-82, 82-83 **FA Amateur Cup:** 3rd round 71-72

Players progressing to Football League: Alan Barnett (Plymouth 1955), Peter Bonetti (Chelsea), Leroy Ambrose (Charlton 1979), Steve Milton (Fulham - via Whyteleafe), Murray Jones (Crystal & Exeter - via Carshalton).
Local Press: Croydon - Advertiser, Midweek Post, Times, Guardian.
96-97 Captain: **P.o.Y.:** **Top scorer:**

HONOURS: Isthmian Lg Div 2 R-up 75-76 95-96, Surrey Snr Cup 81-82 (R-up 76-77), Surrey Prem Cup 86-87, Spartan Lg 63-64, Athenian Lg R-up 71-72 (Div 2 65-66 (R-up 70-71)), Surrey Snr Lg R-up 56-57 60-61 62-63 (Lg Cup 60-61, Charity Cup 53-54 62-63, Res Section 57-58), London Senior Cup R-up 78-79, Suburban Lg South 86-87 (Lg Cup(2)), Southern Yth Lg 85-86 (Lg Cup 85-86 87-88), Berger Yth Cup 78-79.

Croydon FC: *Photo - Andrew Chitty*

PROGRAMME DETAILS:
Pages: 48 **Price:** £1
Editor: Jeremy Mason
(01375 376428)

GRAYS ATHLETIC

Formed: 1890 **Nickname:** The Blues
Colours: Royal & white
Change colours: All yellow.
Midweek matchday: Tuesday

Chairman: Frank Harris **Secretary:** Jeff Saxton, 216 Thundersley Park Road, South Benfleet, Essex SS7 1HP (01268 756964).
Manager: Gary Calder **Asst Man.:** Chris King
Physio: Dave Lawson. **Commercial Manager:** Bill Cherry
Coach: Joe Dunwell **Press Officer:** Gordon Norman (014024 51733)
GROUND Address: Recreation Ground, Bridge Road, Grays RM17 6BZ (01375 391649). **Directions:** Seven minutes walk from Grays station - turn right round one way system, right into Clarence Road, and at end into Bridge Road. Bus No. 370. By road - A13 towards Southend from London, take Grays exit and follow signs to town centre, keep left on one-way system, continue up hill for about half a mile, turn right into Bridge Road, ground half mile on right.
Capacity: 4,500 **Cover:** 1,200 **Seats:** 300 **Floodlights:** Yes
Clubhouse: Bar, pool, darts, bar snacks available. Indoor sports hall, **Stewardess:** Sue Riley (01375 377753)
Club Shop: Selling 'The First Hundred Years', sweaters, T-shirts, replica shirts, scarves, ties, etc. Contact Bill Grove & Dave Smith, 01375 391649
Sponsors: Roehlig & Co (UK) Ltd. London Advertising Centre Ltd, Harris Commercials.

PREVIOUS - Leagues: Athenian 12-14 58-83/ London 14-24 26-39/ Kent 24-26/ Corinthian 45-58.

CLUB RECORDS - Attendance: 9,500 v Chelmsford City, FA Cup Fourth Qualifying Round 1959. **Win:** 12-0 v Tooting (H) London Lge 24/2/23. **Defeat:** 0-12 v Enfield (A) Athenian Lge 20/4/63. **Goalscorer:** Harry Brand 269 (1944-52) **Appearances:** Phil Sammons, 673. **Fee Paid:** For Ian Durant (Canvey Island) **Fee Received:** Undisclosed for Tony Witter (C. Palace) and Dwight Marshall (Plymouth 1991).
Best FA Cup season: 1st Rd 51-52 88-89. **FA Trophy:** 3rd Rd 92-93. **FA Amateur Cup:** 3rd Rd 63-64. **Players progressing to Football League:** J Jordan (Spurs 47), R Kemp (Reading 49), B Silkman & T Banfield (Orient), G O'Reilly (Spurs), W Entwhistle (Bury 83), M Welch (Wimbledon 84), T Witter (C Palace 90), D Marshall (Plymouth 91).
96-97 - Captain: Phil Sammons **P.o.Y.:** Phil Sammons **Top scorer:** Jamie Southon
Local Press: Thurrock Gazette **Local Radio:** BBC Essex, Radio Essex.

HONOURS: Isthmian Div 1 R-up 87-88 (Div 2 Sth 84-85, Lg Cup 91-92); Athenian Lg R-up 82-83, Reserve Section R-up 58-59 (Cup R-up 59-60); Corinthian Lg 45-46 (R-up 51-52 54-55 56-57), Lg Cup(2) 45-47, Mem. Shield(4) 45-47 77-78 79-80; Essex Snr Cup 4 (R-up 6); East Anglian Cup 44-45 (R-up 43-44 54-55); Essex Thameside Tphy 6 (R-up 7); Essex Elizabeth Trophy 76-77 (R-up 65-66); Claridge Tphy 87-88 88-89; Mithras Cup 79-80; Essex Int Cup(3) 56-57 58-60 (Jun Cup 19-20 (R-up 58-59); Essex & Herts Border Comb. East 87-88 (Ancillary Cup 78-79, Comb Cup 82-83); Fred Budden Tphy 86-87; Hornchurch Charity Cup 78-79 86-87; Neale Tphy 50-51; Ford Rate Tphy 83-84 85-86 87-88 (R-up 84-85 86-87); Stan Veness Memorial Trophy (8) 87-96.

Grays Athletic F.C. - Back Row: Donovan Wilson, Russell Penn, Peter Hickles, Richard Cherry, Andy Marsh, Malcom Stewart, Lee Double, Andy Alexander, John Ray. Front Row: Danny Wallace, Darryl Heffer, Barry Roberts, Phil Sammons, Jason Walker, Dean Cox, Kamal Bahbra.

HAMPTON

PROGRAMME DETAILS:
Pages: 28 **Price:** £1
Editor: Secretary

Formed: 1920 **Nickname:** Beavers
Colours: Red & blue/white/blue
Change Colours: White/tangerine/white.
Midweek Matchday: Tuesday
Reserve Team's League: Suburban

Chairman: Robert Hayes **President:** Alan Simpson
Vice Chairman: Ken Gazzard **Press Officer:** Les Rance
Secretary: Adrian Mann, 30 Burniston Court, Manor Rd, Wallington, Surrey SM6 0AD (0181 773 0858).
Manager: Chick Botley **Assistant Manager:** Tony Coombe
Coach: **Physio:** Jim Barrs

GROUND Address: Beveree Stadium, Beaver Close, off Station Rd, Hampton TW12 2BX (0181 979 2456 Club; 0181 941 4936 Boardroom; 0181 941 2838 Office matchdays only)
Directions: A3 out of London, fork left (signed Staines/Esher/Sandown Pk) onto A243, A309 Staines exit to Hampton Ct at 'Scilly Isles' r'bout, left at r'bout after Hampton Court Bridge onto A308, after 1 mile right into Church St (A311), left after White Hart after 200yds into High St, Station Rd on right just before junction with A308.
Capacity: 3,000 **Seats:** 300 **Cover:** 800 **Floodlights:** Yes
Clubhouse: (0181 979 2456). Lounge bar and hall, open on matchdays and training nights. Hall available for hire. **Steward:** Steve Penny.
Club Shop: Sells various club souvenirs & programmes. Contact Stefan Rance (0181 287 4682)
Sponsors: Saft-Nife Ltd.

PREVIOUS - Leagues: Kingston & District 21-33, South West Middx 33-59, Surrey Snr 59-64, Spartan 64-71, Athenian 71-73. **Grounds:** Hatherop Rec (until 1959).

CLUB RECORDS - Win: 11-1 v Eastbourne Utd, Isthmian Lge Div 2 (S), 90-91. **Defeat:** 0-13 v Hounslow Town, Middlesex Senior Cup 62-63. **Goalscorer:** Peter Allen. **Appearances:** Tim Hollands. **Fees - Paid:** £400 for Peter Shodiende (Hendon, 1981). **Received:** £2,500 from APOP (Cyprus) for Ricky Walkes (June 1989).
BEST SEASON - FA Cup: 4th Qual Rd 77-78 (1-2 v Barnet). **FA Vase:** 3rd Rd 91-92 (0-1 v Newport IOW), 95-96 (0-1 v Colllier Row). **FA Trophy:** 1st Rd Prop 83-84 (0-2 v Maidstone Utd). **FA Amateur Cup:** 1st Rd Prop 73-74 (2-4 v Leytonstone)
Players progressing to Football League: Andy Rogers (Southampton, Plymouth, Reading), Dwight Marshall (Plymouth,Luton Town),Paul Rogers(Sheffield Utd.)
96-97 - Captain: Steve Cheshire **P.o.Y.:** Mark Russell **Top scorer:** Steve Cheshire
Local Press: Middx Chronicle, Surrey Comet, Richmond & Twickemham Times, The Informer.

HONOURS: London Snr Cup(2) 86-88; Spartan Lg(4) 64-67 69-70, (R-up 67-68), Lg Cup(4) 64-68 (R-up 2); Surrey Snr Lg 63-64 (Lg Cup R-up 60-61); Middx Charity Cup 69-70 95-96 (R-up 68-69 71-72 89-90 94-95), Middx Snr Cup R-up 71-72 76-77 95-96; Athenian Lg Div 2 R-up 72-73; Southern Comb. Cup 68-69 71-72 76-77 81-82 83-84 85-86 96-97 (R-up 77-78 79-80); Isthmian Lge Div 3 91-92, Lge Div 2 95-96.

Back Row (L-R); Kevin Duffell, Jamie Horton, Darren Powell, Mark Russell, Alan Simpson (President), Jim Wigmore, Derek Bryan, Barry Barnes (Asst Mgr), Robert Hayes (Chr). Centre; Bertie the Beaver (Club Mascot). Front Row; Steve Cheshire, Shaun Mitchell, Peter Wood, Barry Moore, Faye Barton (Matchday Mascot), Danny Collyer, Dave Rattue, Robin Lewis, Steve Stairs.

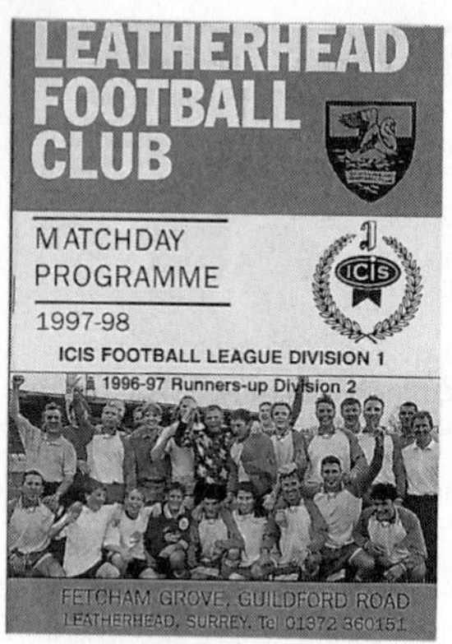

PROGRAMME DETAILS:
Pages: 24 **Price:** 50p
Editor: Bernard Edwards
(01372 454573)

LEATHERHEAD

Founded: 1946 **Nickname:** Tanners
Colours: Green and White.
Change colours: Blue & white
Midweek Matchday: Tuesday
Reserves' League: Suburban (South)

Chairman: David Zackey **President:** Gerald Darby
Vice Chairman: Gerald Darby **Chief Executive:** Bob Davies
Secretary: Gerald Darby, c/o Leatherhead F.C. 01372 360151
Press Officer/Comm. Manager: Bob Davies
Manager: Keith Wenham **Asst. Manager:** Terry Quick
Coach: Bob Davies **Physio:** Brian Mayo.

GROUND Address: Fetcham Grove, Guildford Rd, Leatherhead, Surrey KT22 9AS (01372 360151).
Directions: M25 jct 9 to Leatherhead; follow signs to Leisure Centre, ground adjacent. Half mile from Leatherhead (BR). London Country Buses 479 and 408 - ground opposite bus garage.
Capacity: 3,400 **Seats:** 200 **Cover:** 445 **Floodlights:** Yes
Clubhouse: (0372 360151) Licensed bar open noon - 11pm matchdays. Snacks etc on matchdays.
Club Shop: Yes. 01372 362705 **Sponsors:** Marchant Construction.

PREVIOUS - Leagues: Surrey Snr 46-50/ Metropolitan 50-51/ Delphian 51-58/ Corinthian 58-63/ Athenian 63-72.
Names: None **Grounds:** None.

CLUB RECORDS - Attendance:: 5,500 v Wimbledon, 1976. **Win:** Unknown. **Defeat:** 1-11 v Sutton United.
Career goalscorer: Steve Lunn 96-97 (46). **Career appearances:** P Caswell.
Fee paid: £1,500 to Croydon (B Salkeld). **Fee received:** £1,500 from Croydon (B Salkeld)

BEST SEASON - FA Cup: 4th Round 74-75, 2-3 v Leicester C.(A). Also 2nd Rd 75-76 76-77 78-79, 1st Rd 77-78 80-81
League clubs defeated: Colchester, Brighton 74-75, Cambridge Utd 75-76, Northampton 76-77.
FA Amateur Cup: Semi finalists 70-71 73-74. **FA Trophy:** R-up 77-78

Players progressing to Football League: Chris Kelly (Millwall), B Friend (Fulham), L Harwood (Port Vale), John Humphrey (Millwall).

96-97 - Captain: Steve Lunn **Top Scorer:** Steve Lunn **P.o.Y.:** Steve Lunn
Local Press: Leatherhead Advertiser, Surrey Advertiser **Local Radio:** County Sound.

HONOURS: Isthmian Lg Cup 77-78; Corinthian Lg 62-63; Athenian Ld Div 1 63-64; Surrey Snr Cup 68-69 (R-up 64-65 66-67 74-75 78-79); Surrey Snr Lg 46-47 47-48 48-49 49-50 (Lg Cup 49-50), Snr Shield 68-69, Charity Cup 46-47 49-50); East Surrey Charity Cup 68-69 (R-up 67-68); London Snr Cup R-up 74-75 77-78; Surrey Inter Cup 89-90; Southern Comb. Cup 89-90.

Back Row (L-R); Gerald Darby (Pres), Paul D'Rosiniso, Phil Dunkley, Ray Arnett, Tony Webb, Elliott Davidson, Steve Lammiman, Mark Bryne, Charles Pewbert, Steve Lawson, Tery Quick (Coach), Keith Wenham (Mgr), Bob Davies (Chief Executive). Front Row; Steve Lunn, Stuart Lawson, Alan Whiter, Gani Amet, Nigel Webb, Stuart Culipp, Physio.

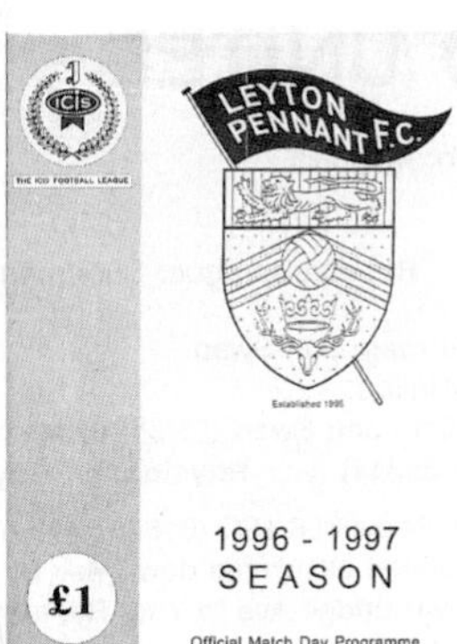

LEYTON PENNANT F.C.
1996 - 1997
SEASON
£1
Official Match Day Programme

PROGRAMME DETAILS:
Pages: 32 **Price:** £1
Editor: John Stacey
(0181 527 8116)

LEYTON PENNANT

Formed: 1868 **Nickname:** Lilywhites
Colours: White/navy/navy
Change colours: All navy
Midweek home matchday: Wednesday
Reserve Team League: Essex & Herts Border Comb.

Chairman: John Stacey **Vice-Chairman:** Tom Kelly
President: George Cross **Secretary:** Andy Perkins, 4 Chestnut Drive, Wanstead, London E11 2TA, (0181 530 4551)
Gen. Manager: Kevin Moran **Press Officer:** Charlie Ward (01295 780639)
Team Manager: Paul Taylor **Coach:** Trevor Harvey
Physio: Christie Keene

GROUND Address: Wadham Lodge Sports Ground, Kitchener Road, Walthamstow, London. E17 4JP (0181 527 2444)
Directions: North Circular Road to Crooked Billet,turn into Chingford Road,then into Brookscroft Road,first on left.Walthamstow Central (Victoria Line tube) one mile away,then buses W21 or 256.
Capacity: 2,000 **Cover:** 600 **Seats:** 200 **Floodlights:** Yes
Clubhouse: (0181 527 2444). Open 11am-11pm Mon-Sat, 12-3 & 7-10.30pm Sun. No hot food. Hot snacks from tea bar on matchdays.
Club Shop: Sells programmes, pennants, scarves, badges etc. Contact Dave Giddings c/o the club. **Sponsors:** Maplin Electronics

PREVIOUS - Leagues: Leyton & District Alliance, South Essex, Southern 05-11, London 20-26, Athenian 27-82, Spartan Lge as Walthamstow Pennant. **Name:** Leyton FC, Leyton Wingate (75-92), Walthamstow Pennant (64-92). **Grounds:** Brisbane Rd (Home of Leyton Orient).
CLUB RECORDS - Attendance: 676 v Aldershot Icis Lge 10/2/96, *(100,000 saw Leyton v Walthamstow Avenue, FA Amateur Cup final at Wembley, April 26th 1952).* **Win:** 10-2 v Horsham 82. **Defeat:** 1-11 v Barnet 46. **Transfer fee paid:** £200 for Dwight Marshall (Hampton). **Transfer fee received:** £6,000 for T Williams (Redbridge Forest). **Career goalscorer:** Steve Lane 118. **Career appearances:** Steve Hamberger 387.
BEST SEASON - FA Trophy: 3rd Rd 86-87. **FA Vase:** 6th Rd 83-84. **FA Cup:** 3rd Rd 09-10. **FA Amateur Cup:** Winners 26-27 27-28, R-up 6. **League clubs defeated in FA Cup:** None
Players progressing to Football League: C Buchan (Sunderland) 10, Casey (Chelsea) 52, K Facey (Orient 52), M Costello (Aldershot 56), D Clark (Orient 61).
96-97 - Captain: Stuart McLean **P.O.Y.:** Paul Salmon **Top scorer:** Che Stadhart
Local Press: Waltham Forest Guardian, Hackney Gazette **Local Radio:** LBC.
HONOURS: Isthmian Lg Div 1 R-up 86-87 (Div 2 North 84-85); Essex Snr Tphy R-up 84-85; Thorn EMI National Floodlight Cup 84-85; London Senior Cup 03-04 (R-up 33-34 37-38 45-46); London Charity Cup 34-35 36-37 (R-up 32-33 46-47 66-67 70-71); London Lg 23-24 24-25 25-26 (R-up 26-27), Lg Cup 56-57; Athenian Lg 28-29 65-66 66-67 76-77 81-82 (R-up 45-46 64-65 77-78), Div 2 Cup R-up 69-70; London Challenge Cup R-up 09-10 27-28 95-96; East Anglian Cup R-up 45-46 72-73; Essex Thameside Trophy 64-65 66-67 81-82 (R-up 63-64); Leyton & Dist. All 1892-93 94-95

Back Row (L-R); Sid Nelson, Joe Harley, Roy Edwards, Paul Salmon, Andy Oniha, Phil Lovell, Ian Brooks, Craig Knox. Front Row; Andy Silk, Mark Salmon, Billy Read, Che Stadhart, Stuart McLean, Andrzej Perkins (Mascot), Jason Geraghty, Robbie Gammons, Paul Sach.

match day programme 80p
1996-97
MAIDENHEAD
UNITED F.C.

MAIDENHEAD UNITED

Formed: 1870 **Nickname:** Magpies
Colours: Black & white stripes/black/red.
Change colours: Red/white/white
Midweek matchday: Tuesday **Reserve League:** Suburban.

Chairman: **Vice Chairman:** Jon Swan
Secretary: Ken Chandler, c/o Maidenhead United
Manager: Alan Devonshire **Press Off.:** Jon Swan (01628 473411)
Commercial Manager: Aviva Swan (011628 36314) **Physio:** Jhn Urry

GROUND Address: York Road, Maidenhead, Berks SL6 1SQ (01628 24739).
Directions: From Maidenhead BR station proceed eastwards down Bell St - grd 300yds. From bus station southwards down Bridge Ave to York Rd, turn right, grd 200yds on left.
Capacity: 3,500 **Cover:** 1,200 **Seats:** 350 **Floodlights:** Yes
Clubhouse: Open some evenings & matchdays. Some hot food.
Club Shop: Yes, wide range of programmes and club souvenirs. Contact Mark Smith (01753 854674). **Sponsors:** None
PREVIOUS - Leagues: Southern 1894-1902/ West Berks 02-04/ Great Western Suburban 04-22/ Spartan 22-39/Great Western Combination 39-45/ Corinthian 45-63/ Athenian 63-73.
Names: Maidenhead FC, Maidenhead Norfolkians. **Grounds:** None

PROGRAMME DETAILS:
Pages: 36 **Price:** £1
Editor: Mark Smith

CLUB RECORDS - Attendance: 7,920 v Southall, FA Amat Cup Q/F 7/3/36. **Career goalscorer:** George Copas 270, 1924-35. **Season's goalscorer:** Jack Palethorpe 66, 1929-30. **Career appearances:** Bert Randall 532, 1950-64. **Win:** 14-1 v Buckingham Town (H), FA Amat. Cup 6/9/52. **Defeat:** 0-14 v Chesham United (A), Spartan Lge 31/3/23. **Transfer fee paid:** £500 to Wycombe for Derek Harris, 1978. **Transfer fee received:** £5,000 from Norwich for Alan Cordice, 1979.

BEST SEASON - FA Cup: Quarter Finals 1873-74 74-75 75-76. **FA Trophy:** 3rd Qual Rd. **FA Amateur Cup:** Semi Final 35-36. **Players progressing to Football League:** A Cordice (Norwich 79), P Priddy (Brentford 72), D Kemp (Plymouth Portsmouth C Palace), L Sanchez (Reading, Wimbledon), E Kelsey, J Palethorpe (Reading 30), B Laryea (Torquay), R Davies (Torquay Reading).
96-97 - Captain: Trevor Roffey **P.o.Y.:** Gary Attrell **Top scorer:** Chuck Agudosi
Local Press: Maidenhead Advertiser, Reading Evening Post. **Local Radio:** 2-Ten FM, Star FM.
HONOURS: Isthmian Lg Div 2 Sth R-up 90-91, Full Members Cup 96-97; Spartan Lg(3) (R-up [2]); Corinthian Lg 57-58 60-61 61-62 (R-up 58-59 59-60, Mem. Shield 56-57 61-62, R-up (4), Neale Cup 48-49 57-58 60-61; Gt Western Suburban Lg 19-20 (R-up 20-21); Berks & Bucks Snr Cup(16), Berks & Bucks Benev. Cup(6) (R-up [2]); Mithras Cup R-up (4); Southern Comb. Cup R-up 81-82.

Back Row (L-R); Tyrone Houston, Francis Duku, Trevor Roffey, A Devonshire (Mgr), Dave Harrison, Kevin Brown, Andrew Eaton, James Parsons (Chr), R Goddard (Res Mgr).

Front Row; Steve Nott-Macaire, Micky Creighton, Brian Connor, Garry Attrell.

Ground; Obi Vlasi, Ben Abbey, Steve Brown.

MOLESEY

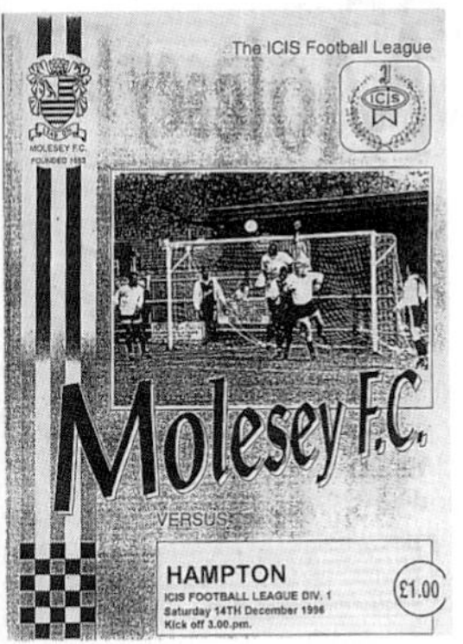

PROGRAMME DETAILS:
Pages: 44 **Price:** £1
Editor: Simon Carthew
c/o the club

Formed: 1950 **Nickname:** The Moles
Colours: White/black/black
Change colours: All Red
Midweek home matchday: Wednesday
Reserve Team's League: Suburban.

Chairman: Norman Clark **President:** Fred Maynard
Secretary/Press Officer: Ben O'Connor (c/o the club)
Manager: Clive Gartell **Coach:** Brian Sparrow
Reserve Manager: Ray Best

GROUND - Address: 412 Walton Road, West Molesey, Surrey KT8 0JG (0181 979 4823). **Directions:** A3 from London to Hook, then A309 to Marquis of Granby pub, right to Hampton Court station, turn left for West Molesey, ground one mile on left.
Capacity: 4,000 **Cover:** 600 **Seats:** 400 **Floodlights:** Yes
Clubhouse: Open every evening and weekend lunchtimes. 2 bars, discos, live artists, darts, bingo, pool. **Steward:** Carol White
Club Shop: Contact John Chambers.

PREVIOUS - Leagues: Surrey Intermediate 53-56, Surrey Snr 56-59, Spartan 59-72, Athenian 72-77. **Name:** Molesey St Pauls 1950-53.

CLUB RECORDS - Attendance: 1,255 v Sutton United, Surrey Senior Cup Semi-Final 1966. **Career Goalscorer:** Michael Rose, 139. **Career Appearances:** Frank Hanley, 453. **Transfer fee paid:** £500 for Chris Vidal (Leatherhead 88). **Transfer fee received:** £5,000 for Chris Vidal (Hythe Town 89).

BEST SEASON - FA Vase: 6th Rd 81-82. **FA Trophy:** 1st Rd replay 90-91.
FA Cup: First Round Proper 94-95 (0-4 at home to Bath City).

Players progressing to Football League: John Finch (Fulham), Cyrille Regis (WBA, Coventry & England).
Local Press: Surrey Comet, Surrey Herald, Molesey News. **Local Radio:** Thames 107.8 FM.
96-97 - Captain: Micky Dalton **P.o.Y.:** Jeremy Jones **Top Scorer:** Mark Wiggins

HONOURS: Isthmian Lg Div 1 R-up 92-93 (Div 2 South R-up 89-90, Lg Cup R-up 92-93), Surrey Senior Lg 57-58, (Lg Charity Cup 56-57), Spartan Lg R-up 59-60 (Lg Cup 61-62 (R-up 63-64)), Surrey Senior Shield R-up 74-75, Southern Combination Cup 90-91 94-95.

Back Row (L-R); Darren Le Tissier, Simon Connell, Kevin Cooper, Barry Gartell, Steve Shaw, David Smith, Chris James, Clive Martland (Physio). Front Row; Roddy Braithwaite, Geoff Taylor, Jeremy Jones, David Kempton, Nick Andrews, Mick Dalton (Capt). *Photo - Garry Letts*

ROMFORD

Reformed: 1992 **Nickname:** The Boro
Colours: Blue & old gold/blue/black
Change colours: Blue & black/black/black
Midweek home matchday: Tuesday (7.45)
Reserve Team's League: Essex & Herts Border West
Club Call: 0891 664 387

Life President: Ron Walker **Chairman:** Bradley Goodwin
Vice-Chairman: Steve Gardener
Secretary: Alan Weatherall, Tel: 0181 593 2182
General Manager: John Goodwin **Team Manager:** Les Whitton
Press Officer: David Fletcher. Tel: 0956 528829
Commercial Manager: John Barrington
Director of Football: Don McGovern
Coach: Don Calder **Physio:** Allen Hyde

PROGRAMME DETAILS:
Pages: 44 **Price:** £1.20
Editor: David Fletcher
Tel: 0956 528829

GROUND - Address: 'Sungate', Collier Row Road, Collier Row, Romford, Essex. Tel: 01708 722766. **Directions:** Take the A12 from London as far as the Moby Dick junction. Turn left and then right at the 1st roundabout into Collier Row Road. The ground entrance is signposted 200 yards on the right. Nearest station is Romford (BR). From directly outside the station the London bus 247 passes within 50 yards of the ground.
Capacity: 2,000 **Cover:** 550 **Seats:** 150 **Floodlights:** Yes
Clubhouse: Open seven days a week 11am - 11pm. **Sponsors:** Carlsberg
Club Shop: Open matchdays, selling replica shirts, programmes etc. Contact Barry Quantrill 01708 705755.

PREVIOUS - **Names:** Romford FC was formed in 1876 but folded in the Great War. The club reformed in 1929 and continued until 1978. In 1992 the club restarted and last season merged with Collier Row - both names being used for that season only. They changed their name in 1997 to Romford.
Leagues: Essex Senior 92-96 **Grounds:** Hornchurch 92-95, Ford United 95-96, Sungate 96-

CLUB RECORDS - Attendance: 820 v Leatherhead (IL2) 15/4/97. **Goalscorer:** Micky Ross 61. **Individual:** Martin Hayes 29 (96-97). **Appearances:** Micky Ross. **Win:** 9-0 v Hullbridge (H) ESL 21/10/95. **Defeat:** 1-7 v St Albans (A) EAC 29/10/96. **Transfer fee paid:** Four figure fee for Wade Falana (Braintree) June 97. **Transfer fee received:** None

BEST SEASON - **FA Cup:** 3rd Qual Rd 94-95 95-96 v St Albans (1-0, 3-1).
FA Vase: 5th Rd 96-97 v Bedlington Terriers 2-1

Local Press: Romford Recorder, Barking & Dagenham Post. **Local Radio:** Essex Radio.
96-97 - Captain: Paul Evans **P.O.Y.:** Paul Evans **Top scorer:** Martin Hayes (29)
HONOURS: Essex Senior Lge Champ 95-96, Lge Cup 95-96; Isthmian Div 2 Champ 96-97.

Martin Hayes, last season's top goalscorer, seen here going past Warren Teasdale of Bedlington Terriers in the FA Vase.
Photo: Roger Turner

PROGRAMME DETAILS:
Pages: 44 **Price:** £1
Editor: Sec. & Stuart Moore
(01784 421118)

STAINES TOWN

Formed: 1892 **Nickname:** The Swans
Colours: Old gold (blue trim)/royal/royal
Change colours: All white.
Midweek matchday: Tuesday
Reserve league: Suburban (since 72).

Chairman: Alan Boon **President:** Nigel Iggulden
Vice Chairman: Ken Williams **Secretary:** Steve Parsons, 3 Birch Green, Staines, Middx TW18 4HA (01784 450420).
Manager: Chris Wainwright **Asst Manager:** Keith Bristow
Physio: Mick Minter/Jug Stephen **Commercial Mgr:** Ken Williams
Press Officer: Stuart Moore (01784 421118)

GROUND - Address: Chertsey Town FC. Alwyns Lane, Chertsey, Surrey KT16 9DW (01932 561774). **Directions:** Alwyns Lane is off Windsor St N end of shopping centre. 10 mins Chertsey (BR).
Capacity: 3,000 **Cover:** 1000 **Seats:** 250 **Floodlights:** Yes
Club HQ & Clubhouse: Staines Town FC, Wheatsheaf Lane, Staines (01784 450420). Fully furnished clubhouse & function hall, open 7-11 matchdays and every evening. Rolls and other snacks available.
Club Shop: Souvenirs available from Harry Trim, 23 Grosvenor Rd, Staines, Middx TW18 2RN. **Sponsors:** Barratt Homes.

PREVIOUS - Leagues: W London All (pre-1900), W London, W Middx (pre-1905), Gt Western Suburban 05-13 20-24, Gt Western Comb, Munitions Lg (World War 1), London Works (World War 1), Hounslow & Dist 19-20, Spartan 24-35 58-71, Middx Sen 43-52/ Parthenon 52-53, Hellenic 53-58, Athenian 71-73. **Names:** Staines Albany and St Peters Institute (merged) in 1895, Staines 05-18, Staines Lagonda 18-25, Staines Vale (2nd World War). **Grounds:** Edgell Rd (St Peters Inst); The Lammas, Shortwood Common, Mill Mead (Hammonds/Wicks/Pursers Farm); Shepperton Road (to 51); Wheatsheaf Lane (51-96) still open for non-sen fixtures.

CLUB RECORDS - Attendance: 2,750 v Banco di Roma (Barassi Cup) 1975 *(70,000 saw 1st leg in Rome).* **Goalscorer:** Alan Gregory 122 **Appearances:** Dickie Watmore 840 **Win:** 14-0 v Croydon (A), Isthmian League Div. 1 19/3/94. **Defeat:** 1-18 v Wycombe Wanderers (A), G West Sub Lge 1909. **Fee Paid:** For R Teale (Slough 81) **Fee Received:** For Scott Taylor (Millwall 95-96).

Best Season - FA Amateur Cup: 3rd Rd 23-24. **FA Trophy:** 2nd Rd 2nd Replay 76-77. **FA Cup:** 1st Rd 84-85 (0-2 at Burton Alb) & 1879-80 & 80-81 (as St Peters Institute).

Players progressing to Football League: R Bennett (Southend 72), J Love (C Palace 75), P Shaw (Charlton 77), E Young (Wolves), G Hill (Millwall), W Stemp (Brighton), M Ferney (Fulham), S Taylor (Millwall & Bolton W).

96-97 - Captain: Mark Fleming **P.o.Y.:** Mark Fleming **Top scorer:** John Gasson

HONOURS: Isthmian Lg Div 1 74-75 88-89 (Div 2 74-75); Athenian Lg Div 2 71-72 (Div 1 R-up 72-73); Spartan Lg 59-60 (R-up 70-71), Lg Cup 68-69 (R-up 60-61 70-71); Hellenic Lg R-up 55-56 (Lg Cup R-up 53-54 55-56); Gt Western Suburban Lg Div 1 R-up 11-12 22-24 (Div 2 (Middx) 20-21); W London All Div 1 1899-1900; W London Lg Div 1 00-01; W Middx Lg 04-05 (R-up 03-04); London Snr Cup R-up 76-77 80-81; Middx Snr Cup(7), (R-up 09-10 32-33 79-80), Snr Charity Cup 94-95; Barassi Cup 76; Southern Comb. Chall. Cup 64-65 66-67 68-69 94-95 96-97,(R-up 67-68 94-95); W Middx Cup 23-24; Staines Cottage Hosp Cup 24-25; Merthyr Middx Charity Shield 90-91,(R-up 94-95); El Canuelo Trophy 92-93 94-95 94-95; Carlsberg Cup 94-95; Melksham Middx Charity Shield 96-97.

Staines Town FC *Photo - F T Lawrence*

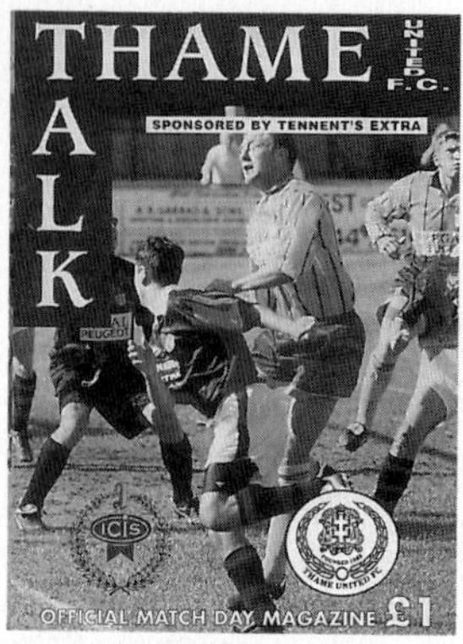

THAME UNITED

Founded: 1883 **Nickname:** United
Colours: Red & black halves/black/red & black hoops.
Change colours: Black & white
Midweek Matchday: Tuesday
Reserves' League: Suburban (West)

Chairman: Jim Tite **Vice Chairman:** Paul K Smith
Secretary: Neil Crocker, 8 Lincoln Place, Thame, Oxford OX9 2ER (01844 213568)
Press Officer: Neil Crocker
Manager: Bob Pratley
Asst Man: Malcolm McIntosh **Physio:** Chris Perkins

GROUND Address: Windmill Road, Thame, Oxon OX9 2DR (01844 213017).
Directions: Into Nelson Street from Market Square. 3 miles from Haddenham & Thame Parkway (BR). Nearest bus stop at Town Hall (half mile away).
Capacity: 2,500 **Seats:** 230 **Cover:** 400 **Floodlights:** Yes
Clubhouse: Open every evening and weekend lunchtimes. Banquetting facilities for 200 (weddings, dinners, dances etc).
Club Shop: No
Sponsors: Tennents Extra

PROGRAMME DETAILS:
Pages: 24 **Price:** £1
Editor: Sally Turner (c/o Club)

PREVIOUS - **Leagues:** Oxon Senior; Hellenic 1959-87; South Midlands 1987-91.
Name: Thame FC.

CLUB RECORDS - **Attendance:** 1,035 v Aldershot, Isthmian Div 2 4/4/94.
Win: 9-0 v Bracknell, 31/10/92
Defeat: 2-11 v Hungerford, FA Cup Prelim. Rd 1984.
Career Goalscorer: Not known
Career Appearances: Steve Mayhew.

BEST SEASON - **FA Cup:** Third Qualifying Round 91-92 (lost 0-4 to Salisbury).

96-97 - Captain: **P.o.Y.** **Top scorer:**
Local Press: Oxford Mail, Thame Gazette, Bucks Free Press. **Local Radio:** BBC Radio Oxford, Fox FM.
HONOURS: Isthmian Lg Div 3 R-up 92-93, Isthmian Lg Div 2 winners 94-95, Hellenic Lg 61-62 69-70 (Premier Div Cup(4)), Sth Mids Lg 90-91, Oxon Snr Cup 1894-95 05-06 08-09 09-10 75-76 80-81 92-93, Oxon Intermediate Cup 76-77 78-79 91-92, Oxon Charity Cup.

Thame United FC: *Photo - Steve Wheeler*

UXBRIDGE

UXBRIDGE F.C.
125 Year Anniversary
OFFICIAL PROGRAMME
SEASON 1996-97
ICIS LEAGUE DIVISION ONE
CANVEY ISLAND
SATURDAY 9th NOVEMBER 1996
KICK-OFF 3.00PM £1.00
MAIN SPONSOR DAGENHAM MOTORS OF UXBRIDGE

PROGRAMME DETAILS:
Pages: 48-56 **Price:** £1.00
Editor: A Peart (01895 443094)
& Roy Green (01895 254784)

Formed: 1871 **Nickname:** The Reds
Colours: Red/white/red
Change colours: Sky & navy blue **OR** White and black
Midweek matchday: Tuesday
Reserves' League: Suburban (North Division).

Chairman: Alan Holloway **Vice-Chairman:** Tom Barnard
Joint President: Tom Barnard & Alan Odell.
Secretary: Graham Hiseman, 96 New Peachey Lane, Cowley, Uxbridge, Middx UB8 3SY (01895 237195).
Press Officer: Andy Peart (01895 443094)
Commercial Manager: Trevor Birch (0181 561 1789)
Manager: George Talbot **Coach:** Micky Nicks **Physio:** Ernie Kempster

GROUND - Address: Honeycroft, Horton Road, West Drayton, Middx UB7 8HX (01895 445830). **Directions:** From West Drayton (BR) turn right then 1st right (Horton Road). Ground 1 mile on left. From Uxbridge (LT) take 222 or U3 bus to West Drayton station, then follow as above. By road, ground 1 mile north of M4 jct 4 taking road to Uxbridge and leaving by first junction and turning left into Horton Rd - ground 500yds on right.
Capacity: 3,770 **Cover:** 760 **Seats:** 339 **Floodlights:** Yes
Clubhouse: (01895 443557). Large clubhouse with bar and function room available for hire. Open every evening and weekend/bank holiday lunchtimes. Hot & cold snacks available on matchdays.
Club Shop: Good selection of souvenirs & programmes. Contact secretary. **Sponsor:** Dagenham Motors

PREVIOUS - Leagues: Southern 1894-99, Gt Western Suburban 1906-19 20-23, Athenian 1919-20 24-37 63-82, Spartan 37-38, London 38-46, Gt Western Comb. 39-45, Corinthian 46-63. **Name:** Uxbridge Town 23-45. **Grounds:** RAF Stadium 23-48, Cleveland Rd 48-78.

CLUB RECORDS - Attendance: 1,000 v Arsenal, floodlight opening 1981. **Career Scorer:** Phil Duff, 153. **Career Appearances:** Roger Nicholls, 1054. **Win:** Unknown. **Defeat:** Unknown. **Transfer fee received:** Unknown. **Transfer fee paid:** Unknown

BEST SEASON - FA Trophy: 1st Rd replay 88-89. **FA Vase:** 4th Rd 83-84. **FA Cup:** 2nd Rd 1873-74. 1st Rd on three other occasions 1883-84 84-85 85-86. **FA Amateur Cup:** Runners-up 1897-98
Players progressing to Football League: William Hill (QPR 1951), Lee Stapleton (Fulham 1952), Gary Churchouse (Charlton A.), Tony Witter (QPR), Guy Butters (Spurs), Michael Meaker (QPR).
96-97 - Captain: Gary Downes **P.o.Y.:** Kevin Cleary **Top Scorer:** Nicky Ryder (25)
Local Press: Uxbridge Gazette & Leader, Uxbridge Recorder. **Local Radio:** Capital, G L R, Star FM.

HONOURS: FA Amateur Cup R-up 1897-98, London Challenge Cup 93-94, Isthmian Lge Div 2 S. R-up 84-85 (Lge Cup R-up 85-86), Athenian Lge Cup R-up 81-82, Res. Section 69-70, Res. Cup 68-69), Corinthian League 59-60 (R-up 48-49, Lge Memorial Shield 50-51 52-53), Middx Senior Cup 1893-94 95-96 1950-51, Middx Senior Charity Cup 07-08 12-13 35-36 81-82 (R-up 69-70 82-83 85-86), Middx Prem Cup R-up 95-96, Allied Counties Yth Lge 92-93 (Lge Cup R-up 86-87, Lge Shield 88-89 92-93), AC Delco Cup R-up 85-86, Suburban Lge North Div Champions 95-96.

Uxbridge FC: *Photo - Andrew Chitty*

PROGRAMME DETAILS:
Pages: 28 **Price:** £1
Editor: Richard Markiewicz
(0181 902 0541 - before 9pm)

WEMBLEY

Formed: 1946. **Nickname:** The Lions
Colours: Red & white/red/red
Change colours: Yellow & navy/navy/navy
Midweek matchday: Tuesday
Reserves' League: Suburban

Chairman: Brian Gumm **President:** Jim Bryan, BEM
Vice Chairman: Eric Stringer **General Manager:** Glen Charles.
Press Officer: Richard Markiewicz (0181 902 0541 before 9pm)
Commercial Manager:
Secretary: Mrs Jean Gumm, 14 Woodfield Avenue, North Wembley, Middx HA0 3NR (0181 908 3353).
Manager: John Walsh **Asst. Manager:** Paul Shields.

GROUND Address: Vale Farm, Watford Road, Sudbury, Wembley HA0 4UR (0181 908 8169).
Directions: Sudbury Town station (Underground) 400 yds, or 10 mins walk from North Wembley (BR) station. Buses 18, 92, 245 & 182.
Capacity: 2,000 **Cover:** 350 **Seats:** 350 **Floodlights:** Yes
Clubhouse: (0181 904 8169). Open every night & weekend lunchtimes. Hot food on matchdays.
Club Shop: No **Sponsors:** G & B Builders.

PREVIOUS - Leagues: Middx 46-49, Spartan 49-51, Delphian 51-56, Corinthian 56-63, Athenian 63-75.
CLUB RECORDS - Attendance: 2,654 v Wealdstone, FA Amateur Cup 52-53.
Career goalscorer: Bill Handrahan 105 (1946-52)
Career appearances: Spud Murphy 505 (78-88).
Win: 11-1 v Hermes, London Senior Cup 1963.
Defeat: 0-16 v Chelsea, London Challenge Cup 59-60.
Transfer fee paid: Nil
Transfer fee received: £10,000 for Gary Roberts (Brentford, 1981).
BEST SEASON - FA Cup: 1st Round Proper 1980-81 (lost 0-3 at Enfield).
FA Trophy: 1st Round proper 91-92 **FA Amateur Cup:** 2nd Round 66-67, 68-69
Players progressing to Football League: Keith Cassells (Watford 1977), Mike O'Donague (Southampton 1979), A McGonigle (Olympiakos), Gary Roberts (Brentford 1980), Richard Cadette (Orient 1984).
96-97 - Captain: Ian Bates **P.o.Y:** Kevin Beckles **Top Scorer:** Keith Boreham
Local Press: Wembley & Harrow Observer. **Local Radio:**

HONOURS: Middx Sen Cup 83-84 86-87 (R-up 55-56 68-69 78-79 87-88 91-92 92-93); Middx Lge 47-48 (Lge Cup 46-47), Middx Charity Cup 67-68(jnt) 80-81 (jnt) 82-83 86-87 94-95,(R-up 83-84 87-88 96-97); Middx Invitation Cup 56-57; Athenian Lge R-up 74-75 (Div 1 R-up 67-68); Corinthian Lge Mem Shield R-up 58-59; Delphian Lge R-up 55-56; Spartan Lge Div 1 West 50-51 (Dunkel Trophy 50-51 jnt); London Sen Cup R-up 55-56; Hitachi Cup SF 83-84; Suburban Lge North 85-86, Lge Cup 84-85 (R-up 83-84).

Wembley FC *Photo - Andrew Chitty*

PROGRAMME DETAILS:
Pages: 36 **Price:** 70p
Editor: Warren Filmer
(0181 660 3255)

WHYTELEAFE

Formed: 1946 **Nickname:** Leafe
Colours: Green & white/white/white
Change colours: Yellow/green.
Midweek matchday: Tuesday
Reserve Team's League: Suburban.

Chairman: Paul Owens **President:** A F Lidbury
Secretary: Ian Robertson, 253 Godstone Road, Whyteleafe, Surrey. CR3 0BD. 01883 622096 (H&B)
Press Officer: Peter Stimpson 01883 348310 (H)
Commercial Manager: Paul Owens
Manager: Lee Richardson **Assistant Man.:** B Donnelly
Coach: Bernie Donnelly **Physio:** J Knapton

GROUND Address: 15 Church Road, Whyteleafe, Surrey CR3 0AR. Tel: 0181 660 5491 *(Ground)* 0181 645 0422 *(Boardroom).*
Directions: Five minutes walk from Whyteleafe (BR) - turn right from station, and left into Church Road.
Capacity: 5,000 **Cover:** 600 **Seats:** 200 **Floodlights:** Yes
Clubhouse: Open every lunchtime and evening. Hot and cold food, pool, darts, gaming machines.
Clubshop: **Sponsors:** Sunday Sport.

PREVIOUS - **Leagues:** Caterham & Edenbridge, Croydon, Thornton Heath & Dist., Surrey Intermediate (East) 54-58, Surrey Senior 58-75, Spartan 75-81, Athenian 81-84.

CLUB RECORDS - **Attendance:** 780
Transfer fee paid: £1,000 for Gary Bowyer (Carshalton)
Transfer fee received: £25,000 for Steve Milton.

BEST SEASON - **FA Vase:** 5th Rd 80-81 85-86. **FA Trophy:** 3rd Qualifying Rd 89-90. **FA Cup:** Third Qualifying Round replay (lost 1-2 after 1-1 draw at Wokingham Town).
Players progressing to Football League: Steve Milton (Fulham).

96-97 - Captain: **P.o.Y.:** **Top scorer:**
Local Press: Croydon Advertiser.
HONOURS: Isthmian League Div 2 South R-up 88-89; Surrey Senior League 68-69 (League Cup R-up 68-69, League Charity Cup 71-72, Reserve Section 62-63 (Challenge Cup 62-63 (R-up 59-60); Surrey Senior Cup 68-69 (R-up 87-88); Surrey Premier Cup R-up 84-85; East Surrey Charity Cup 79-80 (R-up 76-77 77-78); Thornton Heath & Dist League 51-52 (League Cup 51-52, Div 4 R-up 51-52); Edenbridge Charity Cup 51-52; Caterham & Purley Hospital Cup 51-52; Surrey County Intermediate League East Section 1 55-56; Surrey Junior Cup R-up 51-52; Caterham & Edenbridge League Div 3 51-52; Borough of Croydon Charity Cup 56-57; Southern Yth League 89-90 (R-up 88-89, League Cup 88-89 89-90); Southern Count Midweek Floodlit cup 95-96.

Whyteleafe FC: Back Row (L-R); B Donnelly (Ast Mgr), N Hopkins, D Forbes, N Pearson, G Elliott, N Golley, M Smart, D Rose, P Gates, I Paterson, J Knapton (Physio), L Richardson (Mgr). Front Row; D Davenport, D Alger, D Carson, S Milton, M Dodman, A Moore, G Thornton. *Photo - Garry Letts*

WOKINGHAM TOWN

Formed: 1875 **Nickname:** The Town
Colours: Yellow & black/black/black
Change colours: Red/white/red.
Midweek matchday: Tuesday
Reserves' League: Suburban

Chairman: P Walsh **President:** G Gale.
Vice Chairman: R Harrison
Secretary: John Aulsberry, 8 Paice Green, Wokingham RG40 1YN (01189 790441).
Commercial Manager: Roy Merryweather (01189 780253).
Managers: Derek Cottrell & Wayne Wanklyn. **Physio:** Dave Lane
GROUND Address: Town Ground, Finchampstead Road, Wokingham, Berks RG40 2NR (01189 780377).
Directions: Half mile from town centre on A321 (signed Camberley & Sandhurst) Finchampstead Rd - walk down Denmark Street to swimming pool and straight on onto Finchampstead Rd. Half mile from Wokingham (BR) - turn right out of station, walk along Wellington Rd to swimming pool, right into Finchampstead Rd - ground entrance on right immediately after railway bridge.
Capacity: 3,500 **Cover:** 1,500 **Seats:** 300 **Floodlights:** Yes
Clubhouse: Mon-Sat 12-3 & 7-11pm (12-3 & 4.30-11pm Sat matchdays), Sun 12-2.30pm. Hot & cold food & snacks.

PROGRAMME DETAILS:
Pages: 32 **Price:** £1
Editor: Mrs Anne Gale (c/o the club)

Club Shop: Range of club souvenirs. Contact Brian & Sue McKeown at club. **Sponsors:** Higgs & Hill Homes.

PREVIOUS - **Leagues:** Reading & Dist./ Great Western Comb 07-54/ Metropolitan 54-57/ Delphian 57-59/ Corinthian 59-63/ Athenian 63-73. **Grounds:** Oxford Road 1875-1883/ Wellington Road 83-96/ Langborough Rd 96-1906.

CLUB RECORDS - **Attendance:** 3,473 v Norton Woodseats, FA Amateur Cup 57-58. **Career Goalscorer:** Dave Pearce, 79. **Career Appearances:** Dave Cox, 533. **Transfer fee paid:** £5,000 for Fred Hyatt (Burnham, 1990). **Transfer fee received:** £25,000 for Mark Harris (C Palace 88).

BEST SEASON - **FA Cup:** 1st Rd replay 82-83, 0-3 v Cardiff (A) after 1-1. - **League clubs defeated:** None.
FA Trophy: Semi finals 87-88 **FA Amateur Cup:** 4th Rd 57-58

Players progressing to Football League: Ian Kirkwood (Reading 53), John Harley (Hartlepool 76), Kirk Corbin (Cambridge 78), Phil Alexander (Norwich 81), Doug Hatcher (Aldershot 83), Steven Butler & George Torrance (Brentford 84), Mark Harris (C Palace 88), Gary Smart (Oxford 88), Darren Barnard (Chelsea 90), Paul Holsgrove (Luton Town 91), Darron Wilkinson (Brighton) 92.

96-97 - Captain: Andy Russell **P.o.Y.:** Barry Miller **Top scorer:** Andy Gray (18)
Local Press: Wokingham Times, Wokingham News, Reading Evening Post. **Local Radio:** 210 FM

HONOURS: Isthmian Lg R-up 89-90 (Div 1 81-82, Full Members Cup R-up 94-95), Berks & Bucks Snr Cup 68-69 82-83 84-85 95-96, Berks & Bucks Intermediate Cup 52-53.

Tony Gribben of Wokingham clears from Paul Gorman (stripes) of Fisher In the FA Trophy. Photo: Alan Coomes

WORTHING

PROGRAMME DETAILS:
Pages: 48 **Price:** £1
Editor: Neil Wycherley

Formed: 1886 **Nickname:** The Rebels
Colours: Red with blue & white trim/red/red.
Change colours: All blue
Midweek matches: Tuesday.

Chairman: Beau Reynolds **President:** Morty Hollis
Vice Chairman: Ray Smith **Press Officer:** Morty Hollis Tel: 01903 762406
Secretary: Paul Damper, 19 Fletcher Road, Worthing, West Sussex BN14 8EX.
Commercial Manager: David Groom Tel. 01425 638129
Manager: Brian Donnelly
Physio: Andy Neal **Asst Manager:** Glen Geard

GROUND Address: Woodside Road, Worthing, West Sussex BN14 7HQ (01903 239575).
Directions: Follow A24 to town, at end of Broadwater Rd having gone over railway bridge, take 1st right into Teville Rd, take right into South Farm RD, 2nd left into Pavilion Rd, Woodside Rd is first right. Half a mile from Worthing (BR).
Capacity: 4,500 **Seats:** 450 **Cover:** 1,000 **Floodlights:** Yes
Clubhouse: Open two hours before kick-off and closes 11pm. Hot & cold food available.
Shop: Sells a good range of souvenirs & programmes. Open matchdays.
Sponsors: Wessex Cleaning

PREVIOUS - Leagues: West Sussex Sen 1896-04 05-14 19-20/ Brighton, Hove & Dist 19-20/ Sussex County 20-40 45-48/ Corinthian 48-63/ Athenian 63-77.
Grounds: Homefield Park, Beach House Park **Names:** None

CLUB RECORDS - Attendance: 4,500 v Depot Battalion Royal Engineers, FA Amtr Cup 07-08. **Transfer fee paid:** £1,000 for Steve Guille (Bognor Regis Tn 89). **Transfer fee received:** £7,500 for Tim Read (Woking, 1990). **Win:** 25-0 v Littlehampton (H) West Sussex Lge 1911-12. **Defeat:** 0-14 v Southwick (A), Sussex County Lge 1946-47. **Career Goalscorer:** Mick Edmonds 275. **Career Appearances:** Geoff Raynsford

BEST SEASON - FA Vase: 5th Rd 78-79. **FA Trophy:** 3rd Rd Replay 85-86. **FA Amateur Cup:** Quarter-Final replay 07-08. **FA Cup:** 2nd Rd 82-83, (0-4 to Oxford Utd), 1st Rd 36-37, 94-95, (1-3 v AFC Bournemouth).

Players progressing to Football League: Ken Suttle (Chelsea 1948), Alan Arnell & Fred Perry (Liverpool 1954), Craig Whitington (Scarborough, via Crawley Town) 1993, Darren Freeman (Gillingham), Paul Musselwhite (Scunthorpe,Port Vale), Trevor Wood (Port Vale,Walsall), Richard Tiltman (Brighton).

96-97 - Captain: Graham Waller **P.o.Y.:** Graham Waller **Top scorer:** Simon Funnell
Local Press: Evening Argus, Worthing Herald. **Local Radio:** Southern FM.

HONOURS: Isthmian Lg R-up(2) 83-85 (Div 1 82-83, Div 2 81-82 92-93); Athenian Lg Div 1 R-up 63-64, Div 2 R-up 71-72, Lg Cup R-up 72-73, Mem. Shield R-up 63-64; Sussex Snr Cup (20); Sussex RUR Char. Cup (13); Sussex Co. Lg(8) 20-22 26-27 28-29 30-31 33-34 38-40; W Sussex Lg (7); Brighton Char. Cup(9) 29-31 34-35 62-63 69-71 73-74(jt) 80-82; Worthing Char. Cup (10); AFA Invit. Cup 63-64 68-69 73-74 75-76 (Snr Cup R-up 36-37 46-47 48-49); Corinth. Lg Mem. Shield R-up 49-50 (Neale Tphy 58-59); Roy Hayden Mem. Tphy 75(jt), 77 78; Don Morecraft Tphy 72 73 76 81 82; Sussex F'lit Cup(2) 88-90; Sussex I'mediate Cup 34-35 64-65; Brighton Chal. Shield 29-30 31-32.

DIVISION TWO LEAGUE TABLE 1996-97

			Home			Away					
		P	W	D	L	W	D	L	F	A	Pts
1	Collier Row & Romford	42	16	3	2	12	9	0	93	33	96
2	Leatherhead	42	15	3	3	15	2	4	116	45	95
3	Wembley	42	12	5	4	11	6	4	92	45	80
4	Barking	42	13	5	3	9	8	4	69	40	79
5	Horsham	42	14	2	5	8	9	4	78	48	77
6	Edgware Town	42	9	8	4	11	6	4	74	50	74
7	Bedford Town	42	10	3	8	11	5	5	77	43	71
8	Banstead Athletic	42	9	3	9	12	2	7	75	52	68
9	Windsor & Eton	42	8	9	4	9	4	8	65	62	64
10	Leighton Town	42	12	6	3	5	6	10	64	52	63
11	Bracknell Town	42	9	8	4	8	1	12	78	71	60
12	Wivenhoe Town	42	7	6	8	10	3	8	69	62	60
13	Chalfont St Peter	42	9	7	5	5	6	10	53	61	55
14	Hungerford Town	42	8	9	4	6	4	11	68	77	55
15	Metropolitan Police	42	9	2	10	5	5	11	72	75	49
16	Tilbury	42	4	6	11	10	1	10	68	77	49
17	Witham Town	42	4	6	11	7	4	10	39	67	43
18	Egham Town	42	7	3	11	3	6	12	47	86	39
19	Cheshunt	42	4	2	15	5	1	15	37	101	30
20	Ware	42	5	3	13	2	5	14	44	80	29
21	Dorking	42	5	1	15	2	5	14	40	100	27
22	Hemel Hempstead	42	1	2	18	4	4	13	34	125	21

RESULTS GRID 1996-97

HOME TEAM	1	2	3	4	5	6	7	8	9	10	11	12	13	14	15	16	17	18	19	20	21	22
1. Banstead	*	0-1	1-2	0-3	3-1	4-2	2-2	3-0	1-2	2-0	3-0	1-1	5-2	1-2	0-0	1-2	2-3	2-0	1-0	3-0	1-2	1-2
2. Barking	1-1	*	0-0	2-1	1-2	4-0	0-1	4-2	1-1	2-0	2-1	1-0	4-0	2-1	3-1	1-0	2-2	1-0	2-2	1-3	1-0	3-0
3. Bedford	2-3	0-0	*	5-4	1-2	6-0	0-1	1-1	0-3	1-0	1-0	0-1	2-0	3-0	2-1	0-0	1-0	4-1	1-3	1-2	3-0	1-3
4. Bracknell	1-0	2-2	2-1	*	1-1	0-0	0-0	3-2	1-2	6-1	7-1	0-0	3-3	2-4	0-0	4-4	5-1	4-3	1-2	2-0	5-1	0-3
5. Chalfont	0-2	0-1	2-1	1-1	*	4-0	2-2	1-1	0-1	2-0	0-0	1-1	1-3	0-3	2-1	3-0	2-1	3-2	0-0	11	2-0	2-1
6. Cheshunt	0-2	1-1	0-4	0-3	1-0	*	0-1	4-2	1-3	0-1	0-1	0-2	3-5	2-5	0-1	1-0	2-5	2-2	1-4	1-2	1-0	1-2
7. Collier R & R	2-0	2-4	1-1	1-0	3-0	1-0	*	3-1	2-3	3-0	9-2	1-1	3-0	2-1	4-1	2-1	4-2	1-0	1-0	2-0	0-0	4-0
8. Dorking	0-3	0-4	0-3	2-1	0-3	3-1	0-2	*	1-6	0-2	2-3	3-3	0-3	0-3	1-0	2-0	0-2	0-2	1-2	0-2	0-3	2-1
9. Edgware	4-1	0-0	3-0	0-1	1-0	3-1	1-1	2-0	*	1-1	4-0	1-1	1-1	2-3	1-1	1-2	1-0	3-6	1-1	1-1	1-0	2-0
10. Egham	0-4	4-1	0-3	3-2	4-2	0-2	0-3	2-1	1-1	*	0-0	2-1	3-0	1-4	12	1-3	1-4	1-0	0-6	0-1	2-2	1-3
11. Hemel H	0-2	0-2	0-6	0-4	0-1	2-3	0-4	1-5	0-1	1-1	*	2-1	0-1	0-3	0-1	1-4	2-4	0-0	1-4	1-4	0-1	1-4
12. Horsham	3-2	0-0	0-2	4-1	4-0	1-0	1-2	5-0	1-0	1-0	5-1	*	3-1	1-2	3-1	1-1	0-1	3-2	4-2	3-1	6-3	0-2
13. Hungerford	1-3	3-1	2-3	1-0	1-1	2-1	1-1	1-0	2-2	6-4	3-0	0-3	*	0-4	0-0	3-0	4-2	2-2	1-1	0-0	1-1	1-1
14. Leatherhead	3-1	0-1	0-2	4-1	7-0	3-1	2-2	3-0	5-1	4-0	9-0	1-1	2-0	*	2-0	3-0	5-2	2-1	1-1	4-2	0-3	1-0
15. Leighton	2-1	0-3	1-1	2-0	1-0	4-1	2-2	4-0	5-2	2-1	5-0	1-1	2-2	2-2	*	2-0	2-3	3-1	1-2	1-1	2-0	2-1
16. Met Police	0-1	4-0	1-1	4-0	2-0	3-0	0-4	5-1	2-4	2-1	10-4	1-2	2-3	2-4	0-1	*	1-4	0-0	3-2	3-1	2-3	0-2
17. Tilbury	0-0	1-1	2-1	0-1	2-2	1-2	0-4	3-0	0-2	1-1	1-1	2-3	1-1	0-1	1-3	2-1	*	3-1	0-1	1-2	1-2	2-4
18. Ware	0-1	0-0	0-0	0-2	0-4	0-1	0-2	1-0	2-1	1-2	1-1	0-1	2-4	3-2	2-1	4-1	1-3	*	0-4	0-1	0-2	0-3
19. Wembley	4-3	1-2	3-1	4-0	2-0	7-0	2-2	1-1	1-1	1-0	4-2	1-2	3-1	0-2	2-2	1-3	3-1	3-1	*	3-0	0-0	3-0
20. Windsor & E	0-2	2-0	0-4	1-2	2-2	6-0	2-2	1-1	2-2	1-1	2-0	1-1	2-1	1-4	2-0	2-2	4-3	3-1	1-1	*	2-1	1-1
21. Witham	0-1	0-5	0-4	0-1	2-2	1-0	0-1	1-3	0-0	2-2	1-3	0-1	2-0	1-4	0-0	1-0	1-0	1-1	0-3	2-3	*	0-0
22. Wivenhoe	2-5	2-2	0-2	6-1	1-1	0-1	1-3	2-2	1-2	2-2	0-2	5-2	3-2	1-1	2-1	1-1	0-1	3-1	0-2	1-0	3-0	*

DIVISION TWO	10 YEAR RECORD							ICIS LEAGUE		
No of clubs competing N - Div. 2 North, S - Div. 2 South	87/8 (22N&S)	88/9 (22N,21S)	89/0 (22N,21S)	90/1 (22N&S)	91/2 (22)	92/3 (22)	93/4 (22)	94/5 (22)	95/6 (21)	96/7 (22)
Abingdon Town	-	-	3S	1S	-	-	-	-	-	-
Aldershot Town	-	-	-	-	-	-	3	-	-	-
Aveley	21N	9N	2N	-	-	-	10	21	-	-
Banstead Athletic	21S	16S	11S	11S	14	13	9	8	4	8
Barking	-	-	-	-	-	-	-	-	-	4
Barton Rovers	15N	8N	5N	10N	11	18	4	2	-	-
Basildon United	-	-	7N	18N	-	-	-	-	-	-
Bedford Town	-	-	-	-	-	-	-	-	8	7
Berkhamsted Town	4N	15N	17N	5N	18	3	-	-	-	-
Billericay Town	-	6N	15N	3N	3	-	-	-	-	-
Bracknell Town	-	-	-	-	-	-	-	4	9	11
Camberley Town	19S	14S	17S	22S	-	-	-	-	-	-
Canvey Island	-	-	-	-	-	-	-	-	1	-
Chalfont St Peter	1S	-	-	-	-	-	-	10	13	13
Chertsey Town	6S	12S	13S	14S	-	7	2	-	-	-
Cheshunt	-	-	-	-	-	-	-	15	16	19
Clapton	13N	7N	12N	20N	-	-	-	-	-	-
Collier Row & Romford	2N	-	8N	12N	-	-	21	-	5	1
Cove	-	-	-	19S	-	-	-	-	-	-
Croydon	-	-	-	-	-	-	-	7	2	-
Dorking Town	3S	1S	-	-	-	-	-	-	21	21
Eastbourne United	12S	11S	16S	20S	-	-	-	-	-	-
Edgware Town	-	-	-	14N	-	11	11	13	10	6
Egham Town	14S	10S	10S	3S	6	12	14	17	18	18
Epsom & Ewell	5S	9S	14S	13S	-	-	-	-	-	-
Feltham	4S	8S	18S	18S	-	-	-	-	-	-
Finchley	12N	3S	18N	21N	-	-	-	-	-	-
Flackwell Heath	20S	13S	8S	16S	-	-	-	-	-	-
Hampton	-	-	-	12S	-	10	18	6	3	-
Harefield United	13S	5S	12S	7S	19	21	-	-	-	-
Haringey Borough	20N	-	-	-	-	-	-	-	-	-
Harlow Town	5N	1N	-	-	-	-	-	-	-	-
Hemel Hempstead	19N	12N	14N	9N	9	4	13	18	17	22
Hertford Town	22N	10N	3N	15N	-	-	-	-	-	-
Heybridge Swifts	9N	5N	1N	-	-	-	-	-	-	-
Hornchurch	14N	16N	16N	19N	-	-	-	-	-	-
Horsham	15S	20S	21S	15S	-	-	-	-	-	5
Hungerford Town	8S	6S	9S	9S	10	19	16	19	20	14
Kingsbury Town	-	-	-	13N	-	-	-	-	-	-
Leatherhead	-	-	-	10S	4	14	19	12	14	2
Leighton Town	-	-	-	-	-	-	-	-	-	10
Letchworth Garden City	11N	21N	22N	-	-	-	-	-	-	-
Lewes	-	-	-	-	2	-	20	-	-	-
Maidenhead United	11S	17S	5S	2S	-	-	-	-	-	-
Malden Vale	-	-	15S	4S	15	6	6	22	-	-
Metropolitan Police	2S	-	-	-	7	5	8	5	7	15
Molesey	.17S	4S	2S	-	-	-	-	-	-	-
Newbury Town	18S	19S	7S	8S	22	9	1	-	-	-
Oxford City	-	-	-	-	-	-	-	3	-	-
Petersfield	22S	21S	20S	21S	-	-	-	-	-	-
Purfleet	-	2N	-	7N	1	-	-	-	-	-
Rainham Town	16N	19N	21N	8N	16	20	22	-	-	-
Royston Town	17N	18N	9N	16N	-	-	-	-	-	-
Ruislip Manor	9S	7S	4S	5S	5	2	-	-	-	-
Saffron Walden Town	18N	20N	10N	11N	8	8	12	9	15	-
Southall	16S	18S	6S	6S	20	22	-	-	-	-
Southwick Borough	-	-	-	-	21	-	-	-	-	-
Stevenage Borough	-	4N	4N	1N	-	-	-	-	-	-
Thame United	-	-	-	-	-	-	7	1	-	-
Tilbury	3N	17N	6N	17N	-	17	17	14	11	16
Tring Town	10N	3N	19N	22N	-	-	-	-	-	-
Vauxhall Motors	8N	14N	11N	2N	-	-	-	-	-	-
Ware	6N	11N	13N	4N	17	15	15	16	12	20
Wembley	-	-	-	-	-	-	-	-	-	3
Whyteleafe	17S	2S	-	-	-	-	-	-	-	-
Windsor & Eton	-	-	-	-	-	-	-	20	-	9
Witham Town	7N	13N	20N	6N	13	16	5	11	19	17
Wivenhoe Town	1N	-	-	-	-	-	-	-	6	12
Wolverton Town	-	22N	-	-	-	-	-	-	-	-
Worthing	-	-	-	-	12	1	-	-	-	-
Yeading	10S	15S	1S	-	-	-	-	-	-	-

BANSTEAD ATHLETIC

Founded: 1944 **Nickname:** A's. **Colours:** Amber/black/black
Midweek Matchday: Tuesday **Reserves' League:** Suburban **Change colours:** Red & white
Chairman: Terry Molloy **Press Officer:** Colin Darby
Secretary: Gordon Taylor, 116 Kingston Avenue, North Cheam, Surrey SM3 9UF (0181 641 2957).
Manager: Bob Langford. **Asst. Manager/Coach:** Martin Chaplin **Physio:** Kevin Taylor
GROUND Address: Merland Rise, Tadworth, Surrey KT20 5JG (01737 350982). **Directions:** Follow signs to Tattenham Corner (Epsom racecourse), then to Banstead Sports Centre. Ground adjacent to swimming pool. Half a mile from Tattenham Corner (BR). Bus 420 from Sutton stops outside ground. Also buses 406 & 727 from Epsom.
Capacity: 3,500 **Seats:** 250 **Cover:** 800 **Floodlights:** Yes **Club Shop:** No
Clubhouse: Mon-Sat 12-11, Sun 12-2 & 7.30-11. 2 bars, bar snacks available. **Sponsors:** PDM Marketing
PROGRAMME DETAILS: Pages: 38 **Price:** 80p **Editor:** Colin Darby (0181 643 5437)

PREVIOUS - Leagues: Surrey Int., Surrey Snr 49-65, Spartan 65-75, London Spartan 75-79, Athenian 79-84.

CLUB RECORDS - Attendance: 1,400 v Leytonstone, FA Amateur 1953. **Win:** 11-0 **Defeat:** 0-11
Career goalscorer: Harry Clark **Career appearances:** Dennis Wall

BEST SEASON - FA Cup: 3rd Qual.Rd. 86-87. **FA Vase:** Semi - finals 96-97
Players progressing to Football League: W Chesney & B Robinson (Crystal Palace).
96-97 - Captain: Richard Langley **P.o.Y.:** Errol Vassell **Top scorer:** Simon Liddle.

HONOURS: Surrey Snr Lg(6) 50-54 56-57 64-65 (R-up(5) 49-50 54-56 57-59, Lg Cup 57-58, Charity Cup 52-53 58-59), London Spartan Lg R-up 77-78 (Lg Cup(2) 65-67), Surrey Prem. Cup R-up 91-92, 95-96, Surrey Snr Shield 55-56, Gilbert Rice F'lit Cup 81-82 86-87 (R-up(4) 82-86), Athenian Lg Cup(2) 80-82 (R-up 82-83 (SF 79-80)), Surrey Int. Lg(2) 47-49, Surrey Int. Cup 46-47 54-55, E. Surrey Charity Cup(4) 59-60 66-67 76-78 (R-up 79-80, I'mediate Sect. 75-76 (R-up 76-77), Jnr Sect. 81-82), Southern Comb. Cup R-up 69-70, Suburban Lg R-up 86-87, Carlton T.V. Trophy R-Up 95-96.

BARKING

Founded: 1880 **Nickname:** The Blues **Colours:** Blue & white
Midweek matchday: Tuesday **Reserves' League:** None **Change colours:** Red & white
Chairman: John Edgeworth **Vice-Chairman:** Paul Lovell **President:** Terry Lovell
Secretary: Roger Chilvers, 50 Harrow Rd, Barking, Essex IG11 7RA (0181 591 5313).
Press Off.: Derek Pedder, 0181 529 2483 **Manager:** Paul Downes **Asst Man.:** Andy Brennan **Physio:** Allen Hyde
GROUND Address: Mayesbrook Park, Lodge Avenue, Dagenham RM8 2JR (0181 595 6900). **Directions:** Off A13 on A1153 (Lodge Ave), and grd 1 mile on left. Bus 162 from Barking station. Nearest tube Becontree.
Capacity: 2,500 **Cover:** 600 **Seats:** 200 **Floodlights:** Yes **Club Shop:** No
Clubhouse: 2 large bars, open daily 11-11 (Sun 12-11). Hot & cold food. **Sponsors:** Capital Coin Ltd
PROGRAMME DETAILS: Pages: 16 **Price:** 80p **Editor:** Roger Chilvers

PREVIOUS - Leagues: London 1896-98 09-23, South Essex 1898-21, Leyton & Dist 1899-1900, Athenian 23-52.
Names: Barking Rovers, Barking Institute, Barking Woodville, Barking Town.
Grounds: Eastbury Field, Vicage Field (until 1973).

CLUB RECORDS - Attendance: (At Mayesbrook) 1,972 v Aldershot FA Cup 2nd Rd 1978.
Win: 14-0 v Sheppey Utd Mithras Cup 69-70 **Defeat:** 0-8 v Marlow.
Fee received: £6,000 for Alan Hull (Orient). **Fee paid:** None over £1,000
Career goalscorer: Neville Fox 241 (1965-73) **Career appearances:** Bob Makin 566

BEST SEASON - FA Vase: 96-97 **FA Amateur Cup:** Runners-up 26-27 **FA Cup:** 2nd Rd rep. 81-82 1-3 v Gillingham (A) after 1-1. Also 2nd Rd 78-79 79-80 83-84, and 1st Rd 26-27 28-29 78-80.
Recent players to Football League: Kevin Hitchcock, Nottm Forest 83, Dennis Bailey, Fulham 86, Alan Hull, Orient 87
96-97 Captain: Mark Lord **P.o.Y.:** Paul Rogan **Top Scorer:** Paul Rogan

HONOURS: FA Amateur Cup R-up 26-27, Isthmian Lg 78-79 (Lg Cup R-up 76-77), Athenian Lg 34-35 (R-up 24-25), London Lg 20-21 (Div 1 (A) 09-10), South Essex Lg Div 1 1898-99 (R-up 08-09, Div 2 1900-01 01-02 04-05 05-06), London Senior Cup 11-12 20-21 26-27 78-79 (R-up 19-20 75-76 79-80), Essex Senior Cup 1894-95 95-96 1919-20 45-46 62-63 69-70 89-90, Dylon Shield 79-80, Eastern Floodlit R-up 85-86, London Intermediate Cup 85-86.

BEDFORD TOWN

Founded: 1908 **Reformed:** 1989 **Nickname:** Eagles **Colours:** Blue & white
Midweek Matchday: Tuesday **Reserves' Lge:** Sth Mids Lge Res. Div **Change Colours:** Yellow & black
Chairman: David Donnelly. **Vice Chairman:** John Laing. **President:** Allen J Sturgess
Secretary: Barry Stephenson, 9 Aspen Ave., Bedford, Beds MK41 8BX (01234 342276).
Manager: Mick Foster **Asst Manager:** Neal Rodney **Physio:** Mick Dilley
GROUND: Meadow Lane, Cardington, Beds. **Directions:** On A603 Bedford to Sandy rd. Come off A1 at Sandy following signs to Bedford - grd on right. From Bedford take Cardington Rd out of town signed Biggleswade and Sandy.
Capacity: 3,000 **Seats:** 150 **Cover:** 500 **Floodlights:** Yes
Clubhouse: Open matchdays. Bar meals and snacks **Club Shop:** Contact Les Usher (01234 303595)
PROGRAMME DETAILS: Pages: 40 **Price:** 75p **Editor:** Allen Haynes (01525 754476)
Press Officer: Ian Slater (01234 871122) **Sponsors:** Allen Sturges Travel
CLUB RECORDS - Attendance: 3,000 v Peterborough Utd, ground opening 6/8/93. At Allen Park: 1,227 v Bedford Utd, South Midlands League Division One, 26/12/91.
(predecessors: 18,407 v Everton, FA Cup 4th Round 12/2/66).
Career scorer: Jason Reed **Career appearances:** Jason Reed.
PREVIOUS - Leagues: South Midlands 91-94 *(predecessors: Utd Co's 08-39/ Southern 46-82).*
Grounds: Allen Park, Queens Park, Bedford (park pitch) 1991-93
(predecessors: London Rd; Gasworks; Queens Pk; The Eyrie, Raleigh Street).
Players progressing to Football League: Bill Garner (Southend 69), Nicky Platnaeur (Bedford Town, Bristol Rovers 77). Ray Bailey/Derek Bellotti/Billy Brown/Bert Carberry/Peter Hall/Dave Quirke/Bobby Fold (Gillingham 56-67), Phil Driver (Wimbledon 78), Joe Dubois (Grimsby T 53), Ted Duggan (Luton T 56), Harry Duke (Noprwich C 46), John Fahy (Oxford U 64), Ken Flint (Spurs 47), Joe Hooley (Accrington 61), Joe Kirkup (Reading 55), Graham Moxon (Exeter C 75), Bela Olah (Northampton 58), Gary Sergeant (Peterborough U 77), Neil Townsend (Southend U 73).
96-97 - Captain: S Searle **Top Scorer:** Jason Reed **P.o.Y.:** Jason Reed
HONOURS: South Midlands Lg 94-95 (Div 1 92-93, Floodlit Cup 94-95); Hinchingbrook Cup 94-95 94-95; Beds Sen Cup 94-95. *(predecessors: Southern Lg 58-59 (Div 1 69-70), Utd Co's Lg 30-31 32-33 33-34 (R-up 11-12 12-13 13-14 29-30 31-32 34-35 36-37), FA Cup 4th Rd 63-64 65-66, FA Tphy SF 74-75)*

BRACKNELL TOWN

Founded: 1896 **Nickname:** Robins **Colours:** Red & white stripes/red/red
Midweek Matchday: Tuesday **Reserve's League:** Suburban (west) **Change colours:** All blue
Chairman: Dave Mihell **Vice Chairman:** Paul Broome **President:**Jack Quinton.
Secretary: Ian Rich, 50 Woodrow Drive, Wokingham, Berks RG40 1RT (01189 787884)
Manager: Brian Broome **Asst Manager:** Chris Hodge. **Physio:** Karen Cook
GROUND Address: Larges Lane, Bracknell RG12 9AN. Tel: 01344 412305 (club), 01344 300933 (office).
Directions: Off A329 just before Met Office r'bout by Bracknell College, ground 200 yards. From Bracknell (BR)/bus station - right out of station, follow path over bridge, left down steps and follow cycle path ahead, after 300yds follow curve over footbridge, right and follow lane to end, left and ground on left after bend.
Capacity: 2,500 **Seats:** 190 **Cover:** 400 **Floodlights:** Yes
Clubhouse: Members' bar open 11-11 Mon-Sat, 12-3 & 7-10.30 Sun. **Club Shop:** Yes.
PROGRAMME DETAILS: Pages: 32 **Price:** 50p **Editor/Press Officer:** Robert Scully (01344 640721).
PREVIOUS - Leagues: Great Western Comb.; Surrey Snr 63-70; London Spartan 70-75. **Ground/Name:** None
CLUB RECORDS - Attendance: 2,500 v Newquay, FA Amateur Cup 1971.
Career Goalscorer: Richard Whithy **Career Appearances:** James Woodcock
Best season - FA Cup: 4th Qual Rd 88, 1-2 v Cheltenham T., 4th Qual Rd 96, 1-3 v Burton Alb.
Players progressing to Football League: Willie Graham (Brentford).
96-97 - Captain: Dave Osgood **P.o.Y:** Tony Wood **Top Scorer:** Justin Day
HONOURS: Isthmian Lg Div 3 94-95 (Div 2 Sth R-up); Berks & Bucks Snr Cup R-up; Spartan Lg 82-83, R-up (2); Surrey Snr Lg 69-70 (Lg Cup 68-69 69-70).

BRAINTREE TOWN

Founded: **Midweek matches:** Tuesday **Reserves' Lg:** Essex/Herts Border Comb.
Colours: Yellow & blue stripes/blue/yellow **Change colours:** All white **Sponsors:** Asset Paper

Chairman: George Rosling **Vice Chairman:** Ivan Kibble **President:** R F Webb
Secretary: T A Woodley, 19a Bailey Bridge Road, Braintree, Essex CM7 5TT (01376 326234).
Manager: Tony Hall **Asst. Man.:** Phil Boyland **Physio:** Tony Last

GROUND Address: Cressing Road Stadium, Clockhouse Way, Braintree, Essex (01376 345617). **Directions:** From Braintree by-pass, turn into Braintree at the McDonalds r'bout, follow signs for East Braintree Ind. Est. - floodlights on left 1/2 mile into town opp. Orange Tree Pub. Entrance is next left in Clockhouse Way, then left again. 1 mile from Braintree & Bocking (BR). Bus 353 from Witham or town centre stops near the ground. Town centre 20 mins walk.
Capacity: 4,000 **Cover:** 1,500 **Seats:** 292 **Floodlights:** Yes **Club Shop:** Yes
Clubhouse: Open evenings 7.30-11, Sunday 12-2 and Saturday matchday lunchtimes. Full bar facilites.

PROGRAMME DETAILS: Pages: 40 **Price:** £1 **Editor:** Kevin Rosling **Press Officer:** R F Webb (01376 325338)

PREVIOUS - Leagues: North Essex 1898-1925; Essex & Suffolk Border 25-28 55-64; Spartan 28-35; Eastern Co's 35-37 38-39 52-55 70-91; Essex Co. 37-38; London 45-52; Gtr London 64-66; Metropolitan 66-70; Beazer 91-96.
Names: Manor Works 1898-1921; Crittall Ath. 21-68; Braintree & Crittall Ath. 68-81; Braintree FC 81-82.
Grounds: Kings Head Meadow 1898-1903; Spaldings Meadow, Panfield Lane 03-23.

CLUB RECORDS - Attendance: 4,000 v Spurs, charity challenge match, May 1952.
Career Goalscorer: Chris Guy 211, 1983-90 **Career Appearances:** Paul Young 524, 1966-77
Fee Paid: £2,000 for Shane Bailey (Sudbury Town)
Fee Received: £10,000 Matt Metcalf (Brentford) 1993 and John Cheesewright (Colchester) 1993.
Best FA Cup season: 4th Qual. Rd 69-70 85-86 94-95

Players progressing to Football League: John Dick (West Ham & Scotland) 1953, Steve Wright (Wrexham) 1983, John Cheesewright, Birmingham C. 91, Colchester 94; Gary Bennett, Matt Metcalf, Brentford 93; Robbie Reinhelt, Gillingham 93; Miguel de Souza (Birmingham C, Wycombe W); Gary Culling, Colchester U, 94.

96-97 - Captain : Adrian Owers. **Top scorer:** Wade Falana **P.o.Y.:** Gary Culling

HONOURS: Isthmian Lge Div 3 R-up 96-97, Guardian Insurance Cup R-up 96-97; Eastern Counties Lg 36-37 83-84 84-85 (R-up 86-87 87-88 88-89 90-91), Lg Cup 87-88 (R-up 35-36 74-75); Essex County Lg R-up 37-38; London Lg (East) R-up 45-46, Lg Cup 47-48(joint) 48-49 51-52 (R-up 49-50); Metropolitan Lg Cup 69-70; Essex Elizabethan Tphy R-up 68-69; E. Anglian Cup 46-47 68-69 95-96; Essex Sen. Tphy 86-87 (R-up 90-91); Essex & Suffolk Border Lg 59-60 84-85 (Lg Cup 59-60); Nth Essex Lg 05-06 10-11 11-12; Essex Sen Cup 95-96 R-up 96-97; Essex Jnr Cup R-up 04-05 05-06 22-23; RAFA Cup 56-57; Gtr Lon. Ben. Cup 65-66; Worthington Evans Cup 62-63 (jt) 71-72 75-76 (R-up 56-57 60-61 69-70 74-75); Eastern F'lit Cup 85-86 (R-up 94-95); Anglian F'lit Lg 69-70; Jan Havanaar Inter. Tour. 94-95 (R-up 92-93).

CANVEY ISLAND

Formed: 1926 **Midweek matchday:** Tuesday **Colours:** All Yellow
Nickname: Gulls **Reserves' League:** Essex & Herts Border Comb. **Change colours:** Red & white/white/white

Chairman: Ray Cross, 95 Lakeside Path, Canvey Island, Essex SS8 5PD. 01268 684357 (H)
Secretary: Mrs Frances Roche, 56 Harvest Road, Canvey Island SS8 9RP. 01268 698586 (H/Fax)
Manager: Jeff King. 01268 511555 (B) 0850 654321 (Mobile) **Press Officer:** Tony Roche (01268 698586)

GROUND Address: Park Lane, Canvey Island, Essex SS8 7PX (01268 682991).
Directions: A130 from A13 or A127 at Sadlers Farm roundabout, 1 mile right through town centre, first on right past old bus garage. Bus 3 or 151 from Benfleet (BR) to stop after Admiral Jellicoe (PH).
Seats: 165 **Cover:** 250 **Capacity:** 2,500 **Floodlights:** Yes **Clubhouse:** Yes **Club Shop:** Yes

PROGRAMME DETAILS: Pages: 32 **Price:** £1 **Editor:** Rod Hall (01268 697348)

PREVIOUS **Leagues:** Southend & Dist.; Thurrock & Thameside Comb.; Parthenon; Metropolitan; Gtr London 64-71; Essex Senior. **Grounds:** None **Names:** None

CLUB RECORDS - Attendance: 3,250 v Tiverton, FA Vase SF 27/3/93.
Win: 7-1 v Bedford **Defeat:** 7-0 v Halstead
Career appearances: Steve Price (407) **Career goalscorer:** Andy Jones.
Fee received: £3,000 for Ian Durrant **Fee paid:** £ 3,500 for Steve Ward
Best Season - FA Cup: 1st Rd v Brighton (2-2) (replay 1-4) 95-96. **FA Vase:** Semi-final v Tiverton 27/3/93. **FA Trophy:** Prem Rd v Heybridge

Players progressing to Football League: Peter Taylor (Spurs, Crystal Palace & England), Gary Heale (Luton Reading)
96-97 Captain: G Peney Father **P.o.Y.:** Alan Brett **Top scorer:** Andy Jones

HONOURS: Isthmian Lg Div 1 96-97, Div 2 95-96, Div 3 R-up 94-95; Carlton Trophy 95-96; Essex Sen Lg 86-87 92-93 (Lg Cup 79-80 92-93), Trophy R-up 93-94; Harry Fisher Mem. Tphy 93-94; Essex Thameside Trophy 93-94; Parthenon Lge Cup 58-59; Metropolian Lge 67-68 68-69, Cup 67-68 68-69; Thameside 95-96; Res. Lge 95-96, Cup 95-96

CHALFONT St PETER

Midweek home matchday: Tuesday **Colours:** Red with green trim/green/green & red
Chairman: Peter Manson **Manager:** Kevin Stone **Change colours:** Yellow/blue/blue
Secretary: Mal Keenan, 41 Cedar Avenue, Hazlemere, Nr High Wycombe, Bucks HP15 7EA (01494 718332)
GROUND Address: The Playing Fields, Amersham Road, Chalfont St Peter SL9 7BQ Tel: 01753 885797.
Directions: A413 from Uxbridge (London) to Chalfont. Turn left 100 yds after 2nd major roundabout (between Ambulance station and Community Centre. Two miles from Gerrards Cross (BR), regular buses from Slough.
Capacity: 4,500 **Cover:** 220 **Seats:** 220 **Floodlights:** Yes **Club Shop:** Yes
Clubhouse: Open every evening, Saturday afternoons and Sunday lunchtimes.
PROGRAMME DETAILS - Pages: 30 **Price:** 50p **Editor:** Secretary **Press Officer:** Secretary.
PREVIOUS - Leagues: Great Western Combination 1948-58; Parthenon 58-59; London 60-62; Spartan 62-75; London Spartan 75-76; Athenian 76-84.
CLUB RECORDS - Attendance: 2,55 v Watford,benefit match.1985. **Career Appearances:** Colin Davies
Transfer Fee Paid: £750 to Chertsey (Steve Church, March 1989)
Best F.A. Cup season: 3rd Qualifying Rd 85-86 (wins over Banbury, King's Lynn and Barking).
HONOURS: Isthmian Lg Div 2 87-88, Athenian Lg R-up 83-84 (Lg Cup 76-77 82-83), London Spartan Lg Div 2 75-76, Berks & Bucks Intermediate Cup 52-53, FA Tphy 3rd Qualifying Rd 89-90 91-92, FA Vase 4th Rd 87-88, Berks & Bucks Benevolent Cup 64-65.

CHESHUNT

Founded: 1946. **Nickname:** Ambers **Colours:** Gold & black
Midweek matchday: Wednesday **Reserves' Lge:** Essex & Herts Border Comb **Change colours:** All blue
Chairman: George Norman **Vice Chairman:** Paul Cully **President:**
Secretary: Mr Richard Cotterell, 46 Friends Ave, Cheshunt, Herts EN8 8LX
Manager: Dave Steedman **Asst Manager:** Steve Newby **Physio:** Lou Dedman.
GROUND Address: The Stadium, Theobalds Lane, Cheshunt, Herts. **Tel:** 01992 26752
Directions: M25 to junction 25, A10 north towards Hertford, next roundabout third exit to next roundabout, turn left proceed under railway bridge, turn left, ground approx 400 yards on right. 400yds from Theobalds Grove BR station, Buses 310, 242, 311 & 363 to Theobalds Grove station.
Seats: 285 **Cover:** 600 **Capacity:** 2,500 **Floodlights:** Yes **Club Shop:** No
Clubhouse: Yes **Press Officer:** Neil Harrison **Sponsors:** None
PROGRAMME DETAILS - Pages: 20 **Price:** 50p **Editor:** Keith Hughes (01992 627195)
PREVIOUS - Leagues: Athenian 19-20 21-31 64-77; London 20-21 24-25 46-51 55-59; Delphian 51-55; Aetolian 59-62; Spartan 62-64; Isthmian 77-87. **Name:** None **Ground:** None
CLUB RECORDS - Attendance: 7,000 v Bromley, London Senior Cup 1947.
Best season - FA Vase: Qtr Final 81-82 **FA Cup:** 4th Qual. Rd(4)
Players progressing to Football League: Ian Dowie, Ruben Abgula, Steve Sedgeley, Lee Hodges, Paul Marquis, Steve Terry, Neil Prosser, Mario Walsh.
96-97 - Captain: Ian Thurlow **P.o.Y.:** Alfie Norman **Top Scorer:** Panay Panayiotou
HONOURS: Athenian Lg 75-76 (R-up 73-74), Div 1 67-68, Div 2 R-up 65-66, Lg Cup 74-75 75-76; Spartan Lg 62-63, Lg Cup 63-64 92-93, (R-up 89-90); London Lg 49-50 (R-up 56-57), Div 1 47-48 48-49 (R-up 46-47), Div 1 Cup 46-47, Lg Cup R-up 58-59, Park Royal Cup 46-47; Isthmian Lg Div 2 R-up 81-82 (Div 3 R-up 94-95); Herts Snr Cup 23-24 (R-up 48-49 49-50 68-69 69-70 71-72 73-74); Herts Charity Cup 00-01 05-06 (R-up 70-71 74-75 80-81); Herts Charity Shield 46-47 65-66 (52-53 53-54 54-55 63-64 64-65); Herts Snr Centenary Tphy 91-92; East Anglian Cup 74-75 (R-up 75-76); Mithras Floodlit Cup 69-70 (R-up 75-76); London Charity Cup 73-74; Roy Bailey Tphy 90-91 94-95.

L-R, Back Row: Steve Newby (Asst. Man.), Ian Thurlow, Dave Murray, Panay Panayiotou, Danny Kingshott, Sam obeney, Paul Cotterell, Terry Hughes, Lou Dedman (Physio). Front: Dave Steedman (Manager), Lee Judges, Stuart Johnson, Mario Yiannacou, Ross McLean, Noel Lenihan, Alfie Norman.

EDGWARE TOWN

Founded: 1939 **Nickname:** Wares. **Colours:** Green & white Qtrs
Midweek Matchday: Tuesday **Reserve League:** Suburban **Change colours:** All yellow
Chairman: Michael Flynn. **President:** Mr V Deritis **Patron:** Russell Grant.
Secretary: Barry Boreham, 28 St Brides Ave., Edgware, Middx HA8 6BS (0181 952 1685).
Press Officer: Tom Hooks **Manager:** Jim McGleish **Physio:** Sarah Gow **Sponsor:** Philiam Construction
GROUND Address: White Lion Ground, High Street, Edgware HA8 5AQ. **Tel:** 0181 952 6799.
Directions: Turn left out of Edgware tube station (Northern Line), turn left again at crossroads and ground 300yds on right in Edgware High Street behind White Lion pub. Buses 32, 288 and 142.
Capacity: 5,000 **Seats:** 220 **Cover:** 1,500 **Floodlights:** Yes **Club Shop:** No
Clubhouse: Open nightly and Fri, Sat, Sun lunchtimes. Hot & cold food matchdays, cold food lunchtimes.
PROGRAMME DETAILS - Pages: 16 **Price:** 50p **Editor:** Paul Gregory (0181 959 2535).
PREVIOUS - Leagues: Corinthian 46-63; Athenian 64-84; London Spartan 84-90. **Names:** Edgware F.C.
CLUB RECORDS - Attendance: 8,500 v Wealdstone, FA Cup 1948. **Career Appearances:** John Mangan
Career Goalscorer: Steve Newing **Best season - FA Vase:** 5th Round, 1991-92
Players progressing: Brian Stein (Luton), Dave Beasant (Wimbledon), Scott McGleish (Charlton 1994).
Top scorer: Paul McCluskey **96-97 - Captain:** Steve Newing **P.o.Y.:** Paul McCluskey
HONOURS: Isthmian Lg Div 3 91-92; London Spartan Lg 87-88 89-90 (Lg Cup 87-88); Corinthian Lg R-up 53-54, Memorial Shield 52-53 61-62; Athenian Lg R-up 81-82; Middx Snr Lg 40-41 41-42 42-43 43-44 44-45, Cup 47-48 (R-up 73-74 94-95); London Snr Cup R-up 47-48; Middx Border Lg Cup 79-80; Suburban Lg Div R-up 89-90.

EGHAM TOWN

Founded: 1877 **Nickname:** Sarnies/Town **Colours:** All old gold with royal piping
Midweek Matches: Tuesday **Reserves' League:** Suburban **Change colours:** All royal or all white
Chairman: Patrick Bennett **Vice Chairman:** Peter Barnes **President:** Peter Barnes
Club Administrator: Alison Thompson, 138A Thorpe Lea Rd, Egham, Surrey. TW20 8BL (01784 463562)
Press Officer: Mark Ferguson **Managers:** Steve Roberts & Derek Sweetman **Physio:** Alan Maynard
GROUND: Runnymeade Stadium, Tempest Road, Egham, Surrey TW20 8HX (01784 435226).
Directions: M25 jct 13, follow signs to Egham, under M25 at r'bout, left to end, left at mini-r'bout, over railway crossing, left to end (Pooley Green Rd), right, Tempest Rd 2nd right. Bus 41 43 441 from Staines to Pooley Green Rd. Thirty mins walk from Egham or Staines (BR) station.
Capacity: 5,635 **Seats:** 335 **Cover:** 1,120 **Floodlights:** Yes **Club Shop:** No
Clubhouse: (01784 435226) 7-11pm daily & weekend lunchtimes. Members bar and function hall
PROGRAMME: 40 pages, £1 **Editor:** Mark Ferguson (01784 238606 W), Chris Thompson (01784 463562 H)
PREVIOUS - Leagues: Hounslow & District 1896-1914; Surrey Intermediate 19-22; Surrey Senior 22-28 65-67; Spartan 29-33 67-74; Parthenon 64-65; Athenian 74-77. **Names:** Runnymede Rovers 1877-1905; Egham FC 05-63
CLUB RECORDS - Scorer: Mark Butler 50 (91-92). Career record scorer too. **Appearances:** Dave Jones 850+
Attendance: 2,000 - v Select XI, Billy King Memorial 1981. Competitive: 1,400 v Wycombe W., FA Cup 2nd Qual Rd 1972. **Best FA Cup year:** 4th Qual Rd 90-91, 0-2 v Telford Utd (A)
96-97 - Captain: Malcolm Dickinson **P.o.Y.:** Geoff Charles **Top scorer:** Daren Howell (10)
HONOURS: Isthmian Lg Assoc Members Tphy R-up 91-92; Spartan Lg 71-72 (Lg Cup R-up 67-68); Athenian Lg R-up 75-76 (Div 2 74-75); Surrey Snr Cup R-up 91-92, Surrey Snr Lg 22-23, Lg Charity Cup 22-23 (R-up 26-27 34-35); Surrey Intermediate Lg 20-21, Charity Cup 19-20 20-21 (R-up 26-27); North West Surrey Charity Cup 20-21; Egham Twinning Tournament 67-68 71-72 74-75 75-76 76-77 80-81; Southern Comb. Floodlit Cup 77-78 (R-up 83-84).

BEDFORD TOWN F.C. L-R, Back: Eddie lawley, Andy Jukes, Darren Marsh, Martin Baker, Jason Reed, Sean Reedman, Steve Searle, Jason Young, Steve Atkinson, Lee Atfield. Front: Chris Tubbs, Paul Covington, Jon Corbett, Mick Foster (Manager), Lee Bearman, Kevin Lamb, Chris Watts.

EDGWARE TOWN CAPTION - Photo Opposite. L-R, Back Row: A N Other, Steve Hurd, Seamus Finnery, Anthony Whytock, Andy Carter, Gerry Brennan, Lawrence Murphy, John Coleman, Danny Kirby. Front Row: joe Lyons, Busby Finch, Paul McCluskey, Steve Newing, Mark Ivers, Carl Lindo.

BRAINTREE TOWN F.C. L-R, Back: Tony Hall (Manager), john Bishop, Adrian Owers, Neil Grice, Gary Collins, Lee Wilson, Paul Catley, Trevor gunn, Gary Bennett, Shane addington, Tony Last (Physio). Front: Alan Vincent, Russell Tanner, Nicky Simpson, Gary Culling, Shane Bailey, Mascot, Alan Pease, Simon Marshall. Photo: Jon Weaver.

HORSHAM

Founded: 1885 **Nickname:** Hornets **Colours:** Yellow & green halves/green/yellow
Midweek Matches: Tuesday **Reserves' League:** Sussex County **Change colours:** Sky & navy/navy/sky
Chairman: Frank King **Vice Chairman:** Jeff Barratt **President:** Geoff Holtom
Secretary: Eric Mallard, 6 Morrell Avenue, Horsham, West Sussex RH12 4DD (01403 267687 H; 01737 362131 B)
Manager: Mark Dunk **Asst Mgr/Coach:** Sam Chapman. **Physio:** Geoff Brittain.
GROUND: Queen Street, Horsham RH13 5AD (01403 252310). **Directions:** From the station turn left into North Street. Pass the Arts Centre to the traffic lights and turn left. At the next set of lights (200 yards) turn left again into East Street. East Street becomes Queen Street after the Iron Bridge and the ground lies opposite Queens Head public house.
Capacity: 4,500 **Seats:** 300 **Cover:** 3,000 **Floodlights:** Yes **Club Shop:** Yes
Clubhouse: Normal licensing hours. Hot and cold snacks. Dancehall.
PROGRAMME: 40 pages, £1 **Editor:** Adam Hammond (01403 217316) **Sponsors:** Persimmon Homes
Record Attendance: 8,000 v Swindon, FA Cup 1st Rd, November 1966.
Best FA Cup year: 1st Rd 47-48 (lost 1-9 at Notts County), 66-67 (lost 0-3 v Swindon).
PREVIOUS Leagues: W Sussex Sen; Sussex County 26-51; Metropolitan 51-57; Corinthian 57-63; Athenian 63-73.
Grounds: Horsham Park, Hurst Park, Springfield Park
Players progressing to Football League: Jamie Ndah (Barnet), Darren Freeman (Fulham).
96-97 - Captain: Steve Breach. **P.o.Y.:** R Knight **Top scorer:** B Forshaw
HONOURS: Sussex Snr Cup 33-34 38-39 49-50 53-54 71-72 73-74 75-76; Sussex RUR Cup (13); Sussex Floodlight Cup 77-78; Sussex County Lg (7), R-up (4), Lg Cup 45-46 46-47; Metropolitan Lg 51-52; Athenian Lg Div 1 72-73, Div 2 69-70 72-73; West Sussex Sen Lge (4); ICIS Div 3 95-96.

HUNGERFORD TOWN

Founded: 1886 **Nickname:** Crusaders **Colours:** White/blue/white
Midweek Matchday: Tuesday **Reserves' League:** Suburban (West) **Change colours:** All red
Chairman: Alan Holland **Vice Chairman:** Ron Tarry **President:** Sir Seton Wills
Secretary: Eric Richardson, 3 Windermere Way, Thatcham, Berks RG13 4UL (01536 868674).
Press Off.: Ron Tarry (01488 682539) **Manager:** Gerald Smith **Asst Man.:** Colin Moyle **Physio:** Jean Hutchings
GROUND Address: Town Ground, Bulpit Lane, Hungerford RG17 0AY. (01488 682939 -club, 684597 - boardroom, 684597 Fax). **Directions:** M4 jct 14 to A4, right and left at Bear Hotel, through town centre on A338, left into Priory Rd, second left into Bulpit Lane, over crossroads, ground on left. 3/4 mile from Hungerford BR station.
Capacity: 3,000 **Seats:** 172 **Cover:** 200 **Floodlights:** Yes **Club Shop:** Yes
Clubhouse: Open every evening and lunchtimes including Sunday. 2 bars, dancehall, boardroom/committee room, darts, pool, fruit machines. Hot & cold snacks. Stewards: Richard Crook & Chris Barrett (01488 682939).
PROGRAMME: 24 pages, 50p **Editor:** M Wiltshire (01488 682818). **Club Sponsors:** Newbury Saab
PREVIOUS - Leagues: Newbury & D.; Swindon & D.; Hellenic 58-78. **Names:** None **Grounds:** None
CLUB RECORDS - Attendance: 1,684 v Sudbury Town, FA Vase SF 1st leg 88-89 (20,000 v Modena in Italy 1981).
Scorer: Ian Farr (268) **Appearances:** Dean Bailey (approx 400)
Best FA Cup year: 1st Rd 79-80, 1-3 v Slough T. (A)
Players progressing to Football League: Steve Hetzke (Reading, Blackpool, Sunderland), Bruce Walker (Swindon, Blackpool), Des McMahon (Reading), Brian Mundee (Bournemouth, Northampton), Darren Anderson.
97-97 - Captain: Mal Ford **P.o.Y.:** Andy Minturn **Top scorer:** Marcus Richardson (22)
HONOURS: FA Vase SF 77-78 79-80 88-89; Berks & Bucks Snr Cup 81-82 (R-up 75-76 76-77); Hellenic Lg Div 1 70-71, Prem Div Cup 77-78, Div 1 Cup 70-71, Benevolent Cup 60-61; Hungerford Cup 96-97.

LEIGHTON TOWN

Founded: 1885 **Nickname:** Reds **Colours:** Red & white
Midweek Matchday: Tuesday **Reserve's League:** Suburban **Change colours:** All blue
Chairman: Iain S McGregor **President:** Mike Hide
Secretary: Alec Irvine, 12 Rowley Furrows, Linslade, Leighton Buzzard, Beds LU7 7SH (01525 376475).
Press Officer: Iain S McGregor (01525 370142) **Manager:** Peter Lawrence **Physio:** George Lathwell
GROUND: Bell Close, Lake Street, Leighton Buzzard, Beds (01525 373311).
Directions: From bypass (A505) take A4146 (Billington Rd) towards Leighton Buzzard, straight over mini-r'bout & 1st left into car park - ground behind Camden Motors just before town centre. Half mile from Leighton Buzzard (BR) station. Buses from Luton, Aylesbury and Milton Keynes.
Capacity: 2,800 **Seats:** 155 **Cover:** 300 **Floodlights:** Yes **Club Shop:** Yes
Clubhouse: Normal licensing hours. Snack/refreshment bar on matchdays - full rang of hot snacks & drinks.
PROGRAMME: 50p **Editor:** Andrew Massey (01908 613404) **Sponsors:** Camden Motors
PREVIOUS - **Leagues:** Leighton & District; South Midlands 22-24 26-29 46-54 55-56 76-92; Spartan 22-53 67-74; United Counties 74-76. **Name:** Leighton United **Ground:** None
CLUB RECORDS - Attendance: 1,522 v Aldershot T., Isthmian Lg Div 3, 30/1/93
Record win: 7-2. **Record defeat:** 1-6.
Best Season - FA Cup: Third Qual. Round 70-71, 1-2 v St Albans City (A)
96-97 - Captain: Marc Andrews **P.o.Y.:** James Heeps **Top scorer:** Bradley Anderson
HONOURS: Isthmian Lge Div 3 R-up 95-96; Sth Midlands Lg 66-67 91-92, Lg Cup 90-91, O'Brien Tphy 90-91, Reserve Div 1 87-88 91-92 94-95, Res Div 2 76-77, Res Challenge Cup 93-94 94-95; Beds Snr Cup 26-27 67-68 68-69 69-70 92-93; Bucks Charity Cup 94-95; Spartan Lg Div 2 23-24 27-28; Leighton & District Lg, Beds Intermediate Cup(res) 90-91; Beds Yth Cup 91-92 92-93 94-95; Chiltern Youth Lg 94-95, Lg Cup 93-94; East Anglian Yth.Cup 94-95; Assoc Mem Cup 96-97;

MARLOW

Formed: 1870 **Nickname:** The Blues **Colours:** Royal, white trim/royal/royal
Midweek matchday: Tuesday **Reserves' League:** Suburban Premier. **Change colours:** Orange & black
Chairman: Terry Staines **President:** Herbie Swadling **Vice-Chairman:** Michael Watson
Secretary: Paul Burdell, 69 Wycombe Rd., Marlow, High Wycombe (01628 483722)
Press Off./Comm. Man.: Terry Staines. **Information Line** (local call rates): 01628 477032).
Manager: Dave Russell **Coach:** Gary Bree **Physio:** Sarah Cripps.
GROUND Address: Alfred Davis Memorial Ground, Oak Tree Road, Marlow SL7 3ED (01628 483970).
Directions: A404 to Marlow (from M4 or M40), then A4155 towards town centre. Turn right into Maple Rise (by ESSO garage), ground in road opposite (Oak Tree Rd). 1/2 mile from Marlow (BR). 1/4 mile from Chapel Street bus stops.
Capacity: 3,000 **Cover:** 600 **Seats:** 250 **Floodlights:** Yes
Clubhouse: Open matchdays & most evenings. Snack bar open matchdays.
Club Shop: Sells programmes, badges, ties, pens, videos etc. **Sponsors:** The Marlow Building Company
PROGRAMME DETAILS: Pages: 40 **Price:** £1 **Editor:** Terry Staines & John Addaway
PREVIOUS - **Leagues:** Reading & Dist.; Spartan 1908-10 28-65; Great Western Suburban; Athenian 65-84. **Name:** Great Marlow. **Grounds:** Crown Ground 1870-1919); Star Meadow 19-24.
CLUB RECORDS - Attendance: 3,000 v Oxford United, FA Cup 1st Rd 1994. (Ground - 8,000 Slough T. v Wycombe W., Berks & Bucks Snr Cup Final, 1972). **Goalscorer:** Kevin Stone 31. **Appearances:** Mick McKeown 500+. **Fees - Paid:** £5,000 for Richard Evans (Sutton Utd. 94). **Received:** £8,000 for David Lay from Slought Town 94.
BEST SEASON - FA Cup: Semi-Finals 1882; 3rd Rd 92-93 (1-5 v Tottenham); 1st Rd on 19 times - 1871-85 86-88 92-93 1991-92 94-95. **FA Trophy:** 1st Rd 1987-88, 91-92. **FA Vase:** 5th Rd replay 74-75.
Players progressing to Football League: Leo Markham (Watford 1972), Naseem Bashir (Reading).
96-97 - Captain: Andy Leader **P.o.Y.:** Grant Goodall **Top scorer:** C Ayres
HONOURS: Isthmian Lg Div 1 87-88, Div 2 South R-up 86-87, Lg Cup 92-93; Spartan Lg Div 1 37-38 (Div 2 West 29-30); Berks & Bucks Sen Cup (11) + 90-91 94-95.

METROPOLITAN POLICE

Founded: 1919 **Nickname:** Blues **Colours:** All blue
Midweek Matches: Tuesday **Reserves' League:** Suburban **Change colours:** Black & White stripes
Chairman: Des Flanders QPM. **Vice Chairman:** Kes Jones **President:** Sir Paul Condon QPM
Secretary: Tony Brooking, 15 Westmoreland Avenue, Hornchurch, Essex. RM11 2EJ.(01708 450715)
Manager: Mel Thomas **Physio:** Dick Pierce **Club Sponsors:** None
GROUND: Metropolitan Police Sports Ground, Imber Court, East Molesey (0181 398 7358). **Directions:** From London: A3 then A309 to Scilly Isles r'bout, right into Hampton Court Way, left at 1st r'bout into Imber Court Rd - ground faces in 300yds. From M25 jct 10: A3 towards London for 1 mile, A307 through Cobham, left immediately after Sandown Park into Station Rd - ground 1 mile on left. Half mile from either Thames Ditton or Esher BR stations.
Capacity: 3,000 **Seats:** 297 **Cover:** 1,800 **Floodlights:** Yes **Club Shop:** No
Clubhouse: (0181 398 1267). Four bars, dancehall, cafeteria open 9am-11pm. Hot & cold food.
PROGRAMME DETAILS: 10 pages, 50p **Editor/Press Officer:** Cliff Travis (01932 782215).
PREVIOUS - Leagues: Spartan 28-60; Metropolitan 60-71; Southern 71-78. **Grounds:** None **Name:** None
CLUB RECORDS - Attendance: 4,500 v Kingstonian, FA Cup 1934.
Goal Scorer: Mario Russo **Appearances:** Pat Robert
Win: 10-1 v Tilbury 1995 **Defeat:** 1-11 v Wimbledon, 1956
Best FA Cup year: 1st Rd - 32-33, 0-9 v Northampton T. (A); 84-85, 0-3 v Dartford (H); 94-95, 0-3 v Crawley T. (H)
96-97 - Captain: Paul Towler **P.o.Y:** Steve Pope **Top Scorer:** Steve Pope
HONOURS: Isthmian Lg Div 2 R-up 77-78 87-88, Assoc. Members Tphy 94-95; Spartan Lg 28-30(2) 36-37 38-39 45-46 5-55(2), (R-up 47-48), Lg Cup 59-60 (R-up 57-58); Middx Snr Cup 27-28; Surrey Snr Cup 32-33, Charity Shield 38-39; Metropolitan Lg Cup 68-69 (Amtr Cup 68-69 69-70); London Snr Cup R-up 34-35 40-41; Herts & Middx Comb. 39-40.

NORTHWOOD

Founded: 1902 **Nickname:** Woods **Colours:** All red
Midweek Matches: Tuesday **Reserve League:** Suburban **Change colours:** All white
Chairman: Andy Johnson **Vice Chairman:** Geoff Foster **President:** Lothar Hahn
Secretary: Steve Williams, 35 Evelyn Drive, Hatch End, Pinner, Middx HA5 4RL (0181 428 1533 - H & fax).
Manager: Steve Emmanuel **Physio:** George Price **Sponsors:** IFS Freight Forwarding
GROUND: Northwood Park, Chestnut Avenue, Northwood (01923 827148).
Directions: A404 (Pinner-Rickmansworth) - Chestnut Ave. on left by large grey iron railway bridge. Third of a mile from Northwood Hills station (Metropolitan Line) - turn right out of station to r'bout, left into Pinner Rd, left into Chestnut Ave. by Shell petrol station after 300yds. Buses 282 and H11 to Northwood Hills.
Capacity: 2,250 **Seats:** 150 **Cover:** 400 **Floodlights:** Yes **Club Shop:** No
Clubhouse: Weekends and most evenings from 6pm. Bar. Hot and cold food. Pool, juke-box.
PROGRAMME: 52 pgs 80p **Editor:** A Evans (0181 566 2880) **Press Off:** M Russell (01923 827690)
PREVIOUS - Leagues: Harrow & Wembley 32-69; Middx 69-78; Hellenic 79-84; London Spartan 84-92.
Names: Northwood Town **Grounds:** None
CLUB RECORDS - Attendance: 1,324 v Chelsea Friendly July 1995 **Goal Scorer:** Martin Ellis
Appearances: Norman Heslop **Best Season - FA Cup:** 2nd Qual Rd 94-95 **FA Vase:** Qtr finals 96-97
Players progressing to Football League: Gavin Maguire, Derek Payne (Barnet), Warren Patmore (Cambridge).
96-97 - Captain: Sean Glynn **P.o.Y:** Lee Carroll/Sean Glynn **Top Scorer:** Paul Halbert
HONOURS: Isthmian Lg Associate Members Cup 92-93; London Spartan Lg 91-92 (R-up 89-90), Lg Cup 89-90 91-92; Hellenic Lg Div 1 78-79 (Prem Div Cup R-up 81-82); Middx Lg 77-78 (R-up 72-73 76-77), Div 1 R-up 71-72, Challenge Cup 74-75 76-77 77-78; Middx Snr Charity Cup R-up 93-94; Middx Snr Cup SF 91-92 92-93, Jnr Cup 46-47 47-48 48-49; Harrow & Wembley Lg (9); Middlesex Premier Cup 94-95.

TILBURY

Founded: 1900 **Nickname:** Dockers **Colours:** Black & white qtrs/black/red
Midweek Matches: Tuesday **Reserves' League:** Essex & Herts Border Comb. **Change colours:** All red
Chairman: R Nash **Vice Chairman:** T.Harvey **President:** J B Wilson
Secretary: L Brown, 52 Lionel Oxley House, Grays, Essex (01375 409938)
Press Officer: Chairman **Manager:** Shaun McCann **Physio:** Roger Hutton
GROUND: Chadfields, St Chad's Rd, Tilbury, Essex RM18 8NL (01375 23093). **Directions:** BR from Fenchurch Street to Tilbury Town then bus 377 or 20 mins walk. By road: M25 (J 30 or 31) - A13 Southend bound, Tilbury Docks turn off after 4 miles, Chadwell St Mary turn off (left) after 1.5 miles, left again after 400 metres, rt at r'bout (signed Tilbury), rt into St Chad's Rd after half mile, 1st rt into Chadfields.
Capacity: 4,000 **Seats:** 350 **Cover:** 1,000 **Floodlights:** Yes **Club Shop:** No.
Clubhouse: Open every evening, all day Fri. & Sat. and Sun. lunchtimes. Hot & cold food available.
PROGRAMME: 32 pages, 50p **Editor:** Lloyd Brown **Club Sponsors:** None
CLUB RECORDS - Attendance: 5,500 v Gorleston, FA Cup 4th Qual. Rd 19/11/49. **Fee received:** £2,000, Tony Macklin to Grays A., 1990 & Steve Conner to Dartford, 1985 **Win:** 13-2 v Chalfont National (A), London Lge 28/4/92. **Defeat:** 1-10 v Maidstone U. (A), Corinthian Lge 4.9.62, v Met. Police (A), Isthmian Lge. 6/5/95. **Career goalscorer:** Ross Livermore 305 (in 282 games, 58-66). **Career appearances:** Nicky Smith 424 (75-85). **Best Season - FA Cup:** 3rd Rd 77-78, 0-4 v Stoke City (A). 1st Rd 49-50, 0-4 v Notts Co. (A) **FA Amateur Cup:** Quarter Finals
96-97 - Captain: K Lester **P.o.Y:** S Harvey **Top Scorer:** S Harvey (16)
HONOURS: Isthmian Lg Div 1 75-76, (Div 1 Cup 74-75); Athenian Lg 68-69 (Div 2 62-63); London Lg 58-59 59-60 60-61 61-62, Lg Cup 58-59 60-61 61-62, R-up (3); Delphian Lg 67-68 (Div 2 62-63); Essex Snr Cup 60-61 63-64 72-73 74-75 (R-up 46-47 47-48 69-70 71-72 78-79); Essex Professional Cup 75-76; Mithras Cup 72-73 75-76 76-77 78-79 (R-up 71-72 74-75); Essex Elizabethan Tphy 63-64 68-69 (R-up 55-56 59-60 64-65 67-68 70-71); Essex Floodlit Competition 68-69, Anglo-Italian Barassi Cup R-up 75-76; Essex Jnr Cup 08-09 24-25 (R-up 03-04); Stanford Charity Cup 62-63 92-93; Grays & Dist. Lg(numerous); Neale Trophy 65-66; Memorial Shield R-up 87-88.

TOOTING & MITCHAM UTD

Formed: 1932 **Nickname:** Terrors **Colours:** Black & white stripes/black/white
Midweek matchday: Tuesday **Reserve League:** Suburban. **Change colours:** All red.
Chairman: John Buffoni **President:** Cliff Bilham **Vice Chairman:** Alan Simpson
Secretary: Les Roberts, 91 Fernlea Road, Mitcham, Surrey CR4 2HG (01816 465275)
Commercial Manager: John Pollard. **Press Officer:** Jim Silvey 0181 640 5678 (H)
Manager: James Bolton **Coach:** Peter Shaw **Physio:** Danny Keenan
GROUND Address: Sandy Lane, Mitcham, Surrey CR4 2HD (0181 648 3248).
Directions: Tooting (BR) quarter mile. Sandy Lane is off Streatham Road near Swan Hotel.
Capacity: 8,000 **Cover:** 1,990 **Seats:** 1,990 **Floodlights:** Yes **Club Shop:** Yes
Clubhouse: Open every evening and w/end lunches. Food available. **Sponsors:** Claremont Coaches.
PROGRAMME DETAILS: Pages: 24 **Price:** 80p **Editor:** Jim Silvey.
PREVIOUS - Leagues: London 32-37, Athenian 37-56. **Ground:** None **Name:** None
CLUB RECORDS - Goalscorer: Alan Ives 92 (1972-78). **Appearances:** Danny Godwin 470.
Attendance: 17,500 v QPR, FA Cup 2nd Rd 56-57. **Win:** 11-0 v Welton Rovers, FA Amateur Cup 62-63.
Defeat: 1-8 v Kingstonian, Surrey Snr Cup 66-67 & v Redbridge F. (H), Loctite Cup 3rd Rd 19/2/91.
Fee Paid: £9,000 for Dave Flint (Enfield). **Fee Received:** £10,000 for Herbie Smith (Luton).
BEST SEASON - FA Trophy: 2nd Qualifying Rd Replay 71-72 81-82. **FA Amateur Cup:** 1st Rd replay 22-23.
FA Cup: 4th Rd 75-76, 1-3 v Bradford C. (A); 3rd Rd 58-59; 2nd Rd 56-57 76-77; 1st Rd 5 other occasions. -
League clubs defeated: Bournemouth & Boscombe Ath, Northampton 58-59, Swindon 75-76.
Recent players progressing to Football League: Carlton Fairweather & Brian Gayle (Wimbledon 1984)
HONOURS: Isthmian League 57-58 59-60 (Full Members Cup 92-93), Athenian League 49-50 54-55, London Challenge Cup R-up 59-60, Surrey Senior Cup 37-38 43-44 44-45 52-53 59-60 75-76 76-77 77-78, London Senior Cup 42-43 48-49 58-59 59-60 (R-up 43-44 44-45), South Thames Cup 69-70, Surrey Senior Shield 51-52 60-61 61-62 65-66.

WEALDSTONE

Formed: 1899 **Nickname:** The Stones **Colours:** Blue & white quarters
Midweek matches: Tuesday **Reserves' League:** None **Change colours:** Yellow & blue
Chairman: Paul Rumens **Vice Chairman:** Nick Dugard **Admin. & Comm. Man.:** Layne Patterson, c/o Office
Administrative Office: 30 Lowlands Road, Harrow, Middx HA1 3AP (0181 864 3744)
Secretary: Steve Hibberd, 17 Brancaster Rd, Newbury Park, Ilford, Essex IG2 7ER (0181 597 7534).
Manager: Gordon Bartlett **Asst Manager:** Leo Morris **Physio:** Alan Wharton
GROUND: (Share with Edgware Town FC) - White Lion Ground, High Street, Edgware HA8 5AQ. **Tel:** 0181 952 6799.
Clubhouse: Yes, normal licensing hours. **Club Shop:** No **Sponsors:** Jordan Farah
PROGRAMME: 30 pages £1 **Editor:** Roy Couch (0181 907 4421) **Press Officer:** Graham Sharpe

PREVIOUS - Leagues: Willesden & Dist. 1899-1906 08-13; London 1911-22; Middx 13-22; Spartan 22-28; Athenian 28-64; Isthmian 64-71; Southern 71-79 81-82,88-95; GMV Conference 79-81 82-88.
Grounds: College Farm 03-10; Belmont Rd 10-22; Lower Mead Stadium 22-91; Vicarage Rd (Watford FC) 91-93; The Warren (Yeading F.C.)

CLUB RECORDS - Attendance: 13,504 v Leytonstone FA Amateur Cup Fourth Round replay 5/3/49.
Goalscorer: George Duck, 251 **Appearances:** Charlie Townsend, 514
Best FA Cup season: 3rd Rd 77-78, 1-4 v Q.P.R. (A). 1st Rd on 13 occasions.

Players progressing to Football League: include Stuart Pearce (Coventry City 83), Vinnie Jones (Wimbledon 1986), Danny Bailey (Exeter 89), Francis Joseph (Wimbledon & Brentford), Bobby Ryan.

96-97 - Captain: Bryan Hammatt **P.o.Y.:** Fergus Moore **Top scorer:** Roy Marshall

HONOURS: FA Trophy 84-85; FA Amateur Cup 65-66; GMV Conference 84-85; Icis Lge Champ Div 3 96-97; Southern Lg Southern Div 81-82, Div 1 South 73-74, Lg Cup 81-82; Athenian Lg 51-52 (R-up 52-53 58-59 60-61); Spartan Lg R-up 22-23; London Lg Div 2 12-13 (R-up 11-12); London Snr Cup 61-62(joint) (R-up 39-40 51-52 60-61); Middx Snr Cup (11); Middx Senior Charity Cup (11); Capital League 84-85 86-87.

WINDSOR & ETON

Founded: 1892 **Nickname:** Royalists **Colours:** All red with green trim
Midweek matches: Tuesday **Reserves' League:** Suburban (North) **Change colours:** White/black/black
Chairman: Peter Simpson/Kevin Stott **President:** Sir David Hill-Wood, Bt
Secretary: Steve Rowland, 91 Duke Street, Windsor, Berks SL4 1SJ (01753 774528 H, emergency only)
Press Officer: Secretary **Manager:** Allan Davies **Asst Manager:** Alan Rowe **Physio:** Des Hunt
GROUND: Stag Meadow, St Leonards Road, Windsor, Berkshire SL4 3DR (01753 860656).
Directions: A332 from M4 junct 6. Left at r'bout (B3173), left into St Leonards Rd at lights on T-junction, ground 500 yards on right on B3022 opposite Stag & Hounds PH. 1 mile from town centre - pass available to St Leonards Rd. BR to Windsor Central station (from) Slough or Windsor Riverside (change at Staines from Waterloo).
Capacity: 4,500 **Cover:** 650 **Seats:** 400 **Floodlights:** Yes **Club Shop:** Yes
PROGRAMME: 28 pages **Editor:** Eric Richford **Sponsors:** Murex Welding Products **Clubhouse:** Yes

PREVIOUS - Leagues: Southern 1895-96; West Berks; Great Western Suburban 1907-22; Athenian 22-29 63-81; Spartan 29-32; Great Western Comb; Corinthian 45-50; Metropolitan 50-60; Delphian 60-63.

CLUB RECORDS - Attendance: 8,500 (Charity match) **Fee Paid:** £9,000, Keith White (Slough T.)
Fee Received: £45,000, Michael Banton & Michael Barnes (Barnet) **Appearances:** Kevin Mitchell
Best Season - FA Amateur Cup: 4th Rd 21-22 **FA Vase:** Semi-Final 80-81 (QF 79-80)
FA Trophy: 3rd Rd 88-89 **FA Cup:** 2nd Rd replay 83-84. 1st Rd 7 times; 25-26 80-81 82-86 91-92.

Players progressing to Football League: Steve Adams (Charlton 1979), Dave Barnett (Colchester 1988), Vic Woodley (Chelsea & England), Billy Coward (QPR, Walsall), Ken Groves (Preston), Dave Regis (Notts County).

HONOURS: Isthmian Lg Div 1 83-84 (Div 2 R-up 82-83), Athenian Lg 79-80 80-81 (Lg Cup 79-80 (R-up 78-79 80-81), Div 2 Cup 63-64 (R-up 68-69)), Spartan Lg R-up 36-37 37-38 (Div 1 30-31), Metropolitan Lg R-up 53-54 (Lg Amtr Cup 51-52 52-53, Lg Cup 52-53 (R-up 53-54 54-55)), Gt Western Suburban Lg R-up 21-22, Berks & Bucks Snr Cup(11) 10-11 36-38 40-45 61-62 87-89 (R-up 07-08 24-25 26-27 38-39 46-47 62-63), Berks & Bucks Benev. Cup 35-36 37-38 46-47 62-63 (R-up 38-39 47-48 49-50).

WITHAM TOWN

Founded: 1947 **Nickname:** Town **Colours:** Red & black stripes/white/white
Midweek Matches: Tuesday **Reserve's League:** Essex & Herts Border Comb. **Change colours:** Blue & white
Chairman: Mr A Marshall **Vice Chairman:** Reg Wright **President:** B Olley.
Secretary: Jim Claydon, 58 Silver Street, Silver End, Witham, Essex CM8 3QG (01376 584086 H, 01376 583241 x426 B)
Manager: Spencer Pratten **Asst Manager:** George Young **Physio:** John Barwick
GROUND: Spa Road, Witham, Essex CM8 1UN (01376 511198-lounge, 500146-reception, 520996-boardroom).
Directions: From Witham BR (network S.E.) station; through pub car park and follow road to Faulkbourne, at main r'bout turn left and ground is on the right. By road; Off A12 at Witham sign, left at 1st lights (Spinks Lane), right at end of road, follow road under railway bridge - ground 100yds on left.
Capacity: 2,500 **Seats:** 150 **Cover:** 300 **Floodlights:** Yes **Club Shop:** No.
Clubhouse: Open every night and weekend lunctimes. Hot bar snacks. Steward: Richard Green.
PROGRAMME: 24 pages, 60p **Editor:** Alison Gray **Press Officer:** G Vale (01376 513861)
PREVIOUS - **Leagues:** Mid Essex; Essex & Suffolk Border; Essex Senior 71-87. **Ground:** The Park
CLUB RECORDS - Attendance: 800 v Billericay Town, Essex Sen. Lge, May 76 **Win:** 7-0 v Banstead 27/9/94
Defeat: 0-9 v Collier Row 21/10/95. **Goalscorer:** Colin Mitchell **Appearances:** Keith Dent (16 years)
Best Season - FA Vase: 5th Round, 85-86 **FA Cup:** 2nd Qual. Rd 87-88, 88-89, 89-90.
Players progressing to Football League: Steve Tilson (Southend).
96-97 - Captain: George Young **P.o.Y.:** Justin Pearce **Top scorer:** Richard Wyatt
HONOURS: Essex Snr Lg 70-71 85-86 (R-up 84-85 86-87), Tphy 85-86 (R-up 88-89); Essex Thameside Tphy R-up 95-96

WIVENHOE TOWN

Formed: 1925 **Nickname:** The Dragons **Colours:** Royal blue/yellow
Reserves' League: Essex & Suffolk Border Lge **Midweek matchday:** Tuesday **Change colours:** Red/black
Chairman: T.B.A. **Vice Chairman:** Dave Whymark **President:** Harry Welsh
Secretary/Press Officer: Mike Boyle, 15 Daniell Drive, Colchester, Essex (01206 573223).
Manager: Steve Dowman **Asst Manager:** Steve Pitt **Physio:** Barry Wreford
GROUND: Broad Lane Ground, Elmstead Road, Wivenhoe CO7 7HA (01206 823416).
Directions: Coming out of Colchester towards Clacton take first turning (right) towards Wivenhoe, first left and ground clearly visible on right at cross-roads. 1 mile from Wivenhoe (BR).
Capacity: 3,000 **Cover:** 1,300 **Seats:** 250 **Floodlights:** Yes **Club Shop:** Yes
PROGRAMME: 36 pages 80p **Editor:** P Reeve **Clubhouse:** (01206 825380). Open normal pub hours.
PREVIOUS - **Leagues:** Brighlingsea & District 1927-50; Colchester & East Essex 50-71; Essex & Suffolk Border 71-79; Essex Senior 79-86. **Grounds:** Spion Kop; Broomfield; Claude Watcham's Meadow; Vine Farm; Spion Kop; Broomfield; King George V Playing Fields; Essex University. **Name:** Wivenhoe Rangers.
CLUB RECORDS - Attendance: 1,912 v Runcorn, FA Trophy 1st Rd, Feb 1990. **Transfer fee received:** £5,875 for Bobby Mayes (Redbridge Forest). **Win:** 18-0 v Nayland. **Defeat:** 0-8 v Carshalton A. (H), Isthmian Lg 28/8/93. **Career goalscorer:** Paul Harrison, 258 in 350 games. **Career appearances:** Keith Bain, 536. **Best season - FA Cup:** 4th Qual Rd 89-90 2-3 v Halesowen Town (A), 94-95 1-2 v Enfield (H) **FA Trophy:** 2nd Rd replay 89-90 **FA Vase:** 5th Rd 82-83;
Players progressing to Football League: Robert Reinelt (Gillingham) 1993.
HONOURS: Isthmian Lg Div 1 89-90 (Div 2 Nth 87-88); Essex Snr Lg R-up 79-80 81-82 85-86 (Harry Fisher Tphy 83-84 85-86); Essex & Suffolk Border Lg 78-79, Div 1 72-73, Div 2 71-72, Lg Cup R-up(2); Colchester & East Essex Lg 52-53 55-56 (R-up 70-71), Div 1 59-60 69-70, Div 2 R-up 68-69, Lg KO Cup 51-52 52-53 54-55 55-56 (R-up 59-60), Challenge Cup 52-53); Brighlingsea & Dist Lg Div 1 35-36 36-37 47-48 (R-up 37-38), Lg KO Cup 36-37 37-38 47-48, Challenge Cup 36-37; Essex Snr Tphy 87-88.

BANSTEAD ATHLETIC F.C. L-R, Back: Chris Kilby (Coach), Kevin Taylor (Physio), Ochea Ikpa, Simoniddle, Scott Tarr, Ian Kilpatrick, Kelvin Thomas, Bobby Langford (Manager), Martin Chaplin (Coach). Front: Steve Hall, Errol Vassell, Simon Ray, Steve Latuske, Robin Welch, Keith ward, Michael Stratford, Geoff Foreman, Richard Vercesi. Photo: Gary Letts.

DIVISION THREE LEAGUE TABLE 1996-97

			Home			Away					
		P	W	D	L	W	D	L	F	A	Pts
1	Wealdstone	32	14	0	2	10	3	3	72	24	75
2	Braintree Town	32	13	2	1	10	3	3	99	29	74
3	Northwood	32	11	4	1	7	6	3	60	31	64
4	Harlow Town	32	10	1	5	9	3	4	60	41	61
5	Aveley	32	8	4	4	9	2	5	64	39	57
6	East Thurrock Utd.	32	10	3	3	6	3	7	58	51	54
7	Camberley Town	32	8	2	6	7	4	5	55	44	51
8	Wingate & Finchley	32	7	4	5	4	3	9	52	63	40
9	Hornchurch	32	5	4	7	6	2	8	35	51	39
10	Clapton	32	3	4	9	8	2	6	31	49	39
11	Lewes	32	6	6	4	4	2	10	45	53	38
12	Kingsbury Town	32	6	2	8	5	2	9	41	54	37
13	Hertford Town	32	6	3	7	4	3	9	55	65	36
14	Epsom & Ewell	32	4	2	10	4	3	9	62	78	29
15	Flackwell Heath	32	6	3	7	2	2	12	36	71	29
16	Tring Town	32	3	1	12	4	2	10	33	74	24
17	Southall	32	3	2	11	3	2	11	28	69	22

RESULTS GRID 1996-97

	HOME TEAM	1	2	3	4	5	6	7	8	9	10	11	12	13	14	15	16	17
1	Aveley	*	1-2	1-2	1-2	0-4	4-1	1-1	3-1	3-1	5-0	2-0	1-0	2-2	4-1	2-0	1-1	1-1
2	Braintree Town	3-2	*	0-0	6-0	7-1	4-1	6-0	0-0	6-1	4-0	5-3	6-1	1-0	3-0	0-1	2-0	6-0
3	Camberley Town	0-2	0-1	*	1-0	8-3	2-2	3-1	0-1	3-0	2-1	2-0	0-1	3-1	1-1	0-2	0-3	4-2
4	Clapton	0-2	1-11	0-1	*	0-1	0-1	3-1	0-2	0-2	0-0	0-0	2-0	1-1	1-2	5-1	0-1	0-0
5	East Thurrock U	0-0	3-2	2-0	3-0	*	3-2	4-0	1-3	4-2	0-1	4-2	3-0	0-0	3-0	2-2	0-1	2-0
6	Epsom & Ewell	3-5	2-5	2-3	1-2	1-3	*	5-0	3-1	3-1	0-3	1-1	1-1	2-3	2-0	4-3	2-3	4-7
7	Flackwell Heath	0-7	0-3	2-5	0-2	0-0	2-1	*	1-3	1-1	0-3	0-1	2-0	1-1	0-1	5-0	4-0	1-0
8	Harlow Town	3-0	1-1	3-1	1-3	3-2	3-1	3-0	*	2-3	2-1	2-1	0-2	1-3	2-0	1-2	2-1	5-3
9	Hertford Town	0-1	0-1	3-0	1-2	5-1	2-1	2-2	0-2	*	3-1	0-1	4-0	0-1	1-1	4-2	0-2	3-3
10	Hornchurch	0-1	1-5	2-2	0-1	1-1	2-2	2-1	0-2	3-1	*	1-0	2-2	1-0	0-1	2-0	0-3	0-1
11	Kingsbury Town	1-3	1-0	1-2	0-1	3-0	1-3	0-2	3-0	2-3	1-1	*	2-1	0-1	3-1	1-4	0-0	3-0
12	Lewes	6-2	1-1	1-1	3-1	2-3	2-5	0-1	2-2	0-0	1-0	4-1	*	1-1	4-0	1-1	0-1	2-0
13	Northwood	2-0	2-2	1-1	0-0	0-0	2-1	4-1	1-0	7-3	4-0	4-1	4-1	*	3-2	4-1	1-3	1-0
14	Southall	0-4	0-3	2-1	2-2	0-2	2-3	3-1	0-3	1-5	2-3	0-2	0-1	0-1	*	4-0	1-1	0-2
15	Tring Town	0-2	0-2	0-1	0-2	0-2	2-1	2-1	2-3	2-2	0-1	1-2	1-3	1-2	2-0	*	0-3	0-3
16	Wealdstone	1-0	6-0	3-1	2-0	4-1	2-1	3-0	0-2	5-1	2-0	5-0	2-1	0-2	1-0	7-0	*	3-2
17	Wingate & Finchley	1-1	0-1	0-5	2-0	2-0	2-2	4-3	1-1	2-1	2-3	1-4	3-1	1-1	5-1	2-1	0-3	*

LEADING GOALSCORERS

Tot.		Lge	GIC	AMT
31	WADE FALANA (Braintree Town)	29	2	-
25	GARY BENNETT (Braintree Town)	14	8	3
23	PAUL HALBERT (Northwood)	22	-	1
22	ANDY BOXALL (Epsom & Ewell)	21	1	-

AVELEY

Chairman: David Patient **President:** Ken Clay **Press Officer:** Terry King
Secretary: Alan Suttling, 50 Harvey, Grays, Essex RM16 2TX (01375 400741).
Manager: Craig Johnson **Asst Mgr/Coach:** Paul Armstrong **Physio:** Phil Hunter
GROUND: 'Mill Field', Mill Road, Aveley, Essex RM15 4TR (01708 865940). **Directions:** London - Southend A13, turn into Sandy Lane at Aveley. Rainham or Purfleet BR stations then bus No. 723 to the ground.
Capacity: 4,000 **Cover:** 400 **Seats:** 400 **Floodlights:** Yes **Founded:** 1927
Clubhouse: Normal pub hours. Bar snacks and hot food available **Club Shop:** No
Colours: Royal blue/white/royal blue **Change:** Red & white/red/red **Sponsors:** Dagenham Motors
Previous Leagues: Thurrock Combination 46-49/ London 49-57/ Delphian 57-63/ Athenian 63-73.
Midweek matches: Tuesday **Reserves' League:** Essex & Herts Border Comb.
96-97 - Captain: D Allen **P.o.Y.:** Tony Williams **Top Scorer:** Micky White
Honours: Isthmian Lg Div 2 (North) R-up 89-90, Lg (AC Delco) Cup 89-90; London Lg 51-52 54-55 (R-up 55-56, Lg Cup 53-54); Delphian Lg R-up 57-58 (Lg Cup 61-62); Athenian Lg 70-71 (Div 2 R-up 68-69); Essex Junior Cup 47-48 48-49; Essex Thameside Trophy 79-80; Hornchurch Charity Cup 81-82 (R-up 83-84); East Anglian Cup 88-89; FA Amateur Cup QF 70-71; FA Tphy 3rd Qualifying Rd replay 74-75; FA Vase 3rd Rd 89-90.

CAMBERLEY TOWN

Chairman: Ian Waldren **Vice Chairman:** Gordon Foss **President:** Paul Prentice
Secretary: Dave Slater, 33 Blythwood Drive, Frimley, Camberley, Surrey. GU15 1SD (01276 23096).
Manager: Danny McGranaghan **Asst Manager:** Paul Xiberras **Coach:** Paul Holden
Press Officer: Andy Vaughan **Comm. Manager:** Andy Jennings **Physio:** Julia Richards.
Ground: Krooner Park, Krooner Road, off Frimley Rd, Camberley, Surrey GU15 2QP (01276 65392).
Directions: M3 Jct 4, follow signs to Frimley, then B3411 towards Camberley, ground on left opp. 'The Standard' pub.
Capacity: 3,000 **Seats:** 195 **Cover:** 195 **Floodlights:** Yes **Founded:** 1896
Clubhouse: Open matchdays & 2 evenings. Food available from burger bar on matchdays. **Club Shop:** Yes
Colours: Red & white/red/red & white **Change colours:** All yellow **Nickname:** Krooners, Reds or Town
Programme: 24 pages, 50p **Sponsors:** Zip Print **Midweek Matches:** Tuesday **Reserve's League:** Suburban
PREVIOUS - Leagues: Ascot & District; West Surrey; Aldershot Snr; Surrey Snr 22-73; Spartan 73-75; Athenian 75-77 82-84; Isthmian 77-82. **Names:** Camberley & Yorktown 1896-1946; Camberley FC 46-67.
HONOURS: FA Vase QF 85-86, Isthmian Lg Div 2 R-up 78-79, Surrey Snr Lg 30-31 31-32 32-33 (R-up 46-47 61-62, Lg Charity Cup 37-38 51-52 (R-up 31-32 36-37 54-55 72-73)), Surrey Snr Cup 78-79 (R-up 35-36), W. Surrey Lg 13-14 (R-up 12-13), Ascot & Dist Lg 03-04, Surrey Jnr Charity Cup R-up 08-09, Surrey Jnr Cup 1897-98 1909-10 (R-up 07-08), Aldershot Snr Lg 12-13 (Lg Charity Cup R-up 21-22), Southern Comb. Cup 80-81 (R-up 78-79 85-86 87-88).

CLAPTON

Chairman: Ken Harris **President:** Mike Gliksten **Founded:** 1878
Secretary: Steven Walters,10 Buttfield Close,Dagenham Village,Essex.RM10 8TJ. (0181 596 0424).
Press Officer: Secretary **Manager:** Lyndon Lynch **Coach:** Jeff Davis **Physio:** Tony Blackwell
Ground: The Old Spotted Dog, Upton Lane, Forest Gate, London E7 9NP (0181 472 0822).
Directions: BR to Forest Gate, tube to Plaistow (District Line). Official entrance in Upton Lane. Docklands Light Railway to Prince Regent then 325 bus to ground.
Capacity: 2,000 **Seats:** 100 **Cover:** 180. **Floodlights:** Yes **Nickname:** Tons **Club Shop:** Yes
Clubhouse: Open most evenings & match day. Light snacks available. To hire please contact club.
Colours: Red & white stripes/black/black **Change colours:** All blue. **Midweek Matchday:** Tuesday
Programme: 12-16 pages 60p **Editor:** Secretary **Reserves' Lge:** Essex/Herts Border Com.
Previous Leagues: Southern 1894-96 (founder members); London 1896-97. **Sponsors:** Mullalley Const.
96-97 - Captain: Dave Walker **P.o.Y.:** Ben Wood **Top scorer:** Robbie Drake (15)
Hons: FA Amtr Cup 06-07 08-09 14-15 23-24 24-25 (R-up 04-05), Isthmian Lg 10-11 22-23 (R-up 05-06 07-08 09-10 24-25, Div 2 82-83), Essex Thames-side Tphy(2), A.F.A. Invitation Cup(2), London Snr Cup(2), London Charity Cup, Essex Snr Cup(4), First English team to play on the continent, beating a Belgian Select XI over Easter 1890.

CORINTHIAN-CASUALS

Chairman: D G Harrison **Gen Manager:** Steve Bangs.
Secretary: Brian Wakefield, 5 Martingales Close, Richmond, Surrey (0181 940 9208).
Match Secretary: G.Young, (0181 330 6643 H) **Team Manager:** Roger Steer
Ground: King George's Field, Hook Rise South, Tolworth, Surrey KT6 7NA (0181 397 3368).
Directions: A3 to Tolworth r'bout (The Toby Jug). Hook Rise is slip road immediately after the Toby Jug pub. Turn left under railway bridge after a 1/4 mile - grd on right. Half mile from Tolworth (BR); turn left, continue to Toby Jug, then as above. K2 Hoppa bus from Kingston passes ground.
Seats: 126 **Cover:** 500 **Capacity:** 1,700 **Floodlights:** Yes **Founded:** 1939.
Clubhouse: Evenings, matchdays, Sunday lunchtimes. Darts, pool, hot & cold snacks on matchdays.
Programme: 24-48 pages, £1 **Editor:** Gary Brigden (0181 385 0593) **Press Officer:** Secretary
Colours: White/navy/white **Change colours:** Chocolate & pink/sky/sky **Reserves' League:** Suburban
Previous Leagues: Isthmian 39-84, Spartan 84-97 **Best FA Cup season:** 1st Rd replay 85-86.
Players progressing to Football League: Andy Gray, Tony Finnegan, Alan Pardew to Crystal Palace.
Honours: FA Amat Cup R-up 55-56 (SF 56-57), London Spartan Lg R-up 92-93 (Lg Cup R-up 91-92).

CROYDON ATHLETIC

Chairman: Keith Tuckey **Vice Chairman / Press Officer:** Clive Thompson
Secretary: Dean Fisher, Flat 4, 316 Whitehorse Road, Croydon, Surrey CR0 2LE, (0181 405 4300 H, 0171 221 7292 B)
Manager: Micky Taylor **Asst Man.:** Des McCarthy **Physio:** M Reed **Coach:** Leon Maxwell **Kit Man.:** P Courtman
Ground: Mayfields, off Mayfield Road, Thornton Heath, Surrey CR7 6DN (0181-664-8343)
Directions: Follow A23 from London & continue on A23 into Thornton Road. After roundabout take 2nd on right into Silverleigh Road, left fork into Trafford Road which continues into Mayfield Road. To end and turn left and follow narrow road to ground. 1 mile from Norbury (BR). Buses 109, 154.
Seats: 163 **Cover:** 300 **Capacity:** 3,000 **Floodlights:** Yes **Founded:** 1990
Clubhouse: Open every evening & Sunday lunch. **Club Shop:** Yes **Sponsors:** T.C.S. Media
Programme: 52 pages, £1 **Editor:** Secretary **Midweek matches:** Tuesday **Reserve League:** Suburban (S)
Colours: Maroon & white/maroon/maroon **Change colours:** All white
Best season - FA Vase: 3rd Rd 94-95 **FA Cup:** 2nd Qual. Rd 94-95
Top Scorer: Lee May **96-97 - Captain:** Terry Gale **P.o.Y.:** Terry Gale
Honours: London Spartan Lg winners 94-95, R-up 88-89 93-94, (Reserve Div 88-89, R-up 88-89, London Snr Cup R-up 91-92, Southern Youth Lg 92-93, Bearman Harber Mem Trophy 87-88, Wirral Prog 86-87 96-97.

DORKING

Chairman: Jack Collins **President:** Ingram Whittingham **Vice-Chairman:** Ray Collins **Co. Sec.:** Martin Collins
Secretary: David Short, 29 Bennett Close, Cobham, Surrey KT11 1AH (01932 866496)
Manager: Steve Osgood **Asst Manager:** Bryan Stannard **Physio:** Bennie Fishlock
Ground: Meadowbank, Mill Lane, Dorking, Surrey RH4 1DX (01306 884112).
Directions: Mill Lane is off Dorking High St. next to Woolworths and Marks & Spencers opposite the White Horse pub. Fork right in Mill Lane past the Malthouse pub. 1/2 mile from both Dorking and Deepdene (BR) stations.
Capacity: 3,600 **Cover:** 800 **Seats:** 200 **Floodlights:** Yes **Formed:** 1880 **Nickname:** The Chicks
Clubhouse: Open matchdays, w/ends & training nights. Hot & cold food on matchdays. **Club Shop:** Yes
Programme: 48 pages £1 **Editor:** Paul Mason **Press Officer:** Bryan Bletso **Reserve League:** Suburban
Colours: Green & white hoops/green/yellow **Change colours:** All blue **Midweek matches:** Tuesday
Best FA Cup season: 1st Round Proper 92-93, 2-3 v Plymouth A. (H)
Previous Leagues: Surrey Senior 22-56 77-78; Corinthian 56-63; Athenian 63-74 78-80; Southern 74-77.
96-97 - Captain: Tony Leslie **P.o.Y.:** Bryan Stannard **Top scorer:** Alex Harding
Honours: Isthmian Lge Div 2 Sth 88-89, (Full Members Cup R-up 92-93); Surrey Sen Cup R-up 1885-86 1989-90; Surrey Senior Shield (2), R-up (3); Surrey Sen Lge (4), R-up (2), Lge Cup (3); Lge Charity Cup (4), R-up (5); Gilbert Rice F'lit Cup 87-88 (R-up 89-90); Surrey I'mediate Cup 56-57 (R-up 54-55); Southern Comb. Challenge Cup 92-93; FA Trophy 2nd Rd 91-92; FA Vase 3rd Rd(3) 83-84 86-88.

EAST THURROCK UNITED

Chairman: Brian Grover **Vice Chairman:** Harry Caine. **President:** Alan Gower
Secretary: Malcolm Harris, 14 Colne Valley, Upminster, Essex RM14 1QA (017082 28818).
Press Officer: Secretary **Manager:** Tommy Lee **Physio:** Pat Thompson
Ground: Rookery Hill, Corringham, Essex (01375 644166-club, 641009-boardroom).
Directions: A13 London-Southend, take 1014 at Stanford-le-Hope for two and a half miles - ground on left. Two miles from Stanford-le-Hope and Basildon BR stations.
Seats: 160 **Cover:** 360 **Capacity:** 3,000 **Floodlights:** Yes **Founded:** 1969 **Nickname:** Rocks
Clubhouse: Open all day seven days a week. Hot and cold snacks. **Club Shop:** Yes
Programme: 24 pages, 50p **Editor:** Tony Smith (01268 292142)
Colours: Amber/black/black **Change:** Blue/white/white **Reserves' Lge:** Essex/Herts Border Com.
Previous Leagues: Sth Essex Comb.; Gtr London; Metropolitan 72-75; London Spartan 75-79; Essex Snr 79-92.
Players progressing to Football League: Greg Berry (Leyton Orient).
Honours: Metropolitan Lg Div 2 72-73, Essex Snr Lg R-up 88-89 (Lg Cup 88-89 91-92, Harry Fisher Mem. Tphy 83-84 90-91, Sportsmanship Award 81-82 86-87 89-89), Essex Snr Tphy R-up 91-92 95-96, Fred Budden Tphy R-up 89-90, Essex & Herts Border Comb. 89-90 (Lg Cup 89-90).

EPSOM & EWELL

Chairman: Peter Atkins **Vice Chairman:** Stella Lamont **Nickname:** E's **Founded:** 1917
Secretary: David Wilson, 33 Delaporte Close, Epsom, Surrey KT17 4AF (01372 729817).
Press Officer: Sec. **Manager:** Adrian Hill **Coach:** John Wood **Physio:** Jo Morgan
Ground: (Share with Banstead Ath. FC) Merland Rise, Tadworth, Surrey KT20 5JG (01737 350982).
Clubhouse: Normal licensing hours, food available. **Club Shop:** No
Programme: 28/32 pages, 50p **Editor:** Stella Lamont (01737 356245).
Colours: Royal & white **Change:** All yellow **Midweek Matches:** Tuesday **Reserves' League:** Suburban
Best Season - FA Cup: 1st Rd Proper 33-34, lost 2-4 at Clapton Orient.
FA Vase: Finalists 74-75 **FA Trophy:** 2nd Rd Proper 81-82.
Previous Leagues: Surrey Snr 24-27 73-75; London 27-49; Corinthian 49-63; Athenian 63-73 75-77.
96-97 - Captain: Graham Meakin **Top Scorer:** Andy Boxall (25) **P.o.Y.:** Tony Boorman
Hons: F.A. Vase R-up 74-75; London Lg 27-28, R-up (5); Corinthian Lg Memorial Shield 59-60 (R-up 51-52 56-57); Athenian Lg Div 2 R-up 75-76 (Lg Cup R-up 76-77, Div 2 Cup R-up 67-68); Isthmian Lg Div 2 77-78 (Div 1 R-up 83-84); Surrey Snr Lg 25-26 26-27 74-75 (R-up 73-74), Lg Cup 73-74 74-75, Charity Cup 26-27 (R-up 73-74), Surrey Snr Cup 80-81 (R-up 28-29 53-54 83-84); Surrey Snr Shield 32-33 54-55; Surrey Intermediate Cup 29-30, Charity Cup 57-58; Southern Comb. Cup 79-80 (R-up 82-83 92-93).

FLACKWELL HEATH

Chairman: T Glynn **Vice Chairman:** M Baker **President:** Ken Crook
Secretary: Mrs Christine Hobbs, 23 Southfield Rd., Flackwell Heath, Bucks. HP10 9BT (01628-521051)
Ground: Wilks Park, Heath End Rd, Flackwell Heath, High Wycombe, Bucks HP10 9EA (01628 523892).
Directions: M40 jct 4, follow A404 towards High Wycombe, 1st turning into Daws Hill Lane, continue for 2 miles until you see signs for the club, left into Magpie Lane, ground at rear of Magpie (PH). Bus 301 either from bus station or High Street near bottom of Crendon Street which comes from BR station. Ask for Oakland Way.
Capacity: 2,000 **Seats:** 150 **Cover:** Yes **Floodlights:** Yes **Club Shop:** No
Clubhouse: Open every night 6.30-11pm and before and after matches. Hot food in tea bar.
Programme: 18 pages 50p **Reserves' League:** Suburban **Founded:** 1907
Colours: Red/white/red **Change colours:** Yellow/black/yellow **Midweek Matches:** Tuesday
Best F.A. Cup season: 2nd Qualifying Round replay 1990-91 (lost 0-3 at Grays after 2-2 draw).
Previous Leagues: Wycombe & District; Gt Western Comb.; Hellenic 76-82; Athenian 82-84.
96-97 - Captain: Ben Richards **P.o.Y.:** Ben Richards **Top Scorer:** Gary Wiltshire
Hons: Gt Western Combination 57-58 62-63; Hellenic Lg Div 1 R-up 76-77; Berks & Bucks Snr Cup SF 85-86.

FORD UNITED

Chairman: J M Rowe **Vice-Chairman:** George Adams **President:** Paddy Byrne **Manager:** Denis Elliott
Secretary: Michael Ewen, 215 Rush Green Road, Romford, Essex RM7 0JR (01708 724178 H)
Ground: Ford Spts & Soc. Club, Rush Green Rd., Romford (01708 745678). **Directions:** On the A124 (Rush Green road) on left going towards Hornchurch. 2 miles from Romford (BR). Buses 173, 175 87, 106, 23.
Seats: 400 **Cover:** Yes **Capacity:** 3,000 **Floodlights:** Yes **Founded:** 1958 **Club Shop:** No
Clubhouse: 4 bars, 2 dance halls, tea bar, snooker room. **Programme:** Yes **Editor:** Secretary
Colours: L/blue & d/blue/navy/navy **Change:** Green with black & white trim/green/green
Sponsor: Sky Sports **Nickname:** Motormen **Reserves' League:** Essex & Herts Border Comb.
Record Attendance: 58,000 Briggs Sports v Bishop Auckland, at St James Park, Newcastle, FA Amateur Cup.
Previous Leagues: Spartan, Aetolian, Metropolitan
96-97 - Captain: Reg Gardner **Top Scorer:** Jeff Wood **P.o.Y.:** Jeff Wood
Honours: FA Amateur Cup SF 53-54; London Snr Cup 55-56 56-57 94-95; Essex Snr Lge 96-97, Trophy 90-91 91-92, Cup 39-40 49-50 50-51 51-52, R-up 96-97; Spartan Lg 49-50 50-51 55-56 56-57 57-58; London Lg 36-37 38-39; Essex Elizabethan 59-60 60-61 70-71; Gtr London Lg 70-71; Essex Snr Lg 91-92 (R-up 94-95, Lg Cup 85-86; Sportsmanship Award 77-78 79-80 80-81); Essex & Herts Border Comb.(res) 94-95 (Lg Cup 94-95).

HARLOW TOWN

Chairman: Jim Bothwell **Press Officer:** Gavin McWilliams (01279 506848) **Founded:** 1879
Secretary: Jim Aldridge, 1 Brockles Mead, Harlow CM19 4PS (01279 860561)
Manager: Eddie McClusky **Asst. Manager:** Fred Donnelly **Physio:** Malcolm Roddy
Ground: Harlow Sports Centre, Hammarskjold Rd, Harlow CM20 2JF (0279 445319).
Directions: Near town centre, 10 mins walk from Harlow (BR) station.
Capacity: 10,000 **Cover:** 500 **Seats:** 400 **Floodlights:** Yes **Nickname:** Hawks **Club Shop:** No
Clubhouse: Open daily 11-11 (10.30 Sundays). Hot & cold food available. **Sponsors:** BritSec Int. Ltd
Colours: Red & white/white/white **Change:** White & yellow/yellow/yellow **Midweek matches:** Wednesday
Programme: 32 pages, 70p **Editor:** Phil Tuson (0279 416743) **Reserve's League:** Essex & Herts Border Comb.
Previous - Leagues: East Herts (pre-1932); Spartan 32-39 46-54; London 54-61; Delphian 61-63; Athenian 63-73; Isthmian 73-92; inactive 92-93. **Grounds:** Marigolds 1919-22; Green Man Field 22-60.
96-97 - Captain: Dennis Greene **P.o.Y.:** Neil Moore **Top Scorer:** Dennis Greene
Honours: Isthmian Lg Div 1 78-79 (R-up 82-83, Div 2 Nth 88-89, Yth Cup 77-78), Ath'n Lg Div 1 71-72, E Angl. Cup 89-90, Knight F'lit Cup R-up 87-88, Essex Snr Cup 78-79, Essex F'lit Competition R-up 71-72, London Lg Chal. Cup 59-60, Spartan Lg Cup 52-53, Epping Hosp. Cup(3) 46-49, Essex & Herts Border Comb Cup 75-76, Fred Budden Tphy 88-89 89-90, Chelmsford Yth Lg 86-87 (Lg Cup 86-87 87-88).

HEMEL HEMPSTEAD

Chairman: Ted Garnham **President:** Tom Abbott. **Vice President:** Dave Lloyd.
Secretary: Adrian Marson, 1 Pelham Court, Hemel Hempstead HP2 4UN. (01442 243053)
Manager: Mike Vipond **Asst Manager:** Mark Pearson. **Physio:** Chris Hewitt
Ground: Vauxhall Ground, Adeyfield Rd, Hemel Hempstead HP2 4HW (01442 259777) **Nickname:** Hemel
Directions: Euston to Hemel Hempstead Station. H2 or H3 bus to Windmill Rd, Longlands.
Capacity: 3,000 **Seats:** 100 **Cover:** Yes **Floodlights:** Yes **Founded:** 1885 **Club Shop:** Yes
Clubhouse: (01442 259777). 7-11pm weekdays, 12-11pm w/ends & Bank Hols. Tea bar open matchdays
Colours: All red with white trim **Change colours:** All blue **Reserves' League:** Essex & Herts Border Comb.
Programme: 36 pages, 50p **Editor/Press Off.:** Brian Jackson **Sponsors:** Dexion **Midweek Matches:** Tuesday
Previous - Leagues: Spartan 22-52; Delphian 52-63; Athenian 63-77. **Names:** Apsley 1885-1947; Hemel H'stead Town (merged with Hemel H'stead Utd in 1947). **Grounds:** Crabtree Lane (til '71).
Hons: Herts Snr Cup 05-06 07-08 08-09 25-26 61-62 65-66 91-92, Herts Charity Cup/Shield 25-26 34-35 51-52 63-64 76-77 83-84 (R-up 90-91), Spartan Lg 33-34, Herts Intermediate Cup 54-55 65-66 83-84, West Herts St Mary Cup 70-71 75-76 82-83 85-86 90-91 91-92 93-94, Athenian Lg Div 1 R-up 64-65 (Reserves Cup 65-66), Delphian Lg(reserves) 54-55 (Reserves Cup 54-55 61-62).

EPSOM & EWELL F.C. - L-R, Back: Chris Bedworth, Martyn Jones, Nigel Bennett, Graham Morris, Paul Meredith, Steve Smith, Micky Owen, Andy Boxall, Graham Meakin. Front: Gary Meakin (Mascot), Tony Hoy, Tony Boorman, Alan Galloway, Dave Argent, Nick Cawthorne. Photo: Gary Letts

CLAPTON F.C. - L-R, Back: Steven Walters (Hon. Sec.), Keith Meade, Asa Pamplin, Justin Glasgow, Robbie Drake, Ken Harris (Chairman), Lero Mattis, Steve Perkins, Dave Walker (Capt.), Lyndon Lynch (Football Manager), Roy Drake, Tony Blackwell (Physio). Front: Adrian Allen, Marlon Stuart, Gavin Smith, Alan Fenn, Norman McPhee, Ben Wood, Robbie Ford.

KINGSBURY TOWN F.C.

HERTFORD TOWN

President: Bernard Molloy **Chairman:** John Hedley **Vice Chairman:** Graham Wood.
Secretary: Stephen Hedley, 28 Cherry Tree Green, Hertford SG14 2HP (0992 587011).
Press Off.: Graham Showell **Comm. Mgr:** Peter Slade **Manager:** David Whitehead **Physio:** Ray Price
Ground: Hertingfordbury Park, West Street, Hertford (0992 5837011). **Nickname:** The Blues
Directions: Rail to Hertford Nth (from Moorgate) or Hertford East (Liverpool Str.); both 15 mins walk. Green Line bus to town centre then 10 mins walk. By road; off bypass heading east, turn off at Ford garage.
Capacity: 6,500 **Seats:** 200 **Cover:** 1,500 **Floodlights:** Yes **Founded:** 1908
Club Shop: Souvenirs from Graham Showell, 5 Beehive Lane, Welwyn Garden City AL7 4BB. **Clubhouse:** Yes
Colours: Blue & yellow/blue/blue **Change colours:** All red **Midweek Matches:** Tuesday **Sponsors:** None
Programme: 28 pages, 40p **Editor:** Martin Climpson:(01992 589972) **Reserves' Lge:** Essex & Herts Border Comb.
Previous Leagues: Herts Co./ Spartan 21-47 48-59/ Delphian 59-63/ Athenian 63-72/ Eastern Co's 72-73.
Hons: Herts Char. Cup 72-73, Herts Snr Cup 66-67, Hertford Char. Shd 19-20 20-21 35-36 49-50 55-56 59-60, Eastern Co's Lg Cup 72-73, East Anglian Cup 62-63 69-70, Southern Co's Comb. F-lit Cup 94-95, Mithras Cup SF 85-86.

HORNCHURCH

Chairman: Brian Davie **Vice Chairman:** K Nicholls **Manager:** Dave Cox **Physio:** D Edkins
Secretary: Ted Harris, 13 Claremont Gdns, Upminster, Essex RM14 1DW (01708 227891).
Ground: The Stadium, Bridge Avenue, Upminster, Essex RM14 2LX (01708 220080).
Directions: Fenchurch Street to Upminster (BR) then 10 mins walk. Or tube to Upminster Bridge (LT), right outside station, 2nd right into Bridge Ave., ground 150yds on right. By road Bridge Avenue is off A124 between Hornchurch and Upminster. Buses 248, 348, 370, 373 from Romford or Upminster BR stations.
Capacity: 3,000 **Seats:** 300 **Cover:** 350 **Floodlights:** Yes **Founded:** 1923 **Nickname:** Urchins
Clubhouse: Mon-Fri 7.30-11, Sat 12-11, Sun 12-3. Cafeteria open matchdays on ground. **Club Shop:** Yes
Colours: Red & white/red/red **Change colours:** Purple & yellow **Sponsors:** Premier Snacks
Programme: 16-20 pages with admission **Editor/Press Off.:** Rob Monger(01268 490847)
Midweek Matches: Tuesday **Reserves' League:** Essex & Herts Border Comb.
Previous Leagues: Romford 1925-38/ Spartan 38-52/ Delphian 52-59/ Athenian 59-75.
Honours: Athenian Lg 66-67, Romford Lg(2), Essex Snr Trophy R-up 86-87, Essex Jnr Cup, Essex Thameside Tphy 84-85, F.A. Vase 5th Rd 74-75, Isthmian Yth Cup, Carlsberg Trophy R-up 93-94.

KINGSBURY TOWN

Chairman: Allan J Davies **Secretary:** David Thomas, 9 Hillview Gardens, Kingsbury, NW9 0DE
Press Officer: Allan Davies (01895 443761) **Manager:** Peter Blain **Physio:** Margaret Romer
Ground: Silver Jubilee Park, Townsend Lane, Kingsbury, London NW9 7NE (0181 205 1645).
Directions: Underground to Kingsbury, cross road and take bus 183 to Townsend Lane (2 miles) - ground in far left-hand corner of Silver Jubilee Park.
Capacity: 2,500 **Seats:** 165 **Cover:** 400 **Floodlights:** Yes **Nickname:** Kings **Founded:** 1927
Clubhouse: Mon-Fri 7-11, Sat 12-11, Sun 12-2.30 & 7-10.30. Food on matchdays. **Club Shop:** Yes
Colours: Royal/white/royal **Change colours:** Yellow/navy/yellow **Sponsors:** VPA Entertainment Technology.
Programme: 16-20 pages, 50p **Editor:** Allan Davies **Reserves' League:** Suburban **Midweek Matches:** Tuesday
Previous Leagues: Hellenic 27-30 (as Davis Sports)/ Willesden & District 30-43/ Middx Snr 44-47/ Parthenon 47-59// Spartan 59-76 78-81/ Athenian 76-78 81-84.
96-97 - Captain: Niall O'Rourke **P.o.Y.:** Mitchell Morris **Top Scorer:** Randall Ambersley
Hons: FA Vase 4th Rd 74-75; Isthmian Lg Div 2 Nth R-up 85-86; Spartan Lg Cup R-up 59-60 64-65; Parthenon Lg 51-52 (Prem Charity Cup 52-53 53-54; Snr Charity Cup 53-54); Middx Snr Cup R-up 88-89; Middx Charity Cup 85-86 (R-up 88-89); Middx Lg Charity Cup(3) 44-47; Willesden & Dist. Lg R-up 30-31 (Div 2 34-35).

LEWES

Chairman: D Southouse **President:** W D Carr **Manager:** Terry Parris **Asst Man.:** Andy Sinden
Secretary: John Lewis, Marshlands, Kingston Rd, Lewes, East Sussex BN7 3NB (01273 472822).
Ground: The Dripping Pan, Mountfield Road, Lewes BN7 1XN (01273 472100). **Directions:** Two minute walk from Lewes (BR) - turn left out of station and left into Mountfield Road. Ground 100 yards on right.
Capacity: 2,600 **Cover:** 400 **Seats:** 400 **Floodlights:** Yes **Nickname:** Rooks **Founded:** 1885
Clubhouse: (01273 472100). Bar, tea bar, pool, table tennis. **Steward:** P Brook. **Club Shop:** Yes
Colours: Red & Black stripes/black/red **Change colours:** Yellow/green **Midweek matches:** Tuesday
Programme: 32 pages, £1 **Editor:** Martin Burke **Reserves' League:** Sussex Co. Res. Sect.
Previous Leagues: Mid Sussex 1886-1920; Sussex County 20-65; Athenian 65-77.
Honours: Isth. Lg Div 2 R-up 79-80 91-92; Ath'n Lg Div 1 69-70 (Div 2 67-68); Sussex Co. Lg 64-65 (R-up 24-25 33-34 58-59 63-64, Lg Cup 39-40); Mid Sussex Lg 10-11 13-14; Sussex Snr Cup 64-65 70-71 84-85 (R-up 79-80 82-83 87-88); Sussex Royal Ulster Rifles Charity Cup(3) 61-63 64-65; Gilbert Rice F'lit Cup 82-83 88-89; Neale Tphy 68-69; Sussex F'lit Cup 76-77 (SF 83-84); Southern Counties Comb Div 1 80-81.

SOUTHALL

Chairman / Press Officer: J J Loftus **President:** R E Fowler **Founded:** 1871
Secretary: Maria Smith, 20 Berry Lane, Rickmansworth, Herts, WD3 2HH (01923 896803)
Manager: Gregg Phillips **Assistant Manager:** Kenny Lavender **Physio:** George Richardson
Ground: Pendley Sports Centre, Cow Lane, Tring, Herts. HP23 5NS (014428 23075). Sharing with Tring Town for another season. **Ground directions & details:** As Tring Town
Clubhouse: Normal pub hours. Hot snacks available on matchdays. **Club Shop:** No **Nickname:** Fowlers
Colours: Red & white stripes/white/red **Change:** Blue & black **Sponsors:** Loftus Design & Build
Programme: 6 pages, 50p **Editor:** Secretary **Midweek Matchday:** Tuesday **Reserves' Lge:** Middx County
Previous Leagues: Southern 1896-1905; Gt Western Suburban; Herts & Middx; Athenian 19-73.
96-97 - Captain: Paul Harris **P.o.Y.:** Paul Harris **Top Scorer:** Varnava Michael
Hons: FA Amtr Cup R-up 24-25 (SF 25-26 52-53), FA Vase R-up 85-86, Isthmian Lg Div 2 R-up 74-75, Gt Western Suburban Lg 12-13, Athenian Lg 26-27 (R-up 54-55), Middx Snr Cup(12) 07-08 10-11 11-12 12-13 22-23 23-24 24-25 26-27 36-37 44-45 53-54 54-55, Middx Charity Cup 10-11 11-12 13-14 22-23(jt with Botwell Mission) 23-24(jt with Botwell Mission) 27-28 36-37 51-52 68-69 83-84, London Snr Cup SF 35-36 84-85.

TRING TOWN

Chairman: Harry Bowden **Secretary:** Tony Huhn, 6 Sovereign Court, Willow Road, Aylesbury, Bucks HP19 3NL (01296 432496 H, 0956 281797 Mob)
Manager: Paul Burgess **Asst Manager:** Micky Connolly **Physio:** Stuart McCorkindale
Ground: Pendley Sports Centre, Cow Lane, Tring, Herts HP23 5NS (01442 823075).
Directions: One mile from Tring centre on A41 - direct connection to M25 (jct 20) via new A41 bypass. One and a half miles from Tring (BR). Numerous buses from station and Watford-Aylesbury routes serve ground.
Capacity: 2,500 **Seats:** 150 **Cover:** 250 **Floodlights:** Yes **Nickname:** T's. **Founded:** 1904
Clubhouse: All licensing hours. Dancehall, pool, darts, kitchen. **Club Shop:** No
Programme: 24 pages 50p **Editor/Press Officer:** Alan Lee (01702 216063) **Midweek Matchday:** Monday
Colours: Red & white stripes/white/white **Change:** Yellow & blue stripes/blue/blue **Reserves' Lge:** None
Previous Leagues: Gt Western Combination; Spartan 53-75; Athenian 75-77.
Players progressing to Football League: Peter Gibbs (Watford).
Honours: Spartan Lg 66-67, R-up 68-69. Herts Charity Shield winners twice, R-up 4. Athenian Lg Div 2 R-up 76-77, Herts Snr Cup R-up 77-78.

WARE

Chairman: W J Luck **Secretary:** I Bush, 42 Burnett Squ, Hertford, Herts SG14 2HD (01992 587334).
Manager: Steve Ringrose **Coach:** Dermot Drummy **Physio:** Frank Roberts
Ground: Wodson Park, Wadesmill Road, Ware Herts SG12 0HZ (01920 463247).
Directions: A10 off at junction A602 & B1001 (Ware North), turn right at roundabout 300yds, and follow Ware sign, past Rank factory, turn left at main roundabout onto A1170 (Wadesmill Rd). After 3/4 mile stadium on right.
Capacity: 3,300 **Seats:** 312 **Cover:** 500 **Floodlights:** Yes **Nickname:** Blues **Founded:** 1892
Clubhouse: Licensed bar open matchdays. Light snacks at refreshment bar. **Club Shop:** Yes
Programme: 24 pages, 50p **Editor/Press Officer:** Tony Raisborough (01707 656568)
Colours: Blue & white stripes/blue/red **Change colours:** Amber/black **Midweek Matchday:** Tuesday
Reserves' Lge: Essex & Herts Border Comb. **Sponsors:** Charvill Bros Ltd.
Previous Leagues: East Herts; North Middx 07-08; Herts County 08-25; Spartan 25-55; Delphian 55-63; Athenian 63-75.
Honours: Herts Snr Cup 1898-99 03-04 06-07 21-22 53-54, Herts Char. Shield 26-27 56-57 58-59 62-63 85-86, Herts Char. Cup R-up 64-65 65-66 78-79 89-90, Spartan Lg 52-53 (Div 1 Sect.B 51-52, Div 2 Sect.A 26-27), Athenian Lg Div 2 Cup 65-66 72-73, East Anglian Cup 73-74, Herts Co. Lg 08-09 21-22, East Herts Lg 04-05 06-07 (Lg Cup 06-07), Perry Cup 26-27 28-29 37-38 51-52 52-53 53-54 55-56, Dunkels Cup 52-53, Rolleston Cup 39-40 51-52.

WINGATE & FINCHLEY

Chairman: Peter Rebak **Vice Chairman:** **President:** H Whidden.
Secretary: Richard Cooper, c/o Club Tel,0181 446 2217 Fax 0181 343 8194
Press Off.: Harvey Ackerman **Manager:** Bobby Fisher **Coach:** Jeff Bookman **Physio:** Amos Shanaan
Ground: The Abrahams Stadium, Summers Lane, Finchley, London N12 0PD.(0181 446 2217)
Directions: North Circular (A406) to jct with High Road Finchley (A1000), go north and Summers Lane is 200 yds on rt - parking 80 cars. Tube to East Finchley (Northern Line) and then 263 bus to Summers Lane towards North Finchley
Capacity: 8,500 **Seats:** 500 **Cover:** 500 **Floodlights:** Yes **Founded:** 1991 **Nickname:** Blues
Clubhouse: Open during matches. Also tea-bar selling most refreshments. **Club Shop:** No.
Colours: Blue/white/blue **Change Colours:** All red **Midweek matches:** Tuesday
Programme: 24 pages, 50p **Editor:** Marc Morris (0181 371 6008) **Reserve's Lge:** Sub Lge U18
Previous Leagues: (as Wingate & Finchley) South Mids 89-95
96-97 - Captain: Nigel Portman **P.o.Y.:** Andy Myers **Top Scorer:** Andy Myers
Honours: None since Wingate (1946) and Finchley (late 18800s) merged in 1991

COURAGE COMBINED COUNTIES LEAGUE

Chairman: Bill Lale
20 Beverley Gardens, Rustington, Sussex BN16 3LT (01903 770551)

Hon. Secretary: Clive Tidey
22 Silo Road, Farncombe, Godalming, Surrey GU7 3PA (01483 428453)

REVIEW OF SEASON 1996–97

One of the most exciting seasons int he League's history saw Ashford Town (Middlesex) win the title for the third consecutive season, a feat never previously achieved by any club. For much of the season newcomers Corinthian-Casuals had been at the top but with Ashford winning 8-1 at Feltham in midweek prior to the last Saturday of the season, it meant they needed only a point to clinch the championship in their final match which happened to be at home to Corinthian-Casuals.

Casuals themselves needed to win to take the league but in front of a record Combined Counties crowd of 455, Ashford looked stronger on the day, their 4-0 win securing both the match and the title. It was a personal triumph for Ashford manager Dave Kent who has led the Club to all three successes.

In the final weeks of the season all the other contenders had gradually fallen away, with only Bedfont, enjoying their best season for some time, still keeping in touch with a long run of unbroken success. At one point, with both Ashford and Casuals dropping a point or two here and there, they looked as if they may do even better, but in the end they finished third, with Feltham taking 4th place. Thus it was that three Middlesex clubs, with only three miles between them altogether, took three of the top four places.

At the other end of the table, Cranleigh looked doomed to finish in bottom place but after Christmas they rallied to some extent, leaving Raynes Park Vale, Merstham, and Walton Casuals the most likely contenders for the drop. In the end, a 2-5 defeat at Cobham in their final match ensured that Casuals would finish at the bottom by two points. At the time of writing they are facing relegation, with Chessington of the Surrey County Premier League being considered for promotion.

The League will be disappointed to lose Walton Casuals if it comes about, as they had worked so hard to get into the League two seasons ago, achieving miracles to get their ground into shape. They are excellently run and will hopefully soon be back.

Ashford Town (Middx) pictured immediately after beating Corinthian-Casuals 4-0 on the last day of the season to win the title.
Back Row L–R: Nathan Wharf, Don Hanks (physio), Stuart Flurry, Mark Silbeny, Gary Cambridge, Darren Smith, Tim Hollands, Paul German, Paul Burgess, Andrew Mitchell, Jim Heggarty, Lee Holman, Ian Squires (Courage), Simon Kent.
Front Row L–R: Andy Sherwood, Andrew Frost, Graham Hill, Richard McDonald, Baron Jolly, Des Vertannes, Dave Kent (manager) Ian Miles, Dannie Bulman.

In the Premier Challenge Cup, Feltham ensured further Middlesex domination by beating Godalming & Guildford 5-1 in the Final on a perfect Woking pitch. The teams looked evenly matched beforehand, with Godalming, indeed, having inflicted an 8-0 win over their opponents in the League, but on the night Feltham had all the answers, giving an efficient display. Paul Edgehill, who scored a hat-trick, was named 'man of the match', the other two goals coming from Lee Channell.

In national competition, Godalming & Guildford, made the only significant stir in the FA Cup, drawing away at Salisbury Town, but losing the replay at home. In the FA Vase, Reading Town, competing for the first time ever, fought their way through to the 4th Round only to lose narrowly to Banstead, who, of course, went on to the semi-final. On their way to the 4th Round, they achieved a notable success in Jersey against First Tower.

In the County Cups, Reading Town, the holders, again reached the final in the Berks & Bucks Senior Trophy, only to lose after extra time to Abingdon United, whilst in the Middlesex Charity Cup, Ashford Town reached the semi-finals, before losing at Wembley.

Corinthian-Casuals enjoyed some success in the Surrey Senior Cup, including a win over ICIS Premier side Chertsey Town, before losing to Crystal Palace.

The League's leading scorer was Paul German of Ashford Town with 42, eleven ahead of second placed Paul Edgehill of Feltham, who notched 31.

At Reserve level, Godalming & Guildford took the league honours in some style, losing just once, their only defeat coming in the final match at Farnham Town. Bedfont with a late run, finished runners-up

The Reserve Challenge Cup was won by Ashford who beat Ash United by 5 goals to 3 in an exciting final whilst Godalming took the Reserve Shield, in the final match of the season overcoming a determined Reading Town by 2 goals to nil at Farnham Town.

The League's constitution for 1997–98 has yet to be determined at the time of writing. Corinthian-Casuals are hoping for promotion to the ICIS League, if they can get the required work done, whilst Walton Casuals are facing the possibility of relegation. Hartley Wintney may also fall foul of a proposed new rule preventing football taking place on an adjoining pitch whilst a Combined Counties match is in progress.

Croydon Athletic are due to transfer in from the Spartan League whilst Chessington, having finished in 2nd place in the Surrey Premier, are hoping for promotion. There are no contenders this season from either the Chiltonian League or the Middlesex County League.

After the controversies of the previous season at Management Committee level, league administration proceeded fairly smoothly through season 1996–97 and the League's fortunes improved when a sponsorship deal was eventually signed with Courage PLC. Regional Sales Manager Ian Squires took a keen interest in the League, attending a number of matches, and one offshoot of the sponsorship is that once again the League will be fielding a representative team in 1997–98.

There was one very sad note when Assistant Secretary John Whitefoot passed away after a long illness in hospital. John, who had been feeling a little better and had hoped to attend the League's AGM, had been instrumental in bringing about the sponsorship and will be sorely missed after so many years with the League.

Alan Constable
Hon. Fixture Sec.
23 May 1997

FINAL LEAGUE TABLES 1996–97

DIVISION PREMIER	*P*	*W*	*D*	*L*	*F*	*A*	*Pts*
Ashford Town (Middx)	38	27	6	5	107	39	87
Corinthian-Casuals	38	25	8	5	86	36	83
Bedfont	38	23	4	11	94	56	73
Feltham	38	21	3	14	88	67	66
Farnham Town	38	19	7	12	80	42	64
Reading Town	38	17	13	8	62	60	64
Chipstead	38	18	8	12	67	55	62
Sandhurst Town	38	17	10	11	61	63	61
Godalming & Guildford	38	17	8	13	69	47	59
Netherne	38	14	6	18	55	62	48
Viking Sports	38	14	6	18	59	67	48
Hartley Wintney	38	12	11	15	65	78	47
Cove	38	12	11	15	43	59	47
Cobham	38	11	9	18	62	72	42
Westfield	38	10	12	16	34	46	42
Ash United	38	10	8	20	45	64	38
Raynes Park Vale	38	10	6	22	53	90	36
Cranleigh	38	9	6	23	52	88	33
Merstham	38	9	6	23	39	87	33
Walton Casuals	38	9	4	25	47	90	31

THE COURAGE COMBINED COUNTIES LEAGUE 1996–97 — PREMIER DIVISION

HOME TEAM	1	2	3	4	5	6	7	8	9	10	11	12	13	14	15	16	17	18	19	20
Ashford	*	1-1	3-4	2-0	3-1	4-0	2-0	4-1	4-0	5-0	0-1	3-0	2-0	2-0	3-1	4-1	2-4	3-2	4-0	2-1
Ash	2-4	*	0-1	3-0	2-1	1-2	1-3	0-0	1-1	1-1	3-1	1-1	0-2	2-0	3-1	0-2	0-1	1-3	3-0	0-3
Bedfont	0-5	0-1	*	1-2	3-3	2-3	1-1	5-0	0-3	1-4	0-1	2-1	6-0	2-1	3-0	1-1	6-0	3-1	2-3	2-2
Chipstead	0-0	3-0	2-6	*	3-2	0-2	2-1	0-0	1-0	0-3	3-0	1-3	2-1	1-1	1-2	2-3	6-0	1-1	6-0	0-0
Cobham	0-0	2-1	2-5	0-2	*	1-4	3-2	5-1	1-3	1-2	0-4	2-3	0-2	1-2	0-0	2-2	0-1	2-2	5-2	0-0
Cor-Cas	5-1	2-0	3-0	0-1	2-1	*	2-1	5-1	2-0	1-4	1-0	4-3	1-0	3-0	6-1	4-1	1-1	4-0	2-2	0-0
Cove	1-2	2-1	0-2	2-1	1-5	1-0	*	1-0	3-0	2-1	0-0	1-0	1-1	1-0	2-0	2-3	2-2	0-0	2-1	1-1
Cranleigh	0-3	3-0	0-3	2-2	1-2	1-2	3-0	*	1-4	2-8	1-6	3-3	1-2	4-1	1-1	3-1	2-3	3-0	3-2	0-1
Feltham	1-8	8-3	2-3	7-1	4-0	0-2	2-2	3-1	*	2-1	1-2	2-1	3-0	1-3	4-1	10-0	3-2	0-4	4-1	1-0
Farnham	2-2	2-3	2-0	1-2	3-1	2-2	3-0	0-1	4-1	*	0-0	4-0	9-1	2-0	0-0	0-1	0-3	0-2	1-0	2-0
Godg & G	1-5	3-0	0-1	2-2	1-1	0-3	4-1	1-0	8-0	0-0	*	7-0	2-1	4-3	2-0	1-1	1-1	3-0	2-1	3-1
Hartley W	0-5	2-2	1-4	1-1	3-0	1-1	2-2	3-1	1-2	2-2	3-2	*	2-1	2-1	4-1	3-3	1-2	1-0	6-2	0-1
Merstham	1-3	1-1	1-7	0-2	2-5	0-4	3-1	2-1	0-2	1-5	1-0	1-2	*	1-1	3-1	1-1	1-1	0-5	2-0	1-2
Netherne	2-2	1-0	1-3	4-2	0-3	2-0	2-0	2-2	0-1	0-2	2-0	1-3	0-1	*	2-0	1-2	3-3	6-3	4-0	3-0
RP Vale	2-3	0-3	1-2	0-4	1-1	2-6	5-1	3-1	4-2	1-4	1-1	1-1	2-1	2-0	*	2-5	1-6	1-1	1-4	5-3
Reading	1-0	2-1	2-1	2-1	1-1	1-1	0-0	5-0	1-1	2-1	3-1	1-1	2-0	1-1	1-3	*	1-1	1-0	3-1	0-0
Sandhurst	1-3	1-1	3-4	1-5	0-2	0-0	0-0	1-0	2-1	1-0	2-0	4-2	4-2	1-2	0-1	1-2	*	2-1	2-1	0-0
Viking	0-3	3-2	1-3	1-2	2-1	1-2	2-0	2-1	0-3	0-1	2-2	4-2	3-1	0-1	3-2	2-1	4-1	*	0-3	1-1
Walton	2-4	1-0	0-3	0-1	1-3	0-4	2-2	1-4	0-3	0-4	2-1	2-0	1-1	4-0	1-3	3-1	0-1	3-1	*	0-0
Westfield	1-1	0-1	0-2	1-2	1-2	0-0	0-1	1-3	0-3	1-0	1-0	1-1	2-0	1-2	1-0	2-1	2-3	1-2	2-1	*

PREMIER CHALLENGE CUP 1996–97

ROUND ONE

Chipstead	v	Walton Casuals	aet 5-4
Cranleigh	v	Ash United	2-3
Sandhurst Town	v	Ashford Town (Middx)	1-6
Viking Sports	v	Cove	2-1

ROUND TWO

Bedfont	v	Ashford Town (Middx)	aet 0-0
Chipstead	v	Cobham	2-3
Hartley Wintney	v	Farnham Town	2-1
Netherne	v	Corinthian-Casuals	3-5
Reading Town	v	Feltham	aet 1-2
Raynes Park	v	Ash United	aet 0-1
Westfield	v	Godalming & G	0-1
Viking Sports	v	Merstham	1-0

ROUND TWO REPLAY

Ashford Town (Mx) v Bedfont aet 1-0

(match declared void following successful Bedfont protest that insufficient extra time had been played)

ROUND TWO SECOND REPLAY

Ashford Town (Mx) v Bedfont 4-1

ROUND THREE

Ashford Town (Mx)	v	Corinthian-Casuals	1-0
Cobham	v	Godalming & G	1-4
Feltham	v	Ash United	9-2
Viking Sports	v	Hartley Wintney	3-0

SEMI-FINALS

Feltham	v	Viking Sports	6-0
Godalming & G	v	Ashford Town (Middx)	3-1

FINAL (at Woking FC)

Feltham v Godalming & G 5-1

LEADING GOALSCORERS 1996–97

PREMIER DIVISION

Paul German	Ashford Town (Middx)	42
Paul Edgehill	Feltham	31
Clifford West	Corinthian-Casuals	28
David Logie	Bedfont	27
Paul Warner	Farnham Town	26
Lee Channell	Feltham	23
Paul McMahon	Hartley Wintney	20

ASH UNITED

President: Mrs B Wallman
Chairman: Robert J Atkins, 3 Vale Road, Ash Vale, Aldershot, Hants. Tel: 01252 311259 (H)
Secretary: Alex Smith-Gander, 41 Ast Street, Ash, Aldershot, Hants. Tel/Fax: 01252 345221 (H)
Ground: Youngs Drive, off Shawfield Rd, Ash, Nr Aldershot (01252 20385).
Directions: A323 towards Ash, left into Shawfield Rd, right into Ash Church Rd, right at crossroads into Shawfield Rd. 1 mile from both Ash and Ash Vale BR stations.Bus - Stagecoach 20A, 550.
Capacity: 1,500 **Seats:** None **Cover:** Yes **Floodlights:** Yes **Founded:** 1911
Colours: Green/black/black. **Change colours:** All blue or all red. **Midweek Matchday:** Tuesday
Admission: £2 **Programme:** 36 pages, 50p. **Editor:** Gareth Watmore.
Previous Ground: Ash Common Rec. 70-71 **Previous Leagues:** Surrey Snr, Aldershot Snr

ASHFORD TOWN (MIDDX)

Chairman: Robert Parker **Vice Chairman:** Peter Hefferman **President:** E Britzman **Formed:** 1964
Secretary: Alan B J Constable, 30 Marlborough Rd, Ashford, Middx TW15 3QA 01784 885092 (H)
Manager: Dave Kent **Physio:** D Hanks **Press Secretary:** D Baker
Ground: Short Lane, Stanwell, Staines, Middx (01784 245908). **Directions:** M25 jct 13, A30 towards London, 3rd left at footbridge after Ashford Hospital crossroads - ground signposted after quarter of a mile on right down Short Lane. Two miles from Ashford (BR) and Hatton Cross (tube) stations. Bus route - Westlink 116.
Seats: None **Cover:** 75 **Capacity:** 2,000 **Floodlights:** Yes **Nickname:** Ash Trees
Clubhouse: Open 7 days a week. Refreshments always available - hot food on matchdays. **Club Shop:** No
Colours: Tangerine & white/white/tangerine. **Change colours:** All blue **Midweek matchday:** Tuesday
Programme: 24 pages, 50p **Programme Editor:** Secretary **Sponsors:** A. C. Frost Ltd.
PREVIOUS - **Ground:** Clockhouse Lane Rec. **Leagues:** Hounslow & Dist. 64-68; Surrey Intermediate 68-82; Surrey Premier 82-90.
CLUB RECORDS - **Goalscorer:** Andy Smith **Appearances:** Alan Contable 650.
Attendances: 750 v Brentford, friendly 29/7/86.
96-97 Captain: Gary Cambridge **Top Scorer:** Paul German (46) **P.o.Y.:** Paul German
Honours: Combined Co's Lg Champions 94-95, 95-96, 96-97 (Chall. Cup R-up 92-93 94-95, Lg Vase Cup R-up 91-92 94-95), Surrey I'mediate Lg, Surrey Prem. Cup 89-90, Middx Prem. Cup R-up 89-90. Southern Comb Cup 95-96.

BEDFONT

President: Roger Cooper **Chairman:** John Dollimore **Vice Chairman:** K Stone. **Founded:** 1968.
Secretary: Geoff Knock, 187 Northumberland Cres., Bedfont, Middlesex TW14 9SR Tel: 0181 890 6233 (H)
Manager: Alan Humphries **Coach:** Cliff Williamson. **Ass. Man.:** Bob Barnes
Ground: The Orchard, Hatton Rd, Bedfont, Middx. Tel: 0181 890 7264.
Directions: Turn down Faggs Rd opposite Hatton Cross (Picadilly Line) station on Great South Western Rd (A30), then sharp right into Hatton Rd. Ground opposite Duke of Wellington pub.
Seats: None **Cover:** 50 **Capacity:** **Floodlights:** Yes **Clubhouse:** Yes **Midweek matches:** Tuesday
Programme: 28 pages, 50p. Editors: Alan Humphries (01932 563548) and Colin McNeill (0181 384 8410).
Colours: Yellow & blue stripes/blue/blue **Change colours:** Blue/yellow/yellow.
Previous - Names: Bedfont Inst. (est. 1900), Bedfont Rangers (est. 1950) & Fairholme Utd (est. 1953) merged 1968. Club later merged with Interharvester (1973) & Bedfont Eagles (1988). **Ground:** Bedfont Recreation
Honours: Comb. Co's Lg Chal. Vase 92-93 (Res. Div R-up 88-89, Res. Cup R-up 89-90, Grant McClennan Yth Cup 91-92), Middx Lg 73-74 76-77 (Div 1 (Res) 71-72 78-79 79-80, Div 1 Cup 71-72 78-79 79-80), Surrey Prem. Lg 84-85 86-87, Middx I'mediate Cup 69-70 76-77, Inter. Contois Tour. 1992, Liege Euromann Tour. 89, Harold Clayton Cup 90-91, Hounslow & Dist. Lg Div 1 (Res) 86-87.

CHESSINGTON & HOOK UNITED

Chairman: Mr G Ellis, 63 Stormont Way, Chessington, Surrey. KT9 2QW. Tel: 0181 241 2832 (H)
Secretary: Mr A Warwick, 38 Hartfield Road, Chessington, Surrey. KT9 2PW. Tel: 0181 397 1843
Ground: Chalky Lane, Chessington, Surrey. Tel: 013727 29892
Directions: Railway station - Chessington South. Bus - London Transport 71.
Colours: All blue **Change colours:** All purple

CHIPSTEAD

Chairman: D Parsons, 32 Cannons Hill, Old Coulsdon, Surrey. Tel.: 01737 552682 **President:** Keith Rivers
Secretary: Geoff Corner, 20 Sunnymede Avenue, Carshalton Beeches, Surrey SM5 4JF. Tel: 0181 642 0827
Manager: John Sears **Coach:** Paul Duffield **Midweek matchday:** Tuesday.
Ground: High Road, Chipstead, Surrey. Tel: 01737 553250.
Directions: Brighton Road northbound, left into Church Lane, left into Hogcross Lane, right into High Road. One and a half miles from Chipstead (BR). Bus - London County 405, 407.
Seats: 30 **Cover:** 100 **Capacity:** 2,000 **Floodlights:** Yes **Founded:** 1906
Colours: Green/green/black. **Change colours:** Red or Purple/black/black **Programme:** 44 pages
Previous Leagues: Surrey Intermediate 62-82/ Surrey Premier 82-86 **Nickname:** Chips
Hons: Surrey Premier Lg R-up 82-83 83-84 85-86 (Lg Cup 82-83 84-85 85-86), Combined Co's Lg 89-90 (R-up 90-91 92-93, Lg Cup 86-87 90-91 92-93, Elite Class Cup R-up 89-90, Reserve Section Cup 92-93).

Gary Cambridge of Ashford Town (Middx) receives the championship trophy for the 3rd year in succession, following their 4-0 win over runners-up Corinthian Casuals on 10th May. Also in the photo are Ian Squires of Courage plc and Ron Monkley the League President.

Photo: Cranborne Photographic Services.

COBHAM

Chairman: E D Strange **President:** Eric Strange **Nickname:** Hammers **Founded:** 1892
Secretary: Ken Reed, 29 Waterer Gardens, Tadworth, Surrey. KT11 3BD. Tel: 01737 352641.
Manager: R Rembridge **Coach:** M Dickerson **Physio:** C Bird **Midweek matchday:** Tuesday
Ground: Leg O'Mutton Field, Anvil Lane, Downside Bridge Rd, Cobham, Surrey Tel: 01932 865959.
Directions: A3 turnoff A245, A307 (Portsmouth) towards Leatherhead, right into Between Streets, rt into Downside Rd then rt opposite car park. Cobham & Stoke D'Abernon (BR) 2 miles. Bus - Green Line 715, London Country 501, 513.
Capacity: 2,000 **Seats:** None **Cover:** Yes **Floodlights:** No **Club Shop:** No **Programme:** Yes
Colours: All red **Change colours:** All Blue **Sponsor:** Dawson/Strange Photography
Record Gate: 2,000 v Showbiz XI, charity game 1975 **Honours:** Combined Co's Lge Cup, Res Lge (3).

COVE

Chairman: Bob Clark, 3 Linstead Rd., Farnborough, Hants. Tel: 01276 33435 **President:** Ron Brown
Secretary: Graham Brown, 126 Prospect Road, Cove, Farnborough, Hants. GU14 8LB. Tel: 01252 650920
Ground: 7 Squirrels Lane, Farnborough, Hants GU14 8PB. Tel.: 01252 543615.
Directions: Farnborough (BR) 2 miles; right into Union Street, right at lights into Prospect Rd, left into West Heath Rd, right into Romayne close and follow signs to Cove FC. Or, M3 jct 4, follow A325 signed Aldershot & Farnham, right into Prospect Avenue (signposted Cove FC and Farnborough Town FC), then as above.
Capacity: 3,500 **Seats:** 75 **Cover:** 475 **Floodlights:** Yes **Founded:** 1897 **Midweek Matches:** Tuesday
Clubhouse: Mon-Fri 7-11, Sat 12-11, Sunday 12-3 & 7-11. Hot food on matchdays.
Club Shop: No, but souvenirs available in clubhouse. **Reserves' League:** Comb. Cos. 1st Div.
Programme: 30 pages, 50p **Editor:** Graham Brown (01252 650920) **Sponsors:** Sunnyside Removals
Colours: Black & amber/black/black **Change colours:** Red & white stripes/red/red
Honours: Surrey I'mediate Lg; Surrey Prem. Lg x5, R-up x3, Lg Cup x3, Res. Section x4, R-up x4, Res. Cup x2; Combined Co's Lg Cup 81-82; Hants Lg Div 3 x1, Div 4 x1, Div 2 R-up x1; Aldershot - Snr Cup x5, R-up x1, Snr Shield x4, Snr Lg x1, Div 2 x3, Div 2 Cup x1, Div 4 Cup x1.

CRANLEIGH

Chairman: Vic Simmonds **Vice Chairman:** Roy Kelsey **President:** Alan Pavia
Secretary: Roy Kelsey, 2 Wayside Cottages, High St., Bramley, Surrey. Tel: 01483 898117
Manager: Roy Kelsey **Asst Manager:** Paul Jones. **Coach:** Andy Clements.
Ground: Snoxall Playing Fields, Knowle Lane, Cranleigh (01483 275295). **Directions:** A281 from Guildford towards Horsham, at Shalford take B2128 to Cranleigh High Street, right opposite Onslow Arms into Knowle Lane, ground half mile on left. Public transport: Guildford (BR) then bus (Alder Valley) 273 or 283.
Seats: None **Cover:** 50 **Capacity:** 450 **Floodlights:** No **Club Shop:** No.
Clubhouse: Licensed bar. Hot food on matchdays. **Midweek matchday:** Tuesday **Founded:** 1893.
Programme: £1.50 **Editor:** Peter Slater (01483 894245) **Sponsors:** Roger Coupe, Est. Agents
Colours: Blue/black/blue **Change colours:** Yellow/green/yellow **Nickname:** Cranes.
Honours: W Sussex County Times Cup 92-93; F.A. Vase 3rd Rd 92-93.

FARNHAM TOWN

Chairman: Nigel Harrington 01252 716647 (H). **Nickname:** The Town **Founded:** 1921
Secretary: Mrs Barbara Fripp, 70 Lower Farnham Rd., Aldershot, Hampshire. GU12 4EA 01252 657184 (H)
Manager: Peter Browning **Asst Manager:** Roy Atkin **Coach:** A Wyciechowski/A Metcalfe
Ground: Memorial Ground, Babbs Mead, West Street, Farnham, Surrey (01252 715305).
Directions: Take A31, direction Winchester. Take second turning into town at Coxbridge roundabout. Follow West Street until you come to new mini roundabout - The Memorial Ground is on the right.
Capacity: 2,000 **Seats:** None **Cover:** 150 **Floodlights:** Yes **Club Shop:** No
Clubhouse: Open every evening and match days.
Programme: 32 pages 50p **Editor:** Ann Butters **Press Officer:** Charlie White **Sponsors:** Frazer Freight.
Colours: All claret & blue. **Change colours:** Gold, black trim/black/black **Midweek Matchday:** Tuesday
Reserve League: Comb Counties Res Div
Honours: Combined Counties Lg 90-91 91-92, Challenge Cup Prem Div 95-96, Challenge Tphy 91-92 (R-up 89-90).

FELTHAM

Chairman: Willi F P Seuke 0181 386 9630 (H) **Manager:** Carl Taylor. **Asst. Man:** Gary Jenkins
Secretary: John Cronk, 37 Ruskin Ave, Feltham, Middlesex. TW14 9HY. (01817 513663)
Ground: Feltham Arena, Shakespeare Ave., Feltham, Middx TW14 9HY. 0181 384 5048 (club) 0181 890 6905 (ground). **Directions:** BR to Feltham & 5 mins walk thro' Glebelands Park. Buses 90, 285, 117, 237, H24 or H25 to Feltham station, or 116 to top of Shakespeare Ave. By car: M3, M4, A312 Staines road towards Bedfont, 2nd left is Shakespeare Ave.
Capacity: 10,000 **Seats:** 650. **Cover:** 1,500 **Floodlights:** Yes **Club Shop:** No
Clubhouse: Open 7 days a week. 2 bars, dancehall available for hire. **Founded:** 1946.
Programme: 20 pages, 50p. **Editor/Press Off.:** Richard Sevice 01932 - 761544 (Tel) 761744 (Fax)
Colours: Royal blue & white halves/blue/blue. **Change colours:** Red & blue strips. **Midweek Matches:** Wednesday
Reserves' League: Suburban. **Sponsors:** Cowley Security Locksmiths/Damar Glass
96-97 - **Captain:** Phil Heggie **P.o.Y.:** Lee Channell **Top scorer:** Paul Edghill
Honours: Surrey Snr Lg R-up 65-66 (Lg Cup 65-66, Charity Cup 63-64 65-66), Southern Comb. Cup(2)(R-up(2)), Middx Summer Cup, Isthmian Div 2 80-81, Comb. Cos. Lge Co. 96-97

GODALMING & GUILDFORD

Chairman: Dave Allen **President:** W F Kyte **Nickname:** The Weys **Founded:** 1971
Secretary / Press Officer: Eddie Russell, 31 Harts Gardens, Guildford, Surrey GU2 6QB. 01483 635287 (H)
Manager: Mick Wollen **Asst Manager:** Chris Hatchwell **Physio:** Len Brown
Ground: Weycourt, Meadrow, Godalming, Surrey (01483 417520). **Midweek matchday:** Tuesday/Thursday.
Directions: A3100 from Guildford - carry on past Godalming Rugby Club & grd on right after Burmah garage. From Godalming on A3100, grd on left by Leather Bottle pub. Three quarters of a mile from Farncombe BR station.
Capacity: 1,500 **Seats:** Yes **Cover:** 200 **Floodlights:** Yes **Club Shop:** No
Clubhouse: Open Tues, Wed, Thurs eves, matchdays & Sunday lunch. Hot & cold snacks available.
Programme: Yes **Colours:** Green & yellow/green/yellow **Change colours:** Red & blue/blue/blue
Previous Leagues: Surrey Intermediate 71-78/ Surrey County Senior 78-79.
Record Attendance: 600+ - Ex-Guildford City XI v Ex-Football Lg XI. Tony Burge benefit 1991.
Record Goalscorer: Paul Hampshire 123 **Record Appearances:** Andy Metcalfe 287
Players progressing to Football Lge: John Humphreys (Millwall)
Honours: Combined Co's Lg 83-84 (Challenge Trophy 82-83, Reserve Challenge Cup 91-92 (R-up 92-93)), Surrey Intermediate Lg Premier Division Cup 71-72.

HARTLEY WINTNEY

Chairman: Fred Humphreys Tel: 01252 843098 **President:** W A Mitchell **Founded:** 1897
Secretary: Ross Hillair, 17 Rye Close, Farnborough, Hants. GU14 9LU. Tel: 01252 516174 (H)
Ground: Memorial Playing Fields, Green Lane, Hartley Wintney, Hants 01252 843586
Directions: A30 west through Camberley, left at parade of shops at beginning of village then sharp right - ground on right. Two miles from Winchfield (BR). **Midweek matchday:** Tuesday.
Capacity: 2,000 **Seats:** None **Cover:** No **Floodlights:** No **Programme:** Yes **Nickname:** The Row
Colours: Orange/black/orange **Change colours:** White/sky blue/sky blue or All green.
Previous Leagues: Basingstoke/ Aldershot

MERSTHAM

Chairman: Stan Baker **President:** Bill Lawton **Founded:** 1892.
Secretary: Matthew Boardman, 49 Orpin Road, Merstham, Surrey. RH1 3EX Tel: 01737 212543 (H) 0181 770 4818 (B)
Press Officer: Roger Peerless **Manager:** Joe McElligott **Asst Manager:** Colin Humphries
Ground: Merstham Rec., Weldon Way, Merstham, Redhill, Surrey (01737 644046). **Directions:** Leave Merstham village (A23) by School Hill, take 5th right (Weldon Way), clubhouse and car park 100m on right. 10 mins walk from Merstham (BR); down School Hill, under railway bridge, then 5th turning on right into Weldon Way.
Capacity: 2,000 **Seats:** 100 **Cover:** 100 **Floodlights:** Yes **Club Shop:** No
Clubhouse: Across adjacent footpath. Open daily (am & pm). Snacks available.
Programme: Yes **Editor:** Matthew Boardman. **Midweek matches:** Tuesday/Thursday
Colours: Amber/black/amber. **Change colours:** Purple/white/purple **Club Sponsors:** LDC Plant
Previous Leagues: Redhill & Dist./ Surrey Co. S.E. I'mediate/ Surrey Snr 64-78/ London Spartan 78-85.
96-97 - Captain: A Renton **P.o.Y.:** G Smith **Top scorer:** Steve Elliott
Honours: Combined Co's Lg R-up 87-88 89-90 (Elite Class Cup 89-90 (R-up 90-91), Res. Sect. 90-91), Spartan Lg 79-89 (Lg Cup 79-80), Surrey Snr Lg 71-72, Surrey Snr Char. Cup 79-80, E. Surrey Char. Cup 80-81, Surrey I'mediate Lg 52-53.

NETHERNE

Chairman / President: Noel Duffy Tel: 01737 552453. **Secretary:** John Duffy, c/o Netherne FC.
Ground: Netherne Sports Club, Woodplace Lane, Hooley, Coulsdon, Surrey CR5 1YE (01737 553580).
Ground: One mile from end of M23. Turn right off Brighton Rd into Woodplace Lane, follow up hill for about half a mile, ground on left. Approx 20 mins walk from Coulsdon South (BR) station.
Capacity: 2,000 **Seats:** None **Cover:** 50 **Floodlights:** No **Club Shop:** No
Clubhouse: Open matchdays with hot food available over bar. Outside tea also available with hot food.
Programme: 20 pages, 50p **Reserves' League:** Combined Co's Res Div. **Founded:** 1968
Change Colours: Green/white/black **Colours:** Blue & black stripes/black/black
Previous Leagues: Croydon Saturday 68-76; Surrey Eastern Intermediate 76-79;
Surrey South Eastern Intermediate 79-89; Surrey County Premier 89-94.
Club Records - Goalscorer: Michael Rumble 350 **Appearances:** Steve Parker 650
Honours: Surrey Co. Prem. Lg 93-94 (Lg Cup 92-93), Surrey South Eastern Intermediate Comb. 88-89.

RAYNES PARK VALE

President: R Hallett
Chairman: Dave Brenen, 22 The Crescent, Belmont, Surrey. SM2 0BJ. Tel: 0181 296 8626.
Secretary: Paul Armour, 68 Oaks Avenue, Worcester Park, Surrey. KT4 8XD. Tel: 0181 337 4989 (H)
Ground: Grand Drive, Raynes Park. SW20 (0181 542 2193)
Directions: Bus - London Transport 131 & 152. Nearest railway station - Raynes Park.
Colours: Blue & red stripes/blue/red **Change colours:** Green & white stripes/green/green.

READING TOWN

Chairman: Roland Ford, 103 Littleheath Road, Tilehurst, Berkshire RG3 5TG. Tel: 0118 941 2270.
Secretary: Richard Grey, 37 Orchard Grove, Caversham, Reading. RG4 6NF. Tel: 0118 948 2006 (H).
Fixture Sec.: Mrs Pauline Semple, 278 Hemdean Rd., Caversham, Reading RG4 7QT. Tel: 0118 947 9394.
Ground: Reading Town Spts Ground, Scours Lane, Tilehurst, Reading, Berks (0118 945 3555).
Directions: Out of Reading on Oxford road (A329), past Battle Hosp. Scours Lane 1st right after r'bout. Nearest station - Tilehurst or Reading (General). Bus - Reading Bus 17. **Manager:** Dave Crowdy
Seats: No **Cover:** Yes **Programme:** Yes **Sponsors:** Constant Intruder Security **Founded:** 1968.
Clubhouse: Yes **Colours:** Black & red stripes/black/black **Change colours:** All blue.
Honours: Chiltonian Lge Champions 94-95, Res Div 1 R-up 93-94; Berks & Bucks Sen. Trophy 95-96, R-up 96-97.

SANDHURST TOWN

Chairman: Brian Levey. Tel: 01276 32788 **President:** M Watts
Secretary: J E Parker, 24 Florence Rd, College Town, Sandhurst, Berkshire. GU47 0QD Tel: 01276 32308 (H).
Match Sec.: Mrs Gill Levey - 01276 32788 **Manager:** Mel Coombs **Coach:** Ray Clark
Ground: Memorial Ground, Yorktown Rd, Sandhurst (01252 873767).
Directions: A30 westwards through Camberley, right at r-bout with traffic lights onto A321, past superstore turning left the 3rd set of traffic lights on A321 towards Wokingham. Ground situated next to Town & Council offices and Community Sports Centre. Nearest station - Sandhurst. Bus - Bee Line 193, 194.
Seats: None **Cover:** Yes **Floodlights:** Yes **Programme:** Yes **Nickname:** Fizzers
Colours: Red/black/black **Change colours:** All blue **Midweek matchday:** Tuesday.
Previous Leagues: Reading & Dist.; East Berks; Aldershot Snr 79-84; Chiltonian 84-90.
Hons: Combined Co's Lge Chal. Vase R-up 92-93 (Reserve Chal. Cup R-up 91-92), Chiltonian Lge R-up 86-87, Aldershot Snr Lge R-up 83-84; Berks & Bucks Sen. Trophy R-up 92-93.

VIKING SPORTS

Chairman: Brian Lown Tel: 0181 878 9354 (H) 0181 940 3773 (B) **President:** Roy Bartlett **Founded:** 1945
Secretary: John Bennett, 6 Bridge House, Boston Manor Rd, Brentford TW8 9LH (0181 568 9047).
Press Officer: Jamie Cuttica **Manager:** Terry Cross. **Asst Man.:** Jim Curran **Physio:** Ernie Stockwell
Ground: Avenue Park, Western Avenue, Greenford, Middx (0181 578 2706).
Directions: On London-bound carriageway of A40, 300 yds before Greenford flyover and slip road to A4127. 12 mins walk from Greenford (Central Line) station - turn right out of station to A40, turn right - grd 1/4 mile on rght.
Capacity: 450 **Seats:** 50 **Cover:** 100 **Floodlights:** Yes **Midweek matchday:** Tuesday
Clubhouse: Open every evening except Sunday. Hot & cold snacks on matchdays. **Club Shop:** No.
Programme: 12 pages, 50p **Editor:** Secretary **Nickname:** Vikings. **Sponsors:** Measham Self-Drive
Colours: Tangerine/black/tangerine. **Change colours:** Sky blue & maroon/sky blue/sky blue
Previous Leagues: Middx 70-80; Hellenic 80-91
Record Attendance: 180 v Wealdstone, Middx. Sen. Cup, Sept. 96 **Record Goalscorer:** Frank Healy, 43
Players progressing to Football League: Gordon Bartlett (Portsmouth), Alan Devonshire (West Ham), Peter Shaw (Charlton A.)
96-97 - Captain: Tom Heffernan **P.o.Y.:** Tom Heffernan **Top Scorer:** Adrian Nesbeth
Honours: Hellenic Lg Div 1 85-86 (Div 1 Cup R-up 90-91).Co.Counties Lg.(R-Up. 94-95).

WALTON CASUALS

Chairman: Graham James **General Manager:** David Symonds **President:** John Russell
Secretary: Stuart Roberts, 47 Foxholes, Weybridge, Surrey. KT13 0BN. Tel: 01932 845923
Manager: Mick Byrne **Midweek Matchday:** Tuesday. **Nickname:** The Stags **Founded:** 1948.
Ground: Franklin Road Sports Ground, Waterside Drive, Walton-on-Thames, Surrey. KT12 2JG. Tel: 01932 787749 (24hrs ansaphone). **Directions:** Next to Elmbridge Leisure Centre, left off Terrace Road at first roundabout out of Walton centre. Hersham (BR), then bus 564 to Elmbridge Leisure Centre.
Capacity: 1,500 **Seats:** None **Cover:** 80 **Floodlights:** Applied for. **Club Shop:** No
Clubhouse: Matchdays only. Hot food available from Tea Bar.
Programme: 26 pages 50p **Editor/Press Officer:** Stuart Roberts **Sponsors:** John Russell (Allied Dunbar)
Colours: Orange & white/white/white **Change colours:** Red & black/black/black
Previous Leagues: Surrey Premier, Surrey Senior, Surrey Intermediate, Suburban League.
Record Attendance: 178 v Pagham FA Vase 96/97
1996-97 - Top Goalscorer: Mark Postins. **P.o.Y.:** Dave Francis
Honours: Suburban Lge (South) 82-83, (R-up 83-84); Surrey Prem Lge R-up 94-95, S.P.L. Chall Cup 93-94, (R-up 94-95); Surrey Premier Cup R-up 86-87.

WESTFIELD

President: R Hill **Chairman:** S P Perkins, Oakview, Heather Close, Horsell, Surrey. Tel: 01252 547900 (B)
Secretary: Michael Lawrence, 19 Ash Road, Barnsbury Estate, Woking, Surrey. GU22 0BJ. Tel/Fax: 01483 722184
Ground: Woking Park, Kingfield, Woking, Surrey (01483 771106). **Directions:** (Adjacent to Woking FC.) M25 J10 or 11, signposted from outskirts of Town. Ground 1 mile. Woking B.R.Station & buses from Woking.
Capacity: 1,000 **Seats:** None **Cover:** No **Floodlights:** No **Clubhouse:** Yes **Programme:** No
Colours: Yellow/black/yellow **Change colours:** All white **Previous League:** Surrey County Senior Lge.

ESSEX SENIOR LEAGUE

FEEDER TO: ICIS LEAGUE

President: Arthur Diamond

Chairman: Robert Errington

Secretary: David Walls, 77 Thorpedene Gardens, Shoeburyness, Southend on Sea, Essex SS3 9JE

FORD UNITED COME MOTORING IN

Ford United were very worthy Champions, but it took until the last week for them to hit the top and, with it, promotion to the ICIS League and the fastest upgrading of a ground for many a year! This is the 7th club to be elevated in the 10 years we have been in the Pyramid system — a very proud record indeed.

Concord Rangers started the season as favourites with their star line-up and their prolific goalscorers such as Tony Macklin and Martyn Lawrence help them to a record breaking 106 league goals but, because of success in the Vase, East Anglian Cup and other outside competitions, they eventually ran out of steam and had only a Challenge Cup victory, 1-0 over Ford United at Southchurch Park to show for their efforts. One of the most consistent sides in the league and favourites for 97–98 are Great Wakering Rovers who were runners-up for the second year running, having won the league the season before that. With seats bought from Leeds United and Bolton being fitted into their new stand as, it's a Red and White Rose atmosphere at Burroughs Park for the faithful.

The star outfit of the rest of the pack were undoubtedly Stansted who reached the latter qualifying round stage of the FA Cup for the first time and equalled the all time record of 14 straight wins in a row held by Billericay, Heybridge Swifts and Canvey Island. Their matchday programme was also a brilliant piece of work by Alan Russell and their season was highlighted by a surprise visit from Graham Kelly who, by all accounts was made to feel very welcome at this, the grass roots of football. Stansted reached a final, the Harry Fisher Memorial Trophy which was open to all clubs this season but, a disastrous 90th minute own goal gave the trophy to Burnham Ramblers who, themselves were winning their first ever Essex Senior League trophy. This was later joined in the trophy cabinet by the Sportsmanship Award. Both Concord Rangers and Southend Manor reached Round 4 of the Vase and the latter were East Anglian 5-a-side beaten finalists in front of Anglian TV cameras. Southend Manor's Secretary, Dave Kittle was named League Secretary of the Year. The season ended on a sad note with the retirement of both the Vice-Chairman, Vernon Sitch after 16 years as an Officer and Hon Secretary David Wingrove, both having administrative skills that will be sorely missed. A somewhat unique mini-integration of officers with the Essex and Herts Border Combination has now taken place for 97–98 with a number of officers undertaking dual roles. Chairman, Robert Errington pledged his support to the Pyramid and hoped that clubs throughout the whole County of Essex and its Borders will look at the very proud record of the Essex Senior League and consider joining the merry band of brothers!

Robert Errington.

FINAL LEAGUE TABLE 1996–97

DIVISION ONE	*P*	*W*	*D*	*L*	*F*	*A*	*Pts*
Ford United	28	21	6	1	91	24	69
Great Wakering Rovers	28	20	6	2	67	19	66
Concord Rangers	28	19	5	4	106	31	62
Stansted	28	19	2	7	53	37	59
Burnham Ramblers	28	13	6	9	62	40	45
Brentwood	28	11	10	7	46	34	43
Hullbridge Sports	28	13	4	11	52	42	43
Ilford	28	11	3	14	36	40	36
Basildon United*	28	11	5	12	39	52	35
Saffron Walden Town	28	8	8	12	40	39	32
Southend Manor	28	8	5	15	32	42	29
Bowers United	28	8	4	16	32	77	28
East Ham United	28	7	3	18	29	61	24
Sawbridgeworth Town	28	3	3	22	17	69	12
Eton Manor	28	1	4	23	13	108	7

*Basildon United — 3 points deducted, ineligible player.

ESSEX SENIOR LEAGUE RESULTS CHART 1996–97

HOME TEAM	1	2	3	4	5	6	7	8	9	10	11	12	13	14	15
Basildon United	*	1-1	3-3	1-3	1-3	2-1	3-1	2-3	0-0	0-1	1-0	1-1	2-1	1-2	2-0
Bowers United	2-1	*	1-3	3-7	1-5	2-0	2-2	0-5	0-5	2-4	3-2	0-0	1-0	1-0	0-3
Brentwood	1-2	1-1	*	0-2	1-2	4-0	4-0	0-1	0-0	6-1	0-4	2-0	1-1	2-0	0-2
Burnham Ramblers	1-2	2-0	2-2	*	0-4	2-1	4-1	0-2	0-1	0-0	5-1	3-0	3-0	1-1	3-1
Concord Rangers	7-0	7-0	2-2	5-1	*	0-1	9-0	4-4	1-1	2-0	2-1	3-3	5-0	4-0	5-1
East Ham United	0-1	2-1	0-1	1-1	1-9	*	2-1	0-0	0-2	1-3	0-3	1-3	2-0	2-1	0-2
Eton Manor	0-6	0-1	0-1	1-9	0-8	0-5	*	1-6	0-3	1-6	0-0	0-4	2-1	0-3	0-1
Ford United	11-1	8-0	2-2	3-1	2-2	2-1	8-0	*	1-1	4-1	4-0	2-0	1-0	2-0	1-1
Great Wakering Rovers	2-0	6-1	4-1	2-1	3-2	6-0	2-1	2-0	*	4-1	1-0	4-1	6-1	2-1	0-2
Hullbridge Sports	2-1	3-0	0-3	0-2	4-2	2-2	8-0	0-2	1-1	*	0-1	2-1	3-0	1-2	1-2
Ilford	1-2	2-1	0-1	1-0	0-3	3-0	2-1	0-2	2-1	0-3	*	1-1	0-1	0-4	2-1
Saffron Walden Town	2-2	1-2	0-1	1-1	1-0	2-0	3-0	3-4	1-3	0-0	0-0	*	4-0	4-1	1-3
Sawbridgeworth Town	1-0	1-3	0-0	1-4	2-4	1-2	1-1	0-5	1-2	0-2	0-6	2-1	*	0-1	0-3
Southend Manor	0-1	2-1	1-1	2-2	1-2	3-1	0-0	1-3	0-0	1-2	1-3	0-2	4-2	*	0-1
Stansted	2-0	4-2	3-3	3-2	0-4	4-3	6-0	1-3	0-3	2-1	2-1	1-0	1-0	1-0	*

GOALSCORERS FOR THE SEASON 1996–97

Jeff Wood	Ford United	37	Ben Barnett	Southend Manor	13
Tony Macklin	Concord Rangers	36	Des Charley	Ford United–11 with Brentwood	12
Martyn Lawrence	Concord Rangers	24	Alan Hull	Great Wakering Rovers	12
Paul Flack	Great Wakering Rovers	20	Andy Chapman	Saffron Walden Town	11
Gary Hollocks	Burnham Ramblers	19	Mark Saggers	Stansted	11
Gary Hart	Stansted	18	Len Cook	Brentwood	10
Steve Harding	Formerly Burnham Ramblers	17	Jamie Wallace	Ford United	10
Keith Scourfield	Hullbridge Sports	14	Darren Hitchcock	Brentwood	9
Trevor Destouche	Ilford		Wayne Edwards	Basildon United	8

OTHER LEADING GOALSCORERS 1996–97

Sawbridgeworth	Sonuc Soldiray	6	East Ham United	Ayaogo	4
Bowers United	Terry Barrett	5	East Ham United	Duncan	4
East Ham United	Nwachakwu	4	Eton Manor	Richard Mason	2
East Ham United	Ashworth	4	Eton Manor	Noel Duff	2
East Ham United	Dobbs	4			

HARRY FISHER MEMORIAL TROPHY 1996–97

ROUND ONE

Ford United	v	Concord Rangers	1-2	Brentwood	v	Sawbridgeworth	2-1
Bowers United	v	Burnham Ramblers	2-2, 0-5	Stansted	v	Saffron Walden	1-0
East Ham United	v	Ilford	2-3	Hullbridge Sports	v	Basildon United	1-4
Southend Manor	v	Great Wakering Rovers	1-0				

ROUND TWO

Concord Rangers	v	Burnham Ramblers	0-1	Brentwood	v	Eton Manor	4-0
Ilford	v	Southend Manor	1-1, 2-1	Stansted	v	Basildon United	4-0

SEMI-FINAL

Burnham Ramblers	v	Ilford	5-2	Brentwood	v	Stansted	1-2

FINAL

Burnham Ramblers	v	Stansted	2-1

CHALLENGE CUP 1996–97

ROUND ONE

Eton Manor	v	Saffron Walden	1-5	Ford United	v	Gt Wakering Rovers	aet 5-2
Concord Rangers	v	Ilford	2-1	Brentwood	v	Sawbridgeworth	1-1, 3-2
Burnham Ramblers	v	Basildon United	2-0	East Ham United	v	Southend Manor	1-1, 0-3
Bowers United	v	Stansted	0-1				

ROUND TWO

Saffron Walden	v	Concord Rangers	0-1	Ford United	v	Brentwood	2-0
Burnham Ramblers	v	Stansted	0-1	Southend Manor	v	Hullbridge Sports	4-1

SEMI-FINAL

Concord Rangers	v	Stansted	2-0	Ford United	v	Southend Manor	4-0

FINAL

Concord Rangers	v	Ford United	1-0

Retiring Vice-Chairman Vernon Sitch, and Secretary David Wingrove present Mark Jenkins of Concord Rangers with the Challenge Cup. Pic: Robert Errington.

BASILDON UNITED

President: J Oakes **Chairman:** J Moran **Secretary:** Dave Cusack, c/o the club. **Founded:** 1963.
Joint Managers: Dave Cusack & Dave Golding **Press Officer:** Frank Ford (01268 552994
Ground: Gardiners Close, Gardiners Lane, Basildon, Essex SS14 3AW (01268 520268).
Directions: A176 off Southend arterial (A127), left at r'bout into Cranes Farm Road, proceed to end of duel carriageway, left at lights, Gardiners Close is 1st left (Football Club signed). Two and a half miles from Basildon BR station.
Seats: 400 **Cover:** 1,000 **Capacity:** 2,000 **Floodlights:** Yes
Clubhouse: Open lunchtimes, evenings, weekends. Hot food sold.
Programme: 16 pages, Free. **Editor:** P Burch **Midweek Matches:** Wednesday **Club Shop:** No.
Colours: Amber & black stripes **Change:** Green & white squares/white/white **Sponsors:** Orsett Cock
Previous - Name: Armada Sports. **Ground:** Grosvenor Park 63-69. **Leagues:** Grays & Thurrock; Gtr London 68-70; Essex Snr 70-80; Athenian 80-81; Isthmian 81-91. **Record Gate:** 4,000 v West Ham, ground opening 11/8/70
Players progressing to Football League: Jeff Hull (Colchester), Alan Hull (Orient), David Matthews & Steve Tilson (Southend), Jonathan Gould (Coventry City), Ken Charlery (Watford), Steve Jones (West Ham (via Billericay)).
96-97 - Captain: Tommy Scawthorn **Top Scorer:** Wayne Edwards **P.o.Y.:** Wes Faulkner
Honours: Isthmian Lge Div 2 83-83, Essex Senior Lge (5) 76-80 94-95 (Lg Cup 77-78 94-95, Reserve Cup 92-93), Essex Senior Trophy 78-79. Reserve League & Shield 94-95.

BOWERS UNITED

Chairman: P Felfam **Manager:** Tony Cross
Secretary: Ernie D Brown, 92 Quilters Straight, Fryerns, Basildon, Essex SS14 2SJ. 01268 521201 (H)
Ground: Crown Avenue, off Kenneth Rd, Pitsea, Basildon (01268 452068).
Directions: Turn into Rectory Rd from Old London Rd (B1464) at Pitsea Broadway into Kenneth Rd, right at top Crown Ave. 1.25 miles Pitsea (BR). Bus 523 to Rectory Rd, Bowers Guild.
Seats: 200 **Stand:** Yes **Capacity:** 2,000 **Floodlights:** Yes **Founded:** 1946
Clubhouse: Open every night. **Midweek Matches:** Wednesday.
Colours: Red & white/white/red & white **Change colours:** Blue/white/white
Previous Leagues: Thurrock & Thameside Comb.;Olympian **Previous Ground:** Gun Meadow, Pitsea.
Record Gate: 1,800 v Billericay Town, 3rd Rd FA Vase, 15.12.79
Players progressing to Football League: Steve Tilson (Southend Utd).
96-97 - Captain: **Top Scorer:** Terry Barrett **P.o.Y.:**
Honours: Thurrock & Thameside Comb. 58-59; Essex Snr Lg 80-81 (Div 1 Cup 90-91, Harry Fisher Mem. Tphy 91-92, Res. Div R-up 92-93).

BRENTWOOD

Chairman: K J O'Neale **Manager:** Derek Stittle 01708 440486 (H)
Secretary: Colin Harris, 56 Viking Way, Pilgrims Hatch, Brentwood, Essex CM15 9HY. 01277 219564 (H)
Ground: Brentwood Centre, Doddinghurst Rd, Brentwood, Essex. 01277 215151 Ext. 713. **Directions:** Junc. 28 M25, take A12 signposted Brentwood. At Town Centre, turn right and ground is in Doddinghurst Lane at the Leisure Centre.
Cover: Yes **Seats:** **Capacity:** **Floodlights:** No **Founded:** 1955.
Colours: Blue & white stripes/white/white. **Change colours:** Amber/black/black.
Programme: Free with admission **Midweek Matches:** Tuesday **Nickname:** Blues
PREVIOUS - Names: Manor Ath. 55-70, Brentwood Ath. 70-72. **Grounds:** King George, Hartswood, 'Larkins', Ongar (pre-1992), East Ham. **Leagues:** Romford & District, Sth Essex Combination, London & Essex Border, Olympian.
Hons: Olympian Lg Cup 67-68, Essex Inter. Cup 76-77, Essex Lg Cup 75-76 78-79 90-91; Harry Fisher Mem. Trophy 95-96.

BURNHAM RAMBLERS

Chairman: Gordon Brasted **Vice-Chairman:** Ron Hatcher **President:** R J Cole, Esq.
Secretary: Gordon Clark, 20 Church Road, Burnham on Crouch, Essex. Tel. 01621 783212
Manager: Colin Wallington **Asst Manager:** Grant Gordon **Physio:** Cyril Tennant
Ground: Leslie Field, Springfield Rd, Burnham-on-Crouch CM0 8QL (01621 784383).
Directions: On B1010 from South Woodham Ferrers, turn right half mile before town. 15 mins from Burnham (BR).
Seats: 300 **Stand:** Yes **Capacity:** 2,000 **Floodlights:** Yes **Founded:** 1900
Clubhouse: Open Mon-Fri 7-11pm, Sat noon-3 & 5-11pm, Sun noon-3 & 7-9.30pm. Hot meals & snacks available.
Programme: 36 pages, 40p **Editor:** Chairman **Press Officer:** Nigel Radcliffe (01621 783774)
Colours: Royal blue & black/black/black **Change colours:** Red & black/black/black **Nickname:** Ramblers
Midweek matches: Tuesday. **Reserves' Lge:** Essex Snr Div 1 **Record Gate:** 1,500.
Previous - Leagues: N Essex, Mid-Essex, Olympian, S.E. Essex. **Grounds:** Wick Rd, Millfields, Saltcourts (orig.)
Players moving to Football League: I Woolf, West Ham 11, Gordon Brasted, Arsenal 53, John Warner, Colchester 90.
96-97 - Captain: **P.o.Y:** Nicky Wright **Top Scorer:** Gary Hollocks
Honours: Olympian Lg 65-66, Essex I'mediate Cup R-up 81-82, Essex Snr Lg Cup R-up 86-87 89-90 (Reserve Cup 89-90 (R-up 92-93), Reserve Shield R-up 90-91), Harry Fisher Mem. Trophy 96-97, Sportsmanship Award 96-97.

CONCORD RANGERS

President: Albert Lant **Chairman:** Rob Fletcher **Manager:** Lee Patterson **Founded:** 1967.
Secretary: Mrs Carol McKenna, 17 Heeswyck Road, Canvey Island, Essex SS8 9YU. 01268 515048 (H)
Ground: Thames Road, Canvey Island, Essex. SS8 0HP (01268 691780) **Directions:**
Capacity: 1,500 **Cover:** Yes **Seats:** No **Floodlights:** Yes **Midweek Matches:** Tuesday.
Clubhouse: Evenings & weekends **Programme:** 10 pages, 50p **Editor:** Mike Stephenson (01268 684638)
Colours: Yellow & blue/blue/yellow **Change colours:** White/black/black **Club Sponsor:** Aspect Contracts.
Previous - Leagues: Southend & D. All., Essex I'mediate (pre-1991). **Ground:** Waterside
Record - Gate: 1,500 v Lee Chapel North, FA Sunday Cup 89-90. **Win:** 9-0 v Eton Manor, Essex Snr Lge 96-97.
96-97 - Top Scorer: Tony Macklin **Captain:** **P.o.Y.:**
Hons: Southend & Dist. Lge - Lge & Cup 84-85, Southend Alliance - Lge & Cup 87-88, Essex Intermediate Lg Div 2 90-91, Essex Sen. Lge Cup 96-97, Wirral Programme Award 93-94.

EAST HAM UNITED

Chairman: Ted Whatmough, 85 Mill lane, Chadwell Heath, Romford. RM6 6YH. 0181 599 4542 (H)
Secretary: Reuben Gane, 108 Beccles Drive, Barking, Essex IG11 9HZ. 0181 594 7861 (H)
Manager: Reuben Gane **Head of Coaching:** Cornel Dobbs **Trainer:** Lawrie Ashworth
Press Officer: Roland Clooge **Physio:** Regan Cavanagh.
Ground: Ferndale Sports Ground, Pennyroyal Ave., off East Ham Manorway, Cyprus Place, Beckton E6 4NG Tel: 0171 476 5514, Fax: 0181 507 1099. **Directions:** East Ham Manorway - Cyprus Place - Beckton off A13 Newham Way from east or west. Nearest tube - East Ham, then bus 101 to ground, or Cyprus Station (Docklands Light Railway).
Seats: 150 **Cover:** 300 **Capacity:** 2,500 **Floodlights:** Yes **Founded:** 1933.
Clubhouse: Evenings & weekends. **Midweek Matchday:** Tuesday **Nickname:** Hammers.
Colours: Green & white hoops/green/green **Change colours:** Gold/green/gold **Programme:** Yes.
Previous Ground: Whitebarn Lane (previous East Ham Utd, formed 1880 and played in Sth Essex Lge) 1892-1914; Tilletss Farm 1933-46. **Previous Lges:** Spartan, Metropolitan **Previous Name:** Storey Ath. 1933-55
96-97 - Captain: Cornel Dobbs **Top Scorer:** Eddie Nwachukwu **P.o.Y.:** Eddie Nwachukwu
Hons: Metropolitan Lg, FA Vase QF, Essex Snr Tphy 76-77, Gtr London Lg Cup 69-70, London Jnr Cup 46-47, Bob Murrant Memorial Trophy 94-95, Carpathian Charity Cup 94-95. Harry Fisher Memorial Trophy R-U 1994-95.

ETON MANOR

Secretary: George Whiting, c/o 6 Ellen Miller House, Raglen Road, Walthamstow, London E17 9EG.
Chairman: D McCann. **Manager:** David Hill **Coaches:** K Smith, J Fisher **Physio:** C Drane
Ground: (Share with Purfleet FC) **Capacity:** 4,500 **Cover:** 1,000 **Seats:** 300 **Floodlights:** Yes
Address: Thurrock Hotel, Ship Lane, Grays, Essex (01708 868901) (Fax 01708 866705). **Directions:** M25 or A13 to Dartford tunnel r'bout. Ground is fifty yards on right down Ship Lane. Nearest station is Purfleet, two miles from ground.
Clubhouse: Yes **Programme:** 12 pages with entry **Editor:** Secretary **Midweek Matches:** Monday
Colours: Sky & navy/navy/navy **Change colours:** Maroon & green/navy/navy **Nickname:** The Manor
Founded: 1901 **Previous Grounds:** Wildness, Hackney; GUS Sports Ground, Clapton; Walthamstow Avenue FC; Norwegian Ground, Barking; Roding Lane, Buckhurst Hill. **Previous Name:** Wilderness Leyton.
Previous Leagues: London 33-59; Aetolian 59-64; Greater London 64-69; Metropolitan 69-75.
Record Gate: 600 v Leyton Orient, opening of floodlights at Roding Lane. **Club record scorer:** Dave Sams
96-97 - Captain: D Crawley **Top scorer:** D Devor **P.o.Y.:** D Crawley
Hons: Essex Snr Cup R-up 37-38, London Lg 33-34 37-38 52-53 53-54 (R-up 48-49 57-58, Lg Cup 55-56 (R-up 46-47 54-55)), Greater London Lg 64-65, Essex Intermediate Cup 64-65, London Intermediate Cup R-up 33-34 66-67, Essex Snr Lg Sportsmanship Award 75-76 (Div 1 Cup 90-91, Reserve Div 76-77, Reserve Div Cup 91-92).

GREAT WAKERING ROVERS

Chairman: Fred Smith **Vice-Chairman:** Barry Beadle **President:** Eddie Ellis **Founded:** 1919
Secretary: Roger Sampson, 37 Lee Lotts, Gt Wakering, Southend-on-Sea, Essex SS3 0HA. 01702 218794 (H)
Manager: Kevin Maddocks **Assistant Manager:** Eddie Nash. **Physio:** Cleave Taylor.
Ground: Burroughs Park, Little Wakering Hall Lane, Gt Wakering, Southend-on-Sea SS3 0HQ (01702 217812).
Directions: 4a bus from Shoeburyness (BR), 4a or 4b from Southend - alight at British Legion in Gt Wakering alongside which runs Little Wakering Hall Lane. A127 past Southend signposted Gt Wakering. In Gt Wakering, half mile past large Esso garage is along High Street is Little Wakering Hall Lane, ground 250 yds along on left.
Capacity: 1,500 **Cover:** 300 **Seats:** None **Floodlights:** Yes **Club Shop:** No **Nickname:** Rovers
Clubhouse: Weekday evenings, Sat 11-11pm, Sun 12-3 & 7.30-10.30pm. Hot meals, snacks etc available matchdays.
Programme: 24-32 pages, 50p **Editor/Press Officer:** Nobby Johnson (01702 611964). **Sponsors:** PAX (CCTV)
Colours: Green & white stripes/white/green **Change colours:** Yellow & blue stripes/blue/blue
Midweek Matchday: Tuesday **Reserves' League:** Essex & Herts Border Comb
Record Attendance: 500 v Leyton Orient, friendly 18/7/92. **Previous Ground:** Gt Wakering Rec.
Previous Leagues: Southend & District 19-81, Southend Alliance 81-89, Essex Intermediate 89-92.
96-97 Captain: John Heffer. **96-97 P.o.Y.:** **96-97 Top Scorer:** Paul Flack
Honours: Essex I'mediate Cup 91-92, Essex I'mediate Lg Div 2 91-92 (Div 3 90-91, Lg Cup 91-92), Southend Charity Shield 90-91 91-92, Essex Snr Lg. 94-95, Lg Res. Section 94-95 (Wirral Programme Essex Sen. Lg. Award 92-93 94-95).

HULLBRIDGE SPORTS

Chairman: Brian Lloyd **Joint Managers:** David Hughes & Gary Hodson **Founded:** 1945
Secretary: Tony Johnson, 20 Shenfield Gardens, Hutton, Brentwood, Essex CM13 1DT. 01277 224353 (H)
Ground: Lower Road, Hullbridge, Hockley, Essex SS5 6BJ (01702 230420).
Directions: Turn into Rawreth Lane from A130 (left if arriving from Chelmsford), down to mini-r'bout, left, across next mini-r'bout, up hill, ground signed on right just past garage. **Prog. Editor:** Mrs Lynne Ward.
Capacity: **Seats:** No **Cover:** Yes **Floodlights:** No **Midweek matches:** Tues/Thursday.
Clubhouse details: Lounge bar, function hall with bar & changing rooms - set in 16 acre.
Colours: Blue & white stripes/blue/blue **Change colours:** Yellow/Blue/Yellow **Sponsor:** Thermo Shield
Previous Grounds: Pooles Lane Rec. **Previous Leagues:** Southend & Dist., Alliance, Essex I'mediate.
96-97 - Captain: **Top Scorer:** Keith Scourfield **P.o.Y.:**
Honours: Essex Intermediate Snr Div Cup 87-88, Southend & District Lg Div 1 65-66 (Div 2 51-52, Div 3 56-57), French Cup 51-52, Essex Snr Lg Sportsmanship Award 91-92 92-93 94-95.

ILFORD

Chairman: George Hogarth **Manager:** Ray Creek
Secretary: William A Flintham, 15a Maywin Drive, Hornchurch, Essex. RM11 3ST. 01708 454712 (H) 0181 502 6505 (B)
Fixture Secretary: D Quinlan, 25 Burwood Gardens, Rainham, Essex. RM13 8JS. 01708 526323
Ground: Cricklefield Stadium, High Road, Ilford, Essex. IG1 1UB (0181 514 0019)
Directions: Within 5 minutes walk of Seven Kings Station.
Colours: Royal blue & white hoops/navy/royal **Change colours:** Red & white hoops/red/red
Midweek matches: Monday **Programme Editor:** L Llewellyn
Previous League: Spartan 87-95 **Sponsor:** Kelvin Hughes, Intersport.

SAFFRON WALDEN TOWN

Chairman: TBA **Vice Chairman:** Peter Walker. **Founded:** 1872 **Nickname:** Bloods
Secretary: Harry Harvey, 1 New Willow Cottage, Langley Upper Green, Saffron Walden. CB11 4RU. 01799 550615 (H)
Manager: Phil Hopkins **Asst. Man.:** Marc Das **Physio:** Peter White **Press Officer:** D Lightning
Ground: Catons Lane, Saffron Walden, Essex CB10 2DU (01799 22789).
Directions: In Saffron Walden High Street turn into Castle Street, left at T-junction, 1st left by Doctors pub. **Club Sponsors:** Tolly Cobbold.
Capacity: 5,000 **Seats:** 500 **Cover:** 2,000 **Floodlights:** Yes **Clubhouse:** Yes **Club Shop:** Yes
Programme: 24 pages, 40p **Editor:** R Smith (01799 500061) **Midweek Matchday:** Tuesday
Colours: Red & black stipes/black/black **Change cols:** All yellow **Reserves' League:** Essex & Herts Comb.
Previous Leagues: Haverhill & Dist., Stansted & Dist., Cambridgeshire, Nth Essex/ Herts Co., Spartan 33-49 50-54, Parthenon 49-50, Essex Snr 71-74, Eastern Co's 74-84. **Prev. Grounds:** None **Prev. Names:** None.
Record Attendance: 6,000 v Rainham Ath., Essex Junior Cup Final 1926 (played at Crittals, Braintree).
96-97 Top scorer: Andy Chapman **Record Scorer:** John Tipputt **Record Appearances:** Les Page, 700+.
Best F.A. Cup year: Second Qualifying Round replay 84-85 (lost 1-2 at King's Lynn).
Hons: Essex Snr Lg 73-74, Eastern Co's Lg 82-83, Spartan Lg Eastern Div 2 36-37, Essex Snr Tphy 82-83 83-84 84-85, Eastern F'lit Competition 91-92 (R-up 88-89, Nth Thames Group B 82-83), Essex Jnr Cup 1896-97 (R-up 25-26), Cambs Lg R-up 22-23, Essex & Herts Border Lg R-up 25-26(joint), Stansted & Dist. Lg 07-08 08-09 09-10 11-12 20-21 22-23 23-24, Haverhill & Dist. Lg 08-09 22-23 23-24 29-30 33-34.

SAWBRIDGEWORTH TOWN

Chairman: Barry Mutimer **President:** Ron Alder **Founded:** 1890 **Nickname:** Robins
Secretary: Gary Bennett, 21 Sayesbury Road, Sawbridgeworth, Herts, CM21 0EB. 01279 830306 (H)
Manager: Graham Norcott **Coach:** TBA **Physio:** Brian Latchford
Ground: Crofters End, West Road, Sawbridgeworth, Herts. CM21 0DE (01279 722039)
Directions: Three quarters of a mile from the station; up Station Road then into West Road.
Capacity: 1,500 **Seats:** None **Cover:** 250 **Floodlights:** Yes **Club Shop:** **Clubhouse:**
Programme Editor: R Alder (01279 722360) **Press Officer:** Micky Phillips **Sponsor:**
Colours: Red & black stripes/black/red **Change colours:** Green & white hoops/white/green
Previous - Grounds: Hyde Hall, Pishiobury, Hand & Crown. **Leagues:** Essex Olympian, Spartan 36-53.
Record Attendance: 610 v Bishop's Stortford.
Honours: Essex Olympian Lg 71-72; Essex Snr Lg R-up 92-93 94-95; Harry Fisher Mem. Cup 87-88; Lg Cup 94-95 R-up 92-93 93-94, Reserve Div 91-92 92-93 (R-up 93-94), Reserve Shield R-up 92-93); Herts Snr Tphy 90-91 93-94 (R-up 92-93); Herts Charity Shield 92-93 94-95 95-96; Uttlesford Charity Cup 92-93; Herts Intermediate Cup R-up 93-93(res); South Midlands Floodlit Cup R.Up.94-95; Reserve Sect S.M Lge & Lg.Cup R-Up 94-95:

SOUTHEND MANOR

Chairman: Robert Westley **Vice-Chairman:** John Hughes **Nickname:** The Manor
Secretary: Dave Kittle, 15 Seymour Rd, Hadleigh, Benfleet, Essex SS7 2HB. 01702 559581 (H)
Manager: Jeff Short **Coach:** Ross MacIntyre **Physio:**
Ground: Southchurch Park Arena, Lifstan Way, Southend-on-Sea. (01702 615577). **Directions:** A127 then A1159 for 1 mile turn right at second roundabout by Invisible Man PH, due south for 1 mile, ground on right near sea front.
Seats: 500 **Cover:** Yes **Capacity:** 2,000 **Floodlights:** Yes **Founded:** 1955
Clubhouse: Open every evening **Programme:** 10 pages, 50p **Editor/Press Officer:** Paul Docherty.
Colours: Yellow/black/red **Change colours:** White/red/red
Sponsors: Hi-Tech. **Midweek Matchday:** Tuesday. **Reserves Lge:** Essex & Herts Border Comb.
Previous Leagues: Southend Borough Combination, Southend Alliance
Previous Grounds: Victory Spts/ Oakwood Rec.
Record Attendance: 1,521 v Southend Utd, 22/7/91, floodlight opener.
96-97 - Captain: Paul Leggett **Top Scorer:** Ben Barnett **P.o.Y.:** Mick Munroe
Honours: Essex Snr Trophy 92-93, Essex Intermediate Cup 78-79, Essex Snr Lg 90-91 (Lg Cup 87-88, ESL Challenge Cup 89-90, Harry Fisher Mem. Tphy 90-91 92-93 (R-up 91-92)).

STANSTED

Chairman: Terry Shoebridge **General Manager:** Alan Russell **President:** Percy Heal
Secretary: Mrs Denise Murnane, Appletree House, Fullers End, Elsenham, Bishops Stortford. CM22 6DU. 01279 815404 (H&B) **Joint Managers:** Mark Simpson & Don Watters
Ground: Hargrave Park, Cambridge Road, Stansted, Essex. (01279 812897)
Directions: B1383 north of Bishops Stortford on west side of Cambridge Rd. Stansted (BR) - 1/2 mile
Capacity: 2,000 **Seats:** 200 **Cover:** Yes **Floodlights:** Yes **Founded:** 1902 **Nickname:** The blues
Clubhouse: Matchdays till 11pm. Sandwiches available. **Club Shop:** No
Colours: Yellow, blue stripes/blue/yellow **Change:** Blue, black stripes/black/black **Sponsor:** Desavoury Foods
Programme Editor: Secretary **Midweek matches:** Tuesday. **Reserves League:** Cambridgeshire League
Previous - Leagues: Spartan; London; Herts Co. **Grounds:** Greens Meadow; Chapel Hill
96-97 - Captain: Gary Dean **Top Scorer:** G Hart **P.o.Y.:** Gary Dean
Record Attendance: 828 v Whickham (FA Vase 83-84). **Honours:** FA Vase Winners 83-84; Essex Snr Lg R-up 82-83; Essex Snr Lg Cup 83-84, (R-up 72-73 94-95); Harry Fisher Mem Cup 82-83 84-85 (R-up 92-93 93-94); East Anglian Cup 83-84; Courage East F/lit Cup 83-84; Uttlesford Char. Cup 93-84 86-87 88-89 94-95:

TEAM TALK

Easily Britain's best selling national non-league magazine.

NOW IN ITS SEVENTH YEAR

Published by Tony Williams Publications Ltd.
Helland, North Curry, Taunton, Somerset. TA3 6DU.
Tel: 01823 490080 Fax: 01823 490281

Officially featuring all F.A. competitions including
The F.A. Carlsberg Vase
The F.A. Umbro Trophy
The Littlewoods F.A. Cup

and all non-League football
from Conference to County League football

minerva® footballs

SPARTAN SOUTH MIDLANDS FOOTBALL LEAGUE

(A merger between The London Spartan and The South Midlands Football League)

President: B F Smith
Chairman: Pat Burns
Hon. General Secretary: Martyn Mitchell, 26 Leighton Court, Dunstable, Beds. LU6 1EW.
Tel: 01582 667291

Following the merger of The Spartan and the South Midlands Leagues, the two Premier Divisions will continue to run parallel with each other as Premier North and South. At the end of the season probably the top twelve (the exact number to be confirmed) of each division will form a single Premier Division for season 1998–99.

The Present Senior Division would absorb the bottom half of this season's Premier Divisions.

The new competition looks potentially strong and hopefully will have a long and progressive life in the seasons to come.

SOUTH MIDLANDS LEAGUE FINAL LEAGUE TABLES 1996–97

PREMIER DIVISION	P	W	D	L	F	A	Pts
Potters Bar Town	28	18	8	2	53	18	62
Brache Sparta	28	19	5	4	54	20	62
Arlesey Town	28	16	7	5	49	20	55
Toddington Rovers	28	14	4	10	45	29	46
Buckingham Athletic	28	14	3	11	52	34	45
Royston Town	28	13	6	9	47	42	45
London Colney	28	12	8	8	47	41	44
Bedford United	28	10	8	10	44	49	38
Welwyn Garden City	28	9	9	10	45	44	36
Harpenden Town	28	9	7	12	32	33	34
Milton Keynes	28	7	10	11	25	36	31
Letchworth	28	7	7	14	35	50	28
Langford	28	6	6	16	22	56	24
Hoddesdon Town	28	5	7	16	30	55	22
Biggleswade Town	28	2	3	23	21	74	9

SENIOR DIVISION	P	W	D	L	F	A	Pts
Leverstock Green	26	19	3	4	54	19	60
Holmer Green	26	18	1	7	71	21	55
Tring Athletic	26	17	3	6	62	29	54
Stony Stratford Town	26	16	2	8	60	46	50
New Bradwell St Peter	26	13	7	6	49	30	46
Houghton Town	26	10	8	8	31	32	38
Mercedes Benz	26	10	7	9	48	38	37
Risborough Rangers	26	11	4	11	35	50	37
Winslow United	26	10	5	11	40	51	35
Kent Athletic	26	9	5	12	46	57	32
Ampthill Town	26	6	5	15	33	57	23
ACD Tridon	26	5	6	15	33	56	21
Totternhoe	26	2	9	15	27	62	15
The 61 FC (Luton)	26	2	3	21	26	67	9

DIVISION ONE	P	W	D	L	F	A	Pts
Biggleswade United	34	26	4	4	116	35	82
Caddington	34	22	7	5	89	45	72**
De Havilland	34	22	5	7	88	52	71
Crawley Green S&S	34	19	7	8	77	51	64
Old Bradwell United	34	19	6	9	69	49	63
Emberton	34	19	5	10	67	46	62
Bedford Eagles	34	18	6	10	79	48	57*
Scot	34	16	4	14	49	57	52
Walden Rangers	34	14	6	14	70	46	48
Buckingham United	34	13	6	15	66	75	45
Bridger Packaging	34	13	4	17	61	74	43
Luton Old Boys	34	10	7	17	43	53	37
Old Dunstablians	34	10	6	18	62	85	36
Leighton Athletic	34	9	5	20	50	75	32
Flamstead	34	8	6	20	44	80	30
Abbey National (MK)	34	5	9	20	39	92	24
Mursley United	34	6	8	20	53	91	23*
Pitstone & Ivinghoe	34	5	3	26	26	94	18

*3 points deducted **1 point deducted

SPARTAN FOOTBALL LEAGUE FINAL LEAGUE TABLES 1996-97

PREMIER DIVISION	P	W	D	L	F	A	Pts
Barkingside	30	20	6	4	60	23	66
Hillingdon Borough	30	19	8	3	65	31	65
Croydon Athletic	30	18	6	6	56	30	60
St Margaretsbury	30	17	4	9	51	49	55
Beaconsfield Sycob	30	13	10	7	52	28	49
Ruislip Manor	30	14	6	10	74	44	48
Woodford Town	30	13	6	11	42	39	45
Brimsdown Rovers	30	13	5	12	54	52	44
Islington St Mary's	30	9	10	11	38	38	37
Waltham Abbey	30	11	4	15	39	45	37
Amersham Town	30	9	6	15	34	51	33
Hanwell Town	30	8	8	14	49	49	32
Brook House	30	9	5	16	31	55	32
Cockfosters	30	6	6	18	35	57	24
Haringey Borough	30	5	6	19	24	58	21
Harefield United	30	5	6	19	32	87	21

Tottenham Omada recored expunged

DIVISION ONE	P	W	D	L	F	A	Pts
Leyton County	14	10	2	2	34	14	32
Catford Wanderers	14	9	1	4	33	16	25**
Old Roan	14	7	4	3	28	19	25
Trojan	14	7	3	4	25	18	24
Craven	14	6	3	5	39	25	21
Cray Valley	14	4	3	7	25	35	15
Bridon Ropes	14	2	3	9	15	29	9
Classic Inter	14	1	1	12	18	61	4

**3 points deducted
++AC Milla FC failed to complete 90% of its fixtures and as per rule 12(b) all points obtained by or against them have been expunged .

DIVISION TWO	P	W	D	L	F	A	Pts
Odua United	16	11	3	2	47	17	36
Holland Park	16	11	3	2	42	18	36
Clapham	16	10	4	2	44	21	34
Chingford United	16	7	1	8	42	29	22
Leyton Sports	16	5	4	7	31	32	19
Long Lane	16	4	4	8	28	45	16
Doddinghurst	16	4	3	9	25	45	15
Leyton County Res	16	4	2	10	22	34	14
Crofton Albion	16	3	2	11	24	64	11

PREMIER DIVISION NORTH

ARLESEY TOWN

Chairman: John Milton (01582 417815) **Vice-Chairman:** Scott Geekie **President:** Maurice Crouch
Secretary: John Albon, 13 St Johns Rd, Arlesey, Beds SG15 6ST. Tel: 01462 731318 (H & B).
Manager: Robbie O'Keefe **Asst Manager:** **Physio:** Jim Anderson
Ground: Lamb Meadow, Hitchin Rd, Arlesey. Tel: 01462 731448. **Directions:** The ground is situated on the main road thru village. From Hitchin direction the ground is 200 yds past Biggs Wall on left.
Capacity: 8,000 **Seats:** 120 **Cover:** 1,000 **Floodlights:** Yes **Club Shop:**
Clubhouse: Members bar & function room. Open daily 6-11.30, Sat 12-11.30, Sun 12-2.30 & 6-11.30
Programme: 50p **Editor:** Pete Brennan (01462 834455) **Nickname:** Blues **Founded:** 1891
Colours: Sky & navy/navy/navy **Change Colours:** All white.
Sponsors: Milcutt Goldstar **Midweek matchday:** Tuesday **Reserves' League:** South Midlands Lge Res Div
Prev. Lges: Biggleswade & Dist.; Beds. Co. (S. Mids) 22-26,27-28; Parthenon; London 58-60; Utd Co's 33-36 82-92.
Record Attendance: 2,000 v Luton Res, Beds Snr Cup 1906 **Club Record Appearance:** Gary Marshall
Players to progress to Football League: Roland Legate (Luton), Pat Kruse (Brentford, Leicester)
Honours: FA Vase Winners: 1994-5, Utd Co's Lg 84-85 (KO Cup), Sth Mids Lg 51-52 52-53, Premier Champions: 94-95, Chal. Cup 79-80, Prem Div Cup 94-95, Championship Shield 64-65, F'lit Cup, Beds Snr Cup 65-66 78-79.

BEDFORD UNITED

Chairman: John Cleverley **Vice Chairman:** Jim McMullen **President:** D Rostron
Secretary: Geoff Seagrave, 16 Riverview Way, Kempston, Bedford MK42 7BB. 01234 402369 (H)
Manager: Simon Ackroyd **Asst. Man.:** Mark Ackroyd **Coach/Physio:** Dave Petrie
Ground: McMullen Park, Meadow Lane, Cardington, Bedford MK45 3SB (01234 831024)
Directions: M1 jct 13, A421 to Bedford by-pass. Take third exit, A603 sandy, ground 500 yards on left hand side.
Capacity: 5,000 **Seats:** 25 **Cover:** 100 **Floodlights:** Yes **Founded:** 1957
Clubhouse: Open matchdays. Hot & cold snacks and drinks available.
Colours: Blue & White/blue/blue **Change colours:** All red **Nickname:** United
Programme: 24 pages, £1 **Editor:** Robin King (01234 364654) **Press Officer:** Jim McMullem
Midweek matches: Wednesday **Reserves' League:** S. Mids Lge Res. sect. **Club Sponsors:** JDP Finance
Previous - **Leagues:** Bedford & Dist. Lge (57-70 & 80-89); United Cos. Lge 70-80
Name: Printers Diemer-Reynolds (pre'72)
Ground: Allen Park (57-80); Fairhill, Clapham Road (80-93); Hillgrounds, Kempston 93-96).
Record Gate: (at Fairhill) 1500 v Bedford Town, South Midlands League Division One 26/12/92.
Record scorer: Neil Tysoe 220 **Record appearances:** Simon Fordham 418
96-97 - Captain: Tony Brittain **Top Scorer:** Jason Kyle **P.o.Y:** Chris Hyde
Honours: Bedford & Dist Lg Premier Division & Division One, County Junior Cup, Biggleswade KO Cup, Butchers Cup(2), Britania Cup, Bedford Charity Cup.

BIGGLESWADE TOWN

Chairman: Maurice Dorrington **Vice Chairman:** M Jarvis **President:** R Dorrington
Secretary: Graham Arkwright, 21 Willsheres Road, Biggleswade, Beds SG18 0BU (01767 316992).
Manager: D Northfield **Physio:** J Maher **Nickname:** Waders **Founded:** 1874
Ground: 'Fairfield', Fairfield Road, Biggleswade, Beds (01767 312374).
Directions: A1 North r'bout, left immediately after metal bridge into car park. 10 mins walk from Biggleswade (BR).
Capacity: 2,400 **Seats:** 250 **Cover:** 400 **Floodlights:** Yes **Club Shop:** No.
Clubhouse: Open all matchdays. Filled rolls available. Refreshment hut sells hotdogs, teas, coffees, snacks.
Programme: 32 pages, with admission (extra copies 50p). **Editor:** Brian Doggett (01769 318307 (H).
Colours: All green **Change:** Tangerine/black/black **Club Sponsors:** Mantles Ford
Previous Leagues: Biggleswade & Dist. 02-20/ Bedford & Dist. 09-12/ Utd Co's (prev. Northants Lg) 20-39 51-55 63-80/ Spartan 46-51/ Eastern Co's 55-63. **Previous Name:** Biggleswade F.C.
96-97 Top Scorer: G Kinnear **Players moving to Football League:** Darren Hay (Cambridge Utd) 1994
Honours: South Mids Lge Floodlit Cup 95-96; Beds Snr Cup 02-03 07-08 46-47 51-52 61-62 62-63 66-67 73-74, Beds Premier Cup 22-23 27-28, Nth Beds Charity Cup 07-08 09-10 26-27 33-34(joint) 49-50 52-53 54-55 57-58 62-65 67-69 73-74 91-92 94-95, Utd Co's Lg Cup 73-74, Hunts Premier Cup 92-93 93-94(joint) 94-95, Hinchingbrooke Cup 03-04 12-13 92-93, Jess Piggott Trophy 87-88 89-90 91-92 92-93, Key Consul. Res F/Light Cup 89-90.

BRACHE SPARTA

Chairman: Roy Standring **President:** Doug Smith **Nickname:** The Foxes **Founded:** 1960
Secretary: Roy Standring, 37 Taunton Avenue, Luton, Beds. LU2 0Ln. Tel: 01582 736574
Manager: Steve Brinckman **Physio:** Phil Toyer **Colours:** White/navy/white **Change Colours:** All royal
Ground: Foxdell Sports Ground, Dallow Rd, Luton LU1 1UP (01582 20751). **Directions:** Left off A505 to Dunstable into Chaul Lane at r'bout. Proceed across new relief road - ground entrance adjacent to Foxdell Junior School.
Capacity: 400 **Cover:** 100 **Seats:** 25 **Floodlights:** Yes **Midweek matches:** Wednesday
Clubhouse: Open daily 12-3 & 7.30-11. Light snacks & refreshments etc available. **Club Shop:** No
Programme: 30 pages, £2 (incl. admission) **Club Sponsors:** A & E Engineering.
Previous - League: Luton & Dist. **Grounds:** Crawley Green Rd, Luton (public park); Hitchin Town FC (share 93-94).
Club Record Scorer: Keith Denness **Honours:** South Mids Lg R-up 92-93, 96-97 (Div 1 R-up 83-84 87-88, Lg Cup R-up 75-76 80-81 92-93, Prem. Div Cup R-up 91-92, Luton & Dist. Lg 67-68 69-70 70-71 71-72, Wm. Pease Tphy 66-67 67-68 70-71 71-72, Beds I'mediate Cup 71-72 (R-up 68-69 70-71), Beds Jnr Cup 82-83, Leighton Chall. Cup R-up 69-70.

BUCKINGHAM ATHLETIC

Chairman: Alex Miller **President:** J Burgess **Manager:** Malcolm East
Secretary: Chris Forman, 10 Elm Drive, Deanshanger, Milton Keynes. MK19 6JF. Tel: 01908 563526 (H).
Ground: Stratford Fields, Stratford Rd, Buckingham (01280 816945).
Directions: From Milton Keynes take the A422 Stony Stratford-Buckingham road - ground on left just before town centre. From Oxford, Aylesbury or Bletchley, take the ring road to the A422 Stony Stratford roundabout, turn left, the ground is situated at the bottom of the hill on the left.
Capacity: 1,500 **Seats:** No **Cover:** 200 **Floodlights:** Yes **Founded:** 1933
Programme: 10 pages, 50p **Editor:** Tony Checkley, 01280 817826 (H) **Midweek matches:** Wednesday
Colours: All sky & navy blue **Change Colours:** Red & white/white/red **Nickname:** Swans
Previous Leagues: North Bucks; Hellenic. **Players progressing to Football League:** None.
Honours: Sth Mids Lg Div 1 85-86 90-91 (R-up 88-89, Div 1 Cup 90-91), Nth Bucks Lg 84-85 (Lg Cup 83-84, Lg Shield 60-61), Berks & Bucks Jnr Cup 65-66, Buckingham Charity Cup 69-70 71-72.

HARPENDEN TOWN

Chairman: Alan King **Managers:** Mark Nicholls, Paul Woolfrey **Nickname:** The Town **Founded:** 1891
Secretary: Stephen Whiting, 169 Grove Rd, Harpenden, Herts AL5 1SY (01582 761606).
Ground: Rothamsted Park, Amenbury Lane, Harpenden (01582 715724).
Directions: A1081 to Harpenden. Turn left/right at George Hotel into Leyton Rd. Turn left into Amenbury Rd, then left again (50yds) into 'Pay and Display' car park - entrance is signposted thru car park to opposite corner.
Capacity: 1,500 **Seats:** 25 **Cover:** 100 **Floodlights:** Yes **Programme:** 50p **Editor:** Secretary
Midweek matches: Tuesday **Colours:** Yellow/blue/blue **Change Colours:** Red & blue stripes/yellow/yellow
Previous Name: Harpenden FC 1891-1908. **Previous Leagues:** Mid-Herts; Herts County.
Honours: Sth Mids Lg 61-62 64-65 (Championship Shield 67-68, Lg Cup 70-71, Div 1 89-90, Prem Div Tphy 89-90, Reserve Div 89-90), Herts Co. Lg 11-12 49-50 51-52 53-54 (Aubrey Cup 20-21 28-29 50-51 51-52), Mid-Herts Lg 09-10 20-21, Pratt Cup 06-07 08-09 10-11, Herts Jnr Cup 01-02 09-10 11-12 20-21 25-26, Herts I'mediate Cup 52-53, Herts Charity Shield 07-08, Bingham Cox Cup 1896-97 1902-03 09-10 20-21.

HODDESDON TOWN

President: Peter Haynes **Chairman:** Roger Merton **Deputy Chairman:** Stewart Edwards
Secretary: Brenda Timpson, 82 Tolmers Road, Cuffley, Potters Bar, Herts EN6 4JY (01707 874028)
Manager: Alan Moore **Asst Manager:** Paul Surridge **Nickname:** Lilywhites/ Lowfielders **Founded:** 1879
Ground: 'Lowfield', Park View, Hoddesdon, Herts (0992 463133).
Directions: A10, A1170 into Hoddesdon, over 1st r'about, right at 2nd r'about and follow signs to Broxbourne, keeping to the left. Turn right at 1st mini r-about into Cock Lane and 1st right is Park View. Ground 200yds on the left, entrance opposite Park Rd. Nearest BR station is Broxbourne.
Capacity: 3,000 **Seats:** 100 **Cover:** 250 **Floodlights:** Yes **Club Shop:** No.
Clubhouse: Bar and well-stocked Tea Bar with hot food. Open at every home game.
Colours: White/black/black **Change Colours:** All red **Reserves' Lge:** Essex/Herts Border Com
Programme: 88-100 pages 80p **Editor:** Mrs Jane Sinden (01767 631297) **Midweek matchday:** Tuesday
Honours: FA Vase 74-75 (1st winners), Sth Mids Lg Lg Cup 85-86 86-87 91-92 (Premier Div Tphy R-up 92-93), Spartan Lg 70-71 (R-up(3) 71-74, Div 1 35-36, Div 2 'B' 27-28, Lg Cup(2) 70-72), Herts Snr Cup(3) 1886-88 89-90, Herts Charity Shield(4) 47-48 70-72 78-79, Herts Snr Centenary Tphy 86-87, Sth Mids Floodlit Cup 89-90 (R-up 92-93), Waltham Hospital Cup 27-28, Perry Charity Cup(7), East Anglian Cup Group finalists 92-93.

LANGFORD

Chairman: Mick Quinlan **President:** Ted Rutt **Commercial Manager:** Diane Woodward
Secretary: Frank Woodward, 4 West View, Langford, Biggleswade. Beds. SG18 9RT. 01462 701015 (H).
Press Officer: Secretary **Manager:** Gerald Rogers **Asst Mgr:** Andy Wellings **Coach:** Phil Elcock
Ground: Forde Park, Langford Road, Henlow SG16 6AF (0426 816106). **Directions:** Halfway between Langford and Henlow on A6001 Hitchin to Biggleswade road. Bus 177 on main Hitchin-Biggleswade route stops right outside ground.
Capacity: 4,000 **Seats:** 50 **Cover:** 250 **Floodlights:** Yes **Founded:** 1910 **Club Shop:** Yes
Clubhouse: Weekday evenings, matchdays 11am-11pm, Sun 12-3pm. Hot food on matchdays only.
Colours: All red with white trim **Change Colours:** Blue & white
Programme: With admission. **Editors:** Lesley Deveraux 01462 701443 (H); Candy Elcock 01462 700472 (H)
Sponsors: B.B & E.A (Sandy); 'The Boot' Pub & Rest. **Midweek matches:** Tuesday **Nickname:** Reds
Honours: S Mids Lg 88-89 (Lg Cup 73-74 75-76, Prem. Div Tphy 88-89,94-95. O'Brien Div 1 Tphy 84-85), N Beds Charity Cup 27-28 30-31 69-70 75-76 86-87 92-93 94-95, Bedford & Dist. Lg 30-31 31-32 32-33, Bedford I'mediate Cup 68-69, Hinchingbrooke Cup 72-73.

LETCHWORTH GARDEN CITY

Chairman: Adrian Earl **President:** None **Manager:** Grahaem Hopkins
Secretary: June Earl, 92 Bilberry Road, Clifton, Shefford, Beds SG17 5HD. Tel: 01462 816683 (H)
Ground: Baldock Rd, Letchworth, Herts SG6 2GN (01462 684691). **Directions:** Jct 9 (A6141) off A1M over r-about, rt at next r-about, ground on rt. From Luton (A505) thru Hitchin, ground 3 miles after Hitchin. 2 miles from Letchworth (BR).
Capacity: 3,200 **Cover:** 400 **Seats:** 200 **Floodlights:** Yes **Founded:** 1906
Colours: All Blue **Change Colours:** Red & white stripes/red/red **Nickname:** Bluebirds.
Programme: 24 pages, 50p **Editor:** Keith Brown 0385 338584 **Midweek matchday:** Tuesday
Honours: Herts Lg 11-12, Spartan Lg 29-30 35-36 51-52, Delphian Lg 57-58, Athenian Lg 74-75 (Mem. Shield 65-66 66-67), Herts Snr Cup 12-13 35-36 51-52, Herts Charity Shield 22-23 47-48 87-88 91-92, East Anglian Cup 76-77, Woolwich Cup 81-82, Hitchin Cup 81-82.

LONDON COLNEY

Chairman: Bill Gash **Vice Chairman:** P Light **President:** I Holt.
Secretary: Dave Brock, 50 Seymour Rd., St Albans, Herts. AL3 5HW. Tel: 01727 761644 (H)
Ground: Cotslandswick, London Colney (01727 822132). **Manager:** S Seabrook, M Wright **Physio:** J Burt
Directions: From London Colney r'bout (junction of A414/A1081) take A414 towards Watford, after layby (300yds) turn left (hidden turning marked 'Sports Ground') and follow around to gates. Three miles from St Albans (BR).
Capacity: 1,000 **Cover:** 100 **Seats:** 30 **Floodlights:** Yes **Club Shop:**
Clubhouse: Open after games. Hot food available. **Founded:** 1907
Programme: £1 with entry **Editor:** Matt Kelly Tel: 01727 761644 (H) **Nickname:** Blueboys
Colours: All royal blue with white trim **Change Colours:** All Red **Sponsors:** Harris Mortgage & Finance
Previous - Leagues: Mid Herts 1907-54; Herts Co. 07-92. **Ground:** Whitehorse Lane 07-75.
Honours: Sth Mids Lg Snr 94-95 Div R-up 93-94 (Chall. Tphy 93-94, Div 1 R-up 92-93, Herts Co. Lg 56-57 59-60 86-87 88-89 (R-up 57-58 58-59, Aubrey Cup 21-22 22-23 56-57 58-59 81-82, Herts Centenary Tphy 89-90 (R-up 90-91), Herts I'mediate Cup 58-59 74-75 82-83, Herts Charity Shield 61-62 (R-up 59-60), Herts Jnr Cup 54-55, Mid Herts Benevolent Cup 27-28 29-30 48-49 (Benevolent Shield x4 - 51-55, Charity Cup 48-49), St Albans Playing Fields Cup 62-63 73-74 75-76 80-81, Frank Major Tphy 74-75 75-76.

MILTON KEYNES

Chairman: Jacqui Higgins **Managing Director:** A Denman **Founded:** 1993 **Nickname:** None
Secretary: Mr Neasham Galloway, 22 Bascote, Tinkers Bridge, Milton Keynes, MK6 3DW. Tel: 0956 948829
Manager: W Marr **Asst Manager:** A Milne **Physio:** John Butcher
Ground: Manor Fields, Bletchley, Milton Keynes (01908 375256). **Directions:** Old A5 to Fenny Stratford, about 500yds on left go over bridge opposite Belvedere Nursuries into Manor Fields - ground on right.
Capacity: 3,000 **Seats:** 160 **Cover:** 1,000 **Floodlights:** Yes **Club Shop:** No.
Clubhouse: Two bars. Upstairs bar open every evening. Snacks available.
Programme: 16 pages, 40p **Editor:** Drew Dias **Reserves' Lge:** South Mids Res. Div 1A
Colours: Red and black/black/black **Change Colours:** Blue/white/blue **Midweek matches:** Tuesday
Club Records - Attendance: 250 v Bedford Town, S. Mids Lge 30/4/94 **Goalscorer:** Andy McCabe **Appearances:** Andy McCabe **Win:** 8-0 v Long Marston, Leighton Chall. Cup, 15.8.95 **Defeat:** 1-6 v Harpenden T. (A), S Mids Lge Prem. Div. 11/9/93 **Honours:** Leighton Challenge Cup 94-95, 95-96

POTTERS BAR TOWN

Chairman: Peter Waller. **Vice Chairman:** Alan Bolt. **President:** Bert Wright
Secretary: Carole Waller, 26 Queen Annes Grove, Bush Hill Park, Enfield, Middx EN1 2JR (0181 360 7859).
General Manager: Les Eason **Manager:** Ray Kierstenson & Micky Darling **Physio:** Brian Goymer
Ground: Parkfield, The Walk, Potters Bar, Herts EN6 1QN, 01707 654833 **Directions:** M25 jct 24, into Potters Bar along Southgate Rd (A111), at 1st lights rt into High St (A1000), 1/2 mile left into The Walk, ground 200 yds on right (opp. Potters Bar C.C.). BR to Potters Bar - The Walk is opposite station - ground 1/2 mile up hill on left.
Capacity: 2,000 **Seats:** 25 **Cover:** 100 **Floodlights:** Yes **Club Shop:** No
Clubhouse: Sat 12.30-11pm, Sun noon-5pm, Tues & Thurs 7.30-11pm, midweek matchnights 6-11pm.
Programme: 24 pages, £1 **Editor/Press Officer:** Robert Brassett, 0181 364 4058 **Founded:** 1960
Colours: Red & royal stripes/royal/royal **Change colours:** White/red/red
Sponsors: Century 21 Estates **Nickname:** The Grace or The Scholars. **Midweek matches:** Tues. or Wed.
96-97 - Captain: Gary Smith **Top Scorer:** Gary Ferguson **P.o.Y.:** Ryan Harris **Honours:** South Midlands Lge. Prem. Div. 96-97, Plate 96-97; Herts. Sen. Co. Lge. Prem. Div. 90-91, Div. 1 73-74, 81-82, Div. 2 68-69; North London Comb. Prem. Div. 67-68, Div. 1 67-68, Div. 2 R-up 65-66; Barnet & Dist. Lge Prem. Div. R-up 64-65, Div. 1 61-62; Herts Charity Shd. R-up 95-96, Potters Bar Charity Cup 76-77, 95-96, R-up x8; Mid Herts FA - Bingham Cox Cup R-up 94-95.

ROYSTON TOWN

Chairman: Tony Moulding **Vice-Chairman:** Bernard Brown **President:** Alan Barton
Secretary/Press Officer: Trevor Glasscock, 39 Poplar Drive, Royston, Herts. SG8 (01763 230783)
Manager: Paddy Butcher **Asst Mgr:** Bernard Brown **Physio:** Colin Mardell
Ground: Garden Walk, Royston, Herts SG8 7HP (01763 241204). **Directions:** From Baldock, A505 to Royston bypass, right at 2nd island onto A10 towards London, 2nd left is Garden Walk; ground 100 yds on left. From A11, exit 10 turning left onto A505, left at 1st island, 2nd left is Garden Walk. Ten mins walk from Royston (BR).
Capacity: 4,000 **Seats:** 300 **Cover:** 300 **Floodlights:** Yes **Club Shop:** Yes
Clubhouse: Mon-Thurs 7-11, Fri 11-3 & 7-11, Sat 11-3 & 4-11, Sun 12-3. Steward: Mr & Mrs P Nesbitt.
Programme: 16 pages, 30p **Editor:** Steve Langridge (01438 356661) **Nickname:** Crows.
Colours: White/black/black **Change colours:** Red/white/white **Founded:** 1875
Midweek Matches: Tuesday **Reserve League:** Essex & Herts Border Comb. **Sponsors:** ABA Consultants.
96-97 - Capt.: S Moulding **P.o.Y.:** S Brown **Top scorer:** Jon Dobson
Honours: Herts Co. Lg 76-77 (Div 1 69-70 76-77); Sth Mids Lg R-up 79-80 (Div 1 78-79, Chall. Cup R-up 78-79; Herts Charity Shield 81-82 89-90 (R-up 78-79 88-89), Creake Shield 20-21; Cambs Lg Div 2 29-30; Herts Intermediate Cup 88-89 (R-up 89-90), Nth Herts Lg 4 Cup 78-79 79-80 (Div R-up 82-83, Div 3 R-up 81-82, Div 4 R-up 79-80).

BEDFORD UNITED F.C. 1997-98 SQUAD

HODDESDON TOWN F.C. - L-R, Back Row: Ray Greenall (manager), John Walton (Coach), Luke Swift, Dean Stuber, Mark Foster, Gary Cummins, Richard Evans, Joel Miller, Conor McGovern, Ritchie Simmonds, Jim Briggs (Asst. Man.). Front: Stuart Dorward, David Wilson, Dominic Barrett, Pablo Ardiles, Jeff Cross, Mark Kozak, Paul Mann.

TODDINGTON ROVERS

Chairman: Alan Fieldhouse **Vice Chairman:** Brian Horne **President:** Peter Turner
Secretary: Barry Hill, 9 Fairfield Rd, Dunstable,Beds. LU5 4JT. Tel: 01582 471150 (H), 01582 723122 (B).
Manager: Steve Loasby **Asst Man.:** Alan Loasby **Coach:** Roger King **Physio:** John Cullen
Ground: Barton Rovers FC, Sharpenhoe Rd., Barton-le-Clay. Tel: 01582 882607
Directions: From Luton leave A6 at B655. Drive into village then left at Royal Oak P.H. From Bedford take A6 to Luton. Leave A6 & follow signs into village, then right at Royal Oak into Sharpenhoe Rd. Ground entrance 200 yards on left.
Seats: No **Cover:** 100 **Floodlights:** No **Nickname:** Rovers **Founded:** 1894 **Club Shop:** No
Clubhouse: Club use Toddington Social & Services Club. **Midweek matches:** Tuesday
Colours: All black & white stripes **Change Colours:** All Blue. **Press Officer:** Colin Bryson
Programme: 36 pages, 75p **Editor:** Andrew Parker, 01582 599158 (H) **Sponsors:** O'Neill Plant Hire
Honours: South Midlands Lg Snr Div 94-95 (Snr Div Cup 94-95), Luton & District South Beds Lge R-up x3 (Div 1 x3, Div 2 x2, Div 3 x2, Div 4 x1).

WELWYN GARDEN CITY

Chairman: John Newman **Manager:** Ian Priest. **Physio:** Arthur Wood
Secretary: James Bruce, 6 Autumn Grove, Welwyn G.C., Herts AL7 4DB. Tel: 01707 331048 (H).
Ground: Herns Lane, Welwyn Garden City (01707 328470).
Directions: From A1 follow signs for industrial area. Take one-way system opposite Avdel Ltd (signed Hertford B195), take 2nd exit off one-way system. Ground 400 yards on left. One and a half miles from Welwyn GC (BR).
Capacity: 1,500 **Seats:** 40 **Cover:** 120 **Floodlights:** Yes **Founded:** 1921 **Club Shop:** Yes
Clubhouse: Open every night and weekend lunchtimes. Members Bar, Hall. Steward: Dave Parham.
Colours: Maroon & blue/blue/maroon **Change Colours:** Yellow/blue/yellow **Nickname:** Citzens
Programme: 24 pages, 50p **Editor:** Keith Browne (01707 251854) **Midweek Matches:** Tuesday
Best Season - FA Vase: 1st Rd 86-87 **FA Cup:** 1st Qual.Rd. 94-95 **Record Gate:** 600 v Welwyn Garden Utd
Previous - Leagues: Spartan; Metropolitan; Gtr London. **Ground:** Springfields
Honours: Herts Snr Centenary Tphy 84-85 (R-up 88-89), Herts Charity Shield 27-28 86-87 87-88 94-95 (R-up 48-49), Sth Mids Lg 73-74 (R-up 85-86, Div 1 69-70 81-82, Lg Cup R-up 74-75 81-82 88-89, Reserve Cup 85-86).

PREMIER DIVISION SOUTH

AMERSHAM TOWN

Chairman: Howard Lambert **Vice Chairman:** David Holdcroft **President:** Graham Taylor
Secretary: Ian Wright, 80 Somervell Road, Harrow, Middlesex. HA2 8TT
Manager: Paul Pitfield **Coach:** Oscar Ringsell
Ground: Spratley's Meadow, School Lane, Old Amersham, Bucks. (01494 727428).
Directions: From London A413 to Amersham Old town, infront of market hall, right into Church St., first left into School Lane, ground on left past Mill Lane. 1 mile from Amersham Station - BR & underground Metropolitan Line.
Seats: None **Cover:** 100 **Capacity:** 1,500 **Floodlights:** Yes **Founded:** 1890
Clubhouse: Open matchdays. Bar facilities. Teas, coffees and light snacks **Club Shop:** No.
Programme: With admission **Editor/Press Officer:** David Holdcroft 01494 725201 **Sponsors:** Llumarlite Ltd.
Colours: Black & white stripes/black/black **Change colours:** Red/black/black
Midweek matches: Tuesday **Reserve's League:** Middx Co. **Nickname:** Magpies.
Previous Leagues: Wycombe & Dist. Comb.; Aylesbury & Dist.; Chesham; Gt Western Suburban 20-23; Spartan 23-53 61-62; Hellenic 53-61 62-72. **Record Attendance:** 2,000 v Aston V., centenary match 1990 (at Chesham).
96-97 - Captain: Fergal O'Hagan **P.o.Y.:** Danny Kindell **Joint Top scorers:** Ian Huse, Andy Fitzsimons
Honours: Hellenic Lg 63-64 (R-up 64-65 65-66, Div 1 62-63, Cup 53-54), Ldn Spartan Lg R-up 79-80, St Marys Cup 89-90 96-97 (R-up 90-91), Berks & Bucks Jnr Cup 22-23 (Snr Cup SF 79-80 80-81), Wycombe Chal. Cup 23-24.

BARKINGSIDE

President: A Smith **Chairman:** Greg Hall **Manager:** C Edwards **Asst Man.:** A Marsden **Physio:** M Stevens
Secretary/Press Officer: Norman A Ingram, 45 Cheneys Rd, Leytonstone, London E11 3LL. 0181 555 1447 (H)
Ground: Oakside, Station Road, Barkingside, Ilford, Essex (0181 550 3611). **Founded:** 1898
Directions: From London A12 Eastern Avenue to Green Gate, left into Hurns Rd to Barkingside, right into Craven Gardens, right again Carlton Drive leading to Station Road, under bridge and ground entrance on right. Adjacent to Barkingside station (Central Line). From Ilford station (BR) take 169 Bus to Craven Gardens.
Capacity: 1,000 **Seats:** 60 **Cover:** 60 **Floodlights:** Yes **Reserves' League:** Essex & Herts Border Comb.
Clubhouse: Saturdays 1pm-12. midweek matchnights 6.30-11pm. Rolls, hotdogs, hamburgers. **Club Shop:** No.
Colours: All white **Change colours:** All yellow **Midweek matchday:** Tuesday **Sponsors:** Directa
Programme: 12 pages with admission **Editor:** J Brown (0181 500 5125)
96-97 - Captain: G Tamplin **P.o.Y.:** G Munt **Top Scorer:** C Rose **Honours:** Spartan Lge. Prem. Div. 96-97, R-up 90-91 (Harry Sunderland Shld 83-84 (R-up 84-85); London Sen. Cup 96-97; S. Essex Lge R-up 46-47, L'don Lg R-up 49-50 (Lg Cup 55-56 (R-up 52-53 62-63)), Ilford Fest. Cup 51-52, Romford Char. Cup 51-52, Gtr L'don Lg 64-65.

BEACONSFIELD S.Y.C.O.B.

President: D Piercy **Chairman:** Fred Deanus **Manager:** Simon Delahunty
Secretary: Ken Barrett, 31 Stockley End, Abingdon, Oxon OX14 2NF. Tel: 01235 202058 (H), 01235 537080 (B).
Ground: Holloway Park, Slough Road, Beaconsfield, Bucks (01494 676868). **Directions:** M40 (Jct 2), 1st exit to A355. Club 100yds on right. One and a miles from Beaconsfield (BR). Bus 441 Slough/ High Wycombe.
Seats: 250 **Cover:** 250 **Capacity:** 3,000 **Floodlights:** Yes **Founded:** 1994.
Clubhouse: Open eves & matchdays. Bar, Committee Room, Hall, Kitchen, Changing Room **Club Shop:** No
Programme: Yes, £1. **Editor:** Andy Jackson, 17 Boundary Cottages, Chipperfield Rd., Bovingdon, Herts. HP3 0JT.
Midweek Matches: Tuesday **Reserves' League:** Middlesex **Nickname:** SYCOB
Colours: Red & white quarters/black/red & black **Change colours:** All yellow
PREVIOUS - Names: Beaconsfield Utd (1921); Slough Youth Club Old Boys (1941). Clubs merged 1994. **Leagues:** Beaconsfield Utd: Wycombe & District; Maidenhead. *Slough YCOB: Windsor, Slough & District; East Berks; Chiltonian (pre-1994).* **Grounds:** *Slough YCOB: Hatmill Community Centre, Burnham Lane, Slough (pre-1994).*
Best FA Vase season: Beaconsfield: 1st Rd 83-84 85-86 87-88.
Record Gate: 300 Beaconsfield Utd v Chesham Utd, Berks & Bucks Sen Cup 1985.
97-97 - Captain: D Tough **P.o.Y.:** John Milroy **Top Scorer:** Tony Thompson
Honours: *Slough YCOB: Chiltonian Lg Rup 93-94 (Lg Cup 92-93), Slough Town Cup R-up 91-92.*

BRIMSDOWN ROVERS

Chairman/Secretary: Graham Dodd, 57 Roundmoor Drive, Cheshunt, Herts EN8 9HU. 01992 626820 (H&B)
Match Secretary: Tony Beasley, 80 Cobham Road, Fetcham, Leatherhead, Surrey. KT22 9JS. 01372 376820 (H)
Ground Brimsdown Sports & Social Club, Goldsdown Road, Enfield, Middlesex (0181 804 5491).
Directions: BR from Liverpool Street to Brimsdown (half mile away) or Southbury Road. By road off Green Street, itself off Hertford Road (A1010). Buses 191 or 307.
Seats: None **Cover:** 50 **Capacity:** 1,000 **Floodlights:** Yes **Founded:** 1947
Clubhouse: Large lounge & clubroom, games room & stage. 3 bars (300 capacity)
Manager: Harry O'Reilly **Programme:** With admission **Editor:** Peter Wade
Colours: Black & white stripes/black/black **Change colours:** All yellow & blue
Best season - FA Vase: 3rd Rd 93-94 **FA Cup:** 3rd Qual. replay 91-92. **Previous - Leagues:** Northern Suburban **Names:** Durham Rovers; Brimsdown FC. **Record Gate:** 412 v Chesham Utd, FA Cup 3rd Qual. Rd 12/10/91.
96-97 - Captain: Dave Burke **Top Scorer:** Tibbs Corbin **P.o.Y.:** Chris Thomas
Honours: Spartan Lg 92-93. Spartan Lg Cup 95-96.

BROOK HOUSE

President: G Waddock **Chairman:** Mick Ralph **Vice-Chairman:** Barry Crump
Secretary: Barry Crump, 19 Bradenham Road, Hayes, Middlesex UB4 8LP. Tel: 0181 841 3959 (H), 0850 253924 (B).
Manager: Dermot Jackson **Asst. Manager:** Frank Lutt **Press Officer:** Frank Lamb.
Ground: Farm Park, Kingshill Avenue, Hayes, Middlesex (0181 845 0110).
Directions: From North Circular road: A40 Western Ave. to Target r'about, left towards Hayes (A312), over White Hart r'about towards Hayes, right at traffic lights in to Kingshill Ave, ground 1 mile on right. Nearest BR station is Hayes & Harlington, then bus 90 or 195 to Brook House pub. Nearest tube is Northolt (central line), then bus to ground.
Seats: None **Cover:** 75 **Capacity:** 250 **Floodlights:** Yes **Founded:** 1974 **Club Shop:** No
Clubhouse: Open weekdays 7-11pm, Sat noon-11pm, Sun noon-3 & 7-10.30pm
Programme: 10 pages, £1.50 with entry **Editor:** Frank Lamb **Reserve League:** Middlesex County
Colours: Blue & white/white/white **Change colours:** All green **Midweek matchday:** Monday
Best season - FA Vase: Prel Rd 90-91 91-92 93-94. **FA Cup:** 1st Qual Round 93-94.
Players progressing to Football League: Neil Shipperley **Senior Honours:** None.

COCKFOSTERS

Chairman/Press Officer: Frank Brownlie (0181 500 5930) **President:** Vic Bates
Secretary: Graham Bint, 15 Chigwell Park, Chigwell, Essex IG7 5BE (0181 500 7369).
Manager: Derek Townsend **Physio:** Derek Carlisle **Nickname:** Fosters
Ground: Cockfosters Sports Ground, Chalk Lane, Cockfosters, Barnet (0181 449 5833).
Directions: Ground on A111. M25 Jct 24 (Potters Bar), take A111 signed Cockfosters - ground 2 miles on right. Adjacent to Cockfosters underground station (Picadilly Line). Bus 298 to Cockfosters station.
Seats: None **Cover:** 50 **Capacity:** 1,000 **Floodlights:** No **Founded:** 1921.
Clubhouse: 7-11pm Tues & Thurs, 4-11pm Sat, 12-3pm Sun. Hot & cold food on matchdays. **Club Shop:** No.
Programme: 12 pages with entry **Editor:** A Simmons (0181 440 7998) **Midweek matches:** Tuesday
Colours: All Red **Change colours:** All White **Reserve League:** Middx County **Sponsors:** T.S.I. Design
Previous Grounds: None **Previous Name:** Cockfosters Athletic
Previous Leagues: Wood Green & District 21-46/ Northern Suburban 46-66/ Herts Snr Co. 66-91.
Record Gate: 408 v Saffron Walden, Herts Senior County Lg 68-69.
Record win: 10-1 v Rickmansworth T. **Record defeat:** 2-7 v Leggatts Old Boys (both 1968)
Players progressing to Football League: Justin Gentle (Luton, Colchester).
Club record scorer: Peter Benham **Club record appearances:** Bob Davis (500+).
96-97 - Captain: Dave Lee **P.o.Y.:** Dave Lee **Top scorer:** Dean Jones (24)
Honours: London Intermediate Cup 70-71 89-90, Herts Snr Co. Lg 78-79 80-81 83-84 (R-up 82-83 84-85, Aubrey Cup 78-79 84-85 (R-up 70-71 77-78)), Herts Intermediate Cup 78-79 (R-up 71-72 73-74 74-75), Northern Suburban Lg 61-62 (R-up 50-51 65-66, Div 1 49-50 60-61 (R-up 46-47 48-49)), F.A. Vase 2nd Rd 91-92.

HANWELL TOWN

Chairman/Press Officer: Bob Fisher Tel: 0181 952 4142 (H) 0181 519 7511 (B) **President:** Dave Iddiols
Secretary: John A Wake, 38 Warwick Ave., South Harrow, Middx. HA2 8RD. Tel/Fax: 0181 422 1048 (H)
Manager: Roy Nairn **Asst Manager:** Arthur Rowlands **Physio:** Catherine Horne
Ground: Reynolds Field, Perivale Lane, Perivale, Greenford, Middx (0181 998 1701).
Directions: A40(M) west from London, leave opposite Hoover building (B456 for Ealing), turn left into Argyle Road and left into Perivale Lane. Ground is on the left. 500 yards from Perivale tube station (Central line).
Seats: None **Cover:** 200 **Capacity:** 2,000 **Floodlights:** Yes **Founded:** 1948 **Nickname:** The Town
Clubhouse: Saturday matchdays 2-11pm, Tuesdays 6-11pm, Non-matchdays 7.30-11pm. **Club Shop:** No.
Programme: 16 pages, with entry **Editor:** Julie Soutar, c/o The club. **Midweek matchday:** Tuesday
Colours: Black & white stripes/black/black & white **Change:** All red **Reserves' League:** Middx County
Club Records - Attendance.: 600 v Spurs, Floodlights Oct. 89 **Fee received:** £2,000 for Pat Gavin, Gillingham 90
Win: 10-0 v Brook House, Spartan Lge **Goalscorer:** Tony Pickering **Appearances:** Phil Player 617 (20 seasons)
Hons: Spartan Lg 83-84 (Lg Cup R-up 93-94, London Snr Cup 91-92 92-93 (R-up 93-94), Middx Charity Cup R-up 92-93.

HAREFIELD UNITED

Chairman: Keith Ronald. Tel: 01895 824287 **President:** Mr Ivor Mitchell
Secretary: Terry Devereux, 72 Williamson Way, Rickmansworth, Herts WD3 2GL. Tel: 01923 711451 (H/B)
Ground: Preston Park, Breakespeare Road North, Harefield, Middx UB9 6DG (01895 823474).
Directions: M25 junction 16 to M40 East, left at first roundabout, then second left into Harvill Road. Follow this road up the Church Hill into village, right at small roundabout & the ground is on the right. Denham (BR).
Capacity: 2,000 **Seats:** 150 **Cover:** Yes **Floodlights:** Yes **Founded:** 1868 **Nickname:** Hares.
Clubhouse: (01895 823474) Lunchtimes and evenings. Cold snacks (hot on matchdays) **Club Shop:** No
Colours: Red & white/black/black & red **Change colours:** White/black/black **Reserves' League:** Suburban
Programme: 12-40 pages, 30p **Editor:** Terry Deveraux (Sec.) **Midweek Matches:** Tuesday
Previous Leagues: Uxbridge & Dist.; Gt Western Comb. 46-64; Parthenon 64-68; Middx 68-75; Athenian 75-84.
Honours: Middx Premier Cup 85-86, Athenian Lg R-up 83-84, Parthenon Lg 64-65 (Div 1 Cup 65-66), Middx Lg 66-67 68-71 (Lg Cup 66-67 68-69). **Best FA Cup year:** 2nd Qual. Rd replay 80-81, 86-87

HARINGEY BOROUGH

Chairman: Peter Lawlor **Secretary:** George Kilikita, Unit 12A, 16-22 Seven Sisters Rd, London N7 6AE.
Vice-Chairman: T O'Connell Tel: 0171 607 7419 (H), 0181 368 2783 (B)
Ground: Coles Park, White Hart Lane, Tottenham N17 (081 889 1415)
Directions: From M1 take North Circular Road (A406). Leave A406 turning right into Bounds Green Rpad (A109), proceed to end then turn left into Wood Gren High Rd (A105) and then first right into White Hart Lane. Ground is on right 300 yds past New River Sports Centre. Wood Green (Picadilly Line). BR (Eastern Region) to White Hart Lane, W3 bus passes ground A105 or A10 from Nth. Circular to Wood Green.
Seats: 280 **Cover:** Yes **Capacity:** 2,500 **Floodlights:** Yes **Clubhouse:** Open 7 days a week
Colours: Green & white/white/green **Change colours:** Yellow & black/black/yellow
Previous Leagues: London 07-14; Isthmian 19-52 84-88; Spartan 52-54; Delphian 54-63; Athenian 63-84.
Previous Names: Edmonton; Tufnell Park; Tufnell Park Edmonton; Edmonton & Haringey.
Senior Honours: None

HILLINGDON BOROUGH

Chairman: Roy Lovell **Secretary:** Garry Grant, 19 Leveret Close, Leavesden, Watford, Herts.
Commercial Mgr: Ken Rogers WD2 7AX. Tel: 01923 463602 (H).
Manager: John Morris **Asst Man.:** John Toogood **Coach:** Dave Silman **Physio:** Dave Pook
Ground: Middlesex Stadium, Breakspear Road, Ruislip, Middx HA4 7SB (01895 639544).
Directions: From A40 take B467 (signed Ickenham), left at 2nd r'bout into Breakspear Rd South, right after 1 mile by Breakspear pub - ground half mile on left. Nearest station is Ruislip. Bus U1 passes ground.
Seats: 150 **Cover:** 150 **Capacity:** 1,500 **Floodlights:** Yes **Founded:** 1990
Clubhouse: Mon-Fri 7.30-11pm, Sat & Sun lunchtime & 7.30-10.30pm. **Club Shop:** No.
Midweek Matches: Wednesday **Sponsors:** Airport Motor Radiator Co. **Nickname:** Boro.
Colours: White/blue/blue **Change colours:** Red & white stripes/white/red
Programme: 20 pages **Editor / Press Off.:** John Mason (081 868 7551) **Reserves' League:** Suburban
Club Records - Fee Received: £1,000 for Craig Johnson (Wealdstone).
Win: 9-0 v Amersham Town (H), Spartan Lge Prem. Div. 93-94. **Defeat:** 0-8 v Newport AFC
Senior Honours: None

ISLINGTON St MARYS

Chairman: Ian Myclam **Secretary:** Nick Adams, 5 Hambledon Chase, 58 Crouch Hill London N4 4AH.
Tel: 0171 359 6112 Tel: 0171 263 1530 (H), 0171-226 3400 (B), 0370 625235 (M).
Match Secretary: Eddie Webb, 34 Bidwell Gardens, Bounds Green, London, N11 2AU. Tel: 0181 881 0538 (H)
Ground: Coles Park, White Hart Lane, Tottenham N17 (0181 889 1495)
Directions: From M1 take North Circular Road (A406). Leave A406 turning right into Bounds Green Rpad (A109), proceed to end then turn left into Wood Gren High Rd (A105) and then first right into White Hart Lane. Ground is on right 300 yds past New River Sports Centre. Wood Green (Picadilly Line). BR (Eastern Region) to White Hart Lane, W3 bus passes ground A105 or A10 from Nth. Circular to Wood Green.
Capacity: 2,500 **Cover:** Yes **Seating:** 280 **Floodlights:** Yes **Founded:**
Colours: Blue/white/blue **Change Colours:** Black & white/black/white

RUISLIP MANOR

Chairman: Mick Connors **Vice Chairman:** Jim Evans **President:** TBA
Secretary: Andy Torrance, 55 Ryefield Avenue, Hillingdon, Middlesex. 01895 257631.
Manager: Andy Waddock **Asst Manager:** Gary Farrant **Physio:** Gary Strudwick
Ground: Grosvenor Vale, off West End Road, Ruislip, Middx (01895 637487-office, 676168-boardroom)
Directions: A40 to Ruislip, turn off on A4180, right at r'bout into West End Rd, right into Grosvenor Vale after a 1 1/2 miles - ground at end. From Ruislip Manor station (Metropolitan Line) turn left out of station, then 1st right into Shenley Ave, 3rd left into Cranley Dr - ground 150 yds on left.
Capacity: 3,000 **Seats:** 250 **Cover:** 600 **Floodlights:** Yes **Founded:** 1938 **Nickname:** The Manor
Clubhouse: Mon-Fri 12-3.30 & 5.30-11pm, Sat & Sun 12-3 & 7.30-10.30. **Club Shop:** Yes
Programme: 24 **Price:** 50p **Editor / Press Officer:** Steve Szymanski, 01895 637933
Colours: Black & White/black/black **Change colours:** Yellow & blue/yellow/yellow
Midweek Matches: Monday **Reserve League:** Suburban Lge (North) **Sponsors:** Eastcote Birds & Pets
Record Attendance: 2,000 v Tooting & Mitcham United, F.A. Amateur Cup 1962.
Previous Lges: Uxbridge 38-39; Middx Snr 39-46; London 46-58; Spartan 58-65; Athenian 65-84; Isthmian 84-96.
Best F.A. Cup year: Fourth Qual. Round 90-91, 2-5 v Halesowen Town (A)
Players progressing to Football League: Dave Carroll, Paul Barrowcliffe, Michael Meaker, Warren Goodhind, Ray Knowles, Barry & Roy Davies.
96-97 - Captain: Chris Balls **P.O.Y.:** Chris Balls **Top scorer:** Steve Hale, 23
Club Record Appearances: Chris Balls, 350 **Club Record Goalscorer:** Kevin Quinn, 76
Honours: London Lg R-up 51-52 (Div 1 R-up 47-48), Isthmian Lg Div 2 R-up 92-93 (Associate Members Tphy 90-91), Athenian Lg Div 2 72-73, Middx Snr Cup SF(6), Middx Charity Cup R-up 90-91 95-96.

St MARGARETSBURY

Chairman: Trevor I Blacktin **President:** R L Groucott
Secretary: Keith Myall, 30 Crib St, Ware, Herts. SG12 9EX. Tel: 01920 830356 (H), 01920 658502 (B).
Manager: Kelvin Hart **Asst Manager:** Colin Richards **Physio:** Derek Ridgewell
Ground: Station Road, Stanstead St Margarets, Nr Ware, Herts (01920 870473).
Directions: Harlow/Chelmsford exit from A10 to A414, take B181 at Amwell after 300yds towards Stanstead Abotts, ground quarter mile on right. 300yds from St Margaretsbury BR station (Liverpool Str.-Hertford East line).
Seats: 60 **Cover:** 60 **Capacity:** 1,000 **Floodlights:** No **Nickname:** The Bury **Founded:** 1894
Clubhouse: Bar open every evening 7-11, plus Sat 12-2, Sun 12-3. Bar snacks available. **Club Shop:** No
Programme: £2.00 with entry **Editor / Match Sec.:** Jane Free (01920 870431)
Colours: Red & black/black/red & black **Change colours:** All white
Midweek matchday: Tuesday **Reserve League:** Hertford & Dist. **Sponsors:** Universal Office Automation
Previous Leagues: East Herts; Hertford & Dist.; Waltham & District 47-48; Herts Co. 48-92.
Record Attendance: 327 v Wisbech Town, FA Vse 3rd Round 14/12/85.
Honours: Herts Snr Cent Tphy 92-93; Herts Co. Lg Div 2 48-49, Div 3 78-79; Aubrey Cup 48-49 71-72; Res. Div 1 82-83 86-87; Res. Cup 84-85 86-87 87-88); Waltham & Dist Lg 46-47; Spartan Lge 95-96; Roy Bailey Mem Trophy 95-96.

WALTHAM ABBEY

Chairman: Greg Brooker **President:** Dennis Cordell
Secretary: Alex Myers, 88 The Weymarks, Weir Hall Road, Tottenham N17 8LD. Tel/Fax: 0181 808 2706 (H)
Ground: 'Capershotts', Sewardstone Road, Waltham Abbey, Essex (01992 711287).
Directions: Just off M25 jct 26. Waltham Cross (BR Eastern Region) station three miles distant. 242 Bus.
Seats: None **Cover:** 400 **Capacity:** 2,000 **Floodlights:** Yes **Nickname:** The Abbey **Founded:** 1948
Clubhouse: 7-11pm Mon-Fri, 11am-11pm Sat, noon-3pm Sun. Cold snacks, pool, darts. **Club Shop:** No
Programme: 8 pages 50p **Editor:** Alex Myers (Sec.) **Reserves' League:** Essex & Herts Border Comb.
Colours: All green and white **Change colours:** Red & black hoops/red/red **Midweek matches:** Tuesday
Previous Leagues: Northen Suburban
Club Records - Attendance: 1,800 v Spurs, charity game **Scorer:** Paul Holloway **Appearances:** Colin Winter
Best Season - FA Cup: Prel. Rd 90-91 **FA Vase:** Prel. Rd 87-88 88-89 89-90

WOODFORD TOWN

Chairman: Vincent McBean. Tel: 0956 471828 (H), 0171 708 3935 (B).
Secretary: Bill Robertson, 2 Humphrey Close, Clayhill, Ilford, Essex IG5 0RW. Tel: 0181 550 6680 (H), 0171 708 3935 (B).
Ground: Greenwich Borough FC, 'Harrow Meadow', Eltham Green Road, Eltham, London. SE9. Tel: 0181 850 5360.
Directions: Travelling south on Blackwall Tunnel Southern Approach A102 (M) take exit Central London. Turn right at r'about into Shooters Hill Road (A2). At first set of traffic lights turn left into Kidbrooke Park Road (A2213). Proceed to end and turn lef into Eltham Road (A210) and then first left into Eltham Green Road. Ground on the left.
Seats: 50 **Cover:** 50 **Capacity:** 2,500 **Floodlights:** Yes **Programme Editor:** Vincent McBean (Chairman)
Colours: Red & white/red & white/red **Change Colours:** White & black stripes/white/white

BARKINGSIDE F.C. 1996-97 - Spartan League Premier Division Champions
L-R, Back Row: Jason Harris, Neil Hayes (Physio), David Thompson, Lee Parnell, John Buffong, Dean Meek, Billy Roche, Dave Curtis, Glen Tamplin (Captain), Kenrick Roudette, George Munt, Brett Patience. Front: Simon Miller, Chris Rose, Jeff Lennon, Craig Edwards (Manager), Micky Farrell, Tony Atkins, Kevin Field, Lyndon Lennon, Robbie O'Brien.

SENIOR DIVISION

AMPTHILL TOWN

Chairman: Philip Rayner **President:** Gary Williams
Secretary: Eric Turner, 34 Dunstable Street, Ampthill, Beds MK45 2JT. Tel: 01525 403128 (H & B).
Manager: Neil Rodney
Ground: Woburn Road, Ampthill, Beds. (01525 404440)
Directions: From Ampthill Town Centre follow signs to Woburn then 1st right into Ampthill Park.
Capacity: 1,500 **Seats:** 30 **Cover:** 400 **Floodlights:** No **Founded:** 1888.
Colours: Yellow & navy/navy/navy **Change Colours:** Yellow & red/red/red **Nickname:** Town
Previous Grounds: None **Previous Lges:** S Mids 51-65/ Utd Co's 65-91.
Midweek home matchday: Tuesday **Programme:** 16 pages, 50p. **Editor:** Eric Turner (Sec)
Hons: Sth Mids Lg 59-60 (C'ship Shield 58-59 59-60), North Beds Charity Cup 84-85.

BIGGLESWADE TOWN

Chairman: Maurice Dorrington **Vice Chairman:** M Jarvis **President:** R Dorrington
Secretary: Graham Arkwright, 21 Willsheres Road, Biggleswade, Beds SG18 0BU (01767 316992).
Manager: D Northfield **Physio:** J Maher **Nickname:** Waders **Founded:** 1874
Ground: 'Fairfield', Fairfield Road, Biggleswade, Beds (01767 312374).
Directions: A1 North r'bout, left immediately after metal bridge into car park. 10 mins walk from Biggleswade (BR).
Capacity: 2,400 **Seats:** 250 **Cover:** 400 **Floodlights:** Yes **Club Shop:** No.
Clubhouse: Open all matchdays. Filled rolls available. Refreshment hut sells hotdogs, teas, coffees, snacks.
Programme: 32 pages, with admission (extra copies 50p). **Editor:** Brian Doggett (01769 318307 (H).
Colours: All green **Change:** Tangerine/black/black **Club Sponsors:** Mantles Ford
Previous Leagues: Biggleswade & Dist. 02-20/ Bedford & Dist. 09-12/ Utd Co's (prev. Northants Lg) 20-39 51-55 63-80/ Spartan 46-51/ Eastern Co's 55-63. **Previous Name:** Biggleswade F.C.
96-97 Top Scorer: G Kinnear **Players moving to Football League:** Darren Hay (Cambridge Utd) 1994
Honours: South Mids Lge: Res Div 2 87-88, Res Chall Trophy 88-89, S.M. Floodlit Cup 95-96; Beds Snr Cup 02-03 07-08 46-47 51-52 61-62 62-63 66-67 73-74, Beds Premier Cup 22-23 27-28, Nth Beds Charity Cup 07-08 09-10 26-27 33-34(joint) 49-50 52-53 54-55 57-58 62-65 67-69 73-74 91-92 94-95, Utd Co's Lg Cup 73-74, Hunts Premier Cup 92-93 93-94(joint) 94-95, Hinchingbrooke Cup 03-04 12-13 92-93, Jess Piggott Trophy 87-88 89-90 91-92 92-93, Key Consul. Res F/Light Cup 89-90.

CADDINGTON

Chairman: David Mark. Tel: 01582 421404 (H). **Manager:** Leigh Glenister
Secretary: Leigh Glenister, 14 Elaine Gardens, Woodside, Luton, LU1 4DI. Tel: 01582 730502 (H), 01582 477557 (B).
Match Secretary: Fred Rook, 44 Clifford Crescent, Luton. LU4 9HR. Tel: 01582 580453 (H).
Ground: Caddington Recreation Club, Manor Road, Caddington (01582 450151).
Directions: On entering village turn into Manor Road (adjacent to shops and village green), proceed 500 metres: Clubhouse and ground on left side next to Catholic Church.
Capacity: Unknown **Seats:** None **Cover:** None **Floodlights:** No **Clubhouse:** Yes
Colours: Red & black/black/black **Programme:** Yes **Editor:** John Fowler, 01582 732041 (H)
Founded: 1971 **Nickname:** The Oaks **Midweek matchday:** Tuesday or Thursday.
Hons: Beds Intermediate Cup 85-86 92-93 **Record Gate:** 150 v Barton Rvrs, Beds Snr Cup.

HOLMER GREEN

Chairman: Bill Scholes, The Brambles, Penfold Lane, Holmer Green Bucks HP15 6XS. 01494 713867 (H).
Secretary: John Anderson, 1 Jason House, Cressex Rd., High Wycombe, Bucks. HP12 4TT.
Tel: 01494 446128 (H), 01494 465454 (B).
Match Secretary: Ray Ansell, 76 Buckingham Drive, High Wycombe. HP13 7XP. Tel: 01494 535175 (H).
Ground: Watchet Lane, Holmer Green, High Wycombe (01494 711485)
Directions: From Amersham on A404 High Wycombe Road, after approx 2 miles turn right into Sheepcote Dell Road. Continue until end of road by Bat & Ball PH. Turn right then immediate left, continue approx 1/2 mile until 2 mini roundabouts, turn left in front of the Mandarin Duck into Watchet Lane. The ground is 150 yards on the right.
Colours: All Green **Programme:** Yes **Editor:** Bill Scholes (Chairman)

HOUGHTON TOWN

Chairman: David Pigg. Tel: 01582 867058 (H) **Manager:** P Rowe
Secretary: Ken Dye, 9 Luxembourg Close, Luton, Beds LU3 3TD. Tel.: 01582 563378 (H)
Ground: Houghton Town Association Club, Park Road North, Houghton Regis. (01582 864862)
Directions: M1 jct 11, head towards Dunstable, right at island into Poynters Rd, straight over next island keeping left at small r'bout onto Park Rd North - ground on left 10yds before pelican crossing.
Capacity: 200 **Seats:** None **Cover:** Yes **Floodlights:** No **Founded:** 1993
Colours: Green & white/green/white **Change Colours:** All red
Programme: 50p **Editor:** Sally Whitlock, 01582 861181 (H) **Midweek matches:** Tuesday
Hons: South Midlands Lge - Chall Trophy R-up 93-94, Div 1 94-95, Div 1 Cup 94-95, R-up 93-94.

KENT ATHLETIC

Chairman: David Langridge. Tel: 01582 502670 (H)
Secretary: Michael Bayliss, 57 Brickley Road, Leagrave, Luton, Beds. LU4 9EF. Tel: 01582 597894 (H).
Ground: Kent Social Club, Tenby Drive, Leagrave, Luton (01582 582723)
Directions: M1 jct 11 take A505 towards Luton. Take the first turning on the left (Stoneygate Road), straight over at the roundabout and turn right at traffic lights into Beechwood Road. Take the first road on the left and then the first right into Tenby Drive. Ground and car park 100 yards on left.
Colours: Black & white stripes/black/black **Change Colours:** Green & white/white/green
Programme: Yes **Editor:** Lee Sapsford, 01582 502670 (H).

LEVERSTOCK GREEN

Chairman: Bill Dawes, 01442 395748 (H) **Press Officer:** M Connors
Secretary: Steve D Robinson, 11 Connaught Close, Hemel Hempstead, Herts HP2 7AB. Tel: 01442 65734 (H)
Manager: M Goodson **Asst Manager:** H Boycott-Brown
Ground: Pancake Lane, Leverstock Green, Hemel Hempstead. Tel: 01442 246280. **Directions:** From M1 leave at A4147 to 2nd r-about. 1st exit to Leverstock Green, Pancake Lane is on left 300 yrds past the 'Leather Bottle' pub.
Capacity: **Seats:** 25 **Cover:** 100 **Floodlights:** No **Club Shop:** No **Clubhouse:** Yes
Programme: 24 pages, 50p **Editor:** Bill Dawes (Chairman) **Nickname:** The Green **Founded:** 1907
Colours: All white and green **Change Colours:** Green & black/white/black **Sponsor:** Sunshine Cabs
Previous Leagues: West Herts (pre-1950); Herts County 50-91.
Players progressing to Football League: Dean Austin (Tottenham Hotspur).
96-97 - Captain: R Smith **Top scorer:** R Smith **P.o.Y.:** L Attfield
Honours: South Midlands Lge - Sen. Div 96-97, Sen Div Cup R-up 93-94, Herts Centenary Tphy R-up 91-92, Herts Charity Shield R-up 91-92, Frank Major Tphy 1991.

MERCEDES BENZ

Chairman: Bob Flight. Tel: 01604 764433 (H), 01980 245375 (B) **President:** Nigel Wells
Secretary: Peter Baldwin, c/o Mercedes-Benz (UK) Ltd, Tongwell, Milton Keynes MK15 8BA
01604 870457 (H) 01908 245408 (B) 01908 245088 (Fax).
Manager: Cliff Peters **Asst Man.:** Mark Collender **Coach:** Kevin England **Physio:** Nick Booth
Ground: The Barn, Pannier Place, Downs Barn, Milton Keynes, Bucks (01908 245158).
Directions: M1 jct 14, A509 for Milton Keynes, right onto H5 Portway at 1st island, right onto V9 Overstreet at 3rd island, 1st left into Downs Barn Boulevard, 2nd left into Pannier Place, ground at top of hill.
Capacity: 300 **Cover:** No **Seats:** None **Floodlights:** No **Founded:** 1967.
Clubhouse: The Mercedes-Benz Sports & Social Club, 1 mile from ground, open normal licensing hours.
Programme: 16 pages, 50p **Editor:** Stuart Collard, 01908 660796 (H), 01908 600394 (B) **Club Shop:** No
Colours: Royal/navy/navy **Change Colours:** All white **Nickname:** Blues
Midweek matches: Wednesday **Sponsors:** Mercedes-Benz (UK) Ltd **Reserves' league:** S.S.M. Reserve Div.
Previous Leagues: Milton Keynes Sunday; North Bucks & District (pre'93).
Hons: North Bucks Lge - Div 1 90-91, Prem. Div Cup 92-93, I'mediate Tphy 91-92; Daimler-Benz Austrian International Tournament R-up 1990.

NEW BRADWELL ST PETER

Chairman: John Haynes **Vice-Chairman:** K Felce **President:** J P Booden
Secretary: Les Smith, 47 Rowle Close, Stantonbury, Milton Keynes MK14 6BJ. Tel.: 01908 319522 (H)
Manager: S Spooner **Press Officer:** P Smith
Ground: Recreation Ground, Bradwell Road, New Bradwell, Milton Keynes MK13 7AT (01908 313835)
Directions: From M1 Jnt 14 go towards Newport Pagnell, left at 1st r-about into H3 (A422 Monks Way). Over 5 r-abouts, right at 6th island into V6 (Grafton St.), go right the way round (back on yourself) 1st island, 1st left, left at mini-roundabout, ground half mile on left (before bridge).
Nickname: Peters **Seats:** 30 **Cover:** 100 **Floodlights:** No **Founded:** 1902
Clubhouse: Members only (member can sign in 2 guests). Open every evening and w/e lunchtimes. No food.
Colours: Maroon & blue stripes/blue/blue **Change:** Green & yellow halves/green/yellow
Programme: 32 pages, £1 with entry **Editor:** Paul Smith 01908 315766 (H)
Midweek matches: Wednesday **Sponsors:** New Bradwell St Peter V-Presidents.
Hons: South Midlands Lge - Div 1 76-77,83-84, Reserve Div 2 R-up 76-77

RISBOROUGH RANGERS

Chairman: Terry Taylor
Tel: 01844 343309 (H)
Secretary: Derrick J Wallace, 42 Ash Road, Princes Risborough, Bucks, HP27 0BQ Tel.: 01844 345179 (H), 01844 345435 (B).
Manager: Dave Dunsworth **Asst Manager:** Mark Avery **Physio:** Ken Sheppard
Ground: 'Windsor', Horsenden Lane, Princes Risborough. (01844 274176)
Directions: Rear of Princes Risborough BR Station (Chiltern Line). A4010 from Aylesbury thru Princes Risborough, fork right onto A4009, left by thatched cottage, over railway bridge, immediate right ground 150 yds on right.
Capacity: 2,000 **Seats:** 25 **Cover:** 100 **Floodlights:** No **Founded:** 1971
Clubhouse: Yes. Snacks available matchdays. **Club Sponsors:** Systems 3R
Colours: Red & white/black/black **Change Colours:** Blue & white stripes/white/white
Programme: 20+ pages, £1 with entry **Midweek matches:** Tuesday **Club Shop:** No.
Previous League: Wycombe & Dist. **Record Gate:** 1,200 v Showbiz XI **Record scorer:** Craig Smith
Hons: Berks & Bucks Jnr Cup 85-86, Wycombe & District Lg Div 2 85-86 (Div 3 84-85).

SHILLINGTON

Chairman: Jack Farmer. **Secretary:** Aubrey Cole, 32 Greenfields, Shillington, Hitchin, Herts, SG5 3NX.
Tel: 01462 711757 (H) Tel: 01462 711322 (H).
Ground: Playing Field, Greenfields, Shillington, Hitchin, Herts. (01462 711757). **Directions:** From Luton on A6, after bypassing Barton, turn right at large r'about. Through Higham Gobian to Shillington.
From Bedford or Hitchin, A600 to RAF Henlow Camp. At 'Bird in Hand' r'about take exit to Upper Stondon.
Colours: Black & white stripes/black/black. **Programme:** Yes **Editor:** Douglas Riggs, 01462 712695 (H).

STONY STRATFORD TOWN

Chairman: Roger Taylor **Manager:** Peter Sanders **Club Coach:**n Tony Court
Secretary: Maurice J Barber, 26 Boundary Cres., Stony Stratford, Milton Keynes MK11 1DF 01908 567930 (H)
Ground: Sports Ground, Ostlers Lane, Stony Stratford (01908 562267). **Directions:** From Dunstable use old A5, Watling Street. Approaching Bletchley continue on A5 loop road (Hinkley) to end of dual c'way to A422/A508 r'bout. First exit, thru lights, 2nd right into Ostlers Lane. From M1 jct 13 pick up A421 & join A5 (Hinkley) then as above.
Capacity: 2000 **Seats:** 30 **Cover:** 120 **Floodlights:** Yes **Reformed:** 1953 **Club Shop:** No
Clubhouse: Open evenings & weekends **Midweek matches:** Tuesday **Reserves' League:** SSM Res. Div. One
Colours: Sky blue/black/black **Change Colours:** All yellow **Sponsor:** BILDOR Transport & BUSIPRINT
Programme: 28 pages, 50p **Editor:** Ray Cobley 01908 562370 (H) **97-98 Captain:** Zane Flanagan
Honours: Sth Mids Lg R-up 70-71 71-72 (Div 1 93-94, Div 1 Cup 93-94).

THE 61 F.C. (LUTON)

Chairman: Mark Davie **Vice Chairman:** Ms. Nicki Rowley **President:** G B Mapp
Secretary/Manager: Richard Everitt, 44 Somersby Close, Luton LU1 3XB. 01582 485095 (H)
Asst Manager: P Miller **Physio:** N McNully **Comercial Mgr:** Andrew Rowley
Ground: Kingsway, Beverley Road, Luton, Beds. (01582 582965). **Directions:** M1 jct 11, A505 to Luton centre, right at 1st island, 1st left, Beverley Rd is 3rd left, entrance in Beverley Rd, exactly 1 mile junction 11. All Luton to Dunstable buses pass ground - alight at Beech Hill Bowling Club. 1 mile from both Leagrave & Luton BR stations.
Capacity: 2,500 **Cover:** 150 **Seats:** 100 **Floodlights:** No **Formed:** 1961 **Nickname:** Two Blues
Clubhouse: Open every evening and weekend lunchtimes. Hot and cold snacks. **Club Shop:** No.
Programme: 8 pages **Editor:** Andrew Rowley (01582 611292) **Club Sponsors:** Quality Homecrafts
Colours: Sky blue/royal blue/royal **Change colours:** Red/black/red **Midweek matches:** Wednesday
Honours: Beds Snr Cup 83-84.

TOTTERNHOE

Chairman: Jim Basterfield **Vice Chairman:** John Power **President:** Alf Joyce
Secretary: Jim Basterfield, 41 Park Avenue, Totternhoe, Dunstable, Beds LU6 1QF. Tel: 01582 667941 (H)
Manager: Alex Butler **Asst. Man.:** Paul Simmonds **Physio:** Roy Mackerness
Ground: Totternhoe Rec. Ground, Dunstable (01582 606738). **Directions:** Turn off main Dunstable to Tring Road B489. Ground on rt as you enter Totternhoe. 5 miles Leighton Buzzard (BR), 7 miles Luton Bus 61 Luton-Aylesbury
Capacity: 1,000 **Seats:** 30 **Cover:** 200 **Floodlights:** No **Founded:** 1906 **Nickname:** Totts.
Clubhouse: Open evenings 8pm, Saturday after games, Sunday lunchtime. Tea, coffee, soups at matches.
Colours: All red **Change Colours:** White/blue/black **Club Shop:** No **Sponsors:** Building Conservations
Programme: 16 pages with entry **Editor:** Andrew Massey 01908 613404 (H) **Midweek matchday:** Tuesday
Hons: Sth Mids Lg Div 1 61-62 (R-up 68-69 85-86).

TRING ATHLETIC

President: Paul Nichols **Secretary:** Ralph Griffiths, 42 Bedgrove, Aylesbury, Bucks HP21 7BD. Tel: 01296 26425 (H), 01296 393363 x 278 (B).
Chairman: Steve Thomas Tel: 01442 381633 (H)
Manager: Mick Eldridge **Asst Manager:** Ray Brimson **Physio:** Jean Adams
Ground: Miswell Lane, Tring, Herts. (01442 828331) **Directions:** Through Tring on main road towards Aylesbury, right just after Anchor PH into Miswell Lane, pitch approximately 500yds on right opposite Beaconsfield Road. Tring railway station is several miles outside town, but ground can be reached by bus or taxi.
Seats: 25+ **Cover:** 100+ **Floodlights:** No **Founded:** 1958 **Nickname:** Athletic
Clubhouse: Bar, open matchdays, training nights & Sunday lunchtimes. **Club Shop:** No
Colours: Red & black/black/black **Change colours:** Blue & yellow/blue/blue **Sponsors:** Heygates
Programme: 36 pages, 50p **Editor:** Secretary **Midweek matchday:** Wednesday
Honours: West Herts Lg R-up 72-73 (Lg Cup 65-66, Div 1 61-62 64-65 65-66 (R-up 71-72 85-86), Div 2(res) 71-72 (R-up 62-63), Div 3 R-up 83-84, Reserve Cup 72-73), Apsley Snr Cup R-up 71-72 87-88, Marsworth Cup(res) 72-73, Apsley Jnr Cup(res) R-up 94-95.

WINSLOW UNITED

Chairman: Jeff B Robins. **Secretary:** David F Ward, 28 Park Road, Winslow, Buckingham MK18 3DL. Tel: 01296 713202 (H), 01865 781210 (B).
Tel: 01296 714206 (H)
Ground: Recreation Ground, Elmfields Gate, Winslow, Bucks. (01296 713057) **Directions:** A413 from Aylesbury to Winslow, in High Street turn right into Emerald Gate, ground 100yds on left opposite car park. From Milton Keynes take A421 to Buckingham, turn left thru Gt Horwood to Winslow, turn left off High Street into Emerald Gate.
Capacity: 2,000 **Seats:** 25 **Cover:** 100 **Floodlights:** Yes **Founded:** 1891 **Club Shop:** No
Clubhouse: Open every evening except Wed & full weekend. **Programme:** 16 pages with entry
Colours: Yellow/blue/yellow **Change Colours:** Red/white/white **Midweek matches:** Tuesday
Honours: Sth Mids Lg R-up 75-76 (Div 1 74-75), Leighton Challenge Cup 92-93.

DIVISION ONE NORTH

ABBEY NATIONAL (M.K.)

Secretary: Steve White, 5 Hambleton Grove, Emerson Valley, Milton Keynes, Bucks. MK4 2JS. Tel: 01908 505910 (H), 01908 345513 (B).
Ground: Loughton Sports & Social Club, Linceslade Grove, Loughton, Milton Keynes (01908 690668)
Directions: From M1 Jct 14 follow H6, Childs Way for 5 miles until V4 Watling Way (Knowlhill r-about), right to Loughton r-about, right along H5 Portway - 1st right Linceslade Grove.

BEDFORD EAGLES

Secretary: Barry Stephenson, 9 Aspen Avenue, Putnoe, Bedford, MK41 8BX. Tel: 01234 342276 (H), 01234 350931 (B).
Ground: Bedford United FC, The New Eyrie, Meadow Lane Cardington, Bedford MK44 3SB (01234 838448)
Directions: A1 come off at Sandy, follow signs for Bedford, thr Willington, ground on right.

BRIDGER PACKAGING

Secretary: Laurence Jack, 17 Curlew Close, Letchworth, Herts. SG6 4TG. Tel: 01462 625936 (H), 0181 905 1992 (B).
Ground: Letchworth Corner Sports Club, Muddy Lane, Letchworth, Herts. SG6 3TB. (01462 486459)
Directions: A1(M) junc 9 towards Letchworth, over large roundabout, turn left at next roundabout A505 Hitchin, thr lights, turn left at pelican crossing into Muddy Lane.

BUCKINGHAM UNITED

Secretary: Stuart Mackey, 10 Gawcott Fields, Buckingham, Bucks MK18 1TL. Tel: 01280 816903.
Ground: Ford Meadow, Ford Street, Buckingham (01280 816257)
Directions: A421 Buckingham Road, right aty roundabout. At next 'T' junction you are opposite The New Inn Public House and Phillips Rover dealership, go between, ground on left.

CRAWLEY GREEN

Secretary: Neil Ludlow, 159 Cutenhoe Road, Luton, LU1 3NQ. Tel: 01582 486802 (H), 01582 424244 (B).
Ground: Crawley Green Road Recreation Ground (01582 451058).
Directions: M1 junction 10 continue straight on at the roundabout at the end of the motorway slip road into Airport way. At the 4th roundabout turn right into Crawley Green Road, the ground is 800 yards on the left just past Ashcroft.

DE HAVILLAND

Secretary: Roy Ridgway, 85 Garden Ave., Hatfield, Herts AL10 8LH. Tel: 01707 267327 (H).
Ground: De Havilland (Hatfield) Sports & Social Club, Comet Way, Hatfield (01707 263204).
Directions: From south leave A1(M) at Hatfield turn, A1001 to Birchwood r'bout, 1st exit into car park. From north leave A1(M) at Welwyn G.C., A1001 to Birchwood r'bout and 4th exit into car park.

EMBERTON

Secretary: Richard L Dugdale, 9 Stone Court, West Lane, Emberton, Nr Olney, Bucks MK46 5ND. Tel: 01234 711004 (H/B).
Ground: The Playing Field, Hulton Drive, Emberton, Nr Olney, Bucks. (01234 713748)
Directions: M1 jct 14 to Newport Pagnell, right onto A422 at 1st r'bout straight on north towards Olney. Emberton lies before Olney. Turn left at 2nd turning into village and 1st right Hulton Drive. Buses from Northampton, Bedford and Milton Keynes.

FLAMSTEAD

Secretary: Susan Hayward, Greenways, Old Watling Street, Flamstead, St Albans, Herts. AL3 8HL. Tel: 01582 841213 (H)
Ground: Flamstead Sports Assoc., Friendless Lane, Flamstead, St Albans, Herts (0582 841307).
Ground Directions: From Dunstable Town Centre travel south on A5 Trunk Road towards the M1. Follow for approximately 3 miles then turn right opposite Hertfordshire Moat House Hotel. Ground and parking approximately half a mile on the corner of the first right turn.

GREENACRES (HEMEL)

Secretary: Adrian Marson, 1 Pelham Court, Leverstock Green, Hemel Hempstead, Herts. HP2 4Un. Tel: 01442 243053 (H), 0976 447128 (B)
Ground: Berkhamsted Town FC, Broadwater, Lower Kings Road, Berkhamsted, Herts. HP4 2AA. (01442 862815)
Directions: Bypass to the Chesham/Berkhamsted turn off. Turn left at r'about & left at next r'about into Kingshill Way. Take Kings Road to traffic lights, into Lower Kings Rd & left into Broadwater Rd. Ground on the rt.

LEIGHTON ATHLETIC

Secretary: Salvatore Leotta, 28 Ashburnham Crescent, Linslade, Leighton Buzzard, Beds. LU7 7PB. Tel: 01525 382396 (H).
Ground: Memorial Playing Fields, Mentmore Road, Linslade, Leighton Buzzard, Beds (01525 370469)
Directions: On A5 north of Dunstable travelling towards Hockliffe turn left on to A505 Leighton Buzzard bypass. At end of bypass turn right towartds Leighton Buzzard and take the first right immediately after the railway bridge into Cedars Way. At 'T' Junction turn left into Mentmore Road, ground 300 yards on right

LUTON OLD BOYS

Secretary: Terry Owen, 29 Elm Park Close, Houghton Regis, Dunstable, Beds. LU5 5PN. Tel: 01582 863273 (H).
Ground: Luton Old Boys, Dunstable Road, Luton, Beds. (01582 582060)
Directions: On the A505 Luton to Dunstable Road between junction 11 of the M1 and Lex Vauxhall Luton.
Please Note: There is NO right turn when approaching the ground from the Dunstable direction.

MURSLEY UNITED

Secretary: Roger Gurnett, 20 Tweedale Close, Mursley, Milton Keynes MK17 0SB. Tel: 01296 720505 (H).
Ground: Station Road, Mursley, Milton Keynes.
Directions: A421 Bletchley to Buckingham Road, first right in village

OLD BRADWELL UNITED

Secretary: David Bird, 24 Loughton Road, Bradwell, Milton Keynes MK13 9AA. Tel: 01908 315947 (H).
Ground: Abbey Road, Bradwell, Milton Keynes (01908 312355)
Directions: M1 junction 14 go towards Newport Pagnell. Turn left at first roundabout into H3 Honks Way. Go six r'abouts then left onto V6 Grafton Street. Take 1st right at mini-r'about into Rawlins Road and then 2nd left into Loughton Road. Take 1st right into Primrose Road and at the 'T' junction turn right into Abbey Road

OLD DUNSTABLIANS

Secretary: Craig Renfrew, 75B Princes Street. Dunstable. LU6 3AS. Tel: 01582 471794 (H), 01234 265444 (B).
Ground: Lancot Park. Dunstable Road, Totternhoe (01582 663735)
Directions: From Dunstable Town Centre take the B489 Tring Road. At the 4th roundabout turn right, signposted Totternhoe. The pitch is located withion Dunstable Town Cricket Club which is on the right just before entering the village of Totternhoe.

PITSTONE & IVINGHOE

Secretary: Jay Adlem, 22 Maud Janes Close, Ivinghoe, Leighton Buzzard. LU7 9ED. Tel: 01296 668663 (H).
Ground: Pitstone Recreation Ground, Vicarage Road, Pitstone, Bucks (01296 661271)
Directions: Tring Rd (B489) from Dunstable, turn right for Ivinghoe, and continue through to Pitstone r-about; ground left then right. From Aylesbury - left at 'Rising Sun' in Aston Clinton, keep on that road to Pitstone r'bout; ground right then right. Bus 61 from Luton or Aylesbury. Nearest BR stations are Tring or Cheddington.

SCOT

Secretary: Mrs Ann Land, 18 Coleridge Close, Bletchley, Milton Keynes. MK3 5AF. Tel: 01908 372228 (H).
Ground: Selbourne Avenue, Bletchley, Milton Keynes (01908 368881).
Directions: Main roads to Bletchley then A421 Buckingham road, at Glen Garage right into Newton Rd, 2nd left into Selbourne Ave., through railway bridge to bottom of road.

WALDEN RANGERS

Secretary: Irene Oodian, 9 Garfield Court, Handcross Rd, Luton, Beds LU2 8JZ. Tel: 01582 483090 (H), 01582 405060 Ext 2354 (B).
Ground: Breachwood Green Recreation Ground, Chapel Road, Breachwood Green, Nr Kings Walden, Herts (01438 833332). **Directions:** From Luton Airport roundabout (Eaton Green Rd)(away from Vauxhall/ IBC direction) take country road to Breachwood Green (2 miles). From Hitchin on A602, take country road to Preston (6 miles to Breachwood Green).

DIVISION ONE SOUTH

BRIDON ROPES

Secretary: Richard Clements, 3 Fenwick Close, Woolwich, London SE18 4DD. Tel: 0181 244 1167 (H), 01322 442323 (B).
Ground: Meridan Sports Ground, Charlton Park Lane, London, SE7. (0181 856 1923)
Directions: Travelling south on Blackwall Tunnell Southern Approach A102 (M) take exit Central London. Turn left at r'about into Shooters Hill Road (A207) towards Welling. Take sixth turning on the left, Charlton Park Lane. Ground is on the right.

CHESNUT TROJAN

Secretary: Troy Townsend, 54 Grove Park Avenue, Chingford, London E4 8SS. Tel: 0181 527 7911 (H), 0378 652323 (B).
Ground: Beckton United, Manor Way, East Ham E6. (071 476 4857).
Directions: Travelling east on the A13 exit at A117 and turn right under the flyover (Mountain Top Ski Centre on left). Straight on at r'about at junction with Windsor Road the ground is on the right.

CHINGFORD TOWN

Secretary: Kevin Ryan, 3 Elm Lodge, 24-26 Montact Road, Woodford Green, Essex, IG8 9SB. Tel: 0181 559 1671 (H), 0181 529 0485 (B).
Ground: Newgate Street, Chingford, E4. (0181 529 0485).
Directions: Travelling west on A406 turn right onto A104 Woodford New Road. Turn left onto A1009 Chingford Road. Turn right at r'about into Friday Hill, then first right into Chingdale Road and then right into Newgate Street. Ground on the right.

CLASSIC INTER

Secretary: Lloyd Joseph, 27 Benson Avenue, East Ham, London, E6 3EE. Tel: 0181 552 3132 (H), 0181 519 7820 (B - 7pm-10pm Mon-Thur).
Ground: Ive Farm, Villiers Close, Leyton, E10.
Directions: Travelling north on Lower Clapton Road (A107) turn right at r'about into Lea Bridge Road (A104). After approx 2 miles turn right into Church Road (A1006) and proceed for 1/2 mile and then turn right into Villiers Close, the ground is signposted.

CRAY VALLEY

Secretary: Steve Chapman, 97 Yorkland Avenue, Welling, Kent, DA16 2LG. Tel: 0181 304 5387 (H), 0171 260 4085 (B).
Ground: STC, Ivor Grove, New Eltham, SE9. (0181 850 2057).
Directions: Travelling east on Eltham High Street (A210) turn right into Footscray Road (A211). Proceed for 1/2 mile then turn right into Ivor Grove. Ground at end of the road.

CROWN & MANOR

Secretary: Richard Allen, The Crown & Manor Club, Wiltshire Row, Hoxton, London, N1 5OH. Tel: 0171 739 5906 (H&B), 0171 739 3818 (Fax).
Ground: Mile End Stadium, Burdett Road, London, E3. (0181 980 1885).
Directions: Travelling towards central London on A11 turn left by Mile End station into Burdett Road (A1025). Ground is 400 yards on the right.

DODDINGHURST

Secretary: John Kiff, 57 Tangmere Crescent, Hornchurch, Essex, RM12 5PX. Tel: 01708 555413 (H), 01708 441437 (B/Fax).
Ground: Warley Playing Field, The Drive, Chindits Lane, Warley, Brentwood, Essex.
Directions: From M25 or A12 into Brentwood town centre then turn right into Kings Road. Follow road towards Warley Hospital. Ground just before mini-r'about on the left.

HOLLAND PARK

Secretary: jason Clarke, Flat 5, Craigea Lea, 4 Muswell Avenue, London, N10 2EE. Tel: 0181 444 1538 (H), 0958 692788 (B).
Ground: Royal College Hospital, Chelsea Embankment, London, SW3.
Directions: The ground is situated on the Embankment, about 400 metres from Chelsea Bridge going west towards Battersea Bridge.

LEYTON

Secretary: Alan Hunter, Flat E, 86-88 Queens Drive, Finsbury Park, London, N4 2HW. Tel: 0181 809 5057 (H), 0171 588 7511 (B).
Ground: Wingate Leyton Stadium, Lea Bridge Road, Leyton, E10 7LD. (0181 539 5405).
Directions: From north - leave North Circular Road (A406) into Hoe Street (A112). Turn right after first traffic lights into Lea Bridge Road (A104). Ground 300 yards on left. From south - Blackwall Tunnel, A102(M) onto A106. Turn left into Oliver Road and into Church Road (A1006). Turn left into Lea Bridge Road (A104).

LEYTON COUNTY

Secretary: Kirt Kirwan, 120 Malvern Rd, Leytonstone, London E11 3QL. Tel: 0181 539 9210 (H), 0831 222432 (B).
Ground: Leyton County Ground, Crawley Road, London, E10 (0181 539 1924).
Directions: From north - leave North Circular Road (A406) into Hoe Street (A112). Proceed along A112 and after passing Leyton Midland Road station, take 2nd right into Crawley Road. The ground is on the rigt. From south - Blackwall Tunnel, A102(M) onto A106. Turn left into Leyton High Road (A112) and then after 1/2 mile left into Crawley Road.

LEYTON YOUTH

Secretary: Cleveland Mowatt, 3 St Lukes Avenue, Ilford, Essex, IG1 2JA. Tel: 0181 491 3135 (H), 0181 539 1924 (B evening 7-10pm)
Ground: Leyton County Ground, Crawley Road, London, E10 (0181 539 1924).
Directions: From north - leave North Circular Road (A406) into Hoe Street (A112). Proceed along A112 and after passing Leyton Midland Road station, take 2nd right into Crawley Road. The ground is on the rigt. From south - Blackwall Tunnel, A102(M) onto A106. Turn left into Leyton High Road (A112) and then after 1/2 mile left into Crawley Road.

LONG LANE

Secretary: John Cullinane, 181 Bedonwell Road, Bexleyheath, Kent. DA7 5PU. Tel: 01322 431035 (H).
Ground: Kidbrooke Playing Field, Dursley Road, Kidbrooke, SE3 (0181 319 3212)
Directions: Travelling south on Blackwall Tunnel Southern Approach A102(M) take A207 Shooters Hill Road towards Welling. Take first right into East Brook Road, over staggered junction into Woolacombe Road and then first left into Dursley Road. Ground 30 yards on right.

ODUA UNITED

Secretary: Abbey Elegbede, 44 Lilford House, Lilford Road, London, SE5 9QB. Tel: 0171 326 4654 (H), 0956 977218 (B).
Ground: Meridan Sports Ground, Charlton Park Lane, London, SE7. (0181 856 1923)
Directions: Travelling south on Blackwall Tunnell Southern Approach A102 (M) take exit Central London. Turn left at r'about into Shooters Hill Road (A207) towards Welling. Take sixth turning on the left, Charlton Park Lane. Ground is on the right.

OLD ROAN

Secretary: Brian Riley, 33 Buckler Gardens, Mottingham, London, SE9 3BD. Tel: 0181 857 0401 (H), 0181 317 2202 (B).
Ground: John Roan School PLaying Field, Kidbrooke Park Road, London, SE3. (0181 856 1915).
Directions: Travelling south on Blackwall Tunnell Southern Approach A102 (M) take exit Central London. Turn right at r'about into Shooters Hill Road (A2). At first set of traffic lights turn left into Kidbrooke Park Road (A2213). Proceed along past Kidbrooke station, the ground is then 400 yards on the right.

TOTTENHAM OMADA

Secretary: Lindsay Boyaram, 33 Adlington Close, Edmonton, London, N18 1XJ. Tel: 0181 372 2634 (H & B)
Ground: New River Sports Centre, White hart Lane, Woodgreen, London, N22 (0181 889 1050)
Directions: From M1 take North Circular Road (A406). Leave A406 turning right into Bounds Green Road (A109), proceed to end then turn left into Wood Green High Rd (A105) and then first right into White Hart Lane. Ground approx 2 miles on the left.

HERTS SENIOR COUNTY LEAGUE

President: W J R Veneear
Chairman: C T Hudson
Secretary: Mr E H Dear,
48 Wilshere Road, Welwyn, Herts.

FINAL LEAGUE TABLES 1996/97

SENIOR SECTION

PREMIER DIVISION	P	W	D	L	F	A	Pts
Elliott Star	34	28	2	4	100	32	86
Bedmond Sports	34	22	5	7	81	42	71
Cuffley	34	21	5	8	85	40	68
Colney Heath	34	19	8	7	71	39	65
Sun Postal Sports	34	18	7	9	63	40	61
Somersett Ambury V&E	34	18	4	12	69	55	58
Chipperfield Corin.	34	17	6	11	60	47	57
Kings Langley	34	16	6	12	73	61	54
Agrevo Sports	34	15	6	13	61	62	51
Met. Police (Bushey)	34	14	8	12	82	57	50
Oxhey Jets	34	12	10	12	49	55	46
Sandridge Rovers	34	11	7	16	44	60	40
Welwyn	34	10	4	20	50	83	34
Walkern	34	8	5	21	36	78	29
Wormley Rovers	34	7	6	21	33	72	27
St Peters	34	5	10	19	48	76	25
Bovingdon	34	6	7	21	36	89	25
North Mymms	24	4	4	26	32	85	16

DIVISION ONE	P	W	D	L	F	A	Pts
Benington	32	25	4	3	102	21	79
MMS Dynamics	32	24	4	4	89	29	76
Bragbury Athletic	32	21	3	8	75	48	66
Giffen Wheathampstead	32	16	9	7	82	47	57
Malex	32	14	11	7	74	43	53
Herts Police Athletic	32	15	7	10	55	51	52
Standon & Puckeridge	32	13	9	10	46	37	48
Bushey Rangers	32	14	6	12	65	59	48
Evergreen	32	11	10	11	60	57	43
Codicote	32	11	6	15	59	53	39
Emeralds	32	9	6	17	53	63	33
Kimpton Rovers	32	9	6	17	46	69	33
Kodak Hemel H'stead	32	9	5	18	59	86	32
Croxley Guild Astrals	32	8	7	17	33	67	31
Leavesden Sports	32	6	8	18	41	73	26
Park Street Village	32	5	8	19	33	97	23
Sarratt	32	5	5	22	40	112	20

RESERVE SECTION

DIVISION ONE	P	W	D	L	F	A	Pts
Sun Postal Sports	30	21	6	3	65	20	69
Somersett Ambury V&E	30	21	2	7	83	40	65
Bragbury Athletic	30	20	4	6	78	34	64
Bedmond Sports	30	13	6	11	51	40	45
Chipperfield Corinthians	30	12	8	10	56	41	44
Wormley Rovers	30	13	5	12	47	46	44
Colney Heath	30	13	5	12	52	60	44
North Mymms	30	12	6	12	43	40	42
Kings Langley	30	11	8	11	53	52	41
Sandridge Rovers	30	12	5	13	62	78	41
Bovingdon	30	12	4	14	45	47	40
Oxhey Jets	30	11	3	16	45	58	36
Met. Police (Bushey)	30	9	5	16	62	87	32
Cuffley	30	6	8	16	41	60	26
St Peters	30	7	5	18	36	79	26
Walkern	30	6	2	22	33	70	20

DIVISION TWO	P	W	D	L	F	A	Pts
Giffen Wheathampstead	32	27	3	2	128	24	84
Elliott Star	32	25	4	3	88	36	79
Standon & Puckeridge	32	21	4	7	73	35	67
Agrevo Sports	32	18	5	9	93	54	59
Kimpton Rovers	32	17	4	11	76	49	55
Benington	32	16	5	11	53	49	53
Evergreen	32	15	5	12	58	49	50
MMS Dynamics	32	13	7	12	59	55	46
Emeralds	32	13	4	15	36	52	43
Croxley Guild Astrals	32	10	5	16	51	66	35
Welwyn	32	9	7	16	45	75	34
Leavesden Sports	32	9	5	18	46	64	32
Herts Police Athletic	32	9	5	18	38	67	32
Kodak Hemel H'stead	32	9	3	20	47	62	30
Park Street Village	32	8	5	19	35	84	29
Bushey Rangers	32	7	5	20	33	97	26
Sarratt	32	7	2	23	41	82	23

PREMIER DIVISION RESULTS CHART 1996–97

HOME TEAM	1	2	3	4	5	6	7	8	9	10	11	12	13	14	15	16	17	18	19
Agrevo Sports	*	1-2	1-1	0-2	2-2	1-5	0-5	0-3	6-2	1-0	2-2	4-4	2-4	3-2	2-1	2-1	5-1	0-1	
Bedmond Sports	1-1	*	0-1	3-2	1-3	1-0	4-1	1-3	1-1	5-2	0-0	2-1	2-1	p*	5-0	3-0	3-1	6-0	
Bovingdon	0-4	0-4	*	0-2	1-2	1-5	1-7	2-2	4-2	4-2	0-4	1-1	2-2	1-4	0-2	1-5	1-2	1-0	
Chipperfield Cor'ns	2-0	2-0	0-0	*	1-3	2-1	1-4	4-1	4-2	1-0	2-0	2-1	0-1	1-2	3-2	6-1	0-3	0-0	
Colney Heath	2-1	1-1	2-2	2-2	*	2-1	0-4	2-0	0-0	1-0	1-1	3-0	0-0	2-4	3-2	4-0	3-0	3-0	
Cuffley	2-3	1-2	4-2	2-2	4-0	*	2-2	1-3	1-1	5-1	4-0	3-0	3-0	2-1	1-1	3-0	1-0	3-1	
Elliott Star	4-2	2-1	5-1	1-0	0-2	2-0	*	4-0	3-3	2-1	3-0	4-1	1-0	2-0	2-0	2-1	3-2	4-0	
Kings Langley	4-1	3-1	2-4	1-0	0-3	1-4	1-2	*	2-2	3-0	5-1	5-2	2-1	1-3	1-1	8-0	1-3	3-1	
Met. Police (Bushey)	0-1	1-3	4-1	2-1	2-0	0-2	2-4	2-2	*	4-0	2-3	0-0	4-0	2-2	0-4	8-0	12-2	5-1	
North Mymms	2-1	3-4	2-0	2-4	1-3	0-2	0-9	2-2	0-3	*	1-2	1-2	1-4	0-1	2-2	1-2	1-0	0-4	
Oxhey Jets	1-1	1-2	1-0	0-0	0-4	1-2	2-1	2-1	1-3	3-1	*	1-1	0-1	3-5	2-0	1-1	1-1	0-1	
St Peters	2-3	0-5	4-0	5-3	2-5	1-2	0-2	1-2	1-2	0-0	2-3	*	1-1	3-1	0-2	2-2	2-1	3-3	
Sandridge Rovers	0-2	3-0	1-2	0-1	1-0	0-1	0-3	3-4	2-1	1-0	2-2	0-0	*	1-3	0-3	*p	6-3	3-3	
Somersett Ambury	0-2	2-2	3-1	4-2	5-1	3-1	1-3	1-1	0-4	2-1	1-3	4-1	5-1	*	1-1	*p	1-4	0-1	
Sun Postal Sports	2-0	2-3	2-0	1-1	1-0	3-3	0-2	2-1	2-1	3-2	3-1	2-0	6-1	3-1	*	0-1	2-0	3-0	
Walkern	1-3	2--6	1-1	0-2	0-0	1-5	3-2	1-2	1-3	4-1	0-3	1-0	0-2	1-2	0-3	*	2-0	0-0	
Welwyn	1-2	1-4	4-0	1-2	0-6	1-4	1-2	2-0	1-2	0-0	2-2	4-3	3-2	1-4	1-1	0-3	*	3-2	
Wormley Rovers	0-2	0-3	3-0	2-3	0-6	1-5	0-3	2-3	2-0	1-2	0-2	2-2	0-0	0-1	0-1	2-1	0-1	*	

*Non fulfilment points awarded to home club.

AGREVO SPORTS

Secretary: Mrs Marion Howlett, 7 Beckets Square, Berkhamsted, Herts. HP4 1BZ. Tel: 01442 872497 (H). **Ground:** Kitcheners Field, Castle Hill, Berkhamsted. 01442 864937 **Directions:** A4251 into Berkhamsted. At main traffic lights (from Hemel Hempstead) turn right into Lower Kings Rd. At railway station turn left under bridge then 2nd left. Ground entrance is on next corner.

BEDMOND S & S

Secretary: Peter Johnson, 101 Spring Lane, Hemel Hempstead, Herts. HP1 3RB. Tel: 01442 397869 (H) **Ground:** Toms Lane Recreation Ground, Toms Lane, Bedmond. Tel: 01932 267991 **Directions:** MI to junction 8, A414 to 2nd r'about, left on St. Albans route A4147, bear rt. to Bedmond at church (Bedmond Road), right in village into Toms Lane at mini r'about, ground 300 yds on left. Bus 344 from Hemel or Watford.

BENINGTON

Secretary: John Batchelor, 16 Cedar Close, Shefford, Beds. SG17 5RT. 01462 628426 (H), 01438 752146 (B) **Ground:** Benington Recreation Ground, Town Lane, Benington. **Directions:** Leave A1(M) at Stevenage South, over 1st r'about (A602) left at 2nd r'about (Burger King), over next r'about, rt at next one by Swimming Pool, follow signs to Walkern (B1037), turn rt at junction in Walkern, past Walkern FC for approx 800 yds turn left where signed Benington. Thro' Benington, past Bell PH & ground is 800 yds on left.

BRAGBURY ATHLETIC

Secretary: Raymond C Poulter, 292 Jessop Rd., Stevenage, Herts. SG1 5NA. Tel: 01438 358078 (H). **Ground:** British Aerospace Sports & Social Club, Bragbury End, Stevenage, Herts. Tel: 01438 812985. **Directions:** A1(M) to Steveange, take Stevenage South exit (Junct. 7), follow A602 Hertford/Ware signs to Bragbury End, ground on left just past golf course.

CHIPPERFIELD CORINTHIANS

Secretary: Rowland Marshall, 45 Blackwell Drive, Watford, Herts. WD1 4HP. 01923 - 461457(H), 254646(B) **Ground:** Moatfield, Bournehall Lane, Bushey, Herts. Tel: 0181 386 1875. **Directions:** A41 to Hartspring Lane, into Aldenham Rd., left at r'about into the Avenue, rt at top into Herkomer Rd., then 4th on left. Bus - from Watford 142, 258, 306, 706, 719 to Red Lion, Bushey.

COLNEY HEATH

Secretary: Michael Wright, 5 Grove Lea, Hatfield, Herts. AL10 8LA. Tel: 01707 880825 (H). **Ground:** The Pavilion Rec. Ground, High St., Colney Heath, Herts. Tel: 01727 826188. **Directions:** Turn off A414 (was A405) into Colney Heath village, ground is behind school on left.

CUFFLEY

Secretary: Dave Chapman, 51 Woodlands Rd., Hertford. SG13 7JF. Tel: 01992 582358 (H), 0171 480 6410 (B). **Ground:** King George's Playing Fields, Northaw Road East, Cuffley, Herts. Tel: 01707 875395. **Directions:** A121 from Potters bar or Cheshunt, 5 miles from junction 25 or 26 on M25. Bus - 242 from Potters Bar or Cheshunt to Playing Fields, Cuffley.

ELLIOTT STAR

Secretary: Raymond Capper, 28 Alban Crescent, Boreham Wood, Herts. WD6 5JF. Tel: 0181 207 3940 (H). **Ground:** GEC Sports Ground, Rowley Lane, Borehamwood. Tel: 0181 953 5087. **Directions:** A1 from Hatfield to Elstree Moat House, left turn (flyover) into town and turn into Elstree Way. Ground on right behind Clarendon Garage.

KINGS LANGLEY

Secretary: Brian Aldersley, 49 Diamond Rd., Watford. WD2 5EN. Tel: 01923 493462 (H), 01468 906089 (M). **Ground:** Kings Langley FC, Hempstead Rd., Kings Langley. **Directions:** M25, junct. 20 (Aylesbury) then A4251 to Kings Langley. Ground is approx. 1 mile on right.

METROPOLITAN POLICE BUSHEY

Secretary: J R (Jim) Howard, Met. Police Sports Club, Aldenham Road, Bushey, Herts. WD2 3TR. Tel: 01923 674373 (H), 0171 321 7903 (B). **Ground:** Met. Police Sports Club, Aldenham Road, Bushey. Tel: 01923 243947. **Directions:** M1, Junct. 5 take A41 for Harrow/South watford to 1st r'about, rt into Hartspring Lane, leading into Aldenham Road (A4008), ground 1/4 mile on left opposite Caledonian school. Bus - 312 from watford stops outside club.

OXHEY JETS

Secretary: John R Elliott, 7 Brampton Road, South Oxhey, Watford, Herts. WD1 6PF. Tel: 0181 428 6382 (H), 0181 424 5891 (B). **Ground:** Chigwell Gardens, South Oxhey, Watford. Tel: 0181 421 4965. **Directions:** From Watford follow Bushey signs. At Bushey Arches turn rt. into Eastbury Rd., left into Brookdene Ave., cont. along Prestwick Rd. past station. Right into Northwick Rd., then left into Chilwell Gdns. Bus - 348 from Watford, alight at Northwick Rd.

ST. PETERS

Secretary: John Lister, 32 Thirlestane, Lemsford Rd, St. Albans. AL1 3PE. 01727 850246 (H), 01707 651115 (B) **Ground:** William Bird Playing Fields, Toulmin Drive, St. Albans. Tel: 01727 852401. **Directions:** Join St. Albans ring road. Into Batchwood Drive from either A1081 or A5183. Turn right into Green Lane from the former or left from the latter, then 1st left into Toulmin Drive. Ground at the end.

SANDRIDGE ROVERS

Secretary: Graham Hardwick, 21 Woodcock Hill, Sandridge, St. Albans AL4 9EF. 01727 855334 (H), 01483 742200 (B). **Ground:** Spencer Recreation Ground. Tel: 01727 855159 or 835506 clubhouse. **Directions:** Buses 304, 357 & 358 from St. Albans. By road B651 from St Albans or Wheathampstead to High Street. Ground at the rear of the public car park.

SOMERSETT AMBURY V & E

Secretary: John Venables, 156 Crossbrook Street, Cheshunt, Herts. EN8 8JY. Tel: 01992 636991 (H). **Ground:** The V & E Club, Goffs Lane, Cheshunt. Tel: 01992 624281. **Directions:** M25 junct. 25, take A10 north towards Cheshunt. Left at 1st r'about onto B198 (Flamstead End relief road). At 1st r'about right into Goffs Lane. Clubhouse immediately on right.

SUN POSTAL SPORTS

Secretary: Alan Cowland, 132 Bushey Mill Lane, Watford. WD2 4PB. Tel: 01923 233045 (H), 01442 229509 (B). **Ground:** Bellmount Wood Ave., Watford. 01923 227453 **Directions:** By road from Kings Langley to Watford on Hempstead Road, right at Langley Road lights, right at r'about, then 1st left. Ground entrance 50 yds on right.

WORMLEY ROVERS

Secretary: David Smith, 19 Nursery Gardens, Enfield, Middx. EN3 5NG. 0181 804 3608 (H), 01992 445577 (B) **Ground:** Wormley Sports Ground, Church Lane, Wormley. Tel: 01992 460650. **Directions:** Buses 310, 316 from Hertford and London. By road from A10 take A1170, turn off for Broxbourne and Turnford. Left at the 'New River Arms', left again into Church Lane. Ground 1/4 mile on right.

CHILTONIAN FOOTBALL LEAGUE

Hon. Secretary: A R Ford, Pennings Cottage, Aldershot Road, Guildford, Surrey Tel: (01483) 567284

FINAL LEAGUE TABLES 1996/97

PREMIER DIVISION	P	W	D	L	F	A	Pts
Denham United	34	24	6	4	98	29	78
Stocklake	34	23	7	4	109	40	76
Wraysbury	34	23	7	4	113	46	76
Finchampstead	34	19	8	7	75	37	65
Peppard	34	17	8	9	97	46	59
DCA Basingstoke	34	18	5	11	86	57	59
Wooburn Athletic	34	16	7	11	90	59	55
Binfield	34	16	6	12	74	64	54
AFC Wallingford	34	13	10	11	82	73	49
Martin Baker Sports	34	12	9	13	69	78	45
Eton Wick	34	14	2	18	56	72	44
Quarry Nomads	34	14	2	18	62	85	44
Penn & Tylers Green	34	9	11	14	53	52	38
Iver	34	12	2	20	50	84	38
Prestwood*	34	10	3	21	69	112	30
Henley Town	34	5	10	19	50	94	25
Broadmoor Social	34	4	4	26	28	128	16
Old Paludians	34	2	3	29	45	150	9

*deducted three points

DIVISION ONE	P	W	D	L	F	A	Pts
Eton Wick Res.	26	17	8	1	63	33	59
Finchampstead Res.	26	18	1	7	77	34	55
Beaconsfield SYCOB Res.	26	15	9	2	67	35	54
Englefield Green Rovers	26	13	7	6	57	36	46
Drayton Wanderers	26	13	6	7	55	30	45
Denham United Res.	26	11	7	8	52	47	40
Slough Heating	26	9	5	12	61	59	32
Penn & Tylers Green Res.	26	8	8	10	44	47	32
Peppard Res.	26	9	5	12	43	49	32
Chalfont Wasps	26	9	5	12	41	55	32
Wraysbury Res.	26	10	1	15	32	48	31
Binfield Res.	26	4	8	14	26	50	20
Iver Res.	26	4	4	18	40	81	16
AFC Wallingford Res.	26	2	6	18	29	83	12
Vansittart Wanderers	withdrawn						

BON-ACCORD TROPHY (League Cup)

FIRST ROUND

AFC Wallingford	3	Wooburn Athletic	4	#
Binfield	2	Henley Town	1	
Chalfont Wasps	0	Slough Heating	1	
Denham United	2	Cippenham Village	1	
Finchampstead	2	Quarry Nomads	3	
Iver	2	Penn & Tylers Green	2	*!
Martin Baker Sports	5	Englefield Green Rovers	3	*
Peppard	1	Stocklake	2	*$
Byes to 2nd Round:		*Remaining Teams*		

\# AFC Walingford and Wooburn Athletic removed from competition (ineligible players)
$ Stocklake removed from competition (ineligible players)
! Penn & Tylers Green won 4-5 pens.

SECOND ROUND

Broadmoor Social	1	DCA Basingstoke	3
Denham United	1	Peppard	0
Eton Wick	walkover	(*Vansittart Wanders*)	
Martin Baker Sports	3	Binfield	1
Penn & Tylers Green	1	Slough Heating	0
Prestwood	5	Wraysbury	5
Quarry Nomads	7	Drayton Wanderers	2
(*Wooburn Athletic*)	–	Old Paludians	walkover

SECOND ROUND REPLAY

Wraysbury	7	Prestwood	1

THIRD ROUND

Denham United	2	Penn & Tylers Green	1
Eton Wick	10	Old Paludians	1
Martin Baker Sports	0	DCA Basingstoke	3
Wraysbury	0	Quarry Nomads	2

SEMI-FINALS

Denham United 2 Eton Wick 0
(*at Finchampstead Football Club*)

Quarry Nomads 0 DCA Basingstoke 2
(*at Association Football Club Wallingford*)

FINAL

DCA Basingstoke 1 Denham United 1 *
(*at Peppard Football Club*) (Denham United won 5-6 pens)

* After extra time

PREMIER DIVISION CLUBS

AFC WALLINGFORD

Secretary: Mr E Gniadek, 17 Offas Close, Benson, Wallingford, Oxon OX10 6NR (01491 838540)
Ground: Hithercroft, Wallingford, Oxon (01491 835044)
Colours: Red & black/black/red
Change colours: Green & yellow/green/green

BINFIELD

Secretary: V Bradshaw, 21 Audley Way, Ascot, Berks. SL5 8EE (01344 886144)
Ground: Stubbs Hill, Binfield, Berks (01344 860822)
Colours: Red & white/red/red
Change colours: Blue/black/blue

BROADMOOR SOCIAL

Secretary: Mr M A Roberts, 36 Constable Way, College Town, Sandhurst, Berks. (01276 609038)
Ground: Cricket Field Grove, Upper Broadmoor Rd., Crowthorne, Berks (01344 772612)
Colours: Black & white stripes/black/black
Change colours: Red/white/red

DENHAM UNITED

Secretary: Malcolm Taylor, 15 Townson Ave., Northolt, Middlesex. UB5 6PN (0181 845 9986)
Ground: Oxford Road, Denham, Bucks (01895 238717)
Colours: Blue & white/blue/blue
Change colours: Yellow/black/white

ETON WICK

Secretary: Barrie Shurville, 21 Wheatbutts, Eton Wick, Windsor, Berks SL4 6NG (01753 862969)
Ground: Haywards Mead, Eton Wick, Windsor (01753 852749)
Colours: Amber/black/black & amber
Change colours: White/white/white & black

FINCHAMPSTEAD

Secretary: Anna Bradley, 14 Webb Court, Wokingham, Berks. RG40 5YR. 0118 989 2908 (H), 0421 613535(M).
Ground: Memorial Ground, Finchampstead (01734 732890)
Colours: Sky blue & white/blue/white
Change colours: All red

HENLEY TOWN

Secretary: Mr A Kingston, 50 Birdhill Ave., Reading, Berks RG2 7JU. (0118 967 0196)
Ground: The Triangle Ground, Mill Lane, Henley-on-Thames, Oxon (0491 576463)
Colours: White/black/black
Change colours: Claret & blue/white/white

IVER

Secretary: Mr S Law, 59 Grange Way, Iver, Bucks SL0 9NT (01753 819780)
Ground: Lee Barton, High Street, Iver, Bucks (01753 651248)
Colours: Yellow & royal/royal/yellow
Change colours: Coral & navy blue/navy/navy

MARTIN BAKER SPORTS & SOCIAL

Secretary: Chris Cook, 19 Bramble Close, Hillingdon, Middx. 01895 448259 (H), 0374 701114 (B).
Ground: Martin's Field, Tilehouse Lane, Denham, Bucks (01895 833077)
Colours: Blue & black/black/black
Change colours: White/navy/navy

OLD PALUDIANS

Secretary: P Holt, 14 Lime Close, Wokingham, Berks. RG41 4AW. (0118 989 0815)
Ground: Stanley Jones Field, Berry Hill, Taplow, near Maidenhead (01628 21745)
Colours: Maroon/white/maroon
Change colours: Sky blue/navy/navy

PENN & TYLERS GREEN

Secretary: Malcolm James, Woodlands, Forty Green Rd., Forty Green, Beaconsfield, Bucks. HP9 1XS. (01494 677311)
Ground: French School Meadow, Elm Road, Penn, Bucks (01494 815346)
Colours: Blue & white stripes/blue/white
Change colours: All yellow

PEPPARD

Secretary: Chris Boyles, 14 Redwood Ave, Woodley, Reading, Berks RG5 4DR (0118 969 9488)
Ground: Bishops Wood Sports Centre, Horsepond Rd, Gallowstree Common, nr Reading (0118 972 2675)
Colours: All red
Change colours: Sky blue/navy/navy

PRESTWOOD

Secretary: Rupe Perry, Restcot, Perks lane, Prestwood, Bucks HP16 0JG (01494 864744)
Ground: Prestwood Sports Centre, Honor End Lane, Prestwood, Bucks (01494 865946)
Colours: Claret & sky blue/white/white
Change colours: Sky blue/white/white

QUARRY NOMADS

Secretary: K Dalton, 58 Pitts Rd, Headington, Oxon OX3 8AZ (01865 450256)
Ground: St Margarets Road, Headington, Oxford (Clubhouse - 0802 865367)
Colours: Black & white stripes/black/black
Change colours: All yellow

R.S. BASINGSTOKE

Secretary: M Davis, 451 Abbey Road, Popley Abbeys, Basingstoke RG24 9EN (01256 468873)
Ground: Whiteditch Playing Field, Sherborne Rd, Basingstoke. (01256 814618)
Colours: Maroon/Navy/Navy

STOCKLAKE

Secretary: Tom Exton, 116 Narbeth Drive, Aylesbury, Bucks HP20 1PZ (01296 415780)
Ground: Stocklake Sports & Social Club, Hayward Way, Aylesbury, Bucks (01296 23324)
Colours: Yellow/blue/yellow
Change colours: Coral/purple/black

WOOBURN ATHLETIC

Secretary: Mr B Nash, 10 Philip Drive, Flackwell Heath, Bucks HP10 9JB (01628 523293)
Ground: Wooburn Park, Town Lane, Wooburn Green, Bucks (01628 819201/520772)
Colours: All red
Change colours: All royal blue

WRAYSBURY-COOPERS

Secretary: David Jordan, 18 Welland Close, Langley, Bucks SL3 8UZ (01753 546410)
Ground: Memorial Ground, Wraysbury, Bucks (Clubhouse - 01784 482155)
Colours: Red & blue stripes/Blue/red
Change Colours: Blue & black/red/black

READING FOOTBALL LEAGUE

President: Leon Summers

Chairman: John Dell,
The Cottage, 55 Victoria Road, Mortimer,
Reading RG7 3SL. Tel: 0118 933 2156

Secretary: David Jeanes,
6 Hawkesbury Drive, Fords Farm, Calcot,
Reading RG31 5ZP Tel: 0118 941 3926 (B)

SENIOR DIVISION

	P	W	D	L	F	A	Pts
Mortimer	22	16	5	1	63	15	53
Forest O.B.	22	13	5	4	58	34	44
Sutton Exiles	22	11	4	7	49	38	37
AFC Maidenhead	22	11	3	8	39	38	36
South Reading	22	9	8	5	51	35	35
West Reading	22	10	5	7	42	32	35
Cookham Dean	22	9	5	8	37	31	32
Woodley Yeoman	22	8	1	13	36	57	25
Reading Exiles	22	6	6	10	38	43	24
Checkendon Sports	22	7	3	12	27	40	24
Unity	22	4	1	17	23	53	13
Roundhead	22	3	4	15	19	66	13

SENIOR DIVISION ROLL OF HONOUR

	Champions	Runners-up
1989-90	West Reading	Apollo
1990-91	Forest Old Boys	Cookham Dean
1991-92	Reading Exiles	Broadmoor Staff
1992-93	Woodley Arms	Mortimer
1993-94	Mortimer	Reading Exiles
1994-95	Mortimer	Reading Exiles
1995-96	Reading Exiles	Mortimer

PREMIER DIVISION

	P	W	D	L	F	A	Pts
Sonning Common	22	14	5	3	52	18	47
Emmbrook Sports	22	15	2	5	55	23	47
Marlow	22	13	3	6	46	22	*39
SEB Reading	22	11	4	7	55	40	37
Pegasus	22	10	5	7	58	44	35
REME Arborfield	22	10	4	8	64	30	34
IBIS	22	9	4	9	45	59	31
Earlbourne	22	8	4	10	44	56	28
Lower Earley	22	7	6	9	49	50	27
Shinfield	22	6	5	11	48	52	23
Reading Old Blues	22	2	6	14	21	72	12
Cox Green	22	2	2	18	20	91	8

PREMIER DIVISION ROLL OF HONOUR

	Champions	Runners-up
1989-90	Old Prestonians	Marlow United
1990-91	Broadmoor Staff	Mortimer
1991-92	Woodley Arms	Henley Newtown
1992-93	Reading Old Blues	Checkendon Sports
1993-94	AFC Maidenhead	Theale
1994-95	Sutton Exiles	Tilehurst
1995-96	Unity	Roundhead

DIVISION 1 (THAMES)

	P	W	D	L	F	A	Pts
ARM Athletic	22	18	2	2	81	28	56
Highmoor	22	16	3	3	54	26	51
Finchampstead A	22	14	2	6	54	29	44
Reading University	22	10	5	7	45	29	35
Bishopswood manor	22	8	7	7	44	44	31
Mortimer Res.	22	9	4	9	33	48	31
Frilsham & Yattenden	22	9	1	12	47	55	28
Old Presentonians	22	6	6	10	36	45	24
RBC Sweatshop	22	7	3	12	31	46	24
Nettlebed	22	5	4	13	44	63	19
Sonning	22	6	1	15	41	62	19
IBIS Res.	22	2	6	14	25	60	12

DIVISION 1 (KENNET)

	P	W	D	L	F	A	Pts
Westwood Utd.	18	14	0	4	80	29	42
Reading Exiles Res.	18	13	3	2	56	21	42
Goring United	18	12	4	2	82	22	40
Pangbourne	18	9	3	6	36	38	30
Rabson Rovers	18	7	5	6	46	43	26
Caversham Park V	18	7	3	8	45	37	24
Forest O.B. Res.	18	7	2	9	45	43	23
Berks Co. Sports	18	3	3	12	33	68	12
Theale	18	2	3	13	30	69	9
CS Reading	18	2	2	14	25	108	*5

SENIOR DIVISION

A.F.C. MAIDENHEAD
Secretary: Mrs D Saunders, 63 Furze Road, Maidenhead, SL6 7NF. 01628 635994 (H)
Ground: Cox Green School, Highfield Lane, Maidenhead
Colours: Green & white/white/green

CHECKENDON SPORTS
Secretary: Ernie Smith, 10 Emmens Close, Checkendon, Reading RG8 0TU. 01491 681575 (H)
Ground: Playing Field, Checkendon, Reading.
Colours: Maroon & white/black/white

COOKHAM DEAN
Secretary: Rory Gavin, 46 Chiltern Road, Maidenhead SL6 1XA. 01628 632997 (H)
Ground: Alfred Major Rec., Hillcrest Ave., Cookham Rise, Maidenhead.
Colours: Red & black/black/black

EMMBROOK SPORTS CLUB
Secretary: Steve Haynes, 15 Tilney Way, Lower Earley, Reading RG6 4AD. 0118 967 0459 (H)
Ground: Emmbrook Sports Ground, Lowther Road, Emmbrook, Wokingham (01734 780209)
Colours: Blue & white stripes/blue/blue

FOREST OLD BOYS
Secretary: Bob Hulett, 10 Ramsbury Drive, Earley, Reading RG6 7RT. 0118 966 3514 (H)
Ground: Holme Park, Sonning (0118 973 2890)
Colours: Yellow & blue/blue/blue

MORTIMER
Secretary: Steve Dell, 30 Croft Rd, Mortimer, nr Reading RG7 3TS. 0118 933 3821 (H)
Ground: Alfred Palmer Mem. P.F., West End Rd, Mortimer.
Colours: Amber/black/black

READING EXILES
Secretary: Mick Aust, 24 Aylsham Close, Tilehurst, Reading RG30 4XG. 0118 942 1453 (H)
Ground: Palmer Park Sports Stadium, Wokingham Road, Reading
Colours: Royal blue & white/royal/royal

SONNING COMMON
Secretary: Karen Jenkins, 7 Maple Close, Sonning Common, Reading RG4 9NG. 01491 413995 (H)
Ground: Peppard Cricket Club, Peppard Common, Stoke Row Rd. Peppard.
Colours: White/blue/white

SOUTH READING
Secretary: Terence Darlow, Four Horseshoes, 177 Basingstoke Road, Reading RG2 0HY. 0118 987 1604
Ground: Whitley Wood Rec. Gd., Basingstoke Road, Reading
Colours: Yellow/blue/blue
Reserve Colours

SUTTON EXILES
Secretary: Miss Pippa Whybourne, 119 Admirals Court, Reading RG2 0SR. 0118 959 8230 (H)
Ground: Whitley Wood Rec. Gd., Basingstoke Road, Reading.
Colours: All blue

WEST READING
Secretary: Mrs Sue Porton, 6 Hampstead Court, Grovelands Rd, Reading RG30 2QQ. 0118 950 4034 (H)
Ground: Victoria Recreation
Colours: Yellow & black//black/yellow & black

WOODLEY YEOMAN
Secretary: Bob Brodrick, 44 Hilltop Road, Earley, Reading RG6 1DA. 0118 961 7278 (H)
Ground: Woodford Park, Haddon Drive, Woodley
Colours: Blue/blue/black

PREMIER DIVISION

A.R.M. ATHLETIC
Secretary: Andrew Allum, 35 Roundfields, Upper Bucklebury, Reading RG7 6RA. 01635 861903
Ground: Victoria Rec., Kentwood Hill, Tilehurst.

EARLBOURNE
Secretary: Andrew Beach, 24 Quentin Road, Woodley, Reading RG5 3NE. 0118 962 6719 (H)
Ground: Woodford Park, Haddon Drive, Woodley, Reading RG5 4LY (01734 690356)

HIGHMOOR
Secretary: Chris Gallimore, 10 Patrick Road, Caversham, Reading RG4 8DD. 0118 954 3828 (H)
Ground: Highmoor ath. Gd., Highmoor, Henley, Oxon.

IBIS
Secretary: Terry Spice, 75 Hildens Drive, Tilehurst, Reading RG31 5JA. 0118 942 9421
Ground: IBIS Sports Club, Scours Lane, Reading RG3 6AY (0118 942 4130)

MARLOW UNITED
Secretary: Rae Flint, 30 Dean Street, Marlow, Bucks SL7 3AE. 01628 476611
Ground: Gossmore Park, Gossmore Lane, Marlow.

PEGASUS
Secretary: Barry Hoy, 24 Hadleigh Rise, Caversham Park Village, Reading RG4 0RW. 0118 947 6434 (H)
Ground: Emmer Green Recreation Ground

R.E.M.E. ARBORFIELD
Secretary: Peter Davies, 73 Chestnut Cres., Shinfield, Reading RG9 9HA. 0118 988 4107
Ground: Sports Pavilion, Biggs Lane, Princess Marina College, Arborfield

READING EXILES Reserves
(see above)

ROUNDHEAD
Secretary: Eric Wise, 63 St Saviours Rd, Reading RG1 6EJ. 0118 961 0063 (H)
Ground: Coley Park, St Saviours Rd, Coley, Reading.

S.E.B. (READING)
Secretary: George Walker, 9 Springdale, Earley, Reading RG6 5PR. 0118 967 0846 (H)
Ground: Christchurch Meadows, George Street, Caversham, Reading

UNITY
Secretary: Trevor Lowe, 161 Cotswold Way, Tilehurst, Reading RG31 6ST. 0118 945 5133 (H)
Ground: Cintra Park

WESTWOOD
Secretary: Penny Brodie, 58 Devonshire Gardens, Tilehurst, Reading RG31 6FP. 0118 962 4572 (H)
Ground:

SOUTHERN FOOTBALL LEAGUES
Final League Tables 1996-97

MIDDLESEX COUNTY LEAGUE

Premier Division

		P	W	D	L	F	A	Pts
1	Rayners Lane	22	14	5	3	38	22	47
2	Northfield CA V	22	12	7	3	45	24	43
3	Spelthorne Sport	22	12	4	6	32	26	40
4	Willesden (C)	22	12	2	8	62	32	38
5	Stonebridge Tn	22	9	5	8	41	35	32
6	Osterley	22	7	8	7	26	25	29
7	Hanworth Villa	22	8	5	9	35	43	29
8	Pitshanger	22	6	7	9	40	40	25
9	Acton Shamrock	22	6	7	9	31	31	25
10	N Greenford Utd	22	6	4	12	31	44	22
11	Mill End Utd	22	5	5	12	28	56	20
12	Southgate	22	4	3	15	30	62	15

Division One

		P	W	D	L	F	A	Pts
1	Broadfields Utd	16	12	2	2	34	11	38
2	FC Deportivo	16	10	2	4	40	24	32
3	Harrow St Mary's	16	9	1	6	33	16	28
4	Northolt Saints	16	6	4	5	38	33	22
5	Neasden	16	6	2	7	30	28	20
6	Hanwell Viaduct	16	6	2	8	27	26	20
7	Stonebridge Res	16	5	2	9	20	35	17
8	Brentf'd New Inn	16	4	3	9	22	36	15
9	Hayes St Clarets	16	2	4	10	22	57	10
10	Ealing Asyrians	Withdrawn Mid Dec - Record Ex						
11	Mill End Utd Res	Withdrawn Mid Dec - Record Ex						
12	Pitshanger Res	Withdrawn Mid Dec - Record Ex						

ALEX SMITH LEAGUE CUP

HOLDERS: Osterley

Final at Uxbridge FC

Northfield CAV v Willesden Const. 4p2, 2-2

NORTH BERKSHIRE LEAGUE

Division One

		P	W	D	L	F	A	Pts
1	Drayton	20	17	3	0	86	23	37
2	Saxton Rovers	20	12	3	5	65	39	27
3	Long Wittenham	20	11	5	4	59	35	27
4	Shrivenham	20	9	6	5	33	29	24
5	Faringdon Town	20	8	6	6	23	19	22
6	Great Shefford	20	8	3	9	38	45	19
7	Sutton Courtenay	20	6	4	10	43	54	16
8	Didcot Casuals	20	7	2	11	34	47	16
9	Marcham	20	5	5	10	31	46	15
10	Harwell Village	20	4	2	14	25	66	10
11	AERE Harwell	20	2	3	15	34	77	7

Division Two

		P	W	D	L	F	A	Pts
1	Blewbury	24	19	4	1	80	27	42
2	Saxton Rovers R	24	18	2	4	79	32	38
3	Radley	24	16	5	3	86	29	37
4	East Hendred	24	14	4	6	60	27	32
5	Uffington	24	11	8	5	47	26	30
6	Dorchester	24	11	7	6	54	44	29
7	Childrey	24	10	4	10	55	47	24
8	Hanney	24	8	4	12	44	57	20
9	Shrivenham Rs	24	6	6	12	44	47	18
10	Steventon	24	7	2	15	52	68	16
11	Woodcote	24	6	2	16	58	96	14
12	Gt Shefford Rs	24	4	1	19	31	84	9
13	Grove	24	1	1	22	17	123	3

BRIGHTON, HOVE & DISTRICT LEAGUE

Premier Division

		P	W	D	L	F	A	Pts
1	Patcham	20	15	2	3	65	19	47
2	Sussex Univers.	20	13	3	4	46	28	42
3	Rottingdean Villa	20	12	3	5	59	35	39
4	AFC Falcons	20	11	4	5	42	30	37
5	O Verndeanians	20	10	1	9	58	37	31
6	Montpelier Villa	20	6	5	9	23	30	23
7	Rutland	20	7	2	11	25	49	23
8	Portslade Ath	20	6	4	10	30	39	22
9	Midway	20	6	4	10	30	45	22
10	Preston Village	20	5	4	11	29	41	19
11	Brighton BBOB	20	3	0	17	22	76	9

CRAWLEY & DISTRICT LEAGUE

Premier Division

		P	W	D	L	F	A	Pts
1	Godstone	18	15	3	0	74	16	48
2	Edward Sports	18	10	4	4	55	24	34
3	Thomas Bennett	18	9	3	6	41	37	30
4	Phoenix	18	6	7	5	30	25	25
5	Ifield HI	18	7	2	9	31	56	23
6	B O C	18	6	4	8	37	44	22
7	T D Sports	18	6	4	8	18	25	22
8	Longley	18	6	1	11	26	30	19
9	Bluebird Rangers	18	4	3	11	25	51	15
10	Thomas Ath I	18	3	5	10	18	47	14

EAST SUSSEX LEAGUE

Premier Division

		P	W	D	L	F	A	Pts
1	Polegate	16	11	1	4	45	31	34
2	Westfield	16	9	5	2	45	28	32
3	Wadhurst Utd	16	9	3	4	60	19	30
4	Rock a Nore	16	8	4	4	36	17	25
5	Hollington Utd	16	7	2	7	33	35	23
6	Willingdon AFC	16	6	2	8	35	44	20
7	Icklesham Cas.	16	3	3	10	23	60	12
8	Eastbourne Fmen	16	2	5	9	25	43	11
9	Punnetts Town	16	2	5	9	22	47	11

Division One

		P	W	D	L	F	A	Pts
1	Shinewater II	18	13	4	1	65	22	43
2	Northiam '75	18	11	5	2	52	24	38
3	Lt Common Alb	18	11	4	3	52	25	37
4	Bodiham	18	10	6	2	43	23	36
5	Travaux	18	6	4	8	52	50	22
6	Hollington U M	18	5	5	8	46	46	20
7	Robertsbridge	18	5	2	11	28	32	20
8	Pebsham Sibex	18	4	5	9	31	43	17
9	Ticehurst	18	3	2	13	21	57	17
10	Burwash	18	2	3	13	18	56	11

Division Two

		P	W	D	L	F	A	Pts
1	Sandhurst	16	12	0	4	57	21	39
2	Cranbrook	16	10	2	4	42	25	35
3	Claverham	16	10	2	4	49	21	29
4	Peche Hill Select	16	9	2	5	32	25	29

* Sandhurst and Cranbrook Town awarded three points
Claverham deducted three points

SURREY COUNTY PREMIER LEAGUE

Premier Division

		P	W	D	L	F	A	Pts
1	Virginia Water	30	17	7	6	61	39	58
2	Chessington Hk	30	17	6	7	58	30	57
3	Chobham	30	17	6	7	65	40	57
4	Bookham	30	15	9	6	57	34	54
5	Holmesdale	30	15	7	8	64	37	52
6	AFC Guildford	30	16	4	10	62	46	52
6	Ollershaw	30	13	10	7	43	36	49
7	Worcester Park	30	13	7	10	60	49	46
8	Bisley	30	13	6	11	58	59	45
9	Farleigh Rovers	30	12	3	15	50	62	39
10	Coney Hall	30	11	3	16	54	60	36
11	Croydon M O	30	10	1	19	51	89	31
12	Vandyke	30	8	6	16	42	62	30
13	Shottermill	30	8	4	18	42	56	28
14	Sheerwater	30	5	6	19	45	67	21
15	Hersham RBL	30	5	5	20	48	85	20

LEAGUE CUP

FINAL

Ottershaw v Virginia Water 0-1

SURREY COUNTY WESTERN LEAGUE

Division One

		P	W	D	L	F	A	Pts
1	Haslemere	20	15	3	2	49	20	33
2	Tongham	20	12	4	4	55	31	28
3	Merrow	20	12	4	4	46	22	28
4	Marconi S&S	20	10	3	7	44	32	23
5	Horsley	20	8	5	7	36	36	21
6	Worplesdon	20	9	1	10	53	40	19
7	Frimley Green	20	8	3	9	35	36	19
8	Staines Lammas	20	8	1	11	39	37	17
9	Ewhurst	20	7	2	11	38	53	16
10	Windlesham	20	6	2	12	40	63	14
11	Badshot Lea	20	1	0	19	18	83	2

Division Two

		P	W	D	L	F	A	Pts
1	Elstead	22	17	2	3	59	34	36
2	Chiddingfold	22	17	1	4	69	31	35
3	Lightwater	22	15	3	4	64	37	33
4	Ockham	22	12	5	5	52	26	29
5	Wrecclesham	22	13	3	6	59	40	29
6	Woking Pk Hors.	22	10	2	10	63	38	22
7	Witley & District	22	8	5	9	37	40	21
8	Ripley Village	22	9	3	10	39	50	21
9	Surrey Police	22	5	3	14	38	55	13
10	Knaphill	22	6	1	15	46	68	13
11	Burymead	22	3	0	19	28	81	6
12	Bagshott	22	2	2	18	22	76	6

WORTHING LEAGUE

Premier Division

		P	W	D	L	F	A	Pts
1	Sompting	22	18	2	2	69	15	56
2	London Ed Sp	22	17	3	2	75	31	54
3	Northbrook	22	15	3	4	48	22	48
4	AFC Lion	22	11	5	6	46	41	38
5	Maple Leaf Rgrs	22	10	4	8	47	44	34
6	Russell Bourne	22	9	5	8	30	34	32
7	Eurotherm	22	8	6	8	56	36	30
8	St Theresas	22	6	3	13	31	37	21
9	ABS Durrington	22	6	3	13	40	60	21
10	W Terring WMC	22	4	3	15	31	65	15
11	Royal Mail	22	3	4	15	32	75	13
12	Worthing U 'A'	22	3	3	16	36	83	12

MID SUSSEX LEAGUE

Premier Division

		P	W	D	L	F	A	Pts
1	Pease Pottage V	22	14	4	4	74	35	46
2	East Grinstead U	22	13	3	6	57	39	42
3	Nutley	22	11	4	7	54	33	37
4	Maresfield Village	22	11	3	8	34	30	36
5	Wealden	22	9	8	5	46	36	35
6	Lindfield	22	8	8	6	43	40	32
7	Handcross Vlge	22	6	8	8	38	43	26
8	Wisdom Sports	22	6	7	9	29	39	25
9	Clayton	22	6	5	11	35	44	23
10	Plumpton Ath	22	7	2	13	24	42	23
11	Cuckfield	22	6	4	12	29	50	22
12	Felbridge	22	6	2	14	46	78	20

Division One

		P	W	D	L	F	A	Pts
1	Hurstpierpoint	22	16	4	2	73	30	52
2	St Francis H Rs	22	15	3	4	61	25	48
3	Balcombe	22	11	6	5	63	40	39
4	DMS Cuckfield	22	10	5	7	51	45	35
5	Copthorne Rvrs	22	10	4	8	52	43	34
6	Newick	22	9	4	9	53	51	31
7	Ashurstwood	22	8	7	7	35	37	31
8	Village Ditchling	22	9	3	10	37	48	30
9	Chailey	22	7	6	9	35	37	27
10	East Grinstead R	22	7	6	9	33	41	27
11	Anstey Rgrs Res	22	3	4	15	37	66	13
12	Lewes Rovers	22	0	2	20	27	94	2

HFC BANK SOUTHAMPTON LEAGUE

Premier Division

		P	W	D	L	F	A	Pts
1	Ordnance Survey	26	21	3	2	77	23	66
2	Brendon	26	21	2	3	84	25	65
3	B F C (Soton)	26	14	6	6	54	30	48
4	Durley	26	14	5	7	59	37	47
5	West End Sp	26	14	5	7	69	38	46*
6	Fair Oak Amplev.	26	13	1	12	46	52	40
7	Colden Comm. R	26	11	6	9	46	42	39
8	Old Tauntonians	26	8	9	9	43	46	33
9	Esso Fawley Rs	26	8	3	15	38	53	27
10	Bishopstoke S R	26	6	6	14	38	66	24
11	Otterbourne	26	5	7	14	36	61	22
12	AC Delco Res	26	5	6	15	36	53	21
13	Pirelli General R	26	6	3	17	32	58	21
14	Romsey Town Rs	26	4	2	20	31	105	14

* One point deducted

Division One

		P	W	D	L	F	A	Pts
1	North Baddesley	22	18	3	1	58	19	57
2	Ford	22	16	3	3	61	27	51
3	Locks Heath Rs	22	12	2	8	52	38	38
4	Sholing Select	22	12	2	8	41	37	38
5	East Holdre	22	10	5	7	48	42	35
6	AFC Solent	22	10	4	8	56	33	34
7	Codham United	22	8	1	13	39	43	25
8	Lyndhurst	22	7	2	13	41	54	23
9	West End Rs	22	11	1	10	33	49	19
10	Netley Ath Vics	22	3	6	13	34	56	15
11	Hythe Aztecs	22	3	5	14	22	46	14
12	Vosper Thorny R	22	4	2	16	12	63	14

* Fifteen points deducted

COUNTY FOOTBALL ASSOCIATIONS

SECTION

BEDFORDSHIRE F.A.

Secretary: Peter D Brown
19 Lambs Close, Dunstable LU5 4QA (01582) 668013
Tel: (01582) 565111 (County Office) Fax: (01582) 565222

BEDFORDSHIRE SENIOR CUP
(FOUNDED 1894-95)

RECENT FINALS

1991-92	Kempston Rovers	v	Totternhoe	1-0
1992-93	Leighton Town	v	Kempston Rovers	2-1
1993-94	Potton United	v	Stotfold	2-1
1994-95	Bedford Town	v	Toddington Rovers	5-3 (AET)
1995-96	Barton Rovers	v	Bedford Town	0-1

MOST WINS Waterlows 10 Dunstable 9 Luton Clarence 8

1996-97
BEDFORDSHIRE PREMIER CUP

10 CLUBS **HOLDERS: BARTON ROVERS**

PRELIMINARY ROUND

Potton United	v	Stotfold	0-1
Wootton Blue Cross	v	Brache Sparta	2-1

FIRST ROUND

Bedford United	v	Luton Town	1-2
Stotfold	v	Langford	6-0
ArleseyTown	v	Leighton Town	1-2
Wootton Blue Cr	v	Biggleswade Town	4-0

SEMI-FINALS

Stotfold	v	Luton Town	0-2
Wootton Blue Cr	v	Leighton Town	1-2

FINAL

LEIGHTON TOWN v LUTON TOWN 1-2 at Leighton Town FC

BEDFORDSHIRE SENIOR CUP

19 CLUBS **HOLDERS: BEDFORD TOWN**

PRELIMINARY ROUND

Ampthill Town	v	Houghton Town	2-1
Bedford United	v	Langford	1-2
Stotfold	v	Brache Sparta	2-0

FIRST ROUND

Ampthill Town	v	Bedford Town	0-5
Stotfold	v	Barton Rovers	1-2
Kent Athletic	v	Potton United	3*5
Langford	v	Kempston Rovers	0-1
61 FC Luton	v	Biggleswade Town	1*1 0-2
Totternhoe	v	Wootton Blue Cross	0-2
Toddington Rovers	v	Arlesey Town	2*3
ACD Tridon	v	Leighton Town	1-6

SECOND ROUND

Kempston Rovers	v	Wootton Blue Cross	1*1 0-2
Burton Rovers	v	Bedford Town	1-3
Arlesey Town	v	Biggleswade Town	4-1
Potton United	v	Leighton Town	2-0

SEMI-FINALS

Potton United v Wootton Blue Cross 4-1
at Barton Rovers FC

Arlesey Town v Bedford Town 0*0 2-0
at Potton United FC (Replay same venue)

FINAL

ARLESEY TOWN v POTTON UNITED 2*1 at Langford FC

BERKS & BUCKS F.A.

Secretary: Mr W J Gosling,
15a London Street, Faringdon, Oxon SN7 8AG
Tel: (01367) 242099 (County Office) Fax: (01367) 242158

BERKS & BUCKS SENIOR CUP
(FOUNDED 1878-79)
RECENT FINALS

1991-92	Chesham United	v	Windsor & Eton	3-1
1992-93	Chesham United	v	Abingdon Town	1-0
1993-94	Marlow	v	Chesham United	1-0
1994-95	Reading	v	Slough Town	1-0
1995-96	Aylesbury United	v	Wokingham Town	0-1

MOST WINS Wycombe 24 Maidenhead United 15 Marlow 13

1996-97
BERKS & BUCKS SENIOR CUP

20 CLUBS **HOLDERS: WOKINGHAM TOWN**

SECOND QUALIFYING ROUND

Beaconsfield SYCOB	v	Flackwell Heath	0*0 2*1
Windsor & Eton	v	Bracknell Town	2*2 0-4
Marlow	v	Milton Keynes	4-3
Maidenhead Utd	v	Abingdon Town	0-2

FIRST ROUND PROPER

Slough Town	v	Buckingham Town	6-0
Reading	v	Marlow	4-0
Hungerford Town	v	Newport Pagnell Town	1-3
Burnham	v	Beaconsfield SYCOB	1-2
Chalfont St Peter	v	Wokingham Town	0-2
Aylesbury United	v	Chesham United	3-1
Bracknell Town	v	Abingdon Town	3-4
Thatcham Town	v	Wycombe Wanderers	1-3

SECOND ROUND

Aylesbury United	v	Abingdon Town	2-1
Newport Pagnell Tn	v	Wokingham Town	2-1
Slough Town	v	Wycombe Wanderers	2-3
Reading	v	Beaconsfield SYCOB	1-0

SEMI-FINALS

Newport Pagnell Tn	v	Reading	0-3
Wycombe Wand.	v	Aylesbury United	0-1

FINAL

READING	v	AYLESBURY UTD	1-2	at Slough Town FC

BERKS & BUCKS SENIOR TROPHY

34 CLUBS **HOLDERS: READING TOWN**

FIRST QUALIFYING ROUND

Wantage Town	v	Kintbury Rangers	3-2
Winslow United	v	Reading Exiles	1*1 0-4
Mercedes Benz	v	Denham United	2-3
Buckingham Ath	v	Forest Old Boys	5-0

SECOND QUALIFYING ROUND

Martin Baker Sp	v	AFC Newbury	0-3
Milton United	v	Amersham Town	2-3
Finchampstead	v	Iver	1-3
Binfield	v	Olney Town	3-0
Reading Exiles	v	Old Paludians	3-0
Didcot Town	v	Mortimer	1*2
Risborough Rangers	v	Wantage Town	1-0
Abingdon United	v	Wraysbury	2-0
AFC Wallingford	v	New Bradwell St Peter	2-3
Holmer Green	v	Eton Wick	4-0
Sandhurst Town	v	Wooburn Athletic	1-3
Buckingham Ath	v	Broadmoor Social	3-1
Stony Stratford T	v	Denham United	2-0
Penn & Tylers Gn	v	Prestwood	2-0

2 Clubs: Reading Town and Lambourn Sports exempt to

FIRST ROUND PROPER

Lambourn Sports	v	Binfield	2-1
Reading Town	v	AFC Newbury	2-0
Mortimer	v	Stony Stratford Town	2-1
Amersham Town	v	Penn & Tylers Green	2-1
Iver	v	Risborough Rangers	0-2
Reading Exiles	v	Abingdon United	1-3
Buckingham Ath	v	Holmer Green	0-4
Wooburn Athletic	v	New Bradwell St Peter	4-3

SECOND ROUND

Mortimer	v	Amersham Town	0-0 1-0
Lambourn Sports	v	Holmer Green	2-1
Reading Town	v	Wooburn Athletic	6*3
Risborough Rgrs	v	Abingdon United	1-2

SEMI-FINALS

Reading Town	v	Lambourn Sports	1-0
Abingdon United	v	Mortimer	2-1

FINAL

ABINGDON UNITED	v	READING TOWN	2*1	at Marlow FC

BIRMINGHAM F.A.

Secretary: M Pennick FFA,
Ray Hall Lane, Great Barr, Birmingham B43 6JF
Tel: (01213) 574278 (County Office) Fax: (01213) 581661

BIRMINGHAM SENIOR CUP (FOUNDED 1875-76)

RECENT FINALS

1991-92	VS Rugby	v	Birmingham City	3-1
1992-93	Nuneaton Borough	v	VS Rugby	2-0
1993-94	Walsall	v	Hednesford Town	3-0
1994-95	Solihull Borough	v	Aston Villa	2-0
1995-96	Birmingham City	v	Aston Villa	2-0

MOST WINS Aston Villa 19 Birmingham City 7 Kidderminster Harriers 7 Wolverhampton Wanderers 7

1996-97 BIRMINGHAM SENIOR CUP

45 CLUBS **HOLDERS: BIRMINGHAM CITY**

FIRST ROUND

Banbury United	v	Knowle	1-3
Paget Rovers	v	Sutton Coldfield Town	2-1
Sandwell Borough	v	Lye Town	1-2
Wednesfield	v	Brierley Hill Town	2-2 3-1
Halesowen Harriers	v	Bedworth United	3-0
Kings Heath	v	Stratford Town	2-2 2-0
Willenhall Town	v	Boldmere St Michaels	1-2
Redditch United	v	Oldbury United	7-0
Dudley Town	v	Northfield Town	2-0
Gornal Athletic	v	Highgate United	2-0
Coleshill Town	v	Stourbridge	1-3
Worcester City	v	Racing Club Warwick	4-0
Nuneaton Borough	v	Atherstone United	2-0

SECOND ROUND

Darlaston	v	West Bromwich Albion	0-8
Redditch United	v	Wednesfield	5-0
Burton Albion	v	Worcester City	2-0
West Mid Police	v	Evesham United	0-0 1-9
Walsall	v	Solihull Borough	1-1 3-1
VS Rugby	v	Tamworth	2-3
Boldmere St Mick	v	Knowle	2-2 2-1
Halesowen Town	v	Halesowen Harriers	1-1 0-1
Coventry City	v	Hednesford Town	1-0
Moor Green	v	Birmingham City	1-1 2-0
W'mpton Wand'rs	v	Stourbridge @S	3-0
Nuneaton Borough	v	Kings Heath	1-0
Paget Rovers	v	Dudley Town	0-2
Bolehall Swifts	v	Aston Villa	0-2
Gornal Athletic	v	Lye Town	3-0
Cradley Town	v	Tividale	1-2

THIRD ROUND

Moor Green	v	Boldmere St Michaels	3-4
Halesowen Harriers	v	Burton Albion	0-1
Nuneaton Borough	v	West Bromwich Albion	1-2
Tividale	v	Tamworth	1-2
Dudley Town	v	Aston Villa	0-3
Walsall	v	Redditch United	5-1
Coventry City	v	Wolverhampton W	3-1
Evesham United	v	Gornal Athletic	2-1

FOURTH ROUND

Boldmere St Michaels	v	Tamworth	3-3 1-4
Evesham United	v	Coventry City	1-3
Burton Albion	v	Walsall	3-2
West Brom Albion	v	Aston Villa	4-2

SEMI-FINALS

Burton Albion	v	Coventry City	1-0
West Brom Albion	v	Tamworth	0-3

FINAL

BURTON ALBION v TAMWORTH 3-1 at The Lamb Ground, Tamworth FC

CAMBRIDGESHIRE F.A.

Secretary: Roger Pawley,
3 Signet Court, Swanns Road, Cambridge CB5 8LA
Tel: (01223) 576770 (County Office) Fax: (01223) 576780

CAMBRIDGESHIRE INVITATION CUP
(FOUNDED 1950-51)

RECENT FINALS

1991-92	Wisbech Town	v	Cambridge City	2-0
1992-93	Cambridge City	v	Wisbech Town	3-1
1993-94	Chatteris Town	v	Wisbech Town	3-1
1994-95	Wisbech Town	v	Cambridge City	4-2
1995-96	Foxton	v	Mildenhall Town	0-3

MOST WINS Wisbech Town 9 Cambridge City 8 Chatteris Town 7

1996-97
CAMBS INVITATION CUP

12 CLUBS

HOLDERS: MILDENHALL TOWN

PRELIMINARY ROUND

Chatteris Town	v	Histon	
March Town Utd	v	Mildenhall Town	2-1
Ely City	v	Leverington Sports	5-0
Wisbech Town	v	Over Sports	1-0

FIRST ROUND

Histon	v	Cambridge City	2-1
Soham Tn Rangers	v	Ely City	3-2
March Town Utd	v	Foxton	3-1
Newmarket Town	v	Wisbech Town	4-2

SEMI-FINALS

Soham Tn Rangers	v	Histon	0-1
Newmarket Town	v	March Tn United	3-0

FINAL

HISTON v NEWMARKET TN 5p-1 2*2 at Soham Town Rangers FC

CHESHIRE F.A.

Secretary: Alan Collins,
The Cottage, Hartford Moss Rec Centre, Winnington, Northwich, Cheshire CW8 4BG
Tel: (01619) 804706 (H) (01606) 871166 (County Office) Fax: (01606) 871292

CHESHIRE SENIOR CUP
(FOUNDED 1879-80)

RECENT FINALS

1991-92	Macclesfield Town	v	Witton Albion	1-1 (Rep 2-0)
1992-93	Winsford United	v	Witton Albion	3-0
1993-94	Northwich Victoria	v	Runcorn	1-0
1994-95	Witton Albion	v	Altrincham	2-1
1995-96	Hyde United	v	Witton Albion	1-3

MOST WINS Macclesfield Town 18 Northwich Victoria 16 Crewe Alexandra 12 Runcorn 12

1996-97
CHESHIRE SENIOR CUP

13 CLUBS **HOLDERS: WITTON ALBION**

FIRST ROUND

Stalybridge Celtic	v	Winsford United	3-2
Cheadle Town	v	Altrincham	0-6
Runcorn	v	Congleton Town	1-1 1-3
Northwich Victoria	v	Vauxhall GM	0-1
Warrington Town	v	Nantwich Town	1-2

SECOND ROUND

Nantwich Town	v	Stalybridge Celtic	3-1
Vauxhall GM	v	Altrincham	2-1
Hyde United	v	Witton Albion	2-1
Congleton Town	v	Macclesfield Town	1-3

SEMI-FINALS

Hyde United	v	Vauxhall GM	3-1 1-2 4-3
Macclesfield Town	v	Nantwich Town	7-0 2-1 9-1

FINAL

HYDE UNITED v MACCLESFIELD TN 3-0 at The Drill Field, Northwich Victoria FC

CORNWALL F.A.

Secretary: J M Ryder,
Penare, 16 Gloweth View, Truro, Cornwall TR1 3JZ

CORNWALL SENIOR CUP
(FOUNDED 1892-93)

RECENT FINALS

1991-92	Newquay	v	Falmouth Town	1-0
1992-93	Saltash United	v	Launceston	3-2
1993-94	Liskeard Athletic	v	Bodmin Town	2-1
1994-95	Truro City	v	Liskeard Athletic	2-1
1995-96	Porthleven	v	Torpoint Athletic	0-2

MOST WINS Truro City 12 St Austell 11 Penzance 10 St Blazey 10 Torpoint Athletic 10

1996-97
CORNWALL SENIOR CUP

41 CLUBS **HOLDERS: TORPOINT ATHLETIC**

FIRST ROUND

Helston Athletic	v	Ludgvan	4-1	Callington	v	Marazion Blues	7-1
Camelford	v	Goonhavern Athl.	2-2 2-4	St Agnes	v	Illogan RBL	0-2
Bude	v	Mullion	4-1	St Cleer	v	Perranwell	1-3
St Ives Town	v	Mousehole	1-4	St Breward	v	Sticker	3-1
St Just	v	Bugle	2-2 1-0				

9 Clubs with Byes and 14 Clubs Exempt to Second Round

SECOND ROUND

Callington	v	Foxhole Stars	4-1	Launceston*	v	Nanpean Rovers	0-0 T-A
Millbrook	v	Torpoint Athletic	1-1 2-1	Mousehole	v	Bodmin Town	0-3
Padstow United	v	Newquay	1-1 2-4	Pendeen Rovers	v	Falmouth Town	0-7
Penryn Athletic	v	St Blazey	2-2 1-3	Perranwell	v	RNAS Culdrose	1-0
Porthleven	v	St Breward	4-1	St Agnes	v	Helston Athletic	2-1
St Austell	v	Penzance	2-4	St Dennis	v	Saltash United	2-6
St Just	v	Bude	3-0	Troon	v	Goonhavern Ath	2-4
Truro City	v	Roche	3-1	Wadebridge Town	v	Liskeard Athletic	2-2 0-7

(*Tie awarded & Launceston eliminated after it was found they had played an unregistered player in the 0-0 draw)

THIRD ROUND

Callington	v	Truro City	2-7	Falmouth Town	v	Bodmin Town	2-2 4-2
Millbrook	v	Newquay	1-1 3-1	Porthleven	v	Perranwell	3-0
St Agnes	v	Nanpean Rovers	1-4	St Just	v	St Blazey	0-1
Saltash United	v	Penzance	2-5	Liskeard Athletic	v	Goonhavern Athletic	2-1

FOURTH ROUND

Millbrook	v	Nanpean Rovers	1-3	Penzance	v	Liskeard Athletic	0-0 2-1
St Blazey	v	Falmouth Town	0-5	Truro City	v	Porthleven	0-0 3-1

SEMI-FINALS

Falmouth Town	v	Penzance	2-0	Nanpean Rovers	v	Truro City	1-0
at Truro City FC				at St Blazey FC			

FINALS

FALMOUTH TOWN v NANPEAN ROVERS1-1 2-1 at St Blazey FC (both matches)

No Gary Letts - you can't have danger money!

Photo: Eric Marsh

CUMBERLAND FA

Secretary: R Johnson,
72 Victoria Road, Workington, Cumbria CA14 2QT
Tel: (01900) 603979 (County Office)

CUMBERLAND SENIOR CUP
(FOUNDED 1960-61)

RECENT FINALS

1991-92	Gretna	v	Penrith	1-0
1992-93	Carlisle United Res	v	Gretna	0-0 (Rep 3-1)
1993-94	Gretna	v	Carlisle United Res	3-0
1994-95	Gretna	v	Penrith	2-0
1995-96	Cleator Moor Celtic	v	Workington	1-4

MOST WINS Penrith 10 Gretna 8 Haig Colliery 3

1996-97
CUMBERLAND SENIOR CUP

37 CLUBS **HOLDERS: WORKINGTON**

FIRST ROUND

Abbeytown	v	Wigton Harriers	4-0	Langworthy	v	Whitehaven M	0-1
Silloth	v	Northbank Colts	0-2	Windscale	v	Carlisle United	2-3
Carlisle City	v	Northbank	0-1				

SECOND ROUND

Workington	v	Abbeytown	5-2	Carlisle United	v	Silloth Colts	6-0
New Victoria	v	Whitehaven Miners	2-1	British Steel	v	Cumbria Police	BS W-O
Windscale RS	v	Cleator Moor Celtic	1-11	Keswick	v	Inglewood	4-0
Heart Liddlesdale	v	Braithwaite	5-2	Gretna	v	Longtown	4-1
Carleton Rovers	v	Northbank Colts	2-1	Parton United	v	Northbank	0-7
St Bees	v	Whitehaven Amts	1-3	Whitehaven M	v	Greystoke	2-0
Cockermouth	v	Sporting Museum	3*2	Kirkoswald	v	Gillford Park	1-6
Penrith	v	Wetheriggs United	5-0	Alston Town	v	Whitehaven Amt Res	4-0

THIRD ROUND

Heart of Liddlesdale	v	Whitehaven M	3-1	Alston Town	v	Keswick	0-2
Gillford Park	v	British Steel	3-1	Carlisle United	v	Penrith	2-0
Cleator Moor C	v	N Vics/Whitehaven M	0-1	Workington	v	Whitehaven Amts	4-0
Northbank	v	Cockermouth	2-1	Gretna	v	Carleton Rovers	11-0

FOURTH ROUND

Heart of Liddlesdale	v	Workington	2-3	New Victoria	v	Carlisle United	0-6
Keswick	v	Gretna	0-3	Gillford Park	v	Northbank	3-2

SEMI-FINALS

Carlisle United	v	Gillford Park	1-2	Gretna	v	Workington	3-0

FINAL

24/4 & 5/5, P/P water-logged pitch at Carlisle United FC & Gillford Park FC

Gretna's team after their 2-1 win over Gillford Park in the Fianl of the Cumberland Senior Cup.
Back L-R: George Norrie (Coach), Dale Brotherton, Billy Bentley (Physio), Glen Johnstone, Richard Close, Jason Priestley, Mike McCartney, Tony Monaghan, Craig Potts, Shane Biro
Front L-R: Stuart Darley, Jamie Close, Duncan Armstrong, Carl Harwood, Les Armstrong, Craig Watson (Mascot), Paul Taylor

Photo: Alan Watson

DERBYSHIRE F.A.

Secretary: K Compton,
The Grandstand, Moorways Stadium, Moor Lane
Derby DE2 8FB Tel: (01332) 361422

DERBYSHIRE SENIOR CUP
(FOUNDED 1883-84)

RECENT FINALS

1991-92	Matlock Town	v	Stapenhill	3-1 (Agg)
1992-93	Ilkeston Town	v	Alfreton Town	1-1 (Agg) 7-6 (Pens)
1993-94	Gresley Rovers	v	Matlock Town	4-1 (Agg)
1994-95	Alfreton Town	v	Ilkeston Town	8-1 (Agg)
1995-96	Belper Town	v	Gresley Rovers	1-2

MOST WINS Derby County 15 Ilkeston Town 11 Buxton 8 Chesterfield 8 Heanor Town 8

1996-97
DERBYSHIRE SENIOR CUP

26 CLUBS **HOLDERS: GRESLEY ROVERS**

FIRST ROUND

Newhall United	v	Sth Normanton	0-0 0*1	Sandiacre Town	v	Holbrook	3-0
Rolls Royce	v	Sheepbridge	2-0	Shardlow St James	v	Heanor Town	0-2

SECOND ROUND

Mickleover RBL	v	Sth Normanton Ath	1-5	Shirebrook Town	v	Heanor Town	2-3
Mickleover Sports	v	Staveley M W	3-1	Stanton Ilkeston	v	Rolls Royce	1-2
Sandiacre Town	v	Blackwell M W	6-0	Graham St Prims	v	Long Eaton United	2-6

THIRD ROUND

Alfreton Town	v	Sandiacre Town	0V0 T-A	Heanor Town	v	Belper Town	0-2
Borrowash Victoria	v	Gresley Rovers	0-1	Glapwell	v	Buxton	0-2
Stapenhill	v	South Normanton Ath	2-1	Matlock Town	v	Mickleover Sports	4-3
Long Eaton United	v	Derby Rolls Royce	1-3	Ilkeston Town	v	Glossop North End	4-2

(Alfreton Town were found to have fielded an ineligible player and were eliminated with the Tie awarded to Sandiacre Town)

QUARTER-FINALS

Buxton	v	Ilkeston Town	1-5	Stapenhill	v	Matlock Town	0-3
Gresley Rovers	v	Belper Town	4-2	Sandiacre Town	v	Derby Rolls Royce	2-0

SEMI-FINALS

Gresley Rovers	v	Matlock Town	3-0	Sandiacre Town	v	Ilkeston Town	0-1

FINAL (First Leg)

ILKESTON TOWN v GRESLEY ROVERS 1-1

FINAL (Second Leg)

GRESLEY ROVERS v ILKESTON TOWN 2-1=3-2

DEVON F.A.

Secretary: Colin Squirrell,
Coach Road, Newton Abbot, Devon TQ12 1EJ
Tel: (01626) 332077 (County Office) Fax: (01626) 336814

DEVON ST LUKES COLLEGE CUP (FOUNDED 1981-82)

RECENT FINALS

1992-93	Tiverton Town	v	Clyst Rovers	3-0
1993-94	Tiverton Town	v	Bideford	1-0
1994-95	Tiverton Town	v	Bideford	5-1
1995-96	Bideford	v	Torrington	2-1

MOST WINS Tiverton Town 6 Bideford 3 Exmouth Town 3

1996-97 DEVON ST LUKES COLLEGE CUP

11 CLUBS **HOLDERS: BIDEFORD**

FIRST ROUND

Barnstaple Town	v	Crediton United	BT W-O	Exmouth Town	v	Clyst Rovers	0-4
Ilfracombe Town	v	Elmore	3-1				

SECOND ROUND

Bideford	v	Heavitree United	4-1	Dawlish Town	v	Tiverton Town	0-1
Ilfracombe Town	v	Barnstaple Town	*	Torrington	v	Exmouth Town	3-1

* No score given.

SEMI-FINALS

Bideford	v	Torrington	4V1 T-A	Barnstaple Town	v	Tiverton Town	0-2

(After winning the Semi-Final Tie Bideford were found to have fielded an ineligible player and were disqualified and the tie awarded to Torrington.)

FINAL

TIVERTON TOWN v TORRINGTON 6-0 at Ladysmead, Tiverton Town FC

DORSET F.A.

Secretary: P S Hough,
County Ground, Blandford Close, Hamworthy, Poole BH15 4BF
Tel: (01202) 682375 (County Office) Fax: (01202) 666577

DORSET SENIOR CUP
(FOUNDED 1887-88)

RECENT FINALS

1991-92	Wimborne Town	v	Bridport	1-0
1992-93	Weymouth	v	Poole Town	4-0
1993-94	Dorchester Town	v	Poole Town	1-0
1994-95	Hamworthy Eng	v	Poole Town	4-1
1995-96	Dorchester Town	v	St Pauls	3-1

MOST WINS Weymouth 24 Portland United 10 Bridport 9 Poole Town 9

1996-97
DORSET SENIOR CUP

20 CLUBS **HOLDERS: DORCHESTER TOWN**

FIRST ROUND

Bournemouth Sports	v	Blandford	2-1	Parley Sports	v	Hamworthy Engine	1-4
Portland United	v	Sherborne Town	3-1	Flight Refuelling	v	Sturminster Marshall	1V4

SECOND ROUND

Sturminster Newton	v	Wimborne Town	0-1	Bridport	v	Portland United	1-1 2-1
Gillingham Town	v	Hamworthy United	1-1 3-4	Hamworthy Eng FC	v	Flight Refuelling	1-0
Northerners Ath FC	v	Bournemouth Sports	1-3	Poole Town	v	Shaftesbury	2-6
Wareham Rangers	v	Allendale	3-1	Weymouth Sports	v	Swanage T & Herston	1V2

(Swanage Town & Herston were removed from the competition and Weymouth Sports re-instated)

THIRD ROUND

Wimborne Town	v	Weymouth Sports	6-0	Bridport	v	Hamworthy Eng'	1-3
Hamworthy United	v	Wareham Rangers	1-3	Shaftesbury	v	Bournemouth Sports	2-3

SEMI-FINALS

Wimborne Town	v	Hamworthy Engineering	3-1	Wareham Rangers	v	Bournemouth Sports	3-3 2-1

FINAL

WAREHAM R'GERS v WIMBORNE TOWN 0-2 at Dorchester Town FC

DURHAM F.A.

Secretary: J R Walsh,
'Codeslaw', Ferens Park, Durham DH1 1JZ
Tel: 091 384 8653 Fax: (01367) 242158

DURHAM CHALLENGE CUP (FOUNDED 1883-84)

RECENT FINALS

1991-92	Hebburn	v	Billingham Synthonia	2-1
1992-93	Murton	v	Bishop Auckland	2-1
1993-94	Spennymoor United	v	Bishop Auckland	2-2 (Rep 3-2)
1994-95	Spennymoor United	v	South Shields	1-1 (Rep 3-0)
1995-96	Durham City	v	Spennymoor United	0*1

MOST WINS Sunderland 21 Spennymoor United 15 Bishop Auckland 12

1996-97 DURHAM CHALLENGE CUP

45 CLUBS **HOLDERS: SPENNYMOOR UNITED**

PRELIMINARY ROUND

Horden C W	v	Evenwood Town	1-2
Ferryhill Athletic	v	Esh Winning	2-4
Nissan	v	Roker	3-0
Seaham Red Star	v	Ryhope C W	2-1
Washington	v	Billingham Synthonia	2-4
Cleadon	v	Wolviston	2-1
Jarrow	v	Norton & Stockton Anc	2-0
Washington Glebe	v	Cockfield	1-1 0-5
Eppleton C W	v	Hartlepool Utd 'A'	1-7
Hebburny	v	Peterlee	0-1
Ryhope C A	v	Easington	2-3
Shildon	v	Birtley Town	0-2
Annfield Plain	v	South Tyneside Utd	3-1
Hartlepool BWOB	v	Whickham	0-2
Stanley United	v	Willington	3-1
Darlington C S	v	Harton & Westoe	HW W-O

FIRST ROUND

Peterlee	v	Nissan	2-1
Chester Le St Tn	v	Billingham Town	2-4
Cleadon	v	Cockfield	1-3
Bishop Auckland	v	Seaham Red Star	5-1
Jarrow Roofing	v	Hartlepool Utd A	2-2 1-0
West Auckland T	v	Evenwood Town	2-1
Whickham	v	Spennymoor United	0-5
Jarrow	v	South Shields	2-0
Murton	v	Dunston F B	3-1
Brandon United	v	Esh Winning	1-0
Crook Town	v	Tow Law Town	0-0 1-3
Stanley United	v	Shotton Comrades	4-2
Annfield Plain	v	Consett	3-5
Durham City	v	Billingham Synth	1-1 1-0
Birtley Town	v	Easington Colliery	0-1
Harton & Westoe	v	Boldon C A	1-3

SECOND ROUND

Jarrow Roofing	v	Spennymoor United	1-3
Peterlee	v	Durham City	0-2
Jarrow	v	Easington Colliery	2-3
Tow Law Town	v	West Auckland Town	2-3
Bishop Auckland	v	Boldon C A	8-1
Cockfield	v	Billingham Town	1-0
Brandon United	v	Consett	0-2
Murton	v	Stanley United	5-1

THIRD ROUND

Easington Colliery	v	West Auckland Town	0-1
Consett	v	Spennymoor United	0-1
Durham City	v	Bishop Auckland	1-2
Murton	v	Cockfield	2-0

SEMI-FINALS

West Auckland Town	v	Bishop Auckland	1-6
Spennymoor Utd	v	Murton	3-1

FINAL

BISHOP AUCKLAND v SPENNYMOOR UTD 2-0 at Ferens Park, Durham County FA Ground

EAST RIDING F.A.

Secretary: D R Johnson,
52 Bethune Avenue, Hull HU4 7EJ
Tel: (01482) 641458 Fax: 01482 647512

EAST RIDING SENIOR CUP (FOUNDED 1903-04)

RECENT FINALS

1991-92	Bridlington Town	v	Schultz YC	2-1
1992-93	Bridlington Town	v	North Ferriby United	3-1
1993-94	Hall Road Rangers	v	Sculcoates Amateurs	1-0
1994-95	Sculcoates Amateurs	v	Hall Road Rangers	2-1
1995-96	Reckitts	v	Sculcoates Amateurs	1-2

MOST WINS Hull City 25 Bridlington Town 12 Bridlington Trinity 5 North Ferriby United 5

1996-97 EAST RIDING SENIOR CUP

21 CLUBS **HOLDERS: SCULCOATES AMATEURS**

FIRST ROUND

Haltemprice	v	Malet Lambert Y C	4-0
Beverley O G	v	Hall Road Rangers	0-3
Cottingham Sports	v	North Ferriby United	1-3
Dairycoates	v	Norland	4-1
AFC Reckitts	v	Filey Town	1-3

SECOND ROUND

Bulmans	v	Westella & Willerby	2-2 3-2
Ideal Standard	v	Haltemprice	0-3
North Ferriby Utd	v	Dairycoates	3-0
Filey Town	v	East Hull Amateurs	2-0
Kingburn	v	Anlaby United Protech	1-6
Hall Road Rangers	v	Sculcoates Amateurs	2-1
Hilder Foods	v	Smith & Nephew	HF W-O
Hull City AFC	v	Admiral Signs	3-0

THIRD ROUND

Filey Town	v	Hull City AFC	2-0
Haltemprice	v	Anlaby United Protech	5-0
Bulmans	v	North Ferriby United	3-4
Hall Road Rangers	v	Hider Foods	2-1

SEMI-FINALS

Haltemprice	v	Filey Town	0-2
Hall Road Rangers	v	North Ferriby Utd	2-6

Haltemprice v Filey Town at Quennsgate, Bridlington Town FC
Hall Road Rangers v North Ferriby Utd at Church Road, North Ferriby United FC

FINAL

FILEY TOWN v NORTH FERRIBY UTD 0-3 at Boothferry Park, Hull City AFC

EAST RIDING COUNTRY CUP

27 CLUBS **HOLDERS: WARD**

FIRST ROUND

Market Weighton	v	Ward	2-4
Holmpton United	v	Holme Rovers	1-6
Full Measure 2nd	v	Hornsea Town	HT W-O
Hilderthorpe	v	Bridlington Town	0-3
Bridlington Tn Ra	v	Bridlington Labour	0-2
Charles Dickens	v	Flamborough	4-3
Bridlington Rovers	v	Withernsea	0-6
Driffield E I	v	Rudston United	0-0 0-1
Viking Panthers	v	Crown	3-2
Full Measure	v	South Cave United	2-3
Brandesburton	v	Middleton Rovers	MR W-O

SECOND ROUND

Holme Rovers	v	Ward	1-3
Withernsea	v	Bridlington Labour C	0-4
North Cave	v	Shiptonthorpe Utd	2-0
Rudston United	v	Bridlington Town	1-3
Pack Horse	v	Middleton Rovers	2-1
Viking Panthers	v	Tickton	4-1
Filey Town 2nd	v	Charles Dickens	4-2
South Cave Utd	v	Hornsea Town	2-1

THIRD ROUND

Packhorse	v	Filey Town 2nd	3-2
North Cave	v	South Cave United	5-0
Ward	v	Viking Panthers	3-1
Bridlington Labour	v	Bridlington Town	1-2

SEMI-FINALS

Pack Horse	v	North Cave	3-7
Ward FC	v	Bridlington Town	0-4

Pack Horse v North Cave at Hutton Cranswick FC
Ward FC v Bridlington Town at Hunmanby United FC

FINAL

BRIDLINGTON TOWN v NORTH CAVE 1*0 at Queensgate, Bridlington Town FC

ESSEX F.A.

FOUNDED 1882

Secretary: T Alexander,
31 Mildmay Road, Chelmsford CM2 0DN
Tel: (01245) 357727

ESSEX SENIOR CUP
(FOUNDED 1883-84)

RECENT FINALS

1991-92	Redbridge Forest	v	Chelmsford City	3-0
1992-93	Chelmsford City	v	Wivenhoe Town	1-0
1993-94	Grays Athletic	v	Billericay Town	1-0
1994-95	Grays Athletic	v	Billericay Town	1-0
1995-96	Billericay Town	v	Braintree Town	1-2

MOST WINS Ilford 13 Walthamstow Avenue 12 Grays Athletic 8 Leyton 8

1996-97
ESSEX SENIOR CUP

46 CLUBS **HOLDERS: BRAINTREE TOWN**

PRELIMINARY ROUND

Ilford	v	East Ham United	1*4	Brentwood	v	Woodford Town	1-2
Southend Manor	v	Brightlingsea United	3*0	Eton Manor	v	Bowers United	0-4
Basildon United	v	Hullbridge Sports	2-0	Stanway Rovers@Wv		Waltham Abbey	2-1

FIRST ROUND

Basildon United	v	Stansted	2-0	Barkingside	v	Harwich & Parkeston	1-3
Bowers United	v	Concord Rangers	0-2	Ford United	v	Clacton Town	7-0
Maldon Town	v	Woodford Town	5-1	Burnham Ramblers	v	Saffron Walden Town	0-2
East Ham United	v	Stanway Rovers	1*3	Gt Wakering Rvrs	v	Southend Manor	0-1

SECOND ROUND

Aveley	v	Ford United	1-3	Saffron Walden T	v	Clapton	4*5
Hornchurch	v	Billericay Town	0-2	Tilbury	v	Purfleet	1-4
Braintree Town	v	Colchester United	3-1	Wivenhoe Town	v	Barking	3*3 5-1
Witham Town	v	Harlow Town	0-2	Concord Rangers	v	Stanway Rovers	2-1
Leyton Orient	v	Canvey Island @C	1*3	Tiptree United	v	Halstead Town	1-5
Heybridge Swifts	v	Grays Athletic	1-0	Harwich Parkeston	v	Southend United	2-3
East Thurrock Utd	v	Southend Manor	2-0	Dagenham & Rdge	v	C Row & Romford	1*2
Chelmsford City	v	Basildon United	2-0	Leyton Pennant	v	Maldon Town	4*3

THIRD ROUND

Wivenhoe Town	v	Braintree Town	0-2	Leyton Pennant	v	Purfleet	2-3
Southend United	v	Canvey Island	3-1	East Thurrock Utd	v	Concord Rangers	0-2
C Row & Romford	v	Clapton	2-1	Billericay Town	v	Harlow Town	4-2
Halstead Town	v	Ford United	3-4	Heybridge Swifts	v	Chelmsford City	1-0

FOURTH ROUND

Concord Rangers	v	Ford United	0-2	Southend United	v	Heybridge Swifts	5-2
Braintree Town	v	C Row & Romford	2-1	Billericay Town	v	Purfleet	2-3

SEMI-FINALS

Southend United	v	Purfleet	4-1	Ford United	v	Braintree Town	1-3

FINAL

BRAINTREE TOWN v SOUTHEND UNITED 1-2 at Victoria Road, Dagenham & Redbridge FC

ESSEX THAMES-SIDE TROPHY
(FOUNDED 1945-46)

RECENT FINALS

1991-92	Billericay Town	v	Ford United	2-2 (4-2 Pns)
1992-93	Leyton	v	Rainham Town	5-4
1993-94	Canvey Island	v	Grays Athletic	2-2 (4-3 Pns)
1994-95	Purfleet	v	Chelmsford City	2-0
1995-96	Canvey Island	v	Witham Town	5-0

MOST WINS Ilford 13 Walthamstow Avenue 12 Grays Athletic 8 Leyton 8

1996-97
ESSEX THAMES-SIDE TROPHY

25 CLUBS **HOLDERS: CANVEY ISLAND**

FIRST ROUND

Southend Manor	v	Waltham Abbey	4-2
Leyton Pennant	v	Concord Rangers	1-2
Barking	v	Burnham Ramblers	5-1
C Row & Romford	v	Aveley	2-1
Hornchurch	v	Basildon United	3p1 1*1
Clapton	v	East Thurrock Utd	2-3
Gr Waker'g Rovers	v	Ford United	2*3
Tiptree United	v	Tilbury	4-6
Barkingside	v	Billericay Town	1-4

SECOND ROUND

Purfleet	v	Grays Athletic	2-0
Hornchurch	v	C Row & Romford	0-2
Tilbury	v	East Thurrock Utd	0-2
Southend Manor	v	Barking	0*1
Witham Town	v	Ilford (b)	3-4
Chelmsford City	v	Ford United	3-1
Bowers United (b)	v	Canvey Island	2-5
Billericay Town	v	Concord Rangers	3-2

THIRD ROUND

Ilford	v	Billericay Town	1-0
Purfleet	v	Chelmsford City	1-0
Canvey Island	v	East Thurrock Utd	2-0
C Row & Romford	v	Barking	2-3

SEMI-FINALS

Ilford	v	Canvey Island	0-3
Barking	v	Purfleet	4-0

FINAL

CANVEY ISLAND v BARKING 7p8 1*1 at Canvey Island FC

1996-97
EAST ANGLIAN CUP

58 CLUBS **HOLDERS: HEYBRIDGE SWIFTS**

GROUP 1 FIRST ROUND

Sudbury Town	v	Mildenhall Town	0-2
Bury Town	v	Ipswich Wanderers	4-1
Cornard United	v	Felixstowe Port & Tn	1-0

SECOND ROUND

Mildenhall Town	v	Cornard United	2p4 0*0
Halstead Town**	v	Bury Town	4-2

** Bye to this round

GROUP FINAL

Cornard United	v	Halstead Town	0*1

GROUP 2 FIRST ROUND

Stamford	v	Spalding United	6-5
Bourne Town	v	Soham Town Rangers	2-0
Ely City	v	Holbeach United	4-3
March Town Utd	v	Wisbech Town	MTU W-O

SECOND ROUND

Stamford	v	Ely City	S W-O
March Town Utd	v	Bourne Town	4-3

GROUP FINAL

Stamford AFC	v	March Town United	3-0

GROUP 3 FIRST ROUND

Thetford Town	v	Swaftham Town	0-2
Dereham Town @M	v	Mulbarton United	1-4
Diss Town	v	Downham Town	6-3

SECOND ROUND

Swaffham Town	v	Diss Town	0-2
Fakenham Town**	v	Mulbarton United	0A0 1-3

GROUP FINAL

Diss Town	v	Mulbarton United	2-1

GROUP 4 FIRST ROUND

Ware	v	Stansted	2-1
Harlow Town	v	Sawbridgeworth Town	4-0
Letchworth	v	Royston Town	1-2

SECOND ROUND

Ware	v	Royston Town	6-2
Saffron Walden T**	v	Harlow Town	2-3

GROUP FINAL

Ware	v	Harlow Town	4-1

GROUP 5 FIRST ROUND

Somersham Town	v	St Ives Town	1-2
Biggleswade Town	v	Potton United	0-1
Cambridge City	v	Eynesbury Rovers	4*3
Histon	v	Warboys Town	3-2

SECOND ROUND

St Ives Town	v	Cambridge City	0-2
Histon	v	Potton United	1-3

GROUP FINAL

Cambridge City	v	Potton United	1-3

GROUP 6 FIRST ROUND

St Albans City	v	Collier Row & Romford	7-1
Barkingside	v	Hoddesdon Town	3-0
Ford United	v	Harpenden Town	2-0

SECOND ROUND

St Albans City	v	Ford United	1-2
Hertford Town	v	Barkingside	0-4

GROUP FINAL

Ford United	v	Barkingside	2-1

GROUP 7 FIRST ROUND

Hornchurch	v	Southend Manor	1-0
Aveley	v	Maldon Town	3-4
Burnham Ramblers	v	Concord Rangers	0-3

SECOND ROUND

Hornchurch	v	Concord Rangers	0-1
Gt Wakering Rovers	v	Maldon Town	2-0

GROUP FINAL

Concord Rangers	v	Gt Wakering Rovers	20

GROUP 8 FIRST ROUND

Wivenhoe Town	v	Tiptree United	4-1
Braintree Town	v	Witham Town	2-1
Clacton Town	v	Colchester United	0-2

SECOND ROUND

Wivenhoe Town	v	Colchester United	2-6
Harwich P'keston**	v	Braintree Town	0-2

GROUP FINAL

Colchester United	v	Braintree Town	1-0

COMPETITION PROPER QUARTER-FINALS

Ware	v	Halstead Town	1-3
Ford United	v	Colchester United	F W-O
Stamford	v	Diss Town	2*1
Potton United	v	Concord Rangers	5-1

SEMI-FINALS

Halstead Town	v	Stamford	0-1
Potton United	v	Ford United	3-1

FINAL

STAMFORD AFC	v	POTTON UNITED	0-2	at Stamford AFC

GLOUCESTERSHIRE F.A.

Secretary: E J Marsh,
46 Douglas Road, Horfield, Bristol BS7 0JD
Tel: 0117 951 9435

GLOUCESTERSHIRE SENIOR CUP
(FOUNDED 1936-37)
RECENT FINALS

1991-92	Cheltenham Town	v	Gloucester City	4-2 (AET)
1992-93	Gloucester City	v	Yate Town	3-2 (AET)
1993-94	Newport AFC	v	Gloucester City	1-0
1994-95	Cheltenham Town	v	Yate Town	1-1 (5-4 Pns)
1995-96	Cheltenham Town	v	Gloucester City	0-0 (3-1 Pns)

MOST WINS Cheltenham Town 30 Gloucester City 18 Forest Green Rovers 3

1996-97
GLOUCESTERSHIRE SENIOR CUP

6 CLUBS **HOLDERS: CHELTENHAM TOWN**

FIRST ROUND

Forest Grn Rovers	v	Cinderford Town	2-0	Cirencester Town	v	Yate Town	2-0

SEMI-FINALS

Gloucester City	v	Forest Green Rovers	3-0	Cirencester Town	v	Cheltenham Town	1-2

FINAL

GLOUCESTER CITY v CHELTENHAM TOWN 1-2 at Meadow Pk, Sudmeadow Rd, Gloucester City FC

GLOUCESTERSHIRE SENIOR TROPHY
(FOUNDED 1978-79)
RECENT FINALS

1991-92	Cheltenham Saracens	v	Vikings (Stroud)	6-5
1992-93	Hallen	v	Cinderford Town	4-1
1993-94	Mangotsfield United	v	Moreton Town	3-1 (AET)
1994-95	Shortwood United	v	Fairford Town	2-1
1995-96	Cirencester Town	v	Endsleigh	2*1

MOST WINS Mangotsfield United 5 Moreton Town 3 Shortwood United 2

1996-97
GLOUCESTERSHIRE SENIOR TROPHY

32 CLUBS **HOLDERS: CIRENCESTER TOWN**

FIRST ROUND

Stapleton	v	Almondsbury Town	0-4	Brockworth	v	Chelt'ham Saracens	2-2 3-0
Broadwell Amt	v	Ellwood	0-2	Cirencester Utd	v	Tuffley Rovers	2-1
Patchway Town	v	Wotton Rovers	2-4	Harrow Hill	v	Broad Plain House	4-1
Frampton Athletic	v	Pucklechurch Sports	6-1	Old Georgians	v	Shirehampton	0-2
Bitton	v	Bishops Cleeve	4-0	Mangotsfield Utd	v	St Marks C A	4-0
Dursley Town	v	Henbury Old Boys	2-0	D R G	v	Shortwood United	4*1
Cadbury Heath	v	Oldlands	1-3	Endsleigh @BMF	v	Bristol Manor Farm	7-2
Longwell Grn Abb	v	Fairford Town	2-3	Totterdown	v	Hallen	1-2

SECOND ROUND

Ellwood	v	Almondsbury Town	4-2	Fairford Town	v	Hallen	4-1
Wotton Rovers	v	Mangotsfield Town	1-3	Endsleigh	v	Oldlands	1-3
Harrow Hill	v	D R G	1-2	Bitton	v	Frampton Athletic	1-0
Shirehampton	v	Dursley Town	0-2	Brockworth	v	Cirencester United	2-1

THIRD ROUND

Mangotsfield United	v	Fairford Town	5-1	Oldlands	v	Ellwood	1-1 1-2
Bitton	v	Dursley Town	3-3 1-0	Brockworth	v	D R G	1-0

SEMI-FINALS

Bitton	v	Ellwood	6-1	Brockworth	v	Mangotsfield United	2-3
at Oldlands Park, Almondsbury Town FC				at Shortwood United FC			

FINAL

BITTON v MANGOTSFIELD UTD 2-3 at Oaklands Park, Almondsbury Town FC

HAMPSHIRE F.A.

Secretary: R G Barnes,
8 Ashwood Gardens, off Winchester Road
Southampton SO16 7PW Tel: 01703 79110

HAMPSHIRE SENIOR CUP
(FOUNDED 1887-88)

RECENT FINALS

1991-92	Waterlooville	v	Havant Town	1-0
1992-93	Fareham Town	v	Farnborough Town	4-1
1993-94	Havant Town	v	Farnborough Town	1-0
1994-95	Havant Town	v	Farnborough Town	1-0
1995-96	Basingstoke Town	v	Waterlooville	2-0

MOST WINS Southampton 13 Newport 7 Cowes 6

1996-97
HAMPSHIRE SENIOR CUP

48 CLUBS **HOLDERS: BASINGSTOKE TOWN**

FIRST ROUND

Totton	v	Christchurch	1-9	Bass Alton Town	v	Netley Central Sports	0-6
BAT Sports	v	Horndean	4-1	Brockenhurst	v	Petersfield Town	0-2
Colden Common	v	Hayling United	2-0	East Cowes Vics A	v	Liss Athletic	5-1
Gosport Borough	v	Hartley Wintney	2-0	Malshanger	v	Overton United	0-2
Moneyfields	v	Fleetlands	2-2 2-1	New Milton Town	v	A C Delco	4-0
New Street	v	Locksheath	0-2	Pirelli General	v	Romsey Town	3-0
Ryde	v	Bishopstoke Social	2-0	Stockbridge	v	Cove	1-4
Sylvans Sports	v	Blackfield & Langley	4-1	Whitchurch	v	Cowes Sports	2*2 0-4

SECOND ROUND

Aerostructures	v	Sylvans Sports	0-3	AFC Lymington	v	Portsmouth Royal N	3*2
Aldershot Town	v	Havant Town	1-0	Andover	v	Locks Heath	3*0
Bashley	v	Petersfield Town	4-1	Basingstoke Town	v	Cowes Sports	2-1
BAT Sports	v	Overton United	2-0	Christchurch	v	Coldon Common	2*2 O9N
Cove	v	DCA Basingstoke	4-1	East Cowes Vics A	v	Eastleigh	2-0
Fareham Town	v	Moneyfields	2-0	Farnborough Town	v	Fleet Town	4*3
New Milton Town	v	Waterlooville	1-5	Newport IoW	v	Pirelli General	3-0
Ryde	v	Gosport Borough	4-1	Winchester City	v	Netley Central Sports	3-2

THIRD ROUND

AFC Lymingon	v	Colden Common	2-0	Aldershot Town	v	Basingstoke Town	0-2
Andover	v	Winchester City	2-0	Cove	v	Waterlooville	0-4
East Cowes Vics Ath	v	Bashley	1-5	Farnborough Town	v	BAT Sports	6-0
Newport IoW	v	Sylvans Sports	7-0	Ryde	v	Fareham Town	3-1

FOURTH ROUND

Lymington	v	Bashley	1-3	Andover @W	v	Waterlooville	0A2 2-3
Farnborough Town	v	Newport IoW	2*0	Ryde	v	Basingstoke Town	0-1

SEMI-FINALS

Farnborough Town	v	Basingstoke Town	1-2	Waterlooville	v	Bashley	3-1

FINAL

BASINGSTOKE TN	v	WATERLOOVILLE	2-0	at The Dell, Southampton FC

Basingstoke Town after victory over Farnborough in the Hampshire Cup Semi-Final. Also, leaders in ICIS Division I

Photo: Eric Marsh

HEREFORDSHIRE F.A.

Secretary: E R Prescott,
7 Kirkland Close, Hampton Park, Hereford HR1 1XP

HEREFORDSHIRE SENIOR CUP
(FOUNDED 1973-74)

RECENT FINALS

1991-92	Westfields	v	Pegasus Juniors	5-0
1992-93	Hinton	v	Westfields	3-1
1993-94	Hinton	v	Pegasus Juniors	1-1 (Rep 3-2)
1994-95	Hinton	v	Pegasus Juniors	4-1
1995-96	Ross Town	v	Westfields	2-2 (2-4 Pns)

1996-97
HEREFORDSHIRE SENIOR CUP

16 CLUBS

HOLDERS: WESTFIELDS

FIRST ROUND

Pegasus Juniors	v	Golden Valley	2-0	Ross Town	v	Dorstone United	8-0
Ewyas Harold	v	Hereford Lads Club	2-5	Bromyard Town	v	Westfields	2-1
Wellington	v	Weston	3-6	Kington Town	v	Hinton	4-2
Fownhope	v	Woofferton	4-5	Leominster	v	Ledbury Town	4-4 1-4

SECOND ROUND

Hereford Lads Club	v	Bromyard	0-3	Ledbury Town	v	Pegasus Juniors	4*3
Ross Town	v	Woofferton	2-1	Kington Town	v	Weston	10-0

SEMI-FINALS

Bromyard Town	v	Kington Town	1-3	Ledbury Town	v	Ross Town	4-1

FINAL

BROMYARD TOWN v LEDBURY TOWN 3-0 at Edgar Street, Hereford United FC

HERTFORDSHIRE F.A.

Secretary: R G Kibble,
4 The Wayside, Leverstock Green
Hemel Hempstead HP3 8NR

HERTFORDSHIRE SENIOR CUP
(FOUNDED 1886-87)

RECENT FINALS

1991-92	Barnet	v	Hemel Hempstead	4-1
1992-93	Barnet	v	Watford	4-2
1993-94	Watford	v	Stevenage Borough	3-1
1994-95	Watford	v	St Albans City	4-0
1995-96	Barnet	v	Watford	2-1

MOST WINS Hitchin Town 20 Barnet 16 Watford 14

1996-97 HERTFORDSHIRE SENIOR CUP

22 CLUBS **HOLDERS: BARNET**

FIRST ROUND

Cheshunt	v	Harpenden Town	1-2	Hitchin Town	v	Hemel Hempstead	9-0
Bishops Stortford	v	Letchworth	10-1	Sawbridgeworth Tn	v	Ware	3-5
Potters Bar Town	v	Tring Town	2-0	Boreham Wood	v	Berkhamsted Town	5-1

SECOND ROUND

Royston Town	v	Barnet	3*4	Hitchin Town	v	Potters Bar Town	3-0
Baldock Town	v	Watford	0-1	Stevenage Boro	v	Ware	1*2
Harpenden Town	v	Boreham Wood	0-1	St Albans City	v	Hertford Town	6-5
Bishop's Stortford	v	Welwyn Garden City	2-4	London Colney	v	Hoddesdon Town	1-0

THIRD ROUND

Hitchin Town	v	Welwyn Gdn City	0A0 4-0	Barnet	v	Watford	2-0
St Albans City	v	Boreham Wood	1-3	Ware	v	London Colney	1-2

SEMI-FINALS

Boreham Wood	v	Barnet	2-1	London Colney	v	Hitchin Town	0-3

FINAL

BOREHAM WOOD	v	HITCHIN TOWN	1-4	at Clarence Park, St Albans City FC

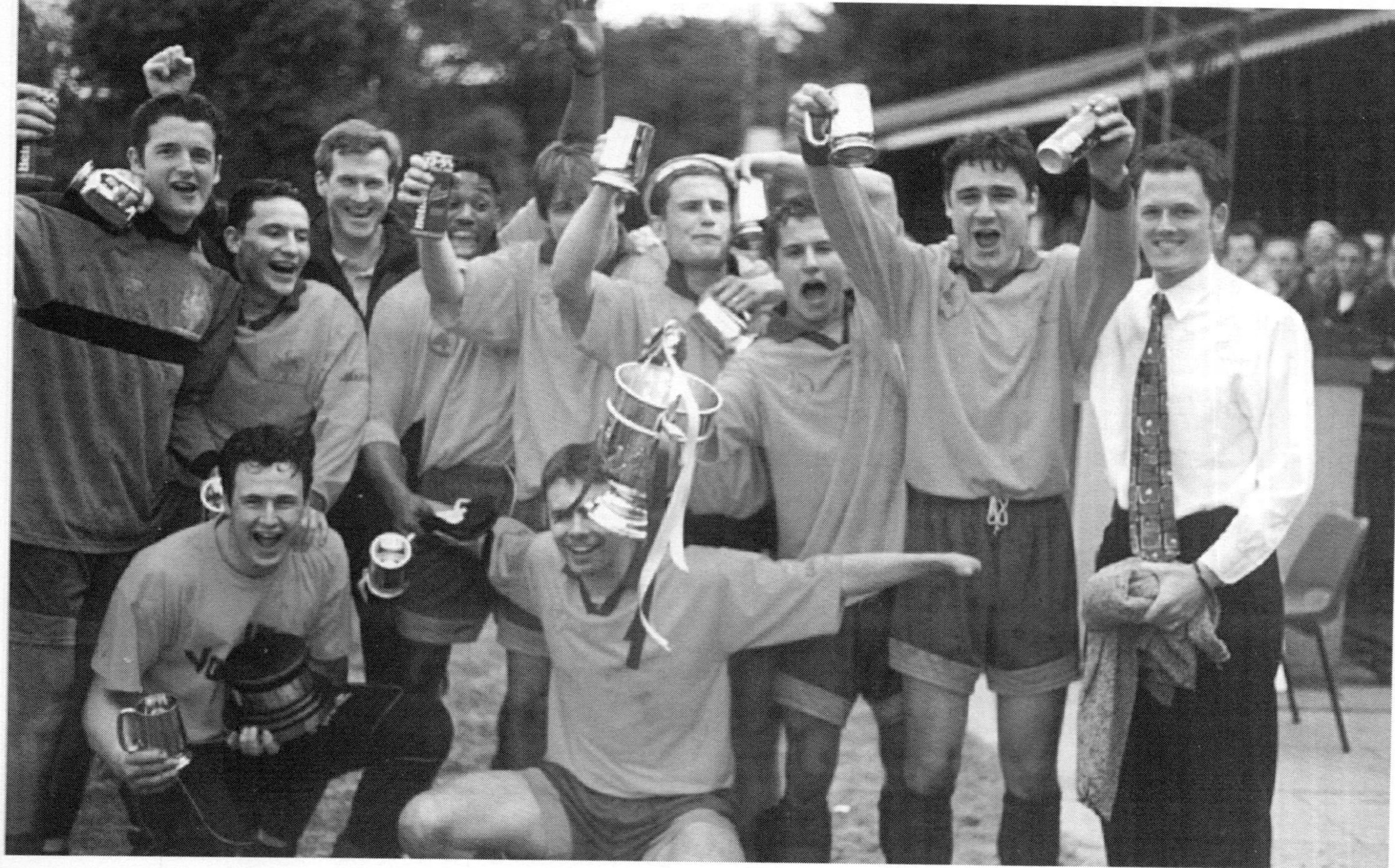

Hitchin Town: Winners of the 1997 Herfordshire Senior Cup

HERTFORDSHIRE CHARITY SHIELD

(FOUNDED 1919-20)

RECENT FINALS

1991-92	Letchworth Gdn City	v	Leverstock Green	1-0
1992-93	Sawbridgeworth Town	v	Leverstock Grn	1-1 (6-5 Pns)
1993-94	London Colney	v	Hoddesdon Town	2-0
1994-95	Sawbridgeworth Town	v	Welwyn Gdn C	2-2 (4-2 Pns)
1995-96	Town	v	Town	0-0

MOST WINS Hertford Town 6 Ware 6 Berkhamstead Town 5

1996-97 HERTFORDSHIRE CHARITY SHIELD

13 CLUBS **HOLDERS: SAWBRIDGEWORTH TOWN**

FIRST ROUND

Potters Bar Town	v	Harpenden Town	2-0
Letchworth	v	Tring Athletic	1-2
Elliott Star	v	Met Police Bushey	5-2
Leverstock Green	v	Sawbridgeworth Town	1-2
Royston Town	v	Hoddesdon Town	3-0

SECOND ROUND

Welwyn Garden City	v	London Colney	3-1
St Margaretsbury	v	Sawbridgeworth Town	3-1
Elliott Star @BW	v	Royston Town	4*5
Tring Athletic	v	Potters Bar Town	5-4

SEMI-FINALS

St Margaretsbury @R	v	Royston Town	6p7 0*0
Welwyn Gdn City	v	Tring Athletic	2-0

FINAL

ROYSTON TOWN v WELWYN GDN CITY 2-1 at Welwyn Garden City FC

Stevenage Borough after victory over St Albans City in the Hertfordshire Charity Cup Final at St Albans on 10th August 1996.

Photo: Eric Marsh

1996-97
HERTFORDSHIRE CENTENARY TROPHY

21 CLUBS **HOLDERS: COLNEY HEATH**

FIRST ROUND

Cuffley	v	Tring Athletic	3-1	Met Police Bushey	v	Leverstock Green	1-2
Bedmond S & S	v	Sandridge Rovers	5-1	North Mymms	v	Welwyn	3-0
Sun Postal Sports	v	Kings Langley	1-0				

SECOND ROUND

Leverstock Green	v	Wormley Rovers	1-2	Bedmond Sports	v	North Mymms	1*0
Oxhey Jets	v	Cuffley	0-1	Somersett A V&E	v	Bovingdon	3-2
Colney Heath	v	Agrevo Sports	2-1	Elliott Star	v	Walkern	9-1
St Peters	v	St Margaretsbury	3-2	Sun Postal Sports	v	Chipperfield Corinthians	3-0

THIRD ROUND

Cuffley	v	Elliott Star	2-0	Somersett A V&E	v	Bedmond Sports	4-1
St Peters	v	Colney Heath	1-3	Sun Postal Sports	v	Wormley Rovers	6-2

SEMI-FINALS

Cuffley	v	Colney Heath	0-2	Sun Postal Sports	v	Somersett Ambury V&E	1-3

FINAL

SOMERSETT A V&E v COLNEY HEATH 1-3 at Wadson Park, Ware FC

1996-97
HERTFORDSHIRE CHARITY CUP

11 CLUBS **HOLDERS: STEVENAGE BOROUGH**

FIRST ROUND

Berkhamsted Town	v	Ware	1-2	Hitchin Town	v	Hertford Town	2-0
Bishop's Stortford	v	Hemel Hempstead	3-1				

SECOND ROUND

Baldock Town	v	Cheshunt	6-1	Ware	v	Tring Town	1-0
St Albans City	v	Bishop's Stortford		Stevenage Boro	v	Hitchin Town	4-2

SEMI-FINALS

Bishop's Stortford	v	Stevenage Borough	1-0	Baldock Town	v	Ware	W W-O

FINAL

BISHOP'S ST'FORD v WARE 4-0 at Bishop's Stortford FC

HUNTINGDONSHIRE F.A.

Secretary: Maurice Armstrong,
1 Chapel End, Gt Gidding, Huntingdon
Cambs PE17 5NP Tel: 01832 293262 (County Office)

HUNTINGDONSHIRE SENIOR CUP
(FOUNDED 1888-89)

RECENT FINALS

1991-92	Eynesbury Rovers	v	Ramsey Town	3-0
1992-93	Eynesbury Rovers	v	Warboys Town	4-2
1993-94	Somersham Town	v	Ortonians	1-0
1994-95	Warboys Town	v	Godmanchester Rovers	2-1
1995-96	Eynesbury Rovers	v	Warboys Town	3*2

MOST WINS St Neots 33 Eynesbury Rovers 12 Huntingdon Town 12

1996-97
HUNTINGDONSHIRE SENIOR CUP

13 CLUBS **HOLDERS: EYNESBURY ROVERS**

FIRST ROUND

Ramsey Town	v	St Neots Town	4-2
Alconbury	v	Huntingdon United	0-1
Yaxley	v	Warboys Town	2*2 1-2
Bluntisham Rngrs	v	Eynesbury Rovers	1-3
Somersham Town	v	Godmanchester Rovers	2*1

SECOND ROUND

Warboys Town	v	Ramsey Town	2-3
St Ives Town	v	Huntingdon United	1-3
Hotpoint	v	Eynesbury Rovers	3*2
Somersham Town	v	Ortonians	2-7

SEMI-FINALS

Ortonians	v	Hotpoint	2-0
Huntingdon United	v	Ramsey Town	HU W-O

FINAL

HUNTINGDON UTD v ORTONIANS 1-2 at Warboys FC

KENT F.A.

Secretary: K T Masters,
69 Maidstone Road, Chatham, Kent ME4 6DT
Tel: 01634 843824

KENT SENIOR CUP (FOUNDED 1888-89)

RECENT FINALS

1991-92	Bromley	v	Hythe Town	3-1
1992-93	Ashford Town	v	Bromley	3-2
1993-94	Margate	v	Dover Athletic	3-2
1994-95	Charlton Athletic	v	Gillingham	4-2
1995-96	Ashford Town	v	Charlton Athletic	3-0

MOST WINS Maidstone United 15 Dartford 9 Northfleet United 9

1996-97 KENT FACIT SENIOR CUP

13 CLUBS **HOLDERS: ASHFORD TOWN**

FIRST ROUND

Erith & Belvedere	v	Dover Athletic	1-4
Gravesend & N'fleet	v	Sittingbourne	0-1
Margate	v	Bromley	0-1
Tonbridge	v	Dartford	1-0
Fisher	v	Welling United	2*1

QUARTER-FINALS

Tonbridge Angels	v	Gillingham	2-3
Bromley	v	Sittingbourne	0A0 5-0
Fisher London	v	Ashford Town	1-0
Dover Athletic	v	Charlton Athletic	1-0

SEMI-FINALS

Dover Athletic	v	Fisher London	2*1
Bromley	v	Gillingham	3-1

FINAL

BROMLEY v DOVER ATHLETIC 4-1 at The New Den, Millwall FC

KENT SENIOR TROPHY (FOUNDED 1874-75)

RECENT FINALS

1991-92	Slade Green	v	Tunbridge Wells	3-1
1992-93	Cray Wanderers	v	Whitstable Town	1-0
1993-94	Alma Swanley	v	Folkestone Invicta	3-1
1994-95	Deal Town	v	Folkestone Invicta	2-2 (5-4 Pns)
1995-96	Dartford	v	Chatham Town	3-0

MOST WINS Alma Swanley 2 Corinthian 2 Faversham Town 2 Fisher Athletic 2 Ramsgate 2

1996-97 KENT PLAAYA SENIOR TROPHY

HOLDERS: DARTFORD

FIRST ROUND

Faversham Town	v	Teynham & Lynsted	2-1
West Wickham	v	Woolwich Town	2*1
Sevenoaks Town	v	Thames Polytechnic	4-0
Ramsgate	v	Tunbridge Wells	1-0
Cray Wanderers	v	Beckenham Town	0*0 3-0
Egerton	v	Folkestone Invicta	4-1
Corinthian	v	Herne Bay	1-2
Deal Town	v	Thamesmead Town	1*3
Furness	v	Hythe United	4-0
Canterbury City	v	Crockenhill	2-0

SECOND ROUND

Chatham Town	v	Thamesmead Town	2-0
Sheppey United	v	Furness	1-2
Greenwich Borough	v	Faversham Town	4-1
Herne Bay	v	Egerton	2-0
West Wickham	v	Lordswood	0-2
Slade Green	v	Sevenoaks Town SG+	W-O
Ramsgate	v	Canterbury City	1-2
Whitstable Town	v	Cray Wanderers	2-1

THIRD ROUND

Furness	v	Lordswood	2-0
Greenwich Borough	v	Canterbury City	9-0
Slade Green	v	Herne Bay	0-3
Whitstable Town	v	Chatham Tn	8p9 1*1 1*1

SEMI-FINALS

Chatham Town	v	Herne Bay	3p4 1*1 1*1
Greenwich Boro	v	Furness	1-0

FINAL

GREENWICH BORO v HERNE BAY 0-2 at Welling United FC

Bromley F.C.: Winners of the 1997 Kent Senior Cup

Photo: K Gillard

LANCASHIRE F.A.

Founded: 28th September 1878
Hon. Secretary: J Kenyon, ACIS,
Northbank, 31a Wellington Street (St Johns), Blackburn BB1 8AU
Tel: 01254 24433 (County Office) Fax: 01254 260095

LANCASHIRE CHALLENGE TROPHY (FOUNDED 1885-86)

RECENT FINALS

1991-92	Gt Harwood Town	v	Southport	3-2
1992-93	Southport	v	Chorley	5-2 (AET)
1993-94	Morecambe	v	Southport	4-3 (AET)
1994-95	Bamber Bridge	v	Morecambe	2-1
1995-96	Bamber Bridge	v	Morecambe	0-1

1996-97
LANCASHIRE ATS TROPHY

25 CLUBS **HOLDERS: MORECAMBE**

FIRST ROUND

Accrington Stanley	v	Blackpool Rovers	6-1
Burscough	v	Atherton Collieries	4-2
Holker O B	v	Nelson	3-2
Leigh RMI	v	Bacup Borough	4-0
Rossendale United	v	Castleton Gabriels	0-3
Atherton L R	v	Daisy Hill	1-0
Darwen	v	Skelmersdale United	0-4
Lancaster City	v	Blackpool Mechanics	9-1
Marine	v	Great Harwood Town	0-1

SECOND ROUND

Accrington Stanley	v	Skelmersdale United	3-1
Burscough	v	Leigh RMI	1-0
Holker Old Boys	v	Great Harwood Tn	2*2 1-3
Radcliffe Borough	v	Barrow	0-1
Bamber Bridge	v	Castleton Gabriels	5-0
Chorley	v	Atherton L Rovers	1-2
Morecambe	v	Clitheroe	5-0
Southport	v	Lancaster City	3-2

THIRD ROUND

Accrington Stanley	v	Barrow	4-1
Burscough	v	Southport	0-0 0-6
Atherton L Rovers	v	Bamber Bridge	1-2
Morecambe	v	Great Harwood Town	2*3

SEMI-FINALS

Accrington Stanley	v	Great Harwood Town	2-1
Bamber Bridge	v	Southport	1-3

FINAL

ACCRINGTON STA. v SOUTHPORT 0-3 at Deepdale, Preston North End FC

LEICESTERSHIRE F.A.

Hon. Secretary: Ron E Barston,
Holmes Park, Dog & Gun Lane, Whetstone LE8 3LJ
Tel: 0116 288 0312 (Home) 0116 286 7828 (County Office) Fax: 0116 286 7828

LEICESTERSHIRE SENIOR CUP
(FOUNDED 1887-88)

RECENT FINALS

1991-92	Friar Lane Old Boys	v	Lutterworth Town	1-0
1992-93	Friar Lane Old Boys	v	Birstall United	2-1 (AET)
1993-94	Ibstock Welfare	v	St Andrews SC	2-1
1994-95	Anstey Nomads	v	Holwell Sports	2-0
1995-96	Leicester City	v	St Andrews	2-1

MOST WINS Leicester City 27 Enderby Town 6 Shepshed Dynamo 6

1996-97 LEICESTERSHIRE 'JELSON HOMES' SENIOR CUP

42 CLUBS **HOLDERS: BIRSTALL UNITED**

FIRST ROUND

Syston St Peters	v	Huncote S & S	2-3
United Collieries	v	Barlestone St Giles	1-0
Newfoundpool	v	Houghton Rangers	3-1
Thringstone M W	v	Cottesmore Amateurs	0-4
Bardon Hill Sports	v	Kirby Muxloe SC	2-3
Lutterworth Town	v	Fosse Imps	1-2
Narb' & L'thorpe	v	Aylestone Park OB	2-3
Saffron Dynamo	v	Highfield Rangers	2-1
North Kilworth	v	Ibstock Welfare	0-1
Coalville	v	Downes Sports	1-3

SECOND ROUND

Stony Stanton	v	Leicester YMCA	2-2 1-0
Saffron Dynamo	v	Friar Lane O B	3-4
Barrow Town	v	Aylestone Park O B	1-3
Barwell	v	Cottesmore Amateurs	3-1
Kirby Muxlow SC	v	St Andrews	2-2 2-1
Loughborough D'	v	Earl Shilton Albion	1-0
United Collieries	v	Asfordby Amateurs	2-3
Huncote Sports	v	Slack & Parr	2-0
Pedigree Petfoods	v	Newfoundpool WMC	1-5
Leics Constabulary	v	Oadby Town	0-3
Holwell Sports	v	Hemington	4-2
Birstall United	v	Anstey Nomads	4-2
Ibstock Welfare	v	Sileby Town	4-0
Anstey Town	v	Downes Sports	1-1 0-3
Quorn	v	Fosse Imps	1-1 1-0
Blaby & Whetstone	v	Harborough Tn Imps	1-1 0-1

THIRD ROUND

Aylestone Park	v	Birstall United	1-2
Loughborough D'mo	v	Ibstock Welfare	2-1
Harborough Tn Imps	v	Stoney Stanton	5-4
Quorn	v	Asfordby Amateurs	3-4
Friar Lane O B	v	Downes Sports	4-2
Kirby Muxloe	v	Holwell Sports	2-2 0*0
Huncote Sports	v	Newfoundpool	2-2 1-3
Oadby Town	v	Barwell	0-3

FOURTH ROUND

Asfordby Amateurs	v	Kirby Muxloe	0-1
Birstall United	v	Barwell	0-1
Friar Lane O B	v	Harborough Town Imps	4-1
Loughboro' D'mo	v	Newfoundpool	2-2 2-1

SEMI-FINALS

Friar Lane Old Boys	v	Kirby Muxloe	4-1
at Quorn FC			
Barwell	v	Loughborough Dynamo	4-1
at Friar Lane Old Boys FC			

FINAL

BARWELL v FRIAR LANE O B 1*0 at Holmes Park, Whetstone, Leics FA

1996-97 LEICESTERSHIRE WESTERBY CHALLENGE CUP

12 CLUBS **HOLDERS: LEICESTER CITY**

FIRST ROUND

Quorn	v	Ibstock Welfare	3-1
Barwell	v	Birstall United	2-0
Oadby Town	v	Anstey Nomads	2-1
Hinckley Town	v	Hinckley Athletic	2-1

SECOND ROUND

Quorn	v	Barwell	1-2
Hinckley Town	v	Leicester City	1-4
Shepshed Dynamo	v	Friar Lane O B	4-1
Oadby Town	v	St Andrews	0-4

SEMI-FINALS

Barwell	v	Shepshed Dynamo	4p5 1*1
at Holmes Park, Leicestershire FA			
St Andrews	v	Leicester City	2-1
at Holmes Park, Leicestershire FA			

FINAL

ST ANDREWS v SHEPSHED D'MO 4p3 3*3 at Filbert Street, Leicester City FC

LINCOLNSHIRE F.A.

Hon. Secretary: Mr F S Richardson,
PO Box 26, 12 Dean Road, Lincoln LN2 4DP
Tel: 01522 524917 (County Office) Fax: 01522 528859

LINCOLNSHIRE SENIOR CUP
(FOUNDED 1935-36)

RECENT WINNERS

1991-92	Grimsby Town
1992-93	Grimsby Town
1993-94	Grimsby Town
1994-95	Grimsby Town
1995-96	Grimsby Town

MOST WINS Grimsby Town 13 Lincoln City 12 Boston United 5

1996-97
LINCOLNSHIRE SENIOR CUP

7 CLUBS **HOLDERS: GRIMSBY TOWN**

FIRST ROUND

Gainsborough Trinity	v	Grimsby Town	0-1	Boston United	v	Scunthorpe United	0-2
Lincoln United	v	Lincoln City	1-0				

SEMI-FINALS

Scunthorpe United	v	Lincoln United	2-1	Grantham Town	v	Grimsby Town	0-3

FINAL

SCUNTHORPE UTD v GRIMSBY TOWN 8p7 3*3 at Glanford Park, Doncaster Rd, Scunthorpe

LINCOLNSHIRE SENIOR 'A' CUP
(FOUNDED 1968-69)

RECENT FINALS

1991-92	Nettleham	v	Lincoln United	3-1
1992-93	Mirrlees Blackstone	v	Bourne Town	1-1 (AET)
1993-94	Brigg Town	v	Lincoln United	5-2
1994-95	Holbeach United	v	Boston Town	1-0
1995-96	Lincoln United	v	Boston Town	2*1

MOST WINS Boston Town 6 Holbeach United 4 Skegness Town 4

1996-97
LINCOLNSHIRE SENIOR 'A' CUP

10 CLUBS **HOLDERS: LINCOLN UNITED**

PRELIMINARY ROUND

Holbeach United	v	Boston Town	2-1	Spalding United	v	Brigg Town	3-2

FIRST ROUND

Stamford AFC	v	Holbeach United	5-1	Nettleham	v	Winterton Rangers	5-4
Spalding United	v	Mirrlees Blackstone	2-0	Louth United	v	Bourne Town	4-2

SEMI-FINALS

Spalding United	v	Nettleham	1-2	Stamford AFC	v	Louth United	1-2

FINAL

LOUTH UNITED v NETTLEHAM 0-2 at Louth United FC

LINCOLNSHIRE SENIOR 'B' CUP
(FOUNDED 1949-50)

RECENT FINALS

1991-92	Harrowby United	v	Hykeham Town	3-0
1992-93	Appleby Frod Ath	v	Humberside United	1-1 (11-10 P)
1993-94	Wyberton	v	Hykeham Town	2-2 (4-1 Pns)
1994-95	Immingham Blos Way	v	Limestone Rangers	3-0
1995-96	Appleby Frod Ath	v	Barton Old Boys	0-2

MOST WINS Brigg Town 5 Appleby Frodingham Athletic 4

1996-97
LINCOLNSHIRE SENIOR 'B' CUP

16 CLUBS **HOLDERS: BARTON OLD BOYS**

FIRST ROUND

Sleaford Town	v	Horncastle Town	2-0
Barton Old Boys	v	Hykeham Town	4-2
Skegness Town	v	Bottesford Town	2-1
Wyberton	v	Grimsby Imm Amt	1-2
Lincoln Moorlands	v	Louth Old Boys	6-0
Harrowby United	v	Ruston Sports	5-2
Appleby Frod'ham	v	Epworth Town LC	5-0
Lymstone Rangers	v	Deeping Rangers	2-0

SECOND ROUND

Sleaford Town	v	Skegness Town	5-0
Barton Old Boys	v	Appleby Frodingham	2-1
Lincoln Moorlands	v	Harrowby United	2-1
Lymstone Rangers	v	Grimsby-Immingham	2-1

SEMI-FINALS

Lincoln Moorlands	v	Sleaford Town	4-2
Barton Old Boys	v	Lymstone Rangers	0-1

FINAL

LINCOLN MRLANDS v LYMSTONE RNGRS 4-0 at Sincil Bank, Lincoln City FC

LIVERPOOL F.A.

Secretary: Fred Hunter
23 Greenfield Road, Liverpool L13 3BN Tel: 01514 27179
Tel: 01512 206089 (County Office) Fax: 0151 2200573

LIVERPOOL SENIOR CUP
(FOUNDED 1977-78)

RECENT FINALS

1991-92	Tranmere Rovers	v	Marine	4-1
1992-93	Southport	v	Burscough	2-1
1993-94	Marine	v	Southport	2-1
1994-95	Tranmere Rovers	v	Marine	2-0 (AET)
1995-96	Everton	v	Tranmere Rovers	Await

details

MOST WINS Marine 5 Liverpool 3 South Liverpool 3

1996-97
LIVERPOOL SENIOR CUP

12 CLUBS **HOLDERS: EVERTON**

FIRST ROUND

Bootle	v	Marine	3-1	Burscough	v	Skelmersdale United	5-1
Knowsley United	v	St Helens Town	1-0	Southport	v	Warrington Town	7-0

SECOND ROUND

Burscough	v	Liverpool	1-2	Southport	v	Tranmere Rovers	3-3 1-2
Everton	v	Prescot Cables	1-0	Bootle	v	Knowsley United	3*4

SEMI-FINALS

Liverpool	v	Everton	tba	Tranmere Rovers	v	Knowsley United	3-1

FINAL

TRANMERE RVRS v LIVERPOOL / EVERTON Awaiting details

Price Patrick & Associates Ltd
The Grange Longmoor Grange
Wokingham
Berks RG40 4EU

Telephone 0118 973 4173
Sponsors

Attention Barrie Whitford/Joseph Brown

CRC
For: Non League
Club Directory

Reference

Tony Williams
Publications Ltd
Helland
North Curry
Taunton TA3 6DU

LONDON F.A.

Secretary: David Fowkes,
Aldworth Grove, London SE13 6HY
Tel: 0181 690 9626 (County Office) Fax: 0181 690 9471

LONDON CHALLENGE CUP (FOUNDED 1990-91)

RECENT FINALS

1991-92	Welling United	v	Dulwich Hamlet	2-0
1992-93	Leyton Orient	v	Barnet	3-2
1993-94	Uxbridge	v	Welling United	3-0
1994-95	St Albans City	v	Fisher	6-0
1995-96	Bromley	v	Leyton Pennant	3*2

1996-97 LONDON CHALLENGE CUP

16 CLUBS **HOLDERS: BROMLEY**

FIRST ROUND

Dulwich Hamlet	v	Metropolitan Police	2-1
Hampton	v	Barking	1-3
Hendon	v	Bromley	2-0
Collier R & Romford	v	Uxbridge	1-4
Tooting & Mitcham	v	Erith & Belvedere	3-0
Leyton Pennant	v	Welling United	1-0
Fisher	v	Boreham Wood	1-2
St Albans City	v	Croydon	4-2

SECOND ROUND

Boreham Wood	v	Tooting & Mitcham	1-2
Barking	v	Hendon	4-3
St Albans City	v	Uxbridge	0-2
Dulwich Hamlet	v	Leyton Pennant	1-2

SEMI-FINALS

Tooting & Mitcham	v	Leyton Pennant	1*1 0-2
Uxbridge	v	Barking	3-2

FINAL

LEYTON PENNANT	v	UXBRIDGE	3-3 0-1	at Craven Cottage, Fulham FC, replay at Hendon FC

LONDON SENIOR CUP (FOUNDED 1887-88)

RECENT FINALS

1991-92	Hanwell Town	v	Croydon Athletic	4-3
1992-93	Hanwell Town	v	Brimsdown Rovers	4-3
1993-94	Ford United	v	Hanwell Town	2-1
1994-95	Wingate & Finchley	v	Tower Hamlets	4-3
1995-96	Kingsbury Town	v	Tottenham Omada	1-2

MOST WINS Walthamstow Avenue 9 Ilford 7 Enfield 6

1996-97 LONDON SENIOR CUP

25 CLUBS **HOLDERS: TOTTENHAM OMADA**

FIRST ROUND

Southall	v	Barkingside	0-4
Bedfont	v	Haringey Borough	4-0
Woolwich Town	v	Corinthian Casuals	1-0
Wingate & Finchley	v	Waltham Abbey	3-2
Hanwell Town	v	Civil Service	1-3
Ford United	v	Hoddesdon Town	2-0
Thames Polytech.	v	St Mary's Islington	2-1
Cockfosters	v	Croydon Athletic	7-0
Cray Wanderers	v	Thamesmead Town	0-2

SECOND ROUND

Ford United	v	Kingsbury Town	5-1
Clapton	v	Woodford Tn	3p2 1*1 0*0
Thames Polytechnic	v	Hillingdon Borough	0-2
Cockfosters	v	East Ham United	3-1
Woolwich Town	v	Thamesmead Town	1*0
Brimsdown Rovers	v	Wingate & Finchley	2-2 1-2
Bedfont	v	Barkingside	3-6
Civil Service	v	Tottenham Omada	0-1

THIRD ROUND

Tottenham Omada	v	Clapton	C W-O
Hillingdon Borough	v	Wingate & Finchley	2-1
Ford United	v	Barkingside	3-4
Cockfosters	v	Woolwich Town	2-1

SEMI-FINALS

Clapton	v	Barkingside	0*0 1-2
Hillingdon Borough	v	Cockfosters	1-0

FINAL

BARKINGSIDE	v	HILLINGDON BORO	2-0	at Imber Court, Metropolitan Police FC

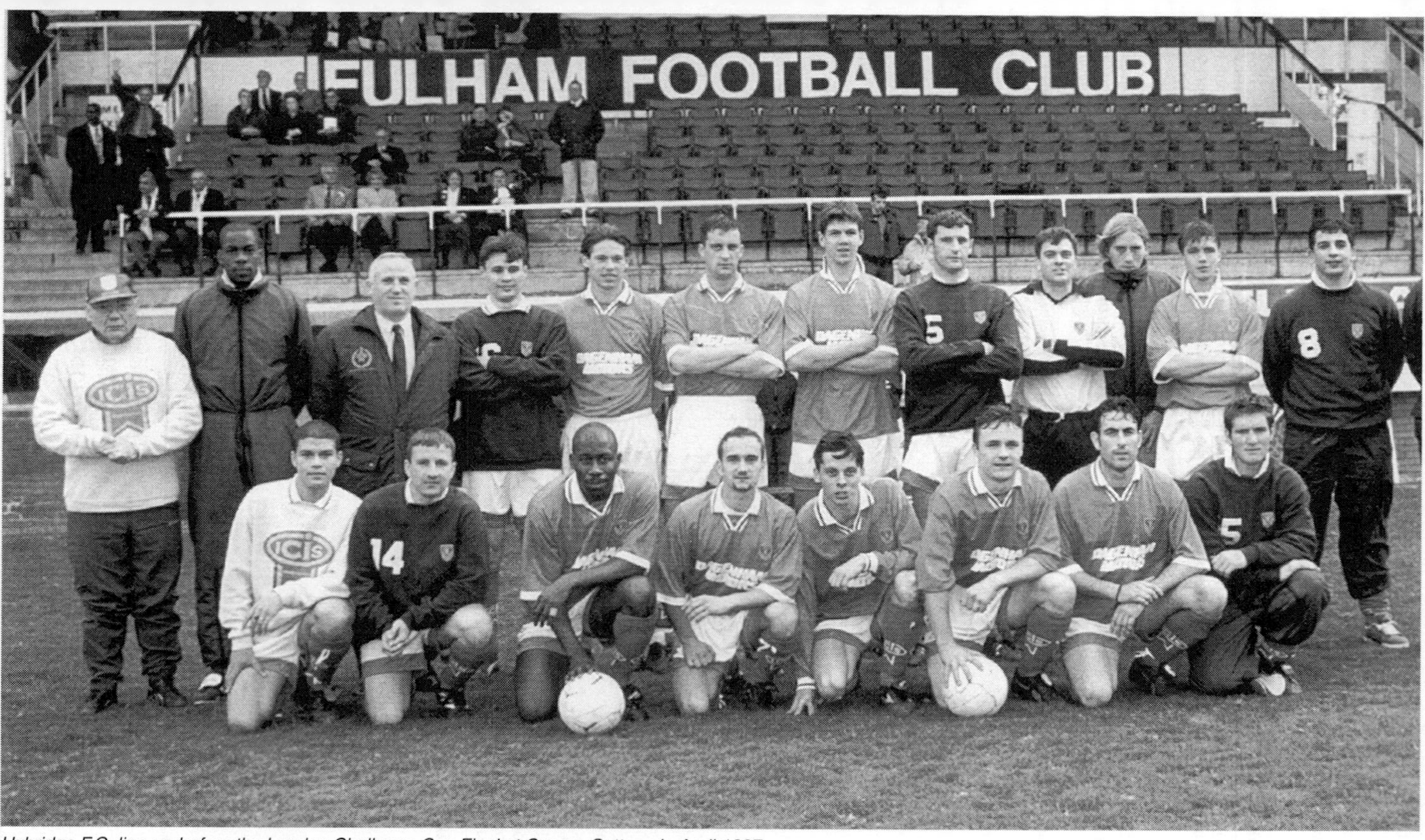

Uxbridge F.C. line-up before the London Challenge Cup Final at Craven Cottage in April 1997
Back Row (L-R): Ernie Kempster (Physio), Andy Campbell, George Talbot (Manager), Darran Wolfe, Kevin Cleary, Mark Gill, Ben Cook, Gary Downes, Sean Dawson, Daryl Pelton, Gavin Bamford, Jeff Priest & Micky Nicks (Coach)
Front Row (L-R): Danny Hawkesworth, Micky Perry, Raoul Sam, Paul Mills, Jamie Cleary, Nicky Ryder, Phil Granville & Alec MacIndoe
Photo: Graham Bowles (Uxbridge Gazette)

MANCHESTER F.A.

Secretary: Fred Brocklehurst,
Sports Complex, Branthingham Road, Chorlton, Manchester M21 1TG
Tel: 01619 984839 (Home) 01618 810299 (County Office) Fax: 01618 816833

MANCHESTER PREMIER CUP
(FOUNDED 1979-80)

RECENT FINALS

1991-92	Ashton United	v	Flixton	2-1
1992-93	Droylsden	v	Curzon Ashton	2-0 (AET)
1993-94	Hyde United	v	Droylsden	4-1
1994-95	Hyde United	v	Trafford	2-1
1995-96	Curzon Ashton	v	Hyde United	2*2 (3-4 Pns)

MOST WINS Curzon Ashton 5 Ashton United 3 Droylsden 2 Hyde United 2 Mossley 2

1996-97
MANCHESTER PREMIER CUP

14 CLUBS **HOLDERS: HYDE UNITED**

FIRST ROUND

Glossop North End	v	Maine Road	3-0		Mossley	v	Castleton Gabriels	5-0
Radcliffe Borough	v	Chadderton	1-0		Curzon Ashton	v	Oldham Town	4-2
Flixton	v	Salford City	4-0		Droylesdon	v	Ashton United	0-6

SECOND ROUND

Curzon Ashton	v	Hyde United	4-3		Mossley	v	Ashton United	0-1
Radcliffe Borough	v	Glossop North End	1-3		Flixton	v	Trafford	2-3

SEMI-FINALS

Ashton United	v	Glossop Nth End	4p5 3*3		Trafford	v	Curzon Ashton	2-0

FINAL

GLOSSOP NTH END v TRAFFORD 5p3 1*1 at Old Trafford, Manchester United FC

MIDDLESEX F.A.

Secretary: Peter Clayton,
39 Roxborough Road, Harrow, Middlesex HA1 1NS
Tel: 01819 093124 (H) 01812 008300 (B)
01814 248524 (City Office) Fax: 0181 862062 (County Office)

MIDDLESEX SENIOR CHARITY CUP
(FOUNDED 1901-02)

RECENT FINALS

1991-92	Chelsea	v	Edgware Town	3-1
1992-93	Harrow Borough	v	Hanwell Town	3-1 (AET)
1993-94	Staines Town	v	Northwood	4-0
1994-95	Wembley	v	Hampton	2-0
1995-96	Hampton	v	Ruislip Manor	3-2

MOST WINS Wealdstone 11 Hayes 10 Southall 10

1996-97
MIDDLESEX SENIOR CHARITY CUP

21 CLUBS **HOLDERS: HAMPTON**

FIRST ROUND

Kingsbury Town	v	Brimsdown Rovers	0-2
Feltham	v	Hillingdon Borough	1-4
Bedfont	v	Harefield United	4-1
Potters Bar Town	v	Brook House	7-0
Waltham Abbey	v	Cockfosters	5p6 1*1

SECOND ROUND

Edgware Town	v	Wealdstone	2-1
Bedfont	v	Uxbridge	1-5
Hillingdon Borough	v	Wembley	5*7
Staines Town	v	Brimsdown	3-1
Northwood	v	Hanwell Town	1-0
Cockfosters	v	Southall	3-1
Ashford Town	v	Ruislip Manor	2-1
Hampton	v	Potters Bar Town	1-0

QUARTER-FINALS

Staines Town	v	Hampton	0-2
Uxbridge	v	Ashford Town	1-2
Cockfosters	v	Wembley	0-5
Northwood	v	Edgware Town	1-3

SEMI-FINALS

Wembley	v	Ashford Town	2-0
Hampton	v	Edgware Town	1-2

FINAL

WEMBLEY v EDGWARE TOWN 0*1 at Vale Farm, Wembley FC

MIDDLESEX SENIOR CUP
(FOUNDED 1888-89)

RECENT FINALS

1991-92	Yeading	v	Wembley	2-1
1992-93	Harrow Borough	v	Wembley	1-0
1993-94	Staines Town	v	Edgware Town	2-1
1994-95	Yeading	v	Staines Town	2-0
1995-96	Hayes	v	Hampton	3-2

MOST WINS Enfield 13 Southall 12 Wealdstone 11

1996-97
MIDDLESEX SENIOR CUP

28 CLUBS **HOLDERS: HAYES**

PRELIMINARY ROUND

Viking Sports	v	Wealdstone	0-2		Harefield United	v	Hillingdon Borough	1-11
Southall	v	Waltham Abbey	3-1		Brook House	v	Potters Bar Town	1-0

FIRST ROUND

Brook House	v	Southall	3-1		Hendon	v	Wealdstone	3*1
Wingate & Finchley	v	Brimsdown Rovers	2-1		Kingsbury Town	v	Wembley	0-1
Ashford Town (Mx)	v	Northwood	1-3		Ruislip Manor	v	Hanwell Town	2-4
Bedfont	v	Feltham	1-0		Hillingdon Borough	v	Cockfosters	5-1

SECOND ROUND

Uxbridge	v	Hampton	4-0		Hayes	v	Wingate & Finchley	4*3
Harrow Borough	v	Staines Town	1*1 2-5		Northwood	v	Hanwell Town	5*3
Hillingdon Borough	v	Edgware Town	1*1 0-4		Brook House	v	Wembley	0-4
Bedfont	v	Enfield	0-2		Hendon	v	Yeading	0-1

QUARTER-FINALS

Northwood	v	Hayes	3-2		Wembley	v	Edgware Town	0-2
Staines Town	v	Enfield	2-0		Uxbridge	v	Yeading	0-2

SEMI-FINALS

Staines Town	v	Edgware Town	4-1		Northwood	v	Yeading	0-4

FINAL

STAINES TOWN v YEADING 6p5 0*0 at Harrow Borough FC

NORFOLK F.A.

Secretary: Ray W Kiddell JP, ACII,
153 Middletons Lane, Hellesdon, Norwich NR6 5SF
Tel: 0603 488222

NORFOLK SENIOR CUP
(FOUNDED 1881-82)

RECENT FINALS

1991-92	Fakenham Town	v	Gorleston	2-2 (Rep 2-1)
1992-93	Wroxham	v	Watton United	3-0
1993-94	Fakenham Town	v	King's Lynn	4-0
1994-95	Fakenham Town	v	Gorleston	2-1
1995-96	Diss Town	v	Wroxham	4-0

MOST WINS King's Lynn 19 Great Yarmouth Town 14 Gorleston 13

1996-97
NORFOLK SENIOR CUP

28 CLUBS **HOLDERS: DISS TOWN**

FIRST ROUND

Poringland Wanderers	v	Mattishall	2*2 3-0		Attleborough	v	North Walsham	1*1 3-0

SECOND ROUND

Lakeford Rangers	v	Poringland Wand'rs	2-0		St Andrews	v	Madra United	4-1
Dereham Town	v	Anglian Windows	2-1		Wymondham Tn	v	Thetford Town	0-7
Wortwell	v	Loddon United	6-1		Blofield United	v	Mulbarton United	2*3
Attleborough	v	Thorpe Village	2*1		Horsford United	v	Norwich United	0-1
Stalham Town	v	Acle United	0-3		Downham Town	v	Swaffham Town	0-1

THIRD ROUND

Acle United	v	Attleborough Town	0-1		Dereham Town	v	Diss Town	1-2
Gt Yarmouth Town	v	Mulbarton United	2-0		Lakeford Rangers	v	Wortwell	3-0
Norwich United	v	St Andrews	1*0		Thetford Town	v	Swaffham Town	2-1
Watton United	v	Fakenham Town	1-2		Wroxham	v	Gorleston	1-0

QUARTER-FINALS

Fakenham Town	v	Diss Town	1-1 1*4		Lakeford Rangers	v	Norwich United	1*1 0-1
Thetford Town	v	Attleborough Town	1-3		Wroxham	v	Gt Yarmouth Town	1-0

SEMI-FINALS

Norwich United	v	Wroxham	0-1		Attleborough Town	v	Diss Town	0-2

FINAL

DISS TOWN	v	WROXHAM	1-4	at Carrow Road, Norwich City FC

NORTHAMPTONSHIRE F.A.

Secretary: Brian Walden,
2 Duncan Close, Red House Road, Moulton Park, Northampton NN3 6WL
Tel: 01604 670741 (County Office) Fax: 01604 670742

NORTHAMPTONSHIRE SENIOR CUP
(FOUNDED 1883-84)

RECENT FINALS

1991-92	Kettering Town	v	Corby Town	1-0
1992-93	Kettering Town	v	Rushden & Diamonds	2-1
1993-94	Rushden & Diamonds	v	Northampton Spencer	5-0
1994-95	Kettering Town	v	Rushden & Diamonds	2-2
				(Rep 2-2, 3-1 Pens)
1995-96	Rothwell Town	v	Rushden & Diamonds	1-0

MOST WINS Kettering Town 28 Northampton Town 11 Peterborough United 11

1996-97
NORTHAMPTONSHIRE 'HILLIER' SENIOR CUP

13 CLUBS **HOLDERS: ROTHWELL TOWN**

FIRST ROUND

Ford Sports	v	Desborough Town	1-1 5-0
N'mpton Spencer	v	Raunds Town	0-4
Corby Town	v	Rothwell Town	4-1
Cogenhoe United	v	Corby S & L	1-0
Brackley Town	v	Long Buckby	1-0

SECOND ROUND

Wellingborough Tn	v	Corby Town	1-2
Kettering Town	v	Rushden & Diamonds	2-1
Ford Sports	v	Raunds Town	3*2
Cogenhoe United	v	Brackley Town	2-1

SEMI-FINALS

Corby Town	v	Daventry Ford Sports	0-3
Kettering Town	v	Cogenhoe United	3-1

FINAL

KETTERING TOWN v FORD SPORTS 3*1 at Rockingham Road, Kettering Town FC

NORTHUMBERLAND F.A.

Secretary: Roland Maughan,
Seymour House, 10 Brenkley Way, Blezard Business Park, Seaton Burn, Newcastle NE13 6DT
Tel: 0191 236 8020

NORTHUMBERLAND SENIOR CUP (FOUNDED 1883-84)

RECENT FINALS

1991-92	Blyth Spartans	v	North Shields	2-1
1992-93	Newcastle Blue Star	v	Newcastle Utd Reserves	2-1
1993-94	Blyth Spartans	v	Newcastle Blue Star	1-0
1994-95	Blyth Spartans	v	Newcastle Utd Reserves	6-2
1995-96	Blyth Spartans	v	Newcastle United	0-3

MOST WINS Blyth Spartans 21 Newcastle United 19 North Shields 12

1996-97 NORTHUMBERLAND SENIOR CUP

12 CLUBS **HOLDERS: NEWCASTLE UNITED RES**

FIRST ROUND

West Allotment C	v	Bedlington Terriers	2-3	Alnwick Town	v	Ashington	1-0
Morpeth Town	v	Seaton Delaval Amt	1-0	Newc' Benfield Pk	v	Whitley Bay	1-2

SECOND ROUND

Bedlington Terriers	v	Newcastle United Res	2-0	Whitley Bay	v	Alnwick Town	5-1
Morpeth Town	v	Blyth Spartans	6-2	Prudhoe Town	v	RTM Newcastle	3-2

SEMI-FINALS

Morpeth Town	v	Whitley Bay	3-0	Bedlington Terriers	v	Prudhoe Town	2-2 4-1

FINAL

BEDLINGTON TER. v MORPETH TOWN 2-0 at St James' Park, Newcastle United FC

NORTHUMBERLAND BENEVOLENT BOWL (FOUNDED 1975-76)

RECENT FINALS

1991-92	Newcastle Benfield Park	v	Blyth Kitty Brewster	1-0
1992-93	West Allot Celtic	v	Walker	4-3
1993-94	Spittal Rovers	v	Longbenton	1-1 (Rep 2-1)
1994-95	Westerhope	v	North Shields St Columbas	2-0
1995-96	Haltwhistle	v	Ponteland United	1-2

MOST WINS Morpeth Town 2 Stobswood Welfare 2

1996-97 NORTHUMBERLAND BENEVOLENT BOWL
Sponsored by "Brother"

12 CLUBS **HOLDERS: PONTELAND UNITED**

FIRST ROUND

Lemington Soc Utd	v	Longbenton	4-1	Walker L'w'd Fosse	v	North Shields Athletic	4-1
N S St Columbas	v	Heaton Stannington	4-1	Gosforth Bohemian	v	Spittal Rovers	2-0

SECOND ROUND

Ponteland United	v	Amble Town	6-0	Walker Ledwood	v	Walker Central	2-1
Gosforth Bohemians	v	Haltwhistle C P	1-2	N S St Columbas	v	Lemington	1-1 0-1

SEMI-FINALS

Lemington	v	Walker Ledwood	1-1 4-0	Haltwhistle C P	v	Ponteland United	2-4

FINAL

LEMINGTON UTD v PONTELAND UTD 1*1 1-0 at Craik Park, Morpeth Town FC

NORTH RIDING F.A.

Secretary: P Kirby,
284 Linthorpe Road, Middlesborough TS1 3QU
Tel: 01642 224585

NORTH RIDING SENIOR CUP
(FOUNDED 1881-82)

RECENT FINALS

1991-92	Scarborough	v	Guisborough Town	3-2 (AET)
1992-93	Guisborough Town	v	Rowntrees	2-0
1993-94	Guisborough Town	v	Pickering Town	2-0
1994-95	Marske United	v	Pickering Town	5-2
1995-96				

MOST WINS Middlesbrough 45 Scarborough 17 South Bank 8 Stockton 8

1996-97
NORTH RIDING SENIOR CUP

17 CLUBS **HOLDERS: YORK CITY**

FIRST PRELIMINARY ROUND

Tees Components	v	Nunthorpe Athletic	3-1	South Bank	v	Stokesley S C	1-3
New Marske S C	v	Fishburn Park	1-2	Loftus W R	v	Rowntrees	1*2

SECOND PRELIMINARY ROUND

Tees Components	v	Stokesley S C	1-2	Rowntrees	v	Fishburn Park	4-0

THIRD PRELIMINARY ROUND

Marske United	v	Stokesley S C	1-2	Northallerton	v	Guisborough Town	3-2
Rowntrees	v	Whitby Town	0-3	Stockton	v	Pickering Town	6p7 2*2

FIRST QUALIFYING ROUND

Stokesley S C	v	Pickering Town	1-6	Northallerton	v	Whitby Town	0-2

SECOND QUALIFYING ROUND

Pickering Town	v	Whitby Town	0-2

SEMI-FINALS

Middlesborough	v	Scarborough	York City	v	Whitby Town

FINAL

NOTTINGHAMSHIRE F.A.

Secretary: W T Annable,
7 Clarendon Street, Nottingham NG1 5HS
Tel: 01602 418954 (County Office) Fax: 01705 724923

NOTTINGHAMSHIRE SENIOR CUP
(FOUNDED 1883-84)

RECENT FINALS

1991-92	Eastwood Town	v	Nottinghamshire Police	2-0
1992-93	Arnold Town	v	Rainworth Miners Welfare	3-1
1993-94	Clipstone Welfare	v	Boots Athletic	3-2
1994-95	Oakham United	v	Clipstone Welfare	3-0
1995-96	Arnold Town	v	Boots Athletic	2-0

MOST WINS Nottingham Forest 17 Sutton Town 17 Notts County 11

1996-97
NOTTINGHAMSHIRE SENIOR CUP

32 CLUBS **HOLDERS: ARNOLD TOWN**

FIRST ROUND

Eastwood Town	v	John Player	3-1	Awsworth Villa	v	Boots Athletic	2-4
Welbeck Colliery	v	Radford	2-1	Ruddington Utd	v	Gedling Town	2-6
Hucknall Town	v	Greenwood Meadows	3-0	Ollerton Town	v	Pelican	0-2
Kimberley Town	v	Southwell City	4*2	Ashfield United	v	City & Sherwood Hosp	6-1
Nuthall	v	Sneinton	2-3	Cotgrave C W	v	Hucknall Rolls Royce	2-1
Rainworth M W	v	Wollerton	5-0	Thoresby C W	v	Dunkirk	0-3
Arnold Town	v	G P T	3-0	Basford United	v	B R S A Retford	2-0
Notts Police	v	Clipstone Welfare	0-4	Blidworth Welfare	v	Worthington Simpsons	4-2

SECOND ROUND

Arnold Town	v	Pelican	2-1	Boots Athletic	v	Blidworth Welfare	3-2
Gedling Town	v	Cotgrave C W	5-0	Rainworth M W	v	Clipstone Welfare	0-3
Welbeck C W	v	Eastwood Town	1-2	Basford United	v	Kimberley Town	3-0
Dunkirk	v	Hucknall Town	0-3	Sneinton	v	Ashfield United	3-2

THIRD ROUND

Arnold Town	v	Sneinton	2-0	Boots Athletic	v	Eastwood Town	1-0
Hucknall Town	v	Gedling Town	3-0	Basford United	v	Clipstone Welfare	2-3

SEMI-FINALS

Arnold Town	v	Hucknall Town	2-1	Boots Athletic	v	Clipstone Welfare	3p2 0*0

FINAL

ARNOLD TOWN v BOOTS ATHLETIC 1-0 at Field Mill, Mansfield Town FC

OXFORDSHIRE F.A.

Secretary: Mr P J Ladbrook,
3 Wilkins Road, Cowley, Oxford OX4 2HY

OXFORDSHIRE SENIOR CUP
(FOUNDED 1884-85)

RECENT FINALS

1991-92	Oxford United Reserves	v	Witney Town	3-1
1992-93	Thame United	v	Banbury United	2-1
1993-94	Witney Town	v	Peppard	1-0
1994-95	Witney Town	v	North Leigh	1-0
1995-96	Thame United	v	Oxford City	1-2

MOST WINS Oxford City 29 Witney Town 9 Oxford United 8

1996-97
OXFORDSHIRE SENIOR CUP

31 CLUBS

HOLDERS: OXFORD CITY

FIRST ROUND

Fritwell	v	Launton Sports	0-2
Chipping Norton Tn	v	Old Woodstock	1-0
Checkendon Sports	v	Wheatley United	CS W-O
Ardley United	v	Chinnor	6-1
Kidlington	v	Adderbury Park	5-0
Sonning Common	v	Worc's College O B	0-1
Woodstock Town	v	Easington Sports	0-6
Charlton United	v	Yarnton	3-3 1-0

SECOND ROUND

Charlton United	v	Carterton Town	1*3
Clanfield	v	Chipping Norton Tn	0-2
Peppard	v	Headington Amateurs	3*1
Bicester Town	v	Checkendon Sport 3A3	2-0
Henley Town	v	Worcester College OB	0-2
North Leigh	v	Watlington	1-0
Launton Sports	v	Quarry Nomads	0-3
Banbury United	v	Ardley United	3*2
Easington Sports	v	Kidlington	1-3
Garsington	v	Eynsham AFC	3-1

THIRD ROUND

Quarry Nomads	v	Garsington	3-0
North Leigh	v	Carterton Town	1-3
Bicester Town	v	Peppard	1*1 0-3
Kidlington	v	Worcester College OB	6-2
Banbury United	v	Chipping Norton Tn	4-2

FOURTH ROUND

Banbury United	v	Witney Town	1-2
Kidlington	v	Oxford City	1-4
Carterton Town	v	Peppard	3-2
Quarry Nomads	v	Thame United	

SEMI-FINALS

Carterton Town	v	Thame United	2-1
at Oxford City FC			
Witney Town	v	Oxford City	1-3
at Witney Town FC			

FINAL

CARTERTON TOWN v OXFORD CITY 4p5 1*1 at Oxford United FC

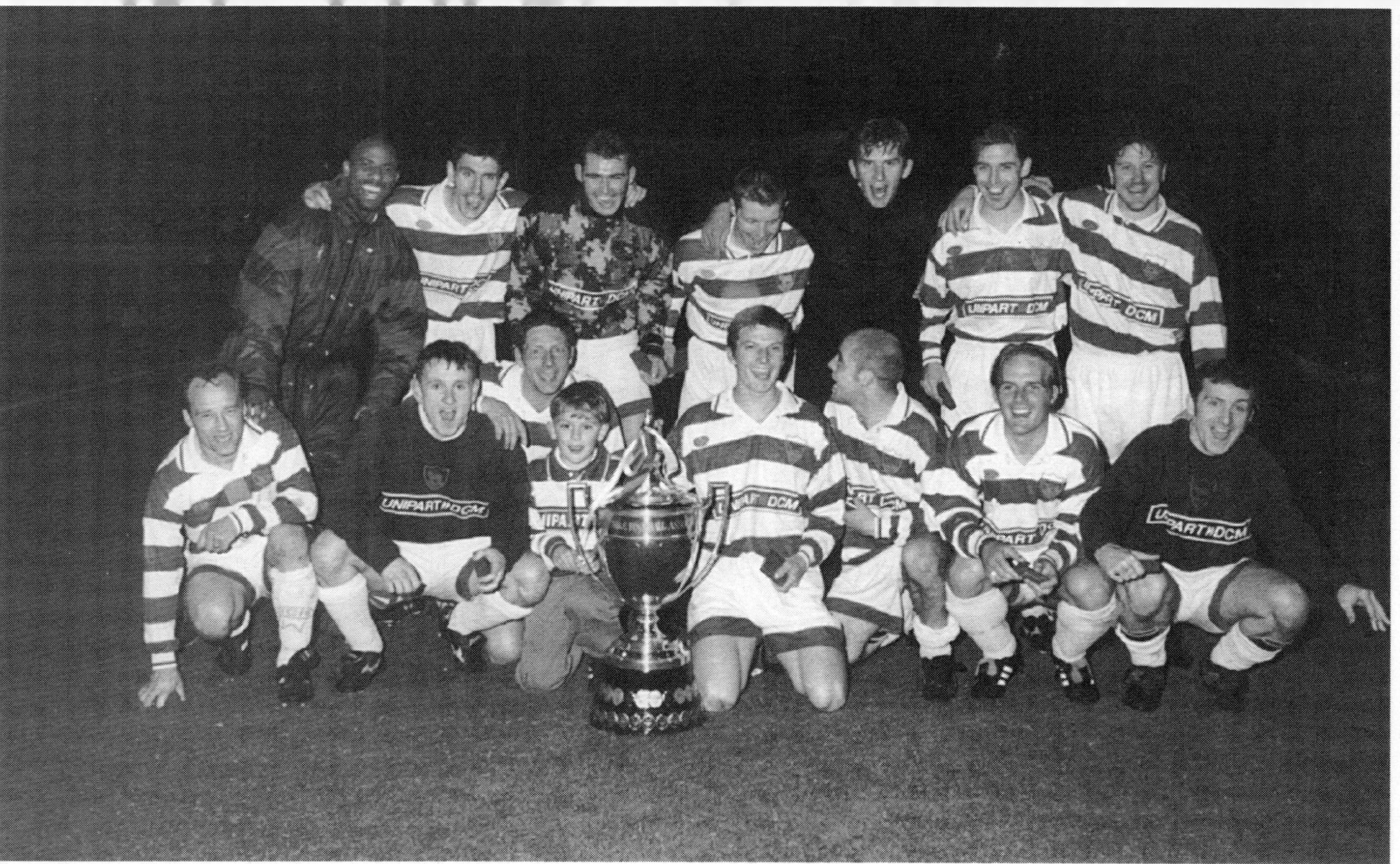

Oxford City, winners of the Oxford Senior Cup

SHEFFIELD & HALLAMSHIRE F.A.

Secretary: G Thompson JP,
Clegg House, 5 Onslow Road, Sheffield S11 7AF
Tel: 01742 670068

SHEFFIELD & HALLAMSHIRE CUP
(FOUNDED 1876-77)

RECENT FINALS

1991-92	Emley	v	Frickley Athletic	1-0
1992-93	Stocksbridge Pk Steels	v	Worksop Town	5-3 (Agg)
1993-94	Sheffield	v	Worksop Town	1-1 (6-5 Pns)
1994-95	Worksop Town	v	Emley	1-0
1995-96	Grimethorpe	v	Stocksbridge Pk Steels	0-1

MOST WINS Sheffield 10 Frickley Athletic 9 Sheffield Wednesday 9

1996-97
SHEFFIELD & HALLAMSHIRE CUP

34 CLUBS **HOLDERS: STOCKSBRIDGE PARK STEELS**

(38 Byes to 2nd Qualifying Round, 12 Clubs Exempt to First Round Proper)

FIRST QUALIFYING ROUND

High Green Villa	v	Mexborough Main St	2-1
Wath Saracens Ath	v	Penistone Church	3-2

SECOND QUALIFYING ROUND

Oughtibridge	v	Avesta Sheffield Sports	2-1
Davy FC	v	Yorkshire Main	5-1
Killamarsh Juniors	v	Throstles Ridgeway	7-0
Wombwell Town	v	Sheffield Lane Top	3-1
A B M FC	v	Wickersley O B	2-3
Harworth Coll Inst	v	Mexborough Athletic	2-1
Sheffield Central'	v	Old Edwardians	1-1 6-2
Phoenix	v	Ecclesfield Red Rose	0-1
J I Case Sports	v	Clifton Rovers	1-2
Grapes Nthn Gen'l	v	Sheffield Bankers	4-2
Frecheville C A	v	Sheffield Hallam UU	2-1
Treeton Welfare	v	Kiveton Sports	6-0
High Green Villa	v	Grimethorpe MW Jnrs	0-1
Queens Hotel	v	Elsecar Mkt Hotel	4*4 1-3
Rossington FC	v	Nemsworth Town	1-2
Thurcroft D Barri	v	Norton Woodseats	1-2
Wombwell Main	v	Maltby M W	5p4 4*4 0*0
Caribbean Sports	v	Parramore Sports	6-2
Swinton Athletic	v	Denaby & Cadeby	1*2
The Wetherby	v	Wath Saracens Ath	7-0

FIRST ROUND PROPER

Wickersley O B	v	Frickley Athletic	0-4
Caribbean Sports	v	Norton Woodseats	0-1
Frecheville CA	v	Grimethorpe M W	0-3
Wombwell Main	v	Stocksbridge Pk St	1-2
Worsbrough Br	v	Emley	1-1 2-5
Parkgate	v	Ecclesfield Red Rose	0-2
Maltby Main	v	Grapes N General	7-1
Elsecar Mkt Hotel	v	Clifton Rovers	0-2
Oughtibridge WM	v	Rossington Main	3-4
Worksop Town	v	The Wetherby	3-2
Sheff Centralians	v	Harworth Coll Inst	1*2
Wombwell Town	v	Sheffield	1*4
Denaby & Cadeby	v	Hemsworth Town	1-3
Brodsworth	v	Killamarsh Juniors	0-1
Davy	v	Treeton Welfare	3-2
Hallam	v	Denaby United	2-0

SECOND ROUND

Stocksbridge Park	v	Rossington Main	2-0
Hemsworth Town	v	Grimethorpe MW	1*0
Davy	v	Clifton Rovers	1-4
Maltby Main	v	Killamarsh Juniors	1-3
Harworth Colliery	v	Hallam	2-1
Sheffield	v	Worksop Town	0-5
Worsbro/Emley	v	Ecclesfield Red Rose	12-0
Frickley Athletic	v	Norton Woodseats	6-1

THIRD ROUND

Harworth Coll Inst	v	Clifton Rovers	3-0
Emley	v	Stocksbridge P S	3-0
Frickley Athletic	v	Worksop Town	1-2
Hemsworth Town	v	Killamarsh Juniors	4-0

SEMI-FINALS (Two Legs)

Harworth Colliery	v	Hemsworth T	2-0 0-0=2-0
Worksop Town	v	Emley	2-0 0-1=2-1

FINAL

HARWORTH C INST v WORKSOP TOWN 0-6 at Hillsborough, Sheffield Wednesday FC

SHROPSHIRE F.A.

Secretary: A W Brett
10-11 High Street, Shrewsbury SY1 1SG
Tel: 01743 362769 Fax: 01743 236145 (Home)

SHROPSHIRE SENIOR CUP
(FOUNDED 1877-78)

RECENT FINALS

1991-92	Telford United	v	Shrewsbury Town	1-0
1992-93	Telford United	v	Shrewsbury Town	2-0
1993-94	Telford United	v	Shrewsbury Town	2-1
1994-95	Shrewsbury Town	v	Telford United	5-1
1995-96	Telford United	v	Shrewsbury Town	0-2

MOST WINS Shrewsbury Town 51 Telford United 34 Oswestry Town 11

1996-97
SHROPSHIRE SENIOR CUP

5 CLUBS **HOLDERS: SHREWSBURY TOWN**

PRELIMINARY ROUND

Shifnal Town	v	Bandon	1-2

SEMI-FINALS

Telford United	v	Bridgenorth Town	5-2
Shrewsbury Town	v	Bandon	6-1

FINAL

SHREWSBURY TN	v	TELFORD UNITED	1-0	at Gay Meadow, Shrewsbury Town FC

SHROPSHIRE COUNTY CUP
(FOUNDED 1966-67)

RECENT FINALS

1991-92	Little Drayton Rngs	v	Shifnal Town	3-0
1992-93	Oakengates Town	v	Albrighton S & S	1-0
1993-94	Ludlow Town	v	Morda United	1-0
1994-95	Ludlow Town	v	Bridgnorth Town Res	3-1
1995-96	Bandon	v	Whitchurch Alport	3-1

MOST WINS GKN Sankey 6 Bridgnorth Town 5 Whitchurch Alport 4

1996-97
SHROPSHIRE COUNTY CUP

20 CLUBS **HOLDERS: BANDON**

FIRST ROUND

Oakengates Town	v	Bridgnorth Town Res	4-1
Ellesmere Rangers	v	Newport	N- W-O
Hadley Town	v	Snailbeach White Star	2-4
Meole Brace	v	Wellington Amateurs	4-3

SECOND ROUND

Morda United	v	St Martins	3-0
Belvidere	v	Newport	0-3
Highley Welfare	v	Hanwood United	1-4
Clee Hill United	v	Oakengates Town	2-2 1-4
Wem Town	v	Ludlow Town	3-5
Meole Brace	v	Little Drayton Rangers	3-1
Star Aluminium	v	Belle Vue Old Boys	1-0
Hadley Town	v	Whitchurch Alport	1-2

THIRD ROUND

Morda United	v	Oakengates Town	4-3
Newport	v	Meole Brace	1-4
Ludlow Town	v	Star Aluminium	1-0
Hanwood United	v	Whitchurch Alport	3-1

SEMI-FINALS

Meole Brace	v	Morda United	1-3
Hanwood United	v	Ludlow Town	0-2

FINAL

MORDA UNITED	v	LUDLOW TOWN	0-2	at Gay Meadow, Shrewsbury Town FC

SOMERSET F.A.

Secretary: Mrs H Marchment,
30 North Road, Midsomer Norton, Bath, Somerset BA3 2QQ
Tel: 01761 410280

SOMERSET SENIOR CUP
(FOUNDED 1895-96)

RECENT FINALS

1991-92	Odd Down	v	Portishead	4-2
1992-93	Brislington	v	Saltford	1-0
1993-94	Bridgwater Town	v	Brislington	1-0
1994-95	Brislington	v	Bridgwater Town	0-0 (5-4 Pns)
1995-96	Bridgwater Town	v	Peasedown Athletic	2-0

MOST WINS Paulton Rovers 12 Radstock Town 12 Welton Rovers 9

1996-97
SOMERSET SENIOR CUP

54 CLUBS **HOLDERS: BRIDGWATER TOWN**

FIRST ROUND

SECOND ROUND

THIRD ROUND

FOURTH ROUND

Westland United	v	Street		Bridgwater Tn Rs	v	Fry's Club	
Nailsea United	v	Wells City		Portishead	v	Peasedown Athletic	

SEMI-FINALS

Portishead	v	Wells City	3-0	Westland United	v	Bridgwater Town Res	1-3

FINAL

BRIDGWATER TN R	v	PORTISHEAD	0-2	at Paulton Rovers FC

SOMERSET PREMIER CUP
(FOUNDED 1948-49)

RECENT FINALS

1991-92	Bristol Rovers	v	Yeovil Town	3-2 (Agg)
1992-93	Bristol Rovers Res	v	Taunton Town	5-1 (Agg)
1993-94	Bath City	v	Bristol Rovers Res	5-4 (Agg)
1994-95	Bath City	v	Taunton Town	2-0 (Agg)
1995-96	Brislington	v	Mangotsfield United	1*1 (6-5 Pns)

MOST WINS Bath City 17 Yeovil Town 14 Bristol City 5

1996-97
SOMERSET PREMIER CUP

20 CLUBS **HOLDERS: BRISLINGTON**

FIRST ROUND

Frome Town	v	Odd Down	3-2	Keynsham Town	v	Wellington	0-2
Bristol Manor Farm	v	Glastonbury	2-0	Mangotsfield Utd	v	Clevedon Town	3-1

SECOND ROUND

Taunton Town	v	Brislington	1-2	Chard Town	v	Paulton Rovers	1-2
Bristol Manor Farm	v	Backwell United	3-2	Mangotsfield Utd	v	Bridgwater Town	1-2
Yeovil Town	v	Frome Town	7-0	Wellington	v	Minehead	2-1
Bristol City	v	Welton Rovers	10-1	Bath City	v	Weston Super Mare	2-4

THIRD ROUND

Brislington	v	Wellington Town	3-0	Bristol City	v	Weston Super Mare	2-0
Paulton Rovers	v	Yeovil Town	0-1	Bristol Manor Farm	v	Bridgwater Town	6p5

SEMI-FINALS

Yeovil Town	v	Brislington	4-2	Bristol Manor Farm	v	Bristol City	0-3

FINAL

BRISTOL CITY v YEOVIL TOWN 1-2 at Yeovil Town FC

STAFFORDSHIRE F.A.

Secretary: G S Brookes
County Showground, Weston Road, Stafford ST18 0DB
Tel: 01785 56994 (County Office) Fax: 01785 224334

STAFFORDSHIRE SENIOR CUP
(FOUNDED 1877-78)

RECENT FINALS

1991-92	Stafford Rangers	v	Chasetown	4-2 (Agg)
1992-93	Stoke City Res	v	Hednesford Town	6-1 (Agg)
1993-94	Macclesfield Town	v	Wednesfield	10-3 (Agg)
1994-95	Stoke City Res	v	Paget Rangers	4-2 (Agg)
1995-96	Leek Town	v	Newcastle Town	4-3 (Agg)

MOST WINS Stoke City 17 Aston Villa 16 West Bromwich Albion 13

1996-97
STAFFORDSHIRE SENIOR CUP

22 CLUBS **HOLDERS: LEEK TOWN**

FIRST ROUND

Eastwood Hanley	v	Macclesfield Town	0-2
Oldbury United	v	Newcastle Town	1-0
Stafford Rangers	v	Bloxwich Town	0-4
Hednesford Town	v	Port Vale	3-0
Rushall Olympic	v	Tamworth	0-5
Stourbridge	v	Knypersley Victoria	0-2

SECOND ROUND

Chasetown	v	Kidsgrove Athletic	0-1
Hednesford Town	v	Tamworth	2-0
Oldbury United	v	Macclesfield Town	0-1
Shifnal Town	v	Rocester	2-1
Halesowen Harriers	v	Bilston Town	2-4
Knypersley Victoria	v	Bloxwich Town	2*1
Pelsall Villa	v	Leek Town	0-3
Stourport Swifts	v	Stoke City	0-5

THIRD ROUND

Leek Town	v	Knypersley Victoria	1-0
Hednesford Town	v	Stoke City	5*3
Shifnal Town	v	Bilston Town	2-2 3*5
Macclesfield Town	v	Kidsgrove Athletic	9-0

SEMI-FINALS

Leek Town	v	Bilston Town	1-2
Macclesfield Town	v	Hednesford Town	5p4 1*1

FINAL (First Leg)

MACCLESFIELD TN	v	BILSTON TOWN	2-1

FINAL (Second Leg)

BILSTON TOWN	v	MACCLESFIELD T	2-2+3-4

SUFFOLK F.A.

Secretary: William M Steward,
2 Millfields, Haughley, Stowmarket IP14 3PU
Tel: 01449 673481

SUFFOLK SENIOR CUP (FOUNDED 1885-86)

RECENT FINALS

1991-92	Whitton United	v	Long Melford	2-0
1992-93	Woodbridge Town	v	Stonham Aspal	5-2 (AET)
1993-94	Woodbridge Town	v	Saxmundham Sports	4-0
1994-95	Grundisburgh	v	Whitton United	2-0
1995-96	Framlingham Town	v	Grundisburgh	0-3

MOST WINS Ipswich Town 16 Lowestoft Town 10 Stowmarket Town 8

1996-97 SUFFOLK SENIOR CUP

32 CLUBS **HOLDERS: GRUNDISBURGH**

FIRST ROUND

East Bergholt Utd	v	Framlingham Town	0-3
Felixstowe P & TRs	v	Brantham & Stutton	1-1 1-5
Walsom le Willow	v	Needham Market	0-1
Cornard United	v	Halesworth Town	0-0 0-2
Brandon Town	v	B T Research	2-1
Ipswich Athletic	v	BS Fonnereau Ath	1-4
Westerfield United	v	Kesgrave	2-4
Haughley United	v	Ashlea	2-0
Sudbury Wdrs Res	v	Walton United	1-3
Lowestoft Tn Rs	v	Oulton Broad & LR	4-0
Nicholians Loco	v	Beccles Town	2-2 2*5
Whitton United	v	Stowmarket Tn Res	0V1
Kirkley	v	Long Melford	3-1
Ipswich Wanderers	v	Grundisburgh	3-0
Achilles	v	Stonham Aspal	0-1
Mildenhall Town	v	Haverhill Rovers	1-2

SECOND ROUND

Brantham & S Utd	v	Walton United	1-0
BS Fonnereau	v	Halesworth Town	4-2
Kesgrave	v	Haverhill Rovers	1-3
Beccles Town	v	Kirkley	0-1
Needham Market	v	Stowmarket Tn Res	1-0
Brandon Town	v	Ipswich Wanderers	0-1
Haughley United	v	Framlingham Town	0-2
Lowestoft Tn Res	v	Stonham Aspal	1-3

THIRD ROUND

Haverhill Rovers	v	Brantham & Sutton Utd	3-0
Framlington Town	v	Stonham Aspal	
Needham Market	v	Kirkley	4-2
BS Fonnereau Ath	v	Ipswich Wanderers	1-1 2-5

SEMI-FINALS

Haverhill Rovers v Stonham Aspal 3*2
at Hadleigh United FC

Needham Market v Ipswich Wanderers 1-2
at Felixstowe Port & Town FC

FINAL

HAVERHILL RVRS v IPSWICH W'DERERS 1-2 at Portman Road, Ipswich Town FC

SUFFOLK PREMIER CUP (FOUNDED 1958-59)

RECENT FINALS

1991-92	Sudbury Town	v	Stowmarket Town	1-0
1992-93	Sudbury Town	v	Brantham Athletic	2-1
1993-94	Newmarket Town	v	Sudbury Town	2-1
1994-95	Newmarket Town	v	Felixstowe Town	1-1 (Rep 1-0)
1995-96	Bury Town	v	Woodbridge Town	0*0 (5-4 Pns)

MOST WINS Sudbury Town 12 Bury Town 10 Lowestoft Town 5

1996-97 SUFFOLK PREMIER CUP

9 CLUBS **HOLDERS: BURY TOWN**

PRELIMINARY ROUND

Hadleigh United v Lowestoft Town 1-2

FIRST ROUND

Stowmarket Town	v	Bury Town	2V2 1V2
Newmarket Town	v	Lowestoft Town	3-3 1-0
Woodbridge Town	v	Sudbury Town	0-2
Felixstowe P & T	v	Sudbury Wanderers	1-3

(Bury Town were found to have fielded an ineligible player and were removed from the competition with Stowmarket Town re-instated)

SEMI-FINALS

Stowmarket Town	v	Sudbury Wanderers	2-1
Newmarket Town	v	Sudbury Town	3*3 2-1

FINAL

NEWMARKET TN v STOWMARKET TN 0*0 1-0 at Sudbury Wanderers FC (Also replay)

SURREY F.A.

(Est. 1877)

Secretary: Peter Adams,
321 Kingston Road, Leatherhead, Surrey KT22 7TU
Tel: 01372 373543

SURREY SENIOR CUP
(FOUNDED 1882-83)

RECENT FINALS

1991-92	Carshalton Athletic	v	Egham Town	3-1
1992-93	Sutton United	v	Carshalton Athletic	2-1
1993-94	Woking	v	Sutton United	3-1
1994-95	Sutton United	v	Carshalton Athletic	3-1
1995-96	Tooting & Mitcham Utd	v	Woking	0-2

MOST WINS Dulwich Hamlet 16 Sutton United 13 Kingstonian 9

1996-97
SURREY SENIOR CUP

33 CLUBS

HOLDERS: WOKING

PRELIMINARY ROUND

Redhill	v	Netherne	0-1

FIRST ROUND

Tooting & Mitcham	v	Cobham	3-2
Sutton United	v	Walton Casuals	3-0
Egham Town	v	Westfield	0-2
Epsom & Ewell	v	Crystal Palace	2-3
Banstead Athletic	v	Farnham Town	3-1
Woking	v	Ashford Town (Mx)	3-0
Metropolitan Police	v	Cranleigh	4-1
Chipstead	v	Kingstonian	1-2
Godalming & Gldfd	v	Leatherhead	1-4
Corinthian Casuals	v	Chertsey Town	1-1 4-2
Whyteleafe	v	Croydon Athletic	4-1
Croydon	v	Merstham	5-0
Molesey	v	Netherne	3-1
Walton & Hersham	v	Camberley Town	6-0
Ash United	v	Dorking	2-5
Carshalton Ath	v	Raynes Park Vale	7-0

SECOND ROUND

Corinthian Casuals	v	Dorking	5-3
Croydon	v	Crystal Palace	1-2
Kingstonian	v	Molesey	1-0
Carshalton Athletic	v	Westfield	3-1
Sutton United	v	Leatherhead	4-0
Whyteleafe	v	Tooting & Mitcham	1-1 1-2
Walton & Hersham	v	Woking	3-2
Banstead Athletic	v	Metropolitan Police	2-1

THIRD ROUND

Tooting & Mitcham	v	Sutton United	1-4
Walton & Hersham	v	Carshalton Athletic	1-2
Corinthian Casuals	v	Crystal Palace	0-3
Banstead Athletic	v	Kingstonian	2-1

SEMI-FINALS

Crystal Palace @S	v	Sutton United	3-1
Carshalton Athletic	v	Banstead Athletic	2-1

FINAL

CARSHALTON ATH v CRYSTAL PALACE 0-1 at Carshalton Athletic FC

Surrey Senior Cup Final 1997: Carshalton Athletic v Crystal Palace. 5th May 1997. Result: 0-1
Left to Right: Adrian Blake, Gary Bowyer, Andy Salako, Jimmy Bolton, Barry Kingsford, Neil Robson, Michael Beard, Sean Daly, Simon Bassey, Eddie Saunders, Phil Dawson, Andy Norman, Dean Thomas, Mark Harmsworth (Captain)

SUSSEX F.A.

Secretary: Mr D Worsfold,
Culver Road, Lancing, West Sussex BN15 9AX
Tel: 01903 753547

SUSSEX SENIOR CUP (FOUNDED 1882-83)

RECENT FINALS

1991-92	Brighton & Hove Alb Res	v	Langney Sports	1-0
1992-93	Wick	v	Oakwood	3-1
1993-94	Brighton & Hove Alb Res	v	Peacehaven & Telscombe	1-0
1994-95	Brighton & Hove Alb Res	v	Bognor Regis Town	2-0
1995-96	Crawley Town	v	Hastings Town	0-1

MOST WINS Worthing 19 Eastbourne Town 12 Southwick 10

1996-97
SUSSEX SENIOR CUP

45 CLUBS

HOLDERS: HASTINGS TOWN

FIRST ROUND

Bosham	v	Worthing United	2-7
Crawley Down V	v	Crowborough Athletic	3-4
Eastbourne United	v	Selgey	2*0
Lancing	v	Steyning Town	2-0
Mile Oak	v	Midhurst & Easebourne	5-1
Saltdean United	v	East Preston	4-1
Three Bridges	v	Withdean	5-0
Chichester City	v	Newhaven	2*2 0-2
East Grinstead	v	Broadbridge Heath	3-1
Horsham	v	Lewes	3-1
Littlehampton T	v	Whitehawk	4-2
Oakwood	v	Southwick	2-1
Sidley United	v	Bexhill Town	3-2

SECOND ROUND

Bognor Regis Town	v	Burgess Hill Town	3-1
Newhaven	v	Shoreham	1-2
East Grinstead	v	Sidley United	0-2
Hailsham Town	v	Mile Oak	2-1
Hastings Town	v	Littlehampton Town	3-5
Oakwood	v	Worthing	0-0 0-1
Peacehaven & Tels	v	Lancing	8-0
St Leonards Smft	v	Crowborough Athletic	9-0
Worthing United	v	Eastbourne Town	1-2
Crawley Town	v	Brighton & Hove	1-3
Eastbourne Utd	v	Arundel	1-2
Hassocks	v	Wick	2-1
Horsham YMCA	v	Langney Sports	3-2
Pagham	v	Portfield	3-5
Ringmer	v	Three Bridges	2-0
Saltdean United	v	Horsham	1-1 1-0

THIRD ROUND

Arundel	v	Sidley United	2-3
Hailsham Town	v	Portfield	1-2
Littlehampton Town	v	Bognor Regis Town	0V4
Worthing	v	Brighton & Hove	3-1
Eastbourne Town	v	Saltdean United	0-1
Hassocks	v	St Leonards	1-4
Horsham YMCA	v	Shoreham	1-3
Ringmer	v	Peacehaven & Tels	2-0

FOURTH ROUND

Saltdean United	v	Littlehampton Town	2-1
Sidley United	v	Portfield	2-4
Ringmer	v	St Leonards	1-3
Shoreham	v	Worthing	2-1

SEMI-FINALS

Portfield v St Leonards Stamcroft 0-3
at Worthing FC

Saltdean United v Shoreham 1-0
at Burgess Hill Town FC

FINAL

SALTDEAN UTD v ST LEONARDS SCFT 1-2 at Woodside Road, Worthing FC

St Leonards Stamcroft with the Sussex Senior Cup

Photo: Roger Turner

SUSSEX ROYAL ULSTER RIFLES CHARITY CUP
(FOUNDED 1896-97)

RECENT FINALS

1991-92	Burgess Hill Town	v	Ringmer	2-1 (AET)
1992-93	Peacehaven & Tels	v	Lancing	2-1
1993-94	Newhaven	v	Pagham	4-0
1994-95	Peacehaven & Tels	v	Stamco	1-0
1995-96	Peacehaven & Tels	v	Saltdean United	1-0

MOST WINS Horsham 13 Worthing 12 Southwick 10

1996-97
SUSSEX ROYAL ULSTER RIFLES CHARITY CUP

36 CLUBS

HOLDERS: PEACEHAVEN & TELSCOMBE

PRELIMINARY ROUND

Bosham	v	East Preston	0-4	Burgess Hill Town	v	Eastbourne Town	1-0
Peacehaven & Tels	v	Whitehawk	4-0	Portfield	v	Wick	3-2

FIRST ROUND

Arundel	v	Chichester City	2-4	Bexhill Town @EG	v	East Grinstead	2*2 3-1
Hassocks	v	Langney Sports	0-3	Littlehampton Tn	v	Midhurst & Easebourne	3-2
Mile Oak	v	Steyning Town	3-1	Newhaven	v	Three Bridges	3*2
Peacehaven & Tels	v	Eastbourne United	3-1	Portfield	v	Horsham YMCA	1-2
Ringmer	v	Oakwood	5-1	Saltdean United	v	Crowborough Athletic	4*2
Selsey	v	Pagham	1-0	Shoreham	v	Broadbridge Heath	5-0
Sidley United	v	Hailsham Town	4*3	Southwick	v	Lancing	4-0
Withdean @BHT	v	Burgess Hill Town	2-4	Worthing United	v	East Preston	1*1 1-3

SECOND ROUND

Chichester City	v	Shoreham @S	0-2	Bexhill Town	v	Saltdean United	0-4
East Preston	v	Selsey	1-2	Burgess Hill Town	v	Ringmer	2-1
Sidley United	v	Langney Sports	3-2	Southwick	v	Littlehampton Town	2-0
Mile Oak	v	Horsham YMCA	2-0	Newhaven	v	Peacehaven & Tels	3*4

THIRD ROUND

Mile Oak	v	Shoreham	1-2	Selsey	v	Saltdean United	2-1
Southwick	v	Peacehaven & Tels	0-3	Burgess Hill Town	v	Sidley United	4-1

SEMI-FINALS

Burgess Hill Town	v	Shoreham	2-3	Selsey	v	Peacehaven & Tels	1*2

FINAL

PEACEHAVEN & T v SHOREHAM 3*3 4-0 at Lancing FC (Replay also)

WESTMORLAND F.A.

Founded: 1897

Secretary: Mr J B Fleming,
Beezon Chambers, off Sandes Avenue, Kendal, Cumbria
Tel: 01539 730946 (County Office)

WESTMORLAND SENIOR CUP
(FOUNDED 1896-97)

RECENT FINALS

1991-92	Coniston	v	Kendal United	4-1
1992-93	Coniston	v	Ambleside	4-2
1993-94	Kendal United	v	Keswick	2-0
1994-95	Kendal United	v	Staveley United	2-1
1995-96	Milnthorpe Corinthians	v	Netherfield Reserves	2-1

MOST WINS Corinthians 11 Netherfield 8 Burneside 7 Windermere 7

1996-97
"WESTMORLAND GAZETTE" SENIOR CHALLENGE CUP

19 CLUBS **HOLDERS: MILNTHORPE CORINTHIANS**

FIRST ROUND

Endmoor KGR	v	Wetheriggs United	1-4		Burneside	v	Kirkby Stephen	2-0
Milnthorpe Corinth	v	Appleby	1-0					

SECOND ROUND

Wetheriggs United	v	Sedbergh	1-0		Shap	v	Staveley United	3*3 2-4
Kendal County	v	Coniston	1-0		Lunesdale United	v	Burneside	B W-O
Grange Amateurs	v	Kendal United	5-1		Milnthorpe Corinth	v	Burton Thistle	3-0
Netherfield Reserves	v	Keswick	1-0		Kirkby Stephen	v	Windermere SC	4-2

THIRD ROUND

Kendal County	v	Kirkby Lonsdale	1-2		Shap/Stavely Utd	v	Wetheriggs United	5-0
Burneside	v	Netherfield Reserves	1-4		Grange Amateurs	v	Milnethorpe Corinth	2-4

SEMI-FINALS

Milnethorpe Corinth	v	Netherfield Reserves	5-3		Kirkby Lonsdale	v	Staveley United	2-1

FINAL

KIRKBY LONSDALE v MILNETHORPE COR 1-2 at Parkside, Kendal, Netherfield FC

WEST RIDING F.A.

Secretary: Roy Carter JP
Fleet Lane, Woodlesford, Leeds LS26 8NX
Tel: 0113 231 0101 (County Office)

WEST RIDING COUNTY CUP
(FOUNDED 1924-25)

RECENT FINALS

1991-92	Goole Town	v	Bradley Rangers	3-2
1992-93	Glasshoughton Welfare	v	Selby Town	4-2
1993-94	Guiseley	v	Goole Town	1-0
1994-95	Farsley Celtic	v	Thackley	2-1
1995-96	Farsley Celtic	v	Guiseley	2-3

MOST WINS Goole Town 11 Farsley Celtic 8 Guiseley 5

1996-97
WEST RIDING COUNTY CUP

19 CLUBS **HOLDERS: GUISELEY**

FIRST ROUND

Halifax Town	v	Harrogate Railway	1-2
Ossett Town	v	Garforth Town	3-1
Tadcaster Albion	v	Liversedge	1-3

SECOND ROUND

Harrogate Town	v	Armthorpe Welfare	0-1
Yorkshire Amateur	v	Ossett Town	0-2
Ossett Albion	v	Liversedge	1V0 1-1 5-0
Pontefract Collieries	v	Glasshoughton Welfare	3-0
Hatfield Main	v	Farsley Celtic	0-3
Harrogate Railway	v	Guiseley	1-2
Bradford Park Ave	v	Eccleshill United	3-1
Thackley	v	Selby Town	1-2

QUARTER-FINALS

Bradford Park Ave	v	Guiseley	4-3
Armthorpe Welfare	v	Pontefract Coll's	3-3 3-2
Ossett Town	v	Ossett Albion	2-3
Selby Town	v	Farsley Celtic	3-4

SEMI-FINALS

Farsley Celtic	v	Ossett Albion	0*0 2-0
Bradford Park Ave	v	Armthorpe Welfare	0-1

FINAL

ARMTHORPE W v FARSLEY CELTIC 0-3 at West Riding County FA Ground, Woodlesford

WILTSHIRE F.A.

Secretary: Mr E M Parry
44 Kennet Avenue, Swindon, Wiltshire SN2 3LG

WILTSHIRE SENIOR CUP
(FOUNDED 1886-87)

RECENT FINALS

1991-92	Wollen Sports	v	Dowton	3-1
1992-93	Bemerton Heath Harl	v	Wollen Sports	3-1
1993-94	Amesbury Town	v	Swindon Supermarine	2-1
1994-95	Purton	v	Downton	1-0
1995-96	Amesbury Town	v	Highworth Town	0-3

MOST WINS Devizes Town 14 Swindon Town 10 Chippenham Town 8

1996-97
WILTSHIRE SENIOR CUP

19 CLUBS **HOLDERS: HIGHWORTH TOWN**

FIRST ROUND

Purton	v	Bradford Town	3-1	Dunbar Athletic	v	G P S Plessey	1-1 0-1
Pewsey Vale	v	Raychem S S	2-1				

SECOND ROUND

Pewsey Vale	v	Aldbourne Park	3-2	Biddestone	v	Wroughton	2-1
Tisbury United	v	Corsham Town	1-3	Purton	v	Bromham	5-1
Marlborough Town	v	Burmah Castrol	0-0 1-0	G P S Plessey	v	Wootton Bassett Town	1-3
Shrewton Town	v	Highworth Town	1-3	Malmesbury Vics	v	Sanford	MV W-O

THIRD ROUND

Purton	v	Biddestone	3-0	Corsham Town	v	Highworth Town	2-0
Malmesbury Vics	v	Pewsey Vale	3p4 1-1 1*1	Wootton Bassett T	v	Marlborough Town	0-0 0-2

SEMI-FINALS

Purton	v	Corsham Town	3-4	Marlborough Town	v	Pewsey Vale	4p2 2*2
at Wootton Bassett Town FC				at Devizes Town FC			

FINAL

CORSHAM TOWN	v	MARLBOROUGH TN	4*1	at Devizes Town FC

WILTSHIRE PREMIER SHIELD
(FOUNDED 1926-27)

RECENT FINALS

1991-92	Trowbridge Town	v	Salisbury City	2-1
1992-93	Trowbridge Town	v	Westbury United	1-0
1993-94	Trowbridge Town	v	Chippenham Town	3-0
1994-95	Trowbridge Town	v	Swindon Supermarine	1-0
1995-96	Chippenham Town	v	Salisbury City	0-2

MOST WINS Swindon Town 26 Salisbury City 10 Trowbridge Town 9

1996-97
WILTSHIRE PREMIER SHIELD

12 CLUBS **HOLDERS: SALISBURY CITY**

FIRST ROUND

Bemerton Heath H	v	Trowbridge Town	2-1	Calne Town	v	Downton	1-2
Chippenham Town	v	Westbury United	0-2	Warminster Town	v	Salisbury City	1-4

SECOND ROUND

Bemerton Heath H	v	Melksham Town	1-0	Downton	v	Swindon Supermarine	0-5
Salisbury City	v	Westbury United	3-0	Devizes Town	v	Amesbury Town	4-0

SEMI-FINALS

Bemerton Heath H	v	Devizes Town	2-3	Swindon S.marine	v	Salisbury City	2-0

FINAL

DEVIZES TOWN	v	SWINDON SUP.MAR.	0-2	at Melksham Town FC

WORCESTERSHIRE F.A.

Secretary: M R Leggatt,
'Fermain', 12 Worcester Road, Evesham, Worcs WR11 4JU
Tel: 01905 612336

WORCESTERSHIRE SENIOR CUP
(FOUNDED 1893-94)

RECENT FINALS

1991-92	Bromsgrove Rovers	v	Sutton Coldfield Town	4-1 (Agg)
1992-93	Kidderminster Harriers	v	Solihull Borough	3-1 (Agg)
1993-94	Bromsgrove Rovers	v	Kidderminster Harriers	5-1 (Agg)
1994-95	Bromsgrove Rovers	v	Moor Green	4-1 (Agg)
1995-96	Bromsgrove Rovers	v	Stourbridge	4-3 (Agg)

1996-97
WORCESTERSHIRE SENIOR CUP

12 CLUBS **HOLDERS: BROMSGROVE ROVERS**

FIRST ROUND

Evesham United	v	Moor Green	0-4
Sutton Coldfield Tn	v	Dudley Town	3-2
Halesowen Town	v	Paget Rangers	2-1
Solihull Borough	v	Redditch United	4-0

SECOND ROUND

Bromsgrove Rovers	v	Stourbridge	0-1
Kidderminster H	v	Haleowen Town	0-3
Worcester City	v	Moor Green	2-2 4*2
Solihull Borough	v	Sutton Coldfield Town	5-0

SEMI-FINALS

Worcester City	v	Stourbridge	3-0
Halesowen Town	v	Solihull Borough	1-2

FINAL (First Leg)

SOLIHULL BORO	v	WORCESTER CITY	0-2

FINAL (Second Leg)

WORCESTER CITY	v	SOLIHULL BORO	1-1=3-1

1996-97
WORCESTERSHIRE SENIOR URN

HOLDERS: PERSHORE TOWN

FIRST ROUND

Stourport Swifts	v	Kidderminster H Res	2-3
Worcester City Res	v	Bromsgrove Rovers Res	5-0
Alvechurch	v	Kings Heath	1-1 0-1
Malvern Town	v	Cradley Town	3-1

SECOND ROUND

Kidderminster H Res	v	Worcester Athletico	9-0
Pegasus Juniors	v	Studley BKL	0-1
Kings Heath	v	Malvern Town	5-1
Pershore Town	v	Worcester City Res	1-3

SEMI-FINALS

Worcester City Res	v	Studley BKL	3-1
Kings Heath	v	Kidderminster H Res	1-0

FINAL (First Leg)

KINGS HEATH	v	WORCESTER C RES	1-0

(Second Leg)

WORCESTER C RES	v	KINGS HEATH	2-3=2-4

THE FOOTBALL LEAGUE OF WALES

Plymouth Chambers, 3 Westgate Street, Cardiff CF1 1DD

President: B Fear **Chairman:** J E Lloyd
Board of Directors: K P Harding, T Lloyd Hughes, D A Jones, D L Jones, J Orells, G Rees, R M Waygood
Secretary: J C Deakin

BARRY TOWN LAND THE TREBLE

Barry Town's dominance of the Welsh domestic scene continued as the Glamorgan club landed the League Cup and Welsh Cup en route to a fantastic treble.

That they would retain the League of Wales title was seldom in doubt as they put their 97 points of the previous championship campaign into the shade as they totted up 105 - some 21 points clear of their nearest challengers, Inter Cardiff. Gary Barnett's side lost just one of their 40 league engagements with 33 of them resulting in victories for his side.

Despite their stranglehold on Welsh football, Barry found themselves unable to transfer their winning sequence onto the European scene, losing 6-0 in aggregate to Dynamo Kiev in the preliminary round of the Champions' League in August.

Inter Cardiff also found the going tough in the UEFA Cup, going down 8-0 to Celtic over two legs of European dominance, while Ebbw Vale produced a credible 0-0 draw at home to Austrian giants Casino Salzburg in the Inter Toto Cup, before going down in their three other matches.

The new season should be an intriguing one with Bangor City set to challenge Barry for the title of top dog under their newly-appointed management team of former Everton favourite Graeme Sharp and the Conwy supremo John Hulse.

Another interesting facet of the campaign will be the introduction of the FAW Invitation Cup. The eight club competition, held in association with BBC Wales, will see LoW clubs Bangor, Conwy, Barry and Newtown lock horns with the "English-system" clubs Wrexham, Swansea City, Cardiff City and Merthyr Tydfil.

Meanwhile, Llansantffraid became the centre of much debate in world footballing circles in July, when they became one of the first clubs to "sell their name". The mid-Wales village, that boasts a population of little over 1,000, will be known as Total Network Solutions after signing a £250,000 sponsorship deal with an Oswestry computer networking firm.

Another point of interest to League of Wales followers will be the relocating of Connah's Quay Nomads. The Deesiders are set to move from The Halfway, their home of 51 years, to a new £1.8m purpose-built stadium at nearby Kelsterton College in January.

William Hughes

LEAGUE OF WALES FINAL LEAGUE TABLE 1996-97

		P	*W*	*D*	*F*	*A*	*Pts*
1	Barry Town	40	33	6	129	26	105
2	Inter Cable Tel	40	26	6	80	32	84
3	Ebbw Vale	40	23	9	87	40	78
4	Caernarfon Town	40	23	9	81	58	78
5	Newton	40	22	5	74	49	71
6	Llansantffraid	40	19	12	78	54	69
7	Conwy United	40	20	8	66	44	68
8	Bangor City	40	20	5	82	62	65
9	Cwmbran Town	40	19	8	71	61	65
10	Porthmadog	40	18	8	64	60	62
11	Connahs Quay	40	16	9	62	64	57
12	Cemaes Bay	40	18	10	62	72	49
13	Aberystwyth Town	40	13	8	67	82	47
14	Caersws	40	11	9	53	77	42
15	Flint Town United	40	11	8	48	76	41
16	Carmarthen Town	40	11	7	41	79	40
17	Welshpool Town	40	10	50	80	39	
18	Ton Pentre	40	12	3	59	99	39
19	Rhyl	40	10	8	51	71	38
20	Holywell Town	40	7	8	52	81	29
21	Briton Ferry	40	5	1	39	129	16

Barry Town

All Time League of Wales Table

96/97	*95/96*		*P*	*W*	*D*	*L*	*F*	*A*	*GD*	*Pts*	*Success %*
1	1	Barry Town	118	79	24	15	292	106	186	261	73.73
2	2	Bangor City	194	113	30	51	409	237	172	369	63.40
3	3	Inter CableTel	194	106	37	51	376	217	159	355	61.00
4	7	Caernarfon	80	39	22	19	158	117	41	139	57.92
5	4	Cwmbran Town	194	95	48	51	318	227	91	333	57.22
6	6	Newtown AFC	194	92	42	60	328	256	72	318	54.64
7	11	Ebbw Vale	194	84	47	63	341	280	61	299	51.37
8	9	Conwy United	194	84	43	67	333	288	45	295	50.69
9	5	Ton Pentre	156	64	35	57	251	251	0	227	48.50
10	8	Flint Town	194	81	32	81	318	307	11	275	47.25
11	12	Aberystwyth	194	75	42	77	326	330	-4	267	45.88
12	13	Connahs Quay	194	74	45	75	312	320	-8	267	45.88
13	19	Llansantffraid	156	57	39	60	247	245	2	210	44.87
14	14	Afan Lido	154	55	41	58	209	238	-29	206	44.59
15	15	CPD Porthmadog	194	70	44	80	328	315	13	254	43.64
16	10	Holywell Town	194	70	43	81	306	315	-9	253	43.47
17	17	Haverfordwest	76	26	15	35	106	147	-41	93	40.79
18	16	Caersws FC	194	60	51	83	294	354	-60	231	39.69
19	20	Cemaes Bay	80	26	17	37	125	152	-27	95	39.58
20	18	Rhyl FC	118	37	22	59	172	223	-51	133	37.57
21	21	Mold Alexandra	114	38	14	62	179	234	-55	128	37.43
22	22	Llanelli AFC	154	43	27	84	239	356	-117	156	33.77
23	0	Carmarthen	40	11	7	22	41	79	-38	40	33.33
24	0	Welshpool	40	10	9	21	50	80	-30	39	32.50
25	23	Briton Ferry	156	34	28	94	217	391	-174	130	27.78
26	24	Llanidloes Town	38	7	9	22	48	93	-45	30	26.30
27	25	Maesteg Park	114	19	28	67	118	243	-125	85	24.85
28	26	Abergavenny	38	7	7	24	36	76	-40	28	24.56
		Summary:	3960	1556	848	1556	6477	6477	5516		

FINAL LEAGUE TABLES 1996-97

Office Visions Welsh League

Div One		P	W	D	L	F	A	D	Pts
1	Haverfordwest	34	25	4	5	111	24	87	79
2	Llanelli	34	21	6	7	76	43	33	69
3	AFC Rhondda	34	20	8	6	65	30	35	68
4	Treowen	34	19	8	7	74	39	35	65
5	Goytre	34	20	5	9	67	43	24	65
6	Afan Lido	34	18	9	7	60	31	29	63
7	Cardiff Corries	34	16	6	12	44	56	-12	54
8	Grange Quins*	34	15	5	14	75	58	17	47
9	Maesteg Park	34	11	11	12	53	52	1	44
10	Port Talbot	34	12	7	15	38	49	-11	43
11	Cardiff CS	34	12	6	16	50	61	-11	42
12	Llanwern	34	10	9	15	49	53	-4	39
13	Aberaman	34	10	8	16	48	63	-15	38
14	Taffs Well	34	9	8	17	39	60	-21	35
15	Abergavenny	34	10	3	21	39	68	-29	33
16	Risca	34	8	5	21	32	69	-37	29
17	Penrhiwceiber	34	6	5	23	31	103	-72	23
18	Caldicot Town	34	4	7	23	37	86	-49	19

* Points deducted

Div Two		P	W	D	L	F	A	D	Pts
1	Bridgend Town	30	22	5	3	74	18	56	71
2	UWIC	30	20	5	5	80	25	55	65
3	Porthcawl Town	30	17	7	6	79	38	41	58
4	Pontardawe	30	17	4	9	88	49	39	55
5	Porth Tywyn	30	16	7	7	61	39	22	55
6	Treharris	30	17	4	9	65	48	17	55
7	BP	30	16	4	10	94	46	48	52
8	Hoover Sports	30	15	4	11	73	55	18	49
9	Caerau	30	13	4	13	62	56	6	43
10	Pontyclun	30	9	10	11	44	54	-10	36
11	Pontypridd	30	9	4	17	46	71	-25	31
12	Ammanford	30	7	6	17	45	82	-37	27
13	Brecon	30	8	3	19	48	126	-78	27
14	Skewen	30	7	5	18	42	65	-23	26
15	Caerleon	30	3	6	21	25	76	-51	15
16	Fields Park/Pont	30	2	6	22	34	112	-78	12

Div Three		P	W	D	L	F	A	D	Pts
1	Gwynfi Utd	30	25	3	2	99	23	76	78
2	Blaenrhondda	30	21	5	4	88	32	56	68
3	Albion Rovers	30	18	4	8	76	35	41	58
4	Milford United	30	14	7	9	55	52	3	49
5	Monkton Swifts	30	12	7	11	50	59	-9	43
6	Newport YMCA	30	11	7	12	54	52	2	40
7	Garw	30	10	8	12	51	64	-13	38
8	Panteg	30	10	7	13	44	53	-9	37
9	Pontlottyn	30	11	4	15	49	59	-10	37
10	Tonyrefail	30	11	4	15	44	60	-16	37
11	Morriston	30	9	9	12	45	51	-6	36
12	Ferndale	30	10	4	16	57	57	0	34
13	Abercynon	30	10	4	16	44	62	-18	34
14	SW Police	30	10	4	16	45	76	-31	34
15	Seven Sisters	30	8	7	15	43	73	-30	31
16	Trelewis	30	5	6	19	41	77	-36	21

Fitlock Welsh Alliance

		P	W	D	L	F	A	Pts
1	Glantraeth	26	20	2	4	96	29	62
2	Llanfairpwll	26	17	6	3	62	30	57
3	Conwy United	26	19	6	5	61	39	47
4	Loco Llanberis	26	12	8	6	52	31	44
5	Halkyn United	26	12	7	7	53	33	43
6	Saltney CC	26	12	4	10	61	54	40
7	Porthmadog	26	12	2	12	44	48	36
8	Nantile Vale	26	10	8	10	54	59	36
9	Prestatyn Town	26	8	9	9	44	40	33
10	Rhyl	26	8	3	15	42	68	27
11	C'fon Town	26	4	11	11	36	53	23
12	Bangor City	26	6	5	15	38	63	23
13	Llangefni Town	26	5	3	18	23	69	18
14	Landyrnog U	26	4	4	18	23	70	16

PA Rowlands Cymru Alliance

		P	W	D	L	F	A	Pts
1	Rhayader T	34	21	12	1	79	25	75
2	Rhydymwyn	34	20	8	6	75	48	68
3	Llandudno	34	19	9	6	84	31	66
4	Oswestry T	34	19	9	6	79	31	66
5	Cefn Druids	34	19	8	7	74	50	65
6	Knighton T	34	19	6	9	68	46	63
7	Lland Wells	34	16	7	11	67	44	55
8	Penrhynch **	34	15	9	10	71	56	48
9	Brymbo B	34	10	14	10	47	48	44
10	Lex XI	34	12	4	18	54	72	40
11	Denbigh T	34	11	5	18	60	70	38
12	Mold Alex*	34	12	5	17	51	64	38
13	Buckley T	34	10	5	19	39	64	35
14	Llanidloes T	34	9	7	18	36	77	34
15	Mostyn	34	8	9	17	46	67	33
16	Penycae	34	9	3	22	40	99	30
17	Ruthin T	34	7	3	24	39	68	24
18	Rhos Aelwyd	34	7	3	24	42	91	24

** 6 Points deducted

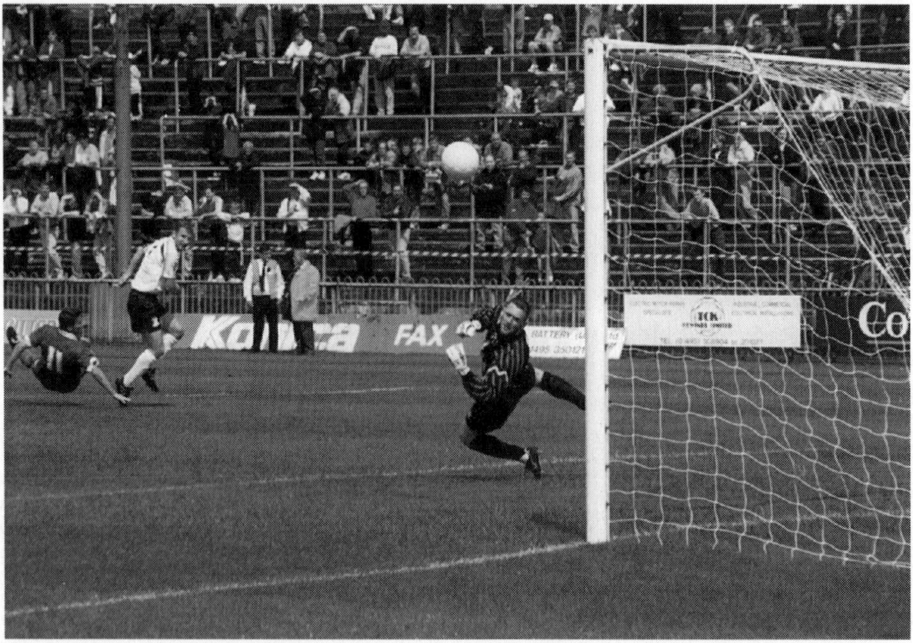

Ebbw Vale played host to French First Division club SC Bastia of Corsica in the Inter Toto Cup. Bastia won 2-1 although this effort hit the post.

Photo: Tim Lancaster

Barry Town in action against Dynamo Kiev at the start of the 1997-98 season.

Welsh Clubs in Europe 1996-97

European Cup Winners Cup Qualifying Round

First Leg (08/08/96)

Llansantffraid FC v KS Ruch Chorzow 1-1

Scorers: Gesior 6 / Thomas 83 **Referee:** E. Olafsson (ISL) **Attendance:** 1558

Llansantffraid Team: *Mulliner, J Whelan, Curtiss, Brown, Arwel Jones, Thomas, Adrian Jones, Evans, Morgan, (Davies 78), Edwards (C Whelan 84), Abercrombie. Subs not used: G Jones, S Jones, Barrett.*

Second Leg (22.08.96)

KS Ruch Chorzow v Llansantffraid FC 5-0 (Ruch win 6-1 on aggregate)

Scorers: A Bak 1, 55, Arwel Jones 47 (og), M Bak 62, 63 **Referee:** S Giownw (CRO) **Attendance:** 6700

Llansantffraid Team: *Mulliner, J Whelan (C Whelan 61), Curtiss, Brown (Davies 57), Arwel Jones, Thomas, Adrian Jones, Evans, Morgan (G Jones 61), Edwards, Abercrombie. Subs not used: S Jones, Barrett.*

UEFA CUP Qualifying Round

First Leg (17/07/96)

Barry Town v Dinaburg Daugavpils 0-0

Referee: J Pratas (POR) **Attendance:** 2500

Barry Town Team: *Ovendale, T Evans, Lloyd, French, York, Norman, Barnett, Loss (Ryan 80), Bird, Jones, C Evans (Pike 62). Subs not used: Mountain, Johnson, O'Gorman.*

Second Leg (24/07/96)

Dinaburg Daugavpils v Barry Town 1-2 (Barry win 2-1 on aggregate)

Scorers: Tarasov 60 / Pike 35, Evans 85) **Referee:** S Dougal (SCO) **Attendance:** 2250

Barry Town Team: *Ovendale, T Evans, Lloyd, French, York, Norman, Barnett, Loss, Bird, Jones, Pike (C Evans 61). Subs not used: Mountain, Johnson, O Gorman, Ryan.*

First Leg (17/7/96)

Newtown AFC v FC Skonto Riga 1-4

Scorers: Brown 90 / Astafyev 37, 71, Lobyanyov 78, 82 **Referee:** J Brito Arceo (ESP) **Attendance:** 2012

Newtown AFC Team: *Barton, J Evans (Thomas 82), M Evans, Reynolds, Wilding, Pike, Williams, Roberts, Holmans (Wickham 76), Brown, Pryce. Subs not used: Haman, Hanmer, Robinson.*

Second Leg (24/7/96)

Skonto Riga v Newtown AFC 3-0 (Skonto win 7-1 on aggregate)

Scorers: Astafayef 45, Ivanov 65, Jelisejev 85 **Referee:** M Milevski (POL) **Attendance:** 3500

Newtown AFC Team: *Barton, J Evans, Wilding, M Evans, Reynolds, Thomas (Pike 70), Roberts, Pryce, Brown, Williams, Robinson. Subs not used: Haman, Hanmer, Wickham.*

UEFA CUP Preliminary Round

First Leg (06/08/96)

Budapesti Vasutas FC v Barry Town 3-1

Scorers: Bukszegi 5, Egressy 42, Farkas 67 (p) / T Evans 14 **Referee:** A Marcel (POR) **Attendance:** 2000

Barry Town Team: *Ovendale, T Evans, Lloyd (Ryan 82), French, York, Norman, Barnett, Loss, Jones, C Evans (O'Gorman 55), PIke (Mountain 89). Subs not used: Johnson, Huggins.*

Second Leg (20/08/96)

Barry Town v Budapesti Vasutas FC 3-1 (Barry Town win 4-2 on penalties)

Scorers: Pike 45 (p), O'Gorman 46, Evans 78 / Egressy 63 **Referee:** A Georgiou (Cyp) **Attendance:** 2500

Barry Town Team: *Mountain, Johnson, Lloyd, French, York, O'Gorman, Barnett, Huggins, Ryan, Pike, Bird. Subs not used: Norman, C Evans, Misbah, Griffith.*

UEFA CUP First Round

First Leg (10/09/96)

Aberdeen FC v Barry Town 3-1

Scorers: Glass 57, Windass 7, Young 65 / Jones 13 **Referee:** A Snoddy (NIR) **Attendance:** 13,400

Barry Town Team: *Ovendale, Johnson, Lloyd, French, York, Barnett, Loss, Bird, Jones, Pike, Ryan. Subs not used: Norman, C Evans, Griffith, O'Gorman, Mountain.*

Second Leg (24/09/96)

Barry Town v Aberdeen FC 3-3 (Aberdeen win 6-4 on aggregate)

Scorers: O'Gorman 4, Ryan 71(p), Bird 82/Dodds 15, 25, Rowson 83 **Referee:** M Lubos (Slo) **Attendance:** 6500

Barry Town Team: *Ovendale, Johnson, Lloyd, French, York, O'Gorman (C Evans 69), Barnett, Pike (Griffith 46), Bird, Jones, Ryan (Huggins). Subs not used: Loss, Mountain.*

23 July 1997: Inter Cable-Tel v Celtic. Celtic's A Thom sends keeper Ellacott the wrong way with a penalty.
Photo: Huw Evans Picture Agency

23 July1997: Inter Cable-Tel v Celtic. Celtic's J McNamara is tackled by W Hewitt.
Photo: Huw Evans Picture Agency

Welsh National League Wrexham Area

Premier Division	P	W	D	L	F	A	Pts
1 Wrexham Colts	26	23	1	2	121	74	70
2 Chirk A.A.A.	26	19	4	3	71	22	61
3 Penley	26	17	4	5	81	53	55
4 Rhostyllen V	26	17	1	8	83	55	52
5 Corwen	26	14	2	10	57	58	44
6 Llay Welfare	26	12	5	9	47	41	41
7 Brit. Aerospace	26	11	3	12	67	70	36
8 Llangollen T	26	10	5	11	61	61	35
9 Cefn Druids R	26	10	2	14	54	57	32
10 Ruthin T Res	26	9	2	15	41	71	29
11 Gresford Ath	26	9	0	17	54	71	27
12 Lex XI Res	26	8	2	16	44	73	26
13 Rhos Aelwyd R	26	2	4	20	26	86	10
14 B. Broughton R	26	2	3	21	31	96	9

Division One	P	W	D	L	F	A	Pts
1 Castell Alun Cts	18	14	2	2	69	24	44
2 Llay Welfare Res	18	10	2	6	38	40	32
3 Glynceiriog	18	8	4	6	43	37	28
4 Brickfield Rgrs	18	8	4	6	38	33	28
5 Bala Town	18	7	6	5	30	28	27
6 Kelloggs	18	8	3	7	36	41	27
7 Gresford Ath Res	18	7	5	6	48	28	26
8 Penycae Res	18	4	6	8	30	42	18
9 Buckley Tn Res	18	3	6	9	27	39	15
10 Ruthin Tn Colts	18	1	2	15	18	65	5

Pentre Broughton resigned, record expunged

Division Two	P	W	D	L	F	A	Pts
1 Owens Corning	22	20	0	2	86	26	60
2 Mynydd Isa	22	15	3	4	54	27	48
3 Glynceirlog Res	22	11	4	7	53	57	37
4 Corwen Res	22	10	4	8	41	37	34
5 Llay Welfare Cts	22	10	4	8	49	47	34
6 Chirk A.A.A. Res	22	9	2	11	52	38	29
7 Llanuwchllyn	22	8	5	9	53	49	29
8 Brit. Aerosp. Res	22	9	2	11	58	56	29
9 Hand Hotel	22	8	4	10	45	54	28
10 Buckley Tn Cts	22	7	3	12	44	54	24
11 Bala Town Res	22	3	5	14	33	66	14
12 Brickfield Rgrs R	22	3	2	17	24	81	11

South Wales Senior League

Division One	P	W	D	L	F	A	Pts
1 Les C/Caerau E	30	24	3	3	126	38	75
2 AFC Llwydcoed	30	23	2	5	104	41	71
3 Bettws FC	30	18	6	6	71	42	60
4 AFC Whitchurch	30	18	4	8	93	63	58
5 Bridgend Street	30	14	8	8	63	43	50
6 Penydarren BC	30	14	1	15	83	76	43
7 Penybryn	30	11	5	14	54	55	41
8 Pentwyn Dynos	30	11	6	13	44	56	38
9 Trefaf YC	30	10	5	15	65	93	38
10 Cogan Con	30	11	4	15	61	90	37
11 St Josephs	30	10	6	14	63	83	36
12 Lisvane	30	12	5	13	56	68	35
13 Grange Albion	30	9	6	15	46	59	32
14 Cadoxton Cons	30	7	2	21	45	75	26
15 Wenvoe Park	30	7	6	17	40	91	24
16 Llangynwyd Rs	30	5	3	21	45	103	15

Division Two	P	W	D	L	F	A	Pts
1 Butetown	30	26	2	2	113	36	80
2 Llanrumney AFC	30	26	0	4	101	37	78
3 Hopkinstown	30	20	2	8	84	46	64
4 Ystrad Mynach	30	16	4	10	68	58	52
5 Penrhiwfer	30	10	3	11	72	55	51
6 Tongwynfais	30	15	4	11	77	67	49
7 BP Barry	30	15	4	11	74	76	49
8 Pontypridd Ath	30	14	5	11	58	51	47
9 Stanleytown	30	12	3	15	81	76	39
10 Cefn Cribwr BC	30	10	5	15	53	68	35
11 Llwynypia WMC	30	9	4	17	62	97	31
12 AFC Rhws	30	8	5	17	58	82	29
13 AFC Rhondda	30	8	4	18	57	84	28
14 Penrhiwceiber	30	8	5	17	61	89	26
15 Nelson Cav's	30	5	2	23	48	85	17
16 Graig Metals	30	4	4	22	40	100	15

Gwent County League

First Division	P	W	D	L	F	A	Pts
1 Chepstow Tn	24	15	6	3	71	32	51
2 Spencer Yth	24	11	10	3	39	25	43
3 Rogerstone	24	12	5	7	47	44	41
4 Fleur-De-Lys	24	11	5	8	50	42	38
5 Tredegar Town	24	12	2	10	51	50	38
6 Pill AFC	24	9	6	9	37	34	33
7 Cwmtillery	24	8	7	9	46	40	31
8 Croesyceillog	24	7	9	8	42	37	30
9 Monmouth Town	24	8	5	11	44	56	29
10 Lliswerry	24	7	8	9	38	52	29
11 Aberbargoed	24	6	6	12	35	40	24
12 RTB Ebbw Vale	24	6	4	14	40	60	22
13 Civil Service	24	5	5	14	25	53	20

Second Division	P	W	D	L	F	A	Pts
1 Girling Ponty	30	22	6	2	98	41	72
2 Cwrn Welfare	30	19	7	4	98	37	64
3 Blaina W Side	30	19	5	6	93	34	62
4 Newport Corin	30	18	4	8	76	45	58
5 Lucas Cwmbran	30	15	9	6	65	47	54
6 Abercarn Town	30	13	7	10	62	52	46
7 Undy Athletic	30	13	6	11	63	63	45
8 Cafn Fforest	30	12	5	13	56	51	41
9 Fairfield United	30	11	5	14	64	70	38
10 Abertillery T	30	10	4	16	52	73	34
11 Christchurch	30	9	4	17	53	75	31
12 Cwmbran Celtic	30	10	1	19	48	76	31
13 Tranch AFC	30	9	3	18	66	87	30
14 Trinant AFC	30	8	6	16	48	75	30
15 AC Pontymister	30	7	6	17	40	74	27
16 Trethomas Mach	30	4	4	22	55	137	16

LEAGUE OF WALES IN EUROPE 1997-98

UEFA CUP PRELIMINARY ROUND

Dynamo Kiev	v	Barry Town	2-0
Barry Town	v	Dynamo Kiev	0-4
Inter Cabletel	v	Celtic	0-3
Celtic	v	Inter Cabletel	5-0

EBBW VALE IN THE INTER-TOTO CUP 1997

Ebbw Vale	v	Casino Graz (Austria)	0-0
Dragoljac (Croatia)	v	Ebbw Vale	4-0
Ebbw Vale	v	Bastia (France)	1-2
Silkeborg (Denmark)	v	Ebbw Vale	6-1

WELSH CLUBS IN THE INTER-TOTO CUP 1995-97

Played: 12 Won: 0 Drew: 2 Lost: 10 For: 3 Against: 37

Connahs Quay Nomads v Caernarfon Town, May 1997
Photo: Deeside Chronicle

Flint (in stripes) v Barry Town, April 1997
Photo: Flint & Holywell Chronicle

Spar Mid Wales League

	P	W	D	L	F	A	Pts
1 Caersws	26	19	5	2	86	33	62
2 Newtown	26	20	1	5	85	20	61

Gwynedd Training League

	P	W	D	L	F	A	Pts
1 Holyhead H'spur	24	17	2	5	82	34	53
2 Hotspur	24	15	2	7	78	39	47

Cambria Housing Anglesey League

	P	W	D	L	F	A	Pts
1 ??mlwch	26	23	0	3	134	21	69
2 ??walchmai	26	17	4	5	105	35	55

Tremont Ford And Rover Mid Wales League (South)

	P	W	D	L	F	A	Pts
1 Newcastle	26	23	2	1	80	21	71
2 Vale of Arrow	26	22	2	2	98	22	68

LAZAROU CARDIFF SUNDAY LEAGUES

Lanterns Restaurant

	P	W	D	L	F	A	Pts
1 Davies Colour	12	8	1	3	33	19	25
2 Ely Region	12	7	2	3	29	24	23

Eversons Sports Trophies

	P	W	D	L	F	A	Pts
1 Quarry Sports	16	10	3	3	53	25	33
2 Athletico New Inn	16	9	5	2	58	31	32

Colorfoto Wales

	P	W	D	L	F	A	Pts
1 Fortuna Athletic	18	14	2	2	72	13	44
2 Cardiff Cosmos L	18	13	3	2	91	34	42

Heps Engineering

	P	W	D	L	F	A	Pts
1 Broadacres	18	16	2	0	81	12	50
2 Idem Papers	18	13	0	5	72	41	39

DEESIDE SUNDAY LEAGUE

Noel Price

Division One	P	W	D	L	F	A	Pts
1 Mold Red Star	20	13	5	2	67	34	31
2 Greenfield NA	20	13	4	3	82	33	30
Division Two							
1 Boot & Ship	20	15	3	2	76	41	33
2 Packet House	20	13	2	5	67	38	28

OLD COLWYN LLANDUDNO SUNDAY LEAGUE

	P	W	D	L	F	A	Pts
1 Crosville	22	20	2	0	160	21	42
2 Hammers	22	19	1	2	154	35	35

PIC-UP SPARES SWANSEA SUNDAY LEAGUE

Division One	P	W	D	L	Pts
1 Mt Dew Rgrs	18	14	2	2	44
2 Fairfield	18	14	0	4	42
Division Two					
1 Windsor	20	17	1	2	52
2 Lady of Lourdes	20	14	1	5	43
Division Three					
1 Duke of York	20	16	3	1	51
2 Old Compass	20	14	4	2	46
Division Four					
1 Cwmfelin Club	22	18	1	3	55
2 Globe Inn	22	17	4	1	55

Tetley Bitter Newtown League

Division One	P	W	D	L	F	A	Pts
1 Churchstoke	16	10	0	6	64	45	30
2 Newtown Fsc	16	9	2	5	58	44	29
Division Two							
1 New Inn	18	16	2	0	94	17	50
2 Elephant & Castle	18	14	0	4	88	31	42

NORTH GWYNEDD & YNYS MON SUNDAY LEAGUE

I & H Griffiths

Division One	P	W	D	L	F	A	Pts
1 Holyhead Ex-Ser	15	13	1	1	73	16	40
2 Gwalchmai Ath	16	11	3	2	88	22	36

Caprice

Division Two	P	W	D	L	F	A	Pts
1 Inter Caer	18	13	3	2	71	26	42
2 Cemaes BS	18	12	3	3	64	32	39

My Scaffolding

Division Three	P	W	D	L	F	A	Pts
1 Ryl Oak M'traeth	18	16	1	1	101	25	46
2 Brynsiencyn	18	12	5	1	84	28	41

TAFF-ELY SUNDAY LEAGUE

Division One	P	W	D	L	F	A	Pts
1 Graig	18	15	1	2	64	29	46
2 Rhydyfelln	18	11	2	5	49	27	35

TAFF-ELY ASSOCIATION FOOTBALL LEAGUE

Senior Saturday League

Premier Division	P	W	D	L	F	A	Pts
1 Abercynon Drag.	14	14	0	0	32	17	42
2 Taffs Well	14	5	5	4	37	30	20
Division One							
1 Graig United	22	18	2	2	66	25	56
2 Trefgaest	22	13	4	5	80	41	43

PIC-UP SPARES SWANSEA SENIOR LEAGUE

Division One	P	W	D	L	Pts
1 West End	22	18	2	2	56
2 Maltsters Sports	22	16	2	4	50
Division Two					
1 PT Colts	20	15	2	3	47
2 Star Athletic	20	13	4	3	43
Division Three					
1 Marquis Arms	22	17	3	2	54
2 PT Stars	22	15	5	2	50
Division Four					
1 Dillwyn Amts	24	17	5	2	56
2 Morriston Sports	24	16	4	4	52
Division Five					
1 Wildfowler	21	19	0	2	57
2 Bryndeg	21	14	3	4	45

ABERAVON SHOPPING CENTRE PORT TALBOT LEAGUE

(Not final, latest available)

Premier Division	P	W	D	L	Pts
1 Abercregan Utd	21	19	1	1	58
2 Glyncorrwg Utd	20	17	2	1	53
Division One					
1 Cornelly Utd	20	16	1	3	49
2 Four Winds	18	14	0	4	42
Division Two					
1 Taibach WMC	21	20	1	0	61

NEATH & DISTRICT LEAGUE

Premier Division

		P	W	D	L	Pts
1	Cwmtawe	22	16	3	3	51
2	Cilfrew	22	14	6	2	48

Division One

		P	W	D	L	Pts
1	Cwmamman Utd	22	17	2	3	53
2	AFC Cimla	22	16	3	3	51

Division Two

		P	W	D	L	Pts
1	Birchgrove Utd	16	12	2	2	38
2	Tonna	16	12	1	3	37

Division Three

		P	W	D	L	Pts
1	Clydach GT	16	11	2	3	35
2	Gwaun-cae-G.	16	9	2	5	29

Reserve Division Three

		P	W	D	L	Pts
1	Giants Grave	18	13	2	3	41
2	Ynysygerwn CC	18	12	2	4	38

Reserve Division Two

		P	W	D	L	Pts
1	Travellers Well	22	16	4	2	52
2	Longford Ath	22	14	2	6	44

Reserve Division Three

		P	W	D	L	Pts
1	Birchgrove Utd	26	20	3	3	63
2	Pontardawe FC	26	17	4	5	55

BRECON LEAGUE

		P	Pts
1	Brecon SC	21	52
2	Sennybridge	21	41

ABERDARE VALLEY

Barlow Mincham

Premier Division

		P	W	D	L	F	A	Pts
1	Aberaman Ex-S	20	16	2	2	91	24	50
2	AFC Llwydooed	20	15	3	2	62	39	48

Phoenix Windows Division One

		P	W	D	L	F	A	Pts
1	Tynte Rovers	14	10	2	2	54	19	32
2	Glandover	14	9	3	2	32	16	30

Tower Colliery Division Two

		P	W	D	L	F	A	Pts
1	Bee Hive	16	15	0	1	64	30	42
2	Cynon Sports	16	10	3	3	75	29	33

CYNGHRAIR FFIGAR ABERYSTWYTH LEAGUE

Adran One

		P	W	D	L	F	A	Pts
1	Padarn United	26	19	6	1	70	17	63
2	Penrhyncoch R	26	17	5	4	68	23	56

Adran Two

		P	W	D	L	F	A	Pts
1	Aberdyfi	30	25	4	1	110	21	79
2	Pardarn Res	30	25	3	2	140	44	78

TALACRE BEACH CARAVAN PARK CLWYD FOOTBALL LEAGUE

Premier Division

		P	W	D	L	F	A	Pts
1	Colwyn B YMCA	26	22	1	3	106	21	67
2	Pilkington FC	25	19	3	3	72	26	60

Division One

		P	W	D	L	F	A	Pts
1	Trefnant Vge FC	20	17	1	2	74	34	52
2	Hawarden R FC	20	14	3	3	86	20	45

Division Two

		P	W	D	L	F	A	Pts
1	Flint Tn Jnrs	20	17	3	0	110	31	54
2	St Asaph C Boys	20	14	3	3	79	40	45

THREEWAYS SUBARU VALE OF CONWY LEAGUE

		P	W	D	L	F	A	Pts
1	Llansannan	30	27	3	0	94	24	84
2	D'mo Dolgarrog	30	21	3	6	104	39	66

NESTLE EAST GWENT LEAGUE

Division One

		P	W	D	L	F	A	Pts
1	Tintern A	26	19	3	4	89	37	61
2	Red & White A	26	18	5	5	87	51	53

Division Two

		P	W	D	L	F	A	Pts
1	Club Santes	20	17	3	0	103	41	52
2	Chepstow B	20	15	4	1	75	35	46

CYNGHRAIR FFIGAR LEAGUE

Division One

		P	W	D	L	Pts
1	Padarn Utd	26	19	6	1	63
2	Penrhyn Res	26	17	5	4	56

Division Two

		P	W	D	L	Pts
1	Aberdyfi	30	25	4	1	79
2	Padarn Res	30	25	3	2	78

L'HIRONDELLE CARDS LEAGUE

Division One

		P	W	D	L	Pts
1	St Dogmaels	22	16	5	1	53
2	Llandysul	22	15	3	4	48

Division Two

		P	W	D	L	Pts
1	Bargod Rang	26	20	1	5	61
2	Lampeter	26	19	3	4	58

Division Three

		P	W	D	L	Pts
1	Lampeter Res	20	16	0	4	48
2	Aberaeron Res	20	12	4	4	40

TANNERS WINES MONTGOMERYSHIRE LEAGUE

Division One

		P	W	D	L	F	A	Pts
1	Waterloo Rovers	16	12	2	2	59	20	38
2	Llanrnaeadr YM	16	12	2	2	52	26	38

Division Two

		P	W	D	L	F	A	Pts
1	Welshpool T Rs	18	15	2	1	58	15	47
2	Dyffryn Banw	18	13	1	4	58	26	40

Division Three

		P	W	D	L	F	A	Pts
1	Coleg Normal	24	20	3	1	94	26	63
2	Bethesda Ath	24	17	4	3	102	26	55

JAMES WILLIAMS PEMBROKESHIRE LEAGUE

Division One

		P	W	D	L	F	A	Pts
1	Hakin United	24	20	2	2	76	16	62
2	Pannar	24	20	1	3	83	24	61

Division Two

		P	W	D	L	F	A	Pts
1	Midford United	26	20	3	3	108	46	63
2	Fishguard	26	20	2	4	89	38	62

Division Three

		P	W	D	L	F	A	Pts
1	H'west CC	24	19	4	1	92	34	61
2	Tenby	24	15	4	4	69	31	52

Reserve Division One

		P	W	D	L	F	A	Pts
1	Marberth	26	23	3	0	132	20	72
2	Hakin Utd	26	23	3	0	118	31	72

Reserve Division Two Play-offs

		P	W	D	L	F	A	Pts
1	Herbrandston	6	4	2	0	22	6	14
2	St Ishmaels	6	1	5	0	16	7	8

DIRECTORY OF CLUBS 1997-98

ABERYSTWYTH TOWN

Chairman: Derek Dawson. **President:** Mr D Jones **Vice-Chairman:**
Secretary: Mr D Dawson, Underwood, Lorweth Avenue, Aberystwyth, SY23 1EW (1970 624548)
Manager: Meirion Appleton **Asst Manager:** **Physio:**
Ground: Park Avenue, Aberystwyth, Dyfed (01970 612122).
Directions: From south: A487, 1st right at Trefachan Bridge to r'bout, 1st right with Park Avenue being 3rd right. From north: A487 and follow one-way system to railway station, at r'bout 1st left with Park Avenue being 3rd right. 5 mins walk from Aberystwyth (BR) - follow as above.
Seats: 300 **Cover:** 1,200 **Capacity:** 4,500 **Floodlights:** Yes **Shop:** Yes
Programme: 24 pages, 60p. **Editor:** Steve Moore (01970 617705). **Press Officer:** David Thomas
Colours: Black & green/black/black. **Change colours:** Yellow/white/white
Sponsors: Continental Cambria Tyres. **Nickname:** Seasiders **Founded:** 1884.
Midweek Matcheday: Wednesday **Reserves League:** Mid-Wales
Record Attendance: 4,500 v Hereford, Welsh Cup 1971.
Previous League: Welsh 1896-97/ Nth Wales Comb. 99-1900/ Montgomeryshire & Dist. 04-20/ Central Wales 21-25 81-87/ Mid-Wales 26-32 51-81/ Cambrian Coast 32-51/ Welsh Lg South 51-63/ Abacus 87-92.
Clubhouse: Open daily noon-3 & 7-12pm. Snacks available.
Club Record Scorer: David Williams 476, 66-83. **Club Record Appearances:** David P Whitney 572, 62-81.
Hons: Welsh Cup 1899-1900; Welsh I'mediate Cup 85-86 87-88; Mid Wales Lg(11) (Lg Cup(7); Welsh Amtr Cup (3); Welsh Lg Div 2 Sth 51-52; Cambrian Coast Lg(8) Central Wales Chal. Cup(6)

BANGOR CITY

President: Lady Pennant **Chairman:** Gwyn Pierce Owen **Vice Chairman:** David Gareth Jones.
Secretary: Alun Griffiths, 12 Lon-Y-Bryn, Menai Bridge, Anglesey, Gwynedd LL57 5NM (01248 712820).
Manager: Graeme Sharp **Asst Manager:** John Hulse **Physio:** Arwel Jones
Ground: The Stadium, Farrar Road, Bangor, Gwynedd (01248 355852)
Directions: Old A5 into Bangor, 1st left before railway station, ground on left by garage.
Seats: 700 **Cover:** 1,200 **Capacity:** 5,000 **Floodlights:** Yes **Shop:** Yes
Programme: 32 pages, 70p **Editor:** Anthony Evans **Press Officer:** Alun Griffiths
Colours: All navy blue **Change colours:** All white
Sponsors: Pentraeth Mazda **Nickname:** Citizens **Founded:** 1876
Midweek Matchedays: Tuesday **Reserve League:** Welsh Alliance.
Record Attendance: 10,000 v Wrexham, Welsh Cup final 78-79.
Previous Leagues:: N Wales Coast 1893-98 1911-12/The Comb 1898-1910/N Wales Comb 30-33/W Mids 32-38/Lancs Comb 38-39 46-50/Ches Co 50-68/NPL 68-79 81-82 84-92/Alliance Prem 79-81 82-84.
Clubhouse: Not on ground
Honours: FA Tphy R-up 83-84; Northern Prem. Lg 81-82 (R-up 86-87, Lg Cup 68-69, Presidents Cup 88-89, Chal. Shield 87-88), Cheshire Co. Lg R-up 53-54 58-59, Lancs Comb. R-up 30-31, League of Wales 94-95 (Lg Cup R-up 94-95), Welsh National Lg 27-28 (R-up 26-27), Nth Wales Coast Lg 1895-96, Welsh Cup 1888-89 95-96 1961-62 (R-up 27-28 60-61 63-64 72-73 77-78 84-85), Nth Wales Chal. Cup 26-27 35-36 36-37 37-38 46-47 51-52 57-58 64-65 67-68, Welsh Amtr Cup 1894-95 96-96 97-98 98-99 1900-01 02-03 04-05 05-06 11-12, Welsh Jnr Cup 1995-96 97-98 1919-20, Welsh All. Alves Cup 49-50 59-60 (Cookson Cup 61-62 68-69 84-85 86-87).

BARRY TOWN

Chairman: Paula O'Halloran **Player Manager:** Gary Barnett
Secretary: Alan Whelan, 132 Westward Rise, Barry, South Glam. CF62 6NQ (01446 737188).
Ground: Jenner Park, Barry (01446 735858)
Directions: M4 jct 33 via Wenvoe (A4050) to Barry. Left at 1st 2 r'bouts to Jenner Park. Nearest rail station is Cadoxton.
Capacity: 3,000 **Floodlights:** Yes **Cover:** Yes **Seats:** 800 **Programme:** Yes
Colours: Yellow/yellow/blue. **Change:** All white
Sponsors: Vale of Glamorgan Council **Nickname:** Dragons **Founded:** 1923.
Midweek Matchedays: Tuesday.
Record Attendance: 7,400 v Queens Park Rangers, FA Cup 1st Rd 1961.
Previous Leagues: Western 08-13/ Southern 13-82 89-93/ Welsh 82-89 94-95.
Best FA Cup season: 2nd Rd 29-30.
Best FA Trophy season: 3rd Qualifying Rd replay 90-91.
Players progressing to Football League: C Simmonds (Millwall) 47, J Brown (Ipswich) 48, D Tennant (Brighton) 48, T Elwell (Swansea) 48, R McLaren (Cardiff) 50, R Howells (Cardiff) 50, C Cairney (Bristol Rovers) 53, D Tapscott (Arsenal) 53, D Ward (Bristol Rovers) 54, J McGhee (Newport) 54, T Quigley (Portsmouth) 55, B Keating (Crewe) 56, J Hartnett (Hartlepool) 57, R Twigg (Notts County) 57, K Webber (Everton) 60, P Issac (Northampton) 1962, L Sheffield (Newport) 62, G Fraser (Newport) 66, R Ferguson (Newport) 69, R Delgado (Luton) 70, G Jones (Luton) 72, R Green (Newport) 72, M Coslett (Newport) 78, P Green (Newport) 84, C Pike (Fulham) 85, I Love (Swansea) 86.
Clubhouse: Open normal licensing hours, 11.00-11.00 daily
96-97 Captain: Andrew York **96-97 Top Scorer:** Tony Bird **96-97 P.o.Y.:** Andrew York
Club Record Goalscorer: Clive Ayres **Club Record Appearances:** Basil Bright.
Honours: Welsh Cup (3); Welsh Trophy 94-95; Southern Lg R-up 20-21; Western Lg R-up 11-12, Welsh Lg (7), Lg Cup (4); South Wales Senior Cup (13); SA Brain Cup (3); League of Wales 95-96 96-97; UEFA Cup 2 Qual Rds 96-97.

CAERNARFON TOWN

President: Jack F Thomas. **Chairman:** G.Lloyd Owen. **Vice-Chairmen:** Eilian Angel
Secretary: Elwyn Watkins, 20 South Penrault, Caernarfon, Gwynedd. LL55 1NS (01286 674045)
Manager: Steve Joel **Coach:** Alan McDonald **Physio:** Ian Humphreys
Ground: The Oval, Marcus Street, Caernarfon, Gwynedd (01286 675002).
Directions: A55 coast road to A487 bypass to Caernarfon. At inner relief road r'bout follow Beddlegert sign, then 2nd right - ground opposite. Nearest BR station is 9 miles distant at Bangor. Local buses to Hendre estate.
Capacity: 3,678 **Seats:** 178 **Cover:** 1,500 **Floodlights:** Yes **Club Shop:** Yes
Programme: 48pgs 70p **Editor:** Marc Roberts **Press Officer:** Geraint Lloyd Owen (01286 830307).
Colours: Yellow/green/yellow **Change colours:** Sky & claret/claret/claret
Sponsors: Bus Eireann (1st Colours). KMP Coaches (Change) **Nickname:** Canaries
Midweek Matchday: Wednesday. **Founded:** 1876 **Reserve Team:** Yes.
Record Attendance: 6,002 v Bournemouth, FA Cup 2nd Rd 1929.
Best FA Trophy season: 1st Round replay 87-88.
Best FA Cup season: 3rd Rd replay 86-87 (lost 0-1 at Barnsley). Also 2nd Rd 29-30.
Previous Leagues: North Wales Coast 06-21/ Welsh National 26-30/ North Wales Combination 32-33/ Welsh Lg (North) 37-76 77-80/ Lancs Combination 80-82/ North West Counties 82-85/ Northern Prem Lge, Prem & Div 1
Players progressing to Football League: Ernie Walley (Spurs), Gwyn Jones (Wolves 1955), Wyn Davies & Haydn Jones (Wrexham 1960 & 64), Tom Walley (Arsenal 1964), Paul Crooks (Stoke 1986), David Martindale & Steve Craven & David Higgins (Tranmere 1987).
Clubhouse: Yes. 2 snooker tables, darts, pool, fruit machines and live entertainment.
96-97 Captain: Paul Tomlinson **96-97 P.o.Y.:** Gary Jones **96-97 Top scorer:** Eifion Williams (42)
Club Record Goalscorer: W Jones 255 (1906-26) **Club Record Appearances:** Walter Jones 306.
Honours: N West Co's Lg R-up 84-85 (Div 2 R-up 82-83); Lancs Comb 81-82 (Lg Cup 80-81); Welsh Lg (North)(4) 46-47 65-66 77-79, R-up(4) 56-58 72-73 79-80; Alves Cup(4) 38-39 74-75 77-79; Cookson 56-57 77-78; N Wales Combination 32-33; Welsh National Lg 26-27 29-30 (R-up 28-29); N Wales Coast Lg 11-12.

CAERSWS

Chairman: Garth Williams **Vice Chairman:** Hadyn Jones **President:** Dilwyn Lewis
Secretary: T M B Jones, 3 Hafren Terrace, Caersws, Powys SY17 5ES (01686 688103).
Manager: Mickey Evans **Asst Manager:** Barry Harding **Physio:** Wynne Jones
Ground: The Recreation Ground, Caersws, Powys.(01686 688753)
Directions: Entering Caersws (between Newtown & Llanidloes on A470) grd entrance on left by bridge.
Seats: 150 **Cover:** 300 **Capacity:** 3,250 **Floodlights:** Yes **Shop:** No.
Programme: 44 pages, 50p **Editor:** Graham Burrows. **Press Officer:** Ivor Williams
Colours: Blue/white/blue **Change colours:** Orange/black/black
Sponsor: British Meat **Nickname:** Bluebirds **Founded:** 1887.
Midweek Matchday: Tuesday **Reserve League:** Mid-Wales.
Record Attendance: 2,795 v Swansea City, Welsh Cup 1990.
Previous Leagues: Mid-Wales (pre-1989)/Cymru Alliance 90-92.
Players progressing to Football League: P Woosnam (Leyton Orient, West Ham United, Aston Villa, Atlanta), M Evans (Wolverhampton Wanderers, Wrexham), K.Lloyd (Hereford U, Cardiff City).
Clubhouse: Not on ground, but in village centre. Normal licensing hours. Food served.
96-97 Captain: Paul Jones **96-97 P.o.Y.:** Paul Jones **96-97 Top Scorer:**
Club Record Scorer: Gareth Davies. **Club Record Appearances:**
Hons: Welsh Amtr Cup 60-61, I'mediate Cup 88-89 (R-up 91-92); Mid-Wales Lg (9) 59-61 62-63 77-78 82-83 85-86 88-90 96-97 (Lg Cup 79-80 82-83 87-88 89-90); Cent. Wales Challenge Cup 77-78 82-83 87-88 89-90 (Yth Cup 69-70 72-73); Montgomeryshire Challenge Cup(18) 52-53 59-60 62-63 69-72 74-75 76-78 83-89 90-91 94-95 94-95 96-97; Montgomeryshire Lg 77-78.

CARMARTHEN TOWN

Chairman: Hugh Jenkins **President:** Anthony Jenkins
Secretary: Alan Latham, 3 Maesdolau, Idole, Carmarthen SA32 8DQ (01267 232432 H), Fax (01267 222851).
Manager: John Mahoney **Asst Manager:** **Physio:** T Poynton/A Underwood
Ground: Richmond Park, Priory Street, Carmarthen Dyfed (01267 232101)
Directions: Proceed into Carmarthen on A48, pich up 440 to Llandilo at the 1st rounabout and follow signs for 800 meters. The ground is on left in Priory Street.
Seats: 120 **Cover:** 750 **Capacity:** 3,000 **Floodlights:** Yes **Club Shop:** Yes
Programme: Yes **Editor:** Alvn Charles
Colours: Gold/black/black **Change colours:** Blue & black/white/blue
Sponsors: Jewson Carmarthen **Nickname:** The Town **Founded:** 1948
Midweek Matchday: Wednesday **Reserve League:** Carmarthenshire Lge
Record Attendance: 3,000 **Previous Leagues:** Welsh League **Clubhouse:** Yes
96-97 Captain: Mark Delaney **96-97 P.o.Y.:** **96-97 Top Scorer:** Mark Dickeson
Honours: Welsh Lge Div 2 59-60, Div 1 95-96, Cup Winners 95-96.

CEMAES YNYS MON

Chairman: J C Davis **President:** I Clews
Secretary: Mrs N Hughes, 12 Maes Garnedd, Tregele, Cemaes Bay, Anglsey LL67 0DR (01407 710297)
Manager: Bryn Howes **Asst Manager:** Steve Edwards **Physio:** G Humphries
Ground: School Lane Stadium, Cemaes Bay, Anglesey (01407 710600)
Directions: A5025 from Brittania Bridge into Anglsey
Seats: 300 **Cover:** 1000 **Capacity:** 3,000 **Floodlights:** Yes **Club Shop:** Yes
Programme: 30 pages 50p **Editor:**
Colours: Yellow/black/black **Change colours:** All red
Sponsors: Various **Nickname:** **Founded:** 1976
Midweek Matchday: Wednesday **Reserve League:** Anglesey Lge
Record Attendance: 721 v Bangor City 95-96
Previous Leagues: Anglesey Lge, Welsh Alliance, Cymru Alliance
Clubhouse: No
96-97 Captain: Tony Clarke **96-97 P.o.Y.:** Mike Maloney **96-97 Top Scorer:** John McNally
Honours: Cookson Cup 91-92 92-93; Welsh Alliance 92-93; Cymru Alliance 94-95

CONNAH'S QUAY NOMADS

Chairman: Mr R Morris **President:** Mr R Jones.
Secretary/Press Officer: Mr Robert Hunter, 40 Brookdale Avenue, Connah's Quay, Deeside, Clywd CH5 4LU (01244 831212(h)/ 520299(b)).
Managers: Neville Powell **Asst Manager:** Gary Wynne **Physio:** Mr M Latter.
Ground: Halfway Ground, Connah's Quay, Deeside, Clwyd.
Directions: On main coast road (A548) from Chester to Rhyl west end of Connah's Quay behind Halfway Hotal.
Seats: 105 **Cover:** 500 **Capacity:** 1,500 **Floodlights:** Yes **Club Shop:** No
Programme: 26 pages, 50p **Editor:** Rachel Morgan
Colours: White/navy/White. **Change colours:** Yellow/blue/yellow
Sponsors: Hallows Associatres Solicitors **Nickname:** Westenders **Founded:** 1946
Midweek Matchday: Tuesday. **Reserve League:** Sealink Welsh Alliance.
Record Attendance: 1,500 v Rhyl, Welsh Cup SF 29/3/93.
Previous Leagues: Clywd/ Welsh Alliance/ Cymru Alliance 90-92.
Clubhouse: No, but Halfway Hotel is adjacent
96-97 Captain: Barry Thukas **96-97 P.o.Y.:** Carl Smyth **96-97 Top Scorer:** Chris Davies
Honours: Welsh Amtr Cup 52-53 54-55, Nth Wales FA Amtr Cup 52-53 54-55, North Wales Coast Challenge Cup, Welsh Intermediate Cup 80-81, Welsh Alliance Cookson Cup 87-88, Welsh Youth Cup 47-48.

CONWY UNITED

Chairman: Graham Rees. **Vice Chairman:** G Evans **President:** K Davies
Secretary: Mr G Rees, 1 Tan y Maes, Glan Conwy LL28 5LQ (01492 573243)
Manager: **Asst Manager:** Steve Myers **Coach:** Chris Camden.
Ground: Morfa Ground, Conwy, Gwynedd (01492 593860).
Directions: Leave A55 on 1st slip road after river tunnel and turn left towards Conwy. Sharp left immediately after overhead railway bridge - ground 400yds on left of Penmaen Rd.
Seats: 150 **Cover:** 400 **Capacity:** 2,500 **Floodlights:** Yes **Shop:** Yes
Programme: 32 pages, 75p **Editor:** Dylan Evans **Press Officer:** G Rees
Colours: Tangerine/black/tangerine **Change colours:** All white
Sponsors: Carlsberg Tetley. **Nickname:** Musselmen **Founded:** 1977.
Midweek Matches: Wednesday **Reserves League:** Gwynedd League
Record Attendance: 600 v Bangor City, Ton Lon Barritt Cup 88
Previous Leagues: Vale of Conwy/ Gwynedd/ Welsh Alliance/ Cymru Alliance.
Players progressing to Football League: Neville Southall (via Winsford to Bury, Everton), Carl Dale (via Rhyl and Bangor to Chester City, Cardiff City).
Clubhouse: Yes,at Ground.
Club Record Goalscorer: Carl Dale **Club Record Appearances:** Gwyn Williams.
Honours: Welsh Alliance 84-85 85-86; Barritt Cup 84-85; Welsh Intermediate Cup 81-82.

CWMBRAN TOWN

Chairman: J C Colley **Vice Chairman:** **President:** John Colley
Secretary: Mr M F SAlway, 10 Hafod Road, Pontthir, Newport, Gwent NP6 1GH (01633 430065 H)
Manager: Tony Willcox **Coach:** Roger Gibbons. **Physio:** Terry Cutlan
Ground: Cwmbran Stadium, Henllys Way, Cwmbran, Gwent (01633 866192 Fax 863324).
Directions: M4 jct 26, follow signs for Cwmbran. At 1st r/about (approx 1.5 miles) take 1st exit & proceed along Cwmbran Drive umtil passing Stadium on right. At r/about take 1st exit, then immediately at next r/about take 3rd exit. Ground entrance 150 yardson right. One and a half miles from Cwmbran (BR).
Seats: 2,201 **Cover:** 1,857 **Capacity:** 8,201 **Floodlights:** Yes **Shop:** Yes
Programme: 28 pages, 50p. **Programme Editor/Press Officer:** Maurice Salway (01633 430065).
Colours: White/blue/white. **Change colours:** All red
Sponsors: Exide Batteries Ltd **Nickname:** The Town **Founded:** 1951.
Midweek Matches: Wednesday. **Reserves League:** None
Record Attendance: 8,148 v Manchester Utd Aug 1994
Previous Leagues: Monmouthshire Snr 51-59/ Welsh 60-92.
Players progressing to Football League: Simon King (Newport 1984), Mark Waite (Bristol Rovers 1984), Nathan Wigg (Cardiff 1993), Chris Watkins (Swansea 1993).
Clubhouse: Pub hours, on ground. Catering facilities.
96-97 Captain: Wayne Goodridge **96-97 P.o.Y.:** Mattie Davies **96-97 Top Scorer:** Mattie Davies
Club Record Scorer: Graham Reynolds **Club Record Appearances:** Mostyn Lewis.
Honours: Lg of W. 92-93; Welsh Lg Div 1 66-67, Welsh Lg Cup 85-86 90-91.

EBBW VALE

President: J S Harrison **Chairman:** D Coughlin **V-Chairmanm** M.Carini.
Secretary: V Reed, Troed yr Afon, Alexander Place, Abercanaid, Merthyr Tydfil CF48 1SJ (01443 692631)
Manager: John Lewis **Asst Manager:** Mick Martin. **Physio:**
Ground: Eugene Cross Park, Ebbw Vale, Gwent (01495 302995).
Directions: From A465 follow signs to Ebbw Vale, 1st left at next two r'bouts - ground on left.
Seats: 1,200 **Cover:** 1,200 **Capacity:** 10,000 **Floodlights:** Yes **Shop:** No
Programme: 26 pages, 50p **Editor:**
Change colours: White & black/white/white **Colours:** Yellow & black/yellow/black
Sponsor: **Nickname:** Cowboys **Founded:** 1950
Midweek matches: Wednesday
Record Attendance: 1,762 v Wrexham, Welsh Cup 1989.
Previous League: Abacus
Clubhouse: Yes open daily share with Rugby Club
96-97 Captain: **96-97 Top Scorer:** **96-97 P.o.Y.:**
Honours: Abacus Lg 87-88 (Div 1 64-65, Southern Div 52-53, Div 2 East 60-61), Sth Wales Lg 03-04, Welsh Cup 25-26, South Wales Snr Cup 04-05, Gwent Snr Cup 24-25 26-27 28-29 32-33 45-46 50-51.

FLINT TOWN UNITED

Chairman: A Baines **Vice Chairman:** J Simon **President:** David Hough.
Secretary: Keith Biggs, 10 Powell Road, Buckley, Flintshire, CH7 2BZX (01244 541789 H)
Manager: Steve Myers **Asst Manager:** S Buxton **Physio:** T Jennings
Ground: Cae-Y-Castell, Marsh Lane, Flint, Clywd CH6 5JP (01352 730982).
Directions: Approaching Flint on A548 from Chester, turn right at signpost for Flint Castle. Ground to right of car park. Flint BR station and bus stops are adjacent to ground.
Seats: 300 **Cover:** 500 **Capacity:** 6,000 **Floodlights:** Yes **Shop:** Yes
Programme: 36 pages, £1 **Editor:** Graham George (01352 735148) **Press Officer:** Norma Bennett
Colours: All black & white **Change colours:** Yelow/white/white
Sponsors: **Nickname:** Silkmen **Founded:** 1886
Midweek matchday: Wednesday **Reserves League:** Clywd
Previous Leagues: Clwyd/ Welsh Alliance/ Cymru Alliance 90-92.
Clubhouse: Yes open every evening and matchdays.
96-97 Captain: A Davies **96-97 Top Scorer:** S Jones **96-97 P.o.Y.:**
Honours: Cymru Alliance 90-91, Welsh Cup 53-54, Welsh Amtr Cup 47-48, Welsh All.(4) 54-57 89-90 (Alves Cup 53-54 89-90, Cookson Cup 52-53 88-89), Welsh Championship Cup 90-91, N. Wales Coast Chal. Cup 90-91, Nth Wales Coast Amtr Cup(8) 09-10 30-36 68-69.

HAVERFORDWEST COUNTY

Chairman: Emile Moore **Manager:** Mark Hopkins
Secretary: C Sales, 46 Wesley Place, Trecwn, Haverfordwest, Pembs SA62 5XR (01348 840083)
Ground: Bridge Meadow Stadium, Haverfordwest Pembs.
Colours: All Blue **Change colours:** Yellow/green/green
Midweek Matchday: Wednesday

INTER-CABLE TEL

Chairman: Max James **President:** **Commercial Mgr:** Colin Hicks
Secretary: John McTavish, 17 Coed Bach, Highlight Park, Barry CF62 8AE (01446 741144)
Manager: George Wood **Asst Manager:** Phil Holme **Physio:** Roy Langley
Ground: Cardiff Athletic Stadium, Leckwith Road, Cardiff (01222 225345)
Directions: M4 Junc 33 to Barry A4232 past Culverhouse Cross turn off onto Leckwith Road, grd on right.
Capacity: 5,000 **Covered:** 2,500 **Seats:** 2,500 **Floodlights:** Yes **Shop:** Yes
Programme: 24 pages, £1 **Editor:** Colin Hicks. **Press Officer:** Clive Harry
Colours: White/black/red **Change colours:** All Yellow
Sponsors: Cabletel **Nickname:** Seagulls **Founded:** 1990.
Midweek Matchdays: Tuesday. **Record Attendance:** 1,500 v Everton August 1996.
Previous Leagues: Barry & District/ South Wales Amateur/ Abacus
96-97 Captain: Sean Wharton **96-97 Top Scorer:** Paul Burrows **96-97 P.o.Y.:** Sean Wharton
Honours: League of Wales R-up 92-93 93-94, Abacus Lg Div 1 86-87, Sth Wales Amtr Lg 84-85 85-86. *As Sully: Sth Wales Amtr Lg Coronation Cup 69-70, Corinthian Cup 78-79, Abacus Lg Div 1 83-84 85-86 89-90 (Div 2 80-81), Sth Wales Snr Cup 80-81 81-82.*

NEWTOWN

President: Trevor Jones **Chairman:** Keith Harding **Manager:** Brian Coyne
Secretary: Mrs S Reynolds, 19 Brynwood Drive, Milford Rd, Newtown, Powys (01686 628089 H), (01686 626965 B), Fax (01681 623813)
Manager: Brian Coyne **Asst Manager:** Jake King. **Physio:** Elwyn Morgan
Ground: Latham Park, Newtown, Powys (01686 623813).
Directions: A43 to Newtown, right at 1st lights into Back Lane & town centre - 400yds left into Park St., 500yds right (at Library) into Park Lane - ground at end.
Seats: 200 **Cover:** 700 **Capacity:** 5,000 **Floodlights:** Yes **Shop:** Yes.
Programme: 36 pages, 50p **Editor:** Keith Harding/ Nigel Bevan. **Press Officer:** John Annerean.
Colours: Red & white/white/red **Change colours:** Blue & yellow/blue/blue
Sponsors: Shell Gas **Nickname:** Robins **Founded:** 1875.
Midweek Matchdays: Tuesday. **Reserves League:** Central Wales
Record Attendance: 5,002 v Swansea City, Welsh Cup 1954.
Previous Leagues: The Combination/ Central Wales/ Northern Premier.
Best FA Trophy year: 3rd Qual. 89-90 **Best FA Cup year:** 2nd Rd 1884-85. Also 1st Rd 1885-86.
Players progressing to Football League: C Lloyd (Orient), J Lovent (C Palace & Exeter), M Bloor (Stoke & Lincoln), I Woan (Nottm Forest), J Hill (Rochdale), R Newlands (Plymouth), M Williams (Shrewsbury).
Clubhouse: Open every evening. Hot/cold snacks, pool, darts.
Honours: Welsh Cup 1878-79 94-95 (R-up 85-65 87-88 96-97), Welsh Amtr Cup 1954-55, Central Wales Lg 75-76 78-79 81-82 86-87 87-88 (R-up 51-52 52-53 55-56 56-57 74-75 82-83, Lg Cup 54-55 56-57 74-75 75-76 81-82 83-84), Arthur Barritt Cup 86-87, Central Wales Cup 74-75 80-81 92-93, Emrys Morgan Cup 80-81.

PORTHMADOG

Chairman: R.J.Havelock **President:** William Pike
Secretary: Mr R I Griffiths, Llyn-yr-Eryr, Ynys, Cricieth, Gwynedd LL52 0PH (01766 810349).
Manager: Colin Hawkins **Physio:** Ifor Roberts
Ground: Y Traeth, Porthmadog, Gwynedd,(01766 514687). **Directions:** At town centre crossroads (by Woolworths) into Snowdon Str., pass RBL/Craft Centre onto unmade track, over railway line - ground on right.
Seats: 100 **Cover:** 400 **Capacity:** 4,000 **Floodlights:** Yes **Club Shop:** No.
Programme: 28 pages, 50p **Editor:** Dylan Ellis. **Founded:** 1884.
Colours: Red & black/black/black **Change:** Yellow/red/red **Nickname:** Porth.
Midweek Matchday: Wednesday. **Reserve League:** Gwynedd.
Record Attendance: 3,500 v Swansea, Welsh Cup 64-65.
Previous Leagues: N Wales/Gwynedd/Bangor & Dist/Lleyn & Dist/Cambrian Coast/Welsh All/Cymru All
Clubhouse: Not on ground (use Midland Hotel), but matchday refreshments available.
Honours: Welsh Amtr Cup(3) 55-58, N. Wales Amtr Cup 37-38 56-57 58-59 62-63, Lge of Wales Cup R-up 92-93, N. Wales Coast Chal. Cup(5) 55-56 73-75 76-78, Welsh All.(8) 02-03 37-38 66-69 74-76 89-90 (Cookson Cup 75-76 89-90, Barritt Cup 77-78, Alves Cup 65-66 73-74 76-77).

RHAYDER TOWN

Chairman: M A Pugh **Manager:** R Cross
Secretary: P Woosnam, Bwthyn Lon, Hazelmere, Rhayader, Powys LD6 5LG (01597 810067)
Ground: The Weirglodd, Bridge Street, Rhayader, Powys (01597 810067)
Colours: White & red/white & red/red **Change Colours:** Jade & white/jade & white/jade
Midweek Matchday: Wednesday

RHYL

Chairman: J B Williams **President:**
Secretary: Mr D Williams, 81A Dyserth Road, Rhyl, LL18 4DT (01745 354773 H)
Ground: Belle Vue, Grange Road, Rhyl, Clwyd (01745 338327).
Directions: A55 Expressway to Rhyl turn-off and follow signs thru Rhuddlan. Follow signs for Sun Centre along Pendyffryn Rd and turn left at junction - ground 200 yards on left.
Capacity: 4,000 **Floodlights:** Yes **Cover:** 1,200 **Seats:** 200 **Shop:** Yes
Programme: 40 pages 80p **Editor:** Andrew Wilson **Press Officer:** John Daley
Colours: White/black/black **Change:** Blue/white/white
Sponsors: **Nickname:** Lilywhites **Founded:** 1883.
Midweek matches: Tuesday.
Record Attendance: 10,000 v Cardiff City, Welsh Cup 1953.
Previous Leagues: Cheshire County/ North West Counties/ Northern Premier/ Cymru Alliance 92-94.
Best FA Cup season: 4th Rd Proper 56-57 (lost 0-3 at Bristol City).
Players progressing to Football League: Ian Edwards, Grenville Millington, Brian Lloyd, Andy Holden, Barry Horne, Andy Jones.
Clubhouse:
Club record scorer: Don Spendlove. **Club record appearances:** Not known.
Honours: Welsh Cup 51-52 52-53 (R-up 29-30 36-37 92-93), Welsh Amateur Cup 72-73, Northern Premier Lg Presidents Cup 84-85, North West Counties Lg R-up 82-83, North Wales Coast Challenge Cup, Cheshire County Lg 47-48 50-51 71-72 (R-up 48-49 49-50 51-52 55-56, Div 2 R-up 81-82, Lg Cup 48-49 51-52 70-71, Div 2 Shield 81-82), Cyrmu Alliance 93-94 (R-up 92-93, Lg Cup 92-93).

TOTAL NETWORK SOLUTIONS

President: Mike Hughes. **Chairman:** Edgar Jones **Vice-Chairman:** Roger Moreton
Secretary: Tony Williams, 5 Maes y Garreg, Llansantffraid, Powys SY22 6BD (01691 828535 H), (01691 828654 B), Fax (01691 828441)
Manager: Graham Breeze **Asst Manager:** Adrian Jones **Physio:** Gordon Evans.
Ground: Recreation Park, Treflan, Llansantffraid (01691 828112).
Directions: A470 between Welshpool and Oswestry, left for Llansantffraid at Llynclys, follow signs to village. Turn opposite Mill silos towards Community Centre. Ground is behind housing estate.
Seats: 120 **Cover:** 250 **Capacity:** 1,500 **Floodlights:** Yes **Shop:** Yes
Programme: 32 pages, 80p **Editor:** Adrian Jones.
Colours: Green/white/white **Change:** Red/black/black.
Sponsors: Total Network Solutions. **Nickname:** The Saints. **Founded:** 1959
Midweek Matchedays: Tuesday **Reserves League:** Mid-Wales
Record Attendance: 2,100 v KS Ruch Chorzow Euro Cup Winners 96
Previous League: Mid-Wales/ Cymru Alliance (pre-1993)
Clubhouse: Normal licensing hours.
96-97 Captain: Garry Evans **96-97 P.o.Y.:** Gary Jones **96-97 Top Scorer:** Adrian Jones
Club Record Goalscorer: Andy Oakley **Club Record Appearances:** Derek Arthur.
Honours: Cymru Alliance 92-93; Welsh Intermediate Cup 92-93; Central Wales Cup 92-93 (R-up 94-95); Central Wales Lg R-up 90-91 94-95 95-96, Lge Cup 95-96; Montgomeryshire Amtr Lg (7), Div 2 80-81, Lg Cup (9), Village Cup (17); Montgomeryshire Cup R-up 82-83; League of Wales Lg.Cup 94-95; Welsh Cup 95-96.

WELSHPOOL

Chairman: M G Edwards. **Manager:** Gareth Cadwallader
Secretary: Mr J A Bartley, 24 Bryn Glas, Welshpool, Powys SY21 7TL (01938 552131 H), (01686 626246 B).
Ground: Maesydre Recreation Ground, Welshpool, Powys.
Directions:
Seats: **Cover:** 100 **Capacity:** **Floodlights:** **Club Shop:**
Colours: White/black/white **Change colours:** Red/black/black
Sponsors: **Nickname:** Seasiders **Founded:** 1878
Midweek Matchday: Wednesday

SCOTTISH FOOTBALL

OVD RUM SCOTTISH JUNIOR CUP

FIRST ROUND

Region		Home	Away	Clubs	Win	Lose	For	Against
Ayrshire	(23)	5	4	9	8	1	36	11
Central	(39)	11	7	18	11	7	42	31
East	(26)	6	3	9	5	4	21	17
Fife	(15)	3	6	9	4	5	17	16
North*	(37)	4	10	14	2	12	15	52
Tayside	(25)	8	7	15	7	8	25	29
TOTAL	*(165)*	*37*	*37*	*74*	*37*	*37*	*156*	*156*

*Kinloss excluded from competition for 1996/97 (and 1997/98) season after failing to fulfil a fixture in 1995/96 compeition)

Largest Home Win:	Glenrothes	v	Maud	7-1
	Greenock	v	Inverurie Juniors	7-1
	Maybole	v	New Elgin	7-1
Largest Away Win:	Elmwood	v	Rob Roy	0-3

Arbroath SC	v	Balleith Thistle	2-0
Ardross WR	v	Deveronside	3-1
Beith	v	Coupar Angus	6-1
Blantyre Vics	v	Kirkcaldy YMCA	1-0
Camelon	v	Kilwinning R	0-0, 0-5
Dunbar Utd	v	Lochore Welfare	2-0
Elmwood	v	Rob Roy	0-3
Fras'burgh U	v	Jeanfield Swifts	2-2, 0-1
Glenafton Ath	v	Kilsyth Rangers	5-1
Greenock	v	Inverurie Juniors	7-1
Linlithgow	v	Wishaw	4-0
Sauchie	v	Stonehouse Violet	3-2
Strathspey Th	v	Lochgelly Albert	1-2
Thorn'wood	v	Dundee East Craigie	3-2
Vale of Leven	v	Aberdeen East End	4-2
Arbroath Vics	v	Bankfoot Athletic	0-2
Armadale Th	v	Stonehaven	4-0
Blairgowrie	v	Rosyth Recreation	3-4
Broughty Ath	v	Carnoustie Panmure	0-2
Cumbernauld	v	Ellon United	3-0
Edinburgh Utd	v	Dairy Thistle	2-3
Forth Wand	v	Johnstone Burgh	1-3
G Perthshire	v	Dundonald Bluebell	2-1
Glenrothes	v	Maud	7-1
Lesmahagow	v	Forres Thistle	5-0
Lossas	v	Steelend Victoria	3-0
Shettleston	v	Livingston United	3-2
Tayport	v	Forfar Albion	5-0
Vale of Clyde	v	Muirkirk	0-2

SECOND ROUND

Region	Home	Away	Clubs	Win	Lose	For	Against
Ayrshire	11	11	22	9	13	41	45
Central	17	15	32	19	13	82	57
East	12	10	22	11	11	41	37
Fife	6	4	10	5	5	27	23
North	8	17	25	9	16	36	78
Tayside	10	7	17	11	6	41	28
TOTAL	*64*	*64*	*128*	*64*	*64*	*268*	*268*

Largest Home Win:	Kelty Hearts	v	Bishopmill United	7-1
Largest Away Win:	RAF Lossiemouth	v	Ormiston Primrose	0-7

Aberdeen LC	v	Dundee North End	1-4
Ardeer Thistle	v	Thorniewood United	1-3
Armadale Th	v	Cumbernauld United	1-2
Ashfield	v	Lesmahagow	0-3
Baillieston	v	Largs T	2-2, 3-3*, 1-2p
Bankfoot Athletic	v	Musselburgh Athletic	0-2
Bellshill Athletic	v	Port Glasgow	0-5
Blantyre Vics	v	Culter	4-1
Buchanhaven	v	Lewis United	2-3
Carluke Rovers	v	Maybole	0-1
Dairy Thistle	v	Maryhill	2-4
Dunbar United	v	Troon	1-3
Dunipace	v	Lanark United	0-6
Fauldhouse United	v	Dyce	4-0
Formartine United	v	Renfrew	1-5
Glenafton Athletic	v	Inverurie Loco Works	2-3
Hurlford United	v	Sunnybank	1-4
Kelty Hearts	v	Bishopmill United	7-1
Kinnoull	v	St Anthonys	2-1
Kirrie Thistle	v	West Calder United	4-0
Lochee Harp	v	Lochgelly Albert	1-1, 4-3
Longside	v	Harthill Royal	1-2
Nairn St Nin.	v	Brechin Victoria	2-1
Newburgh	v	St Josephs	0-0, 2-2*, 4-5p
Petershill	v	Bo'ness United	3-1
RAF Lossie	v	Ormiston Primrose	0-7
Royal Albert	v	Tulliallan Thistle	5-2
St Andrew U	v	Carnoustie Panmure	0-5
Scone Thistle	v	Bonnybridge	3-2
Tayport	v	Larkhall Thistle	0-0, 2-1
Vale of Leven	v	Craigmark B	1-1, 2-1
Whitletts Vics	v	FC Stoneywood	0-1
Annbank United	v	Benburb	2-1
Ardross. WR	v	Banks O'Dee	0-0, 1-2
Arniston R	v	Saltcoats Victoria	3-0
Auchinleck T	v	Kilwinning Rangers	1-0
Banchory ST	v	Turriff United	1-3
Beith	v	Burghead Thistle	6-0
Blackburn United	v	Arthurlie	0-3
Broxburn Athletic	v	Forfar West End	0-1
Cambuslang	v	Kelio Rovers	4-3
Crossgates P	v	Cruden Bay	1-1, 2-0
Downfield	v	Tranent	2-2, 1-3
Dundee Violet	v	Glenrothes	0-1
East Kilbride	v	Hermes	1-3
Fochabers	v	Jeanfield Swifts	1-6
G. Perthshire	v	Lugar Boswell Thistle	1-2
Greenock	v	Bon Accord	1-2
Irvine Victoria	v	Shettleston	0-2
Kilbirnie L	v	Irvine Meadow	2-1
K'tillock RR	v	Cumnock	0-3
Linlithgow R	v	Bathgate Thistle	1-0
Lochee United	v	Shotts Bon Accord	2-5
Montrose R	v	Arbroath Sporting Club	1-0
Neilston	v	Bonnyrigg Rose	4-0
Newt'grange	v	Haddington Athletic	2-0
Pumpherston	v	Hall Russell United	3-1
Rosyth Rec	v	Islavale	5-1
R. Glencairn	v	Pollok	1-3
Sauchie	v	Johnstone Burgh	1-2
Stoneyburn	v	Buckie Rovers	2-1
Thornton Hibs	v	Hill of Beath Hawthorn	0-3
Whitburn	v	Muirkirk	4-3
Yoker Athletic	v	Parkvale	4-0

Above: Scottish Junior Cup First Round
Maybole (Kirkland) v North Elgin

Photo: B Vass

Below: Scottish Junior Cup Second Round Replay
Craigmark Burntonians v Vale of Leven

Photo: B Vass

Right: Scottish Junior Cup
Second Round
Auchinleck Talbot v
Kilwinning Rangers

Photo: B Vass

Below: Scottish Junior Cup
Fourth Round Replay
Troon v FC Stoneywood
Stoney's Martin Lowe rattles the Troon cross bar with this effort

Photo: Alan Watson

Above: Scottish Junior Cup Quarter Final
Fauldhouse United v Pollok

Photo: Chris Sandersay

THIRD ROUND

Region	Home	Away	Clubs	Win	Lose	For	Against
Ayrshire	2	7	9	8	1	27	10
Central	9	10	19	7	12	32	37
East	7	4	11	8	3	29	19
Fife	4	1	5	3	2	6	7
North	6	3	9	5	4	21	18
Tayside	4	7	11	1	10	14	38
TOTAL	*8*	*8*	*16*	*8*	*8*	*21*	*21*

Largest Home Win: Auchinleck Talbot v Forfar West End 5-0
Largest Away Win: Lochee Harp v Kilbirnie Ladeside 1-4
Thorniewood Utd v Ormiston Primrose 1-4

Annbank United	v	Crossgates Primrose	4-0
Auchinleck T	v	Forfar West End	5-0
Cambuslang	v	Kinnoull	1-1, 2-1*
Dundee NE	v	Blantyre Victoria	1-1, 0-3
FC St'wood	v	Troon	1-1, 1-2
Harthill Royal	v	Johnstone Burgh	3-2
H of B Hawth.	v	Montrose Roselea	3-0
Kelty Hearts	v	Lanark United	2-0
Lewis United	v	Neilston	3-2
Newt'grange	v	Renfrew	4-2
Pollok	v	Shotts Bon Accord	2-1
Rosyth Rec.	v	Arniston Rangers	0-3
Shettleston	v	Yoker Athletic	3-0
Sunnybank	v	Maryhill	3-0
Thorniewood	v	Ormiston Primrose	1-4
Vale of Leven	v	Musselburgh Athletic	1-0
Arthurlie	v	Banks O'Dee	3-1
Bon Accord	v	Lugar Boswell Thistle	3-1
Cumbernauld	v	Largs Thistle	0-0, 2-3*
Fauldhouse United	v	Lesmahagow	1-1, 2-1
Glenrothes	v	Port Glasgow	1-0
Hermes	v	Nairn St Ninian	4-2
Inverurie LW	v	Turriff United	2-1
Kirrie Thistle	v	Maybole	1-1, 0-3
Lochee Harp	v	Kilbirnie Ladeside	1-4
Petershill	v	Carnoustie Panmure	4-0
Pumpherston	v	Beith	1-2
Royal Albert	v	Cumnock	0-1
Stoneyburn	v	Scone Thistle	2-2, 2-1
Tayport	v	Linlithgow Rose	3-0
Tranent	v	St Josephs	1-0
Whitburn	v	Jeanfield Swifts	6-3

FOURTH ROUND

Region	Home	Away	Clubs	Win	Lose	For	Against
Ayrshire	7	1	8	4	4	14	18
Central	4	3	7	5	2	15	8
East	1	7	8	3	5	12	15
Fife	0	3	3	1	2	5	5
North	3	2	5	2	3	14	15
Tayside	1	0	1	1	0	1	0
TOTAL	*16*	*16*	*32*	*16*	*16*	*61*	*61*

Annbank United	v	Hill of Beath Hawthorn	0-4
Beith	v	Bon Accord	2-2, 4-3
Cambuslang	v	Ormiston Primrose	4-3
Hermes	v	V of Leven	2-2, 1-1*, 4-2p
Kilbirnie L	v	Arniston Rangers	1-1, 0-1
Maybole	v	Arthurlie	1-3
Pollok	v	Whitburn	2-0
Tayport	v	Shettleston	1-0
Auchinleck T	v	Newtongrange Star	2-1
Blantyre Vics	v	Harthill Royal	2-0
Fauldhouse U	v	Glenrothes	2-0
Inverurie LW	v	Tranent	1-0*
Largs Thistle	v	Lewis United	1-0
Petershill	v	Stoneyburn	1-0
Sunnybank	v	Kelty Hearts	3-1
Troon	v	Cumnock	0-3

FIFTH ROUND

Region	Home	Away	Clubs	Win	Lose	For	Against
Ayrshire	3	1	4	2	2	7	5
Central	2	3	5	4	1	10	7
East	1	2	3	1	2	1	3
Fife	0	1	1	0	1	1	2
North	1	1	2	0	2	1	4
Tayside	1	0	1	1	0	1	0
TOTAL	*8*	*8*	*16*	*8*	*8*	*21*	*21*

Arthurlie	v	Hill of Beath Hawthorn	2-1
Cambuslang	v	Sunnybank	3-1
Hermes	v	Pollok	0-1
Tayport	v	Arniston Rangers	1-0
Beith	v	Fauldhouse	1-1, 0-0*, 6-7p
Cumnock	v	Petershill	1-1, 2-0
Largs Thistle	v	Blantyre Vics	2-2, 0-1
Tranent	v	Auchinleck Talbot	0-1

SIXTH ROUND

Auchinleck Talbot	v	Blantyre Vics	0-3
Cumnock	v	Arthurlie	4-4, 1-2
Cambuslang	v	Tayport	0-1
Fauldhouse U	v	Pollok	0-0

SEMI FINAL

Pollok v Blantyre Victoria 5-0 — *Apr 26 at Adamslie Park, Kirkintilloch*
(Cramner, Barratt, Diver, Lowrie (pen), Anderson)

Tayport v Arthurlie 2-1 — *Apr 30 at Fir Park, Motherwell*
(Hutcheon 2) *(Convery)*

FINAL

Pollok v Tayport 3-1 — *May 18 at Fir Park, Motherwell*
(Diver 2, Elliott) (Ross) HT 2-0 Att: 3523

Pollok: R Lowrie, K Neil, C Cranmer, I Spittal, I Ashcroft, D Elliott, D Fontana, S Bonnar, J Morrison, J Barnett, D Diver
Subs: R Anderson, B Ferguson, P McLean, J Paisley, G Smith

Tayport: F Mann, G Buist, G Paterson, G Miller, K Nicholson, S Wilkie, A Ramsay, S Stewart, S Hutcheon, D Reilly, S Ross
Subs: B Gary, M Spalding, B Coventry, P Reilly, A Kennedy

Referee: B McGarry (Cumbernauld)

OVD Scotttish CupThird Round
Annbank United v Crossgates Primrose
Photo: B Vass

OVD Scotttish CupThird Round Replay
Maybole v Kirrie Thistle
Photo: B Vass

OVD Scotttish CupThird Round
Auchinleck Talbot (5) v Forfar Westend (0)
Talbot's Derek McCulloch (partly hidden) beats Forfar keeper Bruce Glen to put his side 2-0 ahead
Photo: Alan Watson

SCOTTISH JUNIOR CUP
LAST TEN FINALS

1995/96	Tayport	v	Camelon	2-0	at Motherwell FC	Att: 4652
1994/95	Camelon	v	Whitburn	2-0	at Motherwell FC	Att: 8019
1993/94	Largs Thistle	v	Glenafton Ath	1-0	at Motherwell FC	Att: 8668
1992/93	Glenafton Ath	v	Tayport	1-0	at Partick Th FC	Att: 6250
1991/92	Auchinleck T	v	Glenafton Ath	4-0	at Partick Th FC	Att: 8000?
1990/91	Auchinleck T	v	Newtongrange	1-0	at Falkirk FC	Att: 8000?
1989/90	Hill of B Hawth	v	Lesmahagow	1-0	at Kilmarnock FC	Att: 5800
1988/89	Cumnock	v	Ormiston P	1-0	at Kilmarnock FC	
1987/88	Auchinleck T	v	Petershill	1-0	at Kilmarnock FC	Att: 9260
1986/87	Auchinleck T	v	Kilbirnie L	1-1	at Kilmarnock FC	Att: 11027
Replay	Auchinleck T	v	Kilbirnie L	1-0	at Kilmarnock FC	Att: 11300

SCOTTISH JUNIOR REPRESENTATIVE MATCHES

After a break of almost 14 years, the SJFA renewed their matches against the Highland Football League, the last one being on April 24th, 1983, when they won 2-1 at Kirrie Thistle's Westview Park.

This season's match was played on March 4th at Cove Rangers, the Juniors winning by the only goal of the match, scored by Danny Diver of Pollok.

In preparation for the Quadrangular Tournament in Northern Ireland in April, several 'warm up' matches were played:

Bathgate Th v SJFA 0-4 Jan 21st at Bathgate Th FC
(SJFA scorers: Sinclair-Cumnock, Cramner-Pollok, Buchan-Newtongrange)

SJFA v Clydebank 6-3 Mar 24th at Linlithgow Rose
(SJFA scorers: McCulloch-Auchinleck, Spence (2)-Hill of Beath, Diver (2)-Pollok, Stewart-Tayport)

Irvine Meadow v SJFA 1-2 April 6th at Irvine Meadow, (for Meadow's Centenary)
(SJFA scorers: McCulloch (2))

GUINNESS QUADRANGULAR TOURNAMENT

SEMI FINAL April 18th at Holm Park, Armagh City
Scotland v Isle of Man 4-0
(Stewart, Spence 2-1 a pen, Diver)

FINAL April 19th at Lakeview Park, Loughall
Scotland v Northern Ireland 2-1
(Spence 2)

Team (v Isle of Man): Stuart McIntosh *(Kilwinning Rangers)*, Gavin Duncan *(Arthurlie)*, Crauif Brittain *(Ashfield)*, Bryan Smith *(Petershill)*, Iain Ashcroft *(Pollok)*, Derek McCulloch *(Auchinleck Talbot)*, Gary Graham *(Auchinleck Talbot)*, David Fulton *(Arthurlie)*, Danny Diver *(Pollok)*, Billy Spence *(Hill of Beath Hawthorn)*, Steven Stewart *(Tayport)*
Subs: Stuart Allison *(Shettleston)*, Duncan Sinclair *(Cumnock)*, Christy McKenzie *(Camelon)*, David Walker *(Glenafton Athletic)*

Team (v Northern Ireland): as semi final, but with following changes - Allison for McCulloch, McCulloch a sub, and add Graeme Finnan *(Dundee North End)* as a sub.

This was the fourth year of the tournament, with the hosts beaten finalists every season:

1993/94	Scotland	v	Eire	1-0	in Eire
1994/95	N Ireland	v	Scotland	3-2	in Scotland
1995/96	N Ireland	v	Isle of Man	2-1	in Isle of Man
1996/97	Scotland	v	Northern Ireland	2-1	in Northern Ireland

(Left to Right) D McCulloch, D Gray and G Graham of Auchinleck Talbot and Junior Scotland

Photo: B Vass

WHYTE & McKAY WEST OF SCOTLAND CUP

(Competed for as inter-regional competition by Ayrshire and Central Region clubs)

SEMI-FINAL

Arthurlie	v	St Roch's	2-0	June 2nd at Pollok FC
Irvine Meadow	v	Cumnock	3-2	June 3rd at Auchinleck Talbot FC

FINAL

Arthurlie	v	Irvine Meadow	5-0	June 7th at Somervell Park, Cambuslang

(Watson (2), Archer, Nugent, Convery)

LAST FIVE FINALS

1995/96	Petershill	v	Maryhill	0-0*, 2-0p	May 25th at Cambuslang
1994/95	Shettleston	v	Pollok	1-1*, 4-2p	May 28th at Cambuslang
1993/94	Kilwinning R	v	Shettleston	2-0	June 4th at Cambuslang
1992/93	Shettleston	v	Lesmahagow	2-0	June 19th at Cambuslang
1991/92	Pollok	v	Beith	1-0*	June 4th at Cambuslang

(Top Right)
Annbank v Vale of Leven.
Keeper Carson punches McMillan's header clear
Photo: J B Vass

(Middle Right)
Arthurlie striker John Millar pressurises the Vale of Clyde defence in a Whyte & Mackay Cup game
Photo: Chris Sanderson

(Bottom Right)
Pollok go close in their 0-0 draw in a Whyte & Mackay Cup game with Blantyre Vics
Photo: Chris Sanderson

(Bottom Left)
Pollok striker Danny Diver takes on the Blantyre Victoria defence in a Whyte & Mackay Cup game
Photo: Chris Sanderson

AYRSHIRE REGION

FINAL LEAGUE TABLES 1996-97

DIVISION ONE	P	W	D	L	F	A	Pts
Auchinleck Talbot	20	14	4	2	46	20	46
Glenafton Athletic	20	13	3	4	47	27	42
Kilwinning Rangers	20	10	5	5	41	25	35
Beith Juniors	20	10	4	6	38	24	34
Cumnock Juniors	20	9	5	6	41	35	32
Kilbirnie Ladeside	20	9	3	8	33	33	30
Largs Thistle	20	7	3	10	27	32	24
Irvine Meadow XI	20	5	8	7	30	34	23
Dairy Thistle	20	7	2	11	31	38	23
Maybole Juniors	20	2	5	13	34	50	11
Lugar Boswell Th	20	2	2	16	20	70	8

DIVISION TWO	P	W	D	L	F	A	Pts
Troon	22	17	3	2	58	17	54
Muirkirk Juniors	22	14	3	5	49	30	45
Ardrossan Winton R	22	13	4	5	61	28	43
Kello Rovers	22	12	3	7	52	37	39
Irvine Victoria	22	10	7	5	45	33	37
Ardeer Thistle	22	9	5	8	42	46	32
Annbank United	22	9	3	10	38	33	30
Whitletts Victoria	22	7	5	10	42	51	26
Craigmark Burnt.	22	7	5	10	33	47	26
Saltcoats Victoria	22	7	4	11	34	36	25
Darvel Juniors	22	3	2	17	29	65	11
Hurlford United	22	1	2	19	27	87	5

JACKIE SCARLETT SECTIONAL LEAGUE CUP

SEMI-FINAL

Beith v Kilwinning Rangers 0-1
Cumnock v Glenafton Athletic 2-1

FINAL *September 30th at Ayr United FC*

Cumnock v Kilwinning Rangers 1-0
(Scorer: Agnew) *Att: 1862*

IRVINE TIMES AYRSHIRE DISTRICT CUP

FINAL *May 19th at Meadow Park, Irvine*

Auchinleck Talbot v Cumnock 4-0
(Walsh, McCulloch, Thomson (pen), Ellis)

ARDROSSAN & SALTCOATS HERALD AYRSHIRE JUNIOR CUP

FINAL *June 18th at Meadow Park, Irvine*

Auchinleck Talbot v Kilwinning Rangers 2-1
(Thomson 2) *(Archibald)*

NORTH AYRSHIRE CUP

FINAL May 11th at Bellsdale Park, Beith

Irvine Meadow v Kilbirnie Ladeside 3-1
(Rogerson, D Walsh, Thomson) *(M Walsh (pen))*

EAST AYRSHIRE CUP

FINAL *May 20th at Beechwood Park, Auchinleck*

Auchinleck Talbot v Lugar Boswell Thistle 6-0
(Paterson 3, Elkis, Thomson (pen), Shanaghey)

SOUTH AYRSHIRE CUP

FINAL *May 29th at New Pebble Park, Annbank*

Troon v Annbank United 2-0
(Yair, McQueen)

AYRSHIRE SUPER CUP

(Competed for by the three district winners and the Jackie Scarlett Cup winners)

SEMI FINAL

Auchinleck Talbot v Troon 1-1, 3-0p
Cumnock v Irvine Meadow 2-0

FINAL *June 16th at Townhead Park, Cumnock*

Cumnock v Auchinleck Talbot 1-1, 3-1p
(Wilson) *(Thomson)*

Troon - Promotion Celebrations
Ayrshire Region Division Two Champions
Photo: B Vass

Auchinleck Talbot
Winners: Ayrshire Region Division One, Ayrshire District (Irvine Times) Cup, East Ayrshire Cup
Photo: B Vass

(Above) Action from Ayrshire Region Division One: Auchinleck Talbot (McCroy) v Kilwinning Rangers (McLuckie)

(Below) Action from Ayrshire Region Division Two: Troon (Gribben - ex Ayr United) v Whitletts (Coughtrie)

Photos: B Vass

CENTRAL REGION

FINAL LEAGUE TABLES 1996-97

REEBOK LEAGUE PREMIER DIVISION

	P	W	D	L	F	A	Pts
Maryhill	22	15	3	4	52	27	48
Pollok	22	10	10	2	44	23	40
Petershill	22	11	5	6	39	22	38
Shettleston	22	12	0	10	47	41	36
Arthurlie	22	11	2	9	50	35	35
Blantyre Victoria	22	8	6	8	39	35	30
Larkhall Thistle	22	9	3	10	35	50	30
Bailieston	22	6	8	8	32	45	26
Benburb	22	7	3	12	41	52	24
Vale of Leven	22	7	2	13	28	48	23
Rob Roy	22	7	2	13	21	35	23*
Kilsyth Rangers	22	4	6	12	28	44	18

* 3 points deducted

FIRST DIVISION	P	W	D	L	F	A	Pts
Lanark United	26	19	5	2	55	25	59
Lesmagagow	26	16	7	3	54	26	55
Neilston	26	12	10	4	52	26	46
Ashfield	26	11	6	9	43	34	39
Renfrew	26	12	3	11	49	45	39
Cambuslang R'gers	26	10	9	7	51	44	39
Forth Wanderers	26	10	5	11	36	34	35
Vale of Clyde	26	10	5	11	32	43	35
R. Glencairn	26	9	7	10	43	39	34
Cumbernauld Utd	26	9	5	12	40	60	32
Yoker Athletic	26	8	5	13	34	39	29
Greenock	26	8	5	13	34	44	29
East Kilbride Th	26	6	6	14	34	48	24
Dunipace	26	2	2	22	25	74	8

SECOND DIVISION	P	W	D	L	F	A	Pts
Shotts Bon Accord	24	16	6	2	75	21	54
Johnstone Burgh	24	15	3	6	58	32	48
Bellshill Athletic	24	13	6	5	54	32	45

ABERCORN BUILDERS SECTIONAL LEAGUE CUP

FINAL *October 1st at Motherwell FC*

Pollok v Shettleston 4-2

EVENING TIMES CUP WINNERS CUP

FINAL *June 14th at Somervell Park, Cambuslang*

Maryhill v Pollok 2-1

CPS CENTRAL REGIONAL LEAGUE CUP

FINAL *May 31st at Somervell Park, Cambuslang*

Arthurlie v Pollok 2-1 aet

NB. for the 1997/98 season, the sponsors of the above two competitions have 'swapped'. The early season Sectional Cup will now be sponsored by CPS whilst the other will be sponsored by Abercorn Builders.

EAST REGION

FINAL LEAGUE TABLES 1996-97

JOHN WALKER DIVISION ONE

	P	W	D	L	F	A	Pts
Linlithgow Rose	22	13	5	4	46	29	44
Bonnyrigg Rose	22	12	3	7	41	27	39
Bo'ness United	22	11	5	6	46	32	38
Camelon	22	11	5	6	40	34	38
Newtongrange Star	22	9	8	5	35	23	35
Whitburn	22	10	4	8	46	42	34
Arniston Rangers	22	8	5	9	32	33	29
Tranent	22	7	6	9	38	43	27
Armadale Thistle	22	7	5	10	41	54	26
Bonnybridge	22	5	9	8	28	30	24
Harthill Royal	22	4	4	14	28	48	16
Dunbar United	22	3	5	14	22	48	14

JOHN WALKER DIVISION TWO

	P	W	D	L	F	A	Pts
Fauldhouse United	26	19	6	1	69	26	63
Musselburgh Ath.	26	19	4	3	65	24	61
Pumpherston	26	13	6	7	37	25	45
Haddington Athletic	26	12	6	8	53	39	42
Ormiston Primrose	26	12	5	9	62	58	41
Bathgate Thistle	26	11	6	9	39	39	39
Blackburn United	26	11	4	11	39	45	37
Sauchie	26	10	3	13	48	54	33
Dalkeith Thistle	26	8	5	13	38	43	29
Livingston United	26	7	6	13	44	65	27
Stoneyburn	26	7	5	14	41	53	26
West Calder United	26	6	6	14	41	66	24
Edinburgh United	26	5	8	13	46	54	23
Broxburn Athletic	26	3	8	15	29	60	17

SKOL LEAGUE CUP

FINAL *January 8th at Linlithgow Rose FC*

Camelon v Newtongrange Star 0-2

CARLSBERG EAST OF SCOTLAND CUP

FINAL *June 14th at Recreation Park, Pumpherston*

Bo'ness United v Newtongrange S. 3-3*, 1-3p

DAVID MOFFAT CUP

FINAL *June 11 at Newbyres Pk, Gorebridge, Arniston R FC*

Bo'ness United v Newtongrange Star 1-0

(McKinlay (pen))

DALKEITH GLAZING CUP

FINAL *June 9th at Volunteer Park, Armadale*

Linlithgow Rose v Whitburn 3-3, 3-1 pen

(Halcrow, Godfrey (p), Logan) (Ramage, Richardson, Clouston)

'WHITE & McKAY' FIFE & LOTHIANS CUP

(Competed for as an inter-region trophy with clubs from the Fife Region)

FINAL *June 7th at Carmuirs Park, Camelon*

Bo'ness United v Bonnybridge 3-1 aet

FIFE REGION

FINAL LEAGUE TABLE 1996-97

JOHN FYFE LEAGUE

	P	W	D	L	F	A	Pts
Kelty Hearts	28	27	1	0	95	11	55
Hill of Beath Haw.	28	23	1	4	83	20	47
Glenrothes	28	16	7	5	63	29	39
Dundonald Bluebell	28	15	4	9	59	42	34
Thornton Hibs	28	16	1	11	70	54	33
St Andrews United	28	11	9	8	60	39	31
Newburgh	28	10	7	11	58	40	27
Tulliallan Thistle	28	11	5	12	40	60	27
Lochgelly Albert	28	9	8	11	49	55	26
Crossgates Primrs.	28	11	4	13	40	54	26
Oakley United	28	11	3	14	46	68	25
Rosyth Recreation	28	9	5	14	53	48	23
Kirkcaldy YM	28	6	3	19	41	88	15
Steelend Victoria	28	2	4	22	37	99	8
Lochore Welfare	28	1	2	25	20	107	4

PREDDIE SMITH MALACO CUP

FINAL *at Moorside Park, Dundonald*

Thornton Hibs v Rosyth Recreation 3-0

JOHN FYFE CUP

FINAL *at Moorside Park, Dundonald*

Hill of Beath Hawth. v Thornton Hibs 6-0

WHITBREAD CUP

FINAL *at Keirs Park, Hill of Beath*

Glenrothes v Kelty Hearts 2-1

ROSSLYN TROPHY

(Top League Scorers) Kelty Hearts

MONTRAVE CUP

(Good Conduct) Newburgh

NORTH REGION

EAST SECTION

FINAL LEAGUE TABLES 1996-97

BON ACCORD GLASS PREMIER DIVISION

	P	W	D	L	F	A	Pts
Sunnybank	22	16	4	2	58	24	52
FC Stoneywood	22	14	6	2	45	17	48
Bon Accord	22	12	4	6	45	32	40
Culter	22	11	5	6	34	29	38
Inverurie Loco Wks	22	10	5	7	53	35	35
Turriff United	22	9	8	5	45	41	35
Longside	22	6	8	8	35	40	26
Hall Russell United	22	7	4	11	37	45	25
Stonehaven	22	7	4	11	31	48	25
Bank O'Dee	22	4	4	12	41	50	18
East End	22	3	4	15	33	50	13
Banchory St Ternan	22	3	2	17	17	63	11

BON ACCORD GLASS FIRST DIVISION

	P	W	D	L	F	A	Pts
Lewis United	22	17	4	1	69	15	55
Hermes	22	14	3	5	67	30	45
Formartine United	22	13	4	5	61	23	43
Lads Club	22	13	2	7	59	35	41
Cruden Bay	22	12	5	5	48	29	41
Parkvale	22	11	1	10	45	48	34
Buchanhaven H.	22	11	0	11	48	45	33
Fraserburgh United	22	8	1	13	35	47	25
Ellon United	22	5	5	12	26	40	20
Dyce Juniors	22	6	2	14	28	50	20
Maud	22	4	4	14	21	47	14
Inverurie Juniors	22	2	0	20	12	110	6

LATE NEWS: Following the resignation of Bon Accord, a playoff match between East End (third bottom of the Premier Division) and Formartine United (third top in the First Division) will take place at the start of August 1997 to determine which clubs will take the place of Bon Accord in the Premier Division.

'GREAT NORTHERN TROPHIES' NORTH REGIONAL CUP

FINAL *May 10th at New Advocates Park, Aberdeen*

Sunnybank v Bon Accord 3-1

(MacKintosh (p), Cheyne, Sutherland) *(Roberston)*

THE GRILL LEAGUE CUP

FINAL *October 6th at Spain Park, Aberdeen*

Sunnybank v Longside 2-0

(Campbell, MacKintosh (p))

ABERDEEN CABLE TV LEAGUE CUP

FINAL *June 9th at Chris Anderson Stadium, Aberdeen*

Bon Accord v Sunnybank 2-2 aet, 4-3 pen

(Coull, Robertson) *(Lawrie, Sutherland)*

ACORN HEATING CUP

FINAL *June 16th at Heathryfold Park, Aberdeen*

Bon Accord v FC Stoneywood 2-0

(Foote, Robertson)

ARCHIBALD CUP

FINAL *June 11th at Spain Park, Aberdeen*

FC Stoneywood v Culter 4-2 aet

GORDON CAMPBELL CONSTRUCTION TROPHY

FINAL *June 18th at New Advocates Park, Aberdeen*

Sunnybank v Lads Club 4-0

(Brebner 2, Souden 2)

MORRISON TROPHY

FINAL *May 23rd at Denmore Park, Aberdeen*

Hermes v Lewis United 2-1

(Roberts (p), Mearns) *(Johnstone)*

JIMMY GIBB TROPHY

FINAL *June 20th at New Advocates Park, Aberdeen*

Lewis United v Sunnybank 2-3

NORTH REGIONAL CHAMPIONSHIP PLAY-OFF
(Wick Allan Memorial Shield)

FINAL *June 7th at Heathryfold Park, Aberdeen*
Sunnybank v Islavale 1-0
(Flett, Strachan) *(Woolman)*

ARCHIE COOK MEMORIAL TROPHY

FINAL *April 6th at Forest Park, Burghead*
North Section XI v East Section XI 1-1

HAROLD PETRIE MEMORIAL TROPHY

FINAL
Tayside Region XI v North Region XI 4-1

NORTH SECTION

SCOTSGROUP LEAGUE

	P	W	D	L	F	A	Pts
Islavale	26	21	2	3	94	29	65
Buckie Rovers	26	19	6	1	67	30	63
Deveronside	26	18	3	5	73	33	57
New Elgin	26	14	10	2	54	25	52
Burghead Thistle	26	13	5	8	52	41	44
Nairn St Nairn	26	13	3	10	65	55	42
Strathspey Thistle	26	10	7	9	61	46	37
Lossiemouth Utd	26	10	6	10	51	56	36
Bishopmill United	26	8	6	12	49	58	30
Forres Thistle	26	7	5	14	33	49	26
Kinloss	26	7	3	16	50	62	24
RAF Lossiemouth	26	3	8	15	37	73	17
Portgordon United	26	3	2	21	24	88	11
Fochabers	26	2	2	22	25	90	8

MATTHEW CUP

FINAL *June 14th at Canal Park, Banff*
Lossiemouth United v Nairn St Nairn 2-1
(Flett, Strachan) *(Woolman)*

NICHOLSON CUP

FINAL *March 22nd at Black Park, Grantown-on-Spey*
New Elgin v Islavale 3-0

STEWART MEMORIAL TROPHY

FINAL *May 2nd at Grant Park, Lossiemouth*
Burghead Thistle v Islavale 0-2

GORDON WILLIAMSON CUP

FINAL *April 26th at Mosset Park, Forres*
Deveronside v Islavale 2-2 aet, 4-3 pen
(Milne 2) *(Hendry 2)*

ROBERTSON CUP

(1996/97 League placings 1-4)

FINAL *November 1st at Kynoch Park, Keith*
Buckie Rovers v Islavale 1-3

TOM GORDON TROPHY

(1996/97 League placings 5-10)

FINAL *November 30th at Borough Briggs, Elgin*
Bishopmill United v New Elgin 0-3

CONNON CUP

(1996/97 League placings 11-14)

FINAL *October 6th at Mosset Park, Forres*
Burghead Thistle v Strathspey Thistle 1-0

TAYSIDE REGION

FINAL LEAGUE TABLES 1996-97

N C R LEAGUE FIRST DIVISION

	P	W	D	L	F	A	Pts
St Joseph's	26	23	2	1	91	7	71
Tayport	26	22	2	2	64	7	68
North End	26	16	3	7	56	30	54+
Carnoustie P'mure	26	16	4	6	74	40	52
Arbroath SC	26	15	3	8	64	40	48
Kinnoull	26	10	4	12	36	41	31*
Downfield	26	7	7	12	40	45	28
East Craigie	26	6	9	11	32	51	27
Violet	26	6	8	12	32	53	26
Jeanfield Swifts	26	7	5	14	26	66	26
Lochee United	26	6	7	13	30	47	25
Scone Thistle	26	6	4	16	22	66	22
Bankfoot Athletic	26	5	6	15	30	60	21
Forfar Albion	26	5	0	21	34	78	15

+ 3 points awarded * 3 points deducted

N C R LEAGUE DIVISION TWO

	P	W	D	L	F	A	Pts
Kirrie Thistle	20	15	3	2	60	25	48
Forfar West End	20	13	3	4	53	25	42
Elmwood	20	11	4	5	56	40	37
Broughty Athletic	20	9	6	5	41	28	33
Montrose Roselea	20	7	6	7	37	40	27
Lochee Harp	20	6	6	8	42	50	24
Brechin Victoria	20	7	3	10	29	40	24
Coupar Angus	20	6	4	10	36	48	22
Arbroath Victoria	20	6	4	10	37	55	22
Luncarty	20	5	4	11	34	51	19
Blairgowrie	20	1	5	14	33	56	8

DOWNFIELD SC LEAGUE CUP

FINAL *April 27th at Downfield Park, Dundee*
Kirrie Thistle v Forfar West End 1-0
(Nicoll)

INTERSPORT CUP

FINAL *May 20th at Westfield Park, Carnoustie*
Montrose Roselea v Elmwood 3-1
(Gove, Christie, Ferrie) *(Gallagher)*

DJ LAING HOMES CUP

FINAL *June 14th at Glenesk Park, Dundee*
St Joseph's v Carnoustie Panmure 2-1
(Young, McGill) *(Craig)*

WHYTE & McKAY CUP

FINAL *June 3rd at North End Park, Dundee*
St Joseph's v Scone Thistle 4-0
(Devine 2, Kopel, McGill)

TAYCARS TROPHY

FINAL *June 7th at Glenesk Park, Dundee*
St Joseph's v Tayport 2-1
(Kopel, McGill) *(Coventry)*

NORTH END CENTENARY CUP

FINAL *May 31st at North End Park, Dundee*
St Joseph's v Tayport 2-1
(Burns, Jones) *(Stewart)*

NON LEAGUE IN THE SCOTTISH CUP PROPER

FIRST ROUND

Alloa Athletic v Hawick Royal Albert 3-1
(Dwyer, McAnenay, MacKay) (Graham) Att: 452

Elgin City v Whitehill Welfare 0-3
(Wood 2, Millar) Att: 1011

Huntly v Clyde 1-1
(Copeland) (Gibson) Att: 1500

Replay: Clyde v Huntly 3-2 aet
(Annand, McEwan, Mathieson)(Stewart, Copeland) Att: 772

SECOND ROUND

Berwick Rangers v Peterhead 2-1
(McParland) (McCredie) Att: 484

East Stirlingshire v Brora Rangers 4-3
(Inglis, Stirling 2, Abercromby) (Murray, McFee 2-1p) Att: 446

Queens Park v Gala Fairydean 2-1
(Caven, Falconer) (Forrest) Att: 791

Spartans v Arbroath 0-0
Att: 410

Whitehill Welfare v Queen of the South 2-3
(Middlesmist, Millar) (Nesovie, Leslie, Mallan) Att: 350

Replay: Arbroath v Spartans 3-0
(McCarron, Wilie, Grant) Att: 503

QUALIFYING CUP

SOUTH

FIRST ROUND

Annan Athletic	v	Edinburgh University	3-1
Glasgow University	v	Coldstream	2-3
St Cuthbert W	v	Edinburgh City	0-3
Spartans	v	Threave Rov	1-1, 5-1
Whitehill Welfare	v	Wigtown & B	5-0

SECOND ROUND

Annan Athletic	v	Girvan	5-1
Burntisland SY	v	N Stewart	1-1, 2-2, 4-3p
CiS Strollers	v	Vale of Leithen	0-1
Coldstream	v	Preston Ath	2-2, 1-4
Gala Fairydean	v	Selkirk	4-2
Hawick R.A.	v	Edinburgh City	3-1
Spartans	v	Tarff Rovers	5-0
Whitehill Welfare	v	Dalbeattie Star	8-0

THIRD ROUND

Gala Fairydean	v	Preston Athletic	2-0
Hawick R.A.	v	Vale of Leithen	3-3, 2-1
Spartans	v	Burntisland Shipyard	2-1
Whitehill Welfare	v	Annan Athletic	3-1

SEMI-FINAL

Hawick R.A.	v	Gala Fairydean	1-6
Whitehill Welfare	v	Spartans	1-3

FINAL *November 30th at Forthbank, Stirling*

Spartans v Gala Fairydean 2-1
(Govan, McGovern) (Manson)

NORTH

FIRST ROUND

Fraserburgh	v	Rothes	3-0

SECOND ROUND

Brora Rangers	v	Golspie Sutherland	10-0
Clachnacuddin	v	Wick Academy	2-0
Cove Rangers	v	Fraserburgh	3-3, 2-1
Deveronvale	v	Nairn County	3-1
Elgin City	v	Forres Mechanics	3-2
Fort William	v	Buckie Thistle	2-1
Keith	v	Peterhead	1-3
Lossiemouth	v	Huntly	2-3

THIRD ROUND

Brora Rangers	v	Cove Rangers	3-0
Clachnacuddin	v	Peterhead	1-3
Deveronvale	v	Elgin City	0-0, 0-2
Fort William	v	Huntly	1-7

SEMI-FINAL

Brora Rangers	v	Elgin City	1-4
Huntly	v	Peterhead	1-1, 2-1

FINAL *November 16th at Kynoch Park, Keith*

Huntly v Elgin City 2-1
(Copland, Stewart) (M Green)

Team: Huntly: *Gardiner, Yeats, Allan, Copland, Paterson, Rougvie, Gray, Stewart, Selbie, Whyte, Brown (Smith)*
Elgin City: *Pirie, MacLennan, R McHardy, Mone, Moir, Hardie, Whyte, M Green (McGuire), Polworth, D Green, Dunsire*

HIGHLAND LEAGUE

FINAL LEAGUE TABLE 1996-97

	P	W	D	L	F	A	Pts
Huntly	30	21	4	3	86	26	73
Keith	30	21	3	6	76	36	66
Peterhead	30	17	7	6	77	30	58
Lossiemouth	30	18	4	8	66	31	58
Clachnacuddin	30	16	5	9	59	46	53
Fraserburgh	30	15	7	8	56	38	52
Cove Rangers	30	15	5	10	84	47	50
Deveronvale	30	16	2	12	55	54	50
Elgin City	30	13	4	13	64	66	43
Wick Academy	30	9	8	13	41	46	35
Rothes	30	9	8	13	44	52	35
Forres Mechanics	30	8	5	17	40	60	29
Buckie Thistle	30	8	4	18	41	55	28
Brora Rangers	30	5	10	15	43	88	25
Nairn County	30	4	3	23	21	93	15
Fort William	30	2	3	25	31	116	9

HIGHLAND LEAGUE CUP

GROUP A

Cove Rangers	v	Rothes	1-1
Fraserburgh	v	Keith	6-1
Cove Rangers	v	Fraserburgh	1-4
Rothes	v	Keith	1-4
Keith	v	Cove Rangers	0-1
Rothes	v	Fraserburgh	0-6

GROUP B

Buckie Thistle	v	Peterhead	0-4
Huntly	v	Deveronvale	4-0
Buckie Thistle	v	Huntly	0-2
Peterhead	v	Deveronvale	2-1
Deveronvale	v	Buckie Thistle	3-0
Peterhead	v	Huntly	1-3

GROUP C

Forres Mechanics	v	Elgin City	1-7
Lossiemouth	v	Nairn County	2-0
Lossiemouth	v	Forres Mechanics	2-1
Nairn County	v	Elgin City	1-2
Elgin City	v	Lossiemouth	0-2
Nairn County	v	Forres Mechanics	2-4

GROUP D

Clachnacuddin	v	Brora Rangers	3-0
Fort William	v	Wick Academy	0-1
Fort William	v	Clachnacuddin	0-5
Wick Academy	v	Brora Rangers	2-2
Brora Rangers	v	Fort William	6-1
Clachnacuddin	v	Wick Academy	3-0

GROUP A	**P**	**W**	**D**	**L**	**F**	**A**	**Pts**
Fraserburgh	3	3	0	0	16	2	9
Cove Rangers	3	1	1	1	3	5	4
Keith	3	1	0	2	5	8	3
Rothes	3	0	1	2	2	11	1
GROUP B							
Huntly	3	3	0	0	9	1	9
Peterhead	3	2	0	1	7	4	6
Deveronvale	3	1	0	2	4	6	3
Buckie Thistle	3	0	0	3	0	9	0
GROUP C							
Lossiemouth	3	3	0	0	6	1	9
Elgin City	3	2	0	1	9	4	6
Forres Mechanics	3	1	0	2	6	11	3
Nairn County	3	0	0	3	3	8	0
GROUP D							
Clachnacuddin	3	3	0	0	11	0	9
Brora Rangers	3	1	1	1	8	6	4
Wick Academy	3	1	1	1	3	5	4
Fort William	3	0	0	3	1	12	0

SEMI-FINAL

HUNTLY	v	FRASERBURGH	1-2 aet
LOSSIEMOUTH	v	CLACHNACUDDIN	3-1

FINAL *September 14th at Christie Park, Huntly*

FRASERBURGH v LOSSIEMOUTH 1-2

(Hunter) *(Clark, Main)* *Att: 1800*

Teams: Fraserburgh: *Gordon, Milne, Michie, Clark, Killoh (Young), Thomson (McCafferty), Geddes (Norris), Murray, Keith, Hunter, Stephen*

Lossiemouth: *McRitchie, Fiske, Main, Masson, Gerrard, Presslie, Still, Paterson, Rowley (Douglas), Clark, Seaton (MacKenzie)*

McEWANS LAGER NORTH OF SCOTLAND CUP

FIRST ROUND

Elgin City	v	Inverness CT 'A'	3-0
Golspie Suth	v	Wick Academy	0-2
Forres Mechanics	v	Clachnacuddin	2-2, 3-1

SECOND ROUND

Brora Rangers	v	Nairn County	1-4
Elgin City	v	Wick Academy	1-2
Forres Mechanics	v	Fort William	2-1
Lossiemouth	v	Ross County 'A'	4-0

SEMI-FINAL

Lossiemouth	v	Nairn County	1-0
Wick Academy	v	Forres Mechanics	0-0, 1-4

FINAL *March 22nd at Borough Briggs, Elgin*

LOSSIEMOUTH v FORRES MECHANICS 4-1

(Walker, Reid (og), Paterson, Clark) (Minty) *Att: 1382*

Teams: Lossiemouth: *McRitchie, Fiske, Mutch (Rowley), Masson, Gerrard, Walker (Smith), Still, Paterson, Clark, Kellas (McGinlay), Presslie*

Forres Mechanics: *Gray, MacDonald (Houston), Munro, Reid, Walker, Sanderson, Minty (Robertson), Mitchell, Holmes (Watt), Murphy, Brown*

This was Lossiemouth's third successive North of Scotland Cup win

INVERNESS CUP

FIRST ROUND

Clachnacuddin	v	Ross County	1-3
Inverness CT	v	Lossiemouth	4-2
Forres Mechanics	v	Fort William	3-1
Nairn County	v	Brora Rangers	2-1

SEMI-FINAL

Forres Mechanics	v	Inverness CT	0-3
Ross County	v	Nairn County	6-0

THE FINAL is due to be played early in the 1997/98 season, with both clubs fielding their first teams.

JARLAW ABERDEENSHIRE SHIELD

FIRST ROUND

Fraserburgh	v	Keith	1-0
Huntly	v	Cove Rangers	6-3
Peterhead	v	Buckie Thistle	9-1

SEMI-FINAL

Deveronvale	v	Peterhead	1-3
Fraserburgh	v	Huntly	2-1

FINAL *November 27th at Allan Park, Cove*

FRASERBURGH v HUNTLY 6-3 aet

(Hunter 2, McBride 2, Stephen, Killoh) *(Milne 3)* *Att: 500*

Teams: Fraserburgh: *Gordon, Young (M Stephen), Michie, Clark, A Stephen, Geddes (Norris), McCafferty (McBride), Murray, Killoh, Hunter, Milne*

Peterhead: *Pirie, McCreadie (Robertson), Cormack, King, Simpson (Beddie), Bridgeford (Rattray), MacKenzie, Yule, Milne, Brown, Smith*

JARLAW ABERDEENSHIRE CUP

FIRST ROUND

Cove Rangers	v	Keith	1-0
Fraserburgh	v	Buckie Thistle	1-1, 3-1
Huntly	v	Deveronvale	2-1

SEMI-FINAL

Cove Rangers	v	Peterhead	1-2
Fraserburgh	v	Huntly	2-1

FINAL *March 29th at Recreation Park, Peterhead*

FRASERBURGH v PETERHEAD 3-2

(Geddes, Murray, Keith) *(Milne 2)* *Att: 1572*

Teams: Fraserburgh: *Gordon, Milne, Michie, Clark, Stephen (Young), Geddes (Keith), Thomson, Murray (McCafferty), Killoh, Hunter, McBride*

Peterhead: *Pirie, Watson, Cheyne, King, Simpson, Bridgeford, MacKenzie (Buchan), Yule, Milne, Brown, Smith*

Huntley *Back row from left: Arthur Murphy, Niall Grant, Martin Stewart, Doug Rougvie (Manager), John Gardiner, Gary Whyte, Ronnie Smith, Kevin Allan, Andy Pateron. Front row from left: Steve Lennox, Colin MacRonald, Steve Gray, Mike Hendry (Chairman), Eddie Copland, Craig Yeats, Graham Robertson, Stuart Shinnie. 1996/97 P&J League ranking – 1st.*

Peterhead *Back row from left: Ronnie Brown (assistant manager), Craig Watson, Colin Milne, Raymond Cormack, Scott Paterson, Derek Smith, Ivor Price, Mark Simpson, Jim Cheyne, Mark Buchan, Doug Baxter, Sandy Rennie (trainer). Front row from left: Gary Clark, Ray Yule, Ritchie Livingstone, Scott Brown, Dave Watson (manager), Steve King, Sean Beddie, Paul McKenzie. 1996/97 P&J Highland League ranking – 3rd.*

Lossiemouth *Back row from left to right: Ryan Richmond, Norman Kellas, Graeme Masson, Steve McRitchie, Mark McRitchie, Mike McKenzie, Stevie Clinton, Brian Conlon. Front row from left to right: Franny More, Kevin Binnie, Neil Smith, Roy Main, Alan Mair. 1996/97 P&J Highland League ranking – 4th*

__Clachnacuddin__ Back row from left to right: Bruce McCraw, Philip Lamb, John Douglas, Billy Skinner, Barry McCraw, Colin Sinclair, Donian Murray, Alan Richardson, Gavin Deerie. Front row from left to right: David Brennan, Robbie Benson, Graeme Bennett (player-manager), Norman MacMillan, Kevin Corbett. 1996/97 P&J Highland League ranking – 5th

__Fraserburgh__ Back row from left to right: Bill Gordon, Eric West, Jimmy Young, Kris Hunter, Paul Keith, James Geddes, Ina Murray, Kevin Norris, Russell McBride, Andrew Stephen, Keith Stewart. Front row from left to right: Charlie Duncan, Manager, Robbie Duff, James Duthie, Gavin Wemyss, John Thompson, Murray Herd, Scott Clark, Mike McCafferty, Duncan Summers, Steve Eckersley. 1996/97 P&J Highland League ranking – 6th.

__Keith__ Back from left: Martin Allan (manager), John McGachie, Levi Stephen, Derek Nicol, Michael Brown, Keith Watt, Neil Nicol, Paul Dunn, Graham Cadger, Alan Lyons. Front, from left: Neil Gibson, Colin Maver, George Stephen, Darren Still, Bruce Morrison, Neil McPherson, Gary Taylor. 1996/97 P&J Highland League ranking – 2nd

EAST OF SCOTLAND LEAGUE

FINAL LEAGUE TABLES 1996-97

'PRO IV' PREMIER DIVISION

	P	W	D	L	F	A	Pts
Spartans	18	12	5	2	36	17	38
Whitehill Welfare	18	10	6	2	44	18	36
Gala Fairydean	18	10	2	6	31	27	32
Edinburgh Athletic	18	7	5	6	29	26	26
Annan Athletic	18	7	4	7	31	29	25
Edinburgh City	18	7	4	7	40	39	25
Pencaitland	18	6	4	8	21	26	22
Craigroyston	18	6	4	8	23	31	22
Preston Athletic	18	5	6	7	21	23	21
Edinburgh University	18	0	2	16	10	50	2

EAST OF SCOTLAND LEAGUE CUP

SECTION ONE							
C S Strollers	8	7	0	1	16	7	21
Annan Athletic	8	4	2	2	21	15	14
Edinburgh Athletic	8	3	3	2	16	10	12
Selkirk	8	2	0	6	12	24	6
Coldstream	8	1	1	6	15	24	4
SECTION TWO							
Whitehill Welfare	8	6	1	1	43	11	19
Edinburgh City	8	6	1	1	35	9	19
Lothian Thistle	8	4	1	3	28	14	13
Peebles Rovers	8	2	1	5	11	21	7
Heriot Watt Univ.	8	0	0	8	3	65	0
SECTION THREE							
Vale of Leithen	6	3	1	2	11	9	10
Gala Fairydean	6	2	3	1	14	12	9
Graigroyston	6	2	2	2	14	12	8
Kelso United	6	1	2	3	11	17	5
SECTION FOUR							
Spartans	6	5	1	0	12	3	16
Hawick RA	6	4	0	2	13	12	12
Preston Athletic	6	2	1	3	11	12	7
Easthouses Lily	6	0	0	6	2	11	0
SECTION FIVE							
Pencaitland	6	4	0	2	7	3	12
Tollcross United	6	3	2	1	11	7	11
Eyemouth United	6	3	2	1	8	6	11
Edinburgh Univ.	6	0	0	6	4	14	0

PLAY OFF

Spartan	v	Pencaitland	1-2

SEMI-FINAL

Civil Serv Strollers	v	Whitehill Welfare	2-4
Pencaitland	v	Vale of Leithen	1-2

FINAL *December 28th at Pennypit Stadium (Preston Athletic)*

Whitehill Welfare	v	Vale of Leithen	2-0

'CLUB SERVICES' KING CUP

FIRST ROUND

Eyemouth United	v	Selkirk	1-4
Hawick RA	v	Easthouses Lily	2-3
Heriot Watt University	v	Lothian Thistle	0-6
Peebles Rovers	v	Civil Service Strollers	1-1, 2-1
Pencaitland	v	Coldstream	1-0

SECOND ROUND

Easthouses Lily	v	Selkirk	0-0, 2-1
Edinburgh Athletic	v	Peebles Rovers	0-0, 1-0
Gala Fairydean	v	Edinburgh University	3-1
Kelso United	v	Pencaitland	0-0, 0-1
Lothian Thistle	v	Spartans	1-0
Preston Athletic	v	Edinburgh City	3-2
Tollcross United	v	Whitehill Welfare	0-2
Vale of Leithen	v	Craigroyston	3-3, 0-2

THIRD ROUND

Craigroyston	v	Easthouses Lily	4-2
Edinburgh Athletic	v	Preston Athletic	4-2
Pencaitland	v	Gala Fairydean	1-2 aet
Whitehill Welfare	v	Craigroyston	0-2

SEMI-FINAL

Edinburgh Athletic	v	Gala Fairydean	3-2
Whitehill Welfare	v	Craigroyston	0-2

FINAL *May 13th at Pennypit Stadium*

Craigroyston	v	Edinburgh Athletic	2-0

'PRO IV' FIRST DIVISION

	P	W	D	L	F	A	Pts
Lothian Thistle	22	17	3	2	68	21	54
Civil Serv Strollers	22	15	5	2	46	22	50
Selkirk	22	11	5	6	49	36	38
Hawick Royal Albert	22	11	3	8	57	59	36
Peebles Rovers	22	10	4	8	50	35	34
Vale of Leithen	22	10	4	8	54	45	34
Coldstream	22	10	3	9	42	35	33
Tollcross United	22	8	7	7	41	34	31
Kelso United	22	9	3	10	38	50	30
Easthouses Lily	22	5	3	14	27	47	18
Eyemouth United	22	1	6	15	30	63	6*
Heriot Watt Univ.	22	1	2	19	28	83	5

*3 points deducted

'IMAGE PRINTERS' EAST OF SCOTLAND QUALIFYING CUP

FIRST ROUND

Edinburgh Athletic	v	Coldstream	4-1
Gala Fairydean	v	Eyemouth United	6-1
Selkirk	v	Craigroyston	0-2
Tollcross United	v	Kelso United	4-1
Vale of Leithen	v	Whitehill Welfare	0-5

SECOND ROUND

Civil Service Strollers	v	Edinburgh City	0-1
Easthouses Lily	v	Spartans	3-0
Edinburgh University	v	Craigroyston	0-0, 5-1
Gala Fairydean	v	Hawick RA	7-0
Heriot Watt University	v	Tollcross United	0-1
Peebles Rovers	v	Lothian Thistle	2-2, 1-1, 4-5p
Pencaitland	v	Preston Ath (At Preston)	4-1
Whitehill Welfare	v	Edinburgh Athletic	5-1

THIRD ROUND

Easthouses Lily	v	Gala Fairydean	1-4
Edinburgh City	v	Pencaitland	4-1
Lothian Thistle	v	Tollcross United	3-0
Whitehill Welfare	v	Edinburgh University	5-0

SEMI-FINAL

Edinburgh City	v	Lothian Thistle	1-2
Whitehill Welfare	v	Gala Fairydean	2-1

FINAL *April 20th at Pennypit Stadium*

Lothian Thistle	v	Whitehill Welfare	2-1

CITY CUP

SEMI-FINAL

Berwick Rangers	v	Whitehill Welfare	1-1, 4-5p
Livingston	v	Lothian Thistle	2-0

FINAL *April 27th at Livingston FC*

Livingston	v	Whitehill Welfare	2-1

ALEX JACK CUP

FIRST ROUND

Craigroyston	v	Lothian Thistle	0-6
Kelso United	v	Eyemouth United	0-2

SECOND ROUND

Edinburgh Athletic	v	Heriot Watt University	1-1, 4-0
Lothian Thistle	v	Easthouses Lily	1-2
Pencaitland	v	Eyemouth United	8-1
Tollcross United	v	Peebles Rovers	2-2, 2-1

SEMI-FINAL

Easthouses Lily	v	Edinburgh Athletic	1-2
Pencaitland	v	Tollcross United	1-1, 6-5p

FINAL *February 2nd at Whitehill Welfare FC* *Att: 200*

Edinburgh Athletic	v	Pencaitland	1-0

NEWS

*Spartans won the League, breaking a run of championships for Whitehill Welfare
*Ex-Falkirk manager Eamonn Bannon played for Spartans
*Craigroyston, in winning the King Cup, annexed their first ever victory
*Whitehill Welfare are due to open a new pavilion in the 1997/98 season

SOUTH OF SCOTLAND LEAGUE

FINAL LEAGUE TABLE 1996-97

	P	W	D	L	F	A	Pts
Queen of the Sth R	26	17	7	2	90	38	58
Blackwood D'mos	26	16	3	7	58	41	51
St Cuthbert Wdrers	26	15	5	6	72	51	50
Stranraer Athletic	26	15	5	6	52	36	50
Dumfries HSFP	26	13	6	7	59	41	45
Threave Rovers	26	12	6	8	62	47	42
Newton Stewart	26	12	4	10	41	40	40
Maxwelltown HSFP	26	9	6	11	52	58	33
Girvan	26	9	5	12	60	75	32
Creetown	26	7	4	15	53	82	25
Tarff Rovers	26	8	2	16	43	67	26
Annan Athletic	26	7	3	16	52	77	24
Dalbeattie Star	26	5	2	16	44	61	20
Wigtown & Bladnoch	26	6	1	19	40	66	19

SOUTH OF SCOTLAND LEAGUE CUP

WEST SECTION ONE							
Stranraer Athletic	6	5	1	0	21	4	13
Newton Stewart	6	3	2	1	11	6	11
Creetown	6	2	0	4	10	21	6
Tarff Rovers	6	0	1	5	3	14	1
WEST SECTION TWO							
Girvan	4	3	0	1	14	7	9
St Cuthbert W	4	2	1	1	11	7	7
Wigtown & B	4	0	1	3	3	14	1
EAST SECTION ONE							
QOS Reserves	6	5	1	0	24	5	16
Threave Rovers	6	2	1	3	15	17	7
Annan Athletic	6	2	1	3	7	18	4
Dumfries HSFP	6	1	1	4	9	15	4
EAST SECTION TWO							
Maxwelltown	4	3	1	0	13	5	10
Blackwood D	4	2	1	1	12	8	7
Dalbeattie S	4	0	0	4	3	15	0

SEMI-FINAL *(Over two legs)*

Girvan	v	Stranraer Athletic	0-2
Stranraer Athletic	v	Girvan	3-0

(Aggregate: Stranraer Athletic 5-0)

Maxwelltown	v	QOS Reserves	0-3
QOS Reserves	v	Maxwelltown HSFP	3-1

(Aggregate: Queen of the South Reserves won 6-1)

FINAL 1st Leg *August 24th at Stair Park, Stranraer*

STRANRAER ATHLETIC v QOS RESERVES 3-2

(McCulloch, Wilson, Boyd) *(Wilson, Maxwell)* *HT: 1-1*

FINAL 2nd Leg *August 31st at Palmerston Park, Dumfries*

QOS RESERVES v STRANRAER ATHLETIC 3-0

(Bowman 2, Irving) *HT: 1-0*

Aggregate: Queen of the South Reserves won 5-3

JAMES BROWN FAIR PLAY TROPHY

1 Girvan	110	8 Creetown	183
2 QOS Reserves	127	9 Dalbeattie Star	206
3 Wigtown & Blad.	132	10 Blackwood Dynamos	207
4 Threave Rovers	142	11 Newton Stewart	225
5 Stranraer Athletic	147	12 Annan Athletic	236
6 St Cuthbert Wand.	169	13 Maxwelltown HSFP	238
7 Dumfries HSFP	182	14 Tarff Rovers	267

SOUTHERN COUNTIES CHALLENGE CUP

FIRST ROUND			
Annan Athletic	v	Blackwood	3-3 aet, 5-4p
Dumfries HSFP	v	Stranraer	1-3
Maxwelltown HSFP	v	Newton Stewart	6-4
St Cuthbert W	v	Stranraer Athletic	3-0
Tarff Rovers	v	Dalbeatie Star	3-1
Wigtown & B	v	Creetown	5-2
SECOND ROUND			
Annan Athletic	v	Stranraer	2-1
Maxwelltown HSFP	v	Wigtown & B	3-4 aet
St Cuthbert W	v	Tarff Rovers	1-4
Threave Rovers	v	QOS Reserves	2-3
SEMI-FINAL			
QOS Reserves	v	Tarff Rovers	1-0
Wigtown & B	v	Annan Athletic	2-4

FINAL *May 7th at Palmerston Park, Dumfries*

Queen of the Sth Res v Annan Athletic 2-0

(Brydson, Cochrane) *HT: 0-0*

POTTS CUP

FIRST ROUND			
Blackwood D	v	St Cuthbert Wanderers	2-3
Dalbeattie	v	Threave Rovers	1-2
Dumfries HS	v	Tarff Rovers	7-1
Stranraer Athletic	v	Annan Athletic	2-1
SECOND ROUND			
Creetown	v	N Stewart	1-1 aet, 3-4p
Stranraer Athletic	v	St Cuthbert Wanderers	0-1
Threave Rovers	v	Dumfries HSFP	2-0
Wigtown & B	v	Maxwelltown HS	1-2
SEMI-FINAL			
Newton Stewart	v	Maxwelltown HSFP	0-1 aet
St Cuthbert Wanderers	v	Threave Rovers	2-1

FINAL *April 26th at Barbour Hall, Glencaple*

Dumfries HSFP v Stranraer Athletic 0-0 aet, 3-5p

TWEEDIE CUP

FIRST ROUND			
Annan Athletic	v	Creetown	14-0
Dalbeattie S	v	Maxwelltown HSFP	0-6
Dumfries HSFP	v	Wigtown & Bladnoch	3-0
Girvan	v	Stranraer Athletic	2-0
Tarff Rovers	v	Newton Stewart	2-1
SECOND ROUND			
Annan Athletic	v	Girvan	3-2 aet
Blackwood D	v	St Cuthbert Wanderers	1-2
Maxwelltown	v	Dumfries HSFP	2-4
Threave Rovers	v	Tarff Rovers	2-1
SEMI-FINAL			
Annan Athletic	v	Dumfries HSFP	
St Cuthbert Wanderers	v	Threave Rovers	2-8

FINAL *May 10th at Meadow Park, Castle Douglas*

THREAVE ROVERS v ANNAN ATHLETIC 3-0

(M Adams 2, C Adams) *HT: 0-0*

CREE LODGE CUP

FIRST ROUND			
Dalbeattie S	v	Dumfries HSFP	0-4
Maxwelltown	v	St Cuthbert Wanderers	1-2
Newton Stewart	v	Annan Athletic	0-0 aet, 0-3p
Stranraer Athletic	v	Creetown	1-4
Tarff Rovers	v	Girvan	2-1
SECOND ROUND			
Annan Athletic	v	Tarff Rovers	1-1 aet, 5-6p
Dumfries HSFP	v	Creetown	4-0
Threave Rovers	v	St Cuthbert	0-0 aet, 4-2p
Wigtown & B	v	Blackwood Dynamos	2-5
SEMI-FINAL			
Blackwood Dynamos	v	Threave Rovers	1-3
Tarff Rovers	v	Dumfries HSFP	1-1 aet, 5-4p

FINAL *May 3rd at Meadow Park, Castle Douglas*

THREAVE ROVERS v TARFF ROVERS 4-0

(A McGinley 2, M Adams 2) *HT: 2-0*

AYRSHIRE CUP

SEMI-FINAL *April 23rd at Ayr United FC*

Ayr United v Girvan 7-0

LEADING GOALSCORER

(All Competitions) Mark Adams *(Threave Rovers)*

DETROIT TROPHY

(Overall championship based on league points and cup results)

1	Queen of the South Reserves	70
2	Stranraer Athletic	60
3	St Cuthbert Wanderers	58
4=	Dumfries High School FP	56
	Threave Rovers	56

NEWS

Queen of the South are pulling their all conquering reserve side out of the league and cup competitions for 1997/98, how-

AMATEUR & MINOR FOOTBALL

SCOTTISH AMATEUR CUP

A total of 604 clubs entered this season's competition.

SEVENTH ROUND

Glasgow Harp	v	Bourtreehill Ams	1-1, 0-1
Partizan Amateurs	v	Dalziel HSFP	1-1, 1-5
Kilbowie Union	v	Echt Amateurs	1-2
Riverside Athletic	v	Weir Recreation	1-0
Cleland Miners	v	St Pats FP	1-0
Knockentiber Ams	v	Mossblown Ams	5-1
East Kilbride YMCA	v	Benarty Amateurs	2-1
Vale of Clyde	v	Milton Amateurs	1-0

EIGHTH ROUND

East Kilbride YMCA	v	Cleland M	0-0, 2-2 aet, 2-4p
Milton Amateurs	v	Bourtreehill	2-1
Echt Amateurs	v	Knockentiber	1-2
Riverside Athletic	v	Dalziel HSFP	2-4

SEMI-FINAL

Knockentiber Ams	v	Cleland Miners	3-0
Milton Amateurs	v	Dalziel HSFP	Walkover

(Due to using a substitute in the quarter final who had earlier played in the competition with Coatbridge CC, Dalziel HSFP were thrown out of the competition.)

FINAL *May 17th at Hampden Park*

KNOCKENTIBER AMS v MILTON AMATEURS 2-1
(Hunter 2) *(McKechnie)*

*Kilburnie Ladeside (Amber) clear their lines at Cumnock.
Photo: Chtis Sanderson*

AMATEUR FOOTBALL ALLIANCE

Secretary: W.P. Goss,
55 Islington Park Street, London N1 1QB
0171-359 3493 Fax: 0171 359 5027

A F A SENIOR CUP

1ST ROUND PROPER
Nottsborough 4*:5 - 4*:2 Old Addeyans
Bank of England 1 - 0 Old Parkonians
Old Meadonians 2 - 3 Old Lyonian
Ulysses 2 - 4 Cardinal Manning Old Boys
Parkfield 1 - 3 Civil Service
Old Suttonians 6 - 1 Broomfield
Old Wilsonians 3* - 2* Old Cholmeleans
John Fisher Old Boys 1 - 2 Wake Green
Old Aloysians 5 - 1 Old Manorians
Old Latymerians 1 - 0 New Scotland Yard Comets
Hampstead Heathens 1 - 3 Old Tiffinian
Carshalton 9 - 2 Old Malvernian
Latymer Old Boys 4 - 2 Old Owens
Norsemen 1 - 3 Enfield Old Grammarians
Old Tollingtonians 0 - 5 West Wickham
Lancing Old Boys 2:3 - 2:0 Lloyds Bank
Southgate Olympic 3 - 0 Old Elizabethans
Crouch End Vampires 3 - 0 Cuaco
Shene Old Grammarians 1 - 3 Old Tenisonians
Polytechnic 3 - 2 Old Bromleians
Mill Hill Village 2 - 5 Old Buckwellians
St. Mary's College 1 - 3 Old Minchendenians
Cardinal Pole Old Boys 1 - 2 Merton
Midland Bank 9 - 2 Old Salesians
Lensbury 3 - 1 Old Actonians Association
Old Sinjuns 5 - 0 Mill Hill County Old Boys
East Barnet Old Grammarians 6 - 1 Derbyshire Amateurs
Barclays Bank 4 - 1 Old Ignatians
Old Hamptonians 1*:0* - 1*:2* Glyn Old Boys
Southgate County 2 - 0 Kew Association
Fulham Compton Old Boys 0 - 3 Old Vaughanians
Brentham 0* - 4* Witan

2ND ROUND PROPER
Nottsborough 3 - 0 Bank of England
Old Lyonian 1*:3* - 1*:4* Cardinal Manning Old Boys
Civil Service 4 - 1 Old Suttonians
Old Wilsonians 3 - 2 Wake Green
Old Aloysians 2 - 1 Old Latymerians
Old Tiffinian 1 - 2 Carshalton
Latymer Old Boys 4:0 - 4:1 Enfield Old Grammarians
West Wickham 6* - 2* Lancing Old Boys
Southgate Olympic 2 - 3 Crouch End Vampires
Old Tenisonians 3 - 1 Polytechnic
Old Buckwellians 0 - 2 Old Minchendenians
Merton 4 - 0 Midland Bank
Lensbury 4 - 1 Old Sinjuns
East Barnet Old Grammarians 3 - 4 Barclays Bank
Glyn Old Boys 3 - 1 Southgate County
Old Vaughanians 1 - 2 Witan

3RD ROUND PROPER
Nottsborough 4*:5 - 4*:0 Cardinal Manning Old Boys
Civil Service 2 - 1 Old Wilsonians
Old Aloysians 1 - 0 Carshalton
Enfield Old Grammarians 0 - 4? West Wickham
Crouch End Vampires 1* - 0* Old Tenisonians
Old Minchendenians 3 - 2 Merton
Lensbury 3*:4 - 3*:2 Barclays Bank
Glyn Old Boys 2 - 3 Witan

4TH ROUND PROPER
Nottsborough 2 - 3 Civil Service
Old Aloysians 1*:1 - 1*:2 West Wickham
Crouch End Vampires 1 - 0 Old Minchendenians
Lensbury 3 - 1 Witan

SEMI-FINALS
Civil Service 4 - 2 Old Aloysians
Crouch End Vampires 2 - 4 Lensbury
(* - after extra time)

INTERMEDIATE:
Lloyds Bank Res.4 - 1 Civil Service Res.
JUNIOR
Old Finchleians 3rd. 4* - 2* Old Bealonians 3rd.
MINOR
Norsemen 4th. 1 - 0 Hampstead Heathens 4th.
SENIOR NOVETS
Old Actonians Association 5th. 2 - 0 Polytechnic 5th
INTERMEDIATE NOVETS
Old Parmiterians 6th. 2 - 0 Old Camdenians 6th
JUNIOR NOVETS
Old Parmiterians 8th. 2 - 0 National Westminster Bank 7th.
VETERANS
Old Parmiterians Vets. 2 - 1 Old Chigwellians Vets.
0PEN VETERANS
Snaresbrook Vets. 3 - 1 Belstone Vets.
YOUTH
Old Salesians 2 - 1 Old Actonians Association
ESSEX DIVISIONAL SENIOR
Old Foresters 1 - 0 Old Brentwoods
MIDDLESEX DIVISIONAL SENIOR
Cardinal Manning Old Boys 1*:5 - 1*:1 Old Ignatians
SURREY DIVISIONAL SENIOR
Carshalton 1*:0 - 1*:2 Lloyds Bank
ESSEX DIVISIONAL INTERMEDIATE
Leyton County OB Res. 3*:2 - 3*:0 Hale End Athletic Res.
KENT DIVISIONAL INTERMEDIATE
West Wickham Res. 0 - 1 Lloyds Bank Res.
MIDDLESEX DIVISIONAL INTERMEDIATE
Old Actonians Ass'n Res. 2*:4 - 2*:1 Crouch End Vamp. Res.
SURREY DIVISIONAL INTERMEDIATE
Old Thorntonians Res. 2 - 1 South Bank Res.
W E GREENLAND MEMORIAL
Sun Alliance 3 - 0 Gray's Inn
(* - after extra time)

ARTHUR DUNN CUP

Old Foresters 3 Old Salopians 1

ARTHURIAN LEAGUE

PREMIER DIVISION:	P	W	D	L	F	A	Pts
Old Foresters	16	8	5	3	32	15	21
Lancing Old Boys	16	10	1	5	39	23	21
Old Brentwoods	16	8	4	4	47	24	20
Old Carthusians	16	8	4	4	39	33	20
Old Etonians	16	7	3	6	27	28	17
Old Chigwellians	16	6	4	6	31	23	16
Old Cholmeleians	16	7	1	8	27	39	15
Old Reptonians	16	4	2	10	28	53	10
Old Witleians	16	2	0	14	18	50	4

DIVISION 1

	P	W	D	L	F	A	Pts
Old Haberdashers	16	14	0	2	62	17	28
Old Salopians	16	10	5	1	48	26	25
Old Bradfieldians	16	10	2	4	46	27	22
Old Aldenhamians	16	8	1	7	44	28	17
Old Harrovians	16	6	3	7	39	37	15
Old Malvernians	16	6	1	9	35	55	13
Old Haileyburians	16	4	2	10	28	49	10
Old Wykehamists	16	4	0	12	33	67	8
Old Wellingburians	16	2	2	12	27	56	6

DIVISION 2

	P	W	D	L	F	A	Pts
Old Chigwellians Res.	16	13	2	1	49	13	28
Old Cholmeleians Res.	16	12	2	2	49	15	26
Old Etonians Res.	16	9	2	5	40	22	20
Old Carthusians Res.	16	8	1	7	27	26	17
Old Etonians 3rd.	16	8	1	7	29	37	17
Old Foresters Res.	16	5	2	9	17	30	12
Old Cholmeleians 3rd.	16	5	1	10	24	36	11
Lancing Old Boys Res.	16	5	1	10	20	39	11
Old Harrovians Res.	16	1	0	15	16	53	2

DIVISION 3

	P	W	D	L	F	A	Pts
Old Chigwellians 3rd.	18	11	6	1	40	15	28
Old Brentwoods Res.	18	11	3	4	50	27	25
Old Salopians Res.	18	9	3	6	46	38	21
Old Cholmeleians 4th.	18	8	5	5	33	29	21
Old Aldenhamians Res.	18	7	6	5	46	47	20
Old Westminsters	18	7	4	7	44	35	18
Old Eastbournians	18	8	2	8	38	39	18
Old Ardinians	18	7	3	8	41	42	17
Old Foresters 3rd.	18	3	2	13	26	43	8
Old Haberdashers Res.	18	1	2	15	22	71	2 #

(# - Points deducted - breach of rule)

DIVISION 4 Won by Old Millhillians
DIVISION 5 Won by Old Foresters 4th.

Junior League Cup:
O. Chigwellians Res. 3 Old Etonians Res. 1

Derrik Moore Veterans Cup:
O. Cholmeleians Vets 0 O. Etonians Vets 3

LONDON FINANCIAL F.A.

DIVISION ONE

	P	W	D	L	F	A	Pts
Churchill Insurance	16	10	4	2	37	23	24
Morgan Guaranty	16	10	3	3	44	24	23
Royal Bank of Scotland	16	8	3	5	55	42	19
Morgan Stanley Int.	16	8	2	6	51	39	18
Bank America	16	6	4	6	20	23	16
Kleinwort Benson	16	5	5	6	36	31	15
Sun Alliance	16	6	2	8	36	44	14
Coutts	16	2	4	10	28	50	8
Citibank	16	2	3	11	22	43	7

DIVISION TWO

Allied Irish Bank	16	14	1	1	54	9	29
Bowring	16	10	4	2	47	20	24
Eagle Star	16	8	3	5	39	30	19
Temple Bar	16	7	4	5	54	47	18
Granby	16	4	7	5	24	28	15
Chase Manhattan Bank	16	5	4	7	25	30	14
Salomon Brothers	16	5	2	9	27	58	12
Liverpool Victoria	16	3	3	10	26	48	9
Royal Bank of Scot. Res.	16	2	0	14	26	52	4

DIVISION THREE

Vantage	12	10	2	0	36	13	22
Union Bank of Switz.	12	8	1	3	32	18	17
Bankers Trust	12	5	2	5	31	25	12
Century Life	12	4	3	5	21	17	11
ANZ Banking Group	12	4	2	6	23	30	10
Sedgwick Noble Lown.	12	3	3	6	23	32	9
Coutts Res.	12	0	3	9	12	43	3

DIVISION FOUR

Lincoln National	16	13	3	0	53	10	29
Credit Suisse Fin.Prod.	16	12	2	2	44	18	26
Bank America Res.	16	10	1	5	61	31	21
Sun Alliance Res.	16	7	4	5	40	32	18
Churchill Res.	16	5	1	10	35	45	11
Granby Res.	16	5	1	10	22	39	11
Bank of Ireland	16	4	2	10	26	62	10
Royal Bank of Scot. 3rd.	16	2	5	9	24	45	9
Citibank Res.	16	2	5	9	30	53	9

DIVISION FIVE:
8 Teams Won by Standard Chartered Bank

DIVISION SIX:
7 Teams Won by St. Paul International

Challenge Cup:
Lensbury 1 Barclays Bank 2
Senior Cup:
Sun Alliance 2 Morgan Guaranty 3
Senior Plate:
Kleinwort Benson 2 Churchill Insurance 1
Junior Cup:
Century Life 0 Union Bank of Switzerland 4
Junior Plate:
Bank America Res. 5 Granby Res. 2
Minor Cup:
Temple Bar Res. 1 Standard Chartered Bank 3
Minor Plate:
Eagle Star Res. 3 Sun Alliance 3rd. 1
Veterans' Cup:
Lensbury 5 Temple Bar 0
Veterans' Plate:
Citibank 3 Royal Bank of Scotland 2
W A Jewell Memorial:
Morgan Guaranty 5-a-Side
Saunders Shield:
Salomon Brothers 5-a-Side
Sportsmanship Shield:
C. Hoare & Co.

Representative Matches

v Southern Olympian League	Lost	2-4
v Royal Marines	Won	2-1
v Southern Amateur League "B"	Lost	3-4
v Old Boys' League	Lost	0-1
v Stock Exchange F.A.	Drawn	1-1
v Bristol Insurance Institute	Drawn	2-2

LONDON LEGAL LEAGUE

DIVISION ONE

	P	W	D	L	F	A	Pts
Gray's Inn	18	14	2	2	64	15	30
Nabarro Nathanson	18	10	4	4	44	36	24
Herbert Smith	18	9	4	5	45	35	22
Lovell White Durrant	18	9	3	6	34	26	21
Linklaters & Paines	18	8	3	7	31	31	19
Pegasus (Inner Temple)	18	6	5	7	38	44	17
Cameron Markby Hewitt	18	7	1	10	18	39	15
Wilde Sapte	18	6	2	10	31	33	14
Clifford Chance	18	6	0	12	35	70	12
Gouldens	18	3	0	15	16	27	6

DIVISION TWO

Slaughter & May	18	13	3	2	70	14	29
Taylor Joynson Garrett	18	13	3	2	53	19	29
Rosling King	18	11	2	5	50	35	24
Norton Rose	18	8	3	7	43	34	19
Freshfields	18	8	3	7	41	34	19
Macfarlanes	18	7	2	9	53	41	16
S.J. Berwin	18	6	2	10	32	32	14
Allen & Overy	18	5	3	10	26	62	13
D.J. Freeman & Co.	18	5	1	12	21	43	11
Baker & McKenzie	18	2	2	14	14	89	6

DIVISION THREE							
Kennedy's	16	10	3	3	41	25	23
Stephenson Harwood	16	10	2	4	41	13	22
Simmons & Simmons	16	7	5	4	32	22	19
K.P.M.G.	16	6	5	5	24	18	17
McKenna & Co.	16	6	4	6	19	20	16
Barlow Lyde & Gilbert	16	5	4	7	23	36	14
Denton Hall	16	4	3	9	20	27	11
Titmus Sainer Dechert	16	5	1	10	12	29	11
Richards Butler	16	4	3	9	14	36	11

League Challenge Cup:
Gray's Inn 1:2p Linklaters & Paine's 1:4p

Weavers Arms Cup:
Wilde Sapte 5 Nabarro Nathanson 2

Invitation Cup:
Clifford Chance 5 McKenna's 4

LONDON OLD BOYS' CUPS

Senior:
Old Chigwellians 2 - 1 Old Manorians
Intermediate:
Latymer Old Boys Res. 4* - 1* Old Thorntonians
Junior:
Latymer Old Boys 3rd. 1 - 4 Old Tenisonians 3rd.
Minor:
Old Actonians Ass'n 4th. 1 - 0 Old Aloysians 4th.
Novets:
Old Actonians Ass'n 5th. 4* - 3* Old Vaughanians 5th.
Drummond:
Withheld
Nemean:
Old Actonians Ass'n 9th. 2* - 1 Old Addeyans 7th.
Veterans':
Old Meadonians Vets. 4 - 2 Old Salvatorians Vets.

OLD BOYS' INVITATION CUPS

Senior:
Old Tenisonians 2 - 0 Old Parkonians
Junior:
Old Owens Res. 1*:6p - 1*:5p Old Tenisonians Res.
Minor:
Old Tenisonians 3rd. 2 - 1 Glyn Old Boys 3rd.
4th XI:
Old Owens 4th. 1 - 0 Old Finchleians 4th.
5th XI:
Old Stationers 5th. 7 - 3 Old Suttonians 5th.
6th XI:
Old Tenisonians 6th. 3 - 4 Old Finchleians 6th.
7th XI:
Old Suttonians 7th. 5 - 1 East Barnet Old Gramm. 7th.

VETERANS' XI:

Old Tenison. "A" Vets. 1*:5p - 1*:4p Old Tenison. "B" Vets.
(* - after exta time)

MIDLAND AMATEUR ALLIANCE

(Following a merger with Nottingham Spartan & 3 pts. for a win)

PREMIER DIVISION	P	W	D	L	F	A	Pts
Old Elizabethans	20	14	5	1	71	28	47
Lady Bay	20	14	3	3	88	31	45
Bassingfield	20	11	3	6	57	47	36
Caribbean Cavaliers	20	11	1	8	60	37	34
Beeston Town "A"	20	10	2	8	41	42	32
Kirton B. W	20	10	2	8	43	27	32
Derbyshire Amateurs	20	8	5	7	35	36	29
Old Bemrosians	20	6	2	12	42	62	20
Racing Toton	20	5	3	12	49	60	18
Magdala Amateurs "A"	20	4	2	14	28	72	14
County Nalgo	20	3	0	17	6	98	9

DIVISION ONE	P	W	D	L	F	A	Pts
Rylands Athletic	24	16	6	2	67	28	54
Old Elizabethans Res	24	16	5	3	69	29	53
Beeston Old Boys Assn	24	16	3	5	81	36	51
Nott. Univ. Postgrad.	24	15	5	4	75	31	50
Dynamo Baptist	24	10	9	5	59	47	39
Tibshelf Old Boys	24	8	6	10	69	72	30
Woodborough United	24	8	6	10	49	53	30
Nottinghamshire	24	7	7	10	41	60	28
Lady Bay Res	24	6	8	10	48	68	26
Cadland Chilwell	24	6	11	7	29	67	19
Edwinstowe J G	24	4	6	14	34	59	18
Ilkeston Rangers	24	4	5	15	39	72	17
Thistle "S"	24	4	5	15	37	75	17

DIVISION TWO	P	W	D	L	F	A	Pts
Parkhead Academicals	24	18	1	5	88	26	55
Bassingfield Res.	24	16	4	4	77	36	52
Radcliffe Olympic Res	24	15	2	7	75	41	47
Southwell Amateurs	24	15	1	8	69	39	46
Arnold & Carlton Coll.	24	11	4	9	64	44	37
Old Elizabethans 3rd	24	12	2	10	42	33	37
Brunts Old Boys	24	9	5	10	47	54	32
Nottinghamshire Res	24	7	8	9	42	49	29
West-Clif	24	8	4	12	43	61	28
Magdala Amateurs Res	24	8	2	4	48	74	26
Derbyshire Amts. Res	24	5	8	11	54	71	23
Ilkeston Rangers Res	24	7	1	16	39	115	22
Beeston Old Boys Res	24	3	4	17	28	73	13

DIVISION THREE
11 Teams — Won by Hucknall Sports Y C

LEAGUE CUPS:
Senior:
Lady Bay 3 - 1 Southwell Amateurs
Intermediate:
Radcliffe Olympic Res. 4 - 1 Old Elizabethans Res.
Minor:
Hucknall Sports Y C 5 - 1 A S C Dayncourt
H.B. Poole Trophy:
Lady Bay 2 - 1 Old Elizabethans

OLD BOYS' LEAGUE

PREMIER DIVISION	P	W	D	L	F	A	Pts
Old Ignatians	20	15	4	1	53	13	34
Old Aloysians	20	15	4	1	40	18	34
Old Tenisonians	20	11	5	4	25	16	27
Glyn Old Boys	20	8	6	6	37	27	22
Old Hamptonians	20	8	3	9	41	35	19
Cardinal Manning OB	20	7	4	9	32	36	18
Latymer Old Boys	20	5	8	7	25	37	18
Old Vaughanians	20	8	1	11	34	30	17
Old Meadonians	20	5	5	10	32	45	15
Old Kingsburians	20	2	5	13	16	44	9
Clapham Old Xaverians	20	2	3	15	17	51	7

SENIOR DIVISION ONE							
Enfield Old Gramm.	20	13	5	2	68	19	31
Old Suttonians	20	11	7	2	44	20	29
Phoenix Old Boys	20	10	7	3	51	26	27
Old Manorians	20	12	3	5	38	23	27
Old Tiffinians	20	9	3	8	39	46	21
Old Salvatorians	20	6	8	6	31	35	20
Old Wilsonians	20	5	4	11	35	41	14
Old Isleworthians	20	5	3	12	25	39	13
Chertsey Old Salesians	20	5	2	13	25	55	10 *
Old Danes	20	4	2	14	23	57	10
Old Westhamians	20	6	4	10	34	52	8 *

SENIOR DIVISION TWO

Old Buckwellians	20	12	3	5	54	33	27
Old Reigatians	20	10	6	4	35	21	26
Old Tollingtonians	20	11	3	6	53	31	25
Old Camdenians	20	9	3	8	36	36	21
Old Minchendenians	20	9	1	10	44	41	19
Shene Old Gramm.	20	8	3	9	39	43	19
Latymer Old Boys Res.	20	7	5	8	29	35	19
Old Tenisonians Res.	20	7	4	9	39	39	18
Old Meadonians Res.	20	6	4	10	33	43	16
Mill Hill County OB	20	6	4	10	25	50	16
Old Wokingians	20	4	6	10	21	36	14

SENIOR DIVISION THREE

Old Dorkinians	20	12	5	3	48	19	29
Old Sinjuns	20	10	7	3	51	26	27
Phoenix Old Boys Res.	20	10	5	5	55	35	25
Old Addeyans	20	12	1	7	42	30	25
Old Hamptonians Res.	20	8	6	6	41	37	22
Old Southallians	20	6	8	6	32	34	20
Old Aloysians Res.	20	7	4	9	42	43	18
Old Vaughanians Res.	20	6	3	11	30	46	15
Old Salvatorians Res.	20	6	2	12	34	39	14
Wood Green Old Boys	20	4	4	12	22	58	12
Glyn Old Boys Res.	20	2	9	9	20	50	11 *

* - points deducted for breach of rule

Intermediate Division North:
12 Teams — Won by Enfield O. Grammarians Res.
Intermediate Division South:
12 Teams — Won by John Fisher Old Boys
Division One North:
10 Teams — Won by Old Kingsburians Res.
Division One South:
11 Teams — Won by Old Josephians
Division One West:
10 Teams — Won by Old Alpertonians Res.
Division Two North:
11 Teams — Won by Leyton County Old Boys Res.
Division Two South:
11 Teams — Won by Old Wilsonians 3rd.
Division Two West:
10 Teams — Won by Old Alpertonians 3rd.
Division Three North:
11 Teams — Won by Old Aloysians 5th.
Division Three South:
12 Teams — Won by Old Suttonians 5th.
Division Three West:
10 Teams — Won by Old Southallians 3rd.
Division Four North:
9 Teams — Won by Old Camdenians 5th.
Division Four South:
12 Teams — Won by Fitzwilliam Old Boys
Division Four West:
10 Teams — Won by Phoenix Old Boys 4th.
Division Five North:
10 Teams — Won by Old Camdenians 6th.
Division Five South:
10 Teams — Won by John Fisher Old Boys 3rd.
Division Five West:
10 Teams — Won by Old Meadonians 6th.
Division Six North:
8 Teams — Won by Old Egbertians 4th.
Division Six South:
10 Teams — Won by Old Sinjuns 3rd.
Division Six West:
10 Teams — Won by Holland Park Old Boys 3rd.
Division Seven North:
8 Teams — Won by Old Ignatians 6th.
Division Seven South:
11 Teams — Won by Old Tiffinian 6th.
Division Seven West:
9 Teams — Won by Holland Park Old Boys 4th.
Division Eight South:
10 Teams — Won by Chertsey Old Salesians 6th.
Division Eight West:
9 Teams — Won by Old Salvatorians 10th.
Division Nine South:
8 Teams — Won by Old Tiffinian 7th.

SOUTHERN AMATEUR LEAGUE 1996-97

SENIOR SECTION:

FIRST DIVISION	*P*	*W*	*D*	*L*	*F*	*A*	*Pts*
Old Parmiterians	22	15	5	2	51	30	35
Crouch End Vampires	22	10	10	2	33	22	30
Old Actonians Ass.	22	11	5	6	35	20	27
Polytechnic	22	8	8	6	39	34	24
Carshalton	22	7	9	6	29	34	23
Norsemen	22	7	7	8	21	26	21
East Barnet O.Gramm.	22	7	4	11	28	28	18
South Bank Polytechnic	22	5	8	9	35	36	18
West Wickham	22	7	4	11	30	36	18
Civil Service	22	4	10	8	33	44	18
Old Esthameians	22	6	5	11	29	38	17
Nat. West. Bank	22	5	5	12	26	41	15

SECOND DIVISION

Lloyds Bank	22	12	8	2	48	20	32
Lensbury	22	14	2	6	68	31	30
Barclays Bank	22	13	4	5	58	21	30
Alexandra Park	22	12	4	6	45	30	28
Old Latymerians	22	8	7	7	46	38	23
Old Lyonians	22	8	6	8	29	42	22
Old Salesians	22	7	6	9	33	34	20
Old Parkonians	22	7	6	9	33	42	20
Cuaco	22	7	5	10	35	36	19
Winchmore Hill	22	8	3	11	41	51	19
Kew Association	22	4	7	11	32	50	15
Old Stationers	22	1	4	17	14	87	6

THIRD DIVISION

Midland Bank	22	15	3	4	54	29	33
Old Owens	22	14	4	4	62	28	32
Bank of England	22	12	5	5	41	25	29
Southgate Olympic	22	12	5	5	37	23	29
Broomfield	22	11	4	7	54	41	26
Ibis	22	11	3	8	58	41	25
Merton	22	11	3	8	53	36	25
Old Bromleians	22	9	3	10	63	60	21
Alleyn Old Boys	22	5	4	13	39	53	14
Old Westminster Citiz.	22	4	4	14	44	72	12
Reigate Priory	22	3	4	15	20	67	10
Brentham	22	3	2	17	27	77	8

RESERVE TEAMS SECTION:
First Division:
12 Teams — Won by Barclays Bank Res.
Second Division:
12 Teams — Won by Lloyds Bank Res.
Third Division:
12 Teams — Won by Broomfield Res.

3RD. TEAMS SECTION:
First Division:
12 Teams — Won by Old Stationers 3rd.
Second Division:
12 Teams — Won by Old Actonians Association 3rd.
Third Division:
12 Teams — Won by Southgate Olympic 3rd.

4TH. TEAMS SECTION:
First Division:
12 Teams — Won by Old Actonians Association 4th.
Second Division:
12 Teams — Won by Midland Bank 4th.
Third Division:
11 Team — Won by Old Owens 4th.

5TH. TEAMS SECTION:
First Division:
10 Teams — Won by Old Actonians Association 5th.
Second Division:
11 Teams — Won by Norsemen 5th.
Third Division:
11 Teams — Won by Old Westminster Citizens 5th.

6TH. TEAMS SECTION:
First Division:
10 Teams — Won by Old Stationers 6th.
Second Division:
9 Teams — Won by Crouch End Vampires 6th.
Third Division:
7 Teams — Won by East Barnet O. Grammarians 6th.

MINOR SECTION:
First Division:
10 Teams — Won by National Westminster Bank 7th.
Second Division:
10 Teams — Won by Old Parmiterians 8th.
Third Division:
11 Teams — Won by Old Actonians Association 9th.
Fourth Division:
11 Teams — Won by Old Parmiterians 10th.

CHALLENGE CUPS:
Junior:
Crouch End Vampires 3rd. 5 Norsemen 3rd. 1
Minor:
Midland Bank 4th. 4 Norsemen 4th. 1
Senior Novets:
Norsemen 5th. 2 Lloyds Bank 5th. 1
Intermediate Novets:
O. Parmiterians 6th. 2 Polytechnic 6th. 0
Junior Novets:
O. Parmiterians 8th. 4 Norsemen 8th. 1

SOUTHERN OLYMPIAN LEAGUE

SENIOR SECTION:

DIVISION ONE	P	W	D	L	F	A	Pts	
Nottsborough	18	12	2	4	53	24	26	
Old Finchleians	18	12	1	5	7	34	25	
Hale End Athletic	18	9	4	5	48	32	21	*
Southgate County	18	8	3	7	34	39	19	
Parkfield	18	5	6	7	30	36	16	
Witan	18	6	4	8	28	39	16	
St. Mary's College	18	5	5	8	25	34	15	
Ulysses	18	6	3	9	26	38	15	
Wandsworth Borough	18	5	3	10	32	43	13	
Albanian	18	5	3	10	29	43	13	

DIVISION TWO								
Hon. Artillery Company	18	11	5	2	30	11	27	
City of London	18	12	2	4	54	25	26	
Old Simmarobians	18	8	5	5	34	21	21	
Old Grammarians	18	7	5	6	22	20	19	
Westerns	18	8	4	6	34	35	17	*
UCL Academicals	18	6	4	8	30	33	16	
Old Woodhouseians	18	5	5	8	31	35	15	
Mill Hill Village	18	7	1	10	29	42	15	
Ealing Association	18	4	5	9	23	38	13	
Hadley	18	4	0	14	25	52	8	

DIVISION THREE								
Fulham Compton OB	16	12	1	3	52	26	24	*
Hampstead Heathens	16	10	2	4	44	30	22	
B.B.C.	16	10	0	6	51	33	20	
Pegasus (Inner Temple)	16	8	2	6	42	21	18	
Duncombe Sports	16	7	3	6	37	27	17	
Old Bealonians	16	7	1	8	27	24	15	
Old Colfeians	16	6	1	9	22	35	13	
London Welsh	16	6	0	10	27	51	12	
Birkbeck College	16	0	2	14	18	73	2	

DIVISION FOUR								
The Cheshunt Club	18	14	2	2	65	27	30	
Inland Revenue	18	12	2	4	58	33	26	
Mayfield Athletic	18	10	1	7	37	30	21	
New Scot. Yard Comets	18	9	2	7	40	34	20	
Centymca	18	6	6	6	27	32	18	
Cardinal Pole OB	18	9	0	9	41	50	18	
Economicals	18	6	4	8	30	38	15	*
London Airways	18	5	2	11	30	44	12	
Tansley	18	4	2	12	32	51	10	
Brent	18	4	1	13	24	45	9	

* - points deducted - breach of rule

INTERMEDIATE SECTION:
Division One:
10 Teams — Won by Nottsborough Res.
Division Two:
10 Teams — Won by Hale End Athletic Res.
Division Three:
10 Teams — Won by Wandsworth Borough Res.
Division Four:
10 Teams — Won by Old Bealonians 3rd.

JUNIOR SECTION:
Division One: Does not exist
Division Two N:
10 Teams — Won by Albanian 4th..
Division Two S&W:
10 Teams — Won by Old Colfeians Res.
Division Three N:
10 Teams — Won by Parkfield 5th.
Division Three S&W:
10 Teams — Won by Old Colfeians 3rd.

MINOR SECTION:
Division "A" N:
10 Teams — Won by Albanian 6th
Division "A" S&W:
10 Teams — Won by Witan 4th.
Division "B" N:
11 Teams — Won by Old Fairlopians Res.
Division "B" S&W:
10 Teams — Won by Inland Revenue 4th.
Senior Challenge Bowl:
Won by Wandsworth Borough
Senior Challenge Shield:
Won by The Cheshunt Club
Intermediate Challenge Cup:
Won by Nottsborough Res.
Intermediate Challenge Shield:
Won by Ealing Association Res.
Junior Challenge Cup:
Won by Old Bealonians 3rd.
Junior Challenge Shield:
Won by Old Finchleians 3rd.
Mander Cup:
Won by Old Finchleians 4th.
Mander Shield:
Won by Ealing Associaion 4th.
Burntwood Trophy:
Won by Albanian 5th.
Burntwood Shield:
Won by Ealing Association 5th.
Thomas Parmiter Cup:
Won by Parkfield 6th.
Thomas Parmiter Shield:
Won by Old Finchleians 6th.
Veterans' Challenge Cup:
Won by Old Finchleians Vets.
Veterans' Challenge Shield:
Won by Centymca Vets.

LONDON UNIVERSITY XI
REPRESENTATIVE MATCH RESULTS

Old Boys' League	Lost	0-2
Ulysses	Won	3-2
Southern Amateur League	Won	2-1
Arthurian League	Won	3-1
SE Region BUSA	Lost	0-4
Metropolitan Police	Lost	1-3
Army Crusaders	Won	5-4
Southern Olympian League	Won	4-2
Oxford University	Drawn	0-0
Amateur Football Alliance	Lost	2-3

West London Institute, Chelsea XI (twice), Lloyds of London, Cambridge University, London Legal League all lost to bad weather

UNIVERSITY OF LONDON
MENS' INTER-COLLEGIATE LEAGUE

PREMIER DIVISION	*P*	*W*	*D*	*L*	*F*	*A*	*Pts*
Royal Holloway College	14	9	3	2	35	11	30
Queen Mary W'field Coll.	14	8	4	2	27	17	28
Imperial College	14	8	2	4	38	28	26
Goldsmiths' College	14	6	6	2	41	14	24
LSE	14	6	3	5	34	19	21
King's College	14	3	3	8	25	36	12
University College	14	3	1	10	22	53	10
Univ. Coll. & Middx. Hos. Med. Sch.	14	2	0	12	8	52	6

DIVISION ONE							
R'y'l Holloway Coll. Res.	18	13	3	2	55	11	42
LSE Res.	18	10	4	4	47	29	34
R'y'l Holloway Coll. 3rd	18	10	4	4	35	30	34
U.M.D.S.	18	9	4	5	53	31	31
Queen Mary W'field Coll. Res.	18	9	2	7	44	31	29
University College Res.	18	7	4	7	28	39	25
Ch. Cross & W'min. Hosp. MS	18	7	1	10	34	45	22
King's College Hosp.MS	18	5	3	10	32	43	18
R. Lon'n & St. Bart's Hos. MC's	18	3	2	13	12	53	11
St George's Hosp. MS	18	1	5	12	15	43	8

DIVISION TWO
10 Teams — Won by RSM, Imperial College
DIVISION THREE
10 Teams — Won by Mary & Westfield College 3rd.
DIVISION FOUR
10 Teams — Won by Won by Imperial College 4th.
DIVISION FIVE
10 Teams — Won by Won by Wye College, Kent
DIVISION SIX
7 Teams — Won by R. Holloway College 6th.

Challenge Cup:
Goldsmiths' College 1 - 0 London School of Economics
Upper Reserves Cup:
R. Holloway Coll. Res. 5 - 0 London School of Econ.Res.
Lower Reserves Cup:
R. Holloway Coll. 5th. 1 - 3 Q. Mary & Westfield Coll.4th.

United Hospitals:
Senior Cup:
University College Charing Cross & Westminster Hospital Medical School 3 - 4 Hospital Medical School
Junior Cup:
United Medical & Dental 4 - 1 United Medical & Dental Schs. of Guy's & St. Schs. of Guy's & St. Thomas's Hospitals Res.Thomas's Hospitals 3rd.

UNIVERSITY OF LONDON WOMENS' INTER-COLLEGIATE LEAGUE

DIVISION ONE
8 Teams — Won by University College
DIVISION TWO
7 Teams — Won by Royal Free Hospital Res.

Womens' Challenge Cup:
University College 2 - 0 London School of Economics

VARSITY MATCH
OXFORD UNIVERSITY 0
CAMBRIDGE UNIVERSITY 0

LUCKY TO GET NIL!

'Lucky to get nil!' was the remark of a Scottish wag at Murrayfield late in 1951 after the Springboks had put the local international rugby side to the sword by 44 points to nil (62-0 in terms of modern scoring).

At Craven Cottage on the afternoon of Saturday, 29th March, that cynical comment could have been aptly applied to both Oxford and Cambridge after a dull draw, which was a poor advertisement for the game and the country's top universities.

The fact that neither goalkeeper, Oxford's Nick Rutter and Steve Lloyd for Cambridge, had a single difficult save to make provided clear testimony — if any was needed — to the emptiness of the match.

Cambridge had more goalscoring positions, but Echeverria, Watson, Ball and Pett all missed excellent chances. For the Dark Blues Goff, Buckley (on as a substitute) and Kintish went close and in terms of skill Oxford looked the better side, but an excellent Cambridge defence with Ball, Clarance, White and Watson looking solid was given few problems when the opposition came close.

The Dark Blues defence was also its strongest point with Loebinger, Dutton, Lea and O'Brien also looking sound. It was a stalemate from start to finish.

One good feature of the game was the excellent refereeing of Mr E.W. Green, whose control was sensible, clear and unobtrusive. He showed yellow cards to two Light Blues — captain Iain White (possibly harsh) and Mark Pett for pulling down substitute Duncan as he was in full cry. A red card might have been shown by one of the nations high profile referees for the latter, but Mr Green tempered justice with mercy. He was my man of the match.

The crowd numbered 1,504, which may diminish considerably next year. Why should even the keenest wake up early for this kind of stuff? It was no fault of Fulham, who put on a good show, but please, gentlemen, try to do better next time!

BILL MITCHELL

TEAMS
Oxford: N. Rutter, M. Loebinger, B. Dutton, A. Lea, A. O'Brien, *D. Loosemore (captain), *J. Parker, A. Jennings, M. Goff, *A. Bissell (60 for Worthington), *A. Buckley (79 for Loebinger), M. Duncan (81 for Goff), T. Bell (gk) not used.

Cambridge: S. Lloyd, *S. Ball, L. Clarance, *M. Budd, A. Watson, *I. White (captain), *M. Pett, *M. Jolley, R. Williamson, *R. Millar, *D. Echeverria. Substitutes: •A. Thompson (55 for Williamson), S. Ahmed (79 for Echeverria), A. Lewis (84 for Watson), E. Howe (gk) not used.
*Old Blue.

Referee: E.W. Green (Berks & Bucks FA).

For the record: Cambridge lead the series by 45 wins to 41 with 27 matches drawn, but they have not won since December 1987 when the fixture was last played at Wembley.

THE ENGLISH SCHOOLS' F.A.

Hon. Secretary: J C L Williamson, 10 D'Ayncourt Walk, Darnsfield, Nottinghamshire NG22 8DP
Tel: (01623) 882674

Development Officer: M Simmonds, Tel: (0115) 931 3299

THE INTERNATIONAL SEASON UNDER 15

The 1996–97 England Schools' international squad had a very good season, remaining undefeated in their seven 'full' games and finishing eighth out of 32 nations in the Montaigu tournament. The highlight of the season was the 2-1 victory over Germany following an enthralling and exciting second half in front of 40,000 spectators at Wembley Stadium. The match against Scotland at the City Ground, Nottingham was the hundredth match between the two countries at this level and the 1-1 draw meant that the two countries shared the Adidas Victory Shield, the Home International Championship.

The Montaigu tournament, in its tenth year, was a new experience for an England squad and their only defeat in open play from the seven matches came when Holland recorded their first ever victory over England at Under 15 level. The final placing would have been higher but for defeats in penalty shoot-outs by Italy and Slovakia.

RESULTS

adidas Victory Shield

Wales v England 2-3
(Cole, Mike, Armstrong, at Ninian Park, Cardiff)
Norther Ireland v England 0-3
(Taylor, Standing, Armstrong, at Windsor Park, Belfast)
England v Scotland 1-1
(Mike, at City Ground, Nottingham, 7,565)

Invitation Matches

England v France 0-0
(at Old Trafford, 35,000)
Switzerland v England 1-1
(Osman, at Ebikon)
England v Republic of Ireland 3-2
(Mike, Taylor, Burke, at Ewood Park, Blackburn)
England v Germany 2-1
(Osman, Armstrong)

Montaigu Tournament

England v Greece 2-0
England v Israel 3-0
England v Lithuania 1-1
(England won their group)

England v Sweden 2-1
England v Holland 0-2
England v Slovakia 0-0
(Slovakia won on penalties)
England v Italy 1-1
(Italy won on penalties)

APPEARANCES AND GOALSCORERS
(excluding Montaigu Tournament)

Player	Area	Appearances
I. Armstrong	West Lancashire*	5 (+2 sub) (3 goals)
M. Bingham	South Ribble	4 (+1 sub) (GK)
P. Burke	Doncaster	2 (+5 sub) (1 goal)
J. Cole	Islington/Camden*	7 (1 goal)
R. Evans	Swindon*	3 (+1 sub) (GK)
S. Flitcroft	Bolton	4 (+3 sub)
C. Hanson	Middlesbrough	7
M. Maley	Newcastle	6 (capt.)
L. Mike	Trafford*	4 (+3 sub) (3 goals)
C. McCready	Halton*	5 (+1 sub)
C. O'Brien	Liverpool	5 (+1 sub)
L. Osman	West Lancashire	6 (2 goals) (1 app.as capt.)
M. Standing	Brighton	5 (1 goal)
G. Strange	Bolton	2 (+1 sub)
P. Taylor	Wirral	5 (+1 sub) (2 goals)
S. Warnock	West Lancashire	7
R. Wright	Sefton*	

*Indicates player also attending FA National School

Team Manager: J. Owens (St. Helens)
Assistant Team Manager: D. Parnaby (Spennymoor)
Physiotherapist: M. Eales (Liverpool)
Team Doctor: A. Tabor
FA Advisor: A. Gibson

adidas VICTORY SHIELD FINAL TABLE

	P	W	D	L	F	A	Pts
England	3	2	1	0	7	3	5
Scotland	3	2	1	0	4	2	5
Wales	3	0	1	2	3	5	1
N.Ireland	3	0	1	2	0	4	1

England Schools' Under 15 Squad 1996–97

THE INTERNATIONAL SEASON UNDER 18

The Under 18 English Schools' international programme is traditionally more difficult than that of their under 15 counterparts as their continental opponents choose from the whole age range whereas England is limited to those still in full time education. Consequently 1-1 draws with both Holland and Switzerland and a narrow defeat by France with an injury stricken squad were good performances, especially after the squad had suffered a first ever defeat at the hands of the Republic of Ireland.

The Heinz Centenary Shield, previously a triangular tournament between England, Wales and Switzerland, was revamped with Austria, Holland and Northern Ireland also involved. England won their group thanks to their draw with Holland and victory over Wales, and met Switzerland in the final. Extra time could not break the 1-1 deadlock but England won the Shield 5-4 on penalties thanks to a fine save by substitute goalkeeper, Stuart Collar.

RESULTS

Republic of Ireland v England 2-0
at Waterford

Holland v England 1-1
(Leonard) at Zwolle (Heinz Centenary Shield)

England v Wales 2-0
(Robinson, Phelps) at Rushden and Diamonds FC
(Heinz Centenary Shield)

England v France 0-1
at Carrow Road, Norwich

England v Switzerland 1-1
(Sedgemore) (England won 5-4 on penalties) (Heinz Centenary Shield Final at Don Valley Stadium, Sheffield)

APPEARANCES AND GOALSCORERS

S. Anderson	Oxfordshire	0 (+2 sub)
S. Armstrong	Lincolnshire	1 (+1 sub)
J. Bannister	Essex	5
R. Clark	Gloucestershire	4 (GK)
J. Clarke	Essex	5
S. Collar	Berkshire	1 (+2 sub) (GK)
W. Elliott	Hampshire	4 (+1 sub)
S. Futcher	Wiltshire	5
A. Jackson	West Yorkshire	0 (+2 sub)
D. Leonard	Lancashire	3 (1 goal)
G. Phelps	Northumberland	2 (+3 sub) (1 goal)
M. Robinson	West Midlands	3 (+2 sub) (1 goal)
D. Sadler	Somerset	5 (capt.)
A. Sambrook	Kent	5
J. Sedgemore	West Midlands	5 (1 goal)
M. Simpson	Northumberland	1
M. Strode	Devon	5
R. Vickers	Humberside	1 (+ 2 sub)

Team Manager: P. Brackwell (Kettering)
Assistant Team Manager: Dave Cook (London)
Goalkeeping Coach: M. Wallington (Sleaford)
Physiotherapist: A. Gallafant (Middlesbrough)
Doctor: D. Baron

English Schools' FA Under 18 International Squad 1996–97

THE INTER-ASSOCIATION COMPETITIONS
THE E.S.F.A. FUJI FILMS TROPHY 1996–97

FINAL: (First leg at Goodison Park) Liverpool 0 Islington & Camden 2
(Second leg at Highbury) Islington & Camden 1 Liverpool 5

There was a dramatic and controversial conclusion to the English Schools' FA's premier competition, the Fuji Films Trophy when Liverpool reversed a two goal first leg deficit to increase their lead in the all-time winners' list and record their fourteenth success.

The first leg was interrupted by a hailstorm so severe that the players had to leave the field just before half-time. Islington and Camden's enthusiasm was not dampened and two quick goals just after the interval from Jay Bothroyd and Mark Shirley brought hem a deserved victory.

The London side seemed to have done the hard work with this away win and held their lead for 20 minutes of the second leg. A header from Mark Walters for Liverpool halved the deficit and a second goal by John Miles in first half injury time ensured a tense second period.

A superb move, initiated by Bothoyd, was completed by Francis Birch to put Islington back into the lead but England Schools' midfielder, Chris O'Brien made it 3-3 on aggregate. With ten minutes remaining, Liverpool were awarded a penalty, an incident in which Islington's keeper, Adam Mehmet was sent off. Mark Walters missed from the spot but Liverpool made their numerical superiority pay with further goals from O'Brien and Miles to win 5-1 on the night and 5-3 on aggregate, a great disappointment for the home side who had played 40 matches undefeated since coming together as a team.

THE SQUADS

Islington & Camden

Adam Mehmet	Holloway
Alan Dunne	St. Aloysisus
Ricky Alexander	St. Aloysisus
Paul Ellis	St. Aloysisus
Mehmet Unal	Highbury Grove
John Halls	Central Foundn.
Mark Shirley	St. Aloysisus
Tony Webster	Central Foundn.
Jay Bothroyd	Holloway
Danny Wright	Central Foundn.
Francis Birch	St. Aloysisus
Joe Murray	Acland Burghley
Dennis Attoh	Islington Green
Paul Johnson	Holloway
Mark Galvin	St. Aloysisus
Charles Mapes	Hampstead
Michael O'Sullivan	St. Aloysisus

Liverpool

Peter Crookes	St. Margarets
Paul Linn	Bluecoat
Colin Woodcock	St. Francis Xavier
Kevin Nolan	Bluecoat
Chris O'Brien	St. John Almond
Kevin Wright	Breckfield
David Savage	St. Francis Xavier
Tom Kearney	St. John Almond
Michael McLean	Archbishop Beck
Mark Walters	Cardinal Heenan
John Miles	St. Francis Xavier
James Williams	Bluecoat
Darrel Tagoe	St. Francis Xavier
Anthony Bowden	De la Salle
Lee Paul	Cardinal Heenan
Kevin Quick	Campion

ROUTES TO THE FINAL

Islington & Camden

Round 1 v. South Bedfordshire	(A)	5-2
Round 1 v. Barnet	(H)	8-1
Round 3 v. South-East Sussex	(A)	5-2
Round 4 v. Watford	(A)	4-1
Round 5 v. Mid-Hertfordshire	(A)	2-0
Round 6 v. Cardiff	(A)	2-0
Semi-final v. Sefton	(A)	2-0

Liverpool

Round 1 v. Mid-Cheshire	(H)	3-1
Round 2 v. Wigan	(A)	1-0
Round 3 v. Trafford	(H)	8-1
Round 4 v. Bishop Auckland	(H)	4-2
Round 5 v. East Riding	(H)	2-0
Round 6 v. Coventry	(H)	4-2
Semi-final v. Harlow	(H)	aet 5-3

The Islington/Camden squad

Islington and Camden Schools' Under 15's (Runners-up Fuji Films Trophy)

THE E.S.F.A. PREMIER LEAGUE UNDER 16 COUNTY CHAMPIONSHIP

SEMI-FINAL: Oxfordshire 2 Devon 1 (aet)
Northumberland 4 West Midlands 2

FINAL: (at the Manor Ground, Oxford United FC)
Oxfordshire 2 Northumberland 3 (aet)

Underdogs Oxfordshire put up a brave fight against a powerful Northumberland side in the final. In fact, they shocked their opponents by taking an early lead through Robbie Eason who met Jon Townsend's free-kick with a glancing header and it was not until 10 minutes into the second period that Andrew Hay equalised for the north-easterners. Despite brave defending by Oxfordshire with Jonathan Shepheard outstanding, Northumberland went ahead when goalkeeper Sean Leach did well to smother Stephen Warwick's shot but could not stop it rolling over the line.

Oxfordshire then showed the spirit that had brought them three extra time victories en route to the final and two minutes into added time, substitute Lee Nix volleyed home Townsend's cross for a last gasp equaliser.

There was not to be a 'fairy-tale' ending, however, as eight minutes into extra time, the heroic Shepheard mishit a back pass leaving Kris Leighton the simple task of shooting past Leach for the winner.

THE SQUADS
Oxfordshire:
Sean Leach, Craig Farley, Corin Patterson, Gareth Benfield, Jonathan Shepheard, Robbie Eason, Craig Pearman, Michael Hegarty, Ross Weatherstone, Jon Townsend, Darryl Pugh, Subs: Alastair Jarvis, Robin Antonowicz, David Curtis, Lee Nix, Ryan Butler.

Northumberland:
Michael Swann, David Tremble, Mark Lazenby, Darren Fisher, Colin Morton, Stephen Todd, Karl Porter, Stephen Warwick, Kris Leighton, Graham Hogg, Chris Ellis, Andrew Pringle, Andrew Hay, Ross Anderson, Michael Carrick, Mark Maley, James Harmison, Stephen Watson.

Northumberland Schools' Under 16's — Winners of E.S.F.A. Under 16 County Championship

THE E.S.F.A. PREMIER LEAGUE UNDER 19 COUNTY CHAMPIONSHIP

FINAL: (played at Villa Park, Thursday, May 1st 1997)
West Midlands 2 Hampshire 3

West Midlands won the national under 19 County Championship for the second time in their history when they defeated the previously unbeaten Hampshire side in an exciting final. Hampshire got off to a dream start when Michael White's deep cross was headed home at the far post by John Parker after only two minutes. West Midlands drew level after 27 minutes when Michael Crawford's free-kick deflected off the wall to leave Dean Woods helpless but Hampshire went ahead again just before the interval when a defence splitting pass by England Schools' international, Wade Elliott set up Kevin Betsy to chip over the advancing Kearns.

Hampshire withstood a West Midlands barrage for the first 20 minutes of the second period but eventually cracked when David Windsor overstretched to bring Marvin Robinson down in the penalty area in Robinson himself scored from the spot. The winner came in the 72nd minute when Stephen Watson crossed for full back Stephen Swallow to score at the far post.

ROUTES TO THE FINAL

West Midlands		Hampshire	
v. Staffordshire	5-2	v. Wiltshire	4-3
v. Warwickshire	1-0	v. Heredfordshire	5-1
v. Worcestershire	2-0	v. Berkshire	7-1
v. Shropshire	1-0	v. Surrey	3-2 (National quarter-final)
(West Midlands won group)		v. Norfolk	2-1 (National semi-final)
v. Nottinghamshire	3-2 (Midland semi-final)		
v. Lancashire	2-1 (National quarter-final) (aet)		
v. Humberside	3-2 (National semi-final)		

THE SQUADS

West Midlands:
Michael Kearns, Simon Swallow, Michael Crawford, Carl Murphy, Paul Jerrery, Christopher Cooper, Philip Rowe, Steven Watson, Marvin Robinson, Jacke Sedgemore, Tom Neilan, Graham Walmsley, Dean Ricketts, Peter Hegerty, Richard Bannister, David Atack, Andrew Gittins

Hampshire:
Dean Woods, Gary Fulker, Sean Thurgood, Paul King, David Windsor, Ian Jones, Michael White, John Parker, Tom Earles, Kevin Betsy, Wade Elliott, Andrew Chance, Peter Swinney, Nick Hughes, Lee Edwards, Ashley Rowe, Mark Clothier, David Woodfine.

Hampshire Schools' Under 19's Runners-Up E.S.F.A. Under 19 County Championship

THE E.S.F.A. ADIDAS PREDATOR PREMIER UNDER 11 7-A-SIDE CHAMPIONSHIP

Semi-finals and Final at Old Trafford, 19th April, 1997

SEMI-FINAL: Swindon 0 Barnsley 1
Newham 0 Nottingham 1

FINAL: Barnsley 0 Nottingham 0 (Trophy shared)

THE INDIVIDUAL SCHOOLS' COMPETITION
ENGLISH SCHOOLS' SNICKERS UNDER 19 CHAMPIONSHIPS

For the first time, there were two English Schools' Individual Schools' competitions at Under 19 level. For many years the large Further Education and 6th Form Colleges, many with thousands of students,have dominated the single Championship for this age group, their numbers giving them an unfair advantage over schools with 6th Forms. With the support of Snickers, the E.S.F.A. therefore introduced a second national event, open only to schools.

This proved a most successful venture and reached a pleasing climax with both finals played on the same day before more than 3,000 spectators at The Hawthorns (West Bromwich Albion) on April 28th.

THE SCHOOLS' CHAMPIONSHIP FINAL

Monkseaton High School (Whitley Bay) 0 Parmiter's School (Watford) 0
(after extra time — Trophy shared)

Despite the scoreline, the two survivors from over 1200 entries, produced an exciting conclusion to the new competition. Parmiter's man of the match, Tom Butterfield hit the post with an early free-kick, then Graham Sweedy's 30 yard effort was tipped on to the bar by keeper Daniel Craddock, both in the first 15 minutes. The aptly named Gavin Hattrick, Monkseaton's top scorer, was their main threat but once he had limped off with a knee injury, they struggled to hit the target. Both teams gave their all but after extra time, 22 weary players had to settle for a share of the Snickers Trophy.

ROUTES TO THE FINAL

Monkseaton School:
5 matches in the Northumberland County Championship led to qualification for the national stages.

Round 1 v. Gilesgate School (Durham)	2-1
Round 2 v. Rhodesway School (West Yorks)	1-0
Round 3 v. Wolfreton School (Humberside)	2-0
Round 4 v. John Port School (Derbyshire)	1-0
Semi-final v. King's School (Cheshire)	3-1

Parmiter's School:
Qualification by winning the Hertfordshire Championship.

Round 1 v. Barking Abbey School (Essex)	3-3 6-1
Round 2 v. Newmarket School (Suffolk)	3-3. 4-2
Round 3 v. Sprowston High School (Norfolk)	1-1, 5-4 (on penalties)
Round 4 v. Richard Challoner (Surrey)	6-4
Semi-final v. Ardingly School (Sussex)	3-2

THE SCHOOLS AND COLLEGES CHAMPIONSHIP

Although schools may choose to take part in this section rather than that just open to them, it was not surprising to see two 6th Form Colleges in the final. Colchester has nearly 200 students studying Physical Education 'A' level alone and can also choose from the many students in other disciplines. Cardinal Newman is the Catholic 6th Form College in Preston, formed in 1978 by an amalgamation of three educational establishments.

The Final:
Cardinal Newman 6th Form College 1 Colchester 6th Form College 0

There was a strong Preston North End connection with Cardinal Newman's narrow victory in a physical encounter. Joint Manager, Sean Haslegrave was in the professional team's midfield for four years while their goalscorer, David McCann was once on schoolboy forms with the Club. His winning goal came direct from a free-kick after 40 minutes and should have led to a convincing victory. The Morecambe 'duo' of Chris Whittingham and Robert Haworth were dangerous throughout but missed chances and determined Colchester defending kept the score to one.

ROUTES TO THE FINAL

Colchester 6th Form College:
Qualified by winning Essex Championship

Round 1 v. University College (Suffolk)	3-2
Round 2 v. Springwood High School (Norfolk)	6-0
Round 3 v. Palmers College (Essex)	4-3
Round 4 v. Mark Rainham School (Kent)	1-0
Semi-final v. Weald College (Middlesex)	6-0

Cardinal Newman 6th Form College:
Qualified by winning Lancashire Championship

Round 1 v. Carmel College (Merseywide)	2-0
Round 2 v. Stafford College (Staffordshire)	5-1
Round 3 v. Yale College (North Wales)	4-0
Round 4 v. South Cheshire College (Cheshire)	2-1
Semi-final v. St Cuthberts H.S. (Northumberland)	2-1

THE E.S.F.A. GOODYEAR UNDER 16 CHAMPIONSHIP
(IN ASSOCIATION WITH CHANNEL 4)

The Final (played at Molineux Stadium, 5th May 1997):
William Parker School (Hastings) 0 City School (Sheffield) 0
(after extra time; Trophy shared)

The tradition in all English Schools' FA competitions is that, if the final is drawn, the Trophy is shared. Thus, the Goodyear Trophy will be held for 6 months by William Parker and the City School. Yet after 120 minutes, there was a penalty shoot-out which William Parker won 5-4. Why? Simply because, there is an even bigger prize for the winners; as a result of the link between Goodyear and Channel 4, they have the opportunity of an all-expenses paid trip to Italy to play a Sampdoria Youth side prior to a Serie A match with full television exposure.

A 0-0 draw in the final itself sounds rather soulless but both sides contrived to produce excitement galore in almost every imaginable weather conditions. A crowd of nearly 5,000 saw the Hastings school start more impressively but the first 15 minutes set the tone with both keepers William Toal and David Campbell severely tested but never beaten. As the rain poured down in the second half, both sides adapted their game well but still could not defeat those keepers.

THE SQUADS

William Parker:
Will Toal, David Henham, Russell Jones, Sean Ray, Alan Manning, Michael Yardy, Ben Vine, Gareth Barry, Sam Taylor, Gary Pocock, James Pepper. Substitutes: Greg Hobbs, John McSweeney, Russell Keen, Dergham Heider, Tom Cosens.

City School:
David Campbell, Danny Hooper, Jonathan Crossland, Ryan Kirk, Gareth Thomas, David Thonhill, Andrew Potts, Chris Towey, Nathan Salter, Darren Robinson, Adam Burley. Substitutes: Wayne Pass, Gavin Pearce, Nicholas Hague, Chris Hall, Simon Fisher.

ROUTES TO THE FINAL

William Parker

Round 1 v. Howard School (Kent	3-0
Round 2 v. Bishopsholt School (Middlesex)	3-1
Round 3 v. Holloway (Inner London)	4-3
Round 4 v. Ousdale School (Bucks)	2-1
Semi-final v. St Joseph's College (Surrey)	2-2, 1-1

(William Parker 6-5 on penalties)

City School

Round 1 v. William Gee School (Humberside)	3-0
Round 2 v. Thomas Hepburn School (Durham)	5-3
Round 3 v. Lutterworth G.S. (Leicestershire)	2-1
Round 4 v. St Matthew's School (Gr. Manchester)	3-2
Semi-final v. Newall Green (Gr. Manchester)	0-0, 4-1

CHANNEL ISLANDS FOOTBALL REVIEW 1996-97

The jubilant Guernsey squad following their 2-1 Muratti triumph over Jersey
Photo: Guernsey Press Co Ltd

GUERNSEY'S YEAR

For the first time in many years, 1996-97 can truly be said to have been Guernsey's season within the Channel Islands. The prized Muratti Vase is on Guernsey soil for the first time in five years - following a 2-1 victory at the Track in front of a crowd of 3,500 on Bank Holiday Monday, the 5th May. Jersey had taken the lead shortly before half time (an own goal), but an Adrian Exall equaliser within moments of the restart lifted home spirits. The winning goal - a half volley from Steve Brehaut (only drafted into the side at the last minute when Grant Chalmers failed a fitness test) - came only three minutes from time, to send the partizan home crowd delirious. John Nobes became the youngest Guernsey captain (at 21) to lift the premier trophy in Channel Islands football.

He had earlier captained the Guernsey Under 21 side to victory over Jersey in the Under 21 Muratti - played at Jersey's new Springfield Stadium in November - and thus created history by becoming the first Guernsey player to lift two Muratti trophies in the same season. That victory came in a penalty shoot-out (3-1) after 120 minutes of play had failed to produce a goal.

Consolation for Jersey came with a 1-0 after extra time victory in the Under 18 Muratti played at Springfield, and a 1-0 victory in the Schoolboy (Under 15) Muratti, played at the Corbet Field, Guernsey.

Inter Island Club football was also dominated by a Guernsey Club - Sylvans, who became Guernsey Champions for the fourth successive season, clinching the Barclays Priaulx League with something to spare. They went on to secure the Channel Islands Championship (Upton Park Cup) by defeating Jersey Champions Jersey Scottish 1-0 at Springfield - their winner being a wonder goal from Guernsey's top scorer and Player's Player of the Year, Paul Nobes - brother of Guernsey captain John. Sylvans created history by becoming the first Guernsey club to secure all seven Channel Islands senior trophies available to them - adding the two Channel Islands Knock Out trophies (the Wheway Cup and Jeremie Cup), and Guernsey's two Knock-Out cups (the Stranger Charity Cup and Le Vallee Cup), together with the Martinez Cup (played annually between the League Champions and Runners-Up), to the league and Upton. The Guernsey Football Association officially recognised their achievement by striking a special commemorative medal, presented to the Club, their manager Colin Renouf, and to each member of the first team squad.

Two Guernsey clubs, Sylvans and Northerners, entered the Hampshire Senior and Dorset Senior Cups respectively. Northerners suffered defeat in the first round at home to Bournemouth Sports, whilst Sylvans defeated Blackfield & Langley (home), and Aerostructures (away) before suffering their heaviest defeat for some years (0-7) away to Newport (IoW). The game provided proof if any were needed that top Channel Islands sides need to play against stronger opposition on a regular basis if the game is to progress in the Islands.

In late February, the Guernsey Football Association, and all of its member clubs, gave unanimous approval to the concept of a Channel Islands Football League. The proposals of an inter-island working party did not meet with such support in Jersey - with member clubs of the Jersey Football Combination and Sunday Soccer League being split approximately fifty/fifty on the issue. As a result, the Jersey Football Association have adjourned a decision pending further inter-island discussions.

Guernsey and Channel Islands football suffered a great loss at Easter when CI League working party Chairman, and long time advocate of such a league, Rex Bennett, sadly died after a short illness. Football in the Islands will never be quite the same again.

Dave Doroy

BARCLAYS PRIAULX LEAGUE
FINAL LEAGUE TABLE 1996-97

		P	W	D	L	F	A	Pts
1	Sylvans	21	18	1	2	84	22	55
2	Belgrave's	21	14	4	3	65	26	46
3	Northerners	21	11	4	6	54	36	37
4	Rangers	21	9	5	7	42	42	32
5	St Martin's	21	10	1	10	52	49	31
6	Port City	21	6	3	12	30	66	21
7	Vale Recreation	21	2	5	14	27	58	11
8	Rovers	21	1	3	17	20	75	6

JERSEY SCOTTISH SUPREME

JERSEY EUROPEAN FOOTBALL COMBINATION

FINAL LEAGUE TABLES 1996-97

Division One

		P	W	D	L	F	A	Pts
1	Jersey Scottish	16	12	3	1	45	14	39
2	First Tower Utd	16	8	2	6	38	28	26
3	Jersey Wndrs	16	6	6	4	28	29	24
4	St Pauls	16	6	5	5	33	34	23
5	Magpies	16	7	1	8	23	40	22
6	Rozel Rovers	16	6	3	7	35	27	21
7	Portuguese Club	16	5	6	5	24	22	21
8	St Peter	16	5	5	6	30	30	20
9	St Martin	16	1	1	14	11	43	4

Division Two

		P	W	D	L	F	A	Pts
1	Sporting Academ.	16	12	2	2	52	18	38
2	Beeches	16	9	3	4	39	17	30
3	LM Jersey Nthnrs	16	8	2	6	32	28	26
4	St Lawrence	16	8	2	6	29	27	26
5	Oaklands/St Sav.	16	7	2	7	28	32	23
6	Springfield	16	6	3	7	35	25	21
7	St Clement	16	5	3	8	17	27	18
8	Grands Vaux	16	4	3	9	30	42	15
9	Sporting Club Fr.	16	2	2	12	13	54	8

Division Three

		P	W	D	L	F	A	Pts
1	St John	15	8	3	4	32	22	27
2	Grouville	15	7	3	5	22	17	24
3	St Helier	15	6	3	6	27	28	21
4	Trinity	15	4	6	5	20	25	18
5	St Ouen	15	4	5	6	21	22	17
6	St Brelade	15	5	2	8	24	32	17

FIRST TOWER UNITED FC — JERSEY EUROPEAN FOOTBALL COMBINATION

Secretary: Geoff Liron, Yellowstone, 6 La Garenne, Rue De L'Eglise, St Peter, Jersey JE3 7AR (01534 483874 (H) 631666 (B))

Ground: La Hague Manor, La Rue De La Hague, St Peter, Jersey JE3 7DB (01534 485002)

Directions: North on St Peter's main road from Beaumont Hill. Take first right after Star, Tipsy Toad pub. Ground at end of La Route Du Manoir.

Covered Standing: No **Covered Seating:** Yes **Clubhouse:** Yes **Midweek Matchday:**

UPTON PARK TROPHY

Jersey Scottish slipped to a second successive Upton Park Trophy defeat against Guernsey's Sylvans at Springfield. Although competitive, a lack-lustre affair was won with a fine individual goal from Guernsey Muratti striker Paul Nobes. Just after the hour he dispossessed a hesitant Martin Forbes, who had the chance to clear the danger, midway inside the Scottish half.

Nobes, who scored the winner in last year's fixture which also finished 1-0, then raced towards the Scottish penalty area. He firstly jinked one way past two defenders and when they came back again he went between them to lift the ball over and across the face of the advancing goalkeeper.

To Forbes' credit he had kept a quiet rein on his pacey opponent up until the goal but after it Nobes won the tussle.

"It was a blow and Forbsie is gutted", said Scots boss Pat Brennan. "He had him in his pocket until then, the boy wasn't in the game. But he had a lot to do and credit to him he finished it off brilliantly."

Jimmy Reilly in particular, will be kicking himself for missing several gilt edge chances. He hit the crossbar in the opening minute of the second half, nodded the ball straight at the goalkeeper with just him to beat as well as hooking a great effort just wide and gave the ball away on another occasion when a shot could have brought an equaliser.

"It wasn't our day," said Brennan, adding: "On another day Jimmy could have had a hat-trick but nobody will be blaming him as he has had a brilliant season for us and his goals have been instrumental in us getting here."

Scottish: Paul McDermott, Mark McKenna, Martin Forbes, Ryan Lumsden, Robert Fox, Craig Morton, Gary Lightbody, Damon Pih,Adam Greig, Jimmy Reilly, Yazalde Santos. Subs: Paul Carberry, Paul Crompton, Jamie Drummond, Jason O'Prey, Chris McNabb, Lee Nobes.

Sylvans: Ian Drillot, Martin Gauvain, John Nobes, Martin Gallienne, Joel Avery, Mark Coutanche, Steve Brehaut, Grant Chalmers, Jan Renouf, Adie Exall, Paul Nobes. Subs: Duncan Staples, Lunn, Daryl Le Poidevin, Matt Warren, Tony Vance.

Officials: Graham Barber, Steve Landick (J), Tony Sarre (G). Fourth Official: Mark Le Cornu.

Attendance: 630

Guernsey's Player's Player of the Year Paul Nobes of Sylvans in action versus Jersey Scottish in the Upton Park Cup match at Springfield. He emulated Jersey's Graham Le Faux by captaining full and U21 Inter-Island winning sides in one season.

Photo: Guernsey Press Co Ltd

GUERNSEY'S MURATTI SUCCESS

Jersey's hopes of a fifth successive Muratti victory were scotched in Guernsey last May. At the Track Peter Vincenti's much-fancied side failed to deliver and stumbled to a 2-1 defeat after leading 1-0 at the break. And their saviour on countless occasions down the years, goalkeeper Steve Carlyon, accepted that his mistake led to Guernsey's opening goal. Carlyon, who was making his 17th consecutive appearance - a record for a goalkeeper - slipped to the ground while taking a goal-kick after 50 minutes.

The ball was nodded back goalwards by Guernsey's Martin Gauvain from near the half-way line and there appeared no danger. Jersey sweeper Ian Daly left the ball for Carlyon to collect but it bounced up unexpectedly high and over his head. Guernsey's Adie Exall hadn't given up the chase for the ball and with Carlyon now struggling to get back Exall prodded home the equaliser from close range. Spurred on by the goal Guernsey made tactical changes and with Jersey failing to recover from their misfortune, the hosts grabbed a second minutes from the end for an unexpected win.

"I couldn't believe what was happening when the ball popped up like it did," said Carlyon afterwards. "I'm the last line of defence, I didn't get the ball so the goal is down to me."

Jersey, who had by far the better of the opening period also had luck on their side with their goal minutes before half time. Yazalde Santos, one of Jersey's few shining lights, made a brilliant run down the right from inside his own half and whipped a pacey cross into the danger area. Guernsey's Joel Avery deflected the ball goalwards and his team-mate Martin Gauvain could only help it into the goal.

Steve Brehaut shot home Guernsey's winner, from just inside the penalty area, after Carlyon came for a long throw-in but was blocked by a cluster of players, including Guernsey's Jan Renouf who nodded the ball back out to Brehaut.

Guernsey: Ian Drillot, Martin Gauvain, John Nobes, Joel Avery, Rodney Elmy, Mark Coutanche, Jan Renouf, Steve Brehaut, Micky Ogier, Paul Nobes, Adie Exall (Kevin Le Tissier). Subs not used: Robert Smart, Mark Ogier, Michael de la Haye, Ian Chainey.
Jersey: Steve Carlyon, Craig Ferey, Ryan Lumsden, Ian Daly, Craig Morton, Andy Barker, Jon Kellett (Damon Pih), Tony Salaun (De Freitas), Yazalde Santos, Jimmy Reilly (Ross Crick), Chris Hamon. Subs not used: Shaun Maloret, Adam Greig.
Officials: Mike Reed (Birmingham). Assistants: Ted Teed (Guernsey), Russell Barry (Jersey). Fourth official: Kelvin Seeds (Guernsey).

BUT JERSEY WIN ISLAND GAMES

Jersey hosted the Island Games during the summer of 1997 and went on to win the Gold medal in the football section after a 1-0 victory over Ynes Mon (Anglesey) in the final.

Jersey, who beat Guernsey in their group match 4-0, won all five of their matches in the tournament.

In club football, Rozel Rovers retained the Le Riches Cup, the Island's premier knock-out tournament while St Peter won the Charity Cup, a pre-season tournament.

The Island's county trophy, the Wheway Cup, was won by Guernsey's all-conquering Sylvans. The Guernsey side won 2-1 against Rozel Rovers.

ISLE OF MAN FOOTBALL REVIEW 1996-97

PEEL ARE TEAM OF THE SEASON

Whilst it was Douglas High School Old Boys who took the honours in Division One of Manx Football, the team of the season was undoubtedly Peel who showed form that made them likely to return to former glories.

In Division One Old Boys took control from the start and in the 22 matches played they lost only once and drew once to set a record points mark of 61. Goals flowed freely and they averaged over three goals per game, although that did not make them the division's top scorers.

Old Boys were not, however, dominant in cup action as they lost their first match in the FA Vase and failed to win any of the three major Manx Competitions - The F.A., Railway or Hospital Cups.

Peels renaissance coincided with their signing of former Oldham and Manchester City favourite Rick Holden. Holden is now working as a physio at Nobles Hospital on the Island.

Down in the Second Division for the first time in their history Peel came back with a vengeance winning 27 games with only Marown taking points off them in a drawn match. The Westerners scored 154 goals in their successful campaign.

To add to this Peel beat most of the leading first division clubs when they won both The F.A. and Hospital Cups, although replays caused an extension of the season just to deal with their fixtures backlog.

Curiously, however, they won neither of the two cups held purely for second division teams as Colby took the honours in both The Woods and Paul Henry Events and to this they added promotion to the top flight as well as having the Islanders top individual scorer in Basil Kelly. Just one team were relegated, that being Pulrose United.

The Railway Cup went to 1996 champions, St Marys and The Saints were also top scorers in Division One helped by the man with the golden boot, Peter Langridge.

Dave Phillips

Isle of Man Football Association Trophy Winners 1996-97

Division One	DHSOB
Combination One	Rushen
Division Two	Peel
Combination Two	Peel
F A Cup	Peel
Railway Cup	St Marys
Hospital Cup	Peel
Woods Cup	Colby
Paul Henry Cup	Colby
Junior Cup	Rushen
Cowell Cup	Castletown
IoM Bank 14/16	Union Mills
Alan Hawley 14/16	Douglas Royal
'A' 14/16 League	Pulrose
'B' 14/16 League	Corinthians
Fred Faragher Trophy	Marown

TAYLOR WOODROW DIVISION ONE
FINAL LEAGUE TABLE 1996-97

		P	W	D	L	F	A	Pts
1	Old Boys	22	20	1	1	83	19	61
2	Rushen	22	13	7	2	64	25	46
3	St Marys	22	14	3	5	84	28	45
4	Castletown	22	11	5	6	55	36	38
5	St Georges	22	11	5	6	50	34	38
6	Gymnasium	22	11	4	7	63	43	37
7	Police	22	8	7	7	50	50	31
8	Douglas Royal	22	6	3	13	39	56	21
9	Ayre	22	5	5	12	42	66	20
10	Laxey	22	4	4	14	28	51	16
11	Braddan	22	3	2	17	30	76	11
12	Pulrose	22	3	0	19	26	133	9

BOWRING LEAGUE DIVISION TWO
FINAL LEAGUE TABLE 1996-97

		P	W	D	L	F	A	Pts
1	Peel	28	27	1	0	154	16	82
2	Colby	28	21	2	5	147	55	65
3	Corinthians	28	19	4	5	112	56	61
4	Foxdale	28	18	5	5	123	54	59
5	Marown	28	14	3	11	89	66	45
6	Ronaldsway	28	13	2	13	75	78	41
7	Union Mills	28	12	4	12	56	54	40
8	Ramsey	28	11	4	13	68	71	37
9	Michael	28	10	3	15	59	72	33
10	Onchan	28	9	6	13	60	74	33
11	St Johns	28	8	7	13	68	69	31
12	Malew	28	12	3	13	61	93	30
13	Jurby	28	7	1	20	39	135	22
14	Rycob	28	4	3	21	28	94	15
15	Barclays	28	0	2	26	18	172	2

Peel AFC

Ramsey FC

'The Bowl' in Douglas, where Island 'Internationals' are played and the I.o.M. FA have their HQ.

All photos: Andrew Hetherington

WOMEN'S FOOTBALL

The Women's 1996/1997 season turned out to be another fascinating and competitive campaign.

Unlike the one before, it wasn't going to be Croydon's season. They found it that much more difficult to repeat their previous year's success in their attempt to win the Premier League and the FA Women's Cup competition.

Croydon's pre-season signings saw them shoring up their defence by signing Arsenal's experienced centre half and their former treble winner Gill Wylie and the Brighton pair, Welsh defender Lyn Peters and striker Deano Carlin, plus Charlton's speedy winger Iffy Ejim. And they got off to a good start by defeating visitors Liverpool 1-0 only to be held to two home draws, 3-3 by Tranmere Rovers and 2-2 by Everton.

Then they began to string together some good victories including a 5-2 triumph over Doncaster Belles, who had been the dominant force in women's football for many years. Doncaster had reached eleven WFA cup finals, winning six of them. It was the eventual number of defeats (five to be precise) including losing twice to Arsenal that marked Croydon's downfall and they finished third in the league despite winning nine games and drawing four. It turned out to the Arsenal's turn for the championship title. Their successful squad was said to be one of the best that Manager Vic Akers has ever worked with despite having lost their goalkeeper Rosa Serra (Spain's Number One), who went back home. She was replaced by another oustanding Australian player. The Gunners' outfit was completed by picking up the likes of talented ex-Wembley international Kelly Smith, plus two stars from Mill Hill in Natasha Daly and Rachel Yankey, both now England players along with Three Bridges' outstanding centre half Faye White. And the only league game the North London Club lost from eighteen matches was against hosts Doncaster Belles narrowly, losing 0-1 in the opening match of the season, while Wembley were the only side to hold Arsenal to a draw.

That team Wembley (the eventual beaten FA Women's Cup finalists) were to have a say in denying Arsenal the double this season after they knocked them out of the UK Living Women's FA Cup competition at the semi-final stage. Arsenal lost to a single goal by Tracy Koch.

Arsenal to their credit finished off as the newly crowned champions by achieving the best scoring record with 65 goals and the best defensive record having conceded only nine. They also picked up the London County Cup trophy for the third consecutive year by defeating London rivals Millwall Lionesses 2-0 at Hendon FC.

Doncaster Belles were left empty handed for a second consecutive year ending up as runners-up yet again. They did knock out three times League Cup winners Arsenal from the same competition winning 2-1 in the Second Round, but were to slip up to semi-finalists Millwall Lionesses (the team of the season) losing 3-5 on penalties after drawing the game 1-1. Their Manager Mel Woodhall felt he had taken the club as far as he could and decided to bow out of the hot seat which gave an opportunity to former player and reserve manager Julie Chipchase who certainly seemed to instil a bit of enjoyment into their football.

At many stages of the season they led the Premier League but three defeats were too many for Doncaster who eventually salvaged their season by finishing Second. Young defender, England's Claire Utley, was voted Player of the Year with their more senior member with Player's Player of the Year award. Outstanding former England defender Jackie Sherrard was dogged by injury has followed former internationals goalkeeper Tracy Davidson and winger Jan Murray into retirement.

Millwall Lionesses were to have their best season ever. They reached four cup finals and won three trophies. But it was the way they achieved that success combining great young talent - 15 year old and now an England international Danielle Murphy and future regular international and Millwall's Most Improved Player of the season, centre half Katie Chapman with experienced players like midfielder and Millwall's player of the year Lou Waller and key England goalkeeper Pauline Cope - that produced their roll call of awards for the 1996-97. There are twelve trophies in all, won by the senior side right down to the Under 11 team. Including the UK Living FA Women's Cup, FA Women's Premier League Cup, Kent County FA Women's Cup, Greater London League Division 1 Champions, Greater London League Division Six Champions, Greater London League Russell Cup, Southern Girls League Under 14 Division champions, Southern Girls League Under 14 Cup, Southern Girls League Under 11 Division Champions, Southern Girls League Under 11 Cup, LYFA Under 16 Girls Cup and LYFA Under 11 Girls Cup.

Millwall has always been the envy of everyone in women's football purely on their youth policy alone. But this season has seen them come of age. Striker Pru Buckley announced that the Premier League title could be theirs next season. "Everyone had written us off this year and look what we achieved by picking up the League Cup after beating Everton 2-0.

"We convincingly defeated Doncaster Belles 3-0 in the fifth round of the FA Women's Cup, and then we kept our heads by putting out holders Croydon by converting our penalties in the semi-finals."

Millwall in fact went on to lift the cup in an uninspiring final at West Ham United, knocking two goals past the striker-less Wembley side. And of course they collected the Kent County Cup after seeing off finalists Charlton courtesy of a Tina Lindsay goal. Some of Millwall's performances this season have been quite awesome showing off those silky skills which youngsters are being taught these days. Times have changed since my football days in the early eighties when the necessary credential was that you could kick a football and if you could then you were immediately in the first team. But watching the skill, pace and passing ability of these youngsters from Millwall does prove how far the women's game has progressed and being rewarded with lots of silverware can only be good for the future of the women's game. Success is not always the name of the game in every sport and women's football isn't any different.

There are those who had a contrasting season from last year. Take Southampton Saints for instance. They may have signed three key Bristol City players, defender Lyn Amstrong and two 19 year olds in left back Abbie Gould and versatile player Rachel McArthur. But who would believe that after winning the Southern Division last year and promotion to the Premier League this year they would instantly get relegated by finishing second bottom?

They won only three of their eighteen league games, still pipping Ilkeston Town who ended up as bottom of the league. Southampton will play in the Southern Division next year and Ilkeston Town in the Northern Division. Southampton did lift a piece of silverware by winning the Hampshire County Cup final after they defeated rivals Southampton Women 3-2 after extra time.

Veteran Linda Hale, who was part of that successful Southampton side of the seventies winning the WFA Cup eight times, put Southampton Women ahead and Abbie Gould's own goal gave them a commanding 2-0 lead over the Saints, who made an amazing recovery with goals from Rachel McArthur and Sharon Hayes with Angie Fisher scoring the eventual winner in the second period of extra time.

Tranmere Rovers, last year's champions of the Northern Division, had a pretty good year experiencing the big time in top flight Premier League football despite being placed eighth. The Rovers manager Steve Williams admits that they are still a young side and learning all the time. But they do have two outstanding players in youngsters 17 year old Sue Smith and 18 year old Becky Smith both having been picked and played for England in their recent friendlies.

Liverpool, who said goodbye to Manager Joby Humphreys and Assistant John Duffy, welcomed new boss Paul Ashley who has been scouting for the England Manager Ted Copeland. His appointment had prompted a few signings. The Garswood Saints trio, England's Maz Catterill, Shirley Oakford, and Barbara Nodwell, who then became Liverpool's Assistant Manager, went to Liverpool who also produced an excellent league performance to defeat hosts Millwall Lionesses 2-0 with their versatile defender-cum-England cricketer Clare Taylor superb in the heart of their defence but sadly then failed to produce necessary for points and success. They of course had some casualities losing one specific key player in centre half and ex-Doncaster Belles' Louise Ryde, who joined arch rivals Everton.

Liverpool finished a respectable fourth in the league but they, like their hardworking Secretary, Youth Team Manager, Knowsley Football Development Officer and FA County Rep for Women and Girls on Merseyside, Sylvia Gore, know they could do better with the talent they have in England's Karen Burke, Becky Easton and the under-rated Sammy Hayward, a one time England star. But their striker and England's Maria Harper had been ruled out for part of the season with a neck injury sustained during her work as a policewoman.

As for Everton, they picked up two more Liverpool players, Joy McQuiggan and Cathy Gore, as well as Welsh international and Doncaster Belles' Nicky Davies plus Garswood Saints' Lisa Scattergood, Liverpool youth player Tammy Byrne, Liverpool Feds' goalkeeper Terri McGrath and Wigan's Rachel Statt. But they lost Cathy Bell (who is taking time out from the game) and Chris Ashworth who joined Northern Division side Aston Villa (formerly Villa Aztecs).

Everton did produce some great league performances, drawing with defending league champions Croydon 2-2, and then reached their first ever League Cup Final only to blow it against Millwall after having taken the lead through their ever reliable goalscorer Louise Thomas, who along with Joy McQuiggan had alreay picked up a WFA Cup winners medal with Leasow Pacific in 1988 by defeating Friends of Fulham 3-2. Everton finished sixth in the league but on the same 27 points as Millwall Lionesses, who had the better goal difference.

Wembley, who were last season's League Cup winners, lost key players during this season but ended up with a runners-up medal in the FA Women's Cup final. Manager John Jones was pleased that his team won the Middlesex County Cup competition for a fourth consecutive year, and that they had finished seventh in the league this season. But despite losing their three year old home at Wembley's Vale Farm, Sudbury, as they will be moving to Hanwell Town, will still retain the name Wembley. Manager Jones' hard work has paid off by pulling off a two year sponsorship deal that will start next season.

The Northern Division of the National League was won handsomely by newcomers Bradford City, who say the secret of their success is that the club is run by a committee not the players. They lost only one league match from eighteen and that was 3-1 to fifth-placed Wolves. Former Bronte and Scotland player Lorraine Kennedy has been quite outstanding for Bradford all season and they have a a good coach in ex-Coventry and Bradford City player Mick Wood.

Aston Villa (formerly Villa Aztecs) made up for their disappointing 1995-96 season after being relegated from the Premier Division when they finished runners-up - eight points behind league champions Bradford. Villa won the Birmingham County Cup by defeating finalists Tamworth 6-4 with ex-Everton player Chris Ashworth hitting a hat trick.

But Bronte, a club who had been established for a good 26 years, announced they were disbanding on November 2nd when they were due to play Blackburn Rovers in the second round of the FA Women's Cup because they lost their Manager Rob Solk who had left two weeks before to join league rivals Sheffield Wednesday. Loss of players and poor form over the past few years had contributed to their eventual demise. This meant that no club would be relegated from the Northern Division. They will be remembered as the side who produced some top quality England, players including Liverpool's Clare Taylor and Doncaster Belles' five stars in Becky Lonorgan, goalkeeper Debbie Biggins, Izzy Pollard, Chantel Woodhead (now retired) and Sarah Begg plus ex-Arsenal player Sam Britton. Bronte's main claim to fame is having reached the quarter and semi-finals of the FA Women's Cup competition.

It is third time lucky for Berkhamsted Town, who finally were crowned Southern League Champions with promotion to the Premier Division next season. Twice they had been pipped to the Southern Division title by Southampton Saints and Maidstone Tigresses (now disbanded). Despite Wimbledon occupying top spot a good way through the season, they could only claim fourth spot, and Berkhamsted Town took the title with a comfortable three points cushion over final runners-up Brighton & Hove Albion.

They were indebted to Debbie Burton whose hat trick in their last match of the season over Three Bridges to win 4-0 on April 27th earned them the league title. Debbie Gunn along with Michelle Lyons has continued to win caps for Wales.

Oxford United, who were made up mainly of 15 and 16 year olds, can say they benefited from playing in the Southern Division despite being relegated. It didn't help Oxford's cause though when they lost key players, who all joined their former United player and now key England centre defender Carol Harwood at Premier League side Wembley. They were Lois Fiddler, prolific goalscorer Natash Cronin (who missed the entire season because of injury) and Paula Callinin.

Finally, we come to the play offs for a place in the Northern and Southern Division next season with the places finally being filled by Coventry City and Barry Town. The initial run in for the qualifying place for the Northern Division turned into a bit of a fiasco. The Yorkshire & Humberside Division One League Champions, Middlesbrough, who won the title pretty convincingly, had not been put forward until they appealed to the FA to be reinstated.

They won their appeal but not their semi-final play-off match that saw them knocked out by the West Midland Division One league champions Coventry City 1-1 and 2-0 through goals from Becky Wilde and Victoria Watts. Becky Wilde again came to Coventry's rescue scoring the only goal to defeat East Midlands Division One league champions Calverton 1-0 and earn a place in the Northern Division next year. The Southern Division was a more straightforward contest. The South West Division One league champions Barry Town, who boast of no less than seven Welsh players in their team, were the outright winners to play National League football next season.

Firstly they had to see off South East's St Georges by winning 2-0 in the prelim round and then defeated Southern's Reading Royals 4-2 in the semi-final. In the final play-off Barry Town won by 2-1 over Eastern Premier League champions Canary Racers despite Racers going ahead through Jackie Cocker in the 32nd minute. Barry Town had to rely on a second half revival to secure them a Southern Division place with goals from Juliet Payne and Wales' Ayshea Martyn.

Canary Racers had defeated Greater London Regional League runners-up Tottenham Hotspur 3-2 with two goals from Vanessa Kemp and one from Jackie Cocker in the semi-final play-off match. Before meeting Barry Town in the final they had not lost a single league game all season having scored 113 and conceded four goals in the Eastern Region.

While America won the Olympic gold medal beating China in the final in Atlanta with goals from Shannon MacMillan and Tiffeny Milbrett and attracted a crowd of 76,481, the international news in this country wasn't so good when England were knocked out of the current European championships for the first time in seven years.

They failed to reach the latter stages of the competition by losing in the play-offs to Spain (who qualified for the first time) 3-2 on aggregate by losing 2-1 away from home on September 8th and then being held to a 1-1 draw at Tranmere Rovers' ground on September 29th. Spain's and Arsenal's former goalkeeper Rosa Serra was quite outstanding against England.

Since then Manager Ted Copeland has been organising friendlies. On February 27 at Preston North End, England lost 6-4 to the current European champions Germany. But England did make a remarkable recovery having trailed the Germans 5-0; they dispensed with their stifling sweeper (five in defence job) and soon goals materialised from Croydon's Hope Powell (penalty), two from Arsenal's talented player Joanne Broadhurst, and substitute Tranmere Rovers' Sue Smith (scoring on her debut).

A friendly at Sheffield United over rivals Scotland saw England enjoy a sweet 6-0 victory with a hat trick from Broadhurst, two goals from Doncaster Belles' Gillian Coultard, and one from Everton's defender Maureen Marley.

On April 23rd, England lost 2-0 to Italy in Turin. Only after some bizarre substitutions - i.e. taking off Millwall's Number One keeper Pauline Cope for the already injured Liverpool's young Rachel Brown - did Italy manage to break the deadlock after England had equally matched the Italians.

A mini tour to face the Olympic gold medalists and 1991 World cup champions the USA took place in May 1997. On May 9th in San Jose England were defeated 5-0 and then on May 11th in Portland, England suffered another embarrasing defeat losing 6-0. Then on June 8th, England took on the current World champions, Norway, in Lillestrom and lost that friendly encounter 4-0.

England won't relish being drawn against Norway, Germany and Holland as the 1997-1999 Group 3 UEFA qualifying competition for the third FIFA World Cup in the USA in the summer of 1999. But news in the offing that the FA are considering resurrecting an England Under 18 side can only improve the cause of women's football both internationally and domestically.

England are down to play a return friendly with Scotland on August 23rd in Livingston, then will meet Germany away in the UEFA 1st leg qualifier on September 25th.

Wales, who on June 7th 1997 beat hosts Northern Ireland 2-1 in a friendly international at Chiminey Corner FC Belfast, acquired good preparation for their Group six 1997-97 UEFA qualifying matches. They have bee drawn against Poland, Belarus and the Republic of Ireland.

Scotland have been drawn in Group Five of the UEFA qualifying competition for the World Cup, and they are against Estonia, Czech Republic and Lithuania.

Finally the efforts of a certain Assistant Manager of Croydon, Josie Clifford, who in her playing days with QPR Ladies in the 70's won five caps for England, were never officially acknowledged, but, at the London Girls presentation event organised by Manager Paul Iddols in London's Blackheath on Saturday June 21st, Women's FA Secretary Linda Whitehead was there to present Josie her international award.

If you want to hear more about women's football but on a regulary basis, then Women's Football Phoneline is presented by ex Watford footballer Cathy Gibb, who provides up to date information, domestic and international results and news as it happens. And that number is 0891 88 44 30 and you can also hear up to date regional results on 0891 88 44 29.

Cathy Gibb

UK LIVING WOMEN'S F.A. CUP 1996-97

Preliminary Round (08-09-96)

Bedford Bells	1-0	Cambridge United
Truro City	1-7	Barry Town

First Round (29-09-96)

Sunderland	3-4	Chesterfield
(After extra time)		
Newcastle	0-1	Chester Le Street
Chester City	6-0	Brighouse
Trafford	1-3	Liverpool Feds
Newsham PH	1-2	Manchester United
Sheffield Hallam United	1-2	Warrington Town
Darlington	4-2	Runcorn
Doncaster Rovers	8-1	Winsford United
Kirklees	1-3	Leeds United
Bangor City Girls	5-1	Stockport County
Radcliffe Borough	6-0	Wrexham
Haslingden	0-7	Oldham Athletic
Wakefield	7-0	York City
Rochdale	10-0	Deans
Manchester Belle Vue	0-1	Middlesbrough
Wigan	2-1	Hull City
Blackburn Rovers	6-1	Barnsley
Preston Rangers	9-0	Whalley Rangers
Scunthorpe Ironesses	2-3	Stockport
Lowestoft Town	12-0	Rea Valley Rovers
Canary Racers	1-2	Calverton MW
Nettleham	1-2	Birmingham City
Leek Town	1-2	Highfield Rangers
Milton Keynes Athletic	0-3	Coventry City
Belper Town	1-7	Tamworth
Colchester	0-3	Newcastle Town
Pye	1-3	Colchester United
Leicester City	1-0	Norwich United
Cambridge City	3-5	Clacton
Derby County	3-4	Bedford Bells
Haverhill Rovers	2-3	Shrewsbury Town
Abbey Rangers	8-0	Camberwell O Fallopians
Denham United	6-1	Camberley Town
Barnet	3-1	Winchester & Ealing
Charlton	4-1	Farnborough Town
Sawbridgeworth Town	4-1	Stanway
Surbiton Town	2-1	Crowborough Athletic
Hastings Town	1-6	Harlequins
Dunstable	w/o	Chelsea
(Walkover for Chelsea - Dunstable withdrawn)		
Romford	w/o	Slough Town
(Walkover for Slough Town - Romford withdrawn)		
London	9-1	Queens Pk Rgrs LSA
Teynham Gunners	2-8	St Georges (Eltham)
Chelmsford	2-1	Leatherhead
Hassocks	1-2	Harlow Town
(After extra time)		
Collier Row	5-1	Chipstead
Clapton	3-2	Enfield
Newham	5-0	Redbridge Wanderers
Hackney	v	Aylesbury Stocklake
(Abandoned after 77mins due to a serious injury to a Aylesbury Stocklake player)		
Watford & Evergreen	3-2	Chesham United
Dulwich Hamlet	3-2	Gillingham Girls
Tottenham Hotspur	11-0	Stevenage Borough
West Ham	1-2	Fulham
(After extra time)		
Brentford & Hampton	5-0	Luton
Mill Hill United	11-0	Great Wakering Rovers
Cardiff County	1-0	Thame United
Bath City	6-2	Wokingham Town
Clevedon United	0-6	Portsmouth
Bracknell Town	1-9	Yate Town
Binfield	v	Freeway
(Walkover to Binfield - Freeway withdrawn)		
Worcester City	8-3	Newton Abbot
Exeter Rangers	3-7	Bristol City
Okeford United	3-2	Bridgwater Town
Sherborne	3-1	Barnstaple Town
Reading Royals	7-0	Frome
Barry Town	3-1	Plymouth Pilgrims
Swindon Town Spitfires	10-0	Clevedon AFC
Cinderford Town	0-10	Swindon Town
Elmore Eagles	0-4	Cabletel

10 Clubs exempt to Fourth Round

Arsenal, Croydon, Doncaster Belles, Everton, Ilkeston Town, Liverpool, Millwall Lionesses, Southampton Saints, Tranmere Rovers, Wembley

20 Clubs exempt to Second Round

Aston Villa, Berkhamsted Town, Blyth Spartans Kestrels, Bradford City, Brighton & Hove Albion Bronte, Garswood Saints, Huddersfield Town, Ipswich Town, Langford, Leyton Orient, Notts County, Oxford United, Sheffield Wednesday, Stouport Swifts, Three Bridges, Town & County Diamonds, Whitehawk, Wimbledon, Wolverhampton Wanderers

Second Round (03-11-97)

Garswood Saints	2-1	Manchester United
Sheffield Wednesday	8-1	Darlington
Wakefield	8-0	Wigan
Oldham Athletic	11-3	Warrington Town
Blackburn Rovers	w/o	Bronte
(Walkover for Blackburn Rovers - Bronte withdrawn)		
Stockport	3-0	Liverpool Feds
Chester Le Street	w/o	Middlesbrough
(Walkover for Middlesbrough - Chester le Street withdrawn)		
Doncaster Rovers	2-4	Huddersfield Town
Bradford City	1-2	Blyth Spartans Kestrels
Rochdale	0-7	Leeds United
Radcliffe Borough	2-3	Preston Rangers
Chesterfield	1-3	Bangor City Girls
Wolverhampton Wndrs	0-5	Aston Villa
Coventry City	3-1	Leicester City

Town & County Diamonds	0-2	Birmingham City
Tamworth	1-5	Calverton MW
Notts County	0-5	Newcastle Town
Highfield Rangers	4-2	Chester City
Stourport Swifts	3-1	Shrewsbury Town
Tottenham Hotspur	2-1	Wimbledon
Abbey Rangers	4-5	Chelmsford
Brentford & Hampton	1-3	Whiteawk
Harlequins	3-1	Clacton
Berkhamsted Town	8-0	Lowestoft Town
St Georges (Eltham)	2-5	Leyton Orient
Langford	0-1	Chelsea
London	2-2	Sawbridgeworth Town
Sawbridgeworth Town	0-2	London
Brighton & Hove Albion	5-0	Newham
Bedford Bells	0-1	Three Bridges
(After extra time)		
Charlton	0-4	Dulwich Hamlet
Harlow Town	0-4	Mill Hill United
Colchester United	1-4	Collier Row
Ipswich Town	3-0	Surbiton Town
Watford & Evergreen	1-3	Barnet
Fulham	2-3	Clapton
Hackney	3-4	Denham United
Worcester City	0-2	Binfield
Portsmouth	0-1	Oxford United
Reading Royals	5-0	Swindon Town
Bath City	2-2	Okeford United
Okeford United	2-1	Bath City
Barry Town	18-0	Bristol City
Slough Town	0-6	Swindon Town Spitfires
Sherborne	5-2	Yate Town
Cardiff County	1-3	Cabletel

Third Round (01-12-96)

Sheffield Wednesday	3-2	Wakefield
Blackburn Rovers	0-3	Preston Rangers
Leeds United	2-5	Aston Villa
Blyth Spartans Kestrels	1-4	Garswood Saints
Highfield Rangers	1-0	Oldham Athletic
Calverton MW	1-2	Stockport
Coventry City	2-3	Huddersfield Town
Middlesbrough	3-2	Stourport Swifts
Bangor City	2-2	Newcastle Town
(After Extra Time)		
Newcastle Town	1-1	Bangor City
(After extra time, Bangor City won 5-3 on kicks from the penalty mark)		
Dulwich Hamlet	1-6	Berkhamsted Town
Whitehawk	2-1	Binfield
London	0-5	Sherborne
Oxford United	1-4	Reading Royals
Harlequins	0-12	Tottenham Hotspur
Swindon Town Spitfires	0-1	Chelsea
Three Bridges	1-2	Leyton Orient
Collier Row	3-1	Birmingham City
Chelmsford	1-1	Barnet
Barnet	1-1	Chelmsford
(After extra time, Chelmsford won 5-3 on kicks from the penalty mark)		
Okeford	1-2	Denham United
Mill Hill United	0-1	Ipswich Town
Brighton & Hove Albion	7-2	Cabletel
Clapton	1-5	Barry Town

Fourth Round (05-01-97)

Croydon	2-1	Liverpool
Highfield Rangers	2-3	Berkhamsted Town
Chelmsford	2-5	Huddersfield Town
Preston Rangers	12-0	Denham United
Southampton Saints	4-0	Whitehawk
Reading Royals	2-1	Leyton Orient
Doncaster Belles	10-1	Sheffield Wednesday
Ipswich Town	0-8	Middlesbrough
Garswood Saints	3-4	Ilkeston Town
Arsenal	6-0	Barry Town
Tottenham Hotspur	7-2	Collier Row
Sherborne	0-7	Everton
Stockport	2-6	Bangor City
Aston Villa	1-0	Brighton & Hove Albion
Chelsea	0-3	Millwall Lionesses
Tranmere Rovers	1-2	Wembley
(After extra time)		

Fifth Round (02-02-97)

Wembley	1-0	Preston Rangers
(After extra time)		
Southampton Saints	1-1	Berkhamsted Town
(After extra time)		
Berkhamsted Town	3-2	Southampton Saints
Middlesbrough	0-3	Ilkeston Town
Millwall Lionesses	3-0	Doncaster Belles
Bangor City Girls	0-2	Everton (28/1)
Tottenham Hotspur	0-4	Croydon
Reading Royals	2-4	Aston Villa
Arsenal	9-0	Huddersfield Town

Sixth Round (02-03-97)

Croydon	1-0	Everton
Berkhamsted Town	0-0	Wembley
(After extra time)		
Wembly	3-1	Berkhamsted Town
(After extra time)		
Millwall Lionesses	4-1	Aston Villa
(After extra time)		
Ilkeston Town	2-4	Arsenal

Semi-Finals (30-03-97)

Wembley	1-0	Arsenal
(At Boreham Wood FC, attendance 289)		
Millwall Lionesses	1-1	Croydon
(After extra time)		
(Millwall won 3-1 on kicks from the penalty mark)		
(At Dulwich Hamlet, attendance 530)		

Final (04-05-97)

Millwall Lionesses	1-0	Wembley
(At West Ham FC, attendance 3500)		

FA WOMEN'S PREMIER LEAGUE

FINAL LEAGUE TABLES

National Division

		P	W	D	L	F	A	GD	Pts
1	Arsenal	18	15	1	1	65	9	56	49
2	Doncaster Belles	18	13	2	3	44	15	29	41
3	Croydon	18	9	4	5	39	26	13	31
4	Liverpool	18	9	3	6	30	16	14	30
5	Millwall Lionesses	18	7	6	5	20	19	1	27
6	Everton	18	8	3	7	36	36	0	27
7	Wembley	18	6	4	8	26	27	-1	22
8	Tranmere Rovers	18	3	3	12	23	48	-25	12
9	Southampton Saints	18	3	0	15	15	61	-45	9
10	Ilkeston Town	18	1	4	13	14	56	-42	7

Northern Division

		P	W	D	L	F	A	GD	Pts
1	Bradford City	16	15	0	1	56	13	43	45
2	Aston Villa	16	12	1	3	50	15	35	37
3	Blyth Spartans Kstrls	16	9	2	5	40	25	15	29
4	Huddersfield Town	16	8	3	5	37	32	5	27
5	Wolverhampton Wndrs	16	7	1	8	30	29	1	22
6	Sheffield Wednesday	16	4	4	8	25	35	11	16
7	Garswood Saints	16	3	5	8	26	29	-3	14
8	Stouport Swifts	16	3	2	11	22	60	-38	11
9	Notts County	16	0	4	12	21	68	-47	4

Bronte withdrawn - all results expunged

Play off winners: Coventry City

Southern Division

		P	W	D	L	F	A	GD	Pts
1	Berkhamsted Town	18	14	2	2	57	16	41	44
2	Brighton & Hove Alb	18	13	2	3	59	33	25	41
3	Whitehawk	18	12	1	5	39	17	22	37
4	Wimbledon	18	10	2	6	66	28	38	32
5	Three Bridges	18	7	5	6	36	28	8	26
6	Langford	18	7	5	6	28	33	-5	26
7	Ipswich Town	18	5	4	9	24	26	-2	19
8	Leyton Orient	18	3	4	11	27	50	-23	13
9	Town & County	18	2	3	13	18	65	-47	9
10	Oxford United	18	2	2	14	17	75	-58	8

Play off winners: Barry Town

WINNERS, PROMOTION AND RELEGATION MOVEMENT

National Division	**Champions**	Arsenal
	Relegated	Ilkeston Town (to Northern Div), Southampton Saints (to Southern Div)
Northern Division	**Champions**	Bradford City (to National Div)
	Relegated	No Clubs relegated
Southern Division	**Champions**	Berkhamsted Town (to National Div)
	Relegated	Oxford United
League Cup	**Winners**	Millwall Lionesses
	Runners up	Everton

LEADING GOALSCORERS 1996-97

PREMIER DIVISION

Joanne Broadhurst	Arsenal	21
Karen Walker	Doncaster Belles	18
Kerry Davis	Croydon	13
Louse Thomas	Everton	12
Vicky Exley	Doncaster Belles	11
Kelly Smith	Arsenal	11
Andy McGrady	Everton	11
Marieanne Spacey	Arsenal	10
Hope Powell	Croydon	10
Sue Smith	Tranmere Rovers	9
Karen Burke	Liverpool	8
Shirley Oakford	Liverpool	8
Kara Reynolds	Arsenal	7
Rachel Yankey	Arsenal	7

NORTHERN DIVISION

Melanine Garside	Bradford City	25
Lesley Higham	Notts County	17
Clare Mitchell	Huddersfield Town	12
Chris Ashworth	Aston Villa	11
Jane Hurley	Aston Villa	11
Donna Lanagham	Blyth Spartans Kestrels	11
Melanie Reay	Blyth Spartans Kestrels	10
Louise Carter	Wolverhampton Wndrs	9
Jo Mitchell	Huddersfield Town	8
Emma Bowdler	Stouport	8
Angie Gallimore	Garswood	8
Lorraine Kennedy	Bradford City	7
Lorraine Robinson	Aston Villa	7

SOUTHERN DIVISION

Tammy Wayne	Brighton	29
Sarah Whitlock	Wimbledon	18
Emma Mead	Whitehawk	17
Sarah Stanbury	Wimbledon	14
Debbie Burton	Berkhamsted Town	12
Pernille Overbye	Berkhamsted Town	12
Gemma Clark	Langford	10
Dawn Lawrence	Berkhamsted Town	10
Kim Condon	Three Bridges	8
Adel Hinder	Wimbledon	8
Lyn Jacobs	Wimbledon	8
Trudy Mahoney	Langford	8
Cher Beesley	Town & County	7
Lynne McCormick	Whitehawk	7
Bev Payne	Berkhamsted Town	7
Joanne Welham	Ipswich	7

WIRRAL PROGRAMME CLUB

The non profit making Club formed in March, 1967.

Secretary: I.R.W. Runham

3 Tansley Close, Newton, West Kirby, Wirral, L48 9XH Tel: 0151-625-9554

22nd NON-LEAGUE FOOTBALL PROGRAMME OF THE YEAR SURVEY 1996–97

Entries were received from 1026 clubs, nearly 200 less than last year. This is certainly due to the postal problems experienced this year. Many of our letters to league secretaries with details of the survey failed to reach them. We were able to send duplicates to those who contacted us but from phone calls etc received it is obvious many clubs did not get details of the survey. To date I have been unable to get an explanation from the Royal Mail as to why so many letters went astray. With reserve and youth programmes there were 1085 places.

Again there were many superb programmes with numerous clubs showing improvement on last season. It is again pleasing to see clubs issuing for the first time plus some after a gap of many years. ALL clubs that issue a programme are to be congratulated, a single sheet is better than nothing. There would be no programmes without the hard work that the editors and any helpers they can find put in, I'm sure most supporters and many committee members do not realise the time and effort needed to produce a programme, so our special thanks go to all these people. I must also thank all those who sent in programmes for the survey and helped to spread the word, the clubs themselves, their supporters, our members, other collectors, the Football Association, all the League Secretaries, The Non-League Club Directory, Team Talk, Non-League Traveller, Welsh Football and all those who lent us some programmes. Sincere apologies to anyone inadvertently omitted.

Some clubs only issue for a Saturday game, some for special games, some change their style, content, editor, price, etc. during the season; some have special connections with printers etc., often we are not aware of these circumstances. Obviously we can only survey the programmes we receive. Some are from early in the season, others from just before the closing date, most from in between. The results always create a lot of interest with varying points being expressed, some of those we hear second or third hand but most miss our ears, if you have any comments on the survey please let us know. I am sure the day will never come when there is complete agreement over the results, however the more discussion there is over the survey the better, it will keep programmes to the forefront and hopefully maintain or even improve the standards, better still it may encourage more clubs to issue next season.

The club with the winning programme will receive a framed certificate, the winners of each league will also receive a certificate. Please note the programmes have been surveyed, not as many assume voted upon. Marks were awarded to each programme as follows (the maximum marks available for each section are given):- Cover 15 (design 10, match details 5), Page Size 10, Team Layout and position within the programme 10, Results 10, League Tables 10, Price 15, Printing and paper quality 20, Frequency of Issue 20, Value for Money 20, (this takes into account the ratio of adverts to content, the clubs league etc.), Contents 105 (other than those listed) taking into account their relevance to the club, its league, environs etc., the size of the print used, the spacing between the lines, the size of the margins, and if the contents are originals or reproduced (from League bulletins, newspapers, magazines etc.). To gain full marks in the Frequency of Issue section we needed to receive programmes from 10 different matches for each team entered (allowances were made if 10 home games had not been played by the closing date and we were informed of this), the minimum entry was one programme. As many programmes varied from issue to issue all the programmes received were surveyed, the marks in each section were totalled and divided by the number of issues to get the final mark for each section, the marks from each section were then totalled to get the final score. A new standard of marks is set each season so this seasons totals should not be compared with those of earlier seasons as the comparison would almost certainly be inaccurate, a programme identical to last seasons will almost certainly have gained different marks.

We have already received many entries for the Specials section of the survey (for one offs, big cup ties, friendlies, testimonials, charity matches, etc.), the closing date for receiving these is 8th June 1997. To receive the results, expected early July, we should appreciate it if you could send a stamped sae. Thank you.

The results of this seasons survey are as follows:-

Best Non-League Programme Nationally 1996–97			
		NORTHWOOD	189 points
	2nd	LANGNEY SPORTS	183 points
	3rd	DENABY UNITED	180 points

NATIONAL TOP 30 1 Northwood 189. 2 Langney Sports 183. 3 Denaby U 180. 4 Hoddesdon T 177. 5 Hucknall T 175. 6 Denbigh T 166. 7 Gorleston 165. 8 Bashley, Lancing 164. 10 Woking, Raunds T, Peppard 163. 13 Rushden & Diamonds 161. 14 North Shields A 160. 15 Uxbridge 158. 16 Witney T 157. 17 St Leonards Stamcroft, Pelsall Villa 156. 19 Yeovil T 155. 20 Sutton U 154. 21 Aldershot T 153. 22 Chelmsford C, Croydon A, Downham T 152. 25 Truro C, Yateley Green 150. 27 Swindon Supermarine 149. 28 Willenhall T, Anglian Exiles 147.

INDIVIDUAL LEAGUE RESULTS

The first number after the clubs name is the number of programmes received — 10 shows ten or more different programmes were received, or every programme if less than ten matches played, the second number is the total points gained. The leagues are in no particular order.

LEAGUE + No. of entries	**FIRST**	**PTS**	**SECOND**	**PTS**	**THIRD**	**PTS**
Vauxhall Conference (22)	Woking	10-163	Rushden & Diamonds	10-161	Hednesford Town	10-144
Dr. Martens Overall (62)	Bashley	10-164	Raunds Town	10-161	Witney Town	10-157
Prem.Div. (21)	Chelmsford City	10-152	Baldock Town	10-144	Hastings Town	10-140
Mid.Div. (21)	Raunds Town	10-163	Ilkeston Town	10-136	Rothwell Town	10-131
Sth.Div. (20)	Bashley	10-164	Witney Town	10-157	St Leonards Stam	10-156
ICIS Overall (66)	Northwood	10-189	Uxbridge	10-158	Yeovil Town	1-155
Prem.Div. (19)	Yeovil Town	1-155	Sutton United	10-154	Hendon	10-130
Div.1. (19)	Uxbridge	10-158	Aldershot Town	10-153	Whyteleafe	10-135
Div.2. (16)	Collier Row/Romford	10-128	Horsham	10-125	Bedford Town	1-123
Div.3. (12)	Northwood	10-189	Wealdstone	10-146	Epsom & Ewell	10-133
Unibond Overall (42)	Blyth Spartans	10-142	Bradford Park Ave	10-137	Barrow	10-133
Prem.Div. (23)	Blyth Spartans	10-142	Barrow	10-133	Alfretaon Town	10-119
Div.1. (19)	Bradford Park Ave	10-137	Workington	10-130	Matlock Town	1-125
Spartan (9)	Croydon Athletic	10-152	Cockfosters	9-141	Beaconsfield SYCOB	10-126
Combined Counties (9)	Corinthian Casuals	10-139	Walton Casuals	10-129	Ash United	10-124
Essex Senior (8)	Stansted	10-122	Ford United	10-114	Southend Manor	1-109
Winstonlead Kent (13)	Folkestone Invicta	10-135	Herne Bay	1-132	Whitstable Town	10-125
Jewson Wessex (15)	AFC Lymington	10-127	Wimborne Town	10-125	Christchurch	1-120
Unijet Overall (23)	Langney Sports	10-183	Lancing	10-164	Ifield	10-138
Sussex Div.1. (9)	Langney Sports	10-183	Three Bridges	1-135	Burgess Hill Town	10-127
County Div.2. (7)	Lancing	10-164	East Preston	10-131	Broadbridge Heath	10-129
Div. 3. (7)	Ifield	10-138	Buxted	10-96	Seaford Town	1-87
Jewson Overall (25)	Gorleston	10-165	Downham Town	10-152	Somersham Town	10-135
Eastern Prem.Div. (14)	Gorleston	10-165	Sudbury Town Res	10-125	Stowmarket Town	10-123
Counties Div.1. (11)	Downham Town	10-152	Somersham Town	10-135	Needham Market	10-117
Screwfix Overall (18)	Paulton Rovers	1-134	Mangotsfield United	10-125	Amesbury Town	10-116

Direct Prem.Div. (10)	Paulton Rovers	1-134	Mangotsfield United	10-125	Bridgwater Town '84	10-112
Western Div.1. (8)	Amesbury Town	10-116	Glastonbury	10-106	Devizes Town	10-101
Hellenic Overall (19)	Swindon Supermarine	10-149	Abingdon United	10-139	Cirencester United	10-121
Prem.Div. (10)	Swindon Supermarine	10-149	Abingdon United	10-139	Carterton Town	10-110
Div.1. (9)	Cirencester United	10-121	Purton	10-101	Ross Town	10-98
Unlsport Overall (16)	Northampton Spencer	10-127	Yaxley	10-125	Eynesbury Rovers	10-121
United Prem.Div. (13)	Northampton Spencer	10-127	Eynesbury Rovers	10-121	Mirrlees Blackstone	10-119
Div.1. (3)	Yaxley	10-127	St Ives Town	1-77	Rothwell Corinthians	1-58
Minerva Overall (40)	Hoddesdon Town	10-177	Mercedes Benz	10-139	Arlesey Town	10-137
South					Holmer Green	10-137
Midlands Prem.Div. (14)	Hoddesdon Town	10-177	Arlesey Town	10-137	Buckingham Athletic	1-104
Sen.Div. (14)	Mercedes Benz	10-139	Holmer Green	10-137	Leverstock Green	10-115
Div.1. (12)	Old Bradwell United	7-108	Bridger Packaging	1-93	Biggleswade United	1-90
Interlink Exp Mid. A (12)	Pelsall Villa	10-156	Willenhall Town	10-147	Hinckley Athletic	1-146
Carling Overall (39)	St Helens Town	10-141	Newcastle Town	10-136	Clitheroe	10-130
North West Div.1. (20)	St Helens Town	10-141	Newcastle Town	10-136	Clitheroe	10-130
Counties Div.2. (19)	Formby	10-111	Garswood United	10-110		
			Haslingden	10-110		
Northern Overall (27)	Denaby United	10-180	Hucknall Town	10-175	Selby Town	10-133
Counties Prem.Div. (15)	Denaby United	10-180	Hucknall Town	10-175	Selby Town	10-133
East Div. 1. (12)	Borrowash Victoria	10-112	Bridsworth Welfare	10-108	Yorkshire Amateur	1-104
Federation Overall (25)	Chester le Street T	10-117	Billingham Town	10-114	Crook Town	10-104
Brewery					Guisborough Town	1-104
Northern Div.1. (13)	Chester le Street T	10-117	Crook Town	10-104		
			Guisborough Town	1-104		
Div.2. (12)	Billingham Town	10-114	Ashington	1-99		
			Northallerton	10-99		
Middlesex County (8)	Cockfosters Res	2-106	Osterley Town	3-94	Deportivo Galicia	1-93
Dorset Combination (4)	Sturminster Marshall	1-77	Weymouth Sports	1-62	Westland Sports	1-60
Cherry Red Overall (18)	Peppard	10-163	Penn & Tylers Green	10-132	Penn & Tylers G Res	10-130
Chiltonian Prem.Div. (11)	Peppard	10-163	Penn & Tylers Green	10-132	Quarry Nomads	10-119
Other Divs. (7)	Penn & Tylers G Res	10-130	Quarry Nomads Res	10-115	Slough Heating	4-106
Gloucestershire County (4)	Brockworth	10-100	Patchway Town	1-81	Frampton Athletic	1-79
Jewson South Western (7)	Truro City	10-150	Penzance	10-117	Bodmin Town	10-103
Clubsaver Overall (17)	Yateley Green	10-150	Poole Town	10-143	Colden Common	10-133
Hampshire					Mayflower	10-133
Div.1 (10)	Poole Town	10-143	Colden Common	10-133	Fleetlands	1-102
Div.2 (4)	Yateley Green	10-150	Mayflower	10-133	Tadley	10-105
Div.3. (3)	Covies	10-110	Queens Keep	1-78	Laverstock & Ford	1-73
Westward Dev.Devon Co (6)	Newton Abbot Spurs	10-124	Stoke Gabriel	10-119	Ottery St Mary	1-81
Nuclear Elec Kent Co (4)	Tonbridge Rangers	1-101	Tonbridge Rangers Res	4-96	AFC Egerton	1-82
Herts Senior County (3)	Sandridge Rovers	10-124	Metrop Police Bushey	1-91	North Mymms	1-54
Endsleigh Overall (50)	Alvechurch	9-114	Meir K.A.	10-113	Bolehall Swifts	10-103
Midland					Knowle	10-103
Combination Prem.Div. (19)	Alvechurch	9-114	Meir K.A.	10-113	Bolehall Swifts	10-103
					Knowle	10-103
Div.1. (18)	Newhall United	1-98	Hams Hall	10-97	Northfield Town	1-86
Divs. 2, 3 (12)	Enville Athletic	1-100	Badsey Rangers	10-94	Earlswood Town	8-92
Res.Div. (3)	Worcester City Res	10-95	Hinckley Athletic Res	1-68	Boldmere St Michael Res	1-58
Lincolnshire (3)	Sleaford Town	1-92	Grimsby & Immingham	1-70	Wyberton	1-68
Banks Overall (12)	Darlaston Town	1-120	Westfields	10-92	Stourport Swifts	1-81
Brewery Prem.Div. (9)	Darlaston Town	1-120	Westfields	10-92	Stourport Swifts	1-81
West Mids Divs.1N, 1S (3)	Leominster Town	1-61	Great Wyrley	1-57	Bustleholme	1-51
Springbank Vend Midland (3)	Eccleshall	10-112	Stone Dominoes	10-98	Brocton	1-89
Longwell Overall (9)	Attleborough Town	10-104	East Harling	10-99	Beccles Town	10-98
Blake					Holt United	10-98
Anglian Prem.Div. (3)	Ashlea	1-77	Lakeford Rangers '94	1-70	Madra United	1-53
Combination Div.1. (3)	Attleborough Town	10-104	Beccles Town	10-98	Wortwell	1-69
Other Divs. (3)	East Harling	10-99	Holt United	10-98	Hempnall	10-73
B.S. Suffolk & Ipswich (6)	Halesworth Town	1-90	Walsham Le Willows	1-87	Bacton United '89	1-82
Devon & Exeter (3)	Exmouth Amateurs	1-73	Okehampton Argyle	1-68	Dawlish Villa	1-60
Essex Intermediate (4)	Laindon Athletic	10-93	Laindon Athletic Res	10-89	Great Baddow Reserves	4-88
Somerset Senior (4)	Street	1-102	Timsbury Athletic	1-93	Peasedown Athletic	4-77
Oxfordshire Senior (4)	Worcester Coll O.B.	1-79	Chipping Norton Town	1-78	Launton	1-71
Midland Regional All. (5)	Selston Reserves	1-120	Selston	1-112	Arnold Town Reserves	10-94
Northants Combination (4)	Heyford Athletic	6-109	West Haddon	8-108	West Haddon Res	10-104
Notts. Alliance (7)	Rainworth Miners W.	10-138	Teversal Grange	8-94	Welbeck Colliery	1-62
Carlsberg West Cheshire (3)	New Brighton	8-81	Christleton	1-46	Cammell Laird	1-41
Green Insul Mid Cheshire (5)	Rylands	8-145	Rylands Reserves	1-34	Wilmslow Albion	5-124
Redferns Overall (16)	Rossington	1-118	Sandiacre Town	1-115	South Normanton Ath	1-110
Central Sup. Div. (8)	Sandiacre Town	1-115	South Normanton Ath	1-110	Harworth Colliery Inst	1-98
Midlands Prem.Div. (8)	Rossington	1-118	Holbrook	1-80	Mexborough Athletic	1-66
Everards Overall (8)	Coalville	7-112	Loughborough Dynamo	1-105	Saffron Dynamo	1-89
Brewery Prem.Div. (3)	Quorn	1-67	Ayleston Park O.B.	1-56	Kirby Muxloe S.C.	1-45
Leics. Sen. Div. 1 (5)	Coalville	7-112	Loughborough Dynamo	1-105	Saffron Dynamo	1-89
Manchester (8)	Stockport Georgians	1-102	Woodley Sports	3-91	Greater Manchester Pol.	1-81
Northern Alliance (12)	W. Allotment Celtic	10-106	N. Shields St Columbas	9-54	Carlisle City	1-83
Vaux Wearside (6)	North Shields Ath	9-160	Birtley Town	1-77	Wolviston	1-68
SGL Cars West Lancs (6)	Hesketh Bank	1-98	Lytham St Annes	10-92	Carnforth Rangers	1-80
West Overall (11)	York R.I.	10-126	Knaresborough Town	10-123	Carlton Athletic	1-112
Yorkshire Prem.Div. (6)	York R.I.	10-126	Knaresborough Town	10-123	Carlton Athletic	1-112
Other Divs. (5)	Featherstone Coll.	10-110	Magnet Sports Res	1-92	Bramley	1-91
West Riding County (5)	Brighouse Town	10-119	Wibsey	9-101	Golcar United	1-95
Other English Leagues (48)	Colden Common Res	10-135	Ilfield Reserves	5-125	Loughborough Athletic	4-122
Reserves (48)	Colden Common Res	10-135			Rylands Reserves	1-134
	Mercedes Benz Res	10-135				
Suburban (3)	Dulwich Hamlet Res	1-65	Sutton United Reserves	1-59	Aldershot Town Res	1-57
Youth/School (10)	St Andrews U12	10-136	Hucknall Rolls	10-134		
			St Andres U14	10-134		
Youth XI's of Senior XI's (9)	Teversal Grange U13	10-106	Teversal Grange U11	10-102	Sutton United	5-99
F.A. Youth Cup (27)	Sutton United	1-106	St Leonards Stamcroft	1-104	Leighton Town	1-100

TOP NON-LEAGUE TRANSFERS 1996/97

Rodwell, Jim	Halesowen T - Rushden & D	£40,000	
Cramman, Kenny	Gateshead - Rushden & D	£40,000	
Underwood, Paul	Enfield - Rushden & D	£35,000	
Tucker, Mark	Woking - Rushden & D	£35,000	
Foster, Adrian	Hereford U - Rushden & D	£30,000	
Jackson, Justin	Morecambe - Woking	£30,000	
Forinton, Howard	Oxford C - Yeovil T	£20,000	
Carter, Recky	Bromsgrove R - Kettering T	£20,000	
McGrath, Steve	Yeading - Enfield	£19,000	
Leworthy, David	Rushden & D - Kingstonian	£18,000	
Carter, Recky	Kettering T - Solihull B	£17,500	
Thompson, Paul	Gateshead - Stevenage B	£15,000	
Smith, Adie	Bromsgrove R - Kidderminster H	£15,000	
Pickard, Owen	Dorchester T - Yeovil T	£15,000	
Arnold, Ian	Stalybridge C - Kidderminster H	£15,000	
Leworthy, David	Dover A - Rushden & D	£15,000	
Endersby, Lee	Harrow B - Enfield	£15,000	
Cobb, Paul	Purfleet - Dag & Red	£14,000	
Myers, Martin	Telford U - Solihull B	£11,000	
Dennis, Lennie	Welling U - Kingstonian	£10,000	- Trib
Watkins, Dale	Gloucester C - Cheltenham T	£10,000	
Book, Steve	Forest Green R - Cheltenham T	£10,000	
O'Callaghan, Billy	Warrington T - Droylsden	£10,000	
Norbury, Mike	Halifax T - Hednesford T	£10,000	
May, Leroy	Kidderminster H - Kettering T	£10,000	
Hemmings, Tony	Macclesfield T - Hednesford T	£10,000	
Foster, Steve	Telford U - Woking	£10,000	
Bignot, Marcus	Telford U - Kidderminster H	£10,000	
Bellingham, Mark	Chelmsford C - Cheltenham T	£10,000	
Venables, Dave	Stevenage B - Kettering T	£ 9,000	
Niblett, Nigel	Telford U - Hednesford T	£ 8,000	- Trib
Trott, Robin	Welling U - Stevenage B	£ 8,000	
Kelly, Warren	Hayes - Stevenage B	£ 8,000	
Holmes, David	Gloucester C - Burton A	£ 8,000	
Marsden, Tony	Gresley R - Burton A	£ 7,500	
Evans, Stuart	Gresley R - Halesowen T	£ 7,250	
Watson, Liam	Witton Alb - Runcorn	£ 7,000	
Taylor, Steve	Hednesford T - Bromsgrove R	£ 7,000	
May, Leroy	Kettering T - Enfield	£ 7,000	
Francis, Joe	Enfield - Hayes	£ 7,000	
Eshelby, Paul	Alfreton T - Ilkeston T	£ 7,000	
Nuttell, Mick	Burton A - Kettering T	£ 7,500	
Turner, Paul	Yeovil T - St.Albans C	£ 6,000	
Symonds, John	Bedworth U - Cheltenham T	£ 6,000	
Stapleton, Simon	Slough T - Rushden & D	£ 6,000	
Hannigan, Al-James	Rushden & D - Enfield	£ 6,000	

Gaunt, Craig	Bromsgrove R - Kettering T	£ 6,000
Davies, Martin	Cambridge U - Rushden & D	£ 6,000
Bignall, Mike	Stevenage B - Morecambe	£ 6,000
Robinson, David	Ilkeston T - Gresley R	£ 5,500
Blount, Mark	Gresley R - Burton A	£ 5,500
Sparks, Chris	Chertsey T - Hayes	£ 5,000
Morley, Dominic	Knowsley U - Droylsden	£ 5,000
Hannigan, Al-James	Enfield - Yeovil T	£ 5,000
Trott, Dean	Stalybridge C - Leek T	£ 5,000
Scott, Ian	Worcester C - Hinckley T	£ 5,000
Scott, Ian	Kettering T - Worcester C	£ 5,000
Robertson, Paul	Witton Alb - Acc.Stanley	£ 5,000
Pearson, Chris	Hinckley T - Kettering T	£ 5,000
McCue, James	Partick T - Kidderminster H	£ 5,000
Harris, Neil	Maldon T - Camb.C	£ 5,000
Hallam, Mark	Ilkeston T - Hinckley T	£ 5,000
Dennis, Lennie	Sutton U - Welling U	£ 5,000
Kirkup, Andy	Rushden & D - Gloucester C	£ 4,500
Gentle, Justin	Enfield - St.Albans C	£ 4,000
Williams, Mark	Merthyr Tydfil - Newport AFC	£ 4,000
Knapper, John	Eastwood T - Ilkeston T	£ 4,000
Arter, Dave	Ashford T - Gravesend	£ 4,000
Brown, Wayne	Welling U - Kingstonian	£ 3,500
Fenton, Darren	Baldock T - Stevenage B	£ 3,000 - Trib
Wright, Evran	Halesown T - Telford U	£ 3,000
Parker, Jeff	Barrow - Runcorn	£ 3,000
O'Connell, Iain	Dover A - Margate	£ 3,000
Ward, Steve	Grays A - Canvey Is	£ 3,000
Tucker, Jason	Aldershot T - Enfield	£ 3,000
Richardson, John	Enfield - Hendon	£ 3,000
Lyons, Darren	Macclesfield T - Winsford U	£ 3,000
Adams, Darren	Aldershot T - Dover A	£ 3,000
Caffel, Jason	Witney T - Oxford C	£ 2,750
Alsop, Julian	Tamworth - Halesowen T	£ 2,300
Taylor, David	Ilkeston T - Grantham T	£ 2,000
Piggott, Gary	Dudley T - Tamworth	£ 2,000
Hazel, Julian	Wivenhoe T - Bedford T	£ 2,000
Hallam, Mark	Hinckley T - Worcester C	£ 2,000
Twigg, Darren	Leek T - Ashton U	£ 2,000
Sutton, Dave	Leek T - Ashton U	£ 2,000
Sugrue, Jimmy	Hayes - Aldershot T	£ 2,000
Russell, Glen	Baldock T - Chelmsford C	£ 2,000
Clark, Kenny	Worksop T - Matlock T	£ 2,000
Burton, Paul	Westfields - Newport AFC	£ 2,000
Bunce, Nathan	Yeading - Hayes	£ 2,000
Taylor, Stuart	Guiseley - Accrington S	£ 1,500
Bashir, Naseem	St.Albans C - Hendon	£ 1,400
Devereaux, Brian	Halstead T - Braintree T	£ 1,250
Dudley, Derek	Halesowen T - Telford U	£ 1,000
Anderson, Mark	Aldershot T - Bracknell T	£ 1,000

TOP NON-LEAGUE TRANSFERS

(Only those still playing, with an original fee of £6,000 or more are featured)

Alford, Carl	Kettering T - Rushden & D	£85,000	1996
Leworthy, David	Farnborough T - Dover A	£50,000	1993
Smith, Paul	Port Vale - Lincoln C	£48,000	1987
Toman, Andy	Hartlepool - Darlington	£40,000	1989
Lowe, Kenny	Barrow - Barnet	£40,000	1991
Carter, Mark	Runcorn - Barnet	£40,000	1991
Abbott, Gary	Barnet - Enfield	£40,000	1989
Underwood, Paul	Enfield - Rushden & D	£35,000	1997
Charlery, Ken	Fisher A - Maidstone U	£35,000	1989
Foster, Adrian	Hereford U - Rushden & D	£30,000	1997
Stott, Steve	Kettering T - Rushden & D	£30,000	1995
Scott, Keith	Lincoln C - Wycombe W	£30,000	1991
Abbott, Gary	Enfield - Welling U	£30,000	1990
Thomas, Karl	South Liverpool - Colne Dynamoes	£25,000	1989
Norman, Sean	Wealdstone - Chesham U	£25,000	1989
Horton, Duncan	Welling U - Barnet	£25,000	1991
Fergusson, Steve	Worcester C - Gloucester C	£25,000	1990
Barrett, Scott	Stoke C - Colchester U	£25,000	1990
Alford, Carl	Macclesfield T - Kettering T	£25,000	1994
Wilmot, Richard	Scunthorpe U - Halifax T	£20,000	1994
McRobert, Lee	Ashford T - Sittingbourne	£20,000	1993
McDonald, Martin	Macclesfield T - Southport	£20,000	1995
Lee, Andy	Telford U - Colne Dynamoes	£20,000	1989
Collins, Darren	Enfield - Rushden & Diamonds	£20,000	1994
Casey, Kim	Kidderminster H - Cheltenham T	£20,000	1990
Butterworth, Gary	Dag & Red - Rushden & Diamonds	£20,000	1994
Thompson, Steve	Wycombe W - Woking	£19,000	1995
Leworthy, David	Rushden & D - Kingstonian	£18,000	1997
Fielder, Colin	Farnborough T - Slough T	£18,000	1991
Webb, Paul	Bromsgrove R - Kidderminster H	£17,500	1994
Rudge, Simon	Hyde U - Runcorn	£17,500	1989
Portway, Steve	Gravesend - Gloucester C	£17,500	1994
Jones, Gary	Grantham T - Kettering T	£17,500	1990
Joseph, Antone	Telford U - Kidderminster H	£17,000	1989
Ross, Brian	Marine - Chorley	£16,000	1995
Golley, Mark	Sutton U - Maidstone U	£16,000	1988
Thompson, Paul	Gateshead - Stevenage B	£15,000	1997
Smith, Adie	Bromsgrove R - Kidderminster H	£15,000	1997
Pickard, Owen	Dorchester T - Yeovil T	£15,000	1997
Arnold, Ian	Stalybridge C - Kidderminster H	£15,000	1997
Whale, Leroy	Bashley - Enfield	£15,000	1993
Warrilow, Tommy	Crawley T - Hythe T	£15,000	1990
Warmington, Curtis	Carshalton A - Enfield	£15,000	1991
Teale, Shaun	Northwich V - Weymouth	£15,000	1987
Sherwood, Jeff	Yeovil T - Gloucester C	£15,000	1990
Lynch, Tony	Wealdstone - Barnet	£15,000	1990
Jackson, Joe	Worcester C - Yeovil T	£15,000	1990
Handford, Phil	Welling U - Sittingbourne	£15,000	1991
Greene, Dennis	Chelmsford C - Wycombe W	£15,000	1992
Golley, Mark	Maidstone U - Welling U	£15,000	1991
Doherty, Mick	Yeovil T - Runcorn	£15,000	1989
Creaser, Glyn	Barnet - Wycombe W	£15,000	1988
Casey, Paul	Boston U - Lincoln C	£15,000	1987
Arnold, Ian	Kettering T - Stalybridge C	£15,000	1995
Abbott, Gary	Welling U - Barnet	£15,000	1987
Cobb, Paul	Purfleet - Dag & Red	£14,000	1997
Nuttell, Micky	Wycombe W - Boston U	£14,000	1992
Jones, Gary	Grantham T - Kettering T	£14,000	1990
Harvey, Lee	Aylesbury U - Slough T	£14,000	1994
Ashby, Nick	Kettering T - Rushden & D	£14,000	1995
Townsend, Andy	Welling U - Weymouth	£13,500	1986
Doherty, Mick	Maidstone U - Yeovil T	£13,000	1988
Cuggy, Steve	Margate - Hastings T	£13,000	1995

Conning, Peter	Weymouth - Yeovil T	£13,000	1989
Ross, Jeff	Ashford T - Hythe T	£12,500	1990
Phillips, Gary	Reading - Barnet	£12,500	1989
Grocutt, Darren	Burton A - Bromsgrove R	£12,500	1995
Tinson, Darren	Northwich V - Macclesfield T	£12,000	1995
Ricketts, Tony	Bath C - Yeovil T	£12,000	1985
Payne, Derek	Hayes - Barnet	£12,000	1988
Mayers, Kenny	Bamber Bridge - Chorley	£12,000	1995
Burke, Brendan	Witton A - Stalybridge C	£12,000	1993
Blackford, Gary	Fisher A - Barnet	£12,000	1991
Bancroft, Paul	Kidderminster H - Kettering T	£12,000	1990
Bancroft, Paul	Burton A - Kidderminster H	£12,000	1988
Smith, Neil	Cheltenham T - Rushden & D	£11,000	1995
Sayer, Andy	Slough T - Enfield	£11,000	1995
Morton, Neil	Altrincham - Barrow	£11,000	1995
Kurila, Alan	Stafford R - Kidderminster H	£11,000	1990
Morley, Trevor	Corby T - Nuneaton B	£10,200	1980
Dennis, Lennie	Welling U - Kingstonian	£10,000 - Trib	1997
Watkins, Dale	Gloucester C - Cheltenham T	£10,000	1997
Book, Steve	Forest Green R - Cheltenham T	£10,000	1997
Whitehouse, Mark	Burton A - Kidderminster H	£10,000	1989
Whitby, Steve	Wycombe W - Slough T	£10,000	1991
Westley, Graham	Barnet - Wycombe W	£10,000	1987
Watkins, Dale	Grantham T - Rushden & Diamonds	£10,000	1993
Townsend, Chris	Gloucester C - Dorchester T	£10,000	1990
Thomas, Karl	Colne Dynamoes - Witton A	£10,000	1990
Sowerby, Colin	Dartford - Redbridge F	£10,000	1991
Smith, Jimmy	Salisbury C - Cheltenham T	£10,000	1992
Simpson, Wayne	Stafford R - Hednesford T	£10,000	1995
Scott, Keith	Boston U - Wycombe W	£10,000	1991
Rogers, Tony	Dover Ath - Chelmsford C	£10,000	1992
Ricketts, Tony	Yeovil T - Bath C	£10,000	1988
Pearson, Jon	Kidderminster H - Burton A	£10,000	1989
O'Connor, Malcolm	Hyde U - Northwich V	£10,000	1988
Nuttell, Mick	Wycombe W - Boston U	£10,000	1991
Murphy, Frank	Kettering T - Barnet	£10,000	1987
Mogg, David	Bath C - Cheltenham T	£10,000	1987
Meacham, Jeff	Bristol R - Weymouth	£10,000	1988
McCluskie, Jim	Hyde U - Witton A	£10,000	1990
Kitchen, David	Goole T - Stafford R	£10,000	1988
Kelly, Tony	Hayes - Wealdstone	£10,000	1989
Kane, Mark	Chelmsford C - Enfield	£10,000	1991
James, Robbie	Cardiff C - Merthyr Tydfil	£10,000	1992
Hyde, Paul	Hayes - Wycombe W	£10,000	1991
Humphreys, Delwyn	Kidderminster H - Northwich V	£10,000	1995
Humphreys, Delwyn	Bridgnorth T - Kidderminster H	£10,000	1990
Horwood, Neil	Spalding U - Kettering T	£10,000	1990
Holmes, David	Gresley R - Gloucester C	£10,000	1995
Hercules, Cliff	Aylesbury U - Slough T	£10,000	1995
Harlow, David	Kingstonian - Farnborough T	£10,000	1994
Hardy, Martin	Worksop T - Boston U	£10,000	1987
Hadley, Dave	Moor Green - Kidderminster H	£10,000	1993
Grainger, Paul	Telford U - Kidderminster H	£10,000	1992
Doherty, Mick	Weymouth - Maidstone U	£10,000	1987
Cooper, Richard	Weymouth - Yeovil T	£10,000	1989
Coombe, Mark	Salisbury C - Dorchester T	£10,000	1992
Cherry, Richard	Redbridge F - Kingstonian	£10,000	1991
Buglione, Martin	St Johnstone - Sittingbourne	£10,000	1994
Bressington, Graham	Wycombe W - Lincoln C	£10,000	1987
Boyland, Mark	Cheltenham T - Wycombe W	£10,000	1987
Birkby, Dean	Bath C - Yeovil T	£10,000	1995
Beech, Glenn	Boston U - Kettering T	£10,000	1988
Arnold, Ian	Carlisle U - Kettering T	£10,000	1994
Whittaker, Andy	Ashton U - Barrow	£ 9,000	1994
Whittaker, Andy	Netherfield - Ashton U	£ 9,000	1994
Rudge, Simon	Runcorn - Altrincham	£ 9,000	1991
Rudge, Simon	Hyde U - Runcorn	£ 9,000	1989

Laws, David	Bishop Auckland - Weymouth	£ 9,000	1995
Higginbotham, Paul	Barrow - Stalybridge C	£ 9,000	1994
Coe, John	VS Rugny - Rushden & D	£ 9,000	1991
Casey, Kim	Cheltenham T - Wycombe W	£ 9,000	1992
Browne, Steve	Wealdstone - Sutton U	£ 9,000	1992
Niblett, Nigel	Telford U - Hednesford T	£ 8,000 - Trib	1997
Trott, Robin	Welling U - Stevenage B	£ 8,000	1997
Kelly, Warren	Hayes - Stevenage B	£ 8,000	1997
Holmes, David	Gloucester C - Burton A	£ 8,000	1997
Yates, Jason	Bridgnorth T - Clevedon T	£ 8,000	1995
Robbins, Terry	Crawley T - Welling U	£ 8,000	1986
Regis, David	Windsor & Eton - Barnet	£ 8,000	1989
Nuttell, Mick	Peterborough - Cheltenham T	£ 8,000	1989
Newbery, Richard	Wokingham T - Gravesend	£ 8,000	1996
McCluskie, Jim	Mossley - Hyde U	£ 8,000	1989
Lay, David	Marlow - Slough T	£ 8,000	1994
Hughes, Mark	Irlam T - Altrincham	£ 8,000	1989
Hemmings, Tony	Rocester - Northwich V	£ 8,000	1989
Harvey, Lee	Aylesbury U - Slough T	£ 8,000	1995
Grainger, Paul	Wolves - Telford U	£ 8,000	1989
Dent, Nicky	Poole T - Dover A	£ 8,000	1992
Coe, Paul	Rushden & Diamonds - Cambridge C	£ 8,000	1994
Benbow, Ian	Telford U - Merthyr Tydfil	£ 8,000	1993
Singleton, Dave	Taunton T - Weymouth	£ 7,500)	1979
Nuttell, Mick	Burton A - Kettering T	£ 7,500	1997
Marsden, Tony	Gresley R - Burton A	£ 7,500	1997
Wingfield, Phil	Kingstonian - Farnborough T	£ 7,500	1995
Read, Tim	Worthing - Woking	£ 7,500	1990
Myers, Martin	Tamworth - Telford U	£ 7,500	1990
Jackson, Joe	Dover A - Worcester C	£ 7,500	1994
Hedges, Ian	AFC Bournemouth - Bath C	£ 7,500	1991
Freeman, Mark	Gloucester C - Cheltenham T	£ 7,500	1996
Freeman, Mark	Hednesford T - Gloucester C	£ 7,500	1995
Tate, Steve	Havant T - Waterlooville	£ 7,000	1993
Prindiville, Steve	Halifax T - Dag & Red	£ 7,000	1995
Nuttell, Mick	Dag & Red - Rushden & Diamonds	£ 7,000	1994
Kurila, Alan	Burton A - Stafford R	£ 7,000	1989
Jenkins, Steve	Wealdstone - Buckingham T	£ 7,000	1992
Hutchinson, Simon	Eastwood T - Wycombe W	£ 7,000	1990
Freegard, John	Gloucester C - Trowbridge T	£ 7,000	1991
Essex, Steve	Aylesbury U - Stafford R	£ 7,000	1990
Cavell, Paul	Stafford R - Boston U	£ 7,000	1989
Cain, Ian	Fleetwood T - Morecambe	£ 7,000	1989
Browne, Corey	Dover A - Stevenage B	£ 7,000	1995
Boyland, Mark	Aylesbury U - Cheltenham T	£ 7,000	1989
Beattie, Andy	Barnet - Cambridge C	£ 7,000	1991
Abbott, Gary	Welling U - Enfield	£ 7,000	1994
Statham, Gary	VS Rugby - Nuneaton B	£ 6,500	1995
Singleton, Dave	Taunton T - Weymouth	£ 6,500	1980
Evans, Richard	Harrow B - Windsor & Eton	£ 6,500	1986
Roberts, Graham	Dorchester T - Weymouth	£ 6,000)	1979
Turner, Paul	Yeovil T - St.Albans C	£ 6,000	1997
Williams, Tommy	Leyton - Redbridge F	£ 6,000	1991
Tate, Steve	Havant T - Waterlooville	£ 6,000	1993
Stagg, Jeremy	Andover - Bashley	£ 6,000	1989
Shepherd, George	Hyde U - Macclesfield T	£ 6,000	1989
Penman, Jon	Southport - Marine	£ 6,000	1995
Payne, Chris	Billericay T - Dagenham & Red	£ 6,000	1994
Nuttell, Mick	Cheltenham T - Wycombe W	£ 6,000	1991
Murphy, Frank	Nuneaton B - Kettering T	£ 6,000	1986
Killick, Tommy	Wimborne T - Dorchester T	£ 6,000	1994
Killick, Tommy	Wimborne T - Bashley	£ 6,000	1990
Golley, Mark	Welling U - Sutton U	£ 6,000	1992
Fergusson, Steve	Gloucester C - Telford U	£ 6,000	1991
Essex, Steve	Burton A - Aylesbury U	£ 6,000	1988
Doherty, Mick	Runcorn - Farnborough T	£ 6,000	1990
Conroy, Steve	Hitchin T - Kingstonian	£ 6,000	1990
Carroll, Dave	Ruislip Manor - Wycombe W	£ 6,000	1988
Boyle, Martin	Bath C - Cheltenham T	£ 6,000	1992
Boyce, Dave	Waterlooville - Gravesend	£ 6,000	1993
Blewden, Colin	Gravesend - Dover A	£ 6,000	1991

TOP NON-LEAGUE TO LEAGUE TRANSFERS

(Only those still playing with original fees over £10,000 are featured.)

Clarke, Andy	Barnet - Wimbledon	£250,000	1991
Hayles, Barry	Stevenage B. - Bristol R.	£250,000	1997
Hughes, Lee	Kidderminster H - WBA	£200,000	1997
Emblem, Neil	Sittingbourne - Millwall	£175,000	1993
Gridelet, Phil	Barnet - Barnsley	£175,000	1990
Willis, Roger	Barnet - Watford	£175,000	1992
Foster, Steve	Woking - Bristol R	£150,000	1997
Harper, Lee	Sittingbourne - Arsenal	£150,000	1994
Hunt, Andy	Kettering T - Newcastle U	£150,000	1991
Furlong, Paul	Enfield - Coventry C	£130,000	1991
Bignot, Marcus	Kidderminster H. - Crewe A.	£100,000	1997
Collymore, Stan	Stafford R - Crystal Palace	£100,000	1991
Ekoku, Efan	Sutton U - AFC Bournemouth	£100,000	1990
Finnan, Steve	Welling U - Birmingham C	£100,000	1995
Nolan, Ian	Marine - Tranmere R	£100,000	1991
Taylor, Steve	Bromsgrove R - Crystal Palace	£ 90,000	1995
Woan, Ian	Runcorn - Nottingham F	£ 80,000	1990
Forinton, Howard	Yeovil T - Birmingham C	£ 75,000	1997
Barnes, Steve	Welling U - Birmingham C	£ 70,000	1995
Charles, Lee	Chertsey T - QPR	£ 67,500	1995
Hessenthaler, Andy	Redbridge F - Watford	£ 65,000	1991
Harding, Paul	Barnet - Notts Co	£ 60,000	1990
Lake, Mike	Macclesfield T - Sheffield U	£ 60,000	1989
Lilwall, Steve	Kidderminster H - WBA	£ 60,000	1992
Bullock, Darren	Nuneaton B - Huddersfield T	£ 55,000	1993
Barnard, Darren	Wokingham T - Chelsea	£ 50,000	1990
Dodd, Jason	Bath C - Southampton	£ 50,000	1989
Forsyth, Richard	Kidderminster H - Birmingham C	£ 50,000	1995
Hanson, Dave	Hednesford T - Leyton O	£ 50,000	1995
Harle, Michael	Sittingbourne - Millwall	£ 50,000	1994
Little, Colin	Hyde U - Crewe A	£ 50,000	1996
Moody, Paul	Waterlooville - Southampton	£ 50,000	1991
Morah, Ollie	Sutton U - Cambridge U	£ 50,000	1994
Ormerod, Brett	Acc.Stanley - Blackpool	£ 50,000	1997
Richardson, Ian	Dagenham & Red - Birmingham	£ 50,000	1995
Russell, Keith	Hednesford T - Blackpool	£ 50,000	1997
Scott, Andrew	Sutton U - Sheffield U	£ 50,000	1992
Sharp, Lee	Lincoln U - QPR	£ 50,000	1995
Smith, Paul	Hastings T - Nottingham F	£ 50,000	1994
Teale, Shaun	Weymouth - AFC Bournemouth	£ 50,000	1989
Whittington, Craig	Crawley T - Scarborough	£ 50,000	1993
Norris, Steve	Telford U - Scarborough	£ 46,000	1988
Brabin, Gary	Runcorn - Doncaster R	£ 45,000	1994
Farrell, Dave	Redditch U - Aston Villa	£ 45,000	1992
Forbes, Steve	Sittingbourne - Millwall	£ 45,000	1994
Shail, Mark	Yeovil T - Bristol C	£ 45,000	1993
Angell, Brett	Cheltenham T - Derby Co	£ 40,000	1988
Devlin, Paul	Stafford R - Notts Co	£ 40,000	1992
Doherty, Neil	Barrow - Birmingham C	£ 40,000	1994
Jones, Paul	Kidderminster H - Wolves	£ 40,000	1991
Price, Ryan	Stafford R - Birmingham C	£ 40,000	1994
Rammell, Andy	Atherstone U - Manchester U	£ 40,000	1989
Agana, Tony	Weymouth - Watford	£ 35,000	1987
Cox, Ian	Carshalton A - Crystal Palace	£ 35,000	1994
Dalton, Paul	Brandon U - Manchester U	£ 35,000	1988
Impey, Andy	Yeading - QPR	£ 35,000	1990
McRobert, Lee	Sittingbourne - Millwall	£ 35,000	1995
Marshall, Dwight	Grays Ath - Plymouth A	£ 35,000	1991
Nyamah, Kofi	Kettering T - Stoke C	£ 35,000	1996
Pethick, Robbie	Weymouth - Portsmouth	£ 35,000	1993
Pugh, David	Runcorn - Chester C	£ 35,000	1989
Rogers, Paul	Sutton U - Sheffield U	£ 35,000	1992

Townsend, Andy	Weymouth - Southampton	£ 35,000	1985
Wordsworth, Dean	Bromley - Crystal Palace	£ 35,000	1996
Comyn, Andy	Alvechurch - Aston Villa	£ 34,000	1989
Alsop, Julian	Halesowen T - Bristol R	£ 30,000	1997
Barrowcliff, Paul	Stevenage B. - Brentford	£ 30,000	1997
Bullock, Tony	Leek T - Barnsley	£ 30,000	1997
Cotterill, Steve	Burton Alb - Wimbledon	£ 30,000	1989
Dowie, Ian	Hendon - Luton T	£ 30,000	1988
Garner, Darren	Dorchester T - Rotherham	£ 30,000	1995
Gayle, John	Burton Alb - Wimbledon	£ 30,000	1989
Jones, Tom	Weymouth - Aberdeen	£ 30,000	1987
Landon, Richard	Bedworth U - Plymouth A	£ 30,000	1994
McGorry, Brian	Weymouth - AFC Bournemouth	£ 30,000	1991
Morrison, Dave	Chelmsford C - Peterborough U	£ 30,000	1994
Nash, Carlo	Clitheroe - Crystal Palace	£ 30,000	1996
O'Reilly, Justin	Gresley R - Port Vale	£ 30,000	1996
Spink, Dean	Halesowen T - Aston Villa	£ 30,000	1989
Steele, Lee	Northwich V. - Shrewsbury T.	£ 30,000	1997
Williams, Gareth	Gosport B - Aston Villa	£ 30,000	1988
Peake, Trevor	Nuneaton B - Lincoln C	£ 27,750	1979
Burns, Chris	Cheltenham T - Portsmouth	£ 25,000	1991
Clarke, Tim	Halesowen T - Coventry C	£ 25,000	1990
Cooksey, Scott	Bromsgrove R - Peterborough U	£ 25,000	1993
DeSouza, Miguel	Dagenham & Red - Birmingham C	£ 25,000	1994
Gill, Jerry	Yeovil T - Birmingham C	£ 25,000	1997
Harris, Mark	Wokingham T - Crystal Palace	£ 25,000	1988
Hemmings, Tony	Northwich V - Wycombe W	£ 25,000	1993
Holsgrove, Paul	Wokingham T - Luton T	£ 25,000	1991
Jones, Gary	Boston U - Southend U	£ 25,000	1993
Jones, Steve	Cheltenham T - Swansea C	£ 25,000	1995
Leworthy, Dave	Fareham T - Tottenham H	£ 25,000	1984
Macauley, Steve	Fleetwood T - Crewe A	£ 25,000	1992
Martin, Dean	Fisher A - West Ham U	£ 25,000	1991
O'Connor, Martyn	Bromsgrove R - Crystal Palace	£ 25,000	1992
Pearce, Stuart	Wealdstone - Coventry C	£ 25,000	1983
Piggott, Gary	Dudley T - WBA	£ 25,000	1991
Regis, David	Barnet - Notts County	£ 25,000	1990
Taylor, Craig	Dorchester T - Swindon T	£ 25,000	1997
Clarkson, Phil	Fleetwood T - Crewe A	£ 22,500	1991
Jobson, Richard	Burton Alb - Watford	£ 22,000	1982
Jones, Steve	Billericay T - West Ham U	£ 22,000	1992
Crosby, Gary	Grantham T - Nottingham F	£ 20,000	1987
Dixon, Kerry	Dunstable - Reading	£ 20,000	1980
Farrelly, Steve	Macclesfield T - Rotherham	£ 20,000	1995
Flynn, Sean	Halesowen T - Coventry C	£ 20,000	1991
Heald, Greg	Enfield - Peterborough U	£ 20,000	1994
James, Tony	Gainsborough T - Lincoln C	£ 20,000	1988
Liburd, Richard	Eastwood T - Middlesbrough	£ 20,000	1993
McDonald, Martin	Southport - Doncaster R	£ 20,000	1996
McFarlane, Andy	Cradley T - Portsmouth	£ 20,000	1990
Marshall, Lee	Enfield - Norwich C	£ 20,000	1997
Massey, Stuart	Sutton U - Crystal Palace	£ 20,000	1992
Milner, Andy	Netherfield - Rochdale	£ 20,000	1990
Morley, Trevor	Nuneaton B - Northampton T	£ 20,000	1985
Murphy, Matt	Corby T - Oxford U	£ 20,000	1993
Naylor, Tony	Droylsden - Crewe Alexandra	£ 20,000	1990
Ndah, Jaimme	Kingstonian - Torquay U	£ 20,000	1995
Norris, Richard	Marine - Crewe A	£ 20,000	1996
Parrish, Sean	Telford U - Doncaster R	£ 20,000	1994
Parsley, Neil	Witton Alb - Leeds U	£ 20,000	1988
Roberts, Darren	Burton Alb - Wolves	£ 20,000	1992
Scott, Robert	Sutton U - Sheffield U	£ 20,000	1993
Smithers, Tim	Nuneaton B - Oxford U	£ 20,000	1980
Williams, Andy	Solihull B - Coventry C	£ 20,000	1985
Wilson, Kevin	Banbury U - Derby Co	£ 20,000	1979
Pickering, Ally	Buxton - Rotherham U	£ 18,500	1990
Wilkin, Kevin	Cambridge C - Northampton	£ 15,500	1991

Angus, Terry	VS Rugby - Northampton T	£ 15,000	1990
Bodin, Paul	Bath C - Newport Co	£ 15,000	1988
Bullock, Martin	Eastwood T - Barnsley	£ 15,000	1993
Dennis, Tony	Slough T - Cambridge U	£ 15,000	1989
Ferdinand, Les	Hayes - QPR	£ 15,000	1987
Gayle, Mark	Worcester C - Walsall	£ 15,000	1991
Gorman, Paul	Fisher A - Charlton A	£ 15,000	1991
Heathcote, Mick	Spennymoor U - Sunderland	£ 15,000	1987
Hercock, Dave	Cambridge C - Sheff.Wed.	£ 15,000	1996
Hitchcock, Kevin	Barking - Nottingham F	£ 15,000	1983
Lyons, Andy	Fleetwood T - Crewe A	£ 15,000	1992
Pearce, Andy	Halesowen T - Coventry C	£ 15,000	1990
Pritchard, Dave	Telford U - Bristol R	£ 15,000	1994
Robertson, Paul	Runcorn - Doncaster R	£ 15,000	1995
Taylor, Ian	Moor Green - Port Vale	£ 15,000	1992
Taylor, Scott	Staines T - Millwall	£ 15,000	1995
Unsworth, Lee	Ashton U - Crewe A	£ 15,000	1994
Vowden, Colin	Cambridge C - Cambridge U	£ 15,000	1995
Wilcox, Russell	Frickley A - Northampton T	£ 15,000	1986
Wilson, Paddy	Ashton U. - Plymouth A.	£ 15,000	1997
Claridge, Steve	Weymouth - Aldershot	£ 14,000	1988
Bimson, Stuart	Macclesfield T - Bury	£ 12,500	1995
Lyttle, Des	Worcester C - Swansea C	£ 12,500	1992
Austin, Dean	St.Albans C - Southend U	£ 12,000	1990
Dale, Carl	Bangor C - Cardiff C	£ 12,000	1988
Groves, Paul	Burton Alb - Leicester C	£ 12,000	1988
Williams, Paul.A	Woodford T - Charlton A	£ 12,000	1987
Freeman, Clive	Bridlington T - Swansae C	£ 10,500	1990
Alcide, Colin	Emley - Lincoln C	£ 10,000	1995
Bailey, Jon	Enfield - AFC Bournemouth	£ 10,000	1995
Barton, Warren	Leyt & Ilf - Maidstone U	£ 10,000	1989
Black, Tony	Bamber Bridge - Wigan A	£ 10,000	1995
Chalk, Martyn	Louth U - Derby Co	£ 10,000	1990
Collins, Wayne	Winsford U - Crewe A	£ 10,000	1993
Daws, Nicky	Altrincham - Bury	£ 10,000	1992
Eyres, David	Rhyl - Blackpool	£ 10,000	1989
Freestone, Chris	Arnold T - Middlesbrough	£ 10,000	1994
Gittens, Jon	Paget Rangers - Southampton	£ 10,000	1985
Helliwell, Ian	Matlock T - York C	£ 10,000	1987
Illman, Neil	Eastwood T - Plymouth A	£ 10,000	1996
Jones, Graeme	Bridlington T - Doncaster R	£ 10,000	1993
Jones, Nathan	Merthyr Tydfil - Luton T	£ 10,000	1995
Jones, Vinny	Wealdstone - Wimbledon	£ 10,000	1986
Love, Mickey	Hinckley Ath - Wigan Ath	£ 10,000	1995
McGoldrick, Eddie	Nuneaton B - Northampton T	£ 10,000	1986
Metcalf, Matthew	Braintree T - Brentford	£ 10,000	1993
Norbury, Mike	Bridlington T - Cambridge U	£ 10,000	1992
Phillips, Kevin	Baldock T - Watford	£ 10,000	1994
Quinn, Jimmy	Oswestry T - Swindon T	£ 10,000	1981
Richards, Carl	Enfield - AFC Bournemouth	£ 10,000	1986
Royce, Simon	Heybridge Swifts - Southend U	£ 10,000	1991
Samuels, Dean	Boreham Wood - Barnet	£ 10,000	1996
Sheridan, Darren	Winsford U - Barnsley	£ 10,000	1993
Shoemake, Kevin	Welling U - Peterborough U	£ 10,000	1986
Simkin, Darren	Blakenall - Wolves	£ 10,000	1991
Talboys, Steve	Gloucester C - Wimbledon	£ 10,000	1992
Tester, Paul	Cheltenham T - Shrewsbury T	£ 10,000	1983
Todd, Andrew	Eastwood T - Nottingham F	£ 10,000	1996
Toman, Andy	Bishop Auckland - Lincoln C	£ 10,000	1985
Whitlow, Mike	Witton Alb - Leeds U	£ 10,000	1988
Whitney, Jon	Winsford U - Huddersfield T	£ 10,000	1993
Wilding, Peter	Telford U. - Shrewsbury T.	£ 10,000	1997
Williams, Marc	Bangor C - Stockport Co	£ 10,000	1995
Witter, Tony	Grays Ath - Crystal Palace	£ 10,000	1990
Young, Eric	Slough T - Brighton	£ 10,000	1982

ENGLAND SEMI-PROFESSIONAL SQUAD 1996-97

Back Row (left to right): Jim Conway (Physio - Kidderminster H.), David Harlow (Farnborough T.), Lee Hughes (Kidderminster H. - now W.B.A.), Neil Howarth (Macclesfield T.), Scott Cooksey (Hednesford T.), Ron Reid (Manager - now Asst. Man. Oldham Ath.), Paul Gothard (Dagenham & Redbridge), Kevan Brown (Woking), Joe O'Connor (Hednesford T.), Wayne Simpsom (Hednesford T.), Graham Allner (Asst. Man. - Kidderminster H.).

Front Row (left to right): David Leworthy (Rushden & Diamonds - now Kingstonian), Ken Cramman (Rushden & Diamonds), Neil Doherty (Kidderminster H.), Paul Webb (Captain - Kidderminster H.), Jerry Gill (Yeovil T. - now Birmingham C.), Ged Kimmins (Hyde Utd.), Gary Butterworth (Rushden & Diamonds), Mark Gardiner (Macclesfield T.).

Photograph: Sportsfile, Dublin.

ENGLAND

SEMI-PRO CAPS 1979-97 (Max 51)

KEY

E - Eire
I - Italy
F - Finland
G - Gibralter
H - Holland
N - Norway)
S - Scotland
W - Wales

Players who were capped for the first time during the 1996-97 season are boxed.

Gary Abbott (Welling) 87 I(s), S(s), 92 W(s) (3)

David Adamson (Boston Utd) 79 SH, 80 ISH (5)

Tony Agana (Weymouth) 86 E (1)

Carl Alford (Kettering T. & Rushden & Ds) 96 EH (2)

Ian Arnold (Kettering Town) 95 W(s)H (2)

Jim Arnold (Stafford Rangers) 79 SH (2)

Nick Ashby (Kettering & Rushden & Ds) 94 FN, 95 G 96 EH (5)

Noel Ashford (Enfield & Redbridge For.) 82 GHS, 83 IHS, 84 WHSI, 85 WI(s), 86 EE, 87 W(s), IHS, 90 WE, 91 I(s) (21)

John Askey (Macclesfield) 90 W, (1)

Paul Bancroft (Kidderminster H.) 89 IW, 90 IWE, 91 W (6)

Keith Barrett (Enfield) 81 HSI, 82 GIHS, 83 IHS, 84 W(s)HS, 85 IHS (16)

Laurence Batty (Woking) 93 F(s), 95 WHG (4)

Mark Beeney (Maidstone) 89 I(s) (1)

Graham Benstead (Kettering) 94 WFN(s) (3)

Marcus Bignot (Kidderminster H) 97 H (1)

Jimmy Bolton (Kingstonian) 95 G (1)

Gary Brabin (Runcorn) 94 WFN (3)

Colin Brazier (Kidderminster) 87 W (1)

Stewart Brighton (Bromsgrove) 94 W (1)

Steve Brooks (Cheltenham) 88 W(s), 90 WE (3)

Derek Brown (Woking) 94 F(s)N (2)

Kevan Brown (Woking) 95 WHG 96 H 97 E (5)

Corey Browne (Dover) 94 F(s)N(s), 95 H(s) (3)

David Buchanan (Blyth) 86 E(s)E (2)

Brian Butler (Northwich) 93 F (1)

Gary Butterworth (Rushden & Diamonds) 97 EH (2)

GARY BUTTERWORTH *(Rushden & Diamonds) was one of the new cap successes last season.*

Steve Butler (Maidstone) 88 W, 89 IW (3)

Chris Byrne (Macclesfield T.) 97 H (1)

Mark Carter (Runcorn & Barnet) 87 WIHS, 88 W, 89 IW, 90 IE, 91 IW(s) (11)

Kim Casey (Kidderminster) 86 WEE(s), 87 WI (5)

Paul Cavell (Redbridge) 92 W, 93 F (2)

Kevin Charlton (Telford) 85 WI (2)

Andrew Clarke (Barnet) 90 EE (2)

David Clarke (Blyth Spartans)
80 IS(s)H, 81 HSI, 82 IHS, 83 HS, 84 HSI (14)

Gary Clayton (Burton) 86 E (1)

Robert Codner (Barnet) 88 W (1)

John Coleman (Morecambe) 93 F(s) (1)

Darren Collins (Enfield) 93 F(s), 94 WFN (4)

Steve Conner (Dartford, Redbridge & Dagenham & R)
90 I, 91 IW, 92 W, 93 F (5)

David Constantine (Altrincham) 85 IHS, 86 W (4)

Robbie Cooke (Kettering) 89 W(s), 90 I (2)

Scott Cooksey (Hednesford T.) 97 E (1)

Alan Cordice (Wealdstone)
83 IHS, 84 WS(s), I(s), 85 IHS (9)

Ken Cramman (Gateshead & Rushden & Diamonds)
96 E 97 EH (3)

Paul Cuddy (Altrincham) 87 IHS (3)

Paul Culpin (Nuneaton B) 84 W, 85 W(s) IHS (5)

Paul Davies (Kidderminster H.)
86 W, 87 WIS, 88 W, 89 W (6)

John Davison (Altrincham)
79 SH, 80 IS, 81 HSI, 82 GIHS, 83 IHS,
84 WHIS, 85 IHS, 86 WEE (24)

John Denham (Northwich Victoria) 80 H (1)

Peter Densmore (Runcorn) 88 W, 89 I (2)

Phil Derbyshire (Mossley) 83 H(s)S(s) (2)

Mick Doherty (Weymouth) 86 W(s) (1)

Neil Doherty (Kidderminster H.) 97 E (1)

Lee Endersby (Harrow Bor.) 96 H (1)

Mick Farrelly (Altrincham) 87 IHS (3)

Steve Farrelly (Macclesfield) 95 H(s)G(s) (2)

Trevor Finnegan (Weymouth) 81 HS (2)

Richard Forsyth (Kidderminster) 95 WHG (3)

Paul Furlong (Enfield) 90 IEE, 91 IW (5)

Mark Gardiner (Macclesfield T.) 97 E (1)

Jerry Gill (Yeovil T.) 97 E (1)

John Glover (Maidstone Utd) 85 WIHS (4)

Mark Golley (Sutton Utd.)
87 H(s)S, 88 W, 89 IW, 92 W (6)

Paul Gothard (Dagenham & Redb.) 97 E(s) (1)

Phil Gridelet (Hendon & Barnet) 89 IW, 90 WEE (5)

Steve Guppy (Wycombe W.) 93 W (1)

Steve Hancock (Macclesfield) 90 W (1)

David Harlow (Farnborough T.) 97 E(s)H (2)

Barry Hayles (Stevenage Bor.) 96 EH (2

Tony Hemmings (Northwich) 93 F (1

Andy Hessenthaler (Dartford) 90 I (1

Kenny Hill (Maidstone Utd) 80 ISH (3

Mark Hine (Gateshead) 95 W(s)H (2

Simeon Hodson (Kidderminster) 94 WFN (3

Colin Hogarth (Guiseley) 95 WH (2

Steven Holden (Kettering) 94 WFN(s), 95 HG (5

Mark Hone (Welling) 90 I, 93 F, 94 W(s)F(s)N (5

Gary Hooley (Frickley) 85 W (1

Keith Houghton (Blyth Spartans) 79 S (1

Barry Howard (Altrincham) 81 HSI, 82 GIHS (7

Neil Howarth (Macclesfield) 95 H(s) 97 E (2

David Howell (Enfield)
85 H(s)S(s), 86 WE, 87 WIHS, 88 W,
89 IW, 90 IEE (14

Lee Hughes (Kidderminster) 96 EH 97 EH (4

Delwyn Humphreys (Kidderminster H.)
91 W(s), 92 W, 94 WFN, 95 WH (7

Steve Humphries (Barnet) 87 H(s) (1

Nicky Ironton (Enfield) 83 H(s), 84 W (2

Tony Jennings (Enfield)
79 SH, 80 ISH, 81 HSI, 82 GIHS (12

Jeff Johnson (Altrincham)
81 SI, 82 GIHS, 83 IHS, 84 HSI,
84 IHS, 86 W(s)EE (18

Tom Jones (Weymouth) 87 W (1

Anton Joseph (Telford Utd. & Kidderminster H.)
84 S(s), 85 WIHS, 86 W(s), 87 WI(s)H,
88 W, 89 IW, 90 IEE (14

Andy Kerr (Wycombe) 93 W (1

Ged Kimmins (Hyde Utd.) 96 E(s)H(s) 97 E(s) (3

Mike Lake (Macclesfield) 89 I (1

Andy Lee (Telford U. & Witton A.) 89 I(s), 91 IW (3

David Leworthy (Farnborough & Rushden &
Diamonds)
93 W, 94 W 97 EH (4

Kenny Lowe (Barnet) 91 IW (2

Martin McDonald (Macclesfield) 95 G(s) (1

John McKenna (Boston Utd)
88 W(s), 90 IEE, 91 IW, 92 W (

Leroy May (Stafford R.) 95 G(s) (

Bobby Mayes (Redbridge) 92 W (

Paul Mayman (Northwich Vic) 80 IS (

Stewart Mell (Burton) 85 W (

Neil Merrick (Weymouth) 80 I(s)S (

Russell Milton (Dover) 94 FN (

revor Morley (Nuneaton) 84 WHSI, 85 WS(s) (6)

es Mutrie (Blyth Spartans) 79 SH, 80 ISH (5)

lark Newson (Maidstone U) 84 WHSI, 85 W (5)

oug Newton (Burton) 85 WHS (3)

aul Nicol (Kettering T) 91 IW, 92 W (3)

teve Norris (Telford) 88 W(s) (1)

oe O'Connor (Hednesford T.) 97 EH(s) (2)

amon O'Keefe (Mossley) 79 SH (2)

rank Ovard (Maidstone) 81 H(s)S(s)I(s) (3)

ndy Pape (Harrow Bor. & Enfield) 85 W(s)HS, 86 W(s)E 87 WIHS, 88 W, 89 IW, 90 IWE (15)

rian Parker (Yeovil Town) 80 S (1)

teve Payne (Macclesfield T.) 97 H (1)

revor Peake (Nuneaton Bor) 79 SH (2)

avid Pearce (Harrow Bor) 84 I(s) (1)

rendan Phillips (Nuneaton Bor. & Kettering T.) 79 SH, 80 S(s)H (4)

ary Philips (Barnet) 82 G (1)

hil Power (Macclesfield T.) 96 E(s)H(s) (2)

yan Price (Stafford R. & Macclesfield) 92 W(s) 93 WF 96 EH 97 H (6)

teve Prindiville 98 H(s) (1)

imon Read (Farnborough) 92 W(s) (1)

ndy Reid (Altrincham) 95 W (1)

arl Richards (Enfield) 86 E (1)

erek Richardson (Maidstone U) 83 I, 84 W, 86 E (4)

an Richardson (Dagenham & Red) 95 G (1)

evin Richardson (Bromsgrove) 94 WFN (3)

aul Richardson (Redbridge) 92 W, 93 WF (3)

erry Robbins (Welling) 92 W, 93 WF, 94 WFN (6)

eter Robinson (Blyth S) 83 IHS, 84 WI, 85 W (6)

ohn Rogers (Altrincham) 81 HSI, 82 I(s)S (5)

aul Rogers (Sutton) 89 W, 90 IE(2), 91 IW (6)

olin Rose (Witton Alb.) 96 E(s)H (2)

evin Rose (Kidderminster) 94 F(s)N (2)

rian Ross (Marine) 93 W(s)F(s), 94 W(s) 95 WH (5)

eil Sellars (Scarboro) 81 HSI, 82 GH(s)S, 83 IHS (9)

lark Shail (Yeovil T.) 93 W (1)

eter Shearer (Cheltenham) 89 I(s) (1)

aul Shirtliff (Frickley A. & Boston U.) 86 EE, 87 WIH, 88 W, 89 IW, 90 IWEE, 92 W, 93 WF (15)

aul Showler (Altrincham) 91 I(s)W (2)

ordon Simmonite (Boston Utd.) 79 S(s)H(s), 80 ISH (5)

Gary Simpson (Stafford R.) 86 EE, 87 IHS, 90 IWEE (9)

Wayne Simpson (Stafford) 94 FN(s) (2)

Glenn Skivington (Barrow) 90 IWE, 91 IW (5)

Alan Smith (Alvechurch) 82 GIS (3)

Ian Smith (Mossley) 80 ISH(s) (3)

Mark Smith (Stevenage Bor.) 96 EH (2)

Ossie Smith (Runcorn) 84 W (1)

Tim Smithers (Nuneaton), 85 W(s)I, 86 W (3)

Simon Stapleton (Wycombe) 93 W (1)

Mickey Stephens (Sutton), 82 GS(s), 86 WEE(s) (5)

Bob Stockley (Nuneaton Bor) 80 H (1)

Steve Stott (Kettering T. & Rushden & Ds) 95 WH(s)G 96 EH (5)

Peter Taylor (Maidstone) 84 HSI (3)

Steve Taylor (Bromsgrove R.) 95 G (1)

Shaun Teale (Weymouth) 88 W (1)

Stuart Terry (Altrincham) W (1)

Brian Thompson (Yeovil & Maidstone) 79 SH, 81 HSI, 82 IHS, 83 IHS, 84 WHSI (15)

Steve Thompson (Wycombe) 93 W (1)

Kevin Todd (Berwick Rangers) 91 W (1)

Mark Tucker (Woking) 96 E (1)

Tony Turner (Telford) 85 W (1)

David Venables (Stevenage Bor.) 94 W(s), 95 HG 96 EH(s) (5)

David Waite (Enfield) 82 G (1)

Paul Walker (Blyth) 86 WEE(s), 87 S(s) (4)

Steve Walters (Northwich Victoria) 97 H (1)

Mark Ward (Northwich Victoria) 83 S(s) (1)

John Watson (Wealdstone, Scarborough & Maidstone) 79 S(s)H, 80 ISH, 81 HSI, 82 IHS, 83 IHS, 84 W(s)HSI (18)

Liam Watson (Marine) 95 WH(s) (2)

Paul Watts (Redbridge Forest) 89 W, 90 IEE, 91 I, 92 W, 93 WF (8)

Paul Webb (Bromsgrove R & Kidderminster H) 93 F, 94 WFN(s) 95 WHG 96 EH 97 EH (11)

Mark West (Wycombe W) 91 W (1)

Barry Whitbread (Runcorn & Altrincham) 79 SH, 80 ISH, 81 I (6)

Russ Wilcox (Frickley) 86 WE (2)

Colin Williams (Scarborough & Telford Utd.) 81 HS, 82 IHS (5)

Roger Willis (Barnet) 91 I(s) (1)

Paul Wilson (Frickley) 86 W (1)

* * *

LEAGUE INDEX

Leagues are listed alphabetically below with their relevant page numbers. Where a league entry runs to more than one page, the number indicated is that of the first page of the section. As in previous years, sponsors names have been omitted to ease reference. League sponsors, however, get their deserved recognition in the appropriate sections.

ch club is shown with its league & division in brackets. The League Abbreviations used are as follows -

C.Co - Combined Counties
DM - Dr Martens
EAST - Eastern Counties
ESX - Essex Senior
GMVC - Conference
HELL - Hellenic
ICIS - ICIS
KENT - Kent League
M.ALL - Midland Alliance
M.COMB - Midland Combination
NCE - Northern Counties East
NTH - Northern League
NWC - North West Counties
SSM - Spartan South Midlands
SSX - Sussex
UCL - United Counties
UNIB - Unibond League
WALES - League of Wales
WEST - Western League
W.MID - West Midlands
WSX - Wessex